FINDING THE SOLUTION: ELIMINATION METHOD

OBJECTIVE
To eliminate one variable and reduce the solution of the system to the solution of one equation in one variable.

EXAMPLE
Solve the system.
$$\begin{cases} 2x + 3y = 21 & (1) \\ 3x - 4y = 23 & (2) \end{cases}$$

Step 1 **Adjust the coefficients.** If necessary, multiply both equations by appropriate numbers so as to obtain two new equations in which the coefficients of the variable to be eliminated are the opposites of each other.

We arbitrarily select y as the variable to be eliminated.
$$\begin{cases} 8x + 12y = 84 \\ 9x - 12y = 69 \end{cases}$$
Multiply equation (1) by 4.
Multiply equation (2) by 3.

Coefficients are opposites of each other.

Step 2 **Add the equations.** Add the resulting equations in Step 1 to obtain an equation in one variable.
$$\begin{array}{r} 8x + 12y = 84 \\ 9x - 12y = 69 \\ \hline 17x = 153 \end{array}$$
Adding the two equations from Step 1 eliminates the y-terms.

Step 3 **Solve** the equation obtained in Step 2.
$$17x = 153$$
Equation from Step
$$x = \frac{153}{17}$$
Divide both sides b
$$x = 9$$
Simplify.

Finding the Solution
Finding the Solution boxes present important multi-step procedures in a two-column format, illustrating the numbered steps of a procedure with a worked example.

End-of-Section Exercises
Each section ends with a large variety of exercises for you to test your comprehension of the preceding material.

A Exercises Basic Skills and Concepts

In Exercises 1–8, explain whether the given equation defines an exponential function. Give reasons for your answers. Write the base for each exponential function.

1. $y = x^3$
2. $y = 4^x$
3. $y = 2^{-x}$
4. $y = 1^x$
5. $y = x^x$
6. $y = 4^2$
7. $y = 0^x$
8. $y = (1.8)^x$

In Exercises 9–18, evaluate each exponential function for the given value. (Use a calculator if necessary.)

9. $f(x) = 5^{x-1}, f(3)$
10. $f(x) = -2^{x+1}, f(3)$
11. $f(x) = 3^{1-x}, f(3.2)$
12. $f(x) = 6^{x-1}, f(2.8)$
13. $g(x) = -\left(\frac{1}{2}\right)^{x+1}, g(-3.5)$
14. $g(x) = -\left(\frac{2}{3}\right)^{2x-1}, g(2.5)$

23. $h(x) = \left(\frac{1}{4}\right)^x$
24. $f(x) = \left(\frac{1}{10}\right)^x$
25. $f(x) = (1.3)^{-x}$
26. $g(x) = (0.7)^{-x}$

27. How are the graphs in Exercises 19 and 23 related? Can we obtain the graph of Exercise 23 from that of Exercise 19? If so, how?
28. Repeat Exercise 27 for the graphs in Exercises 20 and 24.

Match each exponential function given in Exercises 29–32 with one of the graphs labeled (a), (b), (c), and (d).

29. $f(x) = 5^x$
30. $f(x) = -5^x$
31. $f(x) = 5^{-x}$
32. $f(x) = 5^{-x} + 1$

(a)

(b)

B Exercises Applying the Concepts

79. Suppose that a metal block is cooling so that its temperature T (in °C) is given by $T = 200 \cdot 4^{-0.1t}$, where t is in hours. How long has the cooling been taking place if the block now has a temperature of 100°C?

80. Suppose the worldwide sales (in millions) of a computer chip called pentium p are approximated by
$$s(t) = 50 - 30 \cdot 2^{-t},$$
where t represents the number of years that the pentium p has been on the market.
  a. Find each function value.
    (i) $s(0)$
    (ii) $s(1)$
    (iii) $s(5)$
    (iv) $s(10)$
  b. Graph $y = s(x)$. Find the horizontal asymptote. What is the meaning of this horizontal asymptote?

C Exercises Beyond the Basics

87. Sketch the graph of $f(x) = 2^{|x|} = \begin{cases} 2^x & \text{if } x \ge 0 \\ 2^{-x} & \text{if } x < 0 \end{cases}$ Check for symmetry. Find the range of this function.
88. Sketch the graph of $g(x) = 2^{-|x|}$.
89. Sketch the graph of $g(x) = 2^{x^2}$. Check for symmetry. Find the domain and range of this function.
90. a. Sketch the graph of $h(x) = 2^{-x^2}$.
    b. Find the domain and range of $h(x)$.
    c. Why can't we obtain the graph of $h(x)$ by reflecting the graph of $g(x)$ of Exercise 89 in the y-axis?

91. Let $f(x) = 3^x + 3^{-x}$ and $g(x) = 3^x - 3^{-x}$. Find each of the following:
  a. $f(x) + g(x)$
  b. $f(x) - g(x)$
  c. $[f(x)]^2 - [g(x)]^2$
  d. $[f(x)]^2 + [g(x)]^2$
92. Repeat Exercise 91 for the functions $f(x) = a^x + a^{-x}$ and $g(x) = a^x - a^{-x}$.

Practice Test A

1. Solve the equation $5^{-x} = 125$.
2. Solve the equation $\log_2 x = 5$.
3. State the range of $y = -e^x + 1$, and find the asymptote of its graph.
4. Evaluate $\log_2 \frac{1}{8}$.
5. Solve the exponential equation $\left(\frac{1}{4}\right)^{2-x} = 4$.
6. Evaluate log 0.001 without using a calculator.
7. Rewrite the expression $\ln 3 + 5 \ln x$ in condensed form.
8. Solve the equation $5x^3 e^x - x^4 e^x = 0$.
9. Solve the equation $e^{2x} + e^x - 6 = 0$.
10. Rewrite the expression $\ln \frac{2x^3}{(x+1)^5}$ in expanded logarithmic form.
11. Evaluate $\ln e^{-5}$.
12. Give the equation for the graph obtained by shifting the graph of $y = \ln x$ three units up and one unit right.

13. Sketch the graph of $y = 3^{x-1} + 2$.
14. State the domain of the function $f(x) = \ln(-x) + 4$.
15. Write $3 \ln x + \ln(x^3 + 2)$ form.
16. Solve the equation $\log x =$
17. Find x if $\log_3 9 = 2$.
18. Rewrite the expression $\ln$ form.
19. Suppose that 15,000 dollars paying 7% interest per year amount in the account after pounded quarterly.
20. Suppose the number of His States is approximated by A represents 1960. According Hispanic people were livin

Practice Test B

1. Solve the equation $3^{-x} = 9$.
   (a) $\{2\}$ (b) $\{-2\}$ (c) $\left\{\frac{1}{2}\right\}$ (d) $\left\{-\frac{1}{2}\right\}$ (e) $\{\ln 2\}$
2. Solve the equation $\log_5 x = 2$
   (a) $\{10\}$ (b) $\{25\}$ (c) $\left\{\frac{5}{2}\right\}$ (d) $\left\{\frac{2}{5}\right\}$ (e) $\{2\}$
3. State the range and asymptote of $y = e^x - 1$.
   (a) $(0, \infty); y = -1$ (b) $(-1, \infty); y = -1$
   (c) $(-\infty, \infty); y = -1$ (d) $(-1, \infty); y = 1$
   (e) $(\infty, 1); y = 1$
4. Evaluate $\log_4 64$.
   (a) 16 (b) 8 (c) 2 (d) 3 (e) 4
5. Find the solution of the exponential equation $\left(\frac{1}{3}\right)^{1-x} = 3$.
   (a) $\left\{-\frac{1}{3}\right\}$ (b) $\left\{\frac{1}{3}\right\}$ (c) $\{1\}$ (d) $\{2\}$
6. Evaluate log 0.01.
   (a) -1.99999999 (b) -2 (c) 2 (d) 100
7. Which of the following expressions is equivalent to $\ln 7 + 2 \ln x$?
   (a) $\ln(7 + 2x)$ (b) $\ln(7x^2)$ (c) $\ln(9x)$ (d) $\ln(14x)$
8. Solve the equation $3x^2 e^x + x^3 e^x = 0$.
   (a) $\{-3\}$ (b) $\{0, -3\}$ (c) $\{0\}$ (d) $\varnothing$
9. Solve the equation $e^{2x} - e^x - 6 = 0$.
   (a) $\{-\ln 2\}$ (b) $\{-\ln 3\}$ (c) $\{\ln 6\}$ (d) $\{\ln 3\}$

10. Rewrite the expression $\ln \frac{3x^2}{(x+1)^{10}}$ logarithmic form.
    (a) $\ln 6x - 10 \ln x + 1$
    (b) $2 \ln 3x - 10 \ln(x+1)$
    (c) $2 \ln 3 + 2 \ln x - 10 \ln(x+1)$
    (d) $\ln 3 + 2 \ln x - 10 \ln(x+1)$
11. Find $\ln e^{3x}$.
    (a) 3 (b) $3x$ (c) $3 + x$ (d) x
12. The equation for the graph obtained by shifting the graph of $y = \log_3 x$ two units up and three units left is
    (a) $y = \log_3(x - 3) + 2$ (b) $y = \log_3(x + 3) - 2$
    (c) $y = \log_3(x - 3) - 2$ (d) $y = \log_3(x + 3) + 2$
13. Which of the following four graphs is the graph of $y = 5^{x+1} - 4$?

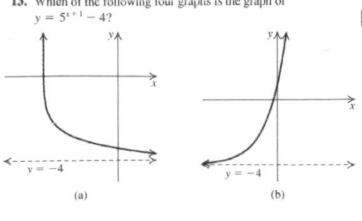

(a)

(b)

End-of-Chapter Material
Each chapter concludes with a Summary of Definitions, Concepts and Formulas, Review Exercises, two Practice Tests, and a Cumulative Review to prove your mastery of the concepts presented in the chapter.

Annotated Instructor's Edition

Precalculus

Annotated Instructor's Edition

Precalculus

J. S. Ratti
University of South Florida

Marcus McWaters
University of South Florida

Boston   San Francisco   New York
London   Toronto   Sydney   Tokyo   Singapore   Madrid
Mexico City   Munich   Paris   Cape Town   Hong Kong   Montreal

Publisher: Greg Tobin
Executive Editor: Anne Kelly
Project Editor: Joanne Ha
Editorial Assistant: Leah Goldberg
Senior Managing Editor: Karen Wernholm
Senior Production Supervisor: Peggy McMahon
Design Supervisor: Barbara T. Atkinson
Text Designer: Carolyn Deacy Design
Cover Designer: Suzanne Heiser, Night & Day Design
Cover Photo: SuperStock
Photo Researcher: Beth Anderson
Media Producer: Ceci Fleming
Software Development: Mary Durnwald & Malcolm Litowitz
Executive Marketing Manager: Becky Anderson
Marketing Coordinator: Bonnie Gill
Senior Author Support/Technology Specialist: Joe Vetere
Rights and Permissions Advisor: Dana Weightman
Manufacturing Manager: Evelyn Beaton
Production Coordination, Technical Illustrations, and
Composition: Pre-Press PMG
Situational Art: Scientific Illustrators

For permission to use copyrighted material, grateful acknowledgment has been made to the copyright holders on page C-1 in the back of the book, which is hereby made part of this copyright page.

Many of the designations used by manufacturers and sellers to distinguish their products are claimed as trademarks. Where those designations appear in this book, and Pearson Education was aware of a trademark claim, the designations have been printed in initial caps or all caps.

The Library of Congress has already cataloged the Student Edition as follows:

Library of Congress Cataloging-in-Publication Data
McWaters, Marcus M.
    Precalculus / Marcus McWaters, Jogindar Ratti. – 1st ed.
    p. cm.
    Includes index.
    ISBN 0-321-29646-X
    1. Algebra—Textbooks. 2. Trancendental functions—Textbooks. I.
    Ratti, J. S. II. Title.
QA152.3.M46 2008
512—dc22   2006050092

ISBN-13 978-0-321-29647-4   ISBN-10 0-321-29647-8

2 3 4 5 6 7 8 9 10—VHP—09 08

To our wives,
Lata and Debra

Foreword

There are many challenges facing today's precalculus students and instructors. Students arrive in this course with varying levels of comprehension from their previous courses. Students often resort to memorization in order to pass the course instead of truly learning the concepts presented. As a result, a textbook needs to get students to a common starting point and engage them in becoming active learners, without sacrificing the solid mathematics that is necessary for conceptual understanding. Instructors in this course are faced with the task of producing students who understand precalculus, are prepared for the next step, and find mathematics useful and interesting. It is our goal to try to help both students and instructors achieve all this and more.

In this text there is a strong emphasis on both concept development and real-life applications. The clearly explained and well developed in-depth coverage of topics such as functions, graphing, the difference quotient, and limiting processes provides thorough preparation for the study of calculus and will improve all students' comprehension of precalculus. There is just-in-time review throughout the text to make sure that all students are beginning with the same foundation of algebra skills. Numerous applications are used to motivate students to apply the concepts and skills learned in precalculus to other courses, including the physical and biological sciences, engineering, and economics, and to on-the-job and everyday problem solving. Students are given ample opportunities throughout this book both to think about important mathematical ideas and to practice and apply algebraic skills.

Another of our goals was to create a book that clearly shows the relevance of what students are learning. Throughout the text, we emphasize why the material being covered is important and how it can be applied. By thoroughly developing mathematical concepts with clearly defined terminology, students also see the *why* behind those concepts, paving the way for a deeper understanding, better retention, less reliance on rote memorization, and, ultimately, more success.

This focus on the students does not mean that we neglected instructors. As instructors ourselves, we know how essential it is to use a book that you believe in and that helps you teach mathematics. To that end, the level of the book was carefully selected so that the material would both be accessible to students and provide them with an opportunity to grow. It is our hope that once you have looked through this textbook, you will see that we were able to fulfill our initial goals of writing for today's students and also for you, the instructor.

Contents

P BASIC CONCEPTS OF ALGEBRA 1

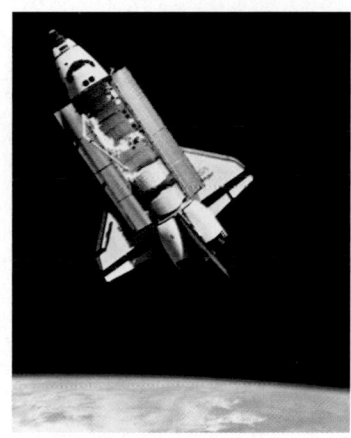

1 EQUATIONS AND INEQUALITIES 86

3   POLYNOMIAL AND RATIONAL FUNCTIONS   317

7 APPLICATIONS OF TRIGONOMETRIC FUNCTIONS 664

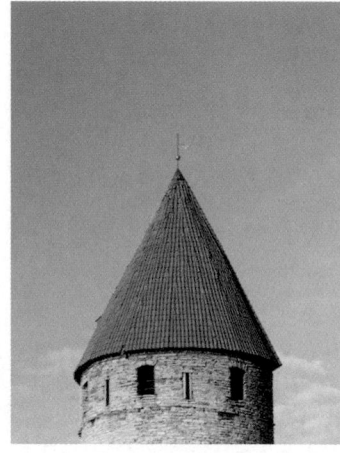

10 THE CONIC SECTIONS 879

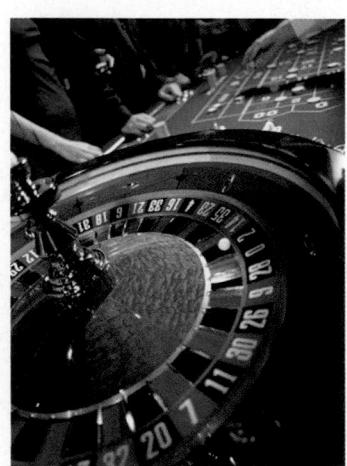

11 FURTHER TOPICS IN ALGEBRA 931

Students begin precalculus classes with widely varying backgrounds. Some haven't taken a math course in several years and may need to spend time reviewing prerequisite topics, while others are ready to jump right into new and challenging material. We have provided review material, in Chapter P and in some of the early sections of other chapters, in such a way that it can be used or omitted, as is appropriate for your course. In addition, students may follow several different paths after completing a precalculus course. Many will continue their study of mathematics in courses such as finite mathematics, statistics, and calculus. For others, this course may be their last mathematics course. Responding to the current and future needs of all of these students was essential in creating this text. Overall, we present our content in a systematic way that illustrates how to study and what to review. We believe that if students use this textbook well, they will succeed in this course.

Features

> **The writing was clear and some topics were explained differently than I've seen before, which was good. I never thought the author was just regurgitating—it seemed fresh.**
> Cindy Shaw, Moraine Valley Community College, Palos Hills, Illinois

Each **chapter opener** includes a description of applications relevant to the content of the chapter, a series of images related to these and other applications, and the list of topics that will be covered in the chapter. In one page, students will see what they are going to learn and why they are learning it.

On the first page of each section is a list of topics that the student should **Review** prior to starting the chapter. Section references with page numbers accompany the suggested review material so that the student can readily find the material. The **Objectives** of the section are then clearly stated and numbered. Each numbered objective is paired with a similarly numbered subsection, so the student can quickly find the section material for a given objective.

The discussion in each section begins with a motivating anecdote or piece of information that is tied to an **application** problem. This problem is solved in an example later in that section, using the mathematics covered in the section. These **section openers** lend continuity to the section and its content, utilizing material from a variety of fields: the physical and biological sciences (including health sciences), economics, art and architecture, the history of mathematics, and more. Of special interest are contemporary topics such as the greenhouse effect and global warming, CAT scans, and computer graphics.

> **My favorite part was the section openers. They were great—they were interesting and relevant, and this is the best part—you actually came back and solved a problem directly related to the opener. I loved these.**
> Catherine Pellish, Front Range Community College, Westminster, Colorado

All **definitions** and **theorems** are boxed for emphasis and titled for ease of reference, as are lists of rules and properties.

The **examples** include a wide range of computational, conceptual, and modern applied problems carefully selected to build confidence, competency, and understanding. Every example has a title that indicates its purpose. Clarifying side comments are provided for each step in the detailed solution of every example. All examples are followed by a **Practice Problem** for students to try so that they can check their understanding of the concept covered.

> **The examples and step-by-step approaches are excellent. The variety of applications is excellent.**
> Marshall Ransom, Georgia Southern University, Statesboro, Georgia

Procedure boxes, interspersed throughout the text, present important procedures in numbered steps. Special **Finding the Solution** boxes present important multistep procedures, such as the steps for doing synthetic division, in a two-column format. The steps of the procedure are given in the left column, and an example is worked, following these steps, in the right column. This approach provides the student with a clear model with which to compare when encountering difficulty in his or her work. **Main Facts** boxes summarize information related to equations and their graphs, such as those of the conic sections.

When appropriate, **historical notes** appear in the margin, giving students information on key people or ideas in the history and development of mathematics. This information is included to add flavor to the subject matter.

> **I like the section openers very much, and historical notes are a real plus in my mind in any book!**
> Gene Garza, Samford University, Birmingham, Alabama

Although the use of graphing calculators is optional in this book, **Technology Connections** give students tips on using their calculators to solve problems, check answers, and reinforce concepts.

Warnings appear as appropriate throughout the text to let students know of common pitfalls that could trip them up in their thinking or calculations.

Periodically, students are reminded in a marginal **Recall** note of a key idea learned earlier in the text that will help them to work through a current problem.

Study Tips give hints for handling newly introduced concepts.

Marginal **By the Way** notes provide students with additional interesting information on nonessential topics in order to keep them engaged in the mathematics presented.

> **I like your application problems because they seemed fresher and more interesting than other books. They aren't all "cookbook" type problems. They should make the students think more.**
> Catherine Pellish, Front Range Community College

Exercises are the heart of any textbook. Knowing this, we made sure that the quantity, quality, and variety of exercises meet every student's needs. The exercises in each exercise set are carefully graded to strengthen the skills developed in the associated section. Exercises are divided into three categories: **A: Basic Skills and Concepts** (developing fundamental skills), **B: Applying the Concepts** (using the section's material to solve real-world problems), and **C: Beyond the Basics** (providing more challenging exercises that give the student an opportunity to reach beyond the material covered in the section). Exercises are paired so that the even-numbered A Exercises closely follow the preceding odd-numbered exercises. All application exercises are titled and relevant to the topics of the section. The A and B Exercises are intended for a typical student, while the C Exercises, generally more theoretical in nature, are suitable for honors students, special assignments, or extra credit.

Critical Thinking exercises, appearing as appropriate, are designed to develop students' higher level thinking skills, and calculator problems are included where needed. Finally, **Group Projects** are provided at the end of many exercise sets so that students can work together to reinforce and extend one another's comprehension of the material.

> **[The exercises] certainly do span a wide range of difficulty levels—from basic to very complex/mature. I applaud the inclusion of the Beyond the Basics and Critical Thinking exercises.**
> James Smith, Columbia State Community College, Columbia, Tennessee

The **chapter-ending** material includes a **Summary of Definitions, Concepts, and Formulas; Review Exercises;** and two **Practice Tests.** The chapter summary gives a brief description of key topics indicating where the material occurs in the text, in order to encourage students to reread sections rather than memorize definitions out of context. The Review Exercises provide students with an opportunity to practice what they have learned in the chapter. Then, the student can take Practice Test A in the usual open-ended format and Practice Test B, covering the same topics, in multiple-choice format. All tests are designed to both increase student comprehension and verify that students have mastered all skills and concepts in the chapter. Mastery of these materials should indicate a true comprehension of the chapter and a likelihood of success on the associated in-class examination.

Cumulative Review Exercises appear at the end of every chapter, starting with Chapter 2, to remind students that mathematics isn't modular and that what is learned in the first part of the book will be useful in later parts of the book and on the final examination.

> **[This text] gives an instructor a reason to teach with enthusiasm.**
> Jason Ramirez, Highline Community College, Des Moines, Washington

Supplements

Student's Solutions Manual

- By Beverly Fusfield
- Provides detailed, worked-out solutions to the odd-numbered end-of-section and Chapter Review exercises and solutions to all of the Practice Tests and Cumulative Review problems
- ISBN 0-321-48670-6

Graphing Calculator Manual

- By Darryl Nester, *Bluffton University*
- Provides instructions and keystroke operations for the TI-83/83+, TI-84+, TI-86, and TI-89
- Keyed directly to text Examples and Technology Connections
- ISBN 0-321-49273-0

Video Lectures on CD with Optional Captioning

- Videos feature Section Summaries and Example Solutions. Section Summaries cover key definitions and procedures from each section. Example Solutions walk students through the detailed solution process for every example in the textbook.
- Ideal for distance learning or supplemental instruction at home or on campus
- Videos include optional text captioning
- ISBN 0-321-48650-1

A Review of Algebra

- By Heidi Howard, *Florida Community College at Jacksonville*
- Provides additional support for those students needing further algebra review
- ISBN 0-201-77347-3

Addison-Wesley Math Tutor Center

- Provides tutoring through a registration number that can be packaged with a new textbook or purchased separately
- Staffed by qualified college mathematics instructors
- Accessible via toll-free telephone, toll-free fax, e-mail, and the Internet at www.aw-bc.com/tutorcenter

Annotated Instructor's Edition

- Answers included on the same page beside the text exercises for quick reference where possible
- ISBN 0-321-29647-8

Instructor's Solutions Manual

- By Beverly Fusfield
- Complete solutions provided for all end-of-section exercises, including the Critical Thinking and Group Projects, Chapter Review exercises, Practice Tests, and Cumulative Review problems
- ISBN 0-321-48357-X

Instructor's Testing Manual

- By Rita Marie O'Brien, *Navarro College*
- Includes diagnostic pretests, chapter tests, and additional test items, grouped by section, with answers provided
- ISBN 0-321-48358-8

TestGen®

- Enables instructors to build, edit, print, and administer tests
- Features a computerized bank of questions developed to cover all text objectives
- Available on a dual-platform Windows/Macintosh CD-ROM
- ISBN 0-321-48538-6

PowerPoint Lecture Presentations and Active Learning Questions

- Features presentations written and designed specifically for this text, including figures and examples from the text
- Active Learning Questions for use with classroom response systems include Multiple Choice questions to review lecture material
- Available within MyMathLab® or from the Instructor Resource Center at www.aw.com/irc

Adjunct Support Center

- Offers consultation on suggested syllabi, helpful tips on using the textbook support package, assistance with content, and advice on classroom strategies
- Available Sunday–Thursday evenings from 5 P.M. to midnight, EST; telephone: 1-800-435-4084; e-mail: AdjunctSupport@aw.com; fax: 1-877-262-9774

Media Resources

MathXL®

MathXL® is a powerful online homework, tutorial, and assessment system that accompanies Addison-Wesley textbooks in mathematics or statistics. With MathXL, instructors can create, edit, and assign online homework and tests using algorithmically generated exercises correlated with the textbook at the objective level. They can also create and assign their own online exercises and import TestGen tests for added flexibility. All student work is tracked in MathXL's online gradebook. Students can take chapter tests in MathXL and receive personalized study plans based on their test results. The study plan diagnoses weaknesses and links students directly to tutorial exercises for the objectives they need to study and on which they need to be retested. Students can also access supplemental animations and video clips directly from selected exercises. MathXL is available to qualified adopters. For more information, visit our Web site at www.mathxl.com, or contact your Addison-Wesley sales representative.

MathXL® Tutorials on CD (ISBN: 0-321-48662-5)

This interactive tutorial CD-ROM provides algorithmically generated practice exercises that are correlated with the exercises in the textbook at the objective level. Every practice exercise is accompanied by an example and a guided solution designed to involve students in the solution process. Selected exercises may also include a video clip to help students visualize concepts. The software provides helpful feedback for incorrect answers and can generate printed summaries of students' progress.

MyMathLab®

MyMathLab® is a series of text-specific, easily customizable online courses for Addison-Wesley textbooks in mathematics and statistics. Powered by CourseCompass™ (Pearson Education's online teaching and learning environment) and MathXL® (our own online homework, tutorial, and assessment system), MyMathLab gives you the tools you need to deliver all or a portion of your course online, whether your students are in a lab setting or working from home. MyMathLab provides a rich and flexible set of course materials, featuring free-response exercises that are algorithmically generated for unlimited practice and mastery. Students can also use online tools, such as video lectures, animations, and a multimedia textbook, to independently improve their understanding and performance. Instructors can use MyMathLab's homework and test managers to select and assign online exercises correlated directly with the textbook, and they can also create and assign their own online exercises and import TestGen tests for added flexibility. MyMathLab's online gradebook—designed specifically for mathematics and statistics—automatically tracks students' homework and test results and gives the instructor control over how to calculate final grades. Instructors can also add offline (paper-and-pencil) grades to the gradebook. MyMathLab is available to qualified adopters. For more information, visit our Web site at www.mymathlab.com or contact your Addison-Wesley sales representative.

InterAct Math Tutorial Web site: www.interactmath.com

Get practice and tutorial help online! This interactive tutorial Web site provides algorithmically generated practice exercises that correlate directly with the exercises in the textbook. Students can retry an exercise as many times as they like, with new values each time, for unlimited practice and mastery. Every exercise is accompanied by an interactive guided solution that provides helpful feedback for incorrect answers, and students can also view a worked-out sample problem that steps them through an exercise similar to the one they're working on.

Video Lectures on CD with Optional Captioning (ISBN: 0-321-48650-1)

The video lectures for this text are available on CD-ROM, making it easy and convenient for students to watch the videos from a computer at home or on campus. The videos feature an engaging team of mathematics instructors who present Section Summaries and Example Solutions. Section Summaries cover key definitions and procedures from each section. Example Solutions walk students through the detailed solution process for every example in the textbook. The format provides distance-learning students with comprehensive video instruction for each section in the book, but also allows students needing only small amounts of review to watch instruction on a specific skill or procedure. The videos have an optional text captioning window; the captions can be easily turned off or on for individual student needs.

Acknowledgments

We would like to express our gratitude to the reviewers of this first edition, who provided such invaluable insights and comments. Their contributions helped shape the development of the text and carry out the vision stated in the preface.

Reviewers

Alison Ahlgren, *University of Illinois at Urbana–Champaign*
Mohammed Aslam, *Georgia Perimeter College*
Ratan Barua, *Miami-Dade College*
Sam Bazzi, *Henry Ford Community College*
Diane Burleson, *Central Piedmont Community College*
Melissa Cass, *State University of New York–New Paltz*
Charles Conrad, *Volunteer State Community College*
Baiqiao Deng, *Columbus State University*
Gene Garza, *Samford University*
Bobbie Jo Hill, *Coastal Bend College*
Yvette Janecek, *Coastal Bend College*
Mohammed Kazemi, *University of North Carolina–Charlotte*
David Keller, *Kirkwood Community College*
Rebecca Leefers, *Michigan State University*
Paul Morgan, *College of Southern Idaho*
Kathy Nickell, *College of DuPage*
Catherine Pellish, *Front Range Community College*
Betty Peterson, *Mercon County*
Marshall Ransom, *Georgia Southern University*
Dr. Traci Reed, *St. Johns River Community College*
Linda Reist, *Macomb Community College*
Jeri Rogers, *Seminole Community College–Oviedo Campus*
Jason Rose, *College of Southern Idaho*
Delphy Shaulis, *University of Colorado–Boulder*
Cindy Shaw, *Moraine Valley Community College*
Cynthia Sikes, *Georgia Southern University*
James Smith, *Columbia State Community College*
Jacqueline Stone, *University of Maryland–College Park*
Kay Stroope, *Phillips County Community College*
Jo Tucker, *Tarrant County College–Southeast*
Tom Worthing, *Hutchinson Community College*
Vivian Zabrocki, *Montana State University–Billings*

Contributors

Jeremy Alm, *Iowa State University*
Ratan Barua, *Miami-Dade College*
Abby Baumgardner, *Blinn College–Bryan*
Edward Bender, *Century College*
Michael Flom, *Normandale Community College*
Tom Hayes, *Montana State University*
Anna Katsoulis, *East Carolina University*
Nicole Lang, *North Hennepin Community College*

Connie Novicoff, *Metropolitan State College of Denver*
Paul Nunez, *Mesa Community College*
Rita Marie O'Brien, *Navarro College*
William Radulovich, *Florida Community College at Jacksonville*
Jason Ramirez, *Highline Community College*
Donna Saye, *Georgia Southern University*
Carol Schmidt, *Lincoln Land Community College*
Julie Turnbow, *Collin Country Community College–Preston*
Chock Wong, *Chaminade University*

Class Testers

Shana Funderburk, *University of North Carolina at Charlotte*
Bobbie Jo Hill, *Coastal Bend College*
Anna Katsoulis, *Eastern Carolina University*
Marcus McWaters, *University of South Florida*
Jeff Norris, *Paris Junior College*
Paul Nuñez, *Mesa Community College*
William Radulovich, *Florida Community College–Jacksonville*
Julie Turnbow, *Collin County Community College*

Our sincerest thanks go out to the legion of dedicated individuals who worked tirelessly to make this book possible. We express special thanks to Abby Tanenbaum for the excellent work she did as the development editor on the text and Beverly Fusfield for her work on the art development. We would also like to express our gratitude to our typist, Beverly DeVine-Hoffmeyer, for her amazing patience and skill. We must also thank Dr. Praveen Rohatgi, Dr. Nalini Rohatgi, and Dr. Bhupinder Bedi for the consulting they provided on all material relating to medicine. Further gratitude is due to Irena Andreevska, Gokarna Aryal, Ferene Tookos, and Christine Fitch for their assistance on the answers to the exercises in the text. In addition, we would like to thank Lauri Semarne, Douglas Ewert, Tom Wegleitner, and Elka Block and Frank Purcell of Twin Prime Editorial, for their meticulous accuracy checking of the text. Thanks are due as well to Sam Blake and Pre-Press PMG for their excellent production work. Finally, our thanks are extended to the professional and remarkable staff at Addison-Wesley. In particular, we would like to thank Greg Tobin, Publisher; Anne Kelly, Executive Editor; Joanne Ha, Project Editor; Leah Goldberg, Editorial Assistant; Peggy McMahon, Senior Production Supervisor; Becky Anderson, Executive Marketing Manager; Bonnie Gill, Marketing Coordinator; Barbara Atkinson, Designer; Cecilia Fleming, Media Producer; Karen Wernholm, Senior Managing Editor; and Joseph Vetere, Senior Author/Technical Art Support.

We invite all who use this book to send any and all suggestions for improvements to Marcus McWaters at marcus@shell.cas.usf.edu.

J. S. Ratti

EDUCATION

Ph.D. Mathematics Wayne State University

TEACHING

Wayne State University (teaching assistant and instructor)

University of Nevada at Las Vegas (instructor)

Oakland University (assistant professor)

University of South Florida (professor and past chairman)

Undergraduate courses taught: college algebra, trigonometry, finite mathematics, calculus (all levels), set theory, differential equations, linear algebra

Graduate courses taught: number theory, abstract algebra, real analysis, complex analysis, graph theory

AWARDS

USF Research Council Grant

USF Teaching Incentive Program (TIP) Award

USF Outstanding Undergraduate Teaching Award

Academy of Applied Sciences grants

RESEARCH

Complex analysis, real analysis, graph theory, probability

PERSONAL INTERESTS

Fan of Tampa Bay Buccaneers

Marcus McWaters

EDUCATION

B.S. Major: mathematics Minor: physics
Louisiana State University New Orleans

Ph.D. Major: mathematics Minor: philosophy
University of Florida

TEACHING

Louisiana State University (teaching assistant)

University of Florida (teaching assistant and graduate fellow)

University of South Florida (associate professor and department chair)

Undergraduate courses taught: college algebra, trigonometry, finite mathematics, calculus, business calculus, life science calculus, advanced calculus, vector calculus, set theory, differential equations, linear algebra

Graduate courses taught: graph theory, number theory, discrete mathematics, geometry, advanced linear algebra, topology, mathematical logic, modern algebra, real analysis

AWARDS

Graduate Fellow, University of Florida
(Center of Excellence Grant)

USF Research Council grant

USF Teaching Incentive Program (TIP) Award

Provost's Award

RESEARCH

Topology, algebraic topology, topological algebra

Founding member, USF Center for Digital and Computational Video

PERSONAL INTERESTS

Traveling with my wife and two daughters, theater, water skiing, racquetball

Basic Concepts of Algebra

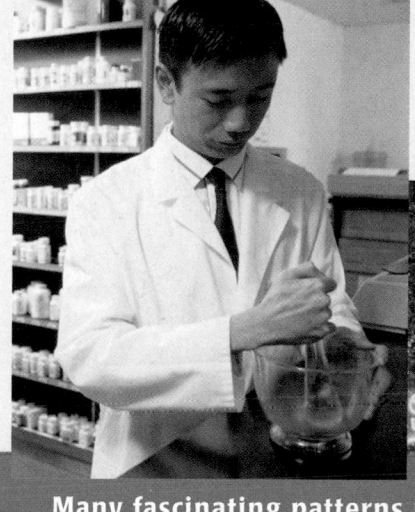

Many fascinating patterns in human and natural processes can be described in the language of algebra. We will investigate events ranging from chirping crickets to the behavior of falling objects.

SECTION P.1 | The Real Numbers and Their Properties

BEFORE STARTING THIS SECTION, REVIEW FROM YOUR PREVIOUS MATHEMATICS TEXTS

1. Arithmetic of signed numbers
2. Arithmetic of fractions
3. Long division involving integers
4. Decimals
5. Arithmetic of real numbers

OBJECTIVES

1 Learn to classify real numbers.

2 Learn the ordering of the real numbers.

3 Learn to specify sets of numbers in roster or set-builder notation.

4 Learn interval notation.

5 Learn absolute value and distance on the number line.

6 Learn the order of operations in arithmetic expressions.

7 Learn to identify and use properties of real numbers.

8 Learn to evaluate algebraic expressions.

Cricket Chirps and Temperature

Crickets are sensitive to changes in air temperature; their chirps speed up as the temperature gets warmer and slow down as it gets cooler. It is possible to use the chirps of the male snowy tree cricket (*Oecanthus fultoni*), common throughout the United States, to gauge temperature. (The insect is found in every U.S. state except Hawaii, Alaska, Montana, and Florida.) By counting the chirps of this cricket, which lives in bushes a few feet from the ground, you can gauge temperature. Snowy tree crickets are more accurate than most cricket species; their chirps are slow enough to count, and they synchronize their singing. To convert cricket chirps to degrees Fahrenheit, count the number of chirps in 14 seconds and then add 40 to get the temperature. To convert cricket chirps to degrees Celsius, count the number of chirps in 25 seconds, divide by 3, and then add 4 to get temperature. In Example 8, we will evaluate algebraic expressions to learn the temperature from the number of cricket chirps. ■

1 Learn to classify real numbers.

Classifying Numbers

In algebra, we use letters such as a, b, x, and y to represent numbers. A letter that is used to represent one or more numbers is called a **variable.** A **constant** is either a specific number, such as 3 or $\frac{1}{2}$, or a letter that represents a fixed (but not necessarily specified) number. Physicists use the letter c as a constant to represent the speed of light ($c = 300,000,000$ meters per second).

We use two variables, a and b, to denote the results of the operations of addition $(a + b)$, subtraction $(a - b)$, multiplication $(a \cdot b$ or $ab)$, and division $\left(a \div b, \text{or } \dfrac{a}{b} \right)$. These operations are called **binary operations,** because each is performed on two numbers. We frequently omit the multiplication sign when writing a product involving two variables (or a constant and a variable), so that $a \cdot b$ and ab indicate the same product. Both a and b are called **factors** in the product $a \cdot b$. This is a good time to recall that we never divide by zero. For $\dfrac{a}{b}$ to represent a real number, b cannot be zero.

STUDY TIP

Here is one difficulty with attempting to divide by 0: If, for example, $\dfrac{5}{0} = a$, then $5 = a \cdot 0$. However, $a \cdot 0 = 0$ for all numbers a. So $5 = 0$, and consequently there is no appropriate choice for $\dfrac{5}{0}$.

Equality of Numbers

The **equal sign,** $=$, is used much like we use the word "is" in English. It means that the number or expression on the left side is equal or equivalent to the number or expression on the right side. We write $a \neq b$ to indicate that a is not equal to b.

Classifying Sets of Numbers

The idea of a set is familiar to us all. We regularly refer to "a set of baseball cards," a "set of CD's," or "a set of dishes." In mathematics, as in everyday life, a **set** is a collection of objects. The objects in the set are called the **elements, or members,** of the set. In the study of algebra, we are interested primarily in sets of numbers.

In listing the elements of a set, it is customary to enclose the listed elements in braces, { }, and separate them by commas.

We distinguish among various sets of numbers.

The numbers we use to count with constitute the set of **natural numbers:** $\{1, 2, 3, 4, \ldots\}$.

The three dots $\ldots$ may be read as "and so on" and indicate that the pattern continues indefinitely.

The **whole numbers** are formed by adjoining the number 0 to the set of natural numbers to obtain $\{ 0, 1, 2, 3, 4, \ldots \}$.

The **integers** consist of the set of natural numbers together with their opposites and 0: $\{ \ldots, -4, -3, -2, -1, 0, 1, 2, 3, 4, \ldots \}$.

The **rational numbers** consist of all numbers that *can* be expressed as the quotient, $\dfrac{a}{b}$, of two integers, where $b \neq 0$.

Examples of rational numbers are $\dfrac{1}{2}$, $\dfrac{5}{3}$, $-\dfrac{4}{17}$, and $\dfrac{7}{100}$. Any integer a can be expressed as the quotient of two integers by writing $a = \dfrac{a}{1}$. Consequently, every integer is also a rational number.

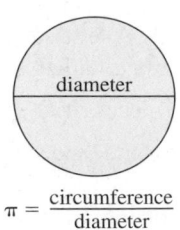

$$\pi = \frac{\text{circumference}}{\text{diameter}}$$

FIGURE P.1

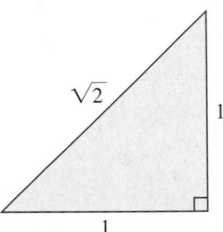

FIGURE P.2

Rational Numbers and Decimals

The rational number $\frac{a}{b}$ can be written as a decimal by using long division. When you take two integers a and b and divide a by b, the result is always either a **terminating decimal,** such as $\left(\frac{1}{2} = 0.5\right)$, or a **nonterminating repeating decimal,** such as $\left(\frac{2}{3} = 0.666\ldots\right)$.

We sometimes place a bar over the repeating digits in a nonterminating repeating decimal. Thus, $\frac{2}{3} = 0.666\ldots = 0.\overline{6}$, and $\frac{13}{11} = 1.181818\ldots = 1.\overline{18}$.

There are decimals that neither terminate nor repeat. Decimals that neither terminate nor repeat represent **irrational numbers.** We can construct such a decimal using only the digits 0 and 1 as follows: 0.01001000100001.... Since each group of zeros contains one more zero than the previous group, no group of digits repeats. Other numbers, such as π (pi, see Figure P.1) and $\sqrt{2}$ (the square root of 2, see Figure P.2), can also be expressed as decimals that neither terminate nor repeat, so they are irrational numbers as well. We can obtain an approximation of an irrational number by using an initial portion of its decimal representation. For example, we can write $\pi \approx 3.14159$ or $\sqrt{2} \approx 1.41421$, where the symbol $\approx$ is read "is approximately equal to."

No familiar process, such as long division, is available for obtaining the decimal representation of an irrational number. However, your calculator can provide a useful approximation for irrational numbers such as $\sqrt{2}$. (Try it!) Since a calculator displays a fixed number of decimal places, it gives a **rational approximation** of an irrational number.

It is usually not easy to determine whether a specific number is irrational. One helpful fact in this regard is that *the square root of any natural number that is not a perfect square is irrational.*

Because rational numbers have decimal representations that either terminate or repeat whereas irrational numbers do not have such representations, *no number is both rational and irrational.*

The rational numbers together with the irrational numbers form the **real numbers.**

The diagram in Figure P.3 shows how various sets of numbers are related. For example, every natural number is also a whole number, an integer, a rational number, and a real number.

FIGURE P.3

2 Learn the ordering of the real numbers.

The Real Number Line

We associate the real numbers with points on a geometric line (imagined to be extended indefinitely in both directions) in such a way that each real number corresponds to exactly one point and each point corresponds to exactly one real number. The point is called the **graph** of the corresponding real number, and the real number is called the **coordinate** of the point. By agreement, *positive numbers* lie to the right of the point corresponding to 0 and *negative numbers* lie to the left of 0. (See Figure P.4.)

Notice that $\frac{1}{2}$ and $-\frac{1}{2}$, 2 and -2, and π and $-\pi$ correspond to pairs of points exactly the same distance from 0, but on opposite sides of 0.

FIGURE P.4

When coordinates have been assigned to points on a line in the manner just described, the line is called a **real number line,** a **coordinate line,** a **real line,** or simply a **number line.** The point corresponding to 0 is called the **origin.**

Inequalities

The real numbers are **ordered** by their size. We say that *a* **is less than** *b* and write $a < b$, provided that $b = a + c$ for some *positive* number *c*. We also write $b > a$, meaning the same thing as $a < b$, and say *b* **is greater than** *a*. On the real line, the numbers increase from left to right. Consequently, *a is to the left of b on the number line when a < b*. Similarly, *a* is to the right of *b* on the number line when $a > b$. We sometimes want to indicate that at least one of two conditions is correct: Either $a < b$ or $a = b$. In this case, we write $a \le b$ or $b \ge a$. The four symbols, $<$, $>$, $\le$, and $\ge$ are called **inequality symbols.**

EXAMPLE 1	Identifying Inequalities

Decide whether each of the following is true or false.

a. $5 > 0$ **b.** $-2 < -3$ **c.** $2 \le 3$ **d.** $4 \le 4$

Solution

a. $5 > 0$ is true, since 5 is to the right of 0 on the number line. (See Figure P.5.)

b. $-2 < -3$ is false, since -2 is to the right of -3 on the number line.

c. $2 \le 3$ is true, since 2 is to the left of 3 on the number line. (Recall that $2 \le 3$ is true if either $2 < 3$ or $2 = 3$.)

d. $4 \le 4$ is true, since $4 \le 4$ is true if either $4 < 4$ or $4 = 4$.

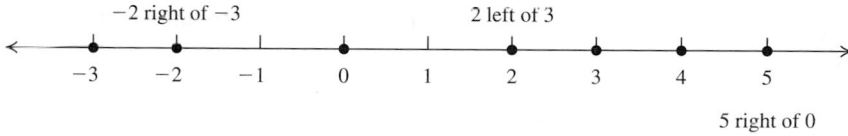

FIGURE P.5

PRACTICE PROBLEM 1 Decide whether each of the following is true or false.

a. $-2 < 0$ **b.** $5 \le 7$ **c.** $-4 < -1$ ■

There are two fundamental properties of inequalities that are intuitively true for all real numbers a, b, and c. We will use these properties throughout this text.

INEQUALITY PROPERTIES

Trichotomy Property: Exactly one of the following is true:

$$a < b, a = b, \text{ or } a > b.$$

Transitive Property: If $a < b$ and $b < c$, then $a < c$.

The trichotomy property says that if two real numbers are not equal, then one is larger than the other. The transitive property says that "less than" works like "smaller than" or "lighter than." Frequently, we read $a > 0$ as "a is positive" instead of "a is greater than 0." We may also read $a < 0$ as "a is negative." If $a \ge 0$, then either $a > 0$ or $a = 0$, and we may say "a is nonnegative."

3 Learn to specify sets of numbers in roster or set-builder notation.

Sets

In order to specify a set, we either

1. List the elements of the set (**roster method**), or
2. Describe the elements of the set (often using **set-builder notation**).

Variables are helpful in describing sets when we use set-builder notation. The notation, $\{x \,|\, x \text{ is a natural number less than 6}\}$ is in set-builder notation and describes the set $\{1, 2, 3, 4, 5\}$, using the roster method.

We read $\{x \,|\, x \text{ is a natural number less than 6}\}$ as "the set of all x such that x is a natural number less than six." Generally, $\{x \,|\, x \text{ has property } P\}$ designates the set of all x such that (the vertical bar is read "such that") x has property P.

It may happen that a description fails to describe any number. For example, consider $\{x \,|\, x < 2 \text{ and } x > 7\}$. Of course, no number can be simultaneously less than 2 and greater than 7, so this set has no members. We refer to a set with no elements as the **empty set** and use the special symbol $\varnothing$ to denote it.

We say that two sets A and B are **equal** if they have exactly the same elements. If each element of a set A is also an element of a set B, we say that A is a **subset** of B. The symbol $\subseteq$ is used to denote the subset relation, so that $A \subseteq B$ is read "A is a subset of B." For example, $\{0, 3\} \subseteq \{0, 1, 2, 3, 4\}$, since 0 and 3 are both elements of the set $\{0, 1, 2, 3, 4\}$.

The **union** of two sets A and B, denoted $A \cup B$, is the set consisting of all elements that are in A *or* B (or both). The **intersection** of A and B, denoted $A \cap B$, is the set consisting of all elements that are in both A *and* B. In other words, $A \cap B$ consists of the elements common to A and B.

EXAMPLE 2   **Forming Set Unions and Intersections**

Find $A \cap B$ and $A \cup B$ if $A = \{-2, -1, 0, 1, 2\}$ and $B = \{-4, -2, 0, 2, 4\}$.

Solution

$A \cap B = \{-2, 0, 2\}$, the set of elements common to both A and B.

$A \cup B = \{-4, -2, -1, 0, 1, 2, 4\}$, the set of elements that are in A or in B (or in both).

■ ■ ■

PRACTICE PROBLEM 2   Find $A \cap B$ and $A \cup B$ if $A = \{-3, -1, 0, 1, 3\}$ and $B = \{-4, -2, 0, 2, 4\}$.

■

4 Learn interval notation.

Intervals

We now turn our attention to graphing certain sets of numbers. That is, we graph each number in a given set. We are particularly interested in sets of real numbers, called **intervals,** whose graphs correspond to special sections of the number line.

If $a < b$, then the set of real numbers between a and b, but not including either a or b, is called the **open interval** from a to b and is denoted by (a, b). (See Figure P.6.) Using set-builder notation, we can write

$$(a, b) = \{x \mid a < x < b\}.$$

$(a, b) = \{x \mid a < x < b\}$

FIGURE P.6

We indicate graphically that the endpoints a and b are excluded from the open interval by drawing a left parenthesis at a and a right parenthesis at b. These parentheses enclose the numbers between a and b.

The **closed interval** from a to b is the set

$$[a, b] = \{x \mid a \leq x \leq b\}.$$

$[a, b] = \{x \mid a \leq x \leq b\}$

FIGURE P.7

The closed interval includes both endpoints a and b. We replace the parentheses by square brackets both in the interval notation and on the graph. (See Figure P.7.) Sometimes we want to include only one endpoint of an interval and exclude the other. Table P.1 on page 8 shows how this is done.

We also want to graph all numbers to the left or right of a given number, such as

$$\{x \mid x > 2\}.$$

The number 2 is not included in this set, and we again indicate this fact graphically by drawing a left parenthesis at 2. We then graph all points to the right of 2, as shown in Figure P.8.

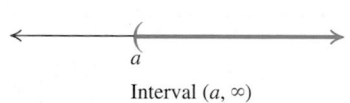

Interval $(2, \infty)$

FIGURE P.8

For any number a, we call $\{x \mid x > a\}$ an **unbounded** (or infinite) **interval** and denote this interval by (a, ∞). The symbol ∞ ("infinity") does not represent a number. The notation (a, ∞) is used to indicate the set of all real numbers that are greater than a, and the symbol ∞ is used to indicate that the interval extends indefinitely to the right of a. (See Figure P.9.)

Interval (a, ∞)

FIGURE P.9

The symbol $-\infty$ is another symbol that does not represent a number. The notation $(-\infty, a)$ is used to indicate the set of all real numbers that are less than a. The notation $(-\infty, \infty)$ represents the set of all real numbers.

Table P.1 lists various types of intervals with which we will be concerned in this book. In the table, when two points a and b are involved, we assume that $a < b$.

TABLE P.1

Interval Notation	Set-Builder Notation	Graph
(a, b)	$\{x \mid a < x < b\}$	
$[a, b]$	$\{x \mid a \leq x \leq b\}$	
$(a, b]$	$\{x \mid a < x \leq b\}$	
$[a, b)$	$\{x \mid a \leq x < b\}$	
(a, ∞)	$\{x \mid x > a\}$	
$[a, \infty)$	$\{x \mid x \geq a\}$	
$(-\infty, b)$	$\{x \mid x < b\}$	
$(-\infty, b]$	$\{x \mid x \leq b\}$	
$(-\infty, \infty)$	$\{x \mid x \text{ is a real number}\}$	

STUDY TIP

The symbols ∞ and $-\infty$ are always used with parentheses, not square brackets. Also, note that $<$ and $>$ are used with parentheses and that $\leq$ and $\geq$ are used with square brackets.

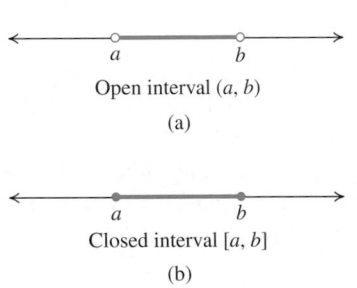

Open interval (a, b)

(a)

Closed interval $[a, b]$

(b)

FIGURE P.10

5 Learn absolute value and distance on the real number line.

An alternative notation for indicating whether endpoints are included uses closed circles to show inclusion and open circles to show exclusion. (See Figure P.10.)

Absolute Value

The **_absolute value_** of a number a, denoted by $|a|$, is the distance between the origin and the point on the number line with coordinate a. The point with coordinate -3 is three units from the origin, so we write $|-3| = 3$ and say that the absolute value of -3 is 3. (See Figure P.11.)

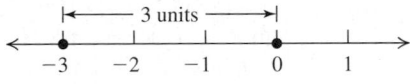

FIGURE P.11

ABSOLUTE VALUE

For any real number a, the **absolute value** of a, denoted $|a|$, is defined by

$$|a| = a \quad \text{if } a \geq 0 \qquad \text{and} \qquad |a| = -a \quad \text{if } a < 0$$

EXAMPLE 3 Determining Absolute Value

Find the absolute value of each of the following.

a. $|4|$ **b.** $|-4|$ **c.** $|0|$ **d.** $|(-3) + 1|$

Solution

a. $|4| = 4$ Since the number inside the absolute value bars is 4, and $4 \geq 0$, just remove the absolute value bars.

STUDY TIP

Finding the absolute value requires knowing whether the number or expression inside the absolute value bars is positive, zero, or negative. If it is positive or zero, you can simply remove the absolute value bars. If it is negative, you remove the bars and change the sign of the number or expression inside the absolute value bars.

b. $|-4| = -(-4) = 4$ Since the number inside the absolute value bars is -4, and $-4 < 0$, remove the bars and change the sign.

c. $|0| = 0$ Since the number inside the absolute value bars is 0, and $0 \geq 0$, just remove the absolute value bars.

d. $|(-3) + 1| = |-2|$ Since the expression inside the absolute value bars is
$$= -(-2) = 2$$ $(-3) + 1 = -2$ and, $-2 < 0$, remove the bars and change the sign.   ■ ■ ■

PRACTICE PROBLEM 3   Find the absolute value of each of the following.

a. $|-10|$ **b.** $|3 - 4|$ **c.** $|2(-3) + 7|$ ■

◆ **WARNING**   The absolute value of a number represents a distance. Because distance can never be negative, the absolute value of a number is never negative; it is always positive or zero. However, if a is not 0, $-|a|$ is always negative. Thus, $-|5.3| = -5.3$, $-|-4| = -4$, and $-|1.\overline{18}| = -1.\overline{18}$.

TECHNOLOGY CONNECTION

 The absolute value function on your graphing calculator will first find the value of the expression entered and then compute its absolute value.

Distance Between Two Points on a Real Number Line

The absolute value is used to define the distance between two points on a number line. The distance between the points corresponding to the numbers 8 and 3 is 5. Notice that $|8 - 3| = |5| = 5$, which leads us to the following definition.

DISTANCE FORMULA ON A NUMBER LINE

If a and b are the coordinates of two points on a number line, then the distance between a and b, denoted by $d(a, b)$, is $|a - b|$. In symbols, $d(a, b) = |a - b|$.

EXAMPLE 4   **Finding the Distance Between Two Points**

Find the distance between -3 and 4 on the number line.

Solution

From Figure P.12, the distance between -3 and 4 can be seen to be 7 units. This answer may also be obtained algebraically by letting $a = -3$ and $b = 4$ in the distance formula:

$$d(-3, 4) = |-3 - 4| = |-7| = -(-7) = 7.$$

FIGURE P.12

Continued on next page.

FIGURE P.13

Notice that if we perform this computation with the order of -3 and 4 reversed, we get the same answer. That is, the distance between 4 and -3 is $|4 - (-3)| = |4 + 3| = |7| = 7$. It is always true that $|a - b| = |b - a|$. (See Figure P.13.) ■ ■ ■

PRACTICE PROBLEM 4   Find the distance between -7 and 2 on the number line. ■

We summarize the properties of absolute value next.

PROPERTIES OF ABSOLUTE VALUE

If a and b are any real numbers, the following properties apply:

Property	**Example**
1. $|a| \geq 0$	$|-5| = 5$, and $5 \geq 0$
2. $|a| = |-a|$	$|3| = |-3|$
3. $|ab| = |a||b|$	$|3(-5)| = |3||-5|$
4. $\left|\dfrac{a}{b}\right| = \dfrac{|a|}{|b|}$	$\left|\dfrac{-7}{3}\right| = \dfrac{|-7|}{|3|}$
5. $|a - b| = |b - a|$	$|2 - 7| = |7 - 2|$
6. $a \leq |a|$	$-2 \leq |-2|, 2 \leq |2|$
7. $|a + b| \leq |a| + |b|$ (the triangle inequality)	$|-2 + 5| \leq |-2| + |5|$

---

6 Learn the order of operations in arithmetic expressions.

Arithmetic Expressions

When we write numbers in a meaningful combination of the basic operations of arithmetic, the result is called an **arithmetic expression.** The real number that results from performing all the operations in the expression is called the **value** of the expression. In arithmetic and in algebra, parentheses ( ) are **grouping symbols** used to indicate which operations are to be performed first. Other common grouping symbols are square brackets [], braces {}, fraction bars, − or /, and absolute value bars, | |.

Evaluating arithmetic expressions requires carefully applying the following coventions for the order in which the operations are done.

THE ORDER OF OPERATIONS

Whenever a fraction bar is encountered, work separately above and below the fraction bar.

When parentheses or other grouping symbols are present, start inside the innermost pair of grouping symbols and work outward.

Step 1   Do operations involving exponents first.

Step 2   Do multiplications and divisions in the order in which they occur, working from left to right.

Step 3   Do additions and subtractions in the order in which they occur, working from left to right.

**TECHNOLOGY
CONNECTION**

The order of operations is built into your graphing calculator.

| EXAMPLE 5 | Evaluating Arithmetic Expressions |

Evaluate each of the following.

a. $3 \cdot 2^5 + 4$ **b.** $5 - (3 - 1)^2$

Solution

a. $3 \cdot 2^5 + 4 = 3 \cdot 32 + 4$ Do operations involving exponents first.
        $= 96 + 4$ Multiplication is done next.
        $= 100$ Addition is done next.

b. $5 - (3 - 1)^2 = 5 - (2)^2$ Work inside the parentheses first.
        $= 5 - 4$ Next do operations involving exponents.
        $= 1$ Subtraction is done next.   ■ ■ ■

PRACTICE PROBLEM 5   Evaluate:

a. $(-3) \cdot 5 + 20$ **b.** $7 - 2 \cdot 3$ **c.** $\dfrac{9 - 1}{4} - 5 \cdot 7$ ■

7 Learn to identify and use properties of real numbers.

Properties of the Real Numbers

When doing arithmetic, we intuitively use important properties of the real numbers. We know, for example, that if we add or multiply two real numbers, the result is a real number. This fact is known as the **closure** property of real numbers. *Throughout this section, unless otherwise stated, a, b, and c represent real numbers.*

The numbers 0 and 1 have special roles among the real numbers. Because 0 preserves the identity of any number under addition ($0 + 3 = 3, 3 + 0 = 3$) and 1 preserves the identity of any number under multiplication ($5 \cdot 1 = 5, 1 \cdot 5 = 5$), we call 0 the **additive identity** and 1 the **multiplicative identity.**

IDENTITY PROPERTIES

$$a + 0 = 0 + a = a \qquad a \cdot 1 = 1 \cdot a = a$$

Two other useful properties of 0 involve multiplication rather than addition.

ZERO-PRODUCT PROPERTIES

$$0 \cdot a = 0 \qquad a \cdot 0 = 0$$

If $a \cdot b = 0$, then $a = 0$ or $b = 0$.

**TECHNOLOGY
CONNECTION**

On your graphing calculator, the *opposite* of a is denoted with a shorter horizontal dash than that used to denote subtraction. It is also placed somewhat higher than the subtraction symbol.

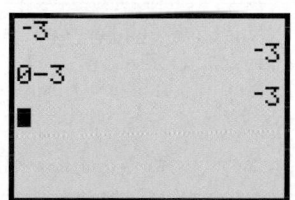

The Additive Inverse

Every real number a has an **opposite** number, denoted $-a$, with the property that the sum of a and $-a$ is 0. The *opposite* of a, $-a$, is also called the **additive inverse** of a. We state this property of real numbers as follows:

> ### ADDITIVE INVERSE PROPERTY
>
> $$a + (-a) = (-a) + a = 0$$

Reciprocals

Every nonzero real number a has an **inverse**, $\dfrac{1}{a}$, with the property that the product of a and $\dfrac{1}{a}$ is 1. The *inverse* $\dfrac{1}{a}$ is also called the **multiplicative inverse,** or **reciprocal,** of a.

> ### MULTIPLICATIVE INVERSE PROPERTY
>
> $$a \cdot \frac{1}{a} = \frac{1}{a} \cdot a = 1 \text{ if } a \neq 0$$

Since $0 \cdot b = 0$ for any number b, the number 0 does not have a multiplicative inverse.

EXAMPLE 6   Finding the Reciprocal

Find the reciprocal of

a. 3   **b.** $-\dfrac{3}{4}$.

Solution

a. The reciprocal of 3 is $\dfrac{1}{3}$, since $3 \cdot \dfrac{1}{3} = 1$.

b. The reciprocal of $-\dfrac{3}{4}$ is $-\dfrac{4}{3}$, since $-\dfrac{3}{4} \cdot -\dfrac{4}{3} = 1$.   ■ ■ ■

PRACTICE PROBLEM 6   Find the reciprocal of

a. $\dfrac{1}{2}$ **b.** -7.   ■

PROPERTIES OF THE REAL NUMBERS

Name	Property	Example
Closure	$a + b$ is a real number	$1 + \sqrt{2}$ is a real number
	$a \cdot b$ is a real number	$2 \cdot \pi$ is a real number.
Commutative	$a + b = b + a$	$4 + 7 = 7 + 4$
	$a \cdot b = b \cdot a$	$3 \cdot 8 = 8 \cdot 3$

(Continued)

PROPERTIES OF THE REAL NUMBERS (CONTINUED)

Name	Property	Example
Associative	$(a + b) + c = a + (b + c)$ $(a \cdot b) \cdot c = a \cdot (b \cdot c)$	$(2 + 1) + 7 = 2 + (1 + 7)$ $(5 \cdot 9) \cdot 13 = 5 \cdot (9 \cdot 13)$
Distributive	$a \cdot (b + c) = a \cdot b + a \cdot c$ $(a + b) \cdot c = a \cdot c + b \cdot c$	$3 \cdot (2 + 5) = 3 \cdot 2 + 3 \cdot 5$ $(2 + 5) \cdot 3 = 2 \cdot 3 + 5 \cdot 3$
Identity	There is a unique real number 0 such that $a + 0 = a$ and $0 + a = a$.	$3 + 0 = 3$ and $0 + 3 = 3$
	There is a unique real number 1 such that $a \cdot 1 = a$ and $1 \cdot a = a$.	$7 \cdot 1 = 7$ and $1 \cdot 7 = 7$
Inverse	There is a unique real number $-a$ such that $a + (-a) = 0$ and $-a + a = 0$.	$5 + (-5) = 0$ and $(-5) + 5 = 0$
	If $a \neq 0$, there is a unique real number $\dfrac{1}{a}$ such that $a \cdot \dfrac{1}{a} = 1$ and $\dfrac{1}{a} \cdot a = 1$.	$4 \cdot \dfrac{1}{4} = 1$ and $\dfrac{1}{4} \cdot 4 = 1$

Subtraction and Division of Real Numbers

You may have noticed that all the properties discussed to this point apply to the operations of addition and multiplication. What about subtraction and division? We see next that subtraction and division can be defined in terms of addition and multiplication.

Subtraction of the number b from the number a is defined with the use of a and $-b$; to subtract b from a, add the opposite of b to a.

Definition of Subtraction

$$a - b = a + (-b)$$

If a and b are real numbers and $b \neq 0$, **division** of a by b is defined with the use of a and $\dfrac{1}{b}$; to divide a by b, multiply a by the reciprocal of b.

Definition of Division

$$a \div b = \frac{a}{b} = a \cdot \frac{1}{b} \quad \text{if } b \neq 0$$

For $b \neq 0$, $\dfrac{a}{b}$ is called the **quotient,** "the **ratio** of a to b," or the **fraction** with **numerator** a and **denominator** b. Here are some useful properties involving opposites, subtraction, and division.

PROPERTIES OF OPPOSITES

$$(-1)\,a = -a \qquad\qquad -(-a) = a \qquad\qquad (-a)b = a(-b) = -(ab)$$

$$(-a)(-b) = ab \qquad\qquad -(a + b) = -a - b \qquad\qquad -(a - b) = b - a$$

$$\frac{-a}{b} = \frac{a}{-b} = -\frac{a}{b} \qquad\qquad \frac{-a}{-b} = \frac{a}{b} \qquad\qquad a(b - c) = ab - ac$$

In order to combine real numbers by means of the division operation, we use the following properties.

PROPERTIES OF FRACTIONS

All denominators are assumed to be nonzero.

$$\frac{a}{c} + \frac{b}{c} = \frac{a + b}{c} \qquad\qquad \frac{a}{b} + \frac{c}{d} = \frac{ad + bc}{bd}$$

$$\frac{a}{b} \cdot \frac{c}{d} = \frac{ac}{bd} \qquad\qquad \frac{a}{b} \div \frac{c}{d} = \frac{a}{b} \cdot \frac{d}{c}$$

$$\frac{ac}{bc} = \frac{a}{b} \qquad\qquad \frac{a}{b} = \frac{c}{d} \quad \text{means} \quad a \cdot d = b \cdot c$$

8 Learn to evaluate algebraic expressions.

Algebraic Expressions

In algebra, any number, constant, variable, or parenthetical group, or any product of these, is called a **term.** A combination of terms using the ordinary operations of addition, subtraction, multiplication, and division (as well as exponentiation and roots, which are discussed later in this chapter) is called an **algebraic expression,** or simply an **expression.** If we replace each variable in an expression with a specific number and we get a real number, the resulting number is called the **value of the algebraic expression.** Of course, this value depends on the numbers we use to replace the variables in the expression. Here are some examples of algebraic expressions:

$$x - 2, \qquad \frac{1}{x} + \sqrt{7}, \qquad \frac{10}{y + 3}, \qquad \sqrt{x} + |y| \div 5.$$

EXAMPLE 7   **Evaluating an Algebraic Expression**

Evaluate the following expressions for the given values of the variables.

a. $[(9 + x) \div 7] \cdot 3 - x$ for $x = 5$

b. $|x| - \dfrac{2}{y}$ for $x = 2$ and $y = -2$

Solution

a. $[(9 + x) \div 7] \cdot 3 - x = [(9 + 5) \div 7] \cdot 3 - 5$ Replace x with 5.

$$= [14 \div 7] \cdot 3 - 5 \quad \text{Work inside the parentheses.}$$
$$= 2 \cdot 3 - 5 \quad \text{Work inside the brackets.}$$
$$= 6 - 5 \quad \text{Then multiply.}$$
$$= 1 \quad \text{The value of the expression}$$

b. $|x| - \dfrac{2}{y} = |2| - \dfrac{2}{-2}$ Replace x with 2 and y with -2.

$$= 2 - \frac{2}{-2} \quad \text{Eliminate the absolute value, } |2| = 2.$$

$$= 2 - (-1) \quad \frac{2}{-2} = -1; \text{ division occurs before subtraction.}$$

$$= 3 \quad \text{The value of the expression} \qquad \blacksquare\ \blacksquare\ \blacksquare$$

PRACTICE PROBLEM 7   Evaluate:

a. $(x - 2) \div 3 + x$ for $x = 3$ b. $7 - \dfrac{x}{|y|}$ for $x = -1, y = 3$. $\blacksquare$

EXAMPLE 8   **Finding the Temperature from Cricket Chirps**

Write an algebraic expression for converting cricket chirps to degrees Celsius. If you count 48 chirps in 25 seconds, what is the Celsius temperature?

Solution

Recall from the introduction to this section that to convert cricket chirps to degrees Celsius, count the chirps in 25 seconds, divide by 3, and then add 4 to get the temperature.

$$\boxed{\begin{array}{c}\text{Temperature in} \\ \text{Celsius degrees}\end{array}} = \boxed{\left(\dfrac{\text{Number of chirps in 25 seconds}}{3}\right) + 4}$$

If we let C = temperature in degrees Celsius and N = number of chirps in 25 seconds, we get the expression

$$C = \frac{N}{3} + 4.$$

Suppose we count 48 chirps in 25 seconds. The Celsius temperature is

$$C = \frac{48}{3} + 4$$
$$= 16 + 4 = 20. \qquad \blacksquare\ \blacksquare\ \blacksquare$$

PRACTICE PROBLEM 8   Use the temperature expression in Example 8 to find the Celsius temperature if 39 chirps are counted in 25 seconds. $\blacksquare$

The **domain** of an algebraic expression having only one variable is the set of all possible numbers that may be used for the variable. For example, division by 0 is not defined, so no number can replace a variable if a denominator of 0 results. Because replacing x by 1 would result in a denominator of 0, the number 1 is excluded from the domain of the expression $\dfrac{1}{x - 1}$. The domain of the expression $\dfrac{1}{x - 1}$ is thus the set of all real numbers x, $x \neq 1$.

| EXAMPLE 9 | **Finding the Domain of an Algebraic Expression** |

Find the domain of the expression $\dfrac{5}{3-x}$.

Solution

Notice that $3 - x = 0$ if $x = 3$.

Since replacing x with 3 in $\dfrac{5}{3-x}$ results in a denominator of 0, the number 3 is not in its domain. If $x \neq 3$, the value of $\dfrac{5}{3-x}$ is a real number. The domain can be expressed in set notation as $\{x \mid x \neq 3\}$, or in interval notation as $(-\infty, 3) \cup (3, \infty)$. ■ ■ ■

PRACTICE PROBLEM 9 Find the domain of the variable x in the expression $\dfrac{2-x}{x+2}$. ■

A Exercises Basic Skills and Concepts

In Exercises 1–8, write each of the following rational numbers as a decimal, and state whether the decimal is repeating or terminating.

1. $\dfrac{1}{3}$ $0.\overline{3}$ repeating
2. $\dfrac{2}{3}$ $0.\overline{6}$ repeating
3. $-\dfrac{4}{5}$ -0.8 terminating
4. $-\dfrac{3}{12}$ -0.25 terminating
5. $\dfrac{3}{11}$ $0.\overline{27}$ repeating
6. $\dfrac{11}{33}$ $0.\overline{3}$ repeating
7. $\dfrac{95}{30}$ $3.1\overline{6}$ repeating
8. $\dfrac{41}{15}$ $2.7\overline{3}$ repeating

In Exercises 9–18, classify each of the following numbers as rational or irrational.

9. -207 rational
10. -114 rational
11. $\sqrt{81}$ rational
12. $-\sqrt{25}$ rational
13. $\dfrac{7}{2}$ rational
14. $-\dfrac{15}{12}$ rational
15. $\sqrt{12}$ irrational
16. $\sqrt{3}$ irrational
17. 0.321 rational
18. $5.8\overline{2}$ rational

In Exercises 19–28, use inequality symbols to write the given statements symbolically.

19. 3 is greater than -2. $3 > -2$
20. -3 is less than -2. $-3 < -2$
21. $\dfrac{1}{2}$ is greater than or equal to $\dfrac{1}{2}$. $\dfrac{1}{2} \geq \dfrac{1}{2}$
22. x is less than $x + 1$. $x < x + 1$

23. 5 is less than or equal to $2x$. $5 \leq 2x$
24. $x - 1$ is greater than 2. $x - 1 > 2$
25. $-x$ is positive. $-x > 0$
26. x is negative. $x < 0$
27. $2x + 7$ is less than or equal to 14. $2x + 7 \leq 14$
28. $2x + 3$ is not greater than 5. $2x + 3 \leq 5$

In Exercises 29–32, fill in the blank with one of the symbols $=$, $<$, or $>$ to produce a true statement.

29. $4 \underline{\ =\ } \dfrac{24}{6}$
30. $-3 \underline{\ <\ } -2$
31. $-4 \underline{\ <\ } 0$
32. $-\dfrac{5}{2} \underline{\ =\ } -2\dfrac{1}{2}$

In Exercises 33–38, use the roster method to write the given sets of numbers. Interpret "between a and b" to include both a and b.

33. The first three natural numbers $\{1, 2, 3\}$
34. The first five natural numbers $\{1, 2, 3, 4, 5\}$
35. The natural numbers between 3 and 7 $\{3, 4, 5, 6, 7\}$
36. The natural numbers between 8 and 11 $\{8, 9, 10, 11\}$
37. The negative integers between -3 and 5 $\{-3, -2, -1\}$
38. The whole numbers between -2 and 4 $\{0, 1, 2, 3, 4\}$

In Exercises 39–52, rewrite each expression without absolute value bars.

39. $|20|$ 20
40. $|12|$ 12
41. $-|-4|$ -4
42. $-|-17|$ -17
43. $\left|\dfrac{5}{7}\right|$ $\dfrac{5}{7}$
44. $\left|\dfrac{-3}{5}\right|$ $\dfrac{3}{5}$

†Due to space constrictions, answers to these exercises may be found in the Answers beginning on page A–1 in the back of the book.

45. $|5 - \sqrt{2}|$ $5 - \sqrt{2}$ **46.** $|\sqrt{2} - 5|$ $5 - \sqrt{2}$

47. $\dfrac{8}{|-8|}$ 1   **48.** $\dfrac{-8}{|8|}$ -1

49. $|5 + |-7||$ 12   **50.** $|5 - |-7||$ 2

51. $||7| - |4||$ 3   **52.** $||4| - |7||$ 3

In Exercises 53–60, use the absolute value to express the distance between the points with coordinates a and b on the number line. Then determine this distance by evaluating the absolute value expression.

53. $a = 3$ and $b = 8$ †   **54.** $a = 2$ and $b = 14$ †

55. $a = -6$ and $b = 9$ †   **56.** $a = -12$ and $b = 3$ †

57. $a = -20$ and $b = -6$ †   **58.** $a = -14$ and $b = -1$ †

59. $a = \dfrac{22}{7}$ and $b = -\dfrac{4}{7}$ †   **60.** $a = \dfrac{16}{5}$ and $b = -\dfrac{3}{5}$ †

In Exercises 61–72, graph each of the given intervals on a separate number line and write the inequality notation for each.

61. $[1, 4]$ †   **62.** $[-2, 2]$ †

63. $(14, 28)$ †   **64.** $\left(\dfrac{1}{2}, \dfrac{9}{2}\right)$ †

65. $(-3, 1]$ †   **66.** $[-6, -2)$ †

67. $[-3, \infty)$ †   **68.** $[0, \infty)$ †

69. $(-\infty, 5]$ †   **70.** $(-\infty, -1]$ †

71. $\left(-\dfrac{3}{4}, \dfrac{9}{4}\right)$ †   **72.** $\left(-3, -\dfrac{1}{2}\right)$ †

In Exercises 73–76, use the distributive property to write each expression without parentheses.

73. $4(x + 1)$ $4x + 4$ **74.** $(-3)(2 - x)$ $-6 + 3x$

75. $5(x - y + 1)$ $5x - 5y + 5$ **76.** $2(3x + 5 - y)$ †

In Exercises 77–80, find the additive inverse and reciprocal of each number.

Number	Additive Inverse	Reciprocal
77. 5	-5	†
78. $-\dfrac{2}{3}$	$\dfrac{2}{3}$	$-\dfrac{3}{2}$
79. 0	0	no reciprocal
80. 1.7	-1.7	†

In Exercises 81–92, name the property of real numbers that justifies the given equality. All variables represent real numbers.

81. $(-7) + 7 = 0$ †   **82.** $5 + (-5) = 0$ †

83. $(x + 2) = 1 \cdot (x + 2)$ †   **84.** $3a = 1 \cdot 3a$ †

85. $7(xy) = (7x)y$ †   **86.** $3 \cdot (6x) = (3 \cdot 6)x$ †

87. $\dfrac{3}{2}\left(\dfrac{2}{3}\right) = 1$ †   **88.** $2\left(\dfrac{1}{2}\right) = 1$ †

89. $(3 + x) + 0 = 3 + x$ †   **90.** $x(2 + y) + 0 = x(2 + y)$ †

91. $(x + 5) + 2y = x + (5 + 2y)$ additive associative

92. $(3 + x) + 5 = x + (3 + 5)$ †

In Exercises 93–102, evaluate each expression for $x = 3$ and $y = -5$.

93. $2(x + y) - 3y$ 11   **94.** $-2(x + y) + 5y$ -21

95. $3|x| - 2|y|$ -1 **96.** $7|x - y|$ 56

97. $\dfrac{x - 3y}{2} + xy$ -6 **98.** $\dfrac{y + 3}{x} - xy$ $\dfrac{43}{3}$

99. $\dfrac{2(1 - 2x)}{y} - (-x)y$ -13 **100.** $\dfrac{3(2 - x)}{y} - (1 - xy)$ $-\dfrac{77}{5}$

101. $\dfrac{\dfrac{14}{x} + \dfrac{1}{2}}{\dfrac{-y}{4}}$ $\dfrac{62}{15}$ **102.** $\dfrac{\dfrac{4}{-y} + \dfrac{8}{x}}{\dfrac{y}{2}}$ $-\dfrac{104}{75}$

In Exercises 103–114, determine the domain of each expression. Write each domain in interval notation.

103. $\dfrac{3}{x - 1}$ $(-\infty, 1) \cup (1, \infty)$ **104.** $\dfrac{-5}{1 - x}$ $(-\infty, 1) \cup (1, \infty)$

105. $\dfrac{x + 2}{x}$ $(-\infty, 0) \cup (0, \infty)$ **106.** $\dfrac{x}{x + 7}$ $(-\infty, -7) \cup (-7, \infty)$

107. $\dfrac{1}{x} + \dfrac{1}{x + 1}$ †   **108.** $\dfrac{2}{x} - \dfrac{3}{x - 5}$ †

109. $\dfrac{7}{(x - 1)(x + 2)}$ †   **110.** $\dfrac{x}{x(x + 3)}$ †

111. $\dfrac{x}{2 - x} + \dfrac{1}{x}$ †   **112.** $\dfrac{5}{x - 3} + \dfrac{4}{3 - x}$ †

113. $\dfrac{5}{x^2 + 1}$ $(-\infty, \infty)$ **114.** $\dfrac{x}{x^2 + 2}$ $(-\infty, \infty)$

B Exercises Applying the Concepts

115. Media players. Let $A =$ the set of people who own MP3 players and $B =$ the set of people who own DVD players.
  a. Describe the set $A \cup B$. †
  b. Describe the set $A \cap B$. †

116. Standard car features. The table on the next page indicates whether certain features are "standard" for each of three types of cars.

	Navigation System	Automatic Transmission	Leather Seats
2005 Lexus SC 430	yes	yes	yes
2005 Lincoln Town Car	no	yes	yes
2005 Infiniti G35 Sport Coupe	no	no	yes

Source: www.autos.yahoo.com

Use the roster method to describe each of the following sets.
a. A = cars in which a navigation system is standard.
b. B = cars in which an automatic transmission is standard.
c. C = cars in which leather seats are standard.
d. $A \cap B$ $A \cap B = \{2005 \text{ Lexus SC } 430\}$
e. $B \cap C$
f. $A \cup B$
g. $A \cup C$

117. Blood pressure. A group of college students had systolic blood pressure readings that ranged from 119.5 to 134.5 inclusive. Let x represent the value of the systolic blood pressure readings. Use inequalities to describe this range of values, and graph the corresponding interval on a number line. †

118. Population projections. Population projections suggest that by the year 2050, the number of people 60 years old or older in the United States will be about 107 million. In 1950, the number of people 60 years old or older in the United States was 30 million. Let x represent the number (in millions) of people in the United States who are 60 years old or older. Use inequalities to describe this population range from 1950 to 2050, and graph the corresponding interval on a number line. *Source:* U.S. Census Bureau. †

119. Heart rate. For exercise to be most beneficial, the optimum heart rate for a 20-year-old person is 120 beats per minute. Use absolute value notation to write an expression that describes the difference between the heart rate achieved by each of the following 20-year-old people and the ideal exercise heart rate. Then evaluate that expression.
a. Latasha: 124 beats per minute $|124 - 120| = 4$
b. Frances: 137 beats per minute $|137 - 120| = 17$
c. Ignacio: 114 beats per minute $|114 - 120| = 6$

120. Downloading music. To download a 4-MB song with a 56-Kbs modem takes an average of 15 minutes. Use absolute value notation to write an expression that describes the difference between this average time and the actual time it took to download the following songs. Then evaluate that expression.
a. *Believe* (Cher): 14 minutes $|15 - 14| = 1$
b. *Caged Bird* (Alicia Keys): 17.5 minutes
c. *Somewhere* (Barbra Streisand): 15 minutes

In Exercises 121 and 122 use the physical interpretation to determine the domain of the variable.

121. Depth and pressure. The pressure p, in pounds per square inch, is related to the depth d, in feet below the surface of an ocean, by $p = \dfrac{5}{11}d + 15$. What is the domain of the variable p? $[0, \infty)$

122. Volume. The volume V of a box that has a square base with a 2-foot side and a height of h feet is $V = 4h$. What is the domain of the variable h? $(0, \infty)$

123. Weight vs. height. The average weight w, in pounds, of a male between 5 feet and 5 feet, 10 inches, tall is related to his height h by $w = \left(\dfrac{11}{2}\right)h - 220$. What is the domain (in inches) of the variable h? $[60, 70]$

124. Pay per hour. The weekly pay A a worker receives for working a 40-hour week or less is given by $A = 10h$, where h represents the number of hours worked in that week. What is the domain of the variable h? $[0, 40]$

Negative calories. In Exercises 125 and 126, use the fact that eating 100 grams of broccoli (a negative-calorie food) actually results in a net *loss* of 55 calories.

125. If a cheeseburger has 522.5 calories, how many grams of broccoli would a person have to consume to have a net gain of zero calories?   950 gr

126. Carmen ate 600 grams of broccoli and now wants to eat just enough French fries so that she has a net calorie intake of zero. If a small order of fries has 165 calories, how many orders does she have to eat?   2 orders

Answers:
116. a. $A = \{2005 \text{ Lexus SC430}\}$
   b. $B = \{2005 \text{ Lexus SC430}, 2005 \text{ Lincoln Town Car}\}$
   c. $C = \{2005 \text{ Lexus SC430}, 2005 \text{ Lincoln Town Car}, 2005 \text{ Infinity G35 Sport Coupe}\}$
   e. $B \cap C = \{2005 \text{ Lexus SC430}, 2005 \text{ Lincoln Town Car}\}$
   f. $A \cup B = \{2005 \text{ Lexus SC430}, 2005 \text{ Lincoln Town Car}\}$
   g. $A \cup C = \{2005 \text{ Lexus SC430}, 2005 \text{ Lincoln Town Car}, 2005 \text{ Infinity G35 Sport Coupe}\}$

Answers:
120. b. $|15 - 17.5| = 2.5$ **c.** $|15 - 15| = 0$

Integer Exponents and Scientific Notation

BEFORE STARTING THIS SECTION, REVIEW

1. Properties of opposites (Section P.1, page 14)

2. Variables (Section P.1, page 3)

3. Decimal notation (Section P.1, page 4)

OBJECTIVES

1 Learn to use integer exponents.

2 Learn to use the rules of exponents.

3 Learn to simplify exponential expressions.

4 Learn to use scientific notation.

Coffee and Candy Consumption in America

In 2002, Americans drank over 2,649,000,000 pounds of coffee and spent more than 13 billion dollars on candy and other confectionery products. The American population at that time was about 280 million. Because our day-to-day activities bring us into contact with much more manageable quantities, most people find large numbers like those just cited a bit difficult to understand. Using exponents, the method of scientific notation allows us to write large and small quantities in a manner that makes comparing such quantities fairly easy. In turn, these comparisons help us get a better perspective on these quantities. In Example 10 of this section, without relying on a calculator, we will see that if we distribute the cost of the candy and other confectionery products used in 2002 evenly among all individuals in the United States, each person would spend over $46. Distributing the coffee used in 2002 evenly among all individuals in the United States gives each person about $9\frac{1}{2}$ pounds of coffee. ■

---

1 Learn to use integer exponents.

Integer Exponents

The area of a square with side 5 feet is $5 \cdot 5 = 25$ square feet.
The volume of a cube whose sides are each 5 feet is $5 \cdot 5 \cdot 5 = 125$ cubic feet.

5 ft

5 ft

Area = 5·5 square feet

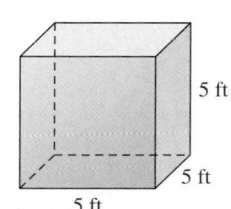

5 ft

5 ft

5 ft

Volume = 5·5·5 cubic feet

A shorter notation for $5 \cdot 5$ is 5^2 and for $5 \cdot 5 \cdot 5$ is 5^3. The number 5 is called the *base* for both 5^2 and 5^3. The number 2 is called the *exponent* in the expression 5^2 and indicates that the base 5 appears as a factor twice.

Definition of a Positive Integer Exponent

If a is a real number and n is a positive integer, then

$$a^n = \underbrace{a \cdot a \cdot \ldots \cdot a}_{n \text{ factors}},$$

where a is the **base** and n is the **exponent**. We adopt the convention that $a^1 = a$.

EXAMPLE 1 Evaluating Expressions that Use Exponents

Evaluate each expression.

a. 5^3 **b.** $(-3)^2$ **c.** -3^2 **d.** $(-2)^3$

Solution

a. $5^3 = 5 \cdot 5 \cdot 5 = 125$

b. $(-3)^2 = (-3)(-3) = 9$ $(-3)^2$ is the opposite of 3, squared.

c. $-3^2 = -3 \cdot 3 = -9$ Multiplication of $3 \cdot 3$ occurs first. (-3^2 is the opposite of 3^2.)

d. $(-2)^3 = (-2)(-2)(-2) = -8$ ▪ ▪ ▪

PRACTICE PROBLEM 1   Evaluate the following.

a. 2^3 **b.** $(3a)^2$ **c.** $\left(\dfrac{1}{2}\right)^4$ ▪

In Example 1, pay careful attention to the fact (from **b** and **c**) that $(-3)^2 \neq -3^2$. In $(-3)^2$, the parentheses indicate that the exponent 2 applies to the base -3, whereas in -3^2, the absence of parentheses indicates that the exponent applies only to the base 3. When n is even, $(-a)^n \neq -a^n$ for $a \neq 0$.

TECHNOLOGY CONNECTION

〰️ The notation for 5^3 on a graphing calculator is 5^3. Any expression on a calculator enclosed in parentheses and followed by ^n will be raised to the nth power. A common error is to forget parentheses when computing an expression such as $(-3)^2$, with the result being -3^2.

```
5^3
              125
(-3)^2
                9
-3^2
               -9
■
```

Definition of Zero and Negative Integer Exponents

For any nonzero number a and any positive integer n,

$$a^0 = 1 \text{ and } a^{-n} = \frac{1}{a^n}.$$

Negative exponents indicate the **reciprocal** of a number. Zero cannot be used as a base with a negative exponent, because zero does not have a reciprocal. Furthermore, **0^0 is not defined.** We shall assume throughout this book that the base is not equal to zero if any of the exponents is negative or zero.

> **EXAMPLE 2**   **Evaluating Expressions that Use Zero or Negative Exponents**

Evaluate. **a.** $(-5)^{-2}$ **b.** -5^{-2} **c.** 8^0 **d.** $\left(\dfrac{2}{3}\right)^{-3}$

Solution

a. $(-5)^{-2} = \dfrac{1}{(-5)^2} = \dfrac{1}{25}$ The exponent -2 applies to the base -5.

b. $-5^{-2} = -\dfrac{1}{5^2} = -\dfrac{1}{25}$ The exponent -2 applies to the base 5.

c. $8^0 = 1$ By definition

d. $\left(\dfrac{2}{3}\right)^{-3} = \dfrac{1}{\left(\dfrac{2}{3}\right)^3} = \dfrac{1}{\dfrac{8}{27}} = \dfrac{27}{8}$ $\left(\dfrac{2}{3}\right)^3 = \dfrac{2}{3}\cdot\dfrac{2}{3}\cdot\dfrac{2}{3} = \dfrac{8}{27}$

■ ■ ■

PRACTICE PROBLEM 2   Evaluate.

a. 2^{-1} **b.** $\left(\dfrac{4}{5}\right)^0$ **c.** $\left(\dfrac{3}{2}\right)^{-2}$ ■

In Example 2, we see that parts **a** and **b** give different results. In part **a** the base is 5 and the exponent is -2, whereas in part **b** we evaluate the ***opposite*** of the expression with base 5 and exponent -2.

2 Learn to use the rules of exponents.

Rules of Exponents

We now review the rules of exponents.

> **RECALL**
>
> In Equation (1), remember that a must be nonzero if the exponent is either zero or negative.

PRODUCT RULE OF EXPONENTS

If a is a real number and m and n are integers, then

(1) $a^m \cdot a^n = a^{m+n}.$

> **EXAMPLE 3**   **Using the Product Rule of Exponents**

Simplify. Use the product rule and (if necessary) the definition of a negative exponent or reciprocal to write each answer without negative exponents.

a. $2x^3 \cdot x^5$ **b.** $x^7 \cdot x^{-7}$ **c.** $(-4y^2)(3y^7)$ **d.** $\dfrac{1}{3^{-2}}$

Solution

a. $2x^3 \cdot x^5 = 2x^{3+5} = 2x^8$ Add exponents: $3 + 5 = 8$.

b. $x^7 \cdot x^{-7} = x^{7+(-7)} = x^0 = 1$ Add exponents: $7 + (-7) = 0$; simplify.

c. $(-4y^2)(3y^7) = (-4)3y^2y^7$ Group the factors with variable bases.
$\qquad = -12y^{2+7}$ Add exponents,
$\qquad = -12y^9$ $2 + 7 = 9$.

Continued on next page.

To evaluate an expression such as 5^{3+4} on a calculator, you must enclose $3+4$ in parentheses. Otherwise, 4 is added to the result of 5^3.

```
5^(3+4)
             78125
5^3+4
               129
■
```

d. $\dfrac{1}{3^{-2}} = \dfrac{1}{\frac{1}{3^2}} = 3^2 = 9$ Negative exponents result in reciprocals.

■ ■ ■

PRACTICE PROBLEM 3 Simplify. Write each answer without using negative exponents.

a. $x^2 \cdot 3x^7$ **b.** $\dfrac{1}{4^{-2}}$ ■

QUOTIENT RULE FOR EXPONENTS

If a is a nonzero real number and m and n are integers, then

(2) $\dfrac{a^m}{a^n} = a^{m-n}.$

STUDY TIP

Remember that if $a \ne 0$, then $a^0 = 1$, so it is okay for a denominator to contain a nonzero base with a zero exponent. For example, $\dfrac{3}{5^0} = \dfrac{3}{1} = 3.$

EXAMPLE 4 **Using the Quotient Rule of Exponents**

Simplify. Use the quotient rule to write each answer without negative exponents.

a. $\dfrac{5^{10}}{5^{10}}$ **b.** $\dfrac{2^{-1}}{2^3}$ **c.** $\dfrac{x^{-3}}{x^5}$

Solution

a. $\dfrac{5^{10}}{5^{10}} = 5^{10-10} = 5^0 = 1$

b. $\dfrac{2^{-1}}{2^3} = 2^{-1-3} = 2^{-4} = \dfrac{1}{2^4} = \dfrac{1}{16}$

c. $\dfrac{x^{-3}}{x^5} = x^{-3-5} = x^{-8} = \dfrac{1}{x^8}.$

■ ■ ■

PRACTICE PROBLEM 4 Simplify. Write each answer without negative exponents.

a. $\dfrac{3^4}{3^0}$ **b.** $\dfrac{5}{5^{-2}}$ **c.** $\dfrac{2x^3}{3x^{-4}}$ ■

POWER RULE FOR EXPONENTS

If a is a real number and m and n are integers, then

(3) $(a^m)^n = a^{mn}.$

EXAMPLE 5 **Using the Power Rule of Exponents**

Simplify. Use the power rule to write each answer without negative exponents.

a. $(5^2)^0$ **b.** $[(-3)^2]^3$ **c.** $(x^3)^{-1}$ **d.** $(x^{-2})^{-3}.$

Solution

a. $(5^2)^0 = 5^{2 \cdot 0} = 5^0 = 1$

b. $[(-3)^2]^3 = (-3)^{2 \cdot 3} = (-3)^6 = 729$ For $(-3)^6$, the base is -3.

c. $(x^3)^{-1} = x^{3(-1)} = x^{-3} = \dfrac{1}{x^3}$

d. $(x^{-2})^{-3} = x^{(-2)(-3)} = x^6$ ■ ■ ■

PRACTICE PROBLEM 5   Simplify. Write each answer without negative exponents.

a. $(7^{-5})^0$ **b.** $(7^0)^{-5}$ **c.** $(x^{-1})^8$ **d.** $(x^{-2})^{-5}$ ■

POWER-OF-A-PRODUCT RULE

If a and b are real numbers and n is an integer, then

(4) $$(a \cdot b)^n = a^n \cdot b^n.$$

EXAMPLE 6   Using the Power-of-a-Product Rule

Simplify. Use the power-of-a-product rule to write each expression without negative exponents.

a. $(3x)^2$ **b.** $(-3x)^{-2}$ **c.** $(-3^2)^3$ **d.** $(xy)^{-4}$ **e.** $(x^2y)^3$

Solution

a. $(3x)^2 = 3^2x^2 = 9x^2$

b. $(-3x)^{-2} = \dfrac{1}{(-3x)^2} = \dfrac{1}{(-3)^2x^2} = \dfrac{1}{9x^2}$ Negative exponents result in reciprocals.

c. $(-3^2)^3 = (-1 \cdot 3^2)^3 = (-1)^3(3^2)^3 = (-1)(3^6) = -729$

d. $(xy)^{-4} = \dfrac{1}{(xy)^4} = \dfrac{1}{x^4y^4}$ Negative exponents result in reciprocals.

e. $(x^2y)^3 = (x^2)^3y^3 = x^{2 \cdot 3}y^3 = x^6y^3$ Recall that $(x^2)^3 = x^{2 \cdot 3}$.   ■ ■ ■

PRACTICE PROBLEM 6   Simplify. Write each answer without negative exponents.

a. $\left(\dfrac{1}{2}x\right)^{-1}$ **b.** $(5x^{-1})^2$ **c.** $(xy^2)^3$ **d.** $(x^{-2}y)^{-3}$ ■

POWER-OF-A-QUOTIENT RULES

If a and b are real numbers and n is an integer, then

(5) $$\left(\dfrac{a}{b}\right)^n = \dfrac{a^n}{b^n}$$ (6) $$\left(\dfrac{a}{b}\right)^{-n} = \left(\dfrac{b}{a}\right)^n = \dfrac{b^n}{a^n}.$$

EXAMPLE 7   Using the Power-of-a-Quotient Rules

Simplify. Use the power-of-a-quotient rules to write each answer without negative exponents.

a. $\left(\dfrac{3}{5}\right)^3$ **b.** $\left(\dfrac{2}{3}\right)^{-2}$

Solution

a. $\left(\dfrac{3}{5}\right)^3 = \dfrac{3^3}{5^5} = \dfrac{27}{125}$ Equation (5)

b. $\left(\dfrac{2}{3}\right)^{-2} = \left(\dfrac{3}{2}\right)^2 = \dfrac{3^2}{2^2} = \dfrac{9}{4}$ Equations (5) and (6)   ■ ■ ■

PRACTICE PROBLEM 7   Simplify. Write each answer without negative exponents.

a. $\left(\dfrac{1}{3}\right)^2$ **b.** $\left(\dfrac{10}{7}\right)^{-2}$ ■

3 Learn to simplify exponential expressions.

Simplifying Exponential Expressions

RULES FOR SIMPLIFYING EXPONENTIAL EXPRESSIONS

An exponential expression is considered **simplified** when

(i)   each base appears only once,

(ii)   no negative or zero exponents are used, and

(iii)   no power is raised to a power.

EXAMPLE 8   Simplifying Exponential Expressions

Simplify the following: **a.** $(-4x^2y^3)(7x^3y)$ **b.** $\left(\dfrac{x^5}{2y^{-3}}\right)^{-3}$.

Solution

a. $(-4x^2y^3)(7x^3y) = (-4)(7)x^2x^3y^3y$ Group factors with the same base.

$= -28x^{2+3}y^{3+1}$ Apply the power rule to add exponents: remember that $y = y^1$.

$= -28x^5y^4$

b. $\left(\dfrac{x^5}{2y^{-3}}\right)^{-3} = \dfrac{(x^5)^{-3}}{(2y^{-3})^{-3}}$ The exponent -3 is applied to both the numerator and the denominator.

$= \dfrac{x^{5(-3)}}{2^{-3}(y^{-3})^{-3}}$ Multiply exponents in the numerator; apply the exponent -3 to each factor in the denominator.

$= \dfrac{x^{-15}}{2^{-3}y^{(-3)(-3)}}$ Power rule for exponents

$$= \frac{x^{-15}}{2^{-3}y^9}$$ $5(-3) = -15; (-3)(-3) = 9$

$$= \frac{x^{-15}x^{15}2^3}{x^{15}2^3 2^{-3}y^9}$$ Multiply numerator and denominator by $x^{15}2^3$.

$$= \frac{2^3}{x^{15}y^9}$$ $x^{-15}x^{15} = x^0 = 1, 2^3 2^{-3} = 2^0 = 1$

$$= \frac{8}{x^{15}y^9}$$ $2^3 = 8$ ■ ■ ■

PRACTICE PROBLEM 8   Simplify each expression.

a. $(2x^4)^{-2}$ **b.** $\dfrac{x^2(-y)^3}{(xy^2)^3}$ ■

4 Learn to use scientific notation.

Scientific Notation

Scientific measurements and calculations often involve very large or very small positive numbers. For example, 1 gram of oxygen contains approximately

$$37,600,000,000,000,000,000,000 \text{ atoms,}$$

and the mass of one oxygen atom is approximately

$$0.0000000000000000000000266 \text{ gram.}$$

Such numbers contain so many zeros that they are awkward to work with in calculations. Fortunately, scientific notation provides a better way to write and work with such large or small numbers.

Scientific notation consists of the product of a number smaller than 10, but no smaller than 1, and a power of 10. That is, scientific notation of a number has the form

$$c \times 10^n,$$

where c is a real number in decimal notation such that $1 \leq c < 10$ and n is an integer.

CONVERTING A DECIMAL NUMBER TO SCIENTIFIC NOTATION

1. Count the number, n, of places the decimal point in the given number must be moved to obtain a number c with $1 \leq c < 10$.

2. If the decimal point is moved n places to the left, the scientific notation is $c \times 10^n$. If the decimal point is moved n places to the right, the scientific notation is $c \times 10^{-n}$.

3. If the decimal point does not need to be moved, the scientific notation is $c \times 10^0$.

EXAMPLE 9   **Converting a Decimal Number to Scientific Notation**

Write each decimal number in scientific notation.

a. 421,000   **b.** 10   **c.** 3.621   **d.** 0.000561

Continued on next page.

TECHNOLOGY CONNECTION

 To write numbers in scientific notation on a graphing calculator, you first must change the "mode" to "scientific." Then, on most graphing calculators, you will see the number displayed as a decimal number, followed by the letter "E," followed by the exponent for 10. So 421000 is shown as 4.21E5, and 0.0018 is shown as 1.8E-3. Some calculators omit the "E."

```
421000
         4.21 E5
0.0018
         1.8 E -3
■
```

STUDY TIP

Note that "small" numbers (numbers less than 1) will have negative exponents in scientific notation and "large" numbers (numbers greater than 10) will have positive exponents in scientific notation.

Solution

a. Since $421{,}000 = 421000.0$, count five spaces to move the decimal point between the 4 and the 2 and produce a number between 1 and 10, namely 4.21.

$$421{,}000 = 4\,2\,1\,0\,0\,0.$$

5 places

Since the decimal point is moved five places to the *left,* the exponent is positive and we write

$$421{,}000 = 4.21 \times 10^5.$$

b. The decimal point for 10 is to the right of the units digit. Count one place to move the decimal point between 1 and 0 and produce a number between 1 and 10, but less than 10, namely 1.

$$10 = 1\,0\,.\,0$$

1 place

Since the decimal point is moved one place to the *left,* the exponent is positive and we write

$$10 = 1.0 \times 10^1.$$

c. The number 3.621 is already between 1 and 10, so the decimal does not need to be moved. We write

$$3.621 = 3.621 \times 10^0.$$

d. The decimal point in 0.000561 must be moved between the 5 and the 6 to produce a number between 1 and 10, namely, 5.61. We count four places as follows:

$$0.0\,0\,0\,5\,6\,1.$$

4 places

Since the decimal point is moved four places to the *right,* the exponent is negative and we write

$$0.000561 = 5.61 \times 10^{-4}.$$ ■ ■ ■

PRACTICE PROBLEM 9   Write 732,000 in scientific notation.   ■

EXAMPLE 10   **Distributing Coffee and Candy in America**

At the beginning of this section, we mentioned that in 2002 Americans drank 2649 million pounds of coffee and spent more than 13 billion dollars on candy and other confectionery products. To see how these products would be evenly distributed among the population, we first convert those numbers to scientific notation.

2649 million is $2{,}649{,}000{,}000 = 2.649 \times 10^9$.
13 billion is $13{,}000{,}000{,}000 = 1.3 \times 10^{10}$.

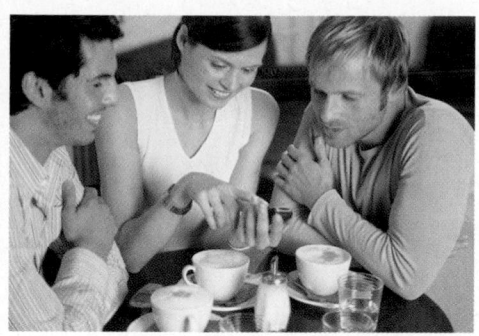

The U.S. population in 2002 was about 280 million, and 280 million is $280,000,000 = 2.8 \times 10^8$.

To distribute the coffee evenly among the population, we divide:

$$\frac{2.649 \times 10^9}{2.8 \times 10^8} = \frac{2.649}{2.8} \times 10 \approx 0.95 \times 10 = 9.5, \text{ or } 9\frac{1}{2} \text{ pounds per person.}$$

To distribute the cost of the candy evenly among the population, we divide:

$$\frac{1.3 \times 10^{10}}{2.8 \times 10^8} = \frac{1.3}{2.8} \times 10^2 \approx 0.464 \times 10^2 = 46.4, \text{ or about } \$46 \text{ per person.} \quad \blacksquare \ \blacksquare \ \blacksquare$$

PRACTICE PROBLEM 10   If the amount spent on candy consumption remains unchanged when the U.S. population reaches 300 million, what is the cost per person when cost is distributed evenly throughout the population?   ■

A Exercises   Basic Skills and Concepts

In Exercises 1–10, name the exponent and the base.

1. 17^3 Exponent: 3, base: 17
2. 10^2 Exponent: 2, base: 10
3. 9^0 Exponent: 0, base: 9
4. $(-2)^0$ Exponent: 0, base: -2
5. $(-5)^5$ Exponent: 5, base: -5
6. $(-99)^2$ †
7. -10^3 Exponent: 3, base: 10
8. $-(-3)^7$ †
9. a^2 Exponent: 2, base: a
10. $(-b)^3$ Exponent: 3, base: $-b$

In Exercises 11–36, evaluate each expression.

11. 6^1 6
12. 3^4 81
13. 7^0 1
14. $(-8)^0$ 1
15. $(2^3)^2$ 64
16. $(3^2)^3$ 729
17. $(3^2)^{-2}$ †
18. $(7^2)^{-1}$ †
19. $(5^{-2})^3$ †
20. $(5^{-1})^3$ †
21. $(4^{-3}) \cdot (4^5)$ 16
22. $(7^{-2}) \cdot (7^3)$ 7
23. $3^0 + 10^0$ 2
24. $5^0 - 9^0$ 0
25. $3^{-2} + \left(\frac{1}{3}\right)^2$ $\frac{2}{9}$
26. $5^{-2} + \left(\frac{1}{5}\right)^2$ $\frac{2}{25}$
27. $\frac{2^{11}}{2^{10}}$ 2
28. $\frac{3^6}{3^8}$ $\frac{1}{9}$
29. $\frac{(5^3)^4}{5^{12}}$ 1
30. $\frac{(9^5)^2}{9^8}$ 81
31. $\frac{2^5 \cdot 3^{-2}}{2^4 \cdot 3^{-3}}$ 6
32. $\frac{4^{-2} \cdot 5^3}{4^{-3} \cdot 5}$ 100
33. $\frac{-5^{-2}}{2^{-1}}$ $-\frac{2}{25}$
34. $\frac{-7^{-2}}{3^{-1}}$ $-\frac{3}{49}$
35. $\left(\frac{11}{7}\right)^{-2}$ $\frac{49}{121}$
36. $\left(\frac{13}{5}\right)^2$ $\frac{25}{169}$

In Exercises 37–74, simplify each expression. Write your answers without negative exponents. Whenever an exponent is negative or zero, assume that the base is not zero.

37. x^4y^0 x^4
38. $x^{-1}y^0$ †
39. $x^{-1}y$ †
40. x^2y^{-2} †
41. $-8x^{-1}$ †
42. $(-8x)^{-1}$ †
43. $x^{-1}(3y^0)$ †
44. $x^{-3}(3y^2)$ †
45. $x^{-1}y^{-2}$ †
46. $x^{-3}y^{-2}$ †
47. $(x^{-3})^4$ †
48. $(x^{-5})^2$ †
49. $(x^{-11})^{-3}$ x^{33}
50. $(x^{-4})^{-12}$ x^{48}
51. $-3(xy)^5$ $-3x^5y^5$
52. $-8(xy)^6$ $-8x^6y^6$
53. $4(xy^{-1})^2$ †
54. $6(x^{-1}y)^3$ †
55. $3(x^{-1}y)^{-5}$ †
56. $-5(xy^{-1})^{-6}$ †
57. $\frac{(x^3)^2}{(x^2)^5}$ $\frac{1}{x^4}$
58. $\frac{x^2}{(x^3)^4}$ $\frac{1}{x^{10}}$
59. $\left(\frac{2xy}{x^2}\right)^3$ $\frac{8y^3}{x^3}$
60. $\left(\frac{5xy}{x^3}\right)^4$ $\frac{625y^4}{x^8}$
61. $\left(\frac{-3x^2y}{x}\right)^5$ $-243x^5y^5$
62. $\left(\frac{-2xy^2}{y}\right)^3$ $-8x^3y^3$
63. $\left(\frac{-3x}{5}\right)^{-2}$ $\frac{25}{9x^2}$
64. $\left(\frac{-5y}{3}\right)^{-4}$ $\frac{81}{625y^4}$
65. $\left(\frac{4x^{-2}}{xy^5}\right)^3$ $\frac{64}{x^9y^{15}}$
66. $\left(\frac{3x^2y}{y^3}\right)^5$ $\frac{243x^{10}}{y^{10}}$
67. $\frac{x^3y^{-3}}{x^{-2}y}$ $\frac{x^5}{y^4}$
68. $\frac{x^2y^{-2}}{x^{-1}y^2}$ $\frac{x^3}{y^4}$
69. $\frac{27x^{-3}y^5}{9x^{-4}y^7}$ $\frac{3x}{y^2}$
70. $\frac{15x^5y^{-2}}{3x^7y^{-3}}$ $\frac{5y}{x^2}$

†Due to space constrictions, answers to these exercises may be found in the Answers beginning on page A–1 in the back of the book.

71. $\dfrac{5a^{-2}bc^2}{a^4b^{-3}c^2}$ $\dfrac{5b^4}{a^6}$

72. $\dfrac{(-3)^2a^5(bc)^2}{(-2)^3a^2b^3c^4}$ $-\dfrac{9a^3}{8bc^2}$

73. $\left(\dfrac{xy^{-3}z^{-2}}{x^2y^{-4}z^3}\right)^{-3}$ $\dfrac{x^3z^{15}}{y^3}$

74. $\left(\dfrac{xy^{-2}z^{-1}}{x^{-5}yz^{-8}}\right)^{-1}$ $\dfrac{y^3}{x^6z^7}$

77. 850,000 8.5×10^5

78. 205,000 2.05×10^5

79. 0.007 7×10^{-3}

80. 0.0019 1.9×10^{-3}

81. 0.00000275 2.75×10^{-6}

82. 0.0000038 3.8×10^{-6}

In Exercises 75–82, write each number in scientific notation.

75. 125 1.25×10^2

76. 247 2.47×10^2

B Exercises   Applying the Concepts

In Exercises 83 and 84, use the fact that when you uniformly stretch or shrink a three-dimensional object in every direction by a factor of a, the volume of the resulting figure is scaled by a factor of a^3. For example, when you uniformly scale (stretch or shrink) a three-dimensional object by a factor of 2, the volume of the resulting figure is scaled by a factor of 2^3, or 8.

83. A display in the shape of a baseball bat has a volume of 135 cubic feet. Find the volume of the display that results by uniformly scaling the figure by a factor of 2. 1080 ft^3

84. A display in the shape of a football has a volume of 675 cubic inches. Find the volume of the display that results by uniformly scaling the figure by a factor of 3. $18,225 \text{ in}^3$

85. The area A of a square with side of length x is given by $A = x^2$. Use this relationship to
 a. Verify that doubling the length of the side of a square floor increases the area of the floor by a factor of 2^2. $(2x)(2x) = 4x^2 = 2^2A$
 b. Verify that tripling the length of the side of a square floor increases the area of the floor by a factor of 3^2. †

86. The area A of a circle with diameter d is given by $A = \pi\left(\dfrac{d}{2}\right)^2$. Use this relationship to
 a. Verify that doubling the length of the diameter of a circular skating rink increases the area of the rink by a factor of 2^2. †
 b. Verify that tripling the length of the diameter of a circular skating rink increases the area of the rink by a factor of 3^2. †

87. The cross section of one type of weight-bearing rod (the surface you would get if you sliced the rod perpendicular to its axis) used in the Olympics is a square, as shown in the accompanying figure. The rod can handle a stress of 25,000 pounds per square inch (psi). The relationship between the stress S that the rod can handle, the load F the rod must carry, and the width w of the cross section is given by the equation $Sw^2 = F$. If $w = 0.25$ inch, find the load the rod can support. $F = 1562.5$

Figure for Exercise 87.

88. The cross section of one type of weight-bearing rod (the surface you would get if you sliced the rod perpendicular to its axis) used in the Olympics is a circle, as shown in the figure. The rod can handle a stress of 10,000 pounds per square inch (psi). The relationship between the stress S that the rod can handle, the load F the rod must carry, and the diameter d of the cross section is given by the equation $S\pi(d/2)^2 = F$. If $d = 1.5$ inches, find the load the rod can support. Use $\pi \approx 3.14$ in your calculation. $F = 17{,}662.5$

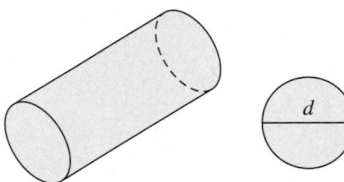

89. Complete the following table:

Celestial Body	Equatorial Diameter (km)	Scientific Notation
Earth	12,700	1.27×10^4 (km)
Moon	3480	3.48×10^3 (km)
Sun	1,390,000	1.39×10^6 (km)
Jupiter	134,000	1.34×10^5 (km)
Mercury	4800	4.8×10^3 (km)

In Exercises 90–95, express the number in each statement in scientific notation.

90. One gram of oxygen contains about

37,600,000,000,000,000,000,000 atoms.

91. One gram of hydrogen contains about

602,000,000,000,000,000,000 atoms.

92. One oxygen atom weighs about

0.0000000000000000000266 kilogram.

93. One hydrogen atom weighs about

0.00000000000000000000167 kilogram.

94. The distance from Earth to the moon is about

380,000,000 meters. 3.8×10^8 m

95. The mass of Earth is about

5,980,000,000,000,000,000,000,000 kilograms.

Answers:
90. 3.76×10^{22} atoms   **91.** 6.02×10^{20} atoms
92. 2.66×10^{-20} kg   **93.** 1.67×10^{-21} kg

Answer:
95. 5.98×10^{24} kg

Polynomials

BEFORE STARTING THIS SECTION, REVIEW

1. Associative, commutative, and distributive properties (Section P.1, page 12)

2. Properties of opposites (Section P.1, page 14)

3. Definition of subtraction (Section P.1, page 13)

4. Power, product, and power-of-a-product rules for exponents (Section P.2, page 21)

OBJECTIVES

1 Learn polynomial vocabulary.

2 Learn to add and subtract polynomials.

3 Learn to multiply polynomials.

4 Learn to use special-product formulas.

Galileo and Free-Falling Objects

At one time, it was widely believed that heavy objects should fall faster than lighter objects, or, more exactly, that the speed of falling objects ought to be proportional to their weights. So if one object is four times as heavy as another, the heavier object should fall four times as fast as the lighter one. Legend has it that Galileo Galilei (1564–1642) disproved this theory by dropping two balls of equal size, one made of lead and the other of balsa wood, from the top of Italy's Leaning Tower of Pisa. Both balls are said to have reached the ground at the same instant when they were released simultaneously from the top of the Tower.

In fact, such experiments "work" properly only in a vacuum, where objects of different mass do fall at the same rate. In the absence of a vacuum, air resistance may greatly affect the rate at which different objects fall. Whether or not Galileo's experiment was actually performed, astronaut David R. Scott successfully performed a version of Galileo's experiment (using a feather and a hammer) on the surface of the moon on August 2, 1971. It turns out that, on Earth (ignoring air resistance), regardless of the weight of the object we hold at rest and then drop, the expression $16t^2$ gives the distance in feet the object falls in t seconds. If we throw the object down with an initial velocity of v_0 feet per second, then the distance the object travels in t seconds is given by the expression

$$16t^2 + v_0 t.$$

In Example 1, we will evaluate such expressions. ■

Polynomial Vocabulary

The height (in feet) of a golf ball above the driving range t seconds after being driven from the tee (at 70 feet per second) is given by the polynomial $70t - t^2$. After 2 seconds $(t = 2)$, the ball is $70(2) - (2)^2 = 136$ feet above the ground. *Polynomials* such as $70t - t^2$ appear frequently in applications.

We begin by reviewing the basic vocabulary of polynomials. A **monomial** is the simplest polynomial in the variable x; it contains one term, and has the form ax^k, where a is a constant and k is either a positive integer or zero. The constant a is called the **coefficient** of the monomial. For $a \neq 0$, the integer k is called the **degree** of the monomial. If $a = 0$, the monomial is 0 and has **no degree.** Any variable may be used in place of x to form a monomial in that variable.

Following are some examples of monomials:

$2x^5$	The coefficient is 2 and the degree is 5.
$-3x^2$	The coefficient is -3 and the degree is 2.
-7	$-7 = -7(1) = -7x^0$. The coefficient is -7 and the degree is 0.
$8x$	The coefficient is 8 and the degree is $1 (x = x^1)$.
x^{12}	The coefficient is $1 (x^{12} = 1 \cdot x^{12})$ and the degree is 12.
$-x^4$	The coefficient is $-1 (-x^4 = (-1) \cdot x^4)$ and the degree is 4.

The expression $5x^{-3}$ is not a monomial, since the exponent of x is negative.

Two monomials in the same variable with the same degree can be combined into one monomial by the distributive property. For example, $-3x^5$ and $9x^5$ can be added: $-3x^5 + 9x^5 = (-3 + 9)x^5 = 6x^5$. Or $-3x^5$ and $9x^5$ can be subtracted: $-3x^5 - 9x^5 = (-3 - 9)x^5 = -12x^5$. Two monomials in the same variable with the same degree are called **like terms.**

POLYNOMIALS IN ONE VARIABLE

A **polynomial** in x is any sum of monomials in x. By combining like terms, we can write any polynomial in the form

$$a_n x^n + a_{n-1}x^{n-1} + \cdots + a_2 x^2 + a_1 x + a_0,$$

where n is either a positive integer or zero and $a_n, a_{n-1}, \ldots a_1, a_0$ are constants, called the **coefficients** of the polynomial. If $a_n \neq 0$, then n, the largest exponent on x, is called the **degree,** and a_n is called the **leading coefficient,** of the polynomial. The monomials $a_n x^n, a_{n-1}x^{n-1} \ldots, a_2 x^2, a_1 x$, and a_0 are the **terms** of the polynomial. The monomial $a_n x^n$ is the **leading term** of the polynomial and a_0 is the **constant term.**

Polynomials can be classified according to the number of terms they have. Polynomials with one term are called **monomials,** polynomials with two *unlike* terms are called **binomials,** and polynomials with three *unlike* terms are called **trinomials.** Polynomials with more than three unlike terms do not have special names.

By agreement, the only polynomial that has *no* degree is the **zero polynomial,** which results when all the coefficients are 0. It is easiest to find the degree of a polynomial when it is written in **descending order**—that is, when the exponents decrease from left to right. In this case, the degree is the exponent of the leading term. A polynomial written in descending order is said to be in **standard form.**

The symbols $a_0, a_1, a_2, \ldots a_n$ in the general notation for a polynomial,

$$a_n x^n + a_{n-1} x^{n-1} + \cdots + a_2 x^2 + a_1 x + a_0$$

are just constants; the numbers to the lower right of a are called subscripts. The notation a_2 is read "a sub 2," a_1 is read "a sub 1," and a_0 is read "a sub 0." This type of notation is used when a large or indefinite number of constants are required. The terms of the polynomial $5x^2 + 3x + 1$ are $5x^2$, $3x$, and 1; the coefficients are 5, 3, and 1; and the degree is 2.

Note that the terms in the general form for a polynomial are connected by the addition symbol $+$. How do we handle $5x^2 - 3x + 1$? Since subtraction is defined in terms of addition, we rewrite

$$5x^2 - 3x + 1 = 5x^2 + (-3)x + 1$$

and see that the terms of $5x^2 - 3x + 1$ are $5x^2$, $-3x$, and 1, and the coefficients are $5, -3$, and 1. (The degree is 2.) Once we recognize this fact, we no longer actually rewrite the polynomial with the $+$ sign separating terms; we just remember that the "sign" is part of both the term and the coefficient.

EXAMPLE 1   Examining Free-Falling Objects

In our introductory discussion about Galileo and free-falling objects, we mentioned two very well-known polynomials:

1. $16t^2$ gives the distance in feet a free-falling object falls in t seconds.

2. $16t^2 + v_0 t$ gives the distance an object falls in t seconds when it is thrown down with an initial velocity of v_0 feet per second. Use these polynomials to

    a. Find how far a wallet dropped from the 86th-floor observatory of the Empire State Building will fall in 5 seconds.

    b. Find how far a quarter thrown down with an initial velocity of 10 feet per second from a hot-air balloon will travel after 5 seconds.

Solution

a. The value of $16t^2$ for $t = 5$ is $16(5)^2 = 400$. The wallet has fallen 400 feet.

b. We replace v_0 by 10 in the polynomial $16t^2 + v_0 t$ to get $16t^2 + 10t$. The value of $16t^2 + 10t$ for $t = 5$ is $16(5)^2 + 10(5) = 450$. The quarter has traveled 450 feet on its downward path after 5 seconds.   ■ ■ ■

PRACTICE PROBLEM 1   Use the information in Example 1 to find out how far a quarter thrown down with an initial velocity of 15 feet per second from a hot-air balloon has traveled after 7 seconds.   ■

2 Learn to add and subtract polynomials.

Adding and Subtracting Polynomials

Like monomials, polynomials are added and subtracted by combining like terms. By convention, we write polynomials in standard form.

EXAMPLE 2   Adding Polynomials

Find the sum of the polynomials

$$-4x^3 + 5x^2 + 7x - 2 \qquad \text{and} \qquad 6x^3 - 2x^2 - 8x - 5.$$

Horizontal Method: Group like terms, and then combine them.

$$(-4x^3 + 5x^2 + 7x - 2) + (6x^3 - 2x^2 - 8x - 5)$$
$$= (-4x^3 + 6x^3) + (5x^2 - 2x^2) + (7x - 8x) + (-2 - 5) \qquad \text{Group like terms.}$$
$$= 2x^3 + 3x^2 - x - 7 \qquad \text{Combine like terms.}$$

A second method for adding polynomials is to arrange them in columns so that like terms appear in the same column.

Column Method:

$$\begin{array}{r} -4x^3 + 5x^2 + 7x - 2 \\ (+)\ \ 6x^3 - 2x^2 - 8x - 5 \\ \hline 2x^3 + 3x^2 - \ x - 7\ \text{(answer)} \end{array}$$

■ ■ ■

PRACTICE PROBLEM 2   Find the sum of

$$7x^3 + 2x^2 - 5 \qquad \text{and} \qquad -2x^3 + 3x^2 + 2x + 1.$$

■

EXAMPLE 3   **Subtracting Polynomials**

Find the difference of the polynomials

$$9x^4 - 6x^3 + 4x^2 - 1 \qquad \text{and} \qquad 2x^4 - 11x^3 + 5x + 3.$$

Horizontal Method: First, using the definition of subtraction, change the sign of each term in the second polynomial. Then add the resulting polynomials by grouping like terms and combining them.

$$(9x^4 - 6x^3 + 4x^2 - 1) - (2x^4 - 11x^3 + 5x + 3)$$
$$= (9x^4 - 6x^3 + 4x^2 - 1) + (-2x^4 + 11x^3 - 5x - 3)$$
$$= (9x^4 - 2x^4) + (-6x^3 + 11x^3) + 4x^2 - 5x + (-1 - 3) \qquad \text{Group like terms.}$$
$$= 7x^4 + 5x^3 + 4x^2 - 5x - 4 \qquad \text{Combine like terms.}$$

The second method for finding the difference of polynomials requires arranging them in columns so that like terms appear in the same column.

Column Method: As before, to find the difference, we first change the sign of each term in the second polynomial and then add.

$$\begin{array}{r} 9x^4 - 6x^3 + 4x^2 \qquad - 1 \\ (+)-2x^4 + 11x^3 \qquad - 5x - 3 \qquad \text{Change signs and then add.} \\ \hline 7x^4 + 5x^3 + 4x^2 - 5x - 4\ \text{(answer)} \end{array}$$

■ ■ ■

PRACTICE PROBLEM 3   Find the difference of:

$$3x^4 - 5x^3 + 2x^2 + 7 \qquad \text{and} \qquad -2x^4 + 3x^2 + x - 5.$$

■

3 Learn to multiply polynomials.

Multiplying Polynomials

We have previously multiplied two monomials, such as $-3x^2$ and $5x^3$, by using the product rule for exponents: $a^m \cdot a^n = a^{m+n}$. We multiply a monomial and a polynomial by combining the product rule and the distributive property.

EXAMPLE 4   **Multiplying a Monomial and a Polynomial**

Multiply $4x^3$ and $3x^2 - 5x + 7$.

$$4x^3(3x^2 - 5x + 7)$$
$$= (4x^3)(3x^2) + (4x^3)(-5x) + (4x^3)(7) \quad \text{Distributive property}$$
$$= (4 \cdot 3)x^{3+2} + 4(-5)x^{3+1} + (4 \cdot 7)x^3 \quad \text{Multiply monomials.}$$
$$= 12x^5 - 20x^4 + 28x^3 \quad \text{Simplify.} \quad ■ \ ■ \ ■$$

PRACTICE PROBLEM 4   Multiply $-2x^3$ and $4x^2 + 2x - 5$.   ■

We can use the distributive property repeatedly to multiply any two polynomials. As with addition, there are two methods.

EXAMPLE 5   **Multiplying Polynomials**

Multiply $4x^2 + 3x$ and $x^2 + 2x - 3$.

Horizontal Method: We treat the second polynomial as a single term and use the distributive property, $(a + b)c = ac + bc$, to multiply it by each of the two terms in the first polynomial.

$$(4x^2 + 3x)(x^2 + 2x - 3)$$
$$= 4x^2(x^2 + 2x - 3) + 3x(x^2 + 2x - 3) \quad \text{Distributive property}$$
$$= 4x^2x^2 + 4x^22x + 4x^2(-3) + 3xx^2 + 3x2x + 3x(-3) \quad \text{Distributive property}$$
$$= 4x^4 + 8x^3 - 12x^2 + 3x^3 + 6x^2 - 9x \quad \text{Product rule}$$
$$= 4x^4 + (8x^3 + 3x^3) + (-12x^2 + 6x^2) - 9x \quad \text{Group like terms.}$$
$$= 4x^4 + 11x^3 - 6x^2 - 9x \quad \text{Combine like terms.}$$

The column method resembles the multiplication of two positive integers written in column form.

Column Method:

$$
\begin{array}{r}
x^2 + 2x - 3 \\
(\times) \qquad 4x^2 + 3x \\
\hline
3x^3 + 6x^2 - 9x \\
4x^4 + \ 8x^3 - 12x^2 \qquad\quad \\
\hline
4x^4 + 11x^3 - 6x^2 - 9x \ \text{(answer)}
\end{array}
$$

Multiply by $3x$:
$(3x)(x^2 + 2x - 3)$.
Multiply by $4x^2$:
$(4x^2)(x^2 + 2x - 3)$.
Combine like terms.   ■ ■ ■

PRACTICE PROBLEM 5   Multiply $5x^2 + 2x$ and $-2x^2 + x - 7$.   ■

The basic multiplication rule for polynomials can be stated as follows.

MULTIPLYING POLYNOMIALS

To multiply two polynomials, multiply each term of one polynomial by every term of the other polynomial and combine like terms.

---

4 Learn to use special-product formulas.

Special Products

Particular polynomial products called *special products* occur frequently enough to deserve special attention. We introduce a very useful method, called F O I L, for multiplying two binomials. Notice that

$$(x + 2)(x - 7) = x(x - 7) + 2(x - 7) \quad \text{Distributive property}$$
$$= x^2 - 7x + 2x - 14 \quad \text{Distributive property}$$
$$= x^2 - 5x - 14 \quad \text{Combine like terms.}$$

Now consider the relationship between the terms of the factors in $(x + 2)(x - 7)$ and the second line, $x^2 - 7x + 2x - 14$, in the computation of the product.

Product of First terms

$$(x + 2)(x - 7) = x^2 - 7x + 2x - 14 \quad \boxed{\text{F}}\text{irst terms: } x \cdot x = x^2$$

Product of Outside terms

$$(x + 2)(x - 7) = x^2 - 7x + 2x - 14 \quad \boxed{\text{O}}\text{utside terms: } x \cdot (-7) = -7x$$

Product of Inside terms

$$(x + 2)(x - 7) = x^2 - 7x + 2x - 14 \quad \boxed{\text{I}}\text{nside terms: } 2 \cdot x = 2x$$

Product of Last terms

$$(x + 2)(x - 7) = x^2 - 7x + 2x - 14. \quad \boxed{\text{L}}\text{ast terms: } 2 \cdot (-7) = -14$$

FOIL METHOD FOR $(A + B)(C + D)$

$$(A + B)(C + D) = \overset{\text{F}}{A \cdot C} + \overset{\text{O}}{A \cdot D} + \overset{\text{I}}{B \cdot C} + \overset{\text{L}}{B \cdot D}$$

EXAMPLE 6   Using the F O I L Method

Use the FOIL method to find the following products.

a. $(2x + 3)(x - 1) = \overset{\text{F}}{(2x)(x)} + \overset{\text{O}}{(2x)(-1)} + \overset{\text{I}}{(3)(x)} + \overset{\text{L}}{(3)(-1)}$
$$= 2x^2 - 2x + 3x - 3$$
$$= 2x^2 + x - 3 \quad \text{Combine like terms.}$$

b. $(3x - 5)(4x - 6) = \overset{\text{F}}{(3x)(4x)} + \overset{\text{O}}{(3x)(-6)} + \overset{\text{I}}{(-5)(4x)} + \overset{\text{L}}{(-5)(-6)}$
$$= 12x^2 - 18x - 20x + 30$$
$$= 12x^2 - 38x + 30 \quad \text{Combine like terms.}$$

c. $(x + a)(x + b) = \overset{\text{F}}{x \cdot x} + \overset{\text{O}}{x \cdot b} + \overset{\text{I}}{a \cdot x} + \overset{\text{L}}{a \cdot b}$
$$= x^2 + bx + ax + a \cdot b \quad xb = bx \text{ (commutative property)}$$
$$= x^2 + (b + a)x + ab \quad \text{Combine like terms.} \quad ■ \ ■ \ ■$$

PRACTICE PROBLEM 6 Use FOIL to find each product.

a. $(4x - 1)(x + 7)$ **b.** $(3x - 2)(2x - 5)$ ■

Squaring a Binomial Sum or Difference

We can find a general formula for the square of any binomial sum $(A + B)^2$ by using FOIL.

$$(A + B)^2 = (A + B)(A + B) = \overset{\text{F}}{A \cdot A} + \overset{\text{O}}{A \cdot B} + \overset{\text{I}}{B \cdot A} + \overset{\text{L}}{B \cdot B}$$

$$= A^2 + AB + AB + B^2 \qquad\qquad AB = BA$$

$$= A^2 + 2AB + B^2 \qquad\qquad AB + AB = 2AB$$

SQUARING A BINOMIAL SUM

$$(A + B)^2 = A^2 + 2AB + B^2$$

A formula such as $(A + B)^2 = A^2 + 2AB + B^2$ can be used in two ways.

EXAMPLE 7   **Finding the Square of a Binomial Sum**

Find $(2x + 3)^2$.

Solution

Pattern Method: In $(2x + 3)^2$, the first term is $2x$ and the second term is 3. Rewrite the formula as

$$\boxed{\begin{array}{c}\text{Square of}\\ \text{sum}\end{array}} = \boxed{\begin{array}{c}\text{Square of}\\ \text{first term}\end{array}} + 2\,\boxed{\begin{array}{c}\text{Product of first}\\ \text{and second terms}\end{array}} + \boxed{\begin{array}{c}\text{Square of}\\ \text{second term}\end{array}}$$

$$(2x + 3)^2 = \quad (2x)^2 \quad + \quad 2 \cdot (2x) \cdot 3 \quad + \quad 3^2$$

$$= 2^2 x^2 + 2 \cdot 2 \cdot 3 \cdot x + 3^2 \qquad \text{Group numerical factors.}$$

$$= 4x^2 + 12x + 9. \qquad\qquad \text{Simplify.}$$

Substitution Method: In the formula $(A + B)^2 = A^2 + 2AB + B^2$, substitute $2x = A$ and $3 = B$. Then

$$(2x + 3)^2 = (2x)^2 + 2 \cdot (2x) \cdot 3 + 3^2$$

$$= 2^2 x^2 + 2 \cdot 2 \cdot 3 \cdot x + 3^2 \qquad \text{Group numerical factors.}$$

$$= 4x^2 + 12x + 9. \qquad\qquad \text{Simplify.} \quad ■ ■ ■$$

PRACTICE PROBLEM 7 Find $(3x + 2)^2$. ■

The definition of subtraction allows us to write any difference $A - B$ as the sum $A + (-B)$. Since $A - B = A + (-B)$, we can use the formula for the square of a binomial sum to find a formula for the square of a binomial difference $(A - B)^2$.

$$(A - B)^2 = [A + (-B)]^2 \qquad\qquad \text{first term} = A, \text{ second term} = -B$$

$$= A^2 + 2A(-B) + (-B)^2$$

$$= A^2 - 2AB + B^2 \qquad\qquad 2A(-B) = -2AB; (-B)^2 = B^2.$$

The Product of the Sum and Difference of Two Terms

SUM AND DIFFERENCE OF TWO TERMS

$$(A + B)(A - B) = A^2 - B^2$$

We leave it for you to use FOIL to verify the formula for finding the product of the sum and difference of two terms.

EXAMPLE 8   **Finding the Product of the Sum and Difference of Two Terms**

Find the product $(3x + 4)(3x - 4)$.

Solution

We use the substitution method; substitute $3x = A$ and $4 = B$ in the formula $(A + B)(A - B) = A^2 - B^2$. Then

$$(3x + 4)(3x - 4) = (3x)^2 - 4^2$$
$$= 9x^2 - 16. \qquad (3x)^2 = 3^2 x^2 = 9x^2 \qquad ■ ■ ■$$

PRACTICE PROBLEM 8   Find the product $(1 - 2x)(1 + 2x)$. ■

The special-products formulas, such as the formulas for squaring a binomial sum or difference, are used often and should be memorized. However, you should be able to derive them from FOIL if you forget them. We list several of these formulas next.

SPECIAL-PRODUCT FORMULAS

A and B represent any algebraic expression.

Formula	**Example**
Sum and difference of two terms	
$(A + B)(A - B) = A^2 - B^2$	$(5x + 2)(5x - 2) = (5x)^2 - 2^2$
	$= 25x^2 - 4$
Squaring a binomial sum or difference	
$(A + B)^2 = A^2 + 2AB + B^2$	$(3x + 2)^2 = (3x)^2 + 2 \cdot (3x)(2) + 2^2$
	$= 9x^2 + 12x + 4$
$(A - B)^2 = A^2 - 2AB + B^2$	$(2x - 5)^2 = (2x)^2 - 2(2x)(5) + 5^2$
	$= 4x^2 - 20x + 25$
Cubing a binomial sum or difference	
$(A + B)^3 = A^3 + 3A^2B + 3AB^2 + B^3$	$(x + 5)^3 = x^3 + 3x^2(5) + 3x(5)^2 + 5^3$
	$= x^3 + 15x^2 + 75x + 125$
$(A - B)^3 = A^3 - 3A^2B + 3AB^2 - B^3$	$(x - 4)^3 = x^3 - 3x^2(4) + 3x(4)^2 + 4^3$
	$= x^3 - 12x^2 + 48x + 64$

(Continued)

SPECIAL-PRODUCT FORMULAS (Continued)

Formula	Example
Sum and Difference of Cubes	
$(A + B)(A^2 - AB + B^2) = A^3 + B^3$	$(x + 2)(x^2 - 2x + 4) = x^3 + 2^3 = x^3 + 8$
$(A - B)(A^2 + AB + B^2) = A^3 - B^3$	$(x - 3)(x^2 + 3x + 9) = x^3 - 3^3 = x^3 - 27$

To this point, we have only investigated polynomials in a single variable. We need to extend our previous vocabulary in order to discuss polynomials in more than one variable. Any product of a constant and two or more variables raised to whole-number powers is a **monomial** in those variables. The constant is called the **coefficient** of the monomial, and the **degree** of the monomial is the sum of all the exponents appearing on its variables. For example, the monomial $5x^3y^4$ is of degree $3 + 4 = 7$ with coefficient 5.

EXAMPLE 9 **Multiplying Polynomials in Two Variables**

Multiply. **a.** $(7a + 5b)(7a - 5b)$ **b.** $(2x + 3y)^2$.

Solution

a. $(7a + 5b)(7a - 5b) = (7a)^2 - (5b)^2$ $(A + B)(A - B) = A^2 - B^2$
$= 49a^2 - 25b^2$ Simplify.

b. $(2x + 3y)^2 = (2x)^2 + 2(2x)(3y) + (3y)^2$ $(A + B)^2 = A^2 + 2AB + B^2$
$= 2^2x^2 + 2 \cdot 2 \cdot 3xy + 3^2y^2$ Apply exponents to each factor.
$= 4x^2 + 12xy + 9y^2$ Simplify.   ■ ■ ■

PRACTICE PROBLEM 9   Multiply $x^2(y + x)$.   ■

A Exercises Basic Skills and Concepts

In Exercises 1–4, determine whether the given expression is a polynomial. If it is, write it in standard form.

1. $1 + x^2 + 2x$ †

2. $x - \dfrac{1}{x}$ No

3. $x^{-2} + 3x + 5$ No

4. $3x^4 + x^7 + 3x^5 - 2x + 1$ †

In Exercises 5–8, find the degree and list the terms of the polynomial.

5. $7x + 3$ degree: 1; terms: $7x$, 3   **6.** $-3x^2 + 7$ †

7. $x^2 - x^4 + 2x - 9$ †   **8.** $x + 2x^3 + 9x^7 - 21$ †

In Exercises 9–18, perform the indicated operations. Write the resulting polynomial in standard form.

9. $(x^3 + 2x^2 - 5x + 3) + (-x^3 + 2x - 4)$ $2x^2 - 3x - 1$

10. $(x^3 - 3x + 1) + (x^3 - x^2 + x - 3)$ $2x^3 - x^2 - 2x - 2$

11. $(2x^3 - x^2 + x - 5) - (x^3 - 4x + 3)$ $x^3 - x^2 + 5x - 8$

12. $(-x^3 + 2x - 4) - (x^3 + 3x^2 - 7x + 2)$ †

13. $(-2x^4 + 3x^2 - 7x) - (8x^4 + 6x^3 - 9x^2 - 17)$ †

14. $3(x^2 - 2x + 2) + 2(5x^2 - x + 4)$ $13x^2 - 8x + 14$

15. $-2(3x^2 + x + 1) + 6(-3x^2 - 2x - 2)$ $-24x^2 - 14x - 14$

16. $2(5x^2 - x + 3) - 4(3x^2 + 7x + 1)$ $-2x^2 - 30x + 2$

17. $(3y^3 - 4y + 2) + (2y + 1) - (y^3 - y^2 + 4)$ †

18. $(5y^2 + 3y - 1) - (y^2 - 2y + 3) + (2y^2 + y + 5)$ †

In Exercises 19–52, perform the indicated operations.

19. $6x(2x + 3)$ $12x^2 + 18x$ **20.** $7x(3x - 4)$ $21x^2 - 28x$

21. $(x + 1)(x^2 + 2x + 2)$ †   **22.** $(x - 5)(2x^2 - 3x + 1)$ †

23. $(3x - 2)(x^2 - x + 1)$ †   **24.** $(2x + 1)(x^2 - 3x + 4)$ †

25. $(x + 1)(x + 2)$ †   **26.** $(x + 2)(x + 3)$ †

27. $(3x + 2)(3x + 1)$ †   **28.** $(x + 3)(2x + 5)$ †

29. $(-4x + 5)(x + 3)$ †   **30.** $(-2x + 1)(x - 5)$ †

31. $(3x - 2)(2x - 1)$ †   **32.** $(x - 1)(5x - 3)$ †

†Due to space constrictions, answers to these exercises may be found in the Answers beginning on page A–1 in the back of the book.

33. $(2x - 3a)(2x + 5a)$ †

34. $(5x - 2a)(x + 5a)$ †

35. $(x + 2)^2 - x^2$ $4x + 4$

36. $(x - 3)^2 - x^2$ $-6x + 9$

37. $(x + 3)^3 - x^3$ †

38. $(x - 2)^3 - x^3$ †

39. $(4x + 1)^2$ $16x^2 + 8x + 1$

40. $(3x + 2)^2$ $9x^2 + 12x + 4$

41. $(3x + 1)^3$ †

42. $(2x + 3)^3$ †

43. $(5 - 2x)(5 + 2x)$ †

44. $(3 - 4x)(3 + 4x)$ †

45. $\left(x + \dfrac{3}{4}\right)^2$ $x^2 + \dfrac{3}{2}x + \dfrac{9}{16}$

46. $\left(x + \dfrac{2}{5}\right)^2$ $x^2 + \dfrac{4}{5}x + \dfrac{4}{25}$

47. $(2x - 3)(x^2 - 3x + 5)$ †

48. $(x - 2)(x^2 - 4x - 3)$ †

49. $(1 + y)(1 - y + y^2)$ †

50. $(y + 4)(y^2 - 4y + 16)$ †

51. $(x - 6)(x^2 + 6x + 36)$ †

52. $(x - 1)(x^2 + x + 1)$ †

In Exercises 53–62, perform the indicated operations.

53. $(x + 2y)(3x + 5y)$ †

54. $(2x + y)(7x + 2y)$ †

55. $(2x - y)(3x + 7y)$ †

56. $(x - 3y)(2x + 5y)$ †

57. $(x - y)^2(x + y)^2$ †

58. $(2x + y)^2(2x - y)^2$ †

59. $(x + y)(x - 2y)^2$ †

60. $(x - y)(x + 2y)^2$ †

61. $(x - 2y)^3(x + 2y)$ †

62. $(2x + y)^3(2x - y)$ †

B Exercises   Applying the Concepts

63. Ticket prices. Theater ticket prices (in dollars) x years after 1997 are described by the polynomial $-0.025x^2 + 0.44x + 4.28$. Find the value of this polynomial for $x = 6$, and state the result as the ticket price for a specific year. †

64. Box-office grosses. Theater box-office grosses (in billions of dollars) x years after 1993 are described by the polynomial $0.035x^2 + 0.15x + 5.17$. Find the value of this polynomial for the year 1997, and state the result as box-office gross for a specific year.   In 1997, it was 6.33 billion dollars

65. Paper shredding. A business that shreds paper products finds that it costs $0.1x^2 + x + 50$ dollars to serve x customers. What does it cost to serve 40 customers? $250.00

66. Gift baskets. A company will produce x (for $x \geq 10$) gift baskets of wine, meat, cheese, and crackers at a cost of $(x - 10)^2 + 5x$ dollars per basket. What is the per basket cost for 15 baskets? $100.00

In Exercises 67 and 68, use the fact (from Example 1) that an object thrown down with an initial velocity of v_0 feet per second will travel $16t^2 + v_0t$ feet in t seconds.

67. Free fall. A sandwich is thrown from a helicopter with an initial downward velocity of 20 feet per second. How far has it fallen after 5 seconds?   500 feet

68. Free fall. A ring is thrown off the Empire State Building with an initial downward velocity of 10 feet per second. How far has it fallen after 2 seconds?   84 feet

69. Cruise ship revenue. A cruise ship decides to reduce ticket prices to its theater by x dollars from the current price of $22.50.

   a. Write a polynomial that gives the new price after the x-dollar deduction. $-x + 22.50$

   b. The revenue is the number of tickets sold times the price of each ticket. If 30 tickets were sold when the price was $22.50 and 10 additional tickets are sold for each dollar the price is reduced, write a polynomial that gives the revenue in terms of x when the original price is reduced by x dollars. $-10x^2 + 225x + 675$

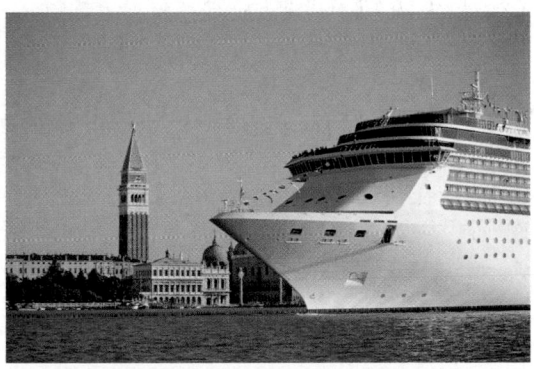

70. Used-car rentals. A dealer who rents used cars wants to increase the monthly rent from the current $250 in n increases of $10.

   a. Write a polynomial that gives the new price after n increases of $10. $10n + 250$

   b. The revenue is the number of cars rented times the monthly rent for each car. If 50 cars can be rented at $250 per month and 2 fewer cars can be rented for each $10 rent increase, write a polynomial that gives the monthly revenue in terms of n. $-20n^2 + 12,500$

SECTION P.4 | Factoring Polynomials

BEFORE STARTING THIS SECTION, REVIEW

1. Exponents (Section P.2, page 20)

2. Polynomials (Section P.3, page 31)

3. Value of algebraic expressions (Section P.1, page 14)

OBJECTIVES

1 Learn to identify and factor out the greatest common monomial factor.

2 Learn to factor trinomials with a leading coefficient of 1.

3 Learn to factor perfect-square trinomials.

4 Learn to factor the difference of squares.

5 Learn to factor the difference and sum of cubes.

6 Learn to factor trinomials.

7 Learn to factor by grouping.

Profit from Research and Development

The finance department of a major drug company projects that an investment of x million dollars in research and development for a specific type of vaccine will return a profit (or loss) of $(0.012x^3 - 32.928)$ million dollars.

The company would have to invest 12 million dollars to get started and is prepared to invest up to 24 million dollars, at a rate of 1 million dollars per year. You could probably stare at this polynomial for a long time without getting a clear picture of what kind of return you could expect from different investments. In Example 7, we will use the methods of this section to rewrite this profit–loss polynomial that will make it easy to explain the result of investing various amounts. ■

The Greatest Common Monomial Factor

The process of factoring polynomials that we study in this section "reverses" the process of multiplying polynomials that we studied in the previous section. To factor any *sum of terms* means to write it as a *product of factors*. Consider the product

$$(x + 3)(x - 3) = x^2 - 9.$$

The polynomials $(x + 3)$ and $(x - 3)$ are called *factors* of the polynomial $x^2 - 9$. When factoring, we start with one polynomial and write it as a product of other polynomials. The polynomials in the product are the **factors** of the given polynomial.

The first thing to look for in factoring a polynomial is a factor that is common to every term. This **common factor** can be "factored out" by the distributive property, $a(b + c) = ab + ac$.

1 Learn to identify and factor out the greatest common monomial factor.

Factoring Out a Monomial

In this section, we will be concerned only with polynomials having integer coefficients. This restriction is called **factoring over the integers.**

Polynomial	Common Factor	Factored Form
$9 + 18y$	9	$9(1 + 2y)$
$2y^2 + 6y$	$2y$	$2y(y + 3)$
$7x^4 + 3x^3 + x^2$	x^2	$x^2(7x^2 + 3x + 1)$
$5x + 3$	No common factor	$5x + 3$

You can verify that any factorization is correct by multiplying the factors. We factored these polynomials by finding the *greatest common monomial factor* of their terms.

FINDING THE GREATEST COMMON MONOMIAL FACTOR

The term ax^n is the **greatest common monomial factor (GCF)** of a polynomial in x (with integer coefficients) if

1. a is the *greatest* integer that divides each of the polynomial coefficients.

2. n is the *smallest* exponent on x found in any term of the polynomial.

EXAMPLE 1   **Factoring by Using the GCF**

Factor. **a.** $16x^3 + 24x^2$ **b.** $5x^4 + 20x^2 + 25x$

Solution

a. The greatest integer that divides both 16 and 24 is 8. The exponents on x are 3 and 2, so 2 is the smallest exponent. Thus, the **GCF** of $16x^3 + 24x^2$ is $8x^2$. We write

$$16x^3 + 24x^2 = 8x^2(2x) + 8x^2(3).$$ Write each term as the product of the GCF and another factor.

$$= 8x^2(2x + 3).$$ Use the distributive property to factor out the GCF.

We can always check the results of factoring by multiplying.

Check: $8x^2(2x + 3) = 8x^2(2x) + 8x^2(3) = 16x^3 + 24x^2$.

b. The greatest integer that divides 5, 20, and 25 is 5. The exponents on x are 4, 2, and 1 $(x = x^1)$, so 1 is the smallest exponent. Thus, the **GCF** of $5x^4 + 20x^2 + 25x$ is $5x$. We write

$$5x^4 + 20x^2 + 25x = 5x(x^3) + 5x(4x) + 5x(5) = 5x(x^3 + 4x + 5).$$

You should check this result by multiplying.   ■ ■ ■

PRACTICE PROBLEM 1   Factor. **a.** $6x^5 + 14x^3$ **b.** $7x^5 + 21x^4 + 35x^2$ ■

Polynomials that cannot be factored as a product of two polynomials (excluding the constant polynomials 1 and -1) are said to be **prime**. A polynomial is said to be **factored completely** when it is written as a product consisting of only prime factors. By agreement, the greatest integer common to all of the terms in the polynomial is not factored. We also allow repeated prime factors to be written as a power of a single factor.

2 Learn to factor trinomials with a leading coefficent of 1.

Factoring Trinomials of the Form $x^2 + bx + c$

Recall that $(x + a)(x + b) = x^2 + (a + b)x + ab$.

We reverse the sides of this equation to get the factoring form
$x^2 + (a + b)x + ab = (x + a)(x + b)$.

EXAMPLE 2   **Factoring $x^2 + bx + c$ by Using the Factors of c**

Factor. **a.** $x^2 + 8x + 15$ **b.** $x^2 - 6x - 16$ **c.** $x^2 + x + 2$

Solution

a. We want integers a and b such that $ab = 15$ and $a + b = 8$.

Factors of 15	1, 15	$-1, -15$	3, 5	$-3, -5$
Sum of factors	16	-16	8	-8

Since the factors 3 and 5 in the third column have a sum of 8,

$$x^2 + 8x + 15 = (x + 3)(x + 5).$$

You should check this answer by multiplying.

b. We must find two integers a and b with $ab = -16$ and $a + b = -6$.

Factors of -16	$-1, 16$	$-2, 8$	$-4, 4$	$1, -16$	$2, -8$	$4, -4$
Sum of factors	15	6	0	-15	-6	0

Since the factors 2 and -8 in the fifth column of the table give a sum of -6,

$$x^2 - 6x - 16 = (x + 2)[x + (-8)] = (x + 2)(x - 8).$$

You should check this answer by multiplying.

c. We must find two integers a and b with $ab = 2$ and $a + b = 1$.

Factors of 2	1, 2	$-1, -2$
Sum of factors	3	-3

The coefficient of the middle term, 1, doesn't appear as the sum of any of the factors of the constant term, 2. Therefore, $x^2 + x + 2$ is prime. ■ ■ ■

PRACTICE PROBLEM 2   Factor. **a.** $x^2 + 6x + 8$ **b.** $x^2 - 3x - 10$ ■

Factoring Formulas

We will investigate how other types of polynomials can be factored by reversing the product formulas on pages 37 and 38.

FACTORING FORMULAS

A and B represent any algebraic expression.

$A^2 - B^2 = (A + B)(A - B)$	Difference of squares
$A^2 + 2AB + B^2 = (A + B)^2$	Perfect square, positive middle term
$A^2 - 2AB + B^2 = (A - B)^2$	Perfect square, negative middle term
$A^3 - B^3 = (A - B)(A^2 + AB + B^2)$	Difference of cubes
$A^3 + B^3 = (A + B)(A^2 - AB + B^2)$	Sum of cubes

---

3 Learn to factor perfect-square trinomials.

Perfect-Square Trinomials

EXAMPLE 3   **Factoring a Perfect-Square Trinomial**

Factor. **a.** $x^2 + 10x + 25$ **b.** $16x^2 - 8x + 1$

Solution

a. The first term, x^2, and the third term, $25 = 5^2$, are perfect squares. Further, the middle term is twice the product of the terms being squared, that is, $10x - 2(5x)$.

$$x^2 + 10x + 25 = x^2 + 2 \cdot 5 \cdot x + 5^2 = (x + 5)^2$$

> **STUDY TIP**
>
> You should always check your answer to any factoring problem by multiplying the factors to verify that the result is the original expression.

b. The first term, $16x^2 = (4x)^2$, and the third term, $1 = 1^2$, are perfect squares. Further, the middle term is the *negative* of twice the product of terms being squared, that is, $-8x = -2(4x)(1)$.

$$16x^2 - 8x + 1 = (4x)^2 - 2(4x)(1) + 1^2 = (4x - 1)^2.$$ ■ ■ ■

PRACTICE PROBLEM 3   Factor. **a.** $x^2 + 4x + 4$ **b.** $9x^2 - 6x + 1$ ■

4 Learn to factor the difference of squares.

Difference of Squares

To factor the difference of squares, we use the special product $(A + B)(A - B) = A^2 - B^2$.

EXAMPLE 4   **Factoring the Difference of Squares**

Factor. **a.** $x^2 - 4$ **b.** $25x^2 - 49$

Solution

a. We write $x^2 - 4$ as the difference of squares.

$$x^2 - 4 = x^2 - 2^2 = (x + 2)(x - 2)$$

b. We write $25x^2 - 49$ as the difference of squares.

$$25x^2 - 49 = (5x)^2 - 7^2 = (5x + 7)(5x - 7)$$ ■ ■ ■

PRACTICE PROBLEM 4   Factor. **a.** $x^2 - 16$ **b.** $4x^2 - 25$ ■

What about the *sum* of two squares? Let's try to factor $x^2 + 2^2 = x^2 + 4$. Notice that $x^2 + 4 = x^2 + 0 \cdot x + 4$, so that the middle term is $0 = 0 \cdot x$. We need two factors, a and b, of 4 whose sum is zero ($a + b = 0$).

Factors of 4	1, 4	−1, −4	2, 2	−2, −2
Sum of factors	5	−5	4	−4

Since no sum of factors is 0, $x^2 + 4$ is prime. A similar result holds regardless of what integer replaces 2 in the process. Consequently, $x^2 + a^2$ is prime for any integer a.

SOME PRIME POLYNOMIALS

If a and c are integers *having no common factors,*

$$ax + c \text{ is prime} \quad \text{and} \quad x^2 + a^2 \text{ is prime.}$$

EXAMPLE 5   **Factoring the Difference of Squares**

Factor. $x^4 - 16$

Solution

We write $x^4 - 16$ as the difference of squares.

$$x^4 - 16 = (x^2)^2 - 4^2 = (x^2 + 4)(x^2 - 4)$$

From Example 4, part **a,** we know that $x^2 - 4 = (x + 2)(x - 2)$. Consequently,

$$
\begin{aligned}
x^4 - 16 &= (x^2 + 4)(x^2 - 4) \\
&= (x^2 + 4)(x + 2)(x - 2). \qquad \text{Replace } x^2 - 4 \text{ by } (x + 2)(x - 2).
\end{aligned}
$$

Since $x^2 + 4$, $x + 2$, and $x - 2$ are prime, $x^4 - 16$ is completely factored.   ■ ■ ■

PRACTICE PROBLEM 5   Factor. $x^4 - 81$ ■

5 Learn to factor the difference and sum of cubes.

Difference and Sum of Cubes

We can also use the special-product formulas to factor the sum and difference of cubes.

$$A^3 - B^3 = (A - B)(A^2 + AB + B^2) \qquad \text{Difference of cubes}$$
$$A^3 + B^3 = (A + B)(A^2 - AB + B^2). \qquad \text{Sum of cubes}$$

EXAMPLE 6   **Factoring the Difference and Sum of Cubes**

Factor. **a.** $x^3 - 64$ **b.** $8x^3 + 125$

Solution

a. We write $x^3 - 64$ as the difference of cubes.

$$x^3 - 64 = x^3 - 4^3 = (x - 4)(x^2 + 4x + 16)$$

b. Write $8x^3 + 125$ as the sum of two cubes.

$$8x^3 + 125 = (2x)^3 + 5^3 = (2x + 5)(4x^2 - 10x + 25)$$ ■ ■ ■

PRACTICE PROBLEM 6   Factor.   **a.** $x^3 - 125$ **b.** $27x^3 + 8$ ■

EXAMPLE 7   **Determining Profit from Research and Development**

In the beginning of this section, we introduced the polynomial $0.012x^3 - 32.928$ that gave the profit (or loss) a drug company would have after an investment of x million dollars and an initial investment of $12 million. If the company will invest an additional $1 million each year, determine when this investment returns a profit. What will the profit (or loss) be in six years?

Solution

First notice that 0.012 is a common factor of both terms of the polynomial, since $32.928 = (0.012)(2744)$. We now factor $0.012x^3 - 32.928$ as follows:

$$0.012x^3 - 32.928 = 0.012x^3 - (0.012)(2744)$$
$$= 0.012(x^3 - 2744) \qquad\qquad \text{Factor out 0.012.}$$
$$= 0.012(x^3 - 14^3) \qquad\qquad 2744 = 14^3$$
$$= 0.012(x - 14)(x^2 + 14x + 196). \qquad \text{Difference of cubes}$$

This product has three factors, and the factor $x^2 + 14x + 196$ is positive for positive values of x, since each term is positive. The sign of the factor $x - 14$ will then determine the sign of the entire polynomial. The factor $x - 14$ is negative if x is less than 14, zero if x equals 14 and positive if x is greater than 14. Consequently, the company receives a profit when x is greater than 14. Since the initial investment is 12 million dollars, with an additional 1 million dollars invested each year, it will be two years before the company breaks even on this venture. Every year thereafter it will profit from the investment. In six years, the company will have invested the initial 12 million dollars, plus an additional 6 million dollars (1 million dollars per year). Thus, the total investment is 18 million dollars. To find the profit (or loss) with 18 million dollars invested, we let $x = 18$ in the profit–loss polynomial:

$$(0.012)(x - 14)(x^2 + 14x + 196)$$
$$= 0.012(18 - 14)(18^2 + (14)(18) + 196) \qquad \text{Replace } x \text{ by 18.}$$
$$= 0.012(4)(772)$$
$$= 37.056 \text{ million dollars.}$$

The company will have made a profit of over 37 million dollars in six years.   ■ ■ ■

PRACTICE PROBLEM 7   In Example 7, what will the profit be in four years?   ■

6 Learn to factor trinomials.

Factoring Trinomials of the Form $Ax^2 + Bx + C$

To factor the general trinomial $Ax^2 + Bx + C$, we begin by supposing that

$$Ax^2 + Bx + C = (ax + b)(cx + d) = acx^2 + (ad + bc)x + bd.$$

We can factor $Ax^2 + Bx + C$ if we can find integers a, b, c, and d such that

$$A = ac \qquad C = bd \qquad B = ad + bc.$$

EXAMPLE 8   **Factoring $Ax^2 + Bx + C$ when $A \neq 1$**

Factor. **a.** $6x^2 + 17x + 7$ **b.** $4x^2 - 8x - 5$

Solution

a. When the leading coefficient is positive we need only consider its positive factors. The positive-factor pairs for 6 are 6, 1 and 2, 3. There are two possible forms for a factorization:

$$6x^2 + 17x + 7 = (6x + \square)(x + \square)$$

or

$$6x^2 + 17x + 7 = (2x + \square)(3x + \square).$$

The numbers to be filled in are factors of 7, the constant term. However, since the middle coefficient is positive, these numbers cannot be -7 and -1. We arrange the factors so that the first- and last-term products work out automatically and then test for the correct middle term, which is the sum of the inside and outside products.
    The following table lists the possible factorizations of $6x^2 + 17x + 7$:

Possible Factorizations	Outside Terms	Inside Terms	Sum of Outside and Inside Products
$(6x + 1)(x + 7)$	$6x, 7$	$1, x$	$(6x)(7) + (1)(x) = 43x$
$(6x + 7)(x + 1)$	$6x, 1$	$7, x$	$(6x)(1) + (7)(x) = 13x$
$(2x + 1)(3x + 7)$	$2x, 7$	$1, 3x$	$(2x)(7) + (1)(3x) = 17x$
$(2x + 7)(3x + 1)$	$2x, 1$	$7, 3x$	$(2x)(1) + (7)(3x) = 23x$

The correct middle term, $17x$, occurs in the *third* row of the table.

$$6x^2 + 17x + 7 = (2x + 1)(3x + 7).$$

b. Since, 4, the leading coefficient of $4x^2 - 8x - 5$, is positive, we need only consider its possible positive factors, namely 4, 1 and 2, 2. There are two possible forms for a factorization:

$$4x^2 - 8x - 5 = (4x + \square)(x + \square)$$

or

$$4x^2 - 8x - 5 = (2x + \square)(2x + \square).$$

The numbers to be filled in are factors of -5, the constant term. Since that term is negative, we use factors that are opposite in sign—that is, 5, -1 and -5, 1.

The following table lists the possible factorizations of $4x^2 - 8x - 5$:

Possible Factorizations	Outside Terms	Inside Terms	Sum of Outside and Inside Products
$(4x - 1)(x + 5)$	$4x, 5$	$-1, x$	$(4x)(5) + (-1)(x) = 19x$
$(4x + 5)(x - 1)$	$4x, -1$	$5, x$	$(4x)(-1) + (5)(x) = x$
$(4x + 1)(x - 5)$	$4x, -5$	$1, x$	$(4x)(-5) + (1)(x) = -19x$
$(4x - 5)(x + 1)$	$4x, 1$	$-5, x$	$(4x)(1) + (-5)(x) = -x$
$(2x - 1)(2x + 5)$	$2x, 5$	$-1, 2x$	$(2x)(5) + (-1)(2x) = 8x$
$(2x + 1)(2x - 5)$	$2x, -5$	$1, 2x$	$(2x)(-5) + (1)(2x) = -8x$

> **STUDY TIP**
>
> After using the techniques just explained to factor several trinomials, you will find that you can often guess the factors without going through all of the steps. Guessing is fine, as long as you check your guesses by using FOIL to multiply. If you guessed incorrectly, you can just guess again.

Notice that the correct middle term, $-8x$, occurs in the last row of the table. Thus,

$$4x^2 - 8x - 5 = (2x + 1)(2x - 5).$$ ■ ■ ■

PRACTICE PROBLEM 8   Factor. **a.** $5x^2 + 11x + 2$ **b.** $9x^2 - 9x + 2$ ■

7 Learn to factor by grouping.

Factoring by Grouping

For polynomials having four terms and a GCF of 1, when none of the preceding factoring techniques apply, we can sometimes group the terms in such a way that each group has a common factor. This technique is called **factoring by grouping.**

EXAMPLE 9   **Factoring by Grouping**

Factor. **a.** $x^3 + 2x^2 + 3x + 6$ **b.** $6x^3 - 3x^2 - 4x + 2$

Solution

a.
$$\begin{aligned} x^3 + 2x^2 + 3x + 6 &= (x^3 + 2x^2) + (3x + 6) \\ &= x^2(x + 2) + 3(x + 2) \quad \text{Factor the binomials.} \\ &= (x^2 + 3)(x + 2) \quad \text{Factor out the common binomial factor } x + 2. \end{aligned}$$

b.
$$\begin{aligned} 6x^3 - 3x^2 - 4x + 2 &= (6x^3 - 3x^2) + (-4x + 2) \\ &= 3x^2(2x - 1) + (-2)(2x - 1) \quad \text{Factor the binomials.} \\ &= (3x^2 - 2)(2x - 1) \quad \text{Factor out the common binomial factor } 2x - 1. \end{aligned}$$

■ ■ ■

PRACTICE PROBLEM 9   Factor. **a.** $x^3 + 3x^2 + x + 3$ **b.** $28x^3 - 20x^2 - 7x + 5$ ■

A Exercises   Basic Skills and Concepts

In Exercises 1–12, factor each polynomial by removing any common monomial factor.

1. $8x - 24$ $8(x - 3)$

2. $5x + 25$ $5(x + 5)$

3. $-6x^2 + 12x$ $-6x(x - 2)$

4. $-3x^2 + 21$ $-3(x^2 - 7)$

5. $7x^2 + 14x^3$ $7x^2(1 + 2x)$

6. $9x^3 - 18x^4$ $9x^3(1 - 2x)$

7. $x^4 + 2x^3 + x^2$ †

8. $x^4 - 5x^3 + 7x^2$ †

†Due to space constrictions, answers to these exercises may be found in the Answers beginning on page A–1 in the back of the book.

9. $3x^3 - x^2$ $x^2(3x - 1)$ **10.** $2x^3 + 2x^2$ $2x^2(x + 1)$

11. $8ax^3 + 4ax^2$ $4ax^2(2x + 1)$ **12.** $ax^4 - 2ax^2 + ax$ †

In Exercises 13–20, factor by grouping.

13. $x^3 + 3x^2 + x + 3$ †   **14.** $x^3 + 5x^2 + x + 5$ †

15. $x^3 - 5x^2 + x - 5$ †   **16.** $x^3 - 7x^2 + x - 7$ †

17. $6x^3 + 4x^2 + 3x + 2$ †   **18.** $3x^3 + 6x^2 + x + 2$ †

19. $12x^7 + 4x^5 + 3x^4 + x^2$ †   **20.** $3x^7 + 3x^5 + x^4 + x^2$ †

In Exercises 21–36, factor each trinomial or state that it is prime.

21. $x^2 + 7x + 12$ †   **22.** $x^2 + 8x + 15$ †

23. $x^2 - 6x + 8$ †   **24.** $x^2 - 9x + 14$ †

25. $x^2 - 3x - 4$ †   **26.** $x^2 - 5x - 6$ †

27. $x^2 - 4x + 13$ prime   **28.** $x^2 - 2x + 5$ prime

29. $2x^2 + x - 36$ †   **30.** $2x^2 + 3x - 27$ †

31. $6x^2 + 17x + 12$ †   **32.** $8x^2 - 10x - 3$ †

33. $3x^2 - 11x - 4$ †   **34.** $5x^2 + 7x + 2$ †

35. $6x^2 - 3x + 4$ prime   **36.** $4x^2 - 4x - 3$ †

In Exercises 37–44, factor each polynomial as a perfect square.

37. $x^2 + 6x + 9$ $(x + 3)^2$ **38.** $x^2 + 8x + 16$ $(x + 4)^2$

39. $9x^2 + 6x + 1$ $(3x + 1)^2$ **40.** $36x^2 + 12x + 1$ $(6x + 1)^2$

41. $25x^2 - 20x + 4$ $(5x - 2)^2$ **42.** $64x^2 + 32x + 4$ $(8x + 2)^2$

43. $49x^2 + 42x + 9$ $(7x + 3)^2$ **44.** $9x^2 + 24x + 16$ $(3x + 4)^2$

In Exercises 45–54, factor each polynomial as the difference of two squares.

45. $x^2 - 64$ $(x - 8)(x + 8)$ **46.** $x^2 - 121$ $(x - 11)(x + 11)$

47. $4x^2 - 1$ $(2x - 1)(2x + 1)$ **48.** $9x^2 - 1$ $(3x - 1)(3x + 1)$

49. $16x^2 - 9$ $(4x - 3)(4x + 3)$ **50.** $25x^2 - 49$ †

51. $x^4 - 1$ †   **52.** $x^4 - 81$ †

53. $20x^4 - 5$ †   **54.** $12x^4 - 75$ †

In Exercises 55–64, factor each polynomial as the sum or difference of two cubes.

55. $x^3 + 64$ †   **56.** $x^3 + 125$ †

57. $x^3 - 27$ †   **58.** $x^3 - 216$ †

59. $8 - x^3$ †   **60.** $27 - x^3$ †

61. $8x^3 - 27$ †   **62.** $8x^3 - 125$ †

63. $40x^3 + 5$ †   **64.** $7x^3 + 56$ †

In Exercises 65–96, factor each polynomial completely. If a polynomial cannot be factored, state that it is prime.

65. $1 - 16x^2$ $(1 - 4x)(1 + 4x)$ **66.** $4 - 25x^2$ $(2 - 5x)(2 + 5x)$

67. $x^2 - 6x + 9$ $(x - 3)^2$ **68.** $x^2 - 8x + 16$ $(x - 4)^2$

69. $4x^2 + 4x + 1$ $(2x + 1)^2$ **70.** $16x^2 + 8x + 1$ $(4x + 1)^2$

71. $2x^2 - 8x - 10$ †   **72.** $5x^2 - 10x - 40$ †

73. $2x^2 + 3x - 20$ †   **74.** $2x^2 - 7x - 30$ †

75. $x^2 - 12x + 36$ $(x - 6)^2$ **76.** $x^2 - 20x + 25$ prime

77. $3x^5 + 12x^4 + 12x^3$ †   **78.** $2x^5 + 16x^4 + 32x^3$ †

79. $9x^2 - 1$ $(3x + 1)(3x - 1)$ **80.** $16x^2 - 25$ †

81. $16x^2 + 24x + 9$ $(4x + 3)^2$ **82.** $4x^2 + 20x + 25$ $(2x + 5)^2$

83. $x^2 + 15$ prime   **84.** $x^2 + 24$ prime

85. $45x^3 + 8x^2 - 4x$ †   **86.** $25x^3 + 40x^2 - 9x$ †

87. $ax^2 - 7a^2x - 8a^3$ †   **88.** $ax^2 - 10a^2x - 24a^3$ †

89. $x^2 - 16a^2 + 8x + 16$ †   **90.** $x^2 - 36a^2 + 6x + 9$ †

91. $3x^5 + 12x^4y + 12x^3y^2$ †   **92.** $4x^5 + 24x^4y + 36x^3y^2$ †

93. $x^2 - 25a^2 + 4x + 4$ †   **94.** $x^2 - 16a^2 + 4x + 4$ †

95. $18x^6 + 12x^5y + 2x^4y^2$ †   **96.** $12x^6 + 12x^5y + 3x^4y^2$ †

B Exercises   Applying the Concepts

97. Garden area. A rectangular garden must have a perimeter of 16 feet. Write a completely factored polynomial whose values give the area of the garden if one side is x feet. †

98. Serving-tray dimensions. A rectangular serving tray must have a perimeter of 42 inches. Write a completely factored polynomial whose values give the area of the tray if one side is x inches. $x(21 - x)$

99. Box construction. A box with an open top is to be constructed from a rectangular piece of cardboard with length 36 inches and width 16 inches by cutting out equal squares of side length x at each corner and then folding up the sides, as shown in the accompanying figure. Write a completely factored polynomial whose values give the volume of the box (volume = length × width × height). $4x(18 - x)(8 - x)$

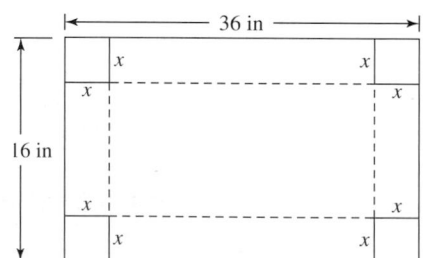

Figure for Exercise 99.

100. Surface area. For the box described in Exercise 99, write a completely factored polynomial whose values give its surface area (surface area = sum of the areas of the five sides). †

101. Area of a washer. As shown in the figure, a washer is made by removing a circular disk from the center of another circular disk of radius 2 cm. If the disk that is removed has radius x, write a completely factored polynomial whose values give the area of the washer. †

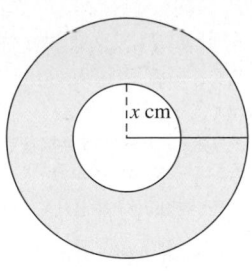

102. Insulation. Insulation must be put into the space between two concentric cylinders. Write a completely factored polynomial whose values give the volume between the inner and outer cylinder if the inner cylinder has radius 3 feet, the outer cylinder has radius x feet, and both cylinders are 8 feet high. $8\pi(x - 3)(x + 3)$

103. Grazing pens. A rancher has 2800 feet of fencing that will fence off a rectangular grazing pen for cattle. One edge of the pen borders a straight river and will need no fence. If the edges of the pen perpendicular to the river are x feet long, write a completely factored polynomial whose values give the area of the pen. $2x(1400 - x)$

104. Centerpiece perimeter. A decorative glass centerpiece for a table has the shape of a rectangle with a semicircular section attached at each end, as shown in the figure. The perimeter of the figure is 48 inches. Write a completely factored polynomial whose values give the area of the centerpiece.

Answers:

101. $\pi(2 - x)(2 + x)$

104. $\dfrac{1}{4}x(96 - \pi x)$

Rational Expressions

BEFORE STARTING THIS SECTION, REVIEW

1. Domain of an expression (Section P.1, page 15)

2. Rational numbers (Section P.1, page 3)

3. Properties of fractions (Section P.1, page 14)

4. Factoring polynomials (Section P.4, page 41)

OBJECTIVES

1 Learn to reduce a rational expression to lowest terms.

2 Learn to multiply and divide rational expressions.

3 Learn to add and subtract rational expressions.

4 Learn to identify and simplify complex fractions.

False Positive in Drug Testing

You are probably aware that the nonmedical use of steroids among adolescents and young adults is an ongoing national concern. In fact, many high schools have required students involved in extracurricular activities to submit to random drug testing. Many methods for drug testing are in use, and those who administer the tests are keenly aware of the possibility of what is termed a "false positive," which occurs when someone who is not a drug user tests positive for using drugs. How likely is it that a student who tests positive actually uses drugs? For a test that is 95% accurate, an expression for the likelihood that a student who tests positive is a nonuser of drugs is

$$\frac{(0.05)(1 - x)}{0.95x + (0.05)(1 - x)},$$

where x is the percent of the student population that uses drugs. This is an example of a rational expression, which we study in this section. In Example 1, we will see that, in a student population among which only 5% of the students use drugs, the likelihood that a student who is a nonuser will test positive is 50% when the test used is 95% accurate. ■

Rational Expressions

Recall that the quotient of two integers, $\frac{a}{b}(b \neq 0)$, is a rational number. When we form the quotient of two polynomials, the result is called a **rational expression.** The following are some examples of rational expressions:

$$\frac{10}{17}, \quad \frac{x+2}{3}, \quad \frac{x+6}{(x-3)(x+4)}, \quad \frac{7}{x^2+1}, \text{ and } \frac{x^2+2x-3}{x^2+5x}.$$

We use the same language to describe rational expressions that we use to describe rational numbers. For $\dfrac{x^2+2x-3}{x^2+5x+6}$, we call x^2+2x-3 the **numerator** and x^2+5x+6 the **denominator.** As with rational numbers, we never allow the denominator to be 0. We write $\dfrac{x+6}{(x-3)(x+4)}$, $x \neq 3$, $x \neq -4$ to indicate that 3 and -4 are not in the domain of this expression.

EXAMPLE 1   Calculating False Positives in Drug Testing

With a test that is 95% accurate, an expression for the likelihood that a student who tests positive for drugs is a nonuser is

$$\frac{(0.05)(1-x)}{0.95x + (0.05)(1-x)},$$

where x is the percentage of the student population that uses drugs. In a student population among which only 5% of the students use drugs, find the likelihood that a student who tests positive is a nonuser.

Solution

We convert 5% to decimal to get $x = 0.05$, and we replace x by 0.05 in the given expression.

$$\frac{(0.05)(1-x)}{0.95x + (0.05)(1-x)} = \frac{(0.05)(1-0.05)}{0.95(0.05) + (0.05)(1-0.05)}$$
$$= 0.50. \qquad\qquad \text{Use a calculator.}$$

Thus, the likelihood that a student who tests positive is a nonuser when the test that is used is 95% accurate is 50%. Because of the high rate of false positives, a more accurate test would be needed. ■ ■ ■

PRACTICE PROBLEM 1   Rework Example 1 for a student population among which only 10% of the students use drugs. ■

1 Learn to reduce a rational expression to lowest terms.

Lowest Terms for a Rational Expression

EXAMPLE 2   Reducing a Rational Expression to Lowest Terms

Simplify each expression.

a. $\dfrac{x^4+2x^3}{x+2}, x \neq -2$ **b.** $\dfrac{x^6-x-6}{x^3-3x^2}, x \neq 0, x \neq 3$

Solution

Factor each numerator and denominator and remove the common factors.

a. $\dfrac{x^4+2x^3}{x+2} = \dfrac{x^3(x+2)}{x+2} = \dfrac{x^3\cancel{(x+2)}}{\cancel{(x+2)}} = x^3.$

Continued on next page.

b. $\dfrac{x^2 - x - 6}{x^3 - 3x^2} = \dfrac{(x+2)(x-3)}{x^2(x-3)} = \dfrac{(x+2)\cancel{(x-3)}}{x^2\cancel{(x-3)}} = \dfrac{x+2}{x^2}.$ ■ ■ ■

PRACTICE PROBLEM 2   Simplify each expression.

a. $\dfrac{2x^3 + 8x^2}{3x^2 + 12x}$ **b.** $\dfrac{x^2 - 4}{x^2 + 4x + 4}$ ■

◆ **WARNING**

Because x^2 is a *term*, not a *factor*, in both the numerator and denominator of $\dfrac{x^2 - 1}{x^2 + 2x + 1}$ you cannot remove x^2. You can remove only *factors* common to both numerator and denominator.

---

2 Learn to multiply and divide rational expressions.

Multiplication and Division of Rational Expressions

We use the same rules for multiplying and dividing rational expressions as we do for rational numbers.

MULTIPLICATION AND DIVISION

For rational expressions $\dfrac{A}{B}$ and $\dfrac{C}{D}$,

$$\dfrac{A}{B} \cdot \dfrac{C}{D} = \dfrac{A \cdot C}{B \cdot D} \qquad \text{and} \qquad \dfrac{\dfrac{A}{B}}{\dfrac{C}{D}} = \dfrac{A}{B} \div \dfrac{C}{D} = \dfrac{A}{B} \cdot \dfrac{D}{C} = \dfrac{AD}{BC}$$

$$\text{if } B \neq 0, D \neq 0 \qquad\qquad \text{if } B \neq 0, C \neq 0, D \neq 0.$$

STUDY TIP

The best strategy to use when multiplying and dividing rational expressions is to factor each numerator and denominator completely and then remove the common factors.

EXAMPLE 3   **Multiplying and Dividing Rational Expressions**

Multiply or divide as indicated. Simplify your answer and leave it in factored form.

a. $\dfrac{x^2 + 3x + 2}{x^3 + 3x} \cdot \dfrac{2x^3 + 6x}{x^2 + x - 2},$ $x \neq 0, x \neq 1, x \neq -2$

b. $\dfrac{\dfrac{3x^2 + 11x - 4}{8x^3 - 40x^2}}{\dfrac{3x + 12}{4x^4 - 20x^3}},$ $x \neq 0, x \neq 5, x \neq -4$

Solution

Factor each numerator and denominator and remove the common factors.

a. $\dfrac{x^2 + 3x + 2}{x^3 + 3x} \cdot \dfrac{2x^3 + 6x}{x^2 + x - 2} = \dfrac{(x+2)(x+1)}{x(x^2+3)} \cdot \dfrac{2x(x^2+3)}{(x-1)(x+2)}$

$= \dfrac{\cancel{(x+2)}(x+1)(2\cancel{x})\cancel{(x^2+3)}}{\cancel{x}\cancel{(x^2+3)}(x-1)\cancel{(x+2)}} = \dfrac{2(x+1)}{x-1}.$

In working with the quotient of two

rational expressions $\dfrac{\dfrac{A}{B}}{\dfrac{C}{D}} = \dfrac{A}{B} \cdot \dfrac{D}{C}$,

there are three polynomials that appear

as denominators: B and D from $\dfrac{A}{B}$

and $\dfrac{C}{D}$, and C from $\dfrac{A}{B} \cdot \dfrac{D}{C}$.

b. $\dfrac{\dfrac{3x^2 + 11x - 4}{8x^3 - 40x^2}}{\dfrac{3x + 12}{4x^4 - 20x^3}} = \dfrac{3x^2 + 11x - 4}{8x^3 - 40x^2} \cdot \dfrac{4x^4 - 20x^3}{3x + 12} = \dfrac{(x + 4)(3x - 1)}{8x^2(x - 5)} \cdot \dfrac{4x^3(x - 5)}{3(x + 4)}$

$$= \dfrac{\overset{x}{\cancel{(x + 4)}(3x - 1)\cancel{(4x^3)}\cancel{(x - 5)}}}{\underset{2}{\cancel{8x^2}\cancel{(x - 5)}(3)\cancel{(x + 4)}}} = \dfrac{(3x - 1)x}{6} = \dfrac{x(3x - 1)}{6}.$$

■ ■ ■

PRACTICE PROBLEM 3 Multiply or divide as indicated. Simplify your answer.

$$\dfrac{\dfrac{x^2 - 2x - 3}{7x^3 + 28x^2}}{\dfrac{4x + 4}{2x^4 + 8x^3}} \qquad x \neq 0, x \neq -4, x \neq -1$$

■

3 Learn to add and subtract rational expressions.

Addition and Subtraction of Rational Expressions

To add and subtract rational expressions, we use the same rules as for adding and subtracting rational numbers.

ADDITION AND SUBTRACTION OF RATIONAL EXPRESSIONS

For rational expressions $\dfrac{A}{D}$ and $\dfrac{C}{D}$ (same denominator $D \neq 0$),

$$\dfrac{A}{D} + \dfrac{C}{D} = \dfrac{A + C}{D} \qquad \text{and} \qquad \dfrac{A}{D} - \dfrac{C}{D} = \dfrac{A - C}{D}.$$

For rational expression, $\dfrac{A}{B}$ and $\dfrac{C}{D}$ $\quad (B \neq 0, D \neq 0)$,

$$\dfrac{A}{B} + \dfrac{C}{D} = \dfrac{AD + BC}{BD} \qquad \text{and} \qquad \dfrac{A}{B} - \dfrac{C}{D} = \dfrac{AD - BC}{BD}.$$

EXAMPLE 4 **Adding and Subtracting Rational Expressions with the Same Denominator**

Add or subtract as indicated. Simplify your answer and leave both numerator and denominator in factored form.

a. $\dfrac{x - 6}{(x + 1)^2} + \dfrac{x + 8}{(x + 1)^2}, x \neq -1$

b. $\dfrac{3x - 2}{x^2 - 5x + 6} - \dfrac{2x + 1}{x^2 - 5x + 6}, x \neq 2, x \neq 3$

Continued on next page.

Solution

a. $\dfrac{x-6}{(x+1)^2} + \dfrac{x+8}{(x+1)^2} = \dfrac{x-6+x+8}{(x+1)^2} = \dfrac{2x+2}{(x+1)^2} = \dfrac{2\cancel{(x+1)}}{(x+1)\cancel{(x+1)}} = \dfrac{2}{x+1}.$

b. $\dfrac{3x-2}{x^2-5x+6} - \dfrac{2x+1}{x^2-5x+6} = \dfrac{(3x-2)-(2x+1)}{x^2-5x+6} = \dfrac{3x-2-2x-1}{x^2-5x+6}$

$$= \dfrac{x-3}{(x-2)(x-3)} = \dfrac{\cancel{x-3}}{(x-2)\cancel{(x-3)}} = \dfrac{1}{x-2}.$$

■ ■ ■

PRACTICE PROBLEM 4   Add or subtract as indicated. Simplify your answers.

a. $\dfrac{5x+22}{x^2-36} + \dfrac{2(x+10)}{x^2-36}$ $x \neq 6, x \neq -6$

b. $\dfrac{4x+1}{x^2+x-12} - \dfrac{3x+4}{x^2+x-12}$ $x \neq -4, x \neq 3$ ■

When adding or subtracting rational expressions with different denominators, we proceed (as with fractions) by finding a common denominator. The one most convenient to use is called the **least common denominator (LCD)** and it is the polynomial of least degree that contains each denominator as a factor. In the simplest case, the LCD is just the product of the denominators.

EXAMPLE 5   **Adding and Subtracting when Denominators Have No Common Factor**

Add or subtract as indicated. Simplify your answer and leave it in factored form.

a. $\dfrac{x}{x+1} + \dfrac{2x-1}{x+3}, x \neq 1, x \neq -3$ **b.** $\dfrac{2x}{x+1} - \dfrac{x}{x+2}, x \neq -1, x \neq -2$

Solution

a. $\dfrac{x}{x+1} + \dfrac{2x-1}{x+3} = \dfrac{x(x+3)}{(x+1)(x+3)} + \dfrac{(2x-1)(x+1)}{(x+1)(x+3)}$ LCD $= (x+1)(x+3)$

$$= \dfrac{x(x+3)+(2x-1)(x+1)}{(x+1)(x+3)} = \dfrac{x^2+3x+2x^2+2x-x-1}{(x+1)(x+3)}$$

$$= \dfrac{3x^2+4x-1}{(x+1)(x+3)}.$$

b. $\dfrac{2x}{x+1} - \dfrac{x}{x+2} = \dfrac{2x(x+2)}{(x+1)(x+2)} - \dfrac{x(x+1)}{(x+1)(x+2)}$ LCD $= (x+1)(x+2)$

$$= \dfrac{2x(x+2)-x(x+1)}{(x+1)(x+2)} = \dfrac{2x^2+4x-x^2-x}{(x+1)(x+2)}$$

$$= \dfrac{x^2+3x}{(x+1)(x+2)} = \dfrac{x(x+3)}{(x+1)(x+2)}.$$

■ ■ ■

PRACTICE PROBLEM 5   Add or subtract as indicated. Simplify your answers.

a. $\dfrac{2x}{x+2} + \dfrac{3x}{x-5}$, $x \neq -2, x \neq 5$ **b.** $\dfrac{5x}{x-4} - \dfrac{2x}{x+3}$, $x \neq 4, x \neq -3$,   ■

TO FIND THE LCD FOR RATIONAL EXPRESSIONS

1. Factor each denominator polynomial completely.

2. Form a product of the different prime factors of each polynomial. (Each distinct factor is used exactly once).

3. Attach to each factor in this product the largest exponent that appears on this factor in *any* of the factored denominators.

EXAMPLE 6   **Finding the LCD for Rational Expressions**

Find the LCD for each pair of rational expressions.

a. $\dfrac{x+2}{x(x-1)^2(x+2)}, \dfrac{3x+7}{4x^2(x+2)^3}$ **b.** $\dfrac{x+1}{x^2-x-6}, \dfrac{2x-13}{x^2-9}$

Solution

a. **Step 1** The denominators are already completely factored.
  Step 2 $4x(x-1)(x+2)$ Product of the different factors
  Step 3 LCD $= 4x^2(x-1)^2(x+2)^3$ The largest exponents are 2, 2, and 3.

b. **Step 1** $x^2 - x - 6 = (x+2)(x-3)$
                 $x^2 - 9 = (x+3)(x-3)$
  Step 2 $(x+2)(x-3)(x+3)$ Product of the different factors
  Step 3 LCD $= (x+2)(x-3)(x+3)$ The largest exponent on each is 1. ■ ■ ■

PRACTICE PROBLEM 6   Find the LCD for each pair of rational expressions.

a. $\dfrac{x^2+3x}{x^2(x+2)^2(x-2)}, \dfrac{4x^2+1}{3x(x-2)^2}$ **b.** $\dfrac{2x-1}{x^2-25}, \dfrac{3-7x^2}{(x^2+4x-5)}$ ■

In adding or subtracting rational expressions with different denominators, the first step is to find the LCD. Here is the general procedure.

PROCEDURE FOR ADDING OR SUBTRACTING RATIONAL EXPRESSIONS WITH DIFFERENT DENOMINATORS.

Step 1   Find the LCD.

Step 2   Using $\dfrac{A}{B} = \dfrac{AC}{BC}$, write each rational expression as a rational expression with the LCD as the denominator.

Step 3   Following the order of operations, add or subtract numerators, keeping the LCD as the denominator.

Step 4   Simplify.

> **EXAMPLE 7** **Using the LCD to Add and Subtract Rational Expressions**

Add or subtract as indicated. Simplify your answer and leave it in factored form.

a. $\dfrac{3}{x^2 - 1} + \dfrac{x}{x^2 + 2x + 1}$, $x \neq 1, x \neq -1$ **b.** $\dfrac{x + 2}{x^2 - x} - \dfrac{3x}{4(x - 1)^2}$, $x \neq 0, x \neq 1$

Solution

a. **Step 1** Note $x^2 - 1 = (x - 1)(x + 1)$ and $x^2 + 2x + 1 = (x + 1)^2$; the LCD is $(x + 1)^2(x - 1)$.

Step 2 $\dfrac{3}{x^2 - 1} = \dfrac{3}{(x - 1)(x + 1)} = \dfrac{3(x + 1)}{(x - 1)(x + 1)^2}$ Multiply numerator and denominator by $x + 1$.

$\dfrac{x}{x^2 + 2x + 1} = \dfrac{x}{(x + 1)^2} = \dfrac{x(x - 1)}{(x + 1)^2(x - 1)}$ Multiply numerator and denominator by $x - 1$.

Steps 3–4 Now add.

$$\dfrac{3}{x^2 - 1} + \dfrac{x}{x^2 + 2x + 1} = \dfrac{3(x + 1)}{(x - 1)(x + 1)^2} + \dfrac{x(x - 1)}{(x - 1)(x + 1)^2}$$

$$= \dfrac{3(x + 1) + x(x - 1)}{(x - 1)(x + 1)^2} = \dfrac{3x + 3 + x^2 - x}{(x - 1)(x + 1)^2}$$

$$= \dfrac{x^2 + 2x + 3}{(x - 1)(x + 1)^2}.$$

b. **Step 1** The LCD is $4x(x - 1)^2$. $x^2 - x = x(x - 1)$

Step 2

$\dfrac{x + 2}{x^2 - x} = \dfrac{x + 2}{x(x - 1)} = \dfrac{(x + 2) \cdot 4(x - 1)}{x(x - 1) \cdot 4(x - 1)} = \dfrac{4(x + 2)(x - 1)}{4x(x - 1)^2}$ Multiply numerator and denominator by $4(x - 1)$.

$\dfrac{3x}{4(x - 1)^2} = \dfrac{(3x)(x)}{4(x - 1)^2(x)} = \dfrac{3x^2}{4x(x - 1)^2}$ Multiply numerator and denominator by x.

Step 3–4 Now subtract.

$$\dfrac{x + 2}{x^2 - x} - \dfrac{3x}{4(x - 1)^2} = \dfrac{4(x + 2)(x - 1)}{4x(x - 1)^2} - \dfrac{3x^2}{4x(x - 1)^2} = \dfrac{4(x + 2)(x - 1) - 3x^2}{4x^2(x - 1)^2}$$

$$= \dfrac{4x^2 + 4x - 8 - 3x^2}{4x(x - 1)^2} = \dfrac{x^2 + 4x - 8}{4x(x - 1)^2}.$$ ■ ■ ■

PRACTICE PROBLEM 7 Add or subtract as indicated. Simplify your answers.

a. $\dfrac{4}{x^2 - 4x + 4} + \dfrac{x}{x^2 - 4}$, $x \neq 2, x = -2$

b. $\dfrac{2x}{3(x - 5)^2} - \dfrac{6x}{2(x^2 - 5x)}$, $x \neq 0, x \neq 5$ ■

4 Learn to identify and simplify complex fractions.

Complex Fractions

A rational expression that contains another rational expression in its numerator or denominator (or both) is called a **complex rational expression** or **complex fraction.** To **simplify** a complex fraction, we write it as a rational expression in lowest terms.

There are two effective methods of simplifying complex fractions.

PROCEDURES FOR SIMPLIFYING COMPLEX FRACTIONS

Method 1   Perform the operations indicated in both the numerator and the denominator of the complex fraction. Then multiply the resulting numerator by the reciprocal of the denominator.

Method 2   Multiply the numerator and the denominator of the complex fraction by the LCD of all the rational expressions that appear in either the numerator or denominator. Simplify the result.

EXAMPLE 8   **Simplifying a Complex Fraction**

Simplify $\dfrac{\dfrac{1}{2} + \dfrac{1}{x}}{\dfrac{x^2 - 4}{2x}}$, $x \neq 0, x \neq 2, x \neq -2$, using each of the two methods.

Solution

Method 1 $\dfrac{\dfrac{1}{2} + \dfrac{1}{x}}{\dfrac{x^2 - 4}{2x}} = \dfrac{\dfrac{x + 2}{2x}}{\dfrac{x^2 - 4}{2x}} = \dfrac{x + 2}{2x} \cdot \dfrac{2x}{x^2 - 4} = \dfrac{x + 2}{2x} \cdot \dfrac{2x}{(x + 2)(x - 2)}$

$$= \dfrac{\cancel{(x + 2)}\cancel{(2x)}}{\cancel{(2x)}\cancel{(x + 2)}(x - 2)} = \dfrac{1}{x - 2}.$$

Method 2   The LCD of $\dfrac{1}{2}, \dfrac{1}{x}$, and $\dfrac{x^2 - 4}{2x}$ is $2x$.

$\dfrac{\dfrac{1}{2} + \dfrac{1}{x}}{\dfrac{x^2 - 4}{2x}} = \dfrac{\left(\dfrac{1}{2} + \dfrac{1}{x}\right)(2x)}{\left(\dfrac{x^2 - 4}{2x}\right)(2x)}$ Multiply numerator and denominator by the LCD.

$$= \dfrac{\dfrac{1}{2}(2x) + \dfrac{1}{x}(2x)}{\left[\dfrac{(x^2 - 4)}{2x}\right](2x)} = \dfrac{x + 2}{x^2 - 4} = \dfrac{\cancel{x + 2}}{(x - 2)\cancel{(x + 2)}} = \dfrac{1}{x - 2}.$$ ■ ■ ■

PRACTICE PROBLEM 8   Simplify: $\dfrac{\dfrac{5}{3x} + \dfrac{1}{3}}{\dfrac{x^2 - 25}{3x}}$, $x \neq 0, x \neq 5, x \neq -5$.   ■

EXAMPLE 9   **Simplifying a Complex Fraction**

Simplify $\dfrac{x}{2x - \dfrac{7}{3 - \dfrac{1}{2}}}$, $x \neq \dfrac{7}{5}$.

Solution

We will use Method 1.

Begin with $\dfrac{7}{3 - \dfrac{1}{2}} = \dfrac{7}{\dfrac{5}{2}} = 7 \cdot \dfrac{2}{5} = \dfrac{14}{5}$.   Replace $3 - \dfrac{1}{2}$ by $\dfrac{5}{2}$.

Then, $\dfrac{x}{2x - \dfrac{7}{3 - \dfrac{1}{2}}} = \dfrac{x}{2x - \dfrac{14}{5}}$ Replace $\dfrac{7}{3 - \dfrac{1}{2}}$ by $\dfrac{14}{5}$.

$= \dfrac{x}{\dfrac{10x - 14}{5}} = x \cdot \dfrac{5}{10x - 14} = \dfrac{5x}{10x - 14} = \dfrac{5x}{2(5x - 7)}$.   ■ ■ ■

PRACTICE PROBLEM 9   Simplify: $\dfrac{5x}{3x - \dfrac{4}{2 - \dfrac{1}{3}}}$, $x \neq \dfrac{4}{5}$.   ■

A Exercises   Basic Skills and Concepts

In Exercises 1–16, reduce each rational expression to lowest terms. Identify all numbers that must be excluded from the domain of the given rational expression.

1. $\dfrac{2x + 2}{x^2 + 2x + 1}$ $\dfrac{2}{x + 1}, x \neq -1$ **2.** $\dfrac{3x - 6}{x^2 - 4x + 4}$ $\dfrac{3}{x - 2}, x \neq 2$

3. $\dfrac{3x + 3}{x^2 - 1}$ †   **4.** $\dfrac{10 - 5x}{4 - x^2}$ †

5. $\dfrac{2x - 6}{9 - x^2}$ †   **6.** $\dfrac{15 + 3x}{x^2 - 25}$ †

7. $\dfrac{2x - 1}{1 - 2x}$ $-1, x \neq \dfrac{1}{2}$ **8.** $\dfrac{2 - 5x}{5x - 2}$ $-1, x \neq \dfrac{2}{5}$

9. $\dfrac{x^2 - 6x + 9}{4x - 12}$ $\dfrac{x - 3}{4}, x \neq 3$ **10.** $\dfrac{x^2 - 10x + 25}{3x - 15}$ †

11. $\dfrac{7x^2 + 7x}{x^2 + 2x + 1}$ $\dfrac{7x}{x + 1}, x \neq -1$ **12.** $\dfrac{4x^2 + 12x}{x^2 + 6x + 9}$ †

13. $\dfrac{x^2 - 11x + 10}{x^2 + 6x - 7}$ †   **14.** $\dfrac{x^2 + 2x - 15}{x^2 - 7x + 12}$ †

15. $\dfrac{6x^4 + 14x^3 + 4x^2}{6x^4 - 10x^3 - 4x^2}$ †   **16.** $\dfrac{3x^3 + x^2}{3x^4 - 11x^3 - 4x^2}$ †

†Due to space constrictions, answers to these exercises may be found in the Answers beginning on page A–1 in the back of the book.

In Exercises 17–34, multiply or divide as indicated. Simplify, and leave the numerator and denominator in your answer in factored form.

17. $\dfrac{x-3}{2x+4} \cdot \dfrac{10x+20}{5x-15}$ 1

18. $\dfrac{6x+4}{2x-8} \cdot \dfrac{x-4}{9x+6}$ $\dfrac{1}{3}$

19. $\dfrac{2x+6}{4x-8} \cdot \dfrac{x^2+x-6}{x^2-9}$ †

20. $\dfrac{25x^2-9}{4-2x} \cdot \dfrac{4-x^2}{10x-6}$ †

21. $\dfrac{x^2-7x}{x^2-6x-7} \cdot \dfrac{x^2-1}{x^2}$ †

22. $\dfrac{x^2-9}{x^2-6x+9} \cdot \dfrac{5x-15}{x+3}$ 5

23. $\dfrac{x^2-x-6}{x^2+3x+2} \cdot \dfrac{x^2-1}{x^2-9}$ $\dfrac{x-1}{x+3}$

24. $\dfrac{x^2+2x-8}{x^2+x-20} \cdot \dfrac{x^2-16}{x^2+5x+4}$ $\dfrac{(x-2)(x+4)}{(x+5)(x+1)}$

25. $\dfrac{2-x}{x+1} \cdot \dfrac{x^2+3x+2}{x^2-4}$ -1

26. $\dfrac{3-x}{x+5} \cdot \dfrac{x^2+8x+15}{x^2-9}$ -1

27. $\dfrac{x+2}{6} \div \dfrac{4x+8}{9}$ $\dfrac{3}{8}$

28. $\dfrac{x+3}{20} \div \dfrac{4x+12}{9}$ $\dfrac{9}{80}$

29. $\dfrac{x^2-9}{x} \div \dfrac{2x+6}{5x^2}$ †

30. $\dfrac{x^2-1}{3x} \div \dfrac{7x-7}{x^2+x}$ $\dfrac{(x+1)^2}{21}$

31. $\dfrac{x^2+2x-3}{x^2+8x+16} \div \dfrac{x-1}{3x+12}$ $\dfrac{3(x+3)}{x+4}$

32. $\dfrac{x^2+5x+6}{x^2+6x+9} \div \dfrac{x^2+3x+2}{x^2+7x+12}$ $\dfrac{x+4}{x+1}$

33. $\left(\dfrac{x^2-9}{x^3+8} \div \dfrac{x+3}{x^3+2x^2-x-2}\right)\dfrac{1}{x^2-1}$ $\dfrac{x-3}{x^2-2x+4}$

34. $\left(\dfrac{x^2-25}{x^2-3x-4} \div \dfrac{x^2+3x-10}{x^2-1}\right)\dfrac{x-2}{x-5}$ $\dfrac{x-1}{x-4}$

In Exercises 35–52, add and subtract as indicated. Simplify, and leave the numerator and denominator in your answer in factored form.

35. $\dfrac{x}{5} + \dfrac{3}{5}$ $\dfrac{x+3}{5}$

36. $\dfrac{7}{4} - \dfrac{x}{4}$ $\dfrac{7-x}{4}$

37. $\dfrac{x}{2x+1} + \dfrac{4}{2x+1}$ $\dfrac{x+4}{2x+1}$

38. $\dfrac{2x}{7x-3} + \dfrac{x}{7x-3}$ $\dfrac{3x}{7x-3}$

39. $\dfrac{x^2}{x+1} - \dfrac{x^2-1}{x+1}$ $\dfrac{1}{x+1}$

40. $\dfrac{2x+7}{3x+2} - \dfrac{x-2}{3x+2}$ $\dfrac{x+9}{3x+2}$

41. $\dfrac{4}{3-x} + \dfrac{2x}{x-3}$ $\dfrac{2(x-2)}{x-3}$

42. $\dfrac{-2}{1-x} + \dfrac{2-x}{x-1}$ $\dfrac{x-4}{x-1}$

43. $\dfrac{5x}{x^2+1} + \dfrac{2x}{x^2+1}$ $\dfrac{7x}{x^2+1}$

44. $\dfrac{x}{2(x-1)^2} + \dfrac{3x}{2(x-1)^2}$ †

45. $\dfrac{7x}{2(x-3)} + \dfrac{x}{2(x-3)}$ †

46. $\dfrac{4x}{4(x+5)^2} + \dfrac{8x}{4(x+5)^2}$ †

47. $\dfrac{x}{x^2-4} - \dfrac{2}{x^2-4}$ $\dfrac{1}{x+2}$

48. $\dfrac{5x}{x^2-1} - \dfrac{5}{x^2-1}$ $\dfrac{5}{x+1}$

49. $\dfrac{x-2}{2x+1} - \dfrac{x}{2x-1}$ †

50. $\dfrac{2x-1}{4x+1} - \dfrac{2x}{4x-1}$ †

51. $\dfrac{-x}{x+2} + \dfrac{x-2}{x} - \dfrac{x}{x-2}$ †

52. $\dfrac{3x}{x-1} + \dfrac{x+1}{x} - \dfrac{2x}{x+1}$ †

In Exercises 53–60, find the LCD for each pair of rational fractions.

53. $\dfrac{5}{3x-6}, \dfrac{2x}{4x-8}$ $12(x-2)$

54. $\dfrac{5x+1}{7+21x}, \dfrac{1-x}{3+9x}$ †

55. $\dfrac{3-x}{4x^2-1}, \dfrac{7x}{(2x+1)^2}$ †

56. $\dfrac{14x}{(3x-1)^2}, \dfrac{2x+7}{9x^2-1}$ †

57. $\dfrac{1-x}{x^2+3x+2}, \dfrac{3x+12}{x^2-1}$ †

58. $\dfrac{5x+9}{x^2-x-6}, \dfrac{x+5}{x^2-9}$ †

59. $\dfrac{7-4x}{x^2-5x+4}, \dfrac{x^2-x}{x^2+x-2}$ †

60. $\dfrac{13x}{x^2-2x-3}, \dfrac{2x^2-4}{x^2+3x+2}$ †

In Exercises 61–76, perform the indicated operations and simplify the result. Leave the numerator and denominator in your answer in factored form.

61. $\dfrac{5}{x-3} + \dfrac{2x}{x^2-9}$ †

62. $\dfrac{3x}{x-1} + \dfrac{x}{x^2-1}$ †

63. $\dfrac{2x}{x^2-4} - \dfrac{x}{x+2}$ †

64. $\dfrac{3x-1}{x^2-16} - \dfrac{2x+1}{x-4}$ †

65. $\dfrac{x-2}{x^2+3x-10} + \dfrac{x+3}{x^2+x-6}$ $\dfrac{2x+3}{(x-2)(x+5)}$

66. $\dfrac{x+3}{x^2-x-2} + \dfrac{x-1}{x^2+2x+1}$ $\dfrac{2x^2+x+5}{(x-2)(x+1)^2}$

67. $\dfrac{2x-3}{9x^2-1} + \dfrac{4x-1}{(3x-1)^2}$ †

68. $\dfrac{3x+1}{(2x+1)^2} + \dfrac{x+3}{4x^2-1}$ †

69. $\dfrac{x-3}{x^2-25} - \dfrac{x-3}{x^2+9x+20}$ †

70. $\dfrac{2x}{x^2-16} - \dfrac{2x-7}{x^2-7x+12}$ †

71. $\dfrac{3}{x^2-4} + \dfrac{1}{2-x} - \dfrac{1}{2+x}$ $\dfrac{2x-3}{(2+x)(2-x)}$

72. $\dfrac{2}{5+x} + \dfrac{5}{x^2-25} + \dfrac{7}{5-x}$ $\dfrac{5(x+8)}{(5-x)(5+x)}$

73. $\dfrac{x+3a}{x-5a} - \dfrac{x+5a}{x-3a}$ †

74. $\dfrac{3x-a}{2x-a} - \dfrac{2x+a}{3x+a}$ †

75. $\dfrac{1}{x+h} - \dfrac{1}{x}$ $\dfrac{h}{x(x+h)}$

76. $\dfrac{1}{(x+h)^2} - \dfrac{1}{x^2}$ †

In Exercises 77–90, perform the indicated operations and simplify the result. Leave the numerator and denominator in your answer in factored form.

77. $\dfrac{\dfrac{2}{x}}{\dfrac{3}{x^2}}$ $\dfrac{2x}{3}$

78. $\dfrac{\dfrac{-6}{x}}{\dfrac{2}{x^3}}$ $-3x^2$

79. $\dfrac{\dfrac{1}{x}}{1-\dfrac{1}{x}}$ $\dfrac{1}{x-1}$

80. $\dfrac{\dfrac{1}{x^2}}{\dfrac{1}{x^2}-1}$ $\dfrac{1}{(1-x)(1+x)}$

81. $\dfrac{\dfrac{1}{x}-1}{\dfrac{1}{x}+1}$ $\dfrac{1-x}{1+x}$

82. $\dfrac{2-\dfrac{2}{x}}{1+\dfrac{2}{x}}$ $\dfrac{2(x-1)}{x+2}$

87. $\dfrac{\dfrac{1}{x+h}-\dfrac{1}{x}}{h}$ †

88. $\dfrac{\dfrac{1}{(x+h)^2}-\dfrac{1}{x^2}}{h}$ †

83. $\dfrac{\dfrac{1}{x}-x}{1-\dfrac{1}{x^2}}-x$

84. $\dfrac{x-\dfrac{1}{x}}{\dfrac{1}{x^2}-1}-x$

89. $\dfrac{\dfrac{1}{x-a}+\dfrac{1}{x+a}}{\dfrac{1}{x-a}-\dfrac{1}{x+a}}$ †

90. $\dfrac{\dfrac{1}{x-a}+\dfrac{1}{x+a}}{\dfrac{x}{x-a}-\dfrac{a}{x+a}}$ $\dfrac{2x}{x^2+a^2}$

85. $x-\dfrac{x}{x+\dfrac{1}{2}}$ $\dfrac{x(2x-1)}{2x+1}$

86. $x+\dfrac{x}{x+\dfrac{1}{2}}$ $\dfrac{x(2x+3)}{2x+1}$

B Exercises   Applying the Concepts

91. Bearing length. The length (in centimeters) of a bearing in the shape of a cylinder is given by $\dfrac{125.6}{\pi r^2}$, where r is the radius of the base of the cylinder. Find the length of a bearing with a diameter of 4 centimeters, using 3.14 as an approximation of π. 10 cm

92. Toy-box height. The height (in feet) of an open toy box that is twice as long as it is wide is given by $\dfrac{13.5-2x^2}{6x}$, where x is the width of the box. Find the height of a toy box that is 1.5 feet wide. 1 ft

93. Diluting a mixture. A 100-gallon mixture of citrus extract and water is 3% citrus extract.
a. Write a rational expression in x whose values give the percentage (in decimal form) of the mixture that is citrus extract when x gallons of water are added to the mixture. †
b. Find the percentage of citrus extract in the mixture if 50 gallons of water are added to it. 2%

94. Acidity in a reservoir. A half-full 400,000-gallon reservoir is found to be 0.75% acid.
a. Write a rational expression in x whose values give the percentage (in decimal form) of acid in the reservoir when x gallons of water are added to it. †
b. Find the percentage of acid in the reservoir if 100,000 gallons of water are added to it. 0.5%

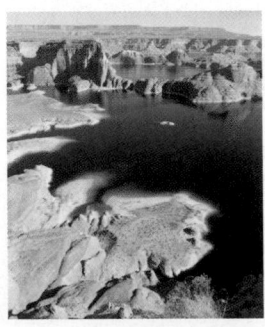

95. Diet lemonade. A company packages its powdered diet lemonade mix in containers in the shape of a cylinder. The top and bottom are made of a tin product that costs 5 cents per square inch. The side of the container is made of a cheaper material that costs one cent per square inch. The height of any cylinder can be found by dividing its volume by the area of its base.
a. If x is the radius of the base (in inches), write a rational expression in x whose values give the cost of each container, assuming that the capacity of the container is 120 cubic inches. †
b. Find the cost of a container whose base is 4 inches in diameter, using 3.14 as an approximation of π. $2.46

Volume = 120 cubic inches

96. Storage containers. A company makes storage containers in the shape of an open box with a square base. The sides of the box are made of a plastic that costs 40 cents per square foot. The height of any box can be found by dividing its volume by the area of its base.
a. If x is the length of the base (in feet), write a rational expression in x whose values give the cost of each container, assuming that the capacity of the container is 2.25 cubic feet. †
b. Find the cost of a container whose base is 1.5 feet long. †

Rational Exponents and Radicals

BEFORE STARTING THIS SECTION, REVIEW

1. Absolute value (Section P.1, page 8)

2. Integer exponents (Section P.2, page 20)

3. Special-product formulas (Section P.3, page 37)

4. Properties of fractions (Section P.1, page 14)

OBJECTIVES

1. Learn to define and evaluate square roots.

2. Learn to simplify square roots.

3. Learn to rationalize denominators and numerators.

4. Learn to define and evaluate nth roots.

5. Learn to combine like radicals.

6. Learn to define and evaluate rational exponents.

Friction and Tap-Water Flow

Suppose that your water company had a large reservoir or water tower 80 meters or more above your cold-water faucet level. If there was no friction in the pipes and you turned on your faucet, the water would come pouring out of the faucet at nearly 90 miles per hour! This fact follows from a result known as Bernoulli's equation, which predicts the velocity of the water (neglecting friction and related turbulence) in this situation to be equal to $\sqrt{2gh}$, where g is the acceleration due to gravity and h is the height of the water level above a hole from which the water escapes.

We can use Bernoulli's equation to calculate the velocity of the water from the faucet by replacing h by 80 meters and g by 10 meters per second per second (a convenient approximation) in the expression $\sqrt{2gh}$ and verifying our statement about the water pouring out at "nearly 90 miles per hour."

Velocity of water

$$= \sqrt{2gh}$$
$$= \sqrt{2(10 \text{ m/s}^2)(80 \text{ m})}$$
$$= \sqrt{1600 \text{ m}^2/\text{s}^2}$$
$$= 40 \text{ m/s (approximately 90 miles per hour)}$$

In Example 3, we will use these same ideas to see how to find the rate at which water is being lost from a punctured water tower. ■

1 Learn to define and evaluate square roots.

Square Roots

When we raise the number 5 to the power 2, we write $5^2 = 25$. The reverse of this squaring process is called finding a **square root.** In the case of 25, we say that 5 is a square root of 25 and write $\sqrt{25} = 5$. In general, we say that b is a square root of a if $b^2 = a$. We can't call 5 *the* square root of 25, because it is also true that $(-5)^2 = 25$, so that -5 is *another* square root of 25.

The symbol $\sqrt{}$, called a **radical sign,** is used to distinguish between 5 and -5, the two square roots of 25. We write $5 = \sqrt{25}$ and $-5 = -\sqrt{25}$ and call $\sqrt{25}$ the *principal square root* of 25.

Definition of Principal Square Root

$$\sqrt{a} = b \quad \text{means} \quad (1)\ b^2 = a \quad \text{and} \quad (2)\ b \geq 0$$

If $\sqrt{a} = b$, then $a = b^2 \geq 0$. Consequently, the symbol $\sqrt{a}$ denotes a real number only when $a \geq 0$. The domain of the expression $\sqrt{x}$ is then $x \geq 0$, or, in interval notation, $[0, \infty)$. The number or expression under the radical sign is called the **radicand,** and the radicand together with the radical sign is called a **radical.**

According to the definition of the square root, there are two tests that the number b must pass in order for the statement $\sqrt{a} = b$ to be correct: (1) $b^2 = a$ and (2) $b \geq 0$. Let's see how these tests are used to decide whether the statements below are true or false.

Statement $\sqrt{a} = b$	Test (1) $b^2 = a$?	Test (2) $b \geq 0$?	Conclusion True when b passes both tests
$\sqrt{4} = 2$	$2^2 = 4$	$2 \geq 0$	**True;** 2 passed both tests.
$\sqrt{4} = -2$	$(-2)^2 = 4$	$-2 \geq 0$	**False;** -2 failed Test (2).
$\sqrt{\frac{1}{9}} = \frac{1}{3}$	$(\frac{1}{3})^2 = \frac{1}{9}$	$\frac{1}{3} \geq 0$	**True;** $\frac{1}{3}$ passed both tests.
$\sqrt{7^2} = 7$	$7^2 = 7^2$	$7 \geq 0$	**True;** 7 passed both tests.
$\sqrt{(-7)^2} = -7$	$(-7)^2 = (-7)^2$	$-7 \geq 0$	**False;** -7 failed Test (2).

The last example (letting x represent -7) shows that $\sqrt{x^2}$ is not always equal to x. Let's apply Test (1) and Test (2) to the statement $\sqrt{x^2} = |x|$, where x represents any real number.

Statement	Test (1)	Test (2)	Conclusion
$\sqrt{x^2} = |x|$	$|x|^2 = x^2$	$|x| \geq 0$	True; $|x|$ passed both tests

---

For any real number x,

$$\sqrt{x^2} = |x|.$$

If $\sqrt{x} = b$, then, by Test (1), $b^2 = x$; replacing b by $\sqrt{x}$ in the equation $b^2 = x$ yields the following result.

> For any nonnegative real number x,
>
> $$(\sqrt{x})^2 = x.$$

EXAMPLE 1   Finding the Square Roots of Perfect Squares and Their Ratios

Find. **a.** $\sqrt{121}$ **b.** $\sqrt{\dfrac{25}{81}}$ **c.** $\sqrt{\dfrac{16}{169}}$

Solution

Write each radicand as a perfect square.

a. $\sqrt{121} = \sqrt{11^2} = 11$ **b.** $\sqrt{\dfrac{25}{81}} = \sqrt{\dfrac{5^2}{9^2}} = \sqrt{\left(\dfrac{5}{9}\right)^2} = \dfrac{5}{9}$

c. $\sqrt{\dfrac{16}{169}} = \sqrt{\dfrac{4^2}{13^2}} = \sqrt{\left(\dfrac{4}{13}\right)^2} = \dfrac{4}{13}.$ ■ ■ ■

PRACTICE PROBLEM 1   Find.

a. $\sqrt{144}$ **b.** $\sqrt{\dfrac{1}{49}}$ **c.** $\sqrt{\dfrac{4}{64}}$ ■

2 Learn to simplify square roots.

Simplifying Square Roots

When working with square roots, we can simplify a radical expression by removing perfect squares that are factors of the radicand from under the radical sign. For example, to simplify $\sqrt{8}$, we write $\sqrt{8} = \sqrt{4 \cdot 2} = \sqrt{4}\sqrt{2} = 2\sqrt{2}$. We rely on the following rules.

> **PRODUCT AND QUOTIENT PROPERTIES OF SQUARE ROOTS**
>
> $$\sqrt{a \cdot b} = \sqrt{a}\sqrt{b} \qquad a \geq 0, b \geq 0$$
>
> $$\sqrt{\dfrac{a}{b}} = \dfrac{\sqrt{a}}{\sqrt{b}} \qquad a \geq 0, b > 0$$

EXAMPLE 2   Simplifying Square Roots

Simplify. **a.** $\sqrt{117}$ **b.** $\sqrt{6}\sqrt{12}$ **c.** $\sqrt{48x^2}$ **d.** $\dfrac{\sqrt{36}}{\sqrt{3}}$ **e.** $\sqrt{\dfrac{25y^3}{9x^2}}, x \neq 0, y \geq 0$

Continued on next page.

Solution

a. $\sqrt{117} = \sqrt{9 \cdot 13} = \sqrt{9}\sqrt{13} = 3\sqrt{13}$

b. $\sqrt{6}\sqrt{12} = \sqrt{6 \cdot 12} = \sqrt{72} = \sqrt{36 \cdot 2} = \sqrt{36}\sqrt{2} = 6\sqrt{2}$

c. $\sqrt{48x^2} = \sqrt{48}\sqrt{x^2} = \sqrt{16 \cdot 3}\sqrt{x^2} = \sqrt{16}\sqrt{3}\sqrt{x^2} = 4\sqrt{3}|x|$

d. $\dfrac{\sqrt{36}}{\sqrt{3}} = \sqrt{\dfrac{36}{3}} = \sqrt{12} = \sqrt{4 \cdot 3} = \sqrt{4}\sqrt{3} = 2\sqrt{3}$

e. $\sqrt{\dfrac{25y^3}{9x^2}} = \dfrac{\sqrt{25y^3}}{\sqrt{9x^2}} = \dfrac{\sqrt{25 \cdot y^2 \cdot y}}{\sqrt{9 \cdot x^2}} = \dfrac{\sqrt{25}\sqrt{y^2}\sqrt{y}}{\sqrt{9}\sqrt{x^2}} = \dfrac{5|y|\sqrt{y}}{3|x|}$ $\quad x \neq 0, y \geq 0$

$\qquad\qquad\qquad\qquad\qquad\qquad\qquad\qquad\qquad = \dfrac{5y\sqrt{y}}{3|x|},$ $\quad y \geq 0, |y| = y.$ ■ ■ ■

PRACTICE PROBLEM 2 Simplify.

a. $\sqrt{20}$ b. $\sqrt{6}\sqrt{8}$ c. $\sqrt{12x^2}$ d. $\sqrt{\dfrac{20y^3}{27x^2}}$ ■

◆ **WARNING**

It is important to note that $\sqrt{a + b} \neq \sqrt{a} + \sqrt{b}$. For example (with $a = 1$ and $b = 4$), $\sqrt{1 + 4} \neq \sqrt{1} + \sqrt{4}$, because $\sqrt{1 + 4} = \sqrt{5}$, whereas $\sqrt{1} + \sqrt{4} = 1 + 2 = 3$, and $\sqrt{5} \neq 3$. Similarly, $\sqrt{a - b} \neq \sqrt{a} - \sqrt{b}$.

EXAMPLE 3   **Calculating Water Flow from a Punctured Water Tower**

The son of the manager of a water company accidentally shoots a hole in the base of the company's large, full water tower with his new .22 Long Rifle. The diameter of the bullet used in the rifle is 223 thousandths of an inch, and the water tower is 20 meters high. What is the initial rate of water flow, in gallons per minute, from the punctured hole?

Solution

We can use Bernoulli's equation to predict the velocity of the water from the hole. If we ignore friction, the velocity of water will be equal to $\sqrt{2gh}$, where g is the acceleration due to gravity and h is the height of the water level above the hole.

We replace h by 20 meters and roughly approximate g by 10 meters per second per second ($g \approx 9.81$ m/s^2) in the expression $\sqrt{2gh}$.

Thus, the velocity of the water is $= \sqrt{2gh}$

$$\approx \sqrt{2(10 \text{ m/s}^2)(20 \text{ m})} = 20 \text{ m/s}$$
$$\approx (20 \text{ m/s})(39.37 \text{ in./m})(60 \text{ s/min}) \qquad 1 \text{ m} \approx 39.37 \text{ in.}$$
$$= 47{,}244 \text{ in./min}$$

Now we need to know two things:

1. That the hole made by the bullet is circular, with diameter 0.223 inch (so the radius is one-half the diameter). Consequently, the area of the hole is $\pi\left(\dfrac{0.223}{2}\right)^2$ square inches.

2. That the volume of water leaving the water tower is given approximately by the area of the hole, multiplied by the velocity of the water flowing through it.

The velocity of the water is 47,244 in./min, so the volume, V, of water leaving the water tower is given by:

$$V = \pi \left(\frac{0.223}{2} \right)^2 (47{,}244) \text{ in.}^3/\text{min} \qquad V = \text{area} \times \text{velocity}$$

$$\approx 1845 \text{ in.}^3/\text{min} \approx 7.4 \text{ gallons/min.} \qquad 1 \text{ in.}^3 = 0.004 \text{ gallon}$$

The initial rate at which water flows from the punctured hole is approximately 7.4 gallons per minute. ■ ■ ■

3 Learn to rationalize denominators and numerators.

Rationalizing Denominators

It is customary to rewrite a quotient involving square roots so that no radical appears in the denominator. The process for eliminating square roots in a denominator is called **rationalizing the denominator.** The special product $(A - B)(A + B) = A^2 - B^2$ is helpful when at least one term of a denominator binomial $A + B$ or $A - B$ is a square root. Here are some examples:

Denominator Factor	Multiply by	New Denominator Contains the Factor
$2 + \sqrt{3}$	$2 - \sqrt{3}$	$(2 + \sqrt{3})(2 - \sqrt{3}) = 2^2 - (\sqrt{3})^2 = 4 - 3 = 1$
$\sqrt{5} - \sqrt{2}$	$\sqrt{5} + \sqrt{2}$	$(\sqrt{5} - \sqrt{2})(\sqrt{5} + \sqrt{2}) = (\sqrt{5})^2 - (\sqrt{2})^2 = 5 - 2 = 3$
$1 + \sqrt{x}$	$1 - \sqrt{x}$	$(1 + \sqrt{x})(1 - \sqrt{x}) = 1^2 - (\sqrt{x})^2 = 1 - x, \ x \geq 0$

EXAMPLE 4   **Rationalizing Denominators**

Rationalize each denominator.

a. $\dfrac{1}{\sqrt{2}}$ **b.** $\dfrac{2}{7 - \sqrt{5}}$

Solution

a. If we multiply numerator and denominator by $\sqrt{2}$, the denominator becomes $\sqrt{2} \cdot \sqrt{2} = (\sqrt{2})^2 = 2$. Consequently,

$$\frac{1}{\sqrt{2}} = \frac{1 \cdot \sqrt{2}}{\sqrt{2} \cdot \sqrt{2}} = \frac{\sqrt{2}}{2}.$$

b. We multiply numerator and denominator by $7 + \sqrt{5}$.

$$\frac{3}{7 - \sqrt{5}} = \frac{3 \cdot (7 + \sqrt{5})}{(7 - \sqrt{5})(7 + \sqrt{5})} = \frac{21 + 3\sqrt{5}}{7^2 - (\sqrt{5})^2} = \frac{21 + 3\sqrt{5}}{49 - 5} = \frac{21 + 3\sqrt{5}}{44}.$$

■ ■ ■

PRACTICE PROBLEM 4   Rationalize each denominator.

a. $\dfrac{7}{\sqrt{8}}$ **b.** $\dfrac{3}{1 - \sqrt{7}}$ **c.** $\dfrac{x}{\sqrt{x} - 3}$ $(x \geq 0)$ ■

4 Learn to define and evaluate *n*th roots.

Other Roots

If *n* is a positive integer, we say that *b* is an *n*th root of *a* if $b^n = a$. We define the **principal** **nth root** of a real number *a*, denoted by the symbol $\sqrt[n]{a}$, as follows.

THE PRINCIPAL *n*th ROOT OF A REAL NUMBER

1. If *a* is positive ($a > 0$), then $\sqrt[n]{a} = b$, provided that $b^n = a$ and $b > 0$.

2. If *a* is negative ($a < 0$) and *n* is odd, then $\sqrt[n]{a} = b$, provided that $b^n = a$.

3. If *a* is negative ($a < 0$) and *n* is even, then $\sqrt[n]{a}$ is not a real number.

We use the same vocabulary for *n*th roots that we used for square roots. That is, $\sqrt[n]{a}$ is called a **radical expression,** $\sqrt{}$ is the **radical sign,** and *a* is the **radicand.** The positive integer *n* is called the **index.** The index 2 is not written; we write $\sqrt{a}$ rather than $\sqrt[2]{a}$ for the principal square root of *a*. It is also common practice to call $\sqrt[3]{a}$ the **cube root** of *a*.

EXAMPLE 5   **Finding Principal *n*th Roots**

Find each root.   **a.** $\sqrt[3]{27}$ **b.** $\sqrt[3]{-64}$ **c.** $\sqrt[4]{16}$ **d.** $\sqrt[4]{(-3)^4}$ **e.** $\sqrt[8]{-46}$

Solution

a. The radicand, 27, is *positive,* so $\sqrt[3]{27} = 3$, because $3^3 = 27$ and $3 > 0$.

b. The radicand, -64, is *negative,* so $\sqrt[3]{-64} = -4$, because $(-4)^3 = -64$.

c. The radicand, 16, is *positive,* so $\sqrt[4]{16} = 2$, because $2^4 = 16$ and $2 > 0$.

d. The radicand, $(-3)^4$, is *positive,* so $\sqrt[4]{(-3)^4} = 3$, because $3^4 = (-3)^4$ and $3 > 0$.

e. The radicand, -46, is *negative* and the index, 8, is even, so $\sqrt[8]{-46}$ is not a real number.   ■ ■ ■

PRACTICE PROBLEM 5   Find each root.

a. $\sqrt[3]{-8}$ **b.** $\sqrt[5]{32}$ **c.** $\sqrt[4]{81}$ **d.** $\sqrt[6]{-4}$ ■

The fact that the definition of the principal *n*th root depends on whether *n* is even or odd results in two rules to replace the square root rule $\sqrt{x^2} = |x|$.

SIMPLIFYING $\sqrt[n]{a^n}$

If *n* is *odd,* then $\sqrt[n]{a^n} = a$.

If *n* is *even,* then $\sqrt[n]{a^n} = |a|$.

The product and quotient rules for square roots can be extended to apply to *n*th roots as well.

PRODUCT AND QUOTIENT RULES FOR *n*th ROOTS

If a and b are real numbers and all the indicated roots are defined, then

$$\sqrt[n]{ab} = \sqrt[n]{a} \cdot \sqrt[n]{b}$$

and

$$\sqrt[n]{\frac{a}{b}} = \frac{\sqrt[n]{a}}{\sqrt[n]{b}}.$$

EXAMPLE 6   Simplifying *n*th Roots

Simplify. **a.** $\sqrt[3]{135}$ **b.** $\sqrt[4]{162a^4}$

Solution

a. We find a factor of 135 that is a perfect cube. Here, $135 = 27 \cdot 5$, and 27 is a perfect cube ($3^3 = 27$). Then

$$\sqrt[3]{135} = \sqrt[3]{27 \cdot 5} = \sqrt[3]{27} \cdot \sqrt[3]{5} = 3\sqrt[3]{5}.$$

b. We find a factor of 162 that is a perfect fourth power. Now, $162 = 81 \cdot 2$, and 81 is a perfect fourth power: $3^4 = 81$. Thus,

$$\sqrt[4]{162a^4} = \sqrt[4]{162}\sqrt[4]{a^4} = \sqrt[4]{81 \cdot 2}|a| = \sqrt[4]{81}\sqrt[4]{2}|a| = 3\sqrt[4]{2}|a|. \quad ■ ■ ■$$

PRACTICE PROBLEM 6   Simplify.

a. $\sqrt[3]{72}$ **b.** $\sqrt[4]{48a^2}$ ■

[5] Learn to combine like radicals.

Like Radicals

Radicals that have the same index and the same radicand are called **like radicals.** Like radicals can be combined with the use of the distributive property.

EXAMPLE 7   Adding and Subtracting Radical Expressions

Simplify. **a.** $\sqrt{45} + 7\sqrt{20}$ **b.** $5\sqrt[3]{80x} - 3\sqrt[3]{270x}$

Solution

a. We find perfect-square factors for both 45 and 20.

$$
\begin{aligned}
\sqrt{45} + 7\sqrt{20} &= \sqrt{9 \cdot 5} + 7\sqrt{4 \cdot 5} \\
&= \sqrt{9}\sqrt{5} + 7\sqrt{4}\sqrt{5} \quad &\text{Product rule} \\
&= 3\sqrt{5} + 7 \cdot 2\sqrt{5} \\
&= 3\sqrt{5} + 14\sqrt{5} \quad &\text{Like radicals} \\
&= (3 + 14)\sqrt{5} \quad &\text{Distributive property} \\
&= 17\sqrt{5}
\end{aligned}
$$

Continued on next page.

b. This time we find perfect-cube factors for both 80 and 270.

$$
\begin{aligned}
5\sqrt[3]{80x} - 3\sqrt[3]{270x} &= 5\sqrt[3]{8 \cdot 10x} - 3\sqrt[3]{27 \cdot 10x} \\
&= 5\sqrt[3]{8} \cdot \sqrt[3]{10x} - 3\sqrt[3]{27} \cdot \sqrt[3]{10x} \qquad \text{Product rule}\\
&= 5 \cdot 2 \cdot \sqrt[3]{10x} - 3 \cdot 3\sqrt[3]{10x} \\
&= 10\sqrt[3]{10x} - 9\sqrt[3]{10x} \qquad \text{Like radicals}\\
&= (10 - 9)\sqrt[3]{10x} \qquad \text{Distributive property}\\
&= \sqrt[3]{10x} \qquad\qquad\qquad\qquad \blacksquare\ \blacksquare\ \blacksquare
\end{aligned}
$$

PRACTICE PROBLEM 7   Simplify.

a. $3\sqrt{12} + 7\sqrt{3}$ **b.** $2\sqrt[3]{135x} - 3\sqrt[3]{40x}$ ▪

Radicals with Different Indexes

Suppose a is a positive real number and m, n, and r are positive integers. Then the property

$$
\sqrt[n]{a^m} = \sqrt[nr]{a^{mr}}
$$

is used to multiply radicals with different indexes.

EXAMPLE 8   **Multiplying Radicals with Different Indexes**

Write $\sqrt{2}\sqrt[3]{5}$ as a single radical.

Solution

Since $\sqrt{2}$ can also be written as $\sqrt[2]{2}$, we have

$$
\sqrt{2} = \sqrt[2]{2} = \sqrt[2\cdot3]{2^3} = \sqrt[6]{2^3},
$$

and similarly,

$$
\sqrt[3]{5} = \sqrt[2\cdot3]{5^2} = \sqrt[6]{5^2}.
$$

Thus, $\sqrt{2}\sqrt[3]{5} = \sqrt[6]{2^3}\sqrt[6]{5^2} = \sqrt[6]{2^3 5^2} = \sqrt[6]{200}.$ $\blacksquare\ \blacksquare\ \blacksquare$

PRACTICE PROBLEM 8   Write $\sqrt{3}\sqrt[5]{2}$ as a single radical.   ▪

6 Learn to define and evaluate rational exponents.

Rational Exponents

Previously, we defined such exponential expressions as 2^3, but what do you think $2^{\frac{1}{3}}$ means? If we want to preserve the power rule of exponents, $(a^n)^m = a^{nm}$, for rational exponents such as $\dfrac{1}{3}$, we must have

$$
(2^{\frac{1}{3}})^3 = 2^{\frac{1}{3}\cdot3} = 2^1 = 2.
$$

Since $(2^{\frac{1}{3}})^3 = 2$, it follows that $2^{\frac{1}{3}}$ is the cube root of 2; that is, $2^{\frac{1}{3}} = \sqrt[3]{2}$.

Such considerations lead to the following definition.

THE EXPONENT $\dfrac{1}{n}$

For any real number a and any integer $n > 1$,

$$a^{\frac{1}{n}} = \sqrt[n]{a}.$$

When n is even and $a < 0$, $\sqrt[n]{a}$ and $a^{\frac{1}{n}}$ are not real numbers.

Notice that the denominator n of the rational exponent is the index of the radical.

EXAMPLE 9   **Evaluating Expressions with Rational Exponents**

Evaluate.   **a.** $16^{\frac{1}{2}}$ **b.** $(-27)^{\frac{1}{3}}$ **c.** $\left(\dfrac{1}{16}\right)^{\frac{1}{4}}$ **d.** $32^{\frac{1}{5}}$ **e.** $(-5)^{\frac{1}{4}}$

Solution

a. $16^{\frac{1}{2}} = \sqrt{16} = 4$

b. $(-27)^{\frac{1}{3}} = \sqrt[3]{-27} = \sqrt[3]{(-3)^3} = -3$

c. $\left(\dfrac{1}{16}\right)^{\frac{1}{4}} = \sqrt[4]{\dfrac{1}{16}} = \sqrt[4]{\left(\dfrac{1}{2}\right)^4} = \dfrac{1}{2}$

d. $32^{\frac{1}{5}} = \sqrt[5]{32} = \sqrt[5]{2^5} = 2$

e. Since the base -5 is negative, and $n = 4$ is even, $(-5)^{\frac{1}{4}}$ is not a real number.

■ ■ ■

PRACTICE PROBLEM 9   Evaluate.

a. $\left(\dfrac{1}{4}\right)^{\frac{1}{2}}$ **b.** $(125)^{\frac{1}{3}}$ **c.** $(-32)^{\frac{1}{5}}$

■

The box below shows a summary of our work so far.

RATIONAL EXPONENTS AND RADICALS

If a is any real number and n is any integer greater than 1, then

	***n* even**	***n* odd**
If $a > 0$,	$\sqrt[n]{a} = a^{\frac{1}{n}}$ is positive.	$\sqrt[n]{a} = a^{\frac{1}{n}}$ is positive.
If $a < 0$,	$\sqrt[n]{a} = a^{\frac{1}{n}}$ is not a real number.	$\sqrt[n]{a} = a^{\frac{1}{n}}$ is negative.
If $a = 0$,	$\sqrt[n]{0} = 0^{\frac{1}{n}} = 0.$	$\sqrt[n]{0} = 0^{\frac{1}{n}} = 0.$

We have defined the expression $a^{\frac{1}{n}}$. How do we define $a^{\frac{m}{n}}$, where m and n are integers, when $n > 1$ and $\sqrt[n]{a}$ is a real number? If we insist that the power-of-a-product rule of exponents holds for rational numbers, then we must have

$$a^{\frac{m}{n}} = a^{\frac{1}{n} \cdot m} = (a^{\frac{1}{n}})^m = (\sqrt[n]{a})^m$$

and

$$a^{\frac{m}{n}} = a^{m \cdot \frac{1}{n}} = (a^m)^{\frac{1}{n}} = \sqrt[n]{a^m}.$$

From this, we arrive at the following definition.

RATIONAL EXPONENTS

$$a^{\frac{m}{n}} = (\sqrt[n]{a})^m = \sqrt[n]{a^m},$$

provided that m and n are integers with no common factors, $n > 1$, and $\sqrt[n]{a}$ is a real number.

Note that the numerator m of the exponent $\dfrac{m}{n}$ is the *exponent of the radical expression* and the denominator n is the *index of the radical*. When n is even and $a < 0$, the symbol $a^{\frac{m}{n}}$ is not a real number.

When rational exponents with negative denominators, such as $\dfrac{3}{-5}$ or $\dfrac{-2}{-7}$, are encountered, we use equivalent expressions, such as $\dfrac{-3}{5}$ and $\dfrac{2}{7}$, respectively, before applying the definition. Note that $(-8)^{\frac{2}{6}} \neq [(-8)^{\frac{1}{6}}]^2$, because $(-8)^{\frac{1}{6}} = \sqrt[6]{-8}$ is not a real number but $(-8)^{\frac{2}{6}}$ is a real number. Writing $\dfrac{2}{6} = \dfrac{1}{3}$ we have

$$(-8)^{\frac{2}{6}} = (-8)^{\frac{1}{3}} = \sqrt[3]{-8} = -2.$$

EXAMPLE 10   **Evaluating Expressions Having Rational Exponents**

Evaluate. **a.** $8^{\frac{2}{3}}$ **b.** $-16^{\frac{5}{2}}$ **c.** $100^{-\frac{3}{2}}$ **d.** $(-25)^{\frac{7}{2}}$

Solution

a. $8^{\frac{2}{3}} = (\sqrt[3]{8})^2 = 2^2 = 4.$

b. $-16^{\frac{5}{2}} = -(\sqrt{16})^5 = -4^5 = -1024$

c. $100^{-3/2} = 100^{-3/2} = (\sqrt{100})^{-3} = \dfrac{1}{(\sqrt{100})^3} = \dfrac{1}{10^3} = \dfrac{1}{1000}.$

d. $(-25)^{7/2} = [(-25)^{1/2}]^7$ Not a real number,

$\qquad = (\sqrt{-25})^7$ because $\sqrt{-25}$ is not a real number   ■ ■ ■

PRACTICE PROBLEM 10   Evaluate

a. $(25)^{2/3}$ **b.** $-36^{3/2}$ **c.** $16^{-5/2}$ **d.** $(-36)^{-1/2}$ ■

The properties of exponents we learned for integer exponents all hold true for rational exponents. For convenience, we list these properties next.

PROPERTIES OF RATIONAL EXPONENTS

If r and s are rational numbers and a and b are real numbers, then

$$a^r \cdot a^s = a^{r+s} \qquad (a^r)^s = a^{rs} \qquad (ab)^r = a^r b^r$$

$$\frac{a^r}{a^s} = a^{r-s} \qquad \left(\frac{a}{b}\right)^r = \frac{a^r}{b^r} \qquad a^{-r} = \frac{1}{a^r} \qquad \left(\frac{a}{b}\right)^{-r} = \left(\frac{b}{a}\right)^r,$$

provided that all the expressions used are defined.

EXAMPLE 11   Simplifying Expressions Having Rational Exponents

Express your answer with only positive exponents. Assume that x represents a positive real number. Simplify.

a. $2x^{\frac{1}{3}} \cdot 5x^{\frac{1}{4}}$ **b.** $\dfrac{21x^{-\frac{2}{3}}}{7x^{\frac{1}{5}}}$ **c.** $\left(x^{\frac{3}{5}}\right)^{-\frac{1}{6}}$

Solution

a. $2x^{\frac{1}{3}} \cdot 5x^{\frac{1}{4}} = 2 \cdot 5x^{\frac{1}{3}} \cdot x^{\frac{1}{4}}$ Group factors with the same base.

$\qquad\qquad = 10x^{\frac{1}{3}+\frac{1}{4}}$ Add exponents of factors with the same base.

$\qquad\qquad = 10x^{\frac{4}{12}+\frac{3}{12}} = 10x^{\frac{7}{12}}.$

b. $\dfrac{21x^{-\frac{2}{3}}}{7x^{\frac{1}{5}}} = \left(\dfrac{21}{7}\right)\left(\dfrac{x^{-\frac{2}{3}}}{x^{\frac{1}{5}}}\right)$ Group factors with the same base.

$\qquad\qquad = 3x^{-\frac{2}{3}-\frac{1}{5}} = 3x^{-\frac{10}{15}-\frac{3}{15}} = 3x^{-\frac{13}{15}} = 3 \cdot \left(\dfrac{1}{x^{\frac{13}{15}}}\right) = \dfrac{3}{x^{\frac{13}{15}}}.$

c. $\left(x^{\frac{3}{5}}\right)^{-\frac{1}{6}} = x^{\left(\frac{3}{5}\right)\left(-\frac{1}{6}\right)} = x^{-\frac{1}{10}} = \dfrac{1}{x^{\frac{1}{10}}}.$ ■ ■ ■

PRACTICE PROBLEM 11   Simplify. Express the answer with only positive exponents.

a. $4x^{\frac{1}{2}} \cdot 3x^{\frac{1}{5}}$ **b.** $\dfrac{25x^{-\frac{1}{4}}}{5x^{\frac{1}{3}}}, x > 0$ **c.** $\left(x^{\frac{2}{3}}\right)^{-\frac{1}{5}}, x > 0$ ■

EXAMPLE 12   Simplifying an Expression Involving Negative Rational Exponents

Simplify $x(x + 1)^{-\frac{1}{2}} + 2(x + 1)^{\frac{1}{2}}$. Express your answer with only positive exponents, and then rationalize the denominator. Assume that $(x + 1)^{-\frac{1}{2}}$ is defined.

Solution

$$x(x + 1)^{-\frac{1}{2}} + 2(x + 1)^{\frac{1}{2}} = \frac{x}{(x + 1)^{\frac{1}{2}}} + \frac{2(x + 1)^{\frac{1}{2}}}{1} \qquad (x + 1)^{-\frac{1}{2}} = \frac{1}{(x + 1)^{\frac{1}{2}}}$$

$$= \frac{x}{(x + 1)^{\frac{1}{2}}} + \frac{2(x + 1)^{\frac{1}{2}}(x + 1)^{\frac{1}{2}}}{(x + 1)^{\frac{1}{2}}}$$

$$= \frac{x + 2(x + 1)}{(x + 1)^{\frac{1}{2}}} = \frac{3x + 2}{(x + 1)^{\frac{1}{2}}} \qquad (x + 1)^{\frac{1}{2}}(x + 1)^{\frac{1}{2}} = x + 1$$

Continued on next page.

To rationalize the denominator $(x + 1)^{\frac{1}{2}} = \sqrt{x + 1}$, multiply both numerator and denominator by $(x + 1)^{\frac{1}{2}}$.

$$\frac{3x + 2}{(x + 1)^{\frac{1}{2}}} = \frac{(3x + 2)(x + 1)^{\frac{1}{2}}}{(x + 1)^{\frac{1}{2}}(x + 1)^{\frac{1}{2}}}$$

$$= \frac{(3x + 2)(x + 1)^{\frac{1}{2}}}{x + 1} \qquad (x + 1)^{\frac{1}{2}}(x + 1)^{\frac{1}{2}} = x + 1. \qquad ■ ■ ■$$

PRACTICE PROBLEM 12   Simplify $x(x + 3)^{-\frac{1}{2}} + (x + 3)^{\frac{1}{2}}$. ■

EXAMPLE 13   **Simplifying Radicals by Using Rational Exponents**

Assume that x represents a positive real number. Simplify.

a. $\sqrt[8]{x^2}$ **b.** $\sqrt[4]{9}\sqrt{3}$ **c.** $\sqrt{\sqrt[3]{x^8}}$

Solution

a. $\sqrt[8]{x^2} = (x^2)^{\frac{1}{8}} = x^{\frac{2}{8}} = x^{\frac{1}{4}} = \sqrt[4]{x}$

b. $\sqrt[4]{9}\sqrt{3} = 9^{\frac{1}{4}} \cdot 3^{\frac{1}{2}} = (3^2)^{\frac{1}{4}} \cdot 3^{\frac{1}{2}} = 3^{\frac{2}{4}} \cdot 3^{\frac{1}{2}} = 3^{\frac{1}{2}} \cdot 3^{\frac{1}{2}} = 3^{\frac{1}{2}+\frac{1}{2}} = 3^1 = 3$

c. $\sqrt{\sqrt[3]{x^8}} = \sqrt{(x^8)^{\frac{1}{3}}} = \sqrt{x^{\frac{8}{3}}} = (x^{\frac{8}{3}})^{\frac{1}{2}} = x^{\frac{8}{3}\cdot\frac{1}{2}} = x^{\frac{4}{3}} = x^{1+\frac{1}{3}} = x^1 \cdot x^{\frac{1}{3}} = x\sqrt[3]{x}$ ■ ■ ■

PRACTICE PROBLEM 13   Simplify. Assume that $x > 0$.

a. $\sqrt[6]{x^4}$ **b.** $\sqrt[4]{25}\sqrt{5}$ **c.** $\sqrt[3]{\sqrt{x^{12}}}$ ■

A Exercises   Basic Skills and Concepts

In Exercises 1–16, evaluate each root or state that the root is not a real number.

1. $\sqrt{64}$ 8

2. $\sqrt{100}$ 10

3. $\sqrt[3]{64}$ 4

4. $\sqrt[3]{125}$ 5

5. $\sqrt[3]{-27}$ −3

6. $\sqrt[3]{-216}$ −6

7. $\sqrt[3]{-\dfrac{1}{8}}$ $-\dfrac{1}{2}$

8. $\sqrt[3]{\dfrac{27}{64}}$ $\dfrac{3}{4}$

9. $\sqrt{(-3)^2}$ 3

10. $-\sqrt{4(-3)^2}$ −6

11. $\sqrt[4]{-16}$ not a real number

12. $\sqrt[6]{-64}$ not a real number

13. $-\sqrt[5]{-1}$ 1

14. $\sqrt[7]{-1}$ −1

15. $\sqrt[5]{(-7)^5}$ −7

16. $-\sqrt[5]{(-4)^5}$ 4

In Exercises 17–41, simplify each expression, using the product and quotient properties for square roots. Assume that x represents a positive real number.

17. $\sqrt{32}$ $4\sqrt{2}$

18. $\sqrt{125}$ $5\sqrt{5}$

19. $\sqrt{18x^2}$ $3x\sqrt{2}$

20. $\sqrt{27x^2}$ $3x\sqrt{3}$

21. $\sqrt{9x^3}$ $3x\sqrt{x}$

22. $\sqrt{8x^3}$ $2x\sqrt{2x}$

23. $\sqrt{6x}\sqrt{3x}$ $3x\sqrt{2}$

24. $\sqrt{5x}\sqrt{10x}$ $5x\sqrt{2}$

25. $\sqrt{15x}\sqrt{3x^2}$ $3x\sqrt{5x}$

26. $\sqrt{2x^2}\sqrt{18x}$ $6x\sqrt{x}$

27. $\sqrt[3]{-8x^3}$ $-2x$

28. $\sqrt[3]{64x^3}$ $4x$

29. $\sqrt[3]{-x^6}$ $-x^2$

30. $\sqrt[3]{-27x^6}$ $-3x^2$

31. $\sqrt{\dfrac{5}{32}}$ $\dfrac{\sqrt{10}}{8}$

32. $\sqrt{\dfrac{3}{50}}$ $\dfrac{\sqrt{6}}{10}$

33. $\sqrt[3]{\dfrac{8}{x^3}}$ $\dfrac{2}{x}$

34. $\sqrt[3]{\dfrac{7}{8x^3}}$ $\dfrac{\sqrt[3]{7}}{2x}$

35. $\sqrt[4]{\dfrac{2}{x^5}}$ $\dfrac{\sqrt[4]{2x^3}}{x^2}$

36. $-\sqrt[4]{\dfrac{5}{16x^5}}$ $-\dfrac{\sqrt[4]{5x^3}}{2x^2}$

37. $\sqrt{\sqrt{x^8}}$ x^2

38. $\sqrt{\dfrac{4x^4}{25y^6}}$ $\dfrac{2x^2}{5y^3}$

39. $\sqrt{\dfrac{9x^6}{y^4}}$ $\dfrac{3x^3}{y^2}$

40. $\sqrt[5]{x^{15}y^5}$ x^3y

41. $\sqrt[4]{x^{16}y^{12}}$ x^4y^3

†Due to space constrictions, answers to these exercises may be found in the Answers beginning on page A–1 in the back of the book.

In Exercises 42–55, simplify each expression. Assume that all variables represent nonnegative real numbers.

42. $2\sqrt{3} + 5\sqrt{3}$ $7\sqrt{3}$

43. $7\sqrt{2} - \sqrt{2}$ $6\sqrt{2}$

44. $6\sqrt{5} - \sqrt{5} + 4\sqrt{5}$ $9\sqrt{5}$

45. $5\sqrt{7} + 3\sqrt{7} - 2\sqrt{7}$ †

46. $\sqrt{98x} - \sqrt{32x}$ $3\sqrt{2x}$

47. $\sqrt{45x} + \sqrt{20x}$ $5\sqrt{5x}$

48. $\sqrt[3]{24} - \sqrt[3]{81}$ $-\sqrt[3]{3}$

49. $\sqrt[3]{54} + \sqrt[3]{16}$ $5\sqrt[3]{2}$

50. $\sqrt[3]{3x} - 2\sqrt[3]{24x} + \sqrt[3]{375x}$ $2\sqrt[3]{3x}$

51. $\sqrt[3]{16x} + 3\sqrt[3]{54x} - \sqrt[3]{2x}$ $10\sqrt[3]{2x}$

52. $\sqrt{2x^5} - 5\sqrt{32x} + \sqrt{18x^3}$ $\sqrt{2x}(x^2 + 3x - 20)$

53. $2\sqrt{50x^5} + 7\sqrt{2x^3} - 3\sqrt{72x}$ $\sqrt{2x}(10x^2 + 7x - 18)$

54. $\sqrt{48x^5y} - 4y\sqrt{3x^3y} + y\sqrt{3xy^3}$ $(2x - y)^2\sqrt{3xy}$

55. $x\sqrt{8xy} + 4\sqrt{2xy^3} - \sqrt{18x^5y}$ $\sqrt{2xy}(2x + 4y - 3x^2)$

In Exercises 56–69, rationalize the denominator of each expression.

56. $\dfrac{2}{\sqrt{3}}$ $\dfrac{2\sqrt{3}}{3}$

57. $\dfrac{10}{\sqrt{5}}$ $2\sqrt{5}$

58. $\dfrac{7}{\sqrt{15}}$ $\dfrac{7\sqrt{15}}{15}$

59. $\dfrac{-3}{\sqrt{8}}$ $-\dfrac{3\sqrt{2}}{4}$

60. $\dfrac{1}{\sqrt{2} + x}$ $\dfrac{\sqrt{2} - x}{2 - x^2}$

61. $\dfrac{1}{\sqrt{5} + 2x}$ $\dfrac{\sqrt{5} - 2x}{5 - 4x^2}$

62. $\dfrac{3}{2 - \sqrt{3}}$ $3(2 + \sqrt{3})$

63. $\dfrac{-5}{1 - \sqrt{2}}$ $5(1 + \sqrt{2})$

64. $\dfrac{1}{\sqrt{3} + \sqrt{2}}$ $\sqrt{3} - \sqrt{2}$

65. $\dfrac{6}{\sqrt{5} - \sqrt{3}}$ $3(\sqrt{5} + \sqrt{3})$

66. $\dfrac{\sqrt{5} - \sqrt{2}}{\sqrt{5} + \sqrt{2}}$ $\dfrac{7 - 2\sqrt{10}}{3}$

67. $\dfrac{\sqrt{7} + \sqrt{3}}{\sqrt{7} - \sqrt{3}}$ $\dfrac{5 + \sqrt{21}}{2}$

68. $\dfrac{\sqrt{x + h} - \sqrt{x}}{\sqrt{x + h} + \sqrt{x}}$ †

69. $\dfrac{a\sqrt{x} + 3}{a\sqrt{x} - 3}$ $\dfrac{a^2x + 6a\sqrt{x} + 9}{a^2x - 9}$

In Exercises 70–79, evaluate each expression without using a calculator.

70. $25^{\frac{1}{2}}$ 5

71. $144^{\frac{1}{2}}$ 12

72. $(-8)^{\frac{1}{3}}$ -2

73. $(-27)^{\frac{1}{3}}$ -3

74. $8^{\frac{2}{3}}$ 4

75. $16^{\frac{3}{2}}$ 64

76. $-25^{-\frac{3}{2}}$ †

77. $-9^{-\frac{3}{2}}$ †

78. $\left(\dfrac{9}{25}\right)^{-\frac{3}{2}}$ $\dfrac{125}{27}$

79. $\left(\dfrac{1}{27}\right)^{-\frac{2}{3}}$ 9

In Exercises 80–81, simplify each expression, leaving your answer with only positive exponents. Assume that all variables represent positive numbers.

80. $x^{\frac{1}{2}} \cdot x^{\frac{2}{5}}$ $x^{\frac{9}{10}}$

81. $x^{\frac{3}{5}} \cdot 5x^{\frac{2}{3}}$ $5x^{\frac{19}{15}}$

82. $x^{\frac{5}{3}} \cdot x^{-\frac{1}{2}}$ $x^{\frac{7}{6}}$

83. $x^{\frac{5}{3}} \cdot x^{-\frac{3}{4}}$ $x^{\frac{11}{12}}$

84. $(8x^6)^{\frac{2}{3}}$ $4x^4$

85. $(16x^3)^{\frac{1}{2}}$ $4x^{\frac{3}{2}}$

86. $(27x^6y^3)^{-\frac{2}{3}}$ †

87. $(16x^4y^6)^{\frac{3}{2}}$ †

88. $\dfrac{15x^{\frac{3}{2}}}{3x^{\frac{1}{4}}}$ $5x^{\frac{5}{4}}$

89. $\dfrac{20x^{\frac{5}{2}}}{4x^{\frac{2}{3}}}$ $5x^{\frac{11}{6}}$

90. $\left(\dfrac{x^{-\frac{1}{4}}}{y^{-\frac{2}{3}}}\right)^{-12}$ $\dfrac{x^3}{y^8}$

91. $\left(\dfrac{27x^{-\frac{5}{2}}}{y^{-3}}\right)^{-\frac{1}{3}}$ $\dfrac{x^{\frac{5}{6}}}{3y}$

In Exercises 92–101, convert each radical expression to its rational exponent form, and then simplify. Assume that all variables represent positive numbers.

92. $\sqrt[4]{3^2}$ $3^{\frac{1}{2}}$

93. $\sqrt[4]{5^2}$ $5^{\frac{1}{2}}$

94. $\sqrt[3]{x^9}$ x^3

95. $\sqrt[3]{x^{12}}$ x^4

96. $\sqrt[3]{x^6y^9}$ x^2y^3

97. $\sqrt[3]{8x^3y^{12}}$ $2xy^4$

98. $\sqrt[4]{9}\sqrt{3}$ 3

99. $\sqrt[4]{49}\sqrt{7}$ 7

100. $\sqrt{\sqrt[3]{x^{10}}}$ $x^{\frac{5}{3}}$

101. $\sqrt{\sqrt[3]{64x^6}}$ $2x$

In Exercises 102–109, convert the given product to a single radical. Assume that all variables represent positive numbers.

102. $\sqrt[3]{2} \cdot \sqrt[5]{3}$ $\sqrt[15]{864}$

103. $\sqrt[3]{3} \cdot \sqrt[4]{2}$ $\sqrt[12]{648}$

104. $\sqrt[3]{x^2} \cdot \sqrt[4]{x^3}$ $x(\sqrt[12]{x^5})$

105. $\sqrt[5]{x^2} \cdot \sqrt[7]{x^5}$ $x(\sqrt[35]{x^4})$

106. $\sqrt[4]{2m^2n} \cdot \sqrt[3]{5m^5n^2}$ †

107. $\sqrt{3xy} \cdot \sqrt[3]{9x^2y^2}$ †

108. $\sqrt[5]{x^4y^3} \cdot \sqrt[6]{x^3y^5}$ †

109. $\sqrt[5]{3a^4b^2} \cdot \sqrt[10]{7a^2b^6}$ †

B Exercises   Applying the Concepts

110. Sign dimensions. A sign in the shape of an equilateral triangle of area A has sides of length $\sqrt{\dfrac{4A}{\sqrt{3}}}$ centimeters. Find the length of a side if the sign has an area of 692 square centimeters. (Use the approximation $\sqrt{3} \approx 1.73$.) 40 cm

111. Return on investment. In order for an initial investment of P dollars to mature to S dollars after two years when the interest is compounded annually, an annual interest rate of

$r = \sqrt{\dfrac{S}{P}} - 1$ is required. Find r if $P = \$1,210,000$ and

$S = \$1,411,344$. 8%

112. Terminal speed. The terminal speed V of a steel ball that weighs w grams and is falling in a cylinder of oil is given

by the equation $V = \sqrt{\dfrac{w}{1.5}}$ centimeters per second. Find the

terminal speed of a steel ball weighing 6 grams. 2 cm/sec

113. Model-airplane speed. A spring-balance scale attached to a wire that holds a model airplane on a circular path indicates the force F on the wire. The speed of the plane V, in m/sec, is given by $V = \sqrt{(rF)/m}$, where m is the mass of the plane (in kilograms) and r is the length of the wire (in meters). What is the top speed of a 2-kilogram plane on an 18-meter wire if the force on the wire at top speed is 49 newtons? 21 m/sec

114. Electronic-game current. The current I (in amperes) in a circuit for an electronic game using W watts and having a

resistance of R ohms is given by $I = \sqrt{\dfrac{W}{R}}$. Find the cur-

rent in a game circuit using 1058 watts and having a resistance of 2 ohms. 23 amp

115. Radius of the moon. The radius of a sphere having volume

V is given by $r = \left(\dfrac{3V}{4\pi}\right)^{\frac{1}{3}}$. If we treat the moon as a sphere

and are told that its volume is 2.19×10^{19} cubic meters, find its radius. Use 3.14 as an approximation for π. 1.74×10^6m

116. Atmospheric pressure. The atmospheric pressure P, measured in pounds per square inch, at an altitude of h miles $(h < 50)$ is given by the equation $P = 14.7(0.5)^{\frac{h}{3.25}}$. Compute the atmospheric pressure at an altitude of 16.25 miles.

117. Force from constrained water. The force F that is exerted on the semicircular end of a trough full of water is approximately $F = 42r^{\frac{3}{2}}$ pounds, where r is the radius of the semicircular end. Find the force if the radius is 3 feet. 218 lb

Answer:
116. 0.46 lb/in.^{2}

| # Topics in Geometry

BEFORE STARTING THIS SECTION, REVIEW

1. Exponents (Section P.2, page 20)

OBJECTIVES

1 Learn to use the Pythagorean Theorem and its converse.

2 Learn to use geometry formulas.

Math in the Movies

Mistakes in mathematics are not unusual and even occur in movies. For example, in MGM's 1939 film version of *The Wizard of Oz,* the scarecrow went to see the wizard to ask him for some brains. Oz, the great and powerful wizard, bestowed upon the scarecrow a diploma with an honorary title of Th.D., "Doctor of Thinkology." The scarecrow, overjoyed at receiving his "brains," immediately decided to impress his friends by reciting the following mathematical statement: "The sum of the square roots of any two sides of an isosceles triangle is equal to the square root of the remaining side." Unfortunately, this statement is incorrect. Homer Simpson makes the same mistake in the introductory scene from the "Springfield" episode of *The Simpsons.* The correct statement that the scarecrow and Homer were attempting is probably the Pythagorean Theorem, a statement about right triangles, not isosceles triangles. (Moreover, it's the sum of the *squares,* not square roots, and the *square* of the remaining side, not its square root, that the theroem states are equal.) In Example 2, we use the Pythagorean Theorem to solve a practical problem. ■

Angles of a Triangle

Frequently, formulas we encounter in algebra come from geometry. We review some topics from geometry in this section, beginning with angles and triangles.

An **acute angle** is an angle of measure greater than $0°$ and less than $90°$.

An **obtuse angle** is an angle of measure greater than $90°$ and less than $180°$.

Any two angles whose measures sum to $180°$ are called **supplementary angles.**

Any two angles whose measures sum to $90°$ are called **complementary angles.**

Theorem. The sum of the measures of the angles of any triangle is $180°$.

Triangles

Triangles may be classified by the number of sides they have of equal length:

Scalene Triangle A triangle in which *no* two sides have equal length.

Isosceles Triangle A triangle with two sides of equal length.

Equilateral Triangle A triangle with all three sides having equal length.

The intuitive idea that two triangles have exactly the same shape (but not necessarily the same size) is captured in the concept of *similar triangles:*

Similar Triangles Two triangles are **similar** if and only if they have equal corresponding angles and their corresponding sides are proportional. (See Figure P.14.)

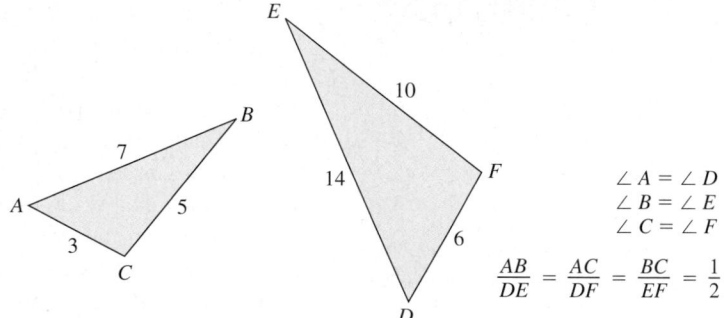

$$\angle A = \angle D$$
$$\angle B = \angle E$$
$$\angle C = \angle F$$

$$\frac{AB}{DE} = \frac{AC}{DF} = \frac{BC}{EF} = \frac{1}{2}$$

FIGURE P.14

Congruent Triangles Two triangles are *congruent* if and only if they have equal corresponding angles and sides.

Included Side A side of a triangle that lies between two angles is called the **included side** of the angles.

Included Angle The angle formed by two sides is the **included angle** of the sides.

CONGRUENT-TRIANGLE THEOREMS

SAS (Side–Angle–Side). If two sides and the included angle of one triangle are equal to the corresponding sides and the included angle of a second triangle, then the two triangles are congruent.
ASA (Angle–Side–Angle). If two angles and the included side of one triangle are equal to the corresponding two angles and the included side of a second triangle, then the two triangles are congruent.
SSS (Side–Side–Side). If the three sides of one triangle are equal to the corresponding sides of a second triangle, then the two triangles are congruent.

1 Learn to use the Pythagorean Theorem and its converse.

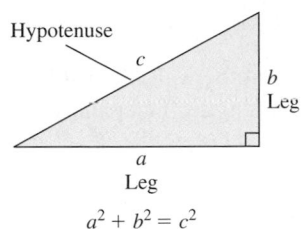

Hypotenuse

c

b
Leg

a
Leg

$a^2 + b^2 = c^2$

FIGURE P.15

Pythagorean Theorem

The *Pythagorean Theorem* states a useful fact about right triangles. A **right triangle** is any triangle that contains a right angle—that is, an angle of 90°. The side of the triangle opposite the 90° angle is called the **hypotenuse;** the other two sides are the **legs** of the triangle. Figure P.15 shows a right triangle with legs of length a and b, and hypotenuse of length c. The symbol $\ulcorner$ is used to identify the right angle.

The Pythagorean Theorem says that the square of the length of the hypotenuse is equal to the sum of the squares of the lengths of the legs. (See Figure P.15). We prove the theorem later in this section.

PYTHAGOREAN THEOREM

If a, b, and c represent the lengths of the two legs and the hypotenuse, respectively, of a right triangle, then

$$a^2 + b^2 = c^2.$$

EXAMPLE 1   **The Pythagorean Theorem**

a. A right triangle has legs of length 3 and 4. Find the length of the hypotenuse.

b. A right triangle has one leg of length 15 and a hypotenuse of length 39. Find the length of the remaining leg.

Solution

a. Let c represent the length of the hypotenuse and a and b represent the lengths of the legs of the right triangle. Then

$$
\begin{aligned}
c^2 &= a^2 + b^2 &&\text{Pythagorean Theorem}\\
c^2 &= 3^2 + 4^2 &&\text{Replace } a \text{ by 3 and } b \text{ by 4.}\\
c^2 &= 25 &&\text{Simplify.}\\
c &= 5 &&c \text{ must be positive, since it is a length.}
\end{aligned}
$$

The length of the hypotenuse is 5.

b. Again, let c represent the length of the hypotenuse and a and b represent the legs of the right triangle. Then

$$
\begin{aligned}
c^2 &= a^2 + b^2 &&\text{Pythagorean Theorem}\\
39^2 &= 15^2 + b^2 &&\text{Replace } c \text{ by 39 and } a \text{ by 15.}\\
39^2 - 15^2 &= b^2 &&\text{Subtract } 15^2 \text{ from both sides.}\\
1296 &= b^2 &&\text{Simplify.}\\
36 &= b &&b \text{ must be positive, since it is a length.}
\end{aligned}
$$

The length of the remaining leg is 36.   ■ ■ ■

PRACTICE PROBLEM 1   A right triangle has legs of lengths 8 and 6. Find the length of the hypotenuse.   ■

EXAMPLE 2   **The Pythagorean Theorem**

You want to change some prices advertised on a letter display fastened 15 feet high on the front wall of your business building. A garden along the front wall forces you to place a ladder 8 feet from the wall. What length ladder is required?

Solution

If a ladder is placed 8 feet from the wall and rests 15 feet high on the wall, the ladder can be viewed as the hypotenuse of a right triangle with legs having lengths 8 feet and 15 feet. (See Figure P.16).

Let c represent the length of the ladder. Then

$$c^2 = a^2 + b^2 \qquad \text{Pythagorean Theorem}$$
$$c^2 = 8^2 + 15^2 \qquad \text{Replace } a \text{ by 8 and } b \text{ by 15.}$$
$$c^2 = 289$$
$$c = 17.$$

A 17-foot ladder will allow you to change the display.   ■ ■ ■

Wall

Ladder

15 ft

8 ft

Ground

FIGURE P.16

PRACTICE PROBLEM 2   In Example 2, suppose the display is fastened 8 feet high and the ladder must be placed 6 feet from the wall. What length ladder is required?   ■

Converse of the Pythagorean Theorem

It is also true that if the square of the length of one side of a triangle equals the sum of the squares of the lengths of the other two sides, then the triangle is a right triangle. The longest side of the triangle is the hypotenuse, and the angle opposite the longest side is the right angle.

CONVERSE OF THE PYTHAGOREAN THEOREM

Suppose a triangle has sides of length a, b, and c. If

$$c^2 = a^2 + b^2,$$

then the triangle is a right triangle, with a right angle opposite the longest side.

EXAMPLE 3   **Converse of the Pythagorean Theorem**

A triangle has sides of length 20, 21, and 29. Is it a right triangle?

Solution

To determine whether the triangle is a right triangle, we first square the length of each side.

$$20^2 = 400, \quad 21^2 = 441, \quad \text{and} \quad 29^2 = 841$$
$$841 = 400 + 441$$

Since the square of the length of the largest side equals the sum of the squares of the lengths of the other two sides, the triangle is a right triangle.   ■ ■ ■

PRACTICE PROBLEM 3   A triangle has sides of length 2, 5, and 6. Is it a right triangle?   ■

2 Learn to use geometry formulas.

Geometry Formulas

Although the area of a rectangle is just the product of its length and width, the general concept of area (and the related concepts of perimeter and volume) is developed with the use of calculus. Fortunately, the formulas for calculating these quantities require only algebra. Figure P.17 next lists some useful formulas from geometry.

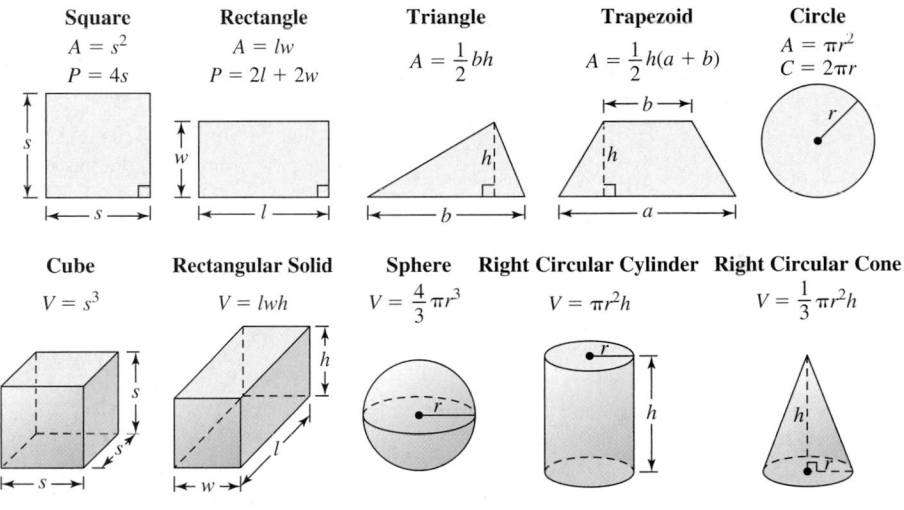

Formulas for area (*A*), circumference (*C*), perimeter (*P*), and volume (*V*)

Square
$A = s^2$
$P = 4s$

Rectangle
$A = lw$
$P = 2l + 2w$

Triangle
$A = \dfrac{1}{2}bh$

Trapezoid
$A = \dfrac{1}{2}h(a + b)$

Circle
$A = \pi r^2$
$C = 2\pi r$

Cube
$V = s^3$

Rectangular Solid
$V = lwh$

Sphere
$V = \dfrac{4}{3}\pi r^3$

Right Circular Cylinder
$V = \pi r^2 h$

Right Circular Cone
$V = \dfrac{1}{3}\pi r^2 h$

FIGURE P.17

A Proof of the Pythagorean Theorem

We start with two identical squares having sides of length $a + b$. (See Figure P.18.) In Figure P.18a, the square is composed of four right triangles, each with legs of lengths a and b and hypotenuse of length c, and one square with area c^2. In Figure P.18b, the square is composed of the same four right triangles that appear in Figure P.18a, together with one square with area a^2 and one square with area b^2.

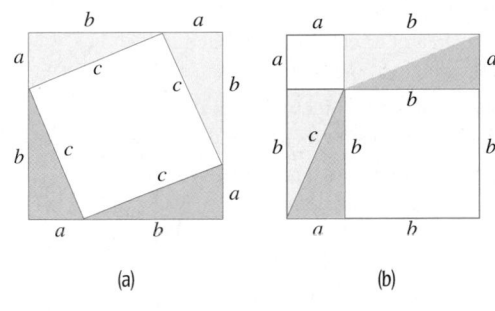

(a)   (b)

FIGURE P.18

Area of the square in Figure P.18a = area of the square in Figure P.18b.

$$\frac{1}{2}ab + \frac{1}{2}ab + \frac{1}{2}ab + \frac{1}{2}ab + c^2 = \frac{1}{2}ab + \frac{1}{2}ab + \frac{1}{2}ab + \frac{1}{2}ab + a^2 + b^2$$

$$2ab + c^2 = 2ab + a^2 + b^2 \qquad \text{Simplify.}$$

$$c^2 = a^2 + b^2 \qquad \begin{array}{l}\text{Subtract } 2ab \text{ from}\\ \text{both sides}\end{array}$$

This completes the proof.

A Exercises   Basic Skills and Concepts

In Exercises 1–6, the lengths of the legs of a right triangle are given. Find the length of the hypotenuse.

1. $a = 7, b = 24$ 25   **2.** $a = 5, b = 12$ 13

3. $a = 9, b = 12$ 15   **4.** $a = 10, b = 24$ 26

5. $a = 3, b = 3$ $3\sqrt{2}$ **6.** $a = 2, b = 4$ $2\sqrt{5}$

In Exercises 7–10, the lengths of one leg, a, and the hypotenuse, c, of a right triangle are given. Find the length of the remaining leg.

7. $a = 15, c = 17$ 8   **8.** $a = 35, c = 37$ 12

9. $a = 14, c = 50$ 48   **10.** $a = 10, c = 26$ 24

In Exercises 11–14, find the area A and the perimeter P of a rectangle with length l and width w.

11. $l = 3, w = 5$ $A = 15, P = 16$

12. $l = 4, w = 3$ $A = 12, P = 14$

13. $l = 10, w = \frac{1}{2}$ $A = 5, P = 21$

14. $l = 16, w = \frac{1}{4}$ $A = 4, P = \frac{65}{2}$

In Exercises 15–18, find the area A of a triangle with base b and altitude h.

15. $b = 3, h = 4$ 6   **16.** $b = 6, h = 1$ 3

17. $b = \frac{1}{2}, h = 12$ 3   **18.** $b = \frac{1}{4}, h = \frac{2}{3}$ $\frac{1}{12}$

In Exercises 19–22, find the area A and the circumference C of a circle with radius r. (Use $\pi \approx 3.14$.)

19. $r = 1$ $A = 3.14, C = 6.28$

20. $r = 3$ $A = 28.26, C = 18.84$

21. $r = \frac{1}{2}$ $A = 0.785, C = 3.14$

22. $r = \frac{3}{4}$ $A = 1.76625, C = 4.71$

In Exercises 23–26, find the volume V of a box with length l, width w, and height h.

23. $l = 1, w = 1, h = 5$ 5

24. $l = 2, w = 7, h = 4$ 56

25. $l = \frac{1}{2}, w = 10, h = 3$ 15

26. $l = \frac{1}{3}, w = \frac{3}{7}, h = 14$ 2

B Exercises   Applying the Concepts

27. Garden area. Find the area of a rectangular garden if the width is 12 feet and the diagonal measures 20 feet. 192 ft²

28. Perimeter of a mural. A mural is 6 feet wide and its diagonal measures 10 feet. Find the perimeter of the mural. 28 ft

29. Dimensions of a computer monitor. The monitor on a portable computer has a rectangular shape with a 15-inch diagonal. If the width of the monitor is 12 inches, what is its height? 9 in.

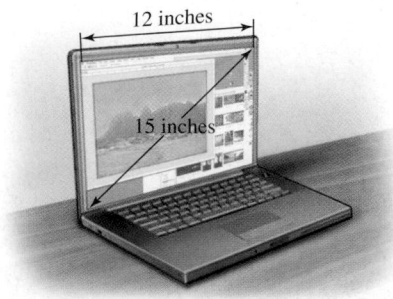

†Due to space constrictions, answers to these exercises may be found in the Answers beginning on page A–1 in the back of the book.

30. **Dimensions of a baseball diamond.** A baseball diamond is actually a square with 90-foot sides. How far does the catcher have to throw the ball to reach second base from home plate? $90\sqrt{2} \approx 127$ ft

31. **Repair problem.** A repairman has to work on an air conditioner's overflow vent located 25 feet above the ground on the side of a house. Shrubs along the house require that a ladder be placed 10 feet from the house. How long must the ladder be in order to reach the overflow vent? $5\sqrt{29} \approx 27$ ft

32. **Building a ramp.** You must build a ramp that allows you to roll a cart from a storeroom into the back of a truck. The rear of the truck must remain 8 feet from the storeroom because of a curb. If the back of the truck is 4 feet above the storeroom floor, how long (in feet) must the ramp be? †

33. **Football field.** The playing surface of a football field (including the end zones) is 120 yards long and 53 yards wide. How far will a player jogging around the perimeter travel? 346 yd

34. **Reflecting pool.** The reflecting pool of the Lincoln Memorial has an approximate perimeter of 4400 feet. The length is approximately 1860 feet more than the width. Find the area of the reflecting pool. 345,100 ft²

35. **Crop circle.** A crop circle with diameter of 787 feet occurred at Milk Hill in Wiltshire, U.K., August 2001. If you walk around the entire edge of the circle, how far will you have walked? (Use $\pi \approx 3.14$.) 2471 ft

36. **Bicycle tires.** The diameter of a bicycle tire is 26 inches. How far will the bicycle travel when the wheel makes one complete turn? (Use $\pi \approx 3.14$.) 81.64 in.

37. **Fishpond border.** A rectangular border a foot and a half wide is built around a rectangular fishpond. If the pond is 6 feet long and 4 feet wide, what is the area of the border? †

38. **Garden fence.** Casper wants to put a decorative fence around his rectangular garden. The garden is 5 feet wide and its diagonal measures 13 feet. How many feet of fencing is required? 34 ft

39. **Oven dimensions.** An oven in the shape of a rectangular box is 2 feet wide, 2.5 feet high, and 3 feet deep. What is the volume of the oven? 15 ft³

40. **Speedway.** A speedway track is constructed by adding semicircular ends to a rectangle, as shown in the figure. Find the area enclosed by the track. 129,542 ft²

Definitions, Concepts, and Formulas

P.1 The Real Numbers and Their Properties

i. **Classifying numbers.**

Natural numbers	$1, 2, 3, \ldots$
Whole numbers	$0, 1, 2, 3, \ldots$
Integers	$\ldots -2, -1, 0, 1, 2, \ldots$
Rational numbers	Numbers that can be expressed as: the quotient $\dfrac{a}{b}$ of two integers, with $b \neq 0$; a terminating or a repeating decimal.
Irrational numbers	Decimals that neither terminate nor repeat.
Real numbers	All the rational and irrational numbers.

ii. **Coordinate line.** Real numbers can be associated with a geometric line called a number line or coordinate line. Numbers associated with points to the right (left) of zero are called positive (negative) numbers.

iii. **Ordering numbers.** $a < b$ means $b = a + c$ for some positive number c.
   Trichotomy property. For two numbers a and b, exactly one of the following is true: $a < b, a = b, b < a$.
   Transitive property. If $a < b$ and $b < c$, then $a < c$.

iv. **Absolute value.**
$$|a| = a \text{ if } a \geq 0 \text{ and } |a| = -a \text{ if } a < 0.$$
   The **distance** between points a and b on a number line is $|b - a|$.

v. **Algebraic properties.**

Commutative	$a + b = b + a, \qquad ab = ba$
Associative	$(a + b) + c = a + (b + c)$
	$(ab)c = a(bc)$
Distributive	$a \cdot (b + c) = a \cdot b + a \cdot c$
	$(a + b) \cdot c = a \cdot c + b \cdot c$
Identity	$a + 0 = 0 + a = a, \qquad a \cdot 1 = 1 \cdot a = a$

Inverse properties:
$$a + (-a) = 0, \qquad a \cdot \frac{1}{a} = 1,$$
$$\text{where } a \neq 0$$

Zero-product properties: $0 \cdot a = 0 = a \cdot 0,$
If $a \cdot b = 0$, then $a = 0$ or $b = 0$.

P.2   Integer Exponents and Scientific Notation

i.   If n is a positive integer, then
$$a^n = \underbrace{a \cdot a \cdots a}_{n \text{ factors}}$$

$$\left. \begin{array}{l} a^0 = 1 \\[2mm] a^{-n} = \dfrac{1}{a^n} \end{array} \right\} \quad a \neq 0$$

ii.   **Rules of exponents.** Denominators and exponents attached to a base of zero are assumed not to be zero.

Product Rule $\qquad a^m \cdot a^n = a^{m+n}$

Quotient Rule $\qquad \dfrac{a^m}{a^n} = a^{m-n}$

Power Rule $\qquad (a^m)^n = a^{mn}$

Power of a product $\quad (a \cdot b)^n = a^n \cdot b^n$

Power of a quotient $\quad \left(\dfrac{a}{b}\right)^n = \dfrac{a^n}{b^n}$

$$\left(\dfrac{a}{b}\right)^{-n} = \left(\dfrac{b}{a}\right)^n = \dfrac{b^n}{a^n}$$

P.3   Polynomials

An algebraic expression of the form
$$a_n x^n + a_{n-1} x^{n-1} + \cdots + a_1 x + a_0,$$
where n is a nonnegative integer, is a polynomial in x.
If $a_n \neq 0$, then n is called the degree of the polynomial.

P.4   Factoring Polynomials

Factoring formulas:
$$A^2 - B^2 = (A - B)(A + B)$$
$$A^2 + 2AB + B^2 = (A + B)^2$$
$$A^2 - 2AB + B^2 = (A - B)^2$$
$$A^3 - B^3 = (A - B)(A^2 + AB + B^2)$$
$$A^3 + B^3 = (A + B)(A^2 - AB + B^2)$$

P.5   Rational Expressions

The quotient of two polynomials is called a rational expression.

i.   **Multiplication and division.**
$$\frac{A}{B} \cdot \frac{C}{D} = \frac{A \cdot C}{B \cdot D}$$

$$\frac{\dfrac{A}{B}}{\dfrac{C}{D}} = \frac{A}{B} \div \frac{C}{D} = \frac{A}{B} \cdot \frac{D}{C} = \frac{A \cdot D}{B \cdot C}$$

All of the denominators are assumed not to be zero.

ii.   **Addition and subtraction.**
$$\frac{A}{B} \pm \frac{C}{D} = \frac{A \cdot D \pm B \cdot C}{B \cdot D}$$

The denominators are assumed not to be zero.

P.6   Rational Exponents and Radicals

i.   If $a > 0$, then $\sqrt[n]{a} = b$ means $a = b^n$ and $b > 0$.

ii.   If $a < 0$ and n is odd, then $\sqrt[n]{a} = b$ means $a = b^n$.
If $a < 0$ and n is even, then $\sqrt[n]{a}$ is not defined.

iii.   When all expressions are defined,
$$a^{\frac{m}{n}} = \sqrt[n]{a^m} = (\sqrt[n]{a})^m; a^{-\frac{m}{n}} = \frac{1}{a^{\frac{m}{n}}}.$$

iv. $\sqrt{a^2} = |a|$.

P.7   Topics in Geometry

i.   An **acute angle** is an angle of measure greater than $0°$ and less than $90°$.

ii.   An **obtuse angle** is an angle of measure greater than $90°$ and less than $180°$.

iii.   Any two angles whose measures sum to $180°$ are called **supplementary angles.**

iv.   Any two angles whose measures sum to $90°$ are called **complementary angles.**

v.   **Theorem.** The sum of the measures of the angles of any triangle is $180°$.

vi.   **Scalene triangle.** A triangle in which *no* two sides have equal length.

vii.   **Isosceles triangle.** A triangle with two sides of equal length.

viii.   **Equilateral triangle.** A triangle with all three sides having equal length.

ix.   **Similar triangles.** Two triangles are **similar** if and only if they have equal corresponding angles and their corresponding sides are proportional.

x.   **Congruent triangles.** Two triangles are **congruent** if and only if they have equal corresponding angles and sides.

xi.   **Included side.** A side of a triangle that lies between two angles is called the **included side** of the angles.

xii.   **Included angle.** The angle formed by two sides is the **included angle** of the sides.

xiii.   **SAS** (Side–Angle–Side). If two sides and the included angle of one triangle are equal to the corresponding sides and the included angle of a second triangle, then the two triangles are congruent.

xiv. ASA (Angle–Side–Angle). If two angles and the included side of one triangle are equal to the corresponding two angles and the included side of a second triangle, then the two triangles are congruent.

xv. SSS (Side–Side–Side). If the three sides of one triangle are equal to the corresponding sides of a second triangle, then the two triangles are congruent.

xvi. A **right triangle** is any triangle that contains a right angle—that is, an angle of 90°. The side of the triangle opposite the 90° angle is called the **hypotenuse**; the other two sides are the **legs** of the triangle.

xvii. Pythagorean Theorem. If a, b, and c represent the lengths of the two legs and the hypotenuse, respectively, of a right triangle, then $a^2 + b^2 = c^2$.

Review Exercises

Basic Skills and Concepts

1. List all the numbers in the set
$$\left\{ 4, \sqrt{7}, -5, \frac{1}{2}, 0.\overline{31}, 0, 0.2, \sqrt{12} \right\} \text{ that are}$$
   a. natural numbers. $\{4\}$
   b. whole numbers. $\{0, 4\}$
   c. integers. $\{-5, 0, 4\}$
   d. rational numbers. †
   e. irrational numbers. $\{\sqrt{7}, \sqrt{12}\}$
   f. real numbers. †

In Exercises 2–5, state which property of the real numbers is being used.

2. $3x + 1 = 1 + 3x$ additive commutative

3. $\pi(x + y) = \pi x + \pi y$ distributive

4. $(x^2 + 1) \cdot 0 = 0 \cdot (x^2 + 1)$ multiplicative commutative

5. $(x^2 + 1) \cdot 1 = x^2 + 1$ multiplicative identity

In Exercises 6–9, write each interval in inequality notation and then graph each interval.

6. $[-2, 3)$ †
7. $(-\infty, 1]$ †
8. $1 \le x < 4$ †
9. $x > 0$ †

In Exercises 10–13, rewrite each expression without absolute value bars.

10. $\dfrac{-12}{|2|}$ -6
11. $|2 - |-3||$ 1
12. $||-5| - |-7||$ 2
13. $|1 - \sqrt{15}|$ $\sqrt{15} - 1$

In Exercises 14–37, evaluate each expression.

14. -5^0 -1
15. $(-4)^3$ -64
16. $\dfrac{2^{18}}{2^{17}}$ 2
17. $2^4 - 5 \cdot 3^2$ -29
18. $(2^3)^2$ 64
19. $-25^{\frac{1}{2}}$ -5
20. $\left(\dfrac{1}{16}\right)^{\frac{1}{4}}$ $\dfrac{1}{2}$
21. $8^{\frac{4}{3}}$ 16

22. $(-27)^{\frac{2}{3}}$ 9
23. $\left(\dfrac{25}{36}\right)^{-\frac{3}{2}}$ $\dfrac{216}{125}$
24. $81^{-\frac{3}{2}}$ †
25. $2 \cdot 5^3$ 250
26. $3^2 \cdot 2^5$ 288
27. $\dfrac{21 \times 10^6}{3 \times 10^7}$ 0.7
28. $\sqrt[4]{10{,}000}$ 10
29. $\sqrt{5^2}$ 5
30. $\sqrt{(-9)^2}$ 9
31. $\sqrt[3]{-125}$ -5
32. $3^{\frac{1}{2}} \cdot 27^{\frac{1}{2}}$ 9
33. $64^{-\frac{1}{3}}$ †
34. $\sqrt{5}\sqrt{20}$ 10
35. $(\sqrt{3} + 2)(\sqrt{3} - 2)$ -1
36. $\left(\dfrac{1}{16}\right)^{-\frac{3}{2}}$ 64
37. $\dfrac{3^{-2} \cdot 7^0}{18^{-1}}$ 2

In Exercises 38–41, evaluate each expression for the given values of x and y.

38. $4(x + 7) + 2y$; $x = 3, y = 4$ 48
39. $\dfrac{y - 6\sqrt{x}}{xy}$; $x = 4, y = 2$ $-\dfrac{5}{4}$
40. $\dfrac{|x|}{x} + \dfrac{|y|}{y}$; $x = 6, y = -3$ 0
41. x^y; $x = 16, y = -\dfrac{1}{2}$ $\dfrac{1}{4}$

In Exercises 42–49, simplify each expression. Write each answer with only positive exponents. Assume that all variables represent positive numbers.

42. $\dfrac{x^{-6}}{x^{-9}}$ x^3
43. $(x^{-2})^{-5}$ x^{10}
44. $\dfrac{x^{-3}}{y^{-2}} \dfrac{y^2}{x^3}$
45. $\left(\dfrac{x^{-3}}{y^{-1}}\right)^{-2}$ $\dfrac{x^6}{y^2}$
46. $\left(\dfrac{xy^3}{x^5 y}\right)^{-2}$ $\dfrac{x^8}{y^4}$
47. $(16x^{-\frac{2}{3}}y^{-\frac{4}{3}})^{\frac{3}{2}}$ $\dfrac{64}{xy^2}$
48. $(49x^{-\frac{4}{3}}y^{\frac{2}{3}})^{-\frac{3}{2}}$ †
49. $\left(\dfrac{64y^{-\frac{9}{2}}}{x^{-3}}\right)^{-\frac{2}{3}}$ $\dfrac{y^3}{16x^2}$

†Due to space constrictions, answers to these exercises may be found in the Answers beginning on page A–1 in the back of the book.

In Exercises 50–66, simplify each expression. Assume that all variables represent positive numbers.

50. $(2x^{\frac{2}{3}})(5x^{\frac{3}{4}})$ $10x^{\frac{17}{12}}$

51. $(7x^{\frac{1}{4}})(3x^{\frac{3}{2}})$ $21x^{\frac{7}{4}}$

52. $\dfrac{32x^{\frac{2}{3}}}{8x^{\frac{1}{4}}}$ $4x^{\frac{5}{12}}$

53. $\dfrac{x^5(2x)^3}{4x^3}$ $2x^5$

54. $\dfrac{(64x^4y^4)^{\frac{1}{2}}}{4y^2}$ $2x^2$

55. $\left(\dfrac{x^2y^{\frac{4}{3}}}{x^{\frac{1}{3}}y}\right)^6$ $x^{10}y^2$

56. $7\sqrt{3} + 3\sqrt{75}$ $22\sqrt{3}$

57. $\dfrac{\sqrt{64}}{\sqrt{11}}$ $\dfrac{8\sqrt{11}}{11}$

58. $\sqrt{180x^2}$ $6x\sqrt{5}$

59. $7\sqrt{6} - 3\sqrt{24}$ †

60. $7\sqrt[3]{54} + \sqrt[3]{128}$ $25\sqrt[3]{2}$

61. $\sqrt{2x}\sqrt{6x}$ $2x\sqrt{3}$

62. $\sqrt{75x^2}$ $5x\sqrt{3}$

63. $\dfrac{\sqrt{100x^3}}{\sqrt{4x}}$ $5x$

64. $5\sqrt{2x} - 2\sqrt{8x}$ $\sqrt{2x}$

65. $4\sqrt[3]{135} + \sqrt[3]{40}$ $14\sqrt[3]{5}$

66. $y\sqrt[3]{56x} - \sqrt[3]{189xy^3}$ $-y\sqrt[3]{7x}$

In Exercises 67–70, rationalize the denominator of each expression.

67. $\dfrac{7}{\sqrt{3}}$ $\dfrac{7\sqrt{3}}{3}$

68. $\dfrac{4}{9 - \sqrt{6}}$ $\dfrac{36 + 4\sqrt{6}}{75}$

69. $\dfrac{1 - \sqrt{3}}{1 + \sqrt{3}}$ $-2 + \sqrt{3}$

70. $\dfrac{2\sqrt{5} + 3}{3 - 4\sqrt{5}}$ $-\dfrac{49 + 18\sqrt{5}}{71}$

71. Write $3.7 \times (6.23 \times 10^{12})$ in scientific notation. †

72. Write $\dfrac{3.19 \times 10^{-9}}{0.02 \times 10^{-3}}$ in decimal notation. 0.0001595

In Exercises 73–82, perform the indicated operations. Leave the resulting polynomial in standard form.

73. $(x^3 - 6x^2 + 4x - 2) + (3x^3 - 6x^2 + 5x - 4)$ †

74. $(10x^3 + 8x^2 - 7x - 3) - (5x^3 - x^2 + 4x - 9)$ †

75. $(4x^4 + 3x^3 - 5x^2 + 9) + (5x^4 + 8x^3 - 7x^2 + 5)$ †

76. $(8x^4 + 4x^3 + 3x^2 + 5) + (7x^4 + 3x^3 + 8x^2 - 3)$ †

77. $(x - 12)(x - 3)$ $x^2 - 15x + 36$

78. $(x - 7)^2$ $x^2 - 14x + 49$

79. $(x^5 - 2)(x^5 + 2)$ $x^{10} - 4$

80. $(4x - 3)(4x + 3)$ $16x^2 - 9$

81. $(2x + 5)(3x - 11)$ $6x^2 - 7x - 55$

82. $(3x - 6)(x^2 + 2x + 4)$ $3x^3 - 24$

In Exercises 83–104, factor each polynomial.

83. $x^2 - 3x - 10$ †

84. $x^2 + 10x + 9$ †

85. $24x^2 - 38x - 11$ †

86. $15x^2 + 33x + 18$ †

87. $x(x + 11) + 5(x + 11)$ †

88. $x^3 - x^2 + 2x - 2$ †

89. $x^4 - x^3 + 7x - 7$ †

90. $9x^2 + 24x + 16$ $(3x + 4)^2$

91. $10x^2 + 23x + 12$ †

92. $8x^2 + 18x + 9$ †

93. $12x^2 + 7x - 12$ †

94. $x^4 - 4x^2$ $x^2(x - 2)(x + 2)$

95. $4x^2 - 49$ $(2x - 7)(2x + 7)$

96. $16x^2 - 81$ †

97. $x^2 + 12x + 36$ $(x + 6)^2$

98. $x^2 - 10x + 100$ prime

99. $64x^2 + 48x + 9$ $(8x + 3)^2$

100. $8x^3 - 1$ †

101. $8x^3 + 27$ †

102. $7x^3 - 7$ †

103. $x^3 + 5x^2 - 16x - 80$ †

104. $x^3 + 6x^2 - 9x - 54$ †

In Exercises 105–118, perform the indicated operation. Simplify your answer.

105. $\dfrac{4}{x - 9} - \dfrac{10}{9 - x}$ $\dfrac{14}{x - 9}$

106. $\dfrac{2}{x^2 - 3x + 2} + \dfrac{6}{x^2 - 1}$ $\dfrac{2(4x - 5)}{(x - 1)(x + 1)(x - 2)}$

107. $\dfrac{3x + 5}{x^2 + 14x + 48} - \dfrac{3x - 2}{x^2 + 10x + 16}$ $\dfrac{22 - 5x}{(x + 2)(x + 6)(x + 8)}$

108. $\dfrac{x + 7}{x^2 - 7x + 6} - \dfrac{5 - 3x}{x^2 - 2x - 24}$ $\dfrac{4x^2 + 3x + 33}{(x - 1)(x - 6)(x + 4)}$

109. $\dfrac{x - 1}{x + 1} - \dfrac{x + 1}{x - 1} - \dfrac{4x}{(x - 1)(x + 1)}$

110. $\dfrac{x^3 - 1}{3x^2 - 3} \cdot \dfrac{6x + 6}{x^2 + x + 1}$ 2

111. $\dfrac{x - 1}{2x - 3} \cdot \dfrac{4x^2 - 9}{2x^2 - x - 1}$ $\dfrac{2x + 3}{2x + 1}$

112. $\dfrac{x^2 + 2x - 8}{x^2 + 5x + 6} \cdot \dfrac{x + 2}{x + 4}$ $\dfrac{x - 2}{x + 3}$

113. $\dfrac{x^2 - 4}{4x^2 - 9} \cdot \dfrac{2x^2 - 3x}{2x + 4}$ $\dfrac{x(x - 2)}{2(2x + 3)}$

114. $\dfrac{3x^2 - 17x + 10}{x^2 - 4x - 5} \cdot \dfrac{x^2 + 3x + 2}{x^2 + x - 2}$ $\dfrac{3x - 2}{x - 1}$

115. $\dfrac{\dfrac{1}{x^2} - x}{\dfrac{1}{x^2} + x}$ †

116. $\dfrac{\dfrac{x}{x - 2} + x}{\dfrac{1}{x^2 - 4}}$ $x(x - 1)(x + 2)$

117. $\dfrac{\dfrac{x}{x - 3} + x}{\dfrac{x}{3 - x} - x}$ -1

118. $\dfrac{x + 2 - \dfrac{18}{x - 5}}{x - 1 - \dfrac{12}{x - 5}} \cdot \dfrac{x + 4}{x + 1}$

Applying the Concepts

119. If a right triangle has legs a and b of lengths 20 and 21, respectively, find the length of the hypotenuse. 29

120. One leg of a right triangle measures 5 inches. The hypotenuse is 1 inch longer than the other leg. Find the length of the hypotenuse. 13 in.

121. Find the area A and the perimeter P of a right triangle with hypotenuse of length 20 and a leg of length 12. †

122. Find the volume V of a box of length $\frac{1}{3}$, width 7, and height 60. 140

123. Find the area of a rectangular rug if its width is 6 feet and its diagonal measures 10 feet. 48 ft^2

124. The amount of alcohol in the body of a person who drinks x grams of alcohol every hour over a relatively long period is $\dfrac{4.2x}{10 - x}$ grams. How many grams of alcohol will be in the body of a person who drinks 2 grams of alcohol every hour (over a relatively long period)? 1.05 gm

125. Because of the earth's curvature, the maximum distance a person can see from a height h above the ground is $\sqrt{7920h + h^2}$, where h is given in miles. What is the maximum distance an airplane pilot can see when the plane is 0.7 mile above the ground? 74.46 mi

126. A contaminated reservoir contains 2% arsenic. The percentage of arsenic in the reservoir can be reduced by adding water. If the reservoir contains a million gallons of water, write a rational expression whose values give the percentage of arsenic in the reservoir when x gallons of water are added to it. †

127. The height (in feet) of an open fruit crate that is three times as long as it is wide is given by $\dfrac{36 - 3x^2}{8x}$, where x is the width of the box. Find the height of a fruit crate that is 2 feet wide. 1.5 ft

128. An object thrown down with an initial velocity of v_0 feet per second will travel $16t^2 + v_0 t$ feet in t seconds. How far has an orange that is dropped from a hot-air balloon traveled after 9 seconds if it has an initial downward velocity of 25 feet per second? 1521 ft

Practice Test

Rewrite each expression without absolute value bars.

1. $|7 - |-3||$ 4

2. $|\sqrt{2} - 100|$ $100 - \sqrt{2}$

3. Evaluate $\dfrac{x - 3y}{2} + xy$ for $x = 5$ and $y = -3$. -8

4. Determine the domain of the variable x in the expression $\dfrac{2x}{(x - 3)(x + 9)}$, and write it in interval notation.

Simplify each expression. Assume that all expressions containing variables are defined.

5. $\left(\dfrac{-3x^2 y}{x}\right)^3$ $-27x^3 y^3$

6. $\sqrt[3]{-8x^6}$ $-2x^2$

7. $\sqrt{75x} - \sqrt{27x}$ $2\sqrt{3x}$

8. $-16^{-\frac{3}{2}}$

9. $\left(\dfrac{x^{-2} y^4}{25x^3 y^3}\right)^{-\frac{1}{2}}$ $\dfrac{5x^{\frac{5}{2}} y^{\frac{1}{2}}}{y}$

10. Rationalize the denominator of the expression $\dfrac{5}{1 - \sqrt{3}}$.

Perform the indicated operations. Write the resulting polynomial in standard form.

11. $4(x^2 - 3x + 2) + 3(5x^2 - 2x + 1)$ $19x^2 - 18x + 11$

12. $(x - 2)(5x - 1)$

13. $(x^2 + 3y^2)^2$

14. A circular rug with radius 5 feet has a border of uniform width. The distance from the center of the rug to the outer edge of the border is x feet. Write a completely factored polynomial that gives the area of the border. $(x - 5)(x + 5)\pi$

Factor each polynomial completely.

15. $x^2 - 5x + 6$

16. $9x^2 + 12x + 4$ $(3x + 2)^2$

17. $8x^3 - 27$ $(2x - 3)(4x^2 + 6x + 9)$

Perform the indicated operations and simplify the result. Leave your answer in factored form.

18. $\dfrac{6 - 3x}{x^2 - 4} - \dfrac{12}{2x + 4}$ $\dfrac{-9}{(x + 2)}$

19. $\dfrac{\frac{1}{x^2}}{9 - \frac{1}{x^2}}$ $\dfrac{1}{(3x + 1)(3x - 1)}$

20. Find the length of the hypotenuse of a right triangle with legs a and b of lengths 35 and 12, respectively. 37

Answers:

4. $x \neq -9, x \neq 3$ **8.** $-\dfrac{1}{64}$ **10.** $-\dfrac{5 + 5\sqrt{3}}{2}$

12. $5x^2 - 11x + 2$ **13.** $x^4 + 6x^2 y^2 + 9y^4$ **15.** $(x - 3)(x - 2)$

CHAPTER 1

Equations and Inequalities

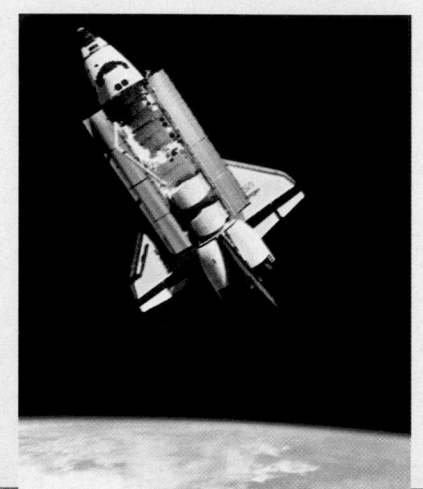

Equations and inequalities are useful in analyzing designs found in the art and architecture of ancient civilizations, in understanding the dazzling geometric constructions that abound in nature, and in solving problems common to industry and daily life.

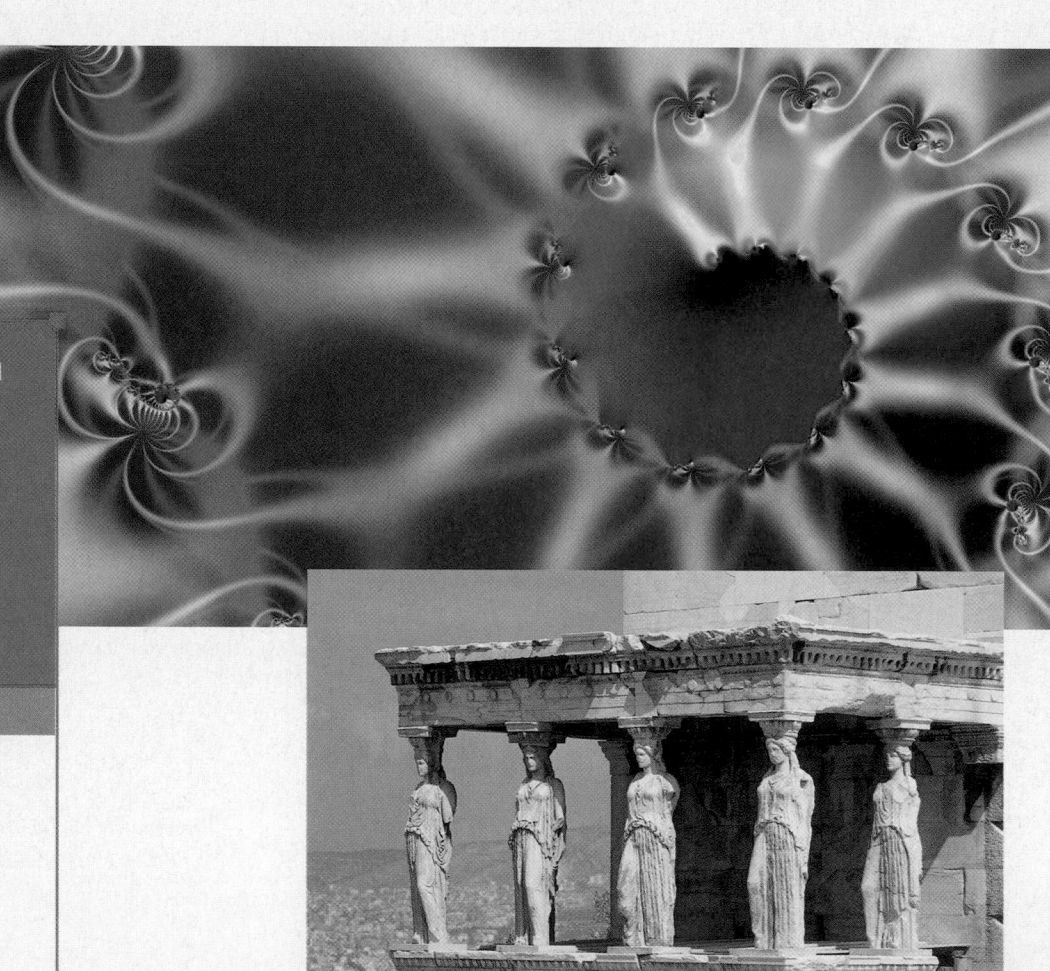

TOPICS

Linear Equations in One Variable

BEFORE STARTING THIS SECTION, REVIEW

1. Algebraic expressions (Section P.1, page 14)
2. Like terms (Section P.3, page 31)
3. Least common denominator (Section P.5, page 54)

OBJECTIVES

1 Learn the vocabulary and concepts used in studying equations.

2 Learn to solve linear equations in one variable.

3 Learn to solve formulas for a specific variable.

4 Learn to solve applied problems by using linear equations.

Bungee-Jumping TV Contestants

England's Oxford Dangerous Sports Club started the modern version of the sport of "bungee" (or bungy) jumping on April 1, 1978, from the Clifton Suspension Bridge in Bristol, England. Bungee cords consist of hundreds of continuous-length rubber strands encased in a nylon sheath. One end of the cord is tied to a solid structure, such as a crane or bridge, and the other end is tied via padded ankle straps to the jumper's ankle. The jumper jumps, and if things go as planned, the cord extends like a rubber band and the jumper bounces up and down until coming to a halt. Suppose that a television adventure program has its contestants bungee jump from a bridge 120 feet above the water. The bungee cord that is used has a 140–150% elongation, meaning that its extended length will be the original length plus a maximum of an additional 150% of its original length. If the show's producer wants to be sure that the jumper doesn't get closer than 10 feet to the water, and if no contestant will be more than 7 feet tall, how long can the bungee cord be? Using the information from this section, we learn in Example 6 that the cord should be about 41 feet long. ■

---

1 Learn the vocabulary and concepts used in studying equations.

Definitions

An **equation** is a statement that two mathematical expressions are equal. For example,

$$7 - 5 = 2$$

is an equation. In algebra, however, we are generally more interested in equations that contain variables.

An **equation in one variable** is a statement that two expressions, with at least one containing the variable, are equal. For example, $2x - 3 = 7$ is an equation in the variable x. The expressions $2x - 3$ and 7 are the *sides* of the equation. The **domain** of the variable in an equation is the set of all real numbers for which both sides of the equation are defined.

> ### EXAMPLE 1   Finding the Domain of the Variable
>
> Find the domain of the variable x in each of the following equations.
>
> **a.** $2 = \dfrac{5}{x - 1}$ **b.** $x - 2 = \sqrt{x}$ **c.** $2x - 3 = 7$

Solution

a. In the equation $2 = \dfrac{5}{x - 1}$, the left side 2 does not contain x, so it is defined for all values of x. Since division by 0 is undefined, $\dfrac{5}{x - 1}$ is not defined if $x = 1$. The domain of x is the set of all real numbers except the number 1. Frequently, when only a few numbers are excluded from the domain of the variable, we write the exceptions on the side of the equation. In this example, if we wanted to specify the domain of the variable, we would simply write $2 = \dfrac{5}{x - 1}, x \neq 1$.

b. The square root of a negative number is not a real number, so $\sqrt{x}$, the right side of the equation $x - 2 = \sqrt{x}$, is defined only when $x \geq 0$. The left side is defined for all real numbers. Thus, the domain of x in this equation is $\{x | x \geq 0\}$, or, in interval notation, $[0, \infty)$.

c. Since both sides of the equation $2x - 3 = 7$ are defined for all real numbers, the domain is $\{x | x \text{ is a real number}\}$, or, in interval notation, $(-\infty, \infty)$.   ■ ■ ■

PRACTICE PROBLEM 1   Find the domain of the variable x in each of the following equations.

a. $\dfrac{x}{3} - 7 = 5$ **b.** $\dfrac{3}{2 - x} = 4$ **c.** $\sqrt{x - 1} = 0$ ■

When the variable in an equation is replaced by a specific value from its domain, the resulting statement may be true or false. For example, in the equation $2x - 3 = 7$, if we let $x = 1$, we obtain

$$2(1) - 3 = 7 \text{ or } -1 = 7,$$

which is obviously false. However, if we replace x by 5, we obtain $2(5) - 3 = 7$, a true statement. Those values (if any) of the variable that result in a true statement are called **solutions** or **roots** of the equation. Thus, 5 is a solution (or root) of the equation $2x - 3 = 7$. We also say that 5 **satisfies** the equation $2x - 3 = 7$. To **solve** an equation means to find all solutions of the equation; the set of all solutions of an equation is called its **solution set**.

An equation that is satisfied by every real number in the domain of the variable is called an **identity.** The equations

$$2(x + 3) = 2x + 6,$$
$$\text{and} \quad x^2 - 9 = (x + 3)(x - 3),$$

are examples of identities. You should recognize that these equations are examples of the distributive property, and the difference of squares, respectively.

An equation that is not an identity, but is true for at least one real number, is called a **conditional equation.** To verify that an equation is a conditional equation, you have to find at least one number that *is* a solution of the equation and at least one number that is *not* a solution of the equation. The equation $2x - 3 = 7$ is an example of a conditional equation: 5 satisfies this equation, but 0 does not.

An equation that *no* number satisfies is called an **inconsistent equation**. The solution set of an inconsistent equation is designated by the empty set symbol, $\varnothing$. The equation $x = x + 5$ is an example of an inconsistent equation. It is inconsistent because no number is 5 more than itself.

Solving an Equation

Equations that have the same solution set are called **equivalent equations**. For example, equations $x = 4$ and $3x = 12$ are equivalent equations with solution set $\{4\}$.

In general, to solve an equation in one variable, we replace the given equation by a sequence of equivalent equations until we obtain an equation whose solution is obvious, such as $x = 4$. The following operations yield equivalent equations.

Generating Equivalent Equations		
Operations	**Given Equation**	**Equivalent Equation**
Simplify expressions on either side by eliminating parentheses, combining like terms, etc.	$(2x - 1) - (x + 1) = 4$	$2x - 1 - x - 1 = 4$ or $x - 2 = 4$
Add (or subtract) the same expression on *both* sides of the equation.	$x - 2 = 4$	$x - 2 + 2 = 4 + 2$ or $x = 6$
Multiply (or divide) *both* sides of the equation by the same *nonzero* expression.	$2x = 8$	$\dfrac{1}{2} \cdot 2x = \dfrac{1}{2} \cdot 8$ or $x = 4$
Interchange the two sides of the equation.	$-3 = x$	$x = -3$

2 Learn to solve linear equations in one variable.

Solving Linear Equations in One Variable

> **LINEAR EQUATIONS**
>
> A **linear equation in one variable**, such as x, is an equation that can be written in the *standard form*
>
> $$ax + b = 0,$$
>
> where a and b are real numbers with $a \neq 0$.

Since the highest exponent on the variable in a linear equation is 1 ($x = x^1$), a linear equation is also called a *first-degree equation*. We can see that the linear equation $ax + b = 0$ with $a \neq 0$ has exactly one solution by using the following two steps:

$$ax + b = 0 \qquad \text{Original equation, } a \neq 0$$
$$ax = -b \qquad \text{Subtract } b \text{ from both sides.}$$
$$x = -\frac{b}{a}. \qquad \text{Divide both sides by } a.$$

In the Finding the Solution box, we describe a step-by-step procedure for solving a linear equation in one variable.

FINDING THE SOLUTION: PROCEDURE FOR SOLVING LINEAR EQUATIONS IN ONE VARIABLE

OBJECTIVE
To solve a linear equation in one variable.

EXAMPLE
Solve $\dfrac{1}{3}x - \dfrac{2}{3} = \dfrac{1}{2}(1 - 3x)$.

Step 1 **Eliminate Fractions.** Multiply both sides of the equation by the least common denominator (LCD) of all the fractions.

$$\frac{1}{3}x - \frac{2}{3} = \frac{1}{2}(1 - 3x) \qquad \text{Original equation}$$

$$6\left(\frac{1}{3}x - \frac{2}{3}\right) = 6 \cdot \frac{1}{2}(1 - 3x) \qquad \text{Multiply both sides by 6 (LCD) to eliminate fractions.}$$

Step 2 **Simplify.** Simplify both sides of the equation by removing parentheses and other grouping symbols (if any) and combining like terms.

$$6 \cdot \frac{1}{3}x - 6 \cdot \frac{2}{3} = 3(1 - 3x) \qquad \text{Distribute on the left side; simplify on the right.}$$

$$2x - 4 = 3 - 9x \qquad \text{Simplify on the left side; distribute on the right.}$$

Step 3 **Isolate the Variable Term.** Add appropriate expressions to both sides, so that when both sides are simplified, the terms containing the variable are on one side and all constant terms are on the other side.

$$2x - 4 + 9x + 4 = 3 - 9x + 9x + 4 \qquad \text{Add } 9x + 4 \text{ to both sides.}$$

Step 4 **Combine Terms.** Combine terms containing the variable to obtain one term that contains the variable as a factor.

$$11x = 7 \qquad \text{Collect like terms and combine constants.}$$

Step 5 **Isolate the Variable.** Divide both sides by the coefficient of the variable to obtain the solution.

$$x = \frac{7}{11} \qquad \text{Divide both sides by 11.}$$

Step 6 **Check the Solution.** Substitute the solution into the original equation.

Check:

Substitute $\dfrac{7}{11}$ for x in both sides of the original equation.

The result should be $-\dfrac{5}{11} = -\dfrac{5}{11}$.

EXAMPLE 2	**Solving a Linear Equation**

Solve: $6x - [3x - 2(x - 2)] = 11$.

Solution

Step 2	$6x - [3x - 2(x - 2)] = 11$	Original equation
	$6x - [3x - 2x + 4] = 11$	Remove innermost parentheses by distributing $-2(x - 2) = -2x + 4$.
	$6x - 3x + 2x - 4 = 11$	Remove square brackets and change the sign of each enclosed term.
	$5x - 4 = 11$	Combine like terms.
Step 3	$5x - 4 + 4 = 11 + 4$	Add 4 to both sides.
Step 4	$5x = 15$	Simplify both sides in Step 3.
Step 5	$\dfrac{5x}{5} = \dfrac{15}{5}$	Divide both sides by 5.
	$x = 3$	Simplify.

The apparent solution is 3.

Step 6   *Check:* Substitute $x = 3$ into the original equation. You should obtain $11 = 11$. Thus, 3 is the only solution of the original equation, so $\{3\}$ is its solution set.   ■ ■ ■

PRACTICE PROBLEM 2   Solve: $3x - [2x - 6(x + 1)] = -1$.   ■

EXAMPLE 3	**Solving a Linear Equation**

Solve: $1 - 5y + 2(y + 7) = 2y + 5(3 - y)$.

Solution

Step 2	$1 - 5y + 2(y + 7) = 2y + 5(3 - y)$	Original equation
	$1 - 5y + 2y + 14 = 2y + 15 - 5y$	Distributive property
	$15 - 3y = 15 - 3y$	Collect like terms and combine constants on each side.
Step 3	$15 - 3y + 3y = 15 - 3y + 3y$	Add $3y$ to both sides.
	$15 = 15$	Simplify.
	$0 = 0$	Subtract 15 from both sides.

We have shown that $0 = 0$ is equivalent to the original equation. The equation $0 = 0$ is always true; its solution set is the set of all real numbers. Therefore, the solution set of the original equation is also the set of all real numbers. Thus, the original equation is an identity.   ■ ■ ■

PRACTICE PROBLEM 3   Solve the equation: $2(3x - 6) + 5 = 12 - (x + 5)$.   ■

> ### TYPES OF LINEAR EQUATIONS
>
> There are three types of linear equations.
>
> 1. A linear equation that is true for all values in the domain of the variable is an *identity*. For example, $2(x - 1) = 2x - 2$.
>
> 2. A linear equation that has a single solution is a *conditional* equation. For example, $2x = 6$.
>
> 3. A linear equation that is not true for any value of the variable is an *inconsistent* equation. For example, $x = x + 2$ is an inconsistent equation. Since no number is 2 more than itself, the solution set of the equation $x = x + 2$ is $\varnothing$. When you try to solve an inconsistent equation, you will obtain a false statement, such as $0 = 2$.

3 Learn to solve formulas for a specific variable.

Formulas

Solving equations that arise from everyday experiences is one of the most important uses of algebra. An equation that expresses a relationship between two or more variables is called a **formula.**

EXAMPLE 4 Converting Temperatures

The formula for converting the temperature in degrees Celsius (C) to degrees Fahrenheit (F) is

$$F = \frac{9}{5}C + 32.$$

If the temperature shows 86° Fahrenheit, what is the temperature in degrees Celsius?

Solution

We first substitute 86 for F in the formula $\quad F = \dfrac{9}{5}C + 32$

to obtain $\qquad\qquad\qquad\qquad 86 = \dfrac{9}{5}C + 32.$

We now solve this equation for C.

$$5(86) = 5\left(\frac{9}{5}C + 32\right) \qquad \text{Multiply both sides by 5.}$$
$$430 = 9C + 160 \qquad \text{Simplify.}$$
$$270 = 9C \qquad \text{Subtract 160 from both sides.}$$
$$\frac{270}{9} = C \qquad \text{Divide both sides by 9.}$$
$$30 = C \qquad \text{Simplify.}$$

Thus, 86° F converts to 30° C. ■ ■ ■

PRACTICE PROBLEM 4 Use the formula in Example 4 to find the temperature in degrees Celsius if the temperature is 50° Fahrenheit. ■

In Example 4, we specified $F = 86$ and solved the equation for C. A more general result can be obtained by assuming that F is a fixed number, or constant, and solving for C. This process is called **solving for a specified variable**.

EXAMPLE 5   **Solving for a Specified Variable**

Solve $F = \dfrac{9}{5}C + 32$ for C.

Solution

$$5F = 5\left(\dfrac{9}{5}C + 32\right)$$ Multiply both sides by 5.

$$5F = 9C + 5 \cdot 32$$ Distributive property

$$5F - 5 \cdot 32 = 9C$$ Subtract $5 \cdot 32$ from both sides.

$$\dfrac{5F - 5 \cdot 32}{9} = C$$ Divide both sides by 9.

$$\dfrac{5}{9}(F - 32) = C \quad \text{or} \quad C = \dfrac{5}{9}(F - 32)$$ Factor.   ■ ■ ■

PRACTICE PROBLEM 5   Solve: $P = 2l + 2w$ for w.   ■

4 Learn to solve applied problems by using linear equations.

Applications

In the next example, we show how the skills learned for solving linear equations are used in solving real-world problems.

EXAMPLE 6   **Bungee-Jumping TV Contestants**

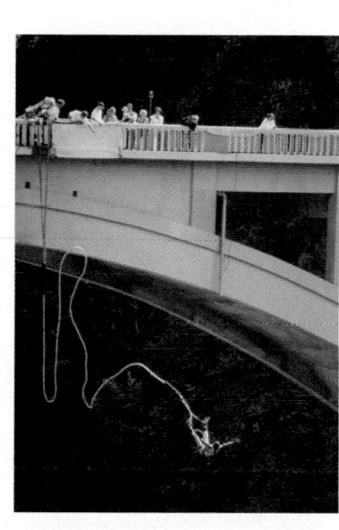

The introduction to this section described a television show on which a bungee cord with 140–150% elongation is used for contestants' bungee jumping from a bridge 120 feet above the water. The show's producer wants to be sure that the jumper doesn't get closer than 10 feet to the water, and no contestant will be more than 7 feet tall. How long can the bungee cord be?

Solution

We want the extended cord plus the length of the jumper's body to be a minimum of 10 feet above the water. To be safe, we will determine the maximum extended length of the cord, add the height of the tallest possible contestant, and ensure that this total length is 10 feet above the water.

Let x = length, in feet, of the cord to be used.

Then $x + 1.5x = 2.5x$ is the maximum extended length (in feet) of the cord (with 150% elongation). We have

Extended cord length	+	Body length	+	10-foot buffer	=	Height of bridge above the water

$$2.5x + 7 + 10 = 120$$ Replace descriptions by arithmetic expressions.

$$2.5x + 17 = 120$$ Combine constants.

$$2.5x = 103$$ Subtract 17 from both sides.

$$x = 41.2 \text{ feet}$$ Divide both sides by 2.5.

If the length of the cord is no more than 41.2 feet, all conditions are met.   ■ ■ ■

PRACTICE PROBLEM 6 What length of cord should be used in Example 6 if the elongation is 200% instead of 140–150%? ■

A Exercises Basic Skills and Concepts

In Exercises 1–5, determine whether the given value of the variable is a solution of the equation.

1. $x - 2 = 5x + 6$
 a. $x = 0$ No   **b.** $x = -2$ Yes

2. $8x + 3 = 14x - 1$
 a. $x = -1$ No   **b.** $x = \dfrac{2}{3}$ Yes

3. $\dfrac{2}{x} = \dfrac{1}{3} + \dfrac{1}{x + 2}$
 a. $x = 4$ Yes   **b.** $x = 1$ No

4. $(x - 3)(2x + 1) = 0$
 a. $x = \dfrac{1}{2}$ No   **b.** $x = 3$ Yes

5. $2x + 3x = 5x$
 a. $x = 157$ Yes   **b.** $x = -2046$ Yes

In Exercises 6–10, find the domain of the variable in each equation. Write the answer in interval notation.

6. $(2 - x) - 4x = 7 - 3(x + 4)$ $(-\infty, \infty)$

7. $\dfrac{y}{y - 1} = \dfrac{3}{y + 2}$ $(-\infty, -2) \cup (-2, 1) \cup (1, \infty)$

8. $\dfrac{1}{y} = 2 + \sqrt{y}$ $(0, \infty)$

9. $\dfrac{3x}{(x - 3)(x - 4)} = 2x + 9$ $(-\infty, 3) \cup (3, 4) \cup (4, \infty)$

10. $\dfrac{1}{\sqrt{x}} = x^2 - 1$ $(0, \infty)$

In Exercises 11–14, determine whether the given equation is an identity. If the equation is not an identity, give a value which demonstrates that fact.

11. $2x + 3 = 5x + 1$ No. $x = 0$

12. $3x + 4 = 6x + 2 - (3x - 2)$ Yes

13. $\dfrac{1}{x + 3} = \dfrac{1}{x} + \dfrac{1}{3}$ No. $x = 1$ **14.** $\dfrac{1}{x} + \dfrac{1}{2} = \dfrac{2 + x}{2x}$ Yes

In Exercises 15–46, solve each equation.

15. $3x + 5 = 14$ $\{3\}$ **16.** $2x - 17 = 7$ $\{12\}$

17. $-10x + 12 = 32$ $\{-2\}$ **18.** $-2x + 5 = 6$ †

19. $3 - y = -4$ $\{7\}$ **20.** $2 - 7y = 23$ $\{-3\}$

21. $7x + 7 = 2(x + 1)$ $\{-1\}$ **22.** $3(x + 2) = 4 - x$ †

23. $3(2 - y) + 5y = 3y$ $\{6\}$ **24.** $9y - 3(y - 1) = 6 + y$ †

25. $4y - 3y + 7 - y = 2 - (7 - y)$ $\{12\}$

26. $3(y - 1) = 6y - 4 + 2y - 4y$ $\{1\}$

27. $3(x - 2) + 2(3 - x) = 1$ †

28. $2x - 3 - (3x - 1) = 6$ †

29. $2x + 3(x - 4) = 7x + 10$ $\{-11\}$

30. $3(2 - 3x) - 4x = 3x - 10$ $\{1\}$

31. $3x + \dfrac{x}{5} - 2 = \dfrac{1}{10} + 2x$ †

32. $\dfrac{1}{4} + 5x - \dfrac{x}{7} = \dfrac{5x}{14} + \dfrac{x}{2}$ †

33. $\dfrac{x + 2}{3} - \dfrac{x}{2} = 7$ $\{-38\}$

34. $\dfrac{x - 1}{3} + \dfrac{2x}{5} = x + 2$ †

35. $\dfrac{x + 1}{2} - \dfrac{2x - 1}{5} = 0$ $\{-7\}$

36. $\dfrac{2x}{3} - \dfrac{1}{2} = \dfrac{2x + 5}{6}$ $\{4\}$

37. $4[x + 2(3 - x)] = 2x + 1$ †

38. $3 - [x - 3(x + 2)] = 4$ †

39. $3(4y - 3) = 4[y - (4y - 3)]$ †

40. $5 - (6y + 9) + 2y = 2(y + 1)$ $\{-1\}$

41. $2x - 3(2 - x) = (x - 3) + 2x + 1$ $\{2\}$

42. $5(x - 3) - 6(x - 4) = -5$ $\{14\}$

43. $\dfrac{2x + 1}{9} - \dfrac{x + 4}{6} = 1$ $\{28\}$

44. $\dfrac{2 - 3x}{7} + \dfrac{x - 1}{3} = \dfrac{3x}{7}$ †

45. $\dfrac{1 - x}{4} + \dfrac{5x + 1}{2} = 3 - \dfrac{2(x + 1)}{8}$ $\left\{\dfrac{4}{5}\right\}$

46. $\dfrac{x + 4}{3} + 2x - \dfrac{1}{2} = \dfrac{3x + 2}{6}$ $\left\{\dfrac{-3}{11}\right\}$

In Exercises 47–58, solve each formula for the indicated variable.

47. $d = rt$ for r †   **48.** $F = ma$ for a †

49. $C = 2\pi r$ for r †   **50.** $A = 2\pi rx + \pi r^2$ for x †

51. $I = \dfrac{E}{R}$ for R $R = \dfrac{E}{I}$ **52.** $A = P(1 + rt)$ for t †

†Due to space constrictions, answers to these exercises may be found in the Answers beginning on page A–1 in the back of the book.

53. $A = \dfrac{(a + b)h}{2}$ for h †   **54.** $T = a + (n - 1)d$ for d †   **57.** $y = mx + b$ for m †   **58.** $ax + by = c$ for y †

55. $\dfrac{1}{f} = \dfrac{1}{u} + \dfrac{1}{v}$ for u †   **56.** $\dfrac{1}{R} = \dfrac{1}{R_1} + \dfrac{1}{R_2}$ for R_2 †

B Exercises   Applying the Concepts

59. Swimming-pool dimensions. The volume of a swimming pool is 2808 cubic feet. If the pool is 18 feet long and 12 feet deep, find its width.   13 ft

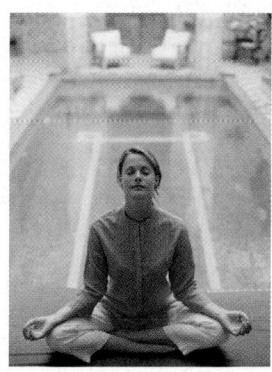

60. Hole dimensions. If a box-shaped hole 7 feet long and 3 feet wide holds 168 cubic feet of dirt, how deep must the hole be? †

61. Geometry. A circle has a circumference of 114π centimeters. Find the radius of the circle.   57 cm

62. Geometry. A rectangle has a perimeter of 28 meters and a width of 5 meters. Find the length of the rectangle.   9 m

63. Storage barrel dimensions. A barrel has a surface area of 6π square meters and a radius of 1 meter. Find the height of the barrel.   2 m

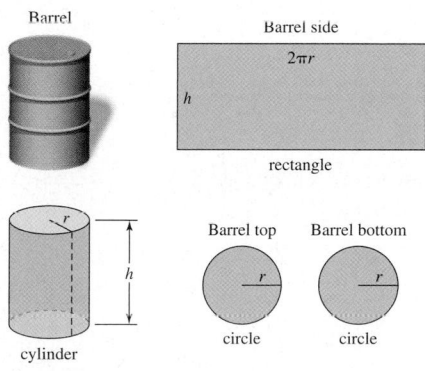

64. Can dimensions. A can has a volume of 148π cubic centimeters and a radius of 2 centimeters. Find the height of the can.   37 cm

65. Geometry. A trapezoid has an area of 66 square feet and a height of 6 feet. If one base is 3 feet, what is the length of the other base?   19 ft

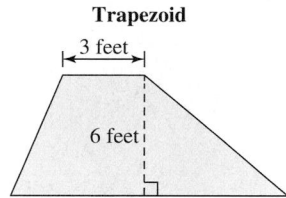

66. Geometry. A trapezoid has an area of 35 square centimeters. If one base is 9 centimeters and the other base is 11 centimeters, find the height of the trapezoid.   3.5 cm

67. Investment. If P dollars are invested at a simple interest rate r (in decimals), the amount A that will be available after t years is

$$A = P + Prt.$$

If $500 is invested at a rate of 6%, how long will it be before the amount of money available is $920? [*Hint*: Use $r = 0.06$.]   14 yr

68. Investment. Using the formula from Exercise 67, determine the amount of money that was invested if $2482 resulted from a 10-year investment at 7%. $1,460

69. Estimating a mortgage note. A rule of thumb for estimating the maximum affordable monthly mortgage note M for prospective homeowners is

$$M = \dfrac{m - b}{4},$$

where m is the gross monthly income and b is the total of the monthly bills. What must the gross monthly income be to justify a monthly note of $427 if monthly bills are $302? $2,010

70. Engineering degrees. Among a group of engineers who had received master's degrees, the annual salary S in dollars was related to two numbers b and a, where

$b =$ the number of years of work experience before receiving the degree and

$a =$ the number of years of work experience after receiving the degree.

The relationship among S, a, and b is given by

$$S = 48{,}917 + 1080b + 1604a.$$

If an engineer had worked eight years before earning her master's degree and was earning \$67,181, how many years did she work after receiving her degree? 6 yr

71. Digital cameras. The price P (in dollars) for which a manufacturer will sell a digital camera is related to the number q of cameras ordered by the formula

$$P = 200 - 0.02q, \text{ for } 100 \le q \le 2000.$$

How many cameras must be ordered in order to pay \$170 per camera? 1500 cameras

72. Boyle's Law. If a volume V_1 of a dry gas under pressure P_1 is subjected to a new pressure P_2, the new volume V_2 of the gas is given by

$$V_2 = \frac{V_1 P_1}{P_2}.$$

If V_2 is 200 cubic centimeters, V_1 is 600 cubic centimeters, and P_1 is 400 millimeters of mercury, find P_2. $P_2 = 1200$ mm

73. Transistor voltage. The voltage gain V of a transistor is related to the generator resistance R_1, the load resistance R_2, and the current gain α by

$$V = \alpha \frac{R_1}{R_2}.$$

If V is 950, and R_1 and R_2 are 100,000 and 100 ohms, respectively, find α. $\alpha = 0.95$

74. Quick ratio. The quick ratio Q of a business is related to its current assets A, its current inventory I, and its current liabilities L, by

$$Q = \frac{A - I}{L}.$$

If $Q = 37{,}000$, $L = \$1500$, and $I = \$3200$, find the current assets. $A = \$55{,}503{,}200$

75. Return on investment. Use the formula $A = P + Prt$ from Exercise 67 to find the amount resulting from a principal of \$1247.65 invested at a rate of 13.91% for a period of 567 days. (Assume a 365-day year.) \$1,517.24

76. Rate of return. Use the formula from Exercise 67 to find the rate of interest if an investment of \$2400 amounts to \$3264 in four years. 9%

C Exercises   Beyond the Basics

77. Explain whether the equations in each pair are equivalent.

   a. $x^2 = x,$ $x = 1$ †
   b. $x^2 = 9,$ $x = 3$ †
   c. $x^2 - 1 = x - 1,$ $x = 0$ †
   d. $\dfrac{x}{x-2} = \dfrac{2}{x-2},$ $x = 2$ †

78. What is wrong with the following argument? †

   Let $x = 1.$

   $x^2 = x$ Multiply both sides by x.

   $x^2 - 1 = x - 1$ Subtract 1 from both sides.

   $\dfrac{x^2 - 1}{x - 1} = \dfrac{x - 1}{x - 1}$ Divide both sides by $x - 1$.

   $\dfrac{(x + 1)\cancel{(x - 1)}}{\cancel{x - 1}} = 1$ Factor $x^2 - 1$.

   $x + 1 = 1$ Remove common factor.

   $1 + 1 = 1$ Replace x by 1 in the previous equation.

   $2 = 1$ Add.

79. Find a value of k so that $3x - 1 = k$ and $7x + 2 = 16$ are equivalent. $k = 5$

80. Find a value of k so that the equation $\dfrac{5}{y-4} = \dfrac{6}{y+k}$ has solution set $\{9\}$. $k = -3$

81. Find a value of k so that the equation $\dfrac{3}{y-2} = \dfrac{4}{y+k}$ is inconsistent. $k = -2$

82. Find a value of k so that the equation
   $\dfrac{1}{x^2 - 9} = \dfrac{1}{(x-3)(x+k)}$ is an identity. $k = 3$

In Exercises 83–88, solve each equation for x.

83. $a(a + x) = b^2 - bx$ $b - a$

84. $9 + a^2 x - ax = 6x + a^2$ †

85. $\dfrac{ax}{b} - \dfrac{bx}{a} = \dfrac{(a+b)^2}{ab}$ $\dfrac{a+b}{a-b}$

86. $\dfrac{2}{3} - \dfrac{x}{3b} - \dfrac{2x+b}{2a} + \dfrac{6b^2 + a^2}{6ab} = 0$ $\dfrac{a+b}{2}$

87. $\dfrac{b(bx-1)}{a} - \dfrac{a(1+ax)}{b} = 1$ $\dfrac{1}{b-a}$

88. $\dfrac{x - 2a}{b} - \dfrac{3}{2} = \dfrac{b-x}{2a} + \dfrac{1}{2}$ $2a + b$

Critical Thinking

89. A pawnshop owner sells two watches for $499 each. On one watch he gained 10%, and on the other he lost 10%. What is his percentage gain or loss? (c)
   a. No loss, no gain   **b.** 10% loss
   c. 1% loss   **d.** 1% gain

90. The price of gasoline increased by 20% from July to August, while your consumption of gas decreased by 20% from July to August. What is the percentage change in your gas bill from July to August? (d)
   a. No change   **b.** 5% decrease
   c. 4% increase   **d.** 4% decrease

Applications of Linear Equations

BEFORE STARTING THIS SECTION, REVIEW

1. Distributive property (Section P.1, page 13)

2. Arithmetic of fractions, least common denominator (Section P.1, page 14)

OBJECTIVES

1 Learn procedures for solving applied problems.

2 Learn to solve finance problems.

3 Learn to solve uniform-motion problems.

4 Learn to solve work-rate problems.

5 Learn to solve mixture problems.

Bomb Threat on the *Queen Elizabeth 2*

While traveling from New York to Southampton, England, the captain of the *Queen Elizabeth 2* received a message that there was a bomb on board and that it was timed to go off during the voyage. A search by crew members proved fruitless, so members of the Royal Marine Special Boat Squadrons bomb disposal unit were flown out on a Royal Air Force Hercules aircraft and parachuted into the Atlantic near the ship, which was 1000 miles from Britain and traveling toward Britain at 32 miles per hour. If the Hercules aircraft could average 300 miles per hour, how long would the passengers have to wait for help to arrive? We learn the answer in Example 4, using the methods of this section. ■

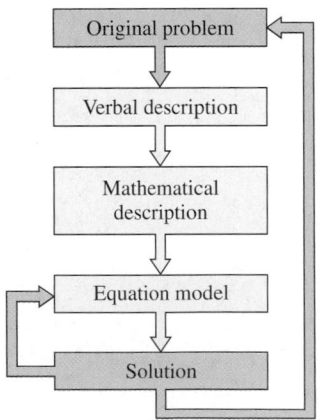

FIGURE 1.1

1 Learn procedures for solving applied problems.

Solving Applied Problems

Practical problems are often introduced through verbal descriptions that do not contain explicit requests for algebraic activity such as "Solve the equation. . . ." Frequently, they describe a situation, perhaps in a physical or financial setting, and ask for a value for some specific quantity that will favorably resolve the situation. The process of translating a practical problem into a mathematical one is called **mathematical modeling.** Generally, we use variables to represent the quantities identified in the verbal description and represent relationships among these quantities with algebraic expressions or equations. Ideally, we reduce the problem to an equation that, when solved, also solves the practical problem. Then we solve the equation and check our result against the practical situation presented in the problem.

You might visualize the modeling process as illustrated in Figure 1.1.

Applied Problems

We provide a general strategy to follow when solving applied problems.

PROCEDURE FOR SOLVING APPLIED PROBLEMS

Step 1. Read the problem as many times as needed to understand it thoroughly. Pay close attention to the question asked to help identify the quantity the variable should represent.

Step 2. Assign a variable to represent the quantity you are looking for, and, when necessary, express all other unknown quantities in terms of this variable. Frequently, it is helpful to draw a diagram to illustrate the problem or to set up a table to organize the information.

Step 3. Write an equation that describes the situation.

Step 4. Solve the equation.

Step 5. Answer the question asked in the problem.

Step 6. Check the answer against the description of the original problem (not just the equation solved in step 4).

---

2 Learn to solve finance problems.

Finance

EXAMPLE 1   **Analyzing Investments**

Tyrick invests $15,000, some in stocks and the rest in bonds. If he invests twice as much in stocks as he does in bonds, how much does he invest in each?

Solution

Step 2 Let $x =$ the amount invested in stocks. The rest of the $15,000 investment ($15,000 $- x$) is invested in bonds. We have one more important piece of information to use:

$$\boxed{\text{Amount invested in stocks, } x} = \boxed{\begin{array}{l}\text{Twice the amount invested} \\ \text{in bonds, } 15,000 - x\end{array}}$$

Step 3 $\qquad\qquad\qquad x = 2(15,000 - x)$ Replace the verbal descriptions with algebraic expressions.

Step 4 $\qquad\qquad\qquad x = 30,000 - 2x$ Distributive property

$\qquad\qquad\qquad\quad 3x = 30,000$ Add $2x$ to both sides.

$\qquad\qquad\qquad\quad\, x = 10,000$ Divide both sides by 3.

Step 5 Tyrick invests $10,000 in stocks and $15,000 $-$ $10,000 = $5000 in bonds.

Step 6 Check in the original problem. If Tyrick invests $10,000 in stocks and $5000 in bonds, then, since 2($5000) = $10,000, he invested twice as much in stocks as he did in bonds. Further, Tyrick's total investment is $10,000 + $5000 = $15,000. ■ ■ ■

PRACTICE PROBLEM 1   Repeat Example 1, but Tyrick now invests three times as much in stocks as he does in bonds. ■

Interest is money paid for the use of borrowed money. For example, while your money is on deposit at a bank, the bank pays you for the right to use the money in your account. The money you are paid by the bank is interest on your deposit. On any loan, the money borrowed for use (and on which interest is paid) is called the **principal.** The **interest rate** is the percent of the principal charged for its use for a specific time period. The most straightforward type of interest computation is described next.

SIMPLE INTEREST

If a principal of P dollars is borrowed for a period of t years with interest rate r (expressed as a decimal) computed yearly, then the total interest paid at the end of t years is

$$I = Prt.$$

Interest computed with this formula is called **simple interest.**

   When interest is computed yearly, the rate r is called an *annual* interest rate (or *per annum* interest rate).

EXAMPLE 2   Solving Problems Involving Simple Interest

Ms. Sharpy invests a total of $10,000 in blue-chip and technology stocks. At the end of a year, the blue chips returned 12% and the technology stocks returned 8% on the original investments. How much was invested in each type of stock if the total interest earned was $1060?

Step 1   We are asked to find two amounts: that invested in blue-chip stocks and that invested in technology stocks. If we know how much was invested in blue-chip stocks, then we know that the rest of the $10,000 was invested in technology stocks.

Step 2   Let $x =$ amount invested in blue-chip stocks. Then

$$10,000 - x = \text{amount invested in technology stocks.}$$

We organize our information in the following table.

Investment	Principal P	Rate r	Time t	Interest $I = Prt$
Blue Chip	x	0.12	1	$0.12x$
Technology	$10,000 - x$	0.08	1	$0.08(10,000 - x)$

$$\boxed{\text{Interest from blue-chip}} \; + \; \boxed{\text{Interest from technology}} \; = \; \boxed{\text{Total interest}}$$

Step 3 $0.12x + 0.08(10,000 - x) = 1060$ Replace descriptions with algebraic expressions.

$12x + 8(10,000 - x) = 106,000$ Multiply by 100 to eliminate decimals.

Step 4 $12x + 80,000 - 8x = 106,000$ Distributive property

$4x = 26,000$ Combine like terms; subtract 80,000 from both sides.

$x = 6500$ Dollars in blue-chip stocks

$10,000 - x = 10,000 - 6500$ Replace x by 6500.

$= 3500$ Dollars in technology stocks

Step 5   Ms. Sharpy invests $3500 in technology stocks and $6500 in blue-chip stocks.

Step 6   Check in the original problem. Now, $3500 + $6500 = $10,000, and

$$12\% \text{ of } \$6500 \text{ is } 0.12(6500) = \$780$$

$$\text{and } 8\% \text{ of } \$3500 \text{ is } 0.08(3500) = \$280.$$

Thus, the total interest earned is $780 + $280 = $1060.   ■ ■ ■

PRACTICE PROBLEM 2   One-fifth of my capital is invested at 5%, one-sixth of my capital at 8%, and the rest at 10% per year. If the annual interest on my capital is $130, what is my capital?   ■

 3 Learn to solve uniform-motion problems.

Uniform Motion

If you drive 60 miles in 2 hours, your average speed is $\frac{60}{2}$ ($=30$) miles per hour. If you multiply your average speed for the trip (30 miles per hour) by the time elapsed (2 hours), you get the distance driven, 60 miles ($60 = 2 \cdot 30$). When solving problems where "rate" refers to the average speed of an object, use the following formula.

UNIFORM MOTION

If an object moves at a rate (average speed) r, then the distance d traveled in time t is

$$d = rt.$$

◆ **WARNING**   Care must be taken to be sure that units of measurement are consistent. If, for example, the rate is given in miles per hour, then the time should be given in hours. If the rate is given in miles per hour and the time is given as 15 minutes, change 15 minutes to $\frac{1}{4}$ hour before using the uniform-motion formula.

EXAMPLE 3   Solving a Uniform-Motion Problem

A motorcycle policeman is chasing a car that is speeding at 70 miles per hour. The policeman is 3 miles behind the car and is traveling 80 miles per hour. How long will it be before the policeman overtakes the car?

Solution

Step 2   We are asked to find the amount of *time* before the policeman overtakes the car. Draw a sketch to help visualize the problem.

FIGURE 1.2

Continued on next page.

Let $x =$ distance in miles the car travels before being overtaken. Then $x + 3 =$ distance in miles the motorcycle travels before overtaking the car. We organize our information in a table.

Object	d (in miles)	r (miles per hour)	$t = \left(\dfrac{d}{r}\right)$ (hours)
Car	x	70	$\dfrac{x}{70}$
Motorcycle	$x + 3$	80	$\dfrac{x + 3}{80}$

Because the time from the start of the chase to the interception point is the same for both the car and the motorcycle, we have

Step 3 $\dfrac{x}{70} = \dfrac{x + 3}{80}.$ The time is the same for both the car and the motorcycle.

Step 4 $8x = 7(x + 3)$ Multiply both sides by the LCD, 560.

$8x = 7x + 21$ Distributive property

$x = 21$ Subtract $7x$ from both sides.

Step 5   The time required to overtake the car is

$$t = \frac{x}{70} = \frac{21}{70} = \frac{3}{10}.$$ Replace x by 21.

In $\dfrac{3}{10}$ of an hour, or 18 minutes, the policeman overtakes the car.

Step 6   Check in the original problem. If the policeman travels for $\dfrac{3}{10}$ of an hour at 80 miles per hour, he travels $d = (80)\left(\dfrac{3}{10}\right) = 24$ miles. The car traveling for this same $\dfrac{3}{10}$ of an hour at 70 miles per hour travels $(70)\left(\dfrac{3}{10}\right) = 21$ miles. Since the policeman travels 3 more miles during that time than the car does (because he started 3 miles behind the car), he does indeed overtake the car.   ■ ■ ■

PRACTICE PROBLEM 3   A train 130 meters long crosses a bridge in 21 seconds. The train is moving at a speed of 25 meters per second. What is the length of the bridge?   ■

EXAMPLE 4   **Dealing with a Bomb Threat on the *Queen Elizabeth II***

In the introduction to this section, the *Queen Elizabeth II* was 1000 miles from Britain and traveling toward Britain at 32 miles per hour. A Hercules aircraft was flying from Britain directly toward the ship and averaging 300 miles per hour. How long would the passengers have to wait for the aircraft to meet the ship?

Solution

The initial separation between the ship and the aircraft is 1000 miles.

Let $t =$ time elapsed when ship and aircraft meet.

Then $32t = $ distance the ship traveled and $300t = $ distance the aircraft traveled.

$$\boxed{\text{Distance the ship traveled}} + \boxed{\text{Distance the aircraft traveled}} = \boxed{1000 \text{ miles}}$$

$$
\begin{aligned}
32t + 300t &= 1000 & &\text{Replace descriptions by algebraic expressions.}\\
332t &= 1000 & &\text{Combine like terms.}\\
t &= \frac{1000}{332} \approx 3.01 & &\text{Divide both sides by 332.}
\end{aligned}
$$

The aircraft and ship meet after about 3 hours.   ■ ■ ■

PRACTICE PROBLEM 4   How long would it take for the aircraft and ship in Example 4 to meet if the aircraft could average 350 miles per hour and were 955 miles away?   ■

4 Learn to solve uniform work-rate problems.

Work Rate

Work-rate problems use an idea much like that of uniform motion. In problems involving rates of work, we assume that the work is done at a uniform rate.

WORK RATE

The portion of a job completed per unit of time is called the **rate of work.**

If a job can be completed in x units of time (seconds, hours, days, etc.), then the portion of the job completed in *one unit of time* (1 second, 1 hour, 1 day, etc.) is $\dfrac{1}{x}$. The portion of the job completed in t *units of time* (t seconds, t hours, t days, etc.) is $t \cdot \dfrac{1}{x}$. When the portion of the job completed is 1, the job is done.

EXAMPLE 5   **Solving a Work-Rate Problem**

One copy machine copies twice as fast as another. If both copiers work together, they can finish a particular job in 2 hours. How long would it take each copier, working alone, to do the job?

Solution

Step 1   Because the speed of one copier is twice the speed of the other, if we find out how long it takes the faster copier to do the job working alone, the slower copier will take twice as long.

Step 2   Let $x = $ the number of hours for the faster copier to complete the job alone.

$2x = $ the number of hours for the slower copier to complete the job alone.

$\dfrac{1}{x} = $ portion of the job the faster copier does in 1 hour.

$\dfrac{1}{2x} = $ portion of the job the slower copier does in one hour.

Continued on next page.

The time it takes both copiers, working together, to do the job is 2 hours. Multiplying the portion of the job each copier does in 1 hour by 2 will give the portion of the completed job done by each copier. We organize our information in a table.

	Portion done in one hour	Time to complete job working together	Portion done by each copier
Faster copier	$\dfrac{1}{x}$	2	$2\left(\dfrac{1}{x}\right) = \dfrac{2}{x}$
Slower copier	$\dfrac{1}{2x}$	2	$2\left(\dfrac{1}{2x}\right) = \dfrac{1}{x}$

Because the job is *completed* in 2 hours, the sum of the portion of the job completed by the faster copier and the portion of the job completed by the slower copier in 2 hours is 1. The model equation can now be written and solved.

Step 3 $\dfrac{2}{x} + \dfrac{1}{x} = 1$ Faster copier portion + slower copier portion = 1.

Step 4 $2 + 1 = x$ Multiply both sides by x.
$\quad\quad\; 3 = x$

Step 5 The faster copier could complete the job, working alone, in 3 hours. The slower copier would require $2(3) = 6$ hours to complete the job.

Step 6 Check in the original problem. The faster copier completes $\dfrac{1}{3}$ of the job in 1 hour. Similarly, the slower copier completes $\dfrac{1}{6}$ of the job in 1 hour.

Thus, in 2 hours, the faster copier has completed $2\left(\dfrac{1}{3}\right) = \dfrac{2}{3}$ of the job and the slower copier has completed $2\left(\dfrac{1}{6}\right) = \dfrac{2}{6} = \dfrac{1}{3}$ of the job. Since $\dfrac{2}{3} + \dfrac{1}{3} = 1$, the copiers have completed the job in 2 hours. ■ ■ ■

PRACTICE PROBLEM 5 A couple took turns washing their sports car on weekends. Jim could usually wash the car in 45 minutes, whereas Anita took 30 minutes for the same job. One weekend they were in a hurry to go to a party, so they worked together. How long did it take them? ■

5 Learn to solve mixture problems.

Mixtures

Mixture problems require combining various ingredients, such as water and antifreeze, to produce a blend with specific characteristics.

EXAMPLE 6   **Solving a Mixture Problem**

A full 6-quart radiator contains 75% water and 25% pure antifreeze. How much of this mixture should be drained and replaced by pure antifreeze so that the resulting 6-quart mixture is 50% pure antifreeze?

Solution

Step 1   We are asked to find the quantity of the radiator mixture that should be drained and replaced by pure antifreeze. The mixture we drain is only 25% pure antifreeze, but is replaced with 100% pure antifreeze.

Step 2   Since we want to find the quantity of mixture drained, let

$$x = \text{number of quarts of mixture drained.}$$

Then x = number of quarts of pure antifreeze added and
$0.25x$ = number of quarts of pure antifreeze drained.
Now we track the pure antifreeze:

Pure antifreeze in final mixture	=	Pure antifreeze in original mixture	−	Pure antifreeze drained from original mixture	+	Pure antifreeze added
(50% of 6)	=	(25% of 6)	−	(25% of x)	+	x

Step 3 $(0.5)(6) = (0.25)(6) - 0.25x + x$ Replace descriptions with algebraic expressions.

Step 4
$3 = 1.5 + 0.75x$ Collect like terms; combine constants.
$1.5 = 0.75x$ Subtract 1.5 from both sides.
$2 = x$ Divide both sides by 0.75.

Step 5   Drain 2 quarts of mixture from the radiator.

Step 6   Check in the original problem. Draining 2 quarts from the original 6 quarts leaves 4 quarts of mixture in the radiator. This mixture consists of 1 quart of pure antifreeze (25%) and 3 quarts of water (75%). Adding 2 quarts of antifreeze to the radiator produces 3 quarts of antifreeze mixed with 3 quarts of water. This is the desired 50% pure antifreeze solution.   ■ ■ ■

PRACTICE PROBLEM 6   How many gallons of 40% sulfuric acid solution should be mixed with 20% sulfuric acid solution to obtain 50 gallons of 25% sulfuric acid solution?   ■

A Exercises   Basic Skills and Concepts

In Exercises 1–10, write an algebraic expression for the specified quantity.

1. Leroy buys roller blades for $327.62, including a sales tax of $6\frac{1}{2}$%. Let x = the price of roller blades before tax. Write an algebraic expression in x for "the tax paid on the roller blades." $0.065x$

2. A lamp-manufacturing company produces 1600 reading lamps a day when it operates in two shifts. The first shift produces only 5/6 as many lamps as the second shift. Let x = the number of lamps per day produced by the second shift. Write an algebraic expression in x for the number of lamps per day produced by the first shift.   †

3. Kim invests $22,000, some in stocks and the rest in bonds. Let x = amount invested in stocks. Write an algebraic expression in x for "the amount invested in bonds."   †

4. An air-conditioning repair bill for $229.50 showed a charge of $72 dollars for parts and remainder of the charge for labor. Let x = number of hours of labor it took to repair the air conditioner. Write an algebraic expression in x for the labor charge per hour.   †

†Due to space constrictions, answers to these exercises may be found in the Answers beginning on page A–1 in the back of the book.

5. Natasha can pick an eight-tree section of orange trees in 4 hours working alone. It takes her brother 5 hours to pick the same section working alone.

     Let t = amount of time it takes Natasha and her brother to pick the eight-tree section working together. Write an algebraic expression in t for

  a. The portion of the job completed by Natasha in t hours. †

  b. The portion of the job completed by Natasha's brother in t hours. †

6. Jermaine can process a batch of tax forms in 3 hours working alone. Ralph can process a batch of tax forms in 2 hours working alone.

     Let t = amount of time it takes Jermaine and Ralph to process a batch of tax forms working together. Write an algebraic expression in t for

  a. The portion of the batch of tax forms completed by Jermaine in t hours. †

  b. The portion of the batch of tax forms completed by Ralph in t hours. †

7. Walnuts sell for $7.40 per pound and raisins sell for $4.60 per pound. Let x = number of pounds of raisins in a 10-pound mixture of walnuts and raisins. Write an algebraic expression in x for

  a. The number of pounds of walnuts in the 10-pound mixture. †

  b. The value of the raisins in the 10-pound mixture. †

  c. The value of the walnuts in the 10-pound mixture. †

8. Dried pears sell for $5.50 per pound and dried apricots sell for $6.25 per pound. Let x = number of pounds of dried pears in the 15-pound mixture of dried pears and dried apricots. Write an algebraic expression in x for

  a. The number of pounds of dried apricots in the 15-pound mixture. †

  b. The value of the dried apricots in the 15-pound mixture. †

  c. The value of the dried pears in the 15-pound mixture. †

9. A pharmacist has 8 liters of a mixture that is 10% alcohol. To strengthen the mixture, the pharmacist adds pure alcohol to it.

     Let x = number of liters of pure alcohol added to the 8-liter mixture. Write an algebraic expression in x for

  a. The number of liters of mixture the pharmacist has once the pure alcohol is added. †

  b. The number of liters of alcohol in the mixture obtained by adding the pure alcohol to the original 8-liter mixture. †

10. A gallon of a 25% saline solution is to be diluted by adding distilled water to it. Let x = number of gallons of distilled water added to the gallon of 25% saline solution. Write an algebraic expression in x for

  a. The number of gallons of saline solution you have once the distilled water is added. †

  b. The percent saline solution obtained by adding the distilled water to the original 25% solution. †

B Exercises   Applying the Concepts

In Exercises 11–48, use mathematical modeling techniques to solve the problems.

11. Chain-store properties. A fast-food chain bought two pieces of land for new stores. The more expensive piece cost $23,000 more than the less expensive one, and the two pieces together cost $147,000. How much did each piece cost? †

12. Administrative salaries. The manager at a wholesale outlet earns $450 more per month than the assistant manager. If their combined salary is $3700 per month, what is the monthly salary of each? $1,625 and $2,075

13. Lottery ticket sales. The lottery ticket sales at Quick Mart for August were 10% above the sales for July. If Quick Mart sold a total of 1113 lottery tickets during July and August, how many tickets were sold in each month? †

14. Sales commission. Jan's commission for February was $15 more than half her commission for March, and her total commission for the two months was $633. Find her commission for each month. February: $221; March: $412

15. Inheritance. An estate valued at $225,000 is to be divided between two sons so that the older son receives four times as much as the younger son. Find each son's share of the estate. Younger son: $45,000; older son: $180,000

16. TV game show. Kevin won $735,000 on a TV game show. He decided to keep a certain amount for himself, give one-half of the amount he kept for himself to his daughter, and one-fourth of the amount he kept for himself to his dad. How much did each person get? †

17. Real estate investment. A real-estate agent invested a total of $4200. Part was invested in a high-risk real-estate venture, and the rest was invested in a savings and loan. At the end of a year, the high-risk venture returned 15% on the women's investment and the savings and loan returned 8% on her investment. Find the amount invested in each if her total income from her investments was $448. †

18. Tax shelter. Mr. Mostafa received an inheritance of $7000. He put part of it in a tax shelter paying 9% and part in a bank paying 6%. If his annual interest totals $540, how much was invested at each rate? †

19. Jogging. Angelina jogs 100 meters in the same time that Harry bicycles 150 meters. If Harry bicycles 15 meters per minute faster than Angelina jogs, find the rate of each. †

20. Overtaking a lead. A car leaves New Orleans traveling 50 kilometers per hour. An hour later, a second car leaves New Orleans following the first car and traveling 70 kilometers per hour. How long will it take the second car to overtake the first? 2.5 hr

21. Butterfat in milk. Two gallons of milk contain 2% butterfat. How many quarts of milk should be drained and replaced by pure butterfat to produce a solution of 2 gallons of milk containing 5% butterfat? (There are 4 quarts in a gallon.) †

22. Gold alloy. A goldsmith has 120 grams of a gold alloy (a mixture of gold and one or more other metals) containing 75% pure gold. How much pure gold must be added to this alloy to obtain an alloy that is 80% pure gold? 30 gr

23. Interest. Ms. Jordan invested $4900, part at 6% and the rest at 8%. If the yearly interest on each investment is the same, how much interest does she receive at the end of the year? †

24. Interest. If $5000 is invested in a bank that pays 5% interest, how much more must be invested in bonds at 8% to earn 6% on the total investment? $2500

25. Separating planes. Two planes leave an airport traveling in opposite directions. One plane travels at 470 kilometers per hour and the other at 430 kilometers per hour. How long will it take them to be 2250 kilometers apart? 2.5 hr

26. Overtaking a bike. Lucas is $\frac{1}{3}$ of a mile away from home, bicycling at 20 miles per hour, when his brother takes off on his bike to catch up. How fast must Lucas's brother go to catch him a mile from home? 30 mph

27. Coffee blends. A coffee wholesaler wants to blend a coffee containing 35% chicory with a coffee containing 15% chicory to produce a 500-kilogram blend of coffee containing 18% chicory. How much of each type is required? †

28. Mixture of nuts. A mixture of nuts contains almonds worth 50¢ a pound, cashews worth $1.00 per pound, and pecans worth 75¢ per pound. If there are three times as many pounds of almonds as cashews in a 100-pound mixture worth 70¢ a pound, how many pounds of each nut does the mixture contain? 30 lb almonds, 10 lb cashews, 60 lb pecans.

29. Retail profit. A retailer's cost for a microwave oven is $480. If he wants to make a profit of 20% of the selling price, at what price should the oven be sold? $600

30. Draining a pool. An old pump can drain a pool in 6 hours working alone. A new pump can drain the pool in 4 hours working alone. How long will it take both pumps to empty the pool working together? 2 h and 24 min

31. Filling a blimp. One type of air blower can fill a blimp (or dirigible) in 6 hours working alone, while a second blower fills the same blimp in 9 hours working alone. How long will it take both blowers working together? 3 h and 36 min

32. Profit from sales. The Beckly Company manufactures shaving sets for $3 and sells them for $5 each. How many shaving sets must be sold in order for the company to recover an initial investment of $40,000 and earn an additional $30,000 as profit? 35,000 shaving sets

33. Overtaking a lead. Karen notices that her husband left for the airport without his briefcase. Her husband drives 40 miles per hour and has a 15-minute head start. If Karen (with the briefcase) drives 60 miles per hour and the airport is 45 miles away, will she catch him before he arrives at the airport? Yes

34. Pay phone coin box. The coin box on a pay phone contained $17.90 in nickels, dimes, and quarters. It contained the same number of nickels as dimes and contained 136 coins in all. How many of each coin did it hold? †

35. Increasing distances. Two cars start out together from the same place. They travel in opposite directions, one of them traveling 7 miles per hour faster than the other. After 3 hours, they are 621 miles apart. How fast is each car traveling? †

36. Shredding hay. A shredder distributes hay across 5/9 of a field in 10 hours working alone. By adding a second shredder, the entire field is finished in another 3 hours. How long would it take the second shredder to do the job working alone? †

37. Draining a pool. A swimming pool has two drainpipes. One can empty the pool in 3 hours and the other can empty the pool in 7 hours. If both drains are open, how long will it take the pool to drain? 2 h and 6 min

38. Population. A 3% increase in the population of a city results in a population of 314,900. What was the former population? †

39. Box construction. An open box is to be constructed from a rectangular sheet of tin 3 meters wide by cutting out a 1-meter square from each corner and folding up the sides. The volume of the box is to be 2 cubic meters. What is the length of the tin rectangle? 4 m

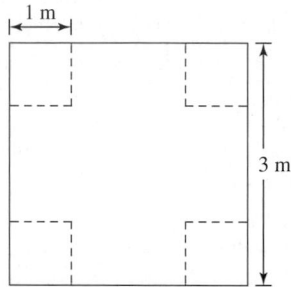

40. Sorting letters. A new letter-sorting machine works twice as fast as the old one. Both sorters working together complete a job in 8 hours. How long would it have taken the new letter sorter to do the job alone? 12 hr

41. Travel time. Aya rode her bicycle from her house to a friend's house and averaged 16 kilometers per hour. It became dark before Aya was ready to return home, so her friend drove her home at a rate of 80 kilometers per hour. If Aya's total traveling time was 3 hours, how far away did her friend live? 40 km

42. Age computation. Eric's grandfather is 57 years older than he is. Five years from now, his grandfather will be four times as old as Eric is at that time. How old is the grandfather? 71 yr

43. Vending machine coins. A vending machine coin box contains nickels, dimes, and quarters. It contains three times as many nickels and four times as many quarters as it does dimes. If the box contains $96.25 in all, how many coins of each kind does it contain? 231 nickels, 77 dimes, 308 quarters

44. Theater ticket sales. A small theater company with 22 seats sold advance-sale tickets for $3.75 and tickets at the door for $4.50. If the company collected $84.00 and sold out completely, how many of each type of ticket did it sell? †

45. Interest rates. Mr. Kaplan invests one sum of money at a certain rate of interest and half that sum at twice the first rate of interest. This arrangement turns out to yield 8% on the total investment. What are the two rates of interest? †

46. Plowing a field. A farmer can plow his field by himself in 15 days. If his son helps, they can do it in 6 days. How long would it take his son to plow it by himself? 10 days

47. Gumdrops. In a jar of red and green gumdrops, 12 more than half the gumdrops are red and the number of green gumdrops is 19 more than half the number of red gumdrops. How many of each color are in the jar? 86 red, 62 green

48. Real-estate investment. A real-estate investor bought acreage for $7200. After reselling three-fourths of the acreage at a profit of $30 per acre, she recovered the $7200. How many acres were sold? 60 acres

C Exercises   Beyond the Basics

Many problems can be solved by modeling procedures introduced in this section other than those presented in the examples in the section. Here are some types for you to try.

49. Suppose you average 75 miles per hour over the first half of your drive from Denver to Las Vegas, but your average speed for the entire trip is 60 miles per hour. What was your average speed for the second half of your drive? 50 mph

50. Davinder (D) and Mikhail (M) were 2 miles apart when they began walking toward each other. D walks at a constant rate of 3.7 miles per hour and M walks at a constant rate of 4.3 miles per hour. When they started, D's dog, who runs at a constant rate of 6 miles per hour, ran to M and then turned back and ran to D. If the dog continued to run back and forth until D and M met, and the dog lost no time turning around, how far did it run? 1.5 mil

51. A mixture contains alcohol and water in the ratio 5:1. On adding 5 liters of water, the ratio of alcohol to water becomes 5:2. Find the quantity of alcohol in the original mixture. 25 l

52. An alloy contains zinc and copper in the ratio 5:8, and another alloy contains zinc and copper in the ratio 5:3. Equal amounts of both the alloys are melted together. Find the ratio of zinc to copper in the new alloy. 105:103

53. Democritus has lived $\frac{1}{6}$ of his life as a boy, $\frac{1}{8}$ of his life as a youth, and $\frac{1}{2}$ of his life as a man and has spent 15 years as a mature adult. How old is Democritus? 72 yr

54. A man and a woman have the same birthday. When he was as old as she is now, the man was twice as old as the woman. When she becomes as old as he is now, the sum of their ages will be 119. How old is the man now? 51 yr

55. How many minutes is it before 6 P.M. if, 50 minutes ago, four times this number was the number of minutes past 3 P.M.? †

56. Two pipes A and B can fill a tank in 24 minutes and 32 minutes, respectively. Initially, both pipes are opened simultaneously. After how many minutes should pipe B be turned off so that the tank is full in 18 minutes? 8 min

57. A small plane was scheduled to fly from Atlanta to Washington, DC. The plane flies at a constant speed of 150 miles per hour. However, the flight was against a head wind of 10 miles per hour. The threat of mechanical failure forced the plane to turn back, and it returned to Atlanta with a tail wind of 10 miles per hour, landing 1.5 hours after it had taken off.
  a. How far had the plane traveled before turning back?
  b. What was the plane's average speed?

58. Three airports A, B, and C, are located on an east–west line. B is 705 miles west of A, and C is 652.5 miles west of B. A pilot flew from A, to B, had a stopover at B for 3 hours, and continued to C. The wind was blowing from the east at 15 miles per hour during the first part of the trip, but it changed to the west at 20 miles per hour during the stopover. The flight time between A and B and between B and C was the same. Find the airspeed of the plane. 455 mph

Critical Thinking

59. Two trains are traveling toward each other on adjacent tracks. One of the trains is 230 feet long and is moving at a speed of 50 miles per hour. The other train is 210 feet long and is traveling at the rate of 60 miles per hour. Find the interval between the moment the trains first meet until they completely pass each other.
  (Remember, 1 mile = 5280 feet.) 2.7 sec

60. Suppose you are driving from point A to point B at x miles per hour and return from B to A at y miles per hour. What is your average speed for the round trip?
  Extend the foregoing problem: You travel along an equilateral triangular path ABC from A to B at x miles per hour, from B to C at y miles per hour, and from C to A at z miles per hour. What is your average speed for the round trip?

Answers:

57. a. 112 mi **b.** $\dfrac{448}{3} = 149.33$ mph

60. $\dfrac{2xy}{x + y}$; $\dfrac{3}{\dfrac{1}{x} + \dfrac{1}{y} + \dfrac{1}{z}}$.

Complex Numbers

Mandelbrot Set
Benoit Mandelbrot
1924–
Mandelbrot was born in Poland into a family with a strong academic tradition. His family moved to France in 1936, where his uncle Szolem Mandelbrot was professor of mathematics at the Collège de France. During World War II, with the constant threat of poverty and need to survive, he was unable to attend very much college. He was largely self-taught. Mandelbrot began his studies at the École Polytechnique in 1944. After graduation, he went to the United States, where he visited the California Institute of Technology (Caltech) and Princeton University. He then found work at IBM, where he used computers to create his famous Mandelbrot set. He is responsible for most of the creation of fractal geometry and chaos theory, two concepts that may change the way mathematics is viewed today.

BEFORE STARTING THIS SECTION, REVIEW

1. Properties of real numbers (Section P.1, page 11)

2. Rules of exponents (Section P.2, page 21)

3. Special products (Section P.3, page 35)

4. Factoring (Section P.4, page 43)

OBJECTIVES

1 Learn the definition of a complex number.

2 Learn to add and subtract complex numbers.

3 Learn to multiply and divide complex numbers.

Fractals and Mandelbrot Sets

In 1967, mathematician Benoit Mandelbrot posed the following question: "How long is the coastline of Great Britain?" Mandelbrot pointed out that repeated measurements of a shoreline on a map produce a wide variety of different lengths. The length of the coastline will depend on detail and scale. Mandelbrot introduced the concept of fractals, which are connected to the shoreline measurement phenomenon, in his groundbreaking book *The Fractal Geometry of Nature*. Fractals are geometric patterns that display *self-similarity* at various scales; that is, the pattern looks the same on every scale. Magnifying a fractal reveals small-scale details similar to the large-scale characteristics. Coastlines and riverbanks show fractal patterns, mountains show fractal patterns, and root structures that prevent erosion also show fractal patterns. It also turns out that weather patterns are related to fractal patterns. The Mandelbrot set (a famous fractal pattern) is a mathematical set that is a collection of complex numbers. The computations used to determine which complex numbers are in a Mandelbrot set require that you know how to multiply and add complex numbers. We give an example of a typical computation for discovering the complex numbers in a Mandelbrot set in Example 4. The Mandelbrot set can be graphically depicted and is both stunning and elegant. ■

Complex Numbers

In the next section, you will learn methods of solving a quadratic equation $ax^2 + bx + c = 0$. Since the squares of real numbers are nonnegative (that is, $x^2 \geq 0$ for any real number x) the quadratic equation $x^2 = -1$ has no solution in the set of real numbers. To remedy this situation, we extend the real number system to a larger system called the complex number system. We define a new number, i, with the following properties:

$$i = \sqrt{-1}, \quad i^2 = -1.$$

1 Learn the definition of a complex number.

Definition of Complex Numbers

A **complex number** is a number of the form

$$a + bi,$$

where a and b are real numbers and $i^2 = -1$.

The **real part** of the complex number $a + bi$ is a.

The **imaginary part** of the complex number $a + bi$ is b.

Two complex numbers are *equal* if and only if their real parts are equal and their imaginary parts are equal.

TECHNOLOGY CONNECTION

Most graphing calculators allow you to work with complex numbers by changing from "real" to $a + bi$ mode. Once the $a + bi$ mode is set, the $\sqrt{-1}$ is recognized as i. The i key is used to enter complex numbers such as $2 + 3i$.

The real and imaginary parts of a complex number can then be found.

A complex number written in the form $a + bi$, where a and b are real numbers, is said to be in **standard form.** A complex number with real part 0, written as just bi, is called a **pure imaginary number.** Real numbers form a subset of complex numbers with imaginary part 0. For example, $-3 = -3 + 0i$.

Complex numbers complete the development of our number system. Figure 1.3 shows how various sets of numbers are related to each other and how they are contained within larger sets.

FIGURE 1.3

We can express the square root of any negative number as the product of a real number and i.

If $a > 0$ is any real number, then $\sqrt{-a} = (\sqrt{a})i$.

BY THE WAY . . .

The great Swiss mathematician Leonhard Euler introduced the symbol i for $\sqrt{-1}$ in 1777. However, electrical engineers often use the letter j for $\sqrt{-1}$, since, in electrical engineering problems, the symbol i is traditionally reserved for the electric current.

EXAMPLE 1   Identifying the Real and the Imaginary Parts of a Complex Number

Identify the real and the imaginary parts of each complex number.

a. $2 + 5i$ **b.** $7 - \dfrac{1}{2}i$ **c.** $3i$ **d.** -9 **e.** 0 **f.** $3 + \sqrt{-25}$

Solution

To identify the real and the imaginary parts, we must express each number in the form $a + bi$.

a. $2 + 5i$ is already written as $a + bi$; real part 2, imaginary part 5.

b. $7 - \dfrac{1}{2}i = 7 + \left(-\dfrac{1}{2}\right)i$; real part 7, imaginary part $-\dfrac{1}{2}$.

c. $3i = 0 + 3i$; real part 0, imaginary part 3.

d. $-9 = -9 + 0i$; real part -9, imaginary part 0.

e. $0 = 0 + 0i$; real part 0, imaginary part 0.

f. $3 + \sqrt{-25} = 3 + (\sqrt{25})i = 3 + 5i$; real part 3, imaginary part 5.   ■ ■ ■

PRACTICE PROBLEM 1   Identify the real and the imaginary part of each complex number.

a. $-1 + 2i$ **b.** $-\dfrac{1}{3} - 6i$ **c.** 8 ■

2 Learn to add and subtract complex numbers.

Addition and Subtraction

ADDITION AND SUBTRACTION OF COMPLEX NUMBERS

For all real numbers a, b, c and d,

$$(a + bi) + (c + di) = (a + c) + (b + d)i;$$
$$(a + bi) - (c + di) = (a - c) + (b - d)i.$$

TECHNOLOGY CONNECTION

In $a + bi$ mode, most graphing calculators perform addition and subtraction of complex numbers with the ordinary addition and subtraction keys.

```
(3+7i)+(2-4i)
              5+3i
(5+9i)-(6-8i)
             -1+17i
```

EXAMPLE 2   Adding and Subtracting Complex Numbers

Write the sum or difference of two complex numbers in standard form.

a. $(3 + 7i) + (2 - 4i)$ **b.** $(5 + 9i) - (6 - 8i)$ **c.** $(2 + \sqrt{-9}) - (-2 + \sqrt{-4})$

Solution

a. $(3 + 7i) + (2 - 4i) = (3 + 2) + [7 + (-4)]i = 5 + 3i$

b. $(5 + 9i) - (6 - 8i) = (5 - 6) + [9 - (-8)]i = -1 + 17i$

c. $(2 + \sqrt{-9}) - (-2 + \sqrt{-4}) = (2 + 3i) - (-2 + 2i)$ $\qquad \sqrt{-9} = 3i, \sqrt{-4} = 2i$

$\qquad\qquad\qquad\qquad\qquad\quad = 2 + 3i + 2 - 2i$

$\qquad\qquad\qquad\qquad\qquad\quad = (2 + 2) + (3 - 2)i = 4 + i$ ■ ■ ■

PRACTICE PROBLEM 2   Write the following complex numbers in standard form.

a. $(1 - 4i) + (3 + 2i)$ **b.** $(4 + 3i) - (5 - i)$ **c.** $(3 - \sqrt{-9}) - (5 - \sqrt{-64})$ ■

◆ **WARNING**   Recall that, if a and b are positive real numbers,

$$\sqrt{a}\sqrt{b} = \sqrt{ab}.$$

However, this property is not true for nonreal numbers. For example,

$$\sqrt{-9}\sqrt{-9} = (3i)(3i) = 9i^2 = 9(-1) = -9,$$

but

$$\sqrt{(-9)(-9)} = \sqrt{81} = 9.$$

Thus,

$$\sqrt{-9}\sqrt{-9} \neq \sqrt{(-9)(-9)}.$$

---

3 Learn to multiply and divide complex numbers.

Multiplying and Dividing Complex Numbers

We multiply complex numbers by first using FOIL (as we did with binomials) and then replacing i^2 by -1. For example,

$$(2 + 5i)(4 + 3i) = \overset{F}{2 \cdot 4} + \overset{O}{2 \cdot 3i} + \overset{I}{5i \cdot 4} + \overset{L}{5i \cdot 3i}$$

$$= 8 + 6i + 20i + 15i^2$$

$$= 8 + 26i + 15(-1) \qquad \text{Replace } i^2 \text{ by } -1.$$

$$= (8 - 15) + 26i$$

$$= -7 + 26i.$$

You should use the FOIL method to multiply complex numbers in standard form, but, for completeness, we now state the product rule formally.

MULTIPLYING COMPLEX NUMBERS

For all real numbers a, b, c, and d,

$$(a + bi)(c + di) = (ac - bd) + (ad + bc)i.$$

EXAMPLE 3   **Multiplying Complex Numbers**

Write the following products in standard form.

a. $(3 - 5i)(2 + 7i)$ **b.** $-2i(5 - 9i)$ **c.** $(3 + \sqrt{-8})(1 + \sqrt{-2})$

Solution

a. $(3 - 5i)(2 + 7i) = \overset{F}{6} + \overset{O}{21i} - \overset{I}{10i} - \overset{L}{35i^2}$

$\qquad\qquad\qquad = 6 + 11i + 35 \qquad \text{Since } i^2 = -1, -35i^2 = 35.$

$\qquad\qquad\qquad = 41 + 11i \qquad\qquad \text{Combine terms.}$

b. $-2i(5 - 9i) = -10i + 18i^2 \qquad \text{Distributive property}$

$\qquad\qquad\quad = -10i - 18 \qquad\quad \text{Since } i^2 = -1, 18i^2 = -18.$

$\qquad\qquad\quad = -18 - 10i$

Continued on next page.

c. $(3 + \sqrt{-8})(1 + \sqrt{-2}) = (3 + \sqrt{8}i)(1 + \sqrt{2}i)$ $\sqrt{-8} = \sqrt{8}i = 2\sqrt{2}i$
$= (3 + 2\sqrt{2}i)(1 + \sqrt{2}i)$ $\sqrt{-2} = \sqrt{2}i$
$= 3 + 3\sqrt{2}i + 2\sqrt{2}i + 2\sqrt{2}\sqrt{2}i^2$ Use FOIL.
$= 3 + 5\sqrt{2}i - 4$ Replace i^2 by -1 and combine terms.
$= -1 + 5\sqrt{2}i$ ■ ■ ■

PRACTICE PROBLEM 3   Write the following products in standard form.

a. $(2 - 6i)(1 + 4i)$ **b.** $-3i(7 - 5i)$ ■

EXAMPLE 4   **Computing Mandelbrot Sets**

The basic computation used (repeatedly) to decide whether or not a complex number z is in the Mandelbrot set is $z^2 + c$, where c is a complex number. Compute $z^2 + c$ for

$$z = 1 + \frac{1}{4}i \text{ and } c = 2 + i.$$

Solution

$$z^2 + c = \left(1 + \frac{1}{4}i\right)\left(1 + \frac{1}{4}i\right) + 2 + i \qquad z^2 = z \cdot z$$

$$= 1 \cdot 1 + \frac{1}{4}i + \frac{1}{4}i + \left(\frac{1}{4}i\right)\left(\frac{1}{4}i\right) + 2 + i \qquad \text{Use FOIL.}$$

$$= 1 - \frac{1}{16} + 2 + \frac{1}{4}i + \frac{1}{4}i + i \qquad \left(\frac{1}{4}i\right)\left(\frac{1}{4}i\right) = -\frac{1}{16}$$

$$= \frac{47}{16} + \frac{3}{2}i \qquad \text{Combine terms.} \quad ■ ■ ■$$

PRACTICE PROBLEM 4   Compute $z^2 + c$ for $z = \frac{1}{2} + \frac{1}{5}i$ and $c = 1 - i$.   ■

THE CONJUGATE OF A COMPLEX NUMBER

If $z = a + bi$, then the conjugate (or complex conjugate) of z is donated by $\bar{z}$ and defined by $\bar{z} = \overline{a + bi} = a - bi$.

Note that the conjugate $\bar{z}$ of a complex number has the same real part as does z, but the sign of the imaginary part is changed. For example $\overline{2 + 7i} = 2 - 7i$ and $\overline{5 - 3i} = \overline{5 + (-3)i} = 5 - (-3)i = 5 + 3i$.

EXAMPLE 5   **Multiplying a Complex Number by Its Conjugate**

Find the product $z\bar{z}$ for each complex number z.

a. $z = 2 + 5i$ **b.** $z = 1 - 3i$

Solution

a. If $z = 2 + 5i$, then $\bar{z} = 2 - 5i$.

$$z\bar{z} = (2 + 5i)(2 - 5i) = 2^2 - (5i)^2 \qquad \text{Difference of squares}$$
$$= 4 - 25i^2 \qquad (5i)^2 = 5^2i^2 = 25i^2$$
$$= 4 - (-25) \qquad \text{Since } i^2 = -1, 25i^2 = -25.$$
$$= 29. \qquad \text{Simplify.}$$

b. If $z = 1 - 3i$, then $\bar{z} = 1 + 3i$.

$$z\bar{z} = (1 - 3i)(1 + 3i) = 1^2 - (3i)^2 \qquad \text{Difference of squares}$$
$$= 1 - 9i^2 \qquad (3i)^2 = 3^2i^2 = 9i^2$$
$$= 1 - (-9) \qquad \text{Since } i^2 = -1, 9i^2 = -9.$$
$$= 10. \qquad \text{Simplify.} \qquad \blacksquare \ \blacksquare \ \blacksquare$$

PRACTICE PROBLEM 5   Find the product $z\bar{z}$ for each complex number z.

a. $z = 1 + 6i$ **b.** $z = -2i$ ■

The results in Example 5 correctly suggest the following theorem.
To write the reciprocal of a nonzero complex number, or the quotient of two complex numbers, in the form $a + bi$, multiply the numerator and denominator by the conjugate of

---

COMPLEX CONJUGATE PRODUCT THEOREM

If $z = a + bi$, then

$$z\bar{z} = a^2 + b^2.$$

---

the denominator. By the Complex Conjugate Product Theorem, the resulting denominator is a real number.

EXAMPLE 6   **Dividing Complex Numbers**

Write the following quotients in standard form.

a. $\dfrac{1}{2 + i}$ **b.** $\dfrac{4 + \sqrt{-25}}{2 - \sqrt{-9}}$

Solution

a. The denominator is $2 + i$, so its conjugate is $2 - i$.

$$\frac{1}{2 + i} = \frac{1(2 - i)}{(2 + i)(2 - i)} \qquad \text{Multiply numerator and denominator by } 2 - i.$$

$$= \frac{2 - i}{2^2 + 1^2} \qquad (2 + i)(2 - i) = 2^2 + 1^2$$

$$= \frac{2 - i}{5} = \frac{2}{5} - \frac{1}{5}i$$

Continued on next page.

Continued on next page.

TECHNOLOGY CONNECTION

In $a + bi$ mode, most graphing calculators perform division of complex numbers with the ordinary division key. The Frac option will display results, using rational numbers.

```
1/(2+i)
          .4-.2i
Ans▶Frac
        2/5-1/5i
■
```

```
(4+√(-25))/(2-√(
-9))
-.5384615385+1....
Ans▶Frac
       -7/13+22/13i
```

The reciprocal of a complex number can also be found with the reciprocal key.

```
(2+i)⁻¹
          .4-.2i
Ans▶Frac
        2/5-1/5i
■
```

b. We write $\sqrt{-25} = 5i$ and $\sqrt{-9} = 3i$, so that $\dfrac{4 + \sqrt{-25}}{2 - \sqrt{-9}} = \dfrac{4 + 5i}{2 - 3i}$.

$$\frac{4 + 5i}{2 - 3i} = \frac{(4 + 5i)(2 + 3i)}{(2 - 3i)(2 + 3i)} \qquad \text{Multiply numerator and denominator by } 2 + 3i.$$

$$= \frac{8 + 12i + 10i + 15i^2}{2^2 + 3^2} \qquad \text{Use FOIL in the numerator;} \quad (2 - 3i)(2 + 3i) = 2^2 + 3^2.$$

$$= \frac{-7 + 22i}{13} \qquad 15i^2 = -15, 8 - 15 = -7$$

$$= -\frac{7}{13} + \frac{22}{13}i. \qquad\qquad ■ \ ■ \ ■$$

PRACTICE PROBLEM 6   Write the following quotients in standard form.

a. $\dfrac{2}{1 - i}$ **b.** $\dfrac{-3i}{4 + \sqrt{-25}}$ ■

A Exercises   Basic Skills and Concepts

In Exercises 1–4, use the definition of equality of complex numbers to find the real numbers x and y such that the equation is true.

1. $2 + xi = y + 3i$ †

2. $x - 2i = 7 + yi$ †

3. $x - \sqrt{-16} = 2 + yi$ †

4. $3 + yi = x - \sqrt{-25}$ †

In Exercises 5–28, perform each operation and write the result in the standard form $a + bi$.

5. $(5 + 2i) + (3 + i)$ $8 + 3i$ **6.** $(6 + i) + (1 + 2i)$ †

7. $(4 - 3i) - (5 + 3i)$ †   **8.** $(3 - 5i) - (3 + 2i)$ $-7i$

9. $(-2 - 3i) + (-3 - 2i)$ †   **10.** $(-5 - 3i) + (2 - i)$ †

11. $3(5 + 2i)$ $15 + 6i$ **12.** $4(3 + 5i)$ $12 + 20i$

13. $-4(2 - 3i)$ $-8 + 12i$ **14.** $-7(3 - 4i)$ $-21 + 28i$

15. $3i(5 + i)$ $-3 + 15i$ **16.** $2i(4 + 3i)$ $-6 + 8i$

17. $4i(2 - 5i)$ $20 + 8i$ **18.** $-3i(5 - 2i)$ $-6 - 15i$

19. $(3 + i)(2 + 3i)$ $3 + 11i$ **20.** $(4 + 3i)(2 + 5i)$ $-7 + 26i$

21. $(2 - 3i)(2 + 3i)$ 13 **22.** $(4 - 3i)(4 + 3i)$ 25

23. $(3 + 4i)(4 - 3i)$ $24 + 7i$ **24.** $(-2 + 3i)(-3 + 10i)$ †

25. $(\sqrt{3} - 12i)^2$ †   **26.** $(-\sqrt{5} - 13i)^2$ †

27. $(2 - \sqrt{-16})(3 + 5i)$ †   **28.** $(5 - 2i)(3 + \sqrt{-25})$ †

In Exercises 29–34, write the conjugate $\bar{z}$ of each complex number z. Then find $z\bar{z}$.

29. $z = 2 - 3i$ †   **30.** $z = 4 + 5i$ †

31. $z = \dfrac{1}{2} - 2i$ †   **32.** $z = \dfrac{2}{3} + \dfrac{1}{2}i$ †

33. $z = \sqrt{2} - 3i$ †   **34.** $z = \sqrt{5} + \sqrt{3}i$ †

In Exercises 35–48, write each quotient in the standard form $a + bi$.

35. $\dfrac{5}{-i}$ $5i$ **36.** $\dfrac{2}{-3i}$ $\dfrac{2}{3}i$

37. $\dfrac{-1}{1 + i}$ $-\dfrac{1}{2} + \dfrac{1}{2}i$ **38.** $\dfrac{1}{2 - i}$ $\dfrac{2}{5} + \dfrac{1}{5}i$

39. $\dfrac{5i}{2 + i}$ $1 + 2i$ **40.** $\dfrac{3i}{2 - i}$ $-\dfrac{3}{5} + \dfrac{6}{5}i$

41. $\dfrac{2 + 3i}{1 + i}$ $\dfrac{5}{2} + \dfrac{1}{2}i$ **42.** $\dfrac{3 + 5i}{4 + i}$ $1 + i$

43. $\dfrac{2 - 5i}{4 - 7i}$ $\dfrac{43}{65} - \dfrac{6}{65}i$ **44.** $\dfrac{3 + 5i}{1 - 3i}$ $-\dfrac{6}{5} + \dfrac{7}{5}i$

45. $\dfrac{2 + \sqrt{-4}}{1 + i}$ 2 **46.** $\dfrac{5 - \sqrt{-9}}{3 + 2i}$ $\dfrac{9}{13} - \dfrac{19}{13}i$

47. $\dfrac{-2 + \sqrt{-25}}{2 - 3i}$ $-\dfrac{19}{13} + \dfrac{4}{13}i$ **48.** $\dfrac{-5 - \sqrt{-4}}{5 - \sqrt{-9}}$ $-\dfrac{19}{34} - \dfrac{25}{34}i$

---

†Due to space constrictions, answers to these exercises may be found in the Answers beginning on page A–1 in the back of the book.

B Exercises   Applying the Concepts

49. Series circuits. If the impedance of a resistor in a circuit is $Z_1 = 4 + 3i$ ohms and the impedance of a second resistor is $Z_2 = 5 - 2i$ ohms, find the total impedance of the two resistors when they are placed in series (the sum of the two impedances). $9 + i$

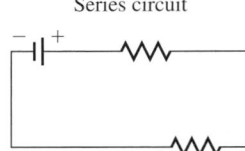

Series circuit

50. Parallel circuits. If the two resistors in Exercise 49 are connected in parallel, the total impedance is given by

$$\frac{Z_1 Z_2}{Z_1 + Z_2}$$

Find the total impedance if the resistors in Exercise 49 are connected in parallel. †

Parallel circuit

As with impedance, the current I and voltage V in a circuit can be represented by complex numbers. The three quantities (voltage V, impedance Z, and current I) are related by the equation $Z = \dfrac{V}{I}$. Thus, if two of these values are given, the value of the third can be found from this equation. In Exercises 51–56, find the value that is not specified.

51. Finding impedance. $I = 7 + 5i$ $V = 35 + 70i$ †

52. Finding impedance. $I = 7 + 4i$ $V = 45 + 88i$ †

53. Finding voltage. $Z = 5 - 7i$ $I = 2 + 5i$ †

54. Finding voltage. $Z = 7 - 8i$ $I = \dfrac{1}{3} + \dfrac{1}{6}i$ †

55. Finding current. $V = 12 + 10i$ $Z = 12 + 6i$ †

56. Finding current. $V = 29 + 18i$ $Z = 25 + 6i$ †

In Exercises 57 and 58, use the definition $|a + bi| = \sqrt{a^2 + b^2}$. For a complex number C, define

$$
\begin{aligned}
z_0 &= 0, \\
z_1 &= C, \\
z_2 &= (z_1)^2 + C = C^2 + C, \\
z_3 &= (z_2)^2 + C = (C^2 + C)^2 + C \\
&\ \ \vdots \\
z_{n+1} &= z_n^2 + C \ \text{(square the previous answer and add } C).
\end{aligned}
$$

The Mandelbrot set is usually displayed by giving each complex number $C = a + bi$ a color determined by the smallest integer n for which $|z_n| \geq 2$. Complex numbers for which $|z_n| < 2$ for every positive integer n are considered to be in the Mandelbrot set. The points in the Mandelbrot set are traditionally colored black. In Exercises 57 and 58, find the color assigned to the given complex number.

For these exercises, use the following assignments.

Smallest value of n for which $|z_n| > 2$	Color
1	Pink
2	Yellow
3	Orange
4	Blue
5	Purple

57. $C = 1 + \dfrac{\sqrt{3}}{2}i$ Yellow   **58.** $C = \dfrac{\sqrt{3}}{2} + \dfrac{1}{2}i$ Orange

C Exercises   Beyond the Basics

In Exercises 59–68, find each power of i and simplify the expression.

59. i^{17} i

60. i^{125} i

61. i^{-7} i

62. i^{-24} 1

63. $i^{10} + 7$ 6

64. $9 + i^3$ $9 - i$

65. $3i^5 - 2i^3$ $5i$

66. $5i^6 - 3i^4$ -8

67. $2i^3(1 + i^4)$ $-4i$

68. $5i^5(i^3 - i)$ 10

In Exercises 69–72, let $z_1 = a + bi$ and $z_2 = c + di$.

69. Prove that $\overline{\overline{z_1}} = z_1$.

70. Prove that $\overline{z_1 + z_2} = \overline{z_1} + \overline{z_2}$.

71. Prove that $\overline{z_1 z_2} = \overline{z_1}\,\overline{z_2}$. Use this fact to prove that $\overline{z^2} = (\overline{z})^2$.

72. Prove that $z_1 + \overline{z_1} = 2a$ and that $z_1 - \overline{z_1} = 2bi$.

73. Prove that the reciprocal of $a + bi$, where not both a and b are zero, is $\dfrac{a}{a^2 + b^2} - \dfrac{b}{a^2 + b^2}i$.

In Exercises 74–77, denote the real part of $z = a + bi$ by $\text{Re}(z)$ and denote the imaginary part of z by $\text{Im}(z)$. Let $w = c + di$. Prove each statement.

74. $\text{Re}(z) = \dfrac{z + \bar{z}}{2}$

75. $\text{Im}(z) = \dfrac{z - \bar{z}}{2i}$

76. $\text{Re}\left(\dfrac{z}{z + w}\right) + \text{Re}\left(\dfrac{w}{z + w}\right) = 1$

77. The product $z\bar{z} = 0$ if and only if $z = 0$.

In Exercises 78–79, use the definition of equality of complex numbers to solve for x and y.

78. $\dfrac{x}{i} + y = 3 + i$ $\quad x = -1, y = 3$

79. $x - \dfrac{y}{i} = 4i + 1$ $\quad x = 1, y = 4$

80. Find all real values of x such that $\dfrac{3 + xi}{1 - i} = 1 + 2i$. $\quad x = 1$

81. Find all real values of x such that $\dfrac{x^2 + 3i}{1 + i} = 6 - 3i$.

82. Find all real values of x and y such that $\dfrac{x + yi}{i} = 5 - 7i$.

83. Find all real values of x and y such that $\dfrac{5x + yi}{2 - i} = 2 + i$.

Critical Thinking

84. State whether the following are true or false.
   a. Every real number is a complex number. True
   b. Every complex number is a real number. False
   c. Every complex number is an imaginary number. False
   d. A real number is a complex number whose imaginary part is 0. True
   e. The product of a complex number and its conjugate is a real number. True

Answers:
   81. $x = -3; 3$ **82.** $x = 7, y = 5$ **83.** $x = 1, y = 0$

SECTION 1.4 | Quadratic Equations

BEFORE STARTING THIS SECTION, REVIEW

1. Factoring (Section P.4, page 41)
2. Square roots (Section P.6, page 62)
3. Rationalizing a denominator (Section P.6, page 65)
4. Linear equations (Section 1.1, page 89)

OBJECTIVES

1 Learn to solve a quadratic equation by factoring.

2 Learn to solve a quadratic equation by the square root method.

3 Learn to solve a quadratic equation by completing the square.

4 Learn to solve a quadratic equation by using the quadratic formula.

5 Learn to solve quadratic equations with complex solutions.

6 Learn to solve applied problems.

The Golden Rectangle

The ancient Greeks, in about the sixth century B.C., sought unifying principles of beauty and perfection, which they believed could be described mathematically. In their study of beauty, the Greeks used the term *golden ratio*. The golden ratio is frequently referred to as "phi," after the Greek sculptor Phidias, and is symbolized by the Greek letter Φ (phi). A geometric figure that is commonly associated with phi is the **golden rectangle** (See Example 11). This rectangle has sides of lengths a and b that are in proportion to the golden ratio. It has been said that the golden rectangle is the most pleasing rectangle to the eye. Numerous examples of art and architecture have employed the golden rectangle. Here are three of them:

The Parthenon

The Mona Lisa

1. The exterior dimensions of the Parthenon in Athens, built in about 440 B.C., form a perfect golden rectangle.

2. Leonardo Da Vinci called the golden ratio the "divine proportion" and featured it in many of his paintings, including the famous *Mona Lisa*. (Try drawing a rectangle around her face.)

The Pyramid of Giza

3. The Great Pyramid of Giza is believed to be 4600 years old, a time long before the Greeks. Its dimensions are also based on the golden ratio.

In Example 11, we shall show that the numerical value of the golden ratio can be found by solving the quadratic equation $x^2 - x - 1 = 0$. ■

QUADRATIC EQUATION

A quadratic equation in the variable x is an equation equivalent to the equation

$$ax^2 + bx + c = 0,$$

where a, b, and c are real numbers and $a \neq 0$.

A quadratic equation written in the form $ax^2 + bx + c = 0$ is said to be in **standard form.** Here are some examples of quadratic equations that are not in standard form:

$$2x^2 - 5x + 7 = x^2 + 3x - 1$$
$$3y^2 + 4y + 1 = 6y - 5$$
$$x^2 - 2x = 3.$$

We shall discuss four methods for solving quadratic equations: (1) by factoring, (2) by taking square roots, (3) by completing the square, and (4) by using the quadratic formula.

We begin by studying real number solutions of quadratic equations.

1 Learn to solve a quadratic equation by factoring.

Factoring Method

Some quadratic equations in the standard form $ax^2 + bx + c = 0$ can be solved by factoring and using the **zero-product property**.

THE ZERO-PRODUCT PROPERTY

Let A and B be two algebraic expressions. Then $AB = 0$ if and only if $A = 0$ or $B = 0$.

EXAMPLE 1   Solving a Quadratic Equation by Factoring

Solve by factoring: $2x^2 + 5x = 3$.

Solution

$$2x^2 + 5x = 3 \qquad \text{Original equation}$$
$$2x^2 + 5x - 3 = 0 \qquad \text{Subtract 3 from both sides.}$$
$$(2x - 1)(x + 3) = 0 \qquad \text{Factor the left side.}$$

We now set each factor equal to 0 and solve the resulting linear equations. The vertical line separates the computations leading to the two solutions.

$$2x - 1 = 0 \quad | \quad x + 3 = 0 \qquad \text{Zero-product property}$$
$$2x = 1 \quad | \quad x = -3 \qquad \text{Isolate the } x \text{ term on one side.}$$
$$x = \frac{1}{2} \quad | \quad x = -3 \qquad \text{Solve for } x.$$

Check: You should check the solutions $x = \frac{1}{2}$ and $x = -3$ in the original equation.

The solution set is $\left\{ \frac{1}{2}, -3 \right\}$.

■ ■ ■

PRACTICE PROBLEM 1   Solve by factoring: $x^2 + 25x = -84$.   ■

EXAMPLE 2   Solving a Quadratic Equation by Factoring

Solve by factoring: $3t^2 = 2t$.

Solution

$$3t^2 = 2t \qquad \text{Original equation}$$
$$3t^2 - 2t = 0 \qquad \text{Subtract } 2t \text{ from both sides.}$$
$$t(3t - 2) = 0 \qquad \text{Factor.}$$
$$t = 0 \quad | \quad 3t - 2 = 0 \qquad \text{Zero-product property}$$
$$t = 0 \quad | \quad 3t = 2 \qquad \text{Isolate the } t \text{ terms on one side.}$$
$$t = 0 \quad | \quad t = \frac{2}{3} \qquad \text{Solve for } t.$$

Check: You should check the solutions $t = 0$ and $t = \frac{2}{3}$ in the original equation.

The solution set is $\left\{ 0, \frac{2}{3} \right\}$.

■ ■ ■

PRACTICE PROBLEM 2   Solve by factoring: $2m^2 = 5m$.   ■

SOLVING A QUADRATIC EQUATION BY FACTORING

Step 1.   Write the given equation in standard form so that one side is 0.

Step 2.   Factor the nonzero side of the equation from Step **1**.

Step 3.   Set each factor obtained in Step **2** equal to 0.

Step 4.   Solve the resulting equations in Step **3**.

Step 5.   Check the solutions obtained in Step **4** in the original equation.

◆ **WARNING**   The factoring method of solving an equation works *only when one of the sides of the equation is* 0. If neither side of an equation is 0, as in $(x + 1)(x - 3) = 10$, we cannot know the value of either factor. For example, we could have $x + 1 = 5$ and $x - 3 = 2$, or $x + 1 = 0.1$ and $x - 3 = 100$, etc. There are countless possibilities for two factors whose product is 10.

EXAMPLE 3	Solving a Quadratic Equation by Factoring

Solve by factoring: $x^2 + 16 = 8x$.

Solution

Step 1 Write the equation in standard form.

$$x^2 + 16 = 8x \qquad \text{Original equation}$$
$$x^2 + 16 - 8x = 0 \qquad \text{Subtract } 8x \text{ from both sides.}$$
$$x^2 - 8x + 16 = 0 \qquad \text{Standard form}$$

Step 2 Factor the left side of the equation.

$$(x - 4)(x - 4) = 0 \qquad \text{Perfect-square trinomial}$$

Steps 3 and 4 Set each factor equal to 0 and solve each resulting equation.

$$
\begin{array}{c|c}
x - 4 = 0 & x - 4 = 0 \\
x = 4 & x = 4
\end{array}
$$

Step 5 Check the solution in the original equation.
Check: $x = 4$, since $x = 4$ is the only possible solution.

$$x^2 + 16 = 8x \qquad \text{Original equation}$$
$$(4)^2 + 16 \overset{?}{=} 8(4) \qquad \text{Replace } x \text{ by 4.}$$
$$32 = 32 ✓$$

Thus, 4 is the only solution of $x^2 + 16 = 8x$, and the solution set is $\{4\}$.

■ ■ ■

PRACTICE PROBLEM 3 Solve by factoring: $x^2 - 6x = -9$. ■

In Example 3, since the factor $(x - 4)$ appears twice in the solution, the number 4 is called a **double root,** or a **root of multiplicity 2,** of the given equation.

2 Learn to solve a quadratic equation by the square root method.

The Square Root Method

The solutions of an equation of the type $x^2 = d$ are obtained by the square root method. Suppose we are interested in solving the equation $x^2 = 3$, which is equivalent to the equation $x^2 - 3 = 0$. Applying the factoring method, but *removing the restriction that coefficients and constants represent only integers,* we have

$$x^2 - 3 = 0$$
$$x^2 - (\sqrt{3})^2 = 0 \qquad \text{Since } 3 = (\sqrt{3})^2$$
$$(x + \sqrt{3})(x - \sqrt{3}) = 0 \qquad \text{Factor (using real numbers).}$$
$$x + \sqrt{3} = 0 \text{ or } x - \sqrt{3} = 0 \qquad \text{Set each factor equal to zero.}$$
$$x = -\sqrt{3} \text{ or } x = \sqrt{3} \qquad \text{Solve for } x.$$

Thus, the solutions of the equation $x^2 = 3$ are $-\sqrt{3}$ and $\sqrt{3}$. Since the solutions differ only in sign, we use the notation $\pm\sqrt{3}$ to write the two numbers $\sqrt{3}$ and $-\sqrt{3}$. In a similar way, we see that, for any nonnegative real number d, the solutions of the quadratic equation $x^2 = d$ are $\pm\sqrt{d}$.

THE SQUARE ROOT PROPERTY

Suppose u is any algebraic expression and $d \geq 0$. If $u^2 = d$, then $u = \pm\sqrt{d}$.

EXAMPLE 4   **Solving an Equation by the Square Root Method**

Solve: $(x - 3)^2 = 5$.

Solution

$$
\begin{array}{ll}
(x - 3)^2 = 5 & \text{Original equation} \\
u^2 = 5 & \text{Let } u = x - 3. \\
u = \pm\sqrt{5} & \text{Square root property} \\
x - 3 = \pm\sqrt{5} & \text{Replace } u \text{ by } x - 3. \\
x = 3 \pm\sqrt{5} & \text{Add 3 to both sides.}
\end{array}
$$

The solution set is $\{3 + \sqrt{5}, 3 - \sqrt{5}\}$.   ■ ■ ■

PRACTICE PROBLEM 4   Solve: $(x + 2)^2 = 5$.   ■

3 Learn to solve a quadratic equation by completing the square.

Completing the Square

A method called **completing the square** can be used to solve quadratic equations that cannot be solved by factoring and are not in the right form to use the square root method. The method requires two steps. First we write a given quadratic equation in the form $(x + k)^2 = d$. Then we solve the equation $(x + k)^2 = d$ by the square root method.

Recall that

$$(x + k)^2 = x^2 + 2kx + k^2.$$

Notice that the coefficient of x on the right side is $2k$, and half of this coefficient is k; that is, $\frac{1}{2}(2k) = k$. We see that the constant term, k^2, in the trinomial $x^2 + 2kx + k^2$ is the *square of one-half the coefficient of x.*

PERFECT-SQUARE TRINOMIAL

A quadratic trinomial in x with coefficient of x^2 equal to 1 is a **perfect-square trinomial** if the constant term is the square of one-half the coefficient of x.

When the constant term is *not* the square of half the coefficient of x we subtract the constant term from both sides and then add a new constant term that will result in a perfect-square trinomial.

Let's first look at some examples to learn what number should be added to $x^2 + bx$ to create a perfect-square trinomial.

$x^2 + bx$	b	$\dfrac{b}{2}$	Add $\left(\dfrac{b}{2}\right)^2$	Result is $\left(x + \dfrac{b}{2}\right)^2$
$x^2 + 6x$	6	3	$3^2 = 9$	$x^2 + 6x + 9 = (x + 3)^2$
$x^2 - 4x$	-4	-2	$(-2)^2 = 4$	$x^2 - 4x + 4 = (x - 2)^2$
$x^2 + 3x$	3	$\dfrac{3}{2}$	$\left(\dfrac{3}{2}\right)^2 = \dfrac{9}{4}$	$x^2 + 3x + \dfrac{9}{4} = \left(x + \dfrac{3}{2}\right)^2$
$x^2 - x$	-1	$-\dfrac{1}{2}$	$\left(-\dfrac{1}{2}\right)^2 = \dfrac{1}{4}$	$x^2 - x + \dfrac{1}{4} = \left(x - \dfrac{1}{2}\right)^2$

Thus, in order to make $x^2 + bx$ a perfect square, we need to add

$$\left[\frac{1}{2}(\text{coefficient of } x)\right]^2 = \left[\frac{1}{2}(b)\right]^2 = \frac{b^2}{4},$$

so that

$$x^2 + bx + \frac{b^2}{4} = \left(x + \frac{b}{2}\right)^2.$$

We say that $\dfrac{b^2}{4}$ was added to $x^2 + bx$ to *complete the square*. (See Figure 1.4.)

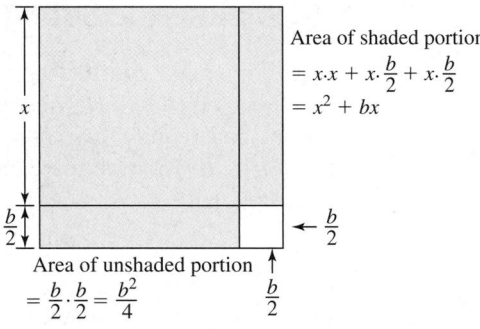

FIGURE 1.4 **Area of a square** $= \left(x + \dfrac{b}{2}\right)^2$

EXAMPLE 5   Solving a Quadratic Equation by Completing the Square

Solve by completing the square: $x^2 + 10x + 8 = 0$.

Solution

First, isolate the constant to the right side.

$$x^2 + 10x + 8 = 0 \qquad \text{Original equation}$$
$$x^2 + 10x = -8 \qquad \text{Subtract 8 from both sides.}$$

Next, add $\left[\dfrac{1}{2}(10)\right]^2 = 5^2 = 25$ to both sides to complete the square on the left side.

$$x^2 + 10x + 25 = -8 + 25 \qquad \text{Add 25 to each side.}$$
$$(x + 5)^2 = 17 \qquad x^2 + 10x + 25 = (x + 5)^2$$
$$u^2 = 17 \qquad \text{Let } u = x + 5.$$
$$u = \pm\sqrt{17} \qquad \text{Solve for } u.$$
$$x + 5 = \pm\sqrt{17} \qquad \text{Replace } u \text{ by } x + 5.$$
$$x = -5 \pm\sqrt{17} \qquad \text{Subtract 5 from each side.}$$

Thus, $x = -5 + \sqrt{17}$ or $x = -5 - \sqrt{17}$, and the solution set is $\{-5 + \sqrt{17}, -5 - \sqrt{17}\}$.   ■ ■ ■

PRACTICE PROBLEM 5   Solve by completing the square: $x^2 - 6x + 7 = 0$.   ■

We summarize the procedure for solving a quadratic equation by completing the square.

METHOD OF COMPLETING THE SQUARE

Step 1.   Rearrange the quadratic equation so that the terms in x^2 and x are on the left side of the equation and the constant term is on the right side.

Step 2.   Make the coefficient of x^2 equal to 1 by dividing both sides of the equation by the original coefficient. (Steps **1** and **2** are interchangeable.)

Step 3.   Add the square of one-half the coefficient of x to both sides of the equation.

Step 4.   Write the equation in the form $(x + k)^2 = d$, using the fact that the left side is a perfect square.

Step 5.   Take the square root of each side, prefixing $\pm$ to the right side.

Step 6.   Solve the two equations from Step **5**.

EXAMPLE 6   **Solving a Quadratic Equation by Completing the Square**

Solve by completing the square: $3x^2 - 4x - 1 = 0$.

Solution

Step 1 $\qquad 3x^2 - 4x - 1 = 0 \qquad$ Note that the coefficient of x^2 is 3.

$\qquad\qquad\quad 3x^2 - 4x = 1 \qquad$ Add 1 to both sides.

Step 2 $\qquad\quad x^2 - \dfrac{4}{3}x = \dfrac{1}{3} \qquad$ Divide both sides by 3.

Step 3 $\quad x^2 - \dfrac{4}{3}x + \left(-\dfrac{2}{3}\right)^2 = \dfrac{1}{3} + \left(-\dfrac{2}{3}\right)^2 \qquad$ Add $\left[\dfrac{1}{2}\left(-\dfrac{4}{3}\right)\right]^2 = \left(-\dfrac{2}{3}\right)^2$ to both sides.

Step 4 $\qquad\qquad \left(x - \dfrac{2}{3}\right)^2 = \dfrac{7}{9} \qquad\qquad x^2 - \dfrac{4}{3}x + \left(-\dfrac{2}{3}\right)^2 = \left(x - \dfrac{2}{3}\right)^2$

Continued on next page.

Step 5 $$x - \frac{2}{3} = \pm\sqrt{\frac{7}{9}}$$ Take the square root of both sides.

$$x - \frac{2}{3} = \pm\frac{\sqrt{7}}{3} \qquad \sqrt{\frac{7}{9}} = \frac{\sqrt{7}}{\sqrt{9}} = \frac{\sqrt{7}}{3}$$

Step 6 $$x = \frac{2}{3} \pm \frac{\sqrt{7}}{3}$$ Add $\frac{2}{3}$ to both sides.

$$x = \frac{2 \pm \sqrt{7}}{3}$$ Add fractions.

The solution set is $\left\{\dfrac{2 - \sqrt{7}}{3}, \dfrac{2 + \sqrt{7}}{3}\right\}$.   ■ ■ ■

PRACTICE PROBLEM 6   Solve by completing the square: $4x^2 - 24x + 25 = 0$.   ■

4 Learn to solve a quadratic equation by using the quadratic formula.

The Quadratic Formula

We can generalize the method of completing the square to derive a formula that gives a solution of *any* quadratic equation.

We solve the standard form of the quadratic equation by completing the square.

$$ax^2 + bx + c = 0, \ a \neq 0.$$

Step 1 $$ax^2 + bx = -c$$ Isolate the constant on the right side.

Step 2 $$x^2 + \frac{b}{a} = -\frac{c}{a}$$ Divide both sides by a.

Step 3 $$x^2 + \frac{b}{a}x + \left(\frac{b}{2a}\right)^2 = \left(\frac{b}{2a}\right)^2 - \frac{c}{a}$$ Add the square of one-half the coefficient of x to both sides.

Step 4 $$\left(x + \frac{b}{2a}\right)^2 = \frac{b^2}{4a^2} - \frac{c}{a}$$ The left side in Step 3 is a perfect square.

$$\left(x + \frac{b}{2a}\right)^2 = \frac{b^2 - 4ac}{4a^2}$$ Combine fractions on the right side.

Step 5 $$x + \frac{b}{2a} = \pm\sqrt{\frac{b^2 - 4ac}{4a^2}}$$ Take the square roots of both sides.

Step 6   Solve the equations in Step 5.

$$x + \frac{b}{2a} = \pm\sqrt{\frac{b^2 - 4ac}{4a^2}}$$ Equations from Step 5

$$x = -\frac{b}{2a} \pm \frac{\sqrt{b^2 - 4ac}}{2|a|}$$ Add $-\dfrac{b}{2a}$ to both sides; $\sqrt{4a^2} = \sqrt{4}\sqrt{a^2} = 2|a|$.

$$x = -\frac{b}{2a} \pm \frac{\sqrt{b^2 - 4ac}}{2a}$$ $\pm 2|a| = \pm 2a$, since $|a| = a$ or $|a| = -a$.

$$x = \frac{-b \pm \sqrt{b^2 - 4ac}}{2a}$$ Combine fractions.

The formula derived in Step 6 is called the **quadratic formula.**

THE QUADRATIC FORMULA

The solutions of the quadratic equation in the standard form $ax^2 + bx + c = 0$ with $a \neq 0$ are given by the formula

$$x = \frac{-b \pm \sqrt{b^2 - 4ac}}{2a}.$$

WARNING   In order to use the quadratic formula, the given quadratic equation must first be put in the standard form. Then determine the values of a (coefficient of x^2), b (coefficient of x), and c (constant term).

EXAMPLE 7   **Solving a Quadratic Equation by Using the Quadratic Formula**

Solve $3x^2 = 5x + 2$ by using the quadratic formula.

Solution

The equation $3x^2 = 5x + 2$ can be rewritten in the standard form by subtracting $5x + 2$ from both sides.

$$3x^2 - 5x - 2 = 0 \qquad \text{Rewrite in standard form.}$$
$$3x^2 + (-5)x + (-2) = 0$$
$$\uparrow \qquad \uparrow \qquad \uparrow \qquad \text{Identify values of } a, b, \text{ and } c \text{ to}$$
$$a \qquad b \qquad c \qquad \text{be used in the quadratic formula.}$$

Then $a = 3, b = -5,$ and $c = -2$, and we have

$$x = \frac{-b \pm \sqrt{b^2 - 4ac}}{2a} \qquad \text{Quadratic formula}$$

$$x = \frac{-(-5) \pm \sqrt{(-5)^2 - 4(3)(-2)}}{2(3)} \qquad \text{Substitute 3 for } a, -5 \text{ for } b, \text{ and } -2 \text{ for } c.$$

$$= \frac{5 \pm \sqrt{25 + 24}}{6} \qquad \text{Simplify.}$$

$$= \frac{5 \pm \sqrt{49}}{6} = \frac{5 \pm 7}{6} \qquad \text{Simplify.}$$

Then

$$x = \frac{5 + 7}{6} = \frac{12}{6} = 2 \text{ or } x = \frac{5 - 7}{6} = \frac{-2}{6} = -\frac{1}{3}, \text{ and the solution set is } \left\{ -\frac{1}{3}, 2 \right\}.$$

You should now solve $3x^2 = 5x + 2$ by factoring to confirm that you get the same result.   ■ ■ ■

PRACTICE PROBLEM 7   Solve by using the quadratic formula: $6x^2 - x - 2 = 0.$ ■

5 Learn to solve quadratic equations with complex solutions.

Quadratic Equations with Complex Solutions

The methods of solving quadratic equations are also applicable to solving quadratic equations with complex solutions.

EXAMPLE 8   Solving Quadratic Equations with Complex Solutions

Solve each equation.

a. $x^2 + 4 = 0$ **b.** $x^2 + 2x + 2 = 0$

Solution

a. Use the square root method.

$$x^2 + 4 = 0 \qquad \text{Original equation}$$
$$x^2 = -4 \qquad \text{Add } -4 \text{ to both sides.}$$
$$x = \pm\sqrt{-4} = \pm(\sqrt{4})i = \pm 2i \qquad \text{Solve for } x.$$

The solution set is $\{-2i, 2i\}$. You should check these solutions.

b. $x^2 + 2x + 2 = 1 \cdot x^2 + 2x + 2 = 0$

$$x = \frac{-2 \pm \sqrt{2^2 - 4(1)(2)}}{2(1)} \qquad \begin{array}{l}\text{Use the quadratic formula} \\ \text{with } a = 1, b = 2, \text{ and } c = 2.\end{array}$$

$$= \frac{-2 \pm \sqrt{-4}}{2} \qquad \text{Simplify.}$$

$$= \frac{-2 \pm 2i}{2} = \frac{2(-1 \pm i)}{2}$$

$$= -1 \pm i$$

The solution set is $\{-1 - i, -1 + i\}$. You should check these solutions.   ■ ■ ■

PRACTICE PROBLEM 8   Solve.

a. $4x^2 + 9 = 0$ **b.** $x^2 = 4x - 13$ ■

The Discriminant

If a, b, and c are real numbers $a \neq 0$, we can predict the number and type of solutions that the equation $ax^2 + bx + c = 0$ will have without solving the equation. In the quadratic formula

$$x = \frac{-b \pm \sqrt{b^2 - 4ac}}{2a},$$

the quantity $b^2 - 4ac$ under the radical sign is called the **discriminant** of the equation. The discriminant reveals the type of solutions of the equation, as shown in the following box.

Discriminant	Solutions
$b^2 - 4ac > 0$	There are two unequal real solutions.
$b^2 - 4ac = 0$	There is one real solution (a root of multiplicity 2).
$b^2 - 4ac < 0$	There are two nonreal complex solutions.

| EXAMPLE 9 | Using the Discriminant |

Use the discriminant to determine the number and type of solutions of each quadratic equation.

a. $x^2 - 4x + 2 = 0$ **b.** $2t^2 + 2t + 19 = 0$ **c.** $4x^2 + 4x + 1 = 0$

Solution

Equation	$b^2 - 4ac$	Conclusion
a. $x^2 - 4x + 2 = 0$	$(-4)^2 - 4(1)(2) = 8 > 0$	Two unequal real solutions
b. $2t^2 + 2t + 19 = 0$	$(2)^2 - 4(2)(19) = -148 < 0$	Two nonreal complex solutions
c. $4x^2 + 4x + 1 = 0$	$(4)^2 - 4(4)(1) = 0$	Exactly one real solution

■ ■ ■

PRACTICE PROBLEM 9   Determine the number and type of solutions:

a. $9x^2 - 6x + 1 = 0$ **b.** $x^2 - 5x + 3 = 0$ **c.** $2x^2 - 3x + 4 = 0$.   ■

6 Learn to solve applied problems.

Applications

| EXAMPLE 10 | Partitioning a Building |

A rectangular building whose depth (from the front of the building) is three times its frontage is divided into two parts by a partition that is 45 feet from, and parallel to, the front wall. If the rear portion of the building contains 2100 square feet, find the dimensions of the building.

Solution

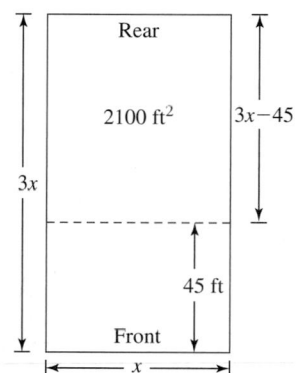

FIGURE 1.5

In solving problems of this type, it is advisable to draw a diagram such as Figure 1.5. We let

$$x = \text{the frontage of the building, in feet.}$$

Then $$3x = \text{the depth of the building, in feet.}$$

and $$3x - 45 = \text{the depth of the rear portion, in feet.}$$

The area of the rear portion of the building is $x(3x - 45)$ square feet. This area is 2100 square feet, so

$$
\begin{aligned}
x(3x - 45) &= 2100 \\
3x^2 - 45x &= 2100 \qquad &\text{Distributive property} \\
3x^2 - 45x - 2100 &= 0 \qquad &\text{Subtract 2100 from both sides.} \\
x^2 - 15x - 700 &= 0 \qquad &\text{Divide both sides by 3.} \\
(x - 35)(x + 20) &= 0 \qquad &\text{Factor.} \\
x - 35 = 0 \text{ or } x + 20 &= 0 \qquad &\text{Zero-product property} \\
x = 35 \quad \text{or} \quad x &= -20 \qquad &\text{Solve for } x.
\end{aligned}
$$

Because the dimensions of the building are positive numbers, we reject $x = -20$. Thus,

$$x = 35 \qquad \text{frontage in feet}$$
$$3x = 105 \qquad \text{depth in feet}$$

Continued on next page.

Check: $3x - 45 = 3(35) - 45 = 105 - 45 = 60$ is the depth of the rear portion, and the area of the rear portion is $60 \cdot 35 = 2100$ square feet.   ■ ■ ■

PRACTICE PROBLEM 10   In Example 10, find approximate dimensions of the building if its depth is five times its frontage.   ■

Golden Rectangle

A rectangle of length p and width q, with $p > q$, is called a *golden rectangle* if you can divide the rectangle into a square with side of length q and a smaller rectangle that is similar to the original one. See Figure 1.6. The ratio of the longer side to the shorter side of a golden rectangle is called the *golden ratio*. In Figure 1.6, the golden ratio is $\dfrac{p}{q}$.

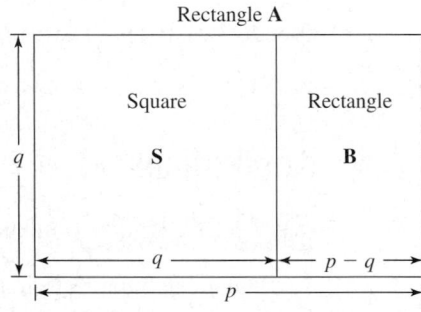

FIGURE 1.6

EXAMPLE 11   **Calculating the Golden Ratio**

Use Figure 1.6 of a golden rectangle to calculate the golden ratio.

Solution

The rectangle **A** in Figure 1.6 is a golden rectangle. This means that we can divide rectangle **A** into a square **S** and a rectangle **B** such that

$$\frac{\text{Longer side of } \mathbf{A}}{\text{Shorter side of } \mathbf{A}} = \frac{\text{Longer side of } \mathbf{B}}{\text{Shorter side of } \mathbf{B}}.$$

Thus, since rectangle **B** is the smaller rectangle, $p - q < q$, and we have

$$\frac{p}{q} = \frac{q}{p - q}$$

$$p(p - q) = q \cdot q \qquad\qquad \text{Multiply both sides by } q(p - q); \text{ simplify.}$$

$$p^2 - pq = q^2 \qquad\qquad \text{Distributive property}$$

$$\left(\frac{p}{q}\right)^2 - \frac{p}{q} = 1 \qquad\qquad \text{Divide both sides by } q^2; \text{ simplify.}$$

$$\Phi^2 - \Phi = 1 \qquad\qquad \text{Replace } \frac{p}{q} \text{ by } \Phi, \text{ the golden ratio.}$$

$$\Phi^2 - \Phi - 1 = 0$$

Write in standard form, treating Φ as the variable.

$$\Phi = \frac{-(-1) \pm \sqrt{(-1)^2 - 4(1)(-1)}}{2(1)}$$

Substitute 1 for a and -1 for both b and c.

$$= \frac{1 \pm \sqrt{5}}{2}$$

Simplify.

Since the ratio of two positive numbers is positive, we reject the negative root $\dfrac{1 - \sqrt{5}}{2}$.

Thus, the golden ratio is

$$\Phi = \frac{1 + \sqrt{5}}{2} \approx 1.618.$$

■ ■ ■

PRACTICE PROBLEM 11   Find the length of a golden rectangle whose width is 36 feet.   ■

A Exercises   Basic Skills and Concepts

In Exercises 1–8, show by substitution whether the number r is a solution of the corresponding quadratic equation.

1. $x^2 + 4x - 12 = 0$; $r = -6$ Yes

2. $x^2 - 8x - 9 = 0$; $r = 9$ Yes

3. $3x^2 + 7x - 6 = 0$; $r = \dfrac{2}{3}$ Yes

4. $2x^2 - 5x - 3 = 0$; $r = -\dfrac{1}{2}$ Yes

5. $x^2 - 4x + 1 = 0$; $r = 2 - \sqrt{3}$ Yes

6. $x^2 - 6x + 1 = 0$; $r = 3 + 2\sqrt{2}$ Yes

7. $4x^2 - 8x + 13 = 0$; $r = 2 + 3i$ No

8. $x^2 - 6x + 13 = 0$; $r = 3 - 2i$ Yes

9. Find k if $x = 1$ is a solution of the equation $kx^2 + x - 3 = 0$. $k = 2$

10. Find k if $x = \sqrt{7}$ is a solution of the equation $kx^2 + x - 3 = 0$. †

In Exercises 11–30, solve each equation by factoring.

11. $x^2 - 5x = 0$ $\{0, 5\}$

12. $x^2 - 5x + 4 = 0$ $\{1, 4\}$

13. $x^2 + 5x = 14$ $\{-7, 2\}$

14. $x^2 - 11x = 12$ $\{-1, 12\}$

15. $x^2 = 5x + 6$ $\{-1, 6\}$

16. $x = x^2 - 12$ $\{-3, 4\}$

17. $2x^2 + 5x - 3 = 0$ †

18. $2x^2 - 9x + 10 = 0$ †

19. $3y^2 + 5y + 2 = 0$ †

20. $6x^2 + 11x + 4 = 0$ †

21. $5x^2 + 12x + 4 = 0$ †

22. $3x^2 - 2x - 5 = 0$ †

23. $2x^2 + x = 15$ †

24. $6x^2 = 1 - x$ †

25. $12x^2 - 10x - 12$ †

26. $-x^2 + 10x + 1200 = 0$ †

27. $18x^2 - 45x = -7$ †

28. $18x^2 + 57x + 45 = 0$ †

29. $4x^2 - 10x - 750 = 0$ †

30. $12x^2 + 43x + 36 = 0$ †

In Exercises 31–40, solve each equation by the square root method.

31. $3x^2 = 48$ $\{-4, 4\}$

32. $2x^2 = 50$ $\{-5, 5\}$

33. $x^2 + 1 = 5$ $\{-2, 2\}$

34. $2x^2 - 1 = 17$ $\{-3, 3\}$

35. $x^2 + 5 = 1$ $\{-2i, 2i\}$

36. $4x^2 + 9 = 0$ †

37. $(x - 1)^2 = 16$ $\{-3, 5\}$

38. $(2x - 3)^2 = 25$ $\{-1, 4\}$

39. $(3x - 2)^2 + 16 = 0$ †

40. $(2x + 3)^2 + 25 = 0$ †

In Exercises 41–50, add a constant term to the expression to make it a perfect square.

41. $x^2 + 4x$ 4

42. $y^2 + 10y$ 25

43. $x^2 + 6x$ 9

44. $y^2 - 8y$ 16

45. $x^2 - 7x$ †

46. $x^2 - 3x$ †

47. $x^2 + \dfrac{1}{3}x$ $\dfrac{1}{36}$

48. $x^2 - \dfrac{3}{2}x$ $\dfrac{9}{16}$

49. $x^2 + ax$ †

50. $x^2 - \dfrac{2a}{3}x$ $\dfrac{a^2}{9}$

In Exercises 51–64, solve each equation by completing the square.

51. $x^2 + 2x - 5 = 0$ †

52. $x^2 + 6x = -7$ †

53. $x^2 - 3x - 1 = 0$ †

54. $x^2 - x - 3 = 0$ †

55. $2r^2 + 3r = 9$ †

56. $3k^2 - 5k + 1 = 0$ †

57. $z^2 - 2z + 2 = 0$ †

58. $x^2 - 6x + 11 = 0$ †

59. $2x^2 - 20x + 49 = -7$ †

60. $4y^2 + 4y + 5 = 0$ †

61. $5x^2 - 6x = 4x^2 + 6x - 3$ †

62. $x^2 + 7x - 5 = x - x^2$ †

63. $5y^2 + 10y + 4 = 2y^2 + 3y + 1$ †

64. $3x^2 - 1 = 5x^2 - 3x - 5$ †

†Due to space constrictions, answers to these exercises may be found in the Answers beginning on page A–1 in the back of the book.

In Exercises 65–80, solve each equation by using the quadratic formula.

65. $x^2 + 2x - 4 = 0$ † **66.** $m^2 + 3m + 2 = 0$ †

67. $6x^2 = 7x + 5$ † **68.** $t^2 + 7 = 4t$ †

69. $3z^2 - 2z = 7$ † **70.** $6y^2 + 11y = 10$ †

71. $3p^2 + 8p + 4 = 0$ † **72.** $8(x^2 - x) = x^2 - 3$ †

73. $x^2 = 5(x - 1)$ † **74.** $(x + 13)(x + 5) = -2$ †

75. $t(t + 1) = 3t^2 + 1$ † **76.** $3(x^2 + 1) = 2x^2 + 4x + 1$ †

77. $2t^2 - 5 = 0$ † **78.** $3k^2 - 48 = 0$ $\{-4, 4\}$

79. $9k^2 + 25 = 0$ † **80.** $3k^2 + 4 = 0$ †

In Exercises 81–88, find the discriminant and determine the number and type of roots of each equation.

81. $4x^2 - 12x + 9 = 0$ † **82.** $3x^2 - 4x + 3 = 0$ †

83. $2y^2 = 6 - y$ † **84.** $9y^2 + 24y = -16$ †

85. $17x - 12 = 6x^2$ † **86.** $5x^2 = 7x - 3$ †

87. $-3x^2 + 21 = 0$ † **88.** $x^2 + 2x + \dfrac{1}{2} = 0$ †

B Exercises Applying the Concepts

89. Dimensions. The length of a rectangular plot is three times its width. If the area of the plot is 10,800 square feet, find the dimensions of the plot. 60 ft by 180 ft

90. Dimensions. The diagonal of a square tile is 4 inches longer than its side. Find the length of the side. $4 + 4\sqrt{2}$ in

91. Finding integers. Find two numbers whose sum is 28 and whose product is 147. 7 and 21

92. Finding integers. Find an integer such that the sum of twice the square of the integer and the integer itself is 55. 5

93. Geometry. The length of a rectangle is 5 centimeters greater than its width. The area of the rectangle is 500 square centimeters. Find the dimensions of the rectangle. 20 cm by 25 cm

94. Geometry. The sides of a rectangle are in the ratio 3:2. The area of the rectangle is 216 square centimeters. Find the dimensions of the rectangle. 12 cm by 18 cm

95. Cutting a wire. A length of wire 16 inches is to be cut into two pieces, and then each piece will be bent to form a square. Find the length of the two pieces if the sum of the areas of the two squares is 10 square inches. 4 in. and 12 in.

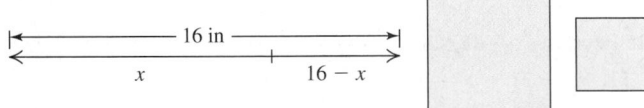

96. Cutting a wire. A piece of wire is 38 inches long. The wire is cut into two pieces, and then each piece is bent to form a square. Find the length of each piece if three times the area of the larger square exceeds the area of the smaller square by 95.75 square inches. 14 in. and 24 in.

97. Manufacturing. The surface area A of a cylinder with height h and radius r is given by the equation $A = 2\pi rh + 2\pi r^2$. A company makes soup cans by using 32π square inches of aluminum sheet for each can. If the height of the can is 6 inches, find the radius of the can. 2 in.

98. Concrete patio. To make a rectangular concrete patio, a homeowner used 70 feet of forming, into which she poured 138 cubic feet of concrete to form a slab 6 inches thick. What were the dimensions of the patio? 12 ft by 23 ft

99. Making a box. The volume of a box is given by the equation $V = $ length · width · height. A topless box is to be made from a square sheet of tin by cutting 5-inch squares from each of the four corners and then shaping the tin into an open box by turning up the sides. If the box is to hold 480 cubic inches, find the size of the piece of tin to be used. 19.8 in. by 19.8 in.

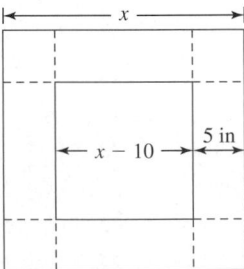

100. Making a box. A 2-inch square is cut from each corner of a rectangular piece of cardboard whose length exceeds the width by 4 inches. The sides are then turned up to form an open box. If the volume of the box is 64 cubic inches, find the dimensions of the box. 8 in. by 4 in. by 2 in.

101. Bus travel. Two buses leave Atlanta at the same time, one traveling west at 40 miles per hour and the other traveling north at 30 miles per hour. When will they be 400 miles apart? after 8 hours

102. Plane travel. Two planes leave San Francisco at 2 P.M. One flew east at a certain speed, and the other flew south at a speed that was 100 kilometers per hour more than the speed of the plane heading east. The planes were 2100 kilometers apart at 5 P.M. How fast was each plane flying? †

103. Dimensions of a family room. The length of a rectangular rug is $\frac{7}{6}$ times its width. The rug is placed on a rectangular family room floor, with a margin of 1 foot all around. The area of the floor is four times that of the margin. Find the dimensions of the family room. 14 ft by 16 ft

104. Gardening. You want to expand your present 25-foot-by-15-foot garden by planting a border of flowers. The border is to be of the same width around the entire garden. The flowers you bought will fill an area of 624 square feet. How wide should the border be? 6 ft

105. Sky divers. Sky divers are in free fall from the time they jump out of a plane until they open their parachutes. A sky diver jumps from 5000 feet. The diver's height h above the ground t seconds after the jump is described by the equation $h = -16t^2 + 5000$. Find the time during which the diver is in free fall if the parachute opens at 1000 feet. 15.8 seconds

106. Physics. Suppose you throw a ball straight up from the ground with a velocity of 112 feet per second. As the ball moves up, gravity slows it. Eventually, the ball begins to fall back to the ground. The height h of the ball after t seconds in the air is given by the equation $h = -16t^2 + 112t$.
 a. Find the height of the ball after 2 seconds.
 b. How long will it take the ball to reach a height of 96 feet?
 c. How long after you throw the ball will it return to the ground?

 a. 160 ft
 b. after 1 sec and after 6 sec
 c. 7 sec

C Exercises   Beyond the Basics

In Exercises 107–112, find the values of k for which the given equation has equal roots.

107. $x^2 - kx + 3 = 0$ †   **108.** $x^2 + 3kx + 8 = 0$ †

109. $2x^2 + kx + k = 0$ 0 or 8   **110.** $kx^2 + 2x + 6 = 0$ †

111. $x^2 + k^2 = 2(k + 1)x$ †   **112.** $kx^2 + (k + 3)x + 4 = 0$ †

113. If r and s are the roots of the quadratic equation $ax^2 + bx + c = 0$, show that
$$r + s = -\frac{b}{a} \quad \text{and} \quad r \cdot s = \frac{c}{a}.$$

114. Find the sum and the product of the roots of the following equations without solving the equation.
 a. $3x^2 + 5x - 5 = 0$ †
 b. $3x^2 - 7x = 1$ †
 c. $\sqrt{3}x^2 = 3x + 4$ †
 d. $(1 + \sqrt{2})x^2 - \sqrt{2}x + 5 = 0$ †

In Exercises 115–116, determine k so that the sum and the product of the roots are equal.

115. $2x^2 + (k - 3)x + 3k - 5 = 0$ 2

116. $5x^2 + (2k - 3)x - 2k + 3 = 0$ $(-\infty, \infty)$

117. Suppose r and s are the roots of the quadratic equation $ax^2 + bx + c = 0$. Show that you can write $ax^2 + bx + c = a(x - r)(x - s)$. Thus, the quadratic trinomial can be written in factored form. †

 [*Hint:* From Exercise 113, $b = -a(r + s)$ and $c = ars$. Substitute in $ax^2 + bx + c$ and factor.]

118. Use Exercise 117 to factor each trinomial.
 a. $4x^2 + 4x - 5$ $(2x + 1 + \sqrt{6})(2x + 1 - \sqrt{6})$
 b. $25x^2 + 40x + 11$ $(5x + 4 + \sqrt{5})(5x + 4 - \sqrt{5})$
 c. $25x^2 - 30x + 34$ $(5x - 3 + 5i)(5x - 3 - 5i)$
 d. $72x^2 + 95x - 1000$ $(9x + 40)(8x - 25)$

119. If we know the roots r and s in advance, then, by Exercise 117, a quadratic equation with roots r and s can be expressed in the form

$$a(x - r)(x - s) = 0.$$

Form a quadratic equation that has the listed numbers as roots.
  a. $-3, 4$ $x^2 - x - 12 = 0$
  b. $5, 5$ $x^2 - 10x + 25 = 0$
  c. $3 + \sqrt{2}, 3 - \sqrt{2}$ $x^2 - 6x + 7 = 0$

120. Solve the equation $3x^2 - 4xy + 5 - y^2 = 0$
  a. For x in terms of y **b.** For y in terms of x.

121. **How to construct a golden rectangle.** Draw a square $ABCD$ with side of length x, as in the accompanying diagram. Let M be the midpoint of DC. The segment MB sweeps out the arc BF, so that F lies on the line through the segment DC. Show that the rectangle $AEFD$ is a golden rectangle.

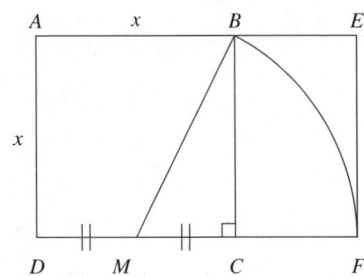

Critical Thinking

122. If the two roots of the quadratic equation $ax^2 + bx + c = 0$ are reciprocals of each other, which of the following must be true? (ii)
  i. $b = c$ **ii.** $a = c$ **iii.** $a = 0$ **iv.** $b = 0$

123. Use Exercise 113 to show that a quadratic equation cannot have three distinct roots.

124. Suppose p is a positive integer greater than 1. Which of the following describe the roots of the equation $x^2 - (p + 1)x + p = 0$? (iv)
  i. real and equal   **ii.** real and irrational
  iii. complex   **iv.** integers and unequal.

125. Amar, Akbar, and Anthony attempt to solve a barely legible quadratic equation written on an old paper. Amar misreads the constant term and finds the solutions 8 and 2. Akbar misreads the coefficient of x and finds the roots -9 and -1. Anthony solves the correct equation. What are Anthony's solutions of the equation?   {1,9}

Answers:

120. a. $\left\{ \dfrac{2y - \sqrt{7y^2 - 15}}{3}, \dfrac{2y + \sqrt{7y^2 - 15}}{3} \right\}$

  b. $\{-2x - \sqrt{7x^2 + 5}, -2x + \sqrt{7x^2 + 5}\}$

Solving Other Types of Equations

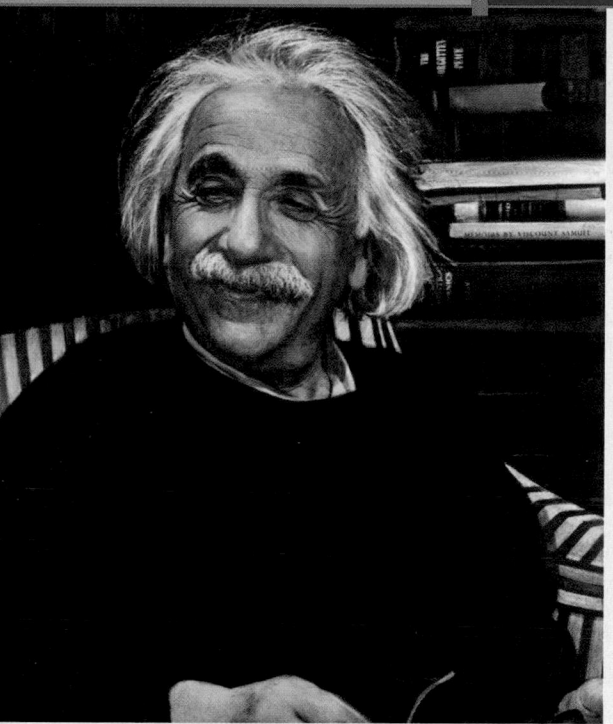

Albert Einstein
1879–1955
Einstein began his schooling in Munich, Germany. Einstein renounced German citizenship in 1896 and entered the Swiss Federal Polytechnic School in Zurich to be trained as a teacher in physics and mathematics. Unable to find a teaching job, he accepted a position as a technical assistant in the Swiss patent office. In 1905, Einstein earned his doctorate from the University of Zurich.

While at the patent office, he produced much of his remarkable work on the Special Theory of Relativity. In 1909, he was appointed Professor Extraordinary at Zurich. In 1914, he was appointed professor at the University of Berlin. He immigrated to America to take the position of professor of physics at Princeton University. By 1949, Einstein was unwell. He drew up his will in 1950.

He left his scientific papers to the Hebrew University in Jerusalem. In 1952, the Israeli government offered the post of second president to Einstein. He politely declined the offer.

One week before his death, Einstein agreed to let Bertrand Russell place his name on a manifesto urging all nations to give up nuclear weapons.

BEFORE STARTING THIS SECTION, REVIEW

1. Factoring (Section P.4, page 41)

2. Radicals (Section P.6, page 62)

3. Quadratic equations (Section 1.4, page 120)

OBJECTIVES

1 Learn to solve equations by factoring.

2 Learn to solve fractional equations.

3 Learn to solve equations involving radicals.

4 Learn to solve equations that are quadratic in form.

Time Dilation

Do you ever feel like time moves really quickly or really slowly? For example, don't the hours fly by when you are hanging out with your best friend, or the seconds drag on endlessly when a dentist is working on your teeth? But you cannot really speed up or slow time down, right? It always "flows" at the same rate.

Einstein said "no." He asserted in his "Special Theory of Relativity" that time is relative. It speeds up or slows down, depending on how fast one object is moving relative to another. He concluded that the closer we come to traveling at the speed of light, the more time will slow down for us relative to someone not moving. He called this slowing of time due to motion *time dilation*. Time dilation can be quantified by the equation

$$t_0 = t\sqrt{1 - \frac{v^2}{c^2}},$$

where $t_0 =$ the "proper time" measured in the moving frame of reference,

$t =$ the time observed in the *fixed* frame of reference,

$v =$ the speed of the moving frame of reference, and

$c =$ the speed of light.

We will investigate this effect in Example 9. ■

1 Learn to solve equations by factoring.

Solving Equations by Factoring

The method of factoring used in solving quadratic equations can also be used to solve certain nonquadratic equations. Specifically, we use the following strategy for solving those equations which can be expressed in factored form with 0 *on one side*.

FINDING THE SOLUTION: PROCEDURE FOR SOLVING EQUATIONS BY FACTORING

OBJECTIVE	EXAMPLE
To use factoring techniques to solve an equation	*Solve $x^3 + 3x^2 = 4x + 12$*

Step 1   Make one side zero. Move all nonzero terms in the equation to one side (say the left side), so that the other side (right side) is 0.

$$x^3 + 3x^2 - 4x - 12 = 0 \qquad \text{Subtract } 4x + 12 \text{ from both sides.}$$

Step 2   Factor the left side.

$$x^2(x + 3) - 4(x + 3) = 0 \qquad \text{Group for factoring.}$$
$$(x + 3)(x^2 - 4) = 0 \qquad \text{Factor out } x + 3.$$
$$(x + 3)(x + 2)(x - 2) = 0 \qquad \text{Factor } x^2 - 4.$$

Step 3   Use the zero-product property. Set each factor in Step 2 equal to 0, and then solve the resulting equations.

$$x + 3 = 0 \quad \text{or} \quad x + 2 = 0 \quad \text{or} \quad x - 2 = 0$$
$$x = -3 \quad \text{or} \quad x = -2 \quad \text{or} \quad x = 2$$

Step 4   Check your solutions.

Check:
Check the solutions in the original equation.

For $x = -3$, $(-3)^3 + 3(-3)^2 \overset{?}{=} 4(-3) + 12$
$$-27 + 27 = -12 + 12 ✔$$

You should also verify that $x = -2$ and $x = 2$ are solutions of $x^3 + 3x^2 = 4x + 12$. The solution set is $\{-3, -2, 2\}$.

EXAMPLE 1   Solving an Equation by Factoring

Solve by factoring: $x^4 = 9x^2$

Solution

Step 1   Move all terms to the left side.

$$x^4 = 9x^2 \qquad \text{Original equation}$$
$$x^4 - 9x^2 = 0 \qquad \text{Subtract } 9x^2 \text{ from both sides.}$$

RECALL

$A^2 - B^2 = (A + B)(A - B)$

Difference of two squares, page 43

Step 2   Factor.

$$x^2(x^2 - 9) = 0 \qquad x^4 - 9x^2 = x^2(x^2 - 9)$$
$$x^2(x + 3)(x - 3) = 0 \qquad x^2 - 9 = (x + 3)(x - 3)$$

Step 3   Set each factor equal to zero.

$$x^2 = 0 \quad \text{or} \quad x + 3 = 0 \quad \text{or} \quad x - 3 = 0 \qquad \text{Zero-product property}$$
$$x = 0 \quad \text{or} \quad x = -3 \quad \text{or} \quad x = 3 \qquad \text{Solve each equation for } x.$$

Step 4   Check.

Let $x = 0$	Let $x = -3$	Let $x = 3$
$(0)^4 \overset{?}{=} 9(0)^2$	$(-3)^4 \overset{?}{=} 9(-3)^2$	$(3)^4 \overset{?}{=} 9(3)^2$
$0 = 0 ✔$	$81 = 81 ✔$	$81 = 81 ✔$

Thus, the solution set of the equation is $\{-3, 0, 3\}$. Note that 0 is a root of multiplicity 2.

■ ■ ■

PRACTICE PROBLEM 1   Solve: $x^4 = 4x^2$ ■

◆ **WARNING**

A common error when solving an equation such as $x^4 = 9x^2$ in Example 1 is to divide both sides by x^2, obtaining $x^2 = 9$, so that ± 3 are the two solutions. This leads to the loss of the solution 0. Remember, we can divide only by quantities that are not 0!

> **EXAMPLE 2**   **Solving an Equation by Factoring**

Solve by factoring: $x^3 - 2x^2 = -x + 2$

Solution

Step 1   **Move all terms to the left side.**

$$x^3 - 2x^2 = -x + 2 \qquad \text{Original equation}$$

$$x^3 - 2x^2 + x - 2 = -x + 2 + x - 2 \qquad \text{Add } x - 2 \text{ to both sides.}$$

$$x^3 - 2x^2 + x - 2 = 0 \qquad \text{Simplify.}$$

Step 2   **Factor.** Since there are four terms, we factor by grouping:

$$(x^3 - 2x^2) + (x - 2) = 0$$

$$x^2(x - 2) + 1 \cdot (x - 2) = 0 \qquad \text{Factor } x^2 \text{ from the first two terms and rewrite } x - 2 \text{ as } 1 \cdot (x - 2).$$

$$(x - 2)(x^2 + 1) = 0 \qquad \text{Factor out the common factor } (x - 2).$$

Step 3   **Set each factor equal to zero.**

$$
\begin{array}{c|c}
x - 2 = 0 & x^2 + 1 = 0 \\
x = 2 & x^2 = -1 \\
& x = \pm i
\end{array}
$$

Step 4   Check.

$$
\begin{array}{c|c|c}
\text{Let } x = 2. & \text{Let } x = i. & \text{Let } x = -i. \\
(2)^3 - 2(2)^2 \overset{?}{=} -2 + 2 & (i)^3 - 2(i)^2 \overset{?}{=} -(i) + 2 & (-i)^3 - 2(-i)^2 \overset{?}{=} -(-i) + 2 \\
8 - 8 \overset{?}{=} 0 & -i + 2 = -i + 2 ✓ & i + 2 = i + 2 ✓ \\
0 = 0 ✓ & &
\end{array}
$$

Thus, the solution set of the equation is $\{2, i, -i\}$.   ■ ■ ■

PRACTICE PROBLEM 2   Solve by factoring: $x^3 - 5x^2 = 4x - 20$ ■

2 Learn to solve fractional equations.

Rational Equations

If at least one algebraic expression with the variable in the denominator appears in an equation, then the equation is a **rational equation.**

When we multiply a rational equation by an expression containing the variable, we may introduce a solution that satisfies the new equation, but does not satisfy the original equation. Such a solution is called an **extraneous solution** or **extraneous root**.

EXAMPLE 3 **Solving a Rational Equation**

Solve: $\dfrac{1}{6} + \dfrac{1}{x+1} = \dfrac{1}{x}$

Solution

Step 1 **Find the LCD.** The LCD from the denominators

$$6, x+1, \text{ and } x \text{ is } 6x(x+1).$$

Step 2 **Multiply both sides of the equation by the LCD, and make the right side 0.**

$$6x(x+1)\left[\frac{1}{6} + \frac{1}{x+1}\right] = 6x(x+1)\left[\frac{1}{x}\right] \qquad \text{Multiply both sides by the LCD.}$$

$$\frac{6x(x+1)}{6} + \frac{6x(x+1)}{x+1} = \frac{6x(x+1)}{x} \qquad \text{Distributive property}$$

$$x(x+1) + 6x = 6(x+1) \qquad \text{Simplify.}$$

$$x^2 + x + 6x = 6x + 6 \qquad \text{Distributive property}$$

$$x^2 + x - 6 = 0 \qquad \text{Subtract } 6x + 6 \text{ from both sides.}$$

Step 3 **Factor.**

$$x^2 + x - 6 = 0$$
$$(x+3)(x-2) = 0 \qquad \text{Factor.}$$

Step 4 **Set each factor equal to zero.**

$$x + 3 = 0 \qquad \text{or} \qquad x - 2 = 0$$
$$x = -3 \qquad \text{or} \qquad x = 2$$

Step 5 **Check.** You should check the solutions, -3 and 2, in the original equation. The solution set is $\{-3, 2\}$. ■ ■ ■

PRACTICE PROBLEM 3 Solve : $\dfrac{1}{x} - \dfrac{12}{5x+10} = \dfrac{1}{5}$ ■

---

3 Learn to solve equations involving radicals.

Equations Involving Radicals

If an equation involves radicals or rational exponents, the method of raising both sides to a positive integer power is often used to remove them. When this is done, the solutions of the new equation always contain the solutions of the original equation. However, in some cases the new equation has *more* solutions than the original equation. For instance, consider the equation $x = 4$. If we square both sides, we get $x^2 = 16$. Notice that the given equation, $x = 4$, has only one solution, namely, 4, whereas the new equation, $x^2 = 16$, has two solutions: 4 and -4. Extraneous solutions may be introduced whenever both sides of an equation are raised to an *even* power, Thus, it is *essential that we check* all solutions obtained after raising both sides of an equation to any even power.

> **EXAMPLE 4** Solving Equations Involving Radicals

Solve: $x = \sqrt{6x - x^3}$

Solution

Since $(\sqrt{a})^2 = a$, we raise both sides of the equation to the second power to eliminate the radical sign. The solutions of the original equation are among the solutions of the equation

$$x^2 = (\sqrt{6x - x^3})^2 \qquad \text{Square both sides of the equation.}$$
$$x^2 = 6x - x^3 \qquad (\sqrt{6x - x^3})^2 = 6x - x^3$$
$$x^3 + x^2 - 6x = 0 \qquad \text{Add } x^3 - 6x \text{ to both sides.}$$
$$x(x^2 + x - 6) = 0 \qquad \text{Factor out } x \text{ from each term.}$$
$$x(x + 3)(x - 2) = 0 \qquad \text{Factor } x^2 + x - 6.$$
$$x = 0, \quad \text{or} \quad x + 3 = 0, \quad \text{or} \quad x - 2 = 0 \qquad \text{Zero-product property}$$
$$x = 0, \quad \text{or} \qquad x = -3, \quad \text{or} \qquad x = 2 \qquad \text{Solve each equation.}$$

Hence, the only possible solutions of $x = \sqrt{6x - x^3}$ are $-3, 0,$ and 2.

Check:

Let $x = -3$.	Let $x = 0$.	Let $x = 2$.
$-3 \overset{?}{=} \sqrt{6(-3) - (-3)^3}$	$0 \overset{?}{=} \sqrt{6(0) - (0)^3}$	$2 \overset{?}{=} \sqrt{6(2) - (2)^3}$
$-3 \overset{?}{=} \sqrt{-18 + 27}$	$0 \overset{?}{=} \sqrt{0}$	$2 \overset{?}{=} \sqrt{12 - 8}$
$-3 \overset{?}{=} \sqrt{9}$	$0 = 0 ✔$	$2 \overset{?}{=} \sqrt{4}$
$-3 \neq 3$		$2 = 2 ✔$

Thus, -3 is an extraneous solution; 0 and 2 are the solutions of the equation $x = \sqrt{6x - x^3}$. The solution set is $\{0, 2\}$. ■ ■ ■

PRACTICE PROBLEM 4 Solve: $x = \sqrt{x^3 - 6x}$ ■

> **EXAMPLE 5** Solving an Equation Involving a Radical

Solve: $\sqrt{2x + 1} + 1 = x$

Solution

Step 1 We begin by isolating the radical to one side of the equation:

$$\sqrt{2x + 1} + 1 = x \qquad \text{Original equation}$$
$$\sqrt{2x + 1} = x - 1. \qquad \text{Subtract 1 from both sides.}$$

Step 2 Next, we square both sides and simplify.

$$(\sqrt{2x + 1})^2 = (x - 1)^2 \qquad \text{Square both sides.}$$
$$2x + 1 = x^2 - 2x + 1 \qquad (\sqrt{a})^2 = a$$
$$2x + 1 - 2x - 1 = x^2 - 2x + 1 - 2x - 1 \qquad \text{Subtract } 2x + 1 \text{ from both sides.}$$
$$0 = x^2 - 4x \qquad \text{Simplify.}$$
$$0 = x(x - 4) \qquad \text{Factor.}$$

Continued on next page.

Step 3   **Set each factor equal to zero.**

$$x = 0 \quad \text{or} \quad x - 4 = 0$$
$$x = 0 \quad \text{or} \quad x = 4 \qquad \text{Solve for } x.$$

Step 4   **Check.**

Let $x = 0$.	Let $x = 4$.
$\sqrt{2(0) + 1} + 1 \overset{?}{=} 0$	$\sqrt{2(4) + 1} + 1 \overset{?}{=} 4$
$\sqrt{1} + 1 \overset{?}{=} 0$	$\sqrt{9} + 1 \overset{?}{=} 4$
$1 + 1 \overset{?}{=} 0$	$3 + 1 \overset{?}{=} 4$
$2 \neq 0$	$4 = 4 \checkmark$

Thus, 0 is an extraneous root; the only solution of the given equation is 4, and the solution set is $\{4\}$.   ■ ■ ■

PRACTICE PROBLEM 5   Solve: $\sqrt{6x + 4} + 2 = x$ ■

We next illustrate a method for solving radical equations that contain two or more square root expressions.

EXAMPLE 6   **Solving an Equation Involving Two Radicals**

Solve: $\sqrt{2x - 1} - \sqrt{x - 1} = 1$

Solution

Step 1   **We first isolate one of the radicals.**

$$\sqrt{2x - 1} - \sqrt{x - 1} = 1 \qquad \text{Original equation}$$
$$\sqrt{2x - 1} = 1 + \sqrt{x - 1} \qquad \text{Add } \sqrt{x - 1} \text{ to both sides to isolate the radical } \sqrt{2x - 1}.$$

Step 2   **Square both sides of the last equation.**

$$(\sqrt{2x - 1})^2 = (1 + \sqrt{x - 1})^2 \qquad \text{Square both sides.}$$
$$2x - 1 = 1^2 + 2 \cdot 1 \cdot \sqrt{x - 1} + (\sqrt{x - 1})^2 \qquad (A + B)^2 = A^2 + 2AB + B^2$$
$$2x - 1 = 1 + 2\sqrt{x - 1} + x - 1 \qquad \text{Simplify; use } (\sqrt{a})^2 = a.$$
$$2x - 1 = 2\sqrt{x - 1} + x \qquad \text{Simplify.}$$

Step 3   **The last equation still contains a radical. We repeat the process of isolating the radical expression.**

$$x - 1 = 2\sqrt{x - 1} \qquad \text{Subtract } x \text{ from both sides and simplify to isolate } 2\sqrt{x - 1}.$$
$$(x - 1)^2 = (2\sqrt{x - 1})^2 \qquad \text{Square both sides.}$$
$$x^2 - 2x + 1 = 4(x - 1) \qquad \text{Use } (A - B)^2 = A^2 - 2AB + B^2 \text{ and } (AB)^2 = A^2 B^2.$$
$$x^2 - 2x + 1 = 4x - 4 \qquad \text{Distributive property}$$
$$x^2 - 6x + 5 = 0 \qquad \text{Add } -4x + 4 \text{ to both sides, simplify.}$$
$$(x - 5)(x - 1) = 0 \qquad \text{Factor.}$$

Step 4   **Set each factor equal to 0.**

$$x - 5 = 0 \quad \text{or} \quad x - 1 = 0$$
$$x = 5 \quad \text{or} \quad\quad x = 1 \qquad \text{Solve for } x.$$

Step 5   **Check.** You should check that the solutions of the original equation are 1 and 5, so the solution set is $\{1, 5\}$.   ■ ■ ■

PRACTICE PROBLEM 6   Solve: $\sqrt{x - 5} + \sqrt{x} = 5$ ■

SOLVING EQUATIONS CONTAINING SQUARE ROOTS

Step 1.   Isolate one radical to one side of the equation.

Step 2.   Square both sides of the equation in Step **1** and simplify.

Step 3.   If the equation obtained in Step **2** contains a radical, repeat Steps **1** and **2** to get an equation that is free of radicals.

Step 4.   Solve the equation obtained in Steps **1–3**.

Step 5.   Check the solutions in the original equation.

---

4   Learn to solve equations that are quadratic in form.

Equations That Are Quadratic in Form

An equation in a variable x is **quadratic in form** if it can be written as

$$au^2 + bu + c = 0 \qquad (a \neq 0),$$

where u is an expression in the variable x. We solve the equation $au^2 + bu + c = 0$ for u. Then the solutions of the original equation can be obtained by replacing u by the expression in x that u represents.

EXAMPLE 7   **Solving an Equation That Is Quadratic in Form by Substitution**

Solve: $(x^2 - 1)^2 - 6(x^2 - 1) - 16 = 0$

Solution

The equation $(x^2 - 1)^2 - 6(x^2 - 1) - 16 = 0$ is not a quadratic equation. However, if we let $u = x^2 - 1$, then $u^2 = (x^2 - 1)^2$. The original equation becomes a quadratic equation if we replace $x^2 - 1$ by u.

$$
\begin{array}{lll}
(x^2 - 1)^2 - 6(x^2 - 1) - 16 = 0 & & \text{Original equation} \\
u^2 - 6u - 16 = 0 & & \text{Replace } x^2 - 1 \text{ by } u. \\
(u + 2)(u - 8) = 0 & & \text{Factor.} \\
u - 8 = 0 \quad \text{or} \quad u + 2 = 0 & & \text{Zero-product property} \\
u = 8 \quad \text{or} \quad\quad u = -2 & & \text{Solve for } u.
\end{array}
$$

Continued on next page.

Since $u = x^2 - 1$, we now find x from $u = -2$ and $u = 8$.

$$
\begin{array}{c|cl}
x^2 - 1 = -2 & x^2 - 1 = 8 & \text{Replace } u \text{ by } x^2 - 1. \\
x^2 = -1 & x^2 = 9 & \text{Add 1 to both sides of each equation.} \\
x = \pm i & x = \pm 3 & \text{Solve for } x.
\end{array}
$$

The equation has four apparent solutions: i, $-i$, 3, and -3.

Check: You should check that i, $-i$, 3, and -3 are solutions of the equation.

Thus, $\{i, -i, 3, -3\}$ is the solution set of the original equation. ■ ■ ■

PRACTICE PROBLEM 7 Solve: $(x + 1)^2 - 3(x + 1) = 40$ ■

◆ **WARNING** When u replaces an expression in the variable x in an equation that is quadratic in form, you are not finished once you have found values for u. You then have to replace u by the expression in x and solve for x.

EXAMPLE 8 **Solving an Equation That Is Quadratic in Form**

Solve: $\left(x + \dfrac{1}{x}\right)^2 - 6\left(x + \dfrac{1}{x}\right) + 8 = 0$

Solution

We let $u = x + \dfrac{1}{x}$. Then $u^2 = \left(x + \dfrac{1}{x}\right)^2$. With this substitution, the original equation becomes a quadratic equation in u.

$$
\begin{array}{ll}
\left(x + \dfrac{1}{x}\right)^2 - 6\left(x + \dfrac{1}{x}\right) + 8 = 0 & \text{Original equation} \\[2mm]
u^2 - 6u + 8 = 0 & \text{Replace } x + \dfrac{1}{x} \text{ by } u. \\[2mm]
(u - 2)(u - 4) = 0 & \text{Factor.} \\[2mm]
u - 2 = 0 \quad \text{or} \quad u - 4 = 0 & \text{Zero-product property} \\[2mm]
u = 2 \quad \text{or} \quad u = 4 & \text{Solve for } u.
\end{array}
$$

Replacing u by $x + \dfrac{1}{x}$ in these equations, we have

$$
x + \dfrac{1}{x} = 2 \quad \text{or} \quad x + \dfrac{1}{x} = 4.
$$

We next solve each of these equations for x.

$$
\begin{array}{ll}
x + \dfrac{1}{x} = 2 & \\[2mm]
x^2 + 1 = 2x & \text{Multiply both sides by } x \text{ (the LCD).} \\[2mm]
x^2 - 2x + 1 = 0 & \text{Subtract } 2x \text{ from both sides; simplify.}
\end{array}
$$

$$(x - 1)^2 = 0 \qquad \text{Factor the perfect-square trinomial.}$$
$$x - 1 = 0 \qquad \text{Square root property}$$
$$x = 1 \qquad \text{Solve for } x.$$

Thus, $x = 1$ is a possible solution of the original equation.

$$x + \frac{1}{x} = 4$$

$$x^2 + 1 = 4x \qquad \text{Multiply both sides by } x \text{ (the LCD).}$$

$$x^2 - 4x + 1 = 0 \qquad \text{Subtract } 4x \text{ from both sides.}$$

$$x = \frac{-(-4) \pm \sqrt{(-4)^2 - 4(1)(1)}}{2(1)} \qquad \begin{array}{l} \text{Quadratic formula:} \\ a = 1, b = -4, c = 1 \end{array}$$

$$x = \frac{4 \pm \sqrt{12}}{2} \qquad \text{Simplify.}$$

$$x = \frac{4 \pm 2\sqrt{3}}{2} \qquad \begin{array}{l} \sqrt{12} = \sqrt{4 \cdot 3} = \\ \sqrt{4}\sqrt{3} = 2\sqrt{3} \end{array}$$

$$x = \frac{2(2 \pm \sqrt{3})}{2} \qquad \text{Factor the numerator.}$$

$$x = 2 \pm \sqrt{3} \qquad \text{Remove the common factor.}$$

Thus, $2 + \sqrt{3}$ and $2 - \sqrt{3}$ are also possible solutions of the original equation. Consequently, the possible solutions of the original equation are 1, $2 + \sqrt{3}$, and $2 - \sqrt{3}$.

You should verify that 1, $2 + \sqrt{3}$, and $2 - \sqrt{3}$ are solutions of the original equation. The solution set is $\{1, 2 - \sqrt{3}, 2 + \sqrt{3}\}$. ■ ■ ■

PRACTICE PROBLEM 8 Solve: $\left(1 + \dfrac{1}{x}\right)^2 - 6\left(1 + \dfrac{1}{x}\right) + 8 = 0$ ■

The next example illustrates the paradoxical effect of time dilation (page 135) when one travels at speeds that are close to the speed of light.

EXAMPLE 9   **Investigating Space Travel (Your Older Sister Is Younger than You Are)**

Your sister is 5 years older than you are. She decides she has had enough of Earth and needs a vacation. She takes a trip to the Omega-One star system. Her trip to Omega-One and back in a spacecraft traveling at an average speed v took 15 years, according to the clock and calendar on the spacecraft. But on landing back on Earth, she discovers that her voyage took 25 years, according to the time on Earth. This means that, although you were 5 years younger than your sister before her vacation, you are 5 years older than her after her vacation! Use the time-dilation equation $t_0 = t\sqrt{1 - \dfrac{v^2}{c^2}}$ from the introduction to this section to calculate the speed of the spacecraft.

Continued on next page.

Solution

Substitute $t_0 = 15$ (moving-frame time) and $t = 25$ (fixed-frame time) to obtain

$$15 = 25\sqrt{1 - \frac{v^2}{c^2}}$$

$$\frac{3}{5} = \sqrt{1 - \frac{v^2}{c^2}} \qquad \text{Divide both sides by 25; } \frac{15}{25} = \frac{3}{5}.$$

$$\frac{9}{25} = 1 - \frac{v^2}{c^2} \qquad \text{Square both sides.}$$

$$\frac{v^2}{c^2} = 1 - \frac{9}{25} \qquad \text{Add } \frac{v^2}{c^2} - \frac{9}{25} \text{ to both sides.}$$

$$\left(\frac{v}{c}\right)^2 = \frac{16}{25} \qquad \text{Simplify.}$$

$$\frac{v}{c} = \pm\frac{4}{5} \qquad \text{Square root property}$$

$$\frac{v}{c} = \frac{4}{5} \qquad \text{Reject the negative value.}$$

$$v = \frac{4}{5}c = 0.8c \qquad \text{Multiply both sides by } c.$$

Thus, the spacecraft must have been traveling at 80% of the speed of light ($0.8c$) when your sister found the "trip of youth." ▪ ▪ ▪

PRACTICE PROBLEM 9 Suppose your sister's trip took 20 years according to the clock and calendar on the spacecraft, but 25 years judging by time on Earth. Find the speed of the spacecraft. ▪

A Exercises ▪ Basic Skills and Concepts

In Exercises 1–10, find the real solutions of each equation by factoring.

1. $x^3 = 2x^2$ $\{0,2\}$

2. $3x^4 - 27x^2 = 0$ $\{-3,0,3\}$

3. $(\sqrt{x})^3 = \sqrt{x}$ $\{0,1\}$

4. $(\sqrt{x})^5 = 16\sqrt{x}$ $\{0,4\}$

5. $x^3 + x = 0$ $\{0\}$

6. $x^3 - 1 = 0$ $\{1\}$

7. $x^4 - x^3 = x^2 - x$ $\{-1,0,1\}$

8. $x^3 - 36x = 16(x - 6)$ †

9. $x^4 = 27x$ $\{0,3\}$

10. $3x^4 = 24x$ $\{0,2\}$

In Exercises 11–20, solve each equation by multiplying both sides by the LCD.

11. $\dfrac{x + 1}{3x - 2} = \dfrac{5x - 4}{3x + 2}$ $\left\{\dfrac{1}{4},2\right\}$

12. $\dfrac{x}{2x + 1} = \dfrac{3x + 2}{4x + 3}$ $\{-1\}$

13. $\dfrac{1}{x} + \dfrac{2}{x + 1} = 1$ †

14. $\dfrac{x}{x + 1} + \dfrac{x + 1}{x + 2} = 1$ †

15. $\dfrac{6x - 7}{x} - \dfrac{1}{x^2} = 5$ †

16. $\dfrac{1}{x} + \dfrac{2}{x + 1} + \dfrac{3}{x + 2} = 0$ †

17. $\dfrac{1}{x} + \dfrac{1}{x - 3} = \dfrac{7}{3x - 5}$ †

18. $\dfrac{x + 3}{x - 1} + \dfrac{x + 4}{x + 1} = \dfrac{8x + 5}{x^2 - 1}$ †

19. $\dfrac{5}{x + 1} - \dfrac{4}{2x + 2} + \dfrac{2}{2x - 1} = \dfrac{13}{18}$ $\left\{\dfrac{1}{26},5\right\}$

20. $\dfrac{6}{2x - 2} - \dfrac{1}{x + 1} = \dfrac{2}{2x + 2} + 1$ $\{-2,3\}$

In Exercises 21–42, solve each equation.

21. $\sqrt{3x + 1} = 2$ $\{1\}$

22. $\sqrt{2x + 3} = 3$ $\{3\}$

23. $\sqrt{x - 1} = -2$ $\varnothing$

24. $\sqrt{3x + 4} = -1$ $\varnothing$

25. $x + \sqrt{x + 6} = 0$ $\{-2\}$

26. $x - \sqrt{6x + 7} = 0$ $\{7\}$

†Due to space constrictions, answers to these exercises may be found in the Answers beginning on page A–1 in the back of the book.

27. $\sqrt{y + 6} = y$ {3}   **28.** $r + 11 = 6\sqrt{r + 3}$ {1,13}

29. $\sqrt{6y - 11} = 2y - 7$ {6}   **30.** $\sqrt{3y + 1} = y - 1$ {5}

31. $t - \sqrt{3t + 6} = -2$ {−2,1}

32. $\sqrt{5x^2 - 10x + 9} = 2x - 1$ {2,4}

33. $\sqrt{x - 3} = \sqrt{2x - 5} - 1$ {3,7}

34. $x + \sqrt{x + 1} = 5$ {3}   **35.** $\sqrt{2y + 9} = 2 + \sqrt{y + 1}$ †

36. $\sqrt{m - 1} = \sqrt{m - 5}$ {9}

37. $\sqrt{7z + 1} - \sqrt{5z + 4} = 1$ {9}

38. $\sqrt{3q + 1} - \sqrt{q - 1} = 2$ {1,5}

39. $\sqrt{2x + 5} + \sqrt{x + 6} = 3$ {−2}

40. $\sqrt{5x - 9} - \sqrt{x + 4} = 1$ {5}

41. $\sqrt{2x - 5} - \sqrt{x - 3} = 1$ {3,7}

42. $\sqrt{3x + 5} + \sqrt{6x + 3} = 3$ {−⅓}

In Exercises 43–64, solve each equation by using an appropriate substitution. Check your answers.

43. $x - 5\sqrt{x} + 6 = 0$ {4, 9}

44. $x - 3\sqrt{x} + 2 = 0$ {1, 4}

45. $2y - 15\sqrt{y} = -7$ $\left\{\dfrac{1}{4}, 49\right\}$

46. $y + 44 = 15\sqrt{y}$ {16, 121}

47. $x^4 - 13x^2 + 36 = 0$ †   **48.** $x^4 - 7x^2 + 12 = 0$ †

49. $2t^4 + t^2 - 1 = 0$ †   **50.** $81y^4 + 1 = 18y^2$ †

51. $p^2 - 3 + 4\sqrt{p^2 - 3} - 5 = 0$ {−2, 2}

52. $x^2 - 3 - 4\sqrt{x^2 - 3} - 12 = 0$ {$-\sqrt{39}, \sqrt{39}$}

53. $(3t + 1)^2 - 3(3t + 1) + 2 = 0$ †

54. $(7z + 5)^2 + 2(7z + 5) - 15 = 0$ †

55. $(\sqrt{y} + 5)^2 - 9(\sqrt{y} + 5) + 20 = 0$ {0}

56. $(2\sqrt{t} + 1)^2 - 2(2\sqrt{t} + 1) - 3 = 0$ {1}

57. $(x^2 - 4)^2 - 3(x^2 - 4) - 4 = 0$ {$-2\sqrt{2}, -\sqrt{3}, \sqrt{3}, 2\sqrt{2}$}

58. $(x^2 + 2)^2 - 5(x^2 + 2) - 6 = 0$ {$-2, 2, -i\sqrt{3}, i\sqrt{3}$}

59. $(x^2 + 3)^2 + (x^2 + 3) - 6 = 0$ {$-i\sqrt{6}, -i, i, i\sqrt{6}$}

60. $(x^2 - 2)^2 + 7(x^2 - 2) + 10 = 0$ {$-i\sqrt{3}, 0, i\sqrt{3}$}

61. $(x^2 - 3x)^2 - 2(x^2 - 3x) - 8 = 0$ {$-1, 1, 2, 4$}

62. $(x^2 - 4x)^2 + 7(x^2 - 4x) + 12 = 0$ {1, 2, 3}

63. $(x^2 + 5x)^2 + 10(x^2 + 5x) + 24 = 0$ {$-4, -3, -2, -1$}

64. $(x^2 + 2x)^2 - 8(x^2 + 2x) + 15 = 0$ †

B Exercises   Applying the Concepts

65. Fractions. The numerator of a fraction is two less than the denominator. The sum of the fraction and its reciprocal is $\dfrac{25}{12}$. Find the numerator and denominator if each is a positive integer. $\frac{6}{8}$

66. Fractions. The numerator of a fraction is five less than the denominator. The sum of the fraction and six times its reciprocal is $\dfrac{25}{2}$. Find the numerator and denominator if each is an integer. $\frac{5}{10}$

67. Investment. Latasha bought some stock for $1800. If the price of each share of the stock had been $18 less, she could have bought five more shares for the same $1800.
  a. How many shares of the stock did she buy? 20 shares
  b. How much did she pay for each share? $90

68. Bus Charter. A civic club charters a bus for one day at a cost of $575. When two more people join the group, each person's cost decreases by $2. How many people were in the original group? 23 people

69. Depth of a well. A stone is dropped into a well, and the time it takes to hear the splash is 4 seconds. Find the depth of the well (to the nearest foot). Assume that the speed of sound is 1100 feet per second and that $d = 16t^2$ is the distance d an object falls in t seconds. 230 ft

70. Estimating the horizon. You are in a hot-air balloon 2 miles above the ocean. (See accompanying diagram.) As far as you can see, you see only water. Given that the radius of the Earth is 3960 miles, how far away is the horizon? 125.87 mi

71. Rate of current. A motorboat is capable of traveling at a speed of 10 miles per hour in still water. On a particular day, it took 30 minutes longer to travel a distance of 12 miles upstream than it took to travel the same distance downstream. What was the rate of the current in the stream on that day? 2 mph

72. Train speed. A freight train requires $2\frac{1}{2}$ hours longer to make a 300-mile journey than an express train does. If the express averages 20 miles per hour faster than the freight train, how long does it take the express train to make the trip? 5 hr

73. Washing the family car. A couple washed the family car in 24 minutes. Previously, when they each had washed the car alone, it took the husband 20 minutes longer to wash the car than the wife. How long did it take the wife to wash the car? 40 min

74. Filling a swimming pool. A small swimming pool can be filled by two hoses together in 1 hour and 12 minutes. The larger hose alone will fill the pool in 1 hour less than the smaller one. How long does it take the smaller hose to fill the pool? 3 hr

75. The area of a rectangular plot. The diagonal and the longer side of a rectangular plot are together three times the length of the shorter side. If the longer side exceeds the shorter side by 100 feet, what is the area of the plot? 120,000 ft²

76. Emergency at sea. You are at sea in your motorboat at a point A located 40 km from a point B that lies 130 kilometers from a hospital on a long, straight road. (See accompanying figure). While at point A, your companion feels sick and has to be taken to the hospital. You call the hospital on your cell phone to send an ambulance. Your motorboat can travel at 40 kilometers per hour, and the ambulance can travel at 80 kilometers per hour. How far from point B will you be when you and the ambulance arrive simultaneously at point C? $BC = 30$ km

77. Planning road construction. Two towns A and B are located 8 and 5 miles, respectively, from a long, straight highway. The points C and D on the highway closest to the two towns are 18 miles apart. (Remember that the shortest distance from a point to a line is the length of the perpendicular segment from the point to the line.) Where should point E be located on the highway so that the sum of the lengths of the roads from A to E and E to B is 23 miles? (See accompanying figure.)
[*Hint*: $205x^2 - 4392x + 18972 = (x - 6)(205x - 3162)$.]

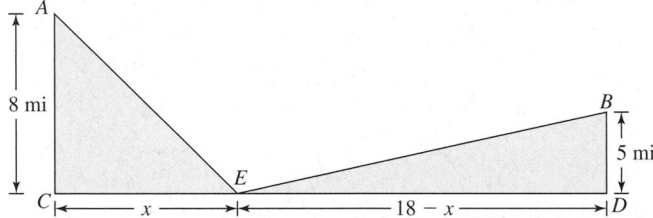

78. Department store purchases. A department store buyer purchased some shirts for $540. Then she sold all but eight of them. On each shirt sold, a profit of $6 (over the purchase price) was made. The shirts sold brought in revenue of $780.
  a. How many shirts were bought initially? 60 shirts
  b. What was the purchase price of each shirt? $9
  c. What was the selling price of each shirt? $15

Answer:
77. $CE = 6$ mi or $CE = \dfrac{3162}{205} \approx 15.4$ mi

C Exercises   Beyond the Basics

In Exercise 79–88, solve each equation by any method.

79. $\left(\dfrac{x^2 - 3}{x}\right)^2 - 6\left(\dfrac{x^2 - 3}{x}\right) + 8 = 0$

80. $\left(\dfrac{x + 2}{3x + 1}\right)^2 - 5\left(\dfrac{x + 2}{3x + 1}\right) + 6 = 0$ $\left\{-\dfrac{1}{8}, 0\right\}$

81. $\sqrt{\sqrt{3x - 2} + 2\sqrt{4x + 1}} = 2\sqrt{2}$ $\{2\}$

82. $\dfrac{5}{x - 1} - \dfrac{3x}{x + 1} = \dfrac{9}{x^2 - 1}$ $\left\{\dfrac{2}{3}, 2\right\}$

83. $\dfrac{x + 2}{x} + \dfrac{2x + 6}{x^2 + 4x} = -\dfrac{1}{x + 4}$ $\{-7, -2\}$

84. $\left(x^2 + \dfrac{1}{x^2}\right) - 7\left(x - \dfrac{1}{x}\right) + 8 = 0$

$\left[\text{Hint: } u = x - \dfrac{1}{x}, u^2 + 2 = x^2 + \dfrac{1}{x^2}\right]$

85. $\left(\dfrac{t}{t + 2}\right)^2 + \dfrac{2t}{t + 2} - 15 = 0$ $\left\{-3, -\dfrac{5}{3}\right\}$

86. $6t^{-2/5} - 17t^{-1/5} + 5 = 0$

87. $2x^{1/3} + 2x^{-1/3} - 5 = 0$

88. $8\sqrt{\dfrac{x}{x + 3}} - \sqrt{\dfrac{x + 3}{x}} = 2$ $\{1\}$

89. Solve $x + \sqrt{x} - 42 = 0$ by using two methods: $\{36\}$
   a. Rationalize the equation and then solve it.
   b. Use the substitution method.

90. Solve $\left(\dfrac{x}{x + 1}\right)^2 - \dfrac{2x}{x + 1} - 8 = 0$ by using two methods:
   a. Use the substitution method.
   b. Multiply by the LCD.

In Exercises 91–94, solve for x in terms of the other variables. (All letters denote positive real numbers.)

91. $\dfrac{x + b}{x - b} = \dfrac{x - 5b}{2x - 5b}$ $\{-5b, 2b\}$

92. $\dfrac{1}{x + a} + \dfrac{1}{x - 2a} = \dfrac{1}{x - 3a}$ $\{a, 5a\}$

93. $3x - 2a = \sqrt{a(3x - 2a)}$ $\left\{\dfrac{2a}{3}, a\right\}$

94. $3a - \sqrt{ax} = \sqrt{a(3x + a)}$ $\{a, 16a\}$

Critical Thinking

In Exercises 95–99, find the value of x.

95. $x = \sqrt{1 + \sqrt{1 + \sqrt{1 + \cdots}}}$ $x = \dfrac{1 + \sqrt{5}}{2}$
   $[\text{Hint: } x = \sqrt{1 + x}.]$

96. $x = \sqrt{20 + \sqrt{20 + \sqrt{20 + \cdots}}}$ $x = 5$

97. $x = \sqrt{n + \sqrt{n + \sqrt{n + \cdots}}}$, where n is a positive integer.

98. $x = 2 + \dfrac{1}{2 + \dfrac{1}{2 + \dfrac{1}{2 + \cdots}}}$ $x = 1 + \sqrt{2}$

99. Assume that $x > 1$. Solve for x: $\{5\}$
$$\sqrt{x + 2\sqrt{x - 1}} + \sqrt{x - 2\sqrt{x - 1}} = 4.$$
$[\text{Hint: } x + 2\sqrt{x - 1} = (x - 1) + 1 + 2\sqrt{x - 1}$
$\qquad\qquad\quad = (\sqrt{x - 1} + 1)^2.]$

Answers:

79. $\{-1, 2 - \sqrt{7}, 3, 2 + \sqrt{7}\}$

84. $\left\{1 - \sqrt{2}, \dfrac{5 - \sqrt{29}}{2}, \dfrac{5 + \sqrt{29}}{2}, 1 + \sqrt{2}\right\}$

86. $\left\{\dfrac{32}{3125}, 243\right\}$ **87.** $\left\{\dfrac{1}{8}, 8\right\}$ **90.** $\left\{-\dfrac{4}{3}, -\dfrac{2}{3}\right\}$

Answer:

97. $x = \dfrac{1}{2} + \dfrac{\sqrt{4n + 1}}{2}$

Linear Inequalities

BEFORE STARTING THIS SECTION, REVIEW

1. Inequalities (Section P.1, page 5)

2. Intervals (Section P.1, page 8)

3. Linear equations (Section 1.1, page 89)

OBJECTIVES

1 Learn the vocabulary for discussing inequalities.

2 Learn to solve and graph linear inequalities.

3 Learn to solve and graph a combined inequality.

4 Learn to solve and graph an inequality involving the reciprocal of a linear expression.

The Bermuda Triangle

The "Bermuda Triangle," or "Devil's Triangle," is the expanse of the Atlantic Ocean between Florida, Bermuda, and Puerto Rico covering approximately 500,000 square miles of sea. This mysterious stretch of sea has an unusually high occurrence of disappearing ships and planes.

For example, on Halloween 1991, pilot John Verdi and his copilot were flying a Grumman Cougar jet over the triangle. They radioed the nearest tower to get permission to increase their altitude. The tower agreed and watched as the jet began the ascent and then disappeared off the radar. The jet didn't fly out of range of the radar, didn't descend, and didn't radio a mayday (distress call). It just vanished, and the plane and crew were never recovered.

One explanation for such disappearances is based on the theory that strange compass readings occur in crossing the Atlantic, due to confusion caused by the three north poles: magnetic (toward which compasses point), grid (the real North Pole, at 90 degrees latitude), and true or celestial north (determined by Polaris, the North Star). To get data to test this theory, a plane set out from Miami to Bermuda with the intention of setting the plane on automatic pilot, once it reached a cruising speed of 300 miles per hour.

The plane was 150 miles along its path from Miami to Bermuda when it reached the 300-mile-per-hour cruising speed and was set on automatic pilot. After what length of time would you be confident in saying that the plane had encountered trouble? The answer to this question is found in Example 2, which uses a linear inequality, the topic discussed in this section. ■

1 Learn the vocabulary for discussing inequalities.

Inequalities

When we replace the equals sign ($=$) in an equation by any of the four inequality symbols $<$, $\leq$, $>$, or $\geq$, the resulting expression is an *inequality*. Here are some examples:

Equation	Replace = by	Inequality
$x = 5$	$<$	$x < 5$
$3x + 2 = 14$	$\leq$	$3x + 2 \leq 14$
$5x + 7 = 3x + 23$	$>$	$5x + 7 > 3x + 23$
$x^2 = 0$	$\geq$	$x^2 \geq 0$

In general, an **inequality** is a statement that one algebraic expression is less than, or is less than or equal to, another algebraic expression. The vocabulary for discussing inequalities is quite similar to that used for equations. The **domain** of a variable in an inequality is the set of all real numbers for which both sides of the inequality are defined. The real numbers that result in a true statement when those numbers are substituted for the variable in the inequality are called **solutions** of the inequality. Since replacing x by 1 in the inequality $3x + 2 \leq 14$ results in the true statement

$$3(1) + 2 \leq 14,$$

the number 1 is a solution of the inequality $3x + 2 \leq 14$. We also say that 1 *satisfies* the inequality $3x + 2 \leq 14$. To **solve** an inequality means to find all solutions of the inequality—that is, its solution set. The most elementary equations, such as $x = 5$, have only one solution. However, even the most elementary inequalities, such as $x < 5$, have infinitely many solutions. In fact, their solution sets are *intervals,* and we frequently graph the solution sets for inequalities in one variable on a number line. The graph of the inequality $x < 5$ is the interval $(-\infty, 5)$, shown in Figure 1.7.

$x < 5$, or $(-\infty, 5)$

FIGURE 1.7

Inequalities are classified in exactly the same way as equations: *conditional, inconsistent,* or *identities.* A **conditional inequality** such as $x < 5$ has in its domain at least one solution and at least one number that is not a solution. An inequality that *no* real number satisfies is called an **inconsistent inequality,** and an inequality that is satisfied by *every* real number in the domain of the variable is called an **identity.**

Because $x^2 = x \cdot x$ is the product of either (1) two positive factors, (2) two negative factors, or (3) two zero factors, x^2 is always either a positive number or zero. That is, x^2 is never negative, or is **nonnegative.** We call this fact the nonnegative identity.

THE NONNEGATIVE IDENTITY

$$x^2 \geq 0$$

for any real number x.

Two inequalities that have exactly the same solution set are called **equivalent inequalities.** The basic method of solving inequalities is similar to the method for solving equations: We replace a given inequality by a series of equivalent inequalities until we arrive at an equivalent inequality, such as $x < 5$, whose solution set we already know.

The following operations produce equivalent inequalities:

1. Simplifying one or both sides of an inequality by combining like terms and eliminating parentheses.
2. Adding or subtracting the same expression on both sides of the inequality.

Caution is required in multiplying or dividing both sides of an inequality by a real number or an expression representing a real number. Notice what happens when we multiply an inequality by -1.

We know that $2 < 3$, but how does $-2 = (-1)(2)$ compare with $-3 = (-1)(3)$? We have $-2 > -3$. See Figure 1.8.

-3 is left of -2 2 is left of 3

FIGURE 1.8

If we multiply (or divide) both sides of the inequality $2 < 3$ by -1 then, in order to get a correct result, we have to exchange the $<$ symbol for the $>$ symbol. This exchange of symbols is called reversing the **sense** or the **direction** of the inequality.

The following chart describes the way multiplication and division affect inequalities.

If C represents a real number, then the following inequalities are all equivalent.

Sign of C	Inequality	Sense	Example
	$A < B$	$<$	$3x < 12$
C positive	$A \cdot C < B \cdot C$	Unchanged	$\frac{1}{3}(3x) < \frac{1}{3}(12)$
C positive	$\dfrac{A}{C} < \dfrac{B}{C}$	Unchanged	$\dfrac{3x}{3} < \dfrac{12}{3}$
C negative	$A \cdot C > B \cdot C$	Reversed	$-\frac{1}{3}(3x) > -\frac{1}{3}(12)$
C negative	$\dfrac{A}{C} > \dfrac{B}{C}$	Reversed	$\dfrac{3x}{-3} > \dfrac{12}{-3}$

Similar results apply when $<$ is replaced throughout by any of the symbols $\leq$, $>$, or $\geq$.

Linear Inequalities

A **linear inequality in one variable** is an inequality that is equivalent to one of the forms

$$ax + b < 0 \quad \text{or} \quad ax + b \leq 0,$$

where a and b represent real numbers and $a \neq 0$.

Inequalities such as $2x - 1 > 0$ and $2x - 1 \geq 0$ are linear inequalities because they are equivalent to $-2x + 1 < 0$ and $-2x + 1 \leq 0$, respectively.

EXAMPLE 1   **Solving and Graphing Linear Inequalities**

Solve each inequality and graph its solution set.

a. $7x - 11 < 2(x - 3)$ **b.** $8 - 3x \leq 2$.

Solution

a. $7x - 11 < 2(x - 3)$

$$7x - 11 < 2x - 6 \qquad \text{Distributive property}$$
$$7x - 11 + 11 < 2x - 6 + 11 \qquad \text{Add 11 to both sides.}$$
$$7x < 2x + 5 \qquad \text{Simplify.}$$
$$7x - 2x < 2x + 5 - 2x \qquad \text{Subtract } 2x \text{ from both sides.}$$
$$5x < 5 \qquad \text{Simplify.}$$
$$\frac{5x}{5} < \frac{5}{5} \qquad \text{Divide both sides by 5.}$$
$$x < 1 \qquad \text{Simplify.}$$

The solution set is $\{x | x < 1\}$, or, in interval notation, $(-\infty, 1)$. The graph is shown in Figure 1.9.

$x < 1$, or $(-\infty, 1)$

FIGURE 1.9

b. $8 - 3x \leq 2$

$$8 - 3x - 8 \leq 2 - 8 \qquad \text{Subtract 8 from both sides.}$$
$$-3x \leq -6 \qquad \text{Simplify.}$$
$$\frac{-3x}{-3} \geq \frac{-6}{-3} \qquad \text{Divide both sides by } -3. \text{ (Reverse the direction of the inequality symbol.)}$$
$$x \geq 2 \qquad \text{Simplify.}$$

The solution set is $\{x | x \geq 2\}$, or, in interval notation, $[2, \infty)$. The graph is shown in Figure 1.10.   ■ ■ ■

$x \geq 2$, or $[2, \infty)$

FIGURE 1.10

PRACTICE PROBLEM 1   Solve each inequality and graph the solution set.

a. $4x + 9 > 2(x + 6) + 1$ **b.** $7 - 2x \geq -3$ ■

EXAMPLE 2   **Calculating the Results of the Bermuda Triangle Experiment**

In the introduction to this section, we discussed an experiment to test the reliability of compass settings and flight by automatic pilot along one edge of the Bermuda Triangle. The plane is 150 miles along its path from Miami to Bermuda, cruising at 300 miles per hour, when it notifies the tower that it is now set on automatic pilot.

The entire trip is 1035 miles, and we want to determine how much time we should let pass before we become concerned that the plane has encountered trouble.

Solution

Let t = time elapsed since the plane went on autopilot. Then:

$$300t = \text{distance the plane has flown in } t \text{ hours}$$
$$150 + 300t = \text{plane's distance from Miami after } t \text{ hours.}$$

Continued on next page.

Concern isn't warranted unless the Bermuda tower doesn't see the plane which means the following is true:

$$\boxed{\text{Plane's distance from Miami}} \geq \boxed{\text{Distance from Miami to Bermuda}}$$

$150 + 300t \geq 1035$	Replace the verbal description by an inequality.
$150 + 300t - 150 \geq 1035 - 150$	Subtract 150 from both sides.
$300t \geq 885$	Simplify.
$\dfrac{300t}{300} \geq \dfrac{885}{300}$	Divide both sides by 300.
$t \geq 2.95$	Simplify.

Since 2.95 is roughly 3 hours, the tower will suspect trouble if the plane has not arrived in 3 hours. ■ ■ ■

PRACTICE PROBLEM 2   How much time should pass in Example 2 if the plane was set on automatic pilot at 340 miles per hour when it was 185 miles from Miami? ■

3 Learn to solve and graph a combined inequality.

Combining Two Inequalities

Sometimes we are interested in inequalities such as $-5 < 2x + 3 \leq 9$. This use of two inequality symbols in a single expression is shorthand for $-5 < 2x + 3$ *and* $2x + 3 \leq 9$ and is called a **combined inequality,** or **compound inequality.** Fortunately, solving such inequalities requires no new principles, as we see in the next example.

EXAMPLE 3   **Solving and Graphing a Compound Inequality**

Solve the inequality $-5 < 2x + 3 \leq 9$ and graph its solution set.

Solution

We must find all real numbers that are solutions of *both* the inequalities

$$-5 < 2x + 3 \text{ and } 2x + 3 \leq 9.$$

Let's first see what happens if we solve these inequalities separately.

$-5 < 2x + 3$	$2x + 3 \leq 9$	Original inequalities
$-5 - 3 < 2x + 3 - 3$	$2x + 3 - 3 \leq 9 - 3$	Subtract 3 from both sides.
$-8 < 2x$	$2x \leq 6$	Simplify.
$\dfrac{-8}{2} < \dfrac{2x}{2}$	$\dfrac{2x}{2} \leq \dfrac{6}{2}$	Divide both sides by 2.
$-4 < x$	$x \leq 3$	Simplify.

The solution of the original pair of inequalities consists of all real numbers x such that $-4 < x$ *and* $x \leq 3$. This solution may be written more compactly as $\{x| -4 < x \leq 3\}$. In interval notation, we write $(-4, 3]$. The graph is shown in Figure 1.11.

$-4 < x \leq 3$, or $(-4, 3]$

FIGURE 1.11

Notice that we did exactly the same thing to both inequalities in each step of the solution process. We can accomplish this simultaneous solution more efficiently by working on both inequalities at the same time as follows:

$$-5 < 2x + 3 \le 9 \qquad \text{Original inequality}$$
$$-5 - 3 < 2x + 3 - 3 \le 9 - 3 \qquad \text{Subtract 3 from each part.}$$
$$-8 < 2x \le 6 \qquad \text{Simplify each part.}$$
$$\frac{-8}{2} < \frac{2x}{2} \le \frac{6}{2} \qquad \text{Divide each part by 2.}$$
$$-4 < x \le 3. \qquad \text{Simplify each part.}$$

The solution set is $\{x \mid -4 < x \le 3\}$, exactly the solution set we obtained previously.

■ ■ ■

PRACTICE PROBLEM 3 Solve and graph $-6 \le 4x - 2 < 4$.   ■

4 Learn to solve and graph an inequality involving the reciprocal of a linear expression.

Inequalities Involving the Reciprocal of a Linear Expression

In the next section, we will solve nonlinear inequalities. However, a "sign property" of reciprocals allows us to exchange certain nonlinear inequalities for equivalent linear inequalities. The **Reciprocal Sign Property** says that any number and its reciprocal have the same sign.

THE RECIPROCAL SIGN PROPERTY

If $x \ne 0$, x and $\dfrac{1}{x}$ are either both positive or both negative. In symbols, if $x > 0$, then $\dfrac{1}{x} > 0$ and if $x < 0$, then $\dfrac{1}{x} < 0$.

EXAMPLE 4   Solving and Graphing an Inequality by Using the Reciprocal Sign Property

Solve and graph $(3x - 12)^{-1} > 0$.

Solution

$$(3x - 12)^{-1} > 0 \qquad \text{Original inequality}$$
$$\frac{1}{3x - 12} > 0 \qquad a^{-1} = \frac{1}{a}; \text{ here, } a = 3x - 12.$$
$$3x - 12 > 0 \qquad \text{Reciprocal Sign Property}$$
$$3x > 12 \qquad \text{Add 12 to both sides.}$$
$$\frac{3x}{3} > \frac{12}{3} \qquad \text{Divide both sides by 3.}$$
$$x > 4.$$

$x > 4$, or $(4, \infty)$

FIGURE 1.12

The solution set is $\{x \mid x > 4\}$, or, in interval notation, $(4, \infty)$.
The graph is shown in Figure 1.12.   ■ ■ ■

PRACTICE PROBLEM 4   Solve and graph $(2x - 8)^{-1} \ge 0$.   ■

If you know that a particular quantity, represented by x, can vary between two values, then the procedures for working with inequalities can be used to find the values between which a linear expression $mx + k$ will vary. We show how to do this in Example 5.

EXAMPLE 5   **Finding the Interval of Values for a Linear Expression**

If $-2 < x < 5$, find real numbers a and b so that $a < 3x - 1 < b$.

Solution

We start with the interval for x:

$$-2 < x < 5$$
$$3(-2) < 3x < 3(5) \qquad \text{Multiply each part by 3 to get } 3x \text{ in the middle.}$$
$$-6 < 3x < 15 \qquad \text{Simplify.}$$
$$-6 - 1 < 3x - 1 < 15 - 1 \qquad \text{Subtract 1 from each part to get } 3x - 1 \text{ in the middle.}$$
$$-7 < 3x - 1 < 14 \qquad \text{Simplify.}$$

We have $a = -7$ and $b = 14$.   ■ ■ ■

PRACTICE PROBLEM 5   If $-3 \leq x \leq 2$, find real numbers a and b so that $a \leq 3x + 5 \leq b$. ■

Our next example demonstrates a practical use of the method shown in Example 5.

EXAMPLE 6   **Finding a Fahrenheit Temperature from a Celsius Range**

The weather in London is predicted to range between $10°$ and $20°$ Celsius during the three-week period you will be working there. To decide what kind of clothes to bring, you want to convert the temperature range to Fahrenheit temperatures. The formula for converting Celsius temperature C to Fahrenheit temperature F is $F = \dfrac{9}{5}C + 32$. What range of Fahrenheit temperatures might you find in London during your stay there?

Solution

First we express the Celsius temperature range as an inequality. Let C = temperature in Celsius degrees.

For the three weeks under consideration $10 \leq C \leq 20$.

We want to know the range of $F = \dfrac{9}{5}C + 32$ when $10 \leq C \leq 20$.

$$10 \leq C \leq 20$$
$$\left(\frac{9}{5}\right)(10) \leq \frac{9}{5}C \leq \left(\frac{9}{5}\right)(20) \qquad \text{Multiply each part by } \frac{9}{5}.$$
$$18 \leq \frac{9}{5}C \leq 36 \qquad \text{Simplify.}$$
$$18 + 32 \leq \frac{9}{5}C + 32 \leq 36 + 32 \qquad \text{Add 32 to each part.}$$
$$50 \leq \frac{9}{5}C + 32 \leq 68 \qquad \text{Simplify.}$$
$$50 \leq F \leq 68 \qquad F = \frac{9}{5}C + 32$$

So, the temperature range from 10° to 20° Celsius corresponds to a range from 50° to 68° Fahrenheit.   ■ ■ ■

PRACTICE PROBLEM 6   What range, in Fahrenheit degrees, corresponds to the range of 15° to 25° Celsius?   ■

A Exercises   Basic Skills and Concepts

In Exercises 1–10, fill in the blank with the correct inequality symbol, using the rules for producing equivalent inequalities.

1. If $x < 8$, then $x - 8$ __$<$__ 0.

2. If $x \leq -3$, then $x + 3$ __$\leq$__ 0.

3. If $x \geq 5$, then $x - 5$ __$\geq$__ 0.

4. If $x > 7$, then $x - 7$ __$>$__ 0.

5. If $\dfrac{x}{2} < 6$, then x __$<$__ 12.

6. If $\dfrac{x}{3} < 2$, then x __$<$__ 6.

7. If $-2x \leq 4$, then x __$\geq$__ -2.

8. If $-3x > 12$, then x __$<$__ -4.

9. If $x + 3 < 2$, then x __$<$__ -1.

10. If $x - 5 \leq 3$, then x __$\leq$__ 8.

In Exercises 11–18, graph the solution set of each inequality and write it in interval notation.

11. $-2 < x < 5$ †

12. $-5 \leq x \leq 0$ †

13. $0 < x \leq 4$ †

14. $1 \leq x < 7$ †

15. $x \geq -1$ †

16. $x > 2$ †

17. $-5x \geq 10$ †

18. $-2x < 2$ †

In Exercises 19–43, solve each inequality. Write the solution in interval notation and graph the solution set.

19. $x + 3 < 6$ †

20. $x - 2 < 3$ †

21. $1 - x \leq 4$ †

22. $7 - x > 3$ †

23. $2x + 5 < 9$ †

24. $3x + 2 \geq 7$ †

25. $3 - 3x > 15$ †

26. $8 - 4x \geq 12$ †

27. $3(x + 2) < 2x + 5$ †

28. $4(x - 1) \geq 3x - 1$ †

29. $3(x - 3) \leq 3 - x$ †

30. $-x - 2 \geq x - 10$ †

31. $6x + 4 > 3x + 10$ †

32. $4(x - 4) > 3(x - 5)$ †

33. $8(x - 1) \leq 7x - 12$ †

34. $3(x + 2) \geq 5x + 18$ †

35. $5(x + 2) \leq 3(x + 1) + 10$ †

36. $x - 4 > 2(x + 8)$ †

37. $9 - 5x \leq 6 - 8x$ †

38. $3 - 2x \leq -7 + 3x$ †

39. $9x - 6 \geq \dfrac{3}{2}x + 9$ †

40. $x - 3 \leq 2 + \dfrac{x}{2}$ †

41. $2 - x \geq 3 + \dfrac{x}{2}$ †

42. $\dfrac{7x - 3}{2} \leq 3x - 4$ †

43. $3 - \dfrac{3x}{2} \leq 1 - 4x$ †

In Exercises 44–58, solve each combined inequality.

44. $3 < x + 5 < 4$ $(-2,-1)$ **45.** $9 \leq x + 7 \leq 12$ $[2,5]$

46. $-4 \leq x - 2 < 2$ $[-2,4)$ **47.** $-3 < x + 5 < 4$ $(-8,-1)$

48. $-9 \leq 2x + 3 \leq 5$ $[-6,1]$ **49.** $-2 \leq 3x + 1 \leq 7$ $[-1,2]$

50. $0 \leq 1 - \dfrac{x}{3} < 2$ $(-3,3]$ **51.** $0 < 5 - \dfrac{x}{2} \leq 3$ $[4,10)$

52. $-1 < \dfrac{2x - 3}{5} \leq 0$ $\left(-1,\dfrac{3}{2}\right]$

53. $-4 \leq \dfrac{5x - 2}{3} < 0$ $\left[-2,\dfrac{2}{5}\right)$

54. $5x \leq 3x + 1 < 4x + 2$ †

55. $3x + 2 < 2x + 3 < 4x - 1$ $\varnothing$

56. $2x > 2 - 2x > 6 + 4x$ $\varnothing$

57. $\dfrac{-5}{2} \geq \dfrac{x - 2}{2} > \dfrac{1}{4}$ $\varnothing$

58. $-\dfrac{1}{2} \leq \dfrac{2x - 3}{2} < \dfrac{5}{4}$ $\left[1,\dfrac{11}{4}\right)$

In Exercises 59–62, solve each reciprocal inequality.

59. $(3x + 6)^{-1} < 0$ $(-\infty,-2)$ **60.** $(2x - 8)^{-1} < 0$ $(-\infty,4)$

61. $(2 - 4x)^{-1} > 0$ $\left(-\infty,\dfrac{1}{2}\right)$ **62.** $(10 - 5x)^{-1} > 0$ $(-\infty,2)$

In Exercises 63–68, find a and b.

63. If $-2 < x < 1$, then $a < x + 7 < b$. $a = 5, b = 8$

64. If $1 < x < 5$, then $a < 2x + 3 < b$. $a = 5, b = 13$

65. If $-1 < x < 1$, then $a < 2 - x < b$. $a = 1, b = 3$

66. If $3 < x < 7$, then $a < 1 - 3x < b$. $a = -20, b = -8$

67. If $0 < x < 4$, then $a < 5x - 1 < b$. $a = -1, b = 19$

68. If $-4 < x < 0$, then $a < 3x + 4 < b$. $a = -8, b = 4$

†Due to space constrictions, answers to these exercises may be found in the Answers beginning on page A–1 in the back of the book.

B Exercises   Applying the Concepts

69. Poster sales. A student club wants to produce a poster as a fund-raising device. The production cost is $1.80 per poster. There are additional expenses of $1200, independent of production or sales. How many posters must be sold at $2 each for the club to make a profit? more than 6000 posters

70. Telemarketing. A telemarketer is paid $25, plus 35% of the difference between the item's selling price and the item's cost. All items sell for at least $50 above cost and at most $125 above cost. For each sale made, over what range can a telemarketer's commission vary? $42.50 to $68.75

71. Appliance markup. The markup over the dealer's cost on a new refrigerator ranges from 15% to 20%. If the dealer's cost is $1750, over what range will the selling price vary?

72. Return on investment. An investor has $5000 to invest for a period of 1 year. Find the range of per annum simple interest rates required to generate interest between $200 and $275 inclusive. 4% to 5.5%

73. Hybrid-car trip. Sometime after passing a truck stop 300 miles from the start of her trip, Cora's hybrid car ran out of gas. If the tank could hold 12 gallons of gasoline, and the hybrid car averaged 40 miles per gallon, find the range of gasoline (in gallons) that could have been in the tank at the start of the trip. 7.5 gal to 12 gal

74. Average grade. Sean has taken three exams and earned scores of 85, 72, and 77 out of a possible 100 points. He needs an average of at least 80 to earn a B in the course. What range of scores on the fourth (and last) 100-point test will guarantee a B in the course? 86 to 100

75. Butterfat content. How much cream that is 30% butterfat must be added to milk that is 3% butterfat in order to have 270 quarts that are at least 4.5% butterfat? at least 15 qt

76. Amplifier cost. The cost of an amplifier to a retailer is $340. At what price can the amplifier be sold if the retailer wants to make a profit of at least 20% of the selling price?

77. Pedometer cost. A company produces a pedometer at a cost of $3 each and sells the pedometer for $5 each. If the company has to recover an initial expense of $4000 before any profit is earned, how many pedometers must be sold to earn a profit in excess of $3000? more than 3500 pedometers

78. Car sales. A car dealer has three times as many SUVs, and twice as many convertibles, as four-door sedans. How many four-door sedans could the dealer have if she has at least 48 cars of these three types? at least 8

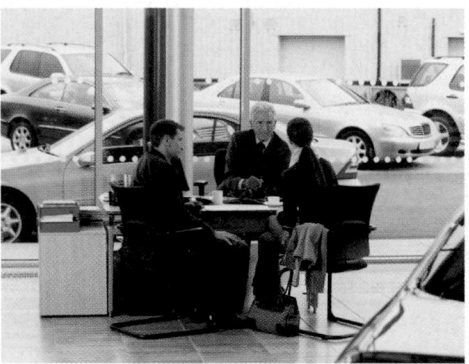

79. Temperature conversion. The formula for converting Fahrenheit temperature F to Celsius temperature C is $C = \dfrac{5}{9}(F - 32)$. What range in Celsius degrees corresponds to a range of 68° to 86° Fahrenheit? 20°C to 30°C

80. Parking expense. The parking cost at the local airport (in dollars) is $C = 2 + 1.75(h - 1)$, where h is the number of hours the car is parked. For what range of hours is the parking cost between $37 and $51? 21 to 29 hr

81. Car rental. Suppose a rental car costs $18 per day, plus $0.25 per mile for each mile driven. What range of miles can be driven to stay within a $30-per-day car rental allowance? 0 to 48 mi

82. Plumbing charges. A plumber charges $42 per hour. A repair estimate includes a fixed cost of $147 for parts and a labor cost that is determined by how long it takes to complete the job. If the total estimate is for at least $210 and at most $294, what interval was estimated for the job? 1.5 to 3.5 hr

Answers:
71. $2012 to $2100
76. at least $425

C Exercises   Beyond the Basics

83. For what value of k does $-2 \le x \le k$ have exactly one solution? $k = -2$

84. For what values of k is $k < x < k + 1$ a conditional inequality? $(-\infty, \infty)$

85. For what value of k is the interval $(-\infty, k]$ the solution set for the linear inequality $ax + b \le 0$ if $a > 0$?

86. What interval is the solution set for the linear inequality $ax + b \ge 0$ if $a < 0$?

87. Solve $0 < (2x + 1)^{-1} < \dfrac{1}{2}$. $\left(\dfrac{1}{2}, \infty\right)$

88. Solve $0 < (3x - 6)^{-1} < \dfrac{2}{3}$. $\left(\dfrac{5}{2}, \infty\right)$

89. Find the domain of x in the expression $\sqrt{3x + 9}$. $[-3, \infty)$

90. Find the domain of x in the expression $\sqrt{3 - x}$. $(-\infty, 3]$

91. Solve the inequality $-a \le bx + c < a$, assuming that $b > 0$.

92. Solve the inequality $-a \le bx + c < a$, assuming that $b < 0$.

Critical Thinking

93. The equation $x = x + 1$ is inconsistent. If possible replace the equality sign in this equation by an appropriate inequality symbol so that the solution set of the resulting inequality is
  a. $\varnothing$. $>$ or $\ge$
  b. $(-\infty, \infty)$. $<$ or $\le$
  c. neither (a) nor (b). not possible

94. Repeat Exercise 93 by beginning with the identity $2(x + 3) = 2x + 6$.

95. Repeat Exercise 93 by beginning with the conditional equation $2x - 3 = 7$.

Answers:

85. $k = -\dfrac{b}{a}$ **86.** $\left(-\infty, -\dfrac{b}{a}\right]$ **91.** $\left[-\dfrac{a + c}{b}, \dfrac{a - c}{b}\right)$

92. $\left(\dfrac{a - c}{b}, -\dfrac{a + c}{b}\right]$

94. a. $<$ or $>$ **b.** $\le$ or $\ge$ **c.** not possible

95. a. not possible   **b.** not possible   **c.** $<, \le, >$ or $\ge$

Polynomial and Rational Inequalities

BEFORE STARTING THIS SECTION, REVIEW

1. Linear equations (Section 1.1, page 89)

2. Quadratic equations (Section 1.4, page 120)

3. Zero-product property (Section 1.4, page 120)

4. Inequalities (Section 1.6, page 148)

OBJECTIVES

1 Learn to solve quadratic inequalities.

2 Learn to solve polynomial inequalities.

3 Learn to solve rational inequalities.

Accident Investigation

Long before the famous traffic fatality in 1997 involving Princess Diana and Dodi Al Fayed, insurance companies and police investigated the scene of traffic accidents for evidence. You have possibly seen investigators measuring skid marks at the scene of an accident. These measurements yield information about the speed the car making the marks was traveling at the time of the accident. Under certain road conditions, such as a wet blacktop surface, the distance (in feet) it takes a car traveling v miles per hour to stop is given by the equation

$$d = 0.05v^2 + v.$$

The skid marks at one accident where these conditions were met were over 75 feet long. The accident occurred in a 25-mile-per-hour speed zone. Was the driver going over the speed limit? We answer this question in Example 2, using the methods of this section. ■

Polynomial Inequalities

When you want to test the chlorine level in a swimming pool you test the water at one place and are confident that the chlorine level is the same throughout the pool. Somewhat like the swimming pool, polynomials have a property that allows you to test *any point* in any interval of numbers that does *not* contain a root of the polynomial, and if the value of the polynomial at that point is positive, the value at *every* point in the interval is also positive. Similarly, if the value at the point tested is negative, the value of the polynomial at *every* point in the interval is also negative. We will learn how to use this property to solve inequalities involving polynomials.

◆ **WARNING**   Before attempting to solve any polynomial or rational inequality, rearrange the inequality so that a polynomial or rational expression is on the left-hand side of the inequality symbol and 0 is on the right-hand side.

1 Learn to solve quadratic inequalities.

Using Test Points to Solve Inequalities

The **test-point** method we describe next works for all quadratic polynomials. We first consider quadratic polynomials that have two distinct real roots. In this case, we find the two roots (using the quadratic formula if necessary) and then make sign graphs of the quadratic polynomial. The two roots divide the number line into three intervals, and the sign of the quadratic polynomial is determined in each interval by testing *any* number in the interval.

EXAMPLE 1   **Using the Test-point Method to Solve a Quadratic Inequality**

Solve $x^2 > 2x + 7$. Write the solution in interval notation and graph the solution set.

Solution

We first rearrange the inequality so that 0 is on the right side.

$x^2 > 2x + 7$	Original inequality
$x^2 - 2x - 7 > 2x + 7 - 2x - 7$	Subtract $2x + 7$ from both sides; remember to change the sign of both terms.
$x^2 - 2x - 7 > 0$	Simplify.

To determine where $x^2 - 2x - 7$ is positive (> 0), we first solve the associated equation.

$$1 \cdot x^2 - 2x - 7 = 0 \qquad \text{Replace } > \text{ by } = \text{ in } x^2 - 2x - 7 > 0.$$

$$x = \frac{-b \pm \sqrt{b^2 - 4ac}}{2a} \qquad \text{Use the quadratic formula to solve } x^2 - 2x - 7 = 0.$$

$$= \frac{-(-2) \pm \sqrt{(-2)^2 - 4(1)(-7)}}{2(1)} \qquad \text{Replace } a \text{ by } 1, b \text{ by } -2, \text{ and } c \text{ by } -7 \text{ in the quadratic formula.}$$

$$= \frac{2 \pm \sqrt{32}}{2} = 1 \pm 2\sqrt{2} \qquad \text{Simplify.}$$

Continued on next page.

The two roots for $x^2 - 2x - 7 = 0$ are $1 - 2\sqrt{2} \approx -1.8$ and $1 + 2\sqrt{2} \approx 3.8$. These roots divide the number line into three intervals, as shown in Figure 1.13. We select a convenient "test point" in each of the three intervals $(-\infty, 1 - 2\sqrt{2})$, $(1 - 2\sqrt{2})$, $(1 + 2\sqrt{2})$, and $(1 + 2\sqrt{2}, \infty)$. The points we selected, namely, -3, 0, and 4, are shown on the number line, but any other three points from each respective interval would work as well. Now evaluate $x^2 - 2x - 7$ for each test point.

Test Interval	Test Point	Value of $x^2 - 2x - 7$	Result
$(-\infty, 1 - 2\sqrt{2})$	-3	$(-3)^2 - 2(-3) - 7 = 8$	Positive
$(1 - 2\sqrt{2}, 1 + 2\sqrt{2})$	0	$(0)^2 - 2(0) - 7 = -7$	Negative
$(1 + 2\sqrt{2}, \infty)$	4	$(4)^2 - 2(4) - 7 = 1$	Positive

The sign of $x^2 - 2x - 7$ at each test point gives the sign of $x^2 - 2x - 7$ for every point in the interval containing that test point. These results are shown in the sign graph in Figure 1.13.

FIGURE 1.13

To find where $x^2 - 2x - 7 > 0$, we locate the "+" signs on the sign graph. Because the "+" signs are to the left of $1 - 2\sqrt{2}$, we include the interval $(-\infty, 1 - 2\sqrt{2})$ in the solution set. Since the "+" signs are also to the right of $1 + 2\sqrt{2}$, we also include the interval $(1 + 2\sqrt{2}, \infty)$ in the solution set. The solution set consists of the numbers that are in either $(-\infty, 1 - 2\sqrt{2})$ or $(1 + 2\sqrt{2}, \infty)$. This can also be written as $(-\infty, 1 - 2\sqrt{2}) \cup (1 + 2\sqrt{2}, \infty)$. The graph of the inequality is shown in Figure 1.14.

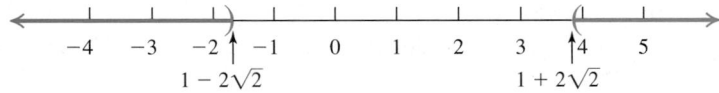

FIGURE 1.14   ■ ■ ■

PRACTICE PROBLEM 1   Solve $x^2 > 2x + 2$. Write the solution in interval notation and graph the solution set.   ■

EXAMPLE 2   **Calculating Speeds from Telltale Skid Marks**

In the introduction to this section, a car involved in an accident left skid marks over 75 feet long. Under the road conditions at the accident, the distance d (in feet) it takes a car traveling v miles per hour to stop is given by the equation

$$d = 0.05v^2 + v.$$

The accident occurred in a 25-mile-per-hour speed zone. Was the driver going over the speed limit?

Solution

To answer the question, we solve the inequality

$$(\text{stopping distance}) > 75 \text{ feet}, \quad \text{or} \quad 0.05v^2 + v > 75.$$

To find out what speeds correspond to a stopping distance of more than 75 feet, we first rearrange the inequality so that only 0 appears on the right side.

$$0.05v^2 + v > 75 \qquad \text{Stopping distance } d > 75 \text{ feet}$$
$$0.05v^2 + v - 75 > 0 \qquad \text{Subtract 75 from both sides.}$$
$$0.05v^2 + v - 75 = 0 \qquad \text{Write the associated equation.}$$
$$5v^2 + 100v - 7500 = 0 \qquad \text{Multiply both sides by 100 to eliminate decimals.}$$
$$v^2 + 20v - 1500 = 0 \qquad \text{Divide both sides by 5.}$$
$$(v + 50)(v - 30) = 0 \qquad \text{Factor.}$$
$$v + 50 = 0 \quad \text{or} \quad v - 30 = 0 \qquad \text{Zero-factor property}$$
$$v = -50 \quad \text{or} \qquad v = 30 \qquad \text{Solve for } v.$$

The two roots, -50 and 30, divide the number line into three test intervals: $(-\infty, -50)$, $(-50, 30)$, and $(30, \infty)$. Now select a convenient test point in each of these intervals. The points we selected, namely, -60, 0, and 40, are shown on the number line in Figure 1.15. Next, we evaluate $0.05v^2 + v - 75$ for each test point.

Test Interval	Test Point	Value of $0.05v^2 + v - 75$	Result
$(-\infty, -50)$	-60	$0.05(-60)^2 + (-60) - 75 = 45$	Positive
$(-50, -30)$	0	$0.05(0)^2 + 0 - 75 = -75$	Negative
$(30, \infty)$	40	$0.05(40)^2 + 40 - 75 = 45$	Positive

The sign of $0.05v^2 + v - 75$ at each test point gives the sign of $0.05v^2 + v - 75$ for every point in the interval containing the test point. These results are shown in the sign graph in Figure 1.15.

FIGURE 1.15

For this situation, we look at only the positive values of v. Note that the numbers corresponding to speeds between 0 and 30 miles per hour (that is, $0 \le v \le 30$) are not solutions of $0.05v^2 + v > 75$. Thus, the car was traveling *more* than 30 miles per hour. The driver was going over the speed limit.   ■ ■ ■

PRACTICE PROBLEM 2   Would the driver in Example 2 have been speeding if the skid marks had been 35 feet long and the accident had taken place in a 20-mile-per-hour speed zone?   ■

Once we rearrange a quadratic inequality so that 0 is on the right side, we set the left side equal to 0 and solve the resulting equation. What if the resulting equation has only one real solution or no real solution?

If the resulting equation has only one real solution, this root divides the number line into two sections, and the sign graph will consist of "0" at the one solution and either all "+" signs or all "−" signs everywhere else. This sign graph can then be used to solve the inequality.

If the resulting equation has no real solution, we use the following result, which is true for all polynomial equations (not just quadratic equations).

ONE-SIGN THEOREM

If a polynomial equation has no real solution, then the polynomial is either always positive or always negative.

EXAMPLE 3   Using the One-sign Theorem to Solve a Quadratic Inequality

Solve: $x^2 - 2x + 2 > 0$.

Solution

This quadratic inequality already has 0 on the right side, so we set the left side equal to 0 to obtain the associated equation. Because there are no obvious factors, we evaluate the discriminant to see if there are any real roots.

$$x^2 - 2x + 2 = 1 \cdot x^2 - 2x + 2 = 0 \qquad a = 1, b = -2, c = 2$$
$$b^2 - 4ac = (-2)^2 - 4(1)(2) \qquad \text{Evaluate the discriminant.}$$
$$= -4 \qquad \text{The discriminant is negative.}$$

Since the discriminant, -4, is negative, $x^2 - 2x + 2 = 0$ has no real roots and $x^2 - 2x + 2$ is either always positive (> 0) or always negative (< 0). To find out which, we can use any value of x as a test point. Calculations with $x = 0$ are simple, so we pick 0 as a test point.

Let $x = 0$. Then $(0)^2 - 2(0) + 2 = 2$, which is positive, so $x^2 - 2x + 2$ is *always* positive. The solution set is the set of all real numbers, which is written in interval notation as $(-\infty, \infty)$.   ■ ■ ■

PRACTICE PROBLEM 3   Solve $x^2 + 2x - 2 > 0$.   ■

2 Learn to solve polynomial inequalities.

Other Polynomial Inequalities

Regardless of the degree of the polynomial in an inequality, if we can factor the polynomial, we can use test points and a sign graph to solve it.

EXAMPLE 4   Solving a Polynomial Inequality

Solve $x^4 \leq 1$. Write the solution in interval notation and graph the solution set.

Solution

We first arrange the inequality so that 0 is on the right-hand side.

$$x^4 \leq 1 \qquad \text{Original inequality}$$
$$x^4 - 1 \leq 0 \qquad \text{Subtract 1 from both sides.}$$

Now we factor the left side.

$$x^4 - 1 \leq 0$$
$$(x^2)^2 - 1 \leq 0 \qquad \text{Rewrite } x^4 \text{ as } (x^2)^2.$$
$$(x^2 - 1)(x^2 + 1) \leq 0 \qquad \text{Factor the difference of squares.}$$
$$(x - 1)(x + 1)(x^2 + 1) \leq 0 \qquad \text{Factor } x^2 - 1 = (x - 1)(x + 1).$$

Next, we find the real solutions of the associated equation.

$$(x - 1)(x + 1)(x^2 + 1) = 0$$ Replace $\leq$ by $=$ in
$$$$ $(x - 1)(x + 1)(x^2 + 1) \leq 0$.

$$x - 1 = 0, \quad \text{or} \quad x + 1 = 0 \quad \text{or} \quad x^2 + 1 = 0$$ Zero-product property

Thus, $x = 1$ or $x = -1$. (The equation $x^2 + 1 = 0$ has no real solution.)

The solutions -1 and 1, of $(x - 1)(x + 1)(x^2 + 1) = 0$ divide the number line into three intervals: $(-\infty, -1), (-1, 1)$ and $(1, \infty)$. See Figure 1.16.

We select convenient test points in each of these three intervals. We pick -2, 0, and 2. Next, we compute the value of $(x - 1)(x + 1)(x^2 + 1)$ at each test point to determine the sign at each point.

Interval	Test Point	Value of $(x - 1)(x + 1)(x^2 + 1)$	Sign
$(-\infty, -1)$	-2	$(-2 - 1)(-2 + 1)((-2)^2 + 1) = 15$	$+$
$(-1, 1)$	0	$(0 - 1)(0 + 1)((0)^2 + 1) = -1$	$-$
$(1, \infty)$	2	$(2 - 1)(2 + 1)((2)^2 + 1) = 15$	$+$

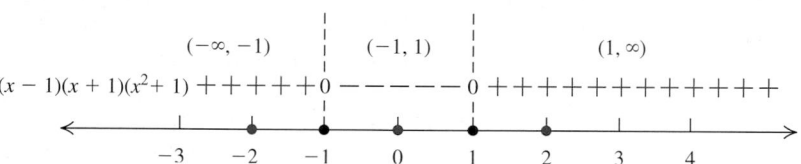

FIGURE 1.16

We see from Figure 1.16 that the solution set consists of all x between -1 and 1, including both -1 and 1. The solution set is shown in Figure 1.17.

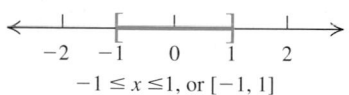

$-1 \leq x \leq 1$, or $[-1, 1]$

FIGURE 1.17   ■ ■ ■

PRACTICE PROBLEM 4   Solve $x^4 \leq 3x^2 + 4$. Write the solution in interval notation and graph the solution set.   ■

3 Learn to solve rational inequalities.

Rational Inequalities

An inequality involving a rational expression rather than a polynomial is called a **rational inequality.** The additional consideration in a rational inequality is the polynomial in the denominator. As with polynomial inequalities, our first step is to rearrange the inequality (if necessary) so that the right side is 0.

EXAMPLE 5   Solving a Rational Inequality

Solve $\dfrac{3}{x - 1} \geq 1$. Write the solution in interval notation and graph the solution set.

Continued on next page.

Solution

We first rewrite $\dfrac{3}{x-1} \geq 1$ to get 0 on the right-hand side.

$$\dfrac{3}{x-1} \geq 1 \qquad \text{Original inequality}$$

$$\dfrac{3}{x-1} - 1 \geq 0 \qquad \text{Subtract 1 from both sides.}$$

$$\dfrac{3 - (x-1)}{x-1} \geq 0 \qquad \text{Use } x - 1 \text{ as a common denominator.}$$

$$\dfrac{4-x}{x-1} \geq 0 \qquad \text{Simplify the numerator.}$$

Solve the following (this can often be done mentally):

$$\text{numerator} = 0 \qquad \text{and} \qquad \text{denominator} = 0.$$
$$4 - x = 0 \qquad\qquad\qquad x - 1 = 0$$
$$4 = x \qquad\qquad\qquad x = 1$$

The numbers 1 and 4 divide the number line into three intervals: $(-\infty, 1), (1, 4)$ and $(4, \infty)$. We choose 0, 2, and 5 as convenient test points in these intervals. The test points are shown on the sign graph in Figure 1.18.

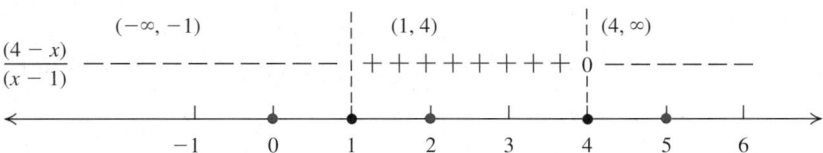

FIGURE 1.18

From the sign graph in Figure 1.18, we determine the real numbers for which $\dfrac{4-x}{x-1}$ is positive (> 0); these are the numbers in the interval $(1, 4)$, as the "+" signs indicate. However, we want to know where $\dfrac{4-x}{x-1}$ is *either* positive *or* 0. The expression $\dfrac{4-x}{x-1}$ is undefined for $x = 1$ and is 0 only if $x = 4$. The solution set is then $\{x \mid 1 < x \leq 4\}$, or, in interval notation, $(1, 4]$. The graph is shown in Figure 1.19. ▪ ▪ ▪

$1 < x \leq 4$, or $(1, 4]$

FIGURE 1.19

PRACTICE PROBLEM 5 Solve $\dfrac{2}{1-3x} > 1$. Write the solution in interval notation and graph the solution set. ▪

WARNING You can't solve a rational inequality by multiplying both sides by the LCD, as you would with a rational equation. Remember that you reverse the sense of an inequality when multiplying by a negative expression. However, when an expression contains a variable, you do not know whether the expression is positive or negative.

A Exercises   Basic Skills and Concepts

In Exercises 1–42, solve each inequality by the test-point method. Write the solution in interval notation.

1. $(x - 3)(x + 2) < 0$ †
2. $(x - 2)(x + 3) < 0$ †
3. $(x + 5)(x - 2) < 0$ †
4. $(x - 5)(x + 2) > 0$ †
5. $(x + 4)(x - 1) \leq 0$ †
6. $(x - 4)(x + 1) \leq 0$ †
7. $(x - 6)(x + 1) \geq 0$ †
8. $(x + 6)(x - 1) \geq 0$ †
9. $x(x + 3) < 0$ $(-3, 0)$
10. $x(x - 3) > 0$ †
11. $x^2 \leq 9$ $[-3, 3]$
12. $x^2 \geq 1$ $(-\infty, -1] \cup [1, \infty)$
13. $25 - x^2 < 0$ †
14. $4 - x^2 > 0$ $(-2, 2)$
15. $x^2 + 4x - 12 \leq 0$ $[-6, 2]$
16. $x^2 - 8x + 7 > 0$ †
17. $6x^2 + 7x - 3 \geq 0$ †
18. $4x^2 - 2x - 2 < 0$ †
19. $25x^2 + 5x - 6 \leq 0$ †
20. $12x^2 - 5x - 7 < 0$ †
21. $(x - 2)^2 \leq 1$ $[1, 3]$
22. $(x + 3)^2 > 9$ †
23. $2x^2 + 5x < 12$ †
24. $6x^2 + 11x \geq 7$ †
25. $2x(x + 3)(x - 3) \leq 0$ †
26. $3x(x + 2)(x - 2) > 0$ †
27. $(x + 3)(x + 1)(x - 1) \geq 0$ $[-3, -1] \cup [1, \infty)$
28. $(x + 4)(x - 1)(x + 2) < 0$ $(-\infty, -4) \cup (-2, 1)$
29. $x^2 - 2x - 2 < 0$ †
30. $x^2 - 4x - 1 \leq 0$ †
31. $x^2 \geq -1$ $(-\infty, \infty)$
32. $2x^2 \geq -5$ $(-\infty, \infty)$
33. $x^2 + 2x < -1$ $\varnothing$
34. $4x^2 + 12x < -9$ $\varnothing$
35. $x^3 - x^2 \geq 0$ $\{0\} \cup [1, \infty)$
36. $x^3 - 9x^2 > 0$ $(9, \infty)$
37. $x^4 \leq 2x^2$ $[-\sqrt{2}, \sqrt{2}]$
38. $x^4 \geq 3x^2$ †
39. $x^2 \geq 1$ $(-\infty, -1] \cup [1, \infty)$
40. $x^3 < -8$ $(-\infty, -2)$
41. $x^4 \leq 16$ $[-2, 2]$
42. $x^4 > 9$ †

In Exercises 43–62, solve each rational inequality. Write the solution in interval notation.

43. $\dfrac{x + 2}{x - 5} < 0$ $(-2, 5)$
44. $\dfrac{x - 3}{x + 1} > 0$ †
45. $\dfrac{3x + 2}{x - 3} \leq 0$ $\left[-\dfrac{2}{3}, 3\right)$
46. $\dfrac{3 - 2x}{4x + 5} \geq 0$ $\left(-\dfrac{5}{4}, \dfrac{3}{2}\right]$
47. $\dfrac{x + 4}{x} < 0$ $(-4, 0)$
48. $\dfrac{x}{x - 2} > 0$ †
49. $\dfrac{x + 1}{x + 2} \leq 3$ †
50. $\dfrac{x - 1}{x - 2} > 3$ $\left(2, \dfrac{5}{2}\right)$
51. $\dfrac{(x - 2)(x + 2)}{x} > 0$ †
52. $\dfrac{(x - 1)(x + 3)}{x - 2} < 0$ †
53. $x + \dfrac{8}{x} \leq 6$ $(-\infty, 0) \cup [2, 4]$
54. $x - \dfrac{12}{x} > 1$ †
55. $2 - \dfrac{2x}{3x - 4} > 0$ †
56. $1 + \dfrac{1}{2 - x} \geq 0$ †
57. $\dfrac{x + 4}{3x - 2} \geq 1$ $\left(\dfrac{2}{3}, 3\right]$
58. $\dfrac{2x - 3}{x + 3} \leq 1$ $(-3, 6]$
59. $3 \leq \dfrac{2x + 6}{2x + 1}$ $\left(-\dfrac{1}{2}, \dfrac{3}{4}\right]$
60. $\dfrac{x - 2}{2x + 1} < -1$ $\left(-\dfrac{1}{2}, \dfrac{1}{3}\right)$
61. $\dfrac{x + 5}{x - 2} > \dfrac{x}{x + 2}$ †
62. $\dfrac{x - 1}{x + 1} > \dfrac{x}{x - 1}$ †

B Exercises   Applying the Concepts

63. **Free-falling object.** The distance d traveled in t seconds by an object dropped from a height h is given by $d = 16t^2$. If a water bottle is dropped from a hot-air balloon when the balloon is between 64 and 100 feet above the ground, how long (in seconds) does it take for the bottle to hit the ground? †

64. **Interest rate.** The amount of money A received at the end of two years when P dollars is invested at a compound rate r is $A = P(1 + r)^2$. A firm is investing \$100,000 for a two-year period and expects to get a return of no less than \$110,000 and no more than \$115,000. What range of interest rates (to the nearest percent) will provide the expected return? 5% to 7%

65. **Temperature.** The number N of water mites in a water sample depends on the temperature t in degrees Fahrenheit and is given by $N = 110t - t^2$. At what temperature will the number of mites exceed 1000? 10°F to 100°F

66. **Falling object.** The height h of an object thrown from the top of a ski lift 1584 feet high after t seconds is $h = -16t^2 + 32t + 1584$. For what times is the height of the object at least 1200 feet? 0 to 6 sec

†Due to space constrictions, answers to these exercises may be found in the Answers beginning on page A–1 in the back of the book.

67. Company profit. The profit P (in millions of dollars) of a company for next year is estimated to satisfy the inequality $P(P - 3) < 4(P - 3)$. What is the estimated profit for this company for next year? Between 3 and 4 million dollars

68. Area of a rectangle. The length of a rectangle is 5 meters larger than the width. Find the range of widths that result in such a rectangle whose area is at least 204 square meters. †

69. Blackjack. A gambler playing blackjack in a casino using four decks noticed that 20% of the cards that had been dealt were jacks, queens, kings, or aces. After x cards had been dealt, he knew that the likelihood that the next card dealt would be a jack, queen, king, or ace is $\dfrac{64 - 0.2x}{208 - x}$. For what values of x is this likelihood greater than 50%? †

70. Area of a triangle. The base of a triangle is 3 centimeters greater than the height. Find the possible heights h so that the area of such a triangle will be at least 5 square centimeters. †

C Exercises   Beyond the Basics

71. Find the numbers k for which the quadratic equation $2x^2 + kx + 2 = 0$ has two real solutions. $(-\infty, -4) \cup (4, \infty)$

72. Find the numbers k for which the quadratic equation $2x^2 + kx + 2 = 0$ has no real solutions. $(-4, 4)$

73. Find the numbers k for which the quadratic equation $x^2 + kx + k = 0$ has two real solutions $(-\infty, 0) \cup (4, \infty)$.

74. Find the numbers k for which the quadratic equation $x^2 + kx + k = 0$ has no real solutions. $(0, 4)$

In Exercises 75–80, find the domain of the variable in each expression.

75. $\sqrt{x^2 - 1}$ $(-\infty, -1] \cup [1, \infty)$ **76.** $\sqrt{x^2 - x - 2}$

77. $\dfrac{1}{\sqrt{1 - x^2}}$ $(-1, 1)$ **78.** $\dfrac{\sqrt{-x}}{x^2 - 9}$ $(-\infty, -3) \cup (-3, 0]$

79. $\sqrt{\dfrac{x - 1}{x + 3}}$ $(-\infty, -3) \cup [1, \infty)$ **80.** $\sqrt{\dfrac{x - 2}{1 - x}}$ $(1, 2]$

81. An import firm pays a tax of $10 on each radio it imports. In addition to this tax, there is a penalty tax that must be paid if more than 1000 radios are imported. The penalty tax is computed by multiplying 5 cents by the number of radios imported in excess of 1000. This tax must be paid on each and every radio imported. If 1006 radios are imported, the penalty tax is $6 \cdot 5 = 30$ cents and is paid on each of the 1006 radios. If the firm wants to spend no more than a total of $640,000 on import taxes, how many radios can it import?

82. A TV quiz program pays a contestant $100 for each correct answer for 10 questions. If all 10 questions are answered correctly, bonus questions are asked. The reward for every correct answer is increased by $50 for each bonus question that is correctly answered. Any incorrect answer ends the game. If 2 bonus questions are answered correctly, the contestant receives $200 *for each of the 12 questions*. If a contestant won more than $3500, how many questions must have been answered correctly? at least 14 questions

Critical Thinking

83. Give an example of a quadratic inequality with each of the following solution sets.
   a. $(-4, 5)$ $(x + 4)(x - 5) < 0$
   b. $[-2, 6]$ $(x + 2)(x - 6) \le 0$
   c. $(-\infty, \infty)$ $x^2 \ge 0$
   d. $\varnothing$ $x^2 < 0$
   e. $\{3\}$ $(x - 3)^2 \le 0$
   f. $(-\infty, 2) \cup (2, \infty)$ $(x - 2)^2 > 0$

84. Give an example of an inequality with each of the following solution sets.
   a. $(-2, 4]$
   b. $[3, 5)$

Is there a quadratic inequality whose solution set is $(2, 5]$?

Answers:

76. $(-\infty, -1] \cup [2, \infty)$ **81.** at most 4000 radios

84. a. $\dfrac{x - 4}{x + 2} \le 0$ **b.** $\dfrac{x - 3}{x - 5} \le 0$ **c.** no

Equations and Inequalities Involving Absolute Value

BEFORE STARTING THIS SECTION, REVIEW

1. Properties of absolute value (Section P.1, page 8)

2. Intervals (Section P.1, page 8)

3. Linear inequalities (Section 1.6, page 148)

OBJECTIVES

1 Learn to solve equations involving absolute value.

2 Learn to solve inequalities involving absolute value.

Rescuing a Downed Aircraft

Rescue crews arrive at an airport in Maine to conduct an air search for a missing Cessna with two persons aboard. If they locate the missing aircraft, they are to mark the global positioning system (GPS) coordinates and notify the mission base. The search planes normally average 110 miles per hour, but weather conditions can affect the average speed by as much as 15 miles per hour (either slower or faster). If a search plane has 30 gallons of fuel and uses 10 gallons of fuel per hour, what is its possible search range (in miles)? In Example 4, we use an inequality involving absolute value to find the plane's possible search range. ■

---

1 Learn to solve equations involving absolute value.

Equations Involving Absolute Value

Recall that, geometrically, the absolute value of a real number a is the distance from the origin on the number line to the point with coordinate a. The definition of absolute value is

$$|a| = a \text{ if } a \geq 0 \qquad \text{and} \qquad |a| = -a \text{ if } a < 0.$$

A summary of the most useful properties of absolute value can be found on page 10 in Section P.1.

Because the only two numbers on the number line that are exactly two units from the origin are 2 and -2, they are the only solutions of the equation $|x| = 2$. (See Figure 1.20.) This simple observation leads to the following rule for solving equations involving absolute value.

FIGURE 1.20

THE SOLUTIONS OF $|u| = a, a \geq 0$

If $a \geq 0$, and u is an algebraic expression, then

$$|u| = a \quad \text{is equivalent to} \quad u = a \text{ or } u = -a.$$

$$|u| = -a \quad \text{has no solution when } a > 0.$$

Note that if $a = 0$, then $u = 0$ is the only solution of $|u| = 0$

EXAMPLE 1   **Solving an Equation Involving Absolute Value**

Solve each equation.

a. $|x + 3| = 0$ **b.** $|2x - 3| - 5 = 8$

Solution

a. Let $u = x + 3$. $|u| = 0$ has only one solution: $u = 0$

$$|x + 3| = 0$$
$$x + 3 = 0 \qquad u = 0$$
$$x = -3$$

Now we check the solution in the original equation.

Check:

$$|x + 3| = 0 \qquad \text{Original equation}$$
$$|-3 + 3| \overset{?}{=} 0 \qquad \text{Replace } x \text{ by } -3.$$
$$|0| = 0 \checkmark \qquad \text{Simplify.}$$

We have verified that -3 is a solution of the original equation.
   The solution set is $\{-3\}$.

b. In order to use the rule for solving equations involving absolute value, we must first isolate the absolute value expression to one side of the equation:

$$|2x - 3| - 5 = 8$$
$$|2x - 3| = 13 \qquad \text{Add 5 to both sides.}$$

$|u| = 13$ is equivalent to $u = 13$ or $u = -13$. Let $u = 2x - 3$; then $|2x - 3| = 13$ is equivalent to

$$2x - 3 = 13 \quad \text{or} \quad 2x - 3 = -13. \qquad u = 13 \text{ or } u = -13$$
$$2x = 16 \qquad\qquad 2x = -10 \qquad \text{Add 3 to both sides of each equation.}$$
$$x = 8 \qquad\qquad x = -5 \qquad \text{Divide both sides by 2.}$$

We leave it to you to check these solutions.
   The solution set is $\{-5, 8\}$. ■ ■ ■

PRACTICE PROBLEM 1   Solve each equation.

a. $|x - 2| = 0$ **b.** $|6x - 3| - 8 = 1$ ■

With a little practice, you may find that you can solve these types of equations without actually writing u and the expression it represents. Then you can just work with the expression itself.

EXAMPLE 2   Solving an Equation of the Form $|u| = |v|$

Solve $|x - 1| = |x + 5|$.

Solution

If $|u| = |v|$, then either u is equal to $|v|$ or u is equal to $-|v|$. Since $|v| = \pm v$ in every case, we have $u = v$ or $u = -v$. Thus,

$$|u| = |v| \text{ is equivalent to } u = v \text{ or } u = -v.$$
$$|x - 1| = |x + 5| \text{ is equivalent to}$$

$$x - 1 = x + 5 \qquad \text{or} \qquad x - 1 = -(x + 5). \qquad \begin{array}{l} u = x - 1, \\ v = x + 5 \end{array}$$

$$-1 = 5 \text{ (False)} \qquad \qquad x = -2 \qquad \qquad \text{Solve for } x.$$

Hence, $x - 1 = x + 5$ has no solution.

The only solution of $|x - 1| = |x + 5|$ is -2, so the solution set is $\{-2\}$. We leave it to you to check this solution.   ■ ■ ■

PRACTICE PROBLEM 2   Solve $|x + 2| = |x - 3|$.   ■

2 Learn to solve inequalities involving absolute value.

Inequalities Involving Absolute Value

The equation $|x| = 2$ has two solutions: 2 and -2. If x is any real number other than 2 or -2, then $|x| < 2$ or $|x| > 2$. Geometrically, this means that x is closer than 2 units to the origin if $|x| < 2$, or farther than 2 units from the origin if $|x| > 2$. Any number x that is closer than 2 units from the origin is in the interval $-2 < x < 2$. (See Figure 1.21 (a).) Any number x that is farther than 2 units from the origin is in either the interval $(-\infty, -2)$ or the interval $(2, \infty)$; that is, either or $x < -2$ or $x > 2$. (See Figure 1.21 (b).)

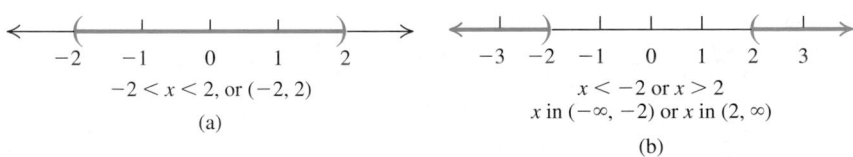

$-2 < x < 2$, or $(-2, 2)$
(a)

$x < -2$ or $x > 2$
x in $(-\infty, -2)$ or x in $(2, \infty)$
(b)

FIGURE 1.21

This discussion is equally valid when we use any positive real number a instead of the number 2, and it leads to the following rules for replacing inequalities involving absolute value with equivalent inequalities that do *not* involve absolute value.

> ### RULES FOR SOLVING ABSOLUTE VALUE INEQUALITIES
>
> If $a > 0$ and u is an algebraic expression, then
>
> 1. $|u| < a$ is equivalent to $-a < u < a$.
> 2. $|u| \le a$ is equivalent to $-a \le u \le a$.
> 3. $|u| > a$ is equivalent to $u < -a$ or $u > a$.
> 4. $|u| \ge a$ is equivalent to $u \le -a$ or $u \ge a$.

EXAMPLE 3 **Solving an Inequality Involving Absolute Value**

Solve the inequality $|4x - 1| \le 9$ and graph the solution set.

Solution

Rule 2 applies here, with $u = 4x - 1$ and $a = 9$.

$$|4x - 1| \le 9 \text{ is equivalent to}$$

$-9 \le 4x - 1 \le 9.$	Rule 2, $-a \le u \le a$
$1 - 9 \le 4x - 1 + 1 \le 9 + 1$	Add 1 to each part.
$-8 \le 4x \le 10$	Simplify.
$-\dfrac{8}{4} \le \dfrac{4x}{4} \le \dfrac{10}{4}$	Divide by 4; the sense of the inequality is unchanged.
$-2 \le x \le \dfrac{5}{2}$	Simplify.

The solution set is $\left\{ x \,\middle|\, -2 \le x \le \dfrac{5}{2} \right\}$; that is, the solution set is the closed interval $\left[-2, \dfrac{5}{2} \right]$. (See Figure 1.22.) ■ ■ ■

$-2 \le x \le \dfrac{5}{2}$, or $\left[-2, \dfrac{5}{2} \right]$

FIGURE 1.22

PRACTICE PROBLEM 3 Solve $|3x + 3| \le 6$ and graph the solution set. ■

Note the following techniques for solving inequalities similar to Example 3.

1. To solve $|4x - 1| < 9$, change $\le$ to $<$ throughout to obtain the solution $\left(-2, \dfrac{5}{2} \right)$.

2. To solve $|1 - 4x| \le 9$, note that $|1 - 4x| = |4x - 1|$ so the solution is exactly that for Example 3, $\left[-2, \dfrac{5}{2} \right]$.

EXAMPLE 4 **Finding the Search Range of an Aircraft**

In the introduction to this section, we wanted to find the possible search range (in miles) for a search plane that has 30 gallons of fuel and uses 10 gallons of fuel per hour. We were told that the search plane normally averages 110 miles per hour, but that weather conditions could affect the average speed by as much as 15 miles per hour (either slower or faster). How do we find the possible search range?

Solution

To find the distance a plane flies (in miles), we need to know both how long (time, in hours) it flies and how fast (speed, in miles per hour) it flies.

Let x = actual speed of the search plane, in miles per hour. We know that the actual speed is within 15 miles per hour of the average speed, 110 miles per hour. That is, |Actual speed − Average speed| ≤ 15 miles per hour.

$$|x - 110| \leq 15 \qquad \text{Replace the verbal description with an inequality.}$$

Solve this inequality for x.

$$-15 \leq x - 110 \leq 15 \qquad \text{Rewrite the inequality using Rule 2.}$$
$$110 - 15 \leq x \leq 110 + 15 \qquad \text{Add 110 to each part.}$$
$$95 \leq x \leq 125 \qquad \text{Simplify.}$$

The actual speed of the search plane is between 95 and 125 miles per hour.

Since the plane uses 10 gallons of fuel per hour and has 30 gallons of fuel, it can fly for $\frac{30}{10}$, or 3 hours. Thus, the actual number of miles the search plane can fly is $3x$.

From $\qquad\qquad\qquad 95 \leq x \leq 125,$

we have $\qquad\qquad 3(95) \leq 3x \leq 3(125) \qquad \text{Multiply each part by 3.}$

$\qquad\qquad\qquad\quad 285 \leq 3x \leq 375 \qquad \text{Simplify.}$

The search plane's range is between 285 and 375 miles.   ■ ■ ■

PRACTICE PROBLEM 4   Repeat Example 4, but let the average speed of the plane be 115 miles per hour and suppose that the wind speed can affect the average speed by 25 miles per hour.   ■

EXAMPLE 5   **Solving an Inequality Involving Absolute Value**

Solve the inequality $|2x - 8| \geq 4$ and graph the solution set.

Solution

Rule 4 applies here, with $u = 2x - 8$ and $a = 4$.

$$|2x - 8| \geq 4 \text{ is equivalent to}$$

$2x - 8 \leq -4$ $\qquad$ or $\qquad$	$2x - 8 \geq 4.$	Rule 4, $u \leq -a$ or $u \geq a$
$2x - 8 + 8 \leq -4 + 8$	$2x - 8 + 8 \geq 4 + 8$	Add 8 to each part.
$2x \leq 4$	$2x \geq 12$	Simplify.
$\dfrac{2x}{2} \leq \dfrac{4}{2}$	$\dfrac{2x}{2} \geq \dfrac{12}{2}$	Divide both sides of each part by 2.
$x \leq 2$	$x \geq 6$	Simplify.

The solution set is $\{x \mid x \leq 2 \text{ or } x \geq 6\}$; that is, the solution set is the set of all real numbers x in either of the intervals $(-\infty, 2]$ or $[6, \infty)$. This set can also be written as $(-\infty, 2] \cup [6, \infty)$. See Figure 1.23.   ■ ■ ■

$x \leq 2$ or $x \geq 6$
$(-\infty, 2] \cup [6, \infty)$

FIGURE 1.23

PRACTICE PROBLEM 5   Solve $|2x + 3| \geq 6$ and graph the solution set.   ■

> **EXAMPLE 6**   **Solving Special Cases of Absolute Value Inequalities**

Solve each inequality.

a. $|3x - 2| > -5$ **b.** $|5x + 3| \leq -2$

Solution

a. Because the absolute value is always nonnegative, $|3x - 2| > -5$ is true for all real numbers x. The solution set is the set of all real numbers; in interval notation, we write $(-\infty, \infty)$.

b. There is no real number with absolute value ≤ -2, because the absolute value of any number is nonnegative. The solution set for $|5x + 3| \leq -2$ is the empty set, $\varnothing$.

■ ■ ■

PRACTICE PROBLEM 6   Solve: **a.** $|5 - 9x| > -3$ **b.** $|7x - 4| \leq -1$.   ■

A Exercises   Basic Skills and Concepts

In Exercises 1–24, solve each equation.

1. $|3x| = 9$ $\{-3,3\}$

2. $|4x| = 24$ $\{-6,6\}$

3. $|-2x| = 6$ $\{-3,3\}$

4. $|-x| = 3$ $\{-3,3\}$

5. $|x + 3| = 2$ $\{-5, -1\}$

6. $|x - 4| = 1$ $\{3,5\}$

7. $|2x - 6| = 8$ $\{-1,7\}$

8. $|3x - 6| = 9$ $\{-1,5\}$

9. $|6x - 2| = 9$ †

10. $|6x - 3| = 9$ $\{-1,2\}$

11. $|2x + 3| - 1 = 0$ †

12. $|2x - 3| - 1 = 0$ $\{1,2\}$

13. $\frac{1}{2}|x| = 3$ $\{-6,6\}$

14. $\frac{3}{5}|x| = 6$ $\{-10,10\}$

15. $\left|\frac{1}{4}x + 2\right| = 3$ $\{-20,4\}$

16. $\left|\frac{3}{2}x - 1\right| = 3$ $\left\{-\frac{4}{3},\frac{8}{3}\right\}$

17. $6|2x - 1| - 8 = 10$ †

18. $5|4x - 1| + 10 = 15$ †

19. $2|3x - 4| - 7 = 7$ †

20. $9|2x - 3| + 2 = -7$ $\varnothing$

21. $|2x + 1| = -1$ $\varnothing$

22. $|3x + 7| = -2$ $\varnothing$

23. $|x^2 - 4| = 0$ $\{-2,2\}$

24. $|9 - x^2| = 0$ $\{-3,3\}$

In Exercises 25–40, solve each inequality.

25. $|3x| < 12$ $(-4,4)$

26. $|2x| \leq 6$ $[-3,3]$

27. $|4x| > 16$ †

28. $|3x| > 15$ †

29. $|x + 1| < 3$ $(-4,2)$

30. $|x - 4| < 1$ $(3,5)$

31. $|x| - 2 \geq 1$ †

32. $|x| + 2 > 7$ †

33. $|2x - 3| < 4$ †

34. $|4x - 6| \leq 6$ $[0,3]$

35. $|2x - 5| > 3$ †

36. $|3x - 3| \geq 15$ †

37. $|3x + 4| \leq 19$ †

38. $|9 - 7x| < 23$ †

39. $|2x - 15| < 0$ $\varnothing$

40. $|x + 5| \leq -3$ $\varnothing$

In Exercises 41–50, solve each inequality and graph the solution set.

41. $\left|\frac{x}{2} - 1\right| < 4$ †

42. $\left|2 - \frac{x}{2}\right| > 1$ †

43. $\left|\frac{x - 8}{2}\right| \leq 4$ †

44. $\left|\frac{2x + 15}{8}\right| > 4$ †

45. $\left|\frac{3}{8}x - 105\right| \geq 0$ †

46. $|27x - 43| \geq 0$ †

47. $\left|3x - \frac{7}{3}\right| - 2 < 3$ †

48. $\left|\frac{x}{2} - 1\right| - 1 \leq \frac{1}{2}$ †

49. $\left|\frac{3}{5}x - 2\right| \leq 4$ †

50. $\left|\frac{x}{2} - \frac{1}{3}\right| > \frac{2}{3}$ †

In Exercises 51–54, solve each equation.

51. $|x + 3| = |x + 5|$ $\{-4\}$

52. $|x + 4| = |x - 8|$ $\{2\}$

53. $|3x - 2| = |6x + 7|$ †

54. $|2x - 4| = |4x + 6|$ †

B Exercises   Applying the Concepts

55. Varying temperatures. The inequality $|T - 75| \le 20$, where T is in degrees Fahrenheit, describes the daily temperature in Tampa during the month of December. Give an interpretation for this inequality if the high and low temperatures in Tampa during December satisfy the equation $|T - 75| = 20$.

56. Scale error. A butcher's scale is accurate to within ± 0.05 pound. A sirloin steak weighs 1.14 pounds on this scale. Let x = actual weight of the steak. Write an absolute value inequality in x whose solution is the range of possible values for the actual weight of the steak. $|x-1.14| \le 0.05$

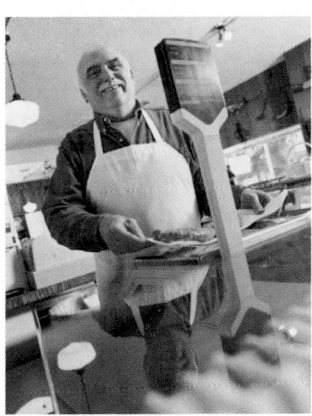

57. Company budget. A company budgets $700 for office supplies. The actual expense for budget supplies must be within $\pm\$50$ of this figure. Let x = actual expense for the office supplies. Write an absolute value inequality in x whose solution is the range of possible amounts for the expense for the office supplies. $|x-700| \le 50$

58. National achievement scores. Suppose 68% of the scores on a national achievement exam will be within ± 90 points of a score of 480. Let x = a score among the 68% just described. Write an absolute value inequality in x whose solution is the range of possible scores within ± 90 points of 480. $|x-480| \le 90$

59. Blood pressure. Suppose that 60% of Americans have a systolic blood pressure reading of 120, plus or minus 6.75. Let x = a blood pressure reading among the 60% just described. Write an absolute value inequality in x whose solution set is the range of possible blood pressure readings within ± 6.75 points of 120. $|x-120| \le 6.75$

60. Gas mileage. A motorcycle has approximately 4 gallons of gas, with an error margin of $\pm\frac{1}{4}$ of a gallon. If the motorcycle gets 37 miles per gallon of gas, how many miles can the motorcycle travel? between 138.75 and 157.25 mil

61. Event planning. An event planner expects about 120 people at a private party. She knows that this estimate could be off by 15 people (more or fewer). Food for the event costs $48 per person. How much might the event planner's food expense be? between $5040 and $6480

62. Company bonuses. Bonuses at a company are usually given to about 60 people each year. The bonuses are $1200 each, and the estimate of 60 recipients may be off by 7 people (more or fewer). How much might the company spend on bonuses this year? between $63,600 and $80,400

63. Fishing revenue. Sarah sells the fish she catches to a local restaurant for 60 cents a pound. She can usually estimate how much her catch weighs to within $\pm\frac{1}{2}$ pound. She estimates that she has 32 pounds of fish. How much might she get paid for her catch? between $18.90 and $19.50

64. Ticket sales. Ticket sales at an amusement park average about 460 on a Sunday. If actual Sunday sales are never more than 25 above or below the average, and if each ticket costs $29.50, how much money might the park take in on a Sunday? between $12,832.50 and $14,307.50

Answer:

55. The temperatures in Tampa during December are between 55°F and 95°F.

C Exercises   Beyond the Basics

In Exercises 65–70, solve each equation or inequality.

65. $|x^2 + 4x - 3| = 5$ †

66. $|x^2 + 3x - 2| = 2$ †

67. $\dfrac{1}{|2x - 1|} < 2$ †

68. $\dfrac{3}{|x + 1|} \geq 1$ $[-4,1) \cup (1,2]$

$\left[\textit{Hint}: 0 < a < b \text{ implies that } \dfrac{1}{a} > \dfrac{1}{b}. \right]$

69. $|x|^2 - 4|x| - 7 \leq 5$ $[-6,6]$ **70.** $2|x|^2 - |x| + 8 < 11$ †

71. Show that if $0 < a < b$ and $0 < c < d < g$, then $ac < bd$.

72. Show that if $0 < a < b < c$ and $0 < e < f < g$, then $ae < bf < cg$.

73. Show that if $x^2 < a$ and $a > 0$, the solution set of the inequality $x^2 < a$ is $\{x| -\sqrt{a} < x < \sqrt{a}\}$, or, in interval notation, $(-\sqrt{a}, \sqrt{a})$.
  [*Hint*: $a = (\sqrt{a})^2$; factor $x^2 - a$.]

74. Show that if $x^2 > a$ and $a > 0$, then the solution set of the inequality $x^2 > a$ is $(-\infty, -\sqrt{a}) \cup (\sqrt{a}, \infty)$.

In Exercises 75–86, write an absolute value inequality with variable x whose solution set is in the given interval(s).

75. $(1, 7)$ $|x - 4| < 3$

76. $[3, 8]$ $|2x - 11| \leq 5$

77. $[-2, 10]$ $|x - 4| \leq 6$

78. $(-7, -1)$ $|x + 4| < 3$

79. $(-\infty, 3) \cup (11, \infty)$ †

80. $(-\infty, -1) \cup (5, \infty)$ †

81. $(-\infty, -5] \cup [10, \infty)$ †

82. $(-\infty, -3] \cup [-1, \infty)$ †

83. (a, b) †

84. $[c, d]$ †

85. $(-\infty, a) \cup (b, \infty)$ †

86. $(-\infty, c] \cup [d, \infty)$ †

87. Varying temperatures. The weather forecast predicts temperatures that will be within 8° of 70° Fahrenheit. Let x = temperature in degrees Fahrenheit. Write an absolute value inequality in x whose solution is the predicted range of temperatures. $|x - 70| \leq 8$

In Exercises 88–93, solve each inequality for x. Use the fact that $|a| \leq |b|$ if and only if $a^2 \leq b^2$.

88. $|x + 1| < |x - 3|$ $(-\infty, 1)$ **89.** $|2x| \leq |x - 5|$ †

90. $\left|\dfrac{x - 1}{x + 1}\right| < 1$ $(0, \infty)$ **91.** $\left|\dfrac{3 - 2x}{1 + x}\right| \leq 4$ †

92. $\dfrac{1}{|x - 4|} - \dfrac{1}{|x + 7|} < 0$ † **93.** $\dfrac{1}{|x - 3|} \geq \dfrac{1}{|x + 4|}$ $\left[-\dfrac{1}{2}, \infty\right)$

Critical Thinking

94. For which values of x is $\sqrt{(x - 3)^2} = x - 3$? $[3, \infty)$

95. For which values of x is $\sqrt{(x^2 - 6x + 8)^2} = x^2 - 6x + 8$? †

96. Solve: $|x - 3|^2 - 7|x - 3| + 10 = 0$. $\{-2, 1, 5, 8\}$
   [*Hint*: Let $u = |x - 3|$.]

Summary   Definitions, Concepts, and Formulas

1.1 Linear Equations in One Variable

i.   An **equation** is a statement that two mathematical expressions are equal.

ii. The **solutions** or **roots** of an equation are those values (if any) of the variable which satisfy the equation.

iii. **Equivalent equations** are equations that have the same solution set.

iv. You can generate equivalent equations by the procedure on page 89.

v.   A linear equation in standard form is $ax + b = 0$.

vi. A **formula** is an equation that expresses a relationship between two or more variables.

1.2 Applications of Linear Equations

i.   **Mathematical modeling** is the process of translating real-world problems into mathematical problems.

ii. **Procedure for solving applied problems:** See page 99.

iii. **Simple Interest:** I = Principal · Rate · Time.

iv. **Uniform Motion:** Distance = Speed · Time

v.   **Work Rate:** If a job can be done in x units of time, then the portion of the job completed in one unit of time is $\dfrac{1}{x}$.

1.3 Complex Numbers

i.   Complex numbers are of the form $a + bi$, where a and b are real numbers and $i = \sqrt{-1}$; $i^2 = -1$.

ii. The number $a - bi$ is called the complex conjugate of $a + bi$.

iii. Operations with complex numbers can be performed as if they are binomials with the variable i. Set $i^2 = -1$ to simplify. Division is performed by first multiplying the numerator and the denominator by the complex conjugate of the denominator.

1.4 Quadratic Equations

i.   The equation $ax^2 + bx + c = 0$ is the **standard form** of the quadratic equation in x.

ii. The **zero-product property:** Let A and B be two algebraic expressions. Then $AB = 0$ if and only if $A = 0$ or $B = 0$.

iii. Square root method: If $u^2 = d$, then $u = \pm\sqrt{d}$.

iv. Method for completing the square: See page 123.

v. The quadratic formula: $x = \dfrac{-b \pm \sqrt{b^2 - 4ac}}{2a}$.

vi. The quantity $b^2 - 4ac$ is called the **discriminant**.

1.5 Solving Other Types of Equations

Remember to check the solutions. Extraneous solutions may be introduced when you

i. Multiply both sides by an LCD that contains a variable or

ii. Raise both sides to an even power.

1.6 Linear Inequalities

i. An **inequality** is a statement that one algebraic expression is less than, or less than or equal to, another algebraic expression.

ii. The real numbers that result in a true statement when they are substituted for the variable in the inequality are called **solutions** of the inequality.

iii. A **linear inequality** is an inequality that can be written in the form $ax + b < 0$. The symbol $<$ can be replaced by $\leq$, $>$, or $\geq$.

1.7 Polynomial and Rational Inequalities

You can use test numbers to solve polynomial or rational inequalities. (See page 159.) Be sure to rearrange the inequality so that a polynomial or rational expression is on the left side and the number 0 is on the right side.

1.8 Equations and Inequalities Involving Absolute Value

i. Definition. $|a| = a$ if $a \geq 0$, and $|a| = -a$ if $a < 0$.

ii. Let u be a variable or an algebraic expression, and let $a > 0$. Then

a. $|u| < a$ if and only if $-a < u < a$.

b. $|u| > a$ if and only if $u < -a$ or $u > a$.
The properties in (a) and (b) are valid if $<$ and $>$ are replaced by $\leq$ and $\geq$, respectively.

Review Exercises

Basic Skills and Concepts

In Exercises 1–18, solve each equation.

1. $5x - 4 = 11$ $\{3\}$

2. $12x + 7 = 31$ $\{2\}$

3. $3(2x - 4) = 9 - (x + 7)$ $\{2\}$ **4.** $4(x + 7) = 40 + 2x$ $\{6\}$

5. $\dfrac{3x - 1}{5} = \dfrac{x + 7}{9}$ $\{2\}$

6. $\dfrac{4x + 3}{7} = \dfrac{5x - 3}{2}$ $\{1\}$

7. $3x + 8 = 3(x + 2) + 2$ †

8. $3x + 8 = 3(x + 1) + 4$ †

9. $x - (5x - 2) = 7(x - 1) - 2$ $\{1\}$

10. $7 + 4(3 + y) = 8(3y - 1) + 3$ †

11. $\dfrac{5 - 6x}{7} = 2 - \dfrac{7 + 4x}{3}$ †

12. $\dfrac{8x - 23}{6} = \dfrac{5}{2}x - \dfrac{1}{3}$ †

13. $\dfrac{2}{x + 3} = \dfrac{5}{11x - 1}$ $\{1\}$

14. $\dfrac{7}{x + 2} = \dfrac{3}{x - 2}$ $\{5\}$

15. $\dfrac{y + 5}{2} + \dfrac{y - 1}{3} = \dfrac{7y + 3}{8} + \dfrac{4}{3}$ $\{11\}$

16. $\dfrac{y - 3}{6} - \dfrac{y - 4}{5} = -\dfrac{1}{6}$ $\{14\}$

17. $|2x - 3| = |4x + 5|$ †

18. $|5x - 3| = |x + 4|$ †

In Exercises 19–22, solve each equation for the indicated variable.

19. $p = k + gt$ for g †

20. $RK = 4 + 3K$ for K †

21. $T = \dfrac{2B}{B - 1}$ for B $B = \dfrac{T}{T - 2}$

22. $S = \dfrac{a}{1 - r}$ for r †

In Exercises 23–40, solve each equation. (Include all complex solutions.)

23. $x^2 - 7x = 0$ $\{0,7\}$

24. $x^2 - 32x = 0$ $\{0,32\}$

25. $x^2 - 3x - 10 = 0$ $\{-2, 5\}$

26. $2x^2 - 9x - 18 = 0$ †

27. $(x - 1)^2 = 2x^2 + 3x - 5$ †

28. $(x + 2)^2 = x(3x + 2)$ †

29. $\dfrac{x^2}{4} + x = \dfrac{5}{4}$ $\{-5, 1\}$

30. $\dfrac{x^2}{4} + \dfrac{7}{16} = x$ $\left\{\dfrac{1}{2}, \dfrac{7}{2}\right\}$

31. $3x(x + 1) = 2x + 2$ †

32. $x^2 - x = 3(5 - x)$ †

33. $x^2 - 3x - 1 = 0$ †

34. $x^2 + 6x + 2 = 0$ †

35. $2x^2 + x - 1 = 0$ †

36. $x^2 + 4x + 1 = 0$ †

37. $3x^2 - 12x - 24 = 0$ †

38. $2x^2 + 4x - 3 = 0$ †

39. $2x^2 - x - 2 = 0$ †

40. $3x^2 - 5x + 1 = 0$ †

In Exercises 41–44, find the discriminant and determine the number and the type of roots.

41. $3x^2 - 11x + 6 = 0$ †

42. $x^2 - 14x + 49 = 0$ †

43. $5x^2 + 2x + 1 = 0$ †

44. $9x^2 = 25$ †

In Exercises 45–64, solve each equation.

45. $\sqrt{x^2 - 16} = 0$ $\{-4, 4\}$

46. $\sqrt{x + 6} = x$ $\{3\}$

47. $\sqrt{4 - 7x} = \sqrt{2x}$ †

48. $t - 2\sqrt{t} + 1 = 0$ $\{1\}$

49. $y - 2\sqrt{y} - 3 = 0$ $\{9\}$

50. $\sqrt{3x + 4} - \sqrt{x - 3} = 3$ $\{4, 7\}$

51. $\sqrt{x - 1} = \sqrt{5 + \sqrt{x}}$ $\{16\}$

†Due to space constrictions, answers to these exercises may be found in the Answers beginning on page A–1 in the back of the book.

52. $\dfrac{1}{(1-x)^2} - \dfrac{7}{1-x} = -10$ $\left\{\dfrac{1}{2}, \dfrac{4}{5}\right\}$

53. $(7x + 5)^2 + 2(7x + 5) - 15 = 0$ †

54. $(x^2 - 1)^2 - 11(x^2 - 1) + 24 = 0$ $\{-3, -2, 2, 3\}$

55. $(\sqrt[3]{x})^2 + 3\sqrt[3]{x} - 4 = 0$ †   **56.** $(\sqrt[3]{x})^2 + \sqrt[3]{x} - 6 = 0$ †

57. $(\sqrt{t} + 5)^2 - 9(\sqrt{t} + 5) + 20 = 0$ $\{0\}$

58. $3\left(\dfrac{y-1}{6}\right)^2 - 7\left(\dfrac{y-1}{6}\right) = 0$ $\{1, 15\}$

59. $4x^4 - 37x^2 + 9 = 0$ †   **60.** $\dfrac{1}{x} + \dfrac{1}{x-1} = \dfrac{5}{6}$ $\left\{\dfrac{2}{5}, 3\right\}$

61. $\dfrac{2x+1}{2x-1} = \dfrac{x-1}{x+1}$ $\{0\}$ **62.** $6 - \dfrac{2}{x} = \dfrac{4}{x-1}$ †

63. $\left(\dfrac{7x}{x+1}\right)^2 - 3\left(\dfrac{7x}{x+1}\right) = 18$ $\left\{-\dfrac{3}{10}, 6\right\}$

64. $\left(\dfrac{4x^2 - 3}{x}\right)^2 = 1$ $\left\{-1, -\dfrac{3}{4}, \dfrac{3}{4}, 1\right\}$

In Exercises 65–88, solve each inequality. Write the solution in interval notation and graph the solution set.

65. $x + 5 < 3$ †   **66.** $2x + 1 < 9$ †

67. $3(x - 3) < 8$ †   **68.** $x + 5 \le 19 + 3x$ †

69. $x + 2 < \dfrac{2}{3}x - 2x$ †   **70.** $2x + 1 \ge \dfrac{5x - 6}{3}$ †

71. $x^2 + 4x - 5 < 0$ †   **72.** $3x^2 - 4x \le 4$ †

73. $x^2 - 2x \ge 15$ †   **74.** $3 \le x - 3 \le 7$ †

75. $-3 \le 2x + 1 \le 7$ †   **76.** $-3 < 3 - 2x < 9$ †

77. $4 \ge \dfrac{3x - 4}{3} > \dfrac{1}{6}$ †   **78.** $-\dfrac{2}{3} \le \dfrac{4(3 - x)}{5} < 1$ †

79. $(5x + 15)^{-1} < 0$ †   **80.** $2x^2 - 4x \ge 6$ †

81. $\dfrac{x}{x-2} \ge 5$ †   **82.** $\dfrac{x+1}{x-1} \le 1$ †

83. $|3x + 2| \le 7$ †   **84.** $|x - 4| \ge 2$ †

85. $4|x - 2| + 8 > 12$ †   **86.** $3|x - 1| + 4 < 10$ †

87. $\left|\dfrac{4 - x}{5}\right| \ge 1$ †   **88.** $\left|\dfrac{1 - x}{6}\right| < 1$ †

Applying the Concepts

89. A circular lens has a circumference of 22 centimeters. Find the radius of the lens. †

90. A rectangle has a perimeter of 18 inches and a length of 5 inches. Find the width of the rectangle. 4 in.

91. A trapezoid has an area of 32 square meters and a height of 8 meters. If one base is 5 meters, what is the length of the other base? 3 m

92. What principal must be deposited for 4 years at 7% annual simple interest in order to earn $354.20 in interest? $1265

93. The volume of a box is 4212 cubic centimeters. If the box is 27 centimeters long and 12 centimeters wide, how high is it? †

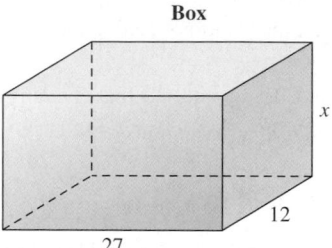

Box

94. The ratio of the current assets of a business to its current liabilities is called the *current ratio* of the business. If the current ratio is 2.7 and the current assets total $256,500, find the current liabilities of the business. $95,000

95. A cylindrical shaft has a volume of 8750π cubic centimeters. If the radius is 5 centimeters, how long is the shaft? †

96. A car dealer deducted 15% of the selling price of a car he had sold on consignment and gave the balance, which was $2210, to the owner. What was the selling price of the car? †

97. The third angle in an isosceles triangle measures 40 degrees more than twice either base angle. Find the number of degrees in each angle of the triangle. $35°, 35°, 110°$

98. A 600-mile trip took 12 hours. Half of the time was spent traveling across flat terrain and half was through hilly terrain. If the average rate over the hilly section was 20 miles per hour slower than the average rate over the flat section, find the two rates and the distance traveled at each rate. †

99. A total of $30,000 is invested in two stocks. At the end of the year, one returned 6% and the second 8% on the original investment. How much was invested in each if the total profit was $2160? $12,000 at 6%, $18,000 at 8%

100. The monthly note on a car that was leased for two years was $250 less than the monthly note on a car that was leased for a year and a half. The total income from the two leases was $21,300. Find the monthly note on each. $400 and $650

101. Two solutions, one containing $4\frac{1}{2}\%$ iodine and the other containing 12% iodine, are to be mixed to produce 10 liters of a 6% iodine solution. How many liters of each are required? †

102. Two cars leave from the same place at the same time, traveling in opposite directions. One travels 5 kilometers per hour faster than the other. After 3 hours, they are 495 kilometers apart. How fast is each car traveling? 80 km/hr, 85

103. A total of 28 handshakes were exchanged at the end of a party. Assuming that everyone shook hands with everyone else, how many people were at the party? 8 people

Practice Test A

1. Solve the equation $5x - 9 = 3x - 5$. {2}

2. Solve the equation $\dfrac{7}{24} = \dfrac{x}{8} + \dfrac{1}{6}$. {1}

3. Solve the equation $\dfrac{1}{x-2} - 5 = \dfrac{1}{x+2}$. $\left\{ -\dfrac{2\sqrt{30}}{5}, \dfrac{2\sqrt{30}}{5} \right\}$

4. The width of a rectangle is 3 centimeters less than the length, and the area is 54 square centimeters. Find the dimensions of the rectangle. 6 cm by 9 cm

5. Solve the equation $x^2 + 36 = -13x$. {−9, −4}

6. If Fran invests \$8200 at 6% per year, how much additional money must she invest at 8% to ensure that the interest she receives each year is 7% of the total investment? $8200

7. A frame of uniform width borders a painting that is 25 inches long and 11 inches high. If the area of the framed picture is 351 square inches, find the width of the border. 1 in.

8. Solve $-6x - 15 = (2x + 5)^2$. †

9. Determine the constant that should be added to the binomial
$$x^2 + \frac{2}{3}x$$
so that it becomes a perfect-square trinomial. Then write and factor the trinomial. †

10. Solve $3x^2 - 5x - 1 = 0$. †

11. A box with a square base and no top is made from a square piece of cardboard by cutting 2-inch squares from each corner and folding up the sides. What length of side must the original cardboard square have if the volume of the box is 50 cubic inches? 9 in.

12. Solve $x^2 + 12x + 33 = 0$. $\{ -6 - \sqrt{3}, -6 + \sqrt{3} \}$

13. Solve the polynomial equation
$$3x^4 - 75x^2 = 0 \quad \{-5, 0, 5\}$$
by factoring and then using the Zero Product Property.

14. Solve the equation
$$3x - 2 - 5\sqrt{x} = 0 \quad \{4\}$$
by making an appropriate substitution.

15. Solve the absolute value equation
$$\left| \frac{1}{3}x + 5 \right| = \left| \frac{2}{3}x + 7 \right|.\ \{-12, -6\}$$

In Problems 16 and 17, solve the inequality. Express the solution set in interval notation.

16. $\dfrac{x}{2} - 5 \geq \dfrac{4x}{9}$ $[90, \infty)$

17. $-4 < 2x - 3 < 4$ †

18. Solve the inequality
$$\left| \frac{2}{3}x - 1 \right| - 2 > \frac{1}{3} \quad (-\infty, -2) \cup (5, \infty)$$
by first rewriting it as an equivalent inequality without absolute value bars. Express the solution set in interval notation.

19. Solve the linear inequality $\dfrac{2}{5}y - 13 \leq -\left(7 + \dfrac{13}{5}y \right)$. †

20. Solve the inequality $0 \leq 5x - 2 \leq 8$. †

Practice Test B

1. Solve the equation $2x - 2 = 5x + 34$. d.

   a. $\left\{\dfrac{17}{4}\right\}$

   b. $\{-18\}$

   c. $\left\{\dfrac{15}{2}\right\}$

   d. $\{-12\}$

2. Solve the equation $\dfrac{z}{2} = 2z + 35$. d.

   a. $\left\{\dfrac{47}{2}\right\}$

   b. $\left\{-\dfrac{47}{2}\right\}$

   c. $\{23\}$

   d. $\left\{-\dfrac{70}{3}\right\}$

3. Solve the equation $\dfrac{1}{t-2} - \dfrac{1}{2} = \dfrac{-2t}{4t-1}$. a.

   a. $\left\{\dfrac{4}{9}\right\}$

   b. $\left\{\dfrac{1}{2}\right\}$

   c. $\left\{\dfrac{2}{3}\right\}$

   d. $\{-2\}$

4. The length of a rectangle is 4 centimeters greater than the width, and the area is 77 square centimeters. Find the dimensions of the rectangle. c.

   a. 11 centimeters by 15 centimeters

   b. 5 centimeters by 9 centimeters

   c. 7 centimeters by 11 centimeters

   d. 9 centimeters by 13 centimeters

5. Solve the equation $x^2 + 12 = -7x$. b.

   a. $\{3, 4\}$

   b. $\{-4, -3\}$

   c. $\{-3, 3, 4\}$

   d. $\{4, 3\}$

6. If Rena invests \$7500 at 7% per year, how much additional money must she invest at 12% to ensure that the interest she receives each year is 10% of the total investment? a.

   a. \$11,250

   b. \$12,375

   c. \$18,000

   d. \$21,000

7. A frame of uniform width borders a painting that is 20 inches long and 13 inches high. If the area of the framed picture is 368 square inches, find the width of the border. d.

   a. 3.5 in.   **b.** 3 in.

   c. 4 in.   **d.** 1.5 in.

8. Solve $-6x - 2 = (3x + 1)^2$. d.

   a. $\varnothing$ **b.** $\left\{-\dfrac{1}{3}\right\}$

   c. $\left\{\dfrac{1}{3}, 1\right\}$ **d.** $\left\{-1, -\dfrac{1}{3}\right\}$

9. Determine the constant that should be added to the binomial

$$x^2 + \dfrac{1}{6}x$$

so that it becomes a perfect–square trinomial. Then write and factor the trinomial. b.

   a. $\dfrac{1}{12}; x^2 + \dfrac{1}{6}x + \dfrac{1}{12} = \left(x + \dfrac{1}{6}\right)^2$

   b. $\dfrac{1}{144}; x^2 + \dfrac{1}{6}x + \dfrac{1}{144} = \left(x + \dfrac{1}{12}\right)^2$

   c. $\dfrac{1}{36}; x^2 + \dfrac{1}{6}x + \dfrac{1}{36} = \left(x + \dfrac{1}{6}\right)^2$

   d. $144; x^2 + \dfrac{1}{6}x + 144 = (x + 12)^2$

10. Solve $7x^2 + 10x + 2 = 0$. a.

   a. $\left\{\dfrac{-5-\sqrt{11}}{7}, \dfrac{-5+\sqrt{11}}{7}\right\}$

   b. $\left\{\dfrac{-5-\sqrt{39}}{7}, \dfrac{-5+\sqrt{39}}{7}\right\}$

   c. $\left\{\dfrac{-5-\sqrt{11}}{14}, \dfrac{-5+\sqrt{11}}{14}\right\}$

   d. $\left\{\dfrac{-10-\sqrt{11}}{7}, \dfrac{-10+\sqrt{11}}{7}\right\}$

11. A box with a square base and no top is made from a square piece of cardboard by cutting 3-inch squares from each corner and folding up the sides. What length of side must the original cardboard square have if the volume of the box is 675 cubic inches. b.

   a. 18 inches   **b.** 21 inches   **c.** 15 inches   **d.** 14 inches

12. Solve $x^2 + 14x + 38 = 0$ d.

   a. $\{7 - \sqrt{38}, 7 + \sqrt{38}\}$ **b.** $\{14 + \sqrt{38}\}$

   c. $\{7 + \sqrt{11}\}$ **d.** $\{-7-\sqrt{11}, -7 + \sqrt{11}\}$

13. Solve the polynomial equation

$$5x^4 - 45x^2 = 0$$

by factoring and then using the Zero Product Property. a.

   a. $\{-3, 0, 3\}$ **b.** $\{-3, 3\}$ **c.** $\{0\}$ **d.** $\{-3\sqrt{5}, 0, 3\sqrt{5}\}$

14. Solve the equation

$$x - 2048 - 32\sqrt{x} = 0$$

by making an appropriate substitution. a.
a. $\{4096\}$ **b.** $\{3072\}$ **c.** $\{8192\}$ **d.** $\{2048\}$

15. Solve the absolute value equation

$$\left|\frac{1}{2}x + 2\right| = \left|\frac{3}{4}x - 2\right|.$$ d.

a. $\{12, 16\}$ **b.** $\varnothing$ **c.** $\{10\}$ **d.** $\{0, 16\}$

In Problems 16 and 17, solve the inequality. Express the solution set in interval notation.

16. $\dfrac{x}{6} - \dfrac{1}{3} \le \dfrac{x}{3} + 1$ d.
a. $(-\infty, -8)$ **b.** $(-\infty, -8)$ **c.** $(-8, \infty)$ **d.** $[-8, \infty)$

17. $-13 \le -3x + 2 < -4$ b.
a. $[-5, -2)$ **b.** $(2, 5]$ **c.** $(-5, -2]$ **d.** $[2, 5)$

18. Solve the inequality

$$8 + \left|1 - \frac{x}{2}\right| \ge 10$$

by first rewriting it as an equivalent inequality without absolute value bars. Express the solution set in interval notation. c.

a. $(-\infty, -6] \cup [2, \infty)$ **b.** $[-2, 6]$
c. $(-\infty, -2] \cup [6, \infty)$ **d.** $[-6, 2]$

19. Solve the linear inequality $\dfrac{2}{3}x - 2 < \dfrac{5}{3}x.$ a.

a. $(-2, \infty)$ **b.** $\infty, 2$ **c.** $(-\infty, -2)$ **d.** $\{-2\}$ **e.** $(2, \infty)$

20. Solve the inequality $0 \le 7x - 1 \le 13.$ a.

a. $\left[\dfrac{1}{7}, 2\right]$ **b.** $(-1, 2]$ **c.** $\dfrac{1}{7}$ **d.** $[-1, 2]$ **e.** $\left(-\infty, \dfrac{1}{7}\right]$

CHAPTER 2

Graphs and Functions

Hurricanes are tracked with the use of coordinate grids, and data from fields as diverse as medicine and sports are related and analyzed by means of functions. The material in this chapter will introduce you to the versatile concepts that are the everyday tools of all dynamic industries.

SECTION 2.1 | The Coordinate Plane

1. The number line (Section P.1, page 5)
2. The Pythagorean Theorem (Section P.7, page 77)

OBJECTIVES

1 Plot points in the Cartesian coordinate plane.

2 Find the distance between two points.

3 Find the midpoint of a line segment.

A Fly on the Ceiling

It is said that one day the French mathematician René Descartes noticed a fly buzzing around on a ceiling made of square tiles. He watched the fly for a long time. He wondered how he could mathematically describe where the fly was. Finally, he realized that he could describe the position of the fly by its distance from the walls of the room. Descartes had just discovered the coordinate plane! In fact, the coordinate plane is sometimes called the Cartesian plane in his honor. The discovery led to the development of analytic geometry, the first mathematical blending of algebra and geometry.

Although the basic idea of graphing with coordinate axes dates all the way back to Apollonius in the second century B.C., Descartes, who lived in the 1600s, gets the credit for coming up with the two-axis system we use today. In Example 2, we will see how the Cartesian plane helps visualize data on smoking. ■

1 Plot points in the Cartesian coordinate plane.

The Coordinate Plane

A visually powerful device for exploring relationships between numbers is the Cartesian plane. A pair of real numbers in which the order is specified is called an **ordered pair** of real numbers. An ordered pair is written by enclosing a pair of numbers in parentheses and separating them by a comma.

The ordered pair (a, b) has **first component** a and **second component** b. Two ordered pairs (x, y) and (a, b) are **equal** if and only if $x = a$ and $y = b$.

Just as the real numbers are identified with points on a line, called the *number line* or the *coordinate line,* the sets of ordered pairs of real numbers are identified with points on a plane called the **coordinate plane** or the **Cartesian plane.** This identification is attributed to Descartes.

STUDY TIP

Although it is common to label the axes *x* and *y*, other letters are also used, especially in applications. In a *uv*-plane, or an *st*-plane, the first letter in the name refers to the horizontal axis, the second to the vertical axis.

We begin with two coordinate lines, one horizontal and one vertical, that intersect at their zero points. The horizontal line (with positive direction to the right) is usually called the **x-axis,** while the vertical line (whose positive direction is up) is usually called the **y-axis.** The point of intersection of the *x*-axis and the *y*-axis is called the **origin.** The *x*-axis and *y*-axis are called **coordinate axes,** and the plane formed by the *x*-axis and *y*-axis is sometimes called the **xy-plane.** The axes divide the plane into four regions called **quadrants,** which are numbered as shown in Figure 2.1. The points on the axes themselves do not belong to any of the quadrants.

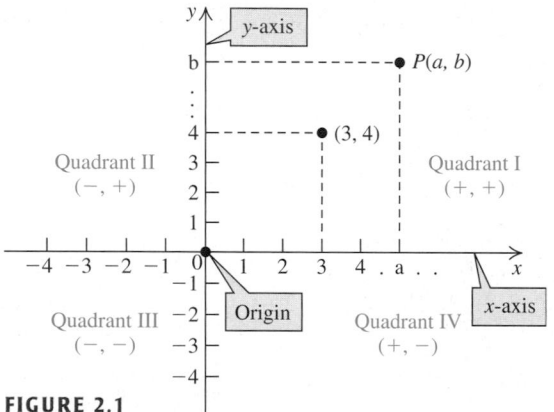

FIGURE 2.1

Figure 2.1 shows how each ordered pair (a, b) of real numbers is associated with a unique point P in the plane, and each point in the plane is associated with a unique ordered pair of real numbers. The first component, a, is called the **x-coordinate** of P, and the second component, b, is called the **y-coordinate** of P, since we have called our horizontal axis the *x*-axis and our vertical axis the *y*-axis.

The *x*-coordinate indicates the point's distance to the right or left of the *y*-axis. The *x*-coordinate is positive if the point is to the right of the *y*-axis, negative if it is to the left of the *y*-axis, and zero if it is on the *y*-axis. Similarly, the *y*-coordinate of a point indicates its distance above, below, or on the *x*-axis. The *y*-coordinate is positive if the point is above the *x*-axis, negative if it is below the *x*-axis, and zero if it is on the *x*-axis. The signs of the *x* and *y* coordinates are shown in Figure 2.1 for each quadrant. We refer to the point corresponding to the ordered pair (a, b) as the **graph of the ordered pair** (a, b) in the coordinate system. However, we frequently ignore the distinction between an ordered pair and its graph. The notation $P(a, b)$ designates the point P in the coordinate plane whose *x*-coordinate is a and whose *y*-coordinate is b.

EXAMPLE 1   **Graphing Points**

Graph the following points in the *xy*-plane:

$A(3, 1)$, $B(-2, 4)$, $C(-3, -4)$, $D(2, -3)$, and $E(-3, 0)$.

Solution

Figure 2.2 shows a coordinate plane, along with the graph of the given points. These points are located by moving left, right, up, or down, starting from the origin (0, 0).

$A(3, 1)$	3 units right, 1 unit up	$D(2, -3)$	2 units right, 3 units down
$B(-2, 4)$	2 units left, 4 units up	$E(-3, 0)$	3 units left, 0 units up or down
$C(-3, -4)$	3 units left, 4 units down		

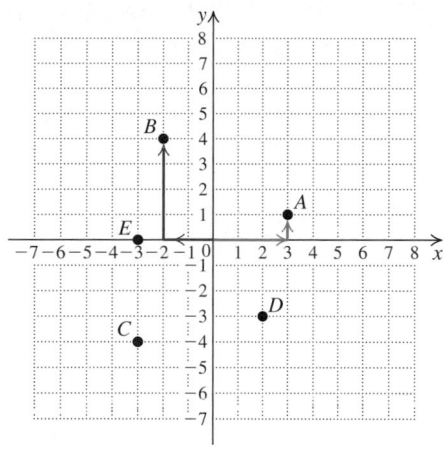

FIGURE 2.2   ■ ■ ■

PRACTICE PROBLEM 1   Plot in the xy-plane:

$$P(-2, 2),\ Q(4, 0),\ R(5, -3),\ S(0, -3),\ \text{and}\ T\left(-2, \frac{1}{2}\right).$$ ■

The next example illustrates how the Cartesian coordinate system allows us to visualize relationships between two variables.

EXAMPLE 2   **Plotting Data on Adult Smokers in the United States**

The data in Table 2.1 show the prevalence of smoking among adults aged 18 years and older in the United States over the years 1997–2003.

TABLE 2.1

Year	1997	1998	1999	2000	2001	2002	2003
Percent of adult smokers	24.7	24.1	23.5	23.2	22.7	22.4	21.6

Source: Center for Disease Control, National Health Interview Survey.

Plot the graph of the ordered pairs (year, percent of adult smokers), where the first coordinate represents a year and the second coordinate represents the percent of adult smokers in that year.

Solution

We let x represent the years 1997 through 2003, and y represent the percent of adult smokers in that year. Since no data are given for the years 0 through 1996, it is customary to indicate these omissions graphically by showing a break in the x-axis. Another way to illustrate the data is to declare a year—say, 1996—as 0. Similar comments apply to the y-axis. The graph of the points (1997, 24.7), (1998, 24.1), (1999, 23.5), (2000, 23.2), (2001, 22.7), (2002, 22.4) and (2003, 21.6) is shown in Figure 2.3 on the next page. The graph shows that the percent of adult smokers has been declining every year since 1997.

Continued on next page.

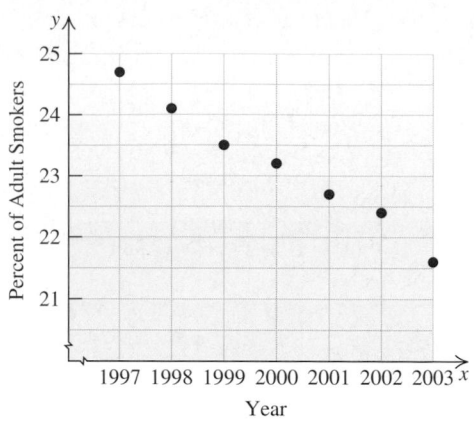

FIGURE 2.3

■ ■ ■

PRACTICE PROBLEM 2   In Example 2, suppose the percent of adult smokers shown in Table 2.1 is decreased by 3 in each year. Write and plot the corresponding ordered pairs (year, percent of adult smokers). ■

The display in Figure 2.3 is called a **scatter diagram** of the data. There are numerous other ways of displaying the data. Two such ways are shown in Figure 2.4(a) and Figure 2.4(b):

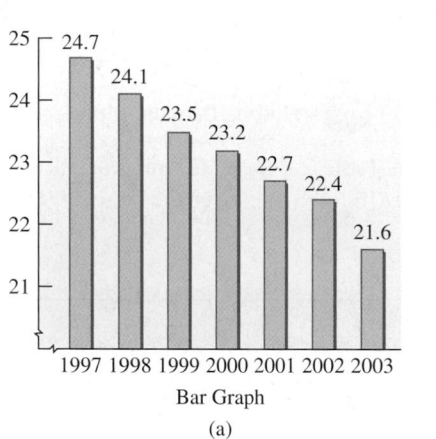

FIGURE 2.4

---

2 Find the distance between two points.

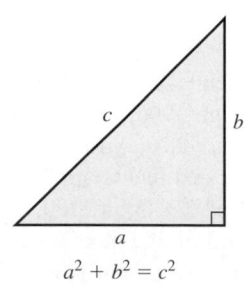

FIGURE 2.5

The Distance Formula

Suppose that a Cartesian coordinate system has the same unit of measurement, such as inches or centimeters, on both axes. We can then calculate the distance between any two points in the coordinate plane in the given unit.

Recall that the Pythagorean Theorem states that, in a **right triangle** with hypotenuse of length c and the other two sides of lengths a and b,

$$a^2 + b^2 = c^2, \qquad \text{Pythagorean Theorem}$$

as shown in Figure 2.5.

Suppose we want to compute the distance between the two points $P(x_1, y_1)$ and $Q(x_2, y_2)$. We draw a horizontal line through the point Q and a vertical line through the point P to form the right triangle PQS, as shown in Figure 2.6.

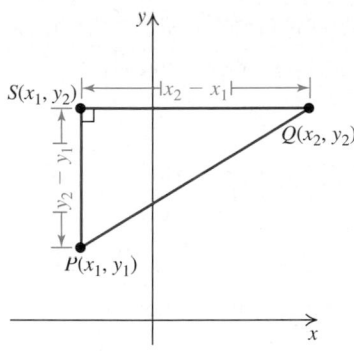

FIGURE 2.6

The length of the horizontal side of the triangle is $|x_2 - x_1|$ and the length of the vertical side is $|y_2 - y_1|$. By the Pythagorean Theorem, we have

$$[d(P, Q)]^2 = |x_2 - x_1|^2 + |y_2 - y_1|^2$$

$$d(P, Q) = \sqrt{|x_2 - x_1|^2 + |y_2 - y_1|^2} \quad \text{Take the square root of both sides.}$$

$$d(P, Q) = \sqrt{(x_2 - x_1)^2 + (y_2 - y_1)^2}, \quad |a - b|^2 = (a - b)^2$$

where $d(P, Q)$ is the distance between P and Q.

THE DISTANCE FORMULA IN THE COORDINATE PLANE

Let $P(x_1, y_1)$ and $Q(x_2, y_2)$ be any two points in the coordinate plane. Then the distance between P and Q, denoted $d(P, Q)$, is given by the **distance formula:**

$$d(P, Q) = \sqrt{(x_2 - x_1)^2 + (y_2 - y_1)^2}.$$

EXAMPLE 3   **Finding the Distance Between Two Points**

Find the distance between the points $P(-2, 5)$ and $Q(3, -4)$.

Solution

Let $(x_1, y_1) = (-2, 5)$ and $(x_2, y_2) = (3, -4)$. Then

$$x_1 = -2, y_1 = 5, x_2 = 3, \text{ and } y_2 = -4.$$

$$\begin{aligned}
d(P, Q) &= \sqrt{(x_2 - x_1)^2 + (y_2 - y_1)^2} && \text{Distance formula} \\
&= \sqrt{[3 - (-2)]^2 + (-4 - 5)^2} && \text{Substitute the values for } x_1, x_2, y_1, y_2. \\
&= \sqrt{5^2 + (-9)^2} && \text{Simplify.} \\
&= \sqrt{25 + 81} && \text{Simplify.} \\
&= \sqrt{106} && \text{Simplify.} \\
&\approx 10.3 && \text{Use a calculator.} \quad ■ ■ ■
\end{aligned}$$

PRACTICE PROBLEM 3   Find the distance between the points $(-5, 2)$ and $(-4, 1)$. ■

In the next example, we use the distance formula and the converse of the Pythagorean Theorem to show that the given triangle is a right triangle.

EXAMPLE 4   **Identifying a Right Triangle**

Let $A(4, 3)$, $B(1, 4)$, and $C(-2, -5)$ be three points in the plane.

a. Sketch the triangle ABC.

b. Find the length of each side of the triangle.

c. Show that ABC is a right triangle.

Continued on next page.

FIGURE 2.7

Solution

a. A sketch of the triangle formed by the three points A, B, and C is shown in Figure 2.7.

b. Using the distance formula, we have

$$d(A, B) = \sqrt{(4 - 1)^2 + (3 - 4)^2} = \sqrt{9 + 1} = \sqrt{10},$$
$$d(B, C) = \sqrt{[1 - (-2)]^2 + [4 - (-5)]^2} = \sqrt{9 + 81} = \sqrt{90},$$
$$d(A, C) = \sqrt{[4 - (-2)]^2 + [3 - (-5)]^2} = \sqrt{36 + 64} = \sqrt{100} = 10.$$

c. We check whether the relationship $a^2 + b^2 = c^2$ holds in this triangle, where a, b, and c denote the lengths of its sides. The longest side, AC, has length 10 units.

$$[d(A, B)]^2 + [d(B, C)]^2 = 10 + 90 \qquad \text{Replace } [d(A, B)]^2 \text{ by } 10$$
$$\text{and } [d(B, C)]^2 \text{ by } 90.$$
$$= 100 = (10)^2 = [d(A, C)]^2.$$

It follows from the converse of the Pythagorean Theorem that the triangle ABC is a right triangle. ■ ■ ■

PRACTICE PROBLEM 4 Is the triangle with vertices $(6, 2)$, $(-2, 0)$, and $(1, 5)$ an isosceles triangle—that is, a triangle with two sides of equal length? ■

EXAMPLE 5 **Applying the Distance Formula to Baseball**

The baseball "diamond" is in fact a square with a distance of 90 feet between each of the consecutive bases. Use an appropriate coordinate system to calculate the distance the ball will travel when the third baseman throws it from third base to first base.

Solution

We can conveniently choose home plate as the origin and place the x-axis along the line from home plate to first base and the y-axis along the line from home plate to third base as shown in Figure 2.8. The coordinates of home plate (O), first base (A), second base (C), and third base (B) are shown in the figure.

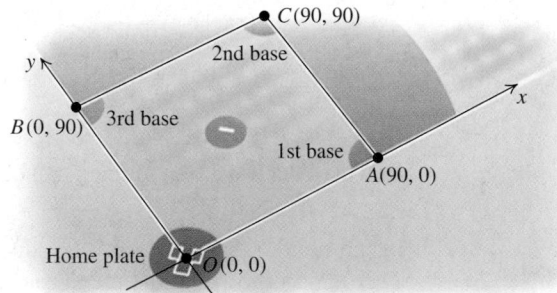

FIGURE 2.8

We are asked to find the distance between the points $A(90, 0)$ and $B(0, 90)$.

$$d(A, B) = \sqrt{(90 - 0)^2 + (0 - 90)^2} \qquad \text{Distance formula}$$
$$= \sqrt{(90)^2 + (-90)^2}$$
$$= \sqrt{2(90)^2} \qquad \text{Simplify.}$$
$$= 90\sqrt{2} \qquad \text{Simplify.}$$
$$\approx 127.28 \text{ feet} \qquad \text{Use a calculator.} \quad ■ ■ ■$$

PRACTICE PROBLEM 5   Young players might play baseball in a square "diamond" with a distance of 60 feet between consecutive bases. Repeat Example 5 for a diamond with these dimensions.   ■

3 Find the midpoint of a line segment.

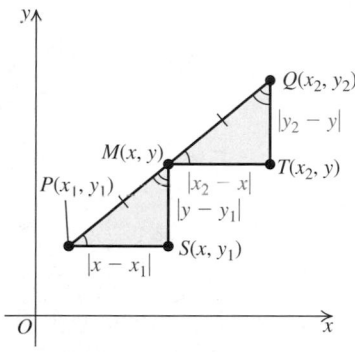

FIGURE 2.9

The Midpoint Formula

THE MIDPOINT FORMULA

The coordinates of the midpoint $M(x, y)$ of the line segment joining $P(x_1, y_1)$ and $Q(x_2, y_2)$ are given by

$$(x, y) = \left(\frac{x_1 + x_2}{2}, \frac{y_1 + y_2}{2} \right).$$

The midpoint formula can be proved by showing that $d(P, M) = d(Q, M)$. See Figure 2.9.

EXAMPLE 6   **Finding the Midpoint of a Line Segment**

Find the midpoint of the line segment joining the points $P(-3, 6)$ and $Q(1, 4)$.

Solution

Let $(x_1, y_1) = (-3, 6)$ and $(x_2, y_2) = (1, 4)$. Then

$$x_1 = -3, y_1 = 6, x_2 = 1, \text{ and } y_2 = 4.$$

$$\text{Midpoint} = \left(\frac{x_1 + x_2}{2}, \frac{y_1 + y_2}{2} \right) \qquad \text{Midpoint formula}$$

$$= \left(\frac{-3 + 1}{2}, \frac{6 + 4}{2} \right) \qquad \text{Substitute values for } x_1, x_2, y_1, y_2.$$

$$= (-1, 5) \qquad \text{Simplify.}$$

Therefore, the midpoint of the line segment joining the points $P(-3, 6)$ and $Q(1, 4)$ is $M(-1, 5)$.   ■ ■ ■

PRACTICE PROBLEM 6   Find the midpoint of the line segment whose endpoints are $(5, -2)$ and $(6, -1)$.   ■

A Exercises ■ Basic Skills and Concepts

1. Plot and label each of the given points in a Cartesian coordinate plane, and state the quadrant, if any, in which each point is located. $(2, 2), (3, -1), (-1, 0), (-2, -5), (0, 0),$ $(-7, 4), (0, 3), (-4, 2)$ †

2. **a.** Write the coordinates of any five points on the x-axis. What do these points have in common? †
   b. Plot the points $(-2, 1), (0, 1), (0.5, 1), (1, 1)$ and $(2, 1)$. Describe the set of all points of the form $(x, 1)$, where x is a real number. †

3. **a.** If the x-coordinate of a point is 0, where does that point lie? †
   b. Plot the points $(-1, 1), (-1, 1.5), (-1, 2), (-1, 3),$ and $(-1, 4)$. Describe the set of all points of the form $(-1, y)$, where y is a real number. †

4. What figure is formed by the set of all points in a Cartesian coordinate plane that have
   a. x-coordinate equal to -3;†
   b. y-coordinate equal to 4? †

5. Let $P(x, y)$ be a point in a coordinate plane.
   a. If the point $P(x, y)$ lies above the x-axis, what must be true of y? $y > 0$
   b. If the point $P(x, y)$ lies below the x-axis, what must be true of y? $y < 0$
   c. If the point $P(x, y)$ lies to the left of the y-axis, what must be true of x? $x < 0$
   d. If the point $P(x, y)$ lies to the right of the y-axis, what must be true of x? $x > 0$

6. Let $P(x, y)$ be a point in a coordinate plane. In which quadrant does P lie
   a. If x and y are both negative? Quadrant III
   b. If x and y are both positive? Quadrant I
   c. If x is positive and y is negative? Quadrant IV
   d. If x is negative and y is positive? Quadrant II

In Exercises 7–16, find (a) the distance between P and Q, and (b) the coordinates of the midpoint of the line segment PQ.

7. $P(2, 1), Q(2, 5)$ **a.** 4 **b.** $(2, 3)$

8. $P(3, 5), Q(-2, 5)$ **a.** 5 **b.** $(0.5, 5)$

9. $P(-1, -5), Q(2, -3)$ **a.** $\sqrt{13}$ **b.** $(0.5, -4)$

10. $P(-4, 1), Q(-7, -9)$ **a.** $\sqrt{109}$ **b.** $(-5.5, -4)$

11. $P(-1, 1.5), Q(3, -6.5)$ **a.** $4\sqrt{5}$ **b.** $(1, -2.5)$

12. $P(0.5, 0.5), Q(1, -1)$ **a.** 1.58 **b.** $(0.75, -0.25)$

13. $P(\sqrt{2}, 4), Q(\sqrt{2}, 5)$ **a.** 1 **b.** $(\sqrt{2}, 4.5)$

14. $P(v - w, t), Q(v + w, t)$ **a.** $2|w|$ **b.** (v, t)

15. $P(t, k), Q(k, t)$ †

16. $P(m, n), Q(-n, -m)$ †

In Exercises 17–24, determine whether the given points are collinear. Points are *collinear* if they can be labeled P, Q, and R, so that $d(P, Q) + d(Q, R) = d(P, R)$.

17. $(0, 0), (1, 2), (-1, -2)$ Yes

18. $(3, 4), (0, 0), (-3, -4)$ Yes

19. $(4, -2), (-2, 8), (1, 3)$ Yes

20. $(9, 6), (0, -3), (3, 1)$ No

21. $(-1, 4), (3, 0), (11, -8)$ Yes

22. $(-2, 3), (3, 1), (2, -1)$ No

23. $(4, -4), (15, 1), (1, 2)$ No

24. $(1, 7), (-7, 8), (-3, 7.5)$ Yes

In Exercises 25–34, identify the triangle PQR as *isosceles* (two sides of equal length), *equilateral* (three sides of equal length), a right triangle, or a *scalene* triangle (three sides of different lengths).

25. $P(-5, 5), Q(-1, 4), R(-4, 1)$ Isosceles, right

26. $P(3, 2), Q(6, 6), R(-1, 5)$ Isosceles

27. $P(-4, 8), Q(0, 7), R(-3, 5)$ Scalene

28. $P(-1, 4), Q(3, -2), R(7, 5)$ Isosceles

29. $P(6, 6), Q(-1, -1), R(-5, 3)$ Scalene

30. $P(0, -1), Q(9, -9), R(5, 1)$ Scalene

31. $P(1, 1), Q(-1, 4), R(5, 8)$ Scalene

32. $P(-4, 4), Q(4, 5), R(0, -2)$ Isosceles

33. $P(1, -1), Q(-1, 1), R(-\sqrt{3}, -\sqrt{3})$ Equilateral

34. $P(-.5, -1), Q(-1.5, 1), R(\sqrt{3} - 1, \sqrt{3}/2)$ Equilateral

35. Show that the points $P(7, -12), Q(-1, 3), R(14, 11),$ and $S(22, -4)$ are the vertices of a square. Find the length of the diagonals. †

36. Repeat Exercise 35 for the points $P(8, -10), Q(9, -11),$ $R(8, -12),$ and $S(7, -11)$. †

37. Find x such that the point $(x, 2)$ is 5 units from $(2, -1)$. †

38. Find y such that the point $(2, y)$ is 13 units from $(-10, -3)$. †

39. Find the point on the x-axis that is equidistant from the points $(-5, 2)$ and $(2, 3)$. $(-\frac{8}{7}, 0)$

40. Find the point on the y-axis that is equidistant from the points $(7, -4)$ and $(8, 3)$. $(0, \frac{4}{7})$

†Due to space constrictions, answers to these exercises may be found in the Answers beginning on page A–1 in the back of the book.

B Exercises Applying the Concepts

41. Population. The table shows the total population of the United States in millions (181 represents 181,000,000). The population is rounded to the nearest million. Plot the data in a Cartesian coordinate system.

Year	Total Population (millions)
1960	181
1965	194
1970	205
1975	216
1980	228
1985	238
1990	250
1995	267
2000	282

Source: U.S. Census Bureau. †

In Exercises 42–45, use the following *vital statistics* table:

	Rate per 1000 population			
Year	Births	Deaths	Marriages	Divorces
1950	24.1	9.6	11.1	2.6
1955	25.0	9.3	9.3	2.3
1960	23.7	9.5	8.5	2.2
1965	19.4	9.4	9.3	2.5
1970	18.4	9.5	10.6	3.5
1975	14.6	8.6	10.0	4.8
1980	15.9	8.8	10.6	5.2
1985	15.8	8.8	10.1	5.0
1990	16.7	8.6	9.4	4.7
1995	14.8	8.8	8.9	4.4
2000	14.4	8.7	8.5	4.2

Source: U.S. Census Bureau.

The table shows the rate per 1000 population of live births, deaths, marriages, and divorces from 1950 to 2000 at five-year intervals. Plot the data in a Cartesian coordinate system, and connect the points with line segments.

42. Plot (year, births). †   **43.** Plot (year, deaths). †

44. Plot (year, marriages). †   **45.** Plot (year, divorces). †

In Exercises 46–48, use the midpoint formula to find the estimate.

46. Murders in USA. In the United States, there were 22,000 murders committed in 1995 and 18,000 in 1997. Assuming that this trend continued, estimate the number of murders committed in 1996. (*Source: U.S. Census Bureau.*) †

47. Spending on prescription drugs. Americans spent 76 billion dollars on prescription drugs in 1997 and 141 billion dollars in 2001. Assuming that this trend continued, estimate the amount spent on prescription drugs during 1998, 1999, and 2000. (*Source: U.S. Census Bureau.*) †

1997   1998   1999   2000

48. Defense spending. The government of the United States spent 320 billion dollars on national defense in 1994 and 400 billion dollars in 2002. Assuming that this trend continued linearly, estimate the amount spent on defense in each of the years 1995–2001. (*Source: Statistical Abstract of the United States.*) †

49. Length of a diagonal. The application of the Pythagorean Theorem in three dimensions involves the relationship between the perpendicular edges of a rectangular block and the solid diagonal of the same block.

In the figure, show that $h^2 = a^2 + b^2 + c^2$.

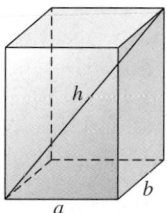

50. Distance. A pilot is flying from Dullsville to Middale to Pleasantville. With reference to an origin, Dullsville is located at (2, 4), Middale at (8, 12), and Pleasantville at (20, 3), all numbers being in 100-mile units.
  a. Locate the positions of the three cities on a Cartesian coordinate plane. †
  b. Compute the distance traveled by the pilot. 2500 miles
  c. Compute the direct distance between Dullsville and Pleasantville. $500\sqrt{13} = 1802.78$ miles

51. Docking Distance. A rope is attached to the bow of a sailboat that is 24 feet from the dock. The rope is drawn in over a pulley 10 feet higher than the bow at the rate of 3 feet per second. Find the distance from the boat to the dock after t seconds. $\sqrt{576 - 156t + 9t^2}$

10 feet

24 feet

C Exercises   Beyond the Basics

a**52.** Use coordinates to prove that the diagonals of a parallelogram bisect each other.
[*Hint:* Choose $(0, 0)$, $(a, 0)$, (b, c), and $(a + b, c)$ as the vertices of a parallelogram.]

53. Let $A(2, 3)$, $B(5, 4)$, and $C(3, 8)$ be three points in a coordinate plane. Find the coordinates of the point D such that the points A, B, C, and D form a parallelogram with
a. AB as one of the diagonals; $(4, -1)$
b. AC as one of the diagonals; $(0, 7)$
c. BC as one of the diagonals. $(6, 9)$
[*Hint:* Use Exercise 52.]

54. Prove that if the diagonals of a quadrilateral bisect each other, then the quadrilateral is a parallelogram. [*Hint:* Choose $(0, 0)$, $(a, 0)$, (b, c), and (x, y) as the vertices of a quadrilateral, and show that $x = a + b, y = c$.]

55. a. Show that $(1, 2)$, $(-2, 6)$, $(5, 8)$, and $(8, 4)$ are the vertices of a parallelogram. [*Hint:* Use Exercise 54.]
b. Find (x, y) if $(3, 2)$, $(6, 3)$, (x, y) and $(6, 5)$ are the vertices of a parallelogram. $x = 9, y = 6$

56. Show that the sum of the squares of the lengths of the sides of a parallelogram is equal to the sum of the squares of the lengths of the diagonals. [*Hint:* Choose $(0, 0)$, $(a, 0)$, (b, c), and $(a + b, c)$ as the vertices of the parallelogram.]

57. Prove that, in a right triangle, the midpoint of the hypotenuse is the same distance from each of the vertices. [*Hint:* Let the vertices be $(0, 0)$, $(a, 0)$, and $(0, b)$.]

58. Show that the midpoints of the sides of any rectangle are the vertices of a rhombus (a quadrilateral with all sides of equal length). [*Hint:* Let the vertices of the rectangle be $(0, 0)$, $(a, 0)$, $(0, b)$, and (a, b).]

59. Show that, in any triangle, the sum of squares of the lengths of the medians is equal to three-fourths the sum of the squares of the lengths of the sides. [*Hint:* Choose $(0, 0)$, $(a, 0)$, and (b, c) as the vertices of a triangle.]

60. Trisecting a line segment. Let $A(x_1, y_1)$ and $B(x_2, y_2)$ be two points in a coordinate plane.
a. Show that the point $C\left(\dfrac{2x_1 + x_2}{3}, \dfrac{2y_1 + y_2}{3}\right)$ is one-third of the way from A to B.
[*Hint:* Show that (i) $d(A, C) + d(C, B) = d(A, B)$ and (ii) $d(A, C) = \dfrac{1}{3}d(A, B)$.]
b. Show that the point $D\left(\dfrac{x_1 + 2x_2}{3}, \dfrac{y_1 + 2y_2}{3}\right)$ is two-thirds of the way from A to B. *The points C and D are called the points of trisection of segment AB.*
c. Find the points of trisection of the line segment joining $(-1, 2)$ and $(4, 1)$. †

Critical Thinking

In Exercises 61–65, describe the set of points $P(x, y)$ in the xy-plane that satisfy the given condition.

61. a. $x = 0$ y-axis **b.** $y = 0$ x-axis
62. a. $xy = 0$ † **b.** $xy \neq 0$ †
63. a. $xy > 0$ † **b.** $xy < 0$ Quadrants II and IV
64. a. $x^2 + y^2 = 0$ $\{(0, 0)\}$ **b.** $x^2 + y^2 \neq 0$ †

65. Describe how to determine the quadrant in which a point lies from the signs of its coordinates. †

Graphs of Equations

BEFORE STARTING THIS SECTION, REVIEW

1. How to plot points (Section 2.1, page 182)

2. Equivalent equations (Section 1.1, page 89)

3. Completing squares (Section 1.4, page 125)

OBJECTIVES

1 Sketch a graph by plotting points.

2 Find the intercepts of a graph.

3 Find the symmetries in a graph.

4 Find the equation of a circle.

Doomsans Discover Deer

A herd of 400 deer was introduced into a small island called Dooms. The natives both liked and admired these beautiful creatures. However, the Doomsans soon discovered that deer meat is excellent food. Also, a rumor spread throughout Dooms that eating deer meat prolonged one's life. The natives then began to hunt the deer. The number of deer, y, after t years from the initial introduction of deer into Dooms is described by the equation $y = -t^4 + 96t^2 + 400$. When does the population of deer become extinct in Dooms? (See Example 6.) ■

---

1 Sketch a graph by plotting points.

Graph of an Equation

When one quantity changes with respect to another quantity, we say that a *relation* exists between the two quantities. The two changing (or varying) quantities in a relation are often represented by *variables*. A relation may sometimes be described by an equation, which may be a formula. The following are examples of equations showing relationships between two variables:

$$y = 2x + 1; \quad x^2 + y^2 = 4; \quad y = x^2; \quad x = y^2; \quad F = \frac{9}{5}C + 32; \quad \text{and } q = -3p^2 + 30.$$

An ordered pair (a, b) is said to **satisfy** an equation with variables x and y if, when a is substituted for x and b is substituted for y in the equation, the resulting statement is true. For example, the ordered pair $(2, 5)$ satisfies the equation $y = 2x + 1$ because replacing x by 2 and y by 5 yields $5 = 2(2) + 1$, a true statement. The ordered pair $(5, -2)$ does not satisfy the equation $y = 2x + 1$, since replacing x by 5 and y by -2 yields $-2 = 2(5) + 1$, which is false. An ordered pair that satisfies an equation is called a **solution** of the equation.

Frequently, for a given equation involving x and y, the numerical values of the variable y can be determined by assigning appropriate values to the variable x. For this reason, y is sometimes referred to as the **dependent variable** and x as the **independent variable.** In the equation $y = 2x + 1$, there are infinitely many choices for x, each resulting in a corresponding value of y. Hence, we have infinitely many solutions of the equation $y = 2x + 1$. When these solutions are plotted as points in the coordinate plane, they constitute the *graph of the equation.* The graph of an equation is thus a geometric picture of its solution set.

TECHNOLOGY CONNECTION

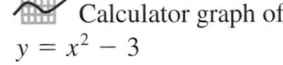 Calculator graph of $y = x^2 - 3$

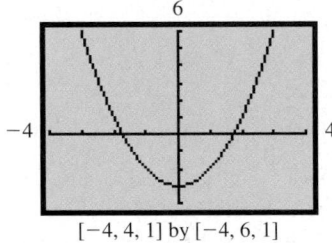

$[-4, 4, 1]$ by $[-4, 6, 1]$

GRAPH OF AN EQUATION

The **graph of an equation** in two variables, such as x and y, is the set of all ordered pairs (a, b) in the coordinate plane that satisfy the equation.

EXAMPLE 1 **Sketching a Graph by Plotting Points**

Sketch the graph of $y = x^2 - 3$.

Solution

There are infinitely many solutions of the equation $y = x^2 - 3$. To find a few, we choose integer values of x between -3 and 3. Then we find the corresponding values of y as shown in Table 2.2.

TABLE 2.2

x	$y = x^2 - 3$	(x, y)
-3	$y = (-3)^2 - 3 = 9 - 3 = 6$	$(-3, 6)$
-2	$y = (-2)^2 - 3 = 4 - 3 = 1$	$(-2, 1)$
-1	$y = (-1)^2 - 3 = 1 - 3 = -2$	$(-1, -2)$
0	$y = 0^2 - 3 = 0 - 3 = -3$	$(0, -3)$
1	$y = 1^2 - 3 = 1 - 3 = -2$	$(1, -2)$
2	$y = 2^2 - 3 = 4 - 3 = 1$	$(2, 1)$
3	$y = 3^2 - 3 = 9 - 3 = 6$	$(3, 6)$

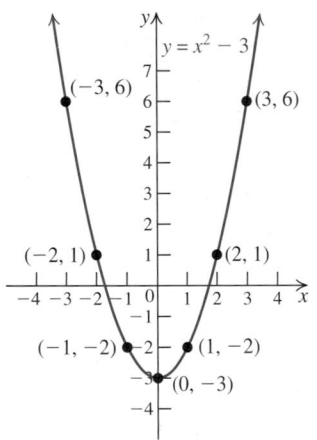

FIGURE 2.10

We plot the seven solutions (x, y) and join them by a smooth curve as shown in Figure 2.10. ■ ■ ■

PRACTICE PROBLEM 1 Sketch the graph of $y = -x^2 + 1$. ■

The bowl-shaped curve sketched in Figure 2.10 is called a *parabola.* It is easy to find parabolas in everyday settings. For example, when you throw a ball, the path it travels is a parabola. Also, the reflector behind a car's headlight is parabolic in shape.

Example 1 suggests the following three steps for sketching the graph of an equation by plotting points.

SKETCHING A GRAPH BY PLOTTING POINTS

Step 1.   Make a representative table of solutions of the equation.

Step 2.   Plot the solutions as ordered pairs in the Cartesian coordinate plane.

Step 3.   Connect the solutions in Step **2** by a smooth curve.

Comment. This point-plotting technique has obvious pitfalls. For instance, many different curves pass through the four points in Figure 2.11. Assume that these points are solutions of a given equation. There is no way to guarantee that any curve we pass through the plotted points is the actual graph of the equation. However, in general, the more solutions that are plotted, the more likely the resulting figure is to be a reasonably accurate graph of the equation.

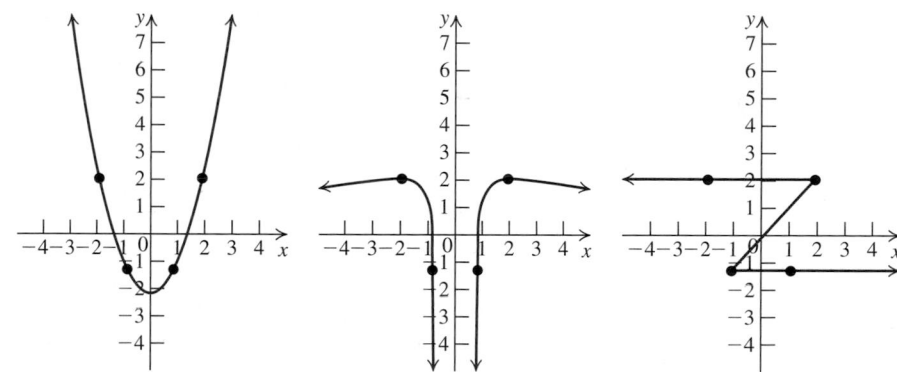

FIGURE 2.11

We now discuss some special features of the graph of an equation.

2 Find the intercepts of a graph.

Intercepts

The points where a graph intersects (crosses or touches) the coordinate axes are of special interest in many problems. Since all points on the x-axis have a y-coordinate of 0, any point where a graph intersects the x-axis has the form $(a, 0)$. (See Figure 2.12.) The number a is called an **x-intercept** of the graph. Similarly, any point where a graph intersects the y-axis has the form $(0, b)$, and the number b is called a **y-intercept** of the graph.

We use the following procedure to find the x- and y-intercepts of the graph of an equation.

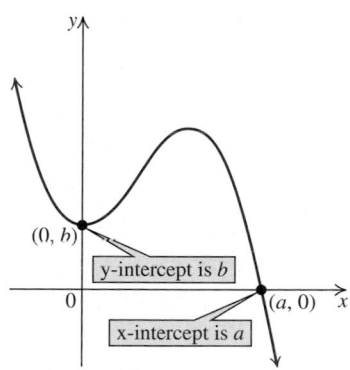

FIGURE 2.12

PROCEDURE FOR FINDING THE INTERCEPTS OF A GRAPH

Step 1 To find the x-intercepts of the graph of an equation, set $y = 0$ in the equation and solve for x.

Step 2 To find the y-intercepts of the graph of an equation, set $x = 0$ in the equation and solve for y.

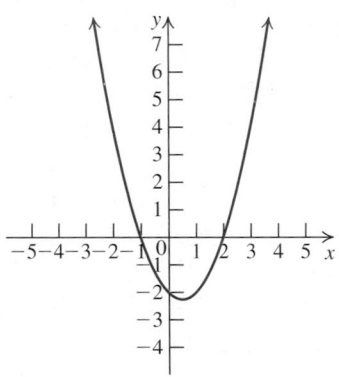

FIGURE 2.13

3 Find the symmetries in a graph.

TECHNOLOGY CONNECTION

Calculator graph of $y = x^2 - x - 2$

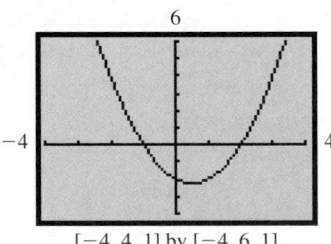

$[-4, 4, 1]$ by $[-4, 6, 1]$

EXAMPLE 2   Finding Intercepts

Find the x- and y-intercepts of the graph of the equation $y = x^2 - x - 2$.

Solution

Step 1   To find the x-intercepts, we set $y = 0$ in the equation and solve for x. Thus $y = x^2 - x - 2$ becomes

$$0 = x^2 - x - 2 \qquad \text{Set } y = 0.$$
$$0 = (x + 1)(x - 2) \qquad \text{Factor.}$$
$$x + 1 = 0 \quad \text{or} \quad x - 2 = 0 \qquad \text{Zero-product property}$$
$$x = -1 \quad \text{or} \qquad x = 2. \qquad \text{Solve each equation for } x.$$

The x-intercepts are -1 and 2.

Step 2   To find the y-intercepts, we set $x = 0$ in the equation $y = x^2 - x - 2$ and solve for y. We obtain

$$y = 0^2 - 0 - 2 \qquad \text{Set } x = 0.$$
$$y = -2. \qquad \text{Solve for } y.$$

The y-intercept is -2.

The graph of the equation $y = x^2 - x - 2$ is shown in Figure 2.13.   ■ ■ ■

PRACTICE PROBLEM 2   Find the intercepts of the graph of $y = 2x^2 + 3x - 2$.   ■

Symmetry

A useful tool for sketching the graph of an equation is the concept of **symmetry,** which means that one portion of the graph is a *mirror image* of another portion.

The idealized mirror used in plane geometry has no thickness and is silvered on both sides, so that it not only reflects an object A into an object B, but also reflects an object B into A. Given any point P on either side of a geometrical mirror, we can construct its reflected image by drawing the perpendicular line segment from P to the mirror and extending this segment to an equal distance on the other side to a point P', so that the mirror (line) perpendicularly bisects the line segment $\overline{PP'}$. See Figure 2.14.

The mirror line is usually called the **axis of symmetry** or **line of symmetry.**

In Figure 2.14, we say that the point P' is the *symmetric image* of the point P with respect to the line l. A knowledge of symmetry reduces the work required to sketch graphs, because we can use information about part of the graph to draw the remainder of the graph.

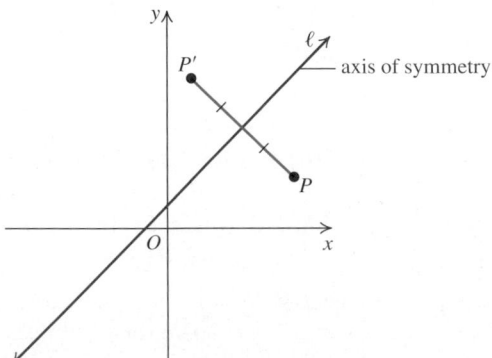

FIGURE 2.14

The following test describes three basic types of symmetries.

TESTS FOR SYMMETRIES

1. A graph is **symmetric with respect to the y-axis** if, for every point (x, y) on the graph, the point $(-x, y)$ is also on the graph. See Figure 2.15(a)

2. A graph is **symmetric with respect to the x-axis** if, for every point (x, y) on the graph, the point $(x, -y)$ is also on the graph. See Figure 2.15(b).

3. A graph is **symmetric with respect to the origin** if, for every point (x, y) on the graph, the point $(-x, -y)$ is also on the graph. See Figure 2.15(c).

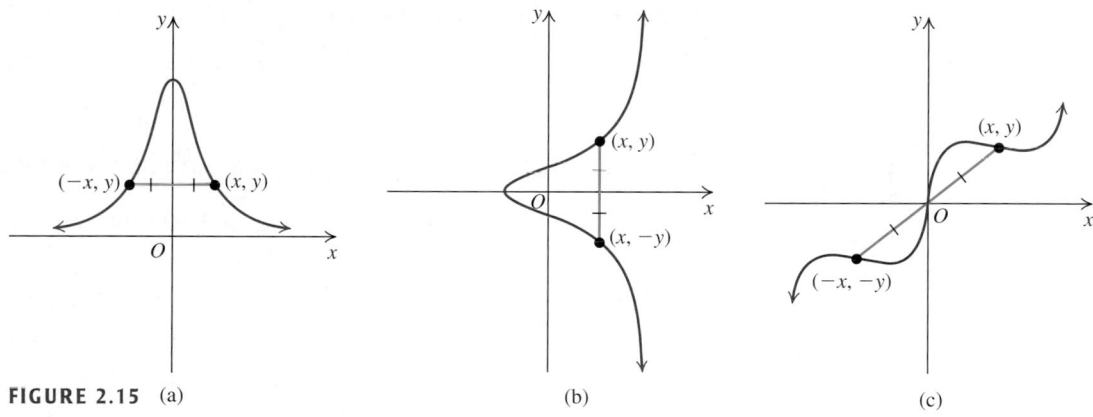

FIGURE 2.15 (a)   (b)   (c)

EXAMPLE 3   **Checking for Symmetry**

Determine whether the graph of the equation $y = \dfrac{1}{x^2 + 5}$ is symmetric with respect to the y-axis.

Solution

To test whether the graph of the given equation is symmetric with respect to the y-axis, we replace x by $-x$ in the given equation, to see if $(-x, y)$ also satisfies the equation.

$$y = \frac{1}{x^2 + 5} \qquad \text{Original equation}$$

$$y = \frac{1}{(-x)^2 + 5} \qquad \text{Replace } x \text{ by } -x.$$

$$y = \frac{1}{x^2 + 5} \qquad \text{Simplify, } (-x)^2 = x^2.$$

Thus, when we replace x by $-x$ in the equation, we obtain the original equation.

Hence, the graph of $y = \dfrac{1}{x^2 + 5}$ is symmetric with respect to the y-axis. ■ ■ ■

PRACTICE PROBLEM 3   Check for symmetry with respect to the y-axis:

$$x^2 - y^2 = 1.$$

■

EXAMPLE 4	Checking for Symmetry

Show that the graph of $x^3 + y^2 - xy^2 = 0$ is symmetric with respect to the x-axis.

Solution

$$
\begin{array}{ll}
x^3 + y^2 - xy^2 = 0 & \text{Original equation} \\
x^3 + (-y)^2 - x(-y)^2 = 0 & \text{Replace } y \text{ by } -y. \\
x^3 + y^2 - xy^2 = 0 & \text{Simplify, } (-y)^2 = y^2.
\end{array}
$$

We obtain the original equation when y is replaced by $-y$. Thus, the graph of the equation is symmetric with respect to the x-axis.   ▪ ▪ ▪

PRACTICE PROBLEM 4   Check for symmetry about the x-axis:

$$x^2 - y^3 = 2.$$ ▪

EXAMPLE 5	Checking for Symmetry with Respect to the Origin

Show that the graph of $y^5 = x^3$ is symmetric with respect to the origin, but not with respect to either axis.

Solution

$$
\begin{array}{ll}
y^5 = x^3 & \text{Original equation} \\
(-y)^5 = (-x)^3 & \text{Replace } x \text{ by } -x \text{ and } y \text{ by } -y. \\
-y^5 = -x^3 & \text{Simplify.} \\
y^5 = x^3 & \text{Multiply both sides by } -1.
\end{array}
$$

Since replacing x by $-x$ and y and $-y$ produces the original equation, $(-x, -y)$ also satisfies the equation and the graph is symmetric with respect to the origin.

The graph of $y^5 = x^3$ is not symmetric with respect to the y-axis, because the point $(1, 1)$ is on the graph, but the point $(-1, 1)$ is not on the graph. Similarly, the graph of $y^5 = x^3$ is not symmetric with respect to the x-axis, since the point $(1, 1)$ is on the graph, but the point $(1, -1)$ is not on the graph.   ▪ ▪ ▪

PRACTICE PROBLEM 5   Check the graph of $x^2 = y^3$ for symmetry in the x-axis, the y-axis, and the origin.   ▪

EXAMPLE 6	Sketching a Graph by Using Intercepts and Symmetry

Initially, there are 400 deer on Dooms island. The number y of deer on the island after t years is described by the equation

$$y = -t^4 + 96t^2 + 400.$$

a.   Sketch the graph of the equation $y = -t^4 + 96t^2 + 400$.

b.   Adjust the graph in part (a) to account for only the physical aspects of the problem.

c.   When does the population of deer become extinct on Dooms?

Solution

a. (i)   First, we find all intercepts. If we set $t = 0$ in the equation
$y = -t^4 + 96t^2 + 400$, we obtain $y = 400$. Thus, the y-intercept is 400.
To find the t-intercepts, we set $y = 0$ in the given equation.

$y = -t^4 + 96t^2 + 400$	Original equation
$0 = -t^4 + 96t^2 + 400$	Set $y = 0$.
$t^4 - 96t^2 - 400 = 0$	Multiply both sides by -1 and interchange sides.
$(t^2 + 4)(t^2 - 100) = 0$	Factor.
$(t^2 + 4)(t + 10)(t - 10) = 0$	Factor $t^2 - 100$.
$t^2 + 4 = 0$ or $t + 10 = 0$ or $t - 10 = 0$	Zero-product property
$t = -10$ or $t = 10$	Solve for t; there is no real solution of $t^2 + 4 = 0$.

The t-intercepts are -10 and 10.

(ii)   Next, we check for symmetry. Note that t replaces x as the independent variable.

Symmetry in the t-axis:
Replacing y by $-y$ gives $-y = -t^4 + 96t^2 + 400$. The pair $(0, -400)$, is a
solution of $-y = -t^4 + 96t^2 + 400$, but not of $y = -t^4 + 96t^2 + 400$. Consequently, the graph is not symmetric in the t-axis.

Symmetry in the y-axis:
Replacing t by $-t$ in the equation $y = -t^4 + 96t^2 + 400$, we obtain
$y = -(-t)^4 + 96(-t)^2 + 400 = -t^4 + 96t^2 + 400$, which is the original
equation. Thus, $(-t, y)$ also satisfies the equation and the graph is symmetric in
the y-axis.

Symmetry in the origin:
Replacing t by $-t$ and y by $-y$ in the equation $y = -t^4 + 96t^2 + 400$, we obtain
$-y = -(-t)^4 + 96(-t)^2 + 400$, or $-y = -t^4 + 96t^2 + 400$. As we saw when
we discussed symmetry in the t-axis, $(0, 400)$ is a solution but $(-0, -400)$ is not a
solution of this equation, so the graph is not symmetric with respect to the origin.

(iii)   Finally, we sketch the graph by first plotting points for $t \geq 0$ (see Table 2.3) and
then using symmetry in the y-axis (see Figure 2.16).

TABLE 2.3

t	$y = -t^4 + 96t^2 + 400$	(t, y)
0	400	$(0, 400)$
1	495	$(1, 495)$
5	2175	$(5, 2175)$
7	2703	$(7, 2703)$
9	1615	$(9, 1615)$
10	0	$(10, 0)$
11	-2625	$(11, -2625)$

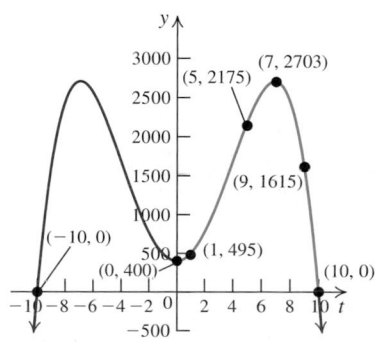

FIGURE 2.16

Continued on next page.

b. The graph pertaining to the physical aspects of the problem is the blue portion in Figure 2.16.

c. The positive *t*-intercept, which is 10, gives the time in years when the deer population of Dooms is 0.   ▪ ▪ ▪

PRACTICE PROBLEM 6   Repeat Example 6 if the initial deer population is 324 and the number of deer on the island after *t* years is given by $y = -t^4 + 77t^2 + 324$.   ▪

---

4 Find the equation of a circle.

Circles

So far, we have seen that an equation in x and y gives rise to a geometric figure that is its graph. Sometimes we can go the other way: A graph is described geometrically in terms of points in the plane, and these points in turn give rise to the equation of the graph in x and y. We illustrate the latter situation in the case of a circle.

Figure 2.17 is the graph of a circle with center $C(h, k)$ and radius r.

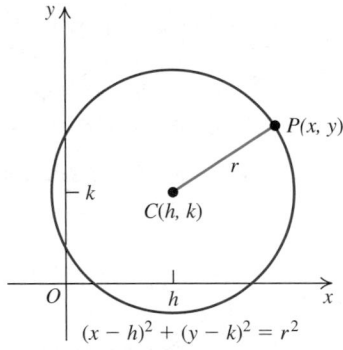

FIGURE 2.17

CIRCLE

A **circle** is a set of points in a Cartesian coordinate plane that are at a fixed distance r from a specified point (h, k). The fixed distance r is called the **radius** of the circle, and the specified point (h, k) is called the **center** of the circle.

A point $P(x, y)$ is on the circle if and only if its distance from the center C is r. Using the notation for the distance between the points P and C, we have:

$$d(P, C) = r$$
$$\sqrt{(x - h)^2 + (y - k)^2} = r \qquad \text{Distance formula}$$
$$(x - h)^2 + (y - k)^2 = r^2 \qquad \text{Square both sides.}$$

The equation $(x - h)^2 + (y - k)^2 = r^2$ is an equation of a circle with radius r and center (h, k). A point (x, y) is on the circle of radius r and center $C(h, k)$ if and only if it satisfies this equation.

THE CENTER-RADIUS FORM FOR THE EQUATION OF A CIRCLE

The equation of a circle with center (h, k) and radius r is

(1) $$(x - h)^2 + (y - k)^2 = r^2.$$

This equation is also called the **standard form** of an equation of a circle with radius r and center (h, k).

EXAMPLE 7   **Finding the Equation of a Circle**

Find the center–radius form of the equation of the circle with center $(-3, 4)$ and radius 7.

Solution

$$(x - h)^2 + (y - k)^2 = r^2 \quad \text{Center–radius form}$$
$$[x - (-3)]^2 + (y - 4)^2 = 7^2 \quad \text{Replace } h \text{ by } -3, \ k \text{ by } 4, \text{ and } r \text{ by } 7.$$
$$(x + 3)^2 + (y - 4)^2 = 49 \quad \text{The desired equation} \quad ■ ■ ■$$

PRACTICE PROBLEM 7   Find the center–radius form of the equation of the circle with center $(3, -6)$ and radius 10.   ■

If an equation in two variables can be written in the standard form (1), then its graph is a circle with center (h, k) and radius r.

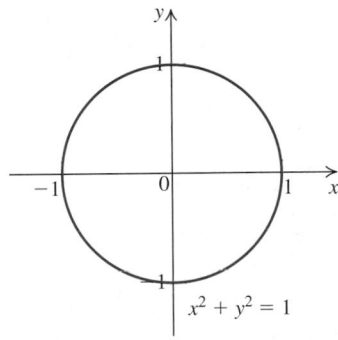

$x^2 + y^2 = 1$

FIGURE 2.18

EXAMPLE 8   **Graphing a Circle**

Graph each equation.

a. $x^2 + y^2 = 1$
b. $(x + 2)^2 + (y - 3)^2 = 25$

Solution

a. The equation $x^2 + y^2 = 1$ can be rewritten as

$$(x - 0)^2 + (y - 0)^2 = 1^2.$$

Comparing this equation with equation (1), we conclude that the given equation is an equation of a circle with center $(0, 0)$ and radius 1. The graph is shown in Figure 2.18. This circle is called the **unit circle.**

b. Rewriting the equation $(x + 2)^2 + (y - 3)^2 = 25$ as

$$[x - (-2)]^2 + (y - 3)^2 = 5^2, \quad x + 2 = x - (-2)$$

we see that the graph of this equation is a circle with center $(-2, 3)$ and radius 5. The graph is shown in Figure 2.19.   ■ ■ ■

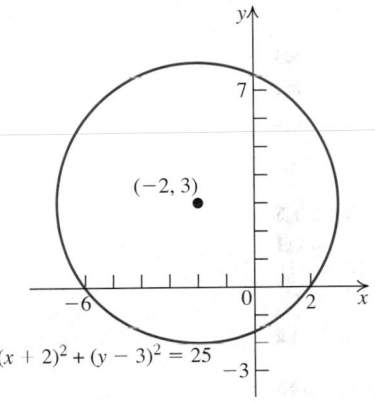

$(-2, 3)$

$(x + 2)^2 + (y - 3)^2 = 25$

FIGURE 2.19

PRACTICE PROBLEM 8   Graph the equation $(x - 2)^2 + (y + 1)^2 = 36$.   ■

TECHNOLOGY CONNECTION

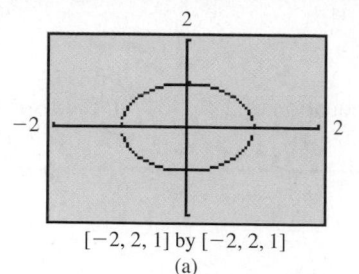

$[-2, 2, 1]$ by $[-2, 2, 1]$
(a)

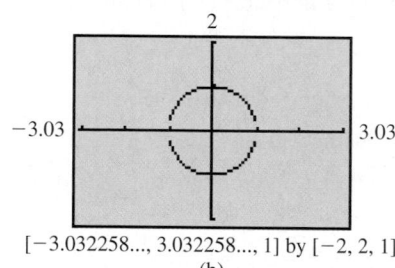

$[-3.032258..., 3.032258..., 1]$ by $[-2, 2, 1]$
(b)

To graph the equation $x^2 + y^2 = 1$ on a graphing calculator, we first solve for y.

$$y^2 = 1 - x^2 \qquad \text{Subtract } x^2 \text{ from both sides.}$$
$$y = \pm\sqrt{1 - x^2} \qquad \text{Square root property}$$

We then graph the two equations

$$Y_1 = \sqrt{1 - x^2} \quad \text{and} \quad Y_2 = -\sqrt{1 - x^2}$$

in the same viewing rectangle. The graph of $y = \sqrt{1 - x^2}$ is the upper semicircle $(y \geq 0)$ and the graph of $y = -\sqrt{1 - x^2}$ is the lower semicircle $(y \leq 0)$. The calculator graph in (a) does not quite look like a circle. The reason is that, on most graphing calculators, the display screen is about two-thirds as high as it is wide. Graphing calculators have options on the ZOOM menu to square the viewing screen. We use the ZSquare option to make the display look like a circle, as shown in (b).

EQUATION ↔ CIRCLE

Note that stating that the equation

$$(x + 3)^2 + (y - 4)^2 = 25$$

represents the circle of radius 5 with center $(-3, 4)$ means two things:

(i) If the values of x and y are a pair of numbers that satisfy the equation, then they are the coordinates of a point on the circle with radius 5 and center $(-3, 4)$.

(ii) If a point is on the circle, then its coordinates satisfy the equation.

Let us expand the squared expressions in the equation of the circle given in the preceding box and then simplify:

$$(x + 3)^2 + (y - 4)^2 = 25 \qquad \text{Given equation}$$
$$x^2 + 6x + 9 + y^2 - 8y + 16 = 25 \qquad \text{Expand squares.}$$
$$x^2 + y^2 + 6x - 8y = 0 \qquad \text{Simplify and rewrite.}$$

In general, if we expand the squared expressions in the standard equation of a circle,

(1) $$(x - h)^2 + (y - k)^2 = r^2,$$

and then simplify, we obtain an equation of the form

(2) $$x^2 + y^2 + ax + by + c = 0.$$

Equation (2) is called the *general form* of the equation of a circle.

GENERAL FORM OF THE EQUATION OF A CIRCLE

The **general form** of the equation of a circle is

$$x^2 + y^2 + ax + by + c = 0.$$

Conversely, suppose that we are given an equation in general form. Then we can convert this equation to standard form by completing the squares on the x- and y-terms. We then obtain an equation of the form

$$(3) \qquad (x - h)^2 + (y - k)^2 = d.$$

If $d > 0$, the graph of equation (3) is a circle with center (h, k) and radius $\sqrt{d}$. If $d = 0$, the graph of equation (3) is the point (h, k). If $d < 0$, there is no graph.

EXAMPLE 9   **Converting the General Form to Center–Radius Form**

Find the center and radius of the circle with equation

$$x^2 + y^2 - 6x + 8y + 10 = 0.$$

RECALL

A quadratic trinomial in the variable x with the coefficient of x^2 equal to 1 is a perfect square if the constant term is the square of one-half the coefficient of x.

Solution

We complete the squares (on both the terms involving x and the terms involving y) to write the given equation in center–radius form.

$x^2 + y^2 - 6x + 8y + 10 = 0$	Original equation
$(x^2 - 6x) + (y^2 + 8y) = -10$	Group the x-terms and y-terms separately; subtract 10 from both sides.
$(x^2 - 6x + 9) + (y^2 + 8y + 16) = -10 + 9 + 16$	Complete the square on both the x-terms and the y-terms by adding 9 and 16 to both sides.
$(x - 3)^2 + (y + 4)^2 = 15$	Factor and simplify.
$(x - 3)^2 + [y - (-4)]^2 = 15$	Rewrite in center–radius form.

Comparing the last equation with the center–radius form, we have $h = 3$, $k = -4$, and $r = \sqrt{15}$. Thus, the given equation represents a circle with center $(3, -4)$ and radius $\sqrt{15} \approx 3.9$.   ■ ■ ■

PRACTICE PROBLEM 9 Find the center and radius of the circle with equation $x^2 + y^2 + 4x - 6y - 12 = 0$.   ■

A Exercises   Basic Skills and Concepts

In Exercises 1–8, determine whether the given points are on the graph of the equation.

Equation	Points
1. $y = x - 1$	$(-3, -4,), (1, 0), (4, 3), (2, 3)$ †
2. $2y = 3x + 5$	$(-1, 1)\ (0, 2), \left(-\dfrac{5}{3}, 0\right), (1, 4)$ †
3. $y = \sqrt{x + 1}$	$(3, 2), (0, 1), (8, -3), (8, 3)$ †
4. $y = \dfrac{1}{x}$	$\left(-3, \dfrac{1}{3}\right), (1, 1), (0, 0), \left(2, \dfrac{1}{2}\right)$ †
5. $x^2 - y^2 = 1$	$(1, 0), (0, -1), (2, \sqrt{3}), (2, -\sqrt{3})$ †
6. $y^2 = x$	$(1, -1), (1, 1)\ (0, 0), (2, -\sqrt{2})$ †

7. Write the x- and y-intercepts of the graph. †

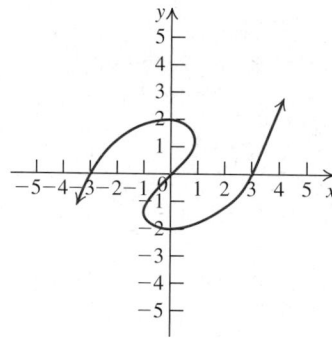

8. Write the x- and y-intercepts of the graph: †

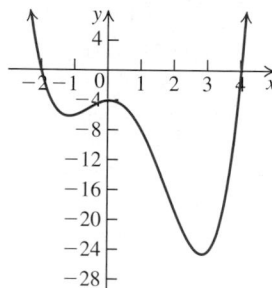

In Exercises 9–30, graph each equation by plotting points. Let $x = -3, -2, -1, 0, 1, 2,$ and 3, where applicable.

9. $y = x + 1$ †

10. $y = x - 1$ †

11. $y = 2x$ †

12. $y = \dfrac{1}{2}x$ †

13. $y = x^2$ †

14. $y = -x^2$ †

15. $y = |x|$ †

16. $y = |x + 1|$ †

17. $y = |x| + 1$ †

18. $y = -|x| + 1$ †

19. $y = 4 - x^2$ †

20. $y = x^2 - 4$ †

21. $y = \sqrt{9 - x^2}$ †

22. $y = -\sqrt{9 - x^2}$ †

23. $y = x^3$ †

24. $y = -x^3$ †

25. $y^3 = x$ †

26. $y^3 = -x$ †

27. $x = |y|$ †

28. $|x| = |y|$ †

29. $y = |2 - x|$ †

30. $|x| + |y| = 1$ †

In Exercises 31–40, find the x- and y-intercepts of the graph of the equation.

31. $3x + 4y = 12$ †

32. $\dfrac{x}{5} + \dfrac{y}{3} = 1$ †

33. $2x + 3y = 5$ †

34. $\dfrac{x}{2} - \dfrac{y}{3} = 1$ †

35. $y = x^2 - 6x + 8$ †

36. $x = y^2 - 5y + 6$ †

37. $x^2 + y^2 = 4$ †

38. $y = \sqrt{9 - x^2}$ †

39. $y = \sqrt{x^2 - 1}$ †

40. $xy = 1$ No x- or y-intercept

In Exercises 41–50, test each equation for symmetry with respect to the x-axis, the y-axis, and the origin.

41. $y = x^2 + 1$ †

42. $x = y^2 + 1$ †

43. $y = x^3 + x$ †

44. $y = 2x^3 - x$ †

45. $y = 5x^4 + 2x^2$ †

46. $y = -3x^6 + 2x^4 + x^2$ †

47. $y = -3x^5 + 2x^3$ †

48. $y = 2x^2 - |x|$ †

49. $x^2y^2 + 2xy = 1$ †

50. $x^2 + y^2 = 16$ †

In Exercises 51–56, specify the center and the radius of each circle.

51. $(x - 2)^2 + (y - 3)^2 = 36$ Center: $(2, 3)$. Radius: 6

52. $(x + 1)^2 + (y - 3)^2 = 16$ Center: $(-1, 3)$. Radius: 4

53. $(x + 2)^2 + (y + 3)^2 = 11$ Center: $(-2, -3)$. Radius: $\sqrt{11}$

54. $\left(x - \dfrac{1}{2}\right)^2 + \left(y + \dfrac{3}{2}\right)^2 = \dfrac{3}{4}$ Center: $\left(\dfrac{1}{2}, -\dfrac{3}{2}\right)$. Radius: $\dfrac{\sqrt{3}}{2}$

55. $(x - a)^2 + (y + b)^2 = r^2$ Center: $(a, -b)$. Radius: $|r|$

56. $(x + a)^2 + (y + b)^2 = 7$ Center: $(-a, -b)$. Radius: $\sqrt{7}$

In Exercises 57–64, find the center–radius form of the equation of a circle that satisfies the given conditions. Graph each equation.

57. Center $(0, 1)$; radius 2 †

58. Center $(1, 0)$; radius 1 †

59. Center $(-1, 2)$; radius $\sqrt{2}$ †

60. Center $(-2, -3)$; radius $\sqrt{7}$ †

61. Center $(3\ -4)$; passing through the point $(-1, 5)$ †

62. Center $(1, 2)$; touching the x-axis †

63. Center $(1, 2)$; touching the y-axis †

64. Diameter with endpoints $(7, 4)$ and $(-3, 6)$ †

†Due to space constrictions, answers to these exercises may be found in the Answers beginning on page A–1 in the back of the book.

In Exercises 65–70, describe the graph of each equation and give the center and radius of each circle.

65. $x^2 + y^2 - 2x - 2y - 4 = 0$ †

66. $x^2 + y^2 - 4x - 2y - 15 = 0$ †

67. $2x^2 + 2y^2 + 4y = 0$ †

68. $3x^2 + 3y^2 + 6x = 0$ †

69. $x^2 + y^2 - x = 0$ †

70. $x^2 + y^2 + 1 = 0$ ∅

B Exercises   Applying the Concepts

In Exercises 71–74, a graph is described *geometrically* as the path of a point $P(x, y)$ on the graph. Find an equation for the graph described.

71. Geometry. $P(x, y)$ is on the graph if and only if the distance from $P(x, y)$ to the x-axis is equal to its distance from the y-axis. $|x| = |y|$

72. Geometry. $P(x, y)$ is the same distance from the two points $(1, 2)$ and $(3, -4)$ †

73. Geometry. $P(x, y)$ is the same distance from the point $(2, 0)$ and the y-axis. †

74. Geometry. $P(x, y)$ is the same distance from the point $(0, 4)$ and the x-axis. †

75. Corporate profits. The equation $P = -0.5t^2 - 3t + 8$ describes the monthly profits (in millions of dollars) of ABCD Corp. for the year 2004, with $t = 0$ representing July 2004.
   a. How much profit did the corporation make in March 2004?
   b. How much profit did the corporation make in October 2004?
   c. Sketch the graph of the equation.
   d. Find the t-intercept. What does it represent?
   e. Find the P-intercept. What does it represent? †

76. Female students in colleges. The equation

$$P = -0.002t^2 + 0.093t + 8.18$$

models the approximate number (in millions) of female college students in the United States for the academic years 1995–2001, with $t = 0$ representing 1995.

   a. Sketch the graph of the equation. †
   b. Find the positive t-intercept. What does it represent? †
   c. Find the P-intercept. What does it represent? †
   (*Source: Statistical Abstract of the United States.*) †

77. Motion. An object is thrown up from the top of a building that is 320 feet high. The equation $y = -16t^2 + 128t + 320$ gives the object's height (in feet) above the ground at any time t (in seconds) after the object is thrown.

   a. What is the height of the object after 0, 1, 2, 3, 4, 5, and 6 seconds? †
   b. Sketch the graph of the equation $y = -16t^2 + 128t + 320$. †
   c. What part of the graph represents the physical aspects of the problem? †
   d. What are the intercepts of this graph, and what do they mean? †

78. Diving for treasure. A treasure-hunting team of divers is placed in a computer-controlled diving cage. The equation $d = \dfrac{40}{3}t - \dfrac{2}{9}t^2$ describes the depth d (in feet) that the cage will descend in t minutes.

   a. Sketch the graph of the equation $d = \dfrac{40}{3}t - \dfrac{2}{9}t^2$. †
   b. What part of the graph represents the physical aspects of the problem? †
   c. What is the total time of the entire diving experiment? †

C Exercises | Beyond the Basics

In Exercises 79–82, sketch the complete graph by using the given symmetry.

79.

y-axis symmetry

80.

x-axis symmetry

81.

origin symmetry

82.

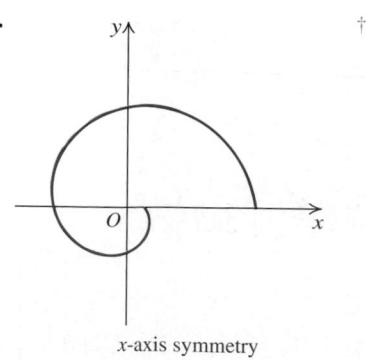

x-axis symmetry

In Exercises 83–88, graph each equation. [Hint: Use the zero-product property of numbers: $ab = 0$ if and only if $a = 0$ or $b = 0$.]

83. $(y - x)(y - 2x) = 0$ †

84. $y^2 = x^2$ †

85. $(y - x)(x^2 + y^2 - 4) = 0$ †

86. $(y - x + 1)(x^2 + y^2 - 6x + 8y + 24) = 0$ †

87. $x^2 - 9y^2 = 0$ †

88. $(y - x - 1)(y - x^2) = 0$ †

89. In the same coordinate system, sketch the graphs of the two circles with equations $x^2 + y^2 - 4x + 2y - 20 = 0$ and $x^2 + y^2 - 4x + 2y - 31 = 0$, and find the area of the region bounded by the two circles. †

90. Sketch the graph (if possible) of each equation.
   a. $x^2 + y^2 + 2x - 2y + 3 = 0$ †
   b. $x^2 + y^2 + 2x - 2y + 2 = 0$ †
   c. $x^2 + y^2 + 2x - 2y - 7 = 0$ †

Critical Thinking

91. Sketch the graph of $y^2 = 2x$, and explain how this graph is related to the graphs of $y = \sqrt{2x}$ and $y = -\sqrt{2x}$. †

92. Show that a graph which is symmetric with respect to the *x*-axis and *y*-axis must be symmetric with respect to the origin. Give an example to show that the converse is not true.

93. True or False? To find the *x*-intercepts of the graph of an equation, set $x = 0$ and solve for *y*. Explain your answer.

94. Write an equation whose graph has *x*-intercepts -2 and 3, and *y*-intercept 6. (Many answers are possible.)

95. Sketch a graph that has
   a. One *x*-intercept and one *y*-intercept. †
   b. Two *x*-intercepts and three *y*-intercepts. †
   c. No intercepts. †
   d. Two *x*-intercepts and no *y*-intercept. †

Answers:
   92. The converse is not true. (See the graph of $y = x$.)
   93. False, because it gives the *y*-intercepts.
   94. For example, $y = -(x + 2)(x - 3)$.

Group Projects

1. a. Show that a circle with diameter having endpoints $A(0, 1)$ and $B(6, 8)$ intersects the x-axis at the roots of the equation $x^2 - 6x + 8 = 0$.

   b. Show that a circle with diameter having endpoints $A(0, 1)$ and $B(a, b)$ intersects the x-axis at the roots of the equation $x^2 - ax + b = 0$.

   c. Use graph paper, ruler, and compass to approximate the roots of the equation $x^2 - 3x + 1 = 0$. Answers may vary slightly.

2. a. Show that a circle with diameter having endpoints $A(1, 0)$ and $B(10, 7)$ intersects the y-axis at the roots of the equation $y^2 - 7y + 10 = 0$.

   b. Show that a circle with diameter having endpoints $A(1, 0)$ and $B(a, b)$ intersects the y-axis at the roots of the equation $y^2 - by + a = 0$.

Lines

BEFORE STARTING THIS SECTION, REVIEW

1. Evaluating algebraic expressions (Section P.1, page 14)
2. Graphs of equations (Section 2.2, page 192)

OBJECTIVES

1 Find the slope of a line.

2 Write the point–slope form of the equation of a line.

3 Write the slope–intercept form of the equation of a line.

4 Recognize the equations of horizontal and vertical lines.

5 Recognize the general form of the equation of a line.

6 Find equations of parallel and perpendicular lines.

A Texan's Tall Tale

Gunslinger Wild Bill Longley's *first* burial took place on October 11, 1878, after he was hanged before a crowd of thousands in Giddings, Texas. Tales of Longley's criminal career are a mixture of facts and his boasts. It is known that Longley killed about three dozen people at the end of the Civil War, when he took up with other young thugs and terrorized the newly freed slaves. Just before his execution, Longley claimed that he had killed only eight men. His story was made into the television series *The Texans*, which aired from 1958 through 1960.

Rumors persisted that Longley's hanging had been a hoax and he had somehow faked his death and escaped execution. In 2001, Longley's descendants had his grave opened to determine whether the remains matched Wild Bill's description: a tall white male, age 27. Both the skeleton and some personal effects suggested that this was indeed Wild Bill. Modern science lent a hand, too: The DNA of Wild Bill's sister's descendant Helen Chapman was a perfect match.

Now the notorious gunman could be buried, back in the Giddings cemetery—for the *second* time. How did the scientists conclude from the skeletal remains that Wild Bill was approximately 6 feet tall? See Example 8. ■

1 Find the slope of a line.

Slope of a Line

In this section, we study various forms of first-degree equations in two variables. Since the graph of such an equation is a straight line, these equations are called **linear equations**. Just as we measure weight or temperature by a number, we will see how a number called the **slope** can be assigned to a line as a measure of the "steepness" of the line.

As we travel from the point $P(x_1, y_1)$ to the point $Q(x_2, y_2)$ on a nonvertical line, we move up or down a certain distance called the **rise.** At the same time, we move horizontally a certain distance, called the **run.** (See Figure 2.20.)

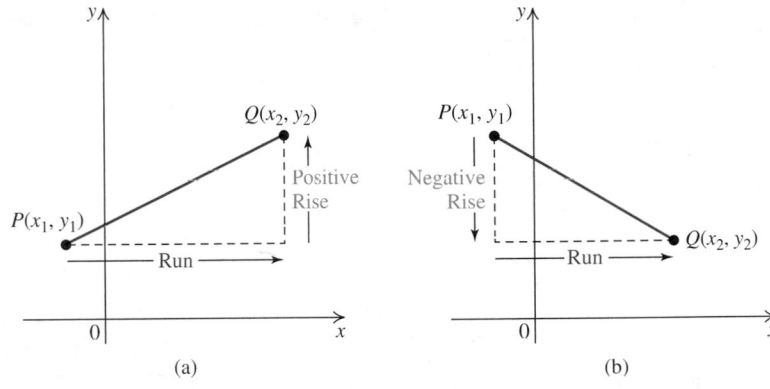

(a)   (b)

FIGURE 2.20

The *rise* is the change in y-coordinates between the points (x_1, y_1) and (x_2, y_2), and the *run* is the corresponding change in the x-coordinates. A positive run indicates movement to the right, as shown in Figure 2.20; a negative run indicates movement to the left. Similarly, a positive rise indicates upward movement; a negative rise indicates downward movement.

SLOPE OF A LINE

The slope of a nonvertical line that passes through the points $P(x_1, y_1)$ and $Q(x_2, y_2)$ is denoted by m and is defined by

$$m = \frac{\text{rise}}{\text{run}} = \frac{y_2 - y_1}{x_2 - x_1}.$$

The slope of a vertical line is undefined.

Since $m = \dfrac{\text{rise}}{\text{run}} = \dfrac{\text{change in } y\text{-coordinates}}{\text{change in } x\text{-coordinates}}$, if the change in x is 1 unit to the right (that is, $x_2 - x_1 = 1$) then the change in y is precisely the slope of the line. Thus, the slope of a line may be interpreted as the **change in y per unit change in x.** In other words, the slope of a line measures the rate of change of y with respect to x. If you have ever done roofing, built a staircase, graded landscaping, or traveled on mountainous roads, you have encountered this rise-over-run concept. For example, when an architect says that the pitch (slope) of a section of the roof is 0.4, he or she means that, for every horizontal distance of 10 feet, the roof ascends 4 feet.

| EXAMPLE 1 | Finding and Interpreting the Slope of a Line |

Sketch the graph of the line that passes through the points $P(1, -1)$ and $Q(3, 3)$. Find and interpret the slope of the line.

Solution

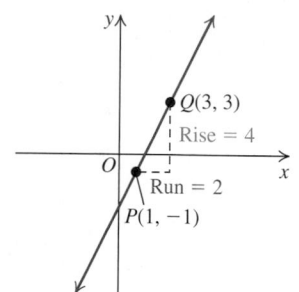

FIGURE 2.21

Any two points determine a line; the graph of the line passing through the points $P(1, -1)$ and $Q(3, 3)$ is sketched in Figure 2.21. The slope m of the line is given by

$$m = \frac{\text{rise}}{\text{run}} = \frac{\text{change in } y\text{-coordinates}}{\text{change in } x\text{-coordinates}}$$

$$= \frac{(y\text{-coordinate of } Q) - (y\text{-coordinate of } P)}{(x\text{-coordinate of } Q) - (x\text{-coordinate of } P)}$$

$$= \frac{(3) - (-1)}{3 - (1)} = \frac{3 + 1}{3 - 1} = \frac{4}{2} = 2.$$

Interpretation

The slope of this line is 2; this means that the value of y increases by exactly 2 units for every *increase* of 1 unit in the value of x. The graph is a straight line rising by 2 units for every one unit we go to the right. ■ ■ ■

PRACTICE PROBLEM 1 Find the slope of the line containing the points $(-7, 5)$ and $(6, -3)$. ■

Figure 2.22 shows several lines passing through the origin. The slope of each line is labeled. The figure shows that the greater the absolute value of the slope, the steeper is the line.

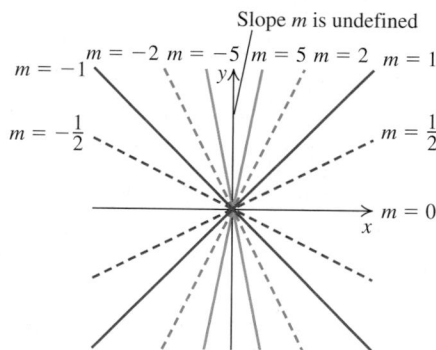

FIGURE 2.22

If two points $P(x_1, y_1)$ and $Q(x_2, y_2)$ are on a vertical line, then $x_2 = x_1$. The calculation of $m = \dfrac{y_2 - y_1}{x_2 - x_1}$ is not defined, because division by 0 is not defined. Thus, the slope of a vertical line is undefined. If $P(x_1, y_1)$ and $Q(x_2, y_2)$ are on a horizontal line, then $y_2 = y_1$. Thus, $y_2 - y_1 = 0$ and the slope of the line is zero.

SLOPES OF VERTICAL AND HORIZONTAL LINES

The slope of a *vertical line* is undefined.
The slope of a *horizontal line* is 0.

2 Write the point–slope form of the equation of a line.

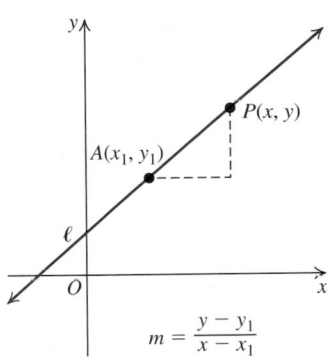

$$m = \frac{y - y_1}{x - x_1}$$

FIGURE 2.23

Equation of a Line

We now find the equation of a line l that passes through the point $A(x_1, y_1)$ and has slope m. Let $P(x, y)$, with $x \neq x_1$, be any point in the plane. Then $P(x, y)$ is on the line l if and only if the slope of the line passing through $P(x, y)$ and $A(x_1, y_1)$ is m. This is true if and only if

$$\frac{y - y_1}{x - x_1} = m.$$

(See Figure 2.23.)

Multiplying both sides by $x - x_1$, we obtain the equation of line l:

$$y - y_1 = m(x - x_1).$$

THE POINT-SLOPE FORM OF THE EQUATION OF A LINE

If a line has slope m and passes through the point (x_1, y_1), then the **point–slope form** of an equation of the line is

$$y - y_1 = m(x - x_1).$$

EXAMPLE 2   Finding an Equation of a Line with Given Point and Slope

Find the point–slope form of the equation of the line passing through the point $(1, -2)$ and with slope $m = 3$. Then solve for y.

Solution

We have $x_1 = 1$, $y_1 = -2$, and $m = 3$.

$$\begin{aligned}
y - y_1 &= m(x - x_1) &&\text{Point–slope form} \\
y - (-2) &= 3(x - 1) &&\text{Substitute } x_1 = 1, y_1 = -2, \text{ and } m = 3. \\
y + 2 &= 3x - 3 &&\text{Simplify.} \\
y &= 3x - 5 &&\text{Subtract 2 from both sides and simplify.}
\end{aligned}$$
■ ■ ■

PRACTICE PROBLEM 2   Find the point–slope form of the equation of the line passing through the point $(-2, -3)$ and with slope $-\frac{2}{3}$. Then solve for y. ■

EXAMPLE 3   Finding an Equation of a Line Passing through Two Given Points

Find the point–slope form of the equation of the line l passing through the points $(-2, 1)$ and $(3, 7)$. Then solve for y.

Continued on next page.

Solution

We first find the slope m of the line l.

$$m = \frac{7 - 1}{3 - (-2)} = \frac{6}{3 + 2} = \frac{6}{5} \qquad m = \frac{y_2 - y_1}{x_2 - x_1}$$

Use the point–slope form with $x_1 = 3$ and $y_1 = 7$.

$$y - y_1 = m(x - x_1) \qquad \text{Point–slope form}$$

$$y - 7 = \frac{6}{5}(x - 3) \qquad \text{Substitute } x_1 = 3, y_1 = 7, \text{ and } m = \frac{6}{5}.$$

$$y - 7 = \frac{6}{5}x - \frac{18}{5} \qquad \text{Distributive property}$$

$$y = \frac{6}{5}x + \frac{17}{5} \qquad \text{Add 7 to both sides and simplify.} \quad ■ \; ■ \; ■$$

Practice Problem 3 Find the point-slope of the equation of a line passing through the points $(-3, -4)$ and $(-1, 6)$. Then solve for y. ■

In Example 3, when using the point–slope form, you could have used the point $(-2, 1)$ for (x_1, y_1), and you would still get the same answer.

3 Write the slope–intercept form of the equation of a line.

EXAMPLE 4   **Finding an Equation of a Line with a Given Slope and y-intercept**

Find the point–slope form of the equation of the line with slope m and y-intercept b. Then solve for y.

Solution

Since the line has y-intercept b, the line passes through the point $(0, b)$. Using the point–slope form, we have

$$y - y_1 = m(x - x_1) \qquad \text{Point–slope form}$$
$$y - b = m(x - 0) \qquad \text{Substitute } x_1 = 0 \text{ and } y_1 = b.$$
$$y - b = mx \qquad \text{Simplify.}$$
$$y = mx + b \qquad \text{Solve for } y. \quad ■ \; ■ \; ■$$

Practice Problem 4 Find the point–slope form of the equation of the line with slope 2 and y-intercept -3. Then solve for y. ■

> ### SLOPE–INTERCEPT FORM OF THE EQUATION OF A LINE
>
> The **slope–intercept form** of the equation of the line with slope m and y-intercept b is
>
> $$y = mx + b.$$

The equation $y = mx + b$ is called the *slope–intercept form* of the equation of a line. The linear equation in the form $y = mx + b$ displays the slope (m, the coefficient of x) and the y-intercept (b, the constant term). Thus, the graph of an equation in the form

$y = mx + b$ is a straight line with slope m and y-intercept b. The number m tells which way and how much the line is tilted; the number b tells where the line intersects the y-axis.

EXAMPLE 5   **Graphing by Using the Slope and y-intercept**

Graph the line whose equation is $y = \dfrac{2}{3}x + 2$.

Solution

The equation

$$y = \frac{2}{3}x \quad + \quad 2$$

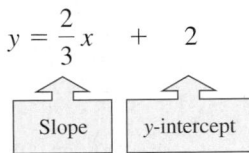

| Slope | y-intercept |

is in the slope-intercept form with slope $\dfrac{2}{3}$ and y-intercept 2. It is sufficient to find two points on the line and then draw a line through the two points. You can use the y-intercept, 2, as one of the points, namely, (0, 2). Use the slope to locate a second point on the line. Since $m = \dfrac{2}{3}$, interpret 2 as the rise and 3 as the run. Thus, from the point (0, 2) you move 3 units to the right (run) and then move 2 units up (rise) to find a second point on the line. This gives $(0 + \text{run}, 2 + \text{rise}) = (0 + 3, 2 + 2) = (3, 4)$ as the second point on the line.

The line joining the points (0, 2) and (3, 4) is shown in Figure 2.24.   ■ ■ ■

FIGURE 2.24

PRACTICE PROBLEM 5   Graph the line with slope $-\dfrac{2}{3}$ and that contains the point (0, 4).   ■

4 Recognize the equations of horizontal and vertical lines.

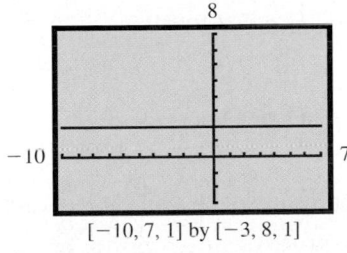
Equations of Horizontal and Vertical Lines

EXAMPLE 6   **Recognizing Horizontal and Vertical Lines**

Discuss the graph of each equation in the xy-plane.

a. $y = 2$ **b.** $x = 4$

Solution

a. The equation $y = 2$ may be considered as an equation in two variables x and y by writing

$$0 \cdot x + y = 2.$$

Any ordered pair of the form $(x, 2)$ is a solution of the equation $0 \cdot x + y = 2$. Some solutions are $(-1, 2)$, $(0, 2)$, $(2, 2)$, and $(7, 2)$. It follows that the graph of $y = 2$ is a line parallel to the x-axis and 2 units above it. The graph is sketched in Figure 2.25 on the next page. The slope of this line is 0.

Continued on next page.

FIGURE 2.25

FIGURE 2.26

b. The equation $x = 4$ may be written as

$$x + 0 \cdot y = 4.$$

Any ordered pair of the form $(4, y)$ is a solution of the equation $x + 0 \cdot y = 4$. Some solutions are $(4, -5)$, $(4, 0)$, $(4, 2)$, and $(4, 6)$. The graph of $x = 4$ is a line parallel to the y-axis and 4 units to the right of it. The graph of the equation $x = 4$ is shown in Figure 2.26. The slope of a vertical line is undefined. ■ ■ ■

PRACTICE PROBLEM 6   Sketch the graphs of the lines $x = -3$ and $y = 7$. ■

GRAPHS OF HORIZONTAL AND VERTICAL LINES

For any constant k, the graph of the equation $y = k$ is a *horizontal line* with slope 0. The graph of the equation $x = k$ is a *vertical line* with undefined slope.

---

5 Recognize the general form of the equation of a line.

General Form of the Equation of a Line

An equation of the form

$$ax + by + c = 0,$$

where a, b, and c are constants and not both a and b are zero, is called the *general form* of the linear equation. Suppose we are given such an equation. There are two cases: $b \neq 0$ or $b = 0$.

    Case (*i*): Suppose $b \neq 0$. In this case, we isolate y on one side of the equation and rewrite the other side in the form $mx + b$ as follows:

$$ax + by + c = 0 \qquad \text{Original equation}$$
$$by = -ax - c \qquad \text{Add } -ax - c \text{ to both sides.}$$
$$y = -\frac{a}{b}x - \frac{c}{b}. \qquad \text{Divide both sides by } b.$$

The last equation is an equation of a line in slope–intercept form. So the slope is $-\dfrac{a}{b}$, and the y-intercept is $-\dfrac{c}{b}$.

Case (*ii*): Suppose $b = 0$. Then $a \neq 0$ (since not both a and b are zero). In this case, the given linear equation becomes

$$ax + 0 \cdot y + c = 0 \qquad \text{Replace } b \text{ by } 0.$$
$$ax + c = 0 \qquad \text{Simplify.}$$
$$x = -\frac{c}{a}.$$

The graph of $x = -\dfrac{c}{a}$ is a vertical line.

GENERAL FORM OF THE EQUATION OF A LINE

The graph of every linear equation

$$ax + by + c = 0,$$

where a, b, and c are constants and not both a and b are zero, is a line. The equation $ax + by + c = 0$ is called the **general form** of the equation of a line.

Calculator graph of
$$y = \frac{3}{4}x + 3$$

$[-10, 7, 1]$ by $[-3, 8, 1]$

EXAMPLE 7   **Graphing a Linear Equation**

Find the slope, *y*-intercept, and *x*-intercept of the line with equation

$$3x - 4y + 12 = 0.$$

Then sketch the graph.

Solution

First, solve for y to write the equation in slope–intercept form:

$$3x - 4y + 12 = 0 \qquad \text{Original equation}$$
$$3x + 12 = 4y \qquad \text{Isolate the } y\text{-term by adding } 4y \text{ to both sides.}$$
$$\frac{3}{4}x + 3 = y \qquad \text{Divide both sides by 4.}$$

Then, from the equation

$$y = \frac{3}{4}x + 3,$$

read off the slope $m = \dfrac{3}{4}$ and the *y*-intercept 3. To find the *x*-intercept, set $y = 0$ in the original equation and obtain $3x + 12 = 0$. Solving for x then yields $x = -4$. Thus, the *x*-intercept is -4.

   To sketch the graph of the equation $3x - 4y + 12 = 0$, it is sufficient to find two points on the graph. The *x*- and *y*-intercepts are -4 and 3, respectively. Sketch the line joining the points $(-4, 0)$ and $(0, 3)$. The graph is shown in Figure 2.27. To help prevent errors, find and graph a third point on the line.   ■ ■ ■

PRACTICE PROBLEM 7   Sketch the graph of the equation $3x + 4y = 24$.   ■

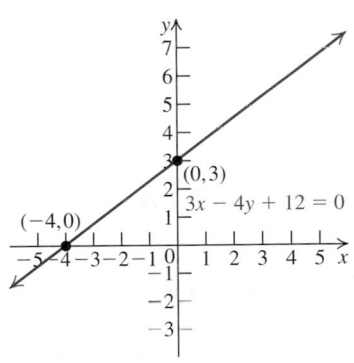

FIGURE 2.27

   Forensic scientists use various clues to determine the identity of deceased individuals. Scientists know that certain bones serve as excellent sources of information about a person's height. The person's height is determined by a set of standard equations containing

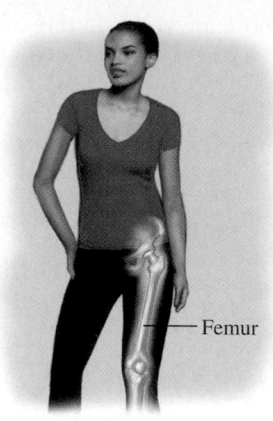
—Femur

scientific information gathered from hundreds of studies. Your upper leg contains a large, single bone called the *femur*. This long bone stretches from the hip (pelvis) socket to the kneecap (patella). The length of the femur can be used to estimate a person's height. Knowing both the gender and race of the individual increases the accuracy of this relationship between the length of the bone and the height of the person.

EXAMPLE 8   Inferring Height from the Femur

The height (H) of a human male is related to the length (x) of his femur by the formula

$$H = 2.6x + 65,$$

where all measurements are in centimeters. The femur of Wild Bill Longley was measured to be between 45 and 46 centimeters. Estimate the height of Wild Bill.

Solution

Substituting $x = 45$ and $x = 46$ into the preceding formula, we have possible heights

$$H_1 = (2.6)(45) + 65$$
$$= 182$$
$$\text{and} \quad H_2 = (2.6)(46) + 65$$
$$= 184.6.$$

Thus, Wild Bill's height was between 182 and 184.6 centimeters. (Recall that 1 inch $\approx$ 2.54 centimeters.)

Converting the foregoing numbers to inches, we conclude that Wild Bill's height was between $\dfrac{182}{2.54} \approx 71.7$ inches and $\dfrac{184.6}{2.54} \approx 72.7$ inches. He was approximately 6 feet tall.

■ ■ ■

PRACTICE PROBLEM 8   Suppose the femur of a person was measured to be between 43 and 44 centimeters. Estimate the height of the person in centimeters.   ■

6 Find equations of parallel and perpendicular lines.

Parallel and Perpendicular Lines

We can use the slopes of lines to decide whether the lines are parallel, perpendicular, or neither. The test is described next.

PARALLEL AND PERPENDICULAR LINES

Let l_1 and l_2 be two distinct lines with slopes m_1 and m_2, respectively. Then
   l_1 is parallel to l_2 if and only if $m_1 = m_2$.
   l_1 is perpendicular to l_2 if and only if $m_1 \cdot m_2 = -1$.
   Any two vertical lines are parallel, and any horizontal line is perpendicular to any vertical line.

In Exercises 107 and 108, you are asked to prove the assertions made in the box. The statement $m_1 \cdot m_2 = -1$ tells us that if the slope of a line l is m, then the slope of a line perpendicular to l is $-\dfrac{1}{m}$. In other words, the slopes of perpendicular lines are *negative*

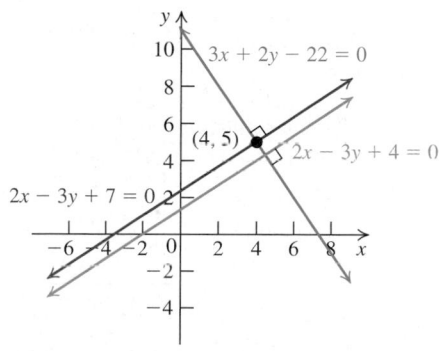

FIGURE 2.28

TECHNOLOGY CONNECTION

Calculator graph of
$y = \dfrac{2}{3}x + \dfrac{4}{3}$ and
$y = \dfrac{2}{3}x + \dfrac{7}{3}$

[−10, 7, 1] by [−3, 8, 1]

reciprocals of each other. For example, if the slope m_1 of a line l_1 is $-\dfrac{3}{4}$, then the slope m_2 of any line l_2 perpendicular to l_1 is $-\dfrac{1}{-\dfrac{3}{4}} = \dfrac{4}{3}$. (See Figure 2.28.)

EXAMPLE 9   Finding Equations of Parallel and Perpendicular Lines

Find equations in general form of the lines that pass through the point (4, 5) and are (a) parallel to and (b) perpendicular to the line $2x - 3y + 4 = 0$.

Solution

We first write the equation $2x - 3y + 4 = 0$ in slope–intercept form to find its slope.

$2x - 3y + 4 = 0$	Original equation
$-3y = -2x - 4$	Add $-2x - 4$ to both sides to isolate the y-term.
$y = \dfrac{2}{3}x + \dfrac{4}{3}$	Divide both sides by -3.

The line $2x - 3y + 4 = 0$ has slope $m = \dfrac{2}{3}$.

a. Any line parallel to the given line also has slope $\dfrac{2}{3}$.

$y - y_1 = m(x - x_1)$	Point–slope form
$y - 5 = \dfrac{2}{3}(x - 4)$	Substitute $x_1 = 4$, $y_1 = 5$, and $m = \dfrac{2}{3}$.
$3(y - 5) = 2(x - 4)$	Multiply both sides by 3.
$3y - 15 = 2x - 8$	Distributive property
$3y - 2x - 7 = 0$	Add $-2x + 8$ to both sides.
$2x - 3y + 7 = 0$	Multiply by -1. (This is because most people prefer a positive x-coefficient.)

The equation $2x - 3y + 7 = 0$ is the general form of the equation of the line through the point (4, 5) and parallel to the line $2x - 3y + 4 = 0$. (See Figure 2.29.)

FIGURE 2.29

Continued on next page.

The lines in part **b.** of Example 9 will not appear perpendicular in the standard viewing window, because each axis has a different scale. Use the ZSquare option on your graphing calculator to make the lines look perpendicular.

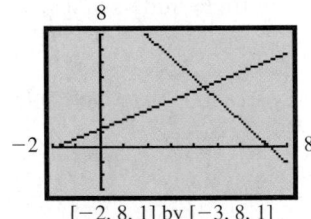

$[-2, 8, 1]$ by $[-3, 8, 1]$

Viewing window before applying ZSquare

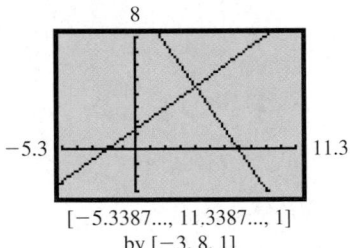

$[-5.3387..., 11.3387..., 1]$
by $[-3, 8, 1]$

After applying ZSquare

b. Since the slope of the given line is $\dfrac{2}{3}$, the slope of any line perpendicular to the given

line is $-\dfrac{1}{\frac{2}{3}} = -\dfrac{3}{2}$. Now use the point–slope form of the equation of the line passing

through the point $(4, 5)$ with slope $-\dfrac{3}{2}$.

$$y - y_1 = m(x - x_1) \qquad \text{Point–slope form}$$

$$y - 5 = -\frac{3}{2}(x - 4) \qquad \text{Substitute } x_1 = 4, y_1 = 5, \text{ and } m = -\frac{3}{2}.$$

$$2(y - 5) = -3(x - 4) \qquad \text{Multiply both sides by 2.}$$

$$2y - 10 = -3x + 12 \qquad \text{Distributive property}$$

$$3x + 2y - 22 = 0 \qquad \text{Add } 3x - 12 \text{ to both sides.}$$

The equation $3x + 2y - 22 = 0$ is the general form of the equation of the line through $(4, 5)$ and perpendicular to the line $2x - 3y + 4 = 0$. (See Figure 2.29.) ■ ■ ■

PRACTICE PROBLEM 9 Find the general form of the equations of the line
a. Through $(-2, 5)$ and parallel to the line containing $(2, 3)$ and $(5, 7)$.
b. Through $(3, -4)$ and perpendicular to the line $4x + 5y + 1 = 0$. ■

Summary

1. We summarize different forms of equations whose graphs are lines.

Form	Equation	Slope	Other information
General	$ax + by + c = 0$ $a \neq 0$, or $b \neq 0$	$-\dfrac{a}{b}$ if $b \neq 0$ Undefined if $b = 0$	x-intercept is $-\dfrac{c}{a}$, $a \neq 0$. y-intercept is $-\dfrac{c}{b}$, $b \neq 0$.
Point–slope	$y - y_1 = m(x - x_1)$	m	Line passes through (x_1, y_1).
Slope–Intercept	$y = mx + b$	m	y-intercept is b; x-intercept is $-\dfrac{b}{m}$ if $m \neq 0$.
Vertical line through (h, k)	$x = h$	undefined	x-intercept is h; no y-intercept if $h \neq 0$.
Horizontal line through (h, k)	$y = k$	0	When $k \neq 0$, no x-intercept; y-intercept is k.

2. Parallel and perpendicular lines: Two lines with slopes m_1 and m_2 are
(a) parallel if $m_1 = m_2$ and (b) perpendicular if $m_1 \cdot m_2 = -1$.

A Exercises   Basic Skills and Concepts

In Exercises 1–8, find the slope of the line through the given pair of points. Without plotting any points, state whether the line is rising, falling, horizontal, or vertical.

1. $(1, 3), (4, 7)$ †
2. $(0, 4), (2, 0)$ -2, falling
3. $(3, -2), (-2, 3)$ -1, falling
4. $(-3, 7), (-3, -4)$ †
5. $(3, -2), (2, -3)$ 1, rising
6. $(0.5, 2), (3, -3.5)$ †
7. $(\sqrt{2}, 1), (1 + \sqrt{2}, 5)$ 4, rising
8. $(1 - \sqrt{3}, 0), (1 + \sqrt{3}, 3\sqrt{3})$ †

9. In the figure, identify the line with the given slope m.
   a. $m = 1$ l_3
   b. $m = -1$ l_2
   c. $m = 0$ l_4
   d. m is undefined. l_1

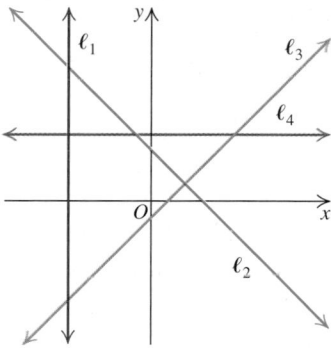

10. Find the slope of each line. (The scale is the same on both axes.) †

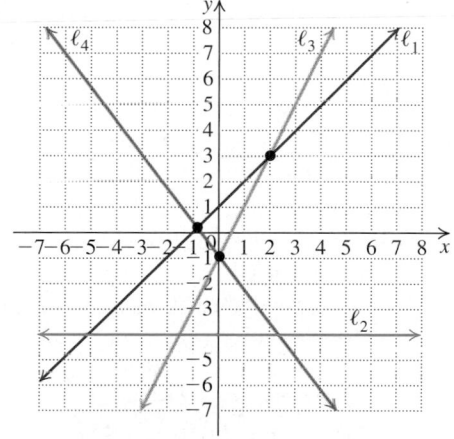

11. a. Write an equation whose graph is the x-axis. $y = 0$
    b. Write an equation whose graph is the y-axis. $x = 0$

12. a. Write an equation whose graph consists of all points with a y-coordinate of -4. $y = -4$
    b. Write an equation whose graph consists of all points with an x-coordinate of 5. $x = 5$

In Exercises 13–18, find an equation in slope–intercept form of the line that passes through the given point and has slope m. Also, sketch the graph of the line by locating the second point with the rise-and-run method.

13. $(0, 4); m = \dfrac{1}{2}$ †
14. $(0, 4); m = -\dfrac{1}{2}$ †
15. $(2, 1); m = -\dfrac{3}{2}$ †
16. $(-1, 0); m = \dfrac{2}{5}$ †
17. $(5, -4); m = -\dfrac{3}{5}$ †
18. $(5, -4); m$ is undefined. †

In Exercises 19–40, use the given conditions to find an equation in slope–intercept form of each of the nonvertical lines. Write vertical lines in the form $x = h$.

19. Passing through $(0, 1)$ and $(1, 0)$ $y = -x + 1$
20. Passing through $(0, 1)$ and $(1, 3)$ $y = 2x + 1$
21. Passing through $(-1, 3)$ and $(3, 3)$ $y = 3$
22. Passing through $(-5, 1)$ and $(2, 7)$ †
23. Passing through $(-2, -1)$ and $(1, 1)$ †
24. Passing through $(-1, -3)$ and $(6, -9)$ †
25. Passing through $\left(\dfrac{1}{2}, \dfrac{1}{4}\right)$ and $(0, 2)$ $y = -\dfrac{7}{2}x + 2$
26. Passing through $(4, -7)$ and $(4, 3)$ $x = 4$
27. A vertical line through $(5, 1.7)$ $x = 5$
28. A horizontal line through $(1.4, 1.5)$ $y = 1.5$
29. A horizontal line through $(0, 0)$ $y = 0$
30. A vertical line through $(0, 0)$ $x = 0$
31. $m = 0$; y-intercept $= 14$ $y = 14$
32. $m = 2$; y-intercept $= 5$ $y = 2x + 5$
33. $m = -\dfrac{2}{3}$; y-intercept $= -4$ $y = -\dfrac{2}{3}x - 4$
34. $m = -6$; y-intercept $= -3$ $y = -6x - 3$
35. x-intercept $= -3$; y-intercept $= 4$ †
36. x-intercept $= -5$; y-intercept $= -2$ †
37. Parallel to $y = 5$; passing through $(4, 7)$ $y = 7$
38. Parallel to $x = 5$; passing through $(4, 7)$ $x = 4$
39. Perpendicular to $x = -4$; passing through $(-3, -5)$ †
40. Perpendicular to $y = -4$; passing through $(-3, -5)$ †
41. Let l_1 be a line with slope $m = -2$. Determine whether the given line l_2 is parallel to l_1, perpendicular to l_1, or neither.
    a. l_2 is the line through the points $(1, 5)$ and $(3, 1)$. parallel
    b. l_2 is the line through the points $(7, 3)$ and $(5, 4)$. neither
    c. l_2 is the line through the points $(2, 3)$ and $(4, 4)$. †

†Due to space constrictions, answers to these exercises may be found in the Answers beginning on page A–1 in the back of the book.

42. A particle initially at $(-1, 3)$ moves along a line of slope $m = 4$ to a new position (x, y).
   a. Find y if $x = 2$. $y = 15$
   b. Find x if $y = 9$. †

In Exercises 43–50, find the slope and intercepts from the equation of the line. Sketch the graph of each equation.

43. $x + 2y - 4 = 0$ †   **44.** $x = 3y - 9$ †

45. $3x - 2y + 6 = 0$ †   **46.** $2x = -4y + 15$ †

47. $x - 5 = 0$ †   **48.** $2y + 5 = 0$ †

49. $x = 0$ †   **50.** $y = 0$ †

51. Show that an equation of a line through the points $(a, 0)$ and $(0, b)$, with a and b nonzero, can be written in the form

$$\frac{x}{a} + \frac{y}{b} = 1.$$

This form is called the **two-intercept form** of the equation of a line.

In Exercises 52–56, use the two-intercept form of the equation of a line found in Exercise 51.

52. Use the two-intercept form to find an equation of the line whose x-intercept is 4 and y-intercept is 3. †

53. Write the equation $2x + 3y = 6$ in the two-intercept form, and read off the x- and y-intercepts. †

54. Repeat Exercise 53 for the equation $3x - 4y + 12 = 0$. †

55. Find an equation of the line that has equal intercepts and passes through the point $(3, -5)$. $y = -x - 2$

56. Find an equation of the line making intercepts on the axes equal in magnitude, but opposite in sign, and passing through the point $(-5, -8)$. $y = x - 3$

57. Find an equation of the line passing through the points $(2, 4)$ and $(7, 9)$. Use the equation to show that the three points $(2, 4)$ and $(7, 9)$, and $(-1, 1)$ are on the same line. †

58. Use the technique of Exercise 57 to check whether the points $(7, 2)$, $(2, -3)$, and $(5, 1)$ are on the same line. †

In Exercises 59–66, determine whether each pair of lines are parallel, perpendicular, or neither.

59. $x = -1$ and $2x + 7 = 9$ Parallel

60. $x = 0$ and $y = 0$ Perpendicular

61. $2x + 3y = 7$ and $y = 2$ Neither

62. $y = 3x + 1$ and $6y + 2x = 0$ Perpendicular

63. $10x + 2y = 3$ and $y + 1 = -5x$ Parallel

64. $4x + 3y = 1$ and $3 + y = 2x$ Neither

65. $3x + 8y = 7$ and $5x - 7y = 0$ Neither

66. $x = 4y + 8$ and $y = -4x + 1$ Perpendicular

In Exercises 67–72, find the equation of the line in slope–intercept form satisfying the given conditions.

67. Parallel to $x + y = 1$; passing through $(1, 1)$ $y = -x + 2$

68. Parallel to $y = 6x + 5$; y-intercept of -2 $y = 6x - 2$

69. Perpendicular to $3x - 9y = 18$; passing through $(-2, 4)$ †

70. Perpendicular to $-2x + y = 14$; passing through $(0, 0)$ †

71. Perpendicular to $y = 6x + 5$; y-intercept of 4 †

72. Parallel to $-2x + 3y - 7 = 0$; passing through $(1, 0)$ †

B Exercises   Applying the Concepts

73. Jet takeoff. Upon takeoff, a jet climbs to 4 miles as it passes over 40 miles of land below it. Find the slope of the jet's climb. †

74. Road gradient. Driving down the Smoky Mountains in Tennessee, Samantha finds that she descends 2000 feet in elevation during the time that she has moved 4 miles horizontally away from a high point on the straight road. Find the slope (gradient) of the road (1 mile = 5280 feet). †

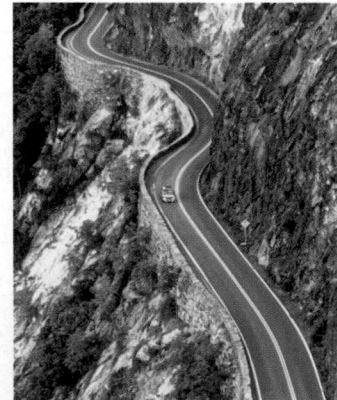

In Exercises 75–82, write an equation of a line in slope–intercept form. To describe this situation, interpret (a) the variables x and y and (b) the meaning of the slope and the y-intercept.

75. Christmas savings account. You currently have \$130 in a Christmas savings account. You deposit \$7 per week into this account. (Ignore interest.) †

76. Golf club charges. Your golf club charges a yearly membership fee of \$1000 and \$35 per session of golf. †

77. Wages. Judy's job at a warehouse pays $11 per hour up to 40 hours per week. If she works over 40 hours in a week, she is paid 1.5 times her usual wage. [*Hint:* You will need two equations.] †

78. Paying off refrigerator. You bought a new refrigerator for $700. You made a down payment of $100 and promised to pay $15 per month. (Ignore interest). †

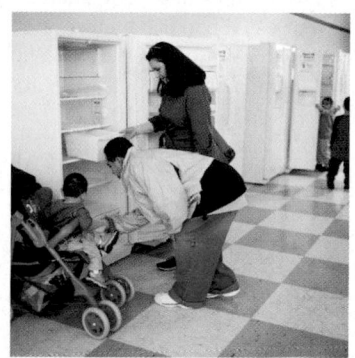

79. Converting currency. In early 2005, according to the International Monetary Fund, 1 U.S. dollar equaled 44 Indian rupees. Convert currency (a) from dollars to rupees and (b) from rupees to dollars. †

80. Life expectancy. In 2004, the life expectancy of a female born in the United States was 82.3 years and was increasing at a rate of 0.27 per year. (Assume that this rate of increase remains constant.) †

81. Manufacturing. A manufacturer produces 50 TV sets at a cost of $17,500 and 75 TV sets at a cost of $21,250. †

82. Demand. The demand for a product is zero units when the price per unit is $100 and 1000 units when the price per unit is zero dollars. †

Exercises 83–84 deal with the topic of **depreciation.** When filing income tax returns, taxpayers (businesses and individuals) can claim deductions for depreciation on items such as cars, computers, and buildings used for business purposes. The government allows these deductions because the value of such assets decreases (depreciates) over time. The simplest method for finding the depreciated value is called **straight-line depreciation** and assumes that the item's value decreases linearly with time.

83. Depreciating a tractor. The value V of a tractor purchased for $14,000 and depreciated linearly at the rate of $1400 per year is given by $v = -1400t + 14,000$, where t represents the number of years since the purchase. Find the value of the tractor after (a) two years and (b) six years. When will the tractor have no value? †

84. Depreciating a computer. A computer is purchased for $3000 and is to be depreciated linearly over four years. Assume that it has no value at the end of the four years.
  a. Find the amount depreciated per year. †
  b. Find a linear equation relating the value V of the computer after t years of purchase. †
  c. Graph the equation in part (b). †

85. Playing for a concert. A famous band is considering playing for a concert and charging $1000, plus $1.50 per person attending the concert. Write an equation relating the income y of the band to the number x of people attending the concert. $y = 1.5x + 1000$

86. Car rental. The U Drive car rental agency charges $30 per day and 25 cents per mile.
   a. Find an equation relating the cost C of renting a car from U Drive for a one-day trip covering x miles. †
   b. Draw the graph of the equation in part (a). †
   c. How much does it cost to rent the car for one day covering 60 miles? †
   d. How many miles were driven if the one-day rental cost was $47.75? †

87. Female prisoners in Florida. The number of females in Florida's prisons rose from 2638 in 1993 to 4796 in 2003. (*Source:* Florida Department of Corrections.)
   a. Find a linear equation relating the number y of women prisoners to the year t. (Take $t = 0$ to represent 1993.) †
   b. Draw the graph of the equation from part (a). †
   c. How many women prisoners were there in 2000? †
   d. Predict the number of women prisoners in 2008. †

88. Fahrenheit and Celsius. In the Fahrenheit temperature scale, water boils at 212°F and freezes at 32°F. In the Celsius scale, water boils at 100° C and freezes at 0°C. Assume that the Fahrenheit temperature F and Celsius temperature C are linearly related.
   a. Find the equation in the slope–intercept form relating F and C, with C as independent variable. †
   b. What is the meaning of slope in part (a)? †
   c. Find the Fahrenheit temperatures, to the nearest degree, corresponding to 40°C, 25°C, −5°C, and −10°C. †
   d. Find the Celsius temperatures, to the nearest degree, corresponding to 100°F, 90°F, 75°F, −10°F and −20°F. †
   e. The normal body temperature in humans ranges from 97.6°F to 99.6°F. Convert this temperature range to degrees Celsius. 36.44°C to 37.55°
   f. When is the Celsius temperature the same numerical value as the Fahrenheit temperature? at −40°

89. Demand equation. A demand equation expresses a relationship between the demand q (the number of items demanded) and the price p per unit. A linear demand equation has the form $q = mp + b$. The slope m (usually negative) measures the change in demand per unit change in price. The y-intercept b gives the demand if the items were given away. A merchant can sell 480 T-shirts per week at a price of $4 each, but can sell only 400 per week if the price per T-shirt is increased to $4.50.
   a. Find a linear demand equation for T-shirts. †
   b. Predict the demand for T-shirts if the price per T-shirt is $5.00. 320.

90. Supply equation. A supply equation expresses a relationship between the supply q (the number of units a supplier is willing to make available) and the unit price p (the price per item). A linear supply equation has the form $q = mp + b$. The slope m is usually positive. A manufacturer of ceiling fans can supply 70 fans per day at $50 apiece and will supply 100 fans a day at a price of $60 per fan.

   a. Find a linear supply equation for the fans from this manufacturer. $q = 3p - 80$
   b. Predict the supply at a price of $62 per fan. 106

91. Lake pollution. In 2002, tests showed that each 1000 liters of water from Lake Heron contained 7 milligrams of a polluting mercury compound. Two years later, tests showed that 8 milligrams of the compound were contained in each 1000 liters of the lake's water. Assuming that the increase in pollutants is linear, find a linear equation relating the year in which the test was given to the number of milligrams of pollutant per 1000 liters of the lake's water. What does your equation predict the pollutant content per 1000 liters of water in Lake Heron to be in 2010? $y = .5x + 7;\ 11$

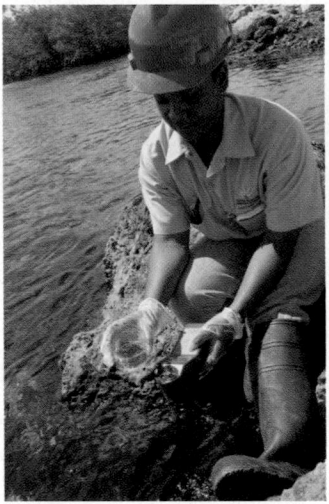

92. Selling shoes. The Alpha shoe manufacturer has determined that the annual cost of making x pairs of its best-selling shoes, α1 (alpha one), is $25 per pair, plus $75,000 in fixed overhead costs. Each pair of shoes that is manufactured is sold wholesale for $50.
   a. Find the equations that model the cost, the revenue, and the profit (Profit = Revenue − Cost). Verify that all three equations are linear. †
   b. Graph the profit equation on the xy-coordinate system. †
   c. What is the slope of the line in part (b)? What is the practical meaning of this slope? †
   d. Find the intercepts of the line in part (b). What is the practical meaning of these intercepts? †

93. Cost. The cost of producing 4 modems is $210.20, and the cost of producing 10 modems is $348.80.
   a. Write a linear equation in slope–intercept form relating cost to the number of modems produced. Sketch a graph of the equation. $y = 23.1x + 117.8$ †
   b. What is the practical meaning of the slope and the intercepts of the equation in part (a)? †
   c. Predict the cost of producing 12 modems. 395

94. Viewers of a TV show. After 5 months, the number of viewers of *The Weekly Show* on TV was 5.73 million. After 8 months, the number of viewers of the show rose to 6.27 million. Assume that the linear model applies.

  a. Write an equation expressing the number of viewers V after x months. $V = 0.18x + 4.83$

  b. Interpret the slope and the intercepts of the line in part (a). †

  c. Predict the number of viewers of the show after 11 months. 6.81 million.

95. Health insurance coverage. In Michigan, 9.4% of the population was not covered by health insurance in 1990. In 1999, the percentage of uninsured people rose to 11.2%. Use the linear model to predict the percentage of people in Michigan who will not be covered in 2010. (*Source:* Michigan Department of Community Health.) 13.4%

96. Oil consumption. The total world consumption of oil increased from 68.200 million barrels per day in 1995 to 73.215 million barrels per day in 1999. Create a linear model involving a relation between the year and the daily oil consumption in that year. Let $t = 0$ represent the year 1995. (*Source:* www.Scaruffi.com) $c = 1.25375t + 68.200$

C Exercises   Beyond the Basics

97. The graph of a line has slope $m = 3$. If $P(-2, 3)$ and $Q(1, c)$ and are points on the graph, find c. $c = 12$

98. Find a real number c such that the line $3x - cy - 2 = 0$ has a y-intercept of -4. †

In Exercises 99–102, show that the three given points are collinear by using (a) slopes and (b) the distance formula.

99. $(0, 1)$, $(1, 3)$, and $(-1, -1)$

100. $(1, 2)$, $(-1, 4)$, and $(2, 1)$

101. $(1, 2)$, $(0, -3)$, and $(-1, -8)$

102. $(1, .5)$, $(2, 0)$, and $(0.5, 0.75)$

103. Show that the triangle with vertices $A(1, 1)$, $B(-1, 4)$, and $C(5, 8)$ is a right triangle by using (a) slopes and (b) the converse of the Pythagorean Theorem.

104. Show that the four points, $A(-4, -1)$, $B(1, 2)$, $C(3, 1)$, and $D(-2, -2)$ are the vertices of a parallelogram. [*Hint:* Opposite sides of a parallelogram are parallel.]

105. Show that the four points $A(-10, 9)$, $B(-2, 24)$, $C(5, 1)$, $D(13, 16)$ are vertices of a square.

106. a. Find an equation of the line that is the perpendicular bisector of the line segment with endpoints $A(2, 3)$ and $B(-1, 5)$. †

  b. Show that $y = x$ is the perpendicular bisector of the line segment with endpoints and $A(a, b)$ and $B(b, a)$.

107. Show that if two nonvertical lines are parallel, their slopes are equal. Start by letting the two lines be l_1: $y = m_1x + b_1$ and l_2: $y = m_2x + b_2$ $(b_1 > b_2)$, and show that if (x_1, y_1) and (x_2, y_2) are on l_1, then $(x_1, y_1 - (b_1 - b_2))$ and $((x_2, y_2 - (b_1 - b_2))$ must be on l_2. Then, by computing m_1 and m_2, show that $m_1 = m_2$. (See the accompanying figure.)

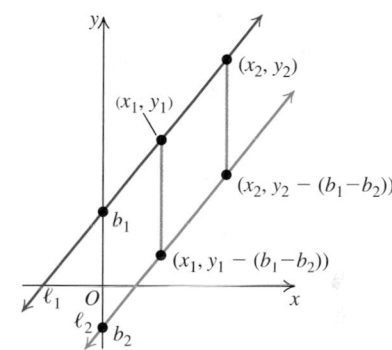

108. If two lines (neither of them vertical) l_1: $y = m_1x$ and l_2: $y = m_2x$ are perpendicular, then $m_1 \cdot m_2 = -1$. In the accompanying figure, use the distance formula and the Pythagorean Theorem to show that triangle AOB is a right triangle. †

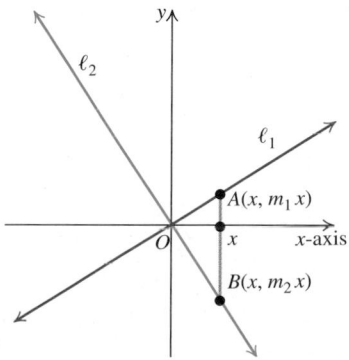

109. Geometry. Use a coordinate plane to prove that if two sides of a quadrilateral are congruent (equal in length) and parallel, then so are the other two sides.

110. Geometry. Use a coordinate plane to prove that the midpoints of the four sides of a quadrilateral are the vertices of a parallelogram.

111. Geometry. Find the coordinates of the point B of a line segment AB, given that $A = (2, 2)$, $d(A, B) = 12.5$, and the slope of the line segment AB is $\dfrac{4}{3}$. (9.5, 12) or (−5.5, −8)

112. Geometry. Show that an equation of a circle with (x_1, y_1) and (x_2, y_2) as endpoints of a diameter can be written in the form

$$(x - x_1)(x - x_2) + (y - y_1)(y - y_2) = 0.$$

[*Hint:* Use the fact that when the two endpoints of a diameter and any other point on the circle are used as vertices for a triangle, the angle opposite the diameter is a right angle.]

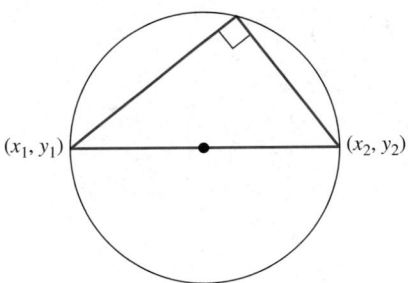

Critical Thinking

113. By considering slopes, show that the points $(1, -1)$, $(-2, 5)$ and $(3, -5)$ lie on the same line.

114. By considering slopes, show that the points $(-9, 6)$, $(-2, 14)$, and $(-1, -1)$ are the vertices of a right triangle.

115. a. The equation $y + 2x + k = 0$ describes a family of lines for each value of k. Sketch the graphs of the members of this family for $k = -3, 0,$ and 2. What is the common characteristic of the family? †

   b. Repeat part (a) for the family of lines $y - kx + 4 = 0$. †

Answers:

113. The slope of the line that passes through $(1, -1)$ and $(-2, 5)$ is -2.
The slope of the line that passes through $(1, -1)$ and $(3, -5)$ is -2.
The slope of the line that passes through $(-2, 5)$ and $(3, -5)$ is -2.

114. The slope of the line that passes through $(-9, 6)$ and $(-2, 14)$ is $\dfrac{8}{7}$.

The slope of the line that passes through $(-9, 6)$ and $(-1, -1)$ is $-\dfrac{7}{8}$.

The slope of the line that passes through $(-2, 14)$ and $(-1, -1)$ is -15.

SECTION 2.4 | Relations and Functions

BEFORE STARTING THIS SECTION, REVIEW

1. Graph of an equation (Section 2.2, page 192)

2. Equation of a circle (Section 2.2, page 198)

OBJECTIVES

1 Learn the definition of a relation.

2 Learn the definition of a function, and learn how to determine which relations are functions.

3 Use functional notation and find function values.

4 Find the domain of a function.

5 Identify the graph of a function.

6 Find the average rate of change of a function.

7 Solve applied problems by using functions.

The Ups and Downs of Drug Levels

Medicines in the form of a pill have a much harder time getting to work than you do. First they get swallowed and dumped into a pool of acid in your stomach. Then they dissolve, leave the stomach, and start getting absorbed, mostly through the lining of the small intestine. Next, the blood from around the intestine carries the medicines to the liver, an organ designed to metabolize (break down) and remove foreign material from the blood. Because of this property of the liver, most drugs have a tough time getting past it. The amount of drug that makes it into your bloodstream, compared with the amount that you put in your mouth, is called the drug's *bioavailability*. If a drug has low bioavailability, then much of the drug is destroyed before it reaches the bloodstream. The amount of drug you take in a pill is calculated to correct for this deficiency, so that the amount you need actually ends up in your blood.

Once the drugs are past the liver, the bloodstream carries them throughout the rest of the body in about one minute. The study of the ways drugs are absorbed and move through the body is called *pharmacokinetics,* or PK for short. PK measures the ups and downs of drug levels in your body. In Example 10, we consider an application of *functions* to the levels of drugs in the bloodstream.

(Adapted from *The ups and downs of drug levels,* by Bob Munk, www.thebody.com/tpan/mayjune_01/druglevels.html) ■

1 Learn the definition of a relation.

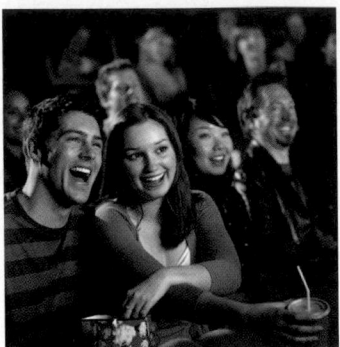

Relations

Consider the following list of the six all-time top grossing movies in the United States through 2005.

Titanic	$600.8 million
Star Wars, Episode IV	$461.0 million
Shrek 2	$441.2 million
E.T.: The Extra-Terrestrial	$435.1 million
Star Wars, Episode I (The Phantom Menace)	$431.1 million
Spider-Man	$403.7 million

(*Source: www.amazon.com*)

For each of the movies listed, there is a corresponding amount of gross sales in millions of dollars. This correspondence can be written as a set of ordered pairs:

$$\{(\textit{Titanic, } \$600.8), (\textit{Star Wars IV, } \$461.0), (\textit{Shrek 2, } \$441.2),$$

$$(\textit{E.T., } \$435.1), (\textit{Star Wars I, } \$431.1), (\textit{Spider-Man, } \$403.7)\}.$$

Ordered pairs are an exceptionally useful method for displaying and organizing correspondences. Any set of ordered pairs is called a **relation.** When relations are written as ordered pairs (x, y), we say that x corresponds to y.

DEFINITION OF A RELATION

Any set of ordered pairs is called a **relation.** The set of all first components is called the **domain** of the relation, and the set of all second components is called the **range** of the relation.

EXAMPLE 1   **Finding the Domain and Range of a Relation**

Find the domain and range of the relation

$$\{(\textit{Titanic, } \$600.8), (\textit{Star Wars IV, } \$461.0), (\textit{Shrek 2, } \$441.2),$$

$$(\textit{E.T., } \$435.1), (\textit{Star Wars I, } \$431.1), (\textit{Spider-Man, } \$403.7)\}.$$

Solution

The domain is the set of all first components, or

$$\{\textit{Titanic, Star Wars IV, Shrek 2, E.T., Star Wars I, Spider-Man}\}.$$

The range is the set of all second components, or

$$\{\$600.8, \$461.0, \$441.2, \$435.1, \$431.1, \$403.7)\}. \qquad ■ ■ ■$$

PRACTICE PROBLEM 1   Find the domain and range of the relation

$$\{(1, 2), (3, 0), (2, -2)\ (-2, -3),\ (-1, 1)\}. \qquad ■$$

2 Learn the definition of a function, and learn how to determine which relations are functions.

Functions

Of particular importance is a special kind of relation called a *function*. A relation with the property that each value in the domain corresponds to *a unique* value in the range is called a *function*.

DEFINITION OF FUNCTION

A **function** from a set X to a set Y is a relation in which each element of X corresponds to one and only one element of Y.

The set X is the domain of the function. The set of those elements of Y which correspond to the elements of X is the range of the function. To decide whether a relation is a function, we must check whether *any* domain element is paired with more than one range element. If this happens, that domain element does not correspond to a *unique* element of Y, and the relation is not a function.

Correspondence Diagrams A relation may be defined by a **correspondence diagram,** in which an arrow points from each domain element to the element or elements in the range that correspond to it. For example, the relation in Example 1 has the following correspondence diagram:

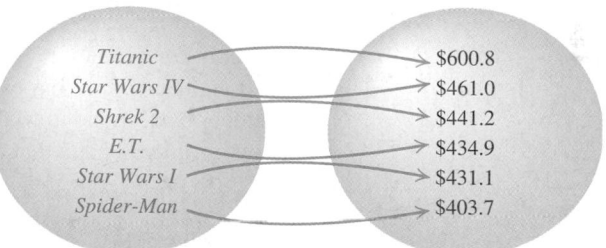

| EXAMPLE 2 | Determining Whether a Relation Is a Function |

Determine whether the relations that follow are functions. The domain of each relation is the family consisting of Malcolm (father), Maria (mother), Ellen (daughter), and Duane (son).

a. For the relation defined by the following diagram, the range consists of the ages of the four family members, and each family member corresponds to that family member's age.

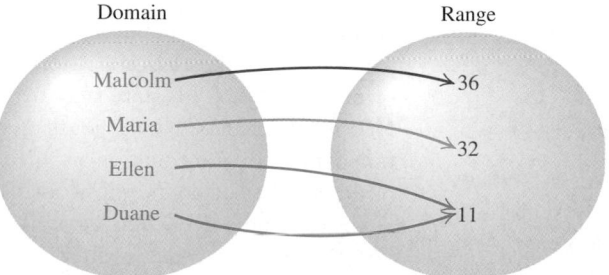

b. For the relation defined by the diagram on the next page, the range consists of the family's home phone number, the office phone numbers for both Malcolm and Maria, and the cell phone number for Maria. Each family member corresponds to all phone numbers at which that family member can be reached.

Continued on next page.

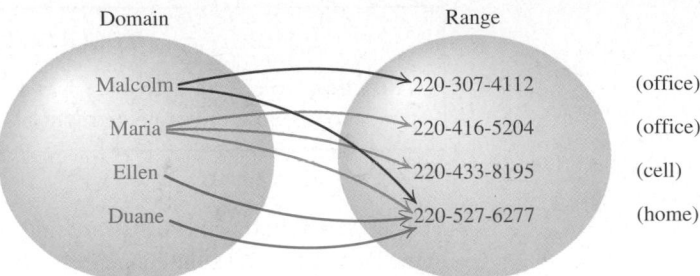

Solution

a. The relation *is* a function, because each element in the domain corresponds to exactly one element in the range. For a function, it is permissible for the same range element to correspond to different domain elements. The set of ordered pairs that define this relation is

$$\{(\text{Malcolm}, 36), (\text{Maria}, 32), (\text{Ellen}, 11), (\text{Duane}, 11)\}.$$

b. The relation *is not* a function, because more than one range element corresponds to the same domain element. For example, both an office phone number and a home phone number correspond to Malcolm.

   The set of ordered pairs that define this relation is

   $$\{(\text{Malcolm}, 220\text{-}307\text{-}4112), (\text{Malcolm}, 220\text{-}527\text{-}6277),$$
   $$(\text{Maria}, 220\text{-}416\text{-}5204), (\text{Maria}, 220\text{-}433\text{-}8195),$$
   $$(\text{Maria}, 220\text{-}527\text{-}6277), (\text{Ellen}, 220\text{-}527\text{-}6277), (\text{Duane}, 220\text{-}527\text{-}6277)\}.$$

■ ■ ■

PRACTICE PROBLEM 2   Replace the family described in Example 2 by your own family. Construct the appropriate correspondence diagrams, and determine whether the relations in **a.** and **b.** are functions.   ■

3 Use functional notation and find function values.

Functional Notation and Values

Often, an equation can be used to define a relation. For example, if you are paid 10 dollars per hour, then the relation between the number of hours, x, that you work and the amount of money, y, that you earn may be expressed by the equation $y = 10x$. The ordered pair (40, 400) indicates that 40 hours of work corresponds to a 400-dollar paycheck. The relation defined by the equation $y = 10x$ is a function, and we say that your pay is a function of the number of hours you work. Because the value of y depends on the given value of x, y is called the *dependent variable* and x is called the *independent variable*.

   We usually use single letters such as f, F, g, G, h, H, and so on as the name of a function. If we choose f as the name of a function, then, for each x in the domain of f, there corresponds a unique y in its range. The number y is denoted by $f(x)$, read as "f of x" or as "f at x". We call $f(x)$ the **value of f at the number x** and say that f *assigns* the value $f(x)$ to x.

   Tables and graphs are often used to describe a function. The data in Table 2.4 (reproduced from Section 2.1) show the prevalence of smoking among adults aged 18 years and older in the United States over the years 1997–2003.

TABLE 2.4

Year	1997	1998	1999	2000	2001	2002	2003
Percent of adult smokers	24.7	24.1	23.5	23.2	22.7	22.4	21.6

Source: Centers for Disease Control, National Health Interview Survey.

The graph in Figure 2.30 is a **scatter diagram** that gives a visual representation of the same information. Scatter diagrams show the relationship between two variables by displaying data as points of a graph. The variable that might be considered the independent variable is plotted on the x-axis, and the dependent variable is plotted on the y-axis. Here, the percent of adult smokers depends on the year and is plotted on the y-axis.

FIGURE 2.30

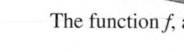

The function f, as a machine

FIGURE 2.31

The function described by both Table 2.4 and Figure 2.30 is $\{(1997, 24.7), (1998, 24.1), (1999, 23.5), (2000, 23.2), (2001, 22.7), (2002, 22.4), (2003, 21.6)\}$. The domain is the set $\{1997, 1998, 1999, 2000, 2001, 2002, 2003\}$, and the range is the set $\{24.7, 24.1, 23.5, 23.2, 22.7, 22.4, 21.6\}$. The function assigns, to each year in the domain, the percent of adult smokers 18 years and older in the United States during that year. Yet another nice way of picturing the concept of a function is as a "machine," as shown in Figure 2.31. If x is in the domain of a function, then the machine accepts it as an "input" and produces the value $f(x)$ as the "output."

◆ **WARNING**

In writing $y = f(x)$, you must distinguish between the symbol f, which is the name of the function, and the symbol $f(x)$, which is a number in the range of f and is the value the function assigns to a given number x in the domain of f. The symbol $f(x)$ does not mean "f times x."

Functions Defined by Equations When the relation defined by an equation in two variables is a function, we can often solve the equation for the dependent variable in terms of the independent variable. For example, the equation $y - x^2 = 0$ can be solved for y in terms of x. That is, from

$$y - x^2 = 0,$$

we have

$$y = x^2.$$

Now we can replace the dependent variable, in this case, y, with functional notation $f(x)$ and express the function as

$$f(x) = x^2 \quad \text{(read "}f\text{ of }x\text{ equals }x^2\text{").}$$

3
↓Input
$f(x) = x^2$
Output
→ $f(3) = 9$

The function f, as a machine

FIGURE 2.32

Here, $f(x)$ plays the role of y and is the value of the function f at x. For example, if $x = 3$ is an element (input value) in the domain of f, the corresponding element (output value) in the range is found by replacing x with 3 in the equation

$$f(x) = x^2,$$

so that $f(3) = 3^2 = 9.$ Replace x by 3.

We say that the value of the function f at 3 is 9. (See Figure 2.32.) In other words, the number 3 in the domain corresponds to the number 9 in the range, and the ordered pair (3, 9) is an ordered pair of the function f.

If a function g is defined by an equation such as $y = x^2 - 6x + 8$, the notation

$$y = x^2 - 6x + 8 \quad \text{and} \quad g(x) = x^2 - 6x + 8$$

define the same function.

EXAMPLE 3   **Evaluating a Function**

Let g be the function defined by the equation

$$y = x^2 - 6x + 8.$$

Evaluate each function value.

a. $g(3)$ **b.** $g(-2)$ **c.** $g\left(\dfrac{1}{2}\right)$ **d.** $g(a + 2)$ **e.** $g(x + h)$

Solution

Since the function defined by the equation $y = x^2 - 6x + 8$ is named g, we replace y by the functional notation $g(x)$ and write

$$g(x) = x^2 - 6x + 8. \qquad \text{Replace } y \text{ by } g(x).$$

In this notation, the independent variable x plays the role of a placeholder. We can think of $g(x) = x^2 - 6x + 8$ as

$$g(\ ) = (\ )^2 - 6(\ ) + 8.$$

a. To find $g(3)$ means to find the output of the function g when the input is 3. We substitute 3 for the variable x in the equation.

$$
\begin{aligned}
g(x) &= x^2 - 6x + 8 & \text{The given equation} \\
g(3) &= 3^2 - 6(3) + 8 & \text{Replace } x \text{ by 3 at each occurrence of } x. \\
&= 9 - 18 + 8 & \text{Simplify.} \\
&= -1
\end{aligned}
$$

The statement $g(3) = -1$ asserts that the value of the function g at 3 is -1.

Just as in part **a,** we can evaluate g at any value x in its domain:

$$g(x) = x^2 - 6x + 8 \qquad\qquad \text{Original equation}$$

b. $g(-2) = (-2)^2 - 6(-2) + 8 = 24 \qquad\qquad$ Replace x by -2 and simplify.

c. $g\left(\dfrac{1}{2}\right) = \left(\dfrac{1}{2}\right)^2 - 6\left(\dfrac{1}{2}\right) + 8 = \dfrac{21}{4} \qquad\qquad$ Replace x by $\dfrac{1}{2}$ and simplify.

d. $g(a + 2) = (a + 2)^2 - 6(a + 2) + 8 \qquad\qquad$ Replace x by $(a + 2)$ in $g(x)$.

$\qquad\qquad\quad = a^2 + 4a + 4 - 6a - 12 + 8 \qquad$ Recall: $(x + y)^2 = x^2 + 2xy + y^2$.

$\qquad\qquad\quad = a^2 - 2a \qquad\qquad\qquad\qquad\quad$ Simplify.

e. $g(x + h) = (x + h)^2 - 6(x + h) + 8 \qquad$ Replace x by $(x + h)$ in $g(x)$.

$\qquad\qquad\quad = x^2 + 2xh + h^2 - 6x - 6h + 8 \quad$ Simplify.   ■ ■ ■

PRACTICE PROBLEM 3   Let g be the function defined by the equation $y = -2x^2 + 5x$. Evaluate each function value.

a. $g(0)$ **b.** $g(-1)$ **c.** $g(x + h)$ ■

EXAMPLE 4   **Determining Whether an Equation Defines a Function**

Determine whether each equation determines y as a function of x.

a. $6x^2 - 3y = 12$ **b.** $y^2 - x^2 = 4$

Solution

Solve each equation for y in terms of x. If more than one value of y corresponds to the same value of x, the equation does not define y as a function of x.

a. $\qquad\qquad 6x^2 - 3y = 12 \qquad\qquad$ Original equation

$6x^2 - 3y + 3y - 12 = 12 + 3y - 12 \qquad$ Add $3y$ to both sides; subtract 12 from both sides.

$\qquad\qquad 6x^2 - 12 = 3y \qquad\qquad$ Simplify.

$\qquad\qquad\quad 2x^2 - 4 = y \qquad\qquad$ Divide both sides by 3.

The last equation shows that only one value of y corresponds to each value of x. For example, if $x = 0$, then $y = 0 - 4 = -4$. Thus, the equation $6x^2 - 3y = 12$ defines y as a function of x.

b. $\qquad\quad y^2 - x^2 = 4 \qquad\qquad$ Original equation

$\qquad y^2 - x^2 + x^2 = 4 + x^2 \qquad$ Add x^2 to both sides.

$\qquad\qquad\quad y^2 = x^2 + 4 \qquad\qquad$ Simplify.

$\qquad\qquad\quad y = \pm\sqrt{x^2 + 4} \qquad$ Square root property

The last equation shows that two values of y correspond to the same value of x. For example, if $x = 0$, then $y = \pm\sqrt{0^2 + 4} = \pm\sqrt{4} = \pm2$. Thus, both 2 and -2 are values of y that correspond to $x = 0$. Therefore, the equation $y^2 - x^2 = 4$ does not define y as a function of x.   ■ ■ ■

PRACTICE PROBLEM 4   Determine whether each equation defines y as a function of x.

a. $2x^2 - y^2 = 1$ **b.** $x - 2y = 5$ ■

4 Find the domain of a function.

The Domain of a Function

If a function is defined by an algebraic equation and its domain is not specified, then we determine the domain of the function from the equation.

> ### AGREEMENT ON DOMAIN
>
> If the domain of a function that is defined by an equation is not explicitly specified, then we take the domain of the function to be the largest set of real numbers that result in real numbers as outputs.

By the way . . .

The word *domain* comes from the Latin word *dominus*, or *master*, which in turn is related to *domus*, meaning *home*. *Domus* is also the root for the words *domestic* and *domicile*.

When we use our agreement to find the domain of a function, it is helpful to find the values of the variable for which the defining expression is not a real number. It is important to remember that

1. Division by zero is undefined and
2. The square root (or any even root) of a negative number is not a real number.

EXAMPLE 5   **Finding the Domain of a Function**

Find the domain of each function.

a. $f(x) = \dfrac{1}{1 - x^2}$ **b.** $g(x) = \sqrt{x}$ **c.** $h(x) = \dfrac{1}{\sqrt{x - 1}}$ **d.** $P(t) = 2t + 1$

Solution

a. The function f is not defined when the denominator $1 - x^2$ is 0. But $1 - x^2 = 0$ if $x = 1$ or $x = -1$. Thus, the domain of f is the set $\{x | x \neq -1 \text{ and } x \neq 1\}$, which in interval notation is written

$$(-\infty, -1) \cup (-1, 1) \cup (1, \infty).$$

b. Since the square root of a negative number is not a real number, negative numbers are excluded from the domain of the function g. The domain of $g(x) = \sqrt{x}$ is $\{x | x \geq 0\}$, or $[0, \infty)$ in interval notation.

c. The function $h(x) = \dfrac{1}{\sqrt{x - 1}}$ has *two* restrictions. The square root of a negative number is not a real number, so, in order for $\sqrt{x - 1}$ to be a real number, we must have $x - 1 \geq 0$. However, we cannot allow $x - 1 = 0$, because $\sqrt{x - 1}$ occurs in the denominator. Therefore, we must have $x - 1 > 0$, or $x > 1$. The domain of h is thus

$$\{x | x > 1\}, \text{ or in interval notation } (1, \infty).$$

d. When any real number is substituted for t in $y = 2t + 1$, a unique real number is determined. The domain is the set of all real numbers: $\{t | t \text{ is a real number}\}$, or in interval notation $(-\infty, \infty)$.   ■ ■ ■

PRACTICE PROBLEM 5   Find the domain of the function

$$f(x) = \frac{1}{\sqrt{1 - x}}.$$ ■

Equality of Functions

Consider the function

$$f(x) = \frac{1}{3x - 2}, \qquad 1 \le x \le 6.$$

The domain of f (specified explicitly in this case) is the set of all real numbers x between 1 and 6 inclusive. However, the domain of the function

$$g(x) = \frac{1}{3x - 2}$$

is not specified explicitly. Consequently, on the basis of our *agreement on domain* the domain of g is the set of all real numbers except $x = \frac{2}{3}$ (because replacing x by $\frac{2}{3}$ makes the denominator equal to zero).

This leads to our next definition.

EQUALITY OF FUNCTIONS

Two functions f and g are equal if and only if

1. f and g have the same domain and
2. $f(x) = g(x)$ for all x in the domain.

Except for some simple situations, finding the range of a function is more difficult than finding the domain.

5 Identify the graph of a function.

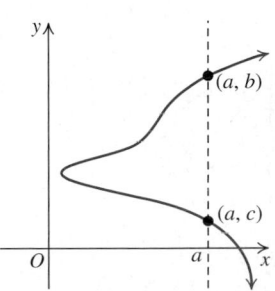

FIGURE 2.33

Graphs of Functions

The graph of any relation is obtained by plotting the ordered pairs of the relation. However, if any vertical line passes through two or more points on the graph of a relation, then the relation is *not* a function. The reason is that any two points on a vertical line have the same first component (the domain element), but *different* second components (range elements). (See Figure 2.33.) We express this statement in a slightly different way as follows:

VERTICAL-LINE TEST

If no vertical line intersects the graph of a relation at more than one point, then the graph is the graph of a function.

EXAMPLE 6   **Identifying the Graph of a Function**

Use the vertical-line test to determine which graphs in Figure 2.34 are graphs of functions.

(a)

(b)

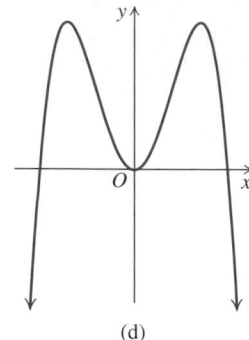

(c)

(d)

FIGURE 2.34

Solution

The graphs in Figures 2.34(a) and 2.34(b) are not graphs of functions, because a vertical line can be drawn through the two points farthest to the left in Figure 2.34(a) and the y-axis is one of many vertical lines that contain more than one point on the graph in Figure 2.34(b). Thus, at least one vertical line intersects each graph at more than one point. The graphs in Figures 2.34(c) and 2.34(d) are the graphs of functions, because no vertical line intersects either graph at more than one point.   ■ ■ ■

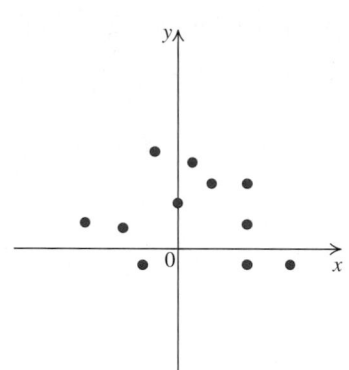

PRACTICE PROBLEM 6   Use the vertical-line test to decide whether the graph in the margin is the graph of a function.   ■

If we use functional notation, we may describe the *graph of a function* as the set of ordered pairs $(x, f(x))$ such that x is in the domain of f.

EXAMPLE 7   **Examining the Graph of a Function**

Let $y = f(x) = x^2 - 2x - 3$.

a. Is the point $(1, -3)$ on the graph of f?
b. Find all values of x such that $(x, 5)$ is on the graph of f.
c. Find all y-intercepts of the graph of f.
d. Find all x-intercepts of the graph of f.

Solution

a. We check whether $(1, -3)$ satisfies the equation $f(x) = x^2 - 2x - 3$.

$$f(x) = x^2 - 2x - 3 \qquad \text{Given equation}$$
$$y = x^2 - 2x - 3 \qquad \text{Replace } f(x) \text{ by } y.$$
$$-3 \overset{?}{=} (1)^2 - 2(1) - 3 \qquad \text{Replace } x \text{ by 1 and } y \text{ by } -3.$$
$$-3 \overset{?}{=} -4 \text{ No!}$$

Thus, $(1, -3)$ is *not* on the graph of f. (See Figure 2.35.)

FIGURE 2.35

b. Substitute 5 for y and solve for x.

$$y = x^2 - 2x - 3 \qquad \text{The given function}$$
$$5 = x^2 - 2x - 3 \qquad \text{Replace } y \text{ by 5 and solve for } x.$$
$$0 = x^2 - 2x - 8 \qquad \text{Subtract 5 from both sides.}$$
$$0 = (x - 4)(x + 2) \qquad \text{Factor } x^2 - 2x - 8.$$
$$x - 4 = 0 \quad \text{or} \quad x + 2 = 0 \qquad \text{Zero-product property}$$
$$x = 4 \quad \text{or} \quad x = -2. \qquad \text{Solve for } x.$$

There are two different values of x for which $(x, 5)$ is on the graph of f, namely, -2 and 4. Both $(-2, 5)$ and $(4, 5)$ are on the graph of f. (See Figure 2.35.)

c. To find the y-intercepts of the graph of f, we find all points (x, y) on the graph, with $x = 0$.

$$y = x^2 - 2x - 3 \qquad \text{The given function}$$
$$y = 0^2 - 2(0) - 3 \qquad \text{Replace } x \text{ by 0 to find the } y\text{-intercept.}$$
$$y = -3 \qquad \text{Simplify.}$$

Thus, the only y-intercept is -3. (See Figure 2.35.)

d. To find the x-intercepts of the graph of f, we find all points (x, y) on the graph, with $y = 0$.

$$y = x^2 - 2x - 3 \qquad \text{The given function}$$
$$0 = x^2 - 2x - 3 \qquad \text{Replace } y \text{ by 0.}$$
$$0 = (x + 1)(x - 3) \qquad \text{Factor } x^2 - 2x - 3.$$
$$x + 1 = 0 \quad \text{or} \quad x - 3 = 0 \qquad \text{Zero-product property}$$
$$x = -1 \quad \text{or} \quad x = 3. \qquad \text{Solve for } x.$$

The x-intercepts of the graph of f are -1 and 3. (See Figure 2.35.) ■ ■ ■

PRACTICE PROBLEM 7   Let $y = f(x) = x^2 + 4x - 5$.

a. Is the point $(2, 7)$ on the graph of f?

b. Find all values of x so that $(x, -8)$ is on the graph of f.

c. Find the y-intercept of the graph of f.

d. Find any x-intercepts of the graph of f.   ■

SUMMARY

A function is usually described in one or more of the following five ways:

1. A set of ordered pairs
2. A correspondence diagram
3. A table of values
4. An equation or a formula
5. A scatter diagram or a graph

Input	Output
x	y or $f(x)$
Independent variable	Dependent variable
Domain is the set of all inputs.	Range is the set of all outputs.

6 Find the average rate of change of a function.

Average Rate of Change

Suppose that your salary increases from 25,000 dollars a year to 40,000 dollars a year over a five-year period. You then have

Change in salary: $40,000 − $25,000 = $15,000,

Average rate of change in salary:

$$\frac{\$40,000 - \$25,000}{5} = \frac{\$15,000}{5} = \$3000 \text{ per year.}$$

Regardless of when you actually received the raises during the five-year period, the final salary is the same as if you received your average annual increase, 3000 dollars, *each* year.

Now we are ready to see how the average rate of change can be defined in a more general setting.

THE AVERAGE RATE OF CHANGE OF A FUNCTION

Let $(a, f(a))$ and $(b, f(b))$ be two points on the graph of a function f. Then the **average rate of change** of $f(x)$ as x changes from a to b is defined by

$$\frac{f(b) - f(a)}{b - a}, \quad a \neq b.$$

EXAMPLE 8   Finding the Average Rate of Change

Find the average rate of change of $f(x) = 2x^2 - 3$ as x changes

a. from $x = 2$ to $x = 4$;

b. from $x = 3$ to $x = 6$;

c. from $x = c$ to $x = c + h, h \neq 0$.

Solution

a. Average rate of change $= \dfrac{f(4) - f(2)}{4 - 2}$ Definition

$= \dfrac{[2(4)^2 - 3] - [2(2)^2 - 3]}{4 - 2}$ $f(4) = 2(4)^2 - 3$ and $f(2) = 2(2)^2 - 3$.

$= \dfrac{29 - 5}{2} = \dfrac{24}{2} = 12$ Simplify.

b. Average rate of change $= \dfrac{f(6) - f(3)}{6 - 3}$ Definition

$= \dfrac{[2(6)^2 - 3] - [2(3)^2 - 3]}{6 - 3}$ Find $f(6)$ and $f(3)$.

$= \dfrac{69 - 15}{3} = \dfrac{54}{3} = 18$ Simplify.

c. Average rate of change $= \dfrac{f(c + h) - f(c)}{(c + h) - c}$ Definition

$= \dfrac{[2(c + h)^2 - 3] - [2(c)^2 - 3]}{c + h - c}$ Find $f(c + h)$ and $f(c)$.

$= \dfrac{[2(c^2 + 2ch + h^2) - 3] - (2c^2 - 3)}{h}$ Expand the binomial square.

$= \dfrac{4ch + 2h^2}{h} = \dfrac{\cancel{h}(4c + 2h)}{\cancel{h}}$ Simplify.

$= 4c + 2h$ Remove common factor h; $h \neq 0$.

■ ■ ■

PRACTICE PROBLEM 8   Find the average rate of change of $f(x) = 1 - x^2$ as x changes from $x = 1$ to $x = 3$.   ■

The average rate of change calculated in Example **8c** is called a *difference quotient*. The difference quotient is an important concept in calculus.

DIFFERENCE QUOTIENT

For a function f, the quantity

$$\frac{f(x + h) - f(x)}{h}, \qquad h \neq 0,$$

is called the **difference quotient.**

EXAMPLE 9   **Evaluating and Simplifying a Difference Quotient**

Let $f(x) = 2x^2 - 3x + 5$. Find and simplify $\dfrac{f(x + h) - f(x)}{h}, h \neq 0$.

Solution

We first find $f(x + h)$ by replacing x with $x + h$ for each occurrence of x in the equation $f(x) = 2x^2 - 3x + 5$.

$f(x) = 2x^2 - 3x + 5$ Original equation

$f(x + h) = 2(x + h)^2 - 3(x + h) + 5$ Replace x by $(x + h)$.

$= 2(x^2 + 2xh + h^2) - 3(x + h) + 5$ $(x + h)^2 = x^2 + 2xh + h^2$

$= 2x^2 + 4xh + 2h^2 - 3x - 3h + 5$ Use the distributive property.

Then we substitute into the difference quotient.

Continued on next page.

$$\frac{f(x+h) - f(x)}{h} = \frac{\overbrace{(2x^2 + 4xh + 2h^2 - 3x - 3h + 5)}^{f(x+h)} - \overbrace{(2x^2 - 3x + 5)}^{f(x)}}{h}$$

$$= \frac{2x^2 + 4xh + 2h^2 - 3x - 3h + 5 - 2x^2 + 3x - 5}{h} \qquad \text{Subtract.}$$

$$= \frac{4xh - 3h + 2h^2}{h} \qquad \text{Simplify.}$$

$$= \frac{\cancel{h}(4x - 3 + 2h)}{\cancel{h}} \qquad \text{Factor out } h.$$

$$= 4x - 3 + 2h \qquad \text{Remove the common factor } h. \qquad ■ ■ ■$$

PRACTICE PROBLEM 9 Repeat Example 9 for $f(x) = -x^2 + x - 3$. ■

7 Solve applied problems by using functions.

Applications

Level of Drugs in Bloodstream When you take a dose of medication, the drug level in the blood goes up quickly. In a little while, it reaches its *peak*, called C_{max} (the maximum concentration). As the drug is removed from your body by the liver or kidneys, drug levels in the blood drop. Just before the next dose enters your bloodstream, drug levels in the blood are at their lowest, a point called the *trough*, or C_{min} (the minimum concentration). The ideal dose should be strong enough to be effective without causing too many side effects. We start by setting upper and lower limits on drug levels in the blood. These levels are shown by the two horizontal lines on a pharmacokinetics (PK) graph. The upper line represents the drug level at which people start to develop serious side effects. The lower line represents the minimum drug level that provides the desired effect. A typical PK graph for a medicine is shown in Figure 2.36.

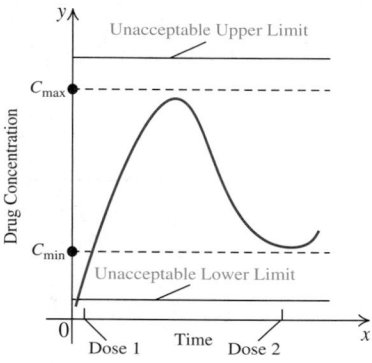

FIGURE 2.36

EXAMPLE 10	**Cholesterol-Reducing Drugs**

Many drugs used to lower high blood cholesterol levels are called *statins* and are very popular and widely prescribed. These drugs, along with proper diet and exercise, help prevent heart attacks and strokes. Recall from the introduction to this section that bioavailability is the amount of a drug you have ingested that makes it into your bloodstream. A statin with a bioavailability of 30% has been prescribed for Boris to treat his cholesterol levels. Boris is to take 20 milligrams of this statin every day. During the same day, one-half of the statin is filtered out of the body. Find the maximum concentration of the statin in the bloodstream on each of the first ten days of using the drug, and graph the result.

Solution

Since the statin has 30% bioavailability and Boris takes 20 milligrams per day, the maximum concentration in the bloodstream is 30% of 20 milligrams, or $20(0.3) = 6$ milligrams from each day's prescription. Because one-half of the statin is filtered out of the body each day, the daily maximum concentration is

$$\frac{1}{2}(\text{previous day's maximum concentration}) + 6.$$

Table 2.5 shows the pattern for the maximum concentration of the drug on each of the first ten days. Each number (except for 6, the first day's maximum concentration) in the second column is computed (to three decimal places) by adding 6 to one-half of the number above it. The graph is shown in Figure 2.37.

TABLE 2.5

Day	Maximum Concentration
1	6.000
2	9.000
3	10.500
4	11.250
5	11.625
6	11.813
7	11.906
8	11.953
9	11.977
10	11.988

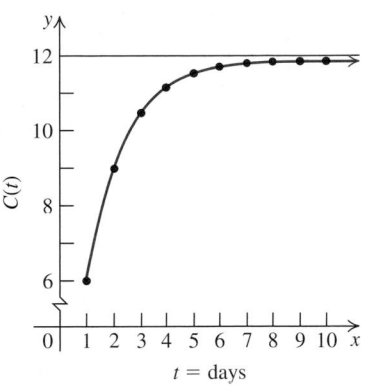

FIGURE 2.37

The graph shows that the maximum concentration of the statin in the bloodstream approaches 12 milligrams if Boris continues to take one pill every day.   ■ ■ ■

PRACTICE PROBLEM 10   In Example 10, use Table 2.5 to find the domain and the range of the function. Also, compute the function value at 6.   ■

Functions in Economics

The important concepts of *breaking even* and *earnings profit or taking a loss* in economics will be discussed throughout this book. We define here some of the elementary functions in economics.

Let x represent the number of units of an item manufactured and sold at a price of p dollars. Then the cost $C(x)$ of producing x items includes the **fixed cost** (such as rent, insurance, product design, setup, promotion, and overhead) and the **variable cost** (which depends on the number of items produced at a certain cost per item).

Linear Cost Function   A linear cost function $C(x)$ is given by

$$C(x) = (\text{variable cost}) + (\text{fixed cost})$$
$$= ax + b,$$

where b is the fixed cost and the cost of producing each item, called the **marginal cost,** is a dollars per item.

Average cost, denoted by $\overline{C}(x)$, is defined by $\overline{C}(x) = \dfrac{C(x)}{x}$.

Linear Price–Demand Function Suppose x items can be sold (demanded) at a price of p dollars per item. Then a linear demand function usually has the form

$$p(x) = -mx + d \qquad \text{expressing } p \text{ as a function of } x,$$

or

$$x(p) = -np + k \qquad \text{expressing } x \text{ as a function of } p,$$

Both expressions indicate that a higher price will result in fewer items sold. The numbers m, d, n, and k are constants that are determined by the particulars of a given situation.

Revenue Function $R(x)$

$$\text{Revenue} = (\text{Price per item}) \times (\text{Number of items sold})$$
$$R(x) = p \cdot x = (-mx + d)x \qquad\qquad p = p(x) = -mx + d$$

Profit Function $P(x)$

$$\text{Profit} = \text{Revenue} - \text{Cost}$$
$$P(x) = R(x) - C(x)$$

A manufacturing company will

(i)   have a *profit* if $P(x) > 0$,

(ii) *break even* if $P(x) = 0$, and

(iii) suffer a *loss* if $P(x) < 0$.

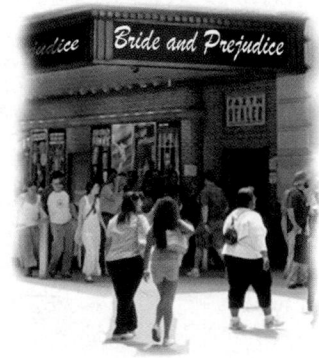

> **EXAMPLE 11**   **Breaking Even**

Metro Entertainment Co. spent $100,000 on production costs for its off-Broadway play *Bride and Prejudice*. Once running, each performance costs $1000 per show and the revenue from each is $2400. Using x to represent the number of shows,

a. Write cost function $C(x)$,

b. Write revenue function $R(x)$,

c. Write profit function $P(x)$.

d. How many showings of *Bride and Prejudice* must be held for Metro to break even?

Solution

a. $C(x) = (\text{Variable cost}) + (\text{fixed cost})$
$$= 1000x + 100{,}000$$

b. $R(x) = (\text{Revenue per show})(\text{Number of shows})$
$$= 2400x$$

c. $P(x) = R(x) - C(x)$
$$= 2400x - (1000x + 100{,}000)$$
$$= 2400x - 1000x - 100{,}000$$
$$= 1400x - 100{,}000$$

d. Metro will break even when $P(x) = 0$. Thus,

$$1400x - 100,000 = 0$$

$$1400x = 100,000 \qquad \text{Add 100,000 to both sides and solve for } x.$$

$$x = \frac{100,000}{1400} \approx 71.429. \qquad \text{Divide both sides by 1400.}$$

Since only a whole number of shows is possible, we say that 72 is the number of shows required for Metro to break even.   ■ ■ ■

PRACTICE PROBLEM 11   Suppose, in Example 11, that once running, each performance costs $1200 and the revenue from each show is $2500. How do the results in Example 11 change?

■

A Exercises   Basic Skills and Concepts

In Exercises 1–12, determine the domain and the range of each relation. State whether the given relation is a function.

1. $\{(-2, 2), (0, 0), (2, 2)\}$ †**2.**$\{(3, 1), (4, 1), (5, 1), (6, 1)\}$ †

3. $\{(-2, -2), (0, 0), (1, 1), (2, 2)\}$ †

4. $\{(4, 2), (9, 3), (4, -2), (9, -3)\}$ †

5. †

6. †

7. †

8. †

9. †

10. †

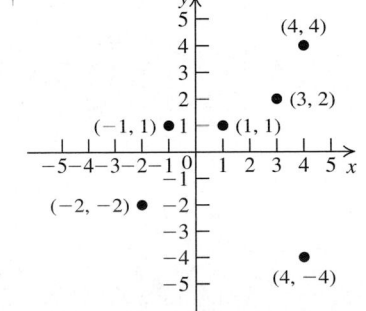

†Due to space constrictions, answers to these exercises may be found in the Answers beginning on page A–1 in the back of the book.

11.

x	y	†
-3	-8	
-1	0	
0	1	
1	0	
2	-3	
3	-8	

12.

x	y	†
0	-1	
3	-2	
8	-3	
0	1	
3	2	
8	2	

In Exercises 13–26, determine whether each equation defines y as a function of x.

13. $x + y = 2$ Yes

14. $x = y - 1$ Yes

15. $y = \dfrac{1}{x}$ Yes

16. $xy = -1$ Yes

17. $y = |x - 1|$ Yes

18. $x = |y|$ No

19. $y = \dfrac{1}{\sqrt{2x - 5}}$ Yes

20. $y = \dfrac{1}{\sqrt{x^2 - 1}}$ Yes

21. $2 - y = 3x$ Yes

22. $3x - 5y = 15$ Yes

23. $x^2 + y = 8$ Yes

24. $x = y^2$ No

25. $x^2 + y^3 = 5$ Yes

26. $x + y^3 = 8$ Yes

In Exercises 27–40, find the domain of each function.

27. $f(x) = -8x + 7$ $(-\infty, \infty)$ **28.** $f(x) = 2x^2 - 11$ $(-\infty, \infty)$

29. $f(x) = \dfrac{1}{x - 9}$ † **30.** $f(x) = \dfrac{1}{x + 9}$ †

31. $h(x) = \dfrac{2x}{x^2 - 1}$ † **32.** $h(x) = \dfrac{x - 3}{x^2 - 4}$ †

33. $G(x) = \dfrac{\sqrt{x - 3}}{x + 2}$ $[3, \infty)$ **34.** $G(x) = \dfrac{\sqrt{x + 3}}{1 - x}$ †

35. $f(x) = \dfrac{3}{\sqrt{4 - x}}$ $(-\infty, 4)$ **36.** $f(x) = \dfrac{x}{\sqrt{2 - x}}$ $(-\infty, 2)$

37. $F(x) = \dfrac{x + 4}{x^2 + 3x + 2}$ † **38.** $F(x) = \dfrac{1 - x}{x^2 + 5x + 6}$ †

39. $g(x) = \dfrac{\sqrt{x^2 + 1}}{x}$ † **40.** $g(x) = \dfrac{1}{x^2 + 1}$ $(-\infty, \infty)$

In Exercises 41–44, use the vertical-line test to determine whether the given graph represents a function.

41. Yes

42. No

43. Yes

44. No

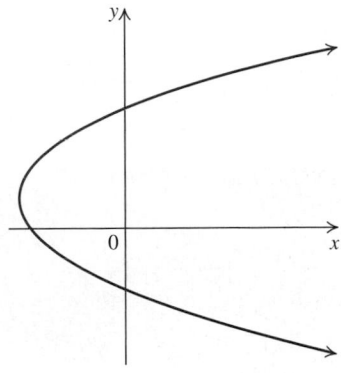

In Exercises 45–48, the graph of a function is given. Find the indicated function values.

45. $f(3)$, $f(5)$, $f(-1)$, $f(-4)$, †

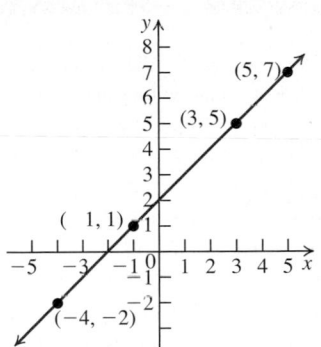

46. $g(-2)$, $g(1)$, $g(3)$, $g(4)$ †

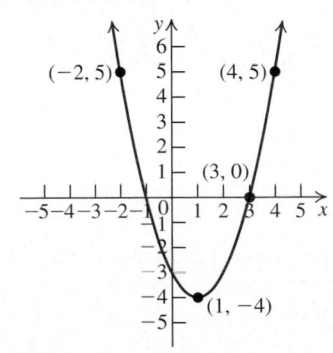

47. $h(-2)$, $h(-1)$, $h(0)$, $h(1)$ †

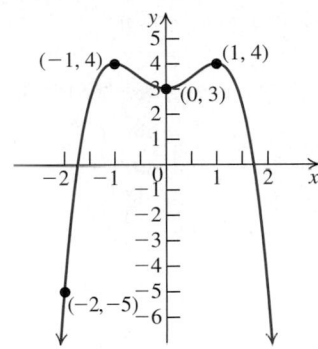

48. $f(-1)$, $f(0)$, $f(1)$ $f(-1) = 4$, $f(0) = 0$, $f(1) = -4$

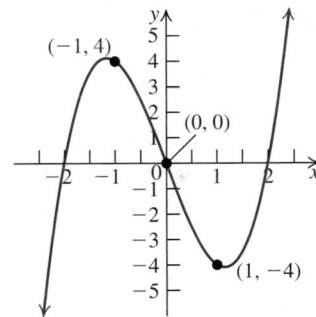

In Exercises 49–52, let $f(x) = x^2 - 3x + 1$, $g(x) = \dfrac{2}{\sqrt{x}}$, and $h(x) = \sqrt{2 - x}$.

49. Find $f(0), g(0), h(0),\ f(a),$ and $f(-x)$. †

50. Find $f(1), g(1), h(1), g(a),$ and $g(x^2)$. †

51. Find $f(-1), g(-1), h(-1),$ h(c), and $h(-x)$. †

52. Find $f(4), g(4), h(4), g(2 + k),$ and $f(a + k)$. †

53. Let $f(x) = \dfrac{2x}{\sqrt{4 - x^2}}$. Find each function value.

   a. $f(0)$ 0   **b.** $f(1)$ $\dfrac{2\sqrt{3}}{3}$

   c. $f(2)$ not defined   **d.** $f(-2)$ not defined

   e. $f(-x)$ $\dfrac{-2x}{\sqrt{4 - x^2}}$

54. Let $g(x) = 2x + \sqrt{x^2 - 4}$. Find each function value.

   a. $g(0)$ not defined

   b. $g(1)$ not defined

   c. $g(2)$ 4

   d. $g(-3)$ $-6 + \sqrt{5}$

   e. $g(-x)$ $-2x + \sqrt{x^2 - 4}$

For each function in Exercises 55–64, compute (for $h \neq 0$)

a. $f(x + h)$; **b.** $f(x + h) - f(x)$; **c.** $\dfrac{f(x + h) - f(x)}{h}$.

55. $f(x) = x$ †

56. $f(x) = 3x + 2$ †

57. $f(x) = x^2$ †

58. $f(x) = x^2 - x$ †

59. $f(x) = 2x^2 + 3x$ †

60. $f(x) = 3x^2 - 2x + 5$ †

61. $f(x) = 4$ †

62. $f(x) = -3$ †

63. $f(x) = \dfrac{1}{x}$ †

64. $f(x) = -\dfrac{1}{x}$ †

65. Let $h(x) = x^2 - x + 1$. Find x such that $(x, 7)$ is on the graph of h. $x = -2$ or 3

66. Let $H(x) = x^2 + x + 8$. Find x such that $(x, 7)$ is on the graph of H. No solution

B Exercises Applying the Concepts

In Exercises 67–70, state whether the given relation is a function and explain why.

67. Each day of the year corresponds to the high temperature in your hometown on that day. †

68. Each year since 1950 corresponds to the cost of a first-class postage stamp on January 1 of that year. †

69. Each letter of the word NUTS corresponds to the states whose names start with that letter. †

70. Each day of the week corresponds to the first names of people currently living in the United States born on that day of the week. †

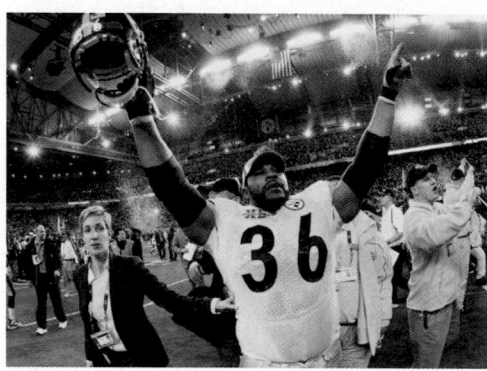

In Exercises 71 and 72, use the table listing the Super Bowl winners for the years 1995–2006.

Year	Super Bowl Winner
1995	San Francisco
1996	Dallas
1997	Green Bay
1998	Denver
1999	Denver
2000	St. Louis
2001	Baltimore
2002	New England
2003	Tampa Bay
2004	New England
2005	New England
2006	Pittsburgh

(*Source:* http://www.superbowl.com/history/boxscores)

71. Consider the relation whose domain values are the years 1995–2006 and whose range values are the corresponding winning teams. Is this relation a function? Explain your answer. Yes, because there is only one winner in each year

72. Consider the relation whose domain values are the names of the winning teams in the table and whose range values are the corresponding years. Is this relation a function? Explain your answer. No, because New England won more than once.

73. Square tiles. The area $A(x)$ of a square tile is a function of the length x of a side of the square. Write a function rule for the area of a square tile. Find and interpret $A(4)$. †

74. Cube. The volume $V(x)$ of a cube is a function of the length x of an edge of the cube. Write a function rule for the volume of a cube. Evaluate the function for a cube with sides of length 3 inches. $V(x) = x^3$. $V(3) = 27$ in.^{3}

75. Surface area. Is the total surface area S of a cube a function of the edge x of the cube? If it is not a function, explain why not. If it is a function, write the function rule $S(x)$ and evaluate $S(3)$. It is a function. $S(x) = 6x^2$, $S(3) = 54$

76. Measurement. One meter equals about 39.37 inches. Write a function rule for converting inches to meters. Evaluate the function for 59 inches. †

77. Cost. A computer notebook manufacturer has a daily fixed cost of 10,500 dollars and a marginal cost of 210 dollars per notebook.
  a. Find the daily cost $C(x)$ of manufacturing x notebooks per day. $C(x) = 210x + 10,500$
  b. Find the cost of producing 50 notebooks per day. $21,000
  c. Find the average cost of a computer notebook if 50 notebooks are manufactured each day. $420
  d. How many notebooks should be manufactured each day so that the average cost per notebook is 315 dollars? 100

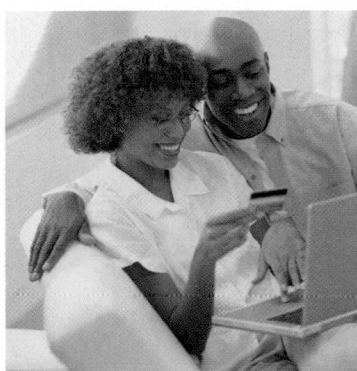

78. Cost. The Just Juice Company has a monthly cost of 20,000 dollars and a marginal cost of 4 dollars per case of juice.
  a. Find the monthly cost $C(x)$ if the company produces x cases of juice per month. $C(x) = 4x + 20,000$
  b. Find the cost of producing 12,000 cases of juice per month. $68,000
  c. Find the average cost of a case of juice in part (b). $5.67
  d. How many cases of juice should be produced each month so that the average cost per case is 4 dollars and 50 cents. 40,000

79. Price–demand. From the past history of the company, analysts for an electronics company produced the price–demand function for its 30-inch LCD televisions. The function is
$$p(x) = 1275 - 25x, \quad 1 \le x \le 30,$$
where p is the wholesale price per TV in dollars and x, in thousands, is the number of TVs that can be sold.
  a. Find and interpret $p(5)$, $p(15)$, and $p(30)$. †
  b. Sketch the graph of $y = p(x)$. †
  c. Find the number of TVs that can be sold at 650 dollars per TV. 25

80. Revenue.
  a. Using the price–demand function $p(x) = 1275 - 25x$, $1 \le x \le 30$, of Exercise 79, write the company's revenue function $R(x)$ and state its domain. †
  b. Find and interpret $R(1)$, $R(5)$, $R(10)$, $R(15)$, $R(20)$, $R(25)$, and $R(30)$. †
  c. Using the data from part (b), sketch the graph of $y = R(x)$. †
  d. Find the number of TVs that must be sold to generate a revenue of 4.7 million dollars.
    [*Hint:* Solve $4700 = 1275x - 25x^2$] 4870

81. Breaking even. Peerless Publishing Company intends to publish Harriet Henrita's next novel. The estimated cost is 75,000 dollars plus 5 dollars and 50 cents for each copy printed. The selling price per copy of the novel is 15 dollars. The bookstores retain 40% of the selling price as commission. Let x represent the number of copies printed and sold.
  a. Find the cost function $C(x)$. $C(x) = 5.5x + 75,000$
  b. Find the revenue function $R(x)$. $R(x) = 9x$
  c. Find the profit function $P(x)$. $P(x) = 3.5x - 75,000$
  d. How many copies of the novel must be sold in order for Peerless to break even? 21,429
  e. What is the profit of the company if 46,000 copies of the novel are sold? $86,000

82. Breaking even. Capital Records Company is planning to produce a CD by the popular rapper Rapit. The fixed cost is 500,000 dollars and the variable cost is 50 cents per CD. The company sells each CD to the record stores for 5 dollars. Let x represent the number of CDs produced and sold.
  a. How many disks must be sold for the company to break even? 111,112
  b. How many CDs must be sold in order for the company to make a profit of 750,000 dollars? 277,778

83. Motion of a projectile. A stone thrown upward with an initial velocity of 128 feet per second will attain a height of h feet in t seconds, where
$$h(t) = 128t - 16t^2, \quad 0 \le t \le 8.$$
  a. What is the domain of h? †
  b. Find $h(2)$, $h(4)$, and $h(6)$. †
  c. How long will it take the stone to hit the ground? †
  d. Sketch a graph of $y = h(t)$. †

84. Housing affordability in the United States. The following table lists the median sale price of existing homes during 1990–2003.

Year	1990	1991	1993	1995	1997	1999	2001	2003
Price in thousands of dollars	97.1	99.7	103.1	111.1	121.8	133.3	147.8	182.1

(*Source:* National Association of Realtors.)

Find the average rate of change of a median-priced home during each period.
a. 1995–1997 5.35
b. 1990–2003 6.54
c. Use your results in (a) and (b) to estimate the median sale price of a home in 1996. †

85. Drug prescription. A certain drug has been prescribed to treat an infection. The patient receives an injection of 16 milliliters of the drug every 4 hours. During this same 4-hour period, the kidneys filter out one-fourth of the drug. Find the concentration of the drug after 4 hours, 8 hours, 12 hours, 16 hours, and 20 hours. Sketch the graph of the concentration of the drug in the bloodstream as a function of time. †

86. Drug prescription. Every day, Jane takes one 500-milligram aspirin tablet that has 80% bioavailability. During the same day, three-fourths of the aspirin is metabolized. Find the maximum concentration of the aspirin in the bloodstream on each of the first ten days of using the drug, and graph the result.

C Exercises   Beyond the Basics

87. Give an example (if possible) of a function matching each description. There are many different correct answers.
a. Its graph is symmetric with respect to the *y*-axis. †
b. Its graph is symmetric with respect to the *x*-axis. †
c. Its graph is symmetric with respect to the origin. †
d. Its graph consists of a single point. $f(x) = \sqrt{-x^2}$
e. Its graph is a horizontal line. $f(x) = 1$
f. Its graph is a vertical line. Not possible

88. Explain whether $f(x)$ and $g(x)$ are equal.
a. $f(x) = 2(\sqrt{x})^2 + 5$, $g(x) = 2x + 5$ †
b. $f(x) = 2(\sqrt[3]{x})^3 + 5$, $g(x) = 2x + 5$ †

In Exercises 89–94, find an expression for $f(x)$ by first solving for *y* and replacing *y* with $f(x)$. Then find the domain of f and compute $f(4)$.

89. $3x - 5y = 15$ †

90. $x = \dfrac{y}{y - 1}$ †

91. $x = \dfrac{2}{y - 4}$ †

92. $xy - 3 = 2y$ †

93. $(x^2 + 1)y + x = 2$ †

94. $yx^2 - \sqrt{x} = -2y$ †

In Exercises 95–100, state whether f and g represent the same function. Explain your reasons.

95. $f(x) = 3x - 4, 0 \le x \le 8$ $g(x) = 3x - 4$ †

96. $f(x) = 3x^2$ $g(x) = 3x^2, -5 \le x \le 5$ †

97. $f(x) = x - 1$ $g(x) = \dfrac{x^2 - 1}{x + 1}$ †

98. $f(x) = \dfrac{x + 2}{x^2 - x - 6}$ $g(x) = \dfrac{1}{x - 3}$ †

99. $f(x) = \dfrac{x^2 - 4}{x - 2}, 2 < x < \infty$
$g(x) = x + 2, 2 < x < \infty$ †

100. $f(x) = \dfrac{x - 2}{x^2 - 6x + 8}, 2 < x < \infty$
$g(x) = \dfrac{1}{x - 4}, 2 < x < \infty$ †

101. Let $f(x) = ax^2 + ax - 3$. If $f(2) = 15$, find *a*. 3

102. Let $g(x) = x^2 + bx + b^2$. If $g(6) = 28$, find *b*. †

103. Let $h(x) = \dfrac{3x + 2a}{2x - b}$. If $h(6) = 0$ and $h(3)$ is undefined, find *a* and *b*. $a = -9, b = 6$

104. Let $f(x) = 2x - 3$. Find $f(x^2)$ and $[f(x)]^2$. †

105. If $g(x) = x^2 - \dfrac{1}{x^2}$, show that $g(x) + g\left(\dfrac{1}{x}\right) = 0$.

106. If $f(x) = \dfrac{x - 1}{x + 1}$, show that $f\left(\dfrac{x - 1}{x + 1}\right) = -\dfrac{1}{x}$.

107. If $f(x) = \dfrac{x + 3}{4x - 5}$ and $t = \dfrac{3 + 5x}{4x - 1}$, show that $f(t) = x$.

Critical Thinking

108. Write an equation of a function with each domain. Answers will vary.

  a. $[2, \infty)$ $y = \sqrt{x - 2}$

  b. $(2, \infty)$ $y = \dfrac{1}{\sqrt{x - 2}}$

  c. $(-\infty, 2]$ $y = \sqrt{2 - x}$

  d. $(-\infty, 2)$ $y = \dfrac{1}{\sqrt{2 - x}}$

109. Consider the graph of the function
$y = f(x) = ax^2 + bx + c, a \neq 0.$

  a. Write an equation whose solution yields the x-intercepts.

  b. Write an equation whose solution is the y-intercept. $y = c$

  c. Write (if possible) a condition under which the graph of $y = f(x)$ has no x-intercepts. $b^2 - 4ac < 0$

  d. Write (if possible) a condition under which the graph of $y = f(x)$ has no y-intercepts. Not possible

Answer:

109. a. $ax^2 + bx + c = 0$

A Library of Functions

1. Equation of a line (Section 2.3, page 209)

2. Absolute value (Section P.1, page 8)

3. Graphs of equations (Section 2.2, page 192)

OBJECTIVES

1 Relate linear functions to linear equations.

2 Understand and graph piecewise functions.

3 Determine whether a function is increasing or decreasing on an interval.

4 Recognize relative maximum and minimum values.

5 Identify even and odd functions.

6 Graph some important functions.

The Megatooth Shark

The giant "Megatooth" shark (*Carcharodon megalodon*), once estimated to be 100 to 120 feet in length, is the largest meat-eating fish that ever lived. The actual size of this shark has been the subject of considerable scientific controversy. Sharks first appeared in the oceans more than 400 million years ago, almost 200 million years before the dinosaurs. A shark's skeleton is made of cartilage that decomposes rather quickly, making complete shark fossils rare. Consequently, scientists rely on calcified vertebrae, fossilized teeth, and small skin scales to reconstruct the evolutionary record of sharks.

The great white shark is the closest living relative to the giant "Megatooth" shark and has been used as a model to reconstruct the "Megatooth." John Maisey, curator at the American Museum of Natural History in New York City, used a partial set of "Megatooth" teeth to make a comparison with the jaws of the great white shark. In Example 2 we will use a formula to calculate the length of the "Megatooth" on the basis of the height of the tooth of the largest known "Megatooth" specimen. ■

1 Relate linear functions to linear equations.

Linear Functions

We know from Section 2.3 that the graph of a linear equation $y = mx + b$ is a straight line with slope m and y-intercept b. For this reason, a function f defined by the equation $f(x) = mx + b$ is called a *linear function*.

LINEAR FUNCTIONS

Let m and b be real numbers. The function $f(x) = mx + b$ is called a **linear function**. If $m = 0$, the function $f(x) = b$ is called a **constant function**. If $m = 1$ and $b = 0$, the resulting function $f(x) = x$ is called the **identity function**. (See Figure 2.38.)

The domain of a linear function is the interval $(-\infty, \infty)$, because the expression $mx + b$ is defined for any real number x. Note that the graph extends indefinitely to the left and right. The range of a nonconstant linear function is also the interval $(-\infty, \infty)$, because the graph extends indefinitely upward and downward. The range of a constant function $f(x) = b$ is the single real number b. (See Figure 2.38(c).)

GRAPH OF $f(x) = mx + b$

The graph of a linear function is a nonvertical line with slope m and y-intercept b.

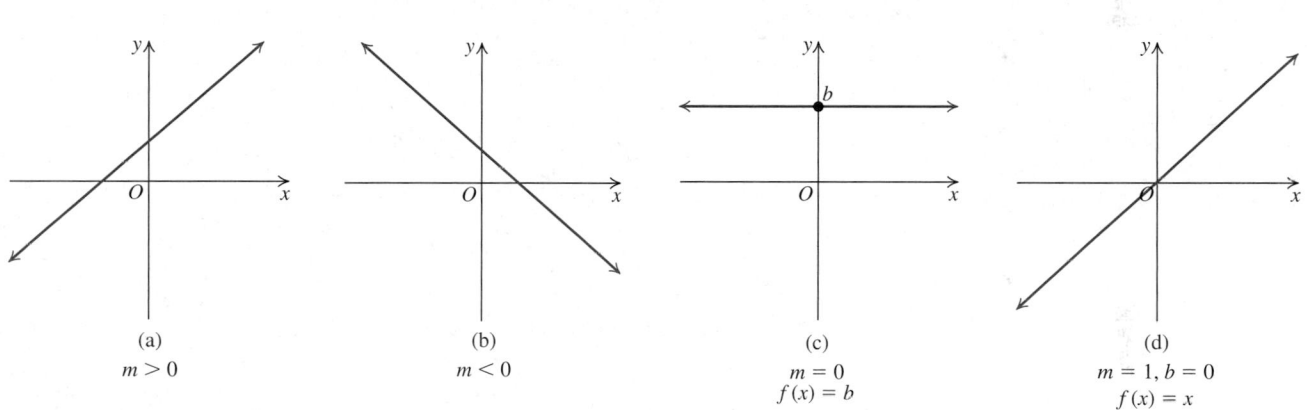

(a)	(b)	(c)	(d)
$m > 0$	$m < 0$	$m = 0$	$m = 1, b = 0$
		$f(x) = b$	$f(x) = x$

FIGURE 2.38

EXAMPLE 1   **Writing a Linear Function**

Write a linear function g for which $g(1) = 4$ and $g(-3) = -2$.

Solution

We first need to find the equation of the line passing through the two points:

$$(x_1, y_1) = (1, 4) \text{ and } (x_2, y_2) = (-3, -2).$$

The slope of the line is given by

$$m = \frac{y_2 - y_1}{x_2 - x_1} = \frac{-2 - 4}{-3 - 1} = \frac{-6}{-4} = \frac{3}{2}.$$

Continued on next page.

FIGURE 2.39

Next, we use the point–slope form of a line.

$$y - y_1 = m(x - x_1) \qquad \text{Point–slope form of a line}$$

$$y - 4 = \frac{3}{2}(x - 1) \qquad \text{Substitute } x_1 = 1, y_1 = 4, \text{ and } m = \frac{3}{2}.$$

$$y - 4 = \frac{3}{2}x - \frac{3}{2} \qquad \text{Distributive property}$$

$$y = \frac{3}{2}x + \frac{5}{2} \qquad \text{Add } 4 = \frac{8}{2} \text{ to both sides and simplify.}$$

$$g(x) = \frac{3}{2}x + \frac{5}{2} \qquad \text{Function notation}$$

The graph of the function $y = g(x)$ is shown in Figure 2.39. ▪ ▪ ▪

PRACTICE PROBLEM 1 Write a linear function g for which $g(-2) = 2$ and $g(1) = 8$. ▪

EXAMPLE 2 **Determining the Length of the "Megatooth" Shark**

The largest known "Megatooth" specimen is a tooth that has a total height of 15.6 centimeters. Calculate the length of the "Megatooth" shark it came from by using the formula

Shark length $= (0.96)$(height of tooth) $- 0.22$,

where shark length is measured in meters and tooth height is measured in centimeters.

Solution

Begin with the formula

Shark length $= (0.96)$(height of tooth) $- 0.22$

Then

$$\text{Shark length} = (0.96)(15.6) - 0.22 \qquad \text{Replace height of tooth by 15.6.}$$
$$= 14.756. \qquad\qquad\qquad\quad \text{Simplify.}$$

This "Megatooth" specimen has a calculated total length of 14.756 meters (48.41 feet).

▪ ▪ ▪

PRACTICE PROBLEM 2 If the "Megatooth" specimen was a tooth measuring 16.4 cm, what would be the length of the "Megatooth" shark from which it came? ▪

2 Understand and graph piecewise functions.

Piecewise Functions

In the definition of some functions, different rules for assigning output values are used over different parts of the domain. Such functions are called **piecewise functions**. For example, in Peach County, Georgia, a section of the interstate highway has a speed limit of 55 miles per hour (mph). If you are caught speeding and your speed is between 56 and 74 mph, your fine is 50 dollars, plus 3 dollars for every mile per hour over 55 mph. For 75 mph and higher, your fine is 150 dollars, plus 5 dollars for every mile per hour over 75 mph.

Let $f(x)$ represent your fine if you are caught speeding at x miles per hour. We can express $f(x)$ as a piecewise function:

$$f(x) = \begin{cases} 50 + 3(x - 55), & 56 \leq x < 75 \\ 150 + 5(x - 75), & x \geq 75 \end{cases}.$$

The expression to the right of $f(x)$ means that if $56 \leq x < 75$, you use $f(x) = 50 + 3(x - 55)$ to compute the value of $f(x)$, which is your fine. For example, if you are caught driving 60 miles per hour, then

$$\begin{aligned} x &= 60 && \text{Your speed when caught} \\ f(x) &= 50 + 3(x - 55) && \text{Expression used for } 56 \leq x < 75 \\ f(60) &= 50 + 3(60 - 55) && \text{Substitute 60 for } x. \\ &= 65 && \text{Simplify.} \end{aligned}$$

Your fine for speeding at 60 miles per hour is \$65. The expression on the right of $f(x)$ also means that if $x \geq 75$, you use $f(x) = 150 + 5(x - 75)$ to compute the value of $f(x)$. For instance, if you are caught driving 90 miles per hour, then

$$\begin{aligned} x &= 90 && \text{Your speed when caught} \\ f(x) &= 150 + 5(x - 75) && \text{Expression used for } x \geq 75 \\ f(90) &= 150 + 5(90 - 75) && \text{Substitute 90 for } x. \\ &= 225 && \text{Simplify.} \end{aligned}$$

Your fine for speeding at 90 miles per hour is \$225.

Graphing Piecewise Functions

Now let's consider how you graph a piecewise function. The **absolute value function,** $f(x) = |x|$, can be expressed as a piecewise function by using the definition of absolute value:

$$f(x) = |x| = \begin{cases} -x & \text{if } x < 0 \\ x & \text{if } x \geq 0 \end{cases}$$

The expression to the right of $|x|$ means that if $x < 0$, we use the equation $y = f(x) = -x$ to find the y-value. So that if $x = -3$, then

$$\begin{aligned} y &= f(x) = -x && \text{Expression used if } x < 0 \\ y &= f(-3) = -(-3) && \text{Substitute } -3 \text{ for } x. \\ &= 3. && \text{Simplify.} \end{aligned}$$

Thus, the point $(-3, 3)$ is on the graph of $y = |x|$. However, if $x \geq 0$, we use the equation $y = f(x) = x$. Thus, if $x = 2$, then

$$\begin{aligned} y &= f(x) = x && \text{Expression used if } x \geq 0 \\ y &= f(2) = 2. && \text{Substitute 2 for } x. \end{aligned}$$

The two pieces $y = -x$ and $y = x$ are each linear functions. We graph the appropriate parts of these lines ($y = -x$ for $x < 0$ and $y = x$ for $x \geq 0$) to form the graph of $y = |x|$. (See Figure 2.40.) The dashed portions in Figure 2.40 are not part of the graph.

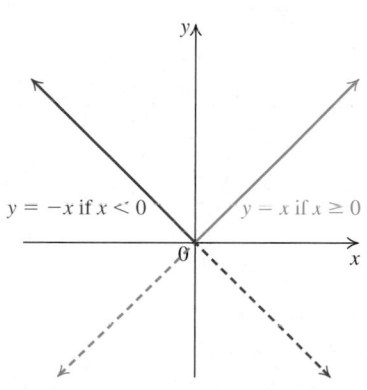

FIGURE 2.40

EXAMPLE 3   Graphing a Piecewise Function

Let

$$F(x) = \begin{cases} 2x^2 & \text{if } x < 1 \\ 3x + 1 & \text{if } x \geq 1 \end{cases}$$

a. Find $F(2)$ and $F(0)$.

b. Sketch the graph of $y = F(x)$.

Solution

a. In order to decide whether to use the rule $y = 2x^2$ or the rule $y = 3x + 1$ for a given value of x, we first note whether $x < 1$ or $x \geq 1$. Since $2 \geq 1$, we find $F(2)$ by using the second part of the definition.

$$F(x) = 3x + 1 \qquad \text{Expression used if } x \geq 1$$
$$F(2) = 3(2) + 1 \qquad \text{Substitute 2 for } x.$$
$$= 6 + 1 \qquad \text{Simplify.}$$
$$= 7$$

Since $0 < 1$, we use the first part of the definition, $F(x) = 2x^2$, to find $F(0)$.

$$F(x) = 2x^2 \qquad \text{Expression used if } x < 1$$
$$F(0) = 2(0)^2 \qquad \text{Substitute 0 for } x.$$
$$= 0 \qquad \text{Simplify.}$$

b. In the definition of F, the formula changes at $x = 1$. We call such numbers the **breakpoints** of the formula. For the function F, the only breakpoint is 1. A useful procedure for graphing piecewise functions is to graph the function separately over the open intervals determined by the breakpoints and then graph the function at the breakpoints themselves. For the function $y = F(x)$, the formula for F specifies that the equation $y = 2x^2$ be used on the interval $(-\infty, 1)$ and the equation $y = 3x + 1$ be used on the interval $(1, \infty)$ and also at the breakpoint 1, so that $y = F(1) = 3(1) + 1 = 4$. We graph $y = 2x^2$ and $y = 3x + 1$ in Figure 2.41(a) and 2.41(b).

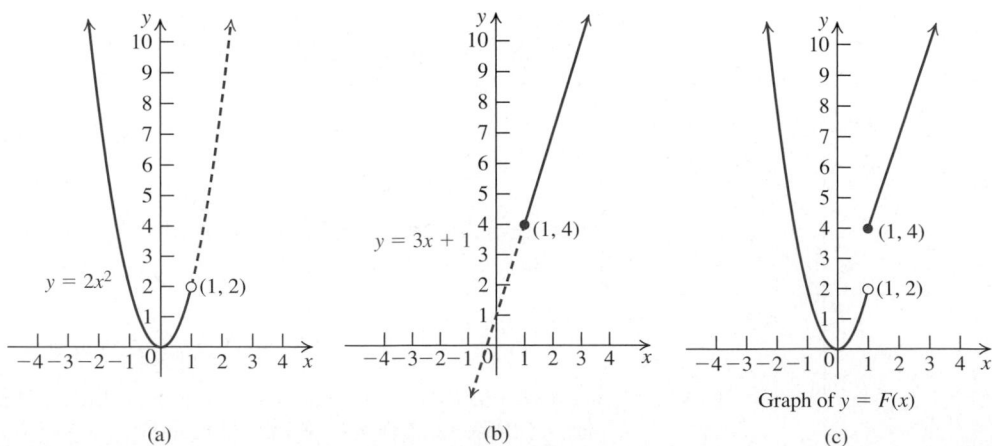

(a)   (b)   (c)

FIGURE 2.41

To obtain a graph of the greatest-integer function, enter $Y_1 = \text{int}(x)$. If you have your calculator set to graph in **connected** mode, you will get the following incorrect graph:

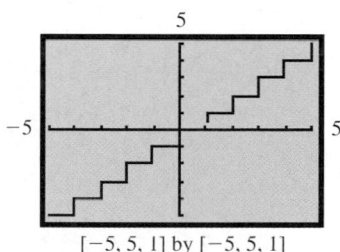

$[-5, 5, 1]$ by $[-5, 5, 1]$

For the graph to appear correctly, you must change from the **connected** to the **dot** mode:

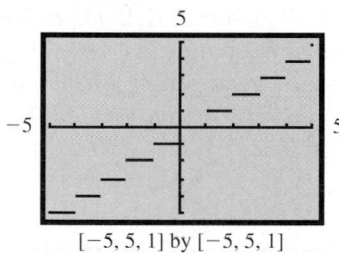

$[-5, 5, 1]$ by $[-5, 5, 1]$

Note that the step from $0 \le x \le 1$ is obscured by the x-axis.

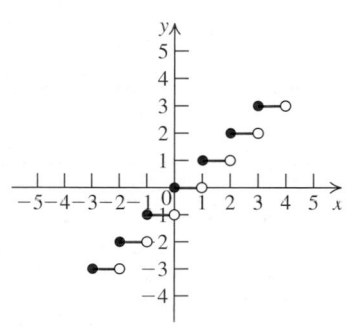

FIGURE 2.42

Notice that for the function F, we only use the solid portions of each graph. Combining these solid portions, we obtain the graph of $y = F(x)$, shown in Figure 2.41(c). When we come to the edge of the part of the graph we are working with, we draw

(i)   a closed circle if that point is included and

(ii) an open circle if the point is excluded.

You may find it helpful to think of this procedure as following the graph of $y = 2x^2$ when x is less than 1 and then jumping to the graph of $y = 3x + 1$ at $x = 1$ and remaining on the graph of $y = 3x + 1$ for x greater than 1.   ■ ■ ■

PRACTICE PROBLEM 3   Let $F(x) = \begin{cases} -x^2 & \text{if } x \le -1 \\ 2x & \text{if } x > -1 \end{cases}$. Find $F(-2)$ and $F(3)$, and sketch the graph of $y = F(x)$.   ■

Some piecewise functions are called **step functions.** Their graphs look like the steps of a staircase.

The **greatest-integer function** is denoted by $[\![x]\!]$, or int(x), where $[\![x]\!]$ = the greatest integer less than or equal to x. For example,

$$[\![2]\!] = 2, \quad [\![2.3]\!] = 2, \quad [\![2.7]\!] = 2, \quad [\![2.99]\!] = 2,$$

because 2 is the greatest integer less than or equal to 2, 2.3, 2.7, and 2.99. Similarly,

$$[\![-2]\!] = -2, \quad [\![-1.9]\!] = -2, \quad [\![-1.1]\!] = -2, \quad [\![-1.001]\!] = -2$$

because -2 is the greatest integer less than or equal to -2, -1.9, -1.1, and -1.001.

In general, if m is an integer such that $m \le x < m + 1$, then $[\![x]\!] = m$. In other words, if x is between two consecutive integers m and $m + 1$, then $[\![x]\!]$ is assigned the smaller integer m.

EXAMPLE 4   **Graphing a Step Function**

Graph the greatest integer function $f(x) = [\![x]\!]$.

Solution

Choose a typical closed interval between two consecutive integers—say, the interval $[2, 3]$. Make a table of values for the interval $2 \le x \le 3$. (See Table 2.6.)

TABLE 2.6

x	2	2.1	2.25	2.5	2.75	2.9	3
$f(x)$	2	2	2	2	2	2	3

We conclude from Table 2.6 that

$$\text{if } 2 \le x < 3, \text{ then } [\![x]\!] = 2.$$

Similarly, we note that

$$\text{if } 1 \le x < 2, \text{ then } [\![x]\!] = 1.$$

Thus, the values of $[\![x]\!]$ are constant between each pair of consecutive integers and jump by one unit at each integer. The graph of $f(x) = [\![x]\!]$ is shown in Figure 2.42.   ■ ■ ■

PRACTICE PROBLEM 4   Find the values of $f(x) = [\![x]\!]$ for $x = -3.4$ and $x = 4.7$.   ■

In Figure 2.42, notice the following features of $f(x) = [\![x]\!]$:

1. The domain of f is $(-\infty, \infty)$.
2. The range of f is the set of all integers.
3. The graph is constant between each pair of consecutive integers.
4. The graph jumps vertically one unit at each integer value in the domain.
5. The function f can be interpreted as a piecewise function:

$$f(x) = [\![x]\!] = \begin{cases} \;\;\vdots \\ -2 \text{ if } -2 \le x < -1 \\ -1 \text{ if } -1 \le x < 0 \\ \;\;0 \text{ if } \;\;\;0 \le x < 1 \\ \;\;1 \text{ if } \;\;\;1 \le x < 2 \\ \;\;\vdots \end{cases}.$$

3 Determine whether a function is increasing or decreasing on an interval.

Increasing and Decreasing Functions

Classifying functions according to how one variable changes with respect to the other variable can be very useful. We introduce some terminology to describe the behavior of a function regarding these changes. Imagine a particle moving from left to right along the graph of a function. This means that the x-coordinate of the point on the graph is getting larger. If the corresponding y-coordinate of the point is getting larger, getting smaller, or staying the same, then the function is called, *increasing, decreasing,* or *constant,* respectively. We state these concepts more precisely as follows.

INCREASING, DECREASING, AND CONSTANT FUNCTIONS

Let f be a function, and let x_1 and x_2 be any two numbers in an open interval (a, b) contained in the domain of f. The symbols a and b represent either real numbers, $-\infty$, or ∞. Then

(i) f is called an **increasing function** on (a, b) if $x_1 < x_2$ implies $f(x_1) < f(x_2)$.

(ii) f is called a **decreasing function** on (a, b) if $x_1 < x_2$ implies $f(x_1) > f(x_2)$.

(iii) f is **constant** on (a, b) if $x_1 < x_2$ implies $f(x_1) = f(x_2)$.

Geometrically, the graph of an increasing function on an open interval (a, b) rises as x-values increase on (a, b). This is because, by definition, as x-values increase from x_1 to x_2 $(x_1 < x_2)$, the y-values also increase, from $f(x_1)$ to $f(x_2)$ (that is, $f(x_1) < f(x_2)$). Similarly, the graph of a decreasing function on (a, b) falls as x-values increase. The graph of a constant function is horizontal, or flat, over the interval (a, b). (See Figure 2.43.)

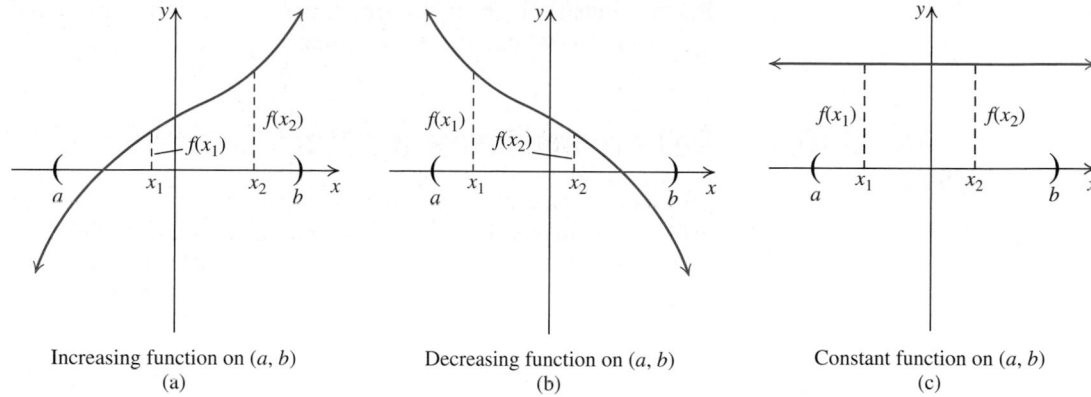

Increasing function on (a, b)
(a)

Decreasing function on (a, b)
(b)

Constant function on (a, b)
(c)

FIGURE 2.43

Of course, not every function always increases or decreases. For example, the function that assigns the height of a ball tossed up in the air to the length of time it is in the air is an example of a function that increases, but also decreases, over different intervals of its domain.

EXAMPLE 5   **Tracking the Behavior of a Function**

From the graph of the function g in Figure 2.44(a), find the intervals over which g is increasing, is decreasing, or is constant.

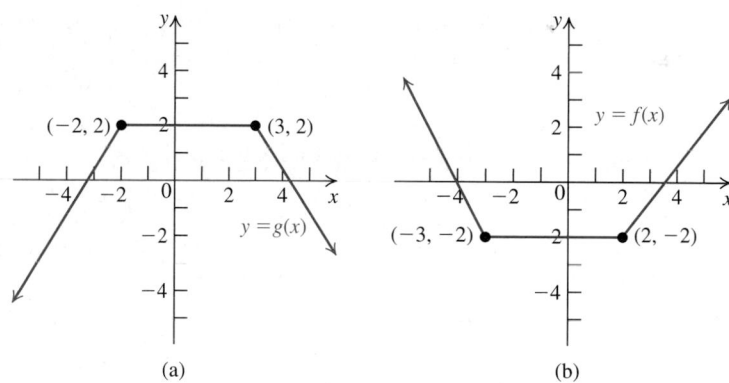

(a)

(b)

FIGURE 2.44

Solution

From the graph in Figure 2.44(a), we observe that the function $y = g(x)$ is

a. increasing on the interval $(-\infty, -2)$,

b. constant on the interval $(-2, 3)$, and

c. decreasing on the interval $(3, \infty)$.   ■ ■ ■

PRACTICE PROBLEM 5   From the graph in Figure 2.44(b), find the intervals over which f is increasing, is decreasing, or is constant.   ■

4 Recognize relative maximum and minimum values.

Relative Maximum and Minimum Values

The y-coordinate of a point that is higher (lower) than any nearby point on a graph is called a *relative maximum* (*relative minimum*) value of the function. Relative maximum and minimum values are the y-coordinates of points corresponding to the peaks and troughs, respectively, of the graph. Here are the corresponding algebraic definitions:

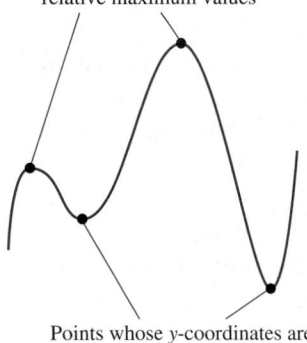

Points whose y-coordinates are relative maximum values

Points whose y-coordinates are relative minimum values

FIGURE 2.45

DEFINITION OF RELATIVE MAXIMUM AND RELATIVE MINIMUM

If a is in the domain of a function f, we say that the value $f(a)$ is a **relative minimum of f** if there is an interval (x_1, x_2) containing a such that

$$f(a) \leq f(x) \text{ for every } x \text{ in the interval } (x_1, x_2).$$

We say that the value $f(a)$ is a **relative maximum of f** if there is an interval (x_1, x_2) containing a such that

$$f(a) \geq f(x) \text{ for every } x \text{ in the interval } (x_1, x_2).$$

Several examples of points whose y-coordinates are either relative minimum or relative maximum values are shown in Figure 2.45. In Section 3.2, you will learn a method for finding the maximum or minimum value for a quadratic function. A graphing calculator can be used to help find or approximate maximum and minimum values for many functions.

5 Identify even and odd functions.

Even and Odd Functions

In Section 2.2, we discussed different types of symmetries for the graph of an equation. In discussing the symmetry of a function, we make the following definitions:

EVEN FUNCTION

A function f is called an **even function** if, for each x in the domain of f, $-x$ is also in the domain of f and

$$f(-x) = f(x).$$

The graph of an even function is symmetric with respect to the y-axis.

EXAMPLE 6   **Graphing the Squaring Function**

Show that the squaring function $f(x) = x^2$ is an even function, and sketch its graph.

Solution

The function $f(x) = x^2$ is even because

$$f(-x) = (-x)^2 \qquad \text{Replace } x \text{ by } -x.$$
$$= x^2 \qquad (-x)^2 = x^2$$
$$= f(x). \qquad \text{Replace } x^2 \text{ by } f(x).$$

We sketch the graph of $f(x) = x^2$ by making a table of values. (See Table 2.7(a).) The graph is obtained by plotting the points from the table in the first quadrant in the coordinate plane and joining these points by a smooth curve. We then use y-axis symmetry to find additional points on the graph of f in the second quadrant. (See Table 2.7(b).)

TABLE 2.7(a)

x	0	$\dfrac{1}{2}$	1	$\dfrac{3}{2}$	2	$\dfrac{5}{2}$	3
$f(x) = x^2$	0	$\dfrac{1}{4}$	1	$\dfrac{9}{4}$	4	$\dfrac{25}{4}$	9

TABLE 2.7(b)

x	0	$-\dfrac{1}{2}$	-1	$-\dfrac{3}{2}$	-2	$-\dfrac{5}{2}$	-3
$f(x) = x^2$	0	$\dfrac{1}{4}$	1	$\dfrac{9}{4}$	4	$\dfrac{25}{4}$	9

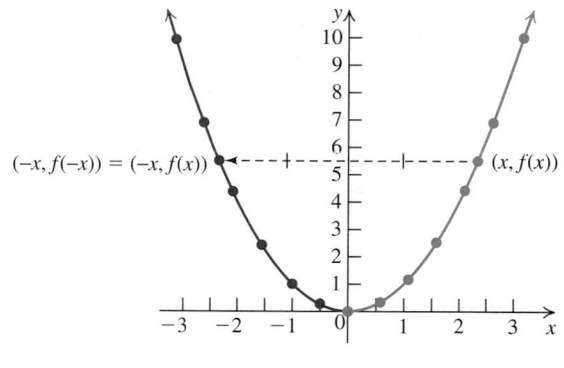

Graph of $f(x) = x^2$

FIGURE 2.46

The graph of $f(x) = x^2$ is shown in Figure 2.46. ▪ ▪ ▪

PRACTICE PROBLEM 6 Show that the function $f(x) = -x^2$ is an even function, and sketch its graph. ▪

ODD FUNCTION

A function f is an **odd function** if, for each x in the domain of f, $-x$ is also in the domain of f and

$$f(-x) = -f(x).$$

The graph of an odd function is symmetric with respect to the origin.

STUDY TIP

The graph of a function can never be symmetric with respect to the x-axis, because the two ordered pairs (x, y) and $(x, -y)$ would then be points on the same vertical line.

EXAMPLE 7 **Graphing the Cubing Function**

Show that the cubing function defined by $g(x) = x^3$ is an odd function, and sketch its graph.

Continued on next page.

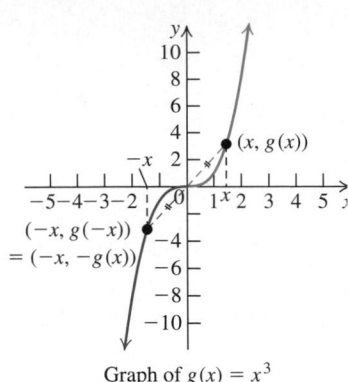

Graph of $g(x) = x^3$

FIGURE 2.47

Solution

The function $g(x) = x^3$ is an odd function because

$$g(-x) = (-x)^3 \qquad \text{Replace } x \text{ by } -x.$$
$$= -x^3 \qquad (-x)^3 = -x^3$$
$$= -g(x). \qquad \text{Replace } x^3 \text{ by } g(x).$$

We sketch the graph of $g(x) = x^3$ by plotting points in the first quadrant and then use symmetry in the origin to extend the graph to the third quadrant. The graph is shown in Figure 2.47.   ■ ■ ■

PRACTICE PROBLEM 7   Show that the function $f(x) = -x^3$ is an odd function, and sketch its graph.   ■

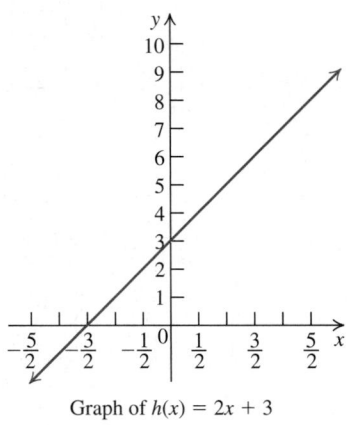

Graph of $h(x) = 2x + 3$

FIGURE 2.48

The function $h(x) = 2x + 3$, whose graph is sketched in Figure 2.48, is neither even nor odd. Notice that the graph is neither symmetric with respect to the y-axis nor symmetric with respect to the origin. To see this algebraically, observe that $h(-x) = 2(-x) + 3 = -2x + 3$, which is not equivalent to either $h(x)$ or $-h(x)$. For example, if $x = 1$, then

$$h(x) = h(1) = 2(1) + 3 = 5 \quad \text{and} \quad -h(x) = -h(1) = -5.$$

However, $h(-x) = h(-1) = 2(-1) + 3 = 1$. Since $1 \neq 5$, $h(-1) \neq h(1)$, so h is not an even function. Also, $h(-1) \neq -h(1)$, so h is not an odd function.

6 Graph some important functions.

Basic Functions

As you progress through this book (and any other mathematics course beyond this one), you will repeatedly come across a relatively small list of basic functions. In the next box, we list some of these common functions of algebra, along with their properties, and include them in a *library of basic functions.* You should try to produce the graphs yourself by plotting points and using symmetries. For all the graphs shown, the unit length is the same on both axes.

Constant Function
$$f(x) = c$$

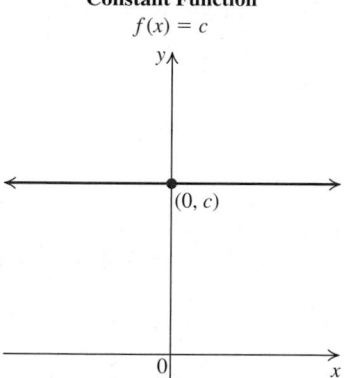

Domain: $(-\infty, \infty)$
Range: $\{c\}$
$f(-3) = c, f(0) = c, f(2) = c$
Constant on $(-\infty, \infty)$
Even function (*y*-axis symmetry)

Identity Function
$$f(x) = x$$

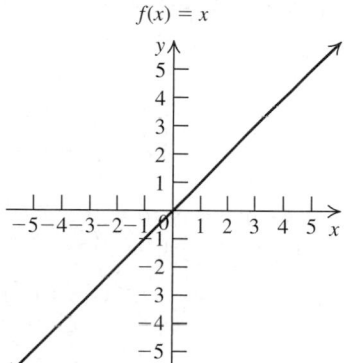

Domain: $(-\infty, \infty)$
Range: $(-\infty, \infty)$
$f(-3) = -3, f(0) = 0, f(2) = 2$
Increasing on $(-\infty, \infty)$
Odd function (origin symmetry)

Squaring Function
$$f(x) = x^2$$

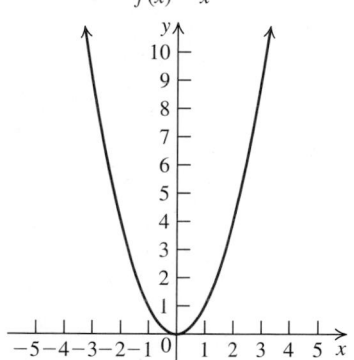

Domain: $(-\infty, \infty)$
Range: $[0, \infty)$
$f(-3) = 9, f(0) = 0, f(2) = 4$
Decreasing on $(-\infty, 0)$
Increasing on $(0, \infty)$
Even function (*y*-axis symmetry)

Cubing Function
$$f(x) = x^3$$

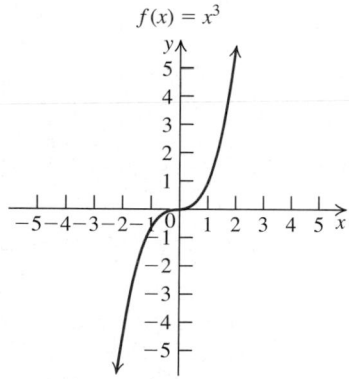

Domain: $(-\infty, \infty)$
Range: $(-\infty, \infty)$
$f(-3) = -27, f(0) = 0, f(2) = 8$
Increasing on $(-\infty, \infty)$
Odd function (origin symmetry)

Absolute Value Function
$$f(x) = |x|$$

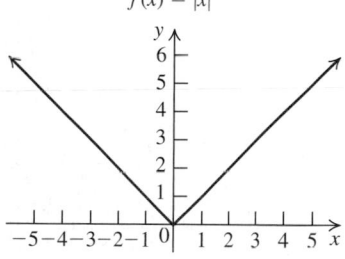

Domain: $(-\infty, \infty)$
Range: $[0, \infty)$
$f(-3) = 3, f(0) = 0, f(2) = 2$
Decreasing on $(-\infty, 0)$
Increasing on $(0, \infty)$
Even function (*y*-axis symmetry)

Square Root Function
$$f(x) = \sqrt{x}$$

Domain: $[0, \infty)$
Range: $[0, \infty)$
$f(-3)$ undefined, $f(0) = 0$,
$f(2) = \sqrt{2}$
Increasing on $(0, \infty)$
Neither even nor odd (no symmetry)

(Continued)

Cube Root Function

$$f(x) = \sqrt[3]{x} = x^{1/3}$$

Domain: $(-\infty, \infty)$
Range: $(-\infty, \infty)$

$f(-3) = -\sqrt[3]{3}$, $f(0) = 0$, $f(2) = \sqrt[3]{2}$

Increasing on $(-\infty, \infty)$
Odd function (origin symmetry)

Reciprocal Function

$$f(x) = \frac{1}{x}$$

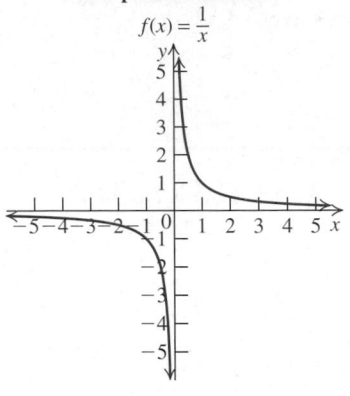

Domain: $(-\infty, 0) \cup (0, \infty)$
Range: $(-\infty, 0) \cup (0, \infty)$

$f(-3) = -\dfrac{1}{3}$, $f(0)$ undefined,

$f(2) = \dfrac{1}{2}$

Decreasing on $(-\infty, 0) \cup (0, \infty)$
Odd function (origin symmetry)

Greatest–Integer Function

$$f(x) = [\![x]\!]$$

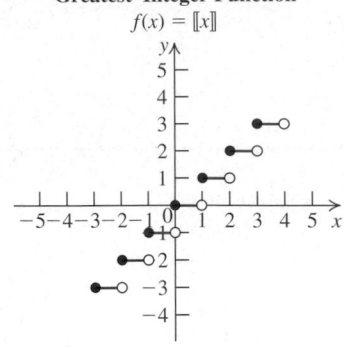

Domain: $(-\infty, \infty)$
Range: $\{... -3, -2, -1, 0, 1, 2, 3, ...\}$

$f(-3) = -3$, $f(0) = 0$, $f(2) = 2$

Neither odd nor even
(no symmetry)

A Exercises   Basic Skills and Concepts

In Exercises 1–10, write a linear function f that has the indicated values. Sketch the graph of f.

1. $f(0) = 1$, $f(-1) = 0$ †
2. $f(1) = 0$, $f(2) = 1$ †
3. $f(-1) = 1$, $f(2) = 7$ †
4. $f(-1) = -5$, $f(2) = 4$ †
5. $f(1) = 1$, $f(2) = -2$ †
6. $f(1) = -1$, $f(3) = 5$ †
7. $f(-2) = 2$, $f(2) = 4$ †
8. $f(2) = 2$, $f(4) = 5$ †
9. $f(0) = -1$, $f(3) = -3$ †
10. $f(1) = \dfrac{1}{4}$, $f(4) = -2$ †

In Exercises 11–18, the graph of a function is given. Use the graph to find each of the following:
a. The domain and the range of the function;
b. The intercepts, if any;
c. The intervals on which the function is increasing, is decreasing, or is constant;
d. Whether the function is even, odd, or neither.

11. †

12. †

13. †

14. †

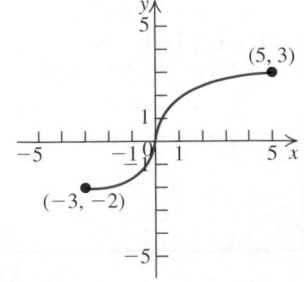

†Due to space constrictions, answers to these exercises may be found in the Answers beginning on page A–1 in the back of the book.

15. †

16. †

17. †

18. †

19. Let

$$f(x) = \begin{cases} x \text{ if } x \geq 2 \\ 2 \text{ if } x < 2 \end{cases}$$

  a. Find $f(1)$, $f(2)$, and $f(3)$. †
  b. Sketch the graph of $y = f(x)$. †

20. Let

$$g(x) = \begin{cases} 2x \text{ if } x < 0 \\ x \text{ if } x \geq 0 \end{cases}$$

  a. Find $g(-1)$, $g(0)$, and $g(1)$. †
  b. Sketch the graph of $y = g(x)$. †

21. Let

$$f(x) = \begin{cases} 1 \text{ if } \quad x > 0 \\ -1 \text{ if } x < 0 \end{cases}$$

  a. Find $f(-15)$ and $f(12)$. †
  b. Sketch the graph of $y = f(x)$. †
  c. Find the domain and the range of f. †

22. Let

$$g(x) = \begin{cases} 2x + 4, \text{ if } \ x > 1 \\ 2x^2 + 2, \text{ if } x \leq 1 \end{cases}$$

  a. Find $g(-3)$, $g(1)$, and $g(3)$. †
  b. Sketch the graph of $y = g(x)$. †
  c. Find the domain and the range of g. †

In Exercises 23–28, find the intervals over which the given function is increasing, is decreasing, or is constant.

23. $f(x) = 2$ †

24. $g(x) = -3$ †

25. $h(x) = 3x + 4$ †

26. $g(x) = -2x + 5$ †

27. $f(x) = 5x^2$ †

28. $h(x) = -x^3$ †

In Exercises 29–42, determine whether the given function is even, odd, or neither. The domain for each of the functions in Exercises 29–32 is $\{-3, -2, -1, 0, 1, 2, 3\}$.

x	-3	-2	-1	0	1	2	3
29. $f(x)$	5	-2	1	0	1	-2	5 †
30. $g(x)$	4	-3	0	2	0	3	-4 †
31. $h(x)$	3	2	1	0	5	2	-3 †
32. $p(x)$	2	3	4	0	-4	-3	-2 †

33. $f(x) = 2x^4 + 4$ even   **34.** $g(x) = 3x^4 - 5$ even

35. $f(x) = 5x^3 - 3x$ odd   **36.** $g(x) = 2x^3 + 4x$ odd

37. $f(x) = \dfrac{1}{x^2 + 4}$ even   **38.** $g(x) = \dfrac{x}{x^2 + 1}$ odd

39. $f(x) = \dfrac{x^3}{x^2 + 1}$ odd   **40.** $g(x) = \dfrac{x^4 + 3}{2x^3 - 3x}$ odd

41. $f(x) = \dfrac{x^2 - 2x}{5x^4 + 4x^2 + 7}$ †   **42.** $g(x) = \dfrac{x^2 + 7}{3x^4 + 16x^2 + 9}$ †

In Exercises 43–50, for each function, find the following:

  a. $f(2x)$ **b.** $2f(x)$

  c. $f(-x)$ **d.** $-f(x)$

  e. $f\left(\dfrac{1}{x}\right)$ **f.** $\dfrac{1}{f(x)}$

43. $f(x) = 3 - 2x$ †   **44.** $f(x) = 5x + 1$ †

45. $f(x) = x^2 - 2x$ †   **46.** $f(x) = x - 4x^2$ †

47. $f(x) = 1 - x^3$ †   **48.** $f(x) = x^3 + x$ †

49. $f(x) = \dfrac{1}{x}$ †   **50.** $f(x) = \dfrac{1}{|x|}$ †

B Exercises   Applying the Concepts

51. Converting volume. To convert the volume of a liquid measured in ounces to a volume measured in liters, we use the fact that 1 liter ≈ 33.81 ounces. Let x denote the volume measured in ounces and y denote the volume measured in liters.
   a. Write an equation for the linear function $y = f(x)$. What are the domain and range of f? †
   b. Compute $f(3)$. What does it mean? †
   c. How many liters of liquid are there in a typical soda can containing 12 ounces of liquid?   0.3549

52. Boiling point and elevation. The boiling point B of water (in degrees Fahrenheit) at elevation h (in thousands of feet) above sea level is given by the linear function $B(h) = -1.8h + 212$.
   a. Find and interpret the intercepts of the function $y = B(h)$. †
   b. Find the domain of this function. †
   c. Find the elevation at which water boils at 98.6°F. Why is this height dangerous to humans? †

53. Pressure at sea depth. The pressure P in atmospheres (atm) at a depth d feet is given by the linear function
$$P(d) = \frac{1}{33}d + 1.$$
   a. Find and interpret the intercepts of $y = P(d)$. †
   b. Find $P(0)$, $P(10)$, $P(33)$, and $P(100)$. †
   c. Find the depth at which the pressure is 5 atmospheres. †

54. Speed of sound. The speed V of sound (in feet per second) in air at temperature T (in degrees Fahrenheit) is given by the linear function $V(T) = 1055 + 1.1T$.
   a. Find the speed of sound at 90°F.   1154 ft/s
   b. Find the temperature at which the speed of sound is 1100 feet per second.   40.91°F

55. Manufacturer's cost. A manufacturer of printers has a total cost per day consisting of a fixed overhead of 6000 dollars plus product costs of 50 dollars per printer.
   a. Express the total cost C as a function of the number x of printers produced. $C = 50x + 6000$
   b. Draw the graph of $y = C(x)$. Interpret the y-intercept. †
   c. How many printers were manufactured on a day when the total cost was 11,500 dollars?   110

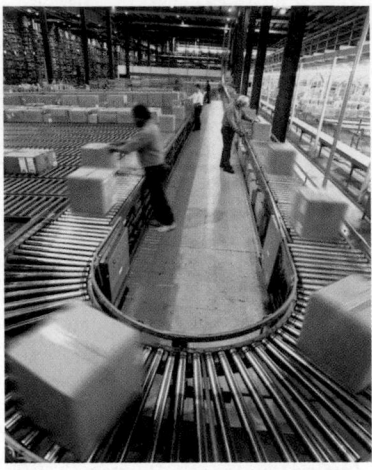

56. Supply function. When the price p of a commodity is 10 dollars per unit, 750 units of it are sold. For every 1 dollar increase in the unit price, the supply q increases by 100 units.
   a. Write the linear function $q = f(p)$. $f(p) = 100p - 250$
   b. Find the supply when the price is 15 dollars per unit.   1250
   c. What is the price at which 1750 units can be supplied? $20

57. Apartment rental. Suppose that a two-bedroom apartment in a neighborhood near your school rents for 900 dollars per month. If you move in after the first of the month, the rent is prorated; that is, it is reduced linearly.
   a. Suppose you move into the apartment x days after the first of the month. (Assume that the month has 30 days.) Express the rent R as a function of x. $R = 900 - 30x$
   b. Compute the rent if you move in 6 days after the first of the month. $720
   c. When did you move into the apartment if the landlord charged you a rent of 600 dollars? †

58. College admissions. The average SAT scores (mathematics and critical reading) for incoming students at Central State College (CSC) have been rising linearly over recent years. In 2002, the average SAT score was 1120; in 2004, it was 1150. (The SAT testing format changed considerably in 2005.)

  a. Express the average SAT score at CSC as a function of time. †
  b. If the trend continues, what will be the average SAT score of incoming students at CSC in 2010? 1240
  c. If the trend continues, when will the average SAT score at CSC be 1300? In 2014

59. Breathing capacity. Suppose the average maximum breathing capacity for humans drops linearly from 100% at age 20 to 40% at age 80. What age corresponds to 50% capacity? 70

60. Drug dosage for children. If a is the adult dosage of a medicine and t is the child's age, then the *Friend's rule* for the child's dosage y is given by the formula $y = \dfrac{2}{25}ta$.

  a. Suppose the adult dosage is 60 milligrams. Find the dosage for a five-year-old child. 24 mg
  b. How old would a child have to be in order to be prescribed an adult dosage? 12.5 yr

61. Air pollution. In Ballerenia, the average number y of deaths per month was observed to be linearly related to the concentration x of sulfur dioxide in the air. Suppose there are 30 deaths when $x = 150$ milligrams per cubic meter and 50 deaths when $x = 420$ milligrams per cubic meter.

  a. Write y as a function of x. †
  b. Find the number of deaths when $x = 350$ milligrams per cubic meter. †
  c. If the number of deaths per month is 45, what is the concentration of sulfur dioxide in the air? 352.5 mg/m³

62. Child shoe sizes. Children's shoe sizes start with size 0, having an insole length L of $3\frac{11}{12}$ inches, and each full size being $\frac{1}{3}$ inch longer.

  a. Write the equation $y = L(S)$, where S is the shoe size. †
  b. Find the length of the insole of a child's shoe of size 4. †
  c. What size (to the nearest half-size) of shoe will fit a child whose insole length is 6.1 inches? 7

63. State income tax. Suppose a state's income tax code states that the tax liability T on x dollars of taxable income is

$$T(x) = \begin{cases} 0.04x & \text{if } 0 \le x < 20,000 \\ 800 + 0.06x & \text{if } x \ge 20,000 \end{cases}.$$

  a. Graph the function $y = T(x)$. †
  b. Find the tax liability on each taxable income. †
    i.   12,000 dollars †
    ii. 20,000 dollars †
    iii. 50,000 dollars †
  c. Find your taxable income if you had each tax liability. †
    i.   600 dollars †
    ii. 1200 dollars †
    iii. 2300 dollars †

64. Federal income tax. The tax table for the 2004 U.S. Income Tax for a single taxpayer is as follows:

If taxable income is over	But not over	The tax is
$0	$7,300	10% of the amount over $0.
$7,300	$29,700	$730 plus 15% of the amount over $7,300.
$29,700	$71,950	$4,090, plus 25% of the amount over $29,700.
$71,950	$150,150	$14,652.50, plus 28% of the amount over $71,950.
$150,150	$326,450	$36,548.50, plus 33% of the amount over $150,150.
$326,450	No limit	$94,727.50, plus 35% of the amount over $326,450.

(*Source:* Internal Revenue Service.)

  a. Express the information given in the table as a six-part piecewise function f, using x as a variable representing taxable income. Then graph the function.
  b. Find the tax liability on each taxable income.
    i.   35,000 dollars †
    ii. 100,000 dollars †
    iii. 500,000 dollars †
  c. Find your taxable income if you had each tax liability †
    i.   3500 dollars †
    ii. 12,700 dollars †
    iii. 35,000 dollars †

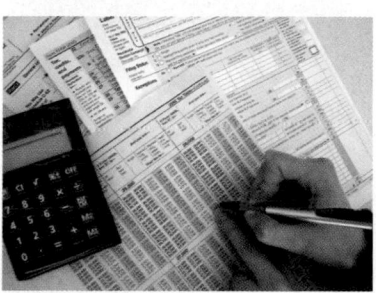

C Exercises   Beyond the Basics

65. Let

$$f(x) = \begin{cases} 3x + 5, & -3 \le x < -1 \\ 2x + 1, & -1 \le x < 2 \\ 2 - x, & 2 \le x \le 4 \end{cases}.$$

a. Find
  i. $f(-2)$, †
  ii. $f(-1)$, and †
  iii. $f(3)$. †
b. Find x when $f(x) = 2$. †
c. Sketch a graph of $y = f(x)$. †

66. Let

$$g(x) = \begin{cases} 3, & -3 \le x < -1 \\ -6x - 3, & -1 \le x < 0 \\ 3x - 3, & 0 \le x \le 1 \end{cases}.$$

a. Find
  i. $g(-2)$, †
  ii. $g\left(\dfrac{1}{2}\right)$, †
  iii. $g(0)$, and **iv** $g(-1)$. †
b. Find x when **i.** $g(x) = 0$ and **ii.** $2g(x) + 3 = 0$. †
c. Sketch a graph of $y = g(x)$. †

In Exercises 67 and 68, a function is given. For each function,
a. Find the domain and range.
b. Find the intervals over which the function is increasing, decreasing, or constant.
c. State whether the function is odd, even, or neither.

67. $f(x) = x - [\![x]\!]$ †   **68.** $f(x) = \dfrac{1}{[\![x]\!]}$ †

69. Let $f(x) = \dfrac{|x|}{x}, x \ne 0$. Find $|f(x) - f(-x)|$. 2

70. The Windchill Index (WCI). Suppose the outside air temperature is T degrees Fahrenheit and the wind speed is v miles per hour. A formula for the WCI based on observations is

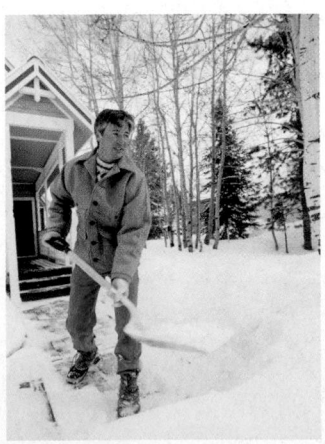

$$WCI = \begin{cases} T, & 0 \le v \le 4 \\ 91.4 + (91.4 - T)(0.0203v - 0.304\sqrt{v} - 0.474), & 4 < v < 45. \\ 1.6T - 55, & v \ge 45 \end{cases}$$

a. Find the WCI to the nearest degree if the outside air temperature is 40°F and
  i. $v = 2$ miles per hour. 40
  ii. $v = 16$ miles per hour. 21.23
  iii. $v = 50$ miles per hour. 9
b. Find the air temperature to the nearest degree if
  i.   the WCI is -58°F and $v = 36$ miles per hour.
  ii. the WCI is -10°F and $v = 49$ miles per hour.

Critical Thinking

71. Postage-rate function. The U.S. Postal Service uses the function $f(x) = -[\![-x]\!]$, called the **ceiling integer function,** to determine postal charges. For instance, if you have an envelope that weighs 3.2 ounces, you will be charged the rate for $f(3.2) = -[\![-3.2]\!] = -(-4) = 4$ ounces. In 2006, it cost 39 cents for the first ounce (or a fraction of it) and 24 cents for each additional ounce (or a fraction of it) to mail a first-class letter in the United States.
a. Express the cost C (in cents) of mailing a letter weighing x ounces. †
b. Graph the function $y = C(x)$. †
c. What are the domain and range of $y = C(x)$? †

72. The cost C of parking a car at the metropolitan airport is 4 dollars for the first hour and 2 dollars for each additional hour or fraction thereof. Write the cost function $C(x)$, where x is the number of parking hours, in terms of the greatest-integer function. $C(x) = 2[\![x]\!] + 4$

73. Car rentals. The weekly cost of renting a compact car from U-Rent is 150 dollars. There is no charge for driving the first 100 miles, but there is a 20-cent charge for each mile (or fraction thereof) driven over 100 miles.
a. Express the cost C of renting a car for a week and driving it for x miles. †
b. Sketch the graph of $y = C(x)$. †
c. How many miles were driven if the weekly rental cost was 190 dollars? 300

Answers:
70. b. (i) -4°F   **(ii)** 28°F
71. a. $C(x) = 24(f(x) - 1) + 39$
   c. Domain: $(0, \infty)$. Range: $\{24n + 39: n$ a nonnegative integer$\}$

Transformations of Functions

BEFORE STARTING THIS SECTION, REVIEW

1. Graphs of basic functions (Section 2.5, page 256)

2. Symmetry (Section 2.2, page 194)

3. Completing the square (Section 1.4, page 125)

OBJECTIVES

1 Learn the meaning of transformations.

2 Use vertical or horizontal shifts to graph functions.

3 Use reflections to graph functions.

4 Use stretching or compressing to graph functions.

Measuring Blood Pressure

Blood pressure is the force of blood per unit area against the walls of the arteries. Blood pressure is recorded as two numbers: the systolic pressure (as the heart beats) and the diastolic pressure (as the heart relaxes between beats). When your doctor tells you that you have a blood pressure of "120 over 80," it means that your blood pressure is rising to a maximum of 120 millimeters of mercury as the heart beats and falling to a minimum of 80 millimeters of mercury as the heart relaxes.

The most precise way to measure blood pressure is to place a small glass tube into an artery and let the blood flow out and up as high as the heart can pump it. That was the way Stephen Hales (1677–1761), the first investigator of blood pressure, learned that a horse's heart could pump blood 8 feet, 3 inches, up a tall tube. Such a test, however, consumed a lot of blood. Jean Louis Marie Poiseuille (1797–1869), greatly improved the process by using a mercury-filled manometer, which allowed a smaller, narrower tube. Even so, a blood pressure check in the 1840s was a very different experience than what we routinely undergo today.

In Example 9, we investigate Poiscuille's Law for the arterial blood flow. ■

1 Learn the meaning of transformations.

Transformations

If a new function is formed by performing certain operations on a given function f, then the graph of the new function is called a **transformation** of the graph of f. For example, the graphs of $y = |x| + 2$ and $y = |x| - 3$ are transformations of the graph of $y = |x|$; that is, the graph of each is a special modification of the graph of $y = |x|$.

2 Use vertical or horizontal shifts to graph functions.

Vertical and Horizontal Shifts

EXAMPLE 1 **Graphing Vertical Shifts**

Let $f(x) = |x|$, $g(x) = |x| + 2$, and $h(x) = |x| - 3$.

a. Sketch the graphs of the functions f and g on the same coordinate plane. Describe how the graph of g relates to the graph of f.

b. Sketch the graphs of the functions f and h on the same coordinate plane. Describe how the graph of h relates to the graph of f.

Solution

a. Make a table of values, and graph the equations $y = f(x)$ and $y = g(x)$.

TABLE 2.8

x	$y = |x|$	$y = |x| + 2$
-5	5	7
-3	3	5
-1	1	3
0	0	2
1	1	3
3	3	5
5	5	7

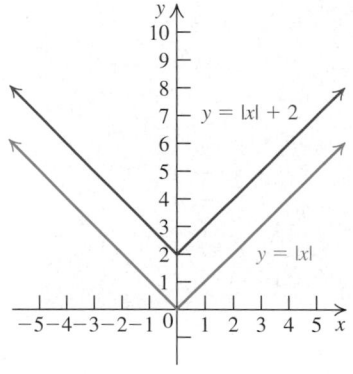

FIGURE 2.49

From Table 2.8 and Figure 2.49, we note that, for each value of x, the value of $y = |x| + 2$ in the third column is 2 more than the value of $y = |x|$ in the second column. Thus, the graph of $y = |x| + 2$ is the graph of $y = |x|$ shifted two units up.

b. Make a table of values, and graph the equations $y = f(x)$ and $y = h(x)$.

TABLE 2.9

x	$y = |x|$	$y = |x| - 3$
-5	5	2
-3	3	0
-1	1	-2
0	0	-3
1	1	-2
3	3	0
5	5	2

FIGURE 2.50

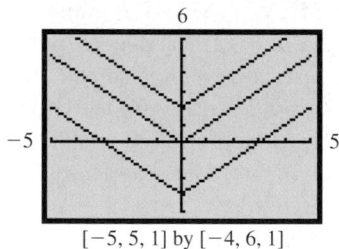

From Table 2.9 and Figure 2.50, we note that, for each value of x, the value of $y = |x| - 3$ in the third column is 3 less than the value of $y = |x|$ in the second column. Thus, the graph of $y = |x| - 3$ is the graph of $y = |x|$ shifted three units down.

■ ■ ■

PRACTICE PROBLEM 1   Let

$$f(x) = x^3, g(x) = x^3 + 1, \text{ and } h(x) = x^3 - 2.$$

Sketch the graphs of all three functions on the same coordinate plane. Describe how the graphs of g and h relate to the graph of f.   ■

Example 1 illustrates the concept of the vertical (up or down) shift of a graph.

VERTICAL SHIFT

Let $c > 0$. The graph of $y = f(x) + c$ is the graph of $y = f(x)$ shifted c units *up*, and the graph of $y = f(x) - c$ is the graph of $y = f(x)$ shifted c units *down*.

EXAMPLE 2   **Writing Functions for Vertical Shifts**

Write a function corresponding to each vertical shift.

a. Shift the graph of $f(x) = (x - 1)^2$, four units down. Express the resulting function in the form $g(x) = ax^2 + bx + c$.

b. Shift the graph of $F(x) = -3x^2 + 1$ three units up. Express the resulting function in the form $G(x) = ax^2 + bx + c$.

Solution

a. When the graph of $y = f(x)$ is shifted four units down, we obtain the graph of $y = f(x) - 4$. Thus, we have the graph of the function

$$
\begin{array}{ll}
g(x) = f(x) - 4 & \text{Subtract 4 from } f(x), \text{ because the shift is down.} \\
g(x) = (x - 1)^2 - 4 & \text{Replace } f(x) \text{ by } (x - 1)^2. \\
\quad = (x^2 - 2x + 1) - 4 & \text{Expand } (x - 1)^2. \\
\quad = x^2 - 2x - 3. & \text{Simplify.}
\end{array}
$$

Thus, $g(x) = ax^2 + bx + c$ where $a = 1, b = -2$, and $c = -3$.

b. When the graph of $y = F(x)$ is shifted three units up, we obtain the graph of $y = F(x) + 3$. Thus, we have the graph of the function

$$
\begin{array}{ll}
G(x) = F(x) + 3 & \text{Add 3 to } F(x), \text{ because the shift is up.} \\
G(x) = (-3x^2 + 1) + 3 & \text{Replace } F(x) \text{ by } -3x^2 + 1. \\
\quad = -3x^2 + 4. & \text{Simplify.}
\end{array}
$$

Thus, $G(x) = ax^2 + bx + c$, where $a = -3, b = 0$, and $c = 4$.   ■ ■ ■

PRACTICE PROBLEM 2   Write a function corresponding to the vertical shift of the graph of $f(x) = (x + 1)^2$ two units down.   ■

We next consider the operation that shifts a graph horizontally.

EXAMPLE 3 **Writing Functions for Horizontal Shifts**

Let $f(x) = x^2$, $g(x) = (x - 2)^2$, and $h(x) = (x + 3)^2$. A table of values for f, g, and h is given in Table 2.10. The graphs of the three functions f, g, and h are shown on the same coordinate plane in Figure 2.51. Describe how the graphs of g and h relate to the graph of f.

TABLE 2.10

x	$y = x^2$	$y = (x - 2)^2$	x	$y = x^2$	$y = (x + 3)^2$
-4	16	36	-4	16	1
-3	9	25	-3	9	0
-2	4	16	-2	4	1
-1	1	9	-1	1	4
0	0	4	0	0	9
1	1	1	1	1	16
2	4	0	2	4	25
3	9	1	3	9	36
4	16	4	4	16	49

(a)   (b)

TECHNOLOGY CONNECTION

The graphs of $y = x^2$, $y = (x + 3)^2$, and $y = (x - 2)^2$ illustrate that these graphs are identical in shape. They differ only in horizontal placement.

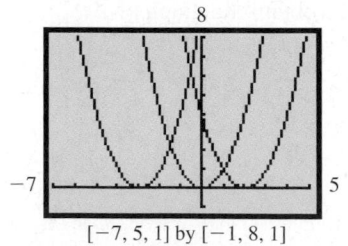

[−7, 5, 1] by [−1, 8, 1]

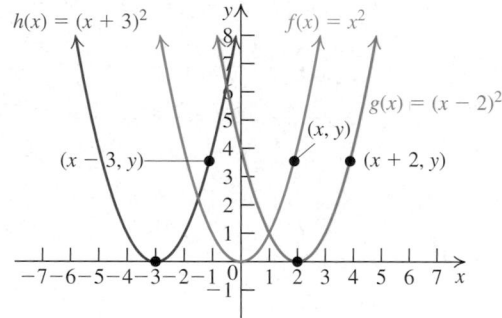

FIGURE 2.51

Solution

The first thing to notice is that all three functions are squaring functions.

a. Note that the right-hand side of the defining equation for g can be obtained by replacing x with $x - 2$ on the right side of the defining equation for f.

$$f(x) = \quad x^2 \qquad \text{Defining equation for } f$$
$$\downarrow$$
$$g(x) = (x - 2)^2. \qquad \text{Replace } x \text{ by } x - 2 \text{ to obtain the defining equation for } g.$$

The x-intercept of f is 0. The x-intercept of g is obtained by solving $g(x) = (x - 2)^2 = 0$ for x. We get $x - 2 = 0$ and obtain $x = 2$.

This means that $(2, 0)$ is a point on the graph of g, whereas $(0, 0)$ is a point on the graph of f. In general, for each point (x, y) on the graph of f, there will be a corresponding point $(x + 2, y)$ on the graph of g. Thus, the graph of $g(x) = (x - 2)^2$ is just the graph of $f(x) = x^2$ shifted two units to the *right*. Noticing that $f(0) = 0$ and $g(2) = 0$ will help you to remember which way to shift the graph. Table 2.10(a) and Figure 2.51 confirm these considerations.

b. The right-hand side of the defining equation for h can be obtained by replacing x by $x + 3$ on the right-hand side of the defining equation for f.

$$f(x) = \quad x^2 \qquad \text{Defining equation for } f$$
$$\downarrow$$
$$h(x) = (x + 3)^2. \qquad \text{Replace } x \text{ by } x + 3 \text{ to obtain the defining equation for } h.$$

As in part (**a**), the x-intercept of f is 0.

To find the x-intercept of h, we solve $h(x) = (x + 3)^2 = 0$. We get $x + 3 = 0$ and find that the x-intercept of h is -3. This means that $(-3, 0)$ is a point on the graph of h, whereas $(0, 0)$ is a point on the graph of f. In general, for each point (x, y) on the graph of f, there will be a corresponding point $(x - 3, y)$ on the graph of h. Thus, the graph of $h(x) = (x + 3)^2$ is just the graph of $f(x) = x^2$ shifted three units to the *left*. Noticing that $f(0) = 0$ and $h(-3) = 0$ will help you to remember which way to shift the graph.

Table 2.10(b) and Figure 2.51 confirm these considerations.   ■ ■ ■

PRACTICE PROBLEM 3   Let

$$f(x) = x^3, g(x) = (x - 1)^3, \text{ and } h(x) = (x + 2)^3.$$

Sketch the graphs of all three functions on the same coordinate plane. Describe how the graphs of g and h relate to the graph of f.   ■

HORIZONTAL SHIFTS

Let $c > 0$. The graph of $y = f(x - c)$ is the graph of $y = f(x)$ shifted c units to the right. The graph of $y = f(x + c)$ is the graph of $y = f(x)$ shifted c units to the left.

A consequence of the description of horizontal shifts is that if we are given the graph of $y = f(x)$, then an equation for the function whose graph is the graph of f shifted c units to the right $(c > 0)$ is obtained by replacing x by $x - c$ in the equation $y = f(x)$. Similarly, an equation for the function whose graph is the graph of f shifted c units to the left $(c > 0)$ is obtained by replacing x by $x + c$ in the equation $y = f(x)$.

EXAMPLE 4   **Combining Vertical and Horizontal Shifts**

Sketch the graph of the function $f(x) = \sqrt{x+2} - 3$.

Solution

We begin with the graph of $y = \sqrt{x}$.

Step 1

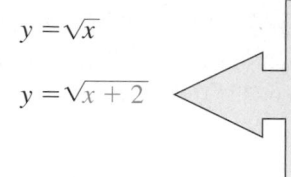

Replace x by $x + 2$ in the equation $y = \sqrt{x}$. This shifts the graph of $y = \sqrt{x}$ left 2 units. (See Figure 2.52.)

Step 2

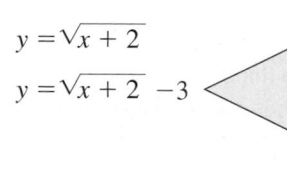

Subtract 3 from the right-hand side of the equation $y = \sqrt{x+2}$. This shifts the graph of $y = \sqrt{x+2}$ down 3 units. (See Figure 2.52.)

FIGURE 2.52

■ ■ ■

PRACTICE PROBLEM 4   Sketch the graph of

$$f(x) = \sqrt{x-2} + 3.$$

■

3 Use reflections to graph functions.

Reflections

Comparing the Graphs of $y = f(x)$ and $y = -f(x)$ Let us now see how the graph of $g(x) = -f(x)$ is related to the graph of $f(x)$. Consider the graph of $f(x) = x^2$, shown in Figure 2.53. Table 2.11 gives some values for $f(x)$ and $g(x) = -f(x)$. We note that the y-coordinate of each point in the graph of $g(x) = -f(x)$ is the negative of the y-coordinate of the corresponding point on the graph of $f(x)$. Thus, the graph of $y = -x^2$ is the reflection of the graph of $y = x^2$ in the x-axis. This means that the points (x, x^2) and $(x, -x^2)$ are the same distance from, but on opposite sides of, the x-axis. (See Figure 2.53.)

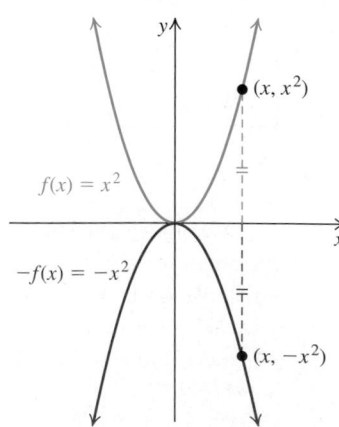

FIGURE 2.53

TABLE 2.11

x	$f(x) = x^2$	$g(x) = -f(x) = -x^2$
-3	9	-9
-2	4	-4
-1	1	-1
0	0	0
1	1	-1
2	4	-4
3	9	-9

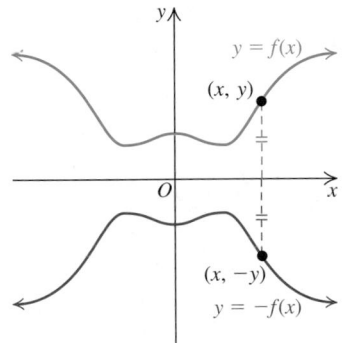

FIGURE 2.54

REFLECTION IN THE x-AXIS

The graph of $y = -f(x)$ is a reflection of the graph of $y = f(x)$ in the x-axis. If a point (x, y) is on the graph of $y = f(x)$, then the point $(x, -y)$ is on the graph of $y = -f(x)$. (See Figure 2.54.)

Comparing the Graphs of $y = f(x)$ and $y = f(-x)$ To compare the graphs of $f(x)$ and $g(x) = f(-x)$, consider the graph of $f(x) = \sqrt{x}$. Then $f(-x) = \sqrt{-x}$. (See Figure 2.55.) Table 2.12 gives some values for $f(x)$ and $g(x) = f(-x)$. The domain of f is $[0, \infty)$ and the domain of g is $(-\infty, 0]$. For each point (x, y) on the graph of f, the corresponding point $(-x, y)$ is on the graph of g. Thus, the graph of $g(x) = f(-x)$ is the reflection of the graph of $y = f(x)$ in the y-axis. This means that the points $(x, \sqrt{x})$ and $(-x, \sqrt{x})$ are the same distance from, but on opposite sides of, the y-axis. (See Figure 2.55.)

TABLE 2.12

x	$f(x) = \sqrt{x}$	$-x$	$g(x) = \sqrt{-x}$
-4	Undefined	4	2
-1	Undefined	1	1
0	0	0	0
1	1	-1	Undefined
4	2	-4	Undefined

FIGURE 2.55

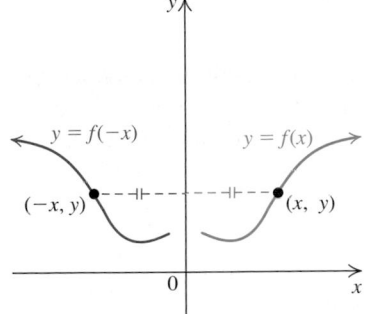

FIGURE 2.56

REFLECTION IN THE y-AXIS

The graph of $y = f(-x)$ is a reflection of the graph of $y = f(x)$ in the y-axis. If a point (x, y) is on the graph of $y = f(x)$, then the point $(-x, y)$ is on the graph of $y = f(-x)$. (See Figure 2.56.)

EXAMPLE 5   **Combining Transformations**

Explain how the graph of $y = -|x - 2| + 3$ can be obtained from the graph of $y = |x|$.

Solution

Start with the graph of $y = |x|$. (See Figure 2.57(a).)

Step 1   Shift the graph of $y = |x|$ two units to the right to obtain the graph of
$y = |x - 2|$. (See Figure 2.57(b).)

(a)

FIGURE 2.57

(b)

(c)

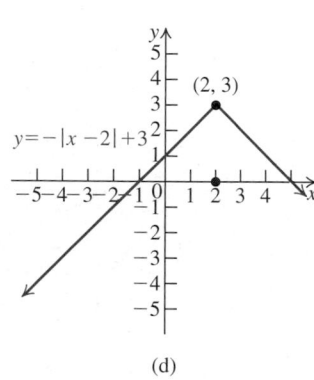

(d)

Step 2   Reflect the graph of $y = |x - 2|$ in the x-axis to obtain the graph of
$y = -|x - 2|$. (See Figure 2.57(c).)

Step 3   Finally, shift the graph of $y = -|x - 2|$, three units up to obtain the graph of
$y = -|x - 2| + 3$. (See Figure 2.57(d).)   ■ ■ ■

PRACTICE PROBLEM 5   Explain how the graph of $y = -(x - 1)^2 + 2$ can be obtained from
the graph of $y = x^2$.   ■

4 Use stretching or
compressing to graph
functions.

Stretching or Compressing

The transformations that result in (vertical or horizontal) shifts or in reflections (in the
y-axis or x-axis) change only the position of the graph in the xy-plane, while the basic
shape of the graph remains unchanged. Such transformations are called **rigid transformations.** We now look at those transformations which distort the shape of a graph. Such
transformations are called **nonrigid transformations.** We consider the relationship of the
graphs of $y = af(x)$ and $y = f(bx)$ to the graph of $y = f(x)$.

Comparing the Graphs of $y = f(x)$ and $y = af(x)$

EXAMPLE 6   **Stretching and Compressing a Function Vertically**

Let $f(x) = |x|$, $g(x) = 2|x|$, and $h(x) = \frac{1}{2}|x|$. Sketch the graphs of f, g, and h on the same
coordinate plane, and describe how the graphs of g and h are related to the graph of f.

Solution

The graphs of $y = |x|$, $y = 2|x|$, and $y = \frac{1}{2}|x|$ are sketched in Figure 2.58. Table 2.13 gives some typical function values.

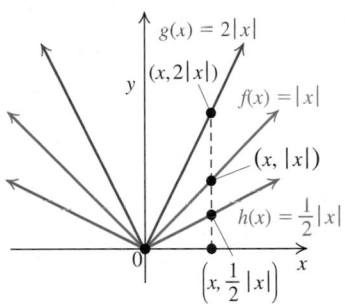

FIGURE 2.58

TABLE 2.13

x	$f(x)$	$g(x)$	$h(x)$
-2	2	4	1
-1	1	2	$\frac{1}{2}$
0	0	0	0
1	1	2	$\frac{1}{2}$
2	2	4	1

The graph of $y = 2|x|$ is the graph of $y = |x|$ vertically stretched (expanded) by multiplying each of its y-coordinates by 2. It is twice as high as the graph of $|x|$ at every real number x. The result is a taller "V"-shaped curve. The graph of $y = 2|x|$ is obtained by multiplying the y-*coordinate* of each point on the graph of $y = |x|$ by 2. (See Figure 2.58.)

The graph $y = \frac{1}{2}|x|$ is the graph of $y = |x|$ vertically compressed (shrunk) by multiplying each of its y-coordinates by $\frac{1}{2}$. It is half as high as the graph of $|x|$ at every real number x. The result is a flatter "V"-shaped curve. Thus, the graph of $y = \frac{1}{2}|x|$ is obtained by multiplying the y-*coordinate* of each point on the graph of $y = |x|$ by $\frac{1}{2}$. (See Figure 2.58.) ■ ■ ■

PRACTICE PROBLEM 6   Let $f(x) = \sqrt{x}$ and $g(x) = 2\sqrt{x}$. Sketch the graphs of f and g on the same coordinate plane, and describe how the graph of g is related to the graph of f. ■

VERTICAL STRETCHING OR COMPRESSING

The graph of $y = af(x)$ is obtained from the graph of $y = f(x)$ by multiplying the y-coordinate of each point on the graph of $y = f(x)$ by a and leaving the x-coordinate unchanged. The result is

1. A **vertical stretch** away from the x-axis if $a > 1$;

2. A **vertical compression** toward the x-axis if $0 < a < 1$.

If $a < 0$, the graph of f is first reflected in the x-axis and then vertically stretched or compressed.

Comparing the Graphs of $y = f(x)$ and $y = f(bx)$ For a given function $f(x)$, we now explore the effect of the constant b in graphing the function $y = f(bx)$. Consider the graphs of $y = f(x)$ and $y = f(2x)$ in Figure 2.59(a). Multiplying the *independent* variable x by 2 compresses the graph $y = f(x)$ horizontally toward the y-axis. The reason is that the value $2x$ is twice the value of x, so that a point on the x-axis will be only half as far from the origin for $y = f(2x)$ to have the same y value as $y = f(x)$.

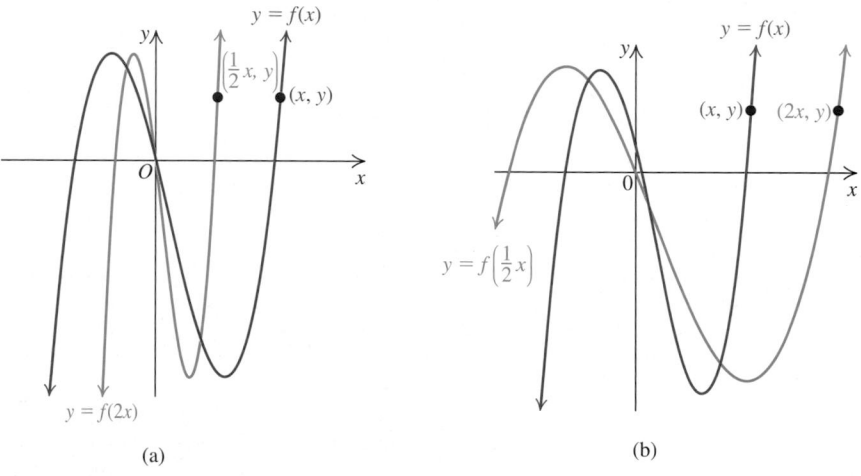

(a)   (b)

FIGURE 2.59

Now consider the graphs of $y = f(x)$ and $y = f\left(\dfrac{1}{2}x\right)$ in Figure 2.59(b). Multiplying the *independent* variable x by $\dfrac{1}{2}$ stretches the graph of $y = f(x)$ horizontally away from the y-axis. The value $\dfrac{1}{2}x$ is half the value of x, so that a point on the x-axis will be twice as far from the origin for $y = f\left(\dfrac{1}{2}x\right)$ to have the same y value as $y = f(x)$. We summarize these observations next.

HORIZONTAL STRETCHING OR COMPRESSING

The graph of $y = f(bx)$ is obtained from the graph of $y = f(x)$ by multiplying the x-coordinate of each point on the graph of $y = f(x)$ by $\dfrac{1}{b}$ and leaving the y-coordinate unchanged. The result is

1. A **horizontal stretch** away from the y-axis if $0 < b < 1$;
2. A **horizontal compression** toward the y-axis if $b > 1$.

If $b < 0$, first obtain the graph of $f(|b|x)$ by stretching or compressing the graph of $y = f(x)$ horizontally. Then reflect the graph of $y = f(|b|x)$ in the y-axis.

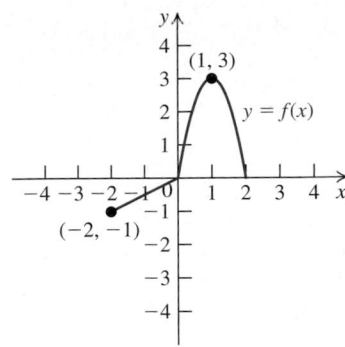

FIGURE 2.60

EXAMPLE 7   Stretching or Compressing a Function Horizontally

The graph of a function $y = f(x)$ is given in Figure 2.60. No formula for f is given. Sketch the graph of each of the related functions.

a. $f\left(\dfrac{1}{2}x\right)$ **b.** $f(2x)$ **c.** $f(-2x)$.

Solution

a. Figure 2.60 shows the graph of $y = f(x)$. To obtain the graph of $y = f\left(\dfrac{1}{2}x\right)$, we stretch the graph of $y = f(x)$ horizontally by a factor of 2. Thus, each graph point (x, y) in Figure 2.60 is transformed to the point $(2x, y)$ in Figure 2.61(a).

b. To obtain the graph of $y = f(2x)$, we compress the graph of $y = f(x)$ horizontally by a factor of $\dfrac{1}{2}$. Thus, each graph point (x, y) in Figure 2.60 is transformed to $\left(\dfrac{1}{2}x, y\right)$ in Figure 2.61(b).

(a)

(b)

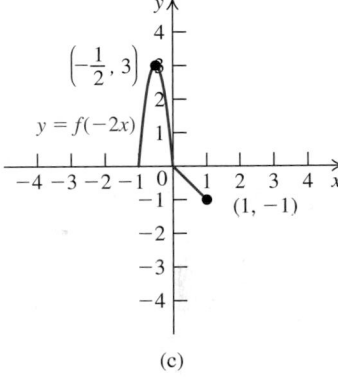

(c)

FIGURE 2.61

c. The graph of $y = f(-2x)$ is the reflection of the graph of $y = f(2x)$ in the y-axis. Thus, we reflect the graph in Figure 2.61(b) in the y-axis to obtain the graph of $y = f(-2x)$. Thus, each graph point (x, y) in Figure 2.61(b) is transformed to the point $(-x, y)$ in Figure 2.61(c). ■ ■ ■

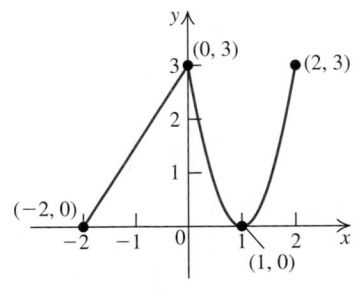

PRACTICE PROBLEM 8   The graph of a function $y = f(x)$ is given in the margin. Sketch the graphs of the following.

a. $f\left(\dfrac{1}{2}x\right)$ **b.** $f(2x)$ ■

Multiple Transformations

When graphing requires more than one transformation of a basic function, it is helpful to consider one transformation at a time.

EXAMPLE 8   **Combining Transformations**

Sketch the graph of the function $f(x) = 3 - 2(x - 1)^2$.

Solution

Begin with the basic function $y = x^2$. Then apply the necessary transformations in a sequence of steps. The result of each step is shown in Figure 2.62.

Step 1	$y = x^2$	Identify a related function whose graph is familiar. In this case, use $y = x^2$. (See Figure 2.62(a).)
Step 2	$y = (x - 1)^2$	Replace x by $x - 1$; shift the graph of $y = x^2$ one unit to the right. (See Figure 2.62(b).)
Step 3	$y = 2(x - 1)^2$	Multiply by 2. Stretch the graph of $y = (x - 1)^2$ vertically by a factor of 2. (See Figure 2.62(c).)
Step 4	$y = -2(x - 1)^2$	Multiply by -1. Reflect the graph of $y = 2(x - 1)^2$ in the x-axis. (See Figure 2.62(d).)
Step 5	$y = 3 - 2(x - 1)^2$	Add 3. Shift the graph of $y = -2(x - 1)^2$ three units up. (See Figure 2.62(e).)

(a)

(b)

(c)

(d)

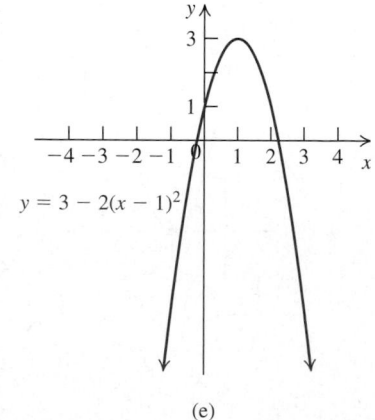

(e)

FIGURE 2.62

■ ■ ■

PRACTICE PROBLEM 8 Sketch the graph of the function

$$f(x) = 3\sqrt{x + 1} - 2.$$ ■

EXAMPLE 9   Using Poiseuille's Law for Arterial Blood Flow

For an artery with radius R, the velocity v of the blood flow at a distance r from the center of the artery is given by

$$v = c(R^2 - r^2),$$

where c is a constant that is determined for a particular artery. (See Figure 2.63.)

To emphasize that the velocity v depends on the distance r from the center of the artery, we write $v = v(r)$, or $v(r) = c(R^2 - r^2)$. Starting with the graph of $y = r^2$, sketch the graph of $y = v(r)$, given that the artery has radius $R = 3$ and $c = 10^4$.

Solution

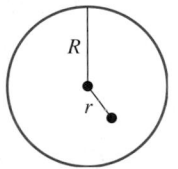

FIGURE 2.63

$v(r) = c(R^2 - r^2)$	Original equation
$v(r) = 10^4(9 - r^2)$	Substitute $c = 10^4$ and $R = 3$.
$v(r) = 9 \cdot 10^4 - 10^4 r^2$	Distributive property

(a)

(b)

(c)

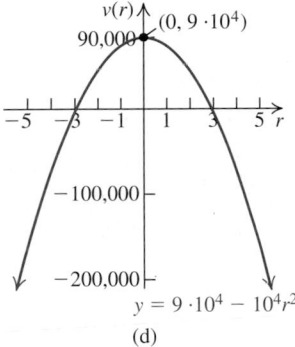

(d)

FIGURE 2.64

We sketch the graph of $y = v(r)$ in Figure 2.64(d) through a sequence of transformations.

Figure 2.64(b) is obtained by stretching the graph of $y = r^2$ (shown in Figure 2.64(a)) vertically by a factor of 10^4.

Figure 2.64(c) is obtained by reflecting the graph of $y = 10^4 \cdot r^2$ (shown in Figure 2.64(b)) in the x-axis.

Figure 2.64(d) is obtained by shifting the graph of $y = -10^4 r^2$ (shown in Figure 2.64(c)) $9 \cdot 10^4$ units up.

The graph in Figure 2.64(d) is the graph of $y = v(r) = 10^4(9 - r^2)$.

The velocity of the blood decreases from the center of the artery ($r = 0$) to the artery wall ($r = 3$), where it ceases to flow. The portions of the graphs in Figure 2.64 corresponding to negative values of r do not have any physical significance, but it is somewhat easier to work with the familiar graph of $y = r^2$.   ■ ■ ■

PRACTICE PROBLEM 9 Suppose in Example 9 that the artery has radius $R = 3$ and that $c = 10^3$. Sketch the graph of $y = v(r)$.   ■

Summary of Transformations of $y = f(x)$

To graph	Draw the graph of f, and	Make these changes to the equation $y = f(x)$	Change the graph point (x, y) to
Vertical shifts for $c > 0$,			
$y = f(x) + c$	Shift the graph of f up c units.	Add c to $f(x)$.	$(x, y + c)$
$y = f(x) - c$	Shift the graph of f down c units.	Subtract c from $f(x)$.	$(x, y - c)$
Horizontal shifts for $c > 0$,			
$y = f(x + c)$	Shift the graph of f to the left c units.	Replace x by $x + c$.	$(x - c, y)$
$y = f(x - c)$	Shift the graph of f to the right c units.	Replace x by $x - c$.	$(x + c, y)$
Reflection in the x-axis			
$y = -f(x)$	Reflect the graph of f in the x-axis.	Multiply $f(x)$ by -1.	$(x, -y)$
Reflection in the y-axis			
$y = f(-x)$	Reflect the graph of f in the y-axis.	Replace x by $-x$.	$(-x, y)$
Vertical stretching or compressing:			
$y = af(x)$	Multiply each y-coordinate of $y = f(x)$ by $\|a\|$. The graph of $y = f(x)$ is stretched vertically away from the x-axis if $a > 1$ and is compressed vertically toward the x-axis if $0 < a < 1$. If $a < 0$, the graph is first reflected in the x-axis and then vertically stretched or compressed.	Multiply $f(x)$ by a.	(x, ay)
Horizontal stretching or compressing:			
$y = f(bx)$	Multiply each x-coordinate of $y = f(x)$ by $\dfrac{1}{\|b\|}$. The graph of $y = f(x)$ is stretched away from the y-axis if $0 < b < 1$ and is compressed toward the y-axis if $b > 1$. If $b < 0$, sketch the graph of $y = f(\|b\|x)$, and then reflect it in the y-axis.	Replace x by bx.	$\left(\dfrac{x}{b}, y\right)$

A Exercises Basic Skills and Concepts

In Exercises 1–14, start with the graph of $f(x)$.

   a. Describe the transformations to the graph of $f(x)$ needed to get the graphs of the given functions $g(x)$ and $h(x)$.

   b. Sketch the graphs of $f(x)$, $g(x)$, and $h(x)$ on the same coordinate plane.

   c. Write the domain and the range of $g(x)$ and $h(x)$.

(c)

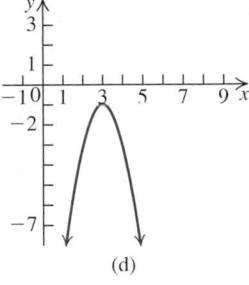
(d)

$f(x)$	$g(x)$	$h(x)$
1. $\sqrt{x}$	$\sqrt{x} + 2$	$\sqrt{x} - 1$ †
2. $\lvert x \rvert$	$\lvert x \rvert + 1$	$\lvert x \rvert - 2$ †
3. x^2	$(x + 1)^2$	$(x - 2)^2$ †
4. $\dfrac{1}{x}$	$\dfrac{1}{x + 2}$	$\dfrac{1}{x - 3}$ †
5. $\sqrt{x}$	$-\sqrt{x}$	$\sqrt{-x}$ †
6. x^2	$-x^2$	$(-x)^2$ †
7. $\lvert x \rvert$	$2\lvert x \rvert$	$\lvert 2x \rvert$ †
8. $\dfrac{1}{x}$	$\dfrac{2}{x}$	$\dfrac{1}{2x}$ †
9. $\sqrt{x}$	$\sqrt{1 - x}$	$-\sqrt{1 - x} + 1$ †
10. x^2	$(x - 1)^2$	$(x - 1)^2 + 3$ †
11. x^3	$(x - 2)^3 + 1$	$-(x + 1)^3 + 2$ †
12. $\lvert x \rvert$	$-\lvert x - 1 \rvert + 2$	$3\lvert x \rvert - 1$ †
13. $\sqrt[3]{x}$	$\sqrt[3]{x} + 1$	$\sqrt[3]{x + 1}$ †
14. $\sqrt[3]{x}$	$2\sqrt[3]{1 - x} + 4$	$-\sqrt[3]{x - 1} + 3$ †

(e)

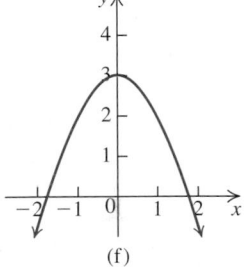
(f)

In Exercises 15–26, match each function with its graph (a)–(l).

15. $y = -\lvert x \rvert + 1$ e

16. $y = -\sqrt{-x}$ c

17. $y = \sqrt{x^2}$ g

18. $y = \dfrac{1}{2}\lvert x \rvert$ h

19. $y = \sqrt{x + 1}$ i

20. $y = 2\lvert x \rvert - 3$ a

21. $y = 1 - 2\sqrt{x}$ b

22. $y = -\lvert x - 1 \rvert + 1$ k

23. $y = (x - 1)^2$ l

24. $y = -x^2 + 3$ f

25. $y = -2(x - 3)^2 - 1$ d

26. $y = 3 - \sqrt{1 - x}$ j

(g)

(h)

(i)

(j)

(a)

(b)

(k)

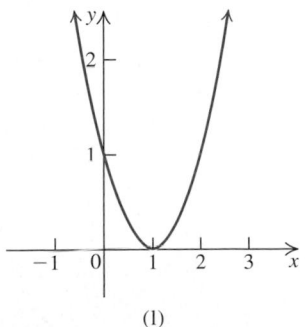
(l)

†Due to space constrictions, answers to these exercises may be found in the Answers beginning on page A–1 in the back of the book.

In Exercises 27–34, write an equation for a function whose graph fits the given description.

27. The graph of $f(x) = x^3$ is shifted two units up. $y = x^3 + 2$

28. The graph of $f(x) = \sqrt{x}$ is shifted three units left. $y = \sqrt{x+3}$

29. The graph of $f(x) = |x|$ is reflected in the x-axis. $y = -|x|$

30. $f(x) = \sqrt{x}$ is reflected in the y-axis. $y = \sqrt{-x}$

31. The graph of $f(x) = x^2$ is shifted three units right, and two units up. $y = (x-3)^2 + 2$

32. The graph of $f(x) = \sqrt{x}$ is shifted three units left, reflected in the x-axis, and shifted two units down. $y = -\sqrt{x+3} - 2$

33. The graph of $f(x) = x^3$ is shifted four units left, stretched vertically by a factor of 3, reflected in the y-axis, and shifted two units up. $y = 3(4-x)^3 + 2$

34. The graph of $f(x) = |x|$ is shifted four units right, stretched vertically by a factor of 2, reflected in the x-axis, and shifted three units down. $y = -2|x-4| - 3$

Answer:
37.

In Exercises 35–42, graph the function $y = g(x)$, given the following graph of $y = f(x)$:

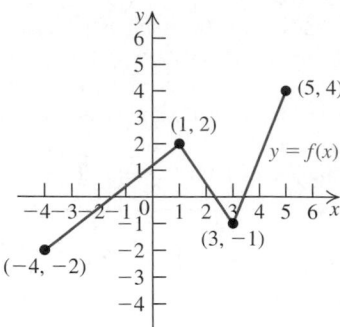

35. $g(x) = f(x) + 1$ †   **36.** $g(x) = -2f(x)$ †

37. $g(x) = f\left(\dfrac{1}{2}x\right)$ **38.** $g(x) = f(-2x)$ †

39. $g(x) = f(x-1)$ †   **40.** $g(x) = f(2-x)$ †

41. $g(x) = -2f(x+1) + 3$ † **42.** $g(x) = -f(-x+1) - 2$

Answer:
42.

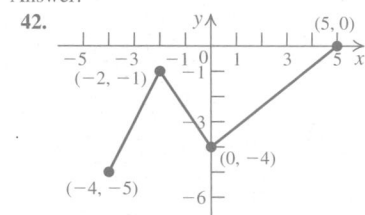

B Exercises Applying the Concepts

In Exercises 43–46, let f be the function that associates the employee number x of each employee of the ABC Corporation with his or her annual salary $f(x)$ in dollars.

43. Across-the-board raise. Each employee was awarded an across-the-board raise of 800 dollars per year. Write a function $g(x)$ to describe the new salary. $g(x) = f(x) + 800$

44. Percentage raise. Suppose each employee of the company was awarded a 5% raise. Write a function $h(x)$ to describe the new salary. $h(x) = 1.05\, f(x)$

45. Across-the-board and percentage raise. Suppose each employee of the company was awarded a 500-dollar across-the-board raise and an additional 2 percent of his or her increased salary. Write a function $p(x)$ to describe these new salaries. $p(x) = 1.02(x + 500)$

46. Across-the-board percentage raise. The employees of the ABC Corporation were divided into two categories: employees making less than 30,000 dollars and employees making 30,000 dollars or more. Employees making 30,000 dollars or more received a 2% raise, while those making less than 30,000 dollars received a 10% raise. Write a piecewise function to describe these new salaries. †

47. Health plan. The ABC Corporation pays for its employee's health insurance at an annual cost (in dollars) given by

$$C(x) = 5{,}000 + 10\sqrt{x-1},$$

where x is the number of employees covered.

a. Use transformations on the graph of $y = \sqrt{x}$ to sketch the graph of $y = C(x)$. †

b. If the company has 400 employees, find its annual outlay for the health coverage. †

48. In Exercise 47, if the insurance company increases the annual cost of health insurance for the ABC Corporation by 10%, write a function that reflects the new annual cost of health coverage. $y = 5500 + 11\sqrt{x - 1}$

49. Demand. The weekly demand for paper hats produced by Mythical Manufacturers is given by

$$x(p) = 109{,}561 - (p + 1)^2,$$

where x represents the number of hats that can be sold at a price of p cents each.
   a. Use transformations on the graph of $y = p^2$ to sketch the graph of $y = x(p)$. †
   b. Find the price at which 69,160 hats can be sold. $2.00
   c. Find the price at which no hats can be sold. $3.30

50. Revenue. The weekly demand for cashmere sweaters produced by the Wool Shop, Inc., is $x(p) = -3p + 600$. The revenue is given by $R(p) = -3p^2 + 600p$. Describe how to sketch the graph of $y = R(p)$ by applying transformations to the graph of $y = p^2$. [*Hint*: First write $R(p)$ in the form $-3(p - h)^2 + k$.] †

51. Daylight. At 60° north latitude, the graph of $y = f(t)$ gives the number of hours of daylight (1 = January; 12 = December). †

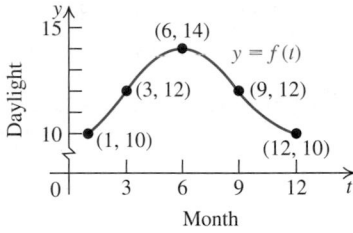

The first coordinate gives the month. The second coordinate gives the hours of daylight.

Sketch the graph of $y = f(t) - 12$ and interpret your result.

52. Use the graph of $y = f(t)$ of Exercise 51 to sketch the graph of $y = 24 - f(t)$. Interpret the result. †

C Exercises   Beyond the Basics

53. Use transformations on $y = \lfloor x \rfloor$ to sketch the graph of
$y = -2\lfloor x - 1 \rfloor + 3.$ †

54. Use transformations on $y = \lfloor x \rfloor$ to sketch the graph of
$y = 3\lfloor x + 2 \rfloor - 1.$ †

In Exercises 55–62, by completing the square on each quadratic expression, use transformations on $y = x^2$ to sketch the graph of $y = f(x)$.

55. $f(x) = x^2 + 4x$
   [*Hint:* $x^2 + 4x = (x^2 + 4x + 4) - 4 = (x + 2)^2 - 4.$] †

56. $f(x) = x^2 - 6x$ †

57. $f(x) = -x^2 + 2x$ †

58. $f(x) = -x^2 - 2x$ †

59. $f(x) = 2x^2 - 4x$ †

60. $f(x) = 2x^2 + 6x + 3.5$ †

61. $f(x) = -2x^2 - 8x + 3$ †

62. $f(x) = -2x^2 + 2x - 1$ †

In Exercises 63–68, sketch the graph of each function.

63. $y = |2x + 3|$ †

64. $y = |\lfloor x \rfloor|$ †

65. $y = |4 - x^2|$ †

66. $y = \left| \dfrac{1}{x} \right|$ †

67. $y = \sqrt{|x|}$ †

68. $y = \lfloor |x| \rfloor$

Critical Thinking

69. Suppose the graph of $y = f(x)$ is given. Using transformations, explain how the graph of $y = g(x)$ differs from the graph of $y = h(x)$.
   a. $g(x) = f(x) + 3,$ $h(x) = f(x + 3)$
   b. $g(x) = f(x) - 1,$ $h(x) = f(x - 1)$
   c. $g(x) = 2f(x),$ $h(x) = f(2x)$
   d. $g(x) = -3f(x),$ $h(x) = f(-3x)$

70. Suppose the graph of $y = f(-4x)$ is given. Explain how to obtain the graph of $y = f(x).$ †

Answers:
69. a. The graph of g is the graph of h shifted three units to the right and three units up.
   b. The graph of g is the graph of h shifted one unit to the left and one unit down.
   c. The graph of g is the graph of h stretched both horizontally and vertically by a factor of two.
   d. The graph of g is the graph of h stretched horizontally by a factor of three, reflected in the y-axis, stretched vertically by a factor of three, and reflected in the x-axis.
70. Stretch the graph of $y = f(-4x)$ horizontally by a factor of four, and reflect the resulting graph in the y-axis.

Combining Functions; Composite Functions

BEFORE STARTING THIS SECTION, REVIEW

1. Domain of a function (Section 2.4, page 230)

2. Area of a circle (Section P.7, page 79)

3. Rational inequalities (Section 1.7, page 163)

OBJECTIVES

1 Learn basic operations on functions.

2 Form composite functions.

3 Find the domain of a composite function.

4 Decompose a function.

5 Apply composition to practical problems.

Exxon Valdez Oil Spill Disaster

The oil tanker *Exxon Valdez* departed from the Trans-Alaska Pipeline terminal at 9:12 P.M., March 23, 1989. After passing through the Valdez Narrows, the tanker encountered icebergs in the shipping lanes, and Captain Hazelwood ordered the vessel to be taken out of the shipping lanes to go around the icebergs. For reasons that remain unclear, the ship failed to make the turn back into the shipping lanes, and the tanker ran aground on Bligh Reef at 12:04 A.M., March 24, 1989.

At the time of the accident, the *Exxon Valdez* was carrying 53 million gallons of oil, and approximately 11 million gallons were spilled. The amount of spilled oil is roughly equivalent to 125 Olympic-sized swimming pools. This spill was one of the largest ever in the United States and is widely considered the number-one spill worldwide in terms of damage to the environment. The spill covered a large area, stretching for 460 miles from Bligh Reef to the tiny village of Chigmik on the Alaska Peninsula. In Example 6, we calculate the area covered by an oil spill. ■

1 Learn basic operations on functions.

Combining Functions

Just as numbers can be added, subtracted, multiplied, and divided to produce new numbers, so functions can be added, subtracted, multiplied, and divided to produce other functions. To add, subtract, multiply, or divide functions, we simply add, subtract, multiply, or divide their range, or output values.

For example, if $f(x) = x^2 - 2x + 4$ and $g(x) = x + 2$, then

$$f(x) + g(x) = (x^2 - 2x + 4) + (x + 2) = x^2 - x + 6.$$

This new function $y = x^2 - x + 6$ is called the sum function $f + g$.

SUM, DIFFERENCE, PRODUCT, AND QUOTIENT OF FUNCTIONS

Let f and g be two functions. The **sum** $f + g$, the **difference** $f - g$, the **product** fg, and the **quotient** $\dfrac{f}{g}$ are functions whose domains consist of those values of x that are common to the domains of f and g. These functions are defined as follows:

(i) Sum $(f + g)(x) = f(x) + g(x)$

(ii) Difference $(f - g)(x) = f(x) - g(x)$

(iii) Product $(fg)(x) = f(x) \cdot g(x)$

(iv) Quotient $\left(\dfrac{f}{g}\right)(x) = \dfrac{f(x)}{g(x)},$ provided that $g(x) \neq 0$.

Note that, in the case of the quotient function $\dfrac{f}{g}$, there is an additional requirement that the values of x for which $g(x) = 0$ be *excluded* from the domain.

EXAMPLE 1   Combining Functions

Let $f(x) = x^2 - 6x + 8$ and $g(x) = x - 2$. Find each of the following functions.

a. $(f + g)(x)$ **b.** $(f - g)(x)$ **c.** $(fg)(x)$ **d.** $\left(\dfrac{f}{g}\right)(x)$

Solution

a. $\begin{aligned}(f + g)(x) &= f(x) + g(x) \\ &= (x^2 - 6x + 8) + (x - 2) \\ &= x^2 - 6x + 8 + x - 2 \\ &= x^2 - 5x + 6\end{aligned}$
    Definition of sum
    Add $f(x)$ and $g(x)$.
    Remove parentheses.
    Combine terms.

b. $\begin{aligned}(f - g)(x) &= f(x) - g(x) \\ &= (x^2 - 6x + 8) - (x - 2) \\ &= x^2 - 6x + 8 - x + 2 \\ &= x^2 - 7x + 10\end{aligned}$
    Definition of difference
    Subtract $g(x)$ from $f(x)$.
    Simplify.
    Combine terms.

c. $\begin{aligned}(fg)(x) &= f(x) \cdot g(x) \\ &= (x^2 - 6x + 8)(x - 2) \\ &= x^2(x - 2) - 6x(x - 2) + 8(x - 2) \\ &= x^3 - 2x^2 - 6x^2 + 12x + 8x - 16 \\ &= x^3 - 8x^2 + 20x - 16\end{aligned}$
    Definition of product
    Multiply $f(x)$ and $g(x)$.
    Distributive property
    Distributive property
    Combine terms.

d. $\left(\dfrac{f}{g}\right)(x) = \dfrac{f(x)}{g(x)}, \quad g(x) \neq 0$ Definition of quotient

$$= \dfrac{x^2 - 6x + 8}{x - 2}, \quad x - 2 \neq 0 \qquad \text{Divide } f(x) \text{ by } g(x).$$

$$= \dfrac{(x - 2)(x - 4)}{x - 2}, \quad x \neq 2 \qquad \text{Factor the numerator.}$$

Since f and g are polynomials, the domain of f and g is the set of all real numbers, or, in interval notation, $(-\infty, \infty)$. Thus, the domain for $f + g$, $f - g$, and fg is $(-\infty, \infty)$.

However, for $\dfrac{f}{g}$, we must exclude those values of x for which $g(x) = x - 2 = 0$. Solving $x - 2 = 0$ for x, we obtain $x = 2$. Hence, the domain for $\dfrac{f}{g}$ is the set of all real numbers x such that $x \neq 2$, or, in interval notation, $(-\infty, 2) \cup (2, \infty)$.   ■ ■ ■

Practice Problem 1   Let $f(x) = 3x - 1$ and $g(x) = x^2 + 2$. Find $(f + g)(x)$, $(f - g)(x)$, $(fg)(x)$, and $\left(\dfrac{f}{g}\right)(x)$.   ■

◆ WARNING   In the expression

(1) $$\left(\dfrac{f}{g}\right)(x) = \dfrac{(x - 2)(x - 4)}{x - 2}, \quad x \neq 2$$

in Example 1, it is tempting to remove the factor $(x - 2)$ and obtain

(2) $$\left(\dfrac{f}{g}\right)(x) = x - 4.$$

However, this is not quite the same function, because the domain of the function defined in equation (2) is $(-\infty, \infty)$, whereas the domain of the actual function $\dfrac{f}{g}$ defined by equation (1) is $(-\infty, 2) \cup (2, \infty)$. It would be correct, however, to write the quotient function in (1) as

$$\left(\dfrac{f}{g}\right)(x) = x - 4, \quad x \neq 2.$$

---

2 Form composite functions.

Composition of Functions

There is yet another way to construct a new function from two functions. Figure 2.65 shows what happens when you apply one function $g(x) = x^2 - 1$ to an input (domain) value x and then apply a second function $f(x) = \sqrt{x}$ to the output value from the first function. In this case, the output from the first function becomes the input for the second function.

FIGURE 2.65

COMPOSITION OF FUNCTIONS

If f and g are two functions, the composition of function f with function g is written as $f \circ g$ and is defined by the equation

$$(f \circ g)(x) = f(g(x)),$$

where the domain of $f \circ g$ consists of those values x in the domain of g for which $g(x)$ is in the domain of f.

Figure 2.66 may help clarify the definition of $f \circ g$.

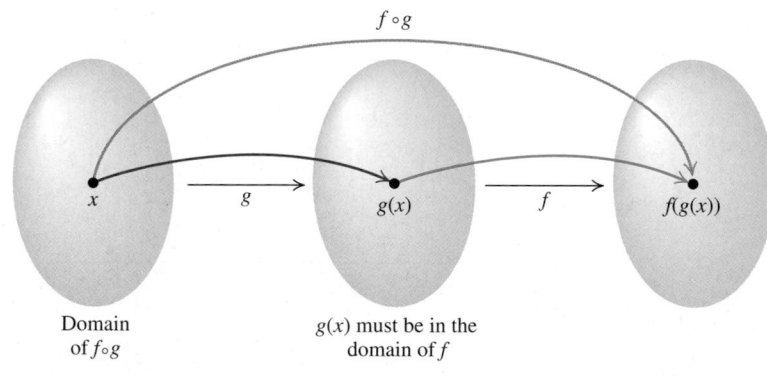

FIGURE 2.66

Evaluating $(f \circ g)(x)$. By definition,

$$(f \circ g)(x) = f(g(x))$$

inner function

outer function

Thus, in order to evaluate $(f \circ g)(x)$, we must

(i) evaluate the inner function g and

(ii) then use the result as the input for the outer function f.

Let's look at some examples.

EXAMPLE 2   **Evaluating a Composite Function**

Let $f(x) = x^3$ and $g(x) = x + 1$. Find each of the following.

a. $(f \circ g)(1)$ **b.** $(g \circ f)(1)$ **c.** $(f \circ f)(-1)$ **d.** $(g \circ g)(-1)$

Solution

a. $(f \circ g)(1) = f(g(1))$ Definition of $f \circ g$
$\quad\quad\quad\quad\quad = f(2)$ $g(1) = 1 + 1 = 2$
$\quad\quad\quad\quad\quad = 2^3$ Evaluate $f(2)$.
$\quad\quad\quad\quad\quad = 8$ Simplify.

b. $(g \circ f)(1) = g(f(1))$ Definition of $g \circ f$
$\qquad\qquad = g(1) \qquad\qquad f(1) = 1^3 = 1$
$\qquad\qquad = 1 + 1 \qquad\quad$ Evaluate $g(1)$.
$\qquad\qquad = 2 \qquad\qquad\;$ Simplify.

c. $(f \circ f)(-1) = f(f(-1))$ Definition of $f \circ f$
$\qquad\qquad\;\; = f(-1) \qquad\quad f(-1) = (-1)^3 = -1$
$\qquad\qquad\;\; = (-1)^3 \qquad\;$ Evaluate $f(-1)$.
$\qquad\qquad\;\; = -1 \qquad\qquad$ Simplify.

d. $(g \circ g)(-1) = g(g(-1))$ Definition of $g \circ g$
$\qquad\qquad\;\; = g(0) \qquad\qquad g(-1) = -1 + 1 = 0$
$\qquad\qquad\;\; = 0 + 1 \qquad\quad$ Evaluate $g(0)$.
$\qquad\qquad\;\; = 1 \qquad\qquad\;\;$ Simplify.   ■ ■ ■

PRACTICE PROBLEM 2   Let $f(x) = -5x$ and $g(x) = x^2 + 1$. Find each of the following.

a. $(f \circ g)(0)$ **b.** $(g \circ f)(0)$ ■

EXAMPLE 3   **Finding Composite Functions**

Let $f(x) = 2x + 1$ and $g(x) = x^2 - 3$. Find each composite function.

a. $(f \circ g)(x)$ **b.** $(g \circ f)(x)$ **c.** $(f \circ f)(x)$

Solution

a. $(f \circ g)(x) = f(g(x))$ Definition of $f \circ g$
$\qquad\qquad = f(x^2 - 3) \qquad$ Replace $g(x)$ by $x^2 - 3$.
$\qquad\qquad = 2(x^2 - 3) + 1 \quad$ Replace x by $x^2 - 3$ in $f(x) = 2x - 1$.
$\qquad\qquad = 2x^2 - 6 + 1 \qquad$ Distributive property
$\qquad\qquad = 2x^2 - 5 \qquad\qquad$ Simplify.
$\qquad$ Thus, $(f \circ g)(x) = 2x^2 - 5$.

b. $(g \circ f)(x) = g(f(x))$ Definition of $g \circ f$
$\qquad\qquad = g(2x + 1) \qquad\quad$ Replace $f(x)$ by $2x + 1$.
$\qquad\qquad = (2x + 1)^2 - 3 \qquad$ Replace x by $2x + 1$ in $g(x) - x^2 \quad 3$.
$\qquad\qquad = 4x^2 + 4x + 1 - 3 \quad (A + B)^2 = A^2 + 2AB + B^2$
$\qquad\qquad = 4x^2 + 4x - 2 \qquad$ Simplify.
$\qquad$ Thus, $(g \circ f)(x) = 4x^2 + 4x - 2$.

c. $(f \circ f)(x) = f(f(x))$ Definition of $f \circ f$
$\qquad\qquad = f(2x + 1) \qquad\quad$ Replace $f(x)$ by $2x + 1$.
$\qquad\qquad = 2(2x + 1) + 1 \qquad$ Replace x by $2x + 1$ in $f(x) = 2x + 1$.
$\qquad\qquad = 4x + 2 + 1 \qquad\quad$ Distributive property
$\qquad\qquad\qquad = 4x + 3 \qquad\quad$ Simplify. ■ ■ ■

PRACTICE PROBLEM 3   Let $f(x) = 2 - x$ and $g(x) = 2x^2 + 1$. Find $(g \circ f)(x)$ and $(f \circ g)(x)$.   ■

Parts **a** and **b** of Example 3 illustrate that, in general, $f \circ g \neq g \circ f$. In other words, the composition of functions is not commutative.

◆ **WARNING**

It is important to note that $f(g(x))$ is not $f(x) \cdot g(x)$. The composition of $f(x)$ and $g(x)$, written as $f(g(x))$, means the output of g is *used as an input* for f, while the product $f(x) \cdot g(x)$ means that the output $f(x)$ is *multiplied* by the output $g(x)$. For example, if $f(x) = 2x + 1$ and $g(x) = x^2 - 3$, then

$$(f \circ g)(5) = f(g(5)) = f(5^2 - 3) = f(22) = 2(22) + 1 = 45,$$

but

$$f(5) \cdot g(5) = [2(5) + 1](5^2 - 3) = (11)(22) = 242.$$

3 Find the domain of a composite function.

Domain of Composite Functions

Let f and g be two functions. The domain of the composite function $f \circ g$ consists of those values of x in the domain of g for which $g(x)$ is in the domain of f. Thus, finding the domain of $f \circ g$ requires us to first find the domain of g. Then, from the domain of g, we exclude those values of x such that $g(x)$ is not in the domain of f.

EXAMPLE 4   **Finding the Domain of a Composite Function**

Let $f(x) = x + 1$ and $g(x) = \dfrac{1}{x}$.

a. Find $(f \circ g)(-1)$. **b.** Find $(g \circ f)(-1)$. **c.** Find $(f \circ g)(x)$ and its domain.
d. Find $(g \circ f)(x)$ and its domain.

Solution

a. $(f \circ g)(-1) = f(g(-1))$ Definition of $f \circ g$

$= f(-1)$ $g(-1) = \dfrac{1}{-1} = -1$

$= -1 + 1$ Replace x by -1 in $f(x) = x + 1$.

$= 0$ Simplify.

b. $(g \circ f)(-1) = g(f(-1))$ Definition of $g \circ f$

$= g(0)$ $f(-1) = -1 + 1 = 0$

not defined   0 is not in the domain of $g(x) = \dfrac{1}{x}$.

c. $(f \circ g)(x) = f(g(x))$ Definition of $f \circ g$

$= f\left(\dfrac{1}{x}\right)$ Replace $g(x)$ by $\dfrac{1}{x}$.

$= \dfrac{1}{x} + 1$ Replace x by $\dfrac{1}{x}$ in $f(x) = x + 1$.

Because 0 is not in the domain of $g(x) = \dfrac{1}{x}$, we must exclude 0 from the domain of $f \circ g$. This is the only restriction on the domain of $f \circ g$, since the domain of f is $(-\infty, \infty)$. Thus, the domain of $f \circ g$ is all real $x, x \neq 0$. In interval notation, the domain of $f \circ g$ is $(-\infty, 0) \cup (0, \infty)$.

d. $(g \circ f)(x) = g(f(x))$ Definition of $g \circ f$

$= g(x + 1)$ Replace $f(x)$ by $x + 1$.

$= \dfrac{1}{x + 1}$ Replace x by $x + 1$ in $g(x) = \dfrac{1}{x}$.

The domain of f is $(-\infty, \infty)$, so we need to exclude from the domain of $g \circ f$ only values of x for which $f(x)$ is not in the domain of g. That is, we must exclude values of x such that $f(x) = 0$ from the domain of $g \circ f$.

We solve the equation $f(x) = 0$.

$$x + 1 = 0 \qquad \text{Replace } f(x) \text{ by } x + 1.$$
$$x = -1 \qquad \text{Add } -1 \text{ to both sides.}$$

Thus, the domain of $g \circ f$ is the set of all real numbers x for which $x \neq -1$. In interval notation, the domain of $g \circ f$ is $(-\infty, -1) \cup (-1, \infty)$.   ■ ■ ■

PRACTICE PROBLEM 4   Let $f(x) = \sqrt{x}$ and $g(x) = 2x + 5$.

a. Find $(g \circ f)(4)$ **b.** Find $(g \circ f)(x)$ and its domain.   ■

4 Decompose a function.

Decomposition of a Function

In the composition of two functions, we combine two functions and create a new function. However, it is sometimes more useful to go the other way—that is, use the concept of composition to *decompose* a function into simpler functions. For example, consider the function $H(x) = \sqrt{x^2 - 2}$. A natural way to write $H(x)$ as the composition of two functions is to let $f(x) = \sqrt{x}$ and $g(x) = x^2 - 2$, so that $f(g(x)) = f(x^2 - 2) = \sqrt{x^2 - 2} = H(x)$.

A function may be decomposed into simpler functions in several different ways by using various expressions in the defining equation for the function representing an "inner" function.

EXAMPLE 5   **Decomposing a Function**

Let $H(x) = \dfrac{1}{\sqrt{2x^2 + 1}}$. Show that each of the following provides a decomposition of $H(x)$.

a. Express $H(x)$ as $f(g(x))$, where $f(x) = \dfrac{1}{\sqrt{x}}$ and $g(x) = 2x^2 + 1$.

b. Express $H(x)$ as $f(g(x))$, where $f(x) = \dfrac{1}{x}$ and $g(x) = \sqrt{2x^2 + 1}$.

Solution

a. $f(g(x)) = f(2x^2 + 1) \qquad$ Replace $g(x)$ by $2x^2 + 1$.

$\qquad\quad = \dfrac{1}{\sqrt{2x^2 + 1}} \qquad$ Since $f(x) = \dfrac{1}{\sqrt{x}}$, replace x by $2x^2 + 1$.

$\qquad\quad = H(x)$

b. $f(g(x)) = f(\sqrt{2x^2 + 1}) \qquad$ Replace $g(x)$ by $\sqrt{2x^2 + 1}$.

$\qquad\quad = \dfrac{1}{\sqrt{2x^2 + 1}} \qquad$ Since $f(x) = \dfrac{1}{x}$, replace x by $\sqrt{2x^2 + 1}$.

$\qquad\quad = H(x)$ ■ ■ ■

PRACTICE PROBLEM 5 Let $H(x) = 2(x - 1)^2 + 3$. Show that $H(x) = f(g(x))$, where $f(x) = 2x^2 + 3$ and $g(x) = x - 1$. ■

5 Apply composition to practical problems.

Applications

EXAMPLE 6 Calculating the Area of an Oil Spill from a Tanker

Oil is spilled from a tanker into the Pacific Ocean. Suppose the area of the oil spill is a perfect circle. (In practice, this does not happen, because of the winds and tides and the location of the coastline.) Suppose that the radius of the oil slick is increasing (because oil continues to spill) at the rate of 2 miles per hour.

a. Express the area of the oil slick as a function of time.

b. Calculate the area covered by the oil slick in 6 hours.

Solution

The area A of the oil slick is a function of its radius r. This function is

$$A = f(r) = \pi r^2.$$

The radius is also a function of time. We are given that r is increasing at the rate of 2 miles per hour. Thus, in t hours, the radius r of the oil slick is given by the function

$$r = g(t) = 2t \quad \text{Distance} = \text{Rate} \times \text{Time}$$

a. The area A of the oil slick is a composite function given by

$$A = f(g(t)) = f(2t) = \pi(2t)^2$$
$$= 4\pi t^2.$$

b. Substitute $t = 6$ (6 hours have passed) into the formula $A = 4\pi t^2$ to obtain the area:

$$A = 4\pi(6)^2 = 4\pi(36)$$
$$= 144\pi \text{ square miles.}$$

The area covered by the oil slick in 6 hours is 144π square miles. ■ ■ ■

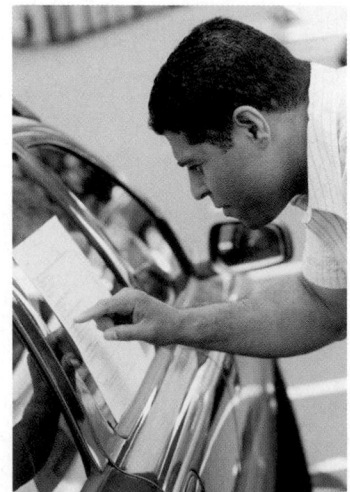

PRACTICE PROBLEM 6 Suppose the oil slick in Example 6 is increasing at a rate of 3 miles per hour. How does this change the results in the example? ■

EXAMPLE 7 Applying Composition to Sales

A car dealer offers an 8% discount off the manufacturer's suggested retail price (MSRP) of x dollars for any new car on his lot. At the same time, the manufacturer offers a $4000 rebate for each purchase of a car.

a. Write a function $f(x)$ that represents the price after the rebate.

b. Write a function $g(x)$ that represents the price after the dealer's discount.

c. Write the functions $(f \circ g)(x)$ and $(g \circ f)(x)$. What do they represent?

d. Calculate $(g \circ f)(x) - (f \circ g)(x)$. Interpret this expression.

Solution

a. The MSRP is x dollars, and the manufacturer's rebate is 4000 dollars for each car. Thus,

$$f(x) = x - 4000$$

represents the price of a car after the rebate.

b. The dealer's discount is 8% of x, or $0.08x$. Hence,

$$g(x) = x - 0.08x = 0.92x$$

represents the price of the car after the dealer's discount.

c. (i) $(f \circ g)(x) = f(g(x))$ Apply the dealer's discount first.
           $= f(0.92x)$ $g(x) = 0.92x$
           $= 0.92x - 4000$ Evaluate $f(0.92x)$, using $f(x) = x - 4000$.

Then, $(f \circ g)(x) = 0.92x - 4000$ represents the price when the dealer's discount is applied first.

    (ii) $(g \circ f)(x) = g(f(x))$ Apply the manufacturer's rebate first.
           $= g(x - 4000)$ $f(x) = x - 4000$
           $= 0.92(x - 4000)$ Evaluate $g(x - 4000)$, using $g(x) = 0.92x$.
           $= 0.92x - 3680$

Thus, $(g \circ f)(x) = 0.92x - 3680$ represents the price when the manufacturer's rebate is applied first.

d. $(g \circ f)(x) - (f \circ g)(x) = (0.92x - 3680) - (0.92x - 4000)$ Subtract function values.

$$= 320 \text{ dollars}$$

This equation shows that it will cost 320 dollars more for any car, regardless of its price, if you apply the rebate first and then the discount.   ■ ■ ■

PRACTICE PROBLEM 7   Suppose in Example 7 that the dealer offers a 6% discount and the manufacturer offers a $4500 rebate. How does this modify the results of the example?   ■

A Exercises   Basic Skills and Concepts

In Exercises 1–6, functions f and g are given. Find each of the given values.

a. $(f + g)(-1)$ **b.** $(f - g)(0)$

c. $(f \cdot g)(2)$ **d.** $\left(\dfrac{f}{g}\right)(1)$

    1. $f(x) = 2x; g(x) = -x$ †

    2. $f(x) = 1 - x^2; g(x) = x + 1$ †

    3. $f(x) = \dfrac{1}{\sqrt{x + 2}}; g(x) = 2x + 1$ †

    4. $f(x) = \dfrac{x}{x^2 - 6x + 8}; g(x) = 3 - x$ †

    5. $f(x) = x^2 + 2x; g(x) = 3 - x$ †

    6. $f(x) = x^2 + 3; g(x) = 3x^3 + 24$ †

In Exercises 7–12, functions f and g are given. Find each of the following functions and state its domain.

a. $f + g$ **b.** $f - g$

c. $f \cdot g$ **d.** $\dfrac{f}{g}$

e. $\dfrac{g}{f}$.

    7. $f(x) = x - 3; g(x) = x^2$ †

    8. $f(x) = 2x - 1; g(x) = x^2$ †

    9. $f(x) = x^3 - 1; g(x) = 2x^2 + 5$ †

   10. $f(x) = x^2 - 4; g(x) = x^2 - 6x + 8$ †

   11. $f(x) = 2x - 1; g(x) = \sqrt{x}$ †

   12. $f(x) = 1 - \dfrac{1}{x}; g(x) = \dfrac{1}{x}$ †

†Due to space constrictions, answers to these exercises may be found in the Answers beginning on page A–1 in the back of the book.

In Exercises 13 and 14, use each diagram to evaluate $(g \circ f)(x)$. Then evaluate $(g \circ f)(2)$ and $(g \circ f)(-3)$.

13. $x \rightarrow \boxed{f(x) = x^2 - 1} \rightarrow \rightarrow \boxed{g(x) = 2x + 3} \rightarrow$ †

14. $x \rightarrow \boxed{f(x) = |x + 1|} \rightarrow \rightarrow \boxed{g(x) = 3x^2 - 1} \rightarrow$ †

In Exercises 15–26, let $f(x) = 2x + 1$ and $g(x) = 2x^2 - 3$. Evaluate each expression.

15. $(f \circ g)(2)$ 11
16. $(g \circ f)(2)$ 47
17. $(f \circ g)(-3)$ 31
18. $(g \circ f)(-5)$ 159
19. $(f \circ g)(0)$ −5
20. $(g \circ f)\left(\dfrac{1}{2}\right)$ 5
21. $(f \circ g)(-c)$ $4c^2 - 5$
22. $(f \circ g)(c)$ $4c^2 - 5$
23. $(g \circ f)(a)$ $8a^2 + 8a - 1$
24. $(g \circ f)(-a)$ $8a^2 - 8a - 1$
25. $(f \circ f)(1)$ 7
26. $(g \circ g)(-1)$ −1

In Exercises 27–32, the functions f and g are given. Evaluate $f \circ g$ and find the domain of the composite function $f \circ g$.

27. $f(x) = \dfrac{2}{x + 1}$; $g(x) = \dfrac{1}{x}$ $\dfrac{2x}{x + 1}$
28. $f(x) = \dfrac{1}{x - 1}$; $g(x) = \dfrac{2}{x + 3}$ $\dfrac{x + 3}{x + 1}$
29. $f(x) = \sqrt{x - 3}$; $g(x) = 2 - 3x$ $\sqrt{-1 - 3x}$
30. $f(x) = \dfrac{x}{x - 1}$; $g(x) = 2 + 5x$ $\dfrac{2 + 5x}{1 + 5x}$
31. $f(x) = |x|$; $g(x) = x^2 - 1$ $|x^2 - 1|$
32. $f(x) = 3x - 2$; $g(x) = |x - 1|$ $3|x - 1| - 2$

In Exercises 33–46, the functions f and g are given. Find each composite function and describe the domain of the resulting function.

a. $f \circ g$
b. $g \circ f$
c. $f \circ f$
d. $g \circ g$

33. $f(x) = 2x - 3$; $g(x) = x + 4$ †

34. $f(x) = x - 3$; $g(x) = 3x - 5$ †
35. $f(x) = 1 - 2x$; $g(x) = 1 + x^2$ †
36. $f(x) = 2x - 3$; $g(x) = 2x^2$ †
37. $f(x) = 2x^2 + 3x$; $g(x) = 2x - 1$ †
38. $f(x) = x^2 + 3x$; $g(x) = 2x$ †
39. $f(x) = x^2$; $g(x) = \sqrt{x}$ †
40. $f(x) = x^2 + 2x$; $g(x) = \sqrt{x + 2}$ †
41. $f(x) = \dfrac{1}{2x - 1}$; $g(x) = \dfrac{1}{x^2}$ †
42. $f(x) = x - 1$; $g(x) = \dfrac{x}{x + 1}$ †
43. $f(x) = |x|$; $g(x) = -2$ †
44. $f(x) = 3$; $g(x) = 5$ †
45. $f(x) = 1 + \dfrac{1}{x}$; $g(x) = \dfrac{1 + x}{1 - x}$ †
46. $f(x) = \sqrt[3]{x + 1}$; $g(x) = x^3 + 1$ †

In Exercises 47–56, express the given function H as a composition of two functions f and g such that $H(x) = (f \circ g)(x)$.

47. $H(x) = \sqrt{x + 2}$ $f(x) = \sqrt{x}$; $g(x) = x + 2$
48. $H(x) = |3x + 2|$. $f(x) = |x|$; $g(x) = 3x + 2$
49. $H(x) = (x^2 - 3)^{10}$ $f(x) = x^{10}$; $g(x) = x^2 - 3$
50. $H(x) = \sqrt{3x^2 + 5}$ $f(x) = \sqrt{x + 5}$; $g(x) = 3x^2$
51. $H(x) = \dfrac{1}{3x - 5}$ $f(x) = \dfrac{1}{x}$; $g(x) = 3x - 5$
52. $H(x) = \dfrac{5}{2x + 3}$ $f(x) = \dfrac{5}{x}$; $g(x) = 2x + 3$
53. $H(x) = \sqrt[3]{x^2 - 7}$ $f(x) = \sqrt[3]{x}$; $g(x) = x^2 - 7$
54. $H(x) = \sqrt[4]{x^2 + x + 1}$ $f(x) = \sqrt[4]{x}$; $g(x) = x^2 + x + 1$
55. $H(x) = \dfrac{1}{|x^3 - 1|}$ $f(x) = \dfrac{1}{|x|}$; $g(x) = x^3 - 1$
56. $H(x) = \sqrt[3]{1 + \sqrt{x}}$ $f(x) = \sqrt[3]{x}$; $g(x) = 1 + \sqrt{x}$

B Exercises   Applying the Concepts

57. **Cost, revenue, and profit.** A retailer purchases x shirts from a wholesaler at a price of 12 dollars per shirt. Her selling price for each shirt is 22 dollars. There is a 7% sales tax in the state. Interpret each of the following functions.
    a. $f(x) = 12x$ Cost function
    b. $g(x) = 22x$ Revenue function
    c. $h(x) = g(x) + 0.07g(x)$ †
    d. $P(x) = g(x) - f(x)$ Profit function

58. **Cost, revenue, and profit.** The demand equation for a product is given by $x = 5000 - 5p$, where x is the number of units produced and sold at price p (in dollars) per unit. The cost (in dollars) of producing x units is given by $C(x) = 4x + 12,000$. Express each of the following as a function of price.
    a. Cost $C(p) = 32,000 - 20p$
    b. Revenue $R(p) = 5000p - 5p^2$
    c. Profit $P(p) = -5p^2 + 5020p - 32,000$

59. Cost and revenue. A manufacturer of radios estimates that his daily cost of producing x radios is given by the equation $C = 350 + 5x$. The equation $R = 25x$ represents the revenue in dollars from selling x radios.

a. Write and simplify the profit function

$$P(x) = R(x) - C(x). \quad P(x) = 20x - 350$$

b. Find $P(20)$. What does the number $P(20)$ represent? †

c. How many radios should the manufacturer produce and sell in order to have a daily profit of 500 dollars? 43

d. Find the composite function $(R \circ x)(C)$. What does this function represent? †

[*Hint*: To obtain $x(C)$, solve $C = 350 + 5x$ for x.] †

60. Mail order. You order merchandise worth x dollars from D-Bay Manufacturers. The company charges you sales tax of 4% of the purchase price, plus a shipping-and-handling fee of 3 dollars plus 2% of the after-tax purchase price.

a. Write a function $g(x)$ that represents the sales tax. †

b. What does the function $h(x) = x + g(x)$ represent? †

c. Write a function $f(x)$ that represents the shipping-and-handling fee.†

d. What does the function

$$T(x) = h(x) + f(x)$$

represent? †

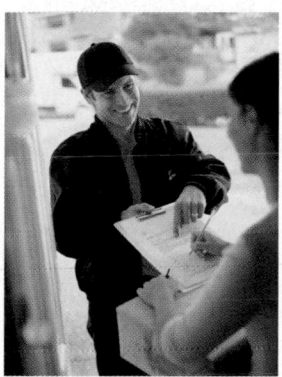

61. Consumer issues. You work in a department store in which employees are entitled to a 30% discount on their purchases. You also have a coupon worth 5 dollars off any item.

a. Write a function $f(x)$ that models discounting an item by 30%. †

b. Write a function $g(x)$ that models applying the coupon. †

c. Use a composition of your two functions from (a) and (b) to model your cost for an item if the clerk applies the discount first and then the coupon. $(g \circ f)(x) = 0.7x - 5$

d. Use a composition of your two functions from (a) and (b) to model your cost for an item if the clerk applies the coupon first and then the discount. †

e. Use the composite functions from (c) and (d) to find how much more an item costs if the clerk applies the coupon first. $1.50

62. Consumer issues. You work in a department store in which employees are entitled to a 20% discount on their purchases. In addition, the store is offering a 10% discount on all items.

a. Write a function $f(x)$ that models discounting an item by 20%. $f(x) = 0.8x$

b. Write a function $g(x)$ that models discounting an item by 10%. $g(x) = 0.9x$

c. Use a composition of your two functions from (a) and (b) to model taking the 20% discount first. †

d. Use a composition of your two functions from (a) and (b) to model taking the 10% discount first. †

e. Use the composite functions from (c) and (d) to decide which discount you would prefer to take first. †

63. Test grades. Professor Harsh gave a test to his college algebra class, and nobody got more than 80 points (out of 100) on the test. One problem worth 8 points had insufficient data, so nobody could solve that problem. The professor adjusts the grades for the class by (1) increasing everyone's score by 10% and (2) giving everyone 8 bonus points. Let x represent the original score of a student.

a. Write statements (1) and (2) as functions $f(x)$ and $g(x)$, respectively. $f(x) = 1.1x; g(x) = x + 8$

b. Find $(f \circ g)(x)$ and explain what it means. †

c. Find $(g \circ f)(x)$ and explain what it means. †

d. Evaluate $(f \circ g)(70)$ and $(g \circ f)(70)$. 85.8 and 85.0

e. Does $(f \circ g)(x) = (g \circ f)(x)$? No

f. Suppose a score of 90 or better qualifies a student to receive an A on the test. What original score will qualify a student to receive an A on the test if the professor used (*i*) $(f \circ g)(x)$; (*ii*) $(g \circ f)(x)$? (*i*) 73.82 (*ii*) 74.55

64. Sales commissions. Henrita works as a salesperson in a department store. Her weekly salary is 200 dollars plus a 3% bonus on weekly sales over 8000 dollars. Suppose her sales in a week are x dollars.

a. Let $f(x) = 0.03x$. What does this mean? †

b. Let $g(x) = x - 8000$. What does this mean? †

c. Which composite function, $(f \circ g)(x)$ or $(g \circ f)(x)$, represents Henrita's bonus? $(f \circ g)(x)$

d. What was her salary for the week in which her sales were 17,500 dollars? $485

e. What were her sales for the week in which her salary was 521 dollars? $18,700

65. Enhancing a fountain. A circular fountain has a radius of x feet. A circular fence is installed around the fountain at a distance of 30 feet from its edge.
  a. Write the function $f(x)$ that represents the area of the fountain. $f(x) = \pi x^2$
  b. Write the function $g(x)$ that represents the entire area enclosed by the fence. $g(x) = \pi(x + 30)^2$
  c. What area does the function $g(x) - f(x)$ represent? †
  d. The cost of the fence was 4200 dollars, installed at the rate of $10\frac{1}{2}$ dollars per running foot (per perimeter foot). You are to prepare an estimate for paving the area between the fence and the fountain at a dollar seventy-five per square foot. To the nearest dollar, what should your estimate be? $16,052

66. Running-track design. An outdoor running track with semicircular ends and parallel sides is constructed. The length of each straight portion of the sides is 180 meters. The track has a uniform width of 4 meters throughout. The inner radius of each semicircular end is x meters.
  a. Write the function $f(x)$ that represents the area enclosed within the *outer* edge of the running track. †
  b. Write the function $g(x)$ that represents the area of the field enclosed within the *inner* edge of the running track. $g(x) = 360x + \pi x^2$
  c. What does the function $f(x) - g(x)$ represent? †
  d. Suppose the inner perimeter of the track is 900 meters.
    (i) Find the area of the track. 3650.26
    (ii) Find the outer perimeter of the track. 925.13 †

67. Area of a disk. The area A of a circular disk of radius r units is given by $A = f(r) = \pi r^2$. Suppose a metal disk is being heated and its radius r is increasing according to the equation $r = g(t) = 2t + 1$, where t is time in hours.
  a. Find $(f \circ g)(t)$. $(f \circ g)(t) = \pi(2t + 1)^2$
  b. Determine A as a function of time. $A(t) = \pi(2t + 1)^2$
  c. Compare parts (a) and (b). They are the same

68. Volume of a balloon. The volume V of a spherical balloon of radius r inches is given by the formula $V = f(r) = \frac{4}{3}\pi r^3$.
  Suppose the balloon is being inflated and its radius is increasing at the rate of 2 inches per second. That is, $r = g(t) = 2t$, where t is time in seconds.
  a. Find $(f \circ g)(t)$. †
  b. Determine V as a function of time. †
  c. Compare parts (a) and (b). They are the same

69. Currency exchange. On March 17, 2006, each British pound (symbol £) was worth 1.7559 U.S. dollars, and each Mexican peso was worth 0.05328 British pound. (*Source:* www.xe.com/ucc)
  a. Write a function f that converts pounds to dollars. †
  b. Write a function g that converts pesos to pounds. †
  c. Which function, $f \circ g$ or $g \circ f$, converts pesos to dollars? $(f \circ g)(x)$
  d. How much was 1000 pesos worth in dollars on March 17, 2006? 93.55

C Exercises   Beyond the Basics

70. Odd and even functions. State whether each of the functions that follow is an odd function, an even function, or neither. Justify your statement.
   a. The sum of two even functions. Even function
   b. The sum of two odd functions. Odd function
   c. The sum of an even function and an odd function. Neither
   d. The product of two even functions. Even function
   e. The product of two odd functions. Even function
   f. The product of an even function and an odd function. †

71. Odd and even function. State whether the composite function $f \circ g$ is an odd function, an even function, or neither in the following situations:
   a. f and g are odd functions. Odd function
   b. f and g are even functions. Even function
   c. f is odd and g is even. Even function
   d. f is even and g is odd. Even function

72. Let $h(x)$ be any function whose domain contains $-x$ whenever it contains x. Show that
   a. $f(x) = h(x) + h(-x)$ is an even function. †
   b. $g(x) = h(x) - h(-x)$ is an odd function. †
   c. $h(x)$ can always be expressed as the sum of an even and an odd function. †

73. Use Exercise 72 to write each of the following functions as the sum of an even function and an odd function.
   a. $h(x) = x^2 - 2x + 3$ †   **b.** $h(x) = [x] + x$ †

Critical Thinking

74. Let $f(x) = \dfrac{1}{[x]}$ and $g(x) = \sqrt{x(2 - x)}$. Find the domain of each of the following functions.
   a. $f(x)$ †
   b. $g(x)$ Domain: [0, 2]
   c. $f(x) + g(x)$ †
   d. $\dfrac{f(x)}{g(x)}$ Domain: [1, 2)

75. For each of the following functions, find the domain of $f \circ f$.
   a. $f(x) = \dfrac{1}{\sqrt{-x}}$ Domain: ∅   **b.** $f(x) = \dfrac{1}{\sqrt{1 - x}}$ †

Inverse Functions

BEFORE STARTING THIS SECTION, REVIEW

1. Vertical-line test (Section 2.4, page 231)

2. Domain and range of a function (Section 2.4, page 230)

3. Composition of functions (Section 2.7, page 283)

4. Line of symmetry (Section 2.2, page 194)

5. Solving linear and quadratic equations (Section 1.1 and 1.4, pages 89; 120)

OBJECTIVES

1 Learn the definition of an inverse function and a relation.

2 Identify one-to-one functions.

3 Find the inverse function.

4 Use inverse functions to find the range of a function.

5 Apply inverse functions in the real world.

Water Pressure on Underwater Devices

The pressure at any depth in the ocean is due to the weight of the overlying water: The deeper you go, the greater is the pressure. Exactly how much does pressure increase with depth? When you go 33 feet deep into water, the pressure increases by 15 pounds per square inch (1 atmosphere). Pressure is a vital consideration in the design of all tools and vehicles that work beneath the water's surface. Work performed by underwater vehicles plays a significant role in the petroleum industry's effort to extract oil beyond the continental shelf, and submarines and diving bells are crucial for military, educational, and industrial uses. To compute the pressure precisely requires a somewhat complicated equation that takes into account the water's salinity, temperature, and slight compressibility. However, a basic formula is given by "pressure equals depth times 15, divided by 33." We thus have pressure (psi) = depth (ft) × 15(psi per atm)/33(ft per atm), where "psi" means "pounds per square inch" and "atm" abbreviates "atmosphere."

For example, if you go 99 feet down under water, that's 45 psi of pressure. If you go 1 mile (5280 feet) down under water, the pressure is (5280 × 15)/33 = 2400 psi. Suppose the pressure gauge on a diving bell breaks and shows a reading of 1800 psi. Determining how far below the surface the bell was when the gauge failed is a straightforward instance of the general concept of inverse functions. We will return to this problem in Example 9. ■

1 Learn the definition of an inverse function and a relation.

Inverses

In Section 2.4, we learned that a relation is any set of ordered pairs. If the ordered pairs in the relation are given as (x, y), then the set of ordered pairs (y, x) with coordinates interchanged is called the **inverse** of the relation. If the relation is a function, the inverse relation may or may not be a function.

EXAMPLE 1   Determining Whether an Inverse Relation Is a Function

TABLE 2.14

Dwayne	590-56-4932
Sophia	599-23-1746
Desmonde	264-31-4958
Carl	432-77-6602
Anna	195-37-4165
Sal	543-71-8026

TABLE 2.15

Dwayne	24
Sophia	26
Desmonde	42
Carl	51
Anna	24
Sal	26

Ray's Music Mart has six employees. Table 2.14 lists the first names and the Social Security numbers of the employees, and Table 2.15 lists the first names and the ages of the employees.

a. Find the inverse of the function defined by Table 2.14, and determine whether the inverse relation is a function.

b. Find the inverse of the function defined by Table 2.15, and determine whether the inverse relation is a function.

Solution

a. Notice that if you are told the Social Security number of an employee, say, 264-31-4958, you can identify that employee from Table 2.14 (in this case, Desmonde). The set of ordered pairs for the function defined by Table 2.14 is

{(Dwayne, 590-56-4932), (Sophia, 599-23-1746), (Desmonde, 264-31-4958),
(Carl, 432-77-6602), (Anna, 195-37-4165), (Sal, 543-71-8026)}.

Every y-value corresponds to exactly one x-value. In this case, interchanging x and y coordinates produces a function, namely,

{(590-56-4932, Dwayne), (599-23-1746, Sophia), (264-31-4958, Desmonde),
(432-77-6602, Carl), (195-37-4165, Anna), (543-71-8026, Sal)}.

Thus, the inverse of the function defined by Table 2.14 is also a function.

b. If you are told the age of an employee, you may not be able to use Table 2.15 to identify that employee. For example, if you are told that the employee is 24 years old, Table 2.15 indicates only that the employee is either Dwayne or Anna. The set of ordered pairs defined by Table 2.15 is

{(Dwayne, 24), (Sophia, 26), (Desmonde, 42), (Carl, 51), (Anna, 24), (Sal, 26)}.

Because there is more than one x-value that corresponds to a y-value ((Dwayne, 24) and (Anna, 24) are examples), interchanging x and y-coordinates does not produce a function. That is, the inverse relation

{(24, Dwayne), (26, Sophia), (42, Desmonde), (51, Carl), (24, Anna,), (26, Sal)}

contains distinct ordered pairs with the same first coordinate.

Thus, the inverse of the function defined by Table 2.15 is *not* a function.   ■ ■ ■

PRACTICE PROBLEM 1   Find the inverse of the function given by the table, and determine whether it is itself a function. The table shows the number of hours each of the employees identified in Example 1 worked the previous week.

Dwayne	47	Carl	55
Sophia	43	Anna	47
Desmonde	50	Sal	46

■

2 Identify one-to-one functions.

The inverse of the function in Example 1(a) is a function because each *y*-value in the range corresponds to exactly one *x*-value in the domain. We call such functions *one-to-one* functions.

DEFINITION OF A ONE-TO-ONE FUNCTION

A function is called a **one-to-one function** if each *y*-value in its range corresponds to only one *x*-value in its domain.

Let f be a one-to-one function. Then the preceding definition implies that, for any two numbers x_1 and x_2 in the domain of f, if $x_1 \neq x_2$, then $f(x_1) \neq f(x_2)$. That is, *f is a one-to-one function if different x-values correspond to different y-values.*

Figure 2.67(a) represents a one-to-one function, and Figure 2.67(b) represents a function that is not one-to-one. The relation shown in Figure 2.67(c) is not a function.

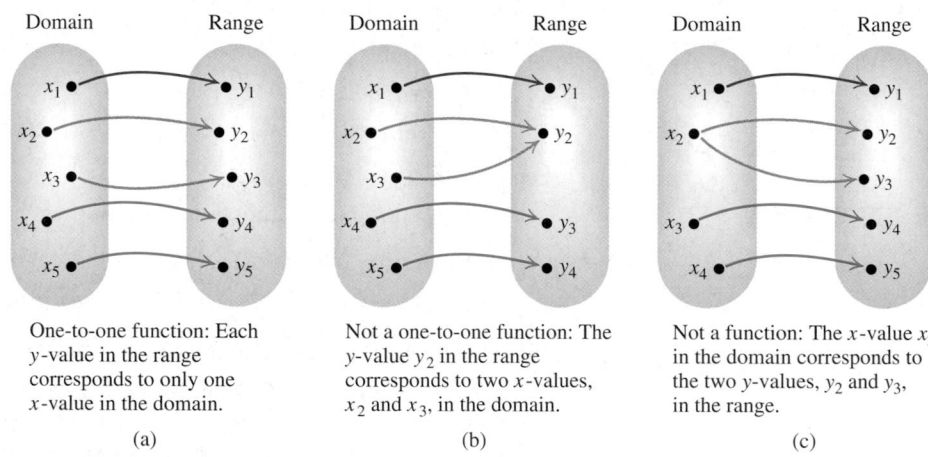

One-to-one function: Each *y*-value in the range corresponds to only one *x*-value in the domain.

(a)

Not a one-to-one function: The *y*-value y_2 in the range corresponds to two *x*-values, x_2 and x_3, in the domain.

(b)

Not a function: The *x*-value x_2 in the domain corresponds to the two *y*-values, y_2 and y_3, in the range.

(c)

FIGURE 2.67

For a function to be one-to-one, different *x*-values must correspond to different *y*-values. Consequently, if a function f is *not* one-to-one, then there are at least two numbers x_1 and x_2 in the domain of f such that $x_1 \neq x_2$ and $f(x_1) = f(x_2)$. Geometrically, this means that the horizontal line passing through the two points $(x_1, f(x_1))$ and $(x_2, f(x_2))$ contains these *two* points on the graph of f. The geometric interpretation of a one-to-one function is called the *horizontal-line test*.

HORIZONTAL-LINE TEST

A function f is one-to-one if no horizontal line intersects the graph of f in more than one point.

| EXAMPLE 2 | **Using the Horizontal-Line Test** |

Use the horizontal-line test to determine which of the following functions are one-to-one.

a. $f(x) = 2x + 5$ **b.** $g(x) = x^2 - 1$ **c.** $h(x) = 2\sqrt{x}$

Solution

From the graphs in Figure 2.68, we see that no horizontal line intersects the graphs of f (Figure 2.68(a)) and h (Figure 2.68(c)) in more than one point; therefore, the functions f and h are one-to-one. The function g is not one-to-one, since the horizontal line $y = 3$ in Figure 2.68(b) (among others) intersects the graph of g at more than one point.   ■ ■ ■

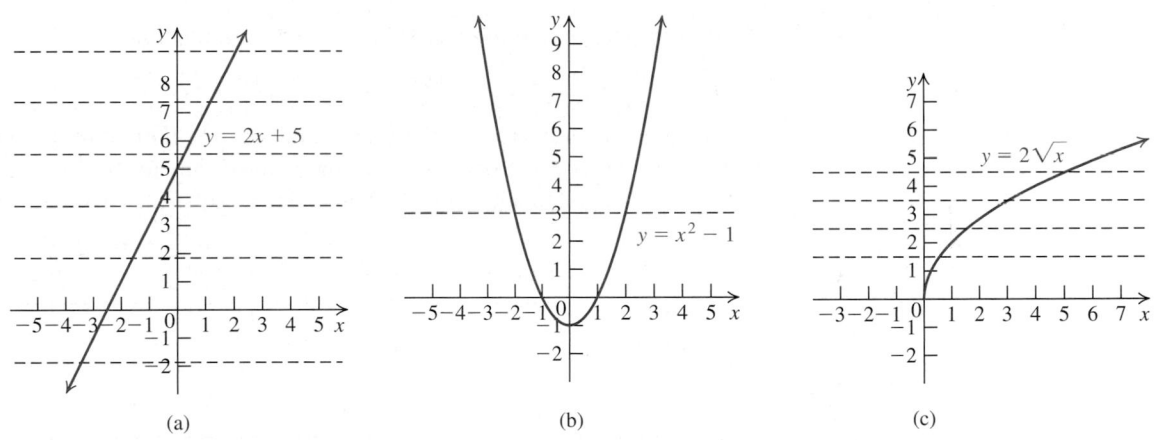

FIGURE 2.68

Practice Problem 2   Use the horizontal-line test to determine whether $f(x) = (x - 1)^2$ is a one-to-one function.   ■

If f is a one-to-one function, then the inverse of f is also a function. We use a special notation, f^{-1}, for the inverse function.

DEFINITION OF f^{-1} FOR A ONE-TO-ONE FUNCTION f

Let f represent a one-to-one function. The inverse of f is also a function, called the **inverse function of f**, and is denoted by f^{-1}. If (x, y) is an ordered pair of f, then (y, x) is an ordered pair of f^{-1}, and we write $x = f^{-1}(y)$. We have $y = f(x)$ if and only if $f^{-1}(y) = x$.

◆ **WARNING**

The notation $f^{-1}(x)$ does not mean $\dfrac{1}{f(x)}$. The expression $\dfrac{1}{f(x)}$ represents the reciprocal of $f(x)$ and is sometimes written as $[f(x)]^{-1}$.

EXAMPLE 3   **Relating the Values of a Function and Its Inverse**

Assume that f is a one-to-one function.

a. If $f(3) = 5$ find $f^{-1}(5)$.   **b.** If $f^{-1}(-1) = 7$, find $f(7)$.

Solution

We know that $y = f(x)$ if and only if $f^{-1}(y) = x$.

a. Let $x = 3$ and $y = 5$. Now $5 = f(3)$ if and only if $f^{-1}(5) = 3$. Thus, $f^{-1}(5) = 3$.
b. Let $y = -1$ and $x = 7$. Now (reading from right to left) $f^{-1}(-1) = 7$ if and only if $f(7) = -1$. Thus, $f(7) = -1$.   ▪ ▪ ▪

PRACTICE PROBLEM 3   Assume that f is a one-to-one function.

a. If $f(-3) = 12$, find $f^{-1}(12)$.   **b.** If $f^{-1}(4) = 9$, find $f(9)$.   ▪

Since the coordinates of the ordered pairs (x, y) of a one-to-one function f are interchanged to obtain the ordered pairs of the inverse function f^{-1}, the domain and range of f are interchanged to obtain the domain and range of f^{-1}. We have

Domain of f = Range of f^{-1} Range of f = Domain of f^{-1}.

Consider the following input–output diagram for $f^{-1} \circ f$:

(x, y) is an ordered pair of f (y, x) is an ordered pair of f^{-1}

input f output   input f^{-1} output
x $\longrightarrow$ y y $\longrightarrow$ x

input $f^{-1} \circ f$ output
x $\longrightarrow$ x

As the preceding diagram shows, $(f^{-1} \circ f)(x) = x$ for all x in the domain of f. Similarly, $(f \circ f^{-1})(x) = x$ for all x in the domain of f^{-1}.

INVERSE FUNCTION PROPERTY

Let f denote a one-to-one function. Then

1. $(f \circ f^{-1})(x) = f(f^{-1}(x)) = x$ for every x in the domain of f^{-1}.
2. $(f^{-1} \circ f)(x) = f^{-1}(f(x)) = x$ for every x in the domain of f.

Not only is it true that $(f \circ f^{-1})(x) = x$ and $(f^{-1} \circ f)(x) = x$, but f^{-1} is the *only* function with this property.

UNIQUE INVERSE FUNCTION PROPERTY

Let f denote a one-to-one function. Then if g is any function such that

$$f(g(x)) = x \text{ for every } x \text{ in the domain of } g \text{ and}$$
$$g(f(x)) = x \text{ for every } x \text{ in the domain of } f, \text{ then}$$

$g = f^{-1}$. That is, g is the inverse function of f.

One interpretation of the equation $(f^{-1} \circ f)(x) = x$ is that f^{-1} undoes anything that f does to x. For example, let

$$f(x) = x + 2 \qquad f \text{ adds 2 to any input } x.$$

To undo what f does to x we should subtract 2 from x. That is, the inverse of f should be

$$g(x) = x - 2. \qquad g \text{ subtracts 2 from } x.$$

Let's verify that $g(x) = x - 2$ is indeed the inverse function of x.

$$
\begin{aligned}
(f \circ g)(x) &= f(g(x)) && \text{Definition of } f \circ g \\
&= f(x - 2) && \text{Replace } g(x) \text{ by } x - 2. \\
&= (x - 2) + 2 && \text{Replace } x \text{ by } x - 2 \text{ in } f(x) = x + 2. \\
&= x && \text{Simplify.}
\end{aligned}
$$

Thus, $(f \circ g)(x) = x$. Also

$$
\begin{aligned}
(g \circ f)(x) &= g(f(x)) && \text{Definition of } g \circ f \\
&= g(x + 2) && \text{Replace } f(x) \text{ by } x + 2. \\
&= (x + 2) - 2 && \text{Replace } x \text{ by } x + 2 \text{ in } g(x) = x - 2. \\
&= x. && \text{Simplify.}
\end{aligned}
$$

EXAMPLE 4   Verifying Inverse Functions

Verify that the following pairs of functions are inverses of each other:

$$f(x) = 2x + 3 \quad \text{and} \quad g(x) = \frac{x - 3}{2}.$$

Solution

We form the compositions of f and g.

$$
\begin{aligned}
f(x) &= 2x + 3 && \text{Given function } f \\
(f \circ g)(x) &= f(g(x)) && \text{Definition of } f \circ g \\
&= f\left(\frac{x - 3}{2}\right) && \text{Replace } g(x) \text{ by } \frac{x - 3}{2}. \\
&= 2\left(\frac{x - 3}{2}\right) + 3 && \text{Replace } x \text{ by } \frac{x - 3}{2} \text{ in } f(x) = 2x + 3. \\
&= (x - 3) + 3 && \text{Simplify.} \\
&= x && \text{Simplify.}
\end{aligned}
$$

Thus, $f(g(x)) = x$.

Continued on next page.

Now find $g(f(x))$.

$$g(x) = \frac{x - 3}{2} \qquad \text{Given function } g$$

$$(g \circ f)(x) = g(f(x)) \qquad \text{Definition of } g \text{ of } f$$

$$= g(2x + 3) \qquad \text{Replace } f(x) \text{ by } 2x + 3.$$

$$= \frac{(2x + 3) - 3}{2} \qquad \text{Replace } x \text{ by } 2x + 3 \text{ in } g(x) = \frac{x - 3}{2}.$$

$$= x \qquad \text{Simplify.}$$

Thus, $g(f(x)) = x$.

Since $f(g(x)) = g(f(x)) = x$, we conclude that f and g are inverses of each other.

■ ■ ■

PRACTICE PROBLEM 4 Verify that $f(x) = 3x - 1$ and $g(x) = \dfrac{x + 1}{3}$ are inverses of each other. ■

In Example 4, notice how the functions f and g neutralize (undo) the effect of one another.

The function f takes an input x, *multiplies* it by 2, and *adds* 3; g neutralizes (or undoes) this effect by *subtracting* 3 and *dividing* by 2. This neutralizing process is illustrated in Figure 2.69. Notice that g reverses both the operations performed by f *and* the order in which they are done.

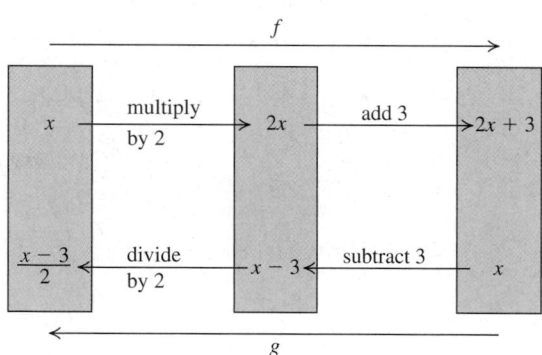

FIGURE 2.69

3 Find the inverse function.

Finding the Inverse Function

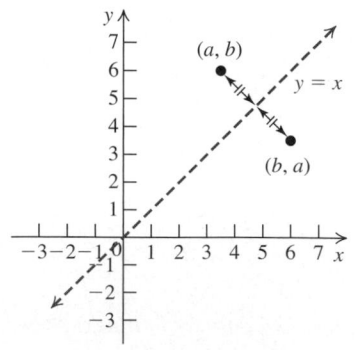

FIGURE 2.70

Let $y = f(x)$ be a one-to-one function; then f has an inverse function. Suppose (a, b) is a point on the graph of f. Then $b = f(a)$. This means that $a = f^{-1}(b)$, so (b, a) is a point on the graph of f^{-1}. Notice that the points (a, b) and (b, a) are symmetric with respect to the line $y = x$, as shown in Figure 2.70. (See Exercises 77 and 78.) That is, if the graph paper is folded along the line $y = x$, the points (a, b) and (b, a) will coincide. We therefore have the following property:

SYMMETRY PROPERTY OF THE GRAPHS OF f AND f^{-1}

The graph of a function f and the graph of f^{-1} are symmetric with respect to the line $y = x$.

> **EXAMPLE 5**   **Finding the Graph of f^{-1} from the Graph of f**

The graph of a function f is shown in Figure 2.71. Sketch the graph of f^{-1}.

Solution

By the horizontal-line test, f is a one-to-one function, so its inverse will also be a function.

The graph of f consists of two line segments: one joining the points $(-3, -5)$ and $(-1, 2)$, and the other joining the points $(-1, 2)$ and $(4, 3)$.

The graph of f^{-1} is the reflection of the graph of f in the line $y = x$. The reflections of the points $(-3, -5), (-1, 2)$, and $(4, 3)$ in the line $y = x$ are $(-5, -3), (2, -1)$ and $(3, 4)$, respectively.

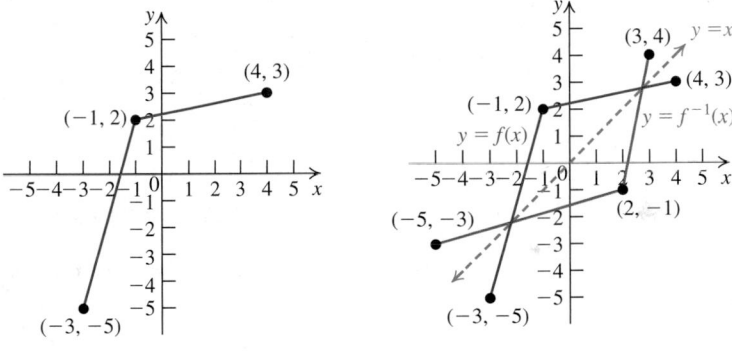

FIGURE 2.71   **FIGURE 2.72**

The graph of f^{-1} consists of two line segments: one joining the points $(-5, -3)$ and $(2, -1)$, and the other joining the points $(2, -1)$ and $(3, 4)$. Figure 2.72 shows the graph of f and f^{-1} on the same coordinate axes.   ■ ■ ■

PRACTICE PROBLEM 5   Use the given graph of a function f to sketch the graph of f^{-1}.   ■

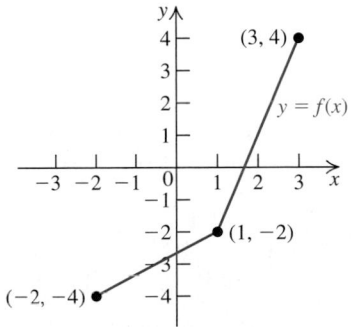

The symmetry property between the graphs of f and f^{-1} tells us that we can find an equation for the inverse function $y = f^{-1}(x)$ from the equation of a one-to-one function $y = f(x)$ by interchanging the roles of x and y in the equation $y = f(x)$. That is, we replace x by y and y by x in the equation $y = f(x)$ to obtain $x = f(y)$. Then we solve the equation $x = f(y)$ for y in terms of x to get $y = f^{-1}(x)$.

Here is a step-by-step procedure for finding the inverse of a one-to-one function:

FINDING THE SOLUTION: PROCEDURE FOR FINDING f^{-1}

OBJECTIVE	EXAMPLE
To find the inverse of a function.	*Find the inverse of $f(x) = 3x - 4$.*

Step 1 Replace $f(x)$ by y in the equation for $f(x)$.

$y = 3x - 4$ Replace $f(x)$ by y.

Step 2 Interchange x and y.

$x = 3y - 4$ Interchange x and y.

Step 3 Solve the equation in Step 2 for y.

$x + 4 = 3y$ Add 4 to both sides.

$\dfrac{x + 4}{3} = y$ Divide both sides by 3.

Step 4 Replace y by $f^{-1}(x)$.

$f^{-1}(x) = \dfrac{x + 4}{3}$

EXAMPLE 6   **Finding the Inverse Function**

Find the inverse of the one-to-one function

$$f(x) = \frac{x + 1}{x - 2}, \quad x \neq 2.$$

Solution

$f(x) = \dfrac{x + 1}{x - 2}, \quad x \neq 2$ Given function

Step 1 $y = \dfrac{x + 1}{x - 2}$ Replace $f(x)$ by y.

Step 2 $x = \dfrac{y + 1}{y - 2}$ Interchange x and y.

Step 3 Solve $x = \dfrac{y + 1}{y - 2}$ for y.   This is the most challenging step.

$\begin{aligned} x(y - 2) &= y + 1 & &\text{Multiply both sides by } y - 2. \\ xy - 2x &= y + 1 & &\text{Distributive property} \\ xy - 2x + 2x - y &= y + 1 + 2x - y & &\text{Add } 2x - y \text{ to both sides.} \\ xy - y &= 2x + 1 & &\text{Simplify.} \\ y(x - 1) &= 2x + 1 & &\text{Factor out } y. \\ y &= \frac{2x + 1}{x - 1} & &\text{Divide both sides by} \\ & & &x - 1, \text{ assuming that } x \neq 1. \end{aligned}$

Step 4 $f^{-1}(x) = \dfrac{2x + 1}{x - 1}, \quad x \neq 1$ Replace y by $f^{-1}(x)$.

To see if our calculations are accurate, we check whether the expression obtained in Step 4 is indeed the inverse of f by computing $f(f^{-1}(x))$ and $f^{-1}(f(x))$.

$$f^{-1}(f(x)) = f^{-1}\left(\frac{x + 1}{x - 2}\right) = \frac{2\left(\dfrac{x + 1}{x - 2}\right) + 1}{\dfrac{x + 1}{x - 2} - 1} = \frac{2x + 2 + x - 2}{x + 1 - x + 2} = \frac{3x}{3} = x.$$

You should also check that $f(f^{-1}(x)) = x$.   ■ ■ ■

PRACTICE PROBLEM 6   Find the inverse of the one-to-one function $f(x) = \dfrac{x}{x + 3}, x \neq -3$. ■

4 Use inverse functions to find the range of a function.

Finding the Range of a Function

In Section 2.4, we mentioned that it is not always easy to determine the range of a function that is defined by an equation. However, suppose a function f has inverse f^{-1}. Then the range of f is the domain of f^{-1}. In those cases where we can find a formula for f^{-1}, we can find the range of f by finding the domain of f^{-1}.

| EXAMPLE 7 | Finding the Domain and Range |

Find the domain and the range of the function $f(x) = \dfrac{x + 1}{x - 2}$ of Example 6.

Solution

The domain of $f(x) = \dfrac{x + 1}{x - 2}$ is the set of all real numbers x such that $x \neq 2$, since 2 is the only number for which $\dfrac{x + 1}{x - 2}$ is not a real number. In interval notation, the domain of f is $(-\infty, 2) \cup (2, \infty)$.

From Example 6, $f^{-1}(x) = \dfrac{2x + 1}{x - 1}, x \neq 1$; therefore,

$$\text{Range of } f = \text{Domain of } f^{-1} = \{x \mid x \neq 1\}.$$

In interval notation, the range of f is $(-\infty, 1) \cup (1, \infty)$. ■ ■ ■

PRACTICE PROBLEM 7   Find the domain and the range of the function $f(x) = \dfrac{x}{x + 3}$. ■

If a function f is not one-to-one, then it does not have an inverse function. Sometimes, by changing its domain, we can produce an interesting function that does have an inverse. (This technique is frequently used in trigonometry.) For example, we saw in Example 2, part (b), that $f(x) = x^2 - 1$ is not a one-to-one function. Hence, $f(x) = x^2 - 1$ does not have an inverse function. However, the horizontal-line test shows that the function

$$g(x) = x^2 - 1, \quad x \geq 0$$

with domain $[0, \infty)$ is one-to-one. (See Figure 2.73.) Therefore, g has an inverse function g^{-1}.

FIGURE 2.73

You can also see that the graphs of $g(x) = x^2 - 1, x \geq 0$ and $g^{-1}(x) = \sqrt{x} - 1$ are symmetric in the line $y = x$ with a graphing calculator.

Enter Y_1, Y_2, and Y_3 as $g(x)$, $g^{-1}(x)$, and $f(x) = x$, respectively.

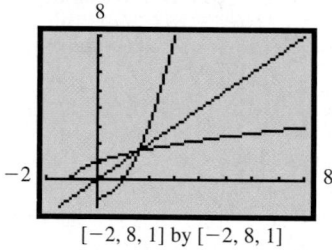

$[-2, 8, 1]$ by $[-2, 8, 1]$

EXAMPLE 8   **Finding an Inverse Function**

Find the inverse of $g(x) = x^2 - 1, x \geq 0$.

Solution

We find g^{-1} by the four-step procedure for finding an inverse function:

$$g(x) = x^2 - 1, \quad x \geq 0 \qquad \text{Original function}$$

Step 1 $y = x^2 - 1, \quad x \geq 0$ Replace $g(x)$ by y.

Step 2 $x = y^2 - 1, \quad y \geq 0$ Interchange x and y.

Step 3 $x + 1 = y^2, \quad y \geq 0$ Add 1 to both sides.

           $y = \pm\sqrt{x + 1}, \quad y \geq 0$ Solve for y.

Since $y \geq 0$ from Step 2, we reject $y = -\sqrt{x + 1}$. Thus, we choose

$$y = \sqrt{x + 1}.$$

Step 4 $g^{-1}(x) = \sqrt{x + 1}$ Replace y by $g^{-1}(x)$.

The graphs of g and g^{-1} are shown in Figure 2.74.

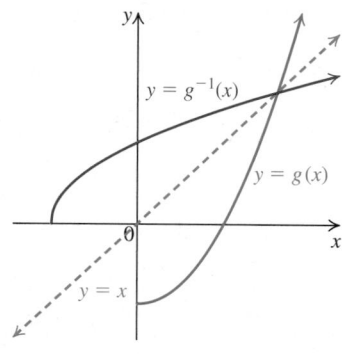

FIGURE 2.74   ■ ■ ■

PRACTICE PROBLEM 8   Find the inverse of $g(x) = x^2 - 1, x \leq 0$.   ■

5   Apply inverse functions in the real world.

Applications

Functions that model real-life situations are frequently expressed as formulas with letters that remind you of the variables they represent. In finding the inverse of a function expressed by a formula, it could be very confusing to interchange the letters. Accordingly, we omit Step 2, keep the letters the same, and just solve the formula for the other variable.

EXAMPLE 9   **Water Pressure on Underwater Devices**

At the beginning of this section, we gave the formula for finding the water pressure p (in pounds per square inch), at a depth d (in feet) below the surface. This formula can be written as $p = \dfrac{15d}{33}$. Suppose the pressure gauge on a diving bell breaks and shows a reading of 1800 psi. Determine how far below the surface the bell was when the gauge failed.

Solution

We want to find the unknown depth in terms of the known pressure. This depth is given by the inverse of the function $p = \dfrac{15d}{33}$.

To find the inverse, we solve the given equation for d.

$$p = \frac{15d}{33} \qquad \text{Original equation}$$

$$33p = 15d \qquad \text{Multiply both sides by 33.}$$

$$d = \frac{33p}{15} \qquad \text{Solve for } d.$$

Now we can use this formula to find how far below the surface the bell was when the gauge failed and read 1800 psi. We let $p = 1800$.

$$d = \frac{33p}{15} \qquad \text{Depth from pressure equation}$$

$$d = \frac{33(1800)}{15} \qquad \text{Replace } p \text{ by 1800.}$$

$$d = 3960$$

The device was 3960 feet below the surface when the gauge failed. ■ ■ ■

PRACTICE PROBLEM 9 In Example 9, suppose the pressure gauge showed a reading of 1650 psi. Determine how far below the surface the bell was when the gauge failed. ■

A Exercises Basic Skills and Concepts

In Exercises 1 and 2, find the inverse of the function defined by the given table and state whether the inverse relation is a function. If the inverse relation is not a function, explain why not.

1.

City	Zip Code
Doddsville, MS	38736
Sacramento, CA	94203
Omaha, NE	68102
Salem, MA	01970
Naalehu, HI	96772

(*Source*: www.USPS.com) †

2.

2006 Chevrolet type	Estimated highway miles per gallon
Malibu	26
Colorado	27
Monte Carlo	31
Impala	27
Equinox	23

(*Source*: www. internetautoguide.com) †

†Due to space constrictions, answers to these exercises may be found in the Answers beginning on page A–1 in the back of the book.

In Exercises 3 and 4, find the inverse of each function and determine whether each inverse is a function.

3. $\{(-13, 3), (-8, 2), (-1, -1), (13, -3), (8, -2), (-1, 1)\}$ †

4. $\{(-3, 10), (-2, 5), (-1, 2), (0, 1), (1, 2), (2, 5), (3, 10)\}$ †

In Exercises 5–12, the graph of a function is given. Use the horizontal-line test to determine whether the function is one-to-one.

5.

one-to-one

† 6.

not one-to-one

7.

not one-to-one

† 8.

one-to-one

9.

not one-to-one

† 10.

not one-to-one

11.

one-to-one

† 12.
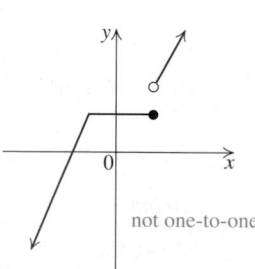
not one-to-one

In Exercises 13–22, assume that the function f is one-to-one.

13. If $f(2) = 7$, find $f^{-1}(7)$. 2

14. If $f^{-1}(4) = -7$, find $f(-7)$. 4

15. If $f(-1) = 2$, find $f^{-1}(2)$. −1

16. If $f^{-1}(-3) = 5$, find $f(5)$. −3

17. If $f(a) = b$, find $f^{-1}(b)$. a

18. If $f^{-1}(c) = d$, find $f(d)$. c

19. Find $(f^{-1} \circ f)(337)$. 337

20. Find $(f \circ f^{-1})(25\pi)$. 25π

21. Find $(f \circ f^{-1})(-1580)$. −1580

22. Find $(f^{-1} \circ f)(9728)$. 9728

23. For $f(x) = 2x - 3$, find each of the following.
   a. $f(3)$ 3
   b. $f^{-1}(3)$ 3
   c. $(f \circ f^{-1})(19)$ 19
   d. $(f \circ f^{-1})(5)$ 5

24. For $f(x) = x^3$, find each of the following.
   a. $f(2)$ 8
   b. $f^{-1}(8)$ 2
   c. $(f \circ f^{-1})(15)$ 15
   d. $(f^{-1} \circ f)(27)$ 27

25. For $f(x) = x^3 + 1$, find each of the following.
   a. $f(1)$ 2 b. $f^{-1}(2)$ 1 c. $(f \circ f^{-1})(269)$ 269

26. For $g(x) = \sqrt[3]{2x^3 - 1}$, find each of the following.
   a. $g(1)$ 1 b. $g^{-1}(1)$ 1 c. $(g^{-1} \circ g)(135)$. 135

In Exercises 27–32, the graph of a function f is given. Sketch the graph of f^{-1}.

27.

† 28.

29.

† 30.

31.

† 32.

In Exercises 33 and 34, use the table of values for $y = f(x)$ to find a table of values for $y = f^{-1}(x)$.

33.

x	−2	−1	0	1	2
$f(x)$	3	4	5	6	7	†

34.

x	-3	-1	1	3	5
$f(x)$	2	0	1	-2	3
†

In Exercises 35–40, show that f and g are inverses of each other by verifying that $f(g(x)) = x = g(f(x))$.

35. $f(x) = 3x + 1$; $g(x) = \dfrac{x - 1}{3}$ †

36. $f(x) = 2 - 3x$; $g(x) = \dfrac{2 - x}{3}$ †

37. $f(x) = x^3$; $g(x) = \sqrt[3]{x}$

38. $f(x) = \dfrac{1}{x}$; $g(x) = \dfrac{1}{x}$

39. $f(x) = \dfrac{x - 1}{x + 2}$; $g(x) = \dfrac{1 + 2x}{1 - x}$

40. $f(x) = \dfrac{3x + 2}{x - 1}$; $g(x) = \dfrac{x + 2}{x - 3}$

41. Find the domain and range of the function f of Exercise 39. †

42. Find the domain and range of the function f of Exercise 40. †

In Exercises 43–54,
a. Determine whether the given function is a one-to-one function.

b. If the function is one-to-one, find its inverse.
c. Sketch the graph of the function and its inverse on the same coordinate axes.

43. $f(x) = 15 - 3x$ †

44. $g(x) = 2x + 5$ †

45. $f(x) = \sqrt{4 - x^2}$ †

46. $f(x) = -\sqrt{9 - x^2}$ †

47. $f(x) = \sqrt{x} + 3$ †

48. $f(x) = 4 - \sqrt{x}$ †

49. $g(x) = \sqrt[3]{x + 1}$ †

50. $h(x) = \sqrt[3]{1 - x}$ †

51. $f(x) = \dfrac{1}{x - 1}, x \neq 1$ †

52. $g(x) = 1 - \dfrac{1}{x}, x \neq 0$ †

53. $f(x) = \sqrt{2 - x}$ †

54. $g(x) = \sqrt{3 + x}$ †

In Exercises 55–58, assume that the given function is one-to-one. Find the inverse of the function. Also, find the domain and the range of the given function.

55. $f(x) = \dfrac{x + 1}{x - 2}, x \neq 2$ †

56. $g(x) = \dfrac{x + 2}{x + 1}, x \neq -1$ †

57. $f(x) = \dfrac{1 - 2x}{1 + x}, x \neq -1$ †

58. $h(x) = \dfrac{x - 1}{x - 3}, x \neq 3$ †

B Exercises   Applying the Concepts

59. Temperature scales. Scientists use the **Kelvin** temperature scale, in which the lowest possible temperature (called absolute zero) is 0 K (K denotes degrees Kelvin).

  The function $K(C) = C + 273$ gives the relationship between the Kelvin temperature (K) and the Celsius temperature (C).

  a. Find the inverse function of $K(C) = C + 273$. What does it represent? †

  b. Use the inverse function from (a) to find the Celsius temperature corresponding to 300 K.   27°C

  c. A comfortable room temperature is 22°C. What is the corresponding Kelvin temperature?   295 K

60. Temperature scales. The boiling point of water is 373 K, or 212°F; the freezing point of water is 273 K, or 32°F. The relationship between Kelvin and Fahrenheit temperature is linear.

  a. Write a linear function expressing $K(F)$ in terms of F. †

  b. Find the inverse of the function in part (a). What does it mean? †

  c. A normal human body temperature is 98.6°F. What is the corresponding Kelvin temperature?   310 K

61. Composition of functions. Use Exercises 59 and 60 and the composition of functions to

  a. Write a function that expresses F in terms of C. †

  b. Write a function that expresses C in terms of F. †

62. Celsius and Fahrenheit temperatures. Show that the functions in (a) and (b) of Exercise 61 are inverse functions. †

63. Currency exchange. Alisha went to Europe last summer. She discovered that when she exchanged her U.S. dollars for euros, she received 25% fewer euros than the number of dollars she exchanged. (She got 75 euros for every 100 U.S. dollars.) When she returned, she got 25% more dollars than the number of euros she exchanged.

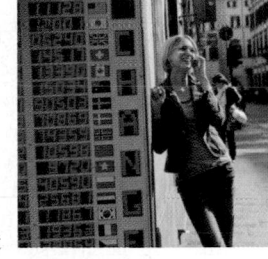

  a. Write each conversion function. †

  b. Show that, in part (a), the two functions are not inverse functions. †

  c. Does Alisha gain or lose money after converting both ways?   She loses money.

64. Hourly wages. Anwar is a short-order cook in a diner. He is paid 4 dollars per hour plus 5% of all the food sales per hour. His average hourly wage w in terms of the food sales of x dollars is $w = 4 + 0.05x$.

  a. Write the inverse function. What does it mean? †

  b. Use the inverse function to estimate the hourly sales at the diner if Anwar averages 12 dollars per hour. $160

65. Hourly wages. In Exercise 64, suppose, in addition, that Anwar is guaranteed a minimum wage of $7 per hour.
  a. Write a function expressing his hourly wage w in terms of food sales per hour. [*Hint:* Use a piecewise function.] †
  b. Does the function in part (a) have an inverse? Explain. †
  c. If the answer in part (b) is yes, then find the inverse function. If the answer is no, then restrict the domain so that the new function has an inverse. †

66. Simple pendulum. If a pendulum is released at a certain point, the **period** is the time it takes for the pendulum to swing along its path and return to the point from which it was released. The period T (in seconds) of a simple pendulum is a function of its length l (in feet) and is given by $T = (1.11)l$.
  a. Find the inverse function. What does it mean? †
  b. Use the inverse function to calculate the length of the pendulum if its period is 2 seconds. 1.8 ft
  c. The convention center in Portland, Oregon, has the longest pendulum in the United States. The pendulum's length is 90 feet. Find the period. 99.9 sec

67. Water supply. Suppose x is the height of the water above the opening at the base of a water tank. The velocity V of water that flows from the opening at the base is a function of x and is given by $V(x) = 8\sqrt{x}$.
  a. Find the inverse function. What does it mean? †
  b. Use the inverse function to calculate the depth of the water in the tank when the flow is (*i*) 30 feet per second and (*ii*) 20 feet per second. †

68. Physics. A projectile is fired from the origin over horizontal ground. Its altitude y (in feet) is a function of its horizontal distance x (in feet) and is given by $y = 64x - 2x^2$.
  a. Find the inverse function.
  b. Use the inverse function to compute the horizontal distance when the altitude of the projectile is (*i*) 32 feet, (*ii*) 256 feet, and (*iii*) 512 feet. †

69. Loan repayment. Chris purchased a car at 0% interest for five years. After making a down payment, she agreed to pay the remaining 36,000 dollars in monthly payments of 600 dollars per month for 60 months.
  a. What does the function $f(x) = 36,000 - 600x$ represent?
  b. Find the inverse of the function in part (a). What does the inverse function represent?
  c. Use the inverse function to find the number of months remaining to make payments if the balance due is 22,000 dollars. †

70. Demand function. A marketing survey finds that the number x (in millions) of computer chips the market will purchase is a function of its price p (in dollars) and is estimated by $x = 8p^2 - 32p + 1200, 0 < p \le 2$.
  a. Find the inverse function. What does it mean?
  b. Use the inverse function to estimate the price of a chip if the demand is 1180.5 million chips. †

C Exercises   Beyond the Basics

In Exercises 71 and 72, show that f and g are inverses of each other by verifying that $f(g(x)) = x = g(f(x))$.

71.

x	1	3	4
$f(x)$	3	5	2

x	3	5	2
$g(x)$	1	3	4

72.

x	1	2	3	4
$f(x)$	-2	0	-3	1

x	-2	0	-3	1
$g(x)$	1	2	3	4

73. Let $f(x) = \sqrt{4 - x^2}$.
  a. Sketch the graph of $y = f(x)$. †
  b. Is f one-to-one? †
  c. Find the domain and the range of f. †

74. Let $f(x) = \dfrac{[x] + 2}{[x] - 2}$, where $[x]$ is the greatest-integer function.
  a. Find the domain of f. Domain: $(-\infty, 2) \cup [3, \infty)$
  b. Is f one-to-one? No

75. Let $f(x) = \dfrac{x}{x+1} = 1 - \dfrac{1}{x+1}$.

   a. Show that f is one-to-one. †

   b. Find the inverse of f. †

   c. Find the domain and the range of f. †

76. Let $g(x) = \sqrt{1 - x^2}, 0 \le x \le 1$.

   a. Show that g is one-to-one. †

   b. Find the inverse of g. †

   c. Find the domain and the range of g. †

77. Let $P(3, 7)$ and $Q(7, 3)$ be two points in the plane.

   a. Show that the midpoint M of the line segment PQ lies on the line $y = x$. †

   b. Show that the line $y = x$ is the perpendicular bisector of the line segment $\overline{PQ}$; that is, show that the line $y = x$ contains the midpoint found in (a) and makes a right angle with $\overline{PQ}$. Hence, the points $(3, 7)$ and $(7, 3)$ are symmetric about the line $y = x$. †

78. Use the procedure outlined in Exercise 77 to show that the points (a, b) and (b, a) are symmetric about the line $y = x$. (See Figure 2.70.) †

79. The graph of $f(x) = x^3$ is given in section 2.5.

   a. Sketch the graph of $g(x) = (x - 1)^3 + 2$ by using transformations of the graph of f. †

   b. Find $g^{-1}(x)$. †

   c. Sketch the graph of $g^{-1}(x)$ by reflecting the graph of g in part (a) in the line $y = x$. †

80. **Inverse of composition of functions.** We show that if f and g have inverses, then

$$(f \circ g)^{-1} = g^{-1} \circ f^{-1}. \text{ (Note the order.)}$$

Let $f(x) = 2x - 1$ and $g(x) = 3x + 4$.

   a. Find the following:

     (i) $f^{-1}(x)$ †   (ii) $g^{-1}(x)$ †

     (iii) $(f \circ g)(x)$ †   (iv) $(g \circ f)(x)$ †

     (v) $(f \circ g)^{-1}(x)$ † (vi) $(g \circ f)^{-1}(x)$ †

     (vii) $(f^{-1} \circ g^{-1})(x)$ † (viii) $(g^{-1} \circ f^{-1})(x)$ †

   b. From part (a), conclude that

     (i) $(f \circ g)^{-1} = g^{-1} \circ f^{-1}$ and

     (ii) $(g \circ f)^{-1} = f^{-1} \circ g^{-1}$. †

81. Repeat Exercise 80 for $f(x) = 2x + 3$ and $g(x) = x^3 - 1$. †

Critical Thinking

82. Does every odd function have an inverse? Explain. †

83. Is there an even function that has an inverse? Explain. †

84. Does every increasing or decreasing function have an inverse? Explain. †

85. A relation R is a set of ordered pairs (x, y). The inverse of R is the set of ordered pairs (y, x).

   a. Give an example of a function such that its inverse relation is not a function. $R = \{(-1, 1),(0, 0),(1, 1)\}$

   b. Give an example of a relation R such that its inverse is a function. $R = \{(-1, 1),(0, 0),(1, 2)\}$

Summary   Definitions, Concepts, and Formulas

2.1 The Coordinate Plane

i. **Ordered Pair.** A pair of numbers in which the order is specified is called an ordered pair of numbers.

ii. **The Distance Formula.** The distance between two points $P(x_1, y_1)$ and $Q(x_2, y_2)$, denoted by $d(P, Q)$, is given by

$$d(P, Q) = \sqrt{(x_2 - x_1)^2 + (y_2 - y_1)^2}.$$

iii. **The Midpoint Formula.** The coordinates of the midpoint $M(x, y)$ of the line segment joining $P(x_1, y_1)$ and $Q(x_2, y_2)$ are given by

$$(x, y) = \left(\frac{x_1 + x_2}{2}, \frac{y_1 + y_2}{2} \right).$$

2.2 Graphs of Equations

i. The graph of an equation in two variables, say, x and y, is the set of all ordered pairs (a, b) in the coordinate plane that satisfy the given equation. A graph of an equation, then, is a picture of its solution set.

ii. **Sketching the graph of an equation by plotting points**

   Step 1 Make a representative table of solutions of the equation.

   Step 2 Plot the solutions in Step 1 as ordered pairs in the coordinate plane.

   Step 3 Connect the representative solutions in Step 2 by a smooth curve.

iii. **Intercepts**

   1. The x-intercept is the x-coordinate of a point on the graph where the graph touches or crosses the x-axis. To find the x-intercepts, set $y = 0$ in the equation and solve for x.

   2. The y-intercept is the y-coordinate of a points on the graph where the graph touches or crosses the y-axis. To find the y-intercepts, set $x = 0$ in the equation and solve for y.

iv. **Symmetry**

   A graph is symmetric with respect to

   (a) the y-axis if, for every point (x, y) on the graph, the point $(-x, y)$ is also on the graph. That is, replacing x by $-x$ in the equation produces an equivalent equation.

(b) the *x*-axis if, for every point (x, y) on the graph, the point $(x, -y)$ is also on the graph. That is, replacing y by $-y$ in the equation produces an equivalent equation.

(c) the *origin* if, for every point (x, y) on the graph, the point $(-x, -y)$ is also on the graph. That is, replacing x by $-x$ and y by $-y$ in the equation produces an equivalent equation.

v. Circle

A circle is a set of points in the coordinate plane that are at a fixed distance r from a fixed point (h, k). The fixed distance r is called the radius of the circle, and the fixed point (h, k) is called the center of the circle. The equation

$$(x - h)^2 + (y - k)^2 = r^2$$

is called the *standard equation* of a circle.

2.3 Lines

i. The slope m of a nonvertical line through the points $P(x_1, y_1)$ and $Q(x_2, y_2)$ is

$$m = \frac{\text{rise}}{\text{run}} = \frac{(y\text{-coordinate of } Q) - (y\text{-coordinate of } P)}{(x\text{-coordinate of } Q) - (x\text{-coordinate of } P)}$$
$$= \frac{y_2 - y_1}{x_2 - x_1}.$$

The slope of a vertical line is undefined. The slope of a horizontal line is 0.

ii. Equation of a line

$$y - y_1 = m(x - x_1) \qquad \text{Point–slope form}$$
$$y = mx + b \qquad \text{Slope–intercept form}$$
$$y = k \qquad \text{Horizontal line}$$
$$x = k \qquad \text{Vertical line}$$
$$ax + by + c = 0 \qquad \text{General form}$$

iii. Parallel and Perpendicular Lines

Two distinct lines with respective slopes m_1 and m_2 are

1. Parallel if $m_1 = m_2$.

2. Perpendicular if $m_1 m_2 = -1$.

2.4 Relations and Functions

i. Any set of ordered pairs is a **relation.** The set of all first components is the **domain,** and the set of all second components is the **range.** The graph of all the ordered pairs is the graph of the relation.

ii. A **function** is a relation in which no two ordered pairs have the same first component. A function is a rule that assigns, to each element x in a set A, exactly one element $f(x)$ in a set B.

iii. Vertical-line test. If each vertical line intersects a graph at no more than one point, the graph is the graph of a function.

iv. If a function f is defined by an equation, then its domain is the largest set of real numbers for which $f(x)$ is a real number.

v. The **average rate of change** of $f(x)$ as x changes from a to b is defined by $\dfrac{f(b) - f(a)}{b - a}, b \neq a$.

vi. The quantity $\dfrac{f(x + h) - f(x)}{h}, h \neq 0$, is called the **difference quotient**.

2.5 A Library of Functions

i. For **piecewise functions,** different rules are used in different parts of the domain.

ii. A function f is **increasing, decreasing,** or **constant** on an interval, depending on whether its graph is respectively rising, falling, or staying the same as you move from left to right on the graph.

iii. A function f is **even** if $f(-x) = f(x)$. The graph of an even function is symmetric with respect to the *y*-axis. A function f is **odd** if $f(-x) = -f(x)$. The graph of an odd function is symmetric with respect to the origin.

iv. Basic Functions

Identity function	$f(x) = x$
Constant function	$f(x) = c$
Squaring function	$f(x) = x^2$
Cubing function	$f(x) = x^3$
Absolute value function	$f(x) = |x|$
Square root function	$f(x) = \sqrt{x}$
Cube root function	$f(x) = \sqrt[3]{x}$
Reciprocal function	$f(x) = \dfrac{1}{x}$
Reciprocal square function	$f(x) = \dfrac{1}{x^2}$
Greatest-integer function	$f(x) = [\![x]\!]$

2.6 Transformations

i. Vertical and horizontal shifts: Let f be a function and c be a positive number.

To Graph	Shift the graph of f by c units
$f(x) + c$	up
$f(x) - c$	down
$f(x - c)$	right
$f(x + c)$	left

ii. Reflections:

To Graph	Reflect the graph of f in the
$-f(x)$	*x*-axis
$f(-x)$	*y*-axis

iii. Stretching and compressing: The graph of $g(x) = af(x)$ for $a > 0$ has the same shape as the graph of $f(x)$ and is taller if $a > 1$ and flatter if $0 < a < 1$. If a is negative, the graph is then reflected in the *x*-axis.

The graph of $g(x) = f(bx)$ for $b > 0$ is obtained from the graph of f by stretching away from the y-axis if $0 < b < 1$ and compressing horizontally toward the y-axis if $b > 1$. If b is negative, the graph is then reflected in the y-axis.

2.7 Combining Functions; Composition

i. Given two functions f and g, for all values of x for which both $f(x)$ and $g(x)$ are defined, the functions can be combined to form **sum, difference, product,** and **quotient** functions.

ii. The **composition** of f and g is defined by $(f \circ g)(x) = f(g(x))$.

   The input of f is the output of g. The domain of $f \circ g$ is the set of all x in the domain of g such that $g(x)$ is in the domain of f.

   In general $f \circ g \neq g \circ f$.

2.8 Inverse Functions

i. A function f is **one-to-one** if, for any x_1 and x_2 in the domain of f, $f(x_1) = f(x_2)$ implies $x_1 = x_2$.

ii. **Horizontal-line test.** If each horizontal line intersects the graph of a function f in at most one point, then f is a one-to-one function.

iii. **Inverse function.** Let f be a one-to-one function. Then g is the inverse of f, and we write $g = f^{-1}$ if $(f \circ g)(x) = x$ for every x in the domain of g and $(g \circ f)(x) = x$ for every x in the domain of f. The graph of f^{-1} is the reflection of the graph of f in the line $y = x$.

Review Exercises

Basic Skills and Concepts

In Exercises 1–8, state whether the given statement is true or false.

1. $(0, 5)$ is the midpoint of the line segment joining $(-3, 1)$ and $(3, 11)$. False

2. The equation $(x + 2)^2 + (y + 3)^2 = 5$ is the equation of a circle with center $(2, 3)$ and radius 5. False

3. If a graph is symmetric with respect to the x-axis and the y-axis, then it must be symmetric with respect to the origin. †

4. If a graph is symmetric with respect to the origin, then it must be symmetric with respect to the x-axis and the y-axis. False

5. In the graph of the equation of the line $3y = 4x + 9$, the slope is 4 and the y-intercept is 9. False

6. If the slope of a line is 2, then the slope of any line perpendicular to it is $\dfrac{1}{2}$. False

7. The slope of a vertical line is undefined. True

8. The equation $(x - 2)^2 + (y + 3)^2 = -25$ is the equation of a circle with center $(2, -3)$ and radius 5. False

In Exercises 9–14, find

a. The distance between the points P and Q.

b. The coordinates of the midpoint of the line segment PQ.

c. The slope of the line containing the points P and Q.

9. $P(3, 5)$, $Q(-1, 3)$ †   **10.** $P(-3, 5)$, $Q(3, -1)$ †

11. $P(4, -3)$, $Q(9, -8)$ †   **12.** $P(2, 3)$, $Q(-7, -8)$ †

13. $P(2, -7)$, $Q(5, -2)$ †   **14.** $P(-5, 4)$, $Q(10, -3)$ †

15. Show that the points $A(0, 5)$, $B(-2, -3)$, and $C(3, 0)$ are the vertices of a right triangle.

16. Show that the points $A(1, 2)$, $B(4, 8)$, $C(7, -1)$, and $D(10, 5)$ are the vertices of a rhombus.

17. Which of the points $(-6, 3)$ and $(4, 5)$ is closer to the origin? †

18. Which of the points $(-6, 4)$ and $(5, 10)$ is closer to the point $(2, 3)$? †

19. Find a point on the x-axis that is equidistant from the points $(-5, 3)$ and $(4, 7)$. †

20. Find a point on the y-axis that is equidistant from the points $(-3, -2)$ and $(2, -1)$. †

In Exercises 21–24, specify whether the given graph has either axis or origin symmetry (or neither).

21.   **22.** †

23.   **24.** 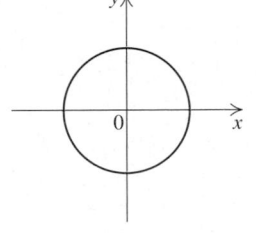 †

In Exercises 25–34, sketch the graph of the given equation. List all intercepts and describe any symmetry of the graph.

25. $x + 2y = 4$ †   **26.** $3x - 4y = 12$ †

†Due to space constrictions, answers to these exercises may be found in the Answers beginning on page A–1 in the back of the book.

27. $y = -2x^2$ †   **28.** $x = -y^2$ †

29. $y = x^3$ †   **30.** $x = -y^3$ †

31. $y = x^2 + 2$ †   **32.** $y = 1 - x^2$ †

33. $x^2 + y^2 = 16$ †   **34.** $y = x^4 - 4$ †

In Exercises 35–37, find the center–radius form of the equation of the circle that satisfies the given conditions.

35. Center $(2, -3)$, radius 5 $(x - 2)^2 + (y + 3)^2 = 25$

36. Diameter with endpoints $(5, 2)$ and $(-5, 4)$ †

37. Center $(-2, -5)$, touching the y-axis †

In Exercises 38–42, describe and sketch the graph of the given equation.

38. $2x - 5y = 10$ †   **39.** $\dfrac{x}{2} - \dfrac{y}{5} = 1$ †

40. $(x + 1)^2 + (y - 3)^2 = 16$ †

41. $x^2 + y^2 - 2x + 4y - 4 = 0$ †

42. $3x^2 + 3y^2 - 6x - 6 = 0$ †

In Exercises 43–47, find the slope–intercept form of the equation of the line that satisfies the given conditions.

43. Passing through $(1, 2)$ with slope -2 $y = -2x + 4$

44. x-intercept 2, y-intercept 5 †

45. Passing through $(1, 3)$ and $(-1, 7)$ $y = -2x + 5$

46. Passing through $(1, 2)$, parallel to x-axis $y = 2$

47. Passing through $(1, 3)$, perpendicular to x-axis $x = 1$

48. Determine whether the lines in each pair are parallel, perpendicular, or neither.

    a. $y = 3x - 2$ and $y = 3x + 2$ parallel

    b. $3x - 5y + 7 = 0$ and $5x - 3y + 2 = 0$ neither

    c. $ax + by + c = 0$ and $bx - ay + d = 0$ perpendicular

    d. $y + 2 = \dfrac{1}{3}(x - 3)$ and $y - 5 = 3(x - 3)$ neither

In Exercises 49–58, graph each relation. State the domain and range of each. Determine which relation determines y as a function of x.

49. $\{(0, 1), (-1, 2), (1, 0), (2, -1)\}$ †

50. $\{(0, 1), (0, -1), (3, 2), (3, -2)\}$ †

51. $x - y = 1$ †   **52.** $y = \sqrt{x - 2}$ †

53. $x^2 + y^2 = 0.04$ †   **54.** $x = -\sqrt{y}$ †

55. $x = 1$ †   **56.** $y = 2$ †

57. $y = |x + 1|$ †   **58.** $x = y^2 + 1$ †

In Exercises 59–76, let $f(x) = 3x + 1$ and $g(x) = x^2 - 2$. Find each of the following.

59. $f(-2)$ -5 **60.** $g(-2)$ 2

61. x if $f(x) = 4$ $x = 1$ **62.** x if $g(x) = 2$ $x = \pm 2$

63. $(f + g)(1)$ 3 **64.** $(f - g)(-1)$ -1

65. $(f \cdot g)(-2)$ -10 **66.** $(g \cdot f)(0)$ -2

67. $(f \circ g)(3)$ 22 **68.** $(g \circ f)(-2)$ 23

69. $(f \circ g)(x)$ $3x^2 - 5$ **70.** $(g \circ f)(x)$ $9x^2 + 6x - 1$

71. $(f \circ f)(x)$ $9x + 4$ **72.** $(g \circ g)(x)$ $x^4 - 4x^2 + 2$

73. $f(a + h)$ $3a + 3h + 1$ **74.** $g(a - h)$ $a^2 - 2ah + h^2 - 2$

75. $\dfrac{f(x + h) - f(x)}{h}$ 3 **76.** $\dfrac{g(x + h) - g(x)}{h}$ $2x + h$

In Exercises 77–82, graph each function and state its domain and range. Determine the intervals over which the function is increasing, decreasing, or constant.

77. $f(x) = -3$ †   **78.** $f(x) = x^2 - 2$ †

79. $g(x) = \sqrt{3x - 2}$ †   **80.** $h(x) = \sqrt{36 - x^2}$ †

81. $f(x) = \begin{cases} x + 1 & \text{if } x \ge 0 \\ -x + 1 & \text{if } x < 0 \end{cases}$ †

82. $g(x) = \begin{cases} x & \text{if } x \ge 0 \\ x^2 & \text{if } x < 0 \end{cases}$ †

In Exercises 83–86, use transformations to graph each pair of functions on the same coordinate axes.

83. $f(x) = \sqrt{x}, g(x) = \sqrt{x + 1}$ †

84. $f(x) = |x|, g(x) = 2|x - 1| + 3$ †

85. $f(x) = \dfrac{1}{x}, g(x) = -\dfrac{1}{x - 2}$ †

86. $f(x) = x^2, g(x) = (x + 1)^2 - 2$ †

In Exercises 87–92, state whether each function is odd, even, or neither. Discuss the symmetry of each graph.

87. $f(x) = x^2 - x^4$ †   **88.** $f(x) = x^3 + x$ †

89. $f(x) = |x| + 3$ †   **90.** $f(x) = 3x + 5$ †

91. $f(x) = \sqrt{x}$ †   **92.** $f(x) = \dfrac{2}{x}$ †

In Exercises 93–96, express each function as a composition of two functions.

93. $f(x) = \sqrt{x^2 - 4}$ †   **94.** $g(x) = (x^2 - x + 2)^{50}$ †

95. $h(x) = \sqrt{\dfrac{x - 3}{2x + 5}}$ †   **96.** $H(x) = (2x - 1)^3 + 5$ †

In Exercises 97–100, determine whether the given function is one-to-one. If the function is one-to-one, find its inverse and sketch the graph of the function and its inverse on the same coordinate axes.

97. $f(x) = x + 2$ †   **98.** $f(x) = -2x + 3$ †

99. $f(x) = \sqrt[3]{x - 2}$ †   **100.** $f(x) = 8x^3 - 1$ †

In Exercises 101 and 102, assume that f is a one-to-one function. Find f^{-1}, and find the domain and range of f.

101. $f(x) = \dfrac{x - 1}{x + 2}, x \ne -2$ †

102. $f(x) = \dfrac{2x + 3}{x - 1}, x \ne 1$ †

103. For the graph of a function f shown on the next page:

    a. Write a formula for f as a piecewise function. †

    b. Find the domain and range of f. †

    c. Find the intercepts of the graph of f. †

d. Draw the graph of $y = f(-x)$. †
e. Draw the graph of $y = -f(x)$. †
f. Draw the graph of $y = f(x) + 1$. †
g. Draw the graph of $y = f(x + 1)$. †
h. Draw the graph of $y = 2f(x)$. †
i. Draw the graph of $y = f(2x)$. †
j. Draw the graph of $y = f\left(\dfrac{1}{2}x\right)$. †
k. Explain why f is one-to-one. †
l. Draw the graph of $y = f^{-1}(x)$. †

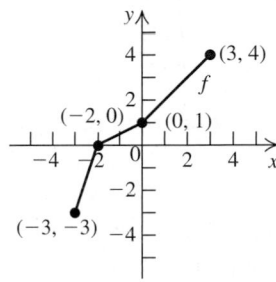

Applying the Concepts

104. Scuba diving. The pressure P on the body of a scuba diver increases linearly as he descends to greater depths d in seawater. The pressure at a depth of 10 feet is 19.2 pounds per square inch, and the pressure at a depth of 25 feet is 25.95 pounds per square inch.
 a. Write the equation relating P and d (with d as independent variable) in slope–intercept form. $P = 0.45d + 14.7$
 b. What is the meaning of the slope and the y-intercept in part (a)? †
 c. Determine the pressure on a scuba diver who is at a depth of 160 feet. 86.7 lb/in.^{2}
 d. Find the depth at which the pressure on the body of the scuba diver is 104.7 pounds per square inch. 200 ft

105. Waste disposal. The Sioux Falls, South Dakota, council considered the following data regarding the cost of disposing of waste material:

Year	1996	2000
Waste (in pounds)	87,000	223,000
Cost	$54,000	$173,000

Source: Sioux Falls Health Department.

Assume that the cost C (in dollars) is linearly related to the waste w (in pounds).
 a. Write the linear equation relating C and w in slope–intercept form. †
 b. Explain the meaning of the slope and the intercepts of the equation in part (a). †

c. Suppose the city has projected 609,000 pounds of waste for the year 2008. Calculate the projected cost of disposing of the waste for the year 2008. †
d. Suppose the city's projected budget for waste collection in 2012 is 1 million dollars. How many pounds of waste can be handled? †

106. Checking your speedometer. A common way to check the accuracy of your speedometer is to drive one or more measured (not odometer) miles, holding the speedometer at a constant 60 miles per hour and checking your watch at the start and end of the measured distance.
 a. How does your watch tell you whether the speedometer is accurate? What mathematics is involved? †
 b. Why shouldn't you use your odometer to measure the number of miles? †

107. Playing blackjack. Chloe, a bright mathematician, read a book on counting cards in blackjack and went to Las Vegas to try her luck. She started with 100 dollars and discovered that the amount of money she had at time t hours after the start of the game could be expressed by the function $f(t) = 100 + 55t - 3t^2$.
 a. What amount of money had Chloe won or lost in the first two hours? She won $98.
 b. What was the average rate at which Chloe was winning or losing money during the first two hours? †
 c. Did she lose all her money? If so, when? †
 d. If she played till she lost all her money, what was the average rate at which she was losing her money? $5/hr

108. Volume discounting. Major cola distributors sell a case (containing 24 cans) of cola to the retailer at a price of $4. They offer a discount of 20% for purchases over 100 cases and a discount of 25% for purchases over 500 cases. Write a piecewise function that describes this pricing scheme. Take x as the number of cases purchased and $f(x)$ as the price paid. †

109. Air pollution. The daily level L of carbon monoxide in a city is a function of the number of automobiles in the city. Suppose $L(x) = 0.5\sqrt{x^2 + 4}$, where x is the number of automobiles (in hundred thousands). Suppose further that the number of automobiles in a given city is growing according to the formula $x(t) = 1 + 0.002t^2$, where t is time in years measured from now.
 a. Form a composite function describing the daily pollution level as a function of time. †
 b. What pollution level is expected in five years? 1.13

110. Toy manufacturing. After being in business for t years, a toy manufacturer is making $x = 5000 + 50t + 10t^2$ GI Jimmy toys per year. The sale price p in dollars per toy has risen according to the formula $p = 10 + 0.5t$. Write a formula for the manufacturer's yearly revenue as
 a. a function of time t. $5t^3 + 125t^2 + 3000t + 50,000$
 b. a function of price p. $40p^3 - 700p^2 + 8000p$

Practice Test A

1. Determine which symmetries the graph of the equation $3x + 2xy^2 = 1$ has. Symmetric about the x-axis

2. Find the x-and y-intercepts of the graph of $y = x^2(x - 3)(x + 1)$. †

3. Graph the equation $x^2 + y^2 - 2x - 2y = 2$. †

4. Write the slope–intercept form of the equation of the line with slope -1 and passing through the point $(2, 7)$. $y = -x + 9$

5. Write an equation of the line parallel to the line $8x - 2y = 7$ and passing through $(2, -1)$. $y = 4x-9$

6. Use $f(x) = -2x + 1$ and $g(x) = x^2 + 3x + 2$ to find $(fg)(2)$. -36

7. Use $f(x) = 2x - 3$ and $g(x) = 1 - 2x^2$ to evaluate $g(f(2))$. †

8. Use $f(x) = x^2 - 2x$ to find $(f \circ f)(x)$. $x^4 - 4x^3 + 2x^2 + 4x$

9. If $f(x) = \begin{cases} x^3 - 2 & \text{if } x \le 0 \\ 1 - 2x^2 & \text{if } > 0 \end{cases}$, then find (a) $f(-1)$, (b) $f(0)$, and (c) $f(1)$. †

10. Find the domain of the function $f(x) = \dfrac{\sqrt{x}}{\sqrt{1 - x}}$. $[0, 1)$

11. Find the domain of the function $f(x) = \sqrt{x^2 + x - 6}$. †

12. Determine the average rate of change of the function $f(x) = 2x + 7$ between $x = 1$ and $x = 4$. 2

13. Determine whether the function $f(x) = 2x^4 - \dfrac{3}{x^2}$ is even, odd, or neither. Even

14. Find the intervals where the function shown is increasing or decreasing. Increasing on $(-\infty, 0) \cup (2, \infty)$, decreasing on $(0, 2)$

15. Suppose that the graph of f is given. Describe how the graph of $y = f(x - 3)$ can be obtained from the graph of f. †

16. A ball is thrown upward from the ground. After t seconds, the height h (in feet) above the ground is given by $h = 25 - (2t - 5)^2$. How many seconds does it take for the ball to reach a height of 25 feet? 2.5 sec

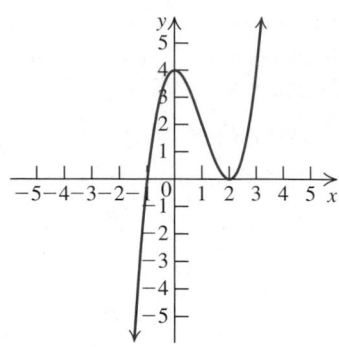

Function for Problem 14

17. If f is a one-to-one function and $f(2) = 7$, find $f^{-1}(7)$. 2

18. Find the inverse function $f^{-1}(x)$ of the one-to-one function $f(x) = \dfrac{2x + 1}{x - 3}$. $f^{-1}(x) = \dfrac{1 + 3x}{x - 2}$

19. Now that Jo has 1000 dollars for a car in her savings account, her dad takes over and deposits 100 dollars each month into her account. Write an equation that relates the total amount of money, A, in Jo's account to the number of months, x, that Jo's dad has been putting money into her account. $A(x) = 100x + 1000$

20. The cost C in dollars for renting a car for one day is a function of the number of miles traveled, m. For a car renting for 30 dollars per day and 25 cents per mile, this function is given by
$$C(m) = 0.25m + 30.$$
   (a) Find the cost of renting the car for one day and driving 230 miles. $87.50
   (b) If the charge for renting the car for one day is 57 dollars and 50 cents, how many miles were driven? 110 mi

Practice Test B

1. The graph of the equation $|x| + 2|y| = 2$ is symmetric with respect to which of the following? d

   I. The origin   **II.** The x-axis   **III.** The y-axis

   (a) I only   **(b)** II only
   (c) III only   **(d)** I, II, and III

2. Which are the x- and y-intercepts of the graph of $y = x^2 - 9$? b

   (a) x-intercept 3, y-intercept -9
   (b) x-intercepts ± 3, y-intercept -9

   (c) x-intercept 3, y-intercept 9
   (d) x-intercepts ± 3, y-intercepts ± 9

3. The slope of a line is undefined if the line is parallel to d

   (a) the x-axis   **(b)** the line $x - y = 0$
   (c) the line $x + y = 0$ **(d)** the y-axis.

4. Which is an equation of the circle with center $(0, -5)$ and radius 7? d

   (a) $x^2 + y^2 - 10y = 0$ **(b)** $x^2 + (y - 5)^2 = 7$
   (c) $x^2 + (y - 5)^2 = 49$ **(d)** $x^2 + y^2 + 10y = 24$

5. Which is an equation of the line passing through $(2, -3)$ and having slope -1? c
   (a) $y + 3 = -(x + 2)$ (b) $y - 3 = -(x - 2)$
   (c) $y + 3 = -(x - 2)$ (d) $y + 3 = -(x + 2)$

6. What is a second point on the line through $(3, 2)$ and having slope $-\dfrac{1}{2}$? c

   (a) $(2, 4)$ (b) $(5, 1)$
   (c) $(7, 0)$ (d) $(4, 4)$

7. Which is an equation of the line parallel to the line $6x - 3y = 5$ and passing through $(-1, 2)$? d
   (a) $y - 2 = -2(x + 1)$ (b) $y - 2 = 6(x + 1)$
   (c) $y - 2 = -6(x + 1)$ (d) $y - 2 = 2(x + 1)$

8. Use $f(x) = 3x - 5$ and $g(x) = 2 - x^2$ to find $(f \circ g)(x)$. b
   (a) $-9x^2 + 30x - 23$ (b) $-3x^2 + 1$
   (c) $3x^2 + 1$ (d) $9x^2 - 30x + 23$

9. Use $f(x) = 2x^2 - x$ to find $(f \circ f)(x)$. a
   (a) $8x^4 - 8x^3 + x$ (b) $8x^4 + x$
   (c) $4x^4 - 4x^3 + x^2 - x$ (d) $4x^4 - x^3 + x^2$
   (e) $-x^4 + 6x^2 - x$

10. If $g(t) = \dfrac{1 - t}{1 + t}$, find $g(a - 1)$. c

    (a) $\dfrac{2 - a}{2 + a}$ (b) $\dfrac{1 - a}{1 + a}$

    (c) $\dfrac{2 - a}{a}$ (d) -1

11. The domain of the function $f(x) = \sqrt{x} + \sqrt{1 - x}$ is a
    (a) $[0, 1]$ (b) $(-\infty, -1] \cup [0, +\infty)$
    (c) $(-\infty, 1]$ (d) $[0, +\infty)$

12. What is the domain of the function $f(x) = \sqrt{x^2 + 6x - 7}$? b
    (a) $(-\infty, -7) \cup (1, \infty)$ (b) $(-\infty, -7] \cup [1, \infty)$
    (c) $[-7, 1]$ (d) $(1, \infty)$

13. Which description of the behavior of the graph drawn here is correct? a
    (a) increasing on $(0, 3)$; decreasing on $(-3, 0) \cup (3, 4)$
    (b) increasing on $(-1, 3)$; decreasing on $(2, -1) \cup (3, 1)$
    (c) increasing on $(-3, 3)$; decreasing on $(2, -1) \cup (3, 1)$
    (d) increasing on $(1.2, 4)$; decreasing on $(-3, -1.4)$

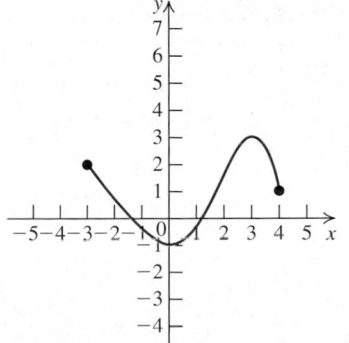

14. Suppose that the graph of f is given. Describe how the graph of $y = f(x + 4)$ can be obtained from the graph of f. a
    (a) By shifting the graph of f 4 units to the left.
    (b) By shifting the graph of f 4 units down.
    (c) By shifting the graph of f 4 units up.
    (d) By shifting the graph of f 4 units to the right.
    (e) By reflecting the graph of f in the x-axis.

15. Suppose that the graph of f is given. Describe how the graph of $y = -2f(x - 4)$ can be obtained from the graph of f. b
    (a) By shifting the graph of f 4 units to the left, then shrinking vertically by a factor of $\dfrac{1}{2}$, and then reflecting the x-axis.
    (b) By shifting the graph of f 4 units to the right, then stretching vertically by a factor of 2, and then reflecting in the x-axis.
    (c) By shifting the graph of f 4 units to the left, then shrinking vertically by a factor of $\dfrac{1}{2}$, and then reflecting the x-axis.
    (d) By shifting the graph of f 4 units to the right, then stretching vertically by a factor of 2, and then reflecting in the y-axis.

16. Which of the following is a one-to-one function? d
    (a) $f(x) = |x + 3|$ (b) $f(x) = x^2$
    (c) $f(x) = \sqrt{x^2 + 9}$ (d) $f(x) = x^3 + 2$

17. If f is a one-to-one function and $f(3) = 5$, then $f^{-1}(5)$ equals c

    (a) $\dfrac{1}{5}$ (b) $\dfrac{1}{3}$

    (c) 3 (d) -5

18. Find the inverse function $f^{-1}(x)$ of $f(x) = \dfrac{1 - 3x}{5 + 2x}$. c

    (a) $\dfrac{1 + 3x}{5 - 2x}$ (b) $\dfrac{5 + 2x}{1 - 3x}$

    (c) $\dfrac{1 - 5x}{3 + 2x}$ (d) $\dfrac{3 + 2x}{1 - 5x}$

19. The ideal weight w (in pounds) for a man of height x inches is found by subtracting 190 from five times his height. Write a linear equation that gives the ideal weight of a man of height x inches. Then find the ideal weight of a man whose height is 70 inches. b

    (a) $w = \dfrac{x + 190}{5}$, 160 lb   (b) $w = 5x - 190$, 160 lb.

    (c) $w = 190 - \dfrac{x}{5}$, 176 lb   (d) $w = \dfrac{x + 190}{5}$, 52 lb

20. Cassie rented an intermediate sedan at 25 dollars per day + 20 cents per mile. How many miles can Cassie travel for 50 dollars? a
    (a) 125
    (b) 1025
    (c) 250
    (d) 175

Cumulative Review Exercises   (Chapters P–2)

1. Simplify:
   (a) $\left(\dfrac{x^3}{y^2}\right)^2\left(\dfrac{y^2}{x^3}\right)^3\dfrac{y^2}{x^3}$
   (b) $\dfrac{x^{-1}y^{-1}}{x^{-1}+y^{-1}}$ $\dfrac{1}{x+y}$

2. Factor:
   (a) $2x^2 + x - 15$ †
   (b) $x^3 - 2x^2 + 4x - 8$ †

3. Combine and simplify:
   (a) $\sqrt{75} + \sqrt{108} - \sqrt{192}$ $3\sqrt{3}$
   (b) $\dfrac{x-1}{x+1} - \dfrac{x-2}{x+2}$ $\dfrac{2x}{(x+1)(x+2)}$

4. Rationalize the denominator:
   (a) $\dfrac{1}{2+\sqrt{3}}$ $2 - \sqrt{3}$
   (b) $\dfrac{1}{\sqrt{5}-2}$ $2 + \sqrt{5}$

In Exercises 5–9, solve each equation for x.

5. (a) $3x - 7 = 5$ $x = 4$ (b) $\dfrac{1}{x-1} = \dfrac{3}{x-1}$ †

6. (a) $x^2 - 3x = 0$ $x = 0; 3$ (b) $x^2 + 3x - 10 = 0$ †

7. (a) $2x^2 - x + 3 = 0$ †   (b) $4x^2 - 12x + 9 = 0$ †

8. (a) $x - 6\sqrt{x} + 8 = 0$ 4, 16
   (b) $\left(x - \dfrac{1}{x}\right)^2 - 10\left(x - \dfrac{1}{x}\right) + 21 = 0$ †

9. (a) $\sqrt{3x - 1} = 2x - 1$ †
   (b) $\sqrt{1 - x} = 2 - \sqrt{2x + 1}$ †

In Exercises 10–14, solve each inequality for x and write the solution in interval notation.

10. (a) $2x - 5 < 11$ $(-\infty, 8)$ (b) $-3x + 4 > -5$ †

11. (a) $x(x - 1) > 0$ †   (b) $(x - 2)(x + 1) < 0$ †

12. (a) $\dfrac{x+1}{x-2} > 0$ †   (b) $\dfrac{x+1}{(x-2)(x-5)} \leq 0$ †

13. (a) $-3 < 2x - 3 < 5$ $(0, 4)$ (b) $5 \leq 1 - 2x \leq 7$ †

14. (a) $|2x - 1| \leq 7$ $[-3, 4]$ (b) $|2x - 3| \geq 5$ †

15. Show that the triangle with vertices $A(5, -2)$, $B(6, 5)$, and $C(2, 2)$ is isosceles. †

16. Sketch the graph of $4x^2 - 9y^2 = 0$. [*Hint:* $4x^2 - 9y^2 = (2x + 3y)(2x - 3y)$.] †

17. Show that the points $(-3, -1)$, $(2, 4)$, $(5, 3)$, and $(6, 2)$ lie on a circle with center $(2, -1)$. †

18. Find the center and radius of the circle with equation $x^2 + y^2 - 6x + 4y + 9 = 0$. Center: $(3, -2)$; radius: 2

In Exercises 19–24, find the slope–intercept form of the equation of the line satisfying the given condition.

19. Slope $= -3$, y-intercept 5. $y = -3x + 5$

20. Slope $= 2$, x-intercept 4. $y = 2x - 8$

21. The line is perpendicular to $y = 2x + 3$ and passes through $(2, -1)$. $y = -0.5x$

22. The line is parallel to $y = 2x + 3$ and passes through $(2, -1)$. $y = 2x - 5$

23. The line is the perpendicular bisector of the line segment joining $(3, -1)$ and $(5, 7)$. $y = -\dfrac{1}{4}x + 4$

24. The line is parallel to $x = -2$ and passes through $(5, 7)$. †

25. Find x if the line through $(x, 5)$ and $(5, 11)$ is parallel to a line with slope 2. $x = 2$

26. Find x if the line through $(x, 3)$ and $(3, 7)$ is perpendicular to a line with slope $\dfrac{1}{2}$. $x = 5$

In Exercises 27–30, graph each equation.

27. $12x = 4y - 6$ †

28. $x^2 - 2x + y^2 - 4y - 4 = 0$ †

29. $f(x) = \sqrt{x + 2} + 3$ †

30. $f(x) = -(x - 1)^2 + 4$ †

31. Ms. Gutiérrez bought some used books for 1650 dollars. She kept 16 of the books and sold the rest at a profit of 10 dollars each. If she recovered her original 1650 dollars from this sale, how many books did she purchase initially? †

32. The monthly note on a car that was leased for two years was 250 dollars less than the monthly note on a car that was leased for a year and a half. The total expense for the two leases was 21,000 dollars. Find the monthly note for each lease. †

33. Let $f(x) = \sqrt{x + 1} - 3$.
    (a) Find the domain of f. † (b) Find the intercepts.
    (c) Find $f(-1)$. †   (d) Solve $f(x) > 0$. †

34. Let $f(x) = \begin{cases} -x & \text{if } x < 0 \\ x^2 & \text{if } x \geq 0 \end{cases}$.
    (a) Find $f(-2)$, $f(0)$, and $f(2)$.
    (b) Find the intervals on which f is increasing, decreasing, or constant. †

35. Let $f(x) = \dfrac{1}{x-2}$ and $g(x) = \dfrac{2}{x}$.
    (a) Find $(f \circ g)(x)$ and state its domain.
    (b) Find $(g \circ f)(x)$ and state its domain.

CHAPTER 3

Polynomial and Rational Functions

Polynomials and rational functions are used in navigation, in computer-aided geometric design, in the study of supply and demand in business, in the design of suspension bridges, in computations determining the force of gravity on planets, and in virtually every area of inquiry requiring numerical approxlmations. Their applicability is so widespread that it is hard to imagine an area in which they have not made an impact.

Quadratic Functions

dennis QUAID

rene RUSSO

YOURS, MINE & OURS

18 kids, one house, no way.

ROCK THE HOUSE!

THANKSGIVING

BEFORE STARTING THIS SECTION, REVIEW

1. Linear functions (Section 2.5, page 246)

2. Completing the square (Section 1.4, page 125)

3. Quadratic formula (Section 1.4, page 127)

4. Transformations (Section 2.6, page 263)

OBJECTIVES

1 Graph a quadratic function in standard form.

2 Graph a quadratic function.

3 Solve problems modeled by quadratic functions.

Yours, Mine, and Ours

The movie *Yours, Mine, and Ours*, released in 1968, is a comedy about the ultimate blended family. The movie was based on the true story of Helen North and Frank Beardsley. Helen, the author of *Who Gets the Drumsticks?* was born on April 5, 1930, and Frank was born on September 11, 1915.

Helen North was a widow with 8 children, and in 1961 she married the widower Frank Beardsley, who had 10 children of his own. The May 1964 issue of *Time* magazine had the following announcement:

May. 1, 1964

Born. To Francis Beardsley, 48, chief warrant officer at the Navy postgraduate school at Monterey, Calif., and Helen North Beardsley, 34: their second child, second daughter; in Carmel, Calif. The couple's 19 other children (he had ten, she eight from previous marriages) all voted on a name for the new Beardsley, came up "unanimously," with Helen Monica.

The film *Yours, Mine, and Ours* details the nuances of everyday life in a house full of children. The poster shown in the margin is from a remake of this popular story. In Example 6, we discuss the maximum possible number of fights among the children in such a family. ■

1 Graph a quadratic function in standard form.

Quadratic Function

A function whose defining equation is a polynomial is called a *polynomial function*. In this section, you will study polynomial functions of degree 2. Such functions are called **quadratic functions.**

QUADRATIC FUNCTION

A function that can be defined by an equation of the form

$$f(x) = ax^2 + bx + c,$$

where a, b, and c, are real numbers with $a \neq 0$, is called a **quadratic function.**

Note that the squaring function $s(x) = x^2$ (whose graph is a parabola) is the quadratic function $f(x) = ax^2 + bx + c$ with $a = 1$, $b = 0$, and $c = 0$. We will show that the graph of any quadratic function can be obtained by applying suitable transformations to the graph of $s(x) = x^2$. Therefore, since the graph of $y = x^2$ is a parabola, the graph of any quadratic function is also a parabola.

We first compare the graphs of $f(x) = ax^2$ for $a > 0$ and $g(x) = ax^2$ for $a < 0$. These are quadratic functions with $b = 0$ and $c = 0$.

$f(x) = ax^2, a > 0$	$g(x) = ax^2, a < 0$
The graph of $f(x) = ax^2$ is obtained from the graph of the squaring function $s(x) = x^2$ by vertically stretching or compressing it. Here are three such graphs on the same axes for $a = 2$, $a = 1$, and $a = \dfrac{1}{2}$:	The graph of $g(x) = ax^2$ is the reflection of the graph of $f(x) = |a|x^2$ in the x-axis. Here are three graphs, for $a = -2$, $a = -1$, and $a = -\dfrac{1}{2}$:

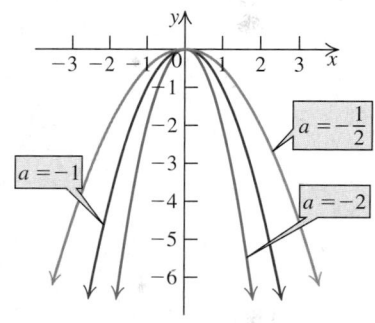

Standard Form of a Quadratic Function

Any quadratic function $f(x) = ax^2 + bx + c$ with $a \neq 0$ can be rewritten in the form $f(x) = a(x - h)^2 + k$, called the **standard form** of the quadratic function f. Now, by using transformations (see Section 2.6), we can obtain the graph of $f(x) = a(x - h)^2 + k$ from the graph of the squaring function $s(x) = x^2$ as follows:

$s(x) = x^2$ — The squaring function

$\downarrow$

$g(x) = (x - h)^2$ — Horizontal translation to the right if $h > 0$ and to the left if $h < 0$

$\downarrow$

$G(x) = a(x - h)^2$ — Vertical stretching or compressing. If $a < 0$, the graph is also reflected in the x-axis.

$\downarrow$

$f(x) = a(x - h)^2 + k$ — Vertical translation, up if $k > 0$ and down if $k < 0$

The preceding transformations show that the graph of a quadratic function $f(x) = a(x - h)^2 + k$ is a parabola that opens up if $a > 0$ and down if $a < 0$. The parabola is symmetric with respect to the vertical line $x = h$. The line of symmetry is called the **axis** (or **axis of symmetry**) of the parabola. The point where the axis meets the parabola is called the **vertex** of the parabola. The vertex of any parabola that opens up is the *lowest point* of the graph, and the vertex of any parabola that opens down is the *highest point* of the graph. The standard form is particularly useful, because it immediately identifies the vertex (h, k). We summarize these observations next.

THE STANDARD FORM OF A QUADRATIC FUNCTION

The quadratic function

$$f(x) = a(x - h)^2 + k, \ a \neq 0$$

is in **standard form.** The graph of f is a parabola with **vertex** (h, k). The parabola is symmetric with respect to the line $x = h$, called the **axis** of the parabola. If $a > 0$, the parabola opens up, and if $a < 0$, the parabola opens down.

EXAMPLE 1 **Finding a Quadratic Function**

Find the standard form of the quadratic function whose graph has vertex $(-3, 4)$ and passes through the point $(-4, 7)$.

Solution

Let $y = f(x)$ be the desired quadratic function in standard form. Then

$y = a(x - h)^2 + k$	Standard form
$y = a[x - (-3)]^2 + 4$	Replace h by -3 and k by 4.
$y = a(x + 3)^2 + 4$	Simplify.
$7 = a(-4 + 3)^2 + 4$	Replace x by -4 and y by 7, because $(-4, 7)$ lies on the graph of $y = f(x)$.
$7 = a + 4$	Simplify.
$a = 3.$	Solve for a.

Hence, the quadratic function is

$$f(x) = 3(x + 3)^2 + 4. \qquad a = 3, h = -3, k = 4$$

■ ■ ■

PRACTICE PROBLEM 1 Find the standard form of the quadratic function whose graph has vertex $(1, -5)$ and passes through the point $(3, 7)$. ■

We give the following general procedure for graphing a quadratic function whose equation is in standard form:

FINDING THE SOLUTION: PROCEDURE FOR GRAPHING $f(x) = a(x - h)^2 + k$

OBJECTIVE	EXAMPLE
To sketch the graph of $f(x) = a(x - h)^2 + k$	*Sketch the graph of* $f(x) = -3(x + 2)^2 + 12$

Step 1   **The graph is a parabola.** Identify a, h, and k.

The graph of $f(x) = -3(x + 2)^2 + 12$

$$= (-3)[x - (-2)]^2 + 12$$
$$\uparrow \qquad \uparrow \qquad \uparrow$$
$$a \qquad h \qquad k$$

is a parabola; $a = -3$, $h = -2$, and $k = 12$.

Step 2   **Determine how the parabola opens.** If $a > 0$, the parabola opens *up*. If $a < 0$, the parabola opens *down*.

Since $a = -3 < 0$, the parabola opens down.

Step 3   **Find the vertex.** The vertex is (h, k). If $a > 0$ (or $a < 0$), the function f has a minimum (or a maximum) value k at $x = h$.

The vertex $(h, k) = (-2, 12)$. Since the parabola opens down, the function f has a maximum value of 12 at $x = -2$.

Step 4   **Find the x-intercepts.** Find the x-intercepts (if any) by setting $f(x) = 0$ and solving the equation $a(x - h)^2 + k = 0$ for x. If the solutions are real numbers, they are the x-intercepts. If not, the parabola either lies above the x-axis (when $a > 0$) or below the x-axis (when $a < 0$).

To find the x-intercepts, set $f(x) = 0$. Then

$0 = -3(x + 2)^2 + 12$	Set $f(x) = 0$.
$3(x + 2)^2 = 12$	Add $3(x + 2)^2$ to both sides.
$(x + 2)^2 = 4$	Divide both sides by 3.
$x + 2 = \pm 2$	Square root property.
$x = -2 \pm 2$	Subtract 2 from both sides.
$x = 0$ or $x = -4$	Solve for x.

The x-intercepts are 0 and -4. The parabola passes through the points $(0, 0)$ and $(-4, 0)$.

Step 5   **Find the y-intercept.** Find the y-intercept by replacing x with 0. Then $f(0) = ah^2 + k$ is the y-intercept.

$f(0) = -3(0 + 2)^2 + 12 = -3(4) + 12 = 0$. The y-intercept is 0.

Step 6   **Sketch the graph.** Plot the points found in Steps 3–5 and join them by a parabola. Show the axis $x = h$ of the parabola by drawing a dashed line.

If there are no x-intercepts, first draw the half of the parabola that passes through the vertex and the y-intercept. Then use the axis of symmetry to draw the other half of the parabola.

The axis of the parabola is the vertical line $x = -2$. The graph of the parabola is shown in the figure.

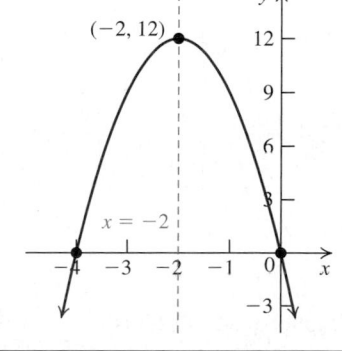

EXAMPLE 2 **Graphing a Quadratic Function in Standard Form**

Graph the quadratic function $f(x) = 2(x - 3)^2 - 8$.

Solution

Step 1 The graph of the given function $f(x) = 2(x - 3)^2 - 8$ is a parabola with

$$a = 2, h = 3, \text{ and } k = -8.$$

Step 2 Since $a = 2$ is greater than 0, the parabola opens *up*.

Step 3 The vertex of the parabola is $(h, k) = (3, -8)$. The function f has a minimum value of -8 at $x = 3$.

Step 4 To find the x-intercepts, set $f(x) = 0$ and solve for x.

$0 = 2(x - 3)^2 - 8$	Set $f(x) = 0$.
$8 = 2(x - 3)^2$	Add 8 to both sides.
$4 = (x - 3)^2$	Divide both sides by 2.
$(x - 3)^2 = 4$	Rewrite if you prefer x terms on the left side.
$x - 3 = \pm 2$	Square root property
$x = 3 \pm 2$	Add 3 to both sides.
$x = 3 + 2 \quad \text{or} \quad x = 3 - 2$	Write separate equations.
$x = 5 \quad \text{or} \quad x = 1$	Simplify.

The x-intercepts are 5 and 1, so the parabola passes through the points $(1, 0)$ and $(5, 0)$.

Step 5 To find the y-intercept, replace x with 0 in the equation

$$f(x) = 2(x - 3)^2 - 8:$$
$$f(0) = 2(0 - 3)^2 - 8$$
$$= 2(9) - 8$$
$$= 18 - 8 = 10$$

The y-intercept is 10, so the parabola passes through the point $(0, 10)$.

Step 6 The axis of the parabola is the vertical line $x = 3$. The parabola opens up. The vertex is $(3, -8)$. The x-intercepts are 1 and 5. The y-intercept is 10. See Figure 3.1. The graph in the figure is the graph of $y = 2x^2$ shifted three units right and eight units down. ■ ■ ■

PRACTICE PROBLEM 2 Graph the quadratic function $f(x) = -2(x + 1)^2 + 3$. ■

TECHNOLOGY CONNECTION

Calculator graph of $f(x) = 2(x - 3)^2 - 8$

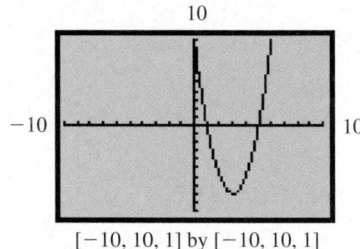

$[-10, 10, 1]$ by $[-10, 10, 1]$

FIGURE 3.1

2 Graph a quadratic function.

Graphing a Quadratic Function $f(x) = ax^2 + bx + c$

A quadratic function $f(x) = ax^2 + bx + c$ can be changed to the standard form $f(x) = a(x - h)^2 + k$ by *completing the square*.

Converting $f(x) = ax^2 + bx + c$ to Standard Form

$$f(x) = ax^2 + bx + c \qquad \text{Original function}$$

$$= a\left(x^2 + \frac{b}{a}x\right) + c \qquad \text{Factor out } a \text{ from } ax^2 + bx.$$

$$= a\left(x^2 + \frac{b}{a}x + \frac{b^2}{4a^2} - \frac{b^2}{4a^2}\right) + c \qquad \text{To complete the square, add and subtract } \left(\frac{1}{2} \cdot \frac{b}{a}\right)^2 = \frac{b^2}{4a^2} \text{ within the parentheses.}$$

$$= a\left(x^2 + \frac{b}{a}x + \frac{b^2}{4a^2}\right) - a \cdot \frac{b^2}{4a^2} + c \qquad \text{Distributive property}$$

$$= a\left(x + \frac{b}{2a}\right)^2 - \frac{b^2}{4a} + c \qquad \left(x + \frac{b}{2a}\right)^2 = x^2 + \frac{b}{a}x + \frac{b^2}{4a^2}$$

Comparing this form with the standard form $f(x) = a(x - h)^2 + k$, we have

$$h = -\frac{b}{2a} \qquad x\text{-coordinate of the vertex}$$

$$\text{and} \quad k = c - \frac{b^2}{4a}. \qquad y\text{-coordinate of the vertex}$$

Notice that $f\left(-\frac{b}{2a}\right) = a\left(-\frac{b}{2a} + \frac{b}{2a}\right)^2 - \frac{b^2}{4a} + c \qquad$ Replace x by $-\frac{b}{2a}$ in the last equation for $f(x)$.

$$= -\frac{b^2}{4a} + c = k.$$

Thus, after you find the x-coordinate $h = -\dfrac{b}{2a}$ of the vertex, calculate $f\left(-\dfrac{b}{2a}\right)$ to find its y-coordinate.

FINDING THE SOLUTION: PROCEDURE FOR GRAPHING $f(x) = ax^2 + bx + c$

OBJECTIVE	EXAMPLE
To graph $y = f(x) = ax^2 + bx + c, a \neq 0$.	Sketch the graph of $f(x) = 2x^2 + 8x - 10$.

Step 1   **The graph is a parabola.** Identify $a, b,$ and c.

The graph of
$$y = f(x) = 2x^2 + 8x - 10$$
is a parabola with $a = 2, b = 8,$ and $c = -10$.

Step 2   **Determine how the parabola opens.** If $a > 0$, the parabola opens *up*; if $a < 0$, the parabola opens *down*.

Since $a = 2 > 0$, the parabola opens up.

Step 3   **Find the vertex (h, k).** Use the vertex formula:
$$(h, k) = \left(-\frac{b}{2a}, f\left(-\frac{b}{2a}\right)\right).$$

$$h = -\frac{b}{2a} = -\frac{8}{2(2)} = -2$$
$$k = f(h) = f(-2)$$
$$= 2(-2)^2 + 8(-2) - 10 \qquad \text{Replace } h \text{ by } -2.$$
$$= -18 \qquad \text{Simplify.}$$

Since the parabola opens up, the function f has a minimum value of -18 at $x = -2$.

Continued on next page.

Step 4   **Find the x-intercepts.** Let $y = f(x) = 0$. Find x by solving the equation $ax^2 + bx + c = 0$. If the solutions are real numbers, they are the x-intercepts. If not, the parabola either lies above the x-axis (when $a > 0$) or below the x-axis (when $a < 0$).

Set $f(x) = 0$ and solve for x.

$$2x^2 + 8x - 10 = 0 \qquad \text{Set } f(x) = 0.$$
$$2(x^2 + 4x - 5) = 0 \qquad \text{Factor out 2.}$$
$$2(x + 5)(x - 1) = 0 \qquad \text{Factor.}$$
$$x + 5 = 0 \quad \text{or} \quad x - 1 = 0 \qquad \text{Zero-product property}$$
$$x = -5 \quad \text{or} \quad x = 1 \qquad \text{Solve for } x.$$

The x-intercepts are -5 and 1, and the corresponding graph points are $(-5, 0)$ and $(1, 0)$.

Step 5   **Find the y-intercept.** Let $x = 0$. The result, $f(0) = c$, is the y-intercept.

Set $x = 0$ to obtain $f(0) = 2(0)^2 + 8(0) - 10 = -10$. The y-intercept is -10, and the parabola passes through the point $(0, -10)$.

Step 6   The parabola is symmetric with respect to its axis, $x = -\dfrac{b}{2a}$. Use this symmetry to find additional points.

The axis of symmetry is $x = -2$. The symmetric image of $(0, -10)$ with respect to the axis $x = -2$ is the point $(-4, -10)$.

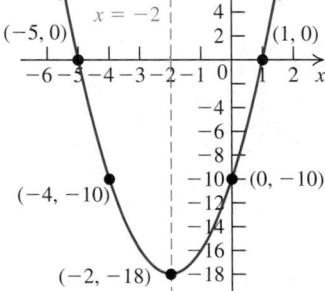

Step 7   Draw a parabola through the points found in Steps 3–6.

The parabola passing through the points in Steps 3–6 is sketched in the figure.

If there are no x-intercepts, just draw the half of the parabola that passes through the vertex and the y-intercept. Then use the axis of symmetry to draw the other half of the parabola.

EXAMPLE 3   **Graphing a Quadratic Function** $f(x) = ax^2 + bx + c$

Graph the quadratic function $f(x) = -2x^2 + 8x - 5$.

Solution

$$y = f(x) = -2x^2 + 8x - 5 \quad \text{Given function}$$

Step 1 $a = -2, b = 8, c = -5$.

Step 2   Since $a = -2 < 0$, the parabola opens down.

Step 3   Find the vertex.
The x-coordinate of the vertex is

$$h = -\frac{b}{2a} = -\frac{8}{2(-2)} = 2.$$
$$k = f(2) = -2(2)^2 + 8(2) - 5$$
$$= -8 + 16 - 5$$
$$= 3.$$

The vertex $(h, k) = (2, 3)$.
Since $a < 0$, the function f has a maximum value of 3 at $x = 2$.

Step 4   Let $f(x) = 0$. Then $-2x^2 + 8x - 5 = 0$. Solve for x:

$$x = \frac{-8 \pm \sqrt{(8)^2 - 4(-2)(-5)}}{2(-2)}$$ Use the quadratic formula.

$$= \frac{4 \pm \sqrt{6}}{2}.$$ Simplify.

The x-intercepts are $\dfrac{4 - \sqrt{6}}{2}$ and $\dfrac{4 + \sqrt{6}}{2}$.

Approximations for the x-intercepts are 0.775 and 3.225, found with a calculator.

Step 5   Let $x = 0$. Then $f(0) = -2(0)^2 + 8(0) - 5 = -5$. The y-intercept is -5, so the parabola passes through the point $(0, -5)$.

Step 6   The axis of symmetry is $x = 2$. Let $x = 1$. Then $y = -2(1)^2 + 8(1) - 5 = 1$. Thus, $(1, 1)$ is a point on the graph. The symmetric image of $(1, 1)$ with respect to the axis $x = 2$ is the point $(3, 1)$. (See Figure 3.2.) Thus, $(3, 1)$ is also on the graph. Similarly, the symmetric image of the y-intercept $(0, -5)$ with respect to the axis $x = 2$ is the point $(4, -5)$. Thus, $(4, -5)$ is also on the graph.

Step 7   The parabola passing through the points found in Steps 3–6 is sketched in Figure 3.2.   ■ ■ ■

FIGURE 3.2

PRACTICE PROBLEM 3   Graph the quadratic function $f(x) = x^2 + 4x + 1$.   ■

EXAMPLE 4   **Identifying the Characteristics of a Quadratic Function from Its Graph**

The graph of the function $f(x) = -2x^2 + 8x - 5$ is shown in Figure 3.2.

a. Find the domain and range of f.

b. Solve the inequality $-2x^2 + 8x - 5 > 0$.

Solution

The graph of $f(x) = -2x^2 + 8x - 5$ in Figure 3.2 is a parabola. The parabola opens down and its vertex is $(2, 3)$.

a. The domain of f is $(-\infty, \infty)$. The graph of f opens down, and the maximum value of f is the y-coordinate of its vertex $(2, 3)$. So the range of f is $(-\infty, 3]$.

b. The x-intercepts of f are $\dfrac{4 - \sqrt{6}}{2} \approx 0.775$ and $\dfrac{4 + \sqrt{6}}{2} \approx 3.225$. The graph of $y = -2x^2 + 8x - 5$ in Figure 3.2 is above the x-axis between these intercepts. Thus, $y = -2x^2 + 8x - 5 > 0$ for the x-values in the interval $\left(\dfrac{4 - \sqrt{6}}{2}, \dfrac{4 + \sqrt{6}}{2} \right)$.

Hence, the solution set of the inequality $-2x^2 + 8x - 5 > 0$ is the interval $\left(\dfrac{4 - \sqrt{6}}{2}, \dfrac{4 + \sqrt{6}}{2} \right)$.   ■ ■ ■

PRACTICE PROBLEM 4   Solve the inequality $3x^2 - 6x - 1 \leq 0$.   ■

TECHNOLOGY CONNECTION

Calculator graph of $f(x) = -2x^2 + 8x - 5$

$[-1, 5, 1]$ by $[-6, 4, 1]$

Part **b** of Example 4 shows that the x-intercepts of the graph of a quadratic function $y = f(x)$ can be used to solve the corresponding quadratic inequality, $y < 0$ or $y > 0$.

Note that if the graph of a quadratic function does not intersect the x-axis, then the solution set of the corresponding inequality is either $(-\infty, \infty)$ or the empty set.

EXAMPLE 5 **Graphing a Quadratic Inequality**

Graph the quadratic function $f(x) = x^2 + 2x + 2$, and solve each quadratic inequality.

a. $x^2 + 2x + 2 > 0$ **b.** $x^2 + 2x + 2 < 0$

Solution

$$y = f(x) = x^2 + 2x + 2 \qquad \text{Given function}$$

Step 1 $a = 1, b = 2, c = 2$

Step 2   Since $a = 1 > 0$, the parabola opens up.

Step 3   Find the vertex (h, k):

$$h = -\frac{b}{2a} = -\frac{2}{2(1)} = -1.$$
$$k = f(-1) = (-1)^2 + 2(-1) + 2 \qquad \text{Replace } x \text{ by } -1 \text{ in } f(x).$$
$$= 1 \qquad \text{Simplify.}$$

Vertex $(h, k) = (-1, 1)$.
  Since $a = 1 > 0$, the function f has a minimum value of 1 at $x = -1$.

Step 4   Find the x-intercepts. Set $f(x) = 0$ and solve for x.

$$x^2 + 2x + 2 = 0 \qquad \text{Set } f(x) = 0.$$
$$x = \frac{-2 \pm \sqrt{(2)^2 - 4(1)(2)}}{2(1)} \qquad \text{Use quadratic formula.}$$
$$= \frac{-2 \pm \sqrt{-4}}{2} \qquad \text{Simplify.}$$
$$= \frac{-2 \pm 2i}{2} \qquad \text{Write } \sqrt{-4} = 2i.$$
$$= -1 \pm i \qquad \text{Simplify.}$$

Since the solutions are not real numbers, the graph of f does not intersect the x-axis. Because the vertex $(-1, 1)$ is above the x-axis and the parabola opens up, the entire graph of f lies above the x-axis.

Step 5   Find the y-intercept. Set $x = 0$ to obtain $f(0) = 2$. The y-intercept is 2.

Step 6   The axis of symmetry is $x = -1$.

Step 7   The points $(-2, 2)$ and $(0, 2)$ are symmetric with respect to the axis of symmetry, $x = -1$. The graph of f is shown in Figure 3.3.

a. The entire graph of f in Figure 3.3 is above the x-axis. Thus, $y = x^2 + 2x + 2 > 0$ for every value of x. Hence, the solution of the inequality $x^2 + 2x + 2 > 0$ in interval notation is $(-\infty, \infty)$.

TECHNOLOGY CONNECTION

Calculator graph of $y = x^2 + 2x + 2$

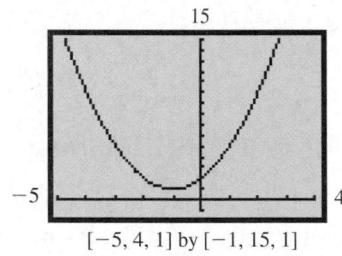

$[-5, 4, 1]$ by $[-1, 15, 1]$

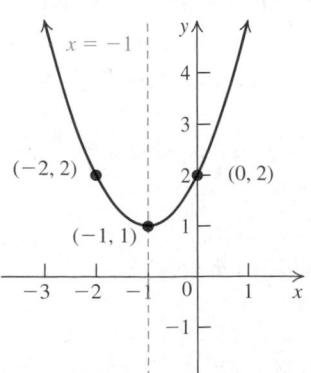

FIGURE 3.3

b. The graph of f in Figure 3.3 is never below the x-axis. Thus, the inequality $y = x^2 + 2x + 2 < 0$ is false for every value of x. Hence, the solution set of the inequality $x^2 + 2x + 2 < 0$ is $\varnothing$.   ■ ■ ■

PRACTICE PROBLEM 5 Sketch the graph of $f(x) = -x^2 + 4x - 7$ and solve the inequality $-x^2 + 4x - 7 > 0$.   ■

3 Solve problems modeled by quadratic functions.

Applications

Many applications of quadratic functions involve finding the maximum or minimum value of the function. Recall that, for a quadratic function $f(x) = ax^2 + bx + c$, the vertex (h, k) is given by $h = -\dfrac{b}{2a}$ and $k = f\left(-\dfrac{b}{2a}\right)$. If $a > 0$, then k is the minimum value of f, and if $a < 0$, then k is the maximum value of f.

EXAMPLE 6   *Yours, Mine, and Ours*

A widower with 10 children marries a widow who also has children. After their marriage, they have their own children. If the total number of children is 24, and we assume that the children of the same parents do not fight, find the maximum possible number of fights among the children. (In this example, a fight between Sean and Misty, no matter how many times they fight, is considered as one fight.)

Solution

STUDY TIP

This example uses a counting principle that we will study further in a later section.

Suppose the widow had x number of children before marriage. Then the couple has $24 - 10 - x = 14 - x$ additional children after their marriage. Since the children of the same parents do not fight, there are no fights among the 10 children the widower brought into the marriage, among the x children the widow brought into the marriage, or among the $14 - x$ children of the couple (widower and widow).

The possible number of fights among the children of

(*i*) the widower (10 children) and the widow (x children) is $10x$,

(*ii*) the widower (10 children) and the couple ($14 - x$ children) is $10(14 - x)$, and

(*iii*) the widow (x children) and the couple ($14 - x$ children) is $x(14 - x)$.

The possible number y of all fights is given by

$$y = 10x + 10(14 - x) + x(14 - x)$$
$$= 10x + 140 - 10x + 14x - x^2 \quad \text{Distributive property}$$
$$= 140 + 14x - x^2 \quad \text{Simplify.}$$

In the quadratic function $y = f(x) = -x^2 + 14x + 140$, we have $a = -1, b = 14$, and $c = 140$.

The vertex (h, k) is given by

$$h = -\frac{b}{2a} = -\frac{14}{2(-1)} = 7,$$
$$k = f(7) = -(7)^2 + 14(7) + 140 = 189.$$

Since $a = -1 < 0$, the function f has maximum value k. Hence, the maximum possible number of fights among the children is 189.   ■ ■ ■

PRACTICE PROBLEM 6   Repeat Example 6 if the widower had eight children from his previous marriage.   ▪

A Exercises   Basic Skills and Concepts

In Exercises 1–8, match each quadratic function with its graph.

1. $y = -\dfrac{1}{3}x^2$ f

2. $y = -3x^2$ d

3. $y = -3(x + 1)^2$ a

4. $y = 2(x + 1)^2$ e

5. $y = (x - 1)^2 + 2$ h

6. $y = (x - 1)^2 - 3$ b

7. $y = 2(x + 1)^2 - 3$ g

8. $y = -3(x + 1)^2 + 2$ c

(a)

(b)

(c)

(d)

(e)

(f)

(g)

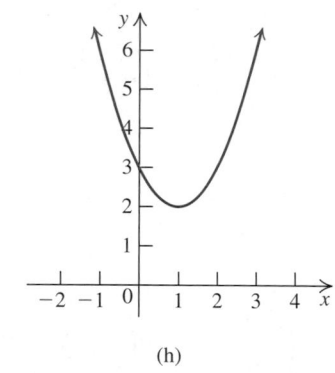

(h)

In Exercises 9–12, find a quadratic function of the form $y = ax^2$ that passes through the given point.

9. $(2, -8)$ $y = -2x^2$

10. $(-3, 3)$ $y = -\dfrac{1}{3}x^2$

11. $(2, 20)$ $y = 5x^2$

12. $(-3, -6)$ $y = -\dfrac{2}{3}x^2$

In Exercises 13–22, find the quadratic function $y = f(x)$ that has the given vertex and whose graph passes through the given point. Write the function in standard form.

13. Vertex $(0, 0)$; passing through $(-2, 8)$ $y = 2x^2$

14. Vertex $(2, 0)$; passing through $(1, 3)$ $y = 3(x - 2)^2$

15. Vertex $(-3, 0)$; passing through $(-5, -4)$ $y = -(x + 3)^2$

16. Vertex $(0, 1)$; passing through $(-1, 0)$ $y = -x^2 + 1$

17. Vertex $(2, 5)$; passing through $(3, 7)$ $y = 2(x - 2)^2 + 5$

18. Vertex $(-3, 4)$; passing through $(0, 0)$ †

19. Vertex $(2, -3)$; passing through $(-5, 8)$ †

20. Vertex $(-3, -2)$; passing through $(0, -8)$ †

21. Vertex $\left(\dfrac{1}{2}, \dfrac{1}{2}\right)$; passing through $\left(\dfrac{3}{4}, -\dfrac{1}{4}\right)$ †

22. Vertex $\left(-\dfrac{3}{2}, -\dfrac{5}{2}\right)$; passing through $\left(1, \dfrac{55}{8}\right)$ †

†Due to space constrictions, answers to these exercises may be found in the Answers beginning on page A–1 in the back of the book.

In Exercises 23–26, the graph of a quadratic function $y = f(x)$ is given. Find the standard form of the function.

23.

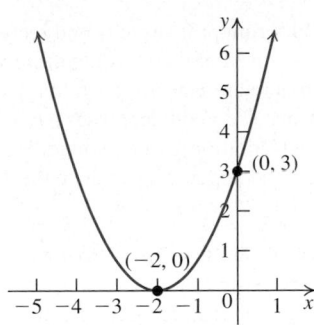

$y = \frac{3}{4}(x + 2)^2$

24.

$y = \frac{2}{9}(x - 3)^2$

25.

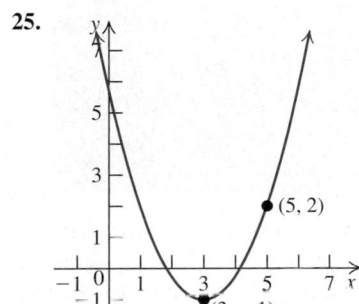

$y = \frac{3}{4}(x - 3)^2 - 1$

26.

$y = -(x - 2)^2 + 5$

In Exercises 27–38, graph the given function by first writing it in the standard form $y = a(x - h)^2 + k$ and then using transformations on $y = x^2$. Find the vertex, the axis, and the intercepts of the parabola.

27. $y = x^2 + 4x$ †

28. $y = x^2 - 2x + 2$ †

29. $y = 6x - 10 - x^2$ †

30. $y = 8 + 3x - x^2$ †

31. $y = 2x^2 - 8x + 9$ †

32. $y = 3x^2 + 12x - 7$ †

33. $y = -3x^2 + 18x - 11$ †

34. $y = -5x^2 - 20x + 13$ †

35. $y = \frac{1}{2}x^2 - 2x + 5$ †

36. $y = \frac{3}{4}x^2 + 6x + 5$ †

37. $y = -\frac{1}{2}x^2 + x - 7$ †

38. $y = -\frac{1}{4}x^2 - \frac{1}{2}x + 3$ †

In Exercises 39–50, (a) determine whether the graph of the given quadratic function opens up or down, (b) find the vertex $\left(-\frac{b}{2a}, f\left(-\frac{b}{2a}\right)\right)$, (c) find the axis of symmetry, (d) find the x- and y-intercepts, and (e) sketch the graph of the function.

39. $y = x^2 - 8x + 15$ †

40. $y = x^2 + 8x + 13$ †

41. $y = x^2 - x - 6$ †

42. $y = x^2 + x - 2$ †

43. $y = x^2 - 2x + 4$ †

44. $y = x^2 - 4x + 5$ †

45. $y = 6 - 2x - x^2$ †

46. $y = 2 + 5x - 3x^2$ †

47. $y = 36x - 3x^2 - 110$ †

48. $y = 2 + 3x^2 - x$ †

49. $y = 12 + x - x^2$ †

50. $y = 9x - 2x^2 - 4$ †

In Exercises 51–58, a quadratic function f is given.

(a) Determine whether the given quadratic function has a maximum value or a minimum value. Then find this value.

(b) Find the range of f.

51. $f(x) = x^2 - 4x + 3$ †

52. $f(x) = -x^2 + 6x - 8$ †

53. $f(x) = -4 + 4x - x^2$ †

54. $f(x) = x^2 - 6x + 9$ †

55. $f(x) = 2x^2 - 8x + 3$ †

56. $f(x) = 3x^2 + 12x - 5$ †

57. $f(x) = -4x^2 + 12x + 7$ †

58. $f(x) = 8x - 5 - 2x^2$ †

In Exercises 59–66, solve the given quadratic inequality by sketching the graph of the corresponding quadratic function.

59. $x^2 - 4 \leq 0$ †

60. $x^2 + 4x + 5 < 0$ †

61. $x^2 - 4x + 3 > 0$ †

62. $x^2 + x - 2 > 0$ †

63. $-6x^2 + x + 7 > 0$ †

64. $-5x^2 + 9x - 4 \leq 0$ †

65. $4x^2 - 28x + 49 \geq 0$ †

66. $\frac{1}{2}x^2 - \frac{3}{4}x + 7 \leq 0$ †

B Exercises   Applying the Concepts

67. Maximizing revenue. A revenue function is given by $R(x) = 15 + 114x - 3x^2$, where x is the number of units produced and sold. Find the value of x for which the revenue is maximum. 19

68. Maximizing revenue. A demand function $p = 200 - 4x$, where p is the price per unit and x is the number of units produced and sold (the demand). Find x for which the revenue is maximum. [Recall that $R(x) = x \cdot p$.] 25

69. Minimizing cost. The total cost of a product is $C = 625 - 50x + x^2$, where x is the number of units produced. Find the value of x for which the total cost is minimum. 25

70. Maximizing profit. A manufacturer produces x items of a product at a total cost of $(50 + 2x)$ dollars. The demand function for the product is $p = 100 - x$. Find the value of x for which the profit is maximum. How much is the maximum profit? [Recall that Profit = Revenue − Cost.] †

71. Geometry. Find the dimensions of a rectangle of maximum area if the perimeter of the rectangle is 80 units. What is the maximum area? †

72. Enclosing area. A rancher with 120 meters of fence intends to enclose a rectangular region along a river (which serves as a natural boundary requiring no fence). Find the maximum area that can be enclosed. 1800 m²

73. Enclosing playing fields. You have 600 meters of fencing, and you have to lay out two identical playing fields. The fields can be side by side as shown in the figure. Find the dimensions and the maximum area of each field. †

74. Enclosing area on a budget. Your budget for constructing a rectangular enclosure which consists of a high surrounding fence and a lower inside fence that divides the enclosure in half is 2400 dollars. The high fence costs 8 dollars per foot and the low fence costs 4 dollars per foot. Find the dimensions and the maximum area of each half of the enclosure. †

75. Maximizing apple yield. From past surveys and records, an orchard owner in northern Michigan has determined that if 26 apple trees per acre are planted, each tree yields 500 apples, on the average. The yield decreases by 10 apples per tree for each additional tree planted. How many trees should be planted per acre to achieve the maximum total yield? 38

76. Buying and selling beef. A steer weighing 300 pounds gains 8 pounds per day and costs 1.00 dollar a day to keep. You bought this steer today at a market price of 1.50 dollars per pound. However, the market price is falling 2 cents per pound per day. When should you sell the steer in order to maximize your profit? After 16 days

77. Going on a tour. A group of students plan a tour. The charge per student is 72 dollars if 20 students go on the trip. If more than 20 students participate, the charge per student is reduced by 2 dollars times the number of students over 20. Find the number of students that will furnish the maximum revenue. What is the maximum revenue? †

78. Computer disks. A 5-inch-radius computer disk contains information in units called *bytes* that are arranged in concentric tracks on the disk. Assume that m bytes per inch can be put on each track. The tracks are uniformly spread (that is, there is a fixed number, say, p, of tracks per inch, measured radially across the disk). If the number of bytes on each track must be the same, where should the innermost track be located to get the maximum number of bytes on the disk? 2.5 inches from the center

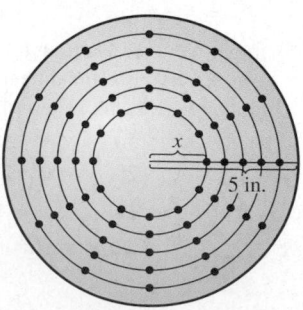

79. Motion of a projectile. A projectile is fired straight up with a velocity of 64 ft/s. Its altitude (height) h after t seconds is given by

$$h(t) = -16t^2 + 64t.$$

  a. What is the maximum height of the projectile? 64 ft
  b. When does the projectile hit the ground? After 4 sec

80. Motion of a projectile. A projectile is shot up from the top of a building 400 feet high with a velocity of 64 feet per second. Its altitude (height) h after t seconds is given by

$$h(t) = -16t^2 + 64t + 400.$$

  a. What is the maximum height of the projectile? 464 ft
  b. When does the projectile hit the ground? After 7.39 sec

81. Architecture. A window is to be constructed in the shape of a rectangle surmounted by a semicircle. If the perimeter of the window is 18 feet, find its dimensions for the maximum area. †

82. Architecture. The shape of the Gateway Arch in St. Louis, Missouri, is a *catenary* curve, which closely resembles a parabola. The function

$$y = f(x) = -0.00635x^2 + 4x$$

models the shape of the arch, where y is the height in feet and x is the horizontal distance from the base of the left side of the arch, in feet.
  a. Graph the function $y = f(x)$. †
  b. What is the width of the arch at the base? 629.92 ft
  c. What is the maximum height of the arch? 629.92 ft

83. Football. The altitude or height h (in feet) of a punted football can be modeled by the quadratic function

$$h = -0.01x^2 + 1.18x + 2,$$

where x (in feet) is the horizontal distance from the point of impact with the punter's foot. (See accompanying figure.)

  a. Find the vertex of the parabola. (59, 36.81)

  b. If the opposing team fails to catch the ball, how far away from the punter does the ball hit the ground (to the nearest foot)? 120 ft

  c. What is the maximum height of the punted ball (to the nearest foot)? 37 ft

  d. The nearest defensive player is 6 feet from the point of impact. How high must the player reach to block the punt (to the nearest foot)? 9 ft

  e. How far downfield has the ball traveled when it reaches a height of 7 feet for the second time? 113.6 ft

84. Field hockey. A *scoop* in field hockey is a pass that propels the ball from the ground into the air. Suppose a player makes a scoop with an upward velocity of 30 feet per second. The function

$$h = -16t^2 + 30t$$

models the altitude or height h in feet at time t in seconds. Will the ball ever reach a height of 16 feet? No.

C Exercises   Beyond the Basics

In Exercises 85–90, find a quadratic function of the form $f(x) = ax^2 + bx + c$ that satisfies the given conditions.

85. The graph of f is obtained by shifting the graph of $y = 3x^2$ two units horizontally to the left and three units vertically up. $f(x) = 3x^2 + 12x + 15$

86. The graph of f passes through the point $(1, 5)$ and has vertex $(-3, -2)$.

87. The graph of f has vertex $(1, -2)$ and y-intercept 4.

88. The graph of f has x-intercepts of 2 and 6 and y-intercept 24. $f(x) = 2x^2 - 16x + 24$

89. The graph of f has x-intercept 7 and y-intercept 14, and $x = 3$ is the axis of symmetry. $f(x) = -2x^2 + 12x + 14$

90. The graph of f is obtained by shifting the graph of $y = x^2 + 2x + 2$ three units horizontally to the right and two units vertically down. $f(x) = x^2 - 4x + 3$

In Exercises 91–94, find two quadratic functions, one opening up and the other down, whose graphs have the given x-intercepts.

91. $-2, 6$ **92.** $-3, 5$

Answers:

86. $f(x) = \dfrac{7}{16}x^2 + \dfrac{21}{8}x + \dfrac{31}{16}$ **87.** $f(x) = 6x^2 - 12x + 4$

91. Opening up: $x^2 - 4x - 12$.
  Opening down: $-x^2 + 4x + 12$.
92. Opening up: $x^2 - 2x - 15$.
  Opening down: $-x^2 + 2x + 15$.

93. $-7, -1$ Opening up: $x^2 + 8x + 7$. Opening down: $-x^2 - 8x - 7$.

94. $2, 10$ Opening up: $x^2 - 12x + 20$. Opening down: $-x^2 + 12x - 20$.

95. Let $f(x) = 4x - x^2$. Solve $f(a + 1) - f(a - 1) = 0$ for a. $a = 2$

96. Let $f(x) = x^2 + 1$. Find $(f \circ f)(x)$.

Critical Thinking

97. **Symmetry about the line $x = h$.** The graph of a polynomial function $y = f(x)$ is symmetric in the line $x = h$ if $f(h + p) = f(h - p)$ for every number p. For

$$f(x) = ax^2 + bx + c, a \neq 0, \text{ set } f(h + p) = f(h - p)$$

and show that $h = -\dfrac{b}{2a}$. This exercise proves that the graph

of a quadratic function is symmetric in its axis $x = -\dfrac{b}{2a}$.

98. In the graph of $y = 2x^2 - 8x + 9$, find the coordinates of the point symmetric to the point $(-1, 19)$ in the axis of symmetry. $(5, 19)$

Answers:

96. $(f \circ f)(x) = x^4 + 2x^2 + 2$
97. $f(h + p) = f(h - p) \Leftrightarrow a(h + p)^2 + b(h + p) + c$
$\qquad\qquad\qquad\qquad = a(h - p)^2 + b(h + p) + c$
$\qquad\qquad \Leftrightarrow ab^2 + 2ab + ap^2 + bh + bp$
$\qquad\qquad\qquad = ab^2 - 2ahp + ap^2 + bh - bp$
$\qquad\qquad \Leftrightarrow 4abp = -2bp \Leftrightarrow 2ahp = -bp$
Since $p \neq 0$, the last equation is equivalent to $2ab = -b$.
Since $a \neq 0$, it follows that $h = -\dfrac{b}{2a}$.

Polynomial Functions

Johannes Kepler (1571–1630)
Kepler was born in Weil in southern Germany and studied at the University of Tübingen. He studied with Michael Mastlin (professor of mathematics), who privately taught him the Copernican theory of the sun-centered universe while hardly daring to recognize it openly in his lectures. Kepler knew that to work out a detailed version of Copernicus's theory, he had to have access to the observations of the Danish astronomer Tycho Brahe (1546–1601). Kepler's correspondence with Tycho resulted in his appointment as Tycho's assistant. Tycho died about 18 months after Kepler's arrival. During these 18 months, Kepler learned enough about Tycho's work to use the material in working out his own major project. He was appointed as Imperial Mathematician by Emperor Rudolf to succeed Tycho Brahe and spent the next 11 years in Prague. He produced the famous three laws of planetary motion. His investigations were published in 1609 in his book *Nova Astronomia*.

BEFORE STARTING THIS SECTION, REVIEW

1. Graphs of equations (Section 2.2, page 192)
2. Solving linear equations (Section 1.1, page 89)
3. Solving quadratic equations (Section 1.4, page 121)
4. Transformations (Section 2.6, page 263)

OBJECTIVES

1. Learn properties of graphs of polynomial functions.
2. Determine the end behavior of polynomial functions.
3. Find the zeros of a polynomial function by factoring.
4. Learn the Relationship between degrees, real zeros, and turning points.
5. Graph polynomial functions.

Kepler's Wedding Reception

Kepler is best known as an astronomer who discovered the three laws of planetary motion. However, Kepler's primary field was not astronomy, but mathematics. He served as a mathematician in Austrian Emperor Mathias's court. After the death of his wife Barbara, Kepler remarried in 1613. His new wife, Susanna, had a crash course in Kepler's character. Legend has it that at his own wedding reception Kepler observed that the Austrian vintners could quickly and mysteriously compute the capacities (volumes) of a variety of wine barrels. Each barrel had a hole, called a *bunghole*, in the middle of its side. The vintner would insert a rod, called the *bungrod*, into the hole until it hit the far corner. Then he would announce the volume. During the reception, Kepler occupied his mind with the problem of finding the volume of wine barrel with a bungrod.

In Example 9, we show you how he solved the problem for barrels that are perfect cylinders. But barrels are not perfect cylinders. Like beer barrels, they are wider in the middle and narrower at the top and bottom, and in between the sides make a graceful curve that appears to be an arc of a circle. So what could be the formula for the volume of such a shape? Kepler tackled this problem in his important book *Nova Stereometria Doliorum Vinariorum* (1615) and developed a complete mathematical theory in relation to it. ■

1 Learn properties of graphs of polynomial functions.

Polynomial Functions

We begin with some terminology. A *polynomial function of degree n* is a function of the form

$$f(x) = a_n x^n + a_{n-1} x^{n-1} + \cdots + a_2 x + a_1 x + a_0,$$

where n is a nonnegative integer and the *coefficients* $a_n, a_{n-1}, \ldots, a_2, a_1, a_0$ are real numbers with $a_n \neq 0$. The term $a_n x^n$ is called the **leading term,** the number a_n (the coefficient of x^n) is called the **leading coefficient,** and a_0 is the **constant term.** A constant function $f(x) = a$ $(a \neq 0)$, which may be written as $f(x) = ax^0$, is a polynomial of degree 0. Since the zero function $f(x) = 0$ can be written in several ways, such as $0 = 0x^6 + 0x = 0x^5 + 0 = 0x^4 + 0x^3 + 0$, and so on, there is no degree assigned to it.

The expression

$$a_n x^n + a_{n-1} x^{n-1} + \cdots + a_2 x + a_1 x + a_0$$

is a **polynomial,** the function f defined by

$$f(x) = a_n x^n + a_{n-1} x^{n-1} + \cdots + a_2 x + a_1 x + a_0$$

is a **polynomial function,** and the equation

$$a_n x^n + a_{n-1} x^{n-1} + \cdots + a_2 x + a_1 x + a_0 = 0$$

is a **polynomial equation.**

In Section 2.5, we discussed polynomial functions of degree 0 and 1. In Section 3.1, we studied polynomial functions of degree 2.

Polynomials of degree 3, 4, and 5 are also called **cubic, quartic,** and **quintic polynomials,** respectively. In this section, we will concentrate on graphing polynomial functions of degree 3 or more.

You might wonder why you should spend time sketching the graph of a polynomial function by hand, since you can always draw such graphs by using a graphing calculator. You are right to a certain extent. But there is a significant issue here of "What you see may not be an accurate graph."

When you draw a graph on a graphing calculator (or a computer), you are drawing the graph in a particular viewing window that is often chosen by the machine. For example, the graph of $y = (x + 8)^2(x - 5)^2$ has x-intercepts -8 and 5, but they do not appear on the calculator graph of the function. You need to know how to adjust the window to show the significant features of the part of the graph that interests you. The way to resolve this problem is through studying graphs algebraically. A thorough study of graphs of functions is given in calculus courses.

TECHNOLOGY CONNECTION

Calculator graph of

$y = (x + 8)^2(x - 5)^2$, using the window

$[-10, 10, 1, -2, 20, 1]$

$[-10, 10, 1]$ by $[-2, 20, 1]$

We next state some properties that are shared by all polynomial functions.

COMMON PROPERTIES OF POLYNOMIAL FUNCTIONS

1. The domain of a polynomial function is the set of all real numbers.

2. The graph of a polynomial function is a **continuous curve.** This means that the graph has no holes or gaps and can be drawn on a piece of paper without lifting your pencil. (See Figure 3.4.)

A continuous curve

(a)

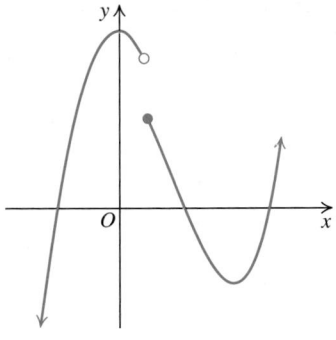

A discontinuous curve. Cannot be the graph of a polynomial function.

(b)

FIGURE 3.4

3. The graph of a polynomial function is a **smooth curve.** This means that the graph of a polynomial function does not contain any sharp corners. (See Figure 3.5.)

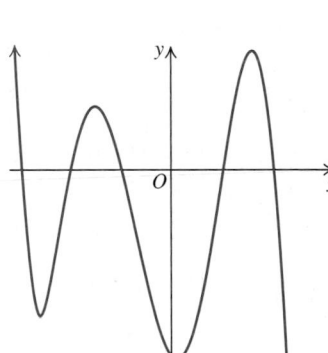

A smooth and continuous curve.

(a)

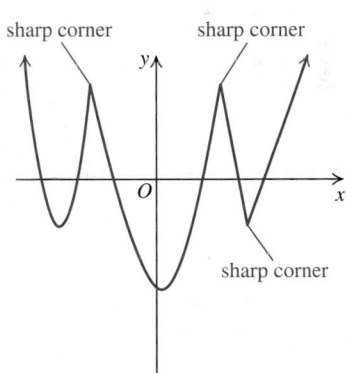

A continuous, but not a smooth, curve; cannot be the graph of a polynomial function.

(b)

FIGURE 3.5

Power Functions

The simplest nth-degree polynomial function is a function of the form $f(x) = ax^n$ and is called a power function.

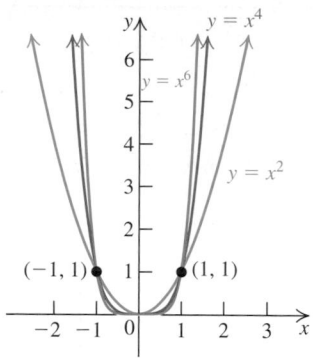

FIGURE 3.6

POWER FUNCTION

A function of the form

$$f(x) = ax^n$$

is called a **power function of degree n,** where a is a nonzero real number and n is a positive integer.

The graph of a power function can be obtained by stretching or shrinking the graph of $y = x^n$ (and reflecting it about the x-axis if $a < 0$). So the basic shape of the graph of a power function $f(x) = ax^n$ is similar to the shape of the graphs of the equations $y = \pm x^n$.

Power Functions of Even Degree   Let $f(x) = ax^n$. If n is even, then $(-x)^n = x^n$. So, in this case, $f(-x) = a(-x)^n = ax^n = f(x)$. Thus, a power function is an even function when n is even. This means that the graph of such a function is symmetric with respect to the y-axis.

The graph of $y = x^n$ (when n is even) is similar to the graph of $y = x^2$; the graphs of $y = x^2$, $y = x^4$, and $y = x^6$ are shown in Figure 3.6.

Comparing the graphs of $y = x^2$ and $y = x^4$, we notice that both graphs pass through the points $(-1, 1)$, $(0, 0)$, and $(1, 1)$. On the interval $-1 < x < 1$, the graph of $y = x^4$ is flatter than the graph of $y = x^2$. (See Exercise 73.) The graph of $y = x^6$ in the interval $(-1, 1)$ is flatter still. However, on the interval $(-\infty, -1) \cup (1, \infty)$, the graph of $y = x^4$ is higher than the graph of $y = x^2$. (See Exercise 74.) In other words, for $|x| > 1$, the graph of $y = x^4$ rises more rapidly than the graph of $y = x^2$. The graph of $y = x^6$ rises still more rapidly.

Power Functions of Odd Degree   Again, let $f(x) = ax^n$. If n is odd, then $(-x)^n = -x^n$. In this case, we have $f(-x) = a(-x)^n = -ax^n = -f(x)$. Thus, the power function $f(x) = ax^n$ is an odd function when n is odd. The graph of such a function is symmetric with respect to the origin. When n is odd, the graph of $f(x) = x^n$ is similar to the graph of $y = x^3$. The graphs of $y = x^3$, $y = x^5$, and $y = x^7$ are shown in Figure 3.7.

If n is an odd positive integer, then the graph of $y = x^n$ passes through the points $(-1, -1)$, $(0, 0)$, and $(1, 1)$. The larger the value of n, the flatter is the graph near the origin (in the interval $-1 < x < 1$), and the more rapidly it rises (or falls) when $|x| > 1$.

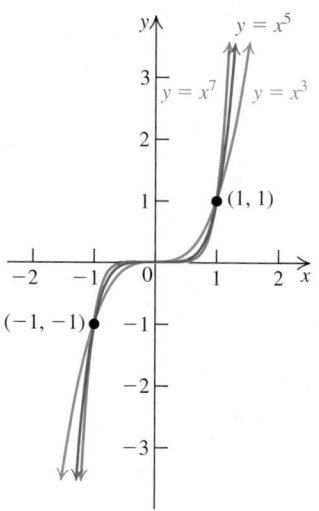

FIGURE 3.7

2 Determine the end behavior of polynomial functions.

End Behavior of Polynomial Functions

Let $y = f(x)$ be a function. We are interested in studying the behavior of $f(x)$ when the independent variable x is large in absolute value. We first describe the intuitive meaning of the expression "*x approaches infinity.*" We say "x approaches infinity" and write this with the notation $x \to \infty$, which means that x gets larger and larger without bound. Intuitively, you may view x as being able to assume values greater than 1, 10, 100, 1000, . . . , without end. Similarly, $x \to -\infty$ (read "x approaches negative infinity") means that x can assume values less than -1, -10, -100, -1000, . . . , without end. Of course, x may be replaced by any other variable.

The behavior of a function $y = f(x)$ as $x \to \infty$ or $x \to -\infty$ is called the **end behavior** of the function. As $x \to \infty$ or $x \to -\infty$, the y-coordinate of a polynomial function $y = f(x)$ may approach ∞ or $-\infty$. In the accompanying box, we describe the behavior of the power function $y = f(x) = ax^n$ as $x \to \infty$ or $x \to -\infty$. Every polynomial function exhibits end behavior similar to one of the four functions $y = x^2$, $y = -x^2$, $y = x^3$, and $y = -x^3$.

End Behavior for the Graph of $y = f(x) = ax^n$

Sign of a	n Even	n Odd
$a > 0$	$y = f(x) \to \infty$ as $x \to \infty$ or $x \to -\infty$. (a) The graph rises to the left and right, similar to $y = x^2$	$y = f(x) \to \infty$ as $x \to \infty$ and $y \to -\infty$ as $x \to -\infty$. (b) The graph rises to the right and falls to the left, similar to $y = x^3$
$a < 0$	$y = f(x) \to -\infty$ as $x \to \infty$ or $x \to -\infty$. (c) The graph falls to the left and right, similar to $y = -x^2$	$y = f(x) \to -\infty$ as $x \to \infty$ and $y \to \infty$ as $x \to -\infty$. (d) The graph rises to the left and falls to the right, similar to $y = -x^3$

TECHNOLOGY CONNECTION

Calculator graph of $P(x) = 2x^3 + 5x^2 - 7x + 11$

$[-8, 8, 2]$ by $[-40, 60, 5]$

In the next example, we show that the end behavior of the given polynomial function is determined by its leading term. If a polynomial $P(x)$ has approximately the same values as $f(x) = ax^n$ when $|x|$ is very large, we write $P(x) \approx ax^n$ when $|x|$ is very large.

EXAMPLE 1   Understanding the End Behavior of a Polynomial Function

Let $P(x) = 2x^3 + 5x^2 - 7x + 11$ be a polynomial function of degree 3. Show that $P(x) \approx 2x^3$ when $|x|$ is very large.

Solution

$$P(x) = 2x^3 + 5x^2 - 7x + 11 \qquad \text{Given polynomial}$$

$$= x^3\left(2 + \frac{5}{x} - \frac{7}{x^2} + \frac{11}{x^3}\right) \qquad \text{Distributive property}$$

Continued on next page.

TABLE 3.1

x	$\dfrac{5}{x}$
10	0.5
10^2	0.05
10^3	0.005
10^4	0.0005

When $|x|$ is very large, the terms $\dfrac{5}{x}$, $-\dfrac{7}{x^2}$, and $\dfrac{11}{x^3}$ are close to 0.

Table 3.1 shows some values of $\dfrac{5}{x}$. (You should compute the values of $-\dfrac{7}{x^2}$, and $\dfrac{11}{x^3}$ for $x = 10$, 10^2, 10^3, and 10^4.) We then have

$$P(x) = x^3\left(2 + \frac{5}{x} - \frac{7}{x^2} + \frac{11}{x^3}\right) \approx x^3(2 + 0 - 0 + 0) \quad \text{when } |x| \text{ is very large}$$

$$= 2x^3. \qquad 2 + 0 - 0 + 0 = 2$$

Hence, the polynomial $P(x) \approx 2x^3$ when $|x|$ is very large. ■ ■ ■

PRACTICE PROBLEM 1 Let $P(x) = 4x^3 + 2x^2 + 5x - 17$. Show that $P(x) \approx 4x^3$ when $|x|$ is very large. ■

The very same technique of Example 1 can be used on any polynomial function to show that the end behavior of a polynomial function is determined by its leading term.

Thus, in terms of end behavior, the graph of a polynomial function behaves as shown in the graphs below. We summarize these observations in the *leading-term test*.

THE LEADING-TERM TEST

Let $f(x) = a_n x^n + a_{n-1}x^{n-1} + \cdots + a_1 x + a_0$ $(a_n \neq 0)$ be a polynomial function. Its leading term is $a_n x^n$. The behavior of the graph of f as $x \to \infty$ or $x \to -\infty$ is similar to one of the following four graphs and is described as shown in each case:

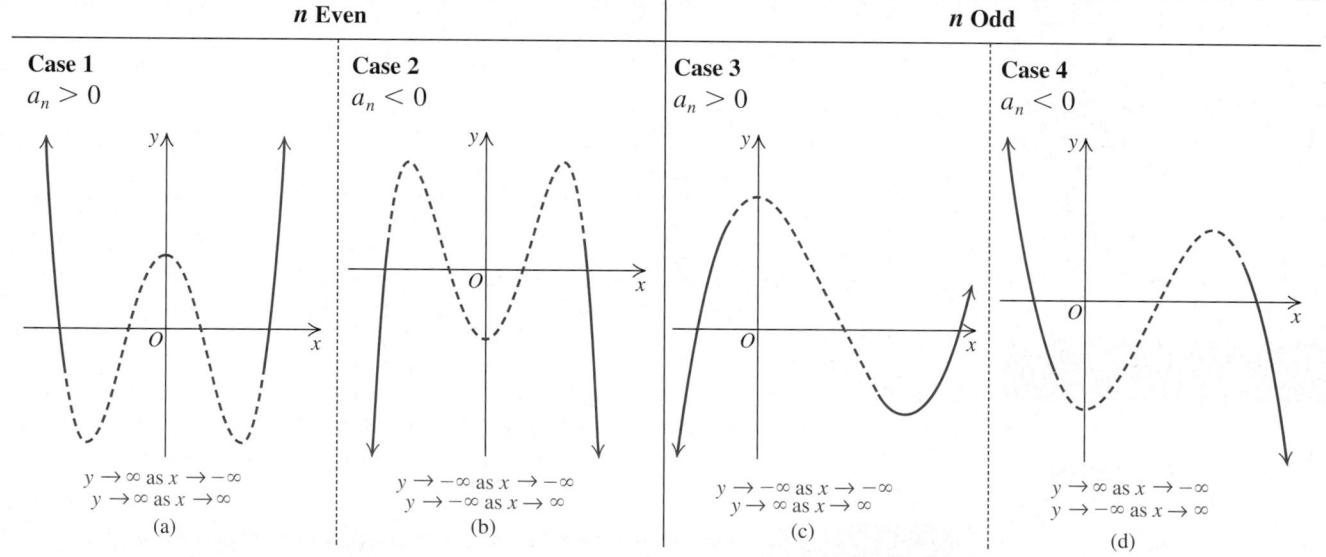

n **Even**		n **Odd**	
Case 1 $a_n > 0$	**Case 2** $a_n < 0$	**Case 3** $a_n > 0$	**Case 4** $a_n < 0$
$y \to \infty$ as $x \to -\infty$ $y \to \infty$ as $x \to \infty$ (a)	$y \to -\infty$ as $x \to -\infty$ $y \to -\infty$ as $x \to \infty$ (b)	$y \to -\infty$ as $x \to -\infty$ $y \to \infty$ as $x \to \infty$ (c)	$y \to \infty$ as $x \to -\infty$ $y \to -\infty$ as $x \to \infty$ (d)

The middle portion of each graph, indicated by the dashed lines, is not determined by this test.

EXAMPLE 2 **Using the Leading-Term Test**

Use the leading-term test to determine the end behavior of the graph of

$$y = f(x) = -2x^3 + 3x + 4.$$

Solution

Here, $n = 3$ (odd) and $a_n = -2 < 0$. Thus, Case 4 applies. The graph of $f(x)$ rises to the left and falls to the right. (See Figure 3.8.) This behavior is described as $y \to \infty$ as $x \to -\infty$ and $y \to -\infty$ as $x \to \infty$. ■ ■ ■

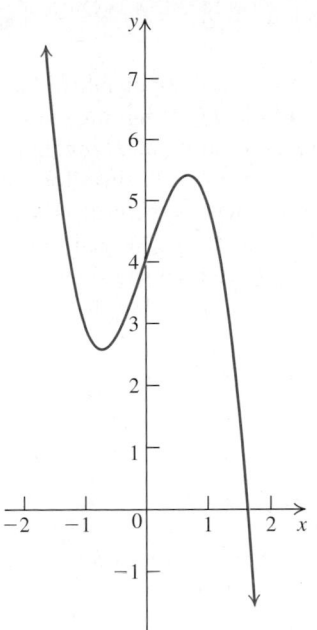

FIGURE 3.8

3 Find the zeros of a polynomial function by factoring.

$f(x) = x^3 + 2x^2 - x - 2$

$[-3, 2, 1]$ by $[-5, 8, 1]$

$g(x) = x^3 - 2x^2 + x - 2$

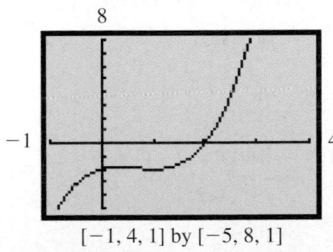

$[-1, 4, 1]$ by $[-5, 8, 1]$

PRACTICE PROBLEM 2 What is the end behavior of $f(x) = -2x^4 + 5x^2 + 3$?   ■

Zeros of a Function

Let f be a function. An input c in the domain of f that produces output 0 is called a *zero* of the function f. For example, if $f(x) = (x - 3)^2$, then 3 is a zero of f because $f(3) = (3 - 3)^2 = 0$. In other words, a number c is a **zero** of f if $f(c) = 0$. The zeros of a function f can be obtained by solving the equation $f(x) = 0$. One way to solve a polynomial equation $f(x) = 0$ is to factor $f(x)$ and then use the zero-product property.

If c is a real number and $f(c) = 0$, then c is called a **real zero** of f. Geometrically, this means that the graph of f has an x-intercept at $x = c$. We summarize our discussion next.

REAL ZEROS OF POLYNOMIAL FUNCTIONS

If f is a polynomial function and c is a real number, then the following statements are equivalent:

1. c is a **zero** of f.
2. c is a **solution** (or **root**) of the equation $f(x) = 0$.
3. c is an **x-intercept** of the graph of f. The point $(c, 0)$ is on the graph of f.

EXAMPLE 3   **Finding the Zeros of a Polynomial Function**

Find all real zeros of each polynomial function.

a. $f(x) = x^3 + 2x^2 - x - 2$ **b.** $g(x) = x^3 - 2x^2 + x - 2$

Solution

a. We first factor $f(x)$ and then solve the equation $f(x) = 0$.

$$
\begin{aligned}
f(x) &= x^3 + 2x^2 - x - 2 && \text{Given function} \\
&= (x^3 + 2x^2) - (x + 2) && \text{Group terms.} \\
&= x^2(x + 2) - 1(x + 2) && \text{Distributive property} \\
&= (x + 2)(x^2 - 1) && \text{Distributive property} \\
&= (x + 2)(x + 1)(x - 1) && \text{Factor } x^2 - 1.
\end{aligned}
$$

$$(x + 2)(x + 1)(x - 1) = 0 \qquad \text{Set } f(x) = 0.$$
$$x + 2 = 0, \quad \text{or} \quad x + 1 = 0, \quad \text{or} \quad x - 1 = 0 \qquad \text{Zero-product property}$$
$$x = -2, \quad \text{or} \quad x = -1, \quad \text{or} \quad x = 1 \qquad \text{Solve each equation.}$$

Thus, the zeros of $f(x)$ are $-2, -1$, and 1. The calculator graph of f supports our solution.

b. By grouping terms, factor $g(x)$ to obtain

$$
\begin{aligned}
g(x) &= x^3 - 2x^2 + x - 2 \\
&= x^2(x - 2) + 1 \cdot (x - 2) && \text{Group terms.} \\
&= (x - 2)(x^2 + 1) && \text{Factor out } x - 2. \\
0 &= (x - 2)(x^2 + 1) && \text{Set } g(x) = 0. \\
\end{aligned}
$$
$$x - 2 = 0, \quad \text{or} \quad x^2 + 1 = 0 \qquad \text{Zero-product property}$$

Solving for x, we obtain 2 as the only real zero of $g(x)$, since $x^2 + 1 > 0$ for all real numbers x. The calculator graph of g supports our conclusion.   ■ ■ ■

PRACTICE PROBLEM 3 Find all real zeros of $f(x) = 2x^3 - 3x^2 + 4x - 6$. ∎

How do we find the zeros of a polynomial of degree 3 or more if we are unable to factor it? The problem of finding the zeros of a polynomial is one of the most important problems of mathematics. You will learn more about finding the zeros of polynomial functions in Sections 3.3 and 3.4. For now, we shall settle for finding approximate values for the zeros of a polynomial function. The Intermediate Value Theorem will be helpful. Recall that the graph of a polynomial function $f(x)$ is a continuous curve. Suppose you locate two numbers a and b such that the function values $f(a)$ and $f(b)$ have opposite signs (one positive and the other negative). Then the continuous graph of f connecting the points $(a, f(a))$ and $(b, f(b))$ must cross the x-axis (at least once) somewhere between a and b. In other words, the function f has a zero between a and b. (See Figure 3.9.) This intuitive concept is stated in the next theorem.

THE INTERMEDIATE VALUE THEOREM

Let a and b be two numbers such that $a < b$. If f is a polynomial function such that $f(a)$ and $f(b)$ have opposite signs, then there is at least one number c, with $a < c < b$, for which $f(c) = 0$.

Notice that Figure 3.9(c) shows more than one zero of f. That is why the Intermediate Value Theorem says that f has *at least one* zero between a and b.

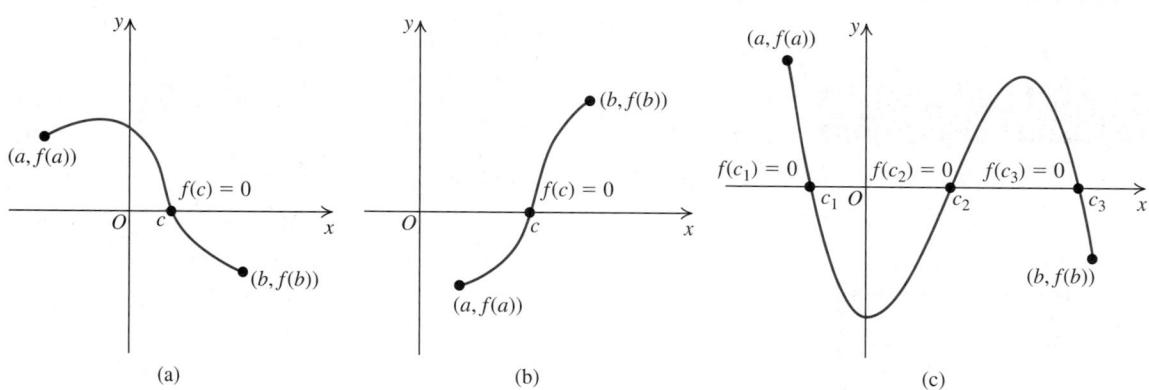

(a)   (b)   (c)

FIGURE 3.9

EXAMPLE 4   Using the Intermediate Value Theorem

Show that the function $f(x) = -2x^3 + 4x + 5$ has a real zero between 1 and 2.

Solution

$$f(x) = -2x^3 + 4x + 5 \qquad \text{Given function}$$
$$f(1) = -2(1)^3 + 4(1) + 5 \qquad \text{Replace } x \text{ by 1 in } f(x).$$
$$= -2 + 4 + 5$$
$$= 7 \qquad \text{Simplify.}$$
$$f(2) = -2(2)^3 + 4(2) + 5 \qquad \text{Replace } x \text{ by 2.}$$
$$= -2(8) + 8 + 5$$
$$= -3 \qquad \text{Simplify.}$$

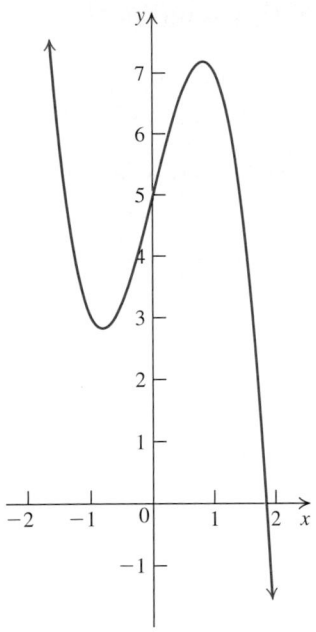

FIGURE 3.10

4 Learn the relationship between degrees, real zeros, and turning points.

Since $f(1)$ is positive and $f(2)$ is negative, they have opposite signs, so, by the Intermediate Value Theorem, the polynomial function $f(x) = -2x^3 + 4x + 5$ has a real zero between 1 and 2. (See Figure 3.10.)   ■ ■ ■

PRACTICE PROBLEM 4 Show that $f(x) = 2x^3 - 3x - 6$ has a real zero between 1 and 2.   ■

In Example 4, if you want to find the zero between 1 and 2 more accurately, you can divide the interval $[1, 2]$ into tenths and find the value of the function at each of the points $1, 1.1, 1.2, \ldots, 1.9$, and 2. When you do this, you will find that

$$f(1.8) = 0.536 \quad \text{and} \quad f(1.9) = -1.118.$$

Thus, by the Intermediate Value Theorem, f has a zero between 1.8 and 1.9. By continuing this process, you can find the zero of f between 1.8 and 1.9 to any degree of accuracy.

Zeros and Turning Points

In Section 3.4, you will study the Fundamental Theorem of Algebra. One of the consequences of this theorem is the following fact:

REAL ZEROS OF A POLYNOMIAL FUNCTION

A polynomial function of degree n with real coefficients has *at most* n real zeros.

EXAMPLE 5 **Finding the Number of Real Zeros**

Find the number of distinct real zeros of the following polynomial functions of degree 3.

a. $f(x) = (x - 1)(x + 2)(x - 3)$ **b.** $g(x) = (x + 1)(x^2 + 1)$
c. $h(x) = (x - 3)^2(x + 1)$

Solution

a. The zeros of $f(x)$ are obtained by solving the equation $f(x) = 0$.

$$f(x) = (x - 1)(x + 2)(x - 3) = 0 \qquad \text{Set } f(x) = 0.$$
$$x - 1 = 0, \quad \text{or} \quad x + 2 = 0, \quad \text{or} \quad x - 3 = 0 \qquad \text{Zero-product property}$$
$$x = 1 \quad \text{or} \quad x = -2 \quad \text{or} \quad x = 3 \qquad \text{Solve for } x.$$

Thus, the polynomial function $f(x) = (x - 1)(x + 2)(x - 3)$ has three real zeros: $1, -2$, and 3.

b.
$$g(x) = (x + 1)(x^2 + 1) = 0 \qquad \text{Set } g(x) = 0.$$
$$x + 1 = 0 \quad \text{or} \quad x^2 + 1 = 0 \qquad \text{Zero-product property}$$
$$x = -1 \qquad \text{Solve for } x.$$

Now, $x^2 + 1 > 0$, for all real x, so the equation $x^2 + 1 = 0$ has no real solution. Hence, -1 is the only real zero of $g(x)$.

c.
$$h(x) = (x - 3)^2(x + 1) = 0 \qquad \text{Set } h(x) = 0.$$
$$(x - 3)^2 = 0, \quad \text{or} \quad x + 1 = 0 \qquad \text{Zero-product property}$$
$$x = 3, \quad \text{or} \quad x = -1 \qquad \text{Solve for } x.$$

The real zeros of $h(x)$ are 3 and -1. Thus, $h(x)$ has two distinct real zeros.   ■ ■ ■

PRACTICE PROBLEM 5   Find the distinct real zeros of $f(x) = (x + 1)^2(x - 3)(x + 5)$.   ■

In Example 5c, the factor $(x - 3)$ appears twice in $h(x)$. [That is, $(x - 3)^2 = (x - 3)(x - 3)$.] We say that 3 is a zero repeated twice, or that 3 is a *zero of multiplicity* 2.

Recall (Section 2.6) that the graph of $y = f(x) = a(x - c)^m$ is the graph of $y = ax^m$ shifted horizontally c units right if $c > 0$ or $|c|$ units left if $c < 0$. Next, we describe the behavior of these graphs near the zero c for even and odd values of m.

Graph of $y = f(x) = a(x - c)^m$

Sign of a	m Even	m Odd
$a > 0$	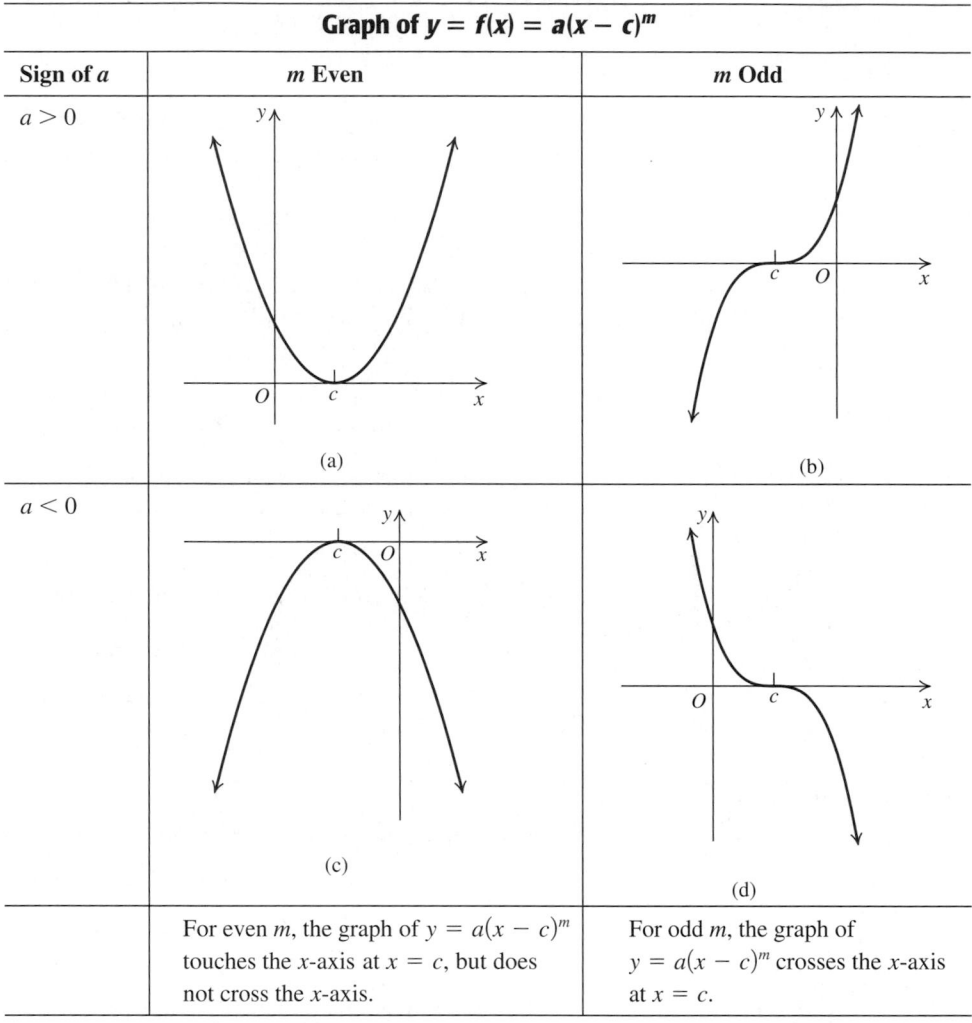 (a)	(b)
$a < 0$	(c)	(d)
	For even m, the graph of $y = a(x - c)^m$ touches the x-axis at $x = c$, but does not cross the x-axis.	For odd m, the graph of $y = a(x - c)^m$ crosses the x-axis at $x = c$.

It can be shown that if c is a zero of multiplicity $m > 1$ of a polynomial function $f(x)$, then the graph of $y = f(x)$ in the vicinity of the x-intercept c behaves like the graph of $y = a(x - c)^m$. The higher the multiplicity of a zero at c, the flatter is the graph at $x = c$.

We next summarize the discussion about the multiplicity of a zero.

MULTIPLICITY OF A ZERO

If c is a zero of a polynomial function $f(x)$ and the corresponding factor $(x - c)$ occurs exactly m times when $f(x)$ is factored, then c is called a **zero of multiplicity m.**

1. If m is odd, the graph of f crosses the x-axis at $x = c$.
2. If m is even, the graph of f touches, but does not cross, the x-axis at $x = c$.

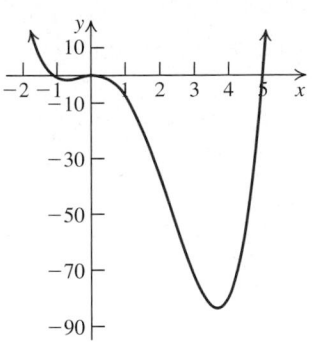

FIGURE 3.11

EXAMPLE 6   **Finding the Zeros and Their Multiplicity**

Find the zeros of the polynomial function $f(x) = x^2(x + 1)(x - 5)$, and give the multiplicity of each zero.

Solution

The polynomial $f(x)$ is already in factored form.

$$f(x) = x^2(x + 1)(x - 5) = 0 \qquad \text{Set } f(x) = 0.$$

$$x^2 = 0, \quad \text{or} \quad x + 1 = 0, \quad \text{or} \quad x - 5 = 0 \qquad \text{Zero-product property}$$

$$x = 0 \quad \text{or} \quad x = -1 \quad \text{or} \quad x = 5 \qquad \text{Solve for } x.$$

$f(x)$ has three distinct zeros: 0, -1, and 5. The zero $x = 0$ has multiplicity 2, and each of the zeros -1 and 5 has multiplicity 1. The graph of f is given in Figure 3.11.

Notice that the graph of f crosses the x-axis at -1 and 5 (the zeros of odd multiplicity), while it touches, but does not cross, the x-axis at $x = 0$ (the zero of even multiplicity).   ■ ■ ■

PRACTICE PROBLEM 6   Write the zeros of $f(x) = (x - 1)^2(x + 3)(x + 5)$, and give the multiplicity of each.   ■

Turning Points   The graph of $f(x) = 2x^3 - 3x^2 - 12x + 5$ is shown in Figure 3.12. The graph has two *turning points:* $(-1, 12)$ and $(2, -15)$. The point $(-1, 12)$ is higher than any nearby point on the graph. On a graphing calculator, it is the highest point on the graph of f within some viewing window. The value $f(-1) = 12$ is a **local** (or **relative**) **maximum** value of f. The point $(2, -15)$ is a **local** (or **relative**) **minimum** point on the graph of f. The local maximum and local minimum points on the graph of a function are called **turning points.** At each turning point, the graph changes direction from increasing to decreasing or from decreasing to increasing.

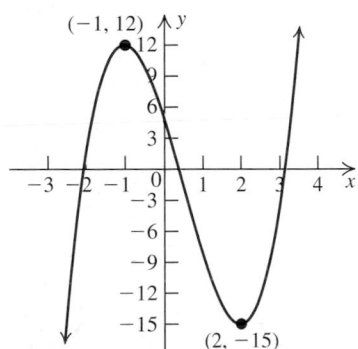

The graph of $f(x) = 2x^3 - 3x^2 - 12x + 5$ has turning points at $(-1, 12)$ and $(2, -15)$.

FIGURE 3.12

The following principle states that the number of turning points of the graph of a polynomial function is less than its degree:

NUMBER OF TURNING POINTS

If $f(x)$ is a polynomial of degree n, then the graph of f has *at most* $(n - 1)$ turning points.

| EXAMPLE 7 | Finding the Number of Turning Points |

Use a graphing calculator and the window $[-10, 10, 1]$ by $[-30, 30, 1]$ to find the number of turning points of the graph of each polynomial function.

a. $f(x) = x^4 - 7x^2 - 18$

b. $g(x) = x^3 + x^2 - 12x$

c. $h(x) = x^3 - 3x^2 + 3x - 1$

Solution

The graphs of f, g, and h (from left to right) are shown in Figure 3.13.

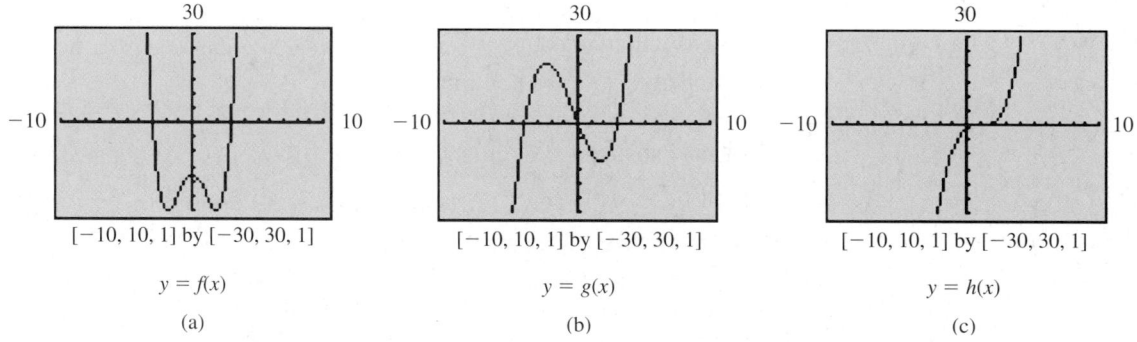

$[-10, 10, 1]$ by $[-30, 30, 1]$ $[-10, 10, 1]$ by $[-30, 30, 1]$ $[-10, 10, 1]$ by $[-30, 30, 1]$

$y = f(x)$ $y = g(x)$ $y = h(x)$

(a)   (b)   (c)

FIGURE 3.13

a. $f(x)$ has two local minimum points and one local maximum point, for a total of three turning points.

b. $g(x)$ has one local maximum point and one local minimum point, for a total of two turning points.

c. $h(x)$ has no turning points. The function $h(x)$ is increasing on the interval $(-\infty, \infty)$.

■ ■ ■

PRACTICE PROBLEM 7 Find the number of turning points of the graph of $f(x) = -x^4 + 3x^2 - 2$. ■

5 Graph polynomial functions.

Graphing a Polynomial Function

The graph of a polynomial function can always be sketched by constructing a table of values for a large number of points and connecting the plotted points with a smooth curve. (In fact, this is just what a graphing calculator does.) Generally, however, this process is a poor way to graph a function by hand, because it is tedious, is error prone, and may give misleading results. Similarly, a graphing calculator approach may also give misleading results, if the viewing window in the calculator is not chosen appropriately. Following is a strategy for graphing a polynomial function:

FINDING THE SOLUTION: GRAPHING A POLYNOMIAL FUNCTION	
OBJECTIVE *To sketch the graph of a polynomial function.*	**EXAMPLE** *Sketch the graph of $f(x) = -x^3 - 4x^2 + 4x + 16$.*

Step 1 **Determine the end behavior.** Apply the leading-term test.

Since the degree, 3, of f is odd and the leading coefficient, -1, is negative, the end behavior (Case 4, page 338) is described by

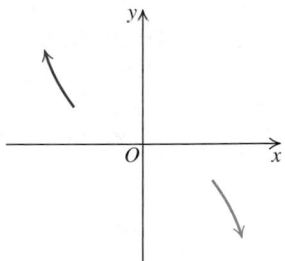

Step 2 **Find the zeros of the polynomial function.** Set $f(x) = 0$. Solve the equation $f(x) = 0$ by factoring or by using a graphing calculator. The zeros will give you the x-intercepts of the graph.

$$-x^3 - 4x^2 + 4x + 16 = 0$$
$$-(x + 4)(x + 2)(x - 2) = 0$$
$$x = -4, x = -2, \text{ or } x = 2$$

There are three zeros, each of multiplicity 1, so the graph crosses the x-axis at each zero.

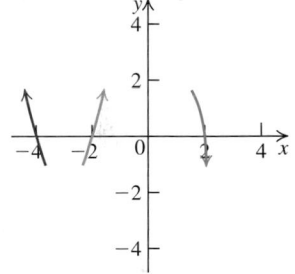

Step 3 **Find the y-intercept** by computing $f(0)$.

The y-intercept is $f(0) = 16$. The graph passes through the point $(0, 16)$.

Step 4 **Use symmetry** to check whether the function is odd, even, or neither.

$$f(-x) = -(-x)^3 - 4(-x)^2 + 4(-x) + 16 = x^3 - 4x^2 - 4x + 16.$$

Since $f(-x) \neq f(x)$, there is no symmetry in the y-axis. Also, since $f(-x) \neq -f(x)$, there is no symmetry with respect to the origin.

Step 5 **Determine the sign of $f(x)$** by using arbitrarily chosen "test numbers" in the intervals defined by the x-intercepts. Find the intervals on which the graph lies above or below the x-axis.

The three zeros -4, -2, and 2 divide the x-axis into four intervals: $(-\infty, -4)$, $(-4, -2)$, $(-2, 2)$, and $(2, \infty)$.

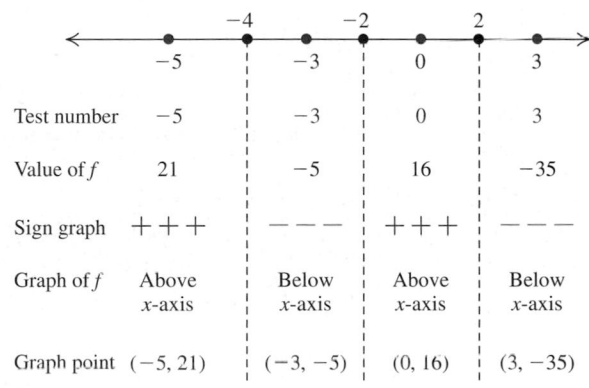

Test number	-5	-3	0	3
Value of f	21	-5	16	-35
Sign graph	$+ + +$	$- - -$	$+ + +$	$- - -$
Graph of f	Above x-axis	Below x-axis	Above x-axis	Below x-axis
Graph point	$(-5, 21)$	$(-3, -5)$	$(0, 16)$	$(3, -35)$

Continued on next page.

Step 6	**Find additional points on the graph.** Use the points associated with the test numbers from Step 5.	The additional points (besides the x-intercepts) are $(-5, 21)$, $(-3, -5)$, $(0, 16)$, and $(3, -35)$.
Step 7	**Draw the graph.** Use the fact that the number of turning points is less than the degree of the polynomial to check whether the graph is drawn correctly.	The graph connecting the x-intercepts and the points in Step **6** by a smooth curve is shown in the figure. The number of turning points is 2, which is less than the degree, 3, of f.

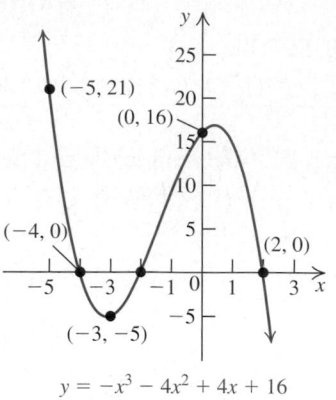

$$y = -x^3 - 4x^2 + 4x + 16$$

EXAMPLE 8 **Graphing a Polynomial Function**

Graph the function $f(x) = x^4 - 10x^2 + 9$.

Solution

Step 1 **Determine end behavior.** Since the degree of the polynomial is even $(n = 4)$ and the leading coefficient is 1 (a positive number), by the leading-term test the graph of $f(x)$ has the same end behavior as $y = x^4$ and rises to both the left and the right. (See Figure 3.14.) This behavior is described as $y \to \infty$ as $x \to -\infty$ and $y \to \infty$ as $x \to \infty$.

FIGURE 3.14

Step 2 **Find the zeros by setting $f(x) = 0$.**

$x^4 - 10x^2 + 9 = 0$	Set $f(x) = 0$.
$(x^2 - 1)(x^2 - 9) = 0$	Factor.
$(x - 1)(x + 1)(x - 3)(x + 3) = 0$	Factor completely.
$x - 1 = 0$, or $x + 1 = 0$, or $x - 3 = 0$, or $x + 3 = 0$	Set each factor equal to 0.
$x = 1$, or $x = -1$, or $x = 3$, or $x = -3$	Solve each equation for x.

There are four zeros, each of multiplicity 1 (odd), so that the graph crosses the x-axis at each of the zeros: -3, -1, 1, and 3. (See Figure 3.15.)

FIGURE 3.15

Step 3 **Find the y-intercept by computing $f(0)$.**

$$f(0) = (0)^4 - 10(0)^2 + 9 = 9.$$

The graph passes through the point $(0, 9)$, so the y-intercept is 9.

Step 4 **Use symmetry.**

$$f(-x) = (-x)^4 - 10(-x)^2 + 9 \quad \text{Replace } x \text{ by } -x \text{ in } f(x).$$
$$= x^4 - 10x^2 + 9 \quad (-x)^4 = x^4, (-x)^2 = x^2$$
$$= f(x).$$

Since $f(-x) = f(x)$, f is an even function. The graph of f is symmetric with respect to the y-axis.

Step 5 **Determine the sign of $f(x)$.** The four zeros -3, -1, 1, and 3 divide the x-axis into five intervals:

$$(-\infty, -3), (-3, -1), (-1, 1), (1, 3), \text{ and } (3, \infty).$$

To determine the sign of $f(x)$ in each interval, we arbitrarily choose test numbers in each interval and examine the value of f at the test numbers.

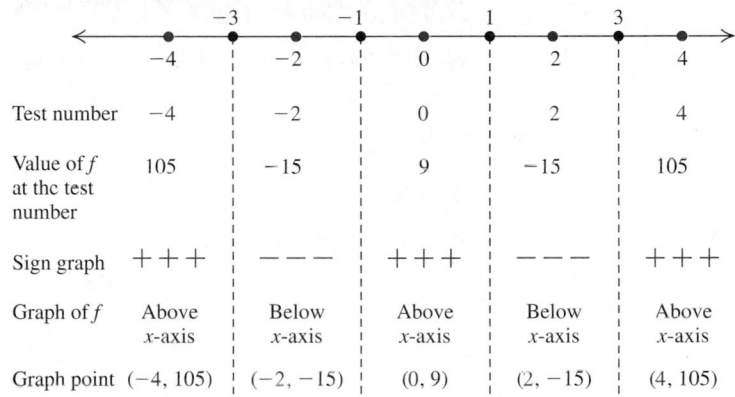

Test number -4	-2	0	2	4
Value of f at the test number	105	-15	9	-15	105
Sign graph $+++$	$---$	$+++$	$---$	$+++$
Graph of f	Above x-axis	Below x-axis	Above x-axis	Below x-axis	Above x-axis
Graph point $(-4, 105)$	$(-2, -15)$	$(0, 9)$	$(2, -15)$	$(4, 105)$

Step 6 **Determine additional graph points.** The additional points are $(-4, 105)$, $(-2, -15)$, $(0, 9)$, $(2, -15)$, and $(4, 105)$.

Step 7 **Draw the graph.** The graph is shown in Figure 3.16.

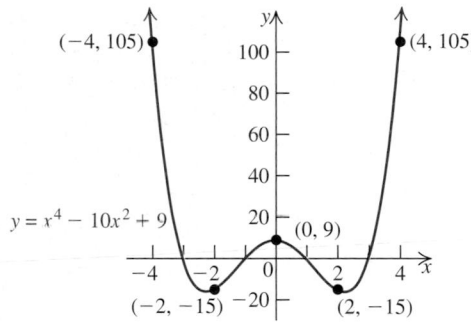

FIGURE 3.16

Figure 3.16 shows the graph of $y = f(x)$: a smooth curve connecting the points we obtained in Step 6. The number of turning points is 3, in agreement with the fact that the number of turning points is less than the degree of the polynomial. ■ ■ ■

PRACTICE PROBLEM 8 Graph $f(x) = -x^4 + 5x^2 - 4$. ■

Volume of a Wine Barrel Kepler first analyzed the problem of finding the volume of a wine barrel for a cylindrical barrel. (Review the information about this problem given in the introduction to this section, and see Figure 3.17). The volume V of a cylinder with radius r and height h is given by the formula $V = \pi r^2 h$. In Figure 3.17, $h = 2z$, so $V = 2\pi r^2 z$. Let x represent the value measured by the rod. Then, by the Pythagorean Theorem,

$$x^2 = 4r^2 + z^2.$$

FIGURE 3.17

Kepler's challenge was to calculate V, given only x—in other words, to express V as a function of x. To solve this problem, Kepler observed the key fact that the Austrian wine barrels were made with the same height-to-diameter ratio. Kepler assumed that the winemakers would have made a smart choice for this ratio, one that would maximize the volume for a fixed value of r. He calculated the ratio to be $\sqrt{2}$.

EXAMPLE 9 **Volume of a Wine Barrel**

Express the volume V of the wine barrel in Figure 3.17 as a function of x. Assume that $\dfrac{\text{height}}{\text{diameter}} = \dfrac{2z}{2r} = \dfrac{z}{r} = \sqrt{2}$.

Solution

We have the following relationships:

$$V = 2\pi r^2 z \qquad \text{Volume with radius } r \text{ and height } 2z$$

$$\frac{z}{r} = \sqrt{2} \qquad \text{Given ratio}$$

$$x^2 = 4r^2 + z^2 \qquad \text{Pythagorean Theorem}$$

$$\frac{x^2}{r^2} = 4 + \frac{z^2}{r^2} \qquad \text{Divide both sides by } r^2.$$

$$\frac{x^2}{r^2} = 4 + 2 = 6. \quad \text{Since } \frac{z}{r} = \sqrt{2}, \frac{z^2}{r^2} = \left(\frac{z}{r}\right)^2 = (\sqrt{2})^2 = 2.$$

From $\dfrac{x^2}{r^2} = 6$, we have $x^2 = 6r^2$ or $r^2 = \dfrac{x^2}{6}$.

Thus, $r = \dfrac{x}{\sqrt{6}}$. From $\dfrac{z}{r} = \sqrt{2}$, we obtain

$$z = \sqrt{2}\, r = \sqrt{2}\,\frac{x}{\sqrt{6}} \qquad \text{Replace } r \text{ by } \frac{x}{\sqrt{6}}$$

$$= \frac{x}{\sqrt{3}}. \qquad \frac{\sqrt{2}}{\sqrt{6}} = \frac{\sqrt{2}}{\sqrt{2}\cdot\sqrt{3}} = \frac{1}{\sqrt{3}}$$

Substituting $z = \dfrac{x}{\sqrt{3}}$ and $r^2 = \dfrac{x^2}{6}$ in the expression for V, we have

$$V = 2\pi r^2 z$$

$$= 2\pi\left(\frac{x^2}{6}\right)\left(\frac{x}{\sqrt{3}}\right) \qquad \text{Replace } z \text{ by } \frac{x}{\sqrt{3}} \text{ and } r^2 \text{ by } \frac{x^2}{6}.$$

$$= \frac{\pi}{3\sqrt{3}}x^3 \qquad \text{Simplify.}$$

$$\approx 0.6046x^3. \qquad \text{Use a calculator.}$$

Consequently, once they knew the value of x from markings on the bungrod that allowed it to be used as a ruler, the Austrian vintners could easily calculate the volume of wine in a barrel by using the formula $V = 0.6046x^3$. ■ ■ ■

PRACTICE PROBLEM 9   Use Kepler's formula to compute the volume of wine (in liters) in a barrel with $x = 70$ cm. Note: 1 decimeter(dm) $= 10$ cm and 1 liter $= (1\text{ dm})^3$. ■

A Exercises   Basic Skills and Concepts

In Exercises 1–16, state which functions are polynomial functions. For those which are polynomial functions, find the degree, the leading term, and the leading coefficient.

1. $f(x) = 2x^5 - 5x^2$ †

2. $f(x) = x^2 + 3|x| - 7$ Not a polynomial function

3. $f(x) = 2x^3 - 5x, \quad 0 \le x \le 2$ Not a polynomial function

4. $f(x) = 3 - 5x - 7x^4$ †

5. $f(x) = \dfrac{2x^3 + 7x}{3}$ †

6. $f(x) = \dfrac{x^2 - 1}{x + 5}$ Not a polynomial function

7. $f(x) = \begin{cases} 2x + 3, & x \ne 0 \\ 1, & x = 0 \end{cases}$ Not a polynomial function

8. $f(x) = \begin{cases} x + 1, & x \ne 1 \\ 2, & x = 1 \end{cases}$ †

9. $f(x) = 5x^2 - 7\sqrt{x}$ Not a polynomial function

10. $f(x) = x^{4.5} - 3x^2 + 7$ Not a polynomial function

11. $f(x) = -7x + 11 + \sqrt{2x^3}$ †

12. $f(x) = \pi x^4 + 1 - x^2$ †

13. $f(x) = \dfrac{x^2 - 1}{x - 1}, \quad x \ne 1$ Not a polynomial function

14. $f(x) = 3x^2 - 4x + 7x^{-2}$ Not a polynomial function

15. $f(x) = 5$ †

16. $f(x) = 0$ †

In Exercises 17–24, state which graphs cannot be the graphs of polynomial functions. Explain your reasons.

17.

Polynomial function

18.

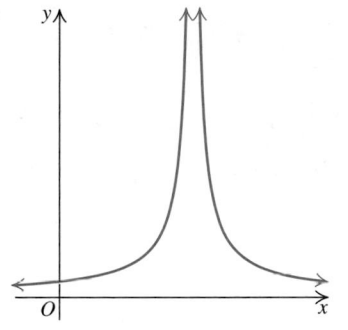

Not a polynomial function.

19.

Polynomial function

20.

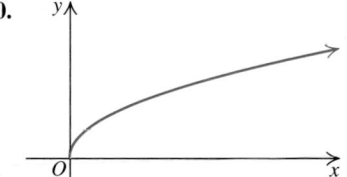

Not a polynomial function.

21.

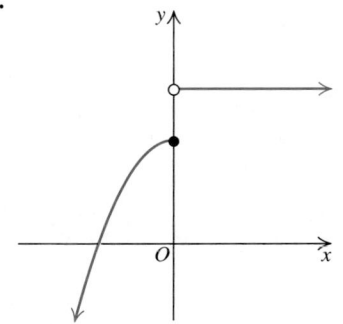

Not a polynomial function.

†Due to space constrictions, answers to these exercises may be found in the Answers beginning on page A–1 in the back of the book.

22.

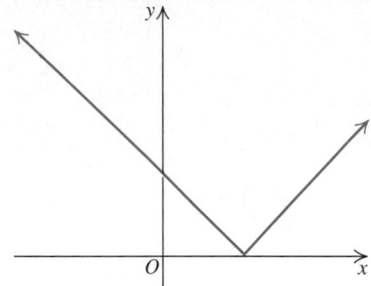

Not a polynomial function.

23.

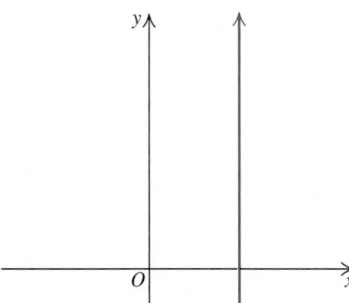

Not a polynomial function.

24.

Not a polynomial function.

(a)

(b)

(c)

(d)

(e)

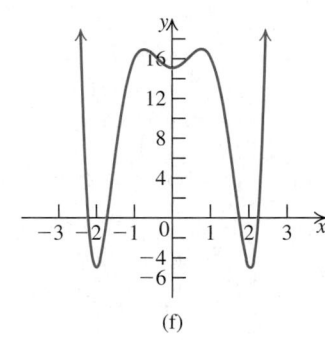

(f)

In Exercises 25–30, match the polynomial function with its graph. Use the leading-term test and the y-intercept.

25. $f(x) = -x^4 + 3x^2 + 4$ c

26. $f(x) = x^6 - 7x^4 + 7x^2 + 15$ f

27. $f(x) = x^4 - 10x^2 + 9$ a

28. $f(x) = x^3 + x^2 - 17x + 15$ e

29. $f(x) = x^3 + 6x^2 + 12x + 8$ d

30. $f(x) = -x^3 - 2x^2 + 11x + 12$ b

In Exercises 31–38, (a) find the zeros of each polynomial function and state the multiplicity for each zero, and (b) state whether the graph crosses, or touches but does not cross, the x-axis at each x-intercept. (c) What is the maximum number of turning points?

31. $f(x) = 5(x - 1)(x + 5)$ †

32. $f(x) = 3(x + 2)^2(x - 3)$ †

33. $f(x) = (x + 1)^2(x - 1)^3$ †

34. $f(x) = 2(x + 3)^2(x + 1)(x - 6)$ †

35. $f(x) = -5\left(x + \dfrac{2}{3}\right)\left(x - \dfrac{1}{2}\right)^2$ †

36. $f(x) = x^3 - 6x^2 + 8x$ †

37. $f(x) = -x^4 + 6x^3 - 9x^2$ †

38. $f(x) = x^4 - 5x^2 - 36$ †

In Exercises 39–52, for each polynomial function f,

a. Describe the end behavior of f.

b. Find the zeros of f. Determine whether the graph of f crosses, or touches but does not cross, the x-axis at each x-intercept.

c. Use the zeros of f and test numbers to find the intervals over which the graph of f is above or below the x-axis.

d. Determine the y-intercept.

e. Find any symmetries of the graph of the function.

f. Determine the maximum number of turning points.

g. Sketch the graph of f.

 h. Use a graphing calculator to support your answers.

39. $f(x) = x^2 + 3$ †

40. $f(x) = x^2 - 4x + 4$ †

41. $f(x) = x^2 + 4x - 21$ †

42. $f(x) = -x^2 + 4x + 12$ †

43. $f(x) = -2x^2(x + 1)$ †

44. $f(x) = x - x^3$ †

45. $f(x) = x^2(x - 1)^2$ †

46. $f(x) = x^2(x + 1)(x - 2)$ †

47. $f(x) = (x - 1)^2(x + 3)(x - 4)$ †

48. $f(x) = (x + 1)^2(x^2 + 1)$ †

49. $f(x) = -x^2(x^2 - 1)(x + 1)$ †

50. $f(x) = -x^2(x^2 - 4)(x + 2)$ †

51. $f(x) = x(x + 1)(x - 1)(x + 2)$ †

52. $f(x) = x^2(x^2 + 1)(x - 2)$ †

B Exercises   Applying the Concepts

53. Drug reaction. Let $f(x) = 3x^2(4 - x)$.

a. Find the zeros of f and their multiplicities. †

b. Sketch the graph of $y = f(x)$. †

c. How many turning points are in the graph of f? 2

d. A particular patient's reaction $R(x)$ to a certain drug, the size of whose dose is x is observed to be $R(x) = 3x^2(4 - x)$. What is the domain of the function $R(x)$? What portion of the graph of $f(x)$ constitutes the graph of $R(x)$? †

 e. Use a graphing calculator to estimate the value of x for which $R(x)$ is a maximum. $x = 2.67$

54. Cough and air velocity. The normal radius of the windpipe of a human adult at rest is approximately 1 cm. When you cough, your windpipe contracts to, say, a radius r. The velocity v at which the air is expelled depends on the radius r and is given by the formula $v = a(1 - r)r^2$, where a is a positive constant.

a. What is the domain of v? [0, 1]

b. Sketch the graph of $v(r)$. †

c. Use a graphing calculator to estimate the value of r for which v is a maximum. 0.67

55. Maximizing revenue. A manufacturer of slacks has discovered that the number x of khakis sold to retailers per week at a price p dollars per pair is given by the formula

$$p = 27 - \left(\frac{x}{300}\right)^2.$$

a. Write the weekly revenue $R(x)$ as a function of x. †

b. What is the domain of $R(x)$? $[0, 900\sqrt{3}]$

c. Graph $y = R(x)$. †

d. Use a graphing calculator to estimate the number of slacks sold to maximize the revenue. 900

e. What is the maximum revenue from part (d)? $16,200

56. Maximizing production. An orange grower in California hires migrant workers to pick oranges during the season. He has 12 employees, and each can pick 400 oranges per hour. He has discovered that if he adds more workers, the production per worker decreases due to lack of supervision. When x new workers (above the 12) are hired, each worker picks $400 - 2x^2$ oranges per hour.

a. Write the number $N(x)$ of oranges picked per hour as a function of x. $N(x) = (x + 12)(400 - 2x^2)$

b. Find the domain of $N(x)$. $[0, 10\sqrt{2}]$

c. Graph the function $y = N(x)$. †

d. Estimate the maximum number of oranges that can be picked per hour. 5950

e. Find the number of employees involved in part (d). 17

57. Making a box. From a rectangular 8 × 15 piece of cardboard, four congruent squares with sides of length x are cut out, one at each corner. (See the figure.) The resulting crosslike piece is then folded to form a box.
  a. Find the volume V of the box as a function of x. †
  b. Sketch the graph of $y = V(x)$. †
  c. Use a graphing calculator to estimate the largest possible value of the volume of the box. 90.74

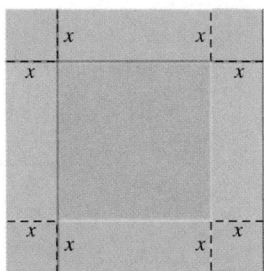

58. Mailing a box. According to Postal Service regulations, the girth plus the length of a parcel sent by Priority Mail may not exceed 108 inches.
  a. Express, as a function of x, the volume V of a rectangular parcel with two square faces (with sides of length x inches) that can be sent by mail. †
  b. Sketch a graph of $V(x)$. †
  c. Use a graphing calculator to estimate the largest possible volume of the box that can be sent by Priority Mail. 11,664 in.³

Girth is 4x

59. Luggage design. AAA Airlines requires that the total outside dimensions (length + width + height) of a piece of checked-in luggage not exceed 62 inches. You have designed a suitcase in the shape of a box whose height (x inches) equals its width. Your suitcase meets AAA's requirements.
  a. Write the volume V of your suitcase as a function of x. †
  b. Graph the function $y = V(x)$. †
  c. Use a graphing calculator to find the approximate dimensions of the piece of luggage with the largest volume that you can check in on this airline. †

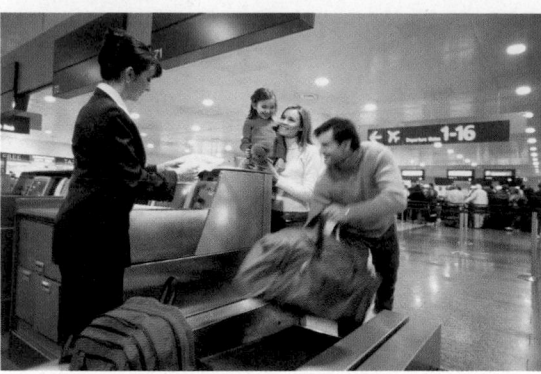

60. Luggage dimensions. American Airlines requires that the total dimensions (length + width + height) of a carry-on bag not exceed 45 inches. You have designed a rectangular boxlike bag whose length is twice its width x. Your bag meets American's requirements.
  a. Write the volume V of your bag as a function of x, where x is measured in inches. †
  b. Graph the function $y = V(x)$. †
  c. Use a graphing calculator to estimate the dimensions of the bag with the largest volume that you can carry on an American flight. (*Source:* sev.prnewswire.com/airline-aviation.) 10 in. × 15 in. × 20 in.

61. Worker productivity. An efficiency study of the morning shift at an assembly plant indicates that the number y of units produced by an average worker t hours after 6:00 A.M. may be modeled by the formula $y = -t^3 + 6t^2 + 16t$.
  a. Sketch the graph of $y = f(t)$. †
  b. Estimate the time in the morning when a worker is most efficient. 11:00 A.M.

62. Death rates from AIDS. According to the *Mortality and Morbidity* report of the U.S. Centers for Disease Control, the following table gives the death rates per 100,000 population from AIDS in the United States for the years 1993–2000.

Year	Death Rate	Year	Death Rate
1993	14.5	1997	6.1
1994	16.2	1998	4.9
1995	16.3	1999	5.4
1996	11.7	2000	5.2

To model the death rate, a data analysis program produced the cubic polynomial
$$P(t) = 0.21594t^3 - 2.226t^2 + 3.7583t + 14.6788,$$
where $t = 0$ represents 1993.
  a. Sketch the graph of $y = P(t)$. †
  b. When does the highest point occur for $0 \le t \le 20$? At $t = 20$

C Exercises   Beyond the Basics

In Exercises 63–72, use transformations of the graph of $y = x^4$ or $y = x^5$ to graph each function $f(x)$. Find the zeros of $f(x)$ and their multiplicity.

63. $f(x) = (x - 1)^4$ †

64. $f(x) = -(x + 1)^4$ †

65. $f(x) = x^4 + 2$ †

66. $f(x) = x^4 + 81$ †

67. $f(x) = -(x - 1)^4$ †

68. $f(x) = \dfrac{1}{2}(x - 1)^4 - 8$ †

69. $f(x) = x^5 + 1$ †

70. $f(x) = (x - 1)^5$ †

71. $f(x) = 8 - \dfrac{(x + 1)^5}{4}$ †

72. $f(x) = 81 + \dfrac{(x + 1)^5}{3}$ †

73. Prove that if $0 < x < 1$, then $0 < x^4 < x^2$. This shows that the graph of $y = x^4$ is flatter than the graph of $y = x^2$ on the interval $(0, 1)$.

74. Prove that if $x > 1$, then $x^4 > x^2$. This shows that the graph of $y = x^4$ is higher than the graph of $y = x^2$ on the interval $(1, \infty)$.

75. Sketch the graph of $y = x^2 - x^4$. Use a graphing calculator to estimate the maximum vertical distance between the graphs $y = x^2$ and $y = x^4$ on the interval $(0, 1)$. Also, estimate the value of x at which this maximum distance occurs. †

76. Repeat Exercise 75 by sketching the graph of $y = x^3 - x^5$. †

In Exercises 77–80, write a polynomial with the given characteristics.

77. A polynomial of degree 3 that has exactly two x-intercepts $f(x) = x^2(x + 1)$

78. A polynomial of degree 3 that has three distinct x-intercepts and whose graph rises to the left and falls to the right †

79. A polynomial of degree 4 that has exactly two distinct x-intercepts and whose graph falls to the left and right †

80. A polynomial of degree 4 that has exactly three distinct x-intercepts and whose graph rises to the left and right †

In Exercises 81–84, find the smallest possible degree of a polynomial with the given graph. Explain your reasons.

81.

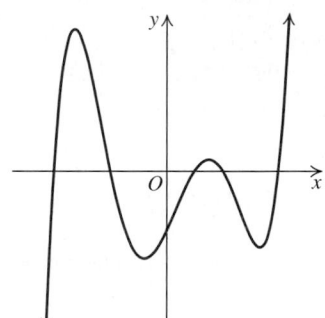

5, because the graph has five x-intercepts

82.

5, because the graph has four turning points

83.

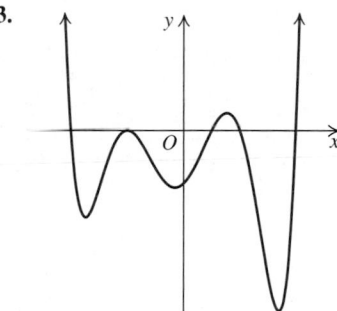

6, because the graph has five turning points

84.

6, because the graph has five turning points

In Exercises 85–88, use the Intermediate Value Theorem to show that each polynomial $P(x)$ has a real zero in the specified interval. Approximate this zero to two decimal places.

85. $P(x) = x^4 - x^3 - 10; [2, 3]$ 2.09

86. $P(x) = x^4 - x^2 - 2x - 5; [1, 2]$ 1.87

87. $P(x) = x^5 - 9x^2 - 15; [2, 3]$ 2.28

88. $P(x) = x^5 + 5x^4 + 8x^3 + 4x^2 - x - 5; [0, 1]$ 0.68

Critical Thinking

89. Is it possible for the graph of a polynomial function to have no y-intercepts? Explain.

90. Is it possible for the graph of a polynomial function to have no x-intercepts? Explain.

91. Is it possible for the graph of a polynomial function of degree 3 to have exactly one local maximum and no local minimum? Explain.

92. Is it possible for the graph of a polynomial function of degree 4 to have exactly one local maximum and exactly one local minimum? Explain.

Answers:

89. No, because the domain of any polynomial function is $(-\infty, \infty)$, which includes the point $x = 0$.

90. Yes. The graph of $f(x) = x^2 + 1$ has no x-intercept.

91. Not possible.

92. Not possible.

SECTION 3.3

Dividing Polynomials and the Rational Zeros Test

BEFORE STARTING THIS SECTION, REVIEW

1. Evaluating expressions using the order of operations (Section P.1, page 10)

2. Multiplying polynomials (Section P.3, page 33)

3. Evaluating a function (Section 2.4, page 228)

4. Factoring trinomials (Section P.4, page 42)

OBJECTIVES

1 Divide polynomials.

2 Use synthetic division.

3 Use the Remainder and Factor Theorems.

4 Use the Rational Zeros Test.

Greenhouse Effect and Global Warming

The **greenhouse effect** refers to the fact that Earth is surrounded by an atmosphere that acts like the transparent cover of a greenhouse, allowing sunlight to filter through while trapping heat. It is becoming increasingly clear that we are experiencing *global warming*. This means that Earth's atmosphere is becoming warmer near its surface. Scientists who study climate agree that global warming is due largely to the emission of "greenhouse gases," such as carbon dioxide (CO_2), chlorofluorocarbons (CFCs), methane (CH_4), ozone (O_3), and nitrous oxide (N_2O). The temperature of Earth's surface increased by 1°F over the 20th century. The late 1990s and early 2000s were some of the hottest years ever recorded. Projections of future warming suggest a global temperature increase of between 2.5°F and 10.4°F by 2100.

Global warming will result in long-term changes in climate, including a rise in average temperatures, unusual rainfalls, and more storms and floods. The sea level may rise so much that people may have to move away from coastal areas. Some regions of the world may become too dry for farming.

The production and consumption of energy is one of the major causes of greenhouse gas emissions. In Example 6, we look at the pattern for the consumption of petroleum in the United States. ■

1 Divide polynomials.

The Division Algorithm and Long Division

In Chapter P, we reviewed the procedures for adding, subtracting, and multiplying two polynomials. In this section, we will review the procedures for dividing polynomials.

The concept of division involving polynomials is quite similar to that of the division of integers. The fact that 5 divides 10 "evenly" is expressed either as $\dfrac{10}{5} = 2$ or as $10 = 5 \cdot 2$. By comparison, the equation

(1) $$x^3 - 1 = (x - 1)(x^2 + x + 1) \qquad \text{Factor, using difference of cubes.}$$

suggests dividing both sides by $x - 1$ to obtain

$$\frac{x^3 - 1}{x - 1} = x^2 + x + 1, \quad x \neq 1.$$

We say that the polynomial $x - 1$ is a factor of $x^3 - 1$.

POLYNOMIAL FACTOR

A polynomial $D(x)$ is a **factor** of a polynomial $F(x)$ if there is a polynomial $Q(x)$ such that $F(x) = D(x) \cdot Q(x)$.

Next, consider the equation

(2) $$x^3 - 2 = (x - 1)(x^2 + x + 1) - 1. \qquad \begin{array}{l}\text{Subtract 1 from both sides}\\\text{of Equation (1).}\end{array}$$

Dividing both sides by $(x - 1)$, we can rewrite Equation (2) in the form

$$\frac{x^3 - 2}{x - 1} = x^2 + x + 1 - \frac{1}{x - 1}, \quad x \neq 1.$$

Here, we say that when the **dividend** $x^3 - 2$ is divided by the **divisor** $x - 1$, the **quotient** is $x^2 + x + 1$ and the **remainder** is -1. In general, we state the following result, called the *division algorithm*:

THE DIVISION ALGORITHM

If a polynomial $F(x)$ is divided by a polynomial $D(x)$, with $D(x) \neq 0$, there are unique polynomials $Q(x)$ and $R(x)$ such that

$$\underset{\text{Dividend}}{F(x)} \quad = \quad \underset{\text{Divisor}}{D(x)} \quad \cdot \quad \underset{\text{Quotient}}{Q(x)} \quad + \quad \underset{\text{Remainder}}{R(x)}$$

Either $R(x)$ is the *zero polynomial*, or the degree of $R(x)$ is less than the degree of $D(x)$.

The division algorithm says that the dividend is equal to the divisor times the quotient plus the remainder. By dividing both sides of the equation in the division algorithm by $D(x)$ we get

$$\frac{F(x)}{D(x)} = Q(x) + \frac{R(x)}{D(x)}.$$

The rational expression $\dfrac{F(x)}{D(x)}$ is **improper** if degree of $F(x) \geq$ degree of $D(x)$. However, the rational expression $\dfrac{R(x)}{D(x)}$ is always **proper,** since by the division algorithm

degree of $R(x) <$ degree of $D(x)$.

For an improper rational expression $\dfrac{F(x)}{D(x)}$, you may recall the **long-division** process shown below for finding the quotient and the remainder.

$$
\begin{array}{r}
3x + 4 \quad \leftarrow \text{Quotient} \\
\text{Divisor} \rightarrow \quad 2x - 1 \overline{\smash{)}6x^2 + 5x + 1} \quad \leftarrow \text{Dividend} \\
\underline{6x^2 - 3x} \qquad (2x - 1)3x \\
8x + 1 \qquad \text{Subtract.} \\
\underline{8x - 4} \qquad (2x - 1)4 \\
\text{Remainder} \rightarrow \quad 5 \qquad \text{Subtract.}
\end{array}
$$

We state the step-by-step procedure involved in the long-division process.

FINDING THE SOLUTION: PROCEDURE FOR LONG DIVISION

OBJECTIVE

Find the quotient and remainder when one polynomial is divided by another.

EXAMPLE

Find the quotient and remainder when $2x^2 + x^5 + 7 + 4x^3$ is divided by $x^2 + 1 - x$.

Step 1 Write the terms in the dividend and the divisor in descending powers of the variable.

Dividend: $x^5 + 4x^3 + 2x^2 + 7$;   *Divisor:* $x^2 - x + 1$

Step 2 Insert terms with zero coefficients in the dividend for any missing powers of the variable.

$$x^5 + 0x^4 + 4x^3 + 2x^2 + 0x + 7$$

Step 3 Divide the first term in the dividend by the first term in the divisor to obtain the first term in the quotient.

$$\frac{x^5}{x^2} = x^3 \quad \text{Divide first terms.}$$

$$
\begin{array}{l}
\; x^3 \\
x^2 - x + 1 \overline{\smash{)}x^5 + 0x^4 + 4x^3 + 2x^2 + 0x + 7}
\end{array}
$$

Step 4 Multiply the divisor by the first term in the quotient, and subtract the product from the dividend.

$$
\begin{array}{l}
\; x^3 \\
x^2 - x + 1 \overline{\smash{)}x^5 + 0x^4 + 4x^3 + 2x^2 + 0x + 7} \\
(-)\underline{x^5 - x^4 + x^3} \qquad x^3(x^2 - x + 1) \\
x^4 + 3x^3 + 2x^2 + 0x + 7 \qquad \text{Remainder}
\end{array}
$$

Subtract.

$$\frac{x^4}{x^2} = x^2 \qquad \frac{4x^3}{x^2} = 4x \qquad \frac{5x^2}{x^2} = 5$$

Step 5 Treat the remainder obtained in Step 4 as a new dividend, and repeat Steps 3 and 4. Continue this process until a remainder is obtained that is of lower degree than the divisor.

$$
\begin{array}{l}
\; x^3 + x^2 + 4x + 5 \\
x^2 - x + 1 \overline{\smash{)}x^5 + 0x^4 + 4x^3 + 2x^2 + 0x + 7} \\
(-)\underline{x^5 - x^4 + x^3} \\
x^4 + 3x^3 + 2x^2 + 0x + 7 \leftarrow \text{New dividend} \\
(-)\underline{x^4 - x^3 + x^2} \qquad x^2(x^2 - x + 1) \\
4x^3 + x^2 + 0x + 7 \qquad \text{Remainder} \\
(-)\underline{4x^3 - 4x^2 + 4x} \qquad 4x(x^2 - x + 1) \\
5x^2 - 4x + 7 \qquad \text{Remainder} \\
(-)\underline{5x^2 - 5x + 5} \qquad 5(x^2 - x + 1) \\
x + 2 \qquad \text{Remainder}
\end{array}
$$

Step 6 Write the quotient and the remainder.

Quotient $= x^3 + x^2 + 4x + 5$ Remainder $= x + 2$

EXAMPLE 1 **Using Long Division**

Divide $x^4 - 13x^2 + x + 35$ by $x^2 - x - 6$.

Solution

Since the dividend does not contain an x^3 term, we use a zero coefficient for the missing term.

$$
\begin{array}{r}
x^2 + x - 6 \quad \leftarrow \text{Quotient} \\
x^2 - x - 6 \overline{)x^4 + 0x^3 - 13x^2 + x + 35} \\
\underline{x^4 - x^3 - 6x^2} \\
x^3 - 7x^2 + x + 35 \\
\underline{x^3 - x^2 - 6x} \\
-6x^2 + 7x + 35 \\
\underline{-6x^2 + 6x + 36} \\
x - 1 \quad \leftarrow \text{Remainder}
\end{array}
$$

The quotient is $x^2 + x - 6$ and the remainder is $x - 1$.

We can write this result in the form

$$\frac{x^4 - 13x^2 + x + 35}{x^2 - x - 6} = x^2 + x - 6 + \frac{x - 1}{x^2 - x - 6}.$$

■ ■ ■

PRACTICE PROBLEM 1   Divide $x^4 + 5x^2 + 2x + 6$ by $x^2 - x + 3$.

■

2 Use synthetic division.

Synthetic Division

You can decrease the work involved in finding the quotient and remainder when the divisor $D(x)$ is of the form $x - a$ by using the process known as *synthetic division*. The procedure is best explained by considering an example.

Long division	Synthetic division
$$\begin{array}{r} 2x^2 + 1x + 6 \\ x - 3\overline{)2x^3 - 5x^2 + 3x - 14} \\ \underline{2x^3 - 6x^2} \\ 1x^2 + 3x - 14 \\ \underline{1x^2 - 3x} \\ 6x - 14 \\ \underline{6x - 18} \\ 4 \end{array}$$	$$\begin{array}{r} 3\,\underline{|}\;\; 2 \quad -5 \quad 3 \quad -14 \\ 6 \quad 3 \quad 18 \\ \hline 2 \quad 1 \quad 6 \;\;\big|\;\; 4 \quad \leftarrow \text{Remainder} \end{array}$$

Each circled term in the long division process is exactly the same as the term above it. Furthermore, the boxed terms are terms in the dividend, written in a new position. If these two sets of terms are eliminated in the synthetic division process, a more efficient format results.

TECHNOLOGY
CONNECTION

 Synthetic division can be done on a graphing calculator. In this problem, enter the first coefficient, 2. Then repeatedly multiply the answer by 3 and add the next coefficient.

```
Ans*3+-5              2
                     1
Ans*3+3
                     6
Ans*3+-14
                     4
```

The essential steps in the process can be carried out as follows:

(i)   Bring down 2 from the first line to the third line.

$$3\overline{\smash{\big)}\,2\quad-5\quad 3\quad-14}$$

2

(ii) Multiply 2 in the third line by the 3 in the divisor position, and place the product, 6, under -5; then add vertically to obtain 1.

$$3\overline{\smash{\big)}\,2\quad-5\quad 3\quad 14}$$

6

2   1

(iii) Multiply 1 by 3, and place the product 3 under 3; then add vertically to obtain 6.

$$3\overline{\smash{\big)}\,2\quad-5\quad 3\quad-14}$$

6   3

2   1   6

(iv) Finally, multiply 6 by 3, and place the product, 18, under -14; then add to obtain 4.

$$3\overline{\smash{\big)}\,2\quad-5\quad 3\quad-14}$$

6   3   18

2   1   6   4

The first three terms, namely, 2, 1, and 6, are the coefficients of the quotient, $2x^2 + x + 6$, and the last term, 4, is the remainder. The procedure for synthetic division is given next.

FINDING THE SOLUTION: PROCEDURE FOR SYNTHETIC DIVISION

OBJECTIVE
To divide a polynomial $F(x)$ by $x - a$.

EXAMPLE
Divide $2x^4 - 3x^2 + 5x - 63$ by $x + 3$.

Step 1   Arrange the coefficients of $F(x)$ in order of *descending powers of x*, supplying zero as the coefficient of each missing power.

$$\big|\;\;2\quad 0\quad -3\quad 5\quad -63$$

Step 2   Replace the divisor $x - a$ by a.

Rewrite $x + 3 = x - (-3); a = -3$

$$-3\overline{\smash{\big)}\,2\quad 0\quad -3\quad 5\quad -63}$$

Step 3   Bring the first (leftmost) coefficient down below the line. Multiply it by a, and write the resulting product one column to the right and above the line.

$$-3\overline{\smash{\big)}\,2\quad 0\quad -3\quad 5\quad -63}$$

-6

$\otimes$

2

⊗ means "multiply by -3."

Step 4   Add the product obtained in Step 3 to the coefficient directly above it, and write the resulting sum directly below it and below the line. This sum is the "newest" number below the line.

$$-3\overline{\smash{\big)}\,2\quad 0\quad -3\quad 5\quad -63}$$

-6

$+$

2   -6

Step 5   Multiply the newest number below the line by a, write the resulting product one column to the right and above the line, and repeat Step 4.

$$-3\overline{\smash{\big)}\,2\quad 0\quad -3\quad 5\quad -63}$$

$-6\quad 18$

$\otimes\; +$

2   -6 15

Continued on next page.

Step 6   Repeat Step 5 until there is a product added to the constant term. Separate the last number below the line by a short vertical line.

$$
\begin{array}{r|rrrrr}
-3 & 2 & 0 & -3 & 5 & -63 \\
   &   & -6 & 18 & -45 & 120 \\
\hline
   & \otimes & + & \otimes + & \otimes + & \otimes + \\
   & 2 & -6 & 15 & -40 & 57
\end{array}
$$

Step 7   The last number below the line is the remainder, and the other numbers, reading from left to right, are the coefficients of the quotient, which has degree one less than the dividend $F(x)$.

$$
\begin{array}{r|rrrrr}
-3 & 2 & 0 & -3 & 5 & -63 \\
   &   & -6 & 18 & -45 & 120 \\
\hline
   & 2 & -6 & 15 & -40 & \vert\, 57
\end{array}
$$

Dividend: degree 4

Quotient: degree 3

$$\underbrace{2x^3 - 6x^2 + 15x - 40}_{\text{Quotient}} \qquad \text{Remainder}$$

EXAMPLE 2   Using Synthetic Division

Use synthetic division to divide $2x^4 + x^3 - 16x^2 + 18$ by $x + 2$.

Solution

Since $x - a = x + 2 = x - (-2)$, we have $a = -2$. Write the coefficients of the dividend in a line, supplying 0 as the coefficient of the missing x-term. Then carry out the steps of synthetic division.

$$
\begin{array}{r|rrrrr}
-2 & 2 & 1 & -16 & 0 & 18 \\
   &   & -4 & 6 & 20 & -40 \\
\hline
   & 2 & -3 & -10 & 20 & \vert\, -22
\end{array}
$$

The quotient is $2x^3 - 3x^2 - 10x + 20$, and the remainder is -22, so the result is

$$\frac{2x^4 + x^3 - 16x^2 + 18}{x + 2} = 2x^3 - 3x^2 - 10x + 20 + \frac{-22}{x + 2}$$

$$= 2x^3 - 3x^2 - 10x + 20 - \frac{22}{x + 2}. \qquad \blacksquare\ \blacksquare\ \blacksquare$$

PRACTICE PROBLEM 2   Use synthetic division to divide $2x^3 + x^2 - 18x - 7$ by $x - 3$.   ■

---

3 Use the Remainder and Factor Theorems.

The Remainder and Factor Theorems

In Example 2, we discovered that if the polynomial $2x^4 + x^3 - 16x^2 + 18$ is divided by $x + 2$, the quotient is $2x^3 - 3x^2 - 10x + 20$ and the remainder is -22. Note that the remainder is a constant.

Now, consider the function F defined by the same polynomial. That is,

$$F(x) = 2x^4 + x^3 - 16x^2 + 18.$$

Let's evaluate F at -2. We have

$$
\begin{aligned}
F(-2) &= 2(-2)^4 + (-2)^3 - 16(-2)^2 + 18 & & \text{Replace } x \text{ by } -2 \text{ in } F(x). \\
&= 2(16) - 8 - 16(4) + 18 & & \text{Simplify.} \\
&= -22. & & \text{Simplify.}
\end{aligned}
$$

Thus, $F(-2) = -22$, which is equal to the remainder obtained earlier. Is it a coincidence that $F(-2)$ is the same number we obtained as the remainder when we divided $F(x)$ by $x + 2$? No, the following theorem asserts that such a result is always true:

THE REMAINDER THEOREM

If a polynomial $F(x)$ is divided by $x - a$, then the remainder R is given by

$$R = F(a).$$

Note that in the statement of the Remainder Theorem, $F(x)$ plays the dual role of representing a polynomial and the function defined by the same polynomial.

The Remainder Theorem has a very simple proof: The division algorithm says that if a polynomial $F(x)$ is divided by a polynomial $D(x) \neq 0$, then

$$F(x) = D(x) \cdot Q(x) + R(x),$$

where $Q(x)$ is the quotient and $R(x)$ is the remainder. Suppose that $D(x)$ is a linear polynomial of the form $x - a$. Since the degree of $R(x)$ is less than the degree of $D(x)$, $R(x)$ is a constant. Call this constant R. In this case, by the division algorithm, we have

$$F(x) = (x - a)Q(x) + R.$$

Replacing x by a in $F(x)$, we obtain

$$F(a) = (a - a)Q(a) + R = 0 + R = R.$$

This proves the Remainder Theorem.

EXAMPLE 3   **Using the Remainder Theorem**

Find the remainder when the polynomial

$$F(x) = 2x^5 - 4x^3 + 5x^2 - 7x + 2$$

is divided by $x - 1$.

Solution

We could find the remainder by either long or synthetic division, but a quicker way is to simply evaluate $F(x)$ when $x = 1$. By the Remainder Theorem, $F(1)$ is the remainder.

$$F(1) = 2(1)^5 - 4(1)^3 + 5(1)^2 - 7(1) + 2 \quad \text{Replace } x \text{ by 1 in } F(x).$$
$$= 2 - 4 + 5 - 7 + 2 = -2.$$

The remainder is -2.   ■ ■ ■

PRACTICE PROBLEM 3   Use the Remainder Theorem to find the remainder when

$$F(x) = x^{110} - 2x^{57} + 5 \text{ is divided by } x - 1. \qquad ■$$

Sometimes, the Remainder Theorem is used in the other direction, to evaluate a polynomial at a specific value of x. This use is illustrated in the next example.

EXAMPLE 4   **Using the Remainder Theorem**

Let $f(x) = x^4 + 3x^3 - 5x^2 + 8x + 75$. Find $f(-3)$.

Solution

One way of solving this problem is to evaluate $f(x)$ when $x = -3$:

$$f(-3) = (-3)^4 + 3(-3)^3 - 5(-3)^2 + 8(-3) + 75 \quad \text{Replace } x \text{ by } -3.$$
$$= 6. \qquad\qquad\qquad\qquad\qquad\qquad\qquad\qquad \text{Simplify.}$$

Another way is to use synthetic division to find the remainder when the polynomial $f(x)$ is divided by $(x + 3)$.

$$
\begin{array}{r|rrrrr}
-3 & 1 & 3 & -5 & 8 & 75 \\
   &   & -3 & 0 & 15 & -69 \\
\hline
   & 1 & 0 & -5 & 23 & \,|\;6
\end{array}
$$

The remainder is 6. By the Remainder Theorem, $f(-3) = 6$.   ■ ■ ■

PRACTICE PROBLEM 4   Use synthetic division to find $f(-2)$, where

$$f(x) = x^4 + 10x^2 + 2x - 20. \qquad\qquad\qquad ■$$

Note that if we divide any polynomial $F(x)$ by $x - a$, we have

$$F(x) = (x - a)Q(x) + R \qquad \text{Division algorithm}$$

$$F(x) = (x - a)Q(x) + F(a). \qquad R = F(a), \text{ by the Remainder Theorem}$$

The last equation says that if $F(a) = 0$, then

$$F(x) = (x - a)Q(x),$$

and $(x - a)$ is a factor of $F(x)$. Conversely, if $(x - a)$ is a factor of $F(x)$, then dividing $F(x)$ by $(x - a)$ gives a remainder of 0. Hence, by the Remainder Theorem, $F(a) = 0$. This argument proves the Factor Theorem:

THE FACTOR THEOREM

A polynomial $F(x)$ has $(x - a)$ as a factor if and only if $F(a) = 0$.

The Factor Theorem shows that if $F(x)$ is a polynomial, then the following problems are equivalent:

1. Factoring $F(x)$.
2. Finding the zeros of the function $F(x)$ defined by the polynomial expression.
3. Solving (or finding the roots of) the polynomial equation $F(x) = 0$.

Note that if a is a zero of the polynomial function $F(x)$, then $F(x) = (x - a)Q(x)$. Any solution of the equation $Q(x) = 0$ is also a zero of $F(x)$. Since the degree of $Q(x)$ is less than the degree of $F(x)$, it is simpler to solve the equation $Q(x) = 0$ to find other possible zeros of $F(x)$. The equation $Q(x) = 0$ is called the **depressed equation** of $F(x)$.

The next example illustrates how to use the Factor Theorem and the depressed equation to solve a polynomial equation.

EXAMPLE 5   Using the Factor Theorem

Given that 2 is a zero of the function $f(x) = 3x^3 + 2x^2 - 19x + 6$, solve the polynomial equation $3x^3 + 2x^2 - 19x + 6 = 0$.

Solution

Since 2 is a zero of $f(x)$, we have $f(2) = 0$. The Factor Theorem tells us that $(x - 2)$ is a factor of $f(x)$. Next, we use synthetic division to divide $f(x)$ by $(x - 2)$.

$$
\begin{array}{r|rrrr}
2 & 3 & 2 & -19 & 6 \\
  &   & 6 & 16 & -6 \\
\hline
  & 3 & 8 & -3 & \;0
\end{array}
$$
← Remainder

coefficients of the quotient, which gives the depressed equation

Thus, since the remainder is 0,

$$f(x) = 3x^3 + 2x^2 - 19x + 6 = (x - 2)(3x^2 + 8x - 3).$$

Any solution of the depressed equation $3x^2 + 8x - 3 = 0$ is a zero of f. In this case, the depressed equation is of degree 2, so any method of solving a quadratic equation may be used to solve it.

$$
\begin{aligned}
f(x) = 3x^3 + 2x^2 - 19x + 6 &= 0 \qquad && \text{Given equation} \\
(x - 2)(3x^2 + 8x - 3) &= 0 \qquad && \text{Synthetic division} \\
(x - 2)(3x - 1)(x + 3) &= 0 \qquad && \text{Factor the trinomial} \\
&&& 3x^2 + 8x - 3. \\
x - 2 = 0 \quad \text{or} \quad 3x - 1 = 0 \quad &\text{or} \quad x + 3 = 0 \qquad && \text{Zero-product property} \\
x = 2 \quad \text{or} \quad x = \tfrac{1}{3} \quad &\text{or} \quad x = -3. \qquad && \text{Solve each equation.}
\end{aligned}
$$

The solution set is $\left\{-3, \dfrac{1}{3}, 2\right\}$.   ■ ■ ■

PRACTICE PROBLEM 5   Solve the equation $3x^3 - x^2 - 20x - 12 = 0$, given that one solution is -2.   ■

Application   Energy is measured in British thermal units (BTU). One BTU is the amount of energy required to raise the temperature of 1 pound of water $1°F$ at or near $39.2°F$; one million BTU is equivalent to 8 gallons of gasoline. Fuels such as coal, petroleum, and natural gas are measured in quadrillion BTU (1 quadrillion $= 10^{15}$), abbreviated "quads."

EXAMPLE 6   Petroleum Consumption

The petroleum consumption C (in quads) in the United States from 1970–1995 can be modeled by the function

$$C(x) = 0.003x^3 - 0.139x^2 + 1.621x + 28.995,$$

where $x = 0$ represents 1970, $x = 1$ represents 1971, and so on.

Continued on next page.

The model indicates that $C(5) = 34$ quads of petroleum were consumed in 1975. Find another year between 1975 and 1995 when the model indicates that 34 quads of petroleum were consumed. (The model was slightly modified from the data obtained from the *Statistical Abstracts of the United States.*)

Solution

Since $x = 5$ represents 1975, we have

$$C(5) = 34$$
$$C(x) = (x - 5)Q(x) + 34 \quad \text{Division algorithm and Remainder Theorem}$$
$$C(x) - 34 = (x - 5)Q(x) \quad \text{Subtract 34 from both sides.}$$

Hence, 5 is a zero of $F(x) = C(x) - 34$, and

$$F(x) = C(x) - 34 = 0.003x^3 - 0.139x^2 + 1.621x - 5.005.$$

Finding another year between 1975 and 1995 when the petroleum consumption was 34 quads requires us to find another zero of $F(x) = C(x) - 34$ that is between 5 and 25. Since 5 is a zero of $F(x)$, we use synthetic division to find the quotient $Q(x)$.

$$
\begin{array}{r|rrrr}
5 & 0.003 & -0.139 & 1.621 & -5.005 \\
  &   & 0.015 & -0.62 & 5.005 \\
\hline
  & 0.003 & -0.124 & 1.001 & 0
\end{array}
$$

We solve the depressed equation $Q(x) = 0$.

$$0.003x^2 - 0.124x + 1.001 = 0 \qquad Q(x) = 0.003x^2 - 0.124x + 1.001$$

$$x = \frac{0.124 \pm \sqrt{(-0.124)^2 - 4(0.003)(1.001)}}{2(0.003)} \qquad \text{Quadratic formula}$$

$$x = 11 \text{ or } x = 30.\overline{3} \qquad \text{Use a calculator.}$$

We reject $x = 30.\overline{3}$, since we are asked to find x between 5 and 25.

Hence, according to this model, in 1981 (the year corresponding to $x = 11$), the petroleum consumption was also 34 quads. ■ ■ ■

PRACTICE PROBLEM 6 The value of $C(x) = 0.23x^3 - 4.255x^2 + 0.345x + 41.05$ is 10 when $x = 3$. Find another positive number x for which $C(x) = 10$. ■

4 Use the Rational Zeros Test.

The Rational Zeros Test

The Factor Theorem can be used to determine whether a specific number a is a zero of a given polynomial function $F(x)$. The following test (see Exercise 101 for a proof) is used to find *possible* rational zeros of a polynomial function with integer coefficients:

THE RATIONAL ZEROS TEST

If $F(x) = a_n x^n + a_{n-1} x^{n-1} + \cdots + a_2 x + a_1 x + a_0$ is a polynomial function with integer coefficients $(a_n \neq 0, a_0 \neq 0)$ and $\dfrac{p}{q}$ is a rational number in lowest terms that is a zero of $F(x)$, then

1. p is a factor of the constant term a_0;
2. q is a factor of the leading coefficient a_n.

EXAMPLE 7   Using the Rational Zeros Test

Find all rational zeros of $F(x) = 2x^3 + 5x^2 - 4x - 3$.

Solution

We first list all *possible* rational zeros of $F(x)$.

$$\text{Possible rational zeros} = \frac{p}{q} = \frac{\text{Factors of the constant term}, -3}{\text{Factors of the leading coefficient, } 2}$$

Factors of -3: $\pm 1, \pm 3$

Factors of 2: $\pm 1, \pm 2$

All combinations can be found by using just the *positive* factors of the leading coefficient. The possible rational zeros are:

$$\frac{\pm 1}{1}, \frac{\pm 1}{2}, \frac{\pm 3}{1}, \frac{\pm 3}{2}$$

or

$$\pm 1, \pm \frac{1}{2}, \pm \frac{3}{2}, \pm 3.$$

There are eight candidates for rational zeros of $F(x)$. We use synthetic division to see if we can find a rational zero among these candidates. We start by testing 1. If 1 is not a rational zero, then we will test other possibilities.

$$
\begin{array}{r|rrrr}
1 & 2 & 5 & -4 & -3 \\
  &   & 2 & 7 & 3 \\
\hline
  & 2 & 7 & 3 & \,|\,0
\end{array}
$$

The zero remainder tells us that $(x - 1)$ is a factor of $F(x)$, with the other factor being $2x^2 + 7x + 3$. Hence,

$$
\begin{aligned}
F(x) &= (x - 1)(2x^2 + 7x + 3) \\
&= (x - 1)(2x + 1)(x + 3). \quad \text{Factor } 2x^2 + 7x + 3.
\end{aligned}
$$

The zeros of $F(x)$ are found by solving the equation $(x - 1)(2x + 1)(x + 3) = 0$.

$$x - 1 = 0 \quad \text{or} \quad 2x + 1 = 0 \quad \text{or} \quad x + 3 = 0 \qquad \text{Zero-product property}$$

$$x = 1 \quad \text{or} \quad x = -\frac{1}{2} \quad \text{or} \quad x = -3 \qquad \text{Solve each equation.}$$

The solution set is $\left\{ 1, -\dfrac{1}{2}, -3 \right\}$. The rational zeros of F are $-3, -\dfrac{1}{2}$, and 1. ■ ■ ■

PRACTICE PROBLEM 7   Find all rational zeros of $F(x) = 2x^3 + 3x^2 - 6x - 8$. ■

A Exercises Basic Skills and Concepts

In Exercises 1–16, use long division to find the quotient and the remainder.

1. $\dfrac{2x^2 - 3x + 4}{x - 1}$ †

2. $\dfrac{b^2 + b - 6}{b + 3}$ †

3. $\dfrac{6x^2 - x - 2}{2x + 1}$ †

4. $\dfrac{12m^2 + 7m - 12}{4m - 3}$ †

5. $\dfrac{4x^3 - 2x^2 + x - 3}{2x - 3}$ †

6. $\dfrac{6x^3 + 6x^2 - 4x + 1}{3x - 2}$ †

7. $\dfrac{6x^3 + x + 4}{2x + 1}$ Quotient: $3x^2 - \dfrac{3}{2}x + \dfrac{5}{4}$; remainder: $\dfrac{11}{4}$

8. $\dfrac{3x^4 - 6x^2 + 3x - 7}{x + 1}$ †

9. $\dfrac{x^5 - 1}{x - 1}$ Quotient: $x^4 + x^3 + x^2 + x + 1$; remainder: 0

10. $\dfrac{6x^6 + 3x^2 + 10}{2x + 3}$ †

11. $\dfrac{x^6 + 5x^3 + 7x + 3}{x^2 + 2}$ Quotient: $x^4 - 2x^2 + 5x + 4$; remainder: $-3x - 5$

12. $\dfrac{4x^3 - 4x^2 - 9x + 5}{2x^2 - x - 5}$ Quotient: $2x - 1$; remainder: 0

13. $\dfrac{y^5 + 3y^4 - 6y^2 + 2y - 7}{y^2 + 2y - 3}$ Quotient: $y^3 + y^2 + y - 5$; remainder: $15y - 22$

14. $\dfrac{z^4 - 2z^2 + 1}{z^2 - 2z + 1}$ Quotient: $z^2 + 2z + 1$; remainder: 0

15. $\dfrac{6x^4 + 13x - 11x^3 - 10 - x^2}{3x^2 - 5 - x}$ Quotient: $2x^2 - 3x + 2$; remainder: 0

16. $\dfrac{x^4 - 9x^2 - 3 - 8x^3 + 16x}{x + 2x^2 - 3}$ †

In Exercises 17–36, use synthetic division to find the quotient and the remainder.

17. $\dfrac{x^3 + 3x^2 - x - 12}{x - 2}$ †

18. $\dfrac{2x^3 + 4x^2 + x - 15}{x - 3}$ †

19. $\dfrac{9x^3 - x^2 - 13x + 6}{x + 5}$ †

20. $\dfrac{x^3 - 7x^2 - 5x + 1}{x + 1}$ †

21. $\dfrac{x^4 + 2x^2 - x - 7}{x - 1}$ †

22. $\dfrac{3x^4 - 6x^2 + 3x - 7}{x - 2}$ †

23. $\dfrac{-2x^3 + 5x^2 + 7x - 8}{x - 3}$ Quotient: $-2x^2 - x + 4$; remainder: 4

24. $\dfrac{-2x^3 - 5x^2 + 3x - 2}{x + 3}$ Quotient: $-2x^2 + x$; remainder: -2

25. $\dfrac{x^5 + x^4 - 7x^3 + 2x^2 + x - 1}{x - 1}$ †

26. $\dfrac{2x^5 + 4x^4 - 3x^3 - 7x^2 + 3x - 2}{x + 2}$ †

27. $\dfrac{x^5 + 1}{x + 1}$ †

28. $\dfrac{x^5 + 1}{x - 1}$ †

29. $\dfrac{x^6 + 2x^4 - x^3 + 5}{x + 1}$ †

30. $\dfrac{x^7 - 1}{x + 1}$ †

31. $\dfrac{2x^5 + 3x^2 + 7}{x - \dfrac{1}{2}}$ †

32. $\dfrac{6x^4 + 3x^3 + 1}{x - \dfrac{1}{3}}$ †

33. $\dfrac{2x^4 - 3x^2 + 5x + 1}{x + \dfrac{3}{2}}$ †

34. $\dfrac{6x^6 - 5x^4 + 3x^2 + 4}{x + \dfrac{2}{3}}$ †

35. $\dfrac{-5x^4}{x + 2}$ †

36. $\dfrac{3x^5}{x - 1}$ †

In Exercises 37–40, use synthetic division and the Remainder Theorem to find each function value. Check your answer by evaluating the function at the given x-value.

37. $f(x) = x^3 + 3x^2 + 1$

  a. $f(1)$ 5

  b. $f(-1)$ 3

  c. $f\left(\dfrac{1}{2}\right)$ $\dfrac{15}{8}$

  d. $f(10)$ 1301

38. $g(x) = 2x^3 - 3x^2 + 1$

  a. $g(-2)$ −27

  b. $g(-1)$ −4

  c. $g\left(-\dfrac{1}{2}\right)$ 0

  d. $g(7)$ 540

39. $h(x) = x^4 + 5x^3 - 3x^2 - 20$

  a. $h(1)$ −17

  b. $h(-1)$ −27

  c. $h(-2)$ −56

  d. $h(2)$ 24

40. $f(x) = x^4 + 0.5x^3 - 0.3x^2 - 20$

  a. $f(0.1)$ −20.0024

  b. $f(0.5)$ −19.95

  c. $f(1.7)$ −10.0584

  d. $f(-2.3)$ 0.3136

In Exercises 41–48, use the Factor Theorem to show that the linear polynomial is a factor of the second polynomial. Check your answer by synthetic division.

41. $x - 1$; $2x^3 + 3x^2 - 6x + 1$

42. $x - 3$; $3x^3 - 9x^2 - 4x + 12$

43. $x + 1$; $5x^4 + 8x^3 + x^2 + 2x + 4$

44. $x + 3$; $3x^4 + 9x^3 - 4x^2 - 9x + 9$

45. $x - 2$; $x^4 + x^3 - x^2 - x - 18$

46. $x + 3$; $x^5 + 3x^4 + x^2 + 8x + 15$

†Due to space constrictions, answers to these exercises may be found in the Answers beginning on page A–1 in the back of the book.

47. $x + 2; x^6 - x^3 - 7x^4 + x^3 + 8x^2 + 5x + 2$

48. $x - 2; 2x^6 - 5x^5 + 4x^4 + x^3 - 7x^2 - 7x + 2$

In Exercises 49–52, find the value of k for which the first polynomial is a factor of the second polynomial.

49. $x + 1; x^3 + 3x^2 + x + k$
 [*Hint:* Let $f(x) = x^3 + 3x^2 + x + k$.
 Then $f(-1) = 0$.] $k = -1$

50. $x - 1; -x^3 + 4x^2 + kx - 2$ $k = -1$

51. $x - 2; 2x^3 + kx^2 - kx - 2$ $k = -7$

52. $x - 1; k^2 - 3kx^2 - 2kx + 6$ $k = 2$ or 3

In Exercises 53–56, use the Factor Theorem to show that the first polynomial *is not* a factor of the second polynomial.
[*Hint:* Show that the remainder is not zero.]

53. $x - 2; -2x^3 + 4x^2 - 4x + 9$ Remainder: 1

54. $x + 3; -3x^3 - 9x^2 + 5x + 12$ Remainder: -3

55. $x + 2; 4x^4 + 9x^3 + 3x^2 + x + 4$ Remainder: 6

56. $x - 3; 3x^4 - 8x^3 + 5x^2 + 7x - 3$ Remainder: 90

In Exercises 57–60, find the set of possible rational zeros of the given function.

57. $f(x) = 3x^3 - 4x^2 + 5$ †

58. $g(x) = 2x^4 - 5x^2 - 2x + 1$ †

59. $h(x) = 4x^4 - 9x^2 + x + 6$ †

60. $F(x) = 6x^6 + 5x^5 + x - 35$ †

In Exercises 61–76, find all rational zeros of the given polynomial function.

61. $f(x) = x^3 - x^2 - 4x + 4$ $\{-2, 1, 2\}$

62. $f(x) = x^3 + x^2 + 2x + 2$ -1

63. $f(x) = x^3 - 4x^2 + x + 6$ $\{-1, 2, 3\}$

64. $f(x) = x^3 + 3x^2 + 2x + 6$ -3

65. $g(x) = 2x^3 + x^2 - 13x + 6$ †

66. $g(x) = 3x^3 - 2x^2 + 3x - 2$ †

67. $g(x) = 6x^3 + 13x^2 + x - 2$ †

68. $g(x) = 2x^3 + 3x^2 + 4x + 6$ †

69. $h(x) = 3x^3 + 7x^2 + 8x + 2$ †

70. $h(x) = 2x^3 + x^2 + 8x + 4$ †

71. $h(x) = x^4 - x^3 - x^2 - x - 2$ $\{-1, 2\}$

72. $h(x) = 2x^4 + 3x^3 + 8x^2 + 3x - 4$ †

73. $F(x) = x^4 - x^3 - 13x^2 + x + 12$ †

74. $G(x) = 3x^4 + 5x^3 + x^2 + 5x - 2$ †

75. $F(x) = x^4 - 2x^3 + x^2 + 2x - 2$ $\{-1, 1\}$

76. $G(x) = x^6 + 2x^4 + x^2 + 2$ No rational zeros

In Exercises 77–80, show that the given equation has no rational roots.

77. $x^2 - 2 = 0$ †

78. $x^3 + 4x + 7 = 0$ †

79. $x^3 + 3x^2 - 1 = 0$ †

80. $x^4 - 2x^3 + 10x^2 - x + 1 = 0$ †

B Exercises Applying the Concepts

81. Geometry. The area of a rectangle is
$(2x^4 - 2x^3 + 5x^2 - x + 2)$ square centimeters. Its length is
$(x^2 - x + 2)$ cm. Find its width. $2x^2 + 1$

82. Geometry. The volume of a rectangular solid is
$(x^4 + 3x^3 + x + 3)$ cubic inches. Its length and width
are $(x + 3)$ and $(x + 1)$ inches, respectively. Find its
height. $x^2 - x + 1$

83. Geometry. Find a point on the parabola $y = x^2$ whose
distance from $(18, 0)$ is $4\sqrt{17}$. $(2, 4)$

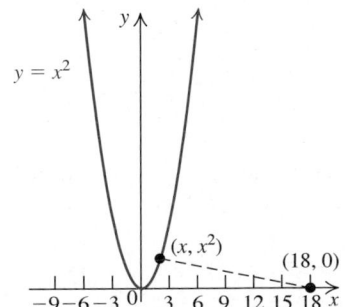

84. Making a box. A square piece of tin 18 inches on each side
is to be made into a box, without a top, by cutting a square
from each corner and folding up the flaps to form the sides.
What size corners should be cut so that the volume of the
box is 432 cubic inches? $x = 3$ in.

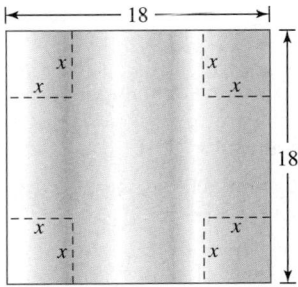

85. Cost function. The total cost of a product (in dollars) is
given by $C(x) = 3x^3 - 6x^2 + 108x + 100$, where x is the
demand for the product. Find the value of x for which the
total cost is 628 dollars. $x = 4$

86. Profit. For the product in Exercise 85, the demand function is $p(x) = 330 + 10x - x^2$. Find the value of x for which the profit is 910 dollars. $x = 5$

87. Production cost. The total cost per month, in thousands of dollars, of producing x printers (with x measured in hundreds) is given by $C(x) = x^3 - 15x^2 + 5x + 50$. How many units must be produced so that the total monthly cost is \$125,000? 15

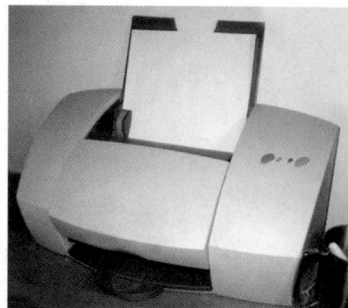

88. Break even. If the demand function for the printers in Exercise 87 is $p(x) = -3x + 3 + \dfrac{74}{x}$, find the number of printers that must be produced and sold to break even. 12

89. Total energy consumption. The total energy consumption (in quads) in the United States from 1970 to 1995 is approximated by the function

$$C(x) = 0.0439x^3 - 1.4911x^2 + 14.224x + 41.76,$$

where $x = 0$ represents 1970. The model indicates that 81 quads of energy was consumed in 1979. Find another

year after 1979 when the model indicates that 81 quads of energy was consumed. (The model was modified from the data obtained from the *Statistical Abstracts of the United States*.) 1990

90. Lottery sales. In the lottery game called *Lotto*, players typically select six digits out of a large field of numbers. Varying prizes are offered for matching three through six numbers drawn by the lottery. Lotto sales (in billions of dollars) in the United States from 1983 through 2003 are approximated by the function

$$s(x) = 0.0039x^3 - 0.2095x^2 + 3.2201x - 2.7505,$$

where $x = 0$ represents 1980. The model indicates that 8.6 billion dollars in Lotto sales occurred in 1985. Find another year after 1985 when the model indicates that 8.6 billion in Lotto sales occurred. (The model was modified from the data obtained from the *Statistical Abstracts of the United States*.) 2001

C Exercises   Beyond the Basics

91. Show that $\dfrac{1}{2}$ is a root of multiplicity 2 of the equation

$$4x^3 + 8x^2 - 11x + 3 = 0.$$

92. Show that $-\dfrac{2}{3}$ is a root of multiplicity 2 of the equation

$$9x^3 + 3x^2 - 8x - 4 = 0.$$

93. If n is a positive integer, find the values of n for which each of the following is true.
  a. $x + a$ is a factor of $x^n + a^n$. *n* is an odd integer.
  b. $x + a$ is a factor of $x^n - a^n$. *n* is an even integer.
  c. $x - a$ is a factor of $x^n + a^n$. there is no such *n*.
  d. $x - a$ is a factor of $x^n - a^n$. *n* is any positive integer.

94. Use Exercise 93 to prove the following:
  a. $7^{11} - 2^{11}$ is exactly divisible by 5.
  b. $(19)^{20} - (10)^{20}$ is exactly divisible by 261.

In Exercises 95–98, show that the given number is irrational. [*Hint:* To show $x = 1 + \sqrt{3}$ is irrational, form the equivalent equations $x - 1 = \sqrt{3}$, $(x - 1)^2 = 3$, and $x^2 - 2x - 2 = 0$, and show that the last equation has no rational roots.]

95. $\sqrt{3}$

96. $\sqrt[3]{4}$

97. $3 - \sqrt{2}$

98. $(9)^{\frac{2}{3}}$

In Exercises 99 and 100, find a polynomial equation of least possible degree with integer coefficients whose roots include the given numbers.

99. $1, -1, 0$ $x^3 - x = 0$

100. $2, 1, -2$

101. In order to prove the rational zeros test, we assume the **Fundamental Theorem of Arithmetic,** which states that "Every integer has a unique prime factorization." Supply reasons for each step in the following proof:

(i) $F\left(\dfrac{p}{q}\right) = 0$ and $\dfrac{p}{q}$ is in lowest terms.

(ii) $a_n\left(\dfrac{p}{q}\right)^n + a_{n-1}\left(\dfrac{p}{q}\right)^{n-1} + \cdots + a_1\left(\dfrac{p}{q}\right) + a_0 = 0$

(iii) $a_n p^n + a_{n-1}p^{n-1}q + \cdots + a_1 pq^{n-1} + a_0 q^n = 0$

(iv) $a_n p^n + a_{n-1}p^{n-1}q + \cdots + a_1 pq^{n-1} = -a_0 q^n$

(v) p is a factor of the left side of (iv).

(vi) p is a factor of $-a_0 q^n$.

(vii) p is a factor of a_0.

(viii) $a_{n-1}p^{n-1}q + \cdots + a_1 pq^{n-1} + a_0 q^n = -a_n p^n$

(ix) q is a factor of the left side of the equation in (viii).

(x) q is a factor of $-a_n p^n$.

(xi) q is a factor of a_n.

102. Find all rational roots of the equation

$$2x^4 + 2x^3 + \frac{1}{2}x^2 + 2x - \frac{3}{2} = 0.$$

[*Hint:* Multiply both sides of the equation by the lowest common denominator.]

Critical Thinking

103. Synthetic division is a process of dividing a polynomial $F(x)$ by $x - a$. Modify the process to use synthetic division so that it finds the remainder when the first polynomial is divided by the second.

a. $2x^3 + 3x^2 + 6x - 2$; $2x - 1$

$$\left[\textit{Hint: } 2x - 1 = 2\left(x - \frac{1}{2}\right). \right] \quad \text{Remainder: } 2$$

b. $2x^3 - x^2 - 4x + 1$; $2x + 3$ Remainder: -2

104. Let $g(x) = 3x^3 - 5cx^2 - 3c^2x + 3c^3$. Use synthetic division to find each function value.
a. $g(-c)$ $-2c^3$
b. $g(2c)$ c^3

Answers:

101. i. Simplifying the fraction if necessary, we can assume that $\dfrac{p}{q}$ is in lowest terms. Since $\dfrac{p}{q}$ is a zero of F, we have $F\left(\dfrac{p}{q}\right) = 0$.

ii. Substitute $\dfrac{p}{q}$ for x in the equation $F(x) = 0$.

iii. Multiply the equation in (ii) by q^n.

iv. Rearrange the equation.

v. The left side of (iv) is $a_n p^n + a_{n-1}p^{n-1}q + \ldots + a_1 pq^{n-1} = p(a_n p^{n-1} + a_{n-1}p^{n-2}q + \ldots + a_1 q^{n-1})$. Therefore, p is a factor.

vi. Because of the equality, p must be a factor of the right side, too.

vii. Since p and q have no common prime factors, p must be a factor of a_0.

viii. Rearrange the terms in the equation in (iii).

ix. The left side of (viii) is $a_{n-1}p^{n-1}q + \ldots + a_1 pq^{n-1} + a_0 q^n = q(a_{n-1}p^{n-1} + \ldots + a_1 pq^{n-2} + a_0 q^{n-1})$. Therefore, q is a factor.

x. Because of the equality, q must be a factor of the right side, too.

xi. Since p and q have no common prime factors, q must be a factor of a_n.

102. Rational roots: $\left\{ -\dfrac{3}{2}, \dfrac{1}{2} \right\}$

Zeros of a Polynomial Function

JEROME CARDAN.

From a scarce Print.

Gerolamo Cardano (1502–1576)
Cardano was trained as a physician, but his range of interests included philosophy, music, gambling, mathematics, astrology, and the occult sciences. Cardano was a colorful man, full of contradictions. His lifestyle was deplorable even by the standards of the times, and his personal life was filled with tragedies. His wife died in 1546. He saw one son executed for wife poisoning. He cropped the ears of a second son who attempted the same crime. In 1570, he was imprisoned for six months for heresy when he published the horoscope of Christ. Cardano spent the last few years in Rome, where he wrote his autobiography, *De Propria Vita*, in which he did not spare the most shameful revelations.

BEFORE STARTING THIS SECTION, REVIEW

1. Long division (Section 3.3, page 357)

2. Synthetic division (Section 3.3, page 358)

3. Rational zeros test (Section 3.3, page 365)

4. Complex numbers (Section 1.3, page 110)

5. Conjugate of a complex number (Section 1.3, page 114)

OBJECTIVES

1. Find the possible number of positive and negative zeros of polynomials.

2. Find the bounds on the real zeros of polynomials.

3. Learn basic facts about the complex zeros of polynomials.

4. Use the Conjugate Pairs Theorem to find zeros of polynomials.

Cardano Accused of Stealing Formula

In 16th-century Italy, it was very difficult to obtain and retain a teaching job at a university. University appointments were mostly temporary. One of the ways a professor convinced the administration that he was worthy of continuing in his position was by winning public challenges. Two contenders for a given position would present each other with a list of problems, and in a public forum some time later, each would present his solutions to the other's problems. As a result, if a person discovered a new method of solving certain problems, it was to his advantage to keep it secret.

In 1535, in a public contest in which the problems were primarily on solving the cubic equation, Nicolo Tartaglia (1499–1557) won over his opponent Antonio Maria Fiore. Gerolamo Cardano (1501–1576), in the hope of learning the secret of solving a cubic equation, invited Tartaglia to visit him. After many promises and much flattery, Tartaglia revealed his method of solution, on the promise, probably given under oath, that Cardano would keep it confidential. When Cardano's book *Ars Magna* (The Great Art) appeared in 1545, the formula and the method of proof were fully disclosed. Angered at this apparent breach of a solemn oath, and feeling cheated out of the rewards of his monumental work, Tartaglia accused Cardano of being a liar and a thief for stealing his formula. Thus began the bitterest feud in the history of mathematics, carried on with name-calling and mudslinging of the lowest order.

As Tartaglia feared, the formula (See Group Project 1) has forever since been known as Cardano's formula for the solution of the cubic equation. ■

1 Find the possible number of positive and negative zeros of polynomials.

Descartes's Rule of Signs

In Section 3.3, you learned how to use the Rational Zeros Test to find the possible rational zeros of a polynomial function with integer coefficients. We now investigate briefly some other useful tests for the real zeros of polynomial functions. One such test, called *Descartes's Rule of Signs,* depends on reading the signs of the coefficients to determine the possible number of positive and negative zeros of a polynomial function.

If the terms of a polynomial are arranged in descending powers of the variable, we say that a **variation of sign** occurs when the signs of two consecutive terms differ. For example, in the polynomial $2x^5 - 5x^3 - 6x^2 + 7x + 3$, the signs of the terms are $+ \ - \ - \ + \ +$. Hence, there are two variations of sign, as follows:

$$+ \quad - \quad - \quad + \quad + .$$

There are three variations of sign in

$$x^5 - 3x^3 + 2x^2 + 5x - 7.$$

DESCARTES'S RULE OF SIGNS

Let $F(x)$ be a polynomial function with real coefficients and with terms written in descending order.

1. The number of positive zeros of F is either equal to the number of variations of sign of $F(x)$ or less than that number by an even integer.

2. The number of negative zeros of F is either equal to the number of variations of sign of $F(-x)$ or less than that number by an even integer.

When using Descartes's Rule, a zero of multiplicity m should be counted as m zeros.

EXAMPLE 1   Using Descartes's Rule of Signs

Find the possible number of positive and negative zeros of

$$f(x) = x^5 - 3x^3 - 5x^2 + 9x - 7.$$

Solution

There are three variations of sign in $f(x)$:

$$f(x) = x^5 - 3x^3 - 5x^2 + 9x - 7.$$
$$+ \text{ to } - \qquad - \text{ to } + \ + \text{ to } -$$

Hence, the number of positive zeros of $f(x)$ is either 3 or $3 - 2 = 1$. (2 is the only even positive integer less than 3.) Furthermore,

$$f(-x) = (-x)^5 - 3(-x)^3 - 5(-x)^2 + 9(-x) - 7$$
$$= -x^5 + 3x^3 - 5x^2 - 9x - 7.$$
$$- \text{ to } + \ + \text{ to } -$$

The polynomial $f(-x)$ has two variations of sign. Hence, the number of negative zeros of $f(x)$ is either 2 or $2 - 2 = 0$.   ■ ■ ■

PRACTICE PROBLEM 1   Find the possible number of positive and negative zeros of
$$f(x) = 2x^5 + 3x^2 + 5x - 1.$$ ■

2 Find the bounds on the real zeros of polynomials.

Bounds on the Real Zeros

If a polynomial function $F(x)$ has no zeros greater than a number k, then k is called an **upper bound** on the zeros of $F(x)$. Similarly, if $F(x)$ has no zeros less than a number k, then k is called a **lower bound** on the zeros of $F(x)$.

The following theorem states the rules for the upper and lower bounds for the zeros of a polynomial function:

RULES FOR BOUNDS

Let $F(x)$ be a polynomial function with real coefficients and a positive leading coefficient. Suppose $F(x)$ is synthetically divided by $x - k$. Then

1. If $k > 0$, and each number in the last row is either zero or positive, then k is an upper bound on the zeros of $F(x)$.

2. If $k < 0$, and numbers in the last row alternate in sign, then k is a lower bound on the zeros of $F(x)$.

If 0 appears in the last row of the synthetic division, then it may be assigned either a positive or a negative sign in determining whether the signs alternate.

EXAMPLE 2   Finding the Bounds on the Zeros

Find upper and lower bounds on the zeros of
$$F(x) = x^4 - x^3 - 5x^2 - x - 6.$$

Solution

By the rational zeros test, the possible rational zeros of $F(x)$ are ± 1, ± 2, ± 3, and ± 6.

There is only one variation of sign in $F(x) = x^4 - x^3 - 5x^2 - x - 6$. Hence, $F(x)$ has only one positive zero. We first try synthetic division by $x - k$ with $k = 1, 2, 3$, and so on. The first integer for which all numbers in the last row are 0 or positive is an upper bound on the zeros of $F(x)$.

$$
\begin{array}{r|rrrrr}
1 & 1 & -1 & -5 & -1 & -6 \\
  &   & 1 & 0 & -5 & -6 \\
\hline
  & 1 & 0 & -5 & -6 & -12 \\
\end{array}
$$
Synthetic division with $k = 1$

$$
\begin{array}{r|rrrrr}
2 & 1 & -1 & -5 & -1 & -6 \\
  &   & 2 & 2 & -6 & -14 \\
\hline
  & 1 & 1 & -3 & -7 & -20 \\
\end{array}
$$
Synthetic division with $k = 2$

$$
\begin{array}{r|rrrrr}
3 & 1 & -1 & -5 & -1 & -6 \\
  &   & 3 & 6 & 3 & 6 \\
\hline
  & 1 & 2 & 1 & 2 & 0 \\
\end{array}
$$
Synthetic division with $k = 3$

←——— All numbers are 0 or positive.

By the rule for bounds, since, for $k = 3$, all numbers in the last row are nonnegative (≥ 0), 3 is an upper bound on the zeros of $F(x)$.

We now try synthetic division by $x - k$ with $k = -1, -2, -3, \ldots$. The first negative integer for which the numbers in the last row alternate in sign is a lower bound on the zeros of $F(x)$.

$$
\begin{array}{r|rrrr}
-1 & 1 & -1 & -5 & -1 & -6 \\
   &   & -1 & 2 & 3 & -2 \\
\hline
   & 1 & -2 & -3 & 2 & -8
\end{array}
\qquad \text{Synthetic division with } k = -1
$$

$$
\begin{array}{r|rrrr}
-2 & 1 & -1 & -5 & -1 & -6 \\
   &   & -2 & 6 & -2 & 6 \\
\hline
   & 1 & -3 & 1 & -3 & 0
\end{array}
\qquad \text{Synthetic division with } k = -2
$$

◄——— These numbers alternate in sign.

Using $k = -2$, we see that the numbers in the last row alternate in sign when 0 is assigned a positive sign. Hence, -2 is a lower bound on the zeros of $F(x)$.   ■ ■ ■

PRACTICE PROBLEM 2   Find upper and lower bounds for the zeros of

$$f(x) = x^3 + 3x^2 + x - 4.$$ ■

3 Learn basic facts about the complex zeros of polynomials.

When we first factor polynomials in algebra, we require that all coefficients be integers. In this case, we say that the polynomial $x^2 - 2$ cannot be factored as a product of two polynomials of nonzero degree. We also say that $x^2 - 2$ cannot be *factored over the integers*. However, if we allow coefficients for polynomials to be real numbers, rather than just integers, we have

$$x^2 - 2 = (x - \sqrt{2})(x + \sqrt{2}). \qquad A^2 - B^2 = (A + B)(A - B)$$

The polynomials $x - \sqrt{2}$ and $x + \sqrt{2}$ use coefficients that are not integers. (Both $\sqrt{2}$ and $-\sqrt{2}$ are irrational numbers.) We say that $x^2 - 2$ is *not prime* when polynomial coefficients can be real numbers (as opposed to being restricted to integers). More succinctly, we say that $x^2 - 2$ can be *factored over the real numbers*. In general, we say that a polynomial $P(x)$ whose coefficients are restricted to membership in a particular set of numbers S can be *factored over S*, provided that $P(x)$ can be factored as a product of two polynomials of nonzero degree with coefficients in S. The Factor Theorem connects the concept of *factors* and *zeros* of a polynomial, and we continue to investigate this connection.

Because the equation $x^2 + 1 = 0$ has no real roots, the polynomial function $P(x) = x^2 + 1$ has no real zeros. However, if we replace x by the complex number i, we have

$$P(i) = i^2 + 1 = (-1) + 1 = 0.$$

Consequently, i is a complex number for which $P(i) = 0$; that is, i is a *complex zero* of $P(x)$. In Section 3.2, we stated that a polynomial of degree n can have at most n real zeros. We now extend our number system to allow the coefficients of polynomials and variables to represent complex numbers. When we want to emphasize that complex numbers may be used in this way, we call the polynomial $P(x)$ a **complex polynomial.** If $P(z) = 0$ for a complex number z, we say that z is a **zero** or a **complex zero** of $P(x)$. In the complex number system, every nth-degree polynomial equation has *exactly* n roots and every nth-degree polynomial can be factored into exactly n linear factors. This fact follows from the Fundamental Theorem of Algebra and also provides the basis for much of our success in factoring polynomials and solving polynomial equations.

FUNDAMENTAL THEOREM OF ALGEBRA

Every polynomial

$$P(x) = a_nx^n + a_{n-1}x^{n-1} + \cdots + a_1x + a_0 \quad (n \geq 1, a_n \neq 0)$$

with complex coefficients $a_n, a_{n-1}, \ldots, a_1, a_0$ has at least one complex zero.

RECALL

If $b = 0$, the complex number $a + bi$ is a real number. Thus, the set of real numbers is a subset of the set of complex numbers.

This theorem was proved by the mathematician Karl Friedrich Gauss at age 20. The proof is beyond the scope of this book, but if we are allowed to use complex numbers, we can use the theorem to prove that every polynomial has a complete factorization.

FACTORIZATION THEOREM FOR POLYNOMIALS

If $P(x)$ is a complex polynomial of degree $n \geq 1$, it can be factored into n (not necessarily distinct) linear factors of the form

$$P(x) = a(x - r_1)(x - r_2) \cdots (x - r_n),$$

where $a, r_1, r_2, \ldots, r_n$ are complex numbers.

To prove the Factorization Theorem for Polynomials, we first observe that if $P(x)$ is a polynomial of degree 1 or higher, then the Fundamental Theorem of Algebra guarantees that there is a zero r_1 such that $P(r_1) = 0$. By the Factor Theorem, $(x - r_1)$ is a factor of $P(x)$ and

$$P(x) = (x - r_1)q_1(x),$$

where the degree of $q_1(x)$ is $n - 1$ and its leading coefficient is a. If $n - 1$ is positive, then we apply the Fundamental Theorem to $q_1(x)$; this gives us a zero, say, r_2, of $q_1(x)$. By the Factor Theorem, $(x - r_2)$ is a factor of $q_1(x)$ and

$$q_1(x) = (x - r_2)q_2(x),$$

where the degree of $q_1(x)$ is $n - 2$ and its leading coefficient is a. Then

$$P(x) = (x - r_1)(x - r_2)q_2(x).$$

This process can be continued until $P(x)$ is completely factored as

$$P(x) = a(x - r_1)(x - r_2) \cdots (x - r_n),$$

where a is the leading coefficient and $r_1, r_2, \ldots, r_n$ are zeros of $P(x)$. The proof is now complete.

In general, the numbers $r_1, r_2, \ldots, r_n$ may not be distinct. As with the polynomials we have encountered previously, if the factor $(x - r)$ appears k times in the complete factorization of $P(x)$, then we say that r is a zero of *multiplicity* k. The polynomial $P(x) = (x - 2)^3(x - i)^2$ has zeros

2 (of multiplicity 3) and i (of multiplicity 2).

The polynomial $P(x) = (x - 2)^3(x - i)^2$ has only 2 and i as its zeros, although it is of degree 5. We have the following result:

NUMBER OF ZEROS THEOREM

A polynomial of degree n has exactly n zeros, provided that a zero of multiplicity k is counted k times.

EXAMPLE 3   **Constructing a Polynomial Whose Zeros Are Given**

Find a polynomial $P(x)$ of degree 4 with a leading coefficient of 2 and zeros $-1, 3, i$, and $-i$. Write $P(x)$

a. in completely factored form;

b. by expanding the product found in part **a.**

Solution

a. Since $P(x)$ has degree 4, we write

$$P(x) = a(x - r_1)(x - r_2)(x - r_3)(x - r_4).   \quad \text{Complete factored form}$$

Now replace the leading coefficient a by 2 and the zeros $r_1, r_2, r_3,$ and r_4 by $-1, 3, i,$ and $-i$ (in any order). Then

$$P(x) = 2[x - (-1)](x - 3)(x - i)[x - (-i)]$$

or

$$P(x) = 2(x + 1)(x - 3)(x - i)(x + i).$$

b. $P(x) = 2(x + 1)(x - 3)(x - i)(x + i).$

$$\begin{aligned}
&= 2(x + 1)(x - 3)(x^2 + 1) &&\text{Expand } (x - i)(x + i). \\
&= 2(x + 1)(x^3 - 3x^2 + x - 3) &&\text{Expand } (x - 3)(x^2 + 1). \\
&= 2(x^4 - 2x^3 - 2x^2 - 2x - 3) &&\text{Expand } (x + 1)(x^3 - 3x^2 + x - 3). \\
&= 2x^4 - 4x^3 - 4x^2 - 4x - 6 &&\text{Distributive property} \qquad ■ ■ ■
\end{aligned}$$

PRACTICE PROBLEM 3   Find a polynomial $P(x)$ of degree 4 with a leading coefficient of 3 and zeros $-2, 1, 1 + i, 1 - i$. Write $P(x)$

a. in completely factored form;   **b.** by expanding the product found in part **a.**   ■

4 Use the Conjugate Pairs Theorem to find zeros of polynomials.

Conjugate Pairs Theorem

In Example 3, we constructed a polynomial that had both i and its conjugate, $-i$, among its zeros. Our next result says that, for all polynomials with real coefficients, nonreal zeros occur in conjugate pairs.

CONJUGATE PAIRS THEOREM

If $P(x)$ is a polynomial function whose coefficients are real numbers and if $z = a + bi$ is a zero of P, then its conjugate, $\bar{z} = a - bi$, is also a zero of P.

To prove the Conjugate Pairs Theorem, let

$$P(x) = a_n x^n + a_{n-1} x^{n-1} + \cdots + a_1 x + a_0,$$

where $a_n, a_{n-1}, \ldots, a_1, a_0$ are real numbers. Now, suppose that $P(z) = 0$. Then we must show that $P(\bar{z}) = 0$ also. We will use the fact that the conjugate of a real number $a = a + 0i$ is identical to the real number a (since, $\bar{a} = a - 0i = a$) and then use the conjugate sum and product properties $\overline{z_1 + z_2} = \bar{z}_1 + \bar{z}_2$, and $\overline{z_1 z_2} = \bar{z}_1 \bar{z}_2$.

$$
\begin{aligned}
P(z) &= a_n z^n + a_{n-1} z^{n-1} + \cdots + a_1 z + a_0 & &\text{Replace } x \text{ by } z. \\
P(\bar{z}) &= a_n (\bar{z})^n + a_{n-1}(\bar{z})^{n-1} + \cdots + a_1 \bar{z} + a_0 & &\text{Replace } z \text{ by } \bar{z}. \\
&= \bar{a}_n \, \overline{z^n} + \bar{a}_{n-1} \, \overline{z^{n-1}} + \cdots + \bar{a}_1 \bar{z} + \bar{a}_0 & &(\bar{z})^k = \overline{z^k}, \ a_k = \bar{a}_k \\
&= \overline{a_n z^n} + \overline{a_{n-1} z^{n-1}} + \cdots + \overline{a_1 z} + \bar{a}_0 & &\bar{z}_1 \bar{z}_2 = \overline{z_1 z_2} \\
&= \overline{a_n z^n + a_{n-1} z^{n-1} + \cdots + a_1 z + a_0} & &\bar{z}_1 + \bar{z}_2 = \overline{z_1 + z_2} \\
&= \overline{P(z)} = \bar{0} = 0 & &P(z) = 0
\end{aligned}
$$

We see that if $P(z) = 0$, then $P(\bar{z}) = 0$, and the theorem is proved.

This theorem has several uses. If, for example, we know that $2 - 5i$ is a zero of a polynomial with real coefficients, then we know that $2 + 5i$ is also a zero. The fact that nonreal zeros occur in conjugate pairs in a polynomial with real coefficients also tells us that there will always be an *even* number of nonreal zeros. Thus, any polynomial with real coefficients of odd degree has at least one zero that is a real number.

ODD-DEGREE POLYNOMIALS WITH REAL ZEROS

Any polynomial $P(x)$ of odd degree with real coefficients must have at least one real zero.

For example, the polynomial $P(x) = 5x^7 + 2x^4 + 9x - 12$ has at least one zero that is a real number, because $P(x)$ has degree 7 (odd degree) and has real numbers as coefficients.

EXAMPLE 4   **Using the Conjugate Pairs Theorem**

A polynomial $P(x)$ of degree 9 with real coefficients has the following zeros: 2, of multiplicity 3; $4 + 5i$, of multiplicity 2; and $3 - 7i$. Write all nine zeros of $P(x)$.

Solution

Since complex zeros occur in conjugate pairs, the conjugate $4 - 5i$ of $4 + 5i$ is a zero of multiplicity 2, and the conjugate $3 + 7i$ of $3 - 7i$ is a zero of $P(x)$. The nine zeros of $P(x)$ are

$$2, 2, 2, 4 + 5i, 4 + 5i, 4 - 5i, 4 - 5i, 3 + 7i, \text{ and } 3 - 7i. \qquad ■ ■ ■$$

PRACTICE PROBLEM 4   A polynomial $P(x)$ of degree 8 with real coefficients has the following zeros: -3 and $2 - 3i$, each of multiplicity 2; and i. Write all eight zeros of $P(x)$.   ■

Every polynomial of degree n has exactly n zeros and can be factored into a product of n linear factors. If the polynomial has real coefficients, then, by the Conjugate Pairs Theorem, its nonreal zeros occur as conjugate pairs. Consequently, if $r = a + bi$ is a zero, then so is $\bar{r} = a - bi$, and both $x - r$ and $x - \bar{r}$ are linear factors of the polynomial. Multiplying these factors, we have

$$\begin{aligned} (x - r)(x - \bar{r}) &= x^2 - (r + \bar{r})x + r\bar{r} & \text{Use FOIL.} \\ &= x^2 - 2ax + (a^2 + b^2). & r + \bar{r} = 2a;\ r\bar{r} = a^2 + b^2 \end{aligned}$$

The quadratic polynomial $x^2 - 2ax + (a^2 + b^2)$ has real coefficients and is *prime* (cannot be factored any further) *over the real numbers*. Thus, each pair of linear factors with complex conjugate zeros can be combined into one prime (or *irreducible*) quadratic factor. We state this result next.

FACTORIZATION THEOREM FOR A POLYNOMIAL WITH REAL COEFFICIENTS

Every polynomial with real coefficients can be uniquely factored over the real numbers as a product of linear factors and/or prime quadratic factors.

EXAMPLE 5   **Finding the Complex Zeros of a Polynomial**

Given that $2 - i$ is a zero of $P(x) = x^4 - 6x^3 + 14x^2 - 14x + 5$, find the remaining zeros.

Solution

Since nonreal zeros occur in conjugate pairs for polynomials with real coefficients, we know that the conjugate of $2 - i$, or $2 + i$, is also a zero of $P(x)$. By the Factorization Theorem, the linear factors $[x - (2 - i)]$ and $[x - (2 + i)]$ appear in the factorization of $P(x)$. Consequently, their product

$$\begin{aligned} [x - (2 - i)][x - (2 + i)] &= (x - 2 + i)(x - 2 - i) \\ &= [(x - 2) + i][(x - 2) - i] & \text{Regroup.} \\ &= (x - 2)^2 - i^2 & A^2 - B^2 = (A + B)(A - B) \\ &= x^2 - 4x + 4 + 1 & \text{Expand } (x - 2)^2. \\ &= x^2 - 4x + 5 & \text{Simplify.} \end{aligned}$$

is also a factor of $P(x)$. We divide $P(x)$ by $x^2 - 4x + 5$ to find the other factor.

RECALL

Dividend =
Quotient · Divisor + Remainder

$$
\begin{array}{r}
x^2 - 2x + 1 \qquad \leftarrow \text{Quotient} \\
x^2 - 4x + 5 \overline{)\, x^4 - 6x^3 + 14x^2 - 14x + 5} \quad \leftarrow \text{Dividend} \\
\underline{x^4 - 4x^3 + 5x^2} \qquad\qquad\qquad \\
-2x^3 + 9x^2 - 14x \qquad\quad \\
\underline{-2x^3 + 8x^2 - 10x} \qquad\quad \\
x^2 - 4x + 5 \\
\underline{x^2 - 4x + 5} \\
0 \qquad \leftarrow \text{Remainder}
\end{array}
$$

Divisor $\rightarrow$

Continued on next page.

Thus,

$$
\begin{aligned}
P(x) &= (x^2 - 2x + 1)(x^2 - 4x + 5) \\
&= (x - 1)(x - 1)(x^2 - 4x + 5) &&\text{Factor } x^2 - 2x + 1. \\
&= (x - 1)(x - 1)[x - (2 - i)][x - (2 + i)]. &&\text{Factor } x^2 - 4x + 5.
\end{aligned}
$$

The zeros of $P(x)$ are 1 (of multiplicity 2), $2 - i$, and $2 + i$.   ■ ■ ■

PRACTICE PROBLEM 5   Given that $2i$ is a zero of $P(x) = x^4 - 3x^3 + 6x^2 - 12x + 8$, find the remaining zeros.   ■

EXAMPLE 6   **Finding the Zeros of a Polynomial**

Find all zeros of the polynomial $P(x) = x^4 - x^3 + 7x^2 - 9x - 18$.

Solution

Since the degree of $P(x)$ is 4, $P(x)$ has four zeros. We use the Rational Zeros Test to find the possible rational zeros:

$$\pm 1, \pm 2, \pm 3, \pm 6, \pm 9, \pm 18.$$

Testing these possible zeros by means of synthetic division, we eventually find that 2 is a zero.

$$
\begin{array}{r|rrrrr}
2 & 1 & -1 & 7 & -9 & -18 \\
  &   & 2 & 2 & 18 & 18 \\
\hline
  & 1 & 1 & 9 & 9 & 0
\end{array}
$$

We now know that $P(2) = 0$, so that $(x - 2)$ is a factor of $P(x)$, and that the quotient is $x^3 + x^2 + 9x + 9$.

We can solve the depressed equation $x^3 + x^2 + 9x + 9 = 0$ by factoring by grouping.

$$
\begin{aligned}
x^3 + x^2 + 9x + 9 &= 0 &&\text{Depressed equation} \\
x^2(x + 1) + 9(x + 1) &= 0 &&\text{Group terms, distributive property} \\
(x^2 + 9)(x + 1) &= 0 &&\text{Distributive property} \\
x^2 + 9 = 0 \quad \text{or} \quad x + 1 &= 0 &&\text{Zero-product property} \\
x^2 = -9 \quad \text{or} \quad x &= -1 &&\text{Solve each equation.} \\
x &= \pm\sqrt{-9} &&\text{Solve } x^2 = -9 \text{ for } x. \\
&= \pm 3i
\end{aligned}
$$

The four zeros of $P(x)$ are $-1, 2, 3i$, and $-3i$. The complete factorization of $P(x)$ is

$$P(x) = x^4 - x^2 + 7x - 9x - 18 = (x + 1)(x - 2)(x - 3i)(x + 3i).$$

■ ■ ■

PRACTICE PROBLEM 6   Find all zeros of the polynomial
$P(x) = x^4 - 8x^3 + 22x^2 - 28x + 16$.   ■

A Exercises Basic Skills and Concepts

In Exercises 1–8, determine the possible number of positive and negative zeros of the given function by using Descartes's Rule of Signs.

1. $f(x) = 5x^3 - 2x^2 - 3x + 4$ †

2. $g(x) = 3x^3 + x^2 - 9x - 3$ †

3. $f(x) = 2x^3 + 5x^2 - x + 2$ †

4. $g(x) = 3x^4 + 8x^3 - 5x^2 + 2x - 3$ †

5. $h(x) = 2x^5 - 5x^3 + 3x^2 + 2x - 1$ †

6. $F(x) = 5x^6 - 7x^4 + 2x^3 - 1$ †

7. $G(x) = -3x^4 - 4x^3 + 5x^2 - 3x + 7$ †

8. $H(x) = -5x^5 + 3x^3 - 2x^2 - 7x + 4$ †

In Exercises 9–16, determine upper and lower bounds on the zeros of the given function.

9. $f(x) = 3x^3 - x^2 + 9x - 3$ Upper bound: $\frac{1}{3}$; lower bound: -1.

10. $g(x) = 2x^3 - 3x^2 - 14x + 21$ Upper bound: $\frac{7}{2}$; lower bound: -3

11. $F(x) = 3x^3 + 2x^2 + 5x + 7$ Upper bound: 1; lower bound: $-\frac{7}{3}$

12. $G(x) = x^3 + 3x^2 + x - 4$ Upper bound: 1; lower bound: -4.

13. $h(x) = x^4 + 3x^3 - 15x^2 - 9x + 31$ †

14. $H(x) = 3x^4 - 20x^3 + 28x^2 + 19x - 13$ †

15. $f(x) = 6x^4 + x^3 - 43x^2 - 7x + 7$ †

16. $g(x) = 6x^4 + 23x^3 + 25x^2 - 9x - 5$ †

In Exercises 17–26, find all solutions of the equation in the complex number system.

17. $x^2 + 25 = 0$ †

18. $9x^2 + 16 = 0$ †

19. $(x - 2)^2 + 9 = 0$ †

20. $(x - 1)^2 + 27 = 0$ †

21. $x^2 + 4x + 4 = -9$ †

22. $x^2 + 2x + 1 = -16$ †

23. $x^3 - 8 = 0$ †

24. $x^4 - 1 = 0$ †

25. $(x - 2)(x - 3i)(x + 3i) = 0$ $\{2, 3i, -3i\}$

26. $(x - 1)(x - 2i)(2x - 6i)(2x + 6i) = 0$ †

In Exercises 27–32, find the remaining zeros of a polynomial $P(x)$ with real coefficients and having the specified degree and zeros.

27. Degree 3; zeros: 2, $3 + i$. $3 - i$

28. Degree 3; zeros: 2, $2 - i$. $2 + i$

29. Degree 4; zeros: 0, 1, $2 - i$. $2 + i$

30. Degree 4; zeros: $-i$, $1 - i$. $i, 1 + i$

31. Degree 6; zeros: 0, 5, i, $3i$. $-i, -3i$

32. Degree 6; zeros: $2i$, $4 + i$, $i - 1$. †

In Exercises 33–36, find the polynomial $P(x)$ with real coefficients having the specified degree, leading coefficient, and zeros.

33. Degree 4, leading coefficient 2, zeros: $5 - i$, $3i$. †

34. Degree 4, leading coefficient -3, zeros: $2 + 3i$, $1 - 4i$ †

35. Degree 5, leading coefficient 7, zeros: 5 (multiplicity 2), 1, $3 - i$. $P(x) = 7x^5 - 119x^4 + 777x^3 - 2415x^2 + 3500x - 1750$

36. Degree 6, leading coefficient 4, zeros: 3, 0 (multiplicity 3), $2 - 3i$. $P(x) = 4x^6 - 28x^5 + 100x^4 - 156x^3$

In Exercises 37–42, use the given zero to find the remaining zeros for each function.

37. $P(x) = x^4 + x^3 + 9x^2 + 9x$, zero: $3i$ $-1, 0, 3i, -3i$

38. $P(x) = x^4 - 2x^3 + x^2 + 2x - 2$, zero: $1 - i$ †

39. $P(x) = x^4 - 2x^3 - 3x^2 + 28x - 24$, zero: $2 + 2i$ †

40. $P(x) = 2x^4 - x^3 + 7x^2 - 4x - 4$, zero: $-2i$ †

41. $P(x) = x^5 - 5x^4 + 2x^3 + 22x^2 - 20x$, zero: $3 - i$ †

42. $P(x) = 2x^5 - 11x^4 + 19x^3 - 17x^2 + 17x - 6$, zero: i †

In Exercises 43–54, find all the zeros of each polynomial function.

43. $P(x) = x^3 - 9x^2 + 25x - 17$ $1, 4 + i, 4 - i$

44. $P(x) = x^3 - 5x^2 + 7x + 13$ $-1, 3 + 2i, 3 - 2i$

45. $P(x) = 3x^3 - 2x^2 + 22x + 40$ †

46. $P(x) = 3x^3 - x^2 + 12x - 4$ †

47. $P(x) = 2x^3 - 9x^2 + 30x - 13$ †

48. $P(x) = 2x^3 - 8x^2 + 7x - 3$ †

49. $P(x) = 2x^4 - 4x^3 + 3x^2 + 9x$ †

50. $P(x) = 9x^4 + 12x^3 - 10x^2 + 4x$ †

51. $P(x) = x^4 - 4x^3 - 5x^2 + 38x - 30$ †

52. $P(x) = x^4 + x^3 + 7x^2 + 9x - 18$ $-2, 1, 3i, -3i$

53. $P(x) = 2x^5 - 11x^4 + 19x^3 - 17x^2 + 17x - 6$ †

54. $P(x) = x^5 - 2x^4 - x^3 + 8x^2 - 10x + 4$ †

C Exercises Beyond the Basics

55. The solutions, -1 and 1, of the equation $x^2 = 1$ are called the square roots of 1. The solutions of the equation $x^3 = 1$ are called the cube roots of 1. Find the cube roots of 1. How many are there? †

56. The solutions of the equation $x^n = 1$, where n is a positive integer, are called the nth roots of 1 or "nth roots of unity." Explain the relationship between the solutions of the equation $x^n = 1$ and the zeros of the complex polynomial $P(x) = x^n - 1$. How many nth roots of 1 are there? †

†Due to space constrictions, answers to these exercises may be found in the Answers beginning on page A–1 in the back of the book.

57. Show that the polynomial function
$P(x) = x^6 + 2x^4 + 3x^2 + 4$ has six nonreal zeros.

58. Show that the polynomial function
$F(x) = x^5 + x^3 + 2x + 1$ has four nonreal zeros.

59. Show that the polynomial function $f(x) = x^7 + 5x + 3$ has six complex zeros.

60. Show that the polynomial function $g(x) = x^3 - x^2 - 1$ has two complex zeros.

Critical Thinking

61. Show that if $r_1, r_2, \ldots, r_n$ are the roots of the equation
$$a_n x^n + a_{n-1} x^{n-1} + \cdots + a_1 x + a_0 = 0 \quad (a_n \neq 0),$$
then the sum of the roots satisfies
$$r_1 + r_2 + \cdots + r_n = -\frac{a_{n-1}}{a_n}.$$

and the product of the roots satisfies
$$r_1 \cdot r_2 \cdot \ldots \cdot r_n = (-1)^n \frac{a_0}{a_n}.$$

[*Hint:* Factor the polynomial; then multiply it out, using $r_1, r_2, \ldots, r_n$, and compare coefficients with those of the original polynomial.]

Group Projects

1. In his book *Ars Magna*, Cardano explained how to solve cubic equations. He considers the following example:
$$x^3 + 6x = 20.$$

a. Explain why this equation has exactly one real solution.

b. Cardano explained the method as follows: "I take two cubes v^3 and u^3 whose difference is 20 and whose product is 2, that is, a third of the coefficient of x. Then, I say that $x = v - u$ is a solution of the equation." Show that if $v^3 - u^3 = 20$ and $vu = 2$, then $x = v - u$ is indeed the solution of the equation $x^3 + 6x = 20$.

c. Solve the system
$$v^3 - u^3 = 20$$
$$vu = 2$$
to find u and v.

d. Consider the equation $x^3 + px = q$, where p is a positive number. Using your work in parts (a), (b), and (c) as a guide, show that the unique solution of this equation is
$$x = \sqrt[3]{\frac{q}{2} + \sqrt{\left(\frac{q}{2}\right)^2 + \left(\frac{p}{3}\right)^3}} - \sqrt[3]{-\frac{q}{2} + \sqrt{\left(\frac{q}{2}\right)^2 + \left(\frac{p}{3}\right)^3}}.$$

e. Consider an arbitrary cubic equation
$$x^3 + ax^2 + bx + c = 0.$$
Show that the substitution $x = y - \dfrac{a}{3}$ allows you to write the cubic equation as
$$y^3 + py = q.$$

2. Use Cardano's method to solve the equation
$x^3 + 6x^2 + 10x + 8 = 0$. $\{-4, -1 + i, -1 - i\}$

Answers:

1. a. According to Descartes's Rule of Signs, the polynomial $x^3 + 6x - 20$ has one positive zero and no negative zero. Therefore, there is exactly one real solution.

b. Substituting $v - u$ for x, we obtain
$$(v - u)^3 + 6(v - u) = v^3 - 3v^2u + 3vu^2 - u^3 + 6(v - u)$$
$$= (v^3 - u^3) + (6 - 3uv)(v - u)$$
$$= 20 - (6 - 3(2))(v - u) = 20.$$
Therefore, $x = v - u$ is the solution.

c. $u = \sqrt[3]{-10 \pm 6\sqrt{3}}$, $v = \dfrac{2}{\sqrt[3]{-10 \pm 6\sqrt{3}}} = \sqrt[3]{10 \pm 6\sqrt{3}}$

Rational Functions

BEFORE STARTING THIS SECTION, REVIEW

1. Domain of a function (Section 2.4, page 230)

2. Zeros of a function (Section 3.2, page 339)

3. Symmetry (Section 2.2, page 194)

4. Quadratic formula (Section 1.4, page 127)

OBJECTIVES

1. Learn the definition of a rational function.

2. Find vertical asymptotes (if any).

3. Find horizontal asymptotes (if any).

4. Graph rational functions.

5. Graph rational functions with oblique asymptotes.

6. Graph revenue curves.

Federal Taxes and Revenues

The federal government of a country levies income taxes on its citizens and corporations to generate revenues. It spends these revenues primarily to pay for the defense of the country, the infrastructure, and social services for the welfare of its citizens. There is a relationship between tax rates and tax revenues. The graph in Figure 3.18 is a rough illustration of a "revenue curve."

All economists agree on the extreme cases. A zero tax rate produces no tax revenues, and with a 100% tax rate no one would bother to work (understandably!), so tax revenue would be zero. It then follows that, in a given economy, there is some optimal tax rate T^* between zero and 100% at which people are willing to maximize their output and still pay their taxes. At the same time, this optimal rate brings in the most revenue for the government. However, since no one knows the actual shape of the revenue curve, it is impossible to find the exact value of T^*.

Notice in Figure 3.18 that between the two extreme rates there are two rates (such as a and b in the figure) that will collect the same amount of revenue. In a democracy (at any given time), politicians can argue that taxes are currently too high (at some point b in Figure 3.18) and should therefore be reduced to encourage incentives and harder work (this is *supply-side economics*), and at the same time the government will generate more revenue. Others can argue that we are well to the left of T^* (at some point a in Figure 3.18), so why not run the experiment by raising the tax rate (for the rich) and observe the results? The choice is the politicians' to make, based upon whether the current rates "seem" to be too high or too low. In Example 9, we will sketch the graph of a revenue curve for a hypothetical economy. ■

FIGURE 3.18

1 Learn the definition of a rational function.

Rational Functions

Recall that each of the sum, difference, and product of two polynomial functions is also a polynomial function. However, the quotient of two polynomial functions is generally *not* a polynomial function. We call the quotient of two polynomial functions a *rational function*.

RATIONAL FUNCTION

A function f that can be expressed in the form

$$f(x) = \frac{N(x)}{D(x)},$$

where the numerator $N(x)$ and the denominator $D(x)$ are polynomials and $D(x)$ is not the zero polynomial, is called a **rational function.** The domain of f consists of all real numbers for which $D(x) \neq 0$.

Examples of rational functions are

$$f(x) = \frac{x - 1}{2x + 1}, \quad g(y) = \frac{5y}{y^2 + 1}, \quad h(t) = \frac{3t^2 - 4t + 1}{t - 2}, \quad \text{and} \quad F(z) = 3z^4 - 5z^2 + 6z + 1.$$

($F(z)$ is considered to have the constant polynomial function $D(z) = 1$ as its denominator.) By contrast, $y = \sqrt{1 - x^2}$ and $G(x) = |x|$ are not rational functions.

EXAMPLE 1   **Finding the Domain of a Rational Function**

Find the domain of each rational function.

a. $f(x) = \dfrac{3x^2 - 12}{x - 1}$ **b.** $g(x) = \dfrac{x}{x^2 - 6x + 8}$ **c.** $h(x) = \dfrac{x^2 - 4}{x - 2}$

Solution

a. The domain of $f(x) = \dfrac{3x^2 - 12}{x - 1}$ is the set of all real numbers x for which $x - 1 \neq 0$ (that is, $x \neq 1$). The domain of f in interval notation is $(-\infty, 1) \cup (1, \infty)$.

b. To find the domain of g, we first find (and exclude from the domain) the values of x for which the denominator $D(x)$ is zero.

$$
\begin{array}{lll}
D(x) = x^2 - 6x + 8 = 0 & \text{Set } D(x) = 0. \\
(x - 2)(x - 4) = 0 & \text{Factor } D(x). \\
x - 2 = 0 \quad \text{or} \quad x - 4 = 0 & \text{Zero-product property} \\
x = 2 \quad \text{or} \quad x = 4 & \text{Solve for } x.
\end{array}
$$

The domain of g is the set of all real numbers x such that $x \neq 2$ and $x \neq 4$. In interval notation, the domain of g is $(-\infty, 2) \cup (2, 4) \cup (4, \infty)$.

c. The domain of $h(x) = \dfrac{x^2 - 4}{x - 2}$ is the set of all real numbers x such that $x \neq 2$.

In interval notation, the domain of h is $(-\infty, 2) \cup (2, \infty)$.   ■ ■ ■

PRACTICE PROBLEM 1   Find the domain of the rational function $f(x) = \dfrac{x-3}{x^2 - 4x - 5}$.   ■

In Example 1, part **(c)**, recall that the functions $h(x) = \dfrac{x^2 - 4}{x - 2} = \dfrac{(x-2)(x+2)}{x-2}$ and $H(x) = x + 2$ are not equal. This is because the domain of $H(x)$ is the set of all real numbers, while the domain of $h(x)$ is the set of all real numbers x such that $x \neq 2$. The graph of $y = H(x)$ is a line with slope 1 and y-intercept 2. The graph of $y = h(x)$ is the same line as $y = H(x)$, except that the point $(2, 4)$ is missing. (See Figure 3.19.)

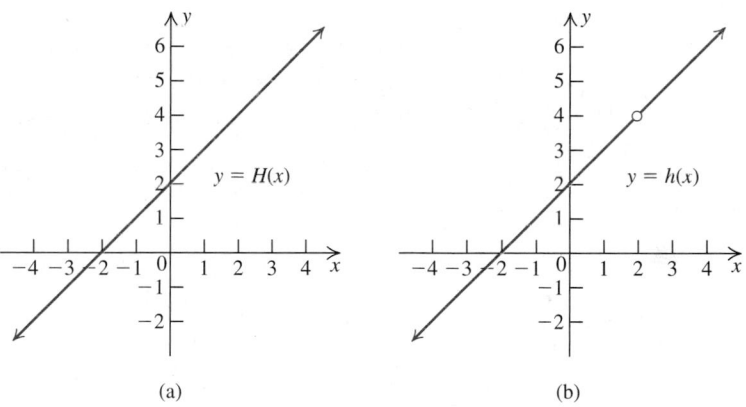

(a)   (b)

FIGURE 3.19

As with the quotient of integers, if the polynomials $N(x)$ and $D(x)$ have no common factors, then the rational function $f(x) = \dfrac{N(x)}{D(x)}$ is said to be in **lowest terms.** If a rational function $f(x) = \dfrac{N(x)}{D(x)}$ is in lowest terms, the zeros of $N(x)$ and $D(x)$ will play an important role in graphing the function f.

2 Find vertical asymptotes (if any).

Vertical Asymptotes

Consider the function $f(x) = \dfrac{1}{x}$. The domain of f is the set of all real numbers except $x = 0$. So far, we have said only that $f(0)$ is undefined, meaning that the function f is not assigned any value at $x = 0$. We now discuss this "undefined" phenomenon by studying the behavior of $f(x)$ "near" the excluded value $x = 0$. Consider the following table:

x	1	0.1	0.01	0.001	0.0002	10^{-9}	10^{-50}
$f(x) = \frac{1}{x}$	1	10	100	1000	5000	10^9	10^{50}

From the table, we see that as x approaches 0 (with $x > 0$), $f(x)$ increases without bound. In symbols, we write "as $x \to 0^+$, $f(x) \to \infty$." This statement is read, "As x approaches 0 *from the right*, $f(x)$ approaches infinity."

In general, the symbol $x \to a^+$ is read "x approaches a from the right," meaning that only values of x that are greater than a may be used, and $x \to a^-$ is read "x approaches a from the left," meaning that only values of x that are less than a may be used.

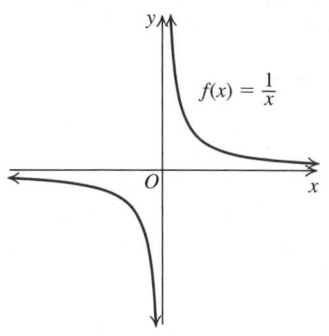

FIGURE 3.20

For the function $f(x) = \dfrac{1}{x}$, we can also make a table of values by choosing negative values of x near zero, such as $x = -1, -0.1, -0.001, \ldots, -10^{-9}$ and so on, and conclude that as $x \to 0^-$, $f(x) \to -\infty$. We say that as x approaches 0 *from the left*, $f(x)$ approaches negative infinity.

The graph of $f(x) = \dfrac{1}{x}$ is the familiar *reciprocal function* from Chapter 2 and is shown in Figure 3.20.

The graph in Figure 3.20 shows that as $x \to 0^+$, $f(x) \to \infty$, and also that as $x \to 0^-$, $f(x) \to -\infty$. The vertical line $x = 0$ is called a *vertical asymptote*.

VERTICAL ASYMPTOTE

The line with equation $x = a$ is called a **vertical asymptote** of the graph of a function f if $|f(x)| \to \infty$ as $x \to a^+$ or $x \to a^-$.

This definition says that if the line $x = a$ is a vertical asymptote of the graph of a rational function f, then the graph of f *near* $x = a$ has the following features (shown in Figure 3.21):

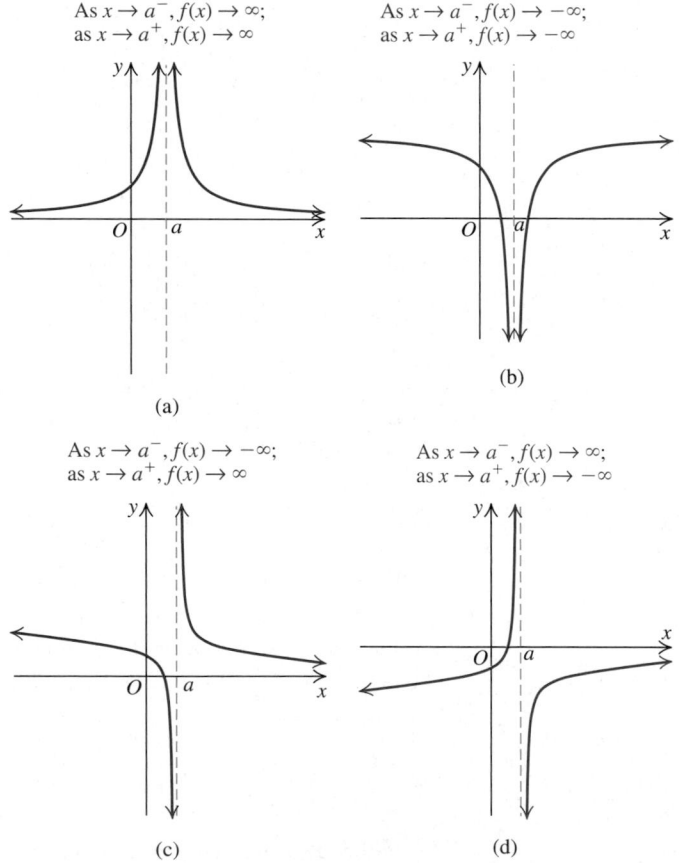

FIGURE 3.21

If $x = a$ is a vertical asymptote for a rational function f, the number a is not in the domain. Hence, the graph of f *does not cross* the vertical asymptote $x = a$. If the graph of a rational function has vertical asymptotes, then they may be located by the following rule:

LOCATING VERTICAL ASYMPTOTES OF RATIONAL FUNCTIONS

If $f(x) = \dfrac{N(x)}{D(x)}$ is a rational function, where $N(x)$ and $D(x)$ do not have a common factor and a is a real zero of $D(x)$, then the line with equation $x = a$ is a vertical asymptote of the graph of f.

The rule says that the vertical asymptotes (if present) are found by locating the real zeros of the denominator $D(x)$.

TECHNOLOGY CONNECTION

Very different graphs are given by graphing calculators for

$$g(x) = \frac{1}{x^2 - 9},$$

depending on whether the mode is set to *connected* or *dot*.

In connected mode, the calculator connects the dots between consecutive display dots (pixels). This produces vertical lines at $x = -3$ and $x = 3$. Dot mode avoids graphing these vertical lines by plotting the same points, but not connecting them. However, dot mode fails to display a continuous graph.

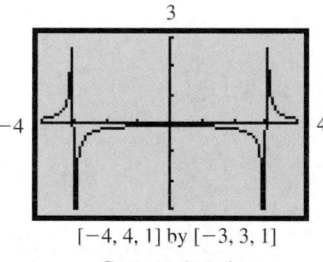

$[-4, 4, 1]$ by $[-3, 3, 1]$

Connected mode

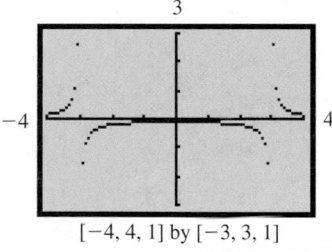

$[-4, 4, 1]$ by $[-3, 3, 1]$

Dot mode

EXAMPLE 2   Finding Vertical Asymptotes

Find all vertical asymptotes of the graph of each rational function.

a. $f(x) = \dfrac{1}{x - 1}$ **b.** $g(x) = \dfrac{1}{x^2 - 9}$ **c.** $h(x) = \dfrac{1}{x^2 + 1}$

Solution

a. There are no common factors in the numerator and denominator of $f(x) = \dfrac{1}{x - 1}$, and the *zero* of the denominator is 1. Thus, the line with equation $x = 1$ is a vertical asymptote of $f(x)$.

b. We first note that the numerator and the denominator of $g(x)$ have no common factor. Factoring $x^2 - 9 = (x + 3)(x - 3)$, we see that the *zeros* of the denominator are -3 and 3. Thus, the lines with equations $x = -3$ and $x = 3$ are the two vertical asymptotes of $g(x)$.

Continued on next page.

TECHNOLOGY CONNECTION

Calculator graph for

$$h(x) = \frac{x^2 - 4}{x - 2}$$

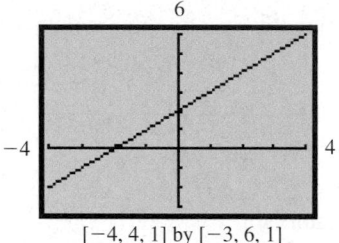

$[-4, 4, 1]$ by $[-3, 6, 1]$

A calculator graph will not show the hole in the graph, but a calculator table shows the situation.

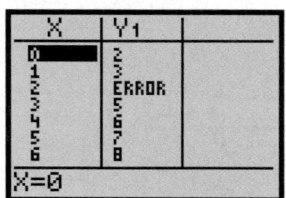

c. The denominator $x^2 + 1$ has no real zeros. Hence, the graph of the rational function $h(x)$ has *no* vertical asymptotes.   ■ ■ ■

PRACTICE PROBLEM 2   Find the vertical asymptotes of the graph of

$$f(x) = \frac{x + 1}{x^2 + 3x - 10}.$$ ■

The next example illustrates that the graph of a rational function may have gaps (missing points) with or without vertical asymptotes.

EXAMPLE 3   **Rational Function Whose Graph Has a Hole**

Find all vertical asymptotes of the graph of each rational function.

a. $h(x) = \dfrac{x^2 - 4}{x - 2}$ **b.** $g(x) = \dfrac{x + 2}{x^2 - 4}$

Solution

a. $h(x) = \dfrac{x^2 - 4}{x - 2}$ Given function

$= \dfrac{(x + 2)(x - 2)}{x - 2}$ Factor $x^2 - 4 = (x + 2)(x - 2)$ in the numerator.

$= x + 2,$ if $x \neq 2$ Simplify.

The graph of $h(x)$ is the line with equation $y = x + 2$ with a gap (hole) corresponding to $x = 2$. (See Figure 3.22.)

The graph of $h(x)$ has no vertical asymptote at the zero, 2, of the denominator, because the numerator and the denominator have the factor $(x - 2)$ in common.

b. We have $g(x) = \dfrac{x + 2}{x^2 - 4}$ Given function

$= \dfrac{x + 2}{(x + 2)(x - 2)}$ Factor $x^2 - 4 = (x - 2)(x + 2)$ in the denominator.

$= \dfrac{1}{x - 2}, x \neq -2$ Simplify.

The graph has a hole at $x = -2$. However, the graph of $g(x)$ also has a vertical asymptote at $x = 2$. (See Figure 3.23.)

FIGURE 3.22

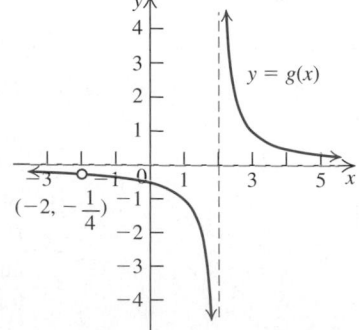

FIGURE 3.23   ■ ■ ■

PRACTICE PROBLEM 3   Find all vertical asymptotes of the graph of $f(x) = \dfrac{3 - x}{x^2 - 9}$.   ■

3 Find horizontal asymptotes (if any).

Horizontal Asymptotes

A vertical asymptote alerts us to examine the behavior of the graph of $y = f(x)$ as x approaches a specific real number, but says nothing about the end behavior of f, that is, the behavior of f as $x \to \pm\infty$. Consider again the function $f(x) = \dfrac{1}{x}$. The larger we make x, the closer $\dfrac{1}{x}$ is to 0. Thus, as $x \to \infty$, $f(x) = \dfrac{1}{x} \to 0$. Similarly, as $x \to -\infty$, $f(x) = \dfrac{1}{x} \to 0$. The x-axis, with equation $y = 0$, is a *horizontal asymptote* of the graph of $f(x) = \dfrac{1}{x}$. Similar considerations show that, for any real number a and any positive integer n, as $|x| \to \infty$, $f(x) = \dfrac{a}{x^n} \to 0$.

HORIZONTAL ASYMPTOTE

The line with equation $y = k$ is a **horizontal asymptote** of the graph of a function f if $f(x) \to k$ as $x \to \infty$ or as $x \to -\infty$.

A line may be a horizontal asymptote with only one of the conditions $f(x) \to k$ as $x \to \infty$ or $f(x) \to k$ as $x \to -\infty$ being satisfied. For example, in Figure 3.24, the line with equation $y = 2$ is a horizontal asymptote of the graph shown because $f(x) \to 2$ as $x \to \infty$. However, this situation is not possible for a rational function.

The graph of a function $y = f(x)$ may cross its horizontal asymptote (in contrast to a vertical asymptote). A vertical asymptote, however, is associated with a zero of the denominator polynomial, and this zero is not in the domain of the function, so there can be no associated point on the graph.

You can see from the graph of $g(x) = \dfrac{x + 2}{x^2 - 4}$, shown in Figure 3.23, that the x-axis (with equation $y = 0$) is a horizontal asymptote. This can be verified algebraically by dividing the numerator and the denominator of g by the highest power of x that appears in the denominator—in this case, x^2.

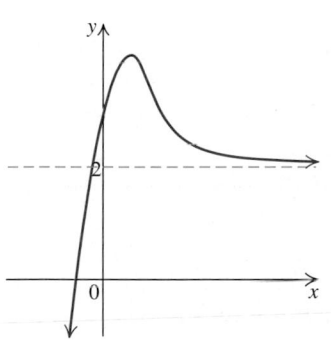

FIGURE 3.24

$$g(x) = \frac{x + 2}{x^2 - 4}$$

$$= \frac{\dfrac{x + 2}{x^2}}{\dfrac{x^4 - 4}{x^2}} \qquad \text{Divide numerator and denominator by } x^2.$$

$$= \frac{\dfrac{x}{x^2} + \dfrac{2}{x^2}}{\dfrac{x^2}{x^2} - \dfrac{4}{x^2}}$$

$$= \frac{\dfrac{1}{x} + \dfrac{2}{x^2}}{1 - \dfrac{4}{x^2}} \qquad \text{Simplify.}$$

As $|x| \to \infty$, the expressions $\dfrac{1}{x}$, $\dfrac{2}{x^2}$, and $\dfrac{4}{x^2}$ all approach 0, so

$$g(x) \to \frac{0 + 0}{1 - 0} = \frac{0}{1} = 0.$$

Since $g(x) \to 0$ as $|x| \to \infty$, the line $y = 0$ (the x-axis) is a horizontal asymptote.

Note that a rational function may have more than one vertical asymptote (see Example 2(b)), but a rational function has at most one horizontal asymptote. The horizontal asymptote (if any) of a rational function may be found by dividing the numerator and denominator by the highest power of x that appears in the denominator and evaluating the resulting expression as $|x| \to \infty$. Alternatively, one may use the following rules:

RULES FOR LOCATING HORIZONTAL ASYMPTOTES

Let f be a rational function given by

$$f(x) = \frac{N(x)}{D(x)} = \frac{a_n x^n + a_{n-1} x^{n-1} + \cdots + a_2 x + a_1 x + a_0}{b_m x^m + b_{m-1} x^{m-1} + \cdots + b_2 x + b_1 x + b_0}, \quad a_n \neq 0, b_m \neq 0,$$

where $N(x)$ and $D(x)$ have no common factors. Then whether the graph of f has one horizontal asymptote or no horizontal asymptote is found by comparing the degree of the numerator, n, with that of the denominator, m:

1. If $n < m$, then the x-axis $(y = 0)$ is the horizontal asymptote.

2. If $n = m$, then the line with equation $y = \dfrac{a_n}{b_m}$ is the horizontal asymptote, where a_n and b_m are the leading coefficients of $N(x)$ and $D(x)$, respectively.

3. If $n > m$, then the graph of f has *no* horizontal asymptote.

EXAMPLE 4   Finding the Horizontal Asymptote

Find the horizontal asymptote (if any) of the graph of each rational function.

a. $f(x) = \dfrac{5x + 2}{1 - 3x}$ **b.** $g(x) = \dfrac{2x}{x^2 + 1}$ **c.** $h(x) = \dfrac{3x^2 - 1}{x + 2}$

Solution

a. The numerator and denominator of $f(x) = \dfrac{5x + 2}{1 - 3x}$ are both of degree 1. The leading coefficient of the numerator is 5 and the leading coefficient of the denominator is -3. Thus, by Rule 2 for locating horizontal asymptotes, the line with equation $y = \dfrac{5}{-3} = -\dfrac{5}{3}$ is the horizontal asymptote of the graph of f.

b. For the function $g(x) = \dfrac{2x}{x^2 + 1}$, the degree of the numerator is 1 and that of the denominator is 2. Since (degree of the denominator) $>$ (degree of the numerator), by Rule 1 for locating horizontal asymptotes, the line with equation $y = 0$ (the x-axis) is the horizontal asymptote of the graph of g.

c. Since the degree of the numerator, 2, of $h(x)$ is greater than the degree of its denominator, 1, by Rule 3 for locating horizontal asymptotes, the graph of h has no horizontal asymptote. ■ ■ ■

PRACTICE PROBLEM 4   Find the horizontal asymptote (if any) of the graph of each function.

a. $f(x) = \dfrac{2x - 5}{3x + 4}$ **b.** $g(x) = \dfrac{x^2 + 3}{x - 1}$ ■

4 Graph rational functions.

Graphing Rational Functions

We sketch the graphs of rational functions by applying the following steps:

FINDING THE SOLUTION: PROCEDURE FOR GRAPHING A RATIONAL FUNCTION

OBJECTIVE	EXAMPLE
Graph $f(x) = \dfrac{N(x)}{D(x)}$, where $N(x)$ and $D(x)$ are polynomials with no common factors.	Sketch the graph of $f(x) = \dfrac{2x^2 - 2}{x^2 - 9}$.

Step 1   **Find the intercepts.** The x-intercepts are found by solving the equation $N(x) = 0$. The y-intercept is $f(0)$.

$$2x^2 - 2 = 0 \qquad \text{Set } N(x) = 0.$$
$$2(x - 1)(x + 1) = 0 \qquad \text{Factor.}$$
$$x - 1 = 0 \quad \text{or} \quad x + 1 = 0 \qquad \text{Zero-product property}$$
$$x = 1 \quad \text{or} \qquad x = -1 \qquad \text{Solve for } x.$$

The x-intercepts are -1 and 1. The graph of f passes through the points $(-1, 0)$ and $(1, 0)$.

$$f(0) = \frac{2(0)^2 - 2}{(0)^2 - 9} \qquad \text{Replace } x \text{ by } 0 \text{ in } f(x).$$

$$= \frac{2}{9} \qquad \text{Simplify.}$$

The y-intercept is $\dfrac{2}{9}$. The graph of f passes through the point $\left(0, \dfrac{2}{9}\right)$.

Step 2   **Find the vertical asymptotes (if any).** Solve $D(x) = 0$. This step gives the vertical asymptotes of the graph. Sketch the vertical asymptotes.

$$x^2 - 9 = 0 \qquad \text{Set } D(x) = 0.$$
$$(x - 3)(x + 3) = 0 \qquad \text{Factor.}$$
$$x - 3 = 0 \quad \text{or} \quad x + 3 = 0 \qquad \text{Zero-product property}$$
$$x = 3 \quad \text{or} \qquad x = -3 \qquad \text{Solve for } x.$$

The vertical asymptotes of the graph of f are the lines $x = -3$ and $x = 3$.

Step 3   **Find the horizontal asymptote (if any).** Use the rules on page 388 for finding the horizontal asymptote of a rational function.

Since $n = m = 2$, by Rule 2 for locating horizontal asymptotes, the horizontal asymptote is the line

$$y = \frac{\text{Leading coefficient of } N(x)}{\text{Leading coefficient of } D(x)} = \frac{2}{1} = 2.$$

Continued on next page.

Step 4   **Test for symmetry.** If $f(-x) = f(x)$, then f is symmetric with respect to the y-axis. If $f(-x) = -f(x)$, then f is symmetric with respect to the origin.

$f(-x) = \dfrac{2(-x)^2 - 2}{(-x)^2 - 9} = \dfrac{2x^2 - 2}{x^2 - 9} = f(x)$. The graph of f is symmetric in the y-axis. This is the only symmetry.

Step 5   **Find the sign of $f(x)$.** Use sign graphs and test numbers associated with the zeros of $N(x)$ and $D(x)$, to determine where the graph of f is above the x-axis and where it is below the x-axis.

The zeros of $N(x)$ and $D(x)$ are $-3, -1, 1$, and 3. These zeros divide the x-axis into five intervals. (See the figure.)

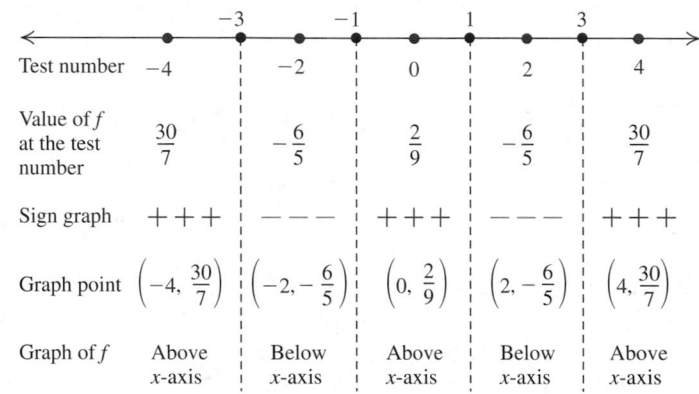

Step 6   **Sketch the graph.** Plot the points and asymptotes found in Steps 1–5 and use symmetry to sketch the graph of f.

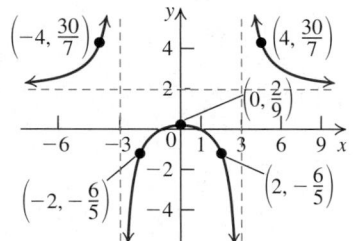

EXAMPLE 5   **Graphing a Rational Function**

Sketch the graph of $f(x) = \dfrac{x}{x^2 - 4}$.

Solution

Step 1   **Find the intercepts.** $f(0) = \dfrac{0}{0 - 4} = 0$. The y-intercept is 0. The graph passes through $(0, 0)$. To find the x-intercepts, set $f(x) = 0$. Then $\dfrac{x}{x^2 - 4} = 0$, or $x = 0$. Thus, $x = 0$ is also the only x-intercept.

Step 2   **Find the vertical asymptotes (if any).** Set $x^2 - 4 = 0$. This gives $x^2 = 4$, or $x = \pm 2$. The domain of f is thus the set of all real numbers x such that $x \neq -2$ and $x \neq 2$. The vertical lines with equations $x = 2$ and $x = -2$ are the vertical asymptotes for the graph of f.

Step 3   **Find the horizontal asymptote (if any).** Since the degree of the denominator, 2, is greater than the degree of the numerator, 1, by Rule **1** for locating horizontal asymptotes, the line with equation $y = 0$ (the x-axis) is the horizontal asymptote.

Step 4   **Test for symmetry.** Here, $f(-x) = \dfrac{-x}{(-x)^2 - 4} = \dfrac{-x}{x^2 - 4} = -f(x)$, so we have symmetry with respect to the origin. This is the only symmetry.

Step 5   **Find the sign of f in the intervals determined by the zeros of the numerator and denominator.** $f(x) = \dfrac{x}{x^2 - 4} = \dfrac{x}{(x - 2)(x + 2)}$. The three zeros, 0, -2, and 2, of the numerator and the denominator divide the x-axis into four intervals:

$$(-\infty, -2), (-2, 0), (0, 2), \text{ and } (2, \infty).$$

To determine the sign of $f(x)$ in each interval, we choose test numbers as shown.

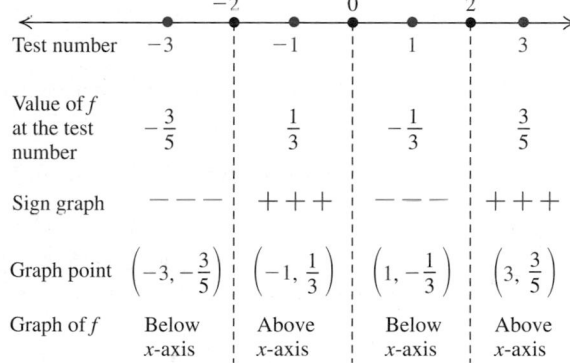

Test number	-3	-1	1	3
Value of f at the test number	$-\dfrac{3}{5}$	$\dfrac{1}{3}$	$-\dfrac{1}{3}$	$\dfrac{3}{5}$
Sign graph	$---$	$+++$	$---$	$+++$
Graph point	$\left(-3, -\dfrac{3}{5}\right)$	$\left(-1, \dfrac{1}{3}\right)$	$\left(1, -\dfrac{1}{3}\right)$	$\left(3, \dfrac{3}{5}\right)$
Graph of f	Below x-axis	Above x-axis	Below x-axis	Above x-axis

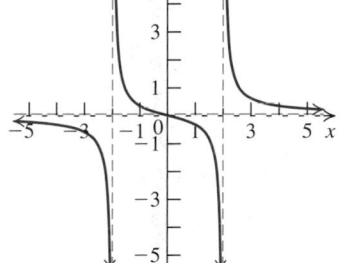

FIGURE 3.25

Step 6   **Sketch the graph.** The graph is shown in Figure 3.25.   ■ ■ ■

PRACTICE PROBLEM 5   Sketch the graph of $f(x) = \dfrac{2x}{x^2 - 1}$.   ■

EXAMPLE 6   **Graphing a Rational Function**

Sketch the graph of $f(x) = \dfrac{x^2 + 2}{(x + 2)(x - 1)}$.

Solution

Step 1   Since $x^2 + 2 > 0$, the graph has no x-intercepts.

$$f(0) = \dfrac{0^2 + 2}{(0 + 2)(0 - 1)} \qquad \text{Replace } x \text{ by } 0 \text{ in } f(x).$$
$$= -1 \qquad \text{Simplify.}$$

The y-intercept is -1.

Step 2   Set $(x + 2)(x - 1) = 0$. Solving for x, we have $x = -2$ or $x = 1$. The vertical asymptotes are the lines $x = -2$ and $x = 1$. The domain is the set of all real numbers except -2 and 1.

Step 3 $f(x) = \dfrac{x^2 + 2}{x^2 + x - 2}$. Rule 2 for locating horizontal asymptotes on page 388 indicates that the horizontal asymptote is $y = \dfrac{1}{1} = 1$, since the leading coefficient for both the numerator and the denominator is 1.

Step 4   **Symmetry.** None

Continued on next page.

Step 5   **Sign intervals.** The zeros of the denominator, -2 and 1, yield the following figure:

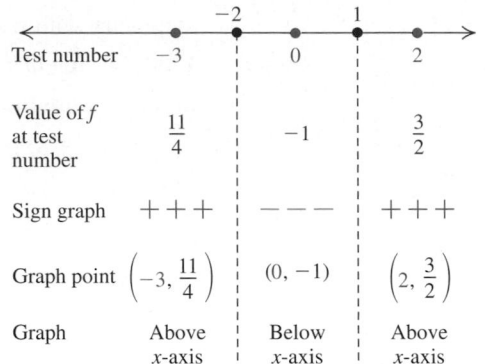

Test number	-3		0		2
Value of f at test number	$\dfrac{11}{4}$		-1		$\dfrac{3}{2}$
Sign graph	$+++$		$---$		$+++$
Graph point	$\left(-3, \dfrac{11}{4}\right)$		$(0, -1)$		$\left(2, \dfrac{3}{2}\right)$
Graph	Above x-axis		Below x-axis		Above x-axis

Step 6   The graph of f is shown in Figure 3.26.   ■ ■ ■

PRACTICE PROBLEM 6   Sketch the graph of $f(x) = \dfrac{2x^2 - 1}{2x^2 + x - 3}$.   ■

Notice in Figure 3.26 that the graph of f crosses the horizontal asymptote $y = 1$. To find the point of intersection, set $f(x) = 1$ and solve for x.

$$\frac{x^2 + 2}{x^2 + x - 2} = 1 \qquad \text{Set } f(x) = 1.$$

$$x^2 + 2 = x^2 + x - 2 \qquad \text{Multiply both sides by } x^2 + x - 2.$$

$$x = 4 \qquad \text{Solve for } x.$$

The graph of f crosses the horizontal asymptote at the point $(4, 1)$.

We know that the graphs of polynomial functions are continuous. The next example shows that the graph of a rational function (other than a polynomial function) may also be continuous.

EXAMPLE 7   **Graphing a Rational Function**

Sketch a graph of $f(x) = \dfrac{x^2}{x^2 + 1}$.

Solution

Step 1   Since $f(0) = 0$ and setting $f(x) = 0$, we have $x = 0$. Thus, 0 is both the x-intercept and the y-intercept for the graph of f.

Step 2   Because $x^2 + 1 > 0$ for all x, the domain is the set of all real numbers. Since there are no zeros for the denominator, there are no vertical asymptotes.

Step 3   By Rule 2 for locating horizontal asymptotes, the horizontal asymptote is $y = 1$.

Step 4 $f(-x) = \dfrac{(-x)^2}{(-x)^2 + 1} = \dfrac{x^2}{x^2 + 1} = f(x)$. The graph is symmetric with respect to the y-axis.

Step 5   The graph of $y = f(x)$ is always above the x-axis except at $x = 0$.

Step 6   The graph of $y = f(x)$ is shown in Figure 3.27.   ■ ■ ■

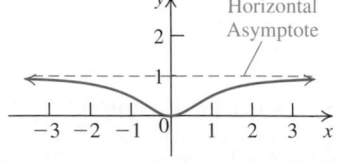

FIGURE 3.26

FIGURE 3.27

PRACTICE PROBLEM 7   Sketch the graph of $f(x) = \dfrac{x^2 + 1}{x^2 + 2}$.   ■

5 Graph rational functions with oblique asymptotes.

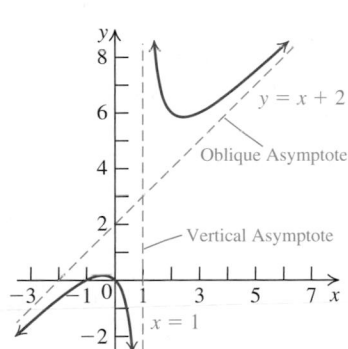

FIGURE 3.28

Oblique Asymptotes

Recall from the rules for locating horizontal asymptotes (page 388) that if the degree of the numerator of a rational function is *greater* than the degree of the denominator, then the graph of the function has no horizontal asymptote. We can still, however, find some useful information.

Suppose

$$f(x) = \frac{N(x)}{D(x)}$$

and the degree of $N(x)$ is greater than the degree of $D(x)$. First use either long division or synthetic division to obtain

$$f(x) = \frac{N(x)}{D(x)} = Q(x) + \frac{R(x)}{D(x)},$$

where the degree of $R(x)$ is less than the degree of $D(x)$. Thus, the x-axis is a horizontal asymptote for $\dfrac{R(x)}{D(x)}$, so as $x \to \infty$ or $x \to -\infty$, the expression $\dfrac{R(x)}{D(x)} \to 0$.

Thus, as $x \to \pm\infty$,

$$f(x) \to Q(x) + 0 = Q(x).$$

This means that as $|x|$ gets very large, the graph of $f(x)$ behaves like the graph of the polynomial $Q(x)$. If the degree of $N(x)$ is exactly one more than the degree of $D(x)$, then $Q(x)$ will be of the form $mx + b$. In this case, $f(x)$ is said to have an **oblique** (or **slanted**) asymptote. For example, by dividing $(x^2 + x)$ by $(x - 1)$, we obtain

$$f(x) = \frac{x^2 + x}{x - 1} = x + 2 + \frac{2}{x - 1}.$$

Now, as $x \to \pm\infty$, the expression $\dfrac{2}{x - 1} \to 0$, so that the graph of f approaches the graph of the oblique asymptote—the line with equation $y = x + 2$, as shown in Figure 3.28.

EXAMPLE 8   **Graphing a Rational Function with an Oblique Asymptote**

Sketch the graph of $f(x) = \dfrac{x^2 - 4}{x + 1}$.

Solution

Step 1   **Intercepts.** $f(0) = \dfrac{0 - 4}{0 + 1} = -4$, so the graph of f passes through the point $(0, -4)$. To find the x-intercepts, set $x^2 - 4 = 0$. We have $x = -2$ and $x = 2$. The x-intercepts are -2 and 2, so the graph of f passes through the points $(-2, 0)$ and $(2, 0)$.

Step 2   **Domain and vertical asymptotes.** Set the denominator, $x + 1$, equal to 0. From $x + 1 = 0$, we get $x = -1$. So the domain is the set of all real numbers except -1, and the line with equation $x = -1$ is a vertical asymptote.

Continued on next page.

Step 3 **Asymptotes.** Since the degree of the numerator is greater than the degree of the denominator, $f(x)$ has no horizontal asymptote. However, by long division,

$$f(x) = \frac{x^2 - 4}{x + 1} = x - 1 + \frac{-3}{x + 1} = x - 1 - \frac{3}{x + 1}.$$

As $x \to \pm\infty$, the expression $\frac{3}{x + 1} \to 0$, so the line with equation $y = x - 1$ is an oblique asymptote. The graph gets close to the line $y = x - 1$ as $x \to \infty$ and as $x \to -\infty$.

Step 4 **Symmetry.** You should check that there is no y-axis or origin symmetry.

Step 5 **Sign of f in the intervals determined by the zeros of the numerator and denominator:**

$$f(x) = \frac{x^2 - 4}{x + 1} = \frac{(x + 2)(x - 2)}{x + 1}$$

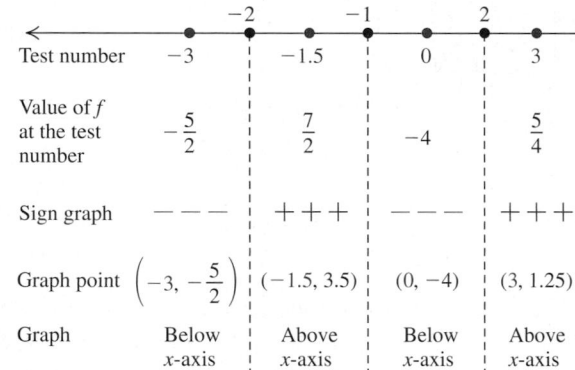

		-2		-1		2	
Test number	-3		-1.5		0		3
Value of f at the test number	$-\dfrac{5}{2}$		$\dfrac{7}{2}$		-4		$\dfrac{5}{4}$
Sign graph	$---$		$+++$		$---$		$+++$
Graph point	$\left(-3, -\dfrac{5}{2}\right)$		$(-1.5, 3.5)$		$(0, -4)$		$(3, 1.25)$
Graph	Below x-axis		Above x-axis		Below x-axis		Above x-axis

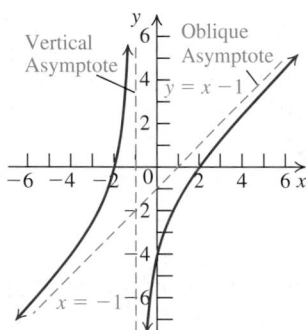

FIGURE 3.29

Step 6 The graph of f is shown in Figure 3.29. ■ ■ ■

PRACTICE PROBLEM 8 Sketch the graph of $f(x) = \dfrac{x^2 + 2}{x - 1}$. ■

6 Graph revenue curves.

Graph of a Revenue Curve

EXAMPLE 9 **Graphing a Revenue Curve**

The revenue curve for an economy of a country is given by

$$R(x) = \frac{x(100 - x)}{x + 10},$$

where x is the tax rate in percent and $R(x)$ is the tax revenue in billions of dollars.

a. Find and interpret $R(10)$, $R(20)$, $R(30)$, $R(40)$, $R(50)$, and $R(60)$.

b. Sketch the graph of $y = R(x)$ for $0 \le x \le 100$.

c. Use a graphing calculator to estimate the tax rate that yields the maximum revenue.

Calculator graph of

$$y = \frac{100x - x^2}{x + 10}.$$

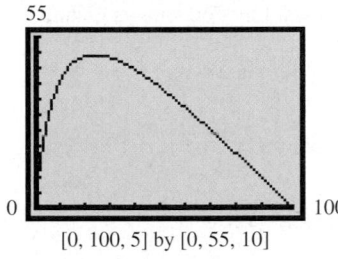

[0, 100, 5] by [0, 55, 10]

Solution

a. $R(10) = \dfrac{10(100 - 10)}{10 + 10} = 45$ billion dollars. This means that if the income is taxed at
the rate of 10%, the total revenue for the government will be 45 billion dollars.
Similarly, $R(20) \approx 53.3$ billion dollars,
$R(30) = 52.5$ billion dollars,
$R(40) = 48$ billion dollars,
$R(50) \approx 41.67$ billion dollars, and
$R(60) \approx 34.3$ billion dollars.

b. The portion of the graph of the rational function $y = R(x)$ for $0 \le x \le 100$ is shown
in Figure 3.30.

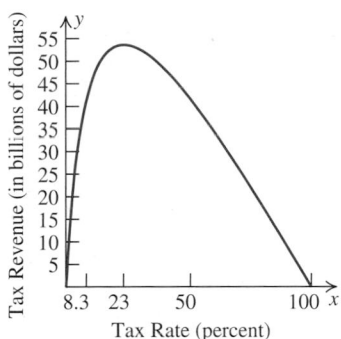

FIGURE 3.30

c. From the calculator graph of

$$Y = \frac{100x - x^2}{x + 10},$$

by using the ZOOM and TRACE features, you can see that the tax rate of about 23%
produces the maximum tax revenue of about 53.67 billion dollars for the government.
(See the Group Project for an algebraic proof.)   ■ ■ ■

A Exercises | Basic Skills and Concepts

In Exercises 1–8, find the domain of each rational function.

1. $f(x) = \dfrac{x - 3}{x + 4}$ †

2. $f(x) = \dfrac{x + 1}{x - 1}$ †

3. $g(x) = \dfrac{x - 1}{x^2 + 1}$ $(-\infty, \infty)$

4. $g(x) = \dfrac{x + 2}{x^2 + 4}$ $(-\infty, \infty)$

5. $h(x) = \dfrac{x - 3}{x^2 - x - 6}$ †

6. $h(x) = \dfrac{x - 7}{x^2 - 6x - 7}$ †

7. $F(x) = \dfrac{2x + 3}{x^2 - 6x + 8}$ †

8. $F(x) = \dfrac{3x - 2}{x^2 - 3x + 2}$ †

†Due to space constrictions, answers to these exercises may be found in the Answers beginning on page A–1 in the back of the book.

In Exercises 9–18, use the graph of the rational function $f(x)$ to complete each statement.

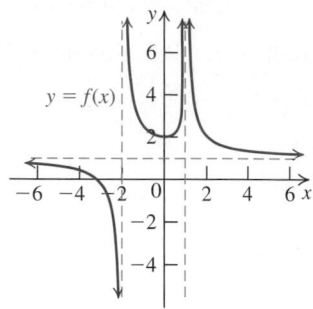

9. As $x \to 1^+$, $f(x) \to$ _____ . ∞

10. As $x \to 1^-$, $f(x) \to$ _____ . ∞

11. As $x \to -2^+$, $f(x) \to$ _____ . ∞

12. As $x \to -2^-$, $f(x) \to$ _____ . $-\infty$

13. As $x \to \infty$, $f(x) \to$ _____ . 1

14. As $x \to -\infty$, $f(x) \to$ _____ . 1

15. The domain of $f(x)$ is _____ . †

16. There are _____ vertical asymptotes. †

17. The equations of the vertical asymptotes of the graph are _____ and _____ . †

18. The equation of the horizontal asymptote of the graph is _____ . †

In Exercises 19–28, find the vertical asymptotes, if any, of the graph of each rational function.

19. $f(x) = \dfrac{x}{x - 1}$ $x = 1$

20. $f(x) = \dfrac{x + 3}{x - 2}$ $x = 2$

21. $g(x) = \dfrac{(x + 1)(2x - 2)}{(x - 3)(x + 4)}$ $x = -4$ and $x = 3$

22. $g(x) = \dfrac{(2x - 1)(x + 2)}{(2x + 3)(3x - 4)}$ $x = -\dfrac{3}{2}$ and $x = \dfrac{4}{3}$

23. $h(x) = \dfrac{x^2 - 1}{x^2 + x - 6}$ †

24. $h(x) = \dfrac{x^2 - 4}{3x^2 + x - 4}$ †

25. $f(x) = \dfrac{x^2 - 6x + 8}{x^2 - x - 12}$ †

26. $f(x) = \dfrac{x^2 - 9}{x^3 - 4x}$ †

27. $g(x) = \dfrac{2x + 1}{x^2 + x + 1}$ †

28. $g(x) = \dfrac{x^2 - 36}{x^2 + 5x + 9}$ †

In Exercises 29–36, find the horizontal asymptote, if any, of the graph of each rational function.

29. $f(x) = \dfrac{x + 1}{x^2 + 5}$ $y = 0$

30. $f(x) = \dfrac{2x - 1}{x^2 - 4}$ $y = 0$

31. $g(x) = \dfrac{2x - 3}{3x + 5}$ $y = \dfrac{2}{3}$

32. $g(x) = \dfrac{3x + 4}{-4x + 5}$ $y = -\dfrac{3}{4}$

33. $h(x) = \dfrac{x^2 - 49}{x + 7}$ †

34. $h(x) = \dfrac{x + 3}{x^2 - 9}$ $y = 0$

35. $f(x) = \dfrac{2x^2 - 3x + 7}{3x^3 + 5x + 11}$ $y = 0$

36. $f(x) = \dfrac{3x^3 + 2}{x^2 + 5x + 11}$ no horizontal asymptote

In Exercises 37–42, match the rational function with its graph.

37. $f(x) = \dfrac{2}{x - 3}$ d

38. $f(x) = \dfrac{x - 2}{x + 3}$ f

39. $f(x) = \dfrac{1}{x^2 - 2x}$ e

40. $f(x) = \dfrac{x}{x^2 + 1}$ b

41. $f(x) = \dfrac{x^2 + 2x}{x - 3}$ a

42. $f(x) = \dfrac{x^2}{x^2 - 4}$ c

a.

b.

c.

d.

e.

f.

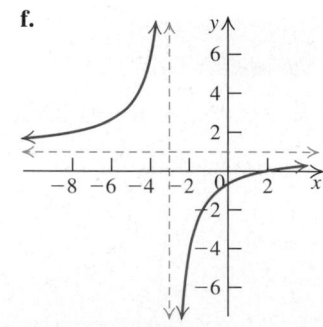

In Exercises 43–62, use the six-step procedure on page 389 to graph each rational function.

43. $f(x) = \dfrac{2x}{x - 3}$ †

44. $f(x) = \dfrac{-x}{x - 1}$ †

45. $f(x) = \dfrac{x}{x^2 - 4}$ †

46. $f(x) = \dfrac{x}{1 - x^2}$ †

47. $g(x) = \dfrac{x^2}{x^2 - 4}$ †

48. $g(x) = \dfrac{x^2}{4 - x^2}$ †

49. $h(x) = \dfrac{-2x^2}{x^2 - 9}$ †

50. $h(x) = \dfrac{4 - x^2}{x^2}$ †

51. $f(x) = \dfrac{2}{x^2 - 2}$ †

52. $f(x) = \dfrac{-2}{x^2 - 3}$ †

53. $g(x) = \dfrac{x + 1}{(x - 2)(x + 3)}$ †

54. $g(x) = \dfrac{x - 1}{(x + 1)(x - 2)}$ †

55. $h(x) = \dfrac{x^2}{x^2 + 1}$ †

56. $h(x) = \dfrac{2x^2}{x^2 + 4}$ †

57. $f(x) = \dfrac{x^2 - 4}{x^2 - 9}$ †

58. $f(x) = \dfrac{x^2 + 4}{x^2 + 1}$ †

59. $g(x) = \dfrac{(x - 2)^2}{x - 2}$ †

60. $g(x) = \dfrac{(x - 1)^2}{x - 1}$ †

61. $h(x) = \dfrac{(x + 3)(x - 4)}{(x + 3)(x - 4)}$ †

62. $h(x) = \dfrac{(x - 1)(x + 1)(x - 2)}{(x - 1)(x + 1)(x - 2)}$ †

In Exercises 63–70, find the oblique asymptote and sketch the graph of each rational function.

63. $f(x) = \dfrac{2x^2 + 1}{x}$ †

64. $f(x) = \dfrac{x^2 - 1}{x}$ †

65. $g(x) = \dfrac{x^3 - 1}{x^2}$ †

66. $g(x) = \dfrac{2x^3 + x^2 + 1}{x^2}$ †

67. $h(x) = \dfrac{x^2 - x + 1}{x + 1}$ †

68. $h(x) = \dfrac{2x^2 - 3x + 2}{x - 1}$ †

69. $f(x) = \dfrac{x^3 - 2x^2 + 1}{x^2 - 1}$ †

70. $h(x) = \dfrac{x^3 - 1}{x^2 - 4}$ †

B Exercises   Applying the Concepts

For Exercises 71 and 72 use the definition: Given a cost function C, the **average cost** of the first x items is found from the formula

$$\overline{C}(x) = \frac{C(x)}{x}, x > 0.$$

71. Average cost. The Genuine Trinket Co. manufactures "authentic" trinkets for gullible tourists. Fixed daily costs are 2000 dollars, and it costs 50 cents to produce each trinket.
  a. Write the cost function C for producing x trinkets. †
  b. Write the average cost $\overline{C}$ of producing x trinkets. †
  c. Find and interpret $\overline{C}(100)$, $\overline{C}(500)$, and $\overline{C}(1000)$. †
  d. Find and interpret the horizontal asymptote of the rational function $\overline{C}(x)$. †

72. Average cost. The monthly cost C of producing x portable CD players is given by

$$C(x) = -0.002x^2 + 6x + 7000.$$

  a. Write the average cost function $\overline{C}(x)$. †
  b. Find and interpret $\overline{C}(100)$, $\overline{C}(500)$, and $\overline{C}(1000)$. †
  c. Find and interpret the oblique asymptote of $\overline{C}(x)$. †

Exercises 73–76 deal with the **law of diminishing returns,** which asserts, "The application of additional units of any one input (labor, land, capital) to fixed amounts of the other inputs yields successively smaller increments in the output of a system of production."

73. Biology: birds collecting seeds. A bird is collecting seed from a field that contains 100 grams of seed. The bird collects x grams of seed in t minutes, where

$$t = f(x) = \frac{4x + 1}{100 - x}, 0 < x < 100.$$

  a. Sketch the graph of $t = f(x)$. †
  b. How long does it take the bird to collect
   (i)   50 grams, about 4 min
   (ii) 75 grams, about 12 min
   (iii) 95 grams, about 76 min
   (iv) 99 grams? 397 min
  c. Complete the following statements if applicable:
   (i)   As $x \to 100^-$, $f(x) \to$ ____. †
   (ii) As $x \to 100^+$, $f(x) \to$ ____. †
  d. Does the bird ever collect all the seed from the field? No

74. Criminology. Suppose the city of Las Vegas decides to be crime free. The estimated cost of catching and convicting $x\%$ of the criminals is given by

$$C(x) = \frac{1000}{100 - x} \text{ million dollars.}$$

a. Find and interpret $C(50)$, $C(75)$, $C(90)$, and $C(99)$. †
b. Sketch a graph of $C(x)$, $0 \leq x < 100$. †
c. What happens to $C(x)$ as $x \to 100^-$? Approaches ∞
d. What percentage of the criminals can be caught and convicted for 30 million dollars? 66.67%

75. Environment. Suppose an environmental agency decides to get rid of the impurities from the water of a polluted river. The estimated cost of removing $x\%$ of the impurities is given by

$$C(x) = \frac{3x^2 + 50}{x(100 - x)} \text{ billion dollars.}$$

a. How much will it cost to remove 50% of the impurities? †
b. Sketch the graph of $y = C(x)$. †
c. Estimate the percentage of the impurities that can be removed at a cost of 30 billion dollars. 90.89%

76. Biology. The growth function $g(x)$ describes the growth rate of organisms as a function of some nutrient concentration x. Suppose

$$g(x) = a\frac{x}{k + x}, \quad x \geq 0,$$

where a and k are positive constants.
a. Find the horizontal asymptote of the graph of $g(x)$. Use the asymptote to explain why a is called the *saturation level* of the nutrient. †
b. Show that k is the half-saturation constant; that is, show that if $x = k$, then $g(x) = \dfrac{a}{2}$.

77. Population of bacteria. The population P (in thousands) of a colony of bacteria at time t (in hours) is given by

$$P(t) = \frac{8t + 16}{2t + 1}, \quad t \geq 0.$$

a. Find the initial population of the colony. (Find the population at $t = 0$ hours.) 16,000
b. What is the long-term behavior of the population? (What happens when $t \to \infty$?) The population will stabilize at 4000.

78. Drug concentration. The concentration c (in milligrams per liter) of a drug in the bloodstream of a patient at time $t \geq 0$ (in hours since the drug was injected) is given by

$$c(t) = \frac{5t}{t^2 + 1}, \quad t \geq 0.$$

 a. By plotting points or by using a graphing calculator, sketch the graph of $y = c(t)$. †
b. Find and interpret the horizontal asymptote of the graph of $y = c(t)$. †
c. Find the approximate time when the concentration of drug in the bloodstream is maximal. †
d. At what time is the concentration level equal to 2 milligrams per liter? †

79. Book publishing. The printing and binding cost for a college algebra book is 10 dollars. The editorial cost is 200,000 dollars. The first 2500 books are samples and are given away free to professors. Let x be the number of college algebra books produced.
a. Write a function f describing the average cost of saleable books. †
b. Find the average cost of a saleable book if 10,000 books are produced. $40
c. How many books must be produced in order to bring the average cost of a saleable book under 20 dollars? †
d. Find the vertical and horizontal asymptotes of the graph of $y = f(x)$. How are they related to the information given? †

80. A "phony" sale. A jewelry merchant at a local mall wants to have a "p percent off" sale. She marks up the stock by q percent to break even with respect to the prices before the sale.
a. Show that $q = \dfrac{p}{1 - p}$, $0 < p < 1$.
b. Sketch the graph of q in part (**a**). †
c. How much should she mark up the stock to break even if she wants to have a "25% off" sale? 33.33%

C Exercises   Beyond the Basics

In Exercises 81–90, use transformations of the graph of $y = \dfrac{1}{x}$ or $y = \dfrac{1}{x^2}$ to graph each rational function $f(x)$.

81. $f(x) = -\dfrac{2}{x}$ †

82. $f(x) = \dfrac{1}{2 - x}$ †

83. $f(x) = \dfrac{1}{(x - 2)^2}$ †

84. $f(x) = \dfrac{1}{x^2 + 2x + 1}$ †

85. $f(x) = \dfrac{1}{(x - 1)^2} - 2$ †

86. $f(x) = \dfrac{1}{(x + 2)^2} + 3$ †

87. $f(x) = \dfrac{1}{x^2 + 12x + 36}$ †

88. $f(x) = \dfrac{3x^2 + 18x + 28}{x^2 + 6x + 9}$ †

89. $f(x) = \dfrac{x^2 - 2x + 2}{x^2 - 2x + 1}$ †

90. $f(x) = \dfrac{2x^2 + 4x - 3}{x^2 + 2x + 1}$ †

91. Sketch and discuss the graphs of the rational functions of the form $y = \dfrac{a}{x^n}$, where a is a nonzero real number and n is a positive integer, in the following cases:
   a. $a > 0$ and n is odd. †
   b. $a < 0$ and n is odd. †
   c. $a > 0$ and n is even. †
   d. $a < 0$ and n is even. †

92. Graphing the reciprocal of a polynomial function.
   Let $f(x)$ be a polynomial function and $g(x) = \dfrac{1}{f(x)}$. Justify the following statements that compare the graphs of $f(x)$ and $g(x)$:
   a. If c is a zero of $f(x)$, then $x = c$ is a vertical asymptote of the graph of $g(x)$. †
   b. If $f(x) > 0$, then $g(x) > 0$, and if $f(x) < 0$, then $g(x) < 0$. †
   c. The graphs of f and g intersect for those values (and only those values) of x for which $f(x) = g(x) = \pm 1$. †
   d. When f is increasing (decreasing, constant) on an interval of its domain, g is decreasing (increasing, constant) on that interval. †

93. Use Exercise 92 to sketch the graphs of $f(x) = x^2 - 4$ and $g(x) = \dfrac{1}{x^2 - 4}$ on the same coordinate axes. †

94. Use Exercise 92 to sketch the graphs of $f(x) = x^2 + 1$ and $g(x) = \dfrac{1}{x^2 + 1}$ on the same coordinate axes. †

95. Recall that the inverse of a function $f(x)$ is written as $f^{-1}(x)$, while the reciprocal of $f(x)$ can be written as either $\dfrac{1}{f(x)}$ or $[f(x)]^{-1}$. The point of this exercise is to make clear that the reciprocal of a function has nothing to do with the inverse of a function. Let $f(x) = 2x + 3$. Find both $[f(x)]^{-1}$ and $f^{-1}(x)$. Compare the two functions. Graph all three functions on the same coordinate axes. †

96. Let $f(x) = \dfrac{x - 1}{x + 2}$. Find $[f(x)]^{-1}$ and $f^{-1}(x)$. Graph all three functions on the same coordinate axes. †

97. Sketch the graph of $g(x) = \dfrac{2x^3 + 3x^2 + 2x - 4}{x^2 - 1}$. Discuss the end behavior of $g(x)$. †

98. Sketch the graph of $f(x) = \dfrac{x^3 - 2x^2 + 1}{x - 2}$. Discuss the end behavior of $f(x)$. †

In Exercises 99–100, the graph of the rational function $f(x)$ crosses the horizontal asymptote. Graph $f(x)$, and find the point of intersection of the curve with its horizontal asymptote.

99. $f(x) = \dfrac{x^2 + x - 2}{x^2 - 2x - 3}$ †

100. $f(x) = \dfrac{4 - x^2}{2x^2 - 5x - 3}$ †

Critical Thinking

In Exercises 101–106, make up a rational function $f(x)$ that has all the characteristics given in the exercise.

101. Has a vertical asymptote at $x = 2$, a horizontal asymptote at $y = 1$, and a y-intercept at $(0, -2)$ †

102. Has vertical asymptotes at $x = 2$ and $x = -1$, a horizontal asymptote at $y = 0$, a y-intercept at $(0, 2)$ and x-intercept at 4 †

103. Has $f\left(\dfrac{1}{2}\right) = 0$; $f(x) \to 4$ as $x \to \pm\infty$,
   $f(x) \to \infty$ as $x \to 1^-$, and $f(x) \to \infty$ as $x \to 1^+$. †

104. Has $f(0) = 0$; $f(x) \to 2$ as $x \to \pm\infty$; has no vertical asymptotes and is symmetric about the y-axis †

105. Has $y = 3x + 2$ as an oblique asymptote; has a vertical asymptote at $x = 1$ †

106. Is it possible for the graph of a rational function to have both a horizontal and an oblique asymptote? Explain. No, because in that case there would be values of x to which two different function values belong, so it would not be a function.

Group Projects   Finding the Range and Turning Points

Find the range of the rational function $y = \dfrac{1}{x^2 + x - 2}$. We first solve the equation for x as follows:

$$y = \frac{1}{x^2 + x - 2} \qquad \text{Original equation}$$

$$(x^2 + x - 2)y = 1 \qquad \begin{array}{l}\text{Multiply both sides by}\\ (x^2 + x - 2).\end{array}$$

$$x^2 y + xy - 2y = 1$$

$$yx^2 + yx - (2y + 1) = 0 \qquad \begin{array}{l}\text{This is a quadratic}\\ \text{equation in } x.\end{array}$$

Use the quadratic formula with $a = y$, $b = y$, and $c = -(2y + 1)$:

$$x = \frac{-y \pm \sqrt{y^2 + 4y(2y + 1)}}{2y}$$

(1) $$x = \frac{-y \pm \sqrt{9y^2 + 4y}}{2y}.$$

Finally, restrictions on y involve making sure that the **discriminant** $9y^2 + 4y \geq 0$, or $y(9y + 4) \geq 0$.

Sign graph

```
          +        −       +
  <———————•————————•——•———————————>
     −1        −4/9    −1/4  0
```

Test points -1 $-\dfrac{4}{9}$ $-\dfrac{1}{4}$ 0

Using the sign graph, we have $y \leq \dfrac{-4}{9}$ or $y \geq 0$. However, equation (1) is not defined for $y = 0$. Thus, the range of

$$f(x) = \frac{1}{x^2 + x - 2} \text{ is } \left(-\infty, \frac{-4}{9}\right] \cup (0, \infty).$$ The value $y = -\dfrac{4}{9}$

is a local maximum value. Substitute $y = -\dfrac{4}{9}$ in (1) to obtain $x = -\dfrac{1}{2}$. Hence, $\left(-\dfrac{1}{2}, -\dfrac{4}{9}\right)$ is a local maximum point on the graph of f.

Use the preceding technique to find the range and turning points (if any) of the graph of each function.

a. $f(x) = \dfrac{x}{x^2 - 4}$ ⠀⠀⠀⠀ (See Example 5)

b. $f(x) = \dfrac{x^2 - 4}{x + 1}$ ⠀⠀⠀⠀ (See Example 8)

c. $R(x) = \dfrac{x(100 - x)}{x + 10}$ ⠀⠀⠀⠀ (See Example 9)

d. $f(x) = \dfrac{x^2 + 2}{(x + 2)(x - 1)}$ ⠀⠀⠀⠀ (See Example 6)

Answers:

a. Range: $(-\infty, \infty)$, no turning points

b. Range: $(-\infty, \infty)$, no turning points

c. Range: $(-\infty, 120 - 20\sqrt{11}) \cup (120 + 20\sqrt{11}, \infty)$; turning points: $(-10 - 10\sqrt{11}, 120 + 20\sqrt{11})$ is a local minimum and $(-10 + 10\sqrt{11}, 120 - 20\sqrt{11})$ is a local maximum.

d. Range: $\left(-\infty, -\dfrac{2\sqrt{2}}{3}\right) \cup \left(\dfrac{2\sqrt{2}}{3}, \infty\right)$;

turning points: $\left(4 - 3\sqrt{2}, -\dfrac{2\sqrt{2}}{3}\right)$ is a local maximum and $\left(4 + 3\sqrt{2}, \dfrac{2\sqrt{2}}{3}\right)$ is a local minimum.

Variation

DÉCOUVERTE DE LA THÉORIE DE LA GRAVITATION UNIVERSELLE.

CAO PUR HOLLANDAIS BENSDORP AMSTERDAM (Hollande)

Sir Isaac Newton
1642–1727

Issac Newton was a mathematician and physicist, one of the foremost scientific intellects of all time. Born at Woolsthorpe, near Grantham in Lincolnshire, where he attended school, he entered Cambridge University in 1661; he was elected a Fellow of Trinity College in 1667 and Lucasian Professor of Mathematics in 1669. He remained at the university, lecturing in most years, until 1696.

As a firm opponent of the attempt by King James II to make the universities into Catholic institutions, Newton was elected Member of Parliament for the University of Cambridge to the Convention Parliament of 1689, and he sat again in 1701–1702.

Meanwhile, in 1696, he moved to London as warden of the Royal Mint. He became master of the Mint in 1699, an office he retained to his death. He was elected a Fellow of the Royal Society of London in 1671, and in 1703 he became president, being annually reelected for the rest of his life. His major work, *Opticks*, appeared the next year; he was knighted in Cambridge in 1705.

> **BEFORE STARTING THIS SECTION, REVIEW**
>
> 1. Equation of a line (Section 2.3, page 209)
> 2. Circumference and area of a circle (Section P.7, page 79)

> **OBJECTIVES**
>
> **1** Solve direct variation problems.
> **2** Solve inverse variation problems.
> **3** Solve joint and combined variation problems.

Newton and the Apple

There is a popular story that Isaac Newton was sitting under an apple tree, an apple fell on his head, and he suddenly thought of the Law of Universal Gravitation. As in all such legends, the story may not be true in detail, but it certainly contains elements of what actually happened.

Before we tell you a more realistic version of this story, let's recall some terminology associated with the motion of objects.

Recall that speed $= \dfrac{\text{distance}}{\text{time}}$.

(i) The **velocity** of an object is the speed of an object in a specific direction.
(ii) **Acceleration:** If the velocity of an object is changing, we say that the object is accelerating. Acceleration is the rate of change of velocity.
(iii) **Force** $= \text{mass} \times \text{acceleration}$.

What really happened with the apple?   Perhaps the correct version of the story is that, upon observing an apple falling from the tree, Newton concluded that the apple accelerated, since the velocity of the apple changed from when it began hanging on the tree (zero velocity) and then moved to the ground. He decided that there must be a force that acts on the apple to cause this acceleration. He called this force "gravity" and the associated acceleration (force = mass × acceleration) the "acceleration due to gravity." He conjectured further that if the force of gravity reaches to the top of the apple tree, it might reach even farther; in particular, might it reach all the way to the moon? In that case, to keep the moon moving in a circular orbit, rather than wandering into outer space, Earth must exert a gravitational force on the moon. Newton realized that the force that brought the apple to the ground and the force that holds the moon in orbit were the same! He concluded that any two objects in the universe exert gravitational attraction on each other, whereupon he gave us the *Law of Universal Gravitation*. (See Example 6.)

Some scientists believe that it was Kepler's Third Law of Planetary Motion (see Exercise 53), not an apple, that led Newton to his Law of Universal Gravitation. ■

1 Solve direct variation problems.

Direct Variation

Two types of relationships between quantities (variables) occur so frequently in mathematics that they are given special names: *direct variation* and *inverse variation*.

Direct variation describes any relationship between two quantities in which any increase (or decrease) in one causes a proportional increase (or decrease) in the other. For example, the sales tax in Tampa, Florida, in 2005 was 7%, so that the sales tax on a 1000-dollar purchase was 70 dollars. If we *double* the purchase to 2000 dollars, the sales tax also *doubles*, to 140 dollars. If we *reduced* the purchase by *half* to 500 dollars, the sales tax is also *reduced* by half, to 35 dollars. We say that the sales tax *varies directly* as the purchase price. The equation

$$\text{Sales tax} = (0.07)\,(\text{Purchase price})$$

expresses the fact that sales tax in Tampa (in 2005) was a constant (0.07) multiple of the purchase price.

STUDY TIP

The statements
"y varies directly as x,"
"y varies as x,"
"y is directly proportional to x,"
"y is proportional to x,"
and "$y = kx, k \neq 0$"
are all used with the same meaning.

> ### DIRECT VARIATION
>
> A quantity y is said to **vary directly** as the quantity x, or y is **directly proportional** to x, if there is a constant k such that $y = kx$. This constant k is called the **constant of variation** or the **constant of proportionality.**

FINDING THE SOLUTION: PROCEDURE FOR SOLVING VARIATION PROBLEMS

OBJECTIVE	EXAMPLE
To solve variation problems.	*Suppose y varies as x, and $x = \dfrac{4}{3}$ when $y = 20$. Find y when $x = 8$.*

Step 1   Write the equation with the constant of variation, k.

y varies as x; then

$$y = kx. \qquad \text{k is a nonzero constant.}$$

Step 2   Substitute the given values of the variables into the equation in Step 1 to find the value of the constant k.

$$20 = k\left(\frac{4}{3}\right) \qquad \text{Replace y by 20 and x by $\dfrac{4}{3}$.}$$

$$20\left(\frac{3}{4}\right) = k\left(\frac{4}{3}\right)\left(\frac{3}{4}\right) \qquad \text{Multiply both sides by $\dfrac{3}{4}$.}$$

$$15 = k \qquad \text{Solve for k.}$$

Step 3   Rewrite the equation in Step 1 with the value of k from Step 2.

$$y = kx \qquad \text{Variation equation from Step 1}$$

$$y = 15x \qquad \text{Replace k by 15.}$$

Step 4   Use the equation from Step 3 to answer the question posed in the problem.

$$y = 15(8) \qquad \text{Replace x by 8.}$$

$$y = 120 \qquad \text{Simplify.}$$

Thus, $y = 120$ when $x = 8$.

EXAMPLE 1   Solving a Direct Variation Problem

Suppose y varies directly as x, and $y = 36$ when $x = 24$. Find y when $x = 60$.

Solution

Step 1   Since y varies directly as x, it follows that, for some constant k, $y = kx$.

Step 2   We are given that when $x = 24$, $y = 36$.

$$36 = k(24) \qquad \text{Substitute } y = 36, x = 24 \text{ in } y = kx.$$

$$\frac{36}{24} = k \qquad \text{Divide both sides by 24.}$$

$$\frac{3}{2} = k \qquad \text{Simplify.}$$

Step 3 $\qquad\qquad\qquad\qquad y = \dfrac{3}{2}x \qquad \text{Replace } k \text{ by } \dfrac{3}{2} \text{ in } y = kx.$

Thus, $y = \dfrac{3}{2}x$ is the equation relating x and y.

Step 4   We find y when $x = 60$.

$$y = \frac{3}{2}x \qquad \text{Equation from Step 3}$$

$$y = \frac{3}{2}(60) \qquad \text{Substitute } x = 60.$$

$$y = 90 \qquad \text{Simplify.}$$

Thus, when $x = 60$, y is 90.   ■ ■ ■

PRACTICE PROBLEM 1   Suppose y varies directly as x. If y is 6 when x is 30, find y when $x = 120$.   ■

EXAMPLE 2   Direct Variation in Electrical Circuits

The current in a circuit connected to a 220-volt battery is 50 amperes. If the current in this circuit is directly proportional to the voltage of the attached battery, what voltage battery is needed to produce a current of 75 amperes?

Solution

Let I = current in amperes and V = voltage in volts of the battery.

Step 1 $\qquad\qquad\qquad\qquad I = kV \qquad I \text{ varies directly as } V.$

Step 2 $\qquad\qquad\qquad\qquad 50 = k(220) \qquad \text{Substitute } I = 50, V = 220.$

$$\frac{50}{220} = k \qquad \text{Divide by 220.}$$

$$\frac{5}{22} = k \qquad \text{Simplify.}$$

Step 3 $\qquad\qquad\qquad\qquad I = \dfrac{5}{22}V \qquad \text{Replace } k \text{ by } \dfrac{5}{22} \text{ in } I = kV.$

Continued on next page.

Step 4   Substitute $I = 75$ in the equation from Step 3 and solve for V.

$$75 = \frac{5}{22}V$$

$$\frac{22}{5} \cdot 75 = V \qquad \text{Multiply both sides by } \frac{22}{5}.$$

$$330 = V \qquad \text{Simplify.}$$

A battery of 330 volts is needed to produce 75 amperes of current.   ▪ ▪ ▪

PRACTICE PROBLEM 2   In Example 2, if the current in the circuit is 60 amperes, what voltage battery is needed to produce a current of 75 amperes?   ▪

We can generalize the concept of direct variation to variation with powers.

DIRECT VARIATION WITH POWERS

"A quantity y varies directly as the nth power of x" means

$$y = kx^n,$$

where k is a nonzero constant and $n > 0$.

Note that when $n = 1$, y varies directly as x, from the previous definition. Consider the formula for the area of a circle $A = \pi r^2$. The relationship between A and r may be described by saying that A varies directly as the square (or second power) of the radius r. In this case, π is the constant of variation.

EXAMPLE 3   **Solving a Problem Involving Direct Variation with Powers**

Suppose that you had forgotten the formula for the volume of a sphere, but were told that the volume V of a sphere varies directly as the cube of its radius r. In addition, you are given that $V = 972\pi$ when $r = 9$. Find V when $r = 6$.

Solution

Step 1 $V = kr^3$ V varies directly as r^3.

Step 2 $V = kr^3$ Equation from Step 1

$$972\pi = k(9)^3 \qquad \text{Replace } V \text{ by } 972\pi \text{ and } r \text{ by } 9.$$

$$972\pi = k(729) \qquad 9^3 = 729$$

$$k = \frac{972\pi}{729} \qquad \text{Solve for } k.$$

$$= \frac{4}{3}\pi \qquad \text{Simplify.}$$

Step 3   Substitute $k = \frac{4}{3}\pi$ in the equation from Step 1.

$$V = \frac{4}{3}\pi r^3.$$

Step 4   We now substitute $r = 6$ in the equation in Step 3 and obtain

$$V = \frac{4}{3}\pi(6)^3$$

$$= 288\pi \text{ cubic units.}$$ ■ ■ ■

PRACTICE PROBLEM 3 y varies directly as the square of x, and $y = 48$ when $x = 2$. Find y when $x = 5$.   ■

2 Solve inverse variation problems.

Inverse Variation

INVERSE VARIATION

A quantity y **varies inversely** as the quantity x, or y is **inversely proportional** to x if

$$y = \frac{k}{x},$$

where k is a nonzero constant.

Suppose a plane takes 4 hours to fly from Atlanta to Denver at an average speed of 300 miles per hour. If we *increase* the average speed to 600 miles per hour (twice the previous speed), the flight time *decreases* to 2 hours (half the previous time). For the Atlanta–Denver trip, the time of flight varies inversely as the speed of the plane:

$$\text{time} = \frac{\text{distance}}{\text{speed}}$$

$$= \frac{k}{\text{speed}}, \text{ where } k = \text{distance between Atlanta and Denver.}$$

We see that the distance is the constant of variation when time and speed are the variables.

EXAMPLE 4   **Solving an Inverse Variation Problem**

Suppose y varies inversely as x, and $y = 35$ when $x = 11$. Find y if $x = 55$.

Solution

Step 1	$y = \dfrac{k}{x}$	y varies inversely as x.
Step 2	$35 = \dfrac{k}{11}$	Substitute $y = 35, x = 11$.
	$35 \cdot 11 = k$	Multiply both sides by 11.
	$385 = k$	Simplify.
Step 3	$y = \dfrac{385}{x}$	Replace k by 385 in $y = \dfrac{k}{x}$.
Step 4	$y = \dfrac{385}{55}$	Replace x by 55.
	$y = 7$	Simplify.

■ ■ ■

PRACTICE PROBLEM 4   *A* varies inversely as *B*, and $A = 12$ when $B = 5$. Find *A* when $B = 3$.   ■

Just as in direct variation, the statement "*y* varies inversely as the *n*th power of *x*" means that $y = \dfrac{k}{x^n}$, where *k* is a nonzero constant and $n > 0$.

BY THE WAY . . .

Light travels at a speed of 299,792,458 meters per second. The distance that light travels in a year is so large that it is a useful unit of distance in astronomy.

1. One light year is approximately 9.46×10^{15} m.
2. The nearest star (other than the Sun) is 4.3 light years away.
3. The Milky Way (our galaxy) is about 100,000 light years in diameter.
4. The most distant objects that astronomers can see are about 18 billion light years away. Thus, the light that we presently see from these objects began its journey to us about 18 billion years ago. Since this is close to the estimated age of the universe, that light is a kind of fossil record of the universe not long after its birth!

EXAMPLE 5   **Solving a Problem Involving Inverse Variation with Powers**

The intensity of light varies inversely as the square of the distance from the light source. If Rita doubles her distance from a light source, what happens to the intensity of light at her new location?

Solution

Let *I* be the intensity of light at a distance *d* from the light source. Since *I* is inversely proportional to the square of *d*, we have:

$$I = \frac{k}{d^2}$$

If we replace *d* by 2*d*, the intensity I_1 at the new location is given by

$$I_1 = \frac{k}{(2d)^2} \qquad \text{Replace } d \text{ by } 2d \text{ in } I = \frac{k}{d^2}.$$

$$I_1 = \frac{k}{4d^2} \qquad (2d)^2 = 2^2 d^2 = 4d^2$$

Thus,

$$\frac{I_1}{I} = \frac{k}{4d^2} \div I \qquad \text{Divide both sides by } I.$$

$$\frac{I_1}{I} = \frac{k}{4d^2} \div \frac{k}{d^2} \qquad \text{Replace } I \text{ by } \frac{k}{d^2}.$$

$$= \frac{k}{4d^2} \times \frac{d^2}{k} \qquad \begin{array}{l}\text{Replace } \div \text{ by } \times \text{ and the divisor}\\ \text{by its reciprocal.}\end{array}$$

$$= \frac{1}{4} \qquad \text{Simplify.}$$

$$\frac{I_1}{I} = \frac{1}{4}$$

Multiplying both sides by *I*, we obtain

$$I_1 = \frac{1}{4}I.$$

This equation tells us that if Rita doubles her distance from the light source, the intensity of light at the new location will be one-fourth of the intensity at the original location.

■ ■ ■

PRACTICE PROBLEM 5   If *y* varies inversely as the square root of *x*, and $y = \dfrac{3}{4}$ when $x = 16$, find *x* when $y = 2$.   ■

3 Solve joint and combined variation problems.

Joint and Combined Variation

In certain situations, different types of variations occur simultaneously in a problem that has more than one independent variable.

The expression *z varies jointly as x and y* means that $z = kxy$, for some nonzero constant k. Similarly, if n and m are positive numbers, then the expression *z varies jointly as the nth power of x and mth power of y* means that $z = kx^n y^m$ for some nonzero constant k.

For example, the volume V of a right circular cylinder with radius r and height h is given by

$$V = \pi r^2 h.$$

Using the vocabulary of variation, we can state this relationship as "The volume V of a right circular cylinder varies jointly as its height h and the square of its radius r." The constant of variation is π.

We can combine the joint variation and inverse variation in a straightforward way. For example, the relationship

$$w = \frac{kx^2 y^3}{\sqrt{z}}$$

may be described as " w varies jointly as the square of x and cube of y, and inversely as the square root of z." The same relationship could also be stated as "w *varies directly as* $x^2 y^3$ *and inversely as* $\sqrt{z}$."

EXAMPLE 6   **Newton's Law of Universal Gravitation**

Newton's Law of Universal Gravitation says that every object in the universe attracts every other object with a force acting along the line of the centers of the two objects and that this attracting force is directly proportional to the product of the two masses and inversely proportional to the square of the distance between the two objects.

a. Write the law symbolically.

b. Estimate the value of g (the acceleration due to gravity) near the surface of Earth. Use the estimates: radius of Earth $R_E = 6.38 \times 10^6$ meters, and mass of Earth $M_E = 5.98 \times 10^{24}$ kilograms.

Solution

a. Let m_1 and m_2 be the masses of the two objects and r be the distance between their centers. (See Figure 3.31.) Let F denote the gravitational force between the objects.

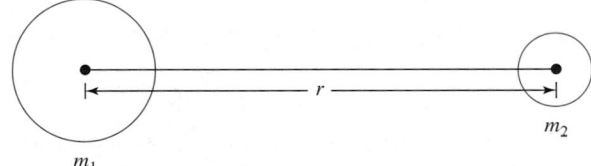

FIGURE 3.31

Then, according to Newton's Law of Universal Gravitation,

$$F = G \cdot \frac{m_1 m_2}{r^2}.$$

Continued on next page.

The constant of proportionality G is called the *universal gravitational constant*. It is termed a "universal constant" because it is thought to be the same at all places and all times and thus universally characterizes the intrinsic strength of the gravitational force. If the masses m_1 and m_2 are measured in kilograms, r is measured in meters, and the force F is measured in newtons, then the value of G is approximately 6.67×10^{-11} cubic meters per kilogram per second squared. This value was experimentally verified by Henry Cavendish in 1795.

b. *Estimating the value of g* (acceleration due to gravity)
We use Newton's Laws: Force = Mass × Acceleration and
$$\text{Force} = G \cdot \frac{m_1 m_2}{r^2}.$$

For an object of mass m near the surface of Earth, we have:

$\text{Force} = G \cdot \dfrac{m_1 m_2}{r^2}$ Law of Universal Gravitation

$\cancel{m} \cdot g = G \cdot \dfrac{\cancel{m} M_E}{R_E^2}$ Force = $m \cdot g$; replace m_1 by m and m_2 by M_E.

$g = G \cdot \dfrac{M_E}{R_E^2}$ Divide both sides by m.

$= \dfrac{(6.67 \times 10^{-11}) \cdot (5.98 \times 10^{24})}{(6.38 \times 10^6)^2}$ Substitute appropriate values for G, M_E, and R_E.

$\approx 9.8 \text{ m/sec}^2$ Use a calculator.   ■ ■ ■

PRACTICE PROBLEM 6 The mass of Mars is about 6.42×10^{23} kilograms, and its radius is about 3397 kilometers. What is the acceleration due to gravity near the surface of Mars? ■

We summarize the steps involved in solving most basic variation problems.

SOLVING VARIATION PROBLEMS

Step 1. Write the equation that models the problem.

a. y varies directly with x.	$y = kx$
b. y varies with the nth power of x.	$y = kx^n$
c. y varies inversely with x.	$y = \dfrac{k}{x}$
d. y varies inversely with the nth power of x.	$y = \dfrac{k}{x^n}$
e. z varies jointly with x and y.	$z = kxy$
f. z varies directly with x and inversely with y.	$z = \dfrac{kx}{y}$

Step 2. Substitute the given values into the equation in Step 1, and solve for k.

Step 3. Rewrite the equation in Step 1 with the value of k from Step 2.

Step 4. Use the equation from Step 3 to answer the question posed in the problem.

Even if a variation problem uses a more involved relationship than those identified in Step 1, once you write the appropriate equation involving k and the variables, you can proceed with Steps 2–4.

A Exercises   Basic Skills and Concepts

In Exercises 1–8, write each statement as an equation.

1. P varies directly as T. $P = kT$

2. P varies inversely as V. †

3. y varies as the square root of x. $y = k\sqrt{x}$

4. F varies jointly as m_1 and m_2. $F = km_1m_2$

5. V varies jointly as the cube of x and fourth power of y. †

6. w varies directly as the square root of x and inversely as y. †

7. z varies jointly as x and u and inversely as square of v. †

8. S varies jointly as the square root of x, the square of y, and the cube of z and inversely as the square of u. †

In Exercises 9–24, use the four-step procedure to solve for the variable requested.

9. x varies directly as y, and $x = 15$ when $y = 30$. Find x if $y = 28$. †

10. y varies directly as x, and $y = 3$ when $x = 2$. Find y when $x = 7$. †

11. s varies directly as the square of t, and $s = 64$ when $t = 2$. Find s when $t = 5$. $k = 16,\quad s = 400$

12. y varies directly as the cube of x, and $y = 270$ when $x = 3$. Find x when $y = 80$. $k = 10,\quad x = 2$

13. r varies inversely as u, and $r = 3$ when $u = 11$. Find r if $u = \dfrac{1}{3}$. $k = 33,\quad r = 99$

14. y varies inversely as z, and $y = 24$ when $z = \dfrac{1}{6}$. Find y if $z = 1$. $k = 4,\quad y = 4$

15. B varies inversely with the cube of A. If $B = 1$ when $A = 2$, find B when $A = 4$. †

16. y varies inversely with the cube root of x, and $y = 10$ when $x = 2$. Find x if $y = 40$. †

17. z varies jointly as x and y, and $z = 42$ when $x = 2$ and $y = 3$. Find y if $z = 56$ and $x = 2$. $k = 7,\quad y = 4$

18. m varies directly as q and inversely as p, and $m = \dfrac{1}{2}$ when $p = 26$ and $q = 13$. Find m when $p = 14$ and $q = 7$. †

19. z varies directly as the square of x, and $z = 32$ when $x = 4$. Find z if $x = 5$. $k = 2,\quad z = 50$

20. u varies inversely as the cube of t, and $u = 9$ when $t = 2$. Find u if $t = 6$. †

21. P varies jointly as T and the square of Q, and $P = 36$ when $T = 17$ and $Q = 6$. Find P when $T = 4$ and $Q = 9$. †

22. a varies jointly as b and the square root of c, and $a = 9$ when $b = 13$ and $c = 81$. Find a when $b = 5$ and $c = 9$. †

23. z varies directly as the square root of x and inversely as the square of y, and $z = 24$ when $x = 16$ and $y = 3$. Find x when $z = 27$ and $y = 2$. $k = 54,\quad x = 4$

24. z varies jointly as u and the cube of v and inversely as the square of w; $z = 9$ when $u = 4$, $v = 3$, and $w = 2$. Find w when $u = 27$, $v = 2$, and $z = 8$. †

In Exercises 25–28, solve for the variable requested without determining the constant of variation, k. Use the fact that if

$$x_1 = ky_1 \text{ and } x_2 = ky_2, \text{ then } \frac{x_1}{y_1} = k = \frac{x_2}{y_2}, \text{ so that } \frac{x_1}{y_1} = \frac{x_2}{y_2}.$$

25. If y is proportional to x, and $y = 12$ when $x = 16$, find y when $x = 8$. $y = 6$

26. If z varies directly as w, and $z = 17$ when $w = 22$, find z when $w = 110$. $z = 85$

27. If y is directly proportional to x, and $y = 100$ for the value x_0 of x, find y when x_0 is doubled—that is, when $x = 2x_0$. $y = 200$

28. If x varies directly as the square root of y, and $x = 2$ when $y = 9$, find y when $x = 3$. †

B Exercises   Applying the Concepts

29. **Hubble constant.** The American astronomer Edwin Powell Hubble (1889–1953) is renowned for having determined that there are other galaxies in the universe beyond the Milky Way. In 1929, he stated that the galaxies observed at a particular time recede from each other at a speed that is directly proportional to the distance between them. The constant of proportionality is denoted by the letter H. Write Hubble's statement in the form of an equation. †

†Due to space constrictions, answers to these exercises may be found in the Answers beginning on page A–1 in the back of the book.

30. **Malthusian doctrine.** The British scientist Thomas Robert Malthus (1766–1834) was a pioneer of population science and economics. In 1798, he stated that populations grow faster than the means that can sustain them. One of his arguments was that the rate of change, R, of a given population is directly proportional to the size P of the population. Write the equation that describes Malthus's argument. $R = kP$, where k is a constant.

31. **Converting units of length.** Use the fact that 1 foot $\approx$ 30.5 centimeters.
  a. Write an equation which expresses the fact that a length measured in centimeters is directly proportional to the length measured in feet.   †
  b. Convert the following measurements into centimeters.
    (i)   8 feet †   (ii)   5 feet, 4 inches †
  c. Convert the following measurements into feet.
    (i)   57 centimeters †   (ii)   1 meter, 24 centimeters †

32. **Converting weight.** Use the fact that 1 kilogram $\approx$ 2.20 pounds.
  a. Write an equation which expresses the fact that a weight measured in pounds is directly proportional to the weight measured in kilograms.   †
  b. Convert the following measurements to pounds.
    (i)   125 grams 0.275 lb
    (ii)   4 kilograms 8.8 lb
    (iii)   2.4 kilograms 5.28 lb
  c. Convert the following measurements to kilograms.
    (i)   27 pounds 12.27 kg
    (ii)   160 pounds 72.73 kg

33. **Protein from soybeans.** The quantity P of protein obtained from dried soybeans is directly proportional to the quantity Q of dried soybeans used. If 20 grams of dried soybeans produces 7 grams of protein, how much protein can be produced from 100 grams of soybeans? 35 g

34. **Wages.** A person's weekly wages W are directly proportional to the number of hours h worked per week. If Samantha earned 600 dollars for a 40-hour week, how much would she earn if she worked only 25 hours in a particular week. What does the constant of proportionality mean?   †

35. **Physics.** The distance d an object falls varies directly as the square of the time t during which it is falling. If an object

falls 64 feet in 2 seconds, how long would it take the object to fall 9 feet?   †

36. **Physics. Hooke's Law** states that the force F required to stretch a spring by x units is directly proportional to x. If a force of 10 pounds stretches a spring by 4 inches, find the force required to stretch a spring by 6 inches.   15 lb

4 in.

10 lb

37. **Chemistry. Boyle's Law** states that at a constant temperature the pressure P of a compressed gas is inversely proportional to its volume V. If the pressure is 20 pounds per square inch when the volume of the gas is 300 cubic inches, what is the pressure when the gas is compressed to 100 cubic inches?   60 lb/in.^{2}

38. **Chemistry.** Scientists use a temperature scale known as the Kelvin temperature scale. The lowest possible temperature (called absolute zero) is 0 K. (K denotes degrees Kelvin.) The relationship between Kelvin temperature (T_K) and Celsius temperature (T_C) is given by $T_K = T_C + 273$.

The pressure P exerted by a gas varies directly as its temperature T_K and inversely as its volume V. Assume that at a temperature of 260 K a gas occupies 13 cubic inches at a pressure of 36 pounds per square inch.
  a. Find the volume of the gas when the temperature is 300 K and the pressure is 40 pounds per square inch.   †
  b. Find the pressure when the temperature is 280 K and the volume is 39 cubic inches.   12.92 lb/in.^{2}

39. **Weight.** The weight of an object varies inversely as the square of the object's distance from the center of Earth. The radius of Earth is 3960 miles.
  a. If an astronaut weighs 120 pounds on the surface of Earth, how much does she weigh 6000 miles above the surface of Earth?   18.97 lb
  b. If a miner weighs 200 pounds on the surface of Earth, how much does he weigh 10 miles below the surface of Earth?   201.01 lb

40. Making a profit. Suppose you wanted to make a profit by buying gold by weight at one altitude and selling at another altitude for the same price per unit weight. Should you buy or sell at the higher altitude? (Use the information from Exercise 39.) Buy.

In Exercises 41 and 42, use Newton's Law of Universal Gravitation. (See Example 6.)

41. Gravity on the moon. The mass of the moon is about 7.4×10^{22} kilograms, and its radius is about 1740 kilometers. How much is the acceleration due to gravity on the surface of the moon? 1.63 m/s^2

42. Gravity on the sun. The mass of the sun is about 2×10^{30} kilograms, and its radius is 696,000 kilometers. How much is the acceleration due to gravity on the surface of the sun? †

2002/06/09 13:19

43. Illumination. The intensity I of illumination from a light source is inversely proportional to the square of the distance d from the source. Suppose the intensity is 320 candlepower at a distance of 10 feet from a light source.
   a. What is the intensity at 5 feet from the source? †
   b. How far away from the source will the intensity be 400 candlepower? 8.94 ft from the source

44. Speed and skid marks. Police estimate that the speed s of a car in miles per hour varies directly as the square root of d, where d in feet is the length of the skid marks left by a car traveling on a dry concrete pavement. A car traveling at 48 miles per hour leaves skid marks of 96 feet.
   a. Write an equation relating s and d. $s = 2\sqrt{6d}$
   b. Use the equation in part (**a**) to estimate the speed of a car whose skid marks stretched (*i*) 60 feet; (*ii*) 150 feet; (*iii*) 200 feet. †
   c. Suppose you are driving at 70 miles per hour and slam on your brakes. How long will your skid marks be? †

45. Simple pendulum. *Periodic motion* is motion that repeats itself over successive equal intervals of time. The time required for one complete repetition of the motion is called the *period*. The period of a simple pendulum varies directly as the square root of its length. What is the effect on the length if the period is doubled?
   (*Note:* The amplitude of a pendulum has no effect on its period. This is what makes pendulums such good timekeepers. Because they invariably lose energy due to friction, their amplitude decreases, but their period remains constant.) †

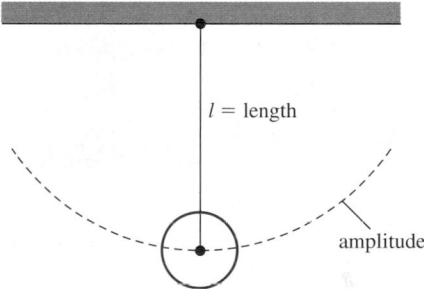

l = length

amplitude

46. Biology. The volume V of a lung is directly proportional to its internal surface area A. A lung with volume 400 cubic centimeters from a certain species has an average internal surface area of 100 square centimeters. Find the volume of a lung of a member of this species if the lung's internal surface area is 120 square centimeters. 480 cm^3

47. Horsepower. The horsepower H of an automobile engine varies directly as the square of the piston radius R and the number N of pistons.
   a. Write the given information in equation form. †
   b. What is the effect on the horsepower if the piston radius is doubled? The horsepower is multiplied by 4.
   c. What is the effect on the horsepower if the number of pistons is doubled? The horsepower is doubled.
   d. What is the effect on the horsepower if the radius of the pistons is cut in half and the number of pistons is doubled? The horsepower is cut in half.

48. Safe load. The safe load that a rectangular beam can support varies jointly as the width and square of the depth of the beam and inversely as its length. A beam 4 inches wide, 6 inches deep, and 25 feet long can support a safe load of 576 pounds. Find the safe load for a beam of the same material, but that is 6 inches wide, 10 inches deep, and 20 feet long. 3000 lb

C Exercises   Beyond the Basics

49. Energy from a windmill. The energy E from a windmill varies jointly as the square of the length l of the blades and the cube of the wind velocity v.

  a. Express the given information as an equation with k as the constant of variation. $E = kl^2v^3$

  b. If blades of length 10 feet and wind velocity 8 miles per hour generate 1920 watts of electric power, find k. †

  c. How much electric power would be generated if the blades were 8 feet long and the wind velocity was 25 miles per hour? $37,500$ W

  d. If the velocity of the wind doubles, what happens to E? †

  e. If the length of blades doubles, what happens to E? †

  f. What happens to E if both the length of the blades and the wind velocity are doubled? E is multiplied by 32.

50. Intensity of light. The intensity of light, I_d, at a distance d from the source of light varies directly as the intensity I of the source and inversely as d^2. It is known that at a distance of 2 meters a 100-watt bulb produces an intensity of approximately 2 watts per square meter.

  a. Find the constant of variation, k. $k = 0.08$

  b. Suppose a 200-watt bulb is located on a wall 2 meters above the floor. What is the intensity of light at a point A that is 3 meters from the wall? 1.23 W/m^2

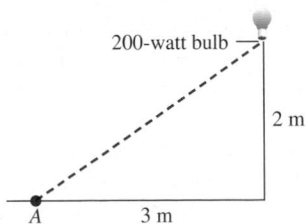

200-watt bulb

2 m

A 3 m

  c. What is the intensity of illumination at the point A in the figure if the bulb is raised by 1 meter? 0.89 W/m^2

51. Metabolic rate. Metabolism is the sum total of all physical and chemical changes that take place within an organism. According to the laws of thermodynamics, all these changes will ultimately release heat, so the metabolic rate is a measure of heat production by an animal. Biologists have found that the normal resting metabolic rate of a mammal is directly proportional to the $\dfrac{3}{4}$ power of its body weight.

The resting metabolic rate of a person weighing 75 kilograms is 75 watts.

  a. Find the constant of proportionality, k. $k = 2.94$

  b. Estimate the resting metabolic rate of a brown bear weighing 450 kilograms. 287.25 W

  c. What is the effect on metabolic rate if the body weight is multiplied by 4? †

  d. What is the approximate weight of an animal with a metabolic rate of 250 watts? 373.93 kg

52. Comparing gravitational forces. The masses of the sun, Earth, and the moon are 2×10^{30} kilograms, 6×10^{24} kilograms, and 7.4×10^{22} kilograms, respectively. The Earth–sun distance is about 400 times the Earth–moon distance. Use Newton's Law of Universal Gravitation to compare the gravitational attraction between the sun and Earth with that between Earth and the moon. †

53. Kepler's Third Law. Suppose an object of mass M_1 orbits around an object of mass M_2. Let r be the average orbital distance in meters between the centers of the two objects, and let T be the orbital period (the time in seconds during which the object completes one orbit). Kepler's Third Law states that T^2 is directly proportional to r^3 and inversely proportional to $M_1 + M_2$.

The constant of proportionality is $\dfrac{4\pi^2}{G}$.

  a. Write the equation that expresses Kepler's Third Law. †

  b. Earth orbits the sun once each year at a distance of about 1.5×10^8 kilometers. Find the mass of the sun. Use these estimates:

  Mass of Earth + Mass of sun ≈ Mass of sun,

  $G = 6.67 \times 10^{-11}$, 1 year $= 3.15 \times 10^7$ seconds. †

54. Use Kepler's Third Law. The moon orbits Earth in about 27.3 days at an average distance of about 384,000 kilometers. Find the mass of Earth. [*Hint:* Convert the period to seconds; also, use Mass of Earth + Mass of moon ≈ Mass of Earth] 6.02×10^{24} kg

55. Spreading a rumor. Let P be the population of a community. The rate R (per day) at which a rumor spreads in the community is jointly proportional to the number N of people who have already heard the rumor and the number $(P - N)$ of people who have not yet heard the rumor.

A rumor about the president of a college is spread in his college community of 10,000 people. Five days after the rumor started, 1000 people had heard it, and it was spreading at the rate of 45 additional people per day.

  a. Write an equation relating R, P, and N. †

  b. Find the constant k of variation. †

  c. Find the rate at which the rumor was spreading when one-half the college community had heard it. †

  d. How many people had heard the rumor when it was spreading at the rate of 100 people per day? 2764 or 7236

Critical Thinking

56. Electricity. The current I in an electric circuit varies directly as the voltage V and inversely as the resistance R. If the resistance is increased by 20%, what percent increase must occur in the voltage to increase the current by 30%? 56%

57. Precious Stones. The value of a precious stone is proportional to the square of its weight.
  a. Calculate the loss incurred by cutting a diamond worth 1000 dollars into two pieces whose weights are in the ratio 2:3. $480
  b. A precious stone worth 25,000 dollars is accidentally dropped and broken into three pieces, the weights of which are in the ratio 5:9:11. Calculate the loss incurred due to breakage. $15,920
  c. A diamond broke into five pieces, the weights of which are in the ratio 1:2:3:4:5. If the resulting loss is 85,000 dollars, find the value of the original diamond. Also, calculate the value of a diamond whose weight is twice that of the original.

Answer:
  57. c. The value of the original diamond is $112,500. The value of a diamond whose weight is twice that of the original is $450,000.

58. Bus service. The profit earned in running a bus service is jointly proportional to the distance and the number of passengers in excess of a certain fixed number. The profit is 80 dollars when 30 passengers are carried over a distance of 40 km and is 180 dollars when 35 passengers are carried over a distance of 60 km. What is the minimum number of passengers that results in no loss? 20

59. Weight of a sphere. The weight of a sphere is directly proportional to the cube of its radius. A metal sphere is known to have a hollow space about its center in the form of a concentric sphere, and its weight is $\dfrac{7}{8}$ times the weight of a solid sphere of the same substance with the same radius. Find the ratio of the inner to the outer radius of the hollow sphere. 1:2

60. Train speed. A locomotive engine without a train can go 24 miles per hour, and its speed is diminished by a quantity that varies directly as the square root of the number of wagons attached. With four wagons, its speed is 20 miles per hour. Find the greatest number of wagons the engine can move. 144

Summary Definitions, Concepts, and Formulas

3.1 Quadratic Functions

  i. A **quadratic function** f is a function of the form
  $$f(x) = ax^2 + bx + c,\ a \neq 0.$$

  ii. The **standard form** of a quadratic function is
  $$f(x) = a(x - h)^2 + k,\ a \neq 0.$$

  iii. The graph of a quadratic function is a transformation of the graph of $y = x^2$.

  iv. The graph of a quadratic function is a parabola with vertex
  $$(h, k) = \left(-\frac{b}{2a},\ f\left(-\frac{b}{2a}\right)\right).$$

  v. The maximum (if $a < 0$) or minimum (if $a > 0$) value of a quadratic function $f(x) = ax^2 + bx + c$ occurs at the vertex of the parabola.

3.2 Polynomial Functions

  i. A function f of the form $f(x) = a_n x^n + a_{n-1} x^{n-1} + \cdots + a_1 x + a_0,\ a_n \neq 0$ is a polynomial function of degree n.

  ii. The graph of a polynomial function is smooth and continuous.

  iii. The end behavior of the graph of a polynomial function depends upon the leading coefficient and the degree of the polynomial.

  iv. The **zeros** of a polynomial function $f(x)$ are the values of x for which $f(x) = 0$.

  v. If, in the factorization of a polynomial function $f(x)$, the factor $(x - a)$ occurs exactly m times, then a is a zero of **multiplicity** m. If m is odd, the graph of $y = f(x)$ crosses the x-axis at a; if m is even, the graph touches the x-axis at a, but does not cross it.

  vi. If the degree of a polynomial function $f(x)$ is n, then $f(x)$ has at most n real zeros and the graph of $f(x)$ has at most $(n - 1)$ turning points.

  vii. **The Intermediate Value Theorem:** Let $f(x)$ be a polynomial function and a and b be two numbers such that $a < b$. If $f(a)$ and $f(b)$ have opposite signs, then there is at least one number c, with $a < c < b$, for which $f(c) = 0$.

  viii. See page 345 for graphing a polynomial function.

3.3 Dividing Polynomials and the Rational Zeros Test

  i. **Division Algorithm:** If a polynomial $F(x)$ is divided by a polynomial $D(x) \neq 0$, there are unique polynomials $Q(x)$ and $R(x)$ such that $F(x) = D(x)Q(x) + R(x)$, where either $R(x) = 0$ or deg $R(x) <$ deg $D(x)$. In words, "The dividend equals the product of the divisor and the quotient, plus the remainder."

  ii. Synthetic division is a shortcut for dividing a polynomial $F(x)$ by $(x - a)$.

iii. Remainder Theorem: If a polynomial $F(x)$ is divided by $(x - a)$, the remainder is $F(a)$.

iv. Factor Theorem: A polynomial function $F(x)$ has $(x - a)$ as a factor if and only if $F(a) = 0$.

v. Rational Zeros Test: If $\dfrac{p}{q}$ is a rational zero in lowest terms for a polynomial function with integer coefficients, then p is a factor of the constant term and q is a factor of the leading coefficient.

3.4 Zeros of a Polynomial Function

i. Descartes's Rule of Signs. Let $F(x)$ be a polynomial function with real coefficients. Then

  a. The number of positive zeros of F is either equal to the number of variations of signs of $F(x)$ or less than that number by an even integer.

  b. The number of negative zeros of F is either equal to the number of variations of sign of $F(-x)$ or less than that number by an even integer.

ii. Rules for Bounds on the Zeros. Suppose a polynomial $F(x)$ is synthetically divided by $x - k$. Then

  a. If $k > 0$ and each number in the last row is either zero or positive, then k is an upper bound on the zeros of $F(x)$.

  b. If $k < 0$ and the numbers in the last row alternate in sign, then k is a lower bound on the zeros of $F(x)$.

iii. The Fundamental Theorem of Algebra. An nth-degree polynomial equation has at least one complex zero.

iv. Factorization Theorem for Polynomials. If $P(x)$ is a polynomial of degree $n \geq 1$, it can be factored into n (not necessarily distinct) linear factors of the form $P(x) = a(x - r_1)(x - r_2) \cdots (x - r_n)$, where $a, r_1, r_2, \ldots, r_n$ are complex numbers.

v. Number-of-Zeros Theorem. A polynomial of degree n has exactly n zeros, provided that a zero of multiplicity k is counted k times.

vi. Conjugate Pairs Theorem. If $a + bi$ is a zero of the polynomial function P (with real coefficients), then $a - bi$ is also a zero of P.

3.5 Rational Functions

i. A function $F(x) = \dfrac{N(x)}{D(x)}$, where $N(x)$ and $D(x)$ are polynomials and $D(x) \neq 0$, is called a rational function. The domain of $F(x)$ is the set of all real numbers except the real zeros of $D(x)$.

ii. The line $x = a$ is a vertical asymptote of the graph of f if $|f(x)| \to \infty$ as $x \to a^+$ or as $x \to a^-$.

iii. If $\dfrac{N(x)}{D(x)}$ is in lowest terms, then the graph of $F(x)$ has vertical asymptotes at the real zeros of $D(x)$.

iv. The line $y = k$ is a horizontal asymptote of the graph of f if $f(x) \to k$ as $x \to \infty$ or as $x \to -\infty$.

v. See page 389 for graphing a rational function.

3.6 Variation

k is a nonzero constant called the constant of variation.

Variation	Equation
y varies directly as x	$y = kx$
y varies with the nth power of x	$y = kx^n$
y varies inversely as x	$y = \dfrac{k}{x}$
y varies inversely as the nth power of x	$y = \dfrac{k}{x^n}$
z varies jointly with the nth power of x and the mth power of y	$z = kx^n y^m$
z varies directly with the nth power of x and inversely with the mth power of y	$z = \dfrac{kx^n}{y^m}$

Review Exercises

Basic Skills and Concepts

In Exercises 1–10, graph each quadratic function by finding (*i*) whether the parabola opens up or down, (*ii*) its vertex, (*iii*) its axis, (*iv*) its x-intercepts, (*v*) its y-intercept, and (*vi*) the intervals over which the function is increasing and decreasing.

1. $y = (x - 1)^2 + 2$ †

2. $y = (x + 2)^2 - 3$ †

3. $y = -2(x - 3)^2 + 4$ †

4. $y = -\dfrac{1}{2}(x + 1)^2 + 2$ †

5. $y = -2x^2 + 3$ †

6. $y = 2x^2 + 4x - 1$ †

7. $y = 2x^2 - 4x + 3$ †

8. $y = -2x^2 - x + 3$ †

9. $y = 3x^2 - 2x + 1$ †

10. $y = 3x^2 - 5x + 4$ †

In Exercises 11–14, determine whether the given quadratic function has a maximum or a minimum value, and then find that value.

11. $f(x) = 3 - 4x + x^2$ †

12. $f(x) = 8x - 4x^2 - 3$ †

13. $f(x) = -2x^2 - 3x + 2$ †

14. $f(x) = \dfrac{1}{2}x^2 - \dfrac{3}{4}x + 2$ †

†Due to space constrictions, answers to these exercises may be found in the Answers beginning on page A–1 in the back of the book.

In Exercises 15–18, graph each polynomial function by using transformations.

15. $f(x) = (x + 1)^3 - 2$ †   **16.** $f(x) = (x + 1)^4 + 2$ †

17. $f(x) = (1 - x)^3 + 1$ †   **18.** $f(x) = x^4 + 3$ †

In Exercises 19–24, for each polynomial function f.

(i) Determine the end behavior of f.

(ii) Determine the zeros of f. State the multiplicity of each zero. Determine whether the graph of f crosses, or touches but does not cross, the axis at each x-intercept.

(iii) Find the x- and y-intercepts of the graph of f.

(iv) Use test numbers to find the intervals over which the graph of f is above or below the x-axis.

(v) Find any symmetry.

(vi) Sketch the graph of $y = f(x)$.

19. $f(x) = x(x - 1)(x + 2)$ † **20.** $f(x) = x^3 - x$ †

21. $f(x) = -x^2(x - 1)^2$ †   **22.** $f(x) = -x^3(x - 2)^2$ †

23. $f(x) = -x^2(x^2 - 1)$ †

24. $f(x) = -(x - 1)^2(x^2 + 1)$ †

In Exercises 25–28, divide by using long division.

25. $\dfrac{6x^2 + 5x - 13}{3x - 2}$ †   **26.** $\dfrac{8x^2 - 14x + 15}{2x - 3}$ †

27. $\dfrac{8x^4 - 4x^3 + 2x^2 - 7x + 165}{x + 1}$ †

28. $\dfrac{x^3 - 3x^2 + 4x + 7}{x^2 - 2x + 6}$ Quotient: $x - 1$; remainder: $13 - 4x$

In Exercises 29–32, divide by using synthetic division.

29. $\dfrac{x^3 - 12x + 3}{x - 3}$ †   **30.** $\dfrac{-4x^3 + 3x^2 - 5x}{x - 6}$ †

31. $\dfrac{2x^4 - 3x^3 + 5x^2 - 7x + 165}{x + 1}$ †

32. $\dfrac{3x^5 - 2x^4 + x^2 - 16x - 132}{x + 2}$ †

In Exercises 33–36, a polynomial function $f(x)$ and a constant c are given. Find $f(c)$ by (i) evaluating the function and (ii) using synthetic division and the Remainder Theorem.

33. $f(x) = x^3 - 3x^2 + 11x - 29; c = 2$ -11

34. $f(x) = 2x^3 + x^2 - 15x - 2; c = -2$ 16

35. $f(x) = x^4 - 2x^2 - 5x + 10; c = -3$ 88

36. $f(x) = x^5 + 2; c = 1$ 3

In Exercises 37–40, a polynomial function $f(x)$ and a constant c are given. Use synthetic division to show that c is a zero of $f(x)$. Use the result to final all zeros of $f(x)$.

37. $f(x) = x^3 - 7x^2 + 14x - 8; c = 2$ $1, 2, 4$

38. $f(x) = 2x^3 - 3x^2 - 12x + 4; c = -2$ †

39. $f(x) = 3x^3 + 14x^2 + 13x - 6; c = \dfrac{1}{3}$ $-3, \ -2, \ \dfrac{1}{3}$

40. $f(x) = 4x^3 + 19x^2 - 13x + 2; c = \dfrac{1}{4}$ †

In Exercises 41–42, use the Rational Zeros Test to list all possible rational zeros of $f(x)$.

41. $f(x) = x^4 + 3x^3 - x^2 - 9x - 6$ †

42. $f(x) = 9x^3 - 36x^2 - 4x + 16$ †

In Exercises 43–46, use Descartes's Rule of Signs and the Rational Zeros Test to find all real zeros of each polynomial function.

43. $f(x) = 5x^3 + 11x^2 + 2x$ †

44. $f(x) = x^3 + 2x^2 - 5x - 6$ $-3, 1, 2$

45. $f(x) = x^3 + 3x^2 - 4x - 12$ $-3, -2, 2$

46. $f(x) = 2x^3 - 9x^2 + 12x - 5$ †

In Exercises 47–52, find all the zeros of $f(x)$, real and nonreal, that are not given.

47. $f(x) = x^3 - 7x + 6$; one zero is 2. $-3, 1, 2$

48. $f(x) = x^4 + x^3 - 3x^2 - x + 2$; 1 is a zero of multiplicity 2. $-2, -1, 1$

49. $f(x) = x^4 - 2x^3 + 6x^2 - 18x - 27$; two zeros are -1 and 3. $-1, \ 3, \ 3i, \ -3i$

50. $f(x) = 4x^3 - 19x^2 + 32x - 15$; one zero is $2 - i$. †

51. $f(x) = x^4 + 2x^3 + 9x^2 + 8x + 20$; one zero is $-1 + 2i$ †

52. $f(x) = x^5 - 7x^4 + 24x^3 - 32x^2 + 64$; $2 + 2i$ is a zero of multiplicity 2. $-1, \ 2 + 2i, \ 2 - 2i$

In Exercises 53–58, solve each equation in the complex number system.

53. $x^3 - x^2 - 4x + 4 = 0$ $\{-2, 1, 2\}$

54. $2x^3 + x^2 - 12x - 6 = 0$ †

55. $4x^3 - 7x - 3 = 0$ †

56. $x^3 + x^2 - 8x - 6 = 0$ $\{-3, \ 1 - \sqrt{3}, \ 1 + \sqrt{3}\}$

57. $x^4 - x^3 - x^2 - x - 2 = 0$ $\{-1, \ 2, \ i, \ -i\}$

58. $x^4 - x^3 - 13x^2 + x + 12 = 0$ $\{-3, -1, 1, 4\}$

In Exercises 59 and 60, show that the given equation has no rational roots.

59. $x^3 + 13x^2 - 6x - 2 = 0$ †

60. $3x^4 - 9x^3 - 2x^2 - 15x - 5 = 0$ †

In Exercises 61 and 62, use the Intermediate Value Theorem to find the value of the real root between 1 and 2 of each equation to two decimal places.

61. $x^3 + 6x^2 - 28 = 0$ 1.88 **62.** $x^3 + 3x^2 - 3x - 7 = 0$ †

In Exercises 63–70, graph each rational function by following the six-step procedure outlined in Section 3.5.

63. $f(x) = 1 + \dfrac{1}{x}$ †

64. $f(x) = \dfrac{2 - x}{x}$ †

65. $f(x) = \dfrac{x}{x^2 - 1}$ †

66. $f(x) = \dfrac{x^2 - 9}{x^2 - 4}$ †

67. $f(x) = \dfrac{x^3}{x^2 - 9}$ †

68. $f(x) = \dfrac{x + 1}{x^2 - 2x - 8}$ †

69. $f(x) = \dfrac{x^4}{x^2 - 4}$ †

70. $f(x) = \dfrac{x^2 + x - 6}{x^2 - x - 12}$ †

Applying the Concepts

71. Variation. If y varies directly as x, and $y = 12$ when $x = 4$, find y when $x = 5$. $y = 15$

72. Variation. If p varies inversely as q, and $p = 4$ when $q = 3$, find p when $q = 4$. $p = 3$

73. Variation. If s varies directly as the square of t, and $s = 20$ when $t = 2$, find s when $t = 3$. $s = 45$

74. Variation. If y varies inversely as x^2, and $y = 3$ when $x = 8$, find x when $y = 12$. $x = \pm 4$

75. Missile path. A missile fired from the origin of a coordinate system follows a path described by the equation $y = -\dfrac{1}{10}x^2 + 20x$, where the x-axis is ground level. Sketch the missile's path, and determine its maximum altitude and where it hits the ground. †

76. Minimizing area. Suppose a wire 20 centimeters long is to be cut into two pieces, each of which will be formed into a square. Find the size of each piece that minimizes the total area. Both pieces must be 10 cm.

77. A farmer wishes to fence off three identical adjoining rectangular pens, each 400 square feet in area. (See the figure.) What should the width and length of each pen be so that the least amount of fence is needed? †

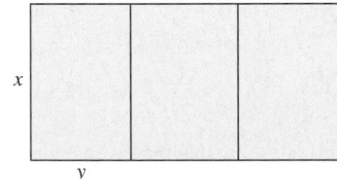

78. Suppose the outer boundary of the pens in Exercise 77 requires heavy fence that costs 5 dollars per foot, but two internal partitions cost 3 dollars per foot. What dimensions x and y will minimize the cost? †

79. Electric circuit. In the circuit shown in the figure, the voltage $V = 100$ volts and the resistance $R = 50$ ohms. We want to determine the size of the remaining resistor (x ohms). The power absorbed by the circuit is given by $p(x) = \dfrac{V^2 x}{(R + x)^2}$.

a. Graph the function $y = p(x)$. †
b. Use a graphing calculator to find the value of x that maximizes the power absorbed. $x = 50$

80. Maximizing area. A sheet of paper for a poster is 18 square feet in area. The margins at the top and bottom are 9 inches each, and the margin on each side is 6 inches. What should the dimensions of the paper be if the printed area is to be a maximum? $36\sqrt{3}$ in. $\times$ $24\sqrt{3}$ in.

81. Maximizing profit. A manufacturer makes and sells printers to retailers at 24 dollars per unit. The total daily cost C in dollars of producing x printers is given by
$$C(x) = 150 + 3.9x + \frac{3}{1000}x^2.$$

a. Write the profit P as a function of x. †
b. Find the number of printers the manufacturer should produce and sell to achieve maximum profit. 3350
c. Find the average cost $\overline{C}(x) = \dfrac{C(x)}{x}$. Graph $y = \overline{C}(x)$. †

82. Meteorology. The function $p = \dfrac{69.1}{a + 2.3}$ relates the atmospheric pressure p in inches of mercury to the altitude a in miles from the surface of Earth.

a. Find the pressure on Mount Kilimanjaro at an altitude of 19,340 feet. 11.59 in.
b. Is there an altitude at which the pressure is 0? No

83. Wages. An employee's wages are directly proportional to the time he or she has worked. Sam earned 280 dollars for 40 hours. How much would Sam earn if he worked for 35 hours? $245

84. Car's stopping distance. The distance required for a car to come to a stop after its brakes are applied is directly proportional to the square of its speed. If the stopping distance for a car traveling at 30 miles per hour is 25 feet, what is the stopping distance for a car traveling at 66 miles per hour? †

85. Illumination. The amount of illumination from a source of light varies directly as the intensity of the source and inversely as the square of the distance from the source. At what distance from a light source of intensity 300 candlepower will the illumination be one-half of the illumination 6 inches away from the source? $6\sqrt{2}$ in.

86. Chemistry. *Charles's Law* states that, at a constant pressure, the volume V of a gas is directly proportional to its temperature T (in Kelvin degrees). If a bicycle tube is filled with 1.2 cubic feet of air at a temperature of 295 K, what will be the volume of the air in the tube if the temperature rises to 310 K while the pressure stays the same? 1.26ft³

87. Electric circuits. The current I (measured in amperes) in an electrical circuit varies inversely as the resistance R (measured in ohms) when the voltage is held constant. The current in a certain circuit is 30 amperes when the resistance is 300 ohms.
 a. Find the current in the circuit if the resistance is decreased to 250 ohms. 36 amp
 b. What resistance will yield a current of 60 amperes? †

88. Safe load. The safe load that a circular column can support varies directly as the square root of its radius and inversely as the square of its length. A pillar with radius 4 inches and length 12 feet can safely support a 20-ton load. Find the load that a pillar of the same material with diameter 6 inches and length 10 feet can safely support. 35.27 ton

89. Spread of disease. An infectious cold virus spreads in a community at a rate R (per day) that is jointly proportional to the number of people who are infected with the virus and the number of people in the community who are not infected yet. After the 10th day of the start of a certain infection, 15% of the total population of 20,000 people of Pollutville had been infected and the virus was spreading at the rate of 255 people per day.
 a. Find the constant of proportionality, k. †
 b. At what rate is the disease spreading when one-half of the population is infected? 500 people per day
 c. Find the number of people infected when the rate of infection reached 95 people per day. 1000 and 19,000

90. Coulomb's law. The electric charge is measured in coulombs. (The charges on an electron and a proton, which are equal and opposite, are approximately 1.602×10^{-19} coulomb.) Coulomb's Law states that the force F between two particles is jointly proportional to their charges q_1 and q_2, and inversely proportional to the square of the distance between the two particles. Two charges are acted upon by a repulsive force of 96 units. What is the force if the distance between the particles is quadrupled? 6 units

Practice Test A

1. Find the x-intercepts of the graph of $f(x) = x^2 - 6x + 2$. †

2. Graph $f(x) = 3 - (x + 2)^2$. †

3. Find the vertex of the parabola described by $y = -7x^2 + 14x + 3$. (1, 10)

4. Find the domain of the function
$$f(x) = \frac{x^2 - 1}{x^2 + 3x - 4}. \quad (-\infty, -4) \cup (-4, 1) \cup (1, \infty).$$

5. Find the quotient and remainder of $\dfrac{x^3 - 2x^2 - 5x + 6}{x + 2}$. †

6. Graph the polynomial function $P(x) = x^5 - 4x^3$. †

7. Find all the zeros of $f(x) = 2x^3 - 2x^2 - 8x + 8$, given that 2 is one of the zeros. $-2, 1, 2$

8. Find the quotient: $\dfrac{-6x^3 + x^2 + 17x + 3}{2x + 3}$. †

9. Use the Remainder Theorem to find the value $P(-2)$ of the polynomial $P(x) - x^4 + 5x^3 - 7x^2 + 9x + 17$. †

10. Find all rational roots of the equation $x^3 - 5x^2 - 4x + 20 = 0$, and then find the irrational roots if there are any. †

11. Find the zeros of the polynomial function
$f(x) = x^4 + x^3 - 15x^2$. †

12. For $P(x) = 2x^{18} - 5x^{13} + 6x^3 - 5x + 9$, list all possible rational zeros found by the Rational Zeros Test, but do not check to see which values are actually zeros. †

13. Describe the end behavior of $f(x) = (x + 3)^3(x - 5)^2$. †

14. Find the zeros and the multiplicity of each zero for $f(x) = (x^2 - 4)(x + 2)^2$. †

15. Determine how many positive and how many negative real zeros the polynomial function $P(x) = 3x^6 + 2x^3 - 7x^2 + 8x$ can have. †

16. Find the horizontal and the vertical asymptotes of the graph of
$$f(x) = \frac{2x^2 + 3}{x^2 - x - 20}. \quad †$$

17. Write an equation that expresses the statement "y is directly proportional to x and inversely proportional to the square of t." †

18. In Problem 17, suppose $y = 6$ when $x = 8$ and $t = 2$. Find y if $x = 12$ and $t = 3$. $y = 4$

19. The cost C of producing x thousand units of a product is given by
$$C = x^2 - 30x + 335 \text{ (dollars)}.$$
Find the value of x for which the cost is minimum. †

20. From a rectangular 8×17 piece of cardboard, four congruent squares with sides of length x are cut out, one at each corner. The sides can then be folded to form a box. Find the volume V of the box as a function of x. †

Practice Test B

1. Find the x-intercepts of the graph of $f(x) = x^2 + 5x + 3$. b

  a. $\dfrac{-5 \pm i\sqrt{13}}{2}$ **b.** $\dfrac{-5 \pm \sqrt{13}}{2}$

  c. $\dfrac{-5 \pm i\sqrt{37}}{2}$ **d.** $\dfrac{-5 \pm \sqrt{37}}{2}$.

2. Which is the graph of $f(x) = 4 - (x - 2)^2$? d

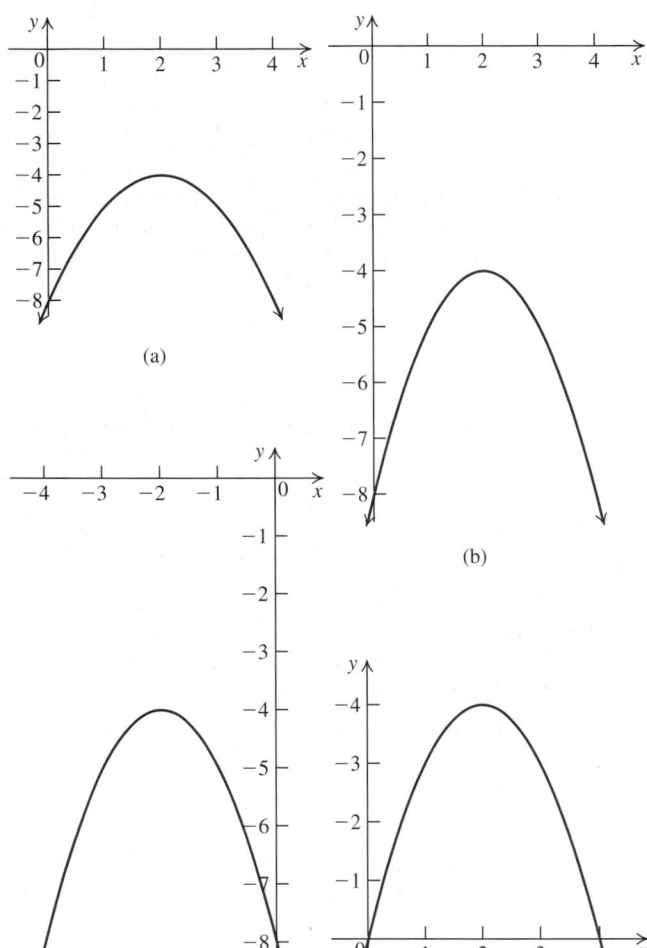

  (a)

  (b)

  (c)

  (d)

3. Find the vertex of the parabola described by
$y = 6x^2 + 12x - 5$. a

  a. $(-1, -11)$ **b.** $(1, -5)$
  c. $(-1, 13)$ **d.** $(1, 13)$

4. Which of the following is *not* in the domain of the function

$$f(x) = \frac{x^2}{x^2 + x - 6}?$$ b

  I. -3
  II. 0
  III. 2
  a. I and II   **b.** I and III
  c. II and III   **d.** I only

5. Find the quotient and remainder when $x^3 - 8x + 6$ is
divided by $x + 3$. d
  a. $x^2 - 8; 2$ **b.** $x^2 - 8; 0$
  c. $x^2 - 3x + 1; x + 3$ **d.** $x^2 - 3x + 1; 3$

6. The graph of the polynomial $P(x) = x^4 + 2x^3$ is c

  (a)   (b)

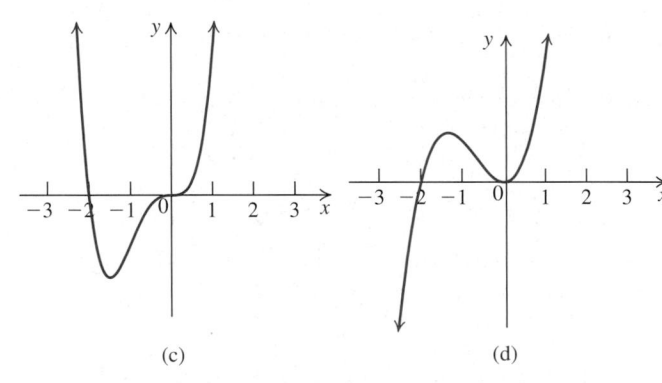

  (c)   (d)

7. Find all the zeros of $f(x) = 3x^3 - 26x^2 + 61x - 30$, given
that 3 is one of the zeros (that is, $f(3) = 0$). c
  a. $3, -5, -\dfrac{2}{3}$ **b.** $3, 2, \dfrac{5}{3}$

  c. $3, 5, \dfrac{2}{3}$ **d.** $3, -2, \dfrac{5}{3}$

8. Find the quotient $\dfrac{-10x^3 + 21x^2 - 17x + 12}{2x - 3}$. b

   a. $x^2 - 3x + 4$ **b.** $-5x^2 + 3x - 4$

   c. $x^2 + 3x - 4$ **d.** $-5x^2 - 4$

9. Use the Remainder Theorem to find the value $P(-3)$ of the polynomial $P(x) = x^4 + 4x^3 + 7x^2 + 10x + 15$. c

   a. 13   **b.** 15   **c.** 21   **d.** 6

10. Find all rational roots of the equation $-x^3 + x^2 + 8x - 12 = 0$, and then find the irrational roots if there are any. a

   a. -3 and 2   **b.** -3 and $\sqrt{2}$

   c. $-1, -2$, and 3   **d.** -3 and $\sqrt{3}$

11. Find the zeros of the polynomial function $f(x) = x^3 + x^2 - 30x$. a

   a. $x = -6, x = 5, x = 0$ **b.** $x = 0, x = -6$

   c. $x = 4, x = 5$ **d.** $x = 0, x = 4, x = 5$

12. For $P(x) = x^{30} - 4x^{25} + 6x^2 + 60$, list all possible rational zeros found by the Rational Zeros Test (but do not check to see which values are actually zeros). d

   a. $\pm2, \pm3, \pm4, \pm5, \pm6, \pm8, \pm10, \pm12, \pm15, \pm20,$ ±30, and ±60

   b. $\pm1, \pm2, \pm3, \pm4, \pm5, \pm6, \pm10, \pm12, \pm15, \pm18, \pm20,$ $\pm24, \pm30$, and ±60

   c. $\pm1, \pm3, \pm4, \pm5, \pm6, \pm12, \pm15, \pm20, \pm30$, and ±60

   d. $\pm1, \pm2, \pm3, \pm4, \pm5, \pm6, \pm10, \pm12, \pm15, \pm20,$ ±30, and ±60

13. Which of the following correctly describes the end behavior of $f(x) = (x + 1)^2(x - 2)^2$? c

   a. $\begin{cases} y \to \infty \text{ as } x \to -\infty \\ y \to -\infty \text{ as } x \to \infty \end{cases}$ **b.** $\begin{cases} y \to -\infty \text{ as } x \to -\infty \\ y \to -\infty \text{ as } x \to \infty \end{cases}$

   c. $\begin{cases} y \to \infty \text{ as } x \to -\infty \\ y \to \infty \text{ as } x \to \infty \end{cases}$ **d.** $\begin{cases} y \to -\infty \text{ as } x \to -\infty \\ y \to \infty \text{ as } x \to \infty \end{cases}$

14. Find the zeros, and the multiplicity of each zero, for $f(x) = (x^2 - 1)(x + 1)^2$. b

   a. $\begin{cases} \text{zero } 1, & \text{multiplicity } 1 \\ \text{zero } -1, & \text{multiplicity } 2 \end{cases}$

   b. $\begin{cases} \text{zero } 1, & \text{multiplicity } 1 \\ \text{zero } -1, & \text{multiplicity } 3 \end{cases}$

   c. $\begin{cases} \text{zero } 1, & \text{multiplicity } 2 \\ \text{zero } -1, & \text{multiplicity } 2 \end{cases}$

   d. $\begin{cases} \text{zero } i, & \text{multiplicity } 2 \\ \text{zero } -1, & \text{multiplicity } 2 \end{cases}$

15. Determine how many positive and how many negative real zeros the polynomial $P(x) = x^5 - 4x^3 - x^2 + 6x - 3$ can have. c

   a. positive 3, negative 2

   b. positive 2 or 0, negative 2 or 0

   c. positive 3 or 1, negative 2 or 0

   d. positive 2 or 0, negative 3 or 1

16. The horizontal and the vertical asymptotes of the graph of $f(x) = \dfrac{x^2 + x - 2}{x^2 + x - 12}$ are c

   a. $x = -2, y = 3, y = -4$

   b. $x = 1, y = 3, y = -4$

   c. $y = 1, x = 3, x = -4$

   d. $y = -2, x = 3, x = -4$

17. Write an equation that expresses the statement that S is directly proportional to the square of t and inversely proportional to the cube of x. d

   a. $S = \dfrac{kt^3}{\sqrt[3]{x}}$ **b.** $S = kt^2x^3$

   c. $S = \dfrac{kt^3}{x^2}$ **d.** $S = \dfrac{kt^2}{x^3}$

18. In Problem 17, suppose $S = 27$ if $t = 3$ and $x = 1$. If $t = 6$ and $x = 3$, then S is b

   a. 54   **b.** 4   **c.** $\dfrac{4}{3}$ **d.** 9

19. The cost C of producing x thousand units of a product is given by b

$$C = x^2 - 24x + 319 \text{ (dollars).}$$

Find the value of x for which the cost is minimum.

   a. 319   **b.** 12   **c.** 175   **d.** 24

20. From a rectangular 10×12 piece of cardboard, four congruent squares with sides of length x are cut out, one at each corner. The sides can then be folded to form a box. Find the volume V of the box as a function of x. d

   a. $V = 2x(10 - x)(12 - x)$

   b. $V = 2x(10 - 2x)(12 - 2x)$

   c. $V = x(10 - x)(12 - x)$

   d. $V = x(10 - 2x)(12 - 2x)$

Cumulative Review Exercises   Chapters 1–3

In Exercises 1–6, solve each equation.

1. $2x + 3 = 11$

2. $|2x - 1| = 5$

3. $x^2 - 2x - 3 = 0$

4. $x^2 + 3x + 1 = 0$

5. $x^3 - 3x^2 - 4x + 12 = 0$ $\{-2, 2, 3\}$

6. $(2x^2 - 1)^2 - 8(2x^2 - 1) + 7 = 0$ $\{-2, -1, 1, 2\}$

In Exercises 7–10, solve each inequality. Write the answer in interval notation.

7. $|2x - 5| < 1$ †

8. $x^2 + 2x - 8 \le 0$ †

9. $(x - 2)^2(x + 1) \le 0$ †

10. $\dfrac{x - 1}{x + 2} < 1$ †

11. Find an equation in center–radius form of the circle with center $(2, -3)$ and radius 4. $(x - 2)^2 + (y + 3)^2 = 16$

12. Find the center and radius of the circle with equation
$$x^2 + y^2 + 2x - 4y - 4 = 0. \; †$$

In Exercises 13–14, find the slope–intercept form of the line satisfying the given condition.

13. The line has slope 3 and passes through $(1, -2)$. $y = 3x - 5$

14. The line is parallel to $2x + 3y = 5$ and passes through $(1, 3)$. †

In Exercises 15 and 16, find the domain of each function.

15. $f(x) = \dfrac{1}{2x + 3}$ †

16. $p(x) = \dfrac{1}{\sqrt{4 - 2x}}$ †

17. Let $f(x) = x^2 - 2x + 3$. Find $f(-2)$, $f(3)$, $f(x + h)$, and $\dfrac{f(x + h) - f(x)}{h}$. †

18. Let $f(x) = \sqrt{x}$ and $g(x) = x^2 + 1$. Find each of the following.

a. $f(g(x))$ †

b. $g(f(x))$ †

c. $f(f(x))$ †

d. $g(g(x))$ †

19. Let $f(x) = \begin{cases} 3x + 2 & \text{if } x \le 2 \\ 4x - 1 & \text{if } 2 < x \le 3. \\ 6 & \text{if } x > 3 \end{cases}$

a. Find $f(1)$, $f(3)$, and $f(4)$. †

b. Sketch the graph of $y = f(x)$. †

20. Let $f(x) = 2x - 3$. Find $f^{-1}(x)$.

21. Use transformations on $y = \sqrt{x}$ to sketch the graph of each function.

a. $f(x) = \sqrt{x + 2}$

b. $g(x) = -2\sqrt{x + 1} + 3$. †

22. Use the Rational Zeros Test to list all possible rational zeros of $f(x) = 2x^4 - 3x^2 + 5x - 6$.

In Exercises 23–26, graph each function.

23. $f(x) = 2x^2 - 4x + 1$ †

24. $f(x) = -x^2 + 2x + 3$ †

25. $f(x) = (x - 1)^2(x + 2)$ †

26. $f(x) = \dfrac{x^2 - 1}{x^2 - 4}$ †

27. Let $f(x) = x^4 - 3x^3 + 2x^2 + 2x - 4$. Given that $1 + i$ is a zero of f, find all zeros of f. $-1, 2, 1 + i, 1 - i$

28. Suppose y varies as the square root of x, and $y = 6$ when $x = 4$. Find y if $x = 9$. 9

29. A drug manufactured by a pharmaceutical company is sold in bulk at a price of 150 dollars per unit. The total production cost (in dollars) for x units in one week is
$$P(x) = 0.02x^2 + 100x + 3000.$$
How many units of the drug must be manufactured and sold in a week to maximize the profit? What is the maximum profit? $1250, \$28,250$

30. The profit (in dollars) for a product is given by
$$P(x) = 0.02x^3 + 48.8x^2 - 2990x + 25,000,$$
where x is the number of units produced and sold. One break-even point occurs when $x = 10$. Use synthetic division to find another break-even point for the product. $x = 50$

Answers:

1. 4

2. $\{-2, 3\}$.

3. $\{-1, 3\}$.

4. $\left\{ -\dfrac{3}{2} + \dfrac{\sqrt{5}}{2}, -\dfrac{3}{2} - \dfrac{\sqrt{5}}{2} \right\}$.

Answers:

20. $f^{-1}(x) = \dfrac{1}{2}x + \dfrac{3}{2}$

22. $-6, -3, -2, -\dfrac{3}{2}, -1, -\dfrac{1}{2}, \dfrac{1}{2}, 1, \dfrac{3}{2}, 2, 3, 6$

CHAPTER 4

Exponential and Logarithmic Functions

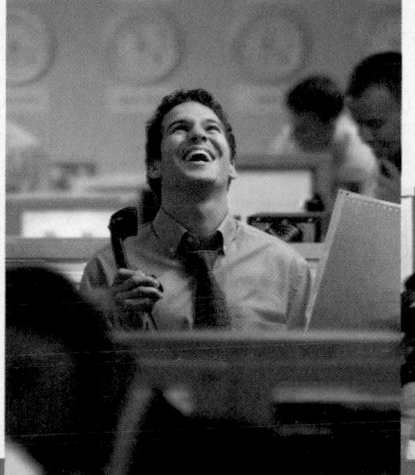

The world of finance, the growth of many populations, the molecular activity that results in an atomic explosion, and countless other everyday events are modeled with exponential and logarithmic functions.

TOPICS

Exponential Functions

BEFORE STARTING THIS SECTION, REVIEW

1. Integer exponents (Section P.2, page 20)

2. Rational exponents (Section P.6, page 69)

3. Graphing and transformations (Section 2.6, page 264)

4. One-to-one functions (Section 2.8, page 296)

5. Increasing and decreasing functions (Section 2.5, page 252)

OBJECTIVES

1 Define an exponential function.

2 Graph exponential functions.

3 Solve exponential equations.

4 Use transformations on exponential functions.

Fooling a King

There once was a wise man named Shashi in the reign of King Rai Bhalit in North West India. One night Shashi invented a wonderful new game called "Shatranj" (chess). The next morning he took it to the king, who marveled at it and was so enchanted that he said to Shashi, "Name your reward." Shashi said that he merely requested that 1 grain of wheat be placed on the first square of the chessboard, 2 grains on the second, 4 on the third, 8 on the fourth, and so on, until all 64 squares had been filled. The king readily agreed to this request, thinking that this man was an eccentric fool for asking for only a few grains of wheat when he could have had gold, jewels, or even his daughter's hand in marriage.

Most chess players know the end of this story. The amount of wheat needed to satisfy Shashi's request (ignoring the problem of stacking so much wheat on each square) is larger than the total amount of wheat harvested in all human history. The king could never fulfill his promise to Shashi, so instead he had him beheaded.

The details of this rapidly growing wheat phenomenon are given on the next page. Table 4.1 shows the number of grains of wheat that need to be stacked up on each square of the chessboard.

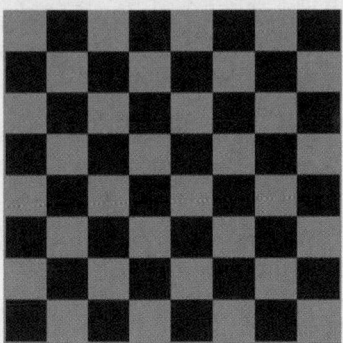

TABLE 4.1 Grains of Wheat on a Chessboard

Square number	Grains placed on this square
1	$1 \, (= 2^0)$
2	$2 \, (= 2^1)$
3	$4 \, (= 2^2)$
4	$8 \, (= 2^3)$
5	$16 \, (= 2^4)$
6	$32 \, (= 2^5)$
.	.
.	.
.	.
63	2^{62}
64	2^{63}

The data in Table 4.1 can be represented or modeled by the function

$$g(n) = 2^{n-1},$$

where $g(n)$ is the number of grains of wheat and n is the number of the square (or the nth square) on the chessboard. Notice that the number of grains of wheat on each square is obtained by doubling the number on the previous square. The function g is an example of an exponential function with base 2, where the values of the variable n are restricted to the numbers $1, 2, 3, \ldots, 64$ used to identify the chessboard squares. The name "exponential function" comes from the fact that the variable (in this case, n) occurs in the exponent. The base 2 is the *growth factor*.

When the rate of growth of a quantity is directly proportional to the existing amount, the growth can be modeled by an exponential function. For example, exponential functions are often used to model the growth of investments and populations, the cell division of living organisms, and the decay of radioactive material. ■

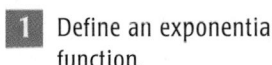 Define an exponential function.

Exponential Functions

EXPONENTIAL FUNCTION

A function f of the form

$$f(x) = a^x, \, a > 0 \text{ and } a \neq 1,$$

is called an **exponential function with base a.** The domain of the exponential function is $(-\infty, \infty)$.

In the definition of the exponential function, we rule out the base $a = 1$, since in this case the function is simply the constant function $f(x) = 1^x$, or $f(x) = 1$. We also exclude bases that are negative, because, for such a base, the function is not defined for every real number. For example, $(-2)^{1/2} = \sqrt{-2}$ is not a real number. Since we want the domain of an exponential function to be the set of all real numbers, we exclude negative numbers as base values for the exponential functions. Other functions that have variables in the exponent, such as $f(x) = 4 \cdot 3^x$, $g(x) = -5 \cdot 4^{3x-2}$, and $h(x) = c \cdot a^x$, $(a > 0, a \neq 1)$, are also called exponential functions.

Evaluate Exponential Functions

We can find the values of an exponential function for rational numbers by using the laws of exponents, as the next example shows.

EXAMPLE 1   **Evaluating Exponential Functions**

a. Let $f(x) = 3^{x-2}$. Find $f(4)$.

b. Let $g(x) = -2 \cdot 10^x$. Find $g(-2)$.

c. Let $h(x) = \left(\dfrac{1}{9}\right)^x$. Find $h\left(-\dfrac{3}{2}\right)$.

Solution

a. $f(4) = 3^{4-2} = 3^2 = 9$

b. $g(-2) = -2 \cdot 10^{-2} = -2 \cdot \dfrac{1}{10^2} = -2 \cdot \dfrac{1}{100} = -0.02$

c. $h\left(-\dfrac{3}{2}\right) = \left(\dfrac{1}{9}\right)^{-\frac{3}{2}} = (9^{-1})^{-\frac{3}{2}} = 9^{\frac{3}{2}} = (\sqrt{9})^3 = 27$ ■ ■ ■

PRACTICE PROBLEM 1   Let $f(x) = \left(\dfrac{1}{4}\right)^x$. Find $f(2)$, $f(0)$, $f(-1)$, $f\left(\dfrac{5}{2}\right)$, and $f\left(-\dfrac{3}{2}\right)$.   ■

Recall that the domain of an exponential function $f(x) = a^x$ $(a > 0, a \neq 1)$ is $(-\infty, \infty)$. In Example 1, we computed the values of exponential functions at some rational numbers. A natural question is, "What is the meaning of a^x when x is an irrational number?" For example, what do expressions such as $3^{\sqrt{2}}$ and 2^{π} mean? It turns out that the definition of a^x (with $a > 0$ and x irrational) requires methods discussed in calculus. However, the basis for the definition can be seen intuitively from the following discussion. Suppose we want to define the number 2^{π}. We first use a rational approximation of π.

From a calculator, we find that

$$\pi \approx 3.14159265.\ldots$$

We successively approximate 2^{π} by the rational powers shown in Table 4.2.

TABLE 4.2

Values of $f(x) = 2^x$ for rational values of x that approach π					
x	3	3.1	3.14	3.141	3.1415
2^x	$2^3 = 8$	$2^{3.1} = 8.5\ldots$	$2^{3.14} = 8.81\ldots$	$2^{3.141} = 8.821\ldots$	$2^{3.1415} = 8.8244\ldots$

It can be shown that there is exactly one number that the powers 2^3, $2^{3.1}$, $2^{3.14}$, $2^{3.141}$, $2^{3.1415}$, ... approach. We define 2^π to be that number. From Table 4.2, we see that $2^\pi \approx 8.82$ (correct to two decimal places). For our work with exponential functions, we will need the following fundamental facts:

1. Exponential functions are defined for all real numbers.
2. The graph of an exponential function is a continuous (unbroken) curve.
3. The rules of exponents hold for all real numbers.

RULES OF EXPONENTS

Let a, b, x, and y be real numbers with $a > 0$ and $b > 0$. Then

$$a^x \cdot a^y = a^{x+y}, \qquad (a^x)^y = a^{xy},$$

$$\frac{a^x}{a^y} = a^{x-y}, \qquad a^0 = 1,$$

$$(ab)^x = a^x b^x, \quad \text{and} \quad a^{-x} = \frac{1}{a^x} = \left(\frac{1}{a}\right)^x.$$

---

2 Graph exponential functions.

Graphing Exponential Functions

We now turn our attention to sketching the graph of an exponential function. Even though the domain of the exponential function $f(x) = a^x$ is the set of all real numbers, we usually choose only the integer values of x (for ease of computation) and find the corresponding values of y. This gives us a selected set of points on the graph of the function. Using your calculator, you can easily evaluate a^x for noninteger values of x. Recall that the graph of a function $f(x)$ is the graph of the equation $y = f(x)$. We use either of the two notations $f(x) = a^x$ and $y = a^x$ to represent a given function.

EXAMPLE 2   **Graphing an Exponential Function with Base $a > 1$**

Graph the exponential function $f(x) = 3^x$.

Solution

First make a table of a few selected values of x and the corresponding values of y, where $y = f(x)$:

x	-3	-2	-1	0	1	2	3
$y = 3^x$	$\dfrac{1}{27}$	$\dfrac{1}{9}$	$\dfrac{1}{3}$	1	3	9	27

Next, plot the points as shown in Figure 4.1(a), and then draw a smooth curve through them to get the graph in Figure 4.1(b).

Continued on next page.

(a)　　　　　　　　　　(b)

FIGURE 4.1

The graph in Figure 4.1(b) is typical of the graphs of exponential functions $f(x) = a^x$ when $a > 1$. Note that the x-axis is the horizontal asymptote of the graph of $y = 3^x$.

■ ■ ■

PRACTICE PROBLEM 2   Sketch the graph of

$$f(x) = 2^x.$$

■

Let's now sketch the graph of an exponential function $f(x) = a^x$ when $0 < a < 1$.

EXAMPLE 3   **Graphing an Exponential Function $f(x) = a^x$, with $0 < a < 1$**

Sketch the graph of $y = \left(\dfrac{1}{2}\right)^x$.

Solution

Make a table similar to that in Example 2:

x	-3	-2	-1	0	1	2	3
$y = \left(\dfrac{1}{2}\right)^x$	8	4	2	1	$\dfrac{1}{2}$	$\dfrac{1}{4}$	$\dfrac{1}{8}$

Plotting these points and drawing a smooth curve through them, we get the graph of $y = \left(\dfrac{1}{2}\right)^x$, shown in Figure 4.2(b). In this graph, as x increases in the positive direction, $y = \left(\dfrac{1}{2}\right)^x$ decreases towards 0. The graph in Figure 4.2 is typical of the graph of an exponential function $y = a^x$ with $0 < a < 1$.

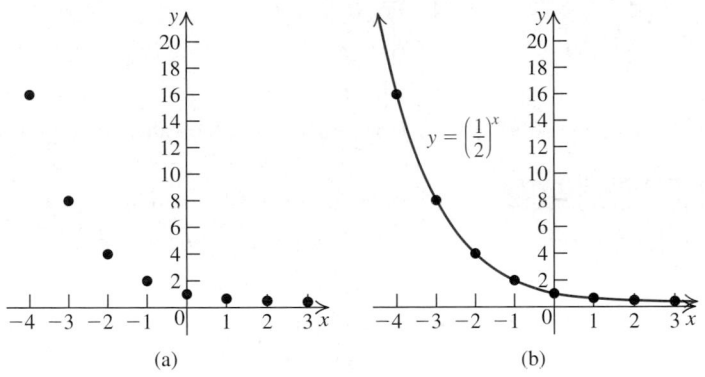

(a)   (b)

FIGURE 4.2   ■ ■ ■

PRACTICE PROBLEM 3   Sketch the graph of

$$f(x) = \left(\frac{1}{3}\right)^x.$$ ■

Since $y = \left(\frac{1}{2}\right)^x = (2^{-1})^x = 2^{-x}$, the graph of $y = \left(\frac{1}{2}\right)^x$ can also be obtained by reflecting the graph of $y = 2^x$ in the y-axis.

In Figure 4.3, we sketch the graphs of four exponential functions on the same set of axes. These graphs illustrate the following general properties of exponential functions.

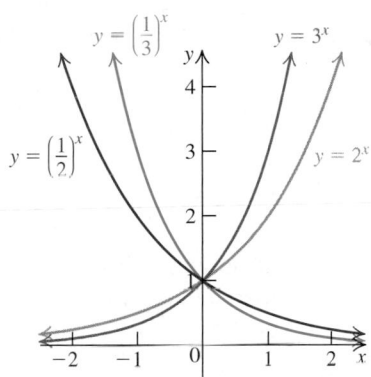

FIGURE 4.3

Properties of Exponential Functions   Let $f(x) = a^x, a > 0, a \neq 1$. Then

1. The domain of $f(x) = a^x$ is $(-\infty, \infty)$.

2. The range of $f(x) = a^x$ is $(0, \infty)$; thus, the entire graph lies above the x-axis.

3. For $a > 1$,

   (i) f is an increasing function; thus, the graph is rising as we move from left to right.

   (ii)   As $x \to \infty$, $y = a^x$ increases indefinitely and very rapidly.

   (iii)   As $x \to -\infty$, the values of $y = a^x$ get closer and closer to 0.

Continued on next page.

4. For $0 < a < 1$,

    (i) f is a decreasing function; thus, the graph is falling as we scan from left to right.

    (ii)   As $x \to -\infty$, $y = a^x$ increases indefinitely and very rapidly.

    (iii) As $x \to \infty$, the values of $y = a^x$ get closer and closer to 0.

RECALL

A function f is one-to-one if, when $f(x_1) = f(x_2)$, then $x_1 = x_2$.

---

5. Each exponential function f is one-to-one. Thus,

    (i)   if $a^{x_1} = a^{x_2}$, then $x_1 = x_2$;

    (ii) f has an inverse.

6. The graph of $f(x) = a^x$ has no x-intercepts. In other words, the graph of $f(x) = a^x$ never crosses the x-axis. Put another way, there is no value of x that will cause $f(x) = a^x$ to equal 0.

7. The graph of $f(x) = a^x$ has y-intercept 1. If we substitute $x = 0$ in the equation $y = a^x$, we obtain $y = a^0 = 1$, which yields 1 as the y-intercept.

REMINDER

Recall that a line $y = b$ is called a horizontal asymptote if $f(x) \to b$ as $x \to \infty$ or as $x \to -\infty$.

8. The x-axis is a horizontal asymptote for every exponential function of the form $f(x) = a^x$.

EXAMPLE 4   Finding a Base Value for an Exponential Function

Find a if the graph of the exponential function $f(x) = a^x$ contains the point $(2, 49)$.

Solution

We write $y = f(x)$, so the graph of the given function is the graph of the equation

$$y = a^x.$$

Since the point $(2, 49)$ is on the graph, we have

$$49 = a^2 \qquad \text{Replace } x \text{ by 2 and } y \text{ by 49.}$$
$$\pm 7 = a \qquad \text{Solve for } a.$$

The solution set is $\{-7, 7\}$. We discard the negative base $a = -7$, since the base for an exponential function must be positive. Therefore, $a = 7$. Hence, the exponential function $f(x) = a^x$ whose graph contains the point $(2, 49)$ is $f(x) = 7^x$.   ■ ■ ■

PRACTICE PROBLEM 4   Find a if the exponential function

$$f(x) = a^x$$

contains the point $(-1, 5)$.   ■

    When we are evaluating $f(x) = a^x$ at some value of x, say, x_0, we are trying to find the second coordinate y of the ordered pair (x_0, y) on the graph of an exponential function, given the first coordinate. In Example 6, we illustrate the method of finding the first coordinate when we are given the second coordinate.

3 Solve exponential equations.

Exponential Equations

In Examples 5 and 6, we use the "one-to-one" property of the exponential function (if $a^x = a^y$, then $x = y$) to solve an exponential equation. This technique works for those equations in which both sides can be written as powers of the same base. Later in the chapter, you will learn how to solve more general exponential equations.

EXAMPLE 5   **Solving an Exponential Equation**

Solve for x: $5^{2x-1} = 25$.

Solution

$$
\begin{aligned}
5^{2x-1} &= 25 && \text{Given equation} \\
5^{2x-1} &= 5^2 && \text{Replace 25 by } 5^2. \\
2x - 1 &= 2 && \text{If } a^x = a^y, \text{ then } x = y. \\
2x &= 3 && \text{Add 1 to both sides.} \\
x &= \frac{3}{2} && \text{Solve for } x.
\end{aligned}
$$

The solution set is $\left\{ \dfrac{3}{2} \right\}$.   ■ ■ ■

PRACTICE PROBLEM 5   Solve for x: $3^{2x+1} = 243$.   ■

EXAMPLE 6   **Finding the First Coordinate, Given the Second**

a. Let $f(x) = 3^{x-2}$. Find x so that $f(x) = \dfrac{1}{27}$.

b. Let $g(x) = 5^{x(x-3)}$. Find x so that $g(x) = \dfrac{1}{25}$.

Solution

a. Since $f(x) = 3^{x-2}$ and $f(x) = \dfrac{1}{27}$, we have

$$
3^{x-2} = \frac{1}{27}
$$

$$
3^{x-2} = 3^{-3} \qquad \frac{1}{27} = \frac{1}{3^3} = 3^{-3}
$$

$$
x - 2 = -3 \qquad \text{If } a^x = a^y, \text{ then } x = y.
$$

$$
x = -1. \qquad \text{Solve for } x.
$$

So the point $\left(-1, \dfrac{1}{27} \right)$ is on the graph of f.

Continued on next page.

b. Since $g(x) = 5^{x(x-3)}$ and $g(x) = \dfrac{1}{25}$, we have

$$5^{x(x-3)} = 5^{-2} \qquad \text{Write } \dfrac{1}{25} = 5^{-2}.$$
$$x(x - 3) = -2 \qquad \text{If } a^x = a^y, \text{ then } x = y.$$
$$x^2 - 3x = -2 \qquad \text{Distributive property}$$
$$x^2 - 3x + 2 = 0 \qquad \text{Add 2 to both sides.}$$
$$(x - 1)(x - 2) = 0 \qquad \text{Factor.}$$
$$\text{Thus, } x = 1 \text{ or } x = 2. \qquad \text{Solve for } x.$$

In this case, there are two points, namely, $\left(1, \dfrac{1}{25}\right)$ and $\left(2, \dfrac{1}{25}\right)$, on the graph of g.

■ ■ ■

PRACTICE PROBLEM 6 Let $f(x) = 5^{3-x}$. Find x such that $f(x) = 625$. ■

---

4 Use transformations on exponential functions.

Transformations on Exponential Functions

We can apply the transformations discussed in Section 2.6 to graph many functions that are related to exponential functions:

Transformations on Exponential Function $f(x) = a^x$

Transformation	Equation	Effect on Graph
Horizontal Shift	$y = a^{x+b}$ $= f(x + b)$	Shift the graph of $y = a^x$, b units (i) left if $b > 0$. (ii) right if $b < 0$.
Vertical Shift	$y = a^x + b$ $= f(x) + b$	Shift the graph of $y = a^x$, b units (i) up if $b > 0$. (ii) down if $b < 0$.
Stretching or Compressing (vertically)	$y = ca^x = cf(x)$	Multiply the y coordinates by c. The graph of $y = a^x$ is vertically (i) stretched if $c > 1$. (ii) compressed if $0 < c < 1$.
Reflection	$y = -a^x = -f(x)$ $y = a^{-x} = f(-x)$	The graph of $y = a^x$ is reflected in the x-axis. The graph of $y = a^x$ is reflected in the y-axis.

EXAMPLE 7 **Sketching Graphs**

Use transformations to sketch the graph of each function.

a. $f(x) = 3^x - 4$ **b.** $f(x) = 3^{x+1}$
c. $f(x) = -3^x$ **d.** $f(x) = -3^x + 2$

State the domain and the range of each function and the horizontal asymptote of its graph.

Solution

Figure 4.4 describes how to sketch the graphs of each of these functions from the graph of the basic exponential function $f(x) = 3^x$.

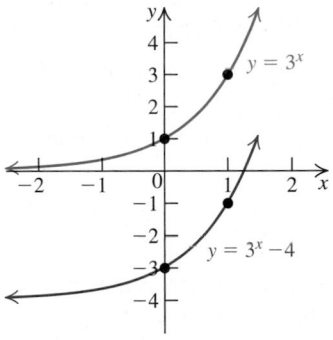

$f(x) = 3^x - 4$
Subtract 4 from 3^x: Shift the
graph of $y = 3^x$, four units down.

(a)

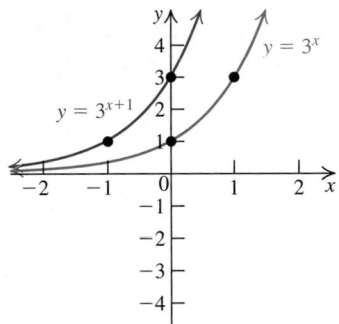

$f(x) = 3^{x+1}$
Replace x in 3^x by $x + 1$: Shift the
graph of $y = 3^x$, one unit left.

(b)

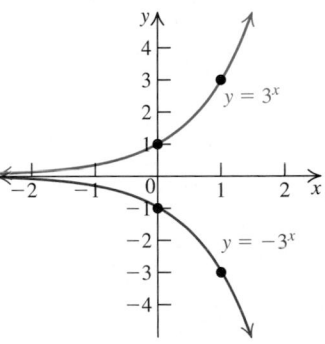

$f(x) = -3^x$
Multiply 3^x by -1: Reflect the graph
of $y = 3^x$ in the x-axis.

(c)

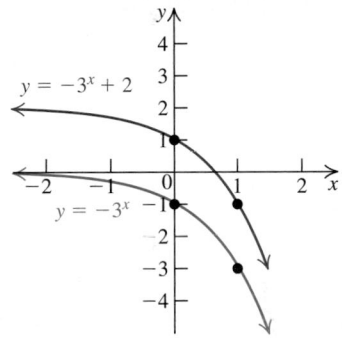

$f(x) = -3^x + 2$
Add 2 to -3^x: Shift the graph of
of $y = -3^x$, two units up.

(d)

FIGURE 4.4

a. The domain of $f(x) = 3^x - 4$ is $(-\infty, \infty)$, the range is $(-4, \infty)$, and the horizontal asymptote is $y = -4$.

b. The domain of $f(x) = 3^{x+1}$ is, $(-\infty, \infty)$ the range is $(0, \infty)$, and the horizontal asymptote is the x-axis $(y = 0)$.

c. The domain of $f(x) = -3^x$ is $(-\infty, \infty)$, the range is $(-\infty, 0)$, and the horizontal asymptote is the x-axis $(y = 0)$.

d. The domain of $f(x) = -3^x + 2$ is $(-\infty, \infty)$, the range is $(-\infty, 2)$, and the horizontal asymptote is $y = 2$. ■ ■ ■

PRACTICE PROBLEM 7   Sketch the graph of $y = 3^{x-1} + 4$. ■

FIGURE 4.5

EXAMPLE 8   Comparing Exponential and Power Functions

Compare the graphs of $f(x) = x^2$ and $g(x) = 2^x$ for $x \geq 0$.

Solution

Figure 4.5 shows the graphs of f and g over the interval [0, 5]. We notice the following:

(i)   The graph of $g(x) = 2^x$ is higher than the graph of $f(x) = x^2$ in the interval [0, 2). Thus, $2^x > x^2$ for $0 \leq x < 2$.

(ii)   The graph of f intersects the graph of g at $x = 2$. Thus, $2^x = x^2$ at $x = 2$. Both values are 4, and (2, 4) is a point on both of the graphs.

(iii)   In the interval (2, 4), the graph of f is higher than the graph of g; that is, $x^2 > 2^x$ for $2 < x < 4$.

(iv)   The graph of f intersects the graph of g again at $x = 4$; that is, $2^x = x^2$ at $x = 4$. Both values are 16, and (4, 16) is a point on both of the graphs.

(v)   For $x > 4$, the graph of g is higher than the graph of f; that is, $2^x > x^2$ for $x > 4$.

PRACTICE PROBLEM 8   Compare the graphs of $f(x) = x^4$ and $g(x) = 4^x$.

The result of Example 8 can be generalized. That is, for large values of x, the exponential function with base $a > 1$ is greater than any power function. In other words, for large values of x, we have

$$a^x > x^n \qquad (a > 1 \text{ and } n \text{ any positive integer}).$$

In fact, for large values of x, any exponential function $y = a^x (a > 1)$ eventually becomes greater than any polynomial function.

EXAMPLE 9   Bacterial Growth

A technician to the French microbiologist Louis Pasteur noticed that a certain culture of bacteria in milk doubles every hour. If the bacteria count $B(t)$ is modeled by the equation

$$B(t) = 2000 \cdot 2^t,$$

with t in hours, find

a.   the initial number of bacteria;

b.   the number of bacteria after 10 hours; and

c.   the time when the number of the bacteria will be 32,000.

Solution

a.   Initial size $B_0 = B(0) = 2000 \cdot 2^0 = 2000 \cdot 1 = 2000$.   Substitute $t = 0$ and simplify.

b. $B(10) = 2000 \cdot 2^{10} = 2,048,000$.   Substitute $t = 10$ and simplify.

c. We have to find t when $B(t) = 32,000$.

$$32,000 = 2000 \cdot 2^t \qquad \text{Let } B(t) = 32,000.$$
$$16 = 2^t \qquad \text{Divide both sides by 2000.}$$
$$2^4 = 2^t \qquad \text{Rewrite 16 as } 2^4.$$
$$4 = t \qquad \text{If } a^x = a^y, \text{ then } x = y.$$

That is, 4 hours from the starting time, the number of bacteria will have increased to 32,000.

■ ■ ■

PRACTICE PROBLEM 9   In Example 9, find the time when the bacteria will be 128,000.   ■

A Exercises   Basic Skills and Concepts

In Exercises 1–8, explain whether the given equation defines an exponential function. Give reasons for your answers. Write the base for each exponential function.

1. $y = x^3$ †

2. $y = 4^x$ †

3. $y = 2^{-x}$ †

4. $y = 1^x$ †

5. $y = x^x$ †

6. $y = 4^2$ †

7. $y = 0^x$ †

8. $y = (1.8)^x$ †

In Exercises 9–18, evaluate each exponential function for the given value. (Use a calculator if necessary.)

9. $f(x) = 5^{x-1}$, $f(3)$ 25

10. $f(x) = -2^{x+1}$, $f(3)$ −16

11. $f(x) = 3^{1-x}$, $f(3.2)$ ≈ 0.089

12. $f(x) = 6^{x-1}$, $f(2.8)$ ≈ 25.158

13. $g(x) = -\left(\dfrac{1}{2}\right)^{x+1}$, $g(-3.5)$ ≈ −5.657

14. $g(x) = -\left(\dfrac{2}{3}\right)^{2x-1}$, $g(2.5)$ $-\dfrac{16}{81} \approx -0.198$

15. $g(x) = \left(\dfrac{1}{4}\right)^{1-2x}$, $g\left(\dfrac{3}{2}\right)$ 16

16. $g(x) = -\left(\dfrac{2}{5}\right)^{3x-1}$, $g\left(\dfrac{4}{3}\right)$ −0.064

17. $h(x) = 1 - 3^{-x}$, $h(1)$ $\dfrac{2}{3}$

18. $h(x) = 3 - 5^{-x}$, $h(2)$ $\dfrac{74}{25}$

In Exercises 19–26, sketch the graph of the given function by making a table of values. (Use a calculator if necessary.)

19. $f(x) = 4^x$ †

20. $g(x) = 10^x$ †

21. $g(x) = \left(\dfrac{3}{2}\right)^{-x}$ †

22. $h(x) = 7^{-x}$ †

23. $h(x) = \left(\dfrac{1}{4}\right)^x$ †

24. $f(x) = \left(\dfrac{1}{10}\right)^x$ †

25. $f(x) = (1.3)^{-x}$ †

26. $g(x) = (0.7)^{-x}$ †

27. How are the graphs in Exercises 19 and 23 related? inverses Can we obtain the graph of Exercise 23 from that of Exercise 19? If so, how? Yes, reflection in the y-axis

28. Repeat Exercise 27 for the graphs in Exercises 20 and 24.

Match each exponential function given in Exercises 29–32 with one of the graphs labeled (a), (b), (c), and (d).

29. $f(x) = 5^x$ (c)

30. $f(x) = -5^x$ (b)

31. $f(x) = 5^{-x}$ (a)

32. $f(x) = 5^{-x} + 1$ (d)

(a)

(b)

(c)

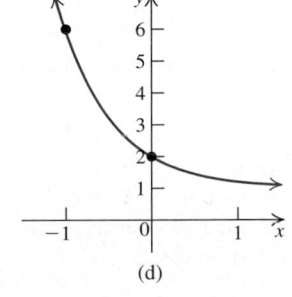

(d)

†Due to space constrictions, answers to these exercises may be found in the Answers beginning on page A–1 in the back of the book.

In Exercises 33–42, graph the equation by using transformations to the graph of the appropriate function in Exercises 19–26.

33. $y = 4^{x-1}$ †

34. $y = -10^x$ †

35. $y = 4^{-x}$ †

36. $y = 7^x + 2$ †

37. $y = -\left(\dfrac{1}{4}\right)^x$ †

38. $y = 4 - 7^x$ †

39. $y = 4 + \left(\dfrac{3}{2}\right)^x$ †

40. $y = \left(\dfrac{1}{10}\right)^x - 1$ †

41. $y = -(1.3)^{-x}$ †

42. $y = 2 - (0.7)^{-x}$ †

In Exercises 43–50, start with the basic exponential function $f(x) = 3^x$, and use transformations to sketch the graph of the function $g(x)$. State the domain and range of $g(x)$ and the horizontal asymptote of its graph.

43. $g(x) = 3^{x-1}$ †

44. $g(x) = 3^{x-1} - 2$ †

45. $g(x) = \dfrac{1}{2}3^{x+1}$ †

46. $g(x) = \dfrac{1}{2}3^{x+1} - 2$ †

47. $g(x) = -2 \cdot 3^{x+1} + 1$ †

48. $g(x) = 2 \cdot 3^{x+1} - 1$ †

49. $g(x) = -2 \cdot 3^{x-1} + 4$ †

50. $g(x) = \dfrac{1}{2} \cdot 3^{-x+1} - 2$ †

In Exercises 51–54, write an equation of each graph in the final position.

51. The graph of $y = 2^x$ is shifted two units left and five units up. $y = 2^{x+2} + 5$

52. The graph of $y = 3^x$ is reflected in the y-axis and then shifted three units right. $y = 3^{-(x+3)}$

53. The graph of $y = \left(\dfrac{1}{2}\right)^x$ is stretched vertically by a factor of 2 and then shifted five units down. †

54. The graph of $y = 2^{-x}$ is reflected in the x-axis and then shifted three units up. $y = -2^{-x} + 3$

In Exercises 55–60, find the exponential function of the form $f(x) = a^x$ that contains the given graph point.

55. $(2, 16)$ $a = 4$

56. $\left(-2, \dfrac{1}{9}\right)$ $a = 3$

57. $(3, 216)$ $a = 6$

58. $\left(3, \dfrac{1}{125}\right)$ $a = \dfrac{1}{5}$

59. $(-2, 16)$ $a = \dfrac{1}{4}$

60. $\left(\dfrac{1}{3}, \dfrac{1}{2}\right)$ $a = \dfrac{1}{8}$

In Exercises 61 and 62, find the exponential function of the form $f(x) = c \cdot a^x$ that contains the two given points.

61. $(0, 3)$ and $(2, 12)$ $y = 3 \cdot 2^x$

62. $(0, 5)$ and $(1, 15)$ $y = 5 \cdot 3^x$

In Exercises 63–78, solve each equation for x by first rewriting both sides as powers of the same base.

63. $3^x = 81$ $x = 4$

64. $9^x = 243$ $x = \dfrac{5}{2}$

65. $4^{|x|} = 128$ $x = \pm\dfrac{7}{2}$

66. $3^{-x} = 27$ $x = -3$

67. $2^{-x+1} = 16$ $x = -3$

68. $4^{x-1} = 1$ $x = 1$

69. $2^x = 4^{2x+1}$ $x = -\dfrac{2}{3}$

70. $(\sqrt{2})^x = \dfrac{1}{16}$ $x = -8$

71. $\left(\dfrac{3}{5}\right)^x = \dfrac{125}{27}$ $x = -3$

72. $\left(\dfrac{2}{3}\right)^x = \left(\dfrac{9}{4}\right)^3$ $x = -6$

73. $2^{|x|} = 16$ $x = \pm4$

74. $4^{-|x|} = \dfrac{1}{128}$ $x = \pm\dfrac{7}{2}$

75. $3^x = (9)^{x-1} \cdot (27)^{1-3x}$ †

76. $5^{x^2} = \left(\dfrac{1}{25}\right)^{-8}$ $x = \pm4$

77. $9^x - 3^x = 0$ $x = 0$

78. $2^{x^2} = (8)^{2x} \cdot \dfrac{1}{256}$. $x = 4, 2$

B Exercises Applying the Concepts

79. Suppose that a metal block is cooling so that its temperature T (in °C) is given by $T = 200 \cdot 4^{-0.1t}$, where t is in hours. How long has the cooling been taking place if the block now has a temperature of 100°C? $t = 5$ hours

80. Suppose the worldwide sales (in millions) of a computer chip called pentium p are approximated by

$$s(t) = 50 - 30 \cdot 2^{-t},$$

where t represents the number of years that the pentium p has been on the market.

a. Find each function value.

(i) $s(0)$ †

(ii) $s(1)$ †

(iii) $s(5)$ †

(iv) $s(10)$ †

b. Graph $y = s(x)$. Find the horizontal asymptote. What is the meaning of this horizontal asymptote? †

81. The population (in thousands) of people of East Indian origin in the United States is approximated by the function

$$p(x) = 750 \cdot (2)^{0.032x},$$

where x is the number of years since 1990.
  a. Find the population of this group in
   (i) 1990 750
   (ii) 2000 936.247 ($\approx$937)
  b. Predict the population in 2010. 1168.746 ($\approx$1169)

(The function $p(x)$ is modeled by the authors from the data from the weekly magazine *India Abroad*.)

82. Suppose we have a large sheet of paper 0.015 centimeter thick, and we tear the paper in half and put the pieces on top of each other. We keep tearing and stacking in this manner, always tearing each piece in half.

How high would the resulting pile of paper be if we continue the process of tearing and stacking

  a. 30 times? 0.015 $\times$ 2^{30} $\approx$ 16,106,127 cm
  b. 40 times? 0.015 $\times$ 2^{40} $\approx$ 16,492,674,420 cm
  c. 50 times? [*Hint:* Use a calculator.] 0.015 $\times$ 2^{50} cm

83. We have a container with a volume of 1000 cubic centimeters. The number of bacteria in this container doubles every minute. Suppose the container is full in 60 minutes. How long did it take for the container to be half full? 59 minutes

84. A box contains radioactive plutonium. The number of kilograms $p(t)$ at time t years is given by the formula

$$p(t) = 2^{-0.0001754t}.$$

Find the amount of plutonium in the box at the following times:
  a. $t = 0$ 1 kg
  b. $t = 800$ 0.9073 kg
  c. $t = 1000$ 0.8855 kg
  d. $t = 10,000$ 0.2965 kg

85. In Exercise 84, how long will it take until only one-half kilogram of plutonium is left in the box? 5701.25 yr

86. The number of bacteria present after t minutes is given by the formula $n(t) = 1000(3)^{0.1t}$.
  a. Find the number of bacteria after
   (i) 5 minutes. (1) 1732.05 ($\approx$1732)
   (ii) 10 minutes. (2) 3000
  b. How long would it take for the bacteria population to reach 9000? 20 minutes

C Exercises Beyond the Basics

87. Sketch the graph of $f(x) = 2^{|x|} = \begin{cases} 2^x & \text{if } x \geq 0 \\ 2^{-x} & \text{if } x < 0 \end{cases}$.
   Check for symmetry. Find the range of this function. †

88. Sketch the graph of $g(x) = 2^{-|x|}$. †

89. Sketch the graph of $g(x) = 2^{x^2}$. Check for symmetry. Find the domain and range of this function. †

90. a. Sketch the graph of $h(x) = 2^{-x^2}$. †
  b. Find the domain and range of $h(x)$. †
  c. Why can't we obtain the graph of $h(x)$ by reflecting the graph of $g(x)$ of Exercise 89 in the y-axis? †

91. Let $f(x) = 3^x + 3^{-x}$ and $g(x) = 3^x - 3^{-x}$. Find each of the following:
  a. $f(x) + g(x)$ $f(x) + g(x) = 2 \cdot 3^x$
  b. $f(x) - g(x)$ $f(x) - g(x) = 2 \cdot 3^{-x}$
  c. $[f(x)]^2 - [g(x)]^2$ $[f(x)]^2 - [g(x)]^2 = 4$
  d. $[f(x)]^2 + [g(x)]^2$. $[f(x)]^2 + [g(x)]^2 = 2(3^{2x} + 3^{-2x})$

92. Repeat Exercise 91 for the functions $f(x) = a^x + a^{-x}$ and $g(x) = a^x - a^{-x}$. †

In Exercises 93–96, solve the given equation for x. [*Hint:* These equations are quadratic in form.]

93. $2^{2x} - 12 \cdot 2^x + 32 = 0$ $x = 2, 3$

94. $3^{2x} - 4 \cdot 3^{x+1} + 27 = 0$ $x = 1, 2$

95. $4(2^x + 2^{-x}) = 17$ $x = 2, -2$

96. $4^{1+x} + 4^{1-x} = 10$ †

97. **Growth of bacteria.** The bacterium *Escherichia coli*, commonly known as *E. coli*, is found in the human digestive tract. Suppose that a colony of *E. coli* started with a single cell, and each *E. coli* cell divides into two cells one-third hour after its own birth. Suppose also that no deaths occur.

   a. Write a function that models the number of *E. coli* cells after t hours. $y(t) = 2^{3t}$

   b. Given that the mass of a single *E. coli* cell is approximately $5 \cdot 2^{-43}$ gram, find the mass of the colony after 10 hours. 5×2^{-13} gm

   c. When will the mass of the colony be 20 grams?
   15 hr

98. **Internet users.** The number of Internet users worldwide was estimated to be 25 million in 1995 and 800 million in 2003. The growth can be approximated by an exponential function.

   a. Find an exponential function of the form $y = c \cdot a^x$ that models the number of Internet users, where $x = 0$ corresponds to 1995 and y corresponds to the number of users in millions.   †

   b. Graph the function and estimate the number of users in 2004.   †

   c. Use the graph to estimate the year when there were 200 million users.   †

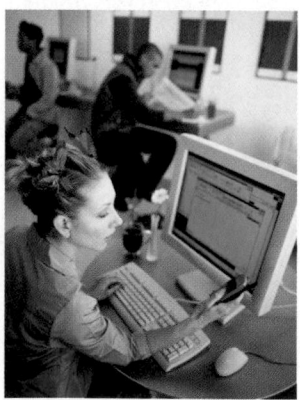

99. **Spread of AIDS.** In 1987, the number of cases of AIDS in the United States was estimated at 50,000. This number was doubling every year. Assume that the trend continued.

   a. Set up a function of the form
   $$f(t) = c \cdot a^{kt}$$
   to describe the number of cases of AIDS, where t is time measured in years from 1987. $f(x) = 50000 \cdot 2^t$

   b. According to the model in (a), how many cases of AIDS were there in 1999?   204,800,000

   c. Use the model to predict the number of cases of AIDS in 2007.   52,428,800,000

   d. According to the model, when was the number of cases of AIDS 1.6 million?   after 5 yr (in 1992)

   e. Is it possible that the number of AIDS cases doubled every year through the year 2007?   †

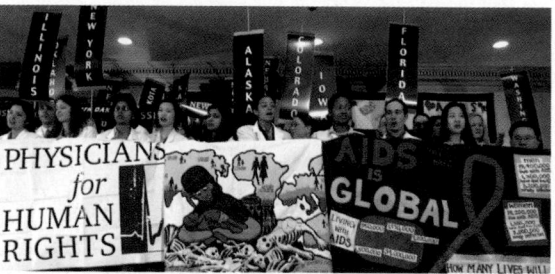

Critical Thinking

100. Give a convincing argument to show that the equation $2^x = k$ has exactly one solution for every $k > 0$. Support your argument with graphs.   †

101. Find all solutions of the equation $2^x = 2x$. How do you know that you have found all solutions?   †

The Natural Exponential Function

BEFORE STARTING THIS SECTION, REVIEW

1. Exponential function (Section 4.1, page 423)

2. Graphing and transformations (Section 2.6, page 264)

OBJECTIVES

1 Develop a compound-interest formula.

2 Understand the number *e*.

3 Graph exponential functions.

4 Evaluate exponential functions.

Descendant Seeks Loan Repayment

George Washington could not tell a lie, but apparently he could leave behind a whopping debt.

In 1777, Jacob DeHaven, a wealthy Pennsylvania trader, responded to a desperate plea from Washington when it seemed that the Revolutionary War was about to be lost. Mr. DeHaven loaned 450,000 dollars worth of gold and supplies to the Continental Congress to rescue the troops at Valley Forge. His loan provided badly needed supplies, provisions, and salaries for the Continental Army. George Washington went on to defeat the British in the war. After the war, the government offered to repay DeHaven's loan in continental dollars, the then worthless currency of the fledging country. But he refused and died penniless in 1812.

In 1990, DeHaven's descendants sued the U.S. government for repayment of the loan. "If I owed the government this money, I would be expected to pay the principal, interest, and any penalties that might have been incurred," said Carolyn Cokerham of San Antonio. Ms. Cokerham is one of nearly 2000 living descendants of DeHaven. These and previous descendants have tried unsuccessfully to get the money repaid through the years. How much money did DeHaven's descendants claim the government owed them on the 1990 anniversary of the loan at the then prevailing interest rate of 6%? See Example 5. ▪

Questions such as these are standard financial management questions. In order to answer these questions, let us first review some of the terminology used in such problems.

Interest A fee charged for borrowing a lender's money is called the *interest*, denoted by I.

Principal The original amount of money borrowed is called the *principal* or initial amount, denoted by P.

Time Suppose P dollars is borrowed. The borrower agrees to pay back the initial P dollars, plus the interest, within a specified period. This period is called the *time* of the loan and is denoted by t.

Interest Rate The *interest rate* is the percent charged for the use of the principal for the given period. The interest rate is expressed as a decimal and denoted by r. Unless stated otherwise, it is assumed to be for one year; that is, r is an annual interest rate.

Simple Interest The amount of interest computed only on the principal is called *simple interest*.

RECALL

$8\% = 8$ percent
$\quad = 8$ per hundred
$\quad = \dfrac{8}{100}$
$\quad = 0.08$

When money is deposited with a bank, the bank becomes the borrower. For example, the statement "One thousand dollars is deposited in an account at 8% interest" means that the principal $P = \$1000$ and the interest rate $r = 0.08$ and the bank is the borrower.

SIMPLE-INTEREST FORMULA

The simple interest I on a principal P at a rate r (expressed as a decimal) per year for t years is

$$I = Prt. \tag{1}$$

EXAMPLE 1   Calculating Simple Interest

Juanita has deposited 8000 dollars in a bank for five years at a simple interest rate of 6%.

a. How much interest will she receive?

b. How much money will she receive at the end of five years?

Solution

a. We use Equation (1) with $P = \$8000$, $r = 0.06$, and $t = 5$.

$$I = Prt$$
$$= \$8000\,(0.06)(5)$$
$$= \$2400.$$

b. The total amount A due her in five years is the sum of the original principal and the interest earned:

$$A = P + I$$
$$= \$8000 + \$2400$$
$$= \$10,400.$$

■ ■ ■

PRACTICE PROBLEM 1   Find the amount received if $10,000 is deposited in a bank at a simple interest rate of 7.5% for 2 years.   ■

In general, with P and r given, the amount $A(t)$ calculated at simple interest and due in t years is found by using the formula

$$A(t) = P + Prt. \tag{2}$$

Equation (2) is a linear function of t. Simple interest problems are examples of **linear growth,** which take place when the growth of a quantity occurs at a constant rate and so can be modeled by a linear function.

1 Develop a compound-interest formula.

Compound Interest

In the real world, the concept of simple interest is almost never used for periods of more than one year. Instead, we replace simple interest with **compound interest**—the interest paid on both the principal and the accrued (previously earned) interest. We illustrate the concept by an example.

Suppose 1000 dollars is deposited in a bank account paying 4% annual interest. At the end of one year, the account will contain the original 1000 dollars, plus the 4% interest earned on the 1000 dollars. That is,

$$\$1000 + (0.04)(\$1000) = \$1040.$$

In the same way, let P represent the initial amount deposited at an interest rate r (expressed as a decimal number) per year. Then the amount A_1 in the account after one year is

$$
\begin{aligned}
A_1 &= P + rP && \text{Principal } P, \text{ plus interest earned} \\
&= P(1 + r). && \text{Factor out } P.
\end{aligned}
$$

During the second year, the account earns interest on the new principal A_1. The amount A_2 in the account after the second year will be equal to A_1, plus the interest earned on A_1.

$$
\begin{aligned}
A_2 &= A_1 + rA_1 && A_1, \text{ plus interest earned} \\
&= A_1(1 + r) && \text{Factor out } A_1. \\
&= P(1 + r)(1 + r) && A_1 = P(1 + r) \\
&= P(1 + r)^2
\end{aligned}
$$

The amount A_3 in the account after the third year is

$$
\begin{aligned}
A_3 &= A_2 + rA_2 && A_2, \text{ plus interest earned} \\
&= A_2(1 + r) && \text{Factor out } A_2. \\
&= P(1 + r)^2(1 + r) && A_2 = P(1 + r)^2 \\
&= P(1 + r)^3.
\end{aligned}
$$

In general, the amount A in the account after t years is given by

$$A = P(1 + r)^t. \tag{3}$$

This type of interest is said to be **compounded annually,** since the interest earned is paid once a year.

> **EXAMPLE 2** **Calculating Compound Interest**

Juanita deposits 8000 dollars in a bank at the interest rate of 6% compounded annually for five years.

a. How much money will she have in her account after five years?

b. How much interest will she receive?

Solution

a. Here, $P = \$8000$, $r = 0.06$, and $t = 5$, so

$$A = P(1 + r)^t \qquad \text{Equation (3)}$$
$$= \$8000(1 + 0.06)^5 \qquad P = \$8000, r = 0.06, t = 5$$
$$= \$8000(1.06)^5$$
$$= \$10{,}705.80. \qquad \text{Use a calculator.}$$

b. Interest $= A - P = \$10{,}705.80 - \$8000 = \$2705.80$. ■ ■ ■

PRACTICE PROBLEM 2 Repeat Example 2 if the bank pays 7.5% interest compounded annually. ■

Comparing the interest in Examples 1 and 2, we see that the effect of compounding Juanita's interest was to make the money grow faster. Observe that, with values of P and r given, the amount $A(t)$ received after t years is

$$A(t) = P(1 + r)^t. \tag{3}$$

The function $A(t)$ in Equation (3) is an exponential function with base $(1 + r)$.

In most savings accounts, the banks or financial institutions pay interest more than once a year. In such cases, a smaller amount of interest is paid more frequently. Suppose that the annual interest rate quoted (also called the **nominal rate**), expressed as the decimal number r is compounded n times per year (at equal intervals) instead of annually. Then, in each period, the interest rate is $\dfrac{r}{n}$, and there are $n \cdot t$ periods in t years. Accordingly, the formula $A(t) = P(1 + r)^t$ can be restated as follows:

COMPOUND INTEREST FORMULA

$$A = P\left(1 + \frac{r}{n}\right)^{nt} \tag{4}$$

A = amount after t years
P = principal
r = annual interest rate (expressed as a decimal number)
n = number of times interest is compounded each year
t = number of years.

The total amount accumulated after t years, denoted by A, is also called the **future value** of the investment.

EXAMPLE 3   **Using Different Compounding Periods to Compare Future Values**

One hundred dollars is deposited in a bank that pays 5% annual interest. Find the future value A after one year if the interest is compounded

(i)   Annually.

(ii) Semiannually.

(iii) Quarterly.

(iv) Monthly.

(v)   Daily.

Solution

In each of the computations that follow, $P = 100$, $r = 0.05$, and $t = 1$. Only n, the number of times interest is compounded each year, is changing. Since $t = 1$, $nt = n(1) = n$.

(i)   Annual Compounding: $A = P\left(1 + \dfrac{r}{n}\right)^{nt}$

$A = 100(1 + 0.05) = \$105.00$ $n = 1; t = 1$

(ii) Semiannual Compounding: $A = P\left(1 + \dfrac{r}{2}\right)^{2}$ $n = 2; t = 1$

$A = 100\left(1 + \dfrac{0.05}{2}\right)^{2}$

$\approx \$105.06$ Use a calculator.

(iii) Quarterly Compounding: $A = P\left(1 + \dfrac{r}{4}\right)^{4}$ $n = 4; t = 1$

$A = 100\left(1 + \dfrac{0.05}{4}\right)^{4}$

$\approx \$105.09$ Use a calculator.

(iv) Monthly Compounding: $A = P\left(1 + \dfrac{r}{12}\right)^{12}$ $n = 12; t = 1$

$A = 100\left(1 + \dfrac{0.05}{12}\right)^{12}$

$\approx \$105.12$ Use a calculator.

(v)   Daily Compounding: $A = P\left(1 + \dfrac{r}{365}\right)^{365}$ $n = 365; t = 1$

$A = 100\left(1 + \dfrac{0.05}{365}\right)^{365}$

$\approx \$105.13$ Use a calculator.

■ ■ ■

Practice Problem 3   Repeat Example 3 if \$5000 is deposited at a 6.5% annual rate.   ■

Leonhard Euler

(1707–1783)

Leonhard Euler was the son of a Calvinist minister from the vicinity of Basel, Switzerland. At 13, Euler entered the University of Basel, pursuing a career in theology, as his father wished. At the university, Euler was tutored by Johann Bernoulli, of the famous Bernoulli family of mathematicians. His interest and skills led him to abandon his theological studies and take up mathematics. Euler obtained his master's degree in philosophy at the age of 16. In 1727, Peter the Great invited him to join the Academy at St. Petersburg. In 1741, he moved to the Berlin Academy, where he stayed until 1766. He then returned to St. Petersburg, where he remained for the rest of his life.

Euler was incredibly prolific, contributing to many areas of mathematics, including number theory, combinatorics, and analysis, as well as its applications to such areas as music and naval architecture. He wrote over 1100 books and papers and left so much unpublished work that it took 47 years after he died for all his work to be published. During his life, his papers accumulated so quickly that he kept a large pile of articles awaiting publication. The Berlin Academy published the papers on top of this pile, so later results often were published before results they depended on or superseded. Euler had 13 children and was able to continue his work while a child or two bounced on his knees. He was blind for the last 17 years of his life, but because of his fantastic memory this affliction did not diminish his mathematical output. The project of publishing his collected works, undertaken by the Swiss Society of Natural Science, is still going on and will require more than 75 volumes.

Compound Interest Formula

Notice in Example 3 that the future value A increases with n, the number of compounding periods. (Of course P, r, and t are fixed.) The question is, If n increases indefinitely (100, 1000, 10,000 times, and so on), does the amount A also increase indefinitely? The surprising answer is no. Let's see what happens as n increases indefinitely. We write $h = \dfrac{n}{r}$. Then, from Equation (4), we have

$$A = P\left(1 + \frac{r}{n}\right)^{nt}$$

$$= P\left[\left(1 + \frac{r}{n}\right)^{\frac{n}{r}}\right]^{rt} \qquad nt = \frac{n}{r} \cdot rt$$

$$= P\left[\left(1 + \frac{1}{h}\right)^{h}\right]^{rt} \qquad h = \frac{n}{r}, \text{ so } \frac{1}{h} = \frac{r}{n}. \qquad (5)$$

Table 4.3 shows what happens to the expression $\left(1 + \dfrac{1}{h}\right)^{h}$ as h takes on increasingly larger values:

TABLE 4.3

h	$\dfrac{1}{h}$	$1 + \dfrac{1}{h}$	$\left(1 + \dfrac{1}{h}\right)^{h}$
1	1	2	2
2	0.5	1.5	2.25
10	0.1	1.1	2.59374
100	0.01	1.01	2.70481
1,000	0.001	1.001	2.71692
10,000	0.0001	1.0001	2.71815
100,000	0.00001	1.00001	2.71827
1,000,000	0.000001	1.000001	2.71828

On the basis of Table 4.3, it appears that as h gets larger and larger, the quantity $\left(1 + \dfrac{1}{h}\right)^{h}$ gets closer and closer to a fixed number. This observation can be proven, and the fixed number is denoted by e in honor of the famous mathematician Leonhard Euler (pronounced "oiler"). The number e, an irrational number, is sometimes called the **Euler number.**

The value of e to 15 places is

$$e = 2.718281828459045.$$

We sometimes write

$$e = \lim_{h \to \infty} \left(1 + \frac{1}{h} \right)^h,$$

which means that when h is very large, the expression $\left(1 + \frac{1}{h} \right)^h$ has a value very close to e.

Note that in Equation (5), as n gets very large, the quantity $h = \frac{n}{r}$ also gets very large, since r is fixed. Thus, the expression inside the brackets approaches e, and so the compounded amount $A = P \left(1 + \frac{r}{n} \right)^{nt}$ approaches Pe^{rt}.

Continuous Compounding. When interest is compounded so that the amount A after one year, with principal P and interest rate r (expressed as a decimal number), is Pe^r, then the interest is said to be compounded continuously. The amount A after t years due to a principal P invested at the rate r per annum, compounded continuously, is given by the following formula:

CONTINUOUS COMPOUND INTEREST FORMULA

$$A = Pe^{rt} \tag{6}$$

A = amount after t years

P = principal

r = annual interest rate (expressed as a decimal number)

t = number of years.

EXAMPLE 4 **Calculating Continuous Compound Interest**

Find the amount when a principal of 8300 dollars is invested at a 7.5% annual rate of interest compounded continuously for eight years and three months.

Solution

We use formula (6), with $P = \$8300$ and $r = 0.075$. We convert eight years and three months to 8.25 years.

$$A = \$8300e^{(0.075)(8.25)} \qquad \text{Use the formula } A = Pe^{rt}.$$
$$\approx \$15,409.83 \qquad \text{Use a calculator.} \qquad ■ \ ■ \ ■$$

PRACTICE PROBLEM 4 Repeat Example 4 if \$9000 is invested at a 6% annual rate.   ■

EXAMPLE 5 **Calculating the Amount of Repaying a Loan**

How much money did the government owe DeHaven's descendants for 213 years on the 450,000-dollar loan at the interest rate of 6%?

Continued on next page.

Solution

a. With simple interest,

$$A = P + Prt = P(1 + rt)$$
$$= \$450{,}000[1 + (0.06)(213)]$$
$$= \$6.201 \text{ million.}$$

b. With interest compounded yearly,

$$A = P(1 + r)^t = \$450{,}000(1 + 0.06)^{213}$$
$$\approx \$1.105 \times 10^{11}$$
$$= \$110.5 \text{ billion.}$$

c. With interest compounded quarterly,

$$A = P\left(1 + \frac{r}{4}\right)^{4t} = \$450{,}000\left(1 + \frac{0.06}{4}\right)^{4(213)}$$
$$\approx \$1.45305 \times 10^{11}$$
$$= \$145.305 \text{ billion.}$$

d. With interest compounded continuously,

$$A = Pe^{rt} = \$450{,}000e^{0.06(213)}$$
$$\approx \$1.5977 \times 10^{11}$$
$$= \$159.77 \text{ billion.}$$

Notice the dramatic difference of more than $14 billion between quarterly and continuous compounding. Notice also the very dramatic difference between simple interest and interest compounded yearly.   ■ ■ ■

PRACTICE PROBLEM 5   Repeat Example 5 if the interest rate is 4%.   ■

3 Graph exponential functions.

The Natural Exponential Function

The exponential function

$$f(x) = e^x$$

with base e is so prevalent in the sciences that it is often referred to as *the* exponential function or the natural exponential function. Most calculators have the key $\boxed{e^x}$ or $\boxed{\text{EXP}}$, which is used to calculate e^x for a given value of x. We use the calculator to obtain e^x to two decimal places for $x = -2, -1, 0, 1,$ and 2 to create Table 4.4.

TABLE 4.4

x	e^x
-2	0.14
-1	0.37
0	1
1	2.72
2	7.39

The graph of $f(x) = e^x$ is sketched in Figure 4.6 by using the ordered pairs in Table 4.4.

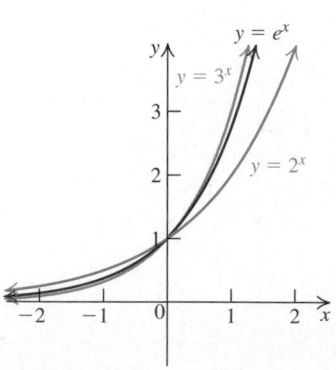

FIGURE 4.6

Since $2 < e < 3$, the graph of $y = e^x$ lies between the graphs $y = 2^x$ and $y = 3^x$. The function $f(x) = e^x$ has all the properties of exponential functions with base $a > 1$ listed in Section 4.1.

The transformations studied in Section 2.6 can be applied to the natural exponential function to obtain the graph of a related function.

EXAMPLE 6   Sketching a Graph

Use transformations to sketch the graph of

$$g(x) = e^{x-1} + 2.$$

Solution

We start with the basic natural exponential function $f(x) = e^x$. We shift the graph of this function 1 unit right to obtain the graph of $y = e^{x-1}$.

We then shift the graph of $y = e^{x-1}$ up 2 units to obtain the graph of $g(x) = e^{x-1} + 2$. See Figure 4.7.

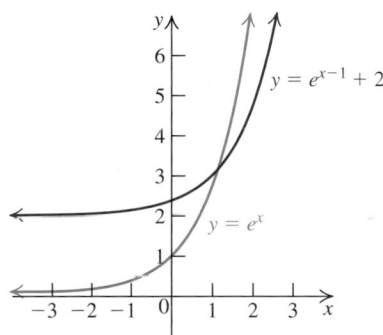

FIGURE 4.7   ■ ■ ■

PRACTICE PROBLEM 6   Sketch the graph of $g(x) = -e^{x-1} - 2$.   ■

Numerous applications of the exponential function are based on the fact that many different quantities have a growth (or decay) rate proportional to their size. Using calculus, we can show that in such cases we obtain the following mathematical model:

MODEL FOR EXPONENTIAL GROWTH OR DECAY

$$A(t) = A_0 e^{kt} \qquad (7)$$

$A(t) = $ the amount at time t,

$A_0 = A(0)$, the initial amount,

$k = $ relative rate of growth $(k > 0)$ or decay $(k < 0)$,

$t = $ time.

---

4 Evaluate exponential functions.

EXAMPLE 7

In the year 2000, the human population of the world was approximately 6 billion and the annual rate of growth was about 2.1 percent. Using the model given by Equation (7), estimate the population of the world in the following years.

a. 2030   **b.** 1990

Solution

a. We use Equation (7) with the year 2000 as $t = 0$.

$$A_0 = 6 \qquad\qquad A_0 = A(0) = 6 \text{ billion}$$
$$k = 0.021 \qquad\quad \text{The growth rate is 2.1\%.}$$
$$t = 30 \qquad\qquad \text{2030 is 30 years after 2000.}$$
$$A(30) = 6e^{(0.021)(30)} \qquad \text{Replace } A_0 \text{ by 6, } k \text{ by 0.021,}$$
$$\text{and } t \text{ by 30 in Equation (7).}$$
$$A(30) \approx 11.265663 \qquad \text{Use a calculator.}$$

Thus, the model predicts that if the rate of growth is 2.1 percent per year, there will be over 11.26 billion people in the world in the year 2030.

b. Again using Equation (7), with

$$A_0 = 6$$
$$k = 0.021$$
$$t = -10, \qquad\qquad \text{1990 is 10 years prior to 2000.}$$

we have

$$A(t) = 6e^{(0.021)(-10)} \qquad \text{Replace } A_0 \text{ by 6, } k \text{ by 0.021,}$$
$$\text{and } t \text{ by } -10 \text{ in (7).}$$
$$= 6e^{(-0.21)} \qquad\qquad \text{Simplify.}$$
$$\approx 4.8635055. \qquad\quad \text{Use a calculator.}$$

Thus, the model predicts that the world had over 4.86 billion people in 1990. (The actual human population of the world in 1990 was 5.28 billion.)   ■ ■ ■

PRACTICE PROBLEM 7   Repeat Example 7 if the annual rate of growth was 2.3%.   ■

A Exercises   Basic Skills and Concepts

In Exercises 1–6, find (a) the future value of the given principal P and (b) the interest earned in the given period.

1. $P = \$5250$ at 8% compounded quarterly for 10 years †

2. $P = \$3500$ at 6.5% compounded annually for 13 years †

3. $P = \$6240$ at 7.5% compounded monthly for 12 years †

4. $P = \$8000$ at 6.5% compounded daily for 15 years †

5. $P = \$7500$ at 5% compounded continuously for 10 years †

6. $P = \$8500$ at $4\frac{3}{4}$% compounded continuously for 8 years †

In Exercises 7–10, find the principal P that will generate the given future value A.

7. $A = \$10,000$ at 8% compounded annually for 10 years †

8. $A = \$10,000$ at 8% compounded quarterly for 10 years †

9. $A = \$10,000$ at 8% compounded daily for 10 years †

10. $A = \$10,000$ at 8% compounded continuously for 10 years †

†Due to space constrictions, answers to these exercises may be found in the Answers beginning on page A–1 in the back of the book.

In Exercises 11–18, starting with the graph of $y = e^x$, use transformations to sketch the graph of each function.

11. $f(x) = e^{-x}$ †

12. $f(x) = -e^x$ †

13. $f(x) = e^{x-2}$ †

14. $f(x) = e^{2-x}$ †

15. $f(x) = 1 + e^x$ †

16. $f(x) = 2 - e^{-x}$ †

17. $f(x) = -e^{x-2} + 3$ †

18. $g(x) = 3 + e^{2-x}$ †

In Exercises 19 and 20, sketch the graph of each function.

19. $f(x) = e^{|x|}$ †

20. $g(x) = e^{-|x|}$ †

B Exercises Applying the Concepts

21. Price appreciation. In 2004, the median price of a house in Miami was $125,000. Assuming a rate of increase of 4% per year, what can we expect the price of such a house to be in 2013? $177,914

22. Price appreciation. In 2004, the median price of a compact car was $14,800. If the rate of increase is assumed to be 6% per year, what can we expect the price of such a car to be in 2010? $20,994

23. Investment. How much should a mother invest at the time her son is born in order to provide him with $80,000 at age 21? Assume that the interest is 7% compounded quarterly. $18,629.40

24. Investment. Sabrina is planning to retire in 20 years. She calculates that she will need $100,000 in addition to the money she will get from her retirement plans (including Social Security). How much should she invest today at 10% compounded daily to accomplish her objective? $13,537.24

25. Depreciation. Trans Trucking Co. purchased a truck for $80,000. The company depreciated the truck at the end of each year at the rate of 15% of its current value. What is the value of the truck at the end of the fifth year? $35,496.43

26. Depreciation. Suppose you bought a car for $21,600. After using the car for three years, you unfortunately wreck it. The insurance company will pay you the depreciated value of the car at the rate of 20% of its previous year's value. How much would you receive from the insurance company if your car was a total loss? $11,059.20

27. Manhattan Island purchase. In 1626, Peter Du Minuit purchased Manhattan Island from the Native Americans for 60 Dutch guilders (about 24 dollars). Suppose the 24 dollars was invested in 1626 at a 6% rate. How much money would that investment be worth in 2006 if the interest was
  a. Simple interest. $571.20
  b. Compounded annually. $99,183,639,920
  c. Compounded monthly. $180,905,950,141
  d. Compounded continuously. $191,480,886,300

28. Investment. Ms. Ann Scheiber retired from government service in 1941 with a monthly pension of 83 dollars and 5000 dollars in savings. At the time of her death in January 1995 at the age of 101, Ms. Scheiber had turned the 5000 dollars to 22 million dollars through shrewd investments in the stock market. She bequeathed all of it to Yeshiva University in New York City. What annual rate of return compounded annually would turn 5000 dollars to a whopping 22 million dollars in 54 years? 16.81%

29. Population. The population of Sometown, USA, was 12,000 in 1990 and grew to 15,000 in 2000. Assume that the population will continue to grow exponentially at the same constant rate. What will be the population of Sometown in 2010? $\left[\textit{Hint: Show that } e^k = \left(\dfrac{5}{4} \right)^{1/10}. \right]$ 18,750

30. Population. The population of the United States was about 250 million in 1990 and 275 million in 2000. Assume that the population will continue to grow exponentially at the same rate. What is the predicted population of the United States in 2020? 332.75 million

31. Medicine. Tests show that a new ointment X helps heal wounds. If A_0 square millimeters is the area of the original wound, then the area A of the wound after n days of application of the ointment X is given by $A = A_0 e^{-0.43n}$. If the area of the original wound was 10 square millimeters, find the area of the wound after 10 days of the application of the new ointment. 0.1357 mm²

32. Medicine. In the model of Exercise 31, suppose the area of the wound after 20 days of the application of the ointment is 0.1 square millimeter. What was the area of the original wound? 543.2 mm²

33. Cooling. The temperature T (in °C) of coffee at time t minutes after its removal from the microwave oven is given by the equation

$$T = 25 + 73e^{-0.28t}.$$

Find the temperature of the coffee at each time listed.
a. $t = 0$ 98°C
b. $t = 10$ 29.44°C
c. $t = 20$ 25.27°C
d. after a long time 25°C

34. Medicine. The radioactive substance iodine-131 is used in measuring heart, liver, and thyroid activity. The quantity Q (in grams) remaining t days after the element is purchased is given by the equation

$$Q = 40e^{-0.086643397t}.$$

Calculate the amount at each time listed.
a. initially purchased 40 gm
b. 8 days after purchase 20 gm
c. 16 days after purchase 10 gm
d. 24 days after purchase 5 gm

C Exercises Beyond the Basics

In Exercises 35–40, sketch the graph of the given function.

35. $f(x) = \begin{cases} e^{-x} & \text{if } x > 0 \\ e^{x} & \text{if } x \le 0 \end{cases}$ †

36. $f(x) = \begin{cases} e^{x} & \text{if } x > 0 \\ -e^{x} & \text{if } x \le 0 \end{cases}$ †

37. $f(x) = \begin{cases} 1 + x & \text{if } x > 0 \\ e^{x} & \text{if } x \le 0 \end{cases}$ †

38. $g(x) = \begin{cases} 1 + x^2 & \text{if } x > 0 \\ e^{-x} & \text{if } x \le 0 \end{cases}$ †

39. $f(x) = \begin{cases} e^{-x} & \text{if } x > 0 \\ 1 & \text{if } x \le 0 \end{cases}$ †

40. $g(x) = \begin{cases} e^{-x} & \text{if } x \le 0 \\ 1 & \text{if } 0 < x < 1 \\ x^2 & \text{if } x \ge 1 \end{cases}$ †

41. Let $f(x) = e^x$. Show that

a. $\dfrac{f(x + h) - f(x)}{h} = e^x \left(\dfrac{e^h - 1}{h} \right)$.

b. $f(x + y) = f(x)f(y)$.

c. $f(-x) = \dfrac{1}{f(x)}$. †

42. You need the following definition for this exercise:
Let $0! = 1$, $1! = 1$, $2! = 2 \cdot 1$, and, in general, $n! = n(n - 1)(n - 2) \cdots 3 \cdot 2 \cdot 1$. The symbol $n!$ is read "n factorial." Now let

$$S_n = 2 + \frac{1}{2!} + \frac{1}{3!} + \frac{1}{4!} + \cdots + \frac{1}{n!}.$$

Compute S_n for $n = 5$, 10, and 15. Compare the resulting values with the value of e on page 442. †

43. The hyperbolic cosine function (abbreviated as $\cosh x$, often pronounced as "*kosh x* or *coshine x*") is defined by

$$\cosh x = \frac{e^x + e^{-x}}{2}.$$

Sketch the graph of $y = \cosh x$ by plotting points. †

44. The hyperbolic sine function (abbreviated as sinh x, often pronounced as "*shine x*") is defined by

$$\sinh x = \frac{e^x - e^{-x}}{2}.$$

Sketch the graph of $y = \sinh x$ by plotting points. †

In Exercises 45–47, prove that the given equations are true for all real numbers.

45. $\cosh(-x) = \cosh x$; this shows that $\cosh x$ is an even function.

46. $\sinh(-x) = -\sinh x$; this shows that $\sinh x$ is an odd function.

47. $(\cosh x)^2 - (\sinh x)^2 = 1$

48. If an investment of P dollars returns A dollars after one year, the **effective annual interest rate** or **annual yield** y is defined by the equation

$$A = P(1 + y).$$

Show that if the sum of P dollars is invested at a nominal rate r per year, compounded m times per year, the effective annual yield y is given by the equation

$$y = \left(1 + \frac{r}{m}\right)^m - 1.$$

49. Calculate the effective annual yield if money is invested at 8% annual rate compounded
  a. quarterly. $y = 0.082432 = 8.2432\%$
  b. monthly. $y = 0.082999 = 8.2999\%$
  c. daily. $y = 0.083277 = 8.3277\%$
  d. continuously. $y - 0.083287 = 8.3287\%$

[*Hint:* Use the formula from Exercise 48.]

50. Sumeet's investment in a mutual fund increased from 30,000 dollars to 45,000 dollars in five years. What was his effective annual yield? 8.447%

[*Hint:* Use $A = P(1 + y)^t$, where t is the number of years and y is the effective annual yield.]

51. Fidelity Federal offers three types of investments paying, respectively,

  9.5 percent continuous interest, yields 9.9658%,
  10 percent simple interest, yields 10%,
  9.6 percent interest compounded monthly.
    yields 10.03%.

Which investment will yield the greatest return? An interest rate of 9.6% will yield the greatest returns

Critical Thinking

52. Let $f(x) = e^{-x^2}$.
  a. Calculate $f(0)$, $f(1)$, $f(2)$, and $f(3)$. (Use a calculator.) †
  b. Find the axis of symmetry of f. y-axis, $(x = 0)$
  c. Find $\lim f(x)$ as $x \to \infty$ and as $x \to -\infty$. $y = 0$
  d. Sketch the graph of f. †

53. An important function in statistics is the probability density function, defined by

$$f(x) = \frac{1}{\sigma\sqrt{2\pi}}\, e^{-\frac{(x-\mu)^2}{2\sigma^2}},$$

where σ (the Greek letter sigma) and μ (the Greek letter mu) are constants with $\sigma > 0$ and μ a real number.
  a. Find the axis of symmetry of f. $x = \mu$
  b. Find $\lim f(x)$ as $x \to \infty$ and as $x \to -\infty$. 0
  c. Describe how to sketch the graph of f from the graph of $y = e^{-x^2}$. Answers will vary.

SECTION 4.3 | Logarithmic Functions

BEFORE STARTING THIS SECTION, REVIEW

1. Finding inverse of a one-to-one function (Section 2.8, page 302)

2. Polynomial and rational inequalities (Section 1.7, page 158)

3. Graphing Transformations (Section 2.6, page 264)

OBJECTIVES

1 Define logarithmic functions.

2 Evaluate logarithms.

3 Find the domains of logarithmic functions.

4 Graph logarithmic functions.

5 Use logarithms to evaluate exponential equations.

The McDonald's Coffee Case

Stella Liebeck of Albuquerque, New Mexico, was in the passenger seat of her grandson's car when she was severely burned by McDonald's coffee in February 1992. Liebeck ordered coffee that was served in a foam cup at the drive-through window of a local McDonald's. While attempting to add cream and sugar to her coffee, Liebeck spilled the entire contents of the cup into her lap. A vascular surgeon determined that Liebeck suffered full-thickness burns (third-degree burns) over 6 percent of her body. She sued McDonald's for damages.

During the preliminary phase of the trial, McDonald's said that, on the basis of a consultant's advice, the company brewed its coffee at 195° to 205°F and held it at between 180° and 190°F to maintain optimal taste.

Coffee served at home is generally between 135° and 140°F. Prior to the Liebeck case, the prestigious Shriner's Burn Institute of Cincinnati had published warnings to the franchise food industry that beverages above 130°F were causing serious scald burns. Liebeck's lawsuit against McDonald's was settled out of court, and both parties agreed to keep the award for damages confidential.

Avoiding further lawsuits. Corporate lawyers have informed McDonald's management that further lawsuits from customers who spill their coffee can be avoided if the temperature of the coffee is 125°F or less when it is delivered to the customers. In Example 10, we will learn how long after brewing the coffee should be held before it is delivered to customers. ■

1 Define logarithmic functions.

Logarithmic Functions

Recall from Section 4.1 that every exponential function

$$f(x) = a^x, a > 0, a \neq 1,$$

is a *one-to-one* function and hence has an inverse function. Figure 4.8 shows the graphs of two typical exponential functions. They are easily seen to be one-to-one functions by the horizontal-line test.

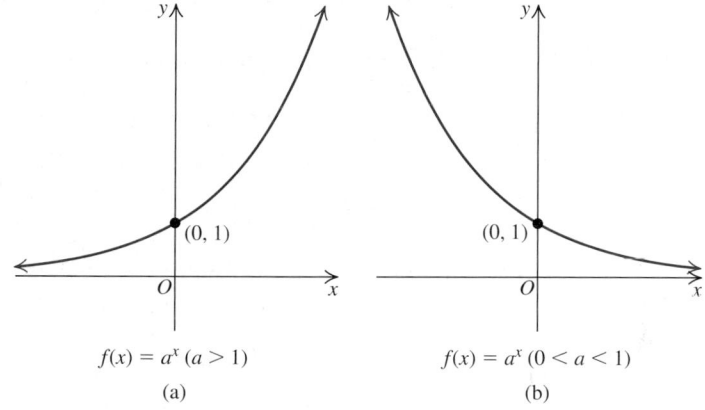

$f(x) = a^x \,(a > 1)$

(a)

$f(x) = a^x \,(0 < a < 1)$

(b)

FIGURE 4.8

In this section, we investigate the problem of finding the inverse of an exponential function. First we consider the exponential function

$$f(x) = 3^x.$$

If we think of an exponential function f as "putting an exponent on" a particular base, then the inverse function f^{-1} must "lift the exponent off" to undo the effect of f, as illustrated below.

$$x \xrightarrow{\;\;f\;\;} 3^x \xrightarrow{\;\;f^{-1}\;\;} x$$

In other words, we are looking for the function f^{-1} such that

$$f^{-1}(f(x)) = x$$

for every x in the domain of f; we also want $f(f^{-1}(x)) = x$ for every x in the domain of f^{-1}.

Let's try to find the inverse of $f(x) = 3^x$ by the procedure outlined in Section 2.8. Recall that f^{-1} is defined by

$$f^{-1}(x) = y \quad \text{if and only if} \quad x = f(y).$$

Step 1   Replace $f(x)$ in the equation $f(x) = 3^x$ by y: $y = 3^x$.

Step 2   Interchange x and y in the equation in Step 1: $x = 3^y$.

Step 3   Solve the equation for y in Step 2. (See the next paragraph.)

In Step 3, we need to solve the equation $x = 3^y$ for y. For some specific values of x, such as $x = 3$ (when $y = 1$) or $x = 27$ (when $y = 3$), we can compute the values of y. What value of y satisfies the equation $5 = 3^y$? There actually is a real number y that solves this equation, but we have not introduced the name for this number yet. (We were in a similar position concerning the solution of $y^3 = 7$ before we introduced the name for the solution, namely, $\sqrt[3]{7}$). We may say that $y =$ "the exponent on 3 that gives 5." The name *logarithm* (or "log" for short) is used to express this exponent. The notation $\log_3 5$ (read as "log of 5 with base 3") is used to express the solution of the equation $5 = 3^y$. This log notation is a new way to write information about exponents. That is, we write $y = \log_3 x$ to mean $x = 3^y$. In other words, $\log_3 x$ *is the exponent y to which 3 must be raised to obtain x.* Thus, the inverse function of the exponential function $f(x) = 3^x$ is written

$$f^{-1}(x) = \log_3 x \qquad \text{or} \qquad y = \log_3 x, \text{ where } y = f^{-1}(x).$$

The previous discussion could be repeated for any base a instead of 3, provided that $a > 0$ and $a \neq 1$.

DEFINITION OF THE LOGARITHMIC FUNCTION

For $x > 0$, $a > 0$, and $a \neq 1$,

$$y = \log_a x \qquad \text{if and only if} \qquad x = a^y.$$

The function $f(x) = \log_a x$ is called the **logarithmic function with base a.**

The definition of the logarithm says that the two equations

$$y = \log_a x \tag{1}$$
$$x = a^y \tag{2}$$

are equivalent. Equation (1) is the *logarithmic form,* and Equation (2) is the *exponential form,* for the same information. For instance, $\log_3 81 = 4$ because 3 must be raised to the fourth power to obtain 81.

EXAMPLE 1   **Converting from Exponential to Logarithmic Form**

Write each exponential equation in logarithmic form.

a. $4^3 = 64$ **b.** $\left(\dfrac{1}{2}\right)^4 = \dfrac{1}{16}$ **c.** $a^{-2} = 7$

Solution

a. $4^3 = 64$ is equivalent to $\log_4 64 = 3$.

b. $\left(\dfrac{1}{2}\right)^4 = \dfrac{1}{16}$ is equivalent to $\log_{1/2} \dfrac{1}{16} = 4$.

c. $a^{-2} = 7$ is equivalent to $\log_a 7 = -2$.   ■ ■ ■

PRACTICE PROBLEM 1   Write each exponential equation in logarithmic form.

a. $9^{-1/2} = \dfrac{1}{3}$ **b.** $p = a^q$ ■

> **EXAMPLE 2**   **Converting from Logarithmic Form to Exponential Form**

Write each logarithmic equation in exponential form.

a. $\log_3 243 = 5$ **b.** $\log_2 5 = x$ **c.** $\log_a N = x$

Solution

a. $\log_3 243 = 5$ is equivalent to $243 = 3^5$.

b. $\log_2 5 = x$ is equivalent to $5 = 2^x$.

c. $\log_a N = x$ is equivalent to $N = a^x$.   ■ ■ ■

PRACTICE PROBLEM 2   Write each logarithmic equation in exponential form.

a. $\log_2 64 = 6$ **b.** $\log_v u = w$ ■

2 Evaluate logarithms.

Evaluating Logarithms

The technique of converting from logarithmic form to exponential form can be used to evaluate some logarithms by inspection.

> **EXAMPLE 3**   **Evaluating Logarithms**

Find the value of each of the following logarithms.

a. $\log_5 25$ **b.** $\log_2 16$ **c.** $\log_{1/3} 9$

d. $\log_7 7$ **e.** $\log_6 1$ **f.** $\log_4 \dfrac{1}{2}$

Solution

Logarithmic Form	Exponential Form	Value
a. $\log_5 25 = y$	$25 = 5^y$ or $5^2 = 5^y$	$y = 2$
b. $\log_2 16 = y$	$16 = 2^y$ or $2^4 = 2^y$	$y = 4$
c. $\log_{1/3} 9 = y$	$9 = \left(\dfrac{1}{3}\right)^y$ or $3^2 = 3^{-y}$	$y = -2$
d. $\log_7 7 = y$	$7 = 7^y$ or $7^1 = 7^y$	$y = 1$
e. $\log_6 1 = y$	$1 = 6^y$ or $6^0 = 6^y$	$y = 0$
f. $\log_4 \dfrac{1}{2} = y$	$\dfrac{1}{2} = 4^y$ or $2^{-1} = 2^{2y}$	$y = -\dfrac{1}{2}$

■ ■ ■

PRACTICE PROBLEM 3   Evaluate.

a. $\log_3 9$ **b.** $\log_9 \dfrac{1}{3}$ ■

> **EXAMPLE 4**   **Using the Definition of Logarithm**

Solve each equation.

a. $\log_5 x = -3$ **b.** $\log_3 \dfrac{1}{27} = y$ **c.** $\log_z 1000 = 3$ **d.** $\log_2(x^2 - 6x + 10) = 1$

Continued on next page.

Solution

a. $\log_5 x = -3$

$\qquad x = 5^{-3}$ Exponential form

$\qquad\quad = \dfrac{1}{5^3} = \dfrac{1}{125}$ $a^{-n} = \dfrac{1}{a^n}$

The solution set is $\left\{\dfrac{1}{125}\right\}$.

b. $\log_3 \dfrac{1}{27} = y$

$\qquad \dfrac{1}{27} = 3^y$ Exponential form

$\qquad 3^{-3} = 3^y$ $\dfrac{1}{27} = \dfrac{1}{3^3} = 3^{-3}$

$\qquad\quad -3 = y$ If $a^x = a^y$, then $x = y$.

The solution set is $\{-3\}$.

c. $\log_z 1000 = 3$

$\qquad 1000 = z^3$ Exponential form

$\qquad 10^3 = z^3$ $1000 = 10^3$

$\qquad\quad 10 = z$ Take the cube root of both sides.

The solution set is $\{10\}$.

d. $\log_2(x^2 - 6x + 10) = 1$

$\qquad x^2 - 6x + 10 = 2^1$ Exponential form

$\qquad x^2 - 6x + 10 = 2$ $2^1 = 2$

$\qquad\quad x^2 - 6x + 8 = 0$ Subtract 2 from both sides.

$\qquad (x - 2)(x - 4) = 0$ Factor.

$\quad x - 2 = 0 \text{ or } x - 4 = 0$ Zero-product property

$\qquad\qquad x = 2 \text{ or } x = 4$ Solve for x.

The solution set is $\{2, 4\}$.   ■ ■ ■

PRACTICE PROBLEM 4   Solve each equation.

a. $\log_2 x = 3$ **b.** $\log_z 125 = 3$ ■

3 Find the domains of logarithmic functions.

Domain of Logarithmic Functions

Since the exponential function $f(x) = a^x$ has domain $(-\infty, \infty)$ and range $(0, \infty)$, its inverse function $f^{-1}(x) = \log_a x$ has domain $(0, \infty)$ and range $(-\infty, \infty)$. Thus, the logarithms of 0 and of negative numbers are not defined, and so expressions such as $\log_a(-2)$ and $\log_a(0)$ are meaningless.

> **EXAMPLE 5**   **Finding the Domain**

Find the domain of each function.

a. $f(x) = \log_3(2 - x)$ **b.** $f(x) = \log_3\left(\dfrac{x - 2}{x + 1}\right)$

Solution

a. Since the domain of the logarithmic function is $(0, \infty)$, the expression $2 - x$ must be positive. In other words, the domain is the set of all real numbers x such that

$$2 - x > 0$$
$$2 > x. \qquad \text{Solve for } x.$$

The domain of f is the interval $(-\infty, 2)$.

b. Since the domain of the logarithmic function is $(0, \infty)$, the expression $\dfrac{x - 2}{x + 1}$ must be positive. In other words, the domain is the set of all real numbers x such that

$$\frac{x - 2}{x + 1} > 0.$$

To solve this inequality, we set

$$\text{numerator} = 0 \quad \text{and} \quad \text{denominator} = 0$$
$$x - 2 = 0 \qquad\qquad x + 1 = 0$$
$$x = 2 \qquad\qquad\quad x = -1$$

The solutions -1 and 2 divide the number line into three intervals: $(-\infty, -1), (-1, 2)$, and $(2, \infty)$. We choose $-2, 0$, and 3 as convenient test points to determine the sign of $\dfrac{x - 2}{x + 1}$ in each of these intervals. From the sign graph in Figure 4.9 we find that the domain of f is $(-\infty, -1) \cup (2, \infty)$.

FIGURE 4.9   ▪ ▪ ▪

PRACTICE PROBLEM 5   Find the domain of

$$f(x) = \log_{10} \sqrt{1 - x}. \qquad\qquad ▪$$

Since $a^1 = a$ and $a^0 = 1$ for any base a, expressing these equations in logarithmic notation gives

$$\log_a a = 1 \text{ and } \log_a 1 = 0.$$

Again, letting $f(x) = a^x$ and $f^{-1}(x) = \log_a x$, the equation

$$f^{-1}(f(x)) = x \text{ can be written as } \log_a a^x = x$$

and the equation

$$f(f^{-1}(x)) = x \text{ can be written as } a^{\log_a x} = x.$$

We summarize these relationships as basic properties of logarithms.

> **BASIC PROPERTIES OF LOGARITHMS**
>
> For any base $a > 0$, with $a \neq 1$,
>
> 1. $\log_a a = 1$.
> 2. $\log_a 1 = 0$.
> 3. $\log_a a^x = x$, for any real number x.
> 4. $a^{\log_a x} = x$, for any $x > 0$.

4 Graph logarithmic functions.

Graphs of Logarithmic Functions

We begin with an example.

EXAMPLE 6 **Sketching a Graph**

Sketch the graph of $y = \log_3 x$.

Solution by plotting points (Method 1) To find selected ordered pairs on the graph of $y = \log_3 x$, we choose the x-values to be powers of 3. For these values, it is easy to compute their logarithms by using Property 3, namely, $\log_3 3^x = x$. We compute the y values in Table 4.5.

TABLE 4.5

x	$y = \log_3 x$	Ordered pair (x, y)
$3^{-3} = \dfrac{1}{27}$	-3	$\left(\dfrac{1}{27}, -3\right)$
$3^{-2} = \dfrac{1}{9}$	-2	$\left(\dfrac{1}{9}, -2\right)$
$3^{-1} = \dfrac{1}{3}$	-1	$\left(\dfrac{1}{3}, -1\right)$
$3^0 = 1$	0	$(1, 0)$
$3^1 = 3$	1	$(3, 1)$
$3^2 = 9$	2	$(9, 2)$

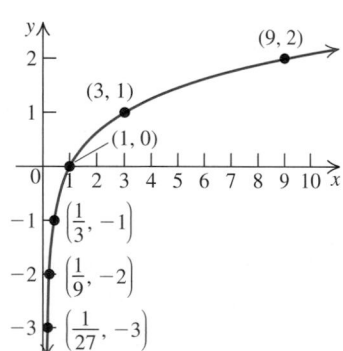

FIGURE 4.10

We plot the ordered pairs listed and connect them with a smooth curve to obtain the graph of $y = \log_3 x$, shown in Figure 4.10.

Solution by using the inverse function (Method 2) Since $y = \log_3 x$ is the inverse of the function $y = f(x) = 3^x$, we first graph the exponential function $y = f(x) = 3^x$. (See Figure 4.11.) Then we reflect the graph $y = 3^x$ in the line $y = x$. The graph of $y = f^{-1}(x) = \log_3 x$ is shown in Figure 4.11.

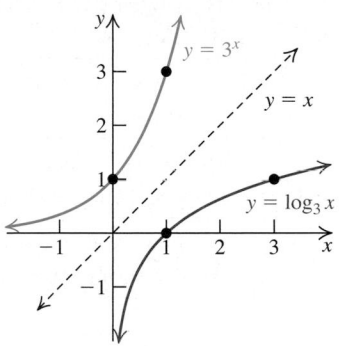

FIGURE 4.11   ■ ■ ■

PRACTICE PROBLEM 6   Sketch the graph of

$$y = \log_2 x.$$ ■

The graph of $y = \log_a x$ with $a > 1$ resembles the graph of $y = \log_3 x$ shown in Figure 4.11. Similarly, the graph of $y = \log_a x$ with $0 < a < 1$ resembles the graph of $y = \log_{1/3} x$ shown in Figure 4.12. These graphs exhibit the following properties of the logarithmic functions (along with the properties of the corresponding inverse exponential functions) on the next page.

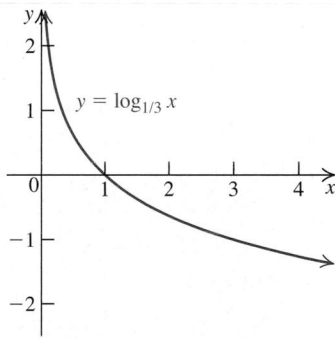

FIGURE 4.12

Properties of Exponential and Logarithmic Functions

Exponential Function $f(x) = a^x$	Logarithmic Function $f(x) = \log_a x$
1. The domain is $(-\infty, \infty)$ and the range is $(0, \infty)$.	The domain is $(0, \infty)$ and the range is $(-\infty, \infty)$.
2. The y-intercept is 1, and there is no x-intercept.	The x-intercept is 1, and there is no y-intercept.
3. The x-axis $(y = 0)$ is the horizontal asymptote.	The y-axis $(x = 0)$ is the vertical asymptote.
4. The function is one-to-one, that is, $a^u = a^v$ if and only if $u = v$.	The function is one-to-one; that is, $\log_a u = \log_a v$ if and only if $u = v$.
5. The function is increasing if $a > 1$ and decreasing if $0 < a < 1$.	The function is increasing if $a > 1$ and decreasing if $0 < a < 1$.

Once we know the shape of a logarithmic graph, we can shift it vertically or horizontally, stretch it, compress it, check answers with it, and interpret the graph.

The graphs of logarithmic functions have one of two basic shapes (one increasing, the other decreasing), determined by the base a, as shown in Figure 4.13.

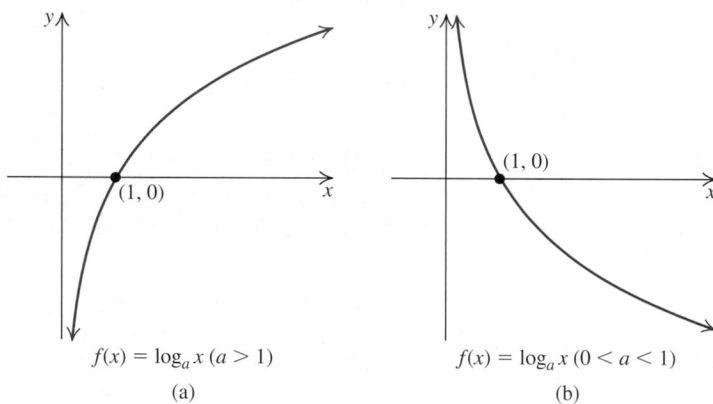

$f(x) = \log_a x \ (a > 1)$ $f(x) = \log_a x \ (0 < a < 1)$

(a)   (b)

FIGURE 4.13

EXAMPLE 7   **Using Transformations**

Start with the graph of $f(x) = \log_3 x$, and use transformations to sketch the graph of each function.

a. $f(x) = \log_3 x + 2$ **b.** $f(x) = \log_3(x - 1)$

c. $f(x) = -\log_3 x$ **d.** $f(x) = \log_3(-x)$

State the domain and range and the vertical asymptote for the graph of each function.

Solution

We start with the graph of $f(x) = \log_3 x$ and use the transformations indicated in Figure 4.14.

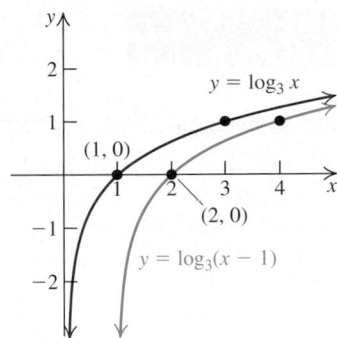

a. $f(x) = \log_3 x + 2$

Add 2 to $\log_3 x$, and shift the graph of $y = \log_3 x$ up two units. Domain: $(0, \infty)$; range: $(-\infty, \infty)$; vertical asymptote: $x = 0$ (y-axis)

b. $f(x) = \log_3(x - 1)$

Replace x by $x - 1$ in $\log_3 x$, and shift the graph of $y = \log_3 x$, right one unit. Domain: $(1, \infty)$; range $(-\infty, \infty)$; vertical asymptote: $x = 1$

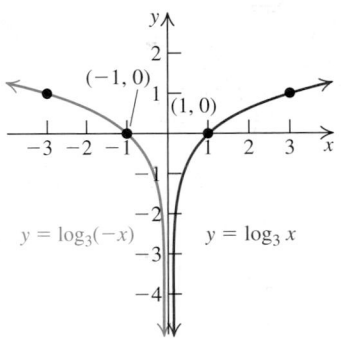

c. $f(x) = -\log_3(x)$

Multiply $\log_3 x$ by -1, and reflect the graph of $y = \log_3 x$ in the x-axis. Domain: $(0, \infty)$; range: $(-\infty, \infty)$; vertical asymptote: $x = 0$

d. $f(x) = \log_3(-x)$

Replace x by $-x$ in $\log_3 x$, and reflect the graph of $y = \log_3 x$ in the y-axis. Domain: $(-\infty, 0)$; range: $(-\infty, \infty)$; vertical asymptote: $x = 0$

FIGURE 4.14   ■ ■ ■

PRACTICE PROBLEM 7   Use transformations to sketch the graph of

$$y = -\log_2(x - 3).$$ ■

Common Logarithms

The logarithm with base 10 is called the **common logarithm** and is denoted by omitting the base:

$$\log x = \log_{10} x.$$

You can find the common logarithms of any positive number with the $\boxed{\text{LOG}}$ key on your calculator. The exact key sequence will vary with different calculators. On most calculators, if you wish to find log 3.7, you press

3.7 $\boxed{\text{LOG}}$ $\boxed{\text{ENTER}}$

or

$\boxed{\text{LOG}}$ 3.7 $\boxed{\text{ENTER}}$

and see the display 0.5682017.

Although we write $\log_{10} 3.7 = 0.5682017$, this really is an approximate value. More appropriately, we should write $\log_{10} 3.7 \approx 0.5682017$.

Thus,

$$y = \log x \quad \text{if and only if} \quad x = 10^{y}.$$

Applying the basic properties of logarithms, (see page 456) to common logarithms, we have:

1. $\log 10 = 1$
2. $\log 1 = 0$
3. $\log 10^{x} = x$
4. $10^{\log x} = x$

We use Property (3) to evaluate the common logarithms of numbers that are powers of 10. For example,

$$\log 1000 = \log 10^{3} = 3$$
$$\text{and} \quad \log 0.01 = \log 10^{-2} = -2.$$

We use a calculator to find the common logarithms of numbers that are not powers of 10 by pressing the "LOG" key.

The graph of $y = \log x$ is similar to the graph in Figure 4.13(a), since the base for $\log x$ is understood to be 10.

EXAMPLE 8   **Using Transformations to Sketch a Graph**

Sketch the graph of

$$y = 2 - \log(x - 2).$$

Solution

We start with the graph of the function $f(x) = \log x$ and use the transformations indicated in Figure 4.15 to sketch the graph.

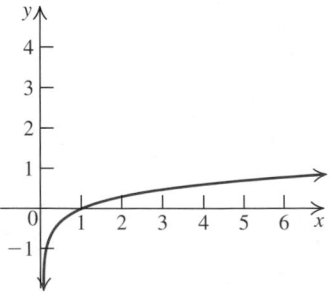

a. $f(x) = \log x$

This is the basic graph from Figure 4.13(a), with $a = 10$.

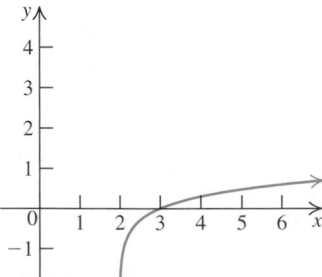

b. $f(x) = \log(x - 2)$

Replace x by $x - 2$ in $\log x$, and shift the graph of $y = \log x$ two units right.

FIGURE 4.15

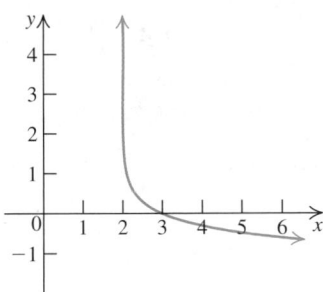

c. $f(x) = -\log(x - 2)$

Multiply $\log(x - 2)$ by -1
and reflect the graph of
$y = \log(x - 2)$ in the x-axis.

d. $f(x) = 2 - \log(x - 2)$

Add 2 to $-\log(x - 2)$ and shift
the graph of $y = -\log(x - 2)$
two units up.

FIGURE 4.15 *(continued)*

The domain of $f(x) = 2 - \log(x - 2)$ is $(2, \infty)$, the range is $(-\infty, \infty)$, and the vertical asymptote is the line $x = 2$. ■ ■ ■

PRACTICE PROBLEM 8   Sketch the graph of

$$y = \log(x - 3) - 2.$$ ■

Natural Logarithms

In most applications in calculus and the sciences, the convenient base for logarithms is the number e. The logarithms with base e are called **natural logarithms** and are denoted by $\ln x$ (read "*ell en x*" or "lawn x"), so that $\ln x = \log_e x$.
Thus,

$$y = \ln x \quad \text{if and only if} \quad x = e^y.$$

Applying the basic properties of logarithms (see page 456) to natural logarithms, we have

1. $\ln e = 1$
2. $\ln 1 = 0$
3. $\ln e^x = x$
4. $e^{\ln x} = x$

We can use Property (3) to evaluate the natural logarithms of powers of e. For evaluating natural logarithms of other numbers, we use the "LN" key on a calculator.

EXAMPLE 9   **Evaluating the Natural Logarithm Function**

Evaluate each expression.

a. $\ln e^4$ **b.** $\ln \dfrac{1}{e^{2.5}}$ **c.** $\ln 3$

Continued on next page.

Solution

a. $\ln e^4 = 4$ Property (3)

b. $\ln \dfrac{1}{e^{2.5}} = \ln e^{-2.5} = -2.5$ Property (3)

c. $\ln 3 \approx 1.0986123$ Use a calculator.   ■ ■ ■

PRACTICE PROBLEM 9   Evaluate each expression.

a. $\ln \dfrac{1}{e}$ **b.** $\ln 2$ ■

5 Use logarithms to solve exponential equations.

Newton's Law of Cooling

When a cool drink is removed from a refrigerator and is placed in a room at normal temperature, the drink warms to the temperature of the room. A pizza baked at a high temperature cools to the temperature of the room when removed from the oven.

In situations such as these, the rate at which an object's temperature is changing at any given time is proportional to the difference between its temperature and the temperature of the surrounding medium. This observation is called *Newton's Law of Cooling,* although, as in the case of a cool drink, it applies to warming as well.

NEWTON'S LAW OF COOLING

Newton's Law of Cooling states that

$$T = T_S + (T_0 - T_S)e^{-kt},$$

where T is the temperature of the object at time t, T_S is the surrounding temperature, and T_0 is the value of T at $t = 0$.

EXAMPLE 10   **McDonald's Hot Coffee**

The local McDonald's franchise has discovered that when coffee is poured from a pot whose contents are at 180°F into a noninsulated pot in the store where the air temperature is 72°F, after 1 minute the coffee has cooled to 165°F. How long should the employees wait before pouring the coffee from this noninsulated pot into cups to deliver it to customers at 125°F?

Solution

We use Newton's Law of Cooling with $T_0 = 180$ and $T_S = 72$. We obtain

$$T = 72 + (180 - 72)e^{-kt},$$

$$T = 72 + 108e^{-kt} \qquad \text{Simplify.} \qquad\qquad (1)$$

From the given data, we have $T = 165$ when $t = 1$. Substituting into Equation (1), we find the value of k:

$$165 = 72 + 108e^{-k}$$ Replace T by 165 and t by 1 in Equation (1), then $kt = k \cdot 1 = k$.

$$93 = 108e^{-k}$$ Subtract 72 from both sides.

$$\frac{93}{108} = e^{-k}$$ Solve for e^{-k}.

$$\ln\left(\frac{93}{108}\right) = -k$$ Write in logarithmic form.

$$-0.1495317 = -k$$ Use a calculator.

$$k = 0.1495317$$ Multiply both sides by -1.

With this value of k, Equation (1) becomes

$$T = 72 + 108e^{-0.1495317t}. \tag{2}$$

From Equation (2), we find t when $T = 125$.

$$125 = 72 + 108e^{-0.1495317t}$$ Replace T by 125 in Equation (2).

$$\frac{125 - 72}{108} = e^{-0.1495317t}$$ Solve for $e^{-0.1495317\,t}$.

$$\frac{53}{108} = e^{-0.1495317t}$$ Simplify.

$$\ln\left(\frac{53}{108}\right) = -0.1495317t$$ Write in logarithmic form

$$t = \frac{-1}{0.1495317}\ln\left(\frac{53}{108}\right)$$ Solve for t.

$$\approx 4.76$$ Use a calculator.

Thus, the employees should wait approximately 4.76 minutes (realistically, about 5 minutes) to deliver the coffee at 125°F to the customers.   ■ ■ ■

PRACTICE PROBLEM 10   Repeat Example 10 if the coffee is to be delivered to the customers at 120°F.   ■

In the next example, we use the mathematical model

$$A = A_0 e^{rt}, \tag{3}$$

where A is the quantity after t units of time, A_0 is the initial (original) quantity when the experiment started $(t = 0)$, and r is the growth or decay rate per period.

EXAMPLE 11   **Chemical Toxins in a Lake**

In a large lake, one-fifth of the water is replaced by clean water each year. A chemical spill deposits 60,000 cubic meters of soluble toxic waste into the lake.

a. How much of this toxin will be left in the lake after four years?

b. How long will it take for the toxic chemical in the lake to be reduced to 6000 cubic meters?

Continued on next page.

Solution

Since one-fifth of the water in the lake is replaced by clean water every year, the decay rate for the toxin is $\frac{1}{5}$; so $r = -\frac{1}{5}$. Thus, with $A_0 = 60{,}000$ and $r = -\frac{1}{5}$, Equation (3) becomes

$$A = 60{,}000e^{\left(-\frac{1}{5}\right)t}, \tag{4}$$

where A is the amount of toxin (in cubic meters) after t years.

a. Substituting $t = 4$ in Equation (4), we get

$$A = 60{,}000e^{\left(-\frac{1}{5}\right)(4)}$$
$$\approx 26{,}959.74 \text{ m}^3. \qquad \text{Use a calculator.}$$

b. We solve Equation (4) for t when $A = 6000$.

$$6000 = 60{,}000e^{\left(-\frac{1}{5}\right)t} \qquad \text{Replace } A \text{ by 6000 in Equation (4).}$$

$$\frac{1}{10} = e^{\left(-\frac{1}{5}\right)t} \qquad \text{Divide both sides by 60,000.}$$

$$0.1 = e^{\left(-\frac{1}{5}\right)t} \qquad \text{Rewrite } \frac{1}{10} \text{ as 0.1.}$$

$$\ln(0.1) = -\frac{1}{5}t \qquad \text{Logarithmic form}$$

$$t = -5\ln(0.1) \qquad \text{Solve for } t.$$

$$\approx 11.51 \text{ years} \qquad \text{Use a calculator.} \qquad \blacksquare\ \blacksquare\ \blacksquare$$

PRACTICE PROBLEM 11   Repeat Example 11 if one-sixth of the water in the lake is replaced by clean water each year. ■

A Exercises   Basic Skills and Concepts

In Exercises 1–12, write each exponential equation in logarithmic form.

1. $5^2 = 25$ †

2. $81^{\frac{1}{2}} = 9$ †

3. $(49)^{-\frac{1}{2}} = \frac{1}{7}$ †

4. $\left(\frac{1}{16}\right)^{\frac{1}{2}} = \frac{1}{4}$ †

5. $\left(\frac{1}{16}\right)^{-\frac{1}{2}} = 4$ †

6. $(a^2)^2 = a^4$ †

7. $10^0 = 1$ †

8. $10^4 = 10{,}000$ †

9. $(10)^{-1} = 0.1$ †

10. $3^x = 5$ †

11. $a^2 = 5$ †

12. $a^e = \pi$ †

In Exercises 13–24, write each logarithmic equation in exponential form.

13. $\log_2 32 = 5$ †

14. $\log_7 49 = 2$ †

15. $\log_{10} 100 = 2$ †

16. $\log_{10} 10 = 1$ †

17. $\log_{10} 1 = 0$ †

18. $\log_a 1 = 0$ †

19. $\log_{10} 0.01 = -2$ †

20. $\log_{1/5} 5 = -1$ †

21. $\log_8 2 = \frac{1}{3}$ $\quad 8^{\frac{1}{3}} = 2$

22. $\log 1000 = 3$ $\quad 10^3 = 1000$

23. $\ln 2 = x$ $\quad e^x = 2$

24. $\ln \pi = a$ $\quad e^a = \pi$

†Due to space constrictions, answers to these exercises may be found in the Answers beginning on page A–1 in the back of the book.

25. Match each logarithmic function with one of the graphs labeled a–f.

   a. $f(x) = \log x$ (f)

   b. $f(x) = -\log|x|$ (a)

   c. $f(x) = -\log(-x)$ (d)

   d. $f(x) = \log(x - 1)$ (b)

   e. $y = (\log x) - 1$ (e)

   f. $f(x) = \log(-1 - x)$ (c)

(a)

(b)

(c)

(d)

(e)

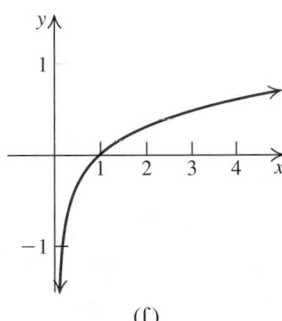

(f)

26. For each given graph below, find a function of the form $f(x) = \log_a x$ that represents the graph.

(a)

(b)

(c)

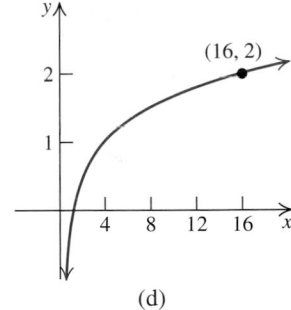

(d)

In Exercises 27–34, graph the given function by using transformations on the appropriate basic graph of the form $y = \log_a x$. State the domain and range of the function and the vertical asymptote of the graph.

27. $f(x) = \log_4(x + 3)$ †

28. $g(x) = \log_{1/2}(x - 1)$ †

29. $y = -\log_5 x$ †

30. $y = 2 \log_7(x)$ †

31. $y = \log_{1/5}(-x)$ †

32. $y = 1 + \log_{1/5}(-x)$ †

33. $y = |\log_3 x|$ †

34. $y = \log_3|x|$ †

In Exercises 35–42, begin with the graph of $f(x) = \log_2 x$ and use transformations to sketch the graph of each function. Find the domain and range of the function and the vertical asymptote of the graph.

35. $y = \log_2(x - 1)$ †

36. $y = \log_2(-x)$ †

37. $y = \log_2(3 - x)$ †

38. $y = \log_2 x$ †

39. $y = 2 + \log_2(3 - x)$ †

40. $y = 4 - \log_2(3 - x)$ †

41. $y = \log_2|x|$ †

42. $y = \log_2 x^2$ †

In Exercises 43–48, begin with the graph of $y = \ln x$ and use transformations to sketch the graph of the given function.

43. $y = \ln(x + 2)$ †

44. $y = \ln(2 - x)$ †

45. $y = -\ln(2 - x)$ †

46. $y = 2\ln x$ †

47. $y = 3 - 2\ln x$ †

48. $y = 1 - \ln(1 - x)$ †

49. Sketch the graph of $f(x) = \begin{cases} \ln x & \text{if } x > 0 \\ \ln(-x) & \text{if } x < 0 \end{cases}$ †

50. Sketch the graph of $f(x) = \begin{cases} \ln(1 - x) & \text{if } x < 1 \\ e^{-x} & \text{if } x \geq 1 \end{cases}$ †

In Exercises 51–66, solve each equation.

51. $\log_5 x = 2$ $x = 25$

52. $\log_5 x = -2$ $x = \dfrac{1}{25}$

53. $\log_5(x - 2) = 3$ $x = 127$

54. $\log_5(x + 1) = -2$ $x = -\dfrac{24}{25}$

55. $\log_2\left(\dfrac{1}{16}\right) = x$ $x = -4$

56. $\log_x\left(\dfrac{1}{5}\right) = -1$ $x = 5$

57. $\log x = 2$ $x = 100$

58. $\log(x - 1) = 1$ $x = 11$

59. $\ln x = 1$ $x = e$

60. $\ln x = 0$ $x = 1$

61. $\log_{16}\sqrt{x - 1} = \dfrac{1}{4}$ $x = 5$

62. $\log_{27}\sqrt[3]{1 - x} = \dfrac{1}{3}$ $x = -26$

63. $\log_a(x - 1) = 0$ $x = 2$

64. $\log_a(x^2 + 5x + 7) = 0$ $x = -3, -2$

65. $\log_2(x^2 - 7x + 14) = 1$ $x = 3, 4$

66. $\log(x^2 + 5x + 16) = 1$ $x = -3, -2$

In Exercises 67–84, evaluate each expression without using a calculator.

67. $\log_5 125$ 3

68. $\log_9 81$ 2

69. $\log 10{,}000$ 4

70. $\log_3 \dfrac{1}{3}$ -1

71. $\log_2 \dfrac{1}{8}$ -3

72. $\log_4 \dfrac{1}{64}$ -3

73. $\log_3 \sqrt{27}$ $\dfrac{3}{2}$

74. $\log_{27} 3$ $\dfrac{1}{3}$

75. $\log_{16} 2$ $\dfrac{1}{4}$

76. $\log_5 \sqrt{125}$ $\dfrac{3}{2}$

77. $\log_7 (49)^{\frac{1}{4}}$ $\dfrac{1}{2}$

78. $\log_3(\log_5 5)$ 0

79. $\log_4(\log_3 81)$ 1

80. $\log_4\left[\log_3(\log_2 8)\right]$ 0

81. $5^{\log_5 7}$ 7

82. $10^{\log 13}$ 13

83. $e^{\ln 5}$ 5

84. $e^{\ln e^2}$ e^2

B Exercises   Applying the Concepts

In Exercises 85–92, use the model $A = A_0 e^{kt}$.

85. Doubling your money. How long would it take to double your money if you invested P dollars at the rate of 8% compounded continuously? 8.66 yr

86. Investment goal. How long would it take to grow your investment from 10,000 dollars to 120,000 dollars at the rate of 10% compounded continuously? 24.85 yr

87. Rate for doubling your money. At what annual rate of return, compounded continuously, would your investment double in six years? 11.55%

88. Rate-of-investment goal. At what annual rate of return, compounded continuously, would your investment grow from 8000 dollars to 50,000 dollars in 25 years? 7.33%

89. Population of Canada. The population of Canada was 27 million in 1995 and 29 million in 2000. Determine the time from 1995 until Canada's population (a) doubles and (b) triples. †

90. Population of Canada. In Exercise 89, find the time from 1995 until Canada's population reaches 50 million. †

91. Water contamination. A chemical is spilled into a reservoir of pure water. The concentration of chemical in the contaminated water is 4%. In one month, 20% of the water in the reservoir is replaced with clean water.

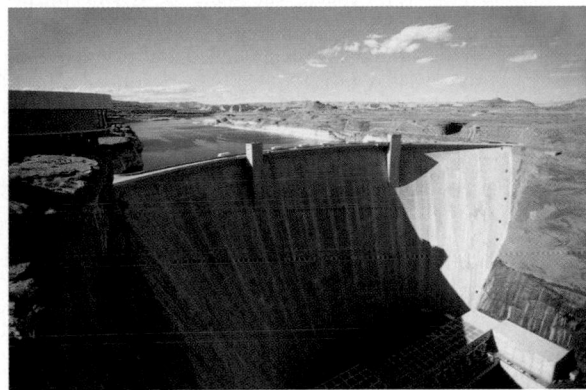

   a. What will be the concentration of the contaminant one year from now? 0.36%

   b. For water to be safe for drinking, the concentration of this contaminant cannot exceed 0.01%. How long will it be before the water is safe for drinking? †

92. Toxic chemicals in a lake. In a lake, one-fourth of the water is replaced by clean water every year. Sixteen thousand cubic meters of soluble toxic chemical spill takes place in the lake. Let $T(n)$ represent the amount of toxin left after n years.

   a. Find a formula for $T(n)$. †

   b. How much toxin will be left after 12 years? †

   c. When will 80% of the toxin be eliminated? †

93. Newton's Law of Cooling. A thermometer is taken from a room at 75°F to the outdoors, where the temperature is 20°F. The reading on the thermometer drops to 50°F after 1 minute.

   a. Find the reading on the thermometer after

      (i)   5 minutes. 22.66

      (ii) 10 minutes. 20.13

      (iii) 1 hour. 20

   b. How long would it take for the reading to drop to 22°F? †

94. Newton's Law of Cooling. The last bit of ice in a picnic cooler has melted ($T_0 = 32°F$). The temperature in the park is 85°F. After 30 minutes, the temperature in the cooler is 40°F. How long will it take for the temperature inside the cooler to reach 50°F? 76 min

95. Cooking salmon. A salmon filet initially at 50°F is cooked in an oven at the constant temperature of 400°F. After 10 minutes, the temperature of the filet rises to 160°F. How long does it take until the salmon is medium rare at 220°F? 17.6 min

96. The time of murder. A forensic specialist took the temperature of a victim's body lying in a street at 2:10 A.M. and found it to be 85.7°F. At 2:40 A.M., the temperature of the body was 84.8°F. When was the murder committed if the air temperature during the night was 55°F? [Remember, normal body temperature is 98.6°F.] At 8:17 P.M. (353 min earlier than 2:10 A.M., assuming that the body temperature is 98.6°F)

C Exercises   Beyond the Basics

97. Finding the domain. Find the domain of the each function.
  a. $f(x) = \log_2(\log_3 x)$ $(1, \infty)$
  b. $f(x) = \log(\ln(x - 1))$ $(2, \infty)$
  c. $f(x) = \ln(\log(x - 1))$ $(2, \infty)$
  d. $f(x) = \log(\log(\log(x - 1)))$ $(11, \infty)$

98. Finding the inverse. Find the inverse of each function in Exercise 97.

99. Present value of an investment. Recall that if P dollars is invested in an account at an interest rate r compounded continuously, then the amount A (called the *future value of P*) in the account t years from now will be $A = Pe^{rt}$. Solving the equation for P, we get $P = Ae^{-rt}$.

Answers:
98. a. 3^{2^x}
  b. $e^{10^x} + 1$
  c. $10^{e^x} + 1$
  d. $1 + 10^{10^{10^x}}$

In this formulation, P is called the present value of the investment.
  a. Find the present value of $100,000 at 7% compounded continuously for 20 years. $24,659.69
  b. Find the interest rate r compounded continuously that is needed to have $50,000 be the present value of $75,000 in 10 years. 4.05%

100. Your uncle is 40 years old, and he wishes to have an annual pension of $50,000 each year at age 65. What is the present value of his pension if the money can be invested at all times at a continuously compounded interest rate of
  a. 5%? $286,504.80
  b. 8%? $84,584.55
  c. 10%? $41,042.50

Rules of Logarithms

King Tut's Golden Mask

BEFORE STARTING THIS SECTION, REVIEW

1. Definition of logarithm (Section 4.3, page 452)

2. Basic properties of logarithms (Section 4.3, page 456)

3. Rules of exponents (Section 4.1, page 425)

OBJECTIVES

1 Learn the rules of logarithms.

2 Change the base of a logarithm.

3 Apply logarithms in growth and decay.

4 Apply logarithms in carbon dating.

The Boy King Tut

Today, the most famous pharaoh of Ancient Egypt is King Nebkheperure Tutankhamun. In popular culture, he has even been given a nickname: "King Tut." He was only 9 years old when he became a pharaoh. In 2005, a team of Egyptian scientists headed by Dr. Zahi Hawass determined that he was 19 years old when he died (around 1346, B.C.)

Tutankhamun was a short-lived boy king who, unlike the great Egyptian Kings Khufu (builder of the Great Pyramid), Amenhotep III (builder of temples throughout Egypt), and Ramesses II (prolific builder and usurper), accomplished nothing significant during his reign. In fact, little was known of him prior to Howard Carter's discovery of his tomb, and the amazing treasures it held, in the Valley of the Kings on November 4, 1922. Carter, with his benefactor Lord Carnarvon at his side, entered the tomb's burial chamber on November 26, 1922. Lord Carnarvon died 7 weeks after entering the burial chamber, giving rise to the theory of the "curse" of King Tut.

The work on the tomb continued until 1933. The tomb contained a pristine mummy of an Egyptian king, lying intact in his original burial furniture. He was accompanied by a small slice of the royal world of the pharaohs: golden chariots, statues of gold and ebony, a fleet of miniature ships to accommodate his trip to the hereafter, his throne of gold, bottles of perfume, precious jewelry, and more. The "Treasures of Tutankhamun" exhibition, first shown at the British Museum in London in 1972, traveled to many countries, including the United States, the Soviet Union, Japan, France, Canada, and Germany. In 2005, almost three decades later, a new exhibition, "Tutankhamun and the Golden Age of the Pharaohs," visited the United States.

In Example 9, we discuss the age of a work of art found in King Tut's tomb. ■

1 Learn the rules of logarithms.

Rules of Logarithms

Recall the basic properties of logarithms from Section 4.3:

$$\log_a a = 1$$

$$\log_a 1 = 0$$

$$\log_a a^x = x$$

$$a^{\log_a x} = x$$

Properties (1) and (2) follow directly from the definition of logarithms. Properties (3) and (4) result from the fact that exponential and logarithmic functions are inverses of one another.

In this section, we shall discuss some important rules of logarithms that are helpful in calculations, simplifications, and applications.

Rules of Logarithms

Let M, N, and a be positive real numbers with $a \neq 1$, and let r be any real number.

Rule	Description	Examples
1. **Product Rule:** $\log_a (MN) = \log_a M + \log_a N$	The logarithm of the product of two (or more) numbers is the sum of the logarithms of the numbers.	$\ln (5 \cdot 7) = \ln 5 + \ln 7$ $\log (3x) = \log 3 + \log x$ $\log_2 (5 \cdot 17) = \log_2 5 + \log_2 17$
2. **Quotient Rule:** $\log_a \left(\dfrac{M}{N}\right) = \log_a M - \log_a N$	The logarithm of the quotient of two numbers is the difference of the logarithms of the numbers.	$\ln \dfrac{5}{7} = \ln 5 - \ln 7$ $\log \left(\dfrac{5}{x}\right) = \log 5 - \log x$
3. **Power Rule:** $\log_a M^r = r \log_a M$	The logarithm of a number to the power r is r times the logarithm of the number.	$\ln 5^7 = 7 \ln 5$ $\log (5)^{3/2} = \dfrac{3}{2} \log 5$ $\log_2 (7)^{-3} = -3 \log_2 7$

Rules 1, 2, and 3 follow from the corresponding rules of the exponents:

$$a^u \cdot a^v = a^{u+v} \quad \text{Product rule}$$

$$\frac{a^u}{a^v} = a^{u-v} \quad \text{Quotient rule}$$

$$(a^u)^r = a^{ur} \quad \text{Power rule}$$

For example, to prove the product rule for logarithms, we let

$$\log_a M = u.$$

Then

$$M = a^u. \qquad \text{Exponential form}$$

Similarly, we let

$$\log_a N = v.$$

Then

$$N = a^v. \qquad\qquad \text{Exponential form}$$

From these equations, we obtain

$$MN = a^u \cdot a^v$$
$$MN = a^{u+v} \qquad\qquad \text{Product rule of exponents}$$
$$\log_a MN = u + v \qquad\qquad \text{Logarithmic form}$$
$$\log_a MN = \log_a M + \log_a N. \quad \text{Replace } u \text{ by } \log_a M \text{ and } v \text{ by } \log_a N.$$

This proves the product rule of logarithms. The quotient rule and the power rule follow from the corresponding rules for exponents in nearly identical fashion and are left as exercises.

EXAMPLE 1 | **Using Rules of Logarithms to Evaluate Expressions**

Given that $\log_5 z = 3$ and $\log_5 y = 2$, evaluate each expression.

a. $\log_5 (yz)$ **b.** $\log_5 (125y^7)$ **c.** $\log_5 \sqrt{\dfrac{z}{y}}$ **d.** $\log_5 \left(z^{\frac{1}{30}} y^5 \right)$

Solution

a. $\log_5 (yz) = \log_5 y + \log_5 z$ Product rule
$$= 2 + 3 \qquad\qquad\qquad \text{Given values}$$
$$= 5$$

b. $\log_5 (125y^7) = \log_5 125 + \log_5 y^7$ Product rule
$$= \log_5 5^3 + \log_5 y^7 \qquad 125 = 5^3$$
$$= 3 + 7 \log_5 y \qquad\qquad \text{Property (3) and power rule}$$
$$= 3 + 7(2) \qquad\qquad\quad \text{Given values}$$
$$= 17$$

c. $\log_5 \sqrt{\dfrac{z}{y}} = \log_5 \left(\dfrac{z}{y}\right)^{\frac{1}{2}}$

$$= \frac{1}{2} \log_5 \frac{z}{y} \qquad\qquad \text{Power rule}$$

$$= \frac{1}{2}(\log_5 z - \log_5 y) \qquad \text{Quotient rule}$$

$$= \frac{1}{2}(3 - 2) \qquad\qquad\quad \text{Given values}$$

$$= \frac{1}{2}$$

d. $\log_5 \left(z^{\frac{1}{30}} y^5 \right) = \log_5 z^{\frac{1}{30}} + \log_5 y^5$ Product rule

$$= \frac{1}{30} \log_5 z + 5 \log_5 y \qquad \text{Power rule}$$

$$= \frac{1}{30}(3) + 5(2) \qquad\qquad \text{Given values}$$

$$= 0.1 + 10 \qquad\qquad\qquad \text{Simplify.}$$

$$= 10.1$$

■ ■ ■

PRACTICE PROBLEM 1 Evaluate each expression for the given values in Example 1.

a. $\log_5 (y/z)$ **b.** $\log_5 (y^2 z^3)$ ■

In many applications in more advanced mathematics courses, the rules of logarithms are used in both directions; that is, the rules are read both from left to right and from right to left. For example, by the product rule of logarithms, we have

$$\log_2 3x = \log_2 3 + \log_2 x.$$

The expression $\log_2 3 + \log_2 x$ is the *expanded form* of the logarithmic expression $\log_2 3x$, while $\log_2 3x$ is the *condensed form*, or the *single logarithmic form*, of $\log_2 3 + \log_2 x$.

EXAMPLE 2 **Writing Expressions in Expanded Form**

Write each expression in expanded form.

a. $\log_2 \dfrac{x^2(x - 1)^3}{(2x + 1)^4}$ **b.** $\log_c \sqrt{x^3 y^2 z^5}$

Solution

a. $\log_2 \dfrac{x^2(x - 1)^3}{(2x + 1)^4} = \log_2 x^2(x - 1)^3 - \log_2 (2x + 1)^4$ Quotient rule

$= \log_2 x^2 + \log_2 (x - 1)^3 - \log_2 (2x + 1)^4$ Product rule

$= 2 \log_2 x + 3 \log_2 (x - 1) - 4 \log_2 (2x + 1)$ Power rule

b. $\log_c \sqrt{x^3 y^2 z^5} = \log_c (x^3 y^2 z^5)^{\frac{1}{2}}$ $\sqrt{a} = a^{1/2}$

$= \dfrac{1}{2} \log_c x^3 y^2 z^5$ Power rule

$= \dfrac{1}{2}[\log_c x^3 + \log_c y^2 + \log_c z^5]$ Product rule

$= \dfrac{1}{2}[3 \log_c x + 2 \log_c y + 5 \log_c z]$ Power rule

$= \dfrac{3}{2} \log_c x + \log_c y + \dfrac{5}{2} \log_c z$ Distributive property ■ ■ ■

PRACTICE PROBLEM 2 Write each expression in expanded form.

a. $\ln \dfrac{2x - 1}{x + 4}$ **b.** $\log \sqrt{\dfrac{4xy}{z}}$ ■

EXAMPLE 3 **Writing Expressions in Condensed Form**

Write each expressions in condensed form.

a. $\log 3x - \log 4y$ **b.** $2 \ln x + \dfrac{1}{2} \ln (x^2 + 1)$

c. $2 \log_2 5 + \log_2 9 - \log_2 75$ **d.** $\dfrac{1}{3}[\ln x + \ln (x + 1) - \ln (x^2 + 1)]$

Solution

a. $\log 3x - \log 4y = \log\left(\dfrac{3x}{4y}\right)$ Quotient rule

b. $2\ln x + \dfrac{1}{2}\ln(x^2+1) = \ln x^2 + \ln(x^2+1)^{\frac{1}{2}}$ Power rule

$\qquad\qquad\qquad\qquad = \ln(x^2\sqrt{x^2+1})$ Product rule

c. $2\log_2 5 + \log_2 9 - \log_2 75 = \log_2 5^2 + \log_2 9 - \log_2 75$ Power rule

$\qquad\qquad\qquad\qquad = \log_2(25\cdot 9) - \log_2 75$ Product rule

$\qquad\qquad\qquad\qquad = \log_2\dfrac{25\cdot 9}{75}$ Quotient rule

$\qquad\qquad\qquad\qquad = \log_2 3$ $\dfrac{25\cdot 9}{75} = \dfrac{9}{3} = 3$

d. $\dfrac{1}{3}[\ln x + \ln(x+1) - \ln(x^2+1)] = \dfrac{1}{3}[\ln x(x+1) - \ln(x^2+1)]$ Product rule

$\qquad\qquad\qquad\qquad = \dfrac{1}{3}\ln\left[\dfrac{x(x+1)}{x^2+1}\right]$ Quotient rule

$\qquad\qquad\qquad\qquad = \ln\sqrt[3]{\dfrac{x(x+1)}{x^2+1}}$ Power rule

■ ■ ■

PRACTICE PROBLEM 3   Write in condensed form: $\dfrac{1}{2}[\log(x+1) + \log(x-1)]$.   ■

WARNING   Be careful when using the rules of logarithms to simplify expressions. For example, there is no general property to rewrite $\log_a(x+y)$.

Specifically,

$$\log_a(x+y) \neq \log_a x + \log_a y. \qquad (5)$$

To see that this is so, let $x = 100$, $y = 10$, and $a = 10$. Then the value of the left side of Equation (5) is

$$\log(100+10) = \log(110)$$
$$\approx 2.0414, \qquad \text{Use a calculator.}$$

while the value of the right side of Equation (1) is

$$\log 100 + \log 10 = \log 10^2 + \log 10 \qquad 100 = 10^2$$
$$= 2\log 10 + \log 10 \qquad \text{Power rule}$$
$$= 2(1) + 1 \qquad \log 10 = 1$$
$$= 3. \qquad \text{Simplify.}$$

So $\log(100+10) \approx 2.0414$, whereas $\log 100 + \log 10 = 3$; thus, $\log(100+10) \neq \log 100 + \log 10$.

◆ **WARNING** To avoid common errors, be aware that in general,

$$\log_a (M + N) \neq \log_a M + \log_a N.$$

$$\log_a (M - N) \neq \log_a M - \log_a N.$$

$$(\log_a M)(\log_a N) \neq \log_a MN.$$

$$\log_a \left(\frac{M}{N}\right) \neq \frac{\log_a M}{\log_a N}.$$

$$\frac{\log_a M}{\log_a N} \neq \log_a M - \log_a N.$$

$$(\log_a M)^r \neq r \log_a M.$$

2 Change the base of a logarithm.

Change of Base

Calculators usually come with two types of log keys: a key for natural logarithms (base e) and a key for common logarithms (base 10). These two types of logarithms are frequently used in applications. Sometimes, however, we need to evaluate logarithms for bases other than e and 10. The *change-of-base formula* helps us convert logarithms from one base to logarithms in another base.

Suppose we are given $\log_b x$ and we are interested in converting it to logarithms with base a. We let

$$u = \log_b x. \tag{6}$$

In exponential form, we have

$$x = b^u. \tag{7}$$

Then

$$\log_a x = \log_a b^u \qquad \text{Take } \log_a \text{ of each side of (7).}$$

$$\log_a x = u \log_a b \qquad \text{Power rule}$$

$$u = \frac{\log_a x}{\log_a b} \qquad \text{Solve for } u.$$

$$\log_b x = \frac{\log_a x}{\log_a b} \qquad \text{Substitute for } u \text{ from (6).} \tag{8}$$

Equation (8) is the change-of-base formula. By choosing $a = 10$ and $a = e$, we can state the change-of-base formula as follows:

CHANGE-OF-BASE FORMULA

Let a, b, and x be positive real numbers with $a \neq 1$ and $b \neq 1$. Then $\log_b x$ can be converted to a different base as follows:

$$\log_b x = \frac{\log_a x}{\log_a b} \quad = \quad \frac{\log x}{\log b} \quad = \quad \frac{\ln x}{\ln b}$$

$$\text{(base } a) \qquad \text{(base 10)} \qquad \text{(base } e)$$

EXAMPLE 4   **Using a Change of Base to Compute Logarithms**

Compute $\log_5 13$ by changing to (a) common logarithms and (b) natural logarithms.

Solution

a. $\log_5 13 = \dfrac{\log 13}{\log 5}$ Change to base 10.

≈ 1.59369 Use a calculator.

b. $\log_5 13 = \dfrac{\ln 13}{\ln 5}$ Change to base e.

≈ 1.59369 Use a calculator.   ■ ■ ■

PRACTICE PROBLEM 4   Find $\log_3 15$.   ■

In some problems, we need to convert $\log_{b^k} a$, $k \neq 0$ from base b^k to base b. We have

$$\log_{b^k} a = \frac{\log_b a}{\log_b b^k} \qquad \text{Change to base } b.$$

$$= \frac{\log_b a}{k \log_b b} \qquad \text{Power rule}$$

$$= \frac{1}{k} \log_b a. \qquad \log_b b = 1$$

Thus,

$$\boxed{\log_{b^k} a = \frac{1}{k} \log_b a.}$$

Using some values of k, we have

$$\log_{1/b} a = -\log_b a \qquad 1/b = b^{-1}, k = -1$$

$$\log_{b^2} a = \frac{1}{2} \log_b a. \qquad k = 2$$

EXAMPLE 5   **Evaluating an Expression**

Find the value of each expression without using a calculator.

a. $\log_5 \sqrt[3]{5}$ **b.** $\log_{1/3} 3$ **c.** $7^{\log_{1/7} 5}$

Solution

a. $\log_5 \sqrt[3]{5} = \log_5 5^{\frac{1}{3}}$ $\sqrt[3]{5} = 5^{\frac{1}{3}}$

$= \dfrac{1}{3} \log_5 5$ Power rule

$= \dfrac{1}{3}$ $\log_5 5 = 1$

b. $\log_{1/3} 3 = \log_{3^{-1}} 3$ $\dfrac{1}{3} = 3^{-1}$

$= -\log_3 3$ $\log_{b^k} = \dfrac{1}{k} \log_b a$ with $k = -1$

$= -1$ $\log_3 3 = 1$

Continued on next page.

c. $7^{\log_{1/7} 5} = 7^{\log_{7^{-1}} 5}$

$\qquad = 7^{-\log_7 5} \qquad\qquad \log_{7^{-1}} 5 = \dfrac{1}{-1} \log_7 5 = -\log_7 5$

$\qquad = (7^{\log_7 5})^{-1} \qquad a^{mn} = (a^n)^m, \ -\log_7 5 = (-1)\log_7 5$

$\qquad = (5)^{-1} \qquad\qquad a^{\log_a x} = x$

$\qquad = \dfrac{1}{5}$

■ ■ ■

PRACTICE PROBLEM 5   Evaluate.

a. $\log_{1/3} 9$ **b.** $5^{\log_{1/5} 7}$ ■

EXAMPLE 6   **Matching Data to an Exponential Curve**

Find the exponential function of the form $f(x) = ae^{bx}$ that passes through the points $(0, 2)$ and $(3, 8)$.

Solution

We are interested in finding the values of a and b. Since the graph of $y = ae^{bx}$ passes through the point $(0, 2)$, we have

$$2 = f(0) = ae^{b(0)} = ae^0 = a \cdot 1 = a,$$

so that $a = 2$. Next, for the graph to pass through the point $(3, 8)$, we must have

$$8 = f(3) = ae^{b(3)} = 2e^{3b} \qquad \text{Replace } a \text{ by } 2.$$

To solve $8 = 2e^{3b}$ for b, we first divide both sides by 2 to obtain

$$4 = e^{3b}$$
$$\ln 4 = 3b \qquad\qquad \text{Logarithmic form}$$
$$b = \frac{1}{3}\ln 4. \qquad \text{Divide both sides by 3.}$$

Thus,

$$f(x) = 2e^{\left(\frac{1}{3}\ln 4\right)x}$$

is the desired exponential function.   ■ ■ ■

PRACTICE PROBLEM 6   Find an exponential function $f(x) = ae^{bx}$ that passes through the points $(0, 5)$ and $(1, 20)$.   ■

3   Apply logarithms in growth and decay.

Growth and Decay Problems

Recall from Section 4.2 that exponential growth (or decay) occurs when a quantity grows (or decreases) at a rate proportional to its size. The standard growth formula is

$$A(t) = A_0 e^{kt},$$

where $A(t) = $ the amount of substance (or population) at time t

$\qquad A_0 = A(0)$ is the initial amount;

k (as a decimal) $=$ relative rate of growth (if $k > 0$) or decay (if $k < 0$);

$\qquad t = $ time.

EXAMPLE 7   **Calculating Carbon Emissions in the United States and China**

In 1995, the United States emitted about 1400 million tons of carbon into the atmosphere (about one-fourth of worldwide emissions). In the same year, China emitted about 850 million tons. Suppose the annual rate of growth of the carbon emissions in the United States and China are 1.5% and 4.5%, respectively. After how many years will China be emitting more carbon into Earth's atmosphere than the United States will?

Solution

We let $t = 0$ correspond to 1995, the year for which we have data. After t years, the amount of carbon emitted by the United States will be

$$A_1(t) = 1400e^{0.015t} \qquad \left(1.5\% = \frac{1.5}{100} = 0.015\right)$$

and that by China will be $A_2(t) = 850e^{0.045t}$.
   We need to find t so that $A_2(t) > A_1(t)$. That is,

$$850e^{0.045t} > 1400e^{0.015t}.$$

We have

$850e^{0.045t} \cdot e^{-0.015t} > 1400e^{0.015t} \cdot e^{-0.015t}$	Multiply both sides by $e^{-0.015t}$.
$850e^{0.03t} > 1400$	Product rule; $e^0 = 1$.
$e^{0.03t} > \dfrac{28}{17}$	Divide both sides by 850 and simplify.
$\ln e^{0.03t} > \ln\left(\dfrac{28}{17}\right)$	$y = \ln x$ is an increasing function, so if $a > b$, then $\ln a > \ln b$.
$0.03t > \ln\left(\dfrac{28}{17}\right)$	$\ln e^x = x$
$t > \dfrac{\ln\left(\dfrac{28}{17}\right)}{0.03}$	Divide both sides by 0.03.
$\approx 16.63.$	Use a calculator.

So, in less than 17 years from 1995 (around the year 2012), under the present assumptions, China will be emitting more carbon into Earth's atmosphere than the United States will.   ■ ■ ■

PRACTICE PROBLEM 7   Repeat Example 7 if the rate of growth of carbon emissions is 1.3% in the United States and 4.7% in China.   ■

4 Apply logarithms in carbon dating.

Radiocarbon Dating

Ordinary carbon, called carbon-12 (^{12}C), is stable and does not decay. However, carbon-14 (^{14}C) is a relatively rare form of carbon that decays radioactively with a **half-life** (*time required for half of any given mass to decay*) of 5700 years. Carbon-14 is constantly produced in Earth's atmosphere by sunlight. When a living organism breathes or eats, it absorbs both carbon-12 and carbon-14. After the organism dies, no more carbon-14 is absorbed, so the age of its remains can be calculated by determining how much carbon-14 has decayed. The method of radiocarbon dating was developed by the American scientist W. F. Libby.

EXAMPLE 8 **Carbon Dating**

A human bone in the Gobi desert is found to contain 30% of the carbon-14 that was originally present. (There are several methods available to determine how much carbon-14 the artifact originally contained.) How long ago did the person die?

Solution

We know that the half-life of carbon-14 is approximately 5700 years. This allows us to calculate k in the equation

$$A(t) = A_0 e^{kt}. \tag{9}$$

To say that a half-life is 5700 years means that $A(t) = \frac{1}{2}A_0$ when $t = 5700$ years. Substituting into Equation (9), we get

$$\frac{1}{2}A_0 = A_0 e^{(5700)k}$$

$$\frac{1}{2} = e^{(5700)k} \qquad \text{Divide both sides by } A_0.$$

$$\ln\left(\frac{1}{2}\right) = 5700k \qquad \text{Logarithmic form}$$

$$k = \frac{\ln\left(\frac{1}{2}\right)}{5700} \qquad \text{Solve for } k.$$

$$\approx -0.0001216. \qquad \text{Use a calculator.}$$

Thus, substituting this value of k into Equation (5), we obtain

$$A(t) = A_0 e^{-0.0001216t}. \tag{10}$$

Since the bone contains 30% of the original carbon-14, we have $A(t) = 0.3A_0$ at the time the bone was tested.

$$0.3A_0 = A_0 e^{-0.0001216t} \qquad \text{Substitute } A(t) = 0.3A_0 \text{ in (10).}$$

$$0.3 = e^{-0.0001216t} \qquad \text{Divide both sides by } A_0.$$

$$\ln(0.3) = -0.0001216t \qquad \text{Logarithmic form}$$

$$t = \frac{\ln(0.3)}{-0.0001216} \approx 9901.09 \qquad \text{Solve for } t \text{ and use a calculator.}$$

The bone comes from a person who died about 9900 years ago. ■ ■ ■

PRACTICE PROBLEM 8 Repeat Example 8 if the human bone contains 20% of the carbon-14 that was originally present. ■

EXAMPLE 9 **King Tut's Treasure**

In 1960, a group of specialists from the British Museum in London investigated whether a piece of art containing organic material found in Tutankhamun's tomb had been made during his reign or (as some historians claimed) whether it belonged to an earlier period. We know that King Tut died in 1346 B.C. and ruled Egypt for 10 years. What percent of the amount of carbon-14 originally contained in the object should be present in 1960 if the object was made during Tutankhamun's reign?

Solution

The half-life of carbon-14 is 5700 years. If A_0 represents the amount of carbon-14 the object originally contained, then, from Equation (10) of Example 8, we have

$$A(t) = A_0 e^{-0.0001216t}. \qquad (11)$$

Let x represent the percent of the original amount of carbon-14 in the object that remains in the object after t years. Thus, xA_0 is the amount of carbon-14 in the object t years after it was made.

$$xA_0 = A_0 e^{-0.0001216t} \qquad \text{Replace } A(t) \text{ by } xA_0 \text{ in Equation (11).}$$
$$x = e^{-0.0001216t} \qquad \text{Divide both sides by } A_0. \qquad (12)$$

The time t that elapsed between King Tut's death and 1960 is

$$t = 1960 + 1346 \qquad \text{1346 B.C. to 1960 A.D.}$$
$$= 3306.$$

Then x_1, the percent of the original amount of carbon-14 remaining in the object (after 3306 years), is

$$x_1 = e^{-0.0001216(3306)} \qquad \text{Replace } t \text{ by 3306 in (12).}$$
$$\approx 0.66897 = 66.897\%.$$

Since King Tut ruled Egypt for 10 years, the time t_1 that elapsed from the beginning of his reign to 1960 is

$$t_1 = 3306 + 10 \qquad t_1 = t + 10$$
$$= 3316.$$

The percent x_2 of the original amount of carbon-14 remaining in the object after 3316 years is

$$x_2 = e^{-0.0001216(3316)} \qquad \text{Replace } t \text{ by 3316 in (12).}$$
$$\approx 0.66816 = 66.816\%.$$

Thus, if the piece of art was made during King Tut's reign, the percent of carbon-14 remaining in 1960 should be between 66.816% and 66.897%.   ■ ■ ■

PRACTICE PROBLEM 9   Repeat Example 9 if the art object was made 194 years before King Tut's death.   ■

A Exercises   Basic Skills and Concepts

In Exercises 1–12, given that $\log x = 2$, $\log y = 3$, $\log 2 \approx 0.3$, and $\log 3 \approx 0.48$, evaluate each expression without using a calculator.

1. $\log 6$ 0.78

2. $\log 4$ 0.6

3. $\log 5$ $\left[\textit{Hint: } 5 = \dfrac{10}{2} \right]$ 0.7

4. $\log (3x)$ 2.48

5. $\log \left(\dfrac{2}{x} \right)$ −1.7

6. $\log x^2$ 4

7. $\log (2x^2 y)$ 7.3

8. $\log xy^3$ 11

9. $\log \sqrt[3]{x^2 y^4}$ $\dfrac{16}{3}$

10. $\log (\log x^2)$ 0.6

11. $\log \sqrt[3]{48}$ 0.56

12. $\log_2 3$ 1.6

In Exercises 13–24, write each expression in expanded form.

13. $\ln [x(x-1)]$ †

14. $\log_2 \left(\dfrac{x-1}{x+3} \right)$ †

15. $\log \dfrac{\sqrt{x^2+1}}{x+3}$ †

16. $\ln \dfrac{x(x+1)}{(x-1)^2}$ †

17. $\log_3 \dfrac{(x-1)^2}{(x+1)^5}$ †

18. $\log_4 \left(\dfrac{x^2-9}{x^2-6x+8} \right)^{\frac{2}{3}}$ †

19. $\log_b xyz$ †

20. $\log_b \sqrt{xyz}$ †

21. $\log_b x^2 y^3 z$ †

22. $\log_b \dfrac{x y^2}{z^3}$ †

23. $\log \sqrt{x \sqrt{yz}}$ †

24. $\log_b (x \log_b b^{\sqrt{yz}})$ †

†Due to space constrictions, answers to these exercises may be found in the Answers beginning on page A–1 in the back of the book.

In Exercises 25–36, write each expression in condensed form.

25. $\log_2 x + \log_2 7$ $\log_2 (7x)$ **26.** $\log_2 x - \log_2 3$ $\log_2 \left(\dfrac{x}{3}\right)$

27. $\log \dfrac{5}{2} - \log \dfrac{7}{9}$ $\log \left(\dfrac{45}{14}\right)$ **28.** $2 \log (x - 1)$ $\log (x - 1)^2$

29. $\dfrac{1}{2} \log x - \log y + \log z$ $\log \left(\dfrac{z\sqrt{x}}{y}\right)$

30. $\dfrac{1}{2}(\log x + \log y)$ $\log (xy)^{1/2}$

31. $\dfrac{1}{5}(\log_2 z + 2 \log_2 y)$ $\log_2 (zy^2)^{1/5}$

32. $\dfrac{1}{3}(\log x - 2 \log y + 3 \log z)$ $\log \left(\dfrac{xz^3}{y^2}\right)^{1/3}$

33. $\ln x + 2 \ln y + 3 \ln z$ $\ln (xy^2z^3)$

34. $2 \ln x - 3 \ln y + 4 \ln z$ $\ln \left(\dfrac{x^2z^4}{y^3}\right)$

35. $2 \ln x - \dfrac{1}{2} \ln (x^2 + 1)$ $\ln \left(\dfrac{x^2}{\sqrt{x^2 + 1}}\right)$

36. $2 \ln x + \dfrac{1}{2} \ln (x^2 - 1) - \dfrac{1}{2} \ln (x^2 + 1)$ $\ln \left(\dfrac{x^2\sqrt{x^2 - 1}}{\sqrt{x^2 + 1}}\right)$

In Exercises 37–48, find the value of each expression without using a calculator.

37. $\log_3 \sqrt{3}$ $\dfrac{1}{2}$ **38.** $\log_{1/4} 4$ -1

39. $\log_3 (\log_2 8)$ 1 **40.** $2^{\log_2 2}$ 2

41. $5^{2 \log_5 3 + \log_5 2}$ 18 **42.** $e^{3 \ln 2 - 2 \ln 3}$ $\dfrac{8}{9}$

43. $10^{3 \log 2 - \log 4}$ 2 **44.** $10^{\log_{1/10} 3}$ $\dfrac{1}{3}$

45. $10^{\log_{100} 3}$ $\sqrt{3}$ **46.** $\log 4 + 2 \log 5$ 2

47. $\log_2 160 - \log_2 5$ 5 **48.** $e^{\log_{e^2} 25}$ 5

In Exercises 49–56, use the change-of-base formula and a calculator to evaluate each logarithm.

49. $\log_2 5$ 2.322 **50.** $\log_4 11$ 1.730

51. $\log_{1/2} 3$ -1.585 **52.** $\log_{\sqrt{3}} 12.5$ 4.598

53. $\log_{\sqrt{5}} \sqrt{17}$ 1.760 **54.** $\log_{15} 123$ 1.777

55. $\log_2 7 + \log_4 3$ 3.6

56. $\log_2 9 - \log_{\sqrt{2}} 5$ -1.474

B Exercises   Applying the Concepts

In Exercises 57–60, find the exponential function of the form $f(x) = ae^{bx}$ that passes through the given points.

57. $(0, 2)$ and $(2, 8)$ $f(x) = 2e^{(\ln 2)x}$

58. $(0, 8)$ and $(2, 5)$ $f(x) = 8e^{x\ln\sqrt{5/8}}$

59. $(0, 100)$ and $(5, 1000)$ $f(x) = 100e^{\frac{x}{5}\ln 10}$

60. $(0, 10)$ and $(10, 2)$ $f(x) = 10e^{-\frac{x}{10}\ln 5}$

In Exercises 61–64, assume the exponential growth model $A(t) = A_0 e^{kt}$ and a world population of 6.5 billion in 2006.

61. Rate of population growth. If the world adds about 90 million people in 2007, then what is the rate of growth? †

62. Population. Use the rate of growth from Exercise 61 to estimate the year in which the world population will be
   a. 12 billion. 2051
   b. 20 billion. 2088

63. Population growth. If the population must stay below 20 billion during the next 100 years, what is the maximum acceptable annual rate of growth? 1.12%

64. Population decline. If world population must decline below 5 billion during the next 25 years, what must be the annual rate of decline? 1.05%

65. Continuous compounding. One thousand dollars is deposited in a bank at 10% interest compounded continuously. How many years will it take the thousand dollars to grow to 3500 dollars? 12.53 yr

66. Continuous compounding. At what rate of interest, compounded continuously, will an investment double in six years? 11.55%

67. Half-life. Iodine-131, a radioactive substance that is effective in locating brain tumors, has a half-life of only 8 days. A hospital purchased 20 grams of the substance, but had to wait 5 days before it could be used. How much of the substance was left after 5 days? 12.969 gm

68. Half-life. Plutonium-241 has a half-life of 13 years. A laboratory purchased 10 grams of the substance, but did not use it for 2 years. How much of the substance was left after 2 years? 8.9885 gm

69. Half-life. Tritium is used in nuclear weapons to increase their power. It decays at the rate of 5.5% per year. Calculate the half-life of tritium. 12.60 yr

70. Half-life. Sixty grams of magnesium-28 decayed into 7.5 grams after 63 hours. What is the half-life of magnesium-28? 21 hr

Effective medicine dosage. Use the following model in Exercises 71–74: The concentration $C(t)$ of a drug administered to a patient intravenously jumps to its highest level almost immediately. The concentration subsequently decays exponentially according to the law

$$C(t) = C_0 e^{-kt},$$

where $C(0) = C_0$. The physician administering the drug would like to have

$$m < C(t) < M,$$

where m is the concentration below which the drug is ineffective and M is the concentration above which the drug is dangerous.

71. **Drug concentration.** Suppose, for a certain drug, the following results were obtained: Immediately after the drug was administered, the concentration was 5 milligrams per milliliter. Ten hours later, the concentration had dropped to 1.5 milligrams per milliliter. Determine the value of k for this drug. $k = 0.1204$

72. **Drug concentration.** Suppose, for the drug of Exercise 71, the maximum safe level is $M = 12$ milligrams per milliliter and the minimum effective level is $m = 3$ milligrams per milliliter. Assume an initial concentration of M, find the maximum possible time between doses of this drug. 11.5 hr

73. **Half-life.** The half-life of Valium® is 36 hours. Suppose a patient receives 16 milligrams of the drug at 8 A.M. How much Valium® is in the patient's blood at 4 P.M. the same day? 13.7 gm

74. **Half-life.** The half-life of aspirin in the blood is 12 hours. Estimate the time required for the aspirin to decay to 90% of the original amount ingested. 1.82 hr

C Exercises   Beyond the Basics

75. Show that
$$\log_b \left(\sqrt{x^2 + 1} - x\right) + \log_b \left(\sqrt{x^2 + 1} + x\right) = 0.$$

76. Show that
$$\log_b \left(\sqrt{x + 1} + \sqrt{x}\right) = -\log_b \left(\sqrt{x + 1} - \sqrt{x}\right).$$

77. Show that $(\log_b a)(\log_a b) = 1$.

78. Show that $\log \dfrac{a}{b} + \log \dfrac{b}{a} = 0$.

79. Write $\log_2 x = \dfrac{\ln x}{\ln 2}$ by the change-of-base formula. Then use a graphing calculator to sketch the graph of $y = \log_2 x$. †

80. Sketch the graph of $y = \log_5 (x + 3)$. †

81. By the power rule for logarithms, $\log x^2 = 2 \log x$. However, the graphs of $f(x) = \log x^2$ and $g(x) = 2 \log x$ are not identical. Explain why. †

82. Simplify each expression.
    a. $\log \left(\dfrac{a}{b}\right) + \log \left(\dfrac{b}{a}\right) + \log \left(\dfrac{c}{a}\right) + \log \left(\dfrac{a}{c}\right)$ 0
    b. $\log \left(\dfrac{a^2}{bc}\right) + \log \left(\dfrac{b^2}{ca}\right) + \log \left(\dfrac{c^2}{ab}\right)$ 0
    c. $\log_2 3 \cdot \log_3 4$ 2
    d. $\log_a b \cdot \log_b c \cdot \log_c a$ 1

83. Find the number of digits in N if $\log_2 (\log_2 N) = 4$. 5

84. Let $f(x) = \log_a x$. Show that
    a. $f\left(\dfrac{1}{x}\right) = -f(x) = \log_{1/a} x$.
    b. $\dfrac{f(x + h) - f(x)}{h} = \log_a \left(1 + \dfrac{h}{x}\right)^{\frac{1}{h}}, h \neq 0.$

85. State whether each of the following is true or false for all permissible values of the variable.
    a. $\log (x + 2) = \log x + \log 2$ False
    b. $\log 2x = \log x + \log 2$ True
    c. $\log_2 3x = 3 \log_2 x$ False
    d. $(\log_3 2x)^4 = 4 \log_3 2x$ False
    e. $\log_5 x^2 = 2 \log_5 x$ True
    f. $\log \dfrac{x}{3} = \log x - \log 3$ True
    g. $\log \dfrac{x}{4} = \dfrac{\log x}{\log 4}$ False
    h. $\ln \left(\dfrac{1}{x}\right) = -\ln x$ True
    i. $\log_2 x^2 = (\log_2 x)(\log_2 x)$ False
    j. $\log |10x| = 1 + \log |x|$ True

86. a. Prove the quotient rule for logarithms:
    $$\log_a \dfrac{M}{N} = \log_a M - \log_a N.$$
    b. Prove the power rule for logarithms:
    $$\log_a M^r = r \log_a M.$$

Critical Thinking

87. **What went wrong?** Find the error in the following argument:
$$3 < 4$$
$$3 \log \dfrac{1}{2} < 4 \log \dfrac{1}{2}$$
$$\log \left(\dfrac{1}{2}\right)^3 < \log \left(\dfrac{1}{2}\right)^4$$
$$\log \dfrac{1}{8} < \log \dfrac{1}{16}$$
$$\dfrac{1}{8} < \dfrac{1}{16}$$
$$2 < 1$$

Since $\log \dfrac{1}{2}$ is a negative number, $3 < 4$ implies
$$3 \log \left(\dfrac{1}{2}\right) > 4 \log \left(\dfrac{1}{2}\right).$$

Exponential and Logarithmic Equations

BEFORE STARTING THIS SECTION, REVIEW

1. One-to-one property of exponential functions (Section 4.1, page 428).

2. One-to-one property of logarithmic functions (Section 4.3, page 458).

3. Rules of logarithms (Section 4.4, page 470).

OBJECTIVES

1 Solve exponential equations.

2 Solve applied problems involving exponential equations.

3 Solve logarithmic equations.

4 Use the logistic growth model.

Logistic Growth Model

In Section 4.2, we discussed a mathematical model of population growth given by the equation

$$A(t) = A_0 e^{kt}. \tag{1}$$

Equation (1) represents a realistic model for a biological population with plenty of food and enough space to grow and facing no threat from predators.

However, most populations are constrained by limitations on resources—for example, plants as food for the animals of a particular species to eat. In the 1830s the Belgian scientist P. F. Verhulst added another constraint into the population growth model: *There is a limited sustainable maximum population M of a species that the habitat can support*. In population biology, *M* is called the *carrying capacity*.

Verhulst replaced Equation (1) by

$$P(t) = \frac{M}{1 + ae^{-kt}}, \tag{2}$$

where *k* is the rate of growth and *a* is a constant. In 1840, using the data from the first five U.S. censuses, he made a prediction of the U.S. population for the year 1940. As things turned out it was off by less than 1%.

The mathematical model represented by Equation (2) is called the *logistic growth model* or the *Verhulst model*. Both *logistic* and *logarithm* share the Greek root *logos*, meaning "reckoning" or "ratio." Verhulst introduced the term *logistique* to refer to the "loglike" qualities of the *S*-shaped graph of Equation (2). (See Figure 4.16.)

To sketch the graph of $y = P(t) = \dfrac{M}{1 + ae^{-kt}}$, we notice that the *y*-intercept is

$$P(0) = \frac{M}{1 + ae^0} = \frac{M}{1 + a}.$$

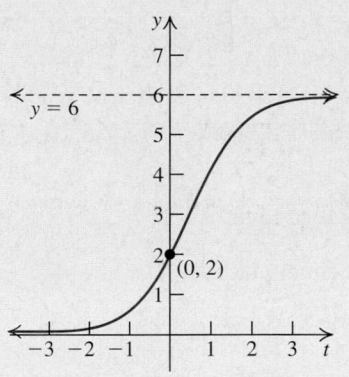

FIGURE 4.16

As t approaches ∞, the quantity ae^{-kt} approaches 0 (since k is positive). Consequently, the denominator $1 + ae^{-kt}$ of $P(t)$ approaches 1; thus, $P(t)$ approaches M.

Hence, $y = M$ is a horizontal asymptote. Similarly, as t approaches $-\infty$, e^{-kt} approaches ∞. In this case, the denominator $1 + ae^{-kt}$ of $P(t)$ approaches ∞ if $a > 0$ (or $-\infty$ if $a < 0$), and $P(t)$ approaches 0.

Thus, $y = 0$ (the t-axis) is also a horizontal asymptote. The graph of $y = \dfrac{6}{1 + 2e^{-1.5t}}$ is sketched i`n Figure 4.16.

In Example 9, we will again discuss the logistic function defined by Equation (2). ■

---

1 Solve exponential equations.

Solving Exponential Equations

An equation containing terms of the form $a^x (a > 0, a \neq 1)$ is called an exponential equation. Here are some examples of simple exponential equations:

$$2^x = 15 \qquad 9^x = 3^{x+1} \qquad 7^x = 13^{2x} \qquad 5 \cdot 2^{x-3} = 17$$

If both sides of an equation can be expressed as a power of the same base, then we can use the one-to-one property of exponential functions (if $a^x = a^y$ then $x = y$) to solve the equation. This strategy for solving exponential equations was utilized in Section 4.1. We revisit the method in the next example.

> **EXAMPLE 1**   **Solving an Exponential Equation of "Common Base" Type**

Solve each equation.

a. $25^x = 125$ **b.** $9^x = 3^{x+1}$

Solution

a.

$25^x = 125$	Given equation
$(5^2)^x = 5^3$	$25 = 5^2, 125 = 5^3$
$5^{2x} = 5^3$	Power rule for exponents
$2x = 3$	One-to-one property
$x = \dfrac{3}{2}$	Solve for x.

The solution set is $\left\{\dfrac{3}{2}\right\}$.

b.

$9^x = 3^{x+1}$	Given equation
$(3^2)^x = 3^{x+1}$	$9 = 3^2$
$3^{2x} = 3^{x+1}$	Power rule of exponents
$2x = x + 1$	One-to-one property
$2x - x = 1$	Subtract x from both sides.
$x = 1$	Simplify.

The solution set is $\{1\}$.   ■ ■ ■

PRACTICE PROBLEM 1 Solve each equation. **a.** $3^x = 243$ **b.** $8^x = 4$ ■

Logarithms are used to solve those equations for which both sides cannot be readily expressed with the same base. The next example illustrates this strategy.

EXAMPLE 2 **Solving Exponential Equations by "Taking Logarithms"**

Solve each equation and approximate the result to three decimal places.

a. $2^x = 15$ **b.** $5 \cdot 2^{x-3} = 17$

Solution

a.

$$2^x = 15 \qquad \text{Given equation}$$

$$\ln 2^x = \ln 15 \qquad \text{Take the natural log of both sides.}$$

$$x \ln 2 = \ln 15 \qquad \text{Power rule of logarithms}$$

$$x = \frac{\ln 15}{\ln 2} \qquad \text{Divide both sides by } \ln 2.$$

$$\approx 3.907 \qquad \text{Use a calculator.}$$

b.

$$5 \cdot 2^{x-3} = 17 \qquad \text{Given equation}$$

$$2^{x-3} = \left(\frac{17}{5}\right) \qquad \text{Divide both sides by 5.}$$

$$\ln 2^{x-3} = \ln\left(\frac{17}{5}\right) \qquad \text{Take the natural log of both sides.}$$

$$(x-3)\ln 2 = \ln\left(\frac{17}{5}\right) \qquad \text{Power rule of logarithms}$$

$$x - 3 = \frac{\ln\left(\frac{17}{5}\right)}{\ln 2} \qquad \text{Divide both sides by } \ln 2.$$

$$x = \frac{\ln\left(\frac{17}{5}\right)}{\ln 2} + 3 \qquad \text{Add 3 to both sides.}$$

$$\approx 4.766 \qquad \text{Use a calculator.} \qquad ■\ ■\ ■$$

PRACTICE PROBLEM 2 Solve the equation $e^{2x-1} = 10$. ■

The method used in Example 2 is summarized next.

PROCEDURE FOR SOLVING EXPONENTIAL EQUATIONS

Step 1. Isolate the exponential expression on one side of the equation.

Step 2. Take the common or natural logarithm of both sides of the equation in Step 1.

Step 3. Use the power rule $\log_a M^r = r \log_a M$ to "bring down the exponent."

Step 4. Solve for the variable.

> **EXAMPLE 3**   **Solving an Exponential Equation with Different Bases**

Solve the equation $5^{2x-3} = 3^{x+1}$ and approximate the answer to three decimal places.

Solution

When different bases are involved, we begin with Step 2 of the procedure just summarized.

$5^{2x-3} = 3^{x+1}$	Given equation
$\ln 5^{2x-3} = \ln 3^{x+1}$	Take the natural log of both sides.
$(2x - 3) \ln 5 = (x + 1) \ln 3$	Power rule of logarithms
$2x \ln 5 - 3 \ln 5 = x \ln 3 + \ln 3$	Distributive property
$2x \ln 5 - x \ln 3 = \ln 3 + 3 \ln 5$	Collect terms containing x on one side.
$x(2 \ln 5 - \ln 3) = \ln 3 + 3 \ln 5$	Factor out x on the left side.
$x = \dfrac{\ln 3 + 3 \ln 5}{2 \ln 5 - \ln 3}$	Solve for x to obtain an *exact* solution.
≈ 2.795	Use a calculator. ■ ■ ■

PRACTICE PROBLEM 3   Solve the equation $3^{x+1} = 2^{2x}$.   ■

> **EXAMPLE 4**   **An Exponential Equation of Quadratic Form**

Solve the equation $3^x - 8 \cdot 3^{-x} = 2$.

Solution

Multiply both sides of the equation by 3^x to obtain

$3^x(3^x - 8 \cdot 3^{-x}) = 2(3^x)$	
$3^{2x} - 8 \cdot 3^0 = 2 \cdot 3^x$	Distributive property; $3^x \cdot 3^{-x} = 3^0$
$3^{2x} - 8 = 2 \cdot 3^x$	$3^0 = 1$
$3^{2x} - 2 \cdot 3^x - 8 = 0.$	Subtract $2 \cdot 3^x$ from both sides.

The last equation is quadratic in form. To see this, we let $y = 3^x$; then $y^2 = (3^x)^2 = 3^{2x}$. Thus,

$3^{2x} - 2 \cdot 3^x - 8 = 0$	
$y^2 - 2y - 8 = 0$	Substitute: $y = 3^x$, $y^2 = 3^{2x}$.
$(y + 2)(y - 4) = 0$	Factor.
$y + 2 = 0 \quad$ or $\quad y - 4 = 0$	Zero product property
$y = -2 \quad$ or $\quad y = 4$	Solve for y.
$3^x = -2 \quad$ or $\quad 3^x = 4.$	Replace y by 3^x.

But $3^x = -2$ is not possible, since $3^x > 0$ for all numbers x.

Thus, the only solution of the original exponential equation is found by solving the equation

$3^x = 4$	
$\ln 3^x = \ln 4$	Take the natural log of both sides.
$x \ln 3 = \ln 4$	Power rule of logarithms
$x = \dfrac{\ln 4}{\ln 3}$	An exact solution
≈ 1.262	Use a calculator. ■ ■ ■

PRACTICE PROBLEM 4   Solve the equation $e^{2x} - 4e^x - 5 = 0$.   ■

2 Solve applied problems involving exponential equations.

Applications of Exponential Equations

EXAMPLE 5   **Solving a Population Growth Problem**

The following table shows the approximate population and annual growth rate of the United States and Pakistan in 2005:

Country	Population	Annual Population Growth Rate
United States	295 million	1.0%
Pakistan	162 million	3.1%

Source: www.cia.gov

Use the alternate population model $P(t) = P_0(1 + r)^t$ and the information in the table, and assume that the growth rate for each country stays the same. In this model, P_0 is the initial population and t is the time in years since 2005.

a. Use the model to estimate the population of each country in 2015.

b. If the current growth rate continues, in what year will the population of the United States be 350 million?

c. If the current growth rate continues, in what year will the population of Pakistan be the same as the population of the United States?

Solution

The given model is: $$P(t) = P_0(1 + r)^t \qquad (3)$$

a. Since we begin in 2005, for the U.S. population $P_0 = 295$. In 10 years, 2015, the population of the United States will be

$$295(1 + 0.01)^{10} \approx 325.86 \text{ million.} \qquad P_0 = 295, r = 0.01, t = 10 \text{ in } (3)$$

In the same way, the population of Pakistan in 2015 will be

$$162(1 + 0.031)^{10} \approx 219.84 \text{ million.} \qquad P_0 = 162, r = 0.031, t = 10 \text{ in } (3)$$

b. To find the year when the population of the United States will be 350 million, we solve for t in the equation

$$350 = 295(1 + 0.01)^t \qquad P = 350, P_0 = 295, r = 0.01 \text{ in } (3)$$

$$\frac{350}{295} = (1.01)^t \qquad \text{Divide both sides by 295.}$$

$$\ln\left(\frac{350}{295}\right) = \ln(1.01)^t \qquad \text{Take natural logs of both sides.}$$

$$\ln\left(\frac{350}{295}\right) = t \ln(1.01) \qquad \text{Power rule for logarithms}$$

$$t = \frac{\ln\left(\dfrac{350}{295}\right)}{\ln(1.01)} \approx 17.18 \qquad \text{Solve for } t \text{ and use a calculator.}$$

The population of the United States will be 350 million after approximately 17.18 years from 2005—that is, sometime in the year 2022.

c. To find when the population of the two countries will be same, we solve for t in the equation

$$295(1 + 0.01)^t = 162(1 + 0.031)^t$$

$$295(1.01)^t = 162(1.031)^t$$

$$\frac{295}{162} = \left(\frac{1.031}{1.01}\right)^t \qquad \text{Divide both sides by } 162(1.01)^t \text{ and rewrite.}$$

$$\ln\left(\frac{295}{162}\right) = \ln\left(\frac{1.031}{1.01}\right)^t \qquad \text{Take natural logs of both sides.}$$

$$\ln\left(\frac{295}{162}\right) = t \ln\left(\frac{1.031}{1.01}\right) \qquad \text{Power rule for logarithms}$$

$$t = \frac{\ln\left(\dfrac{295}{162}\right)}{\ln\left(\dfrac{1.031}{1.01}\right)} \qquad \text{Solve for } t.$$

$$\approx 29.13 \text{ years} \qquad \text{Use a calculator.}$$

Thus, the population of the two countries will be the same in about 29.13 years, that is, sometime in the year 2034. ■ ■ ■

PRACTICE PROBLEM 5   Repeat Example 5 if the rates of growth for the United States and Pakistan are 1.1% and 3.3%, respectively. ■

3 Solve logarithmic equations.

Solving Logarithmic Equations

Equations that contain terms of the form $\log_a x$ are called **logarithmic equations.** Here are some examples of logarithmic equations:

$$\log_2 x = 4 \qquad \log_3(2x - 1) = \log_3(x + 2) \qquad \log_2(x - 3) + \log_2(x - 4) = 1$$

To solve an equation such as $\log_2 x = 4$, we rewrite it in the equivalent exponential form:

$$\log_2 x = 4 \text{ means } x = 2^4 = 16.$$

Thus, $x = 16$ is a solution of the equation $\log_2 x = 4$. Because the domain of logarithmic functions consists of positive numbers, we must check apparent solutions of logarithmic equations in the original equation.

EXAMPLE 6   **Solving a Logarithmic Equation**

Solve: $4 + 3 \log_2 x = 1$.

Solution

$$4 + 3 \log_2 x = 1 \qquad \text{Original equation}$$
$$3 \log_2 x = 1 - 4 \qquad \text{Subtract 4 from both sides.}$$
$$3 \log_2 x = -3 \qquad \text{Simplify.}$$
$$\log_2 x = -1 \qquad \text{Divide both sides by 3.}$$
$$x = 2^{-1} \qquad \text{Exponential form}$$
$$x = \frac{1}{2}$$

Continued on next page.

Check $x = \dfrac{1}{2}$:

$$4 + 3 \log_2 x = 1 \qquad \text{Original equation}$$
$$4 + 3 \log_2 2^{-1} \overset{?}{=} 1 \qquad \text{Substitute } x = \dfrac{1}{2} = 2^{-1}.$$
$$4 + 3(-1) \log_2 2 \overset{?}{=} 1 \qquad \text{Power rule for logarithms}$$
$$4 - 3 \overset{?}{=} 1 \qquad \log_2 2 = 1$$
$$1 = 1 \qquad \text{yes}$$

This check shows that the solution set is $\left\{ \dfrac{1}{2} \right\}$. ■ ■ ■

PRACTICE PROBLEM 6 Solve: $1 + 2 \ln x = 4$. ■

If each side of an equation can be expressed as a single logarithm with the same base, then we can use the one-to-one property of logarithms to solve the equation.

REMINDER

The one-to-one property of logarithms says that if $\log_a x = \log_a y$, then $x = y$.

EXAMPLE 7 **Using the One-to-One Property of Logarithms**

Solve: $\log_4 x + \log_4 (x + 1) = \log_4 (x - 1) + \log_4 6$.

Solution

$$\log_4 x + \log_4 (x + 1) = \log_4 (x - 1) + \log_4 6 \qquad \text{Original equation}$$
$$\log_4 [x(x + 1)] = \log_4 [6(x - 1)] \qquad \begin{array}{l}\text{Product rule:}\\ \log_a M + \log_a N = \log_a MN\end{array}$$
$$x(x + 1) = 6(x - 1) \qquad \text{One-to-one property}$$
$$x^2 + x = 6x - 6 \qquad \text{Distributive property}$$
$$x^2 - 5x + 6 = 0 \qquad \text{Add } -6x + 6 \text{ to both sides.}$$
$$(x - 2)(x - 3) = 0 \qquad \text{Factor.}$$
$$x - 2 = 0 \text{ or } x - 3 = 0 \qquad \text{Zero product property}$$
$$x = 2 \text{ or } x = 3 \qquad \text{Solve for } x.$$

Now we check these possible solutions in the original equation.

Check $x = 2$:

$$\log_4 x + \log (x + 1) \overset{?}{=} \log_4 (x - 1) + \log_4 6$$
$$\log_4 2 + \log_4 (2 + 1) \overset{?}{=} \log_4 (2 - 1) + \log_4 6$$
$$\log_4 2 + \log_4 3 \overset{?}{=} \log_4 1 + \log_4 6$$
$$\log_4 2 + \log_4 3 \overset{?}{=} 0 + \log_4 6$$
$$\log_4 (2 \cdot 3) \overset{?}{=} \log_4 6$$
$$\log_4 6 \overset{?}{=} \log_4 6$$
$$\text{yes}$$

Check $x = 3$:

$$\log_4 x + \log (x + 1) \overset{?}{=} \log_4 (x - 1) + \log_4 6$$
$$\log_4 3 + \log_4 (3 + 1) \overset{?}{=} \log_4 (3 - 1) + \log_4 6$$
$$\log_4 3 + \log_4 4 \overset{?}{=} \log_4 2 + \log_4 6$$
$$\log_4 (3 \cdot 4) \overset{?}{=} \log_4 (2 \cdot 6)$$
$$\log_4 12 \overset{?}{=} \log_4 12$$
$$\text{yes}$$

The solution set is $\{2, 3\}$. ■ ■ ■

PRACTICE PROBLEM 7 Solve: $\ln (x + 5) + \ln (x + 1) = \ln (x - 1)$. ■

| **EXAMPLE 8** | **Using the Product and Quotient Rules** |

Solve: **a.** $\log_2 (x - 3) + \log_2 (x - 4) = 1$ **b.** $\log_3 (x - 1) - \log_3 (x - 3) = 1$.

Solution

a.
$$\log_2 (x - 3) + \log_2 (x - 4) = 1 \qquad \text{Original equation}$$
$$\log_2 [(x - 3)(x - 4)] = 1 \qquad \text{Product rule for logarithms}$$
$$(x - 3)(x - 4) = 2^1 \qquad \text{Exponential form}$$
$$x^2 - 7x + 12 = 2 \qquad \text{Expand } (x - 3)(x - 4).$$
$$x^2 - 7x + 10 = 0 \qquad \text{Subtract 2 from both sides.}$$
$$(x - 2)(x - 5) = 0 \qquad \text{Factor.}$$
$$x - 2 = 0 \quad \text{or} \quad x - 5 = 0 \qquad \text{Zero product property}$$
$$x = 2 \quad \text{or} \qquad x = 5 \qquad \text{Solve for } x.$$

We check the possible solutions in the original equation.

Check $x = 2$	**Check $x = 5$**
$\log_2 (x - 3) + \log_2 (x - 4) = 1$	$\log_2 (x - 3) + \log_2 (x - 4) = 1$
$\log_2 (2 - 3) + \log_2 (2 - 4) \overset{?}{=} 1$	$\log_2 (5 - 3) + \log_2 (5 - 4) \overset{?}{=} 1$
$\log_2 (-1) + \log_2 (-2) \overset{?}{=} 1$	$\log_2 2 + \log_2 1 \overset{?}{=} 1$
no	$1 + 0 = 1$
	$1 = 1$

Since logarithms are not defined for negative numbers, the number 2 does not satisfy the original equation. The solution set is $\{5\}$.

yes (under Check $x=5$)

b.
$$\log_3 (x - 1) - \log_3 (x - 3) = 1 \qquad \text{Original equation}$$
$$\log_3 \left(\frac{x - 1}{x - 3} \right) = 1 \qquad \text{Quotient rule for logarithms}$$
$$\left(\frac{x - 1}{x - 3} \right) = 3^1 \qquad \text{Exponential form}$$
$$x - 1 = 3(x - 3) \qquad \text{Multiply both sides by } (x - 3).$$
$$x - 1 = 3x - 9 \qquad \text{Distributive property}$$
$$8 = 2x \qquad \text{Simplify.}$$
$$4 = x \qquad \text{Divide both sides by 2.}$$

Check the possible solution, 4, in the original equation.

Check $x = 4$.

$$\log_3 (x - 1) - \log_3 (x - 3) = 1 \qquad \text{Original equation}$$
$$\log_3 (4 - 1) - \log_3 (4 - 3) \overset{?}{=} 1 \qquad \text{Replace } x \text{ by 4.}$$
$$\log_3 3 - \log_3 1 \overset{?}{=} 1 \qquad \text{Simplify.}$$
$$1 - 0 \overset{?}{=} 1 \qquad \text{Since } \log_3 3 = 1 \text{ and } \log_3 1 = 0.$$
$$1 \overset{?}{=} 1$$

yes

The solution set is $\{4\}$.   ■ ■ ■

yes

The solution set is $\{4\}$.

■ ■ ■

4 Use the logistic growth model.

PRACTICE PROBLEM 8 Solve: $\log_3 (x - 8) + \log_3 x = 2$.

■

Pierre Frençors Verhulst

(1804–1849)

Pierre Verhulst was born and educated in Brussels, Belgium. He received his Ph.D. from the University of Ghent in 1825. Influenced by Lambert Quetelet, he became interested in social statistics. Verhulst's research on the law of population growth is important. The assumed belief before Quetelet and Verhulst worked on population growth was that an increasing population as a function of time was given by

$$P(t) = P_0(1 + k)^t \quad \text{or}$$
$$P(t) = P_0 e^{kt}.$$

Verhulst showed that there are forces which tend to prevent the population growth according to these laws. He discovered the model given by Equation (2).

On the basis of his model, Verhulst predicted that the upper limit (M) of the Belgium population would be 9,400,000. In fact, the population in 1994 was 10,119,000. But for the effect of immigration, his prediction looked good.

EXAMPLE 9 **Using the Logistic Growth Model**

Suppose the carrying capacity M of the human population on Earth is 35 billion. In 1987, the world population was about 5 billion. Use the logistic growth model of P. F. Verhulst to calculate the average rate, k, of growth of the population, given that the population was about 6 billion in 2003.

$$P(t) = \frac{M}{1 + ae^{-kt}} \qquad \text{From page 482} \qquad (2)$$

Solution

We consider 1987 to be the starting time. So, substituting $t = 0$, $P(0) = 5$, and $M = 35$ into Equation (2), we have

$$5 = \frac{35}{1 + ae^{-k(0)}} = \frac{35}{1 + a}. \text{ Thus,}$$

$$5 = \frac{35}{1 + a}$$

$$5(1 + a) = 35 \qquad \text{Multiply both sides by } 1 + a.$$

$$1 + a = 7 \qquad \text{Divide both sides by 5.}$$

$$a = 6. \qquad \text{Subtract 1 from both sides.}$$

Equation (2), with $M = 35$ and $a = 6$, becomes

$$P(t) = \frac{35}{1 + 6e^{-kt}} \qquad (4)$$

We now solve Equation (4) for k, given that $t = 16$ (for 2003) and $P(16) = 6$.

$$6 = \frac{35}{1 + 6e^{-16k}} \qquad \text{Replace } P(t) \text{ by 6 and } t \text{ by 16 in (4).}$$

$$6(1 + 6e^{-16k}) = 35 \qquad \text{Multiply both sides by } 1 + 6e^{-16k}.$$

$$6 + 36e^{-16k} = 35 \qquad \text{Distributive property}$$

$$36e^{-16k} = 29 \qquad \text{Subtract 6 from both sides.}$$

$$e^{-16k} = \frac{29}{36} \qquad \text{Divide both sides by 36.}$$

$$-16k = \ln\left(\frac{29}{36}\right) \qquad \text{Logarithmic form}$$

$$k = -\frac{1}{16}\ln\left(\frac{29}{36}\right) \qquad \text{Divide both sides by } -16.$$

$$k \approx 0.0135 \qquad \text{Use a calculator.}$$

$$= 1.35\%$$

Thus, the average growth rate of the world population was approximately 1.35%. ■ ■ ■

A Exercises   Basic Skills and Concepts

In Exercises 1–16, solve each equation.

1. $2^x = 16$ $x = 4$

2. $3^x = 243$ $x = 5$

3. $8^x - 32$ $x = 5/3$

4. $5^{x-1} = 1$ $x = 1$

5. $4^{|x|} = 128$ $x = \pm 7/2$

6. $9^{|x|} = 243$ $x = \pm 5/2$

7. $5^{-|x|} = 625$ $\varnothing$

8. $3^{-|x|} = 81$ $\varnothing$

9. $\ln x = 0$ $x = 1$

10. $\ln(x - 1) = 1$ $x = 1 + e$

11. $\log_2 x = -1$ $x = 1/2$

12. $\log_2(x + 1) = 3$ $x = 7$

13. $\log_3 |x| = 2$ $x = \pm 9$

14. $\log_2 |x + 1| = 3$ $x = 7, -9$

15. $\dfrac{1}{2}\log x - 2 = 0$ $x = 10{,}000$

16. $\dfrac{1}{3}\log(x + 1) - 1 = 0$ $x = 999$

In Exercises 17–42, solve each exponential equation and approximate the result, correct to three decimal places.

17. $2^x = 3$ $x = 1.585$

18. $3^x = 5$ $x = 1.465$

19. $3^{1-x} = 7$ $x = -0.771$

20. $2^{1-x} = 9$ $x = -2.170$

21. $5^{1-2x} = 6$ $x = -0.057$

22. $3^{2-3x} = 11$ $x = -0.061$

23. $2^{2x+3} = 15$ $x = 0.453$

24. $3^{2x+5} = 17$ $x = -1.210$

25. $5 \cdot 2^x - 7 = 10$ $x = 1.765$

26. $3 \cdot 5^x + 4 = 11$ $x = 0.526$

27. $3 \cdot 4^{2x-1} + 4 = 14$ $x = 0.934$

28. $2 \cdot 3^{4x-5} - 7 = 10$ $x = 1.740$

29. $5^{1-x} = 2^x$ $x = 0.699$

30. $3^{2x-1} = 2^{x+1}$ $x = 1.191$

31. $\dfrac{5}{2 + 3^x} = 4$ $\varnothing$

32. $\dfrac{7}{3 + 5 \cdot 2^x} = 4$ $\varnothing$

33. $20(1.03)^t = 500$ $t = 108.897$

34. $3(1.02)^t = 40$ $t = 130.804$

35. $(1.065)^t = 2$ $t = 11.007$

36. $(1.0725)^t = 2$ $t = 9.903$

37. $2^{2x} - 4 \cdot 2^x = 21$ $x = 2.807$

38. $4^x - 4^{-x} = 2$ $x = 0.636$

39. $9^x - 6 \cdot 3^x + 8 = 0$ $x = 0.631$ or 1.262

40. $\dfrac{3^x + 5 \cdot 3^{-x}}{3} = 2$ $x = 0, 1.465$

41. $\dfrac{3^x - 3^{-x}}{3^x + 3^{-x}} = \dfrac{1}{4}$ $x = 0.232$

42. $\dfrac{e^x - e^{-x}}{e^x + e^{-x}} = \dfrac{1}{3}$ $x = 0.347$

In Exercises 43–60, solve each logarithmic equation.

43. $3 + \log(2x + 5) = 2$ $x = -49/20$

44. $1 + \log(3x - 4) = 0$ $x = 41/30$

45. $\log(x^2 - x - 5) = 0$ $x = 3, -2$

46. $\log(x^2 - 6x + 9) = 0$ $x = 4, 2$

47. $\log_4(x^2 - 7x + 14) = 1$ $x = 5, 2$

48. $\log_4(x^2 + 5x + 10) = 1$ $x = -3, -2$

49. $\ln(2x - 3) - \ln(x + 5) = 0$ $x = 8$

50. $\log(x + 8) + \log(x - 1) = 1$ $x = 2$

51. $\log x + \log(x + 9) = 1$ $x = 1$

52. $\log_5(3x - 1) - \log_5(2x + 7) = 0$ $x = 8$

53. $\log_a(5x - 2) - \log_a(3x + 4) = 0$ $x = 3$

54. $\log(x - 1) + \log(x + 2) = 1$ $x = 3$

55. $\log_6(x + 2) + \log_6(x - 3) = 1$ $x = 4$

56. $\log_2(3x - 2) - \log_2(5x + 1) = 3$ $\varnothing$

57. $\log_3(2x - 7) - \log_3(4x - 1) = 2$ $\varnothing$

58. $\log_4 \sqrt{x + 3} - \log_4 \sqrt{2x - 1} = \dfrac{1}{4}$ $x = 5/3$

59. $\log_7 3x + \log_7(2x - 1) = \log_7(16x - 10)$ $x = 2/3, 5/2$

60. $\log_3(x + 1) + \log_3 2x = \log_3(3x + 1)$ $x = 1$

---

†Due to space constrictions, answers to these exercises may be found in the Answers beginning on page A–1 in the back of the book.

B Exercises   Applying the Concepts

61. Investment. Find the time required for an investment of 10,000 dollars to grow to 18,000 dollars at an annual interest rate of 6% if the interest is compounded
    a. Yearly. 10.087 yr   **b.** Quarterly. 9.870 yr
    c. Monthly. 9.821 yr   **d.** Daily. 9.797 yr
    e. Continuously. 9.796 yr

62. Investment. How long will it take for an investment of 100 dollars to double in value if the annual rate of interest is 7.2% compounded
    a. Yearly. 9.970 yr   **b.** Quarterly. 9.713 yr
    c. Monthly. 9.656 yr   **d.** Continuously. 9.627 yr

In Exercises 63–68, use the following table, which shows various statistics for Canada, Mexico, and the United Kingdom in 1988, and assume the same annual growth rate to continue for each country. Use the continuous compounding model.

Item	Canada	Mexico	United Kingdom
Population	26 million	82.7 million	57.1 million
Annual growth rate	0.9%	2.1%	0.3%
Price/liter of milk	$1.19	$.67	$0.95
Price/kilogram of bread	$1.76	$1.31	$1.40
Annual inflation rate	4%	7.8%	5.3%

63. Annual growth rate. Find all of the data for each country for each year.
    a. 2012 †   **b.** 2018 †

64. Annual growth rate. When will the population of Mexico reach 250 million people? In 2041 (after 52.7 yr)

65. Annual growth rate. In what year will the population of Canada be 60 million people? In 2081 (after 92.9 yr)

66. Annual growth rate. In Mexico in 1988, the average person spent approximately $500 on food. Use the inflation rate to calculate the cost of this food in the year
    a. 2012. $3250.64,   **b.** 2018. $5190.62

67. Annual growth rate. In each country, when will the price of a kilogram of bread be 10 dollars? †

68. Annual growth rate. In what year will the price of a liter of milk be the same in both Mexico and United Kingdom? †

69. Inflation. The rate of inflation in the fictional land of Sardonia is such that the price of a car costing 20,000 dollars in U.S. currency will double in eight years. What will be the price of this car in five years? What is the annual rate of inflation? $r \approx 8.66\%$, $30,837.52

70. Doubling Time. An amount P dollars is deposited in a regular bank account. How long does it take to double the initial investment (called the **doubling time**) if
    a. The interest rate is r, compounded annually. †
    b. The interest rate is r (per year), compounded continuously. †

71. Population growth. It is estimated that in t years from 2000 the population of Sardonia will be

$$P(t) = \frac{32}{5 + 3e^{-kt}} \text{ million.}$$

    a. Find the average rate of growth if the population of Sardonia in 2004 was 4.2 million. †
    b. What was the population of Sardonia in 2002? †
    c. Sketch the graph of $y = P(t)$. †
    d. What will the population of Sardonia be in 2020? †
    e. What will happen to the population in the long run? †

72. Epidemic outbreak. An epidemic spread through a community so that t weeks after the outbreak the number of people who became infected is given by the function

$$f(t) = \frac{20,000}{1 + ae^{-kt}},$$

where 20,000 people of the community are susceptible to the disease. If 1000 people were infected initially, and 8999 had been infected by the end of the 4th week, find the number of people infected after
    a. 8 weeks. 18,542   **b.** 16 weeks. 19,994

73. Spreading a rumor. A malicious rumor was started by a jealous student on an isolated college campus of 5000 students. The number of people who heard the rumor anytime up to t days after it was started is given by the function

$$R(t) = \frac{5000}{1 + ae^{-kt}}.$$

Half the college students had heard the rumor by 10 days after it started.
   a. Find a and k and graph the function $y = R(t)$. †
   b. How many students would have heard the rumor by 15 days after it started? 4930
   c. How many students will have heard the rumor in the long run? 5000

74. Biological growth. In his laboratory experiment in 1934, G. F. Gause placed paramecia (unicellular microorganisms) in 5 cubic centimeters of a saline (salt) solution with a constant amount of food and measured their growth on a daily basis. He found that the population $P(t)$ after t days was approximated by

$$P(t) = \frac{4490}{1 + e^{5.4094 - 1.0255t}}, \quad t \geq 0.$$

   a. What was the initial size of the paramecia? 20
   b. What was the carrying capacity of the medium? 4490
   c. Graph the equation $y = P(t)$. †

75. Marriage rate. The marriage rate in the United States in 1990 was 0.98%, and there were about 2,448,000 marriages that year. (*Source:* Department of Health and Human Services.)
   Use the model $M(t) = M_0(1 + r)^t$, with a constant marriage rate and $t = 0$ corresponding to the year 1990 to estimate
   a. the number of marriages in 2010. $M(20) = 2,975,218$
   b. the year in which the number of marriages will be 4 million. The year 2041.

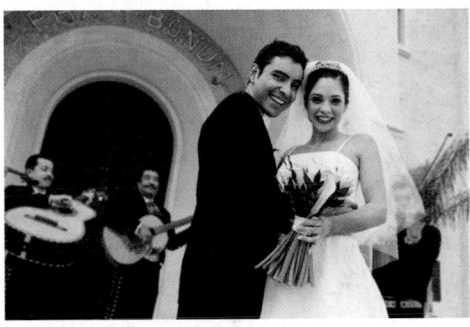

76. Divorce rate. The divorce rate in the United States in 1990 was 0.47%, and there were 1,175,000 divorces that year. Use the model $D(t) = D_0(1 + r)^t$, with a constant divorce rate and $t = 0$ corresponding to the year 1990 to estimate
   a. the number of divorces in 2010. 1,290,524
   b. the year in which the number of divorces will be 2 million. In 2104

77. Light absorption in physics. The light intensity I (in lumens) at a depth of x feet in Lake Elizabeth is given by

$$\log\left(\frac{I}{12}\right) = -0.025x.$$

   a. Find the light intensity at a depth of 30 feet. 2.134 lm
   b. At what depth is the light intensity 4 lumens? 19.08 ft

78. Rule of 70. Bankers use the **rule of 70** to estimate the doubling time for money invested at different rates. The rule of 70 states that

$$\text{Doubling time} \approx \frac{70}{100r} \text{ years,}$$

where r is the annual interest rate (expressed as a decimal number). Explain why this formula works. $\ln(2) \approx 0.69$

C Exercises   Beyond the Basics

79. Solve for t: $P = \dfrac{M}{1 + e^{-kt}}$. $t = \dfrac{1}{k} \ln \left(\dfrac{P}{M - P} \right)$

80. Find k so that
  a. $2^x = e^{kx}$; 0.693   **b.** $e^x = 2^{kx}$. 1.443

81. If $x = \dfrac{e^y - e^{-y}}{e^y + e^{-y}}$, show that $y = \dfrac{1}{2} \ln \left(\dfrac{1 + x}{1 - x} \right)$.

82. If $x = \dfrac{a^y + a^{-y}}{a^y - a^{-y}}$, show that $y = \dfrac{1}{2} \log_a \left(\dfrac{x + 1}{x - 1} \right)$.

83. If $\dfrac{\log x}{2} = \dfrac{\log y}{3} = \dfrac{\log z}{5} \ (= k)$, show that
  a. $xy = z$;   **b.** $y^2 z^2 = x^8$.
  [*Hint:* First express x, y, and z in terms of k.]

84. The pressure P and the volume V of a gas are related by the formula
$$PV^\alpha = k,$$
where α and k are constants that depend on the gas. Find α for a given gas with $P_1 = 2$ atmospheres (atm), $V_1 = 3.2$ cubic feet, $P_2 = 3$ atm, and $V_2 = 2.3$ cubic feet. $\alpha = 1.228$

85. **Annuity.** The future value A of an ordinary annuity with payment size R, periodic rate i, and a term of n payments is given by the formula $A = R \dfrac{(1 + i)^n - 1}{i}$. Solve this equation for n.

86. The present value P of an annuity with payment size R, periodic rate i, and a term of n payments is given by the formula
$$P(1 + i)^n = R \dfrac{(1 + i)^n - 1}{i}.$$ Solve this equation for n.

Critical Thinking

In Exercises 87–90, solve each equation for x.

87. $(\log x)^2 = \log x$ $x = 1.10$

88. $\log_2 x + \log_4 x = 6$ $x = 16$

89. $\log_4 x^2 (x - 1)^2 - \log_2 (x - 1) = 1$ $x = 2$

90. $\log (\log x^{10}) = 1$ $x = 10$

91. Find the value of $\log_2 \log_2 \log_3 \log_3 27^3$. 0

92. If $f(x) = \log_a \left(\dfrac{1 + x}{1 - x} \right)$, show that $f \left(\dfrac{2x}{1 + x^2} \right) = 2 f(x)$.

93. If $\log 3 = 0.477$ and $(1000)^x = 3$, then the value of x is a
  a. 0.159. **b.** 10. **c.** 0.0477. **d.** 0.0159.

94. The simplified value of $\log (\log x^2) - \log (\log x)$ is c.
  a. 2. **b.** $\dfrac{1}{2}$ **c.** $\log 2$. **d.** $2 \log x$.

Answers:

85. $n = \dfrac{\ln \left(\dfrac{R + iA}{R} \right)}{\ln (1 + i)}$ **86.** $n = \dfrac{\ln \left(\dfrac{R}{R - iP} \right)}{\ln (1 + i)}$

Summary   Definitions, Concepts and Formulas

4.1 Exponential Functions

i. A function $f(x) = a^x$, with $a > 0$ and $a \neq 1$, is called an exponential function with base a.
  Rules of exponents: $a^x a^y = a^{x+y}$, $\dfrac{a^x}{a^y} = a^{x-y}$, $(a^x)^y = a^{xy}$,
$$a^0 = 1, a^{-x} = \dfrac{1}{a^x}$$

ii. Exponential functions are one-to-one: If $a^x = a^y$, then $x = y$.

iii. If $a > 1$, then $f(x) = a^x$ is an increasing function; $f(x) \to \infty$ as $x \to \infty$ and $f(x) \to 0$ as $x \to -\infty$.

iv. If $0 < a < 1$, then $f(x) = a^x$ is a decreasing function; $f(x) \to 0$ as $x \to \infty$ and $f(x) \to \infty$ as $x \to -\infty$

v. The graph of $f(x) = a^x$ has y-intercept 1, and the x-axis is a horizontal asymptote.

4.2 The Natural Exponential Function

i. *Simple-interest formula.* If P dollars is invested at an interest rate r per year for t years, then the simple interest is given by the formula $I = Prt$.

ii. *Compound interest.* P dollars invested at annual rate r compounded n times per year for t years amounts to
$$A_n = P \left(1 + \dfrac{r}{n} \right)^{nt}.$$

iii. The Euler constant $e = \lim\limits_{h \to \infty} \left(1 + \dfrac{1}{h} \right)^h \approx 2.718$.

iv. *Continuous compounding.* P dollars invested at an annual rate r compounded continuously for t years amounts to $A = Pe^{rt}$.

v. The function $f(x) = e^x$ is the natural exponential function.

4.3 Logarithmic Functions

i. $y = \log_a x$ if and only if $x = a^y$.

ii. *Basic properties:* $\log_a a = 1$, $\log_a 1 = 0$,
$$\log_a a^x = x, a^{\log_a x} = x \quad \text{Inverse properties}$$

iii. The domain of $\log_a x$ is $(0, \infty)$, the range is $(-\infty, \infty)$, and the y-axis is a vertical asymptote. The x-intercept is 1.

iv. Logarithmic functions are one-to-one: If $\log_a x = \log_a y$, then $x = y$.

v. If $a > 1$, then $f(x) = \log_a x$ is an increasing function; $f(x) \to \infty$ as $x \to \infty$ and $f(x) \to -\infty$ as $x \to 0^+$.

vi. If $0 < a < 1$, then $f(x) = \log_a x$ is a decreasing function; $f(x) \to -\infty$ as $x \to \infty$ and $f(x) \to \infty$ as $x \to 0^+$.

vii. The common logarithmic function is $y = \log x$ (base 10); the natural logarithmic function is $y = \ln x$ (base e).

4.4 Rules of Logarithms

i. *Rules of logarithms:*

$$\log_a MN = \log_a M + \log_a N \quad \text{Product rule}$$

$$\log_a \frac{M}{N} = \log_a M - \log_a N \quad \text{Quotient rule}$$

$$\log_a M^r = r \log_a M \quad \text{Power rule}$$

ii. *Change-of-base formula:* $\log_b x = \dfrac{\log_a x}{\log_a b} = \dfrac{\log x}{\log b} = \dfrac{\ln x}{\ln b}$

$$\text{(base } a) \quad \text{(base 10)} \quad \text{(base } e)$$

4.5 Exponential and Logarithmic Equations

An *exponential equation* is an equation in which a variable occurs in one or more exponents.

A *logarithmic equation* is an equation that involves the logarithm of a function of the variable.

Exponential and logarithmic equations are solved by using some or all of the following techniques:

i. Using the one-to-one property of exponential and logarithmic functions

ii. Converting from exponential to logarithmic form or vice versa

iii. Using the product, quotient, and power rules for exponents and logarithms

---

Review Exercises

Basic Skills

In Exercises 1–10, state whether the given statement is true or false.

1. $f(x) = a^x$ is an exponential function if $a > 0$. False

2. The graph of $f(x) = 4^x$ approaches the x-axis as $x \to -\infty$. True

3. The domain of $f(x) = \log(2 - x)$ is $(-\infty, 2]$. False

4. $u = 10^v$ means $\log u = v$. True

5. The inverse of $f(x) = \ln x$ is $g(x) = e^x$. True

6. The graph of $y = a^x$ $(a > 0, a \neq 1)$ always contains the points $(0, 1)$ and $(1, a)$. True

7. $\ln(M + N) = \ln M + \ln N$ False

8. $\log \sqrt{300} = 1 + \dfrac{1}{2} \log 3$ True

9. $f(x) = 2^{-x}$ and $g(x) = \left(\dfrac{1}{2}\right)^x$ have the same graph. True

10. $\ln u = \dfrac{\log u}{\log e}$ True

In Exercises 11–18, match the function with its graph in (a)–(h).

11. $f_1(x) = \log_2 x$ h

12. $f_2(x) = 2^x$ c

13. $f_3(x) = \log_2(3 - x)$ f

14. $f_4(x) = \log_{1/2} x$ d or e

15. $f_5(x) = -\log_2 x$ d or e

16. $f_6(x) = \left(\dfrac{1}{2}\right)^x$ b

17. $f_7(x) = 3 - 2^{-x}$ a

18. $f_8(x) = \dfrac{6}{1 + 2e^{-x}}$ g

(a)

(b)

(c)

(d)

(e)

(f)

(g)

(h)

†Due to space constrictions, answers to these exercises may be found in the Answers beginning on page A–1 in the back of the book.

In Exercises 19–30, use transformations on an appropriate graph to graph each function. Determine the domain, range, and asymptotes (if any).

19. $f(x) = 2^{-x}$ †

20. $g(x) = 2^{-0.5x}$ †

21. $h(x) = 3 + 2^{-x}$ †

22. $f(x) = e^{|x|}$ †

23. $g(x) = e^{-|x|}$ †

24. $h(x) = e^{-x+1}$ †

25. $f(x) = \ln(-x)$ †

26. $g(x) = 2 \ln|x|$ †

27. $h(x) = 2 \ln(x - 1)$ †

28. $f(x) = 2 - \left(\dfrac{1}{2}\right)^x$ †

29. $g(x) = 2 - \ln(-x)$ †

30. $h(x) = 3 + 2 \ln(5 + x)$ †

In Exercises 31–34, sketch the graph of the given function, using two steps:

i. find the *y*-intercept;   **ii.** find $\lim\limits_{x\to\infty} f(x)$ and $\lim\limits_{x\to-\infty} f(x)$.

31. $f(x) = 3 - 2e^{-x}$ †

32. $f(x) = \dfrac{5}{2 + 3e^{-x}}$ †

33. $f(x) = e^{-x^2}$ †

34. $f(x) = 3 - \dfrac{6}{1 + 2e^{-x}}$ †

In Exercises 35–38, first find *a* and *k*, and then evaluate the function.

35. Let $f(x) = a(2^{kx})$, with $f(0) = 10$ and $f(3) = 640$. Find $f(2)$. $a = 10, k = 2, f(2) = 160$

36. Let $f(x) = 50 - a(5^{kx})$, with $f(0) = 10$ and $f(2) = 0$. Find $f(1)$. $a = 40, k = 0.06932, f(1) = 5.28$

37. Let $f(x) = \dfrac{4}{1 + a\,e^{-kx}}$, with $f(0) = 1$ and $f(3) = \dfrac{1}{2}$. Find $f(4)$. $a = 3, k = -0.2824, f(4) = 0.38890$

38. Let $f(x) = 6 - \dfrac{3}{1 + ae^{-kx}}$, with $f(0) = 5$ and $f(4) = 4$. Find $f(10)$. $a = 2, k = 0.3466, f(10) = 3.1764$

In Exercises 39–42, write each logarithm in expanded form.

39. $\ln(xy^2z^3)$ $\ln x + 2\ln y + 3\ln z$

40. $\log(x^3\sqrt{y - 1})$ $3\log x + \dfrac{1}{2}\log(y - 1)$

41. $\ln\left[\dfrac{x\sqrt{x^2 + 1}}{(x^2 + 3)^2}\right]$ $\ln x + \dfrac{1}{2}\ln(x^2 + 1) - 2\ln(x^2 + 3)$

42. $\ln\sqrt{\dfrac{x^3 + 5}{x^3 - 7}}$ $\dfrac{1}{2}[\ln(x^3 + 5) - \ln(x^3 - 7)]$

In Exercises 43–48, write *y* as a function of *x*.

43. $\ln y = \ln x + \ln 3$ $y = 3x$

44. $\ln y = \ln(C) + kx$; *C* and *k* are constants. $y = Ce^{kx}$

45. $\ln y = \ln(x - 3) - \ln(y + 2)$ $y = -1 \pm \sqrt{x - 2}$

46. $\ln y = \ln x - \ln(x^2 y) - 2\ln y$ †

47. $\ln y = \dfrac{1}{2}\ln(x - 1) + \dfrac{1}{2}\ln(x + 1) - \ln(x^2 + 1)$ †

48. $\ln(y - 1) = \dfrac{1}{x} + \ln(y)$ †

In Exercises 49–66, solve each equation.

49. $3^x = 81$ 4

50. $5^{x-1} = 625$ 5

51. $2^{x^2 + 2x} = 16$ $-1 \pm \sqrt{5}$

52. $3^{x^2 - 6x + 8} = 1$ $\{2, 4\}$

53. $3^x = 23$ †

54. $2^{x-1} = 5.2$ †

55. $273^x = 19$ †

56. $27 = 9^x \cdot 3^{x^2}$ $\{1, -3\}$

57. $3^k = e^{kx}$ $\ln 3$

58. $a^{2x-1} = b$ †

59. $x^{\ln x} = e$ †

60. $2^{2^x} = 8$ †

61. $\log_3(x + 2) - \log_3(x - 1) = 1$ 2.5

62. $\log_5(3x + 7) + \log_5(x - 5) = 2$ 6

63. $2\ln 3x = 3\ln x$ 9

64. $2\log x = \ln e$ $\sqrt{10}$

65. $2^x - 8 \cdot 2^{-x} - 7 = 0$ 3

66. $3^x - 24 \cdot 3^{-x} = 10$ †

Applying the Concepts

67. You have 7000 dollars to invest for seven years. Which investment will provide the greater return, 5% compounded yearly or 4.75% compounded monthly? †

68. How long will it take 8000 dollars to grow to 20,000 dollars if the rate of interest is 7% compounded continuously?   13.09 yr

69. The formula $P(t) = 32e^{0.003t}$ models the population of Canada, in millions, *t* years after 2004.
   a. Estimate the population of Canada in 2014.   32.975 million
   b. According to this model, when will the population of Canada be 60 million?   209.54 yr (or in 2214)

70. The formula $C(t) = 100 + 25e^{.03t}$ models the average cost of a house in Sometown, U.S.A., *t* years after 2000. The cost is expressed in thousands of dollars.
   a. Sketch the graph of $y = C(t)$. †
   b. Estimate the average cost in 2010. †
   c. According to this model, when will the average cost of a house in Sometown be 250,000 dollars? †

71. An experimental drug was injected into the bloodstream of a rat. The concentration $C(t)$ of the drug (in micrograms per milliliter of blood) after t hours was modeled by the function

$$C(t) = 0.3e^{-0.47t}, \quad 0.5 \le t \le 10.$$

  a. Graph the function $y = C(t)$ for $0.5 \le t \le 10$. †

  b. When will the concentration of the drug be 0.029 micrograms per milliliter? (1 microgram $= 10^{-6}$ gram.) †

72. X-ray technicians are shielded by a wall insulated with lead. The equation $x = \dfrac{1}{152} \log\left(\dfrac{I_0}{I}\right)$ measures the thickness x (in centimeters) of the lead insulation required to reduce the initial intensity I_0 of X-rays to the desired intensity I.

  a. What thickness of lead is required to reduce the intensity of X-rays to one-tenth of their initial intensity? †

  b. What thickness of lead is required to reduce the intensity of X-rays to $\dfrac{1}{40}$ of their initial intensity? †

  c. How much is the intensity reduced if the lead insulation is 10 centimeters thick? †

73. Chai (a certain kind of tea) is made by adding boiling water ($212°$ F) to the chai mix. Suppose you are sitting in a room with the air temperature at $75°$F. You make chai, and according to Newton's law of cooling, the temperature of the chai t minutes after it is boiled is given by a function of the form $f(t) = 75 + ae^{-kt}$. After 1 minute, the temperature of the chai falls to $200°$F. How long will it take for the chai to be drinkable at $150°$F? $t = 6.57$ min

74. Approximately $P(t) = \dfrac{6}{1 + 5e^{-.7t}}$ thousand people had caught a new form of influenza anytime up to t weeks after its outbreak.

  a. Sketch the graph of $y = P(t)$. †

  b. How many people had the disease initially? †

  c. How many people had contracted the disease after 4 weeks? †

  d. If the trend continues, how many people in all will contract the disease? †

75. The population density x miles from the center of a town called Greenville is approximated by the equation $D(x) = 5e^{0.08x}$ thousand people per square mile.

  a. What is the population density at the center of Greenville? 5 thousand people/square mile

  b. What is the population density 5 miles from the center of Greenville? 7.459 thousand people/square mile

  c. Approximately how far from the center of Greenville would the density be 15,000 people per square mile? †

76. Assume that in 2000 the population of the United States was 280 million and in the same year the number of vehicles was 200 million. Suppose the population of the United States is growing at the rate of 1% per year, while the number of vehicles in the United States is growing at the rate of 3%. In what year will there be an average of one vehicle per person? 16.82 years (i.e., in 2017)

77. **Light intensity.** The *Bouguer–Lambert Law* states that the intensity I of sunlight filtering down through water at a depth x (in meters) decreases according to the exponential

decay function $I = I_0e^{-kx}$, where I_0 is the intensity at the surface and $k > 0$ is an absorption constant that depends on the murkiness of the water. Suppose the absorption constant of Carrollwood Lake was experimentally determined to be $k = 0.73$. How much light has been absorbed by the water at a depth of 2 meters? $I = 0.2322I_0$

78. The strength of a TV signal usually fades out due to a damping effect of cable lines. If I_0 is the initial strength of the signal, then its strength I at a distance x miles is measured by the formula $I = I_0e^{-kx}$, where $k > 0$ is a damping constant that depends on the type of wire used. Suppose the damping constant has been measured experimentally to be $k = 0.003$. What fraction of the signal is lost at a distance of 10 miles? 20 miles? †

79. **Walking speed in a city.** In 1976, Marc and Helen Bernstein discovered that in a city with population p the average speed s (in feet per second) that a person walks on main streets can be approximated by the formula

$$s(p) = 0.04 + 0.86 \ln p.$$

  a. What is the average walking speed of pedestrians in Tampa (population 470,000)? 11.27 ft/sec

  b. What is the average walking speed of pedestrians in Bowman, Georgia (population 450)? 5.29 ft/sec

  c. What is the estimated population of a town in which the estimated average walking speed is 4.6 feet per second? †

80. **Drinking and driving.** Just after Eric had his last drink, the alcohol level in his bloodstream was 0.26 (milligram of alcohol per milliliter of blood). After one-half hour, his alcohol level was 0.18. The alcohol level $A(t)$ in a person follows the exponential decay law:

$$A(t) = A_0e^{-kt},$$

where $k > 0$ depends on the individual.

  a. What is the value of A_0 for Eric? 0.26

  b. What is the value of k for Eric? $k = 0.74$

  c. If the legal driving limit for alcohol level is 0.08, how long should Eric wait (after his last drink) before he will legally be able to drive? $t = 1.59$ hr $\approx$ 1 hr, 34 min

81. **Bacteria culture.** The mass $m(t)$ in grams of a bacteria culture grows according to the logistic growth model

$$m(t) = \dfrac{6}{1 + 5e^{-0.7t}},$$

where t is time measured in days.

  a. What is the initial mass of the culture? 1 gm

  b. What happens to the mass in the long run? †

  c. When will the mass reach 5 grams? 4.6 days

82. **A learning model.** The number of units $n(t)$ produced per day after t days of training is given by

$$n(t) = 60(1 - e^{-kt}),$$

where $k > 0$ is a constant that depends on the individual.

  a. Estimate k for Rita, who produced 20 units after 1 day of training. $k = 0.41$

  b. How many units will Rita produce per day after 10 days of training? $58.90 \approx 59$ units

  c. How many days should Rita be trained if we expect her to produce 40 units per day? $2.7 \approx 3$ days

Practice Test A

1. Solve the equation $5^{-x} = 125$. $x = -3$

2. Solve the equation $\log_2 x = 5$. $x = 32$

3. State the range of $y = -e^x + 1$, and find the asymptote of its graph. Range $= (-\infty, 1)$, horizontal asymptote $y = 1$

4. Evaluate $\log_2 \dfrac{1}{8}$. -3

5. Solve the exponential equation $\left(\dfrac{1}{4}\right)^{2-x} = 4$. $x = 3$

6. Evaluate $\log 0.001$ without using a calculator. -3

7. Rewrite the expression $\ln 3 + 5 \ln x$ in condensed form. †

8. Solve the equation $5x^3 e^x - x^4 e^x = 0$. $\{0, 5\}$

9. Solve the equation $e^{2x} + e^x - 6 = 0$. $\ln 2$

10. Rewrite the expression $\ln \dfrac{2x^3}{(x+1)^5}$ in expanded logarithmic form. $\ln 2 + 3 \ln x - 5 \ln (x+1)$

11. Evaluate $\ln e^{-5}$. -5

12. Give the equation for the graph obtained by shifting the graph of $y = \ln x$ three units up and one unit right. †

13. Sketch the graph of $y = 3^{x-1} + 2$. †

14. State the domain of the function $f(x) = \ln (-x) + 4$. †

15. Write $3 \ln x + \ln (x^3 + 2) - \dfrac{1}{2} \ln (3x^2 + 2)$ in condensed form. †

16. Solve the equation $\log x = \log 6 - \log (x - 1)$. $x = 3$

17. Find x if $\log_x 9 = 2$. $x = 3$

18. Rewrite the expression $\ln \sqrt{2x^3 y^2}$ in expanded logarithmic form. $\frac{1}{2}[\ln 2 + 3 \ln x + 2 \ln y]$

19. Suppose that 15,000 dollars is invested in a savings account paying 7% interest per year. Write the formula for the amount in the account after t years if the interest is compounded quarterly. $A(t) = 15000(1.0175)^{4t}$

20. Suppose the number of Hispanic people living in the United States is approximated by $H = 15,000e^{0.02t}$, where $t = 0$ represents 1960. According to this model, about how many Hispanic people were living in the United States in 1980? †

Practice Test B

1. Solve the equation $3^{-x} = 9$. b
   (a) $\{2\}$ (b) $\{-2\}$ (c) $\left\{\dfrac{1}{2}\right\}$ (d) $\left\{-\dfrac{1}{2}\right\}$ (e) $\{\ln 2\}$

2. Solve the equation $\log_5 x = 2$. b
   (a) $\{10\}$ (b) $\{25\}$ (c) $\left\{\dfrac{5}{2}\right\}$ (d) $\left\{\dfrac{2}{5}\right\}$ (e) $\{2\}$

3. State the range and asymptote of $y = e^{-x} - 1$. b
   (a) $(0, \infty); y = -1$ (b) $(-1, \infty); y = -1$
   (c) $(-\infty, \infty); y = -1$ (d) $(-1, \infty); y = 1$
   (e) $(\infty, 1); y = 1$

4. Evaluate $\log_4 64$. d
   (a) 16 (b) 8 (c) 2 (d) 3 (e) 4

5. Find the solution of the exponential equation $\left(\dfrac{1}{3}\right)^{1-x} = 3$. d
   (a) $\left\{-\dfrac{1}{3}\right\}$ (b) $\left\{\dfrac{1}{3}\right\}$ (c) $\{1\}$ (d) $\{2\}$

6. Evaluate $\log 0.01$. b
   (a) -1.99999999 (b) -2 (c) 2 (d) 100

7. Which of the following expressions is equivalent to $\ln 7 + 2 \ln x$? b
   (a) $\ln (7 + 2x)$ (b) $\ln (7x^2)$ (c) $\ln (9x)$ (d) $\ln (14x)$

8. Solve the equation $3x^2 e^x + x^3 e^x = 0$. b
   (a) $\{-3\}$ (b) $\{0, -3\}$ (c) $\{0\}$ (d) $\varnothing$

9. Solve the equation $e^{2x} - e^x - 6 = 0$. d
   (a) $\{-\ln 2\}$ (b) $\{-\ln 3\}$ (c) $\{\ln 6\}$ (d) $\{\ln 3\}$

10. Rewrite the expression $\ln \dfrac{3x^2}{(x+1)^{10}}$ in expanded logarithmic form. d
    (a) $\ln 6x - 10 \ln x + 1$
    (b) $2 \ln 3x - 10 \ln (x + 1)$
    (c) $2 \ln 3 + 2 \ln x - 10 \ln (x + 1)$
    (d) $\ln 3 + 2 \ln x - 10 \ln (x + 1)$

11. Find $\ln e^{3x}$. b
    (a) 3 (b) $3x$ (c) $3 + x$ (d) x

12. The equation for the graph obtained by shifting the graph of $y = \log_3 x$ two units up and three units left is d
    (a) $y = \log_3 (x - 3) + 2$ (b) $y = \log_3 (x + 3) - 2$
    (c) $y = \log_3 (x - 3) - 2$ (d) $y = \log_3 (x + 3) + 2$

13. Which of the following four graphs is the graph of $y = 5^{x+1} - 4$? b

(a)

(b)

(c)

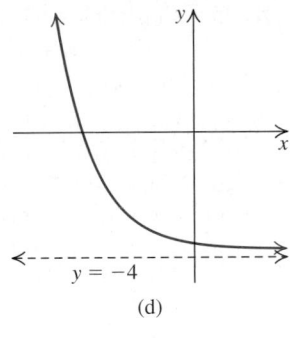

(d)

14. Find the domain of the function $f(x) = \ln(1 - x) + 3$. a
(a) $(-\infty, 1)$ (b) $(1, \infty)$ (c) $(-\infty, -1)$
(d) $(-\infty, 3)$ (e) $(3, \infty)$

15. Write $\ln x - 2\ln(x^2 + 1) + \dfrac{1}{2}\ln(x^4 + 1)$ in condensed form. a

(a) $\ln \dfrac{x\sqrt{x^4 + 1}}{(x^2 + 1)^2}$ (b) $\ln \dfrac{x}{x^2 + 1}$

(c) $\ln(x - (x^2 + 1)^2 + (x^4 + 1)^{1/2})$

(d) $2\ln \dfrac{x(1 + x^4)}{x^2 + 1}$

16. Solve the equation $\log x = \log 12 - \log(x + 1)$. d

(a) $\left(\dfrac{11}{2}\right)$ (b) $\left(\dfrac{13}{2}\right)$ (c) $\{3, -4\}$ (d) $\{3\}$ (e) $\left\{\dfrac{2}{12}\right\}$

17. Find x if $\log_x 16 = 4$. b
(a) 4   (b) 2   (c) 64   (d) $\dfrac{1}{4}$ (e) 16

18. Rewrite the expression $\ln \sqrt[3]{5x^2y^3}$ in expanded logarithmic form. c

(a) $\dfrac{1}{3}(\ln 5x^2 + \ln y^3)$ (b) $\dfrac{1}{3}(2\ln 5x + 3\ln y)$

(c) $\dfrac{1}{3}(\ln 5 + 2\ln x + 3\ln y)$ (d) $\dfrac{1}{3}\ln 5 + 2\ln x + 3\ln y$

(e) $\dfrac{1}{3}\ln 5 + 2 + \ln x + 3 + \ln y$

19. Suppose that 12,000 dollars is invested in a saving account paying 10.5% interest per year. Write the formula for the amount in the account after t years if the interest is compounded monthly. d
(a) $A = 12,000(1.105)^t$ (b) $A = 12,000(1.525)^{2t}$
(c) $A = 12,000(1,2625)^{4t}$ (d) $A = 12,000(1.00875)^{12t}$

20. The population of a certain city is growing according to the model $P = 10,000\log_5(t + 5)$, where t is time in years. If $t = 0$ corresponds to the year 2000, what will the population of the city be in the year 2020? b
(a) 30,000   (b) 20,000
(c) 50,000   (d) 10,000

Cumulative Review Exercises Chapters 1–4

1. Find the x- and y-intercepts of the graph of the equation $x^2 + (y - 1)^2 = 1$. Check for symmetry with respect to both axes and the origin. †

2. Solve each equation.
(a) $\dfrac{1}{2}x - \dfrac{2}{3} = \dfrac{3}{4}x + \dfrac{1}{12}$ †   (b) $\sqrt{x - 1} - \sqrt{6 - x} = 1$ †

3. Solve the inequality $\dfrac{x - 2}{2x + 1} > 0$ and write the answer in interval notation. $(-\infty, -1/2) \cup (2, \infty)$

4. Write the slope–intercept form of the equation of the line that passes through $(-2, 4)$ and is perpendicular to the line $2x + 3y = 17$. †

5. Find the domain of $f(x) = \log \dfrac{x - 2}{x + 3}$. $(-\infty, -3) \cup (2, \infty)$

6. Evaluate the function $f(x) = \begin{cases} 2x - 3, & x < 1 \\ 2x^2 + 1, & x \geq 1 \end{cases}$ at each value specified.
 a. $f(-2)$ -7 b. $f(0)$ -3 c. $f(3)$. 19

7. Identify the basic function, and then use transformations to sketch the graph of the function $f(x) = 3\sqrt{x + 1} - 2$. †

8. Let $f(x) = 3\sqrt{x}$ and $g(x) = -\dfrac{1}{x}$.
Find and write the domain of $(f \circ g)(x)$ in interval notation. †

9. Determine whether the function has an inverse function, and if so, find the inverse function.
(a) $f(x) = 2x^3 + 1$ †
(b) $f(x) = |x|$ No
(c) $f(x) = \ln x$. Yes, $f^{-1}(x) = e^x$

10. Divide
(a) $\dfrac{2x^3 + 3x + 1}{x^2 + 1}$ using long division †

(b) $\dfrac{2x^4 + 7x^3 - 2x + 3}{x + 3}$ using synthetic division †

11. Find a polynomial function of least degree with integer coefficients and that has the given zeros.
(a) $1, 2, -3$ $(x - 1)(x - 2)(x + 3) = x^3 - 7x + 6$
(b) $1, -1, i, -i$ $x^4 - 1$

12. Use rules of logarithms to rewrite the following expressions in expanded form.

(a) $\log_2 5x^3$ $\log_2 5 + 3 \log_2 x$

(b) $\log_a \sqrt[3]{\dfrac{x\, y^2}{z}}$ $\frac{1}{3}[\log_a x + 2 \log_a y - \log_a z]$

(c) $\ln \dfrac{3\sqrt{x}}{5y}$. $\ln 3 + \frac{1}{2} \ln x - \ln 5 - \ln y$

13. Use rules of logarithms to rewrite the following expressions in condensed form.

(a) $\dfrac{1}{2}(\log x + \log y)$ $\log \sqrt{xy}$

(b) $3 \ln x - 2 \ln y$ $\ln \dfrac{x^3}{y^2}$

14. Use a calculator to evaluate the expression. Round your answer to three decimal places.

(a) $\log_9 17$ 1.289

(b) $\log_3 25$ 2.930

(c) $\log_{1/2} 0.3$ 1.737

15. Solve each equation.

(a) $\log_6 (x + 3) + \log_6 (x - 2) = 1$ $\{3\}$

(b) $5^{x^2 - 4x + 5} = 25$ $\{1, 3\}$

(c) $3.1^{x-1} = 23$ 3.77

16. Find all possible rational zeros of
$$f(x) = x^4 - x^3 - 2x^2 - 2x + 4.$$
Also, find upper and lower bounds for the zeros of f.

17. Let $f(x) = (x - 1)^3(x + 2)^2(x - 3)$.

(a) Find the zeros of f, along with their multiplicities.

(b) What is the behavior of f near each zero?

(c) What is the end behavior of f?

(d) Sketch the graph of f.

18. Let $f(x) = \dfrac{(x - 1)(x + 2)}{(x - 3)(x + 4)}$.

(a) Find the vertical asymptotes of f (if any).

(b) Find the horizontal asymptotes of f (if any).

(c) Find the intervals over which $f(x) > 0$ or $f(x) < 0$.

(d) Sketch the graph of f.

Answers:

16. Rational zeros $\{1, 2\}$; upper bound 3, lower bound -1

17. a. $1, 1, 1, -2, -2, 3$

b. At $x = 1$ and $x = 3$, the graph crosses the x-axis. At $x = -2$, the graph touches, but does not cross, the x-axis.

c. $f(x) \to \infty$ as $x \to \infty$; $f(x) \to \infty$ as $x \to -\infty$

18. a. Vertical asymptotes $x = 3, x = -4$

b. Horizontal asymptotes $y = 1$

c. $f(x) > 0$ on $(-\infty, -4) \cup (-2, 1) \cup (3, \infty)$
$f(x) < 0$ on $(-4, -2) \cup (1, 3)$

CHAPTER 5

Trigonometric Functions

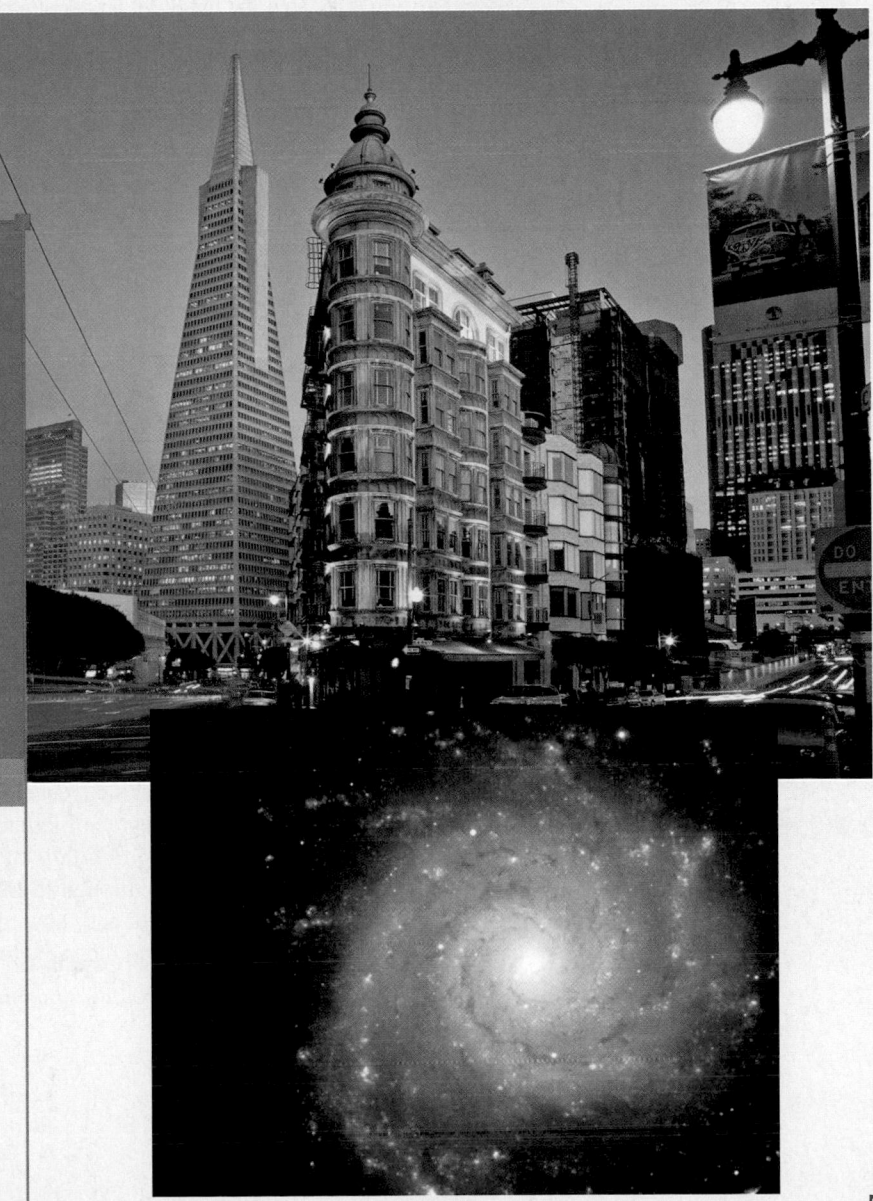

Angles are vital for activities ranging from taking photographs to designing layouts for city streets. Scientists use angles and basic trigonometry to measure remote distances such as the distance between mountain peaks or the distances between planets. Angles are universally used to specify locations on Earth via longitude and latitude. In this chapter we begin the study of trigonometry and its many uses.

TOPICS

Angles and Their Measure

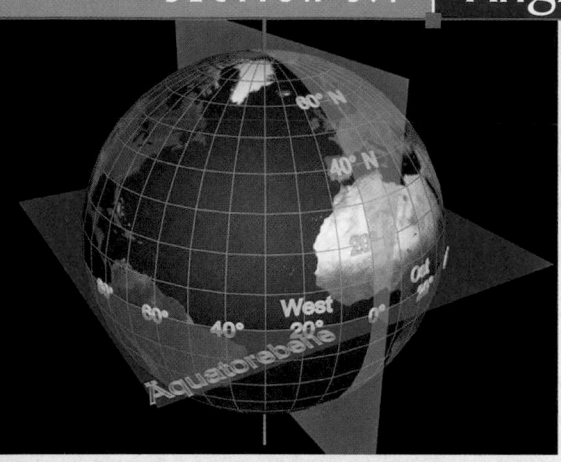

BEFORE STARTING THIS SECTION, REVIEW

1. Circumference and area of a circle (Section P.7, page 79)

OBJECTIVES

1 Learn the vocabulary associated with angles.

2 Use degree and radian measure.

3 Convert between degree and radian measure.

4 Find complements and supplements.

5 Find the length of an arc of a circle.

6 Compute linear and angular speed.

7 Find the area of a sector.

Latitude and Longitude

Any location on Earth can be described by two numbers, its *latitude* and its *longitude*. To explain how these two location numbers are assigned, we imagine that the Earth is a sphere, though actually the shape is slightly oval.

Lines of latitude are parallel circles of different size around the sphere representing Earth. The longest circle is the equator, with latitude 0, while at the poles the circles shrink to a point.

Lines of longitude (also called *meridians*) are circles of identical size that pass through both the North Pole and the South Pole as they circle the globe. Every such circle must cross the equator. The equator is divided into 360 degrees, and the longitude of a location is the value in degrees where the meridian through the location meets the equator. For historical reasons, the meridian near the old Royal Astronomical Observatory in Greenwich, England, is the one chosen as 0 longitude.

Today this prime meridian is marked with a brass band stretching across the yard of the Observatory. Longitude is measured from the prime meridian, with positive values going east (0 to 180) and negative values going west (0 to −180). Both 180-degree longitudes share the same line, in the middle of the Pacific Ocean. At the equator, the distance on Earth's surface for each one degree of latitude or longitude is just over 69 miles.

Every location on Earth is then identified by the meridian and the latitude lines that pass through it. In Example 7, we will explain how latitude values are assigned and how they can be used to compute distances between cities having the same longitude. ■

1 Learn the vocabulary associated with angles.

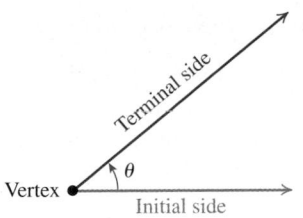

FIGURE 5.1

Angles

A **ray** is a portion of a line made up of a point, called the **endpoint**, and all points on the line on one side of the endpoint. An **angle** is formed by rotating a ray about its endpoint. The ray in its original position is called the **initial side**, while the ray in its new position after the rotation is called the **terminal side**. The endpoint is called the **vertex** of the angle. A curved arrow drawn near the vertex indicates both the direction and amount of rotation from the initial side to the terminal side of the angle. (See Figure 5.1.)

The Greek letters α (alpha), β (beta), γ (gamma), and θ (theta) are often used to name angles.

If the rotation of the initial side to the terminal side is counterclockwise, the result is a **positive angle**; if the rotation is clockwise, the result is a **negative angle**. See Figure 5.2. Rotation in both directions is unrestricted. Angles that have the same initial and terminal sides are called **coterminal** angles. In Figure 5.2(c), α and β are different angles, but are coterminal.

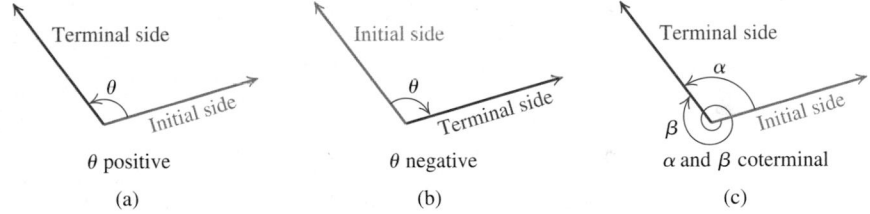

FIGURE 5.2

An angle in a rectangular coordinate system is said to be in **standard position** if its vertex is at the origin and its initial side coincides with the positive x-axis. All the angles in Figure 5.3 are in standard position. If the terminal side of an angle in standard position lies on the x-axis or the y-axis, the angle is said to be a **quadrantal angle**. If the terminal side of an angle θ lies in a quadrant rather than on a coordinate axis, we say that θ *lies in that quadrant.* See Figure 5.3.

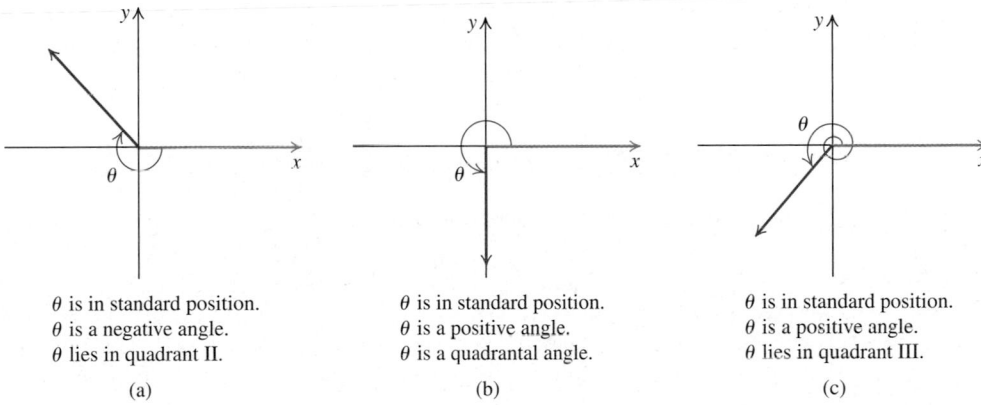

FIGURE 5.3

We measure angles by determining the amount of rotation from the initial side to the terminal side, indicated by a curved arrow that also shows direction. We examine two units of measurement for angles, *degrees* and *radians*.

2 Use degree and radian measure.

Measuring Angles by Using Degrees

A measure of **one degree** (denoted by 1°) is assigned to an angle resulting from a rotation $\frac{1}{360}$ of a complete revolution counterclockwise about the vertex. An angle formed by rotating the initial side counterclockwise 1 full rotation until the terminal side coincides with the initial side has measure 360 degrees, written as 360°.

Angles are classified according to their measures. As illustrated in Figure 5.4, an **acute angle** is any angle with measure between 0° and 90°; a **right angle** is an angle with measure 90°, or $\frac{1}{4}$ of a counterclockwise revolution; an **obtuse angle** is any angle with measure between 90° and 180°; and a **straight angle** is an angle with measure 180°, or $\frac{1}{2}$ of a counterclockwise revolution. Also in Figure 5.4, several angles measured in degrees are shown.

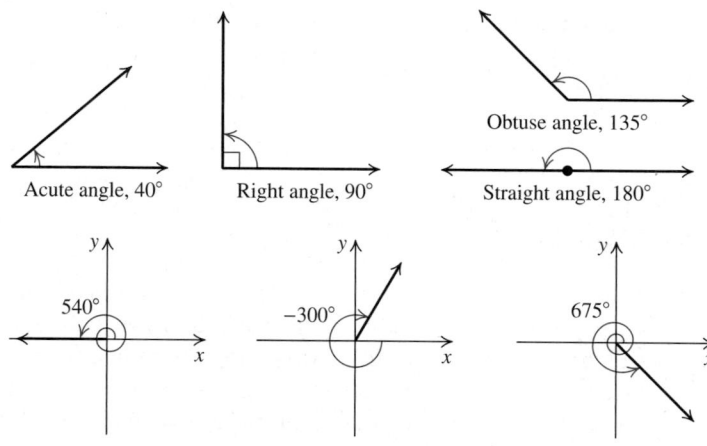

FIGURE 5.4

There is no numerical limit to the measure of an angle, because the terminal side can be rotated either clockwise or counterclockwise without limitation.

FIGURE 5.5

FIGURE 5.6

EXAMPLE 1   **Drawing an Angle in Standard Position**

Draw each angle in standard position.

a. 60°   **b.** 135°   **c.** −240°   **d.** 405°

Solution

a. Since $60 = \frac{2}{3}(90)$, a 60° angle is $\frac{2}{3}$ of a 90° angle. See Figure 5.5.

b. Since $135 = 90 + 45$, a 135° angle is a counterclockwise rotation of 90°, followed by $\frac{1}{2}$ of a 90° counterclockwise rotation. See Figure 5.6.

c. Since $-240 = -180 - 60$, a −240° angle is a clockwise rotation of 180°, followed by a clockwise rotation of 60°. See Figure 5.7.

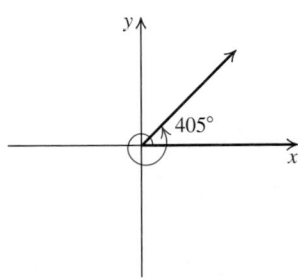

FIGURE 5.7

FIGURE 5.8

d. Since $405 = 360 + 45$, a 405° angle is one complete counterclockwise rotation of 360°, followed by $\dfrac{1}{2}$ of a 90° counterclockwise rotation. See Figure 5.8.   ■ ■ ■

PRACTICE PROBLEM 1   Draw a 225° angle in standard position.   ■

Today it is common to divide degrees into fractional parts, using *decimal degree notation* such as 30.5°. Traditionally, however, degrees were expressed in terms of *minutes* and *seconds*. One **minute**, denoted by 1′, is defined as $\dfrac{1}{60}$ (1°), and one **second**, denoted 1″, is defined as $\dfrac{1}{3600}$ (1°). An angle measuring 27 degrees, 14 minutes, and 39 seconds is written as 27°14′39″.

Since $\dfrac{1}{3600} = \dfrac{1}{60} \cdot \dfrac{1}{60}$, we have $1'' = \dfrac{1}{3600}(1°) = \dfrac{1}{60}\left[\dfrac{1}{60}(1°)\right] = \dfrac{1}{60}(1').$

RELATIONSHIP BETWEEN DEGREES, MINUTES, AND SECONDS

$1' = \dfrac{1}{60}(1°) = \left(\dfrac{1}{60}\right)°$ $1° = 60'$

$1'' = \dfrac{1}{3600}(1°) = \left(\dfrac{1}{3600}\right)°$ $1'' = \dfrac{1}{60}(1')$ $1' = 60''$

We use these relationships to convert between degree, minute, second (DMS), and decimal degree notation. For Example,

$$30' = 30 \cdot 1' = 30 \cdot \dfrac{1}{60}(1°) = 0.5(1°) = 0.5°.$$

We have $18°30' = 18° + 30' = 18° + 0.5° = 18.5°.$

Since $0.2° = \dfrac{2}{10}(1°) = \dfrac{2}{10}(60') = 12',$

we have $39.2° = 39° + 0.2° = 39° + 12' = 39°12'.$

EXAMPLE 2   **Converting Between DMS and Decimal Notation**

a. Convert 24°8′15″ to decimal degree notation, rounded to two decimal places.

b. Convert 67.526° to DMS notation, rounded to the nearest second.   ⋮

Solution

a. $24°8'15'' = 24° + 8' + 15''$

$\qquad\qquad = 24° + 8 \cdot 1' + 15 \cdot 1''$ Rewrite.

$\qquad\qquad = 24° + 8\left(\dfrac{1}{60}\right)° + 15\left(\dfrac{1}{3600}\right)°$ $1' = \left(\dfrac{1}{60}\right)°, 1'' = \left(\dfrac{1}{3600}\right)°$

$\qquad\qquad \approx 24.14°$ Use a calculator.

Continued on next page.

b. $67.526° = 67° + 0.526°$

$= 67° + 0.526 \cdot 1°$	Rewrite.
$= 67° + 0.526(60')$	$1° = 60'$
$= 67° + 31.56'$	Use a calculator.
$= 67° + 31' + 0.56'$	
$= 67° + 31' + 0.56 \cdot 1'$	Rewrite.
$= 67° + 31' + 0.56(60'')$	$1' = 60''$
$= 67° + 31' + 33.6''$	Use a calculator.
$\approx 67°31'34''$	Rounded to nearest second

■ ■ ■

PRACTICE PROBLEM 2

a. Convert $13°9'22''$ to decimal degree notation, rounded to two decimal places.

b. Convert $41.275°$ to DMS notation, rounded to the nearest second.

■

Radian Measure

An angle whose vertex is at the center of a circle is called a **central angle**. A positive central angle formed by rotating the initial ray through an arc of the circle of length equal to the radius of the circle is said to have measure **1 radian**. See Figure 5.9. (The central angle intercepts the arc along the circle from the initial side to the terminal side.)

Because the circumference of a circle of radius r is $2\pi r \approx 6.28r$, 6 arcs of length r can be consecutively marked off on a circle of radius r, leaving only a small portion of the circumference uncovered. See Figure 5.10.

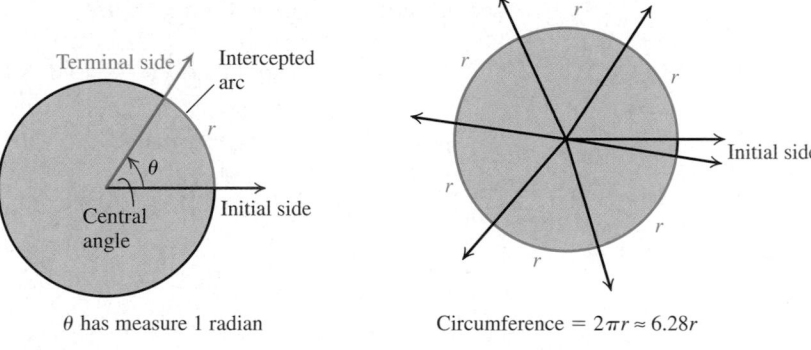

θ has measure 1 radian

FIGURE 5.9

Circumference $= 2\pi r \approx 6.28r$

FIGURE 5.10

Each of the positive central angles in Figure 5.10 that intercepts an arc of length r has measure 1 radian, so the measure of one complete revolution is a little more than 6 radians. For convenience, in this book (unless otherwise specified) a central angle means a positive central angle.

RADIAN MEASURE OF A CENTRAL ANGLE

The radian measure θ of a central angle that intercepts an arc of length s on a circle of radius r is defined by

$$\theta = \frac{s}{r} \text{ radians.}$$

<table>
<tr><td>

3 Convert between degrees and radian measure.

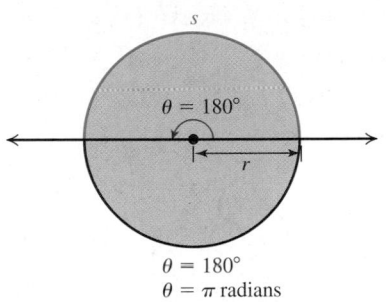

$\theta = 180°$
$\theta = \pi$ radians

FIGURE 5.11

</td><td>

Relationship between Degrees and Radians

To discover a relationship between degrees and radians, consider a central angle with measure $\theta = 180°$, in a circle of radius r. See Figure 5.11. The length of the arc, s, that is intercepted by this angle with measure $\theta = 180°$ is $\frac{1}{2}$ the circumference of the circle. Thus,

$$s = \frac{1}{2}(\text{circumference})$$

$$s = \frac{1}{2}(2\pi r) = \pi r. \qquad \text{Circumference} = 2\pi r$$

The radian measure for $\theta = 180°$ can now be found.

$$180° = \theta = \frac{s}{r} \text{ radians} \qquad \text{Radian measure of a central angle}$$

$$= \frac{\pi r}{r} \text{ radians} \qquad \text{Replace } s \text{ by } \pi r.$$

$$= \pi \text{ radians} \qquad \text{Simplify.}$$

We have the relationship $\boxed{180° = \pi \text{ radians}}$.

Dividing both sides of the equation $180° = \pi$ radians by either 180 or π provides a basic conversion formula.

</td></tr>
</table>

CONVERTING BETWEEN DEGREES AND RADIANS

$$1 \text{ degree} = \frac{\pi}{180} \text{ radian}$$

$$1 \text{ radian} = \frac{180}{\pi} \text{ degrees}$$

$$\theta° = \theta\left(\frac{\pi}{180}\right) \text{ radians}$$

$$\theta \text{ radians} = \theta\left(\frac{180}{\pi}\right) \text{ degrees}$$

EXAMPLE 3   **Converting from Degrees to Radians**

Convert each angle from degrees to radians.

a. 30°   **b.** 90°   **c.** −225°   **d.** 55°

Solution

To convert degrees to radians, multiply degrees by $\frac{\pi}{180°}$.

Continued on next page.

a. $30° = 30° \cdot \dfrac{\pi}{180°} = \dfrac{30\pi}{180} = \dfrac{\pi}{6}$ radian

b. $90° = 90° \cdot \dfrac{\pi}{180°} = \dfrac{90\pi}{180} = \dfrac{\pi}{2}$ radians

c. $-225° = -225° \cdot \dfrac{\pi}{180°} = \dfrac{-225\pi}{180} = -\dfrac{5\pi}{4}$ radians

d. $55° = 55° \cdot \dfrac{\pi}{180°} = \dfrac{55\pi}{180} \approx 0.96$ radian   ■ ■ ■

PRACTICE PROBLEM 3 Convert $-45°$ to radians.   ■

Angles that are fractions of a complete rotation are usually expressed in radian measure as fractional multiples of π, rather than as decimals. Thus, we write $30°$ as $\dfrac{\pi}{6}$ radian, which is the exact value, instead of writing the approximation $30° \approx 0.52$ radian.

EXAMPLE 4   **Converting from Radians to Degrees**

Convert each angle in radians to degrees.

a. $\dfrac{\pi}{3}$ radians   **b.** $-\dfrac{3\pi}{4}$ radians   **c.** 1 radian

Solution

To convert radians to degrees, multiply radians by $\dfrac{180°}{\pi}$.

a. $\dfrac{\pi}{3}$ radians $= \dfrac{\pi}{3} \cdot \dfrac{180°}{\pi} = \left(\dfrac{180}{3}\right)° = 60°$

b. $-\dfrac{3\pi}{4}$ radians $= -\dfrac{3\pi}{4} \cdot \dfrac{180°}{\pi} = \left(-\dfrac{3}{4}\right)180° = -135°$

c. 1 radian $= 1 \cdot \dfrac{180°}{\pi} \approx 57.3°$ ■ ■ ■

PRACTICE PROBLEM 4 Convert $\dfrac{3\pi}{2}$ radians to degrees.   ■

Figure 5.12 includes the degree and radian measures of some commonly used angles. With practice, you should be able to make these conversions without using the figure.

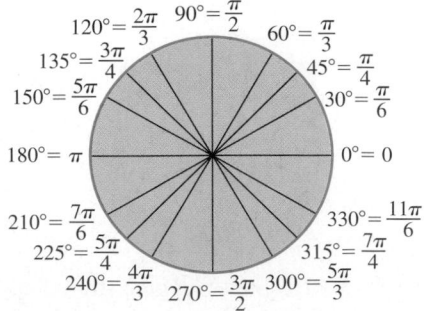

$120° = \dfrac{2\pi}{3}$ $90° = \dfrac{\pi}{2}$ $60° = \dfrac{\pi}{3}$

$135° = \dfrac{3\pi}{4}$ $45° = \dfrac{\pi}{4}$

$150° = \dfrac{5\pi}{6}$ $30° = \dfrac{\pi}{6}$

$180° = \pi$ $0° = 0$

$210° = \dfrac{7\pi}{6}$ $330° = \dfrac{11\pi}{6}$

$225° = \dfrac{5\pi}{4}$ $315° = \dfrac{7\pi}{4}$

$240° = \dfrac{4\pi}{3}$ $270° = \dfrac{3\pi}{2}$ $300° = \dfrac{5\pi}{3}$

FIGURE 5.12

4 Find complements and supplements.

Complements and Supplements

Two positive angles are **complements** (or **complementary angles**) if the sum of their measures is 90°. Thus, two angles with measures 50° and 40° are complements because 50° + 40° = 90°. Each angle is the complement of the other.

Two positive angles are **supplements** (or **supplementary angles**) if the sum of their measures is 180°. Thus, two angles with measures 120° and 60° are supplements because 120° + 60° = 180°.

STUDY TIP

A positive angle with measure ≥ 90° does not have a complement. A positive angle with measure ≥ 180° does not have a supplement.

EXAMPLE 5   Finding Complements and Supplements

Find the complement and the supplement of the given angle or explain why the angle has no complement or supplement.

a. 73°   **b.** 110°

Solution

a. Let θ represent the complement of 73°. Then θ is positive, and $\theta + 73° = 90°$, so $\theta = 90° - 73° = 17°$. The complement of 73° is 17°.

Let α represent the supplement for 73°. Then α is positive, and $\alpha + 73° = 180°$, so $\alpha = 180° - 73° = 107°$. The supplement of 73° is 107°.

b. If θ is a positive angle, then $\theta + 110° > 90°$. Thus, 110° does not have a complement.

Let α represent the supplement of 110°. Then α is positive, and $\alpha + 110° = 180°$, so $\alpha = 180° - 110° = 70°$. The supplement of 110° is 70°.   ■ ■ ■

PRACTICE PROBLEM 5   Find the complement and the supplement for 67° or explain why 67° does not have a complement or a supplement.   ■

When radian measure is used, two positive angles are complements when the sum of their measures is $\dfrac{\pi}{2}$ radians (equivalent to 90°) and are supplements when the sum of their measures is π radians (equivalent to 180°).

Length of an Arc of a Circle

5 Find the length of an arc of a circle.

The formula for the radian measure θ of a central angle that intercepts an arc of length s is:

$$\theta = \frac{s}{r}$$

Multiplying both sides of this equation by r yields $s = r\theta$, a formula for the length s of the arc intercepted by a central angle with radian measure θ in a circle of radius r.

ARC LENGTH FORMULA

$$s = r\theta$$

EXAMPLE 6 **Finding Arc Length of a Circle**

A circle has a radius of 18 inches. Find the length of the arc intercepted by a central angle with measure 210°.

Solution

To use the arc length formula, we must first convert the central angle measure from degrees to radians.

$$s = r\theta \qquad \text{Arc length formula}$$

$$s = 18\left(\frac{7\pi}{6}\right) \qquad \theta = 210° = 210°\left(\frac{\pi}{180°}\right) = \frac{7\pi}{6} \text{ radians.}$$

$$= 21\pi \qquad \text{Simplify.}$$

$$\approx 65.97 \text{ inches} \qquad \text{Use a calculator.} \qquad\qquad ■ \quad ■ \quad ■$$

PRACTICE PROBLEM 6 A circle has a radius of 2 meters. Find the length of the arc intercepted by a central angle with measure 225°. ■

EXAMPLE 7 **Finding the Distance between Cities**

We discussed longitude and latitude in the introduction to this section. We obtain the latitude of a location L anywhere on Earth by first finding the point of intersection, P, between the meridian through L and the equator. The latitude of L is the angle formed by rays drawn from the center of Earth to points L and P, with the ray through P being the initial ray. See Figure 5.13a.

Billings, Montana, is due north of Grand Junction, Colorado. Find the distance between Billings (latitude 45°48′ N) and Grand Junction (latitude 39°7′ N). Use 3960 miles as the radius of Earth. The N in 45°48′ N means the location is north of the equator.

Solution

Because Billings is due north of Grand Junction, the same meridian passes through both cities. The distance between the cities is then the length of the arc, s, on this meridian intercepted by the central angle, θ, that is the difference in their latitudes. See Figure 5.13b.

FIGURE 5.13a

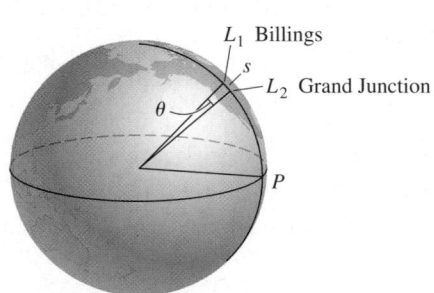

FIGURE 5.13b

The measure of angle θ is $45°48' - 39°7' = 6°41'$. To use the arc length formula $s = r\theta$, we must first convert the angle $6°41'$ to radians.

$$\theta = 6°41' \approx 6.6833° = 6.6833\left(\frac{\pi}{180}\right) \text{ radian } \approx 0.117 \text{ radian}$$

We use this value of θ and $r = 3960$ miles in the arc length formula:

$$s = r\theta$$
$$s \approx (3960)(0.117) \text{ miles } \approx 463 \text{ miles.}$$ ■ ■ ■

PRACTICE PROBLEM 7   Chicago, Illinois, is due north of Pensacola, Florida. Find the distance between Chicago (latitude $41°51'$ N) and Pensacola (latitude $30°25'$ N). Use $r = 3960$ miles.   ■

6 Compute linear and angular speed.

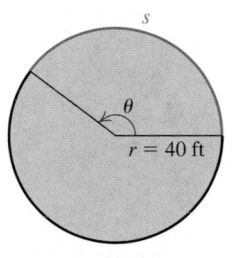

$s = 100$ ft
$\theta = 2.5$ radians

FIGURE 5.14

Linear and Angular Speed

If a skater skates 100 feet in 5 seconds, then her *average speed, v,* is given by

$$v = \frac{\text{distance}}{\text{time}} = \frac{100 \text{ feet}}{5 \text{ seconds}} = 20 \text{ feet per second.}$$

Suppose now that the skater is skating around the circumference of a circular skating rink with radius 40 feet. See Figure 5.14. In 5 seconds, the skater travels an arc of length 100 feet and moves through an angle θ, where

$$\theta = \frac{s}{r} = \frac{100}{40} = 2.5 \text{ radians.}$$

We say that the skater is traveling at an (average) *angular speed* of ω (omega), given by

$$\omega = \frac{\theta}{t} = \frac{2.5}{5} = 0.5 \text{ radian per second.}$$

We call the average speed, $v = \frac{100}{5} = 20$ feet per second, the (average) *linear speed* to distinguish it from the (average) *angular speed,* $\omega = \frac{2.5}{5} = 0.5$ radian per second.

Notice that $v = 20 = 40(0.5) = r\omega$.
We define these ideas more generally as follows.

LINEAR AND ANGULAR SPEED

Suppose an object travels around a circle of radius r. If the object travels through an angle of θ radians and an arc of length s, in time t, then

1. $v = \dfrac{s}{t}$ is the (average) **linear speed** of the object; and

2. $\omega = \dfrac{\theta}{t}$ is the (average) **angular speed** of the object.

Further, since $s = r\theta$ (replacing s by $r\theta$ in **1.** and using **2.**), we have

3. $v = r\omega$.

> **EXAMPLE 8** **Finding Angular and Linear Speed from Revolutions per Minute**

A model plane is attached to a swivel so that it flies in a circular path at the end of a 12-foot wire at the rate of 15 revolutions per minute. Find the angular speed and the linear speed of the plane.

12 ft

Solution

Because angular speed is measured in radians per unit of time, we must first convert revolutions per minute into radians per minute. Recall that

$$1 \text{ revolution} = 360° = 2\pi \text{ radians}.$$

Then 15 revolutions = $15 \cdot 2\pi$ radians.
Thus, the angular speed $\omega = 15 \cdot 2\pi = 30\pi$ radians per minute.
Linear speed is given by

$$
\begin{aligned}
v &= r\omega \\
&= 12 \cdot 30\pi \text{ feet per minute} && \text{Replace } r \text{ by 12 and } \omega \text{ by } \\
& && 30\pi \text{ radians per minute.} \\
&\approx 1131 \text{ feet per minute} && \text{Use a calculator.} \quad \blacksquare \ \blacksquare \ \blacksquare
\end{aligned}
$$

PRACTICE PROBLEM 8 Find the angular speed and the linear speed of the plane in Example 8 if the wire is 10 feet long and the plane flies at a rate of 18 revolutions per minute. ■

7 Find the area of a sector.

Area of a Sector

A **sector** of a circle is a region bounded by the two sides of a central angle and the intercepted arc.

Suppose that θ is the radian measure of a central angle of a circle of radius r. See Figure 5.15. To find a formula for the area of the sector of the circle formed by this central angle θ, we use the proportion:

$$\frac{\text{area of a sector}}{\text{area of a circle}} = \frac{\text{length of the intercepted arc}}{\text{circumference of the circle}}$$

Letting $A = $ area of the sector, this equation becomes

$$
\begin{aligned}
\frac{A}{\pi r^2} &= \frac{r\theta}{2\pi r} && \text{Area of a circle} = \pi r^2, \text{ circumference} = 2\pi r \\
& && \text{Arc length formula } s = r\theta \\
A &= \pi r^2 \left(\frac{r\theta}{2\pi r} \right) && \text{Multiply both sides by } \pi r^2. \\
&= \frac{1}{2} r^2 \theta && \text{Simplify.}
\end{aligned}
$$

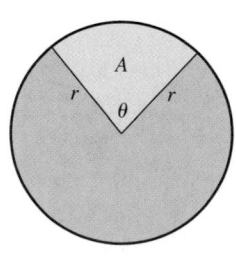

A
r θ r

FIGURE 5.15

AREA OF A SECTOR

The area A of a sector of a circle of radius r formed by a central angle with radian measure θ is:

$$A = \frac{1}{2}r^2\theta$$

EXAMPLE 9   **Finding the Area of a Sector of a Circle**

How many square inches of pizza have you eaten (rounded to the nearest square inch) if you eat a sector of an 18-inch diameter pizza whose edges form a 30° angle? See Figure 5.16.

Solution

We must first convert 30° to radians in order to use the formula for the area of a sector. The radius of the pizza is $\frac{1}{2}$ the diameter, or 9 inches, and $30° = \frac{\pi}{6}$ radian.

$$A = \frac{1}{2}r^2\theta \qquad \text{Area of a sector formula}$$

$$= \frac{1}{2}9^2\left(\frac{\pi}{6}\right) \qquad \text{Replace } r \text{ by 9 and } \theta \text{ by } \frac{\pi}{6}.$$

$$\approx 21 \text{ square inches} \qquad \text{Use a calculator.}$$

You have eaten about 21 square inches of pizza.   ■ ■ ■

PRACTICE PROBLEM 9   Find the area of a sector of the circle of radius 10 inches formed by an angle of 60°. Round the answer to two decimal places.   ■

FIGURE 5.16

A Exercises   Basic Skills and Concepts

In Exercises 1–8, draw each angle in standard position.

1. 30° †

2. 150° †

3. −120° †

4. −330° †

5. $\frac{5\pi}{3}$ †

6. $\frac{11\pi}{6}$ †

7. $-\frac{4\pi}{3}$ †

8. $-\frac{13\pi}{4}$ †

In Exercises 9–14, convert each angle to decimal degree notation. Round your answers to two decimal places.

9. 70°45′ 70.75°

10. 38°38′ 38.63°

11. 23°42′30″ 23.71°

12. 45°50′50″ 45.85°

13. −15°42′57″ −15.72°

14. −70°18′13″ −70.30°

In Exercises 15–20, convert each angle to DMS notation. Round your answers to the nearest second.

15. 27.32° 27°19′12″

16. 120.64° 120°38′24″

17. 13.347° 13°20′49″

18. 110.433° 110°25′59″

19. 19.0511° 19°3′4″

20. 82.7272° 82°43′38″

In Exercises 21–30, convert each angle from degrees to radians. Express each answer as a multiple of π.

21. 45° †

22. 60° †

23. −180° −π

24. −210° †

25. 315° †

26. 330° †

27. 480° †

28. 450° †

29. −510° †

30. −420° †

In Exercises 31–40, convert each angle from radians to degrees.

31. $\frac{\pi}{2}$ 90°

32. $\frac{3\pi}{4}$ 135°

33. $-\frac{5\pi}{4}$ −225°

34. $-\frac{3\pi}{2}$ −270°

35. $\frac{5\pi}{3}$ 300°

36. $\frac{11\pi}{6}$ 330°

†Due to space constrictions, answers to these exercises may be found in the Answers beginning on page A–1 in the back of the book.

37. $\dfrac{5\pi}{2}$ 450°

38. $\dfrac{17\pi}{6}$ 510°

39. $-\dfrac{11\pi}{4}$ −495°

40. $-\dfrac{7\pi}{3}$ −420°

In Exercises 41–44, convert each angle from degrees to radians. Express your answer as a decimal rounded to two decimal places.

41. 12° 0.21 radians

42. 127° 2.22 radians

43. −84° −1.47 radians

44. −175° −3.05 radians

In Exercises 45–48, convert each angle from radians to degrees. Express your answer as a decimal rounded to two decimal places.

45. 0.94 53.86°

46. 5 286.48°

47. −8.21 −470.40°

48. −6.28 −359.82

In Exercises 49–54, find the complement and the supplement of the given angle or explain why the angle has no complement or supplement.

49. 47° †

50. 75° †

51. 120° †

52. 160° †

53. 210° †

54. −50° †

In Exercises 55–58, find the radian measure of a central angle of each circle of radius r that intercepts each arc of length s. Round your answers to three decimal places.

55. $r = 25$ inches, $s = 7$ inches 0.28 radians

56. $r = 5$ feet, $s = 6$ feet 1.2 radians

57. $r = 10.5$ centimeters, $s = 22$ centimeters 2.095 radians

58. $r = 60$ meters, $s = 120$ meters 2 radians

In Exercises 59–62, find the length of the arc on each circle of radius r meters intercepted by a central angle θ. Round your answers to three decimal places.

59. $r = 3$, $\theta = 25°$ 1.309 m

60. $r = 0.7$, $\theta = 357°$ 4.362 m

61. $r = 6.5$, $\theta = 12$ radians 78 m

62. $r = 6$, $\theta = \dfrac{\pi}{6}$ radians 3.142 m

63. Find the area of a sector of a circle of radius 6 inches formed by a central angle of 40°. Round your answer to two decimal places. 12.57 square inches

64. Find the area of a sector of a circle of radius 1.5 feet formed by a central angle of 60°. Round your answer to two decimal places. 1.18 square feet

B Exercises Applying the Concepts

65. Wheel ratios. An automobile is pushed so that its wheels turned three-quarters of a revolution. If the tires have a radius of 15 inches, how many inches has the car moved? †

66. Nautical miles. A nautical mile is the length of an arc of the equator intercepted by a central angle of 1′. Using 3960 miles for the value of the radius of the Earth, express 1 nautical mile in terms of standard (**statute**) miles. 1.15 miles

67. Angles on a clock. What is the radian measure of the smaller central angle made by the hands of a clock at 4:00? Express your answer as a rational multiple of π. †

68. Angles on a clock. What is the radian measure of the larger central angle made by the hands of a clock at 7:00? Express your answer as a rational multiple of π. †

69. Diameter of a pizza. You are told that a slice of pizza whose edges form a 25° angle with an outer crust edge 4 inches long was found in a gym locker. What was the diameter of the original pizza? Round your answer to the nearest inch. 18 inches

70. Arc of a pendulum. How far does the tip of a 5-foot pendulum travel as it swings through an angle of 30°? Round your answer to two decimal places. 2.62 feet

71. Lifting a shark. A shark is suspended by a wire wound around a pulley of radius 4 inches. The shark must be raised 6 inches more to be completely off the ground. Through how

many degrees must the pulley be rotated counterclockwise to accomplish the 6-inch lift? Round your answer to the nearest degree. 86°

72. Security cameras. A security camera rotates through an angle of 120°. To the nearest foot, what is the arc width of the field of view 40 feet from the camera? 84 feet

73. Pulley wheels. Two pulleys are connected by a belt so that when one pulley rotates, the linear speeds of the belt and both pulleys are the same. (See the figure.) The radius of the smaller pulley is 2 inches, and the radius of the larger pulley is 5 inches. A point on the belt travels at a rate of 600 inches per minute.

a. Find the angular speed of the larger pulley. †
b. Find the angular speed of the smaller pulley. †

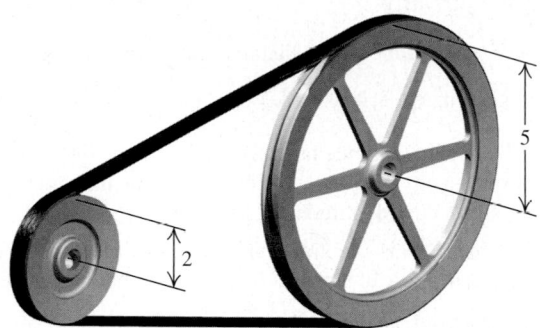

74. **Ferris wheel speed.** A Ferris wheel in Vienna, Austria, has a diameter of approximately 61 meters. Assume that it takes 90 seconds for the Ferris wheel to make one complete revolution.

a. Find the angular speed of the Ferris wheel. Round your answer to two decimal places. †
b. Find the linear speed of the Ferris wheel in meters per second. Round your answer to two decimal places. †

75. **Bicycle speed.** A bicycle's wheels are 24 inches in diameter. If the bike is traveling at a rate of 25 miles per hour, find the angular speed of the wheels. Round your answer to two decimal places. 132,000 radians per hour

76. **Bicycle speed.** A bicycle's wheels are 30 inches in diameter. If the angular speed of the wheels is 11 radians per second, find the speed of the bicycle in inches per second. †

77. **Hard disk speed.** Hard disks are circular disks that store data in your computer. Suppose a circular hard disk is 3.75 inches in diameter. If the disk rotates at 7200 revolutions

per minute, what is the linear speed of a point on the edge of the disk (in inches per minute)? †

In Exercises 78–81, the latitude of any location on Earth is the angle formed by the two rays drawn from the center of Earth to the location and to the equator. The ray through the location is the initial ray. Use 3960 miles as the radius of Earth.

78. **Distance between cities.** Indianapolis, Indiana, is due north of Montgomery, Alabama. Find the distance between Indianapolis (north latitude 39°44′ N) and Montgomery (latitude 32°23′ N). ≈ 508 miles

79. **Distance between cities.** Pittsburgh, Pennsylvania, is due north of Charleston, South Carolina. Find the distance between Pittsburgh (north latitude 40°30′ N) and Charleston (latitude 32°54′ N). ≈ 525 miles

80. **Distance between cities.** Amsterdam, the Netherlands, is due north of Lyon, France. Find the distance between Amsterdam (north latitude 52°23′ N) and Lyon (latitude 45°42′ N). ≈ 462 miles

81. **Distance between cities.** Adana, Turkey (north latitude 36°59′ N) is due north of Jerusalem, Israel (latitude 31°47′ N). Find the distance between Adana and Jerusalem. ≈ 359 miles

82. **Difference in latitudes.** Miles City, Montana, is 440 miles due north of Boulder, Colorado. Find the difference in the latitudes of these two cities, assuming that the radius of Earth is 3960 miles. 6.366°

83. **Difference in latitudes.** Lincoln, Nebraska, is 554 miles due north of Dallas, Texas. Find the difference in the latitudes of these two cities, assuming that the radius of Earth is 3960 miles. ≈ 7.958°

84. **Linear speed at the equator.** Earth rotates on an axis that goes through both the North and South Poles. It makes one complete revolution in 24 hours. If the distance from the axis to any location on the equator is 3960 miles, find the linear speed (in miles per hour) of a location on the equator. ≈ 1037 miles per hour

C Exercises   Beyond the Basics

85. Use the fact that $\theta + \pi$ and $\theta - \pi$ are coterminal angles to prove that $\dfrac{5\pi}{3}$ and $-\dfrac{\pi}{3}$ are coterminal.

86. Show that if α is the complement of θ, then $\alpha + \dfrac{\theta}{2}$ is the complement of $\dfrac{\theta}{2}$.

87. Find the smallest positive integer n, such that θ and $\theta - \dfrac{n\pi}{2}$ are coterminal. 4

88. Find the smallest positive integer n, such that θ and $\theta + \dfrac{n\pi}{3}$ are coterminal. 6

89. Show that if the linear speed of a point on a rotating circular disk of radius r is v, then the linear speed of the midpoint on a radius is $\dfrac{1}{2}v$.

90. Show that if A is the area of a sector of a circle of radius r formed by a central angle with radian measure θ, then $4A$ is the area of a sector of a circle of radius $2r$ formed by a central angle with radian measure θ.

91. Show that if A is the area of a sector of a circle of radius r formed by a central angle with radian measure θ, then $\frac{1}{2}A$ is the area of a circle of radius r formed by a central angle of radian measure $\frac{1}{2}\theta$.

92. **Pulley wheels.** Two pulleys are connected by a belt (see figure) so that when one pulley rotates, the linear speeds of the belt and both pulleys are the same. Suppose the radius of the smaller pulley is r and the radius of the larger pulley is r_1. If the angular speed of the smaller pulley is ω and the angular speed of the larger pulley is ω_1, show that $\frac{r}{\omega_1} = \frac{r_1}{\omega}$.

93. **Pulley wheels.** In Exercise 92, let $r = 6$ inches and $r_1 = 8$ inches. If the point B in the figure of Exercise 92 has a velocity of 88 feet per second, find
a. the angular and the linear velocity of point A.
b. the angular and the linear velocity of point C.

Critical Thinking

94. Arrange the following radian measures from smallest to largest: $\pi, \frac{3\pi}{2}, 3, 4$. $3, \pi, 4, \frac{3\pi}{2}$

95. Which line of latitude has smaller radius, the line of latitude through a city of latitude $30°40'13''$, or the line of latitude through a city of latitude $40°30'13''$?

96. Assume that θ is a central angle in a circle of radius r that intercepts an arc of length s. Show that if θ has radian measure less than $\frac{\pi}{2}$, then the central angle that intercepts an arc of length $\frac{\pi r}{2} - s$ and θ are complementary angles.

Answers:
93. a. $\omega_A = 176$ radians per second. $v_A = 1056$ inches per second.
b. $\omega_C = 132$ radians per second. $v_C = 1056$ inches per second.
95. The line of latitude through $40°40'¢13''$.
96. The length of the arc $\frac{\pi r}{2} - s = \frac{\pi r}{2} - r\theta = r\left(\frac{\pi}{2} - \theta\right). \frac{\pi}{2} - \theta$ is the complement of θ.

Group Project

In about 250 B.C., the philosopher Eratosthenes estimated the radius of Earth, based on what might appear to be scant information. He knew that the city of Syene (modern Aswan) is directly south of the city of Alexandria and that Syene and Alexandria are (in modern units) about 500 miles apart. He also knew that in Syene at noon on a midsummer day, an upright rod casts no shadow, but makes a $7°12'$ angle with a vertical rod at Alexandria, and that then the sun's rays at Syene are effectively parallel to the sun's rays at Alexandria. Explain how, by measuring the length of the shadow in Alexandria at noon on the summer solstice when there was no shadow in Syene, Eratosthenes could measure the circumference of the Earth.

Right Triangle Trigonometry

Mount Kilimanjaro

BEFORE STARTING THIS SECTION, REVIEW

1. Rationalizing the denominator (Section P.6, page 65)

2. Acute angle definition (Section P.7, page 75)

3. Pythagorean Theorem (Section P.7, page 77)

4. Similar triangles (Section P.7, page 76)

5. Functions (Section 2.4, page 225)

OBJECTIVES

1 Define trigonometric functions of acute angles.

2 Evaluate trigonometric functions of acute angles.

3 Evaluate trigonometric functions for the special angles 30°, 45°, and 60°.

4 Use right triangle trigonometry in applications.

Measuring Mount Kilimanjaro

Trigonometry developed as a result of attempts to solve practical problems in astronomy, navigation, and land measurement. The word "trigonometry," coined by Pitiscus in 1594, is derived from two Greek words, *trigonon* (triangle) and *metron* (measure), and means "triangle measurement."

Measuring objects that are generally inaccessible is one of the many successes of trigonometry. In Example 7, we use trigonometry to approximate the height of Mount Kilimanjaro, Tanzania. Mount Kilimanjaro is the highest mountain in Africa. ■

1 Define trigonometric functions of acute angles.

RECALL

In a right triangle, the side opposite the right angle is called the hypotenuse, and the other two sides are called the legs.

Trigonometric Ratios and Functions

Consider a right triangle with one of its acute angles labeled θ. In Figure 5.17, the capital letters A, B, and C designate the vertices of the triangle, and the lower-case letters a, b, and c, respectively, represent the lengths of the sides opposite these angles.

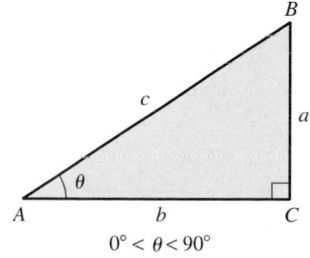

a = length of the side opposite θ
b = length of the side adjacent to θ
c = length of the hypotenuse

$0° < \theta < 90°$

FIGURE 5.17

There are six ratios that can be formed with the lengths of these sides: $\frac{a}{c}, \frac{b}{c}, \frac{a}{b}, \frac{b}{a}, \frac{c}{b}$, and $\frac{c}{a}$. These ratios are used to define the *six trigonometric functions of the acute angle* θ. We use the words "opposite" for the length of the leg opposite to θ, "adjacent" for the length of the leg adjacent to θ, and "hypotenuse" for the length of the hypotenuse.

RIGHT TRIANGLE DEFINITIONS OF THE TRIGONOMETRIC FUNCTIONS OF AN ACUTE ANGLE θ

$$\sin\theta = \frac{\text{opposite}}{\text{hypotenuse}} = \frac{a}{c} \qquad \csc\theta = \frac{\text{hypotenuse}}{\text{opposite}} = \frac{c}{a}$$

$$\cos\theta = \frac{\text{adjacent}}{\text{hypotenuse}} = \frac{b}{c} \qquad \sec\theta = \frac{\text{hypotenuse}}{\text{adjacent}} = \frac{c}{b}$$

$$\tan\theta = \frac{\text{opposite}}{\text{adjacent}} = \frac{a}{b} \qquad \cot\theta = \frac{\text{adjacent}}{\text{opposite}} = \frac{b}{a}$$

Notice that the ratios that define the functions in the second column in the box are reciprocals of those in the first column. The full names for these six trigonometric functions are **sine, cosine, tangent, cosecant, secant,** and **cotangent.** The customary abbreviations for the values of these functions of an angle θ are **sin θ, cos θ, tan θ, csc θ, sec θ,** and **cot θ,** respectively, as shown in the box.

Because any two right triangles having acute angle θ are similar, the ratios of corresponding sides depend only on the angle θ, not on the size of the triangle. Three right triangles with acute angle θ are shown in Figure 5.18.

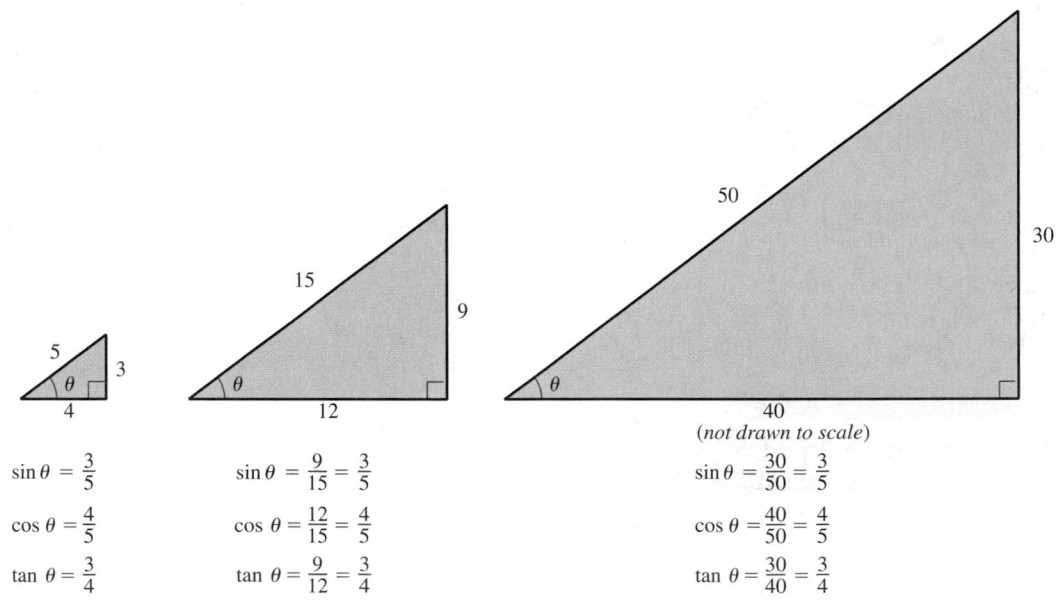

FIGURE 5.18

For each triangle, the six trigonometric values are identical. Recall that $\csc\theta$, $\sec\theta$, and $\cot\theta$ are the reciprocals of $\sin\theta$, $\cos\theta$, and $\tan\theta$, respectively. Consequently, for any of the triangles in Figure 5.18, we have $\csc\theta = \dfrac{5}{3}$, $\sec\theta = \dfrac{5}{4}$, and $\cot\theta = \dfrac{4}{3}$.

2 Evaluate trigonometric functions of acute angles.

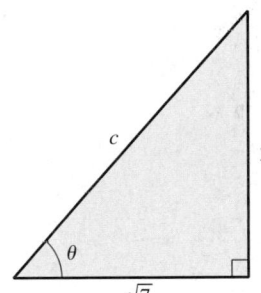

FIGURE 5.19

EXAMPLE 1   **Finding the Values of Trigonometric Functions**

Find the exact values for the six trigonometric functions of the angle θ in Figure 5.19.

Solution

To find the values for the six trigonometric functions of θ, we must first find the value of c, the length of the hypotenuse.

$$a^2 + b^2 = c^2 \qquad \text{Pythagorean Theorem}$$
$$(3)^2 + \left(\sqrt{7}\right)^2 = c^2 \qquad \text{Replace } a \text{ by 3 and } b \text{ by } \sqrt{7}.$$
$$9 + 7 = c^2$$
$$16 = c^2$$
$$4 = c \qquad c \text{ is a positive number.}$$

Now, with $c = 4$, $a = 3$, and $b = \sqrt{7}$, we have:

$$\sin\theta = \frac{\text{opposite}}{\text{hypotenuse}} = \frac{3}{4} \qquad\qquad \csc\theta = \frac{\text{hypotenuse}}{\text{opposite}} = \frac{4}{3}$$

$$\cos\theta = \frac{\text{adjacent}}{\text{hypotenuse}} = \frac{\sqrt{7}}{4} \qquad\qquad \sec\theta = \frac{\text{hypotenuse}}{\text{adjacent}} = \frac{4}{\sqrt{7}} = \frac{4\sqrt{7}}{7}$$

$$\tan\theta = \frac{\text{opposite}}{\text{adjacent}} = \frac{3}{\sqrt{7}} = \frac{3\sqrt{7}}{7} \qquad\qquad \cot\theta = \frac{\text{adjacent}}{\text{opposite}} = \frac{\sqrt{7}}{3}$$

These are exact values; using a calculator would yield approximate values.   ■ ■ ■

PRACTICE PROBLEM 1   Find the exact values for the six trigonometric functions of the acute angle θ in a right triangle if the length of the side opposite θ is 4 and the length of the hypotenuse is 5.   ■

EXAMPLE 2   **Finding Remaining Trigonometric Function Values from a Given Value**

Find the other five trigonometric function values of θ, given that θ is an acute angle of a right triangle with $\sin\theta = \dfrac{2}{5}$.

Solution

Since

$$\sin\theta = \frac{2}{5} = \frac{\text{opposite}}{\text{hypotenuse}}$$

Continued on next page.

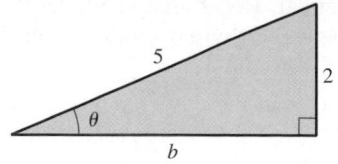

FIGURE 5.20

we draw a right triangle with hypotenuse of length 5 and the side opposite θ of length 2. See Figure 5.20. Then

$$5^2 = 2^2 + b^2 \qquad \text{Pythagorean Theorem}$$
$$b^2 = 5^2 - 2^2 \qquad \text{Subtract } 2^2 \text{ from both sides.}$$
$$b^2 = 21 \qquad\quad \text{Simplify.}$$
$$b = \sqrt{21}. \qquad b \text{ is a positive number.}$$

For this triangle we have:

$$c = \text{length of the hypotenuse} = 5$$
$$a = \text{length of the opposite side} = 2$$
$$b = \text{length of the adjacent side} = \sqrt{21}$$

Thus,

$$\sin \theta = \frac{\text{opposite}}{\text{hypotenuse}} = \frac{2}{5} \qquad\qquad \csc \theta = \frac{\text{hypotenuse}}{\text{opposite}} = \frac{5}{2}$$

$$\cos \theta = \frac{\text{adjacent}}{\text{hypotenuse}} = \frac{\sqrt{21}}{5} \qquad\qquad \sec \theta = \frac{\text{hypotenuse}}{\text{adjacent}} = \frac{5}{\sqrt{21}} = \frac{5\sqrt{21}}{21}$$

$$\tan \theta = \frac{\text{opposite}}{\text{adjacent}} = \frac{2}{\sqrt{21}} = \frac{2\sqrt{21}}{21} \qquad \cot \theta = \frac{\text{adjacent}}{\text{opposite}} = \frac{\sqrt{21}}{2} \qquad ■■■$$

3 Evaluate trigonometric functions for the special angles 30°, 45°, and 60°.

PRACTICE PROBLEM 2   Find the other five trigonometric function values of θ, given that θ is an acute angle of a right triangle with $\cos \theta = \dfrac{1}{3}$.   ■

Function Values for Some Special Angles

We can use the Pythagorean Theorem to find the exact values of the trigonometric functions for the angles with measure 30°, 45°, and 60° by examining the relationships between the side lengths in two "special" right triangles.

Consider an isosceles right triangle in which the length of each of the two legs of equal length is 1. Because the triangle has two sides of equal length, the two acute angles have equal measure, α. See Figure 5.21.

Since the sum of the measures of the angles in a triangle is 180°, we have $\alpha + \alpha = 90°$, so $2\alpha = 90°$ and $\alpha = 45°$. As is customary, we let $c =$ length of the hypotenuse; then

$$1^2 + 1^2 = c^2 \qquad \text{Pythagorean Theorem}$$
$$2 = c^2$$
$$c = \sqrt{2}. \qquad c \text{ is a positive number.}$$

Thus, a right triangle in which both legs have length 1 has a hypotenuse of length $\sqrt{2}$ and contains two 45° angles. See Figure 5.22. We call this an *isosceles right triangle*, or a **45–45–90 triangle**.

FIGURE 5.21

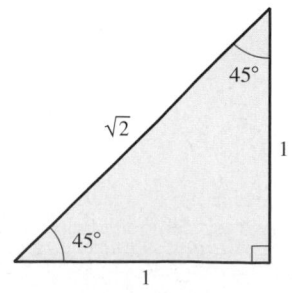

FIGURE 5.22

EXAMPLE 3 **Finding the Trigonometric Functions Values for 45°**

Use Figure 5.22 to find $\sin 45°$, $\cos 45°$, and $\tan 45°$.

Solution

Referring to Figure 5.22, we have:

$$\sin 45° = \frac{\text{opposite}}{\text{hypotenuse}} = \frac{1}{\sqrt{2}} = \frac{\sqrt{2}}{2}$$

$$\cos 45° = \frac{\text{adjacent}}{\text{hypotenuse}} = \frac{1}{\sqrt{2}} = \frac{\sqrt{2}}{2}$$

$$\tan 45° = \frac{\text{opposite}}{\text{adjacent}} = \frac{1}{1} = 1$$

■ ■ ■

PRACTICE PROBLEM 3   Use Figure 5.22 to find $\csc 45°$, $\sec 45°$, and $\cot 45°$.   ■

RECALL

An *equilateral triangle* is a triangle with all three sides of equal length. The measure of each angle of an equilateral triangle is 60°.

Now consider an equilateral triangle with side length 2, as shown in Figure 5.23(a). The perpendicular segment (dashed) in Figure 5.23(b) divides this triangle into two congruent right triangles.

We find the length of the perpendicular segment by applying the Pythagorean Theorem to one of the triangles. Let h denote the length of the perpendicular segment, which is a leg of both congruent right triangles. See Figure 5.23(b).

We can use either triangle to find the exact values of all six trigonometric functions for both 30° and 60° angles. We have

$2^2 = h^2 + 1^2$ Pythagorean Theorem

$h^2 = 2^2 - 1^2$ Subtract 1^2 from both sides and interchange sides.

$h^2 = 3$ Simplify.

$h = \sqrt{3}$ h is positive.

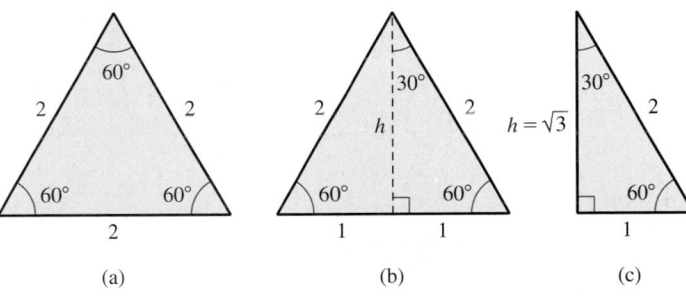

(a)   (b)   (c)

FIGURE 5.23

The resulting right triangle whose acute angles measure 30° and 60° is given in Figure 5.23(c). We call this a **30–60–90 triangle.**

TECHNOLOGY CONNECTION

 To use a calculator to find the value of a trigonometric function for an angle θ measured in degrees, you must set the calculator to degree mode. For example, in degree mode, to find the value cos 30°, press the $\boxed{\cos}$ key, enter 30, and press $\boxed{\text{ENTER}}$. The result is shown as a decimal. You can verify that your calculator gives this same decimal value for $\dfrac{\sqrt{3}}{2}$.

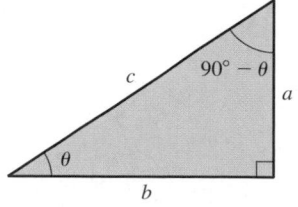

EXAMPLE 4 Finding the Trigonometric Functions Values for 30°

Use Figure 5.23(c) to find the values of the six trigonometric functions of 30°.

Solution

Referring to Figure 5.23(c), we have:

$$\sin 30° = \frac{\text{opposite}}{\text{hypotenuse}} = \frac{1}{2} \qquad \csc 30° = \frac{\text{hypotenuse}}{\text{opposite}} = \frac{2}{1} = 2$$

$$\cos 30° = \frac{\text{adjacent}}{\text{hypotenuse}} = \frac{\sqrt{3}}{2} \qquad \sec 30° = \frac{\text{hypotenuse}}{\text{adjacent}} = \frac{2}{\sqrt{3}} = \frac{2\sqrt{3}}{3}$$

$$\tan 30° = \frac{\text{opposite}}{\text{adjacent}} = \frac{1}{\sqrt{3}} = \frac{\sqrt{3}}{3} \qquad \cot 30° = \frac{\text{adjacent}}{\text{opposite}} = \frac{\sqrt{3}}{1} = \sqrt{3}$$
■ ■ ■

PRACTICE PROBLEM 4 Use Figure 5.23(c) to find the values of the six trigonometric functions of 60°. ■

You should be able to reconstruct the triangles used to find the values for the six trigonometric functions for 30°, 45°, and 60°, as these values occur frequently. Remember that the values depend only on the *acute angle itself*, and not on the size of the triangle. We summarize the values obtained so far in Table 5.1, using both degree and radian measures.

TABLE 5.1 Trigonometric Function Values of Some Common Angles

θ (degrees)	θ (radians)	sin θ	cos θ	tan θ	csc θ	sec θ	cot θ
30°	$\dfrac{\pi}{6}$	$\dfrac{1}{2}$	$\dfrac{\sqrt{3}}{2}$	$\dfrac{\sqrt{3}}{3}$	2	$\dfrac{2\sqrt{3}}{3}$	$\sqrt{3}$
45°	$\dfrac{\pi}{4}$	$\dfrac{\sqrt{2}}{2}$	$\dfrac{\sqrt{2}}{2}$	1	$\sqrt{2}$	$\sqrt{2}$	1
60°	$\dfrac{\pi}{3}$	$\dfrac{\sqrt{3}}{2}$	$\dfrac{1}{2}$	$\sqrt{3}$	$\dfrac{2\sqrt{3}}{3}$	2	$\dfrac{\sqrt{3}}{3}$

Complements

Because 30° and 60° are acute angles in the same right triangle, the same six possible ratios of the lengths of the sides of the triangle are used to compute the values of the trigonometric functions for both angles. Notice that $\cos 30° = \sin 60°$, $\sin 30° = \cos 60°$, and $\tan 30° = \cot 60°$. Taking reciprocals of these values extends this relationship to the remaining three trigonometric functions.

The prefix "co-" (in cosine, cotangent, and cosecant) stands for *complement*. In general, for any acute angle θ in a right triangle, the other acute angle is its complement, $90° - \theta$. See Figure 5.24.

Computations similar to those in Example 4 lead to the relationships given next.

FIGURE 5.24

COMPLEMENTARY RELATIONSHIPS

The value of any trigonometric function of an acute angle θ is equal to the cofunction of the complement of θ. This is true whether θ is measured in degrees or in radians.

θ in degrees

$$\sin \theta = \cos (90° - \theta) \qquad \cos \theta = \sin (90° - \theta)$$
$$\tan \theta = \cot (90° - \theta) \qquad \cot \theta = \tan (90° - \theta)$$
$$\sec \theta = \csc (90° - \theta) \qquad \csc \theta = \sec (90° - \theta)$$

If θ is measured in radians, replace 90° by $\dfrac{\pi}{2}$.

EXAMPLE 5   Finding Trigonometric Function Values of a Complementary Angle

a. Given that $\cot 68° \approx 0.4040$, find $\tan 22°$.

b. Given that $\cos 72° \approx 0.3090$, find $\sin 18°$.

Solution

a. Note that $68° = 90° - 22°.$ Thus,

$$\tan 22° = \cot (90° - 22°) = \cot 68° \approx 0.4040.$$

b. Here, $72° = 90° - 18°.$ Thus,

$$\sin 18° = \cos (90° - 18°) = \cos 72° \approx 0.3090.$$ ■ ■ ■

PRACTICE PROBLEM 5

a. Given that $\csc 21° \approx 2.7904$, find $\sec 69°$.

b. Given that $\tan 75° \approx 3.7321$, find $\cot 15°$.   ■

4 Use trigonometry in applications.

Applications

Angles that are measured between a line of sight and a horizontal line occur in many applications and are called *angles of elevation,* or *angles of depression.* If the line of sight is *above* the horizontal line, the angle between these two lines is called the **angle of elevation.** If the line of sight is *below* the horizontal line, the angle between the two lines is called the **angle of depression.**

For example, suppose that you are taking a picture of a friend who has climbed to the top of the Arc de Triomphe in Paris. See Figure 5.25. The angle your eyes rotate

Angle of elevation

Angle of depression

FIGURE 5.25

through as your gaze changes from straight ahead to looking at your friend is the angle of elevation.

The angle your friend's eyes rotate through as she changes from looking straight ahead to looking down at you (no pun intended) is the angle of depression.

EXAMPLE 6   **Finding the Height of a Cloud**

To determine the height of a cloud at night, a farmer shines a spotlight straight upward to a spot on the cloud. The angle of elevation to this same spot on the cloud from a point located 150 feet horizontally from the spotlight is 68.2°. Find the height of the cloud.

Solution

In Figure 5.26, h represents the height of the cloud, in feet. We have

$$\tan 68.2° = \frac{h}{150}$$

$$h = 150 \tan 68.2° \qquad \text{Multiply both sides by 150.}$$

$$h \approx 375 \qquad\qquad\quad \text{Use a calculator.}$$

The height of the cloud is approximately 375 feet.   ■ ■ ■

FIGURE 5.26

PRACTICE PROBLEM 6   From an observation deck 425 feet high, on the top of a lighthouse, the angle of depression to a ship at sea is 4.2°. How many miles is the ship from a point at sea level directly below the observation deck?   ■

EXAMPLE 7   **Measuring the Height of Mount Kilimanjaro**

A surveyor wants to measure the height of Mount Kilimanjaro by using the known height of a nearby mountain. The nearby location is at an altitude of 8720 feet, the distance between that location and Mount Kilimanjaro's peak is 4.9941 miles, and the angle of elevation from the lower location is 23.75°. See Figure 5.27. Use this information to find the approximate height of Mount Kilimanjaro.

4.9941 mi

23.75°

h

8720 ft

FIGURE 5.27

Solution

The sum of the side length h and the location height of 8720 feet gives the approximate height of Mount Kilimanjaro. Let h be measured in miles. Use the definition of $\sin\theta$, for $\theta = 23.75°$.

$$\sin\theta = \frac{\text{opposite}}{\text{hypotenuse}} = \frac{h}{4.9941}$$

$$h = (4.9941)\sin\theta \qquad \text{Multiply both sides by 4.9941.}$$

$$= (4.9941)\sin 23.75° \qquad \text{Replace } \theta \text{ by } 23.75°.$$

$$h \approx 2.0114 \qquad \text{Use a calculator.}$$

Because 1 mile = 5280 feet,

$$2.0114 \text{ miles} = (2.0114)(5280)$$

$$\approx 10,620 \text{ feet}$$

Thus, the height of Mount Kilimanjaro

$$\approx 10,620 + 8720 = 19,340 \text{ feet.} \qquad ■ ■ ■$$

PRACTICE PROBLEM 7   The height of the nearby location to Mount McKinley, Alaska, is 12,870 feet, its distance to Mount McKinley's peak is 3.3387 miles, and the angle of elevation θ is 25°. What is the approximate height of Mount McKinley?   ■

EXAMPLE 8   **Finding the Width of a River**

To find the width of a river, a surveyor sights straight across the river from a point A on her side to a point B on the opposite side. See Figure 5.28. She then walks 200 feet upstream to a point C. The angle θ that the line of sight from point C to point B makes with the river bank is 58°. How wide is the river?

Solution

The points $A, B,$ and C are the vertices of a right triangle with acute angle $\theta = 58°$.
     Let w represent the width of the river. From Figure 5.28 we have

$$\frac{w}{200} = \tan 58° \qquad \tan\theta = \frac{\text{opposite}}{\text{adjacent}}$$

$$w = 200\tan 58° \qquad \text{Multiply both sides by 200.}$$

$$w \approx 320.07 \text{ feet} \qquad \text{Use a calculator.}$$

The river is about 320 feet wide at the point A.   ■ ■ ■

FIGURE 5.28

PRACTICE PROBLEM 8 From a point on the edge of one of two parallel rooftop sides, a point directly opposite is identified on the other rooftop. From a second point 25 feet from the first point along the rooftop edge, a second sighting to the point on the opposite rooftop is made, and the angle θ that this line of sight makes with the rooftop is found to be 60°. How far apart are the two buildings? Round your answer to the nearest foot. ▪

A Exercises ▪ Basic Skills and Concepts

In Exercises 1–6, find the exact values for the six trigonometric functions of the angle θ in each figure. Rationalize the denominator where necessary.

1.

2.

3.

4.

5.

6.

In Exercises 7–12, use each given trigonometric function value of θ to find the five other trigonometric function values of the acute angle θ. Rationalize the denominators where necessary.

7. $\cos \theta = \dfrac{2}{3}$ †

8. $\sin \theta = \dfrac{3}{4}$ †

9. $\tan \theta = \dfrac{5}{3}$ †

10. $\cot \theta = \dfrac{6}{11}$ †

11. $\sec \theta = \dfrac{13}{12}$ †

12. $\csc \theta = 4$ †

In Exercises 13–20, match each expression on the left with its value on the right. Do not use a calculator or refer to any of the earlier pages in this section. Some values may be used more than once or not at all.

13. $\sin 45°$ (d)

14. $\cos 30°$ (a)

15. $\tan 60°$ (g)

16. $\csc 30°$ (f)

17. $\sin 60°$ (a)

18. $\cot 45°$ (b)

19. $\sec 60°$ (f)

20. $\tan 30°$ (e)

(a) $\dfrac{\sqrt{3}}{2}$

(b) 1

(c) $\dfrac{2\sqrt{3}}{3}$

(d) $\dfrac{\sqrt{2}}{2}$

(e) $\dfrac{\sqrt{3}}{3}$

(f) 2

(g) $\sqrt{3}$

(h) $\sqrt{2}$

In Exercises 21–26, find the trigonometric function values of each corresponding complementary angle.

21. Given that $\sin 58° \approx 0.8480$, find $\cos 32°$. 0.8480

22. Given that $\cos 37° \approx 0.7986$, find $\sin 53°$. 0.7986

23. Given that $\tan 27° \approx 0.5095$, find $\cot 63°$. 0.5095

24. Given that $\cot 49° \approx 0.8693$, find $\tan 41°$. 0.8693

25. Given that $\sec 65° \approx 2.3662$, find $\csc 25°$. 2.3662

26. Given that $\csc 78° \approx 1.0223$, find $\sec 12°$. 1.0223

†Due to space constrictions, answers to these exercises may be found in the Answers beginning on page A–1 in the back of the book.

B Exercises   Applying the Concepts

27. Positioning a ladder. An 18-foot ladder is resting against a wall of a building in such a way that the top of the ladder is 14 feet above the ground. How far is the foot of the ladder from the base of the building? ≈11 feet

28. Positioning a ladder. The ladder from Exercise 27 is placed against a wall so that the foot of the ladder is 7 feet from the base of the wall. How high up the wall will the ladder reach? ≈17 feet

In Exercises, 29 and 30 use the following definitions:
The **vertical rise** of a ski lift is the vertical distance traveled when a lift car goes from the bottom terminal to the top terminal. The **slope length** is the linear distance a lift car travels as it moves from the bottom terminal to the top terminal. We treat the *slope length* as the hypotenuse, and the *vertical rise* as the side opposite the angle formed by the horizontal line at the bottom terminal and the lift cables.

29. Ski lift dimensions. Find the horizontal distance a lift car passes over if the vertical rise is 295 meters and the slope length is 1070 meters. ≈1029 meters

30. Ski lift dimensions. Find the vertical rise (to the nearest foot) for a ski lift with slope length 2050 feet if the angle formed by a horizontal line at the bottom terminal and the lift cable is 16°. ≈565 feet

31. Ski lift height. If a skier travels 5000 feet up a ski lift whose angle of inclination is 30°, how high above his starting level is he? 2500 feet

32. Shadow length. At a time when the sun's rays make a 50° angle with the horizontal, how long is the shadow cast by a 6-foot man standing on flat ground? ≈5 feet

33. Height of a tree. The angle relative to the horizontal from the top of a tree to a point 110 feet from its base (on flat ground) is found to be 15°. Find the height of the tree, to the nearest foot. ≈29 feet

34. Height of a cliff. The angle of elevation from a rowboat moored 75 feet from a cliff is 73.8°. Find the height of the cliff, to the nearest foot. ≈258 feet

35. Height of a flagpole. A flagpole is supported by a 30-foot tension wire attached to the flagpole and to a stake in the ground. If the ground is flat and the angle the wire makes with the ground is 40°, how high up the flagpole is the wire attached? Round your answer to the nearest foot. ≈19 feet

36. Flying a kite. A girl 5 feet tall is flying a kite. How long must the string be in order for her to raise the kite 200 feet above the ground if the string makes a 28°4′ angle with the ground? ≈414 feet

37. Height of a shadow. Find the height of a pine tree that casts a 93-foot shadow on the ground if the angle of elevation of the sun is 24°35′. ≈43 feet

38. Width of a river. Sal and his friend are on opposite sides of a river. To find the width of the river, each of them hammered a stake on his bank of the river in such a way that the distance between the two stakes approximates the width of the river. Sal walks 10 feet away from his stake along the river and finds that the line of sight from his new position to his friend's stake across the river and the line of sight to his own stake form a 73°34′ angle. How wide is the river? ≈34 feet

39. Measuring the Empire State Building. From a neighboring building's 13th-floor window that is 128 meters above the ground, the angle of elevation of the top of the Empire State Building is 59°20′, while the angle of depression of the base is 40°29′. How far away from the neighboring building, and how tall, is the Empire State Building? †

40. Sighting a mortar station. The angle of depression from a helicopter 3000 feet directly above an allied mortar station to an enemy supply depot is 13°. How far is the depot from the mortar station? ≈12,994 feet

41. Distance between Earth and the moon. If the radius of Earth is 3960 miles and angle A (the latitude of A) is 89°3′, find the distance between the center of Earth and the center of the moon. ≈238,844 miles

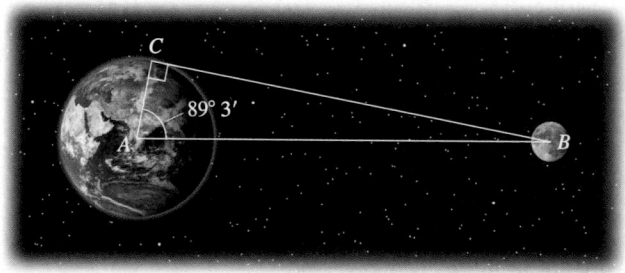

In Exercises 42 and 43, use the figure to find the radius r for the given latitudes (values of θ). Use 3960 miles for the radius of Earth.

42. Latitude. Find the radius of the 50th parallel (of latitude).

43. Latitude. Find the radius of the 53rd parallel (of latitude).

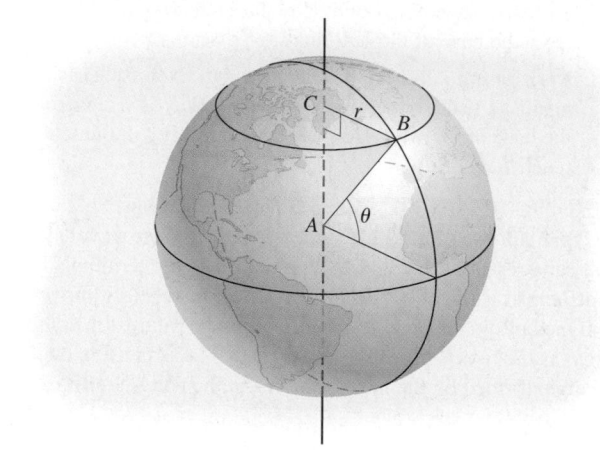

Answers:
42. ≈ 2545 miles   **43.** ≈ 2383 miles

C Exercises   Beyond the Basics

In Exercises 44–50, use the figure and the given values to find each specified side length, angle, and trigonometric function value. Round your answer to three decimal places.

44. $a = 8, b = 10$ Find c, $\sin\theta$, and $\tan\theta$. †

45. $a = 18, b = 3$ Find c, $\sin\theta$, and $\cos\theta$. †

46. $a = 23, b = 7$ Find $\cos\theta$ and $\tan\theta$. †

47. $a = 19, b = 27$ Find c, $\cos\theta$, and $\tan\theta$. †

48. $\theta = 30°, a = 9$ Find $\sin\theta$, b and c. †

49. $\theta = 30°, a = 5$ Find b and c. †

50. $\theta = 60°, a = 7$ Find α, b, and c. †

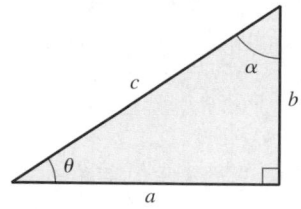

51. Height of an airplane. From a tower 150 feet high, with the sun directly overhead, an airplane and its shadow

have an angle of elevation of 67.4° and an angle of depression of 8.1°, respectively. Find the height of the airplane. ≈2682 feet

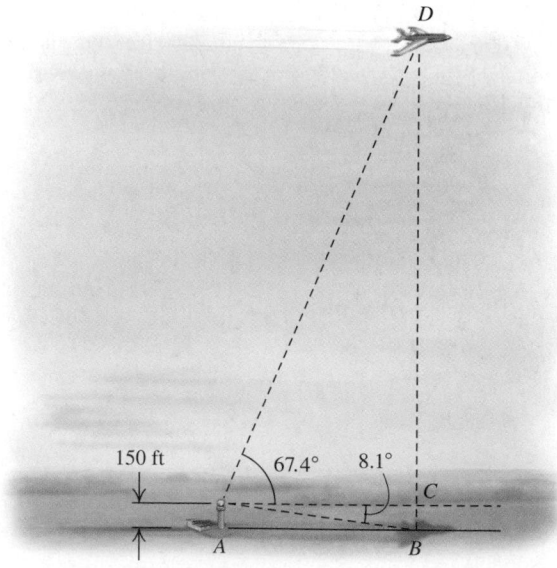

52. **Camera angle.** Raphael stands 12 feet from a large painting on a wall. He sets his camera 5 feet 6 inches above the floor. If the bottom edge of the painting is 4 feet above the floor and the angle of elevation from the camera to the top of the painting is 50°, find the height of the painting to the nearest tenth of a foot. ≈15.8 feet

53. **Height of a building.** The WCNC-TV Tower in Dallas, North Carolina, is 600 meters high. Suppose that a building is erected such that the base of the building is on the same plane as the base of the tower, the angle of elevation from the top of the building to the top of the tower is 75.24°, and the angle of depression from the top of the building to the foot of the tower is 60.05°. How high would the building have to be? (*Source:* en.wikipedia.org) ≈188.27 meters

54. **Height of a building.** Suppose that from the top of the Empire State Building (which is about 1250 feet high) the angle of depression to the top of a second building is 55.8°, and the angle of depression to the bottom of the second building is 67.7°. Find the height of the second building. ≈496 feet

55. In the figure below, show that $h = \dfrac{d}{\cot\alpha - \cot\beta}$.

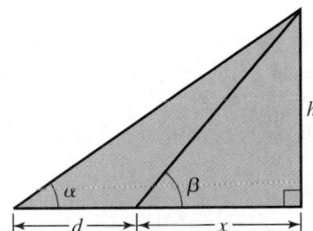

56. **Height of a plane.** A plane flies directly over two tracking stations that are 500 meters apart on a level plain. The plane flies in the direction from Station A to Station B. After the plane has passed Station B, an observer at Station B records the angle of elevation as 38.9°. At the same time an observer at station A records the angle of elevation as 36.9°. What is the plane's altitude? ≈5402 meters
[*Hint:* Use Exercise 55.]

57. **Measuring the Statue of Liberty.** While sailing toward the Statue of Liberty, a sailor in a boat observed that at a certain point the angle of elevation of the tip of the torch was 25°. After sailing another 100 meters toward the statue, the angle of elevation became 41°50′. How tall is the Statue of Liberty? ≈97 meters

58. **Speed of a plane.** A plane flying at an altitude of 12,000 feet finds the angle of depression for a building ahead of the plane to be 10.4°. With the building still straight ahead, two minutes later the angle of depression is 25.6°. Find the speed of the plane relative to the ground (in feet per minute). ≈20,168.5 feet per minute

59. In the figure below, show that $h = \dfrac{d}{\cot\alpha + \cot\beta}$.

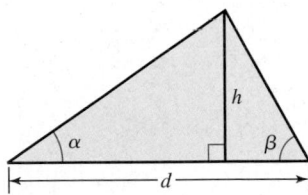

60. Find the area of the following triangle. ≈20 square units

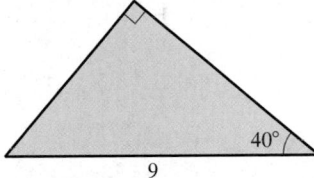

[*Hint:* Use Exercise 59.]

61. Find the area of triangle *ABC*. ≈48 square units

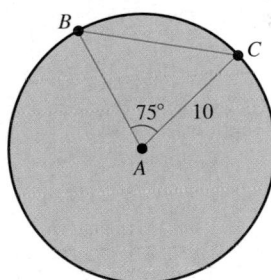

Critical Thinking

62. Draw a right triangle with acute angle θ. Then use the definitions of sin θ and cos θ together with the Pythagorean Theorem to show that $\sin^2\theta + \cos^2\theta = 1$.

63. In a right triangle with acute angle θ, what value must the adjacent side have in order for the length of the opposite side to represent tan θ? 1

64. Use the result of Exercise 63 to compare tan α and tan β if α and β are acute angles and the measure of α is less than the measure of β. tan β > tan α

Trigonometric Functions of Any Angle; Unit Circle

BEFORE STARTING THIS SECTION, REVIEW

1. Rationalizing a denominator (Section P.6, page 65)

2. Distance between two points (Section 2.1, page 185)

3. Unit circle (Section 2.2, page 199)

OBJECTIVES

1 Evaluate trigonometric functions of any angle.

2 Determine the signs of the trigonometric functions.

3 Find a reference angle.

4 Find the area of an SAS triangle.

5 Use the unit circle definitions of the trigonometric functions.

6 Apply the basic trigonometric identities.

Angles and Cell Towers

Angles that are not acute are everywhere. A popular photo lens has a 185° field of view, the rearview mirror in a car reflects a view considerably wider than 90°, and lights such as search beams and disco lights rotate through very large angles, as do rotating wheels, fans, and parts in many types of machinery. In this section, given an angle of any size, we associate an acute angle (called a *reference angle*) with the given angle that often allows us to evaluate a trigonometric function of the given angle using the reference angle. In Example 8, we will learn how to compute a triangular area determined by three cellular telephone towers.

In Section 5.2, we defined the trigonometric functions for acute angles. However, to understand the most important applications of trigonometry we will need to extend these definitions to include all angles. ■

---

1 Evaluate trigonometric functions of any angle.

Trigonometric Functions of Angles

Consider an angle θ in standard position, as shown in Figure 5.29. Let P be any point on the terminal ray of θ, and let (x, y) be the coordinates of P. The distance between the origin $O\,(0, 0)$ and the point P is $r = \sqrt{(x - 0)^2 + (y - 0)^2} = \sqrt{x^2 + y^2}$.

We define the six trigonometric functions, **sine**, **cosine**, **tangent**, **cosecant**, **secant**, and **cotangent,** for any angle θ by using the same abbreviations we used in the previous section.

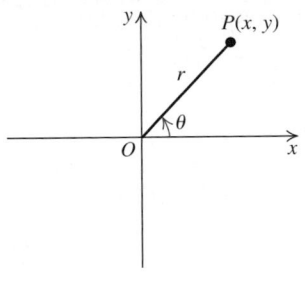

FIGURE 5.29

DEFINITION OF THE TRIGONOMETRIC FUNCTIONS OF ANY ANGLE θ

Let $P(x, y)$ be any point on the terminal ray of an angle θ in standard position (other than the origin), and let $r = \sqrt{x^2 + y^2}$. Then $r > 0$, and:

$$\sin\theta = \frac{y}{r} \qquad\qquad \csc\theta = \frac{r}{y} \quad (y \neq 0)$$

$$\cos\theta = \frac{x}{r} \qquad\qquad \sec\theta = \frac{r}{x} \quad (x \neq 0)$$

$$\tan\theta = \frac{y}{x} \quad (x \neq 0) \qquad\qquad \cot\theta = \frac{x}{y} \quad (y \neq 0)$$

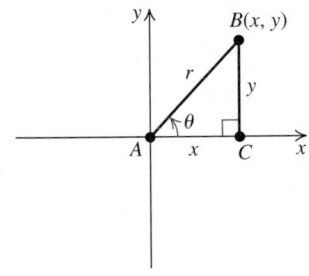

FIGURE 5.30

Now consider a right triangle with acute angle θ and vertices A, B, and C. Place the triangle so that θ is in standard position, as shown in Figure 5.30. If (x, y) are the coordinates of the vertex B, then $r^2 = x^2 + y^2$, so $r = \sqrt{x^2 + y^2}$, and

$$\sin\theta = \frac{\text{opposite}}{\text{hypotenuse}} = \frac{y}{r} \qquad \csc\theta = \frac{\text{hypotenuse}}{\text{opposite}} = \frac{r}{y}$$

$$\cos\theta = \frac{\text{adjacent}}{\text{hypotenuse}} = \frac{x}{r} \qquad \sec\theta = \frac{\text{hypotenuse}}{\text{adjacent}} = \frac{r}{x}$$

$$\tan\theta = \frac{\text{opposite}}{\text{adjacent}} = \frac{y}{x} \qquad \cot\theta = \frac{\text{adjacent}}{\text{opposite}} = \frac{x}{y}$$

Notice that *for acute angles, the definitions from the previous section give the same values for all six trigonometric functions as do the definitions in this section.* Consequently, the trigonometric function values we computed in Section 5.2, such as those for $30°$, $45°$, and $60°$, are the same values that we would obtain by using the more general definitions given in this section.

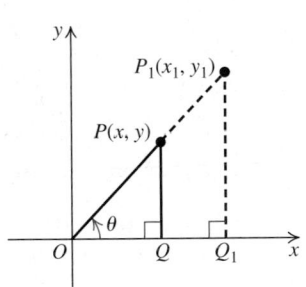

FIGURE 5.31

In Figure 5.31, triangles POQ and P_1OQ_1 are similar by Angle-Angle Similarity, so the ratios of corresponding sides are equal. Thus, letting $r = \sqrt{x^2 + y^2}$ and $r_1 = \sqrt{x_1^2 + y_1^2}$, we have $\sin\theta = \dfrac{y}{r} = \dfrac{y_1}{r_1}$, $\cos\theta = \dfrac{x}{r} = \dfrac{x_1}{r_1}$, and so on. This shows that the values of the trigonometric functions do not depend on the choice of the point $P(x, y)$ on the terminal side of θ.

> **EXAMPLE 1** **Finding Trigonometric Function Values**

Suppose that θ is an angle whose terminal side contains the point $P(-1, 3)$. Find the exact values of the six trigonometric functions of θ.

Solution

Since $x = -1$, and $y = 3$ (see Figure 5.32), we have

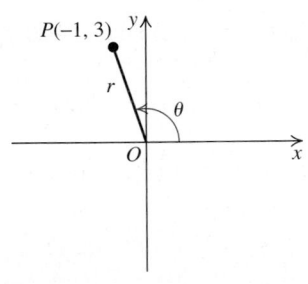

FIGURE 5.32

$$
\begin{aligned}
r &= \sqrt{x^2 + y^2} && \text{Definition of } r \\
&= \sqrt{(-1)^2 + 3^2} && \text{Replace } x \text{ by } -1 \text{ and } y \text{ by } 3. \\
&= \sqrt{10} && \text{Simplify.}
\end{aligned}
$$

Continued on next page.

Replacing x by -1, y by 3, and r by $\sqrt{10}$ in the definition of the trigonometric functions, we have:

$$\sin\theta = \frac{y}{r} = \frac{3}{\sqrt{10}} = \frac{3\sqrt{10}}{10} \qquad\qquad \csc\theta = \frac{r}{y} = \frac{\sqrt{10}}{3}$$

$$\cos\theta = \frac{x}{r} = \frac{-1}{\sqrt{10}} = -\frac{\sqrt{10}}{10} \qquad\qquad \sec\theta = \frac{r}{x} = \frac{\sqrt{10}}{-1} = -\sqrt{10}$$

$$\tan\theta = \frac{y}{x} = \frac{3}{-1} = -3 \qquad\qquad \cot\theta = \frac{x}{y} = \frac{-1}{3} = -\frac{1}{3} \qquad ■ ■ ■$$

PRACTICE PROBLEM 1 Suppose that θ is an angle whose terminal side contains the point $P(2, -5)$. Find the exact values of the six trigonometric functions of θ. ■

Since the value of each trigonometric function of an angle in standard position is completely determined by the position of the terminal side, the following statements are true:

1. Coterminal angles are assigned identical values by the six trigonometric functions.
2. The signs of the values of the trigonometric functions are determined by the quadrant containing the terminal side.
3. For any integer n, in degree measure θ and $\theta + n360°$ are coterminal angles, and in radian measure θ and $\theta + 2\pi n$ are coterminal angles.

Some frequently used consequences of these observations are given next.

TRIGONOMETRIC FUNCTION VALUES OF COTERMINAL ANGLES

θ in degrees	**θ in radians**
$\sin\theta = \sin(\theta + n360°)$	$\sin\theta = \sin(\theta + 2\pi n)$
$\cos\theta = \cos(\theta + n360°)$	$\cos\theta = \cos(\theta + 2\pi n)$

These equations hold for any integer n.

If an angle θ is measured in degrees, we use the degree symbol when indicating a trigonometric function value, such as $\cos 60°$ or $\tan 28°$. If θ is measured in radians, then no symbol is used when indicating a trigonometric function value (for example, $\sin\dfrac{\pi}{4}$, $\sec\pi$, and $\cos 16$). Notice that if one of the coordinates of a point on the terminal side of a quadrantal angle is 0, then this coordinate cannot appear in a denominator. If the terminal side is on the x-axis, then the y-coordinate is 0, so the cotangent $\left(\cot\theta = \dfrac{x}{y}\right)$ and the cosecant $\left(\csc\theta = \dfrac{r}{y}\right)$ functions are undefined. If the terminal side is on the y-axis, then the x-coordinate is 0 and the tangent $\left(\tan\theta = \dfrac{y}{x}\right)$ and the secant $\left(\sec\theta = \dfrac{r}{x}\right)$ functions are undefined.

> **EXAMPLE 2**   **Finding the Values of the Trigonometric Functions of Quadrantal Angles**

Find the values (if any) of the six trigonometric functions of each angle.

a. $\theta = 0° = 0$ **b.** $\theta = 90° = \dfrac{\pi}{2}$

Solution

First choose a point on the terminal side of each angle, as shown in Figure 5.33. Then use the definitions of the trigonometric functions.

a. $\theta = 0° = 0$ radians; $x = 1, y = 0$, and $r = \sqrt{1^2 + 0^2} = 1$,

$$\sin 0° = \sin 0 = \frac{y}{r} = \frac{0}{1} = 0 \qquad\qquad \cos 0° = \cos 0 = \frac{x}{r} = \frac{1}{1} = 1$$

$$\tan 0° = \tan 0 = \frac{y}{x} = \frac{0}{1} = 0 \qquad\qquad \sec 0° = \sec 0 = \frac{r}{x} = \frac{1}{1} = 1$$

Because the y-coordinate of P is 0, $\csc 0°$ and $\cot 0°$ are undefined.

b. $\theta = 90° = \dfrac{\pi}{2}$ radians; $x = 0, y = 1$, and $r = \sqrt{0^2 + 1^2} = 1$,

$$\sin 90° = \sin \frac{\pi}{2} = \frac{y}{r} = \frac{1}{1} = 1 \qquad\qquad \cos 90° = \cos \frac{\pi}{2} = \frac{x}{r} = \frac{0}{1} = 0$$

$$\csc 90° = \csc \frac{\pi}{2} = \frac{r}{y} = \frac{1}{1} = 1 \qquad\qquad \cot 90° = \cot \frac{\pi}{2} = \frac{x}{y} = \frac{0}{1} = 0$$

Because the x-coordinate of Q is 0, $\sec 90°$ and $\tan 90°$ are undefined.   ■ ■ ■

PRACTICE PROBLEM 2   Find the values (if any) of the six trigonometric functions of each angle.

a. $\theta = 180° = \pi$ **b.** $\theta = 270° = \dfrac{3\pi}{2}$ ■

Table 5.2 summarizes these facts about quadrantal angles.

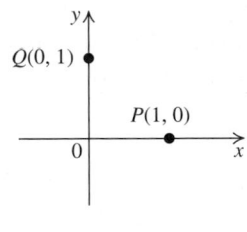

FIGURE 5.33

TABLE 5.2 Trigonometric Function Values of Quadrantal Angles

θ (degrees)	θ (radians)	sin θ	cos θ	tan θ	cot θ	sec θ	csc θ
0°	0	0	1	0	undefined	1	undefined
90°	$\dfrac{\pi}{2}$	1	0	undefined	0	undefined	1
180°	π	0	−1	0	undefined	−1	undefined
270°	$\dfrac{3\pi}{2}$	−1	0	undefined	0	undefined	−1
360°	2π	0	1	0	undefined	1	undefined

Signs of the Trigonometric Functions

2 Determine the signs of the trigonometric functions.

For angles that are not quadrantal angles, the sign of any trigonometric function depends on the quadrant in which the terminal side of θ lies. The value of r used in defining the trigonometric function value of any angle is always *positive*, so that the signs of the coordinates x and y of a point on the terminal side determine the sign of the values of the trigonometric functions.

If θ lies in quadrant I, then both x and y are positive, so all six trigonometric function values are positive. However, if θ lies in quadrant II, then x is negative and y is positive, so only $\sin\theta = \dfrac{y}{r}$ and $\csc\theta = \dfrac{r}{y}$ are positive. If θ lies in quadrant III, then x and y are both negative, so only $\tan\theta = \dfrac{y}{x}$ and $\cot\theta = \dfrac{x}{y}$ are positive. If θ lies in quadrant IV, then x is positive and y is negative, so only $\cos\theta = \dfrac{x}{r}$ and $\sec\theta = \dfrac{r}{x}$ are positive. Figure 5.34 summarizes the signs of the trigonometric functions.

RECALL

If $a \neq 0$ is any real number, then a and $\dfrac{1}{a}$ are either both positive or both negative.

II	I
$(-, +)$	$(+, +)$
$\sin\theta > 0,$	All positive
$\csc\theta > 0$	
$\tan\theta > 0,$	$\cos\theta > 0,$
$\cot\theta > 0$	$\sec\theta > 0$
$(-, -)$	$(+, -)$
III	IV

FIGURE 5.34

EXAMPLE 3 **Determining the Quadrant in Which an Angle Lies**

If $\tan\theta > 0$ and $\cos\theta < 0$, in which quadrant does θ lie?

Solution

Because $\tan\theta > 0$, θ must lie in quadrant I or in quadrant III. However, $\cos\theta > 0$ for θ in quadrant I, so θ must lie in quadrant III. ◾ ◾ ◾

PRACTICE PROBLEM 3 If $\sin\theta > 0$ and $\cos\theta < 0$, in which quadrant does θ lie? ◾

STUDY TIP

The sentence "All Students Take Calculus" can be useful in remembering which trigonometric functions are positive in quadrants I – IV. Use the first letter of each word in this phrase;

A ll functions (I),

S ine (II)

T angent (III)

C osine (IV)

and recall that a and $\dfrac{1}{a}$ have the same sign.

EXAMPLE 4 **Evaluating Trigonometric Functions**

Given that $\tan\theta = \dfrac{3}{2}$ and $\cos\theta < 0$, find the exact values of $\sin\theta$ and $\sec\theta$.

Solution

Because $\tan\theta > 0$ and $\cos\theta < 0$, θ lies in quadrant III. We want to identify a point (x, y) in quadrant III that is on the terminal side of θ. We have

$$\tan\theta = \frac{y}{x} = \frac{3}{2},$$

and because the point (x, y) is in quadrant III, both x and y must be negative. See Figure 5.35. If we choose $x = -2$ and $y = -3$, then

$$\tan\theta = \frac{y}{x} = \frac{-3}{-2} = \frac{3}{2}.$$

Further, $r = \sqrt{x^2 + y^2} = \sqrt{(-2)^2 + (-3)^2} = \sqrt{4 + 9} = \sqrt{13}$.

From $x = -2$, $y = -3$, and $r = \sqrt{13}$, we can find $\sin\theta$ and $\sec\theta$.

$$\sin\theta = \frac{y}{r} = \frac{-3}{\sqrt{13}} = -\frac{3\sqrt{13}}{13} \qquad \sec\theta = \frac{r}{x} = \frac{\sqrt{13}}{-2} = -\frac{\sqrt{13}}{2}$$ ◾ ◾ ◾

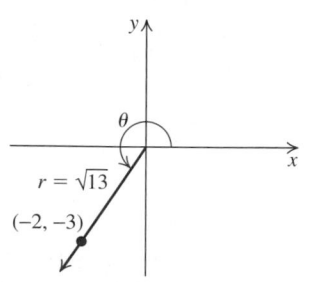

FIGURE 5.35

PRACTICE PROBLEM 4 Given that $\tan\theta = -\dfrac{4}{5}$ and $\cos\theta > 0$, find the exact values of $\sin\theta$ and $\sec\theta$. ◾

3 Find a reference angle.

Reference Angle

For any angle θ, there is a corresponding acute angle called its *reference angle*, whose trigonometric function values are identical to those of θ, except possibly for the sign.

DEFINITION OF A REFERENCE ANGLE

Let θ be an angle in standard position that is not a quadrantal angle. The **reference angle** for θ is the positive acute angle θ′("theta prime") formed by the terminal side of θ and the positive or negative *x*-axis.

If θ lies in quadrant I, then θ = θ′. The reference angles for positive angles in each of the four quadrants $(0° < θ < 360°)$ are shown in Figure 5.36.

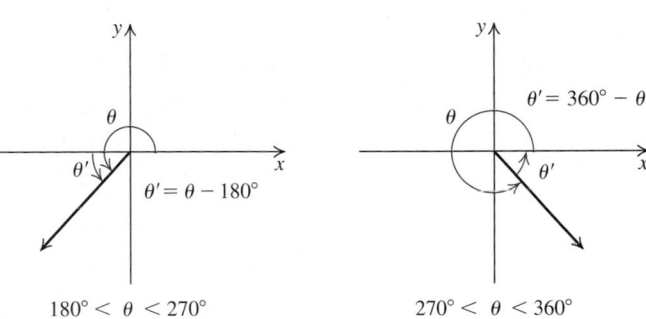

FIGURE 5.36

If θ is measured in radians, and $0 < θ < 2π$, we have $θ′ = θ$, $θ′ = π − θ$, $θ′ = θ − π$, and $θ′ = 2π − θ$, for θ in quadrants I, II, III, and IV, respectively.

EXAMPLE 5   **Identifying Reference Angles**

Find the reference angle, θ′, for each angle θ.

a. $θ = 250°$ **b.** $θ = \dfrac{3π}{5}$ **c.** $θ = 5.75$

Continued on next page.

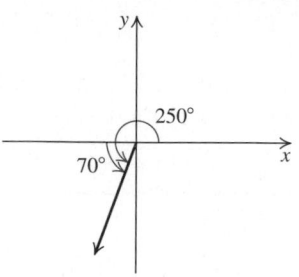

FIGURE 5.37

Solution

a. Because 250° lies in quadrant III, the reference angle is $\theta' = \theta - 180°$. Thus, $\theta' = 250° - 180° = 70°$. See Figure 5.37.

b. Note that $\dfrac{3\pi}{5}$ lies in quadrant II; consequently the reference angle is $\theta' = \pi - \theta$.

$\theta' = \pi - \dfrac{3\pi}{5} = \dfrac{5\pi}{5} - \dfrac{3\pi}{5} = \dfrac{2\pi}{5}$. See Figure 5.38.

c. Since no degree symbol appears in $\theta = 5.75$, θ has radian measure. Now $\dfrac{3\pi}{2} \approx 4.71$ and $2\pi \approx 6.28$. So θ lies in quadrant IV, and $\theta' = 2\pi - \theta$. Thus, $\theta' = 2\pi - 5.75 \approx 6.28 - 5.75 = 0.53$. See Figure 5.39. ■ ■ ■

FIGURE 5.38

PRACTICE PROBLEM 5   Find the reference angle, θ', for each angle θ.

a. $\theta = 175°$ **b.** $\theta = \dfrac{5\pi}{3}$ **c.** $\theta = 8.22$ ■

As you will learn later, there are convenient methods for finding the values of the trigonometric functions for $-\theta$ from the values of the function for θ. Consequently, we will not need to find reference angles for negative angles.

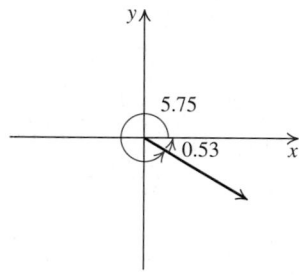

FIGURE 5.39

Using Reference Angles   A reference angle is used to find the values of trigonometric functions of any angle θ. For example, consider the reference angle θ' of the angle θ in Figure 5.40. Let $P(x, y)$ be a point on the terminal side of θ in quadrant III. From the definition of trigonometric functions, we have

$$\cos\theta = \frac{x}{r} = \frac{-|x|}{r} \quad x \text{ is negative.}$$

In the right **reference triangle** *POM* in Figure 5.40, we have

$$\cos\theta' = \frac{\text{adjacent}}{\text{hypotenuse}} = \frac{|x|}{r}, \text{ thus, } \cos\theta = -\cos\theta'.$$

In general, $\cos\theta$ and $\cos\theta'$ have the same value except possibly for the sign. The same is true for the other five trigonometric functions.

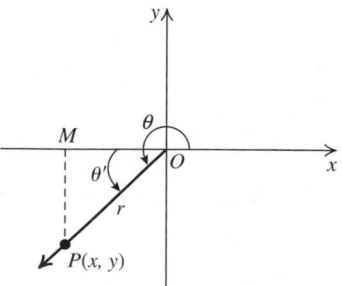

FIGURE 5.40

We next give a three-step procedure for using reference angles to find trigonometric function values.

FINDING THE SOLUTION: PROCEDURE FOR USING REFERENCE ANGLES TO FIND TRIGONOMETRIC FUNCTION VALUES

OBJECTIVE	EXAMPLE
The **objective** is to find the value of any trigono-metric function of a positive angle θ.	Find $\sin 1320°$.

Step 1 If the degree measure of θ is greater than 360°, find a coterminal angle for θ with degree measure between 0° and 360°. Otherwise, use θ in Step 2.

Dividing 1320° by 360° gives a quotient of 3 and a remainder of 240°. Thus, $1320° = 3(360°) + 240°$, so 240° is coterminal with 1320°.

Step 2 Find the reference angle θ' for the angle resulting from Step 1. Write the trigonometric function of the acute angle, θ'.

Because 240° is in quadrant III, its reference angle θ' is

$$\theta' = 240° - 180° = 60°,$$

and

$$\sin \theta' = \sin 60° = \frac{\sqrt{3}}{2} \quad \text{See page 522.}$$

Step 3 Choose the correct sign for the trigonometric function of θ based on the quadrant in which θ lies.

Because the sine is *negative* in quadrant III, we have

$$\sin 240° = -\sin 60° = -\frac{\sqrt{3}}{2}.$$

Thus, $\sin 1320° = \sin 240° = -\dfrac{\sqrt{3}}{2}.$

EXAMPLE 6   Using the Reference Angle to Find Values of Trigonometric Functions

Find the exact value of each expression.

a. $\tan 330°$ **b.** $\sec \dfrac{59\pi}{6}$

Solution

a. Step 1   Since 330° is between 0° and 360°, we proceed to find its reference angle.
   Step 2   Because 330° is in quadrant IV, its reference angle θ' is

$$\theta' = 360° - 330° = 30°.$$

$$\tan \theta' = \tan 30° = \frac{\sqrt{3}}{3}. \qquad \text{See page 522.}$$

   Step 3   In quadrant IV, $\tan \theta$ is negative, so

$$\tan 330° = -\tan 30° = -\frac{\sqrt{3}}{3}.$$

b. Step 1 Since the radian measure of $\dfrac{59\pi}{6}$ is greater than 2π, its degree measure is greater than $360°$.

$$\frac{59\pi}{6} = \frac{11\pi + 48\pi}{6} = \frac{11\pi}{6} + 8\pi, \text{ so}$$

$\dfrac{11\pi}{6}$ is an angle between 0 and 2π that is coterminal with $\dfrac{59\pi}{6}$.

Step 2 Because $\dfrac{11\pi}{6}$ is in quadrant IV, its reference angle θ' is

$$\theta' = 2\pi - \frac{11\pi}{6} = \frac{\pi}{6}.$$

$$\sec\theta' = \sec\frac{\pi}{6} = \frac{2\sqrt{3}}{3} \qquad \text{See page 522.}$$

Step 3 In quadrant IV, $\sec\theta > 0$, so

$$\sec\frac{11\pi}{6} = \sec\frac{\pi}{6} = \frac{2\sqrt{3}}{3}$$

and

$$\sec\frac{59\pi}{6} = \sec\frac{11\pi}{6} = \frac{2\sqrt{3}}{3}. \qquad\qquad ■ ■ ■$$

PRACTICE PROBLEM 6 Find the exact value of each expression.

a. $\sin 1035°$ **b.** $\cot\dfrac{17\pi}{6}$ ■

Area of a Triangle

4 Find the area of an SAS triangle.

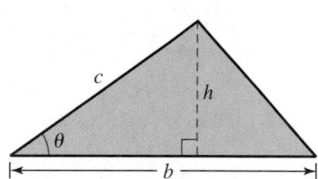

FIGURE 5.41

Recall that the area K of a triangle is given by the formula

$$\text{Area} = \frac{1}{2}(\text{base})(\text{height}),$$

or

$$K = \frac{1}{2}bh.$$

If θ is an acute angle in a triangle (see Figure 5.41), then $\sin\theta = \dfrac{h}{c}$, so $h = c\sin\theta$. The area of this triangle is given by

$$K = \frac{1}{2}bh = \frac{1}{2}bc\sin\theta. \qquad \text{Replace } h \text{ by } c\sin\theta.$$

The angle θ shown in Figure 5.42 is an obtuse angle. Here $\theta' = 180° - \theta$ is the reference angle for θ and $\sin\theta = \sin\theta' = \dfrac{h}{c}$. Thus,

$$h = c\sin\theta' = c\sin\theta$$

$$K = \frac{1}{2}bh = \frac{1}{2}bc\sin\theta. \qquad \text{Replace } h \text{ by } c\sin\theta.$$

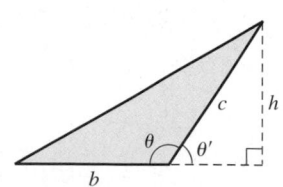

FIGURE 5.42

AREA OF A TRIANGLE

In any triangle, if θ is the included angle between sides of lengths b and c, the area K of the triangle is given by:

$$K = \frac{1}{2} bc \sin \theta$$

EXAMPLE 7   **Finding the Area of a Triangle**

Find the area of the triangle ABC in Figure 5.43.

Solution

We are given the angle of measure $62°$ between the sides of lengths 36 feet and 29 feet. The area K of the triangle ABC is given by

$$K = \frac{1}{2} bc \sin \theta \qquad \text{Area formula}$$

$$= \frac{1}{2} (36)(29) \sin 62° \qquad b = 36, c = 29, \theta = 62°$$

$$\approx 460.9 \text{ square feet.} \qquad \text{Use a calculator.} \quad ■ \quad ■ \quad ■$$

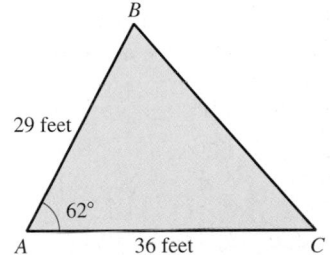

FIGURE 5.43

B

29 feet

62°

A   36 feet   C

PRACTICE PROBLEM 7   Find the area of triangle ABC if the lengths of the sides AC and BC are 27 feet and 38 feet, respectively, and the measure of the angle between these sides is $47°$.

■

EXAMPLE 8   **Finding a Triangular Area Determined by Cellular Telephone Towers**

Three cell towers are set up on three mountain peaks. Suppose the lines of sight from tower A to towers B and C form an angle of $120°$, and the distances between tower A and towers B and C are 3.6 miles and 4.2 miles, respectively. Find the area of the triangle having these three towers as vertices.

Solution

The area of a triangle (see Figure 5.44) with angle θ included between sides of lengths b and c is

$$A = \frac{1}{2} bc \sin \theta$$

$$= \frac{1}{2} (3.6)(4.2) \sin 120° \qquad \text{Replace } b \text{ by 3.6, } c \text{ by 4.2, and } \theta \text{ by } 120°$$

$$= \frac{1}{2} (3.6)(4.2) \sin 60° \qquad \theta' = 180° - 120° = 60° \text{ and } \sin 120° = \sin 60°$$

$$= \frac{1}{2} (3.6)(4.2) \frac{\sqrt{3}}{2} \qquad \sin 60° = \frac{\sqrt{3}}{2}$$

$$\approx 6.55 \text{ square miles.} \qquad \text{Use a calculator.} \quad ■ \quad ■ \quad ■$$

FIGURE 5.44

3.6 mi   A   4.2 mi

120°

B   C

PRACTICE PROBLEM 8   Rework Example 8, where the given distances are 5.1 and 3.8 miles and the included angle measures $150°$.

■

5 Use the unit circle definitions of the trigonometric functions.

Trigonometric Functions and the Unit Circle

With the aid of a circle of radius 1 (called a **unit circle**) centered at the origin of a rectangular coordinate system, we can interpret length on a number line as both the length of an arc and as the radian measure of the angle that intercepts the arc.

Recall from Section 5.1 that a central angle with measure θ radians in a circle of radius r intercepts an arc of length $s = r\theta$. In a unit circle, $r = 1$, so the length, s, of the arc intercepted by an angle of measure θ radians is $s = 1 \cdot \theta$, or $s = \theta$. That is, the *radian measure* and the *arc length* of an arc intercepted by a central angle in a unit circle are identical. See Figure 5.45(a). Now draw a copy of the real number line so that it is tangent to the circle at the point $(1, 0)$. See Figure 5.45(b). The origin (0 point) for the number line is placed at $(1, 0)$. The unit length on the number line is the same as on the coordinate axes, and the positive portion of the number line is above the x-axis.

FIGURE 5.45

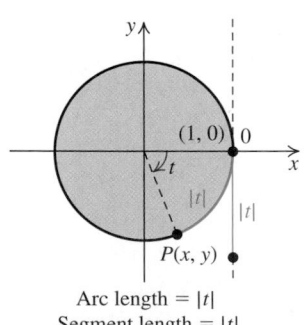

Arc length $= |t|$
Segment length $= |t|$

FIGURE 5.46

Given a real number t, with $t \geq 0$, we locate t on the tangent number line and think of "wrapping" the segment from 0 to t *counterclockwise* around the circle, arriving at a point $P(x, y)$ that marks the endpoint of an arc of length t from $(1, 0)$ to P. In this way, each real number t, $t \geq 0$, corresponds to a unique point P on the unit circle. Notice that because the circumference of the unit circle is 2π, if $t > 2\pi$, you must go around the circle more than once to arrive at the point P.

For $t < 0$, we modify the procedure used for $t \geq 0$ by now "wrapping" the segment from 0 to t *clockwise* around the circle, this time arriving at a point $P(x, y)$ that marks the endpoint of an arc of length $|t|$. See Figure 5.46. The negative angle having the x-axis for its initial side and the ray from the origin through the point $P(x, y)$ as its terminal side has radian measure t.

A substantial amount of information can be gained from the representation of real numbers as arcs on the unit circle. For example, let t be a positive real number, and let $P(x, y)$ be the point on the unit circle associated with t. See Figure 5.47(a). The point $P(x, y)$ is on the terminal side of the angle with radian measure t that intercepts the arc from $(1, 0)$ to P. Remember that in a unit circle $r = 1$.

Applying the definitions of the trigonometric functions of any angle (see page 531) to the unit circle (substituting 1 for r), we obtain

$$\sin t = \sin(t \text{ radians}) = \frac{y}{1} = y \qquad \cos t = \cos(t \text{ radians}) = \frac{x}{1} = x$$

$$\tan t = \frac{y}{x} = \frac{\sin t}{\cos t}, \cot t = \frac{y}{x} = \frac{\cos t}{\sin t}, \quad \csc t = \frac{1}{y} = \frac{1}{\sin t}, \text{ and } \sec t = \frac{1}{x} = \frac{1}{\cos t}.$$

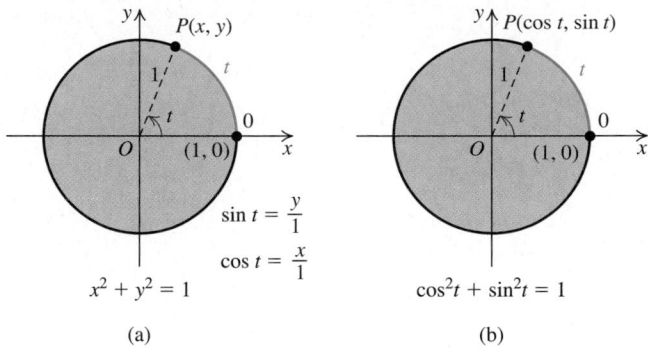

FIGURE 5.47

We previously defined the six trigonometric functions of an acute angle by using ratios of the side lengths in a right triangle (see Section 5.2, page 518) and of *any* angle by using ratios of x, y, and r (see page 531). The unit circle approach allows us to define the trigonometric functions of real numbers.

UNIT CIRCLE DEFINITIONS OF THE TRIGONOMETRIC FUNCTIONS OF REAL NUMBERS

Let t be any real number and let $P(x, y)$ be the point on the unit circle associated with t. Then

$$\sin t = y \qquad\qquad \csc t = \frac{1}{y}, (y \neq 0)$$

$$\cos t = x \qquad\qquad \sec t = \frac{1}{x}, (x \neq 0)$$

$$\tan t = \frac{y}{x}, (x \neq 0) \qquad\qquad \cot t = \frac{x}{y}, (y \neq 0)$$

Because these definitions are based on the unit circle, when the trigonometric functions are discussed in this context, they are often called the **circular functions**. This approach is important for graphing trigonometric functions and in calculus.

We see that a point P on the unit circle associated with a real number t has coordinates $(\cos t, \sin t)$. See Figure 5.47(b).

6 Apply the basic trigonometric identities.

Basic Trigonometric Identities

The equation for the unit circle is:

$$x^2 + y^2 = 1 \qquad\qquad \text{The center is } (0,0); \text{ the radius is } 1.$$

This leads to the identity:

$$(\cos t)^2 + (\sin t)^2 = 1 \qquad \text{Replace } x \text{ by } \cos t \text{ and } y \text{ by } \sin t.$$

By agreement, we write $\cos^2 t$ instead of $(\cos t)^2$ and $\sin^2 t$ instead of $(\sin t)^2$. A similar agreement holds for powers of all the trigonometric functions.

The equation $x^2 + y^2 = 1$ yields two other useful identities.

$$x^2 + y^2 = 1$$

$$\frac{x^2}{x^2} + \frac{y^2}{x^2} = \frac{1}{x^2}, x \neq 0 \qquad \text{Divide both sides by } x^2.$$

$$1 + \left(\frac{y}{x}\right)^2 = \left(\frac{1}{x}\right)^2 \qquad \text{Simplify.}$$

$$1 + \left(\frac{\sin t}{\cos t}\right)^2 = \left(\frac{1}{\cos t}\right)^2 \qquad \text{Replace } x \text{ by } \cos t \text{ and } y \text{ by } \sin t.$$

$$1 + \tan^2 t = \sec^2 t \qquad \frac{\sin t}{\cos t} = \tan t, \frac{1}{\cos t} = \sec t$$

Dividing both sides of the equation $x^2 + y^2 = 1$ by y^2 leads to the identity

$$1 + \cot^2 t = \csc^2 t.$$

The three identities resulting from the equation $x^2 + y^2 = 1$ are called the **Pythagorean identities** because the Pythagorean Theorem is the basis for this equation. We list these and several other useful identities next.

BASIC TRIGONOMETRIC IDENTITIES

Quotient and Reciprocal Identities

$$\tan t = \frac{\sin t}{\cos t} \qquad \cot t = \frac{\cos t}{\sin t} \qquad \csc t = \frac{1}{\sin t} \qquad \sec t = \frac{1}{\cos t}$$

Pythagorean Identities

$$\cos^2 t + \sin^2 t = 1 \qquad 1 + \tan^2 t = \sec^2 t \qquad 1 + \cot^2 t = \csc^2 t$$

EXAMPLE 9   **Finding the Exact Value of a Trigonometric Function Using the Pythagorean Identities**

a.   Given $\sin t = \dfrac{1}{3}$ and $\cos t < 0$, find $\cos t$ and $\tan t$.

b.   Given $\sec t = -2$ and $\tan t > 0$, find $\tan t$.

Solution

a.   Use the Pythagorean identity involving $\sin t$.

$$\cos^2 t + \sin^2 t = 1 \qquad \text{Pythagorean identity}$$

$$\cos^2 t + \left(\frac{1}{3}\right)^2 = 1 \qquad \text{Replace } \sin t \text{ by } \frac{1}{3}.$$

$$\cos^2 t = 1 - \frac{1}{9} \qquad \text{Subtract } \frac{1}{9} = \left(\frac{1}{3}\right)^2 \text{ from both sides.}$$

$$\cos^2 t = \frac{8}{9} \qquad \text{Simplify.}$$

$$\cos t = \pm\sqrt{\frac{8}{9}} = \pm\frac{2\sqrt{2}}{3} \qquad \text{Square root property}$$

$$\cos t = -\frac{2\sqrt{2}}{3} \qquad\qquad \cos t < 0 \text{ is given.}$$

$$\tan t = \frac{\sin t}{\cos t} = \frac{\dfrac{1}{3}}{-\dfrac{2\sqrt{2}}{3}} \qquad \text{Replace } \sin t \text{ by } \frac{1}{3} \text{ and } \cos t \text{ by } -\frac{2\sqrt{2}}{3}.$$

$$= -\frac{1}{2\sqrt{2}} \qquad\qquad \text{Simplify.}$$

$$= -\frac{\sqrt{2}}{4} \qquad\qquad \text{Rationalize the denominator.}$$

   b. Use the Pythagorean identity involving $\sec t$.

$$1 + \tan^2 t = \sec^2 t \qquad \text{Pythagorean identity}$$
$$1 + \tan^2 t = (-2)^2 \qquad \text{Replace } \sec t \text{ by } -2.$$
$$\tan^2 t = 3 \qquad \text{Subtract 1 from both sides and simplify.}$$
$$\tan t = \pm\sqrt{3} \qquad \text{Square root property}$$
$$\tan t = \sqrt{3} \qquad \tan t > 0 \text{ is given.} \qquad ■\ ■\ ■$$

PRACTICE PROBLEM 9 Given $\cos t = -\dfrac{2}{3}$ and $\sin t > 0$, find $\sin t$ and $\tan t$. ■

We will discuss and work with trigonometric identities in detail in Chapter 6.

A Exercises   Basic Skills and Concepts

In Exercises 1–8, a point on the terminal side of each angle θ is given. Find the exact values of the six trigonometric functions of θ.

1. $(-4, 3)$ †
2. $(-3, 5)$ †
3. $(-\sqrt{3}, -1)$ †
4. $(-1, -2)$ †
5. $(3, 3)$ †
6. $(-2, -2)$ †
7. $(12, -5)$ †
8. $(7, -2)$ †

In Exercises 9–16, use the given information to find each quadrant in which θ lies.

9. $\sin\theta < 0$ and $\cos\theta < 0$ †
10. $\sin\theta < 0$ and $\tan\theta > 0$ †
11. $\sin\theta > 0$ and $\cos\theta < 0$ †
12. $\tan\theta > 0$ and $\csc\theta < 0$ †
13. $\cos\theta > 0$ and $\csc\theta < 0$ †
14. $\cos\theta < 0$ and $\cot\theta > 0$ †
15. $\sec\theta < 0$ and $\csc\theta > 0$ †
16. $\sec\theta < 0$ and $\tan\theta > 0$ †

In Exercises 17–24, find the exact values of the remaining trigonometric functions of θ from the given information.

17. $\cos\theta = -\dfrac{5}{13}$, θ in quadrant III †

18. $\tan\theta = -\dfrac{3}{4}$, θ in quadrant IV †

19. $\cot\theta = -\dfrac{3}{4}$, θ in quadrant II †

20. $\sec\theta = \dfrac{4}{\sqrt{7}}$, θ in quadrant IV †

21. $\sin\theta = \dfrac{3}{5}$, $\tan\theta < 0$ †
22. $\cot\theta = \dfrac{3}{2}$, $\sec\theta > 0$ †

23. $\sec\theta = 3$, $\sin\theta < 0$ †
24. $\tan\theta = -2$, $\sin\theta > 0$ †

In Exercises 25–32, find the reference angle for each angle.

25. $120°$ $60°$
26. $275°$ $85°$
27. $500°$ $40°$
28. $420°$ $60°$
29. $\dfrac{17\pi}{3}$ $\dfrac{2\pi}{3}$
30. $\dfrac{19\pi}{4}$ $\dfrac{\pi}{4}$
31. $\dfrac{28\pi}{6}$ $\dfrac{\pi}{3}$
32. $\dfrac{31\pi}{6}$ $\dfrac{\pi}{6}$

†Due to space constrictions, answers to these exercises may be found in the Answers beginning on page A–1 in the back of the book.

In Exercises 33–44, find the exact value of each expression.

33. $\cos 120°$ †

34. $\sin 315°$ †

35. $\tan 510°$ †

36. $\cot 750°$ $\sqrt{3}$

37. $\sec 210°$ †

38. $\csc 300°$ †

39. $\sin \dfrac{7\pi}{6}$ $-\dfrac{1}{2}$

40. $\cos \dfrac{4\pi}{3}$ $-\dfrac{1}{2}$

41. $\sec \dfrac{15\pi}{4}$ $\sqrt{2}$

42. $\cot \dfrac{19\pi}{4}$ -1

43. $\sin \dfrac{29\pi}{3}$ $-\dfrac{\sqrt{3}}{2}$

44. $\tan \dfrac{55\pi}{3}$ $\sqrt{3}$

In Exercises 45–52, find the area of a triangle ABC (see the figure) with the given information.

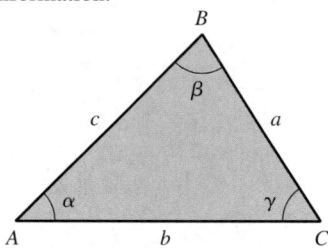

45. $\alpha = 57°$, $b = 30$ inches, $c = 52$ inches 654.2 sq in.

46. $\beta = 110°$, $a = 20$ centimeters, $c = 27$ centimeters 253.7 sq cm

47. $\gamma = 46°$, $a = 15$ kilometers, $b = 22$ kilometers

48. $\alpha = 146.7°$, $b = 16.7$ feet, $c = 18.6$ feet 85.3 sq ft

49. $\beta = 38.6°$, $a = 12$ millimeters, $c = 16.7$ millimeters

50. $\beta = 112.5°$, $a = 151.6$ feet, $c = 221.8$ feet

51. $\gamma = 107.3°$, $a = 271$ feet, $b = 194.3$ feet

52. $\alpha = 131.8°$, $b = 15.7$ millimeters, $c = 18.2$ millimeters 106.5 sq mm

In Exercises 53–60, use the Pythagorean identities to find the exact value of each expression.

53. Given $\sin t = \dfrac{2}{5}$ and $\cos t < 0$, find $\cos t$. $\cos t = -\dfrac{\sqrt{21}}{5}$

54. Given $\cos t = \dfrac{1}{6}$ and $\sin t < 0$, find $\sin t$. $\sin t = -\dfrac{\sqrt{35}}{6}$

55. Given $\sec t = -5$ and $\tan t < 0$, find $\tan t$. $\tan t = -2\sqrt{6}$

56. Given $\cot t = 4$ and $\csc t < 0$, find $\csc t$. $\csc t = -\sqrt{17}$

57. Given $\tan t = -3$ and $\sec t > 0$, find $\sec t$. $\sec t = \sqrt{10}$

58. Given $\csc t = -6$ and $\cos t > 0$, find $\cos t$.

59. Given $\sin t = -\dfrac{3}{4}$ and $\cos t < 0$, find $\sec t$. $\sec t = -\dfrac{4\sqrt{7}}{7}$

60. Given $\cos t = \dfrac{3}{5}$ and $\sin t > 0$, find $\csc t$. $\csc t = \dfrac{5}{4}$

Answers:

47. 118.7 sq km **49.** 62.5 sq m

50. 15,532.7 sq ft **51.** 25,136.6 sq ft

58. $\cos t = \dfrac{\sqrt{35}}{6}$

B Exercises   Applying the Concepts

61. **Area of the Bermuda Triangle.** The angle formed by the lines of sight from Ft. Lauderdale, Florida, to Bermuda and to San Juan, Puerto Rico, is approximately 67°. The distance from Ft. Lauderdale to Bermuda is 1026 miles, and the distance from Ft. Lauderdale to San Juan is 1046 miles. Find the area of the Bermuda Triangle, which is formed with these cities as vertices. 493,941 square miles

62. **Landscaping.** A triangular region between the three streets shown in the figure will be landscaped for $30 a square foot. How much will the landscaping cost? $5250

Figure for Exercise 62

63. **A safety chain.** A piece of heavy equipment has two 8-foot metal arms that make a V with the horizontal plane and form an angle of 118° at their base. A contractor wants to put a chain from the top of one arm to the top of the other, for safety. How long must the chain be? ≈ 13.72 feet

64. Removing a buoy. A crane is situated on the edge of a sheer cliff. It has a 12-foot arm that makes an angle of 120° with the horizontal, and drops a hook straight down to a metal buoy that must be pulled from the water. (See the figure.) How far is the center of the buoy from the cliff? 6 feet

65. Surface area of a pyramid. A pyramid has a square base and four triangular faces. The angle that a side of the base makes with one of the triangular face edges is 40°. (See the figure.) The edge of the base is 23 meters, and the edge of the face (base to top) is 22 meters. Find the surface area of a face of the pyramid. 162.6 square meters

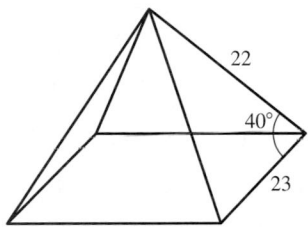

C Exercises   Beyond the Basics

66. Use the values $\dfrac{\sqrt{0}}{2}, \dfrac{\sqrt{1}}{2}, \dfrac{\sqrt{2}}{2}, \dfrac{\sqrt{3}}{2}, \dfrac{\sqrt{4}}{2}$, and the figure to write the values for $\sin\theta$ and $\cos\theta$ for $\theta = 0°$, $\theta = 30°$, $\theta = 45°$, $\theta = 60°$, and $\theta = 90°$. †

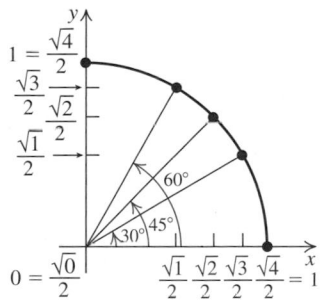

67. Use the coordinates of a point (x, y) on the terminal side of an angle θ to show that $\cos(\theta + \pi) = -\cos\theta$. †

68. Use the coordinates of a point (x, y) on the terminal side of an angle θ to show that $\sin(\theta + \pi) = -\sin\theta$. †

69. Use the coordinates of a point (x, y) on the terminal side of an angle θ to show that $\tan(\theta + \pi) = \tan\theta$. †

70. If $\sin\theta = -\dfrac{7}{16}$ and θ is in quadrant IV, find $\sin(-\theta)$. $\dfrac{7}{16}$

71. If $\cos\theta = 0.03$ and θ is in quadrant IV, find $\cos(-\theta)$. 0.03

72. If $\tan\theta = 5$ and θ is in quadrant I, find $\tan(-\theta)$. −5

73. If $\sec\theta = -2$ and θ is in quadrant II, find $\sec(-\theta)$. −2

74. If $\csc\theta = -3$ and θ is in quadrant IV, find $\csc(-\theta)$. 3

75. Find all values of θ, with $-360° < \theta < 0°$, measured in degrees, for which $\tan\theta = 1$. −135°, −315°

76. Find a formula for the reference angle θ', of a negative angle θ, with $-180° < \theta < -90°$. $\theta + 180°$

77. Find a formula for the reference angle θ', of a negative angle θ, with $-270° < \theta < -180°$. $-(\theta + 180°)$

78. Find a formula for the reference angle θ', of a negative angle θ, with $-360° < \theta < -270°$. $\theta + 360°$

Critical Thinking

79. Show that $\sin\theta \le 1$ and $\cos\theta \le 1$, for any acute angle θ. [*Hint:* For any real numbers x and y, $x^2 + y^2 \ge x^2$.]

80. Show that $-1 \le \sin\theta \le 1$ and $-1 \le \cos\theta \le 1$, for any angle θ.

81. Find the area of the shaded region in the figure. †

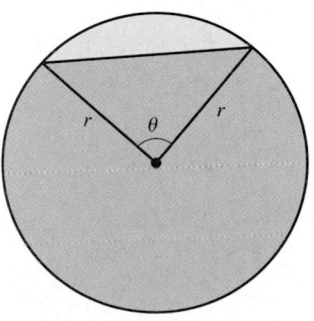

Graphs of the Sine and Cosine Functions

BEFORE STARTING THIS SECTION, REVIEW

1. Equation of a circle (Section 2.2, page 198)

2. Transformations of functions (Section 2.6, page 263)

3. Unit circle definitions of the sine and cosine (Section 5.3, page 541)

OBJECTIVES

1 Define periodic functions.

2 Graph the sine and cosine functions.

3 Find the amplitude and period of sinusoidal functions.

4 Find the phase shift and graph sinusoidal functions of the forms $y = a \sin b(x - c)$ and $y = a \cos b(x - c)$.

Global Warming and Weather Cycles

The current global warming debate has stirred considerable interest in the way the climate exhibits periodic fluctuations. During our winter, because the Northern Hemisphere tilts away from the sun, it receives less direct solar radiation than does the Southern Hemisphere, which tilts towards the sun. In the Northern Hemisphere, the summer solstice (the longest day of the year) occurs on or around June 21, and the winter solstice (the shortest day of the year) occurs on or about December 21. In the Southern Hemisphere, the seasons are reversed. One feature of our climate is the variation in the number of hours of daylight at different latitudes. The length of a day is one of the many phenomena that can be described by the trigonometric functions we study in this section. In Example 11, we will see how to model the number of daylight hours that the city of Paris enjoys throughout the year. ■

1 Define periodic functions.

Periodic Functions

It is not difficult to think of examples of behavior that repeat a particular pattern over and over. For example, no matter where you live, the sun appears in a dependable pattern throughout the year. Naturalists find that certain animal populations vary in a regular pattern over time. The beam from a lighthouse will sweep out a very regular pattern. The blood pressure for a typical individual will fluctuate rhythmically. The idea of predictably repeatable behavior is captured mathematically in the definition of a *periodic function*.

In this section, we will focus on the graphs of the sine and cosine functions and transformations of these graphs. In order to graph these functions on an xy-coordinate system, we will use x as the independent variable and y as the dependent variable, so we will write $y = \sin x$ rather than $y = \sin t$.

> **DEFINITION OF A PERIODIC FUNCTION**
> A function f is said to be **periodic** if there is a positive number p such that
> $$f(x + p) = f(x)$$
> for every x in the domain of f.
>   The smallest value of p (if there is one) for which $f(x + p) = f(x)$ is called the
> **period** of f. The graph of f over any interval of length p is called one **cycle** of the graph.

Because $\sin(x + 2\pi) = \sin x$ and $\cos(x + 2\pi) = \cos x$, both the sine and cosine functions are periodic functions. The period for each of the sine and cosine functions is 2π. (See Exercise 72.)

2 Graph the sine and cosine functions.

Graph of the Sine Function

We can use a table of values for $y = \sin x$ (Table 5.3), where $0 \le x \le 2\pi$ and x radians either is a quadrantal angle or has $\dfrac{\pi}{6}, \dfrac{\pi}{4}$, or $\dfrac{\pi}{3}$ as a reference angle, to sketch the graph of $y = \sin x$ for $0 \le x \le 2\pi$.

TABLE 5.3

x	0	$\dfrac{\pi}{6}$	$\dfrac{\pi}{4}$	$\dfrac{\pi}{3}$	$\dfrac{\pi}{2}$	$\dfrac{2\pi}{3}$	$\dfrac{3\pi}{4}$	$\dfrac{5\pi}{6}$	π	$\dfrac{7\pi}{6}$	$\dfrac{5\pi}{6}$	$\dfrac{4\pi}{3}$	$\dfrac{3\pi}{2}$	$\dfrac{5\pi}{3}$	$\dfrac{7\pi}{4}$	$\dfrac{11\pi}{6}$	2π
$\sin x$	0	0.5	0.71	0.87	1	0.87	0.71	0.5	0	-0.5	-0.71	-0.87	-1	-0.87	-0.71	-0.5	0

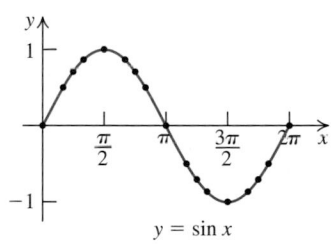

FIGURE 5.48

Connecting these points with a smooth curve gives us the graph in Figure 5.48. Only $0, \dfrac{\pi}{2}, \pi, \dfrac{3\pi}{2}$, and 2π are marked on the x-axis, but all the ordered pairs $(x, \sin x)$ given in Table 5.3 are plotted on the curve.

For any real number x, recall from Section 5.3 that $(\cos x, \sin x)$ is the point on the unit circle associated with x. In this situation the horizontal axis is labeled the u-axis. See Figure 5.49. Consequently, $-1 \le \sin x \le 1$; that is, the range of the sine function is $[-1, 1]$.

Because x can be any real number, there is no restriction on the values of x for $y = \sin x$. Thus, the domain of the sine function is $(-\infty, \infty)$. The fact that the sine function is periodic with period 2π allows us to sketch the complete graph of $y = \sin x$ by extending the graph in Figure 5.48 indefinitely to the left and to the right, in every successive interval of length 2π. See Figure 5.50.

FIGURE 5.49

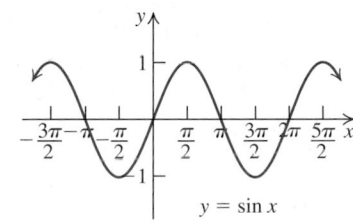

FIGURE 5.50

Graph of the Cosine Function

We can use the same method for graphing $y = \cos x$ that we used for $y = \sin x$. Table 5.4 gives the values for $y = \cos x$, where $0 \leq x \leq 2\pi$ and x radians either is a quadrantal angle or has $\dfrac{\pi}{6}, \dfrac{\pi}{4}$, or $\dfrac{\pi}{3}$ as a reference angle.

TABLE 5.4

x	0	$\dfrac{\pi}{6}$	$\dfrac{\pi}{4}$	$\dfrac{\pi}{3}$	$\dfrac{\pi}{2}$	$\dfrac{2\pi}{3}$	$\dfrac{3\pi}{4}$	$\dfrac{5\pi}{6}$	π	$\dfrac{7\pi}{6}$	$\dfrac{5\pi}{6}$	$\dfrac{4\pi}{3}$	$\dfrac{3\pi}{2}$	$\dfrac{5\pi}{3}$	$\dfrac{7\pi}{4}$	$\dfrac{11\pi}{6}$	2π
$\cos x$	1	0.87	0.71	0.5	0	-0.5	-0.71	-0.87	-1	-0.87	-0.71	-0.5	0	0.5	0.71	0.87	1

Connecting these points with a smooth curve gives the graph in Figure 5.51. Again, only $0, \dfrac{\pi}{2}, \pi, \dfrac{3\pi}{2}$, and 2π are marked on the x-axis, but all the ordered pairs $(x, \cos x)$ given in Table 5.4 are plotted on the curve. From the fact that $(\cos x, \sin x)$ is a point on the unit circle, we have $-1 \leq \cos x \leq 1$, so the range of the cosine function is $[-1, 1]$. See Figure 5.52.

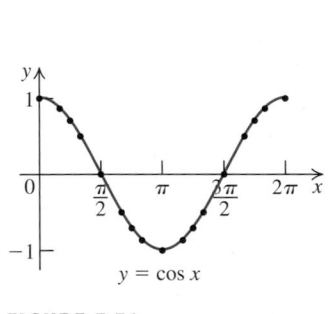

FIGURE 5.51

$y = \cos x$

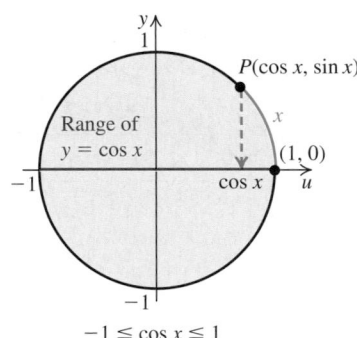

FIGURE 5.52

$-1 \leq \cos x \leq 1$

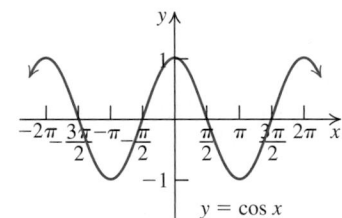

FIGURE 5.53

$y = \cos x$

As with the sine function, there is no restriction on the values of x for $y = \cos x$, so the domain of the cosine function is $(-\infty, \infty)$. The complete graph of $y = \cos x$ can be drawn by extending the graph in Figure 5.51 indefinitely to the left and right, in every successive interval of length 2π. See Figure 5.53.

Properties of the Sine and Cosine Functions

Let t be a positive real number and let $P(x, y)$ be the point on the unit circle associated with t. The angle intercepted by the arc from $(1, 0)$ to $P(x, y)$ has measure t radians. See Figure 5.54.

The two right triangles OMP and OMQ shown in Figure 5.54 are congruent by SSS Congruence. Consequently, the negative angle in standard position with the terminal side passing through the point $Q(x, -y)$ has measure $-t$. Thus, since the circle has radius 1,

$$P(x, y) = (\cos t, \sin t) \quad \text{and} \quad Q(x, -y) = (\cos(-t), \sin(-t)).$$

So we have $\cos(-t) = x = \cos t$ and $\sin(-t) = -y = -\sin t$. From $\sin(-t) = -\sin t$, we learn that the sine function is an *odd* function, and so its graph is symmetric with

FIGURE 5.54

respect to the origin. Similarly, since $\cos(-t) = \cos t$, the cosine function is an *even* function, and so its graph is symmetric with respect to the *y*-axis.

PROPERTIES OF THE SINE AND COSINE FUNCTIONS

Sine Function

1. Period: 2π
2. Domain: $(-\infty, \infty)$
3. Range: $[-1,1]$
4. Odd: $\sin(-t) = -\sin t$

Cosine Function

1. Period: 2π
2. Domain: $(-\infty, \infty)$
3. Range: $[-1,1]$
4. Even: $\cos(-t) = \cos t$

---

3 Find the amplitude and period of sinusoidal functions.

Amplitude and Period

In Section 2.6, we studied transformation of functions. In this section, we consider transformations of the form $y = a\sin bx$ and $y = a\cos bx$. The number $|a|$ in $y = a\sin bx$ and $y = a\cos bx$ is called the **amplitude** and is the largest value of y obtained by the function. We begin by examining the graphs obtained when $b = 1$.

EXAMPLE 1   **Graphing** $y = a \sin x$

Graph $y = 3\sin x$, $y = \dfrac{1}{3}\sin x$, and $y = \sin x$ on the same coordinate system over the interval $[-2\pi, 2\pi]$.

Solution

We begin with the graph of $y = \sin x$ and multiply the *y*-coordinate of each point on this graph by 3 to get the graph of $y = 3\sin x$. This results in stretching the graph of $y = \sin x$ vertically by a factor of 3. See Figure 5.55. Similarly, we multiply the *y*-coordinate on the graph of $y = \sin x$ by $\dfrac{1}{3}$ to get the graph of $y = \dfrac{1}{3}\sin x$. This results in compressing the graph of $y = \sin x$ vertically by a factor of $\dfrac{1}{3}$. See Figure 5.55.

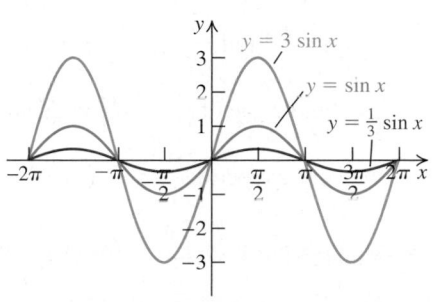

FIGURE 5.55   ■ ■ ■

PRACTICE PROBLEM 1   Graph $y = 5\sin x$, $y = \dfrac{1}{5}\sin x$, and $y = \sin x$ on the same coordinate system over the interval $[-2\pi, 2\pi]$.   ■

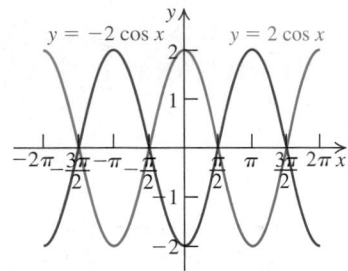

FIGURE 5.56

EXAMPLE 2   Graphing $y = a\cos x$

Graph $y = -2\cos x$ over the interval $[-2\pi, 2\pi]$. Find the amplitude and range of the function.

Solution

Begin with the graph of $y = \cos x$, multiply the y-coordinate of each point on the graph of $y = \cos x$ by 2 to stretch the graph vertically by a factor of 2 to get the graph of $y = 2\cos x$. Next, reflect the graph of $y = 2\cos x$ in the x-axis to produce the graph of $y = -2\cos x$. See Figure 5.56. The amplitude is $|-2| = 2$, the largest value attained by $y = -2\cos x$; the smallest value attained is -2. Thus, the range of $y = -2\cos x$ is $[-2, 2]$.   ■ ■ ■

PRACTICE PROBLEM 2   Graph $y = 5\cos x$ over the interval $[-2\pi, 2\pi]$. Find the amplitude and range of the function.   ■

Both the sine and cosine functions have period 2π, and for $b > 0$, $0 \le bx \le 2\pi$ is equivalent to $0 \le x \le \dfrac{2\pi}{b}$. This means that as x takes on the values from 0 to $\dfrac{2\pi}{b}$, the expression bx takes on the values from 0 to 2π.

The graphs of $y = \sin bx$ and $y = \cos bx$ have similar shapes to those of $y = \sin x$ and $y = \cos x$, respectively, but they are compressed or expanded horizontally so that they complete one cycle over any interval of length $\dfrac{2\pi}{b}$. Consequently, the functions $y = \sin bx$ and $y = \cos bx$ both have period $\dfrac{2\pi}{b}$. When $b < 0$, we can use the facts that $\sin(-x) = -\sin x$ and $\cos(-x) = \cos x$ to rewrite the given function in a form where $b > 0$. For example, $y = \sin(-3x) = -\sin 3x$.

EXAMPLE 3   Graphing $y = \sin bx$

Graph one cycle of the graphs of $y = \sin 3x$, $y = \sin \dfrac{1}{3}x$, and $y = \sin x$ on the same coordinate system.

Solution

We begin with the graph of $y = \sin x$ and adjust its period, 2π, by dividing 2π by 3 to get the period $\dfrac{2\pi}{3}$ of $y = \sin 3x$. We then compress the graph of $y = \sin x$ horizontally so that one cycle of $y = \sin 3x$ is completed on the interval $\left[0, \dfrac{2\pi}{3}\right]$. See Figure 5.57. Similarly, to get the period of $y = \sin \dfrac{1}{3}x$, we adjust the period of the sine function by dividing 2π by $\dfrac{1}{3}$, resulting in $\dfrac{2\pi}{\dfrac{1}{3}} = 6\pi$. We then expand the graph of $y = \sin x$ horizontally so that one cycle for $y = \sin \dfrac{1}{3}x$ is completed on the interval $[0, 6\pi]$. See Figure 5.57.   ■ ■ ■

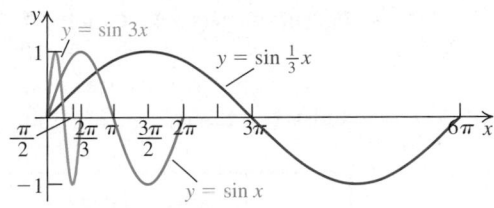

FIGURE 5.57

PRACTICE PROBLEM 3   Graph one cycle of the graphs of $y = \sin\dfrac{1}{2}x$ and $y = \sin x$ on the same coordinate system.   ■

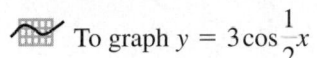

TECHNOLOGY CONNECTION

To graph $y = 3\cos\dfrac{1}{2}x$ with a graphing calculator, choose Radian mode and these WINDOW settings.

$X \min = 0$
$X \max = 4\pi$
$X \text{ scl} = \pi/2$
$Y \min = -4$
$Y \max = 4$
$Y \text{ scl} = 1$

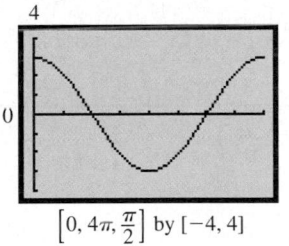

$\left[0, 4\pi, \dfrac{\pi}{2}\right]$ by $[-4, 4]$

EXAMPLE 4   **Graphing $y = a\cos bx$**

Graph $y = 3\cos\dfrac{1}{2}x$ over a one-period interval.

Solution

Beginning with the graph of $y = \cos x$, we adjust the period 2π by dividing by $\dfrac{1}{2}$, to get

$$\frac{2\pi}{\dfrac{1}{2}} = 4\pi. \qquad \text{Replace } b \text{ by } \frac{1}{2} \text{ in } \frac{2\pi}{b}.$$

Next we multiply the y-coordinate of each point on the graph of $y = \cos\dfrac{1}{2}x$ by 3 to stretch this graph vertically by a factor of 3. To sketch the graphs, it is helpful to divide the period, 4π, into 4 quarters, starting at 0. The five endpoints of the four subintervals give the highest point, the lowest point, and the x-intercepts of the graph. Then graph the function from

$$0 \text{ to } \frac{1}{4} \text{ (period)} \longrightarrow 0 \text{ to } \frac{1}{4}(4\pi) = \pi$$

$$\frac{1}{4} \text{ (period) to } \frac{1}{2} \text{ (period)} \longrightarrow \pi \text{ to } \frac{1}{2}(4\pi) = 2\pi$$

$$\frac{1}{2} \text{ (period) to } \frac{3}{4} \text{ (period)} \longrightarrow 2\pi \text{ to } \frac{3}{4}(4\pi) = 3\pi$$

$$\frac{3}{4} \text{ (period) to } 1 \text{(period)} \longrightarrow 3\pi \text{ to } 4\pi$$

See Figure 5.58. The graph can then be extended indefinitely to the left and right. The amplitude is 3, so the largest value of y is 3; the range is $[-3, 3]$.

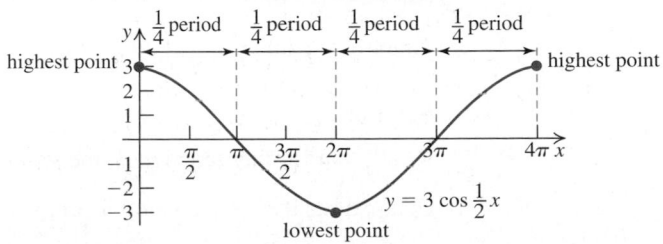

FIGURE 5.58

■ ■ ■

PRACTICE PROBLEM 4 Graph $y = 2\cos 2x$ over a one-period interval. ∎

The next box summarizes what we have learned about graphing the functions $y = a\sin bx$ and $y = a\cos bx$.

CHANGING THE AMPLITUDE AND PERIOD OF THE SINE AND COSINE FUNCTIONS

The functions $y = a\sin bx$ and $y = a\cos bx$ ($b > 0$) have amplitude $|a|$ and period $\dfrac{2\pi}{b}$.

If $a > 0$, the graphs of $y = a\sin bx$ and $y = a\cos bx$ are similar to the graphs of $y = \sin x$ and $y = \cos x$, respectively, with two changes.

1. The range is $[-a, a]$.

2. One cycle is completed over the interval $\left[0, \dfrac{2\pi}{b}\right]$.

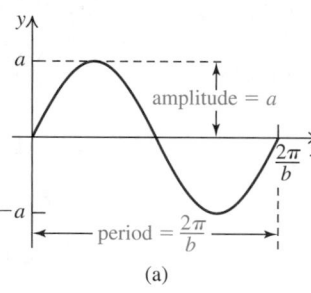

(a)

$$y = a\sin bx, \ (a > 0)$$

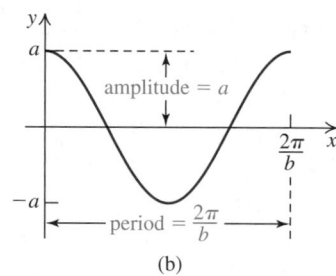

(b)

$$y = a\cos bx, \ (a > 0)$$

If $a < 0$, the graphs are the reflections of the graph of $y = |a|\sin bx$ and $y = |a|\cos bx$, respectively, in the x-axis.

---

4 Find the phase shift and to graph sinusoidal functions of the forms $y = a\sin b(x - c)$ and $y = a\cos b(x - c)$.

Phase Shift

The sine and cosine graphs and transformations of these graphs are called **sinusoidal** graphs or curves. The method of graphing one cycle of a sinusoidal graph by finding a starting point and breaking the period into quarters, as we did in Example 4, is particularly helpful when a horizontal shift is involved. In the simplest cases, however, the methods developed in Chapter 2 are easily applied.

EXAMPLE 5 **Graphing $y = a\sin(x - c)$**

Graph $y = \sin\left(x - \dfrac{\pi}{2}\right)$ over a one-period interval.

Solution

Recall that for any function f, the graph of $y = f(x - c)$ is the graph of $y = f(x)$, shifted right c units if $c > 0$, and left $|c|$ units if $c < 0$. Comparing the equation $y = \sin\left(x - \dfrac{\pi}{2}\right)$

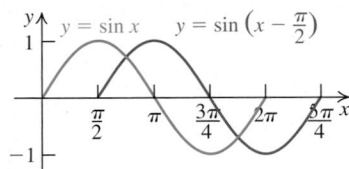

FIGURE 5.59

with $y = \sin x$, we see that $y = \sin\left(x - \dfrac{\pi}{2}\right)$ has the form $y = \sin(x - c)$, where $c = \dfrac{\pi}{2}$.

Therefore, the graph of $y = \sin\left(x - \dfrac{\pi}{2}\right)$ is the graph of $y = \sin x$ shifted right $\dfrac{\pi}{2}$ units. See Figure 5.59.

■ ■ ■

PRACTICE PROBLEM 5 Graph $y = \cos\left(x - \dfrac{\pi}{4}\right)$ over a one-period interval. ■

Before describing the general procedure for graphing the sinusoidal functions $y = a\sin b(x - c)$ and $y = a\cos b(x - c)$, with $b > 0$, we find the value of x for which $b(x - c) = 0$. This number is called the **phase shift**. Let

$$b(x - c) = 0$$

$$x - c = 0 \qquad \text{Divide both sides by } b.$$
$$x = c \qquad \text{Add } c \text{ to both sides.}$$

The phase shift is the amount by which the graphs of $y = a\sin bx$ and $y = a\cos bx$ are shifted horizontally. These graphs are shifted right if $c > 0$ and left if $c < 0$. To graph a cycle of either function, we start the cycle at $x = c$ and then divide the period into fourths. We describe this procedure next.

FINDING THE SOLUTION: PROCEDURE FOR GRAPHING $y = a \sin b(x - c)$ AND $y = a \cos b(x - c)$

OBJECTIVE
*The **objective** is to graph a function of the form $y = a\sin b(x - c)$ or $y = a\cos b(x - c)$, with $b > 0$, finding the amplitude, period, and phase shift.*

EXAMPLE
Find the amplitude, period, and phase shift and sketch the graph of $y = 3\sin 2\left(x - \dfrac{\pi}{4}\right)$ over a one-period interval.

Step 1 Find the amplitude, period, and phase shift.

amplitude $= |a|$

period $= \dfrac{2\pi}{b}$

phase shift $= c$

1. $y = 3\sin 2\left(x - \dfrac{\pi}{4}\right)$

$a = 3,\ b = 2,\ c = \dfrac{\pi}{4}.$

amplitude $= 3$

period $= \dfrac{2\pi}{2} = \pi$

phase shift $= \dfrac{\pi}{4}$ $\qquad$ To the right, since $\dfrac{\pi}{4} > 0$

Step 2 The starting point for the cycle is $x = c$. The interval over which one complete cycle occurs is $\left[c, c + \dfrac{2\pi}{b}\right].$

2. Starting point: $x = \dfrac{\pi}{4}$

One cycle is graphed over

$$\left[\dfrac{\pi}{4}, \dfrac{\pi}{4} + \pi\right].$$

begin end
cycle cycle

Step 3 Divide the interval $\left[c, c + \dfrac{2\pi}{b}\right]$ into four equal parts, each of length $\dfrac{1}{4}(\text{period}) = \dfrac{1}{4}\left(\dfrac{2\pi}{b}\right)$. This requires 5 points: a starting point $c,\ c + \dfrac{1}{4}\left(\dfrac{2\pi}{b}\right)$, $c + \dfrac{1}{2}\left(\dfrac{2\pi}{b}\right),\ c + \dfrac{3}{4}\left(\dfrac{2\pi}{b}\right)$, and $c + \dfrac{2\pi}{b}$.

3. $\dfrac{1}{4}(\text{period}) = \dfrac{1}{4}(\pi) = \dfrac{\pi}{4}$

$\text{starting point} = \dfrac{\pi}{4}$

$\text{2nd point} = \dfrac{\pi}{4} + \dfrac{1}{4}(\pi) = \dfrac{\pi}{2}$

$\text{3rd point} = \dfrac{\pi}{4} + \dfrac{1}{2}(\pi) = \dfrac{3\pi}{4}$

$\text{4th point} = \dfrac{\pi}{4} + \dfrac{3}{4}(\pi) = \pi$

$\text{end point} = \dfrac{\pi}{4} + \pi = \dfrac{5\pi}{4}$

Step 4 If $a > 0$, for $y = a \sin b(x - c)$, sketch one cycle of the sine curve, starting at $(c, 0)$, through the points $\left(c + \dfrac{\pi}{2b}, a\right)$, $\left(c + \dfrac{\pi}{b}, 0\right), \left(c + \dfrac{3\pi}{2b}, -a\right)$, and $\left(c + \dfrac{2\pi}{b}, 0\right)$. For $y = a \cos b(x - c)$, sketch one cycle of the cosine curve, starting at (c, a), through the points $\left(c + \dfrac{\pi}{2b}, 0\right), \left(c + \dfrac{\pi}{b}, -a\right)$, $\left(c + \dfrac{3\pi}{2b}, 0\right)$, and $\left(c + \dfrac{2\pi}{b}, a\right)$. If $a < 0$, reflect the graph of $y = |a| \sin b(x - c)$ or $y = |a| \cos b(x - c)$ in the x-axis.

4.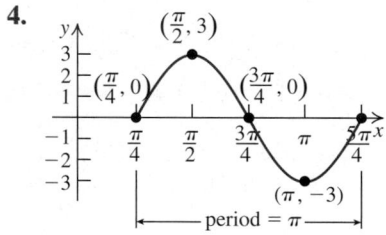

EXAMPLE 6   **Finding the Amplitude, Period, and Phase Shift**

Find the amplitude, period, and phase shift of the function

$$y = -4 \sin \dfrac{2}{3}(x - \pi).$$

Solution

Compare the given equation with the equation $y = a \sin b(x - c)$ to identify the values of a, b, and c.

$$y = -4 \sin \dfrac{2}{3}(x - \pi)$$
$$\uparrow \quad\ \uparrow \qquad \uparrow$$
$$a \quad\ b \qquad\ c$$

$$\text{amplitude} = |a| = |-4| = 4$$

$$\text{period} = \frac{2\pi}{b} = \frac{2\pi}{\dfrac{2}{3}} = 3\pi$$

$$\text{phase shift} = c = \pi \qquad \text{To the right, since } \pi > 0 \qquad\qquad ■ \quad ■ \quad ■$$

PRACTICE PROBLEM 6   Find the amplitude, period, and phase shift of the function

$$y = \frac{1}{3}\cos\frac{2}{5}\left(x + \frac{\pi}{6}\right). \qquad\qquad ■$$

EXAMPLE 7   Graphing $y = a \cos b(x - c)$

Graph $y = -\cos 2\left(x + \dfrac{\pi}{2}\right)$ over a one-period interval.

Solution

Use the steps from the procedure for graphing $y = a\cos b(x - c)$.

Step 1   Here $y = -\cos 2\left(x + \dfrac{\pi}{2}\right) = (-1)\cos 2\left[x - \left(-\dfrac{\pi}{2}\right)\right]$

$$\qquad\qquad\qquad\qquad\qquad \uparrow \qquad\quad \uparrow \qquad\qquad \uparrow$$

$$\qquad\qquad\qquad\qquad a = -1 \quad b = 2 \quad c = -\frac{\pi}{2}$$

$$\text{amplitude } = |a| = |-1| = 1$$

$$\text{period } = \frac{2\pi}{b} = \frac{2\pi}{2} = \pi$$

$$\text{phase shift} = c = -\frac{\pi}{2} \qquad \text{To the left, since } -\frac{\pi}{2} < 0$$

Step 2   The starting point for the cycle is $x = -\dfrac{\pi}{2}$.

One cycle is graphed over the interval $\left[-\dfrac{\pi}{2}, -\dfrac{\pi}{2} + \pi\right] = \left[-\dfrac{\pi}{2}, \dfrac{\pi}{2}\right]$.

Step 3 $\dfrac{1}{4}(\text{period}) = \dfrac{1}{4}(\pi) = \dfrac{\pi}{4}$

$$\text{starting point } = -\frac{\pi}{2}$$

$$\text{2nd point } = -\frac{\pi}{2} + \frac{1}{4}(\pi) = -\frac{\pi}{4}$$

$$\text{3rd point } = -\frac{\pi}{2} + \frac{1}{2}(\pi) = 0$$

$$\text{4th point } = -\frac{\pi}{2} + \frac{3}{4}(\pi) = \frac{\pi}{4}$$

$$\text{endpoint } = -\frac{\pi}{2} + \pi = \frac{\pi}{2}$$

Continued on next page.

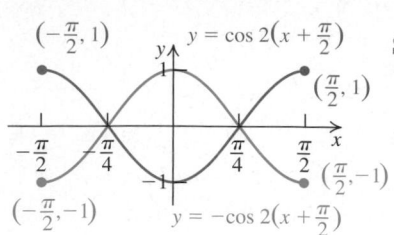

FIGURE 5.60

Step 4 Because $a = -1 < 0$, we first graph $y = |-1| \cos 2\left(x + \dfrac{\pi}{2}\right)$ by sketching one cycle, beginning at $\left(-\dfrac{\pi}{2}, 1\right)$, through the points $\left(-\dfrac{\pi}{4}, 0\right)$, $(0, -1)$, $\left(\dfrac{\pi}{4}, 0\right)$, and $\left(\dfrac{\pi}{2}, 1\right)$. We then reflect this graph in the x-axis to obtain the graph of $y = -\cos 2\left(x + \dfrac{\pi}{2}\right)$. See Figure 5.60. ■ ■ ■

PRACTICE PROBLEM 7 Graph $y = -2\cos 3(x + \pi)$ over a one-period interval. ■

To graph the function of the form $y = a\sin(bx - k)$ or $y = a\cos(bx - k)$, with $b > 0$, we first note that

$$bx - k = b\left(x - \dfrac{k}{b}\right). \qquad \text{Factor out } b.$$

Consequently, to graph these functions, we rewrite their equations.

$$y = a\sin(bx - k) = a\sin b\left(x - \dfrac{k}{b}\right)$$

$$y = a\cos(bx - k) = a\cos b\left(x - \dfrac{k}{b}\right)$$

We can then use the procedures for graphing the functions of the form $y = a\sin b(x - c)$ and $y = a\cos b(x - c)$ by letting $\dfrac{k}{b} = c$.

EXAMPLE 8 **Finding the Period and Phase Shift**

Find the period and the phase shift of each function.

a. $y = 2\cos\left(3x - \dfrac{\pi}{2}\right)$ **b.** $y = 3\sin(\pi x + 2)$

Solution

a.
$$y = 2\cos\left(3x - \dfrac{\pi}{2}\right) \qquad \text{The given function}$$

$$= 2\cos 3\left(x - \dfrac{\pi}{6}\right) \qquad \text{Distributive property}$$

$$\qquad\quad \underset{a}{\uparrow} \quad \underset{b}{\uparrow} \quad \underset{c}{\uparrow} \qquad \text{Compare with } y = a\cos b(x - c).$$

$$\text{Period} = \dfrac{2\pi}{b} = \dfrac{2\pi}{3} \qquad \text{Replace } b \text{ by 3.}$$

$$\text{Phase shift} = c = \dfrac{\pi}{6} \qquad \text{To the right, since } \dfrac{\pi}{6} > 0$$

b. $\quad y = 3\sin(\pi x + 2)$ The given function

$\qquad y = 3\sin \pi\left[x - \left(-\dfrac{2}{\pi}\right)\right]$ Distributive property

$\qquad\qquad \underset{a}{\uparrow}\ \underset{b}{\uparrow} \qquad\qquad \underset{c}{\uparrow}$

$\qquad$ Period $= \dfrac{2\pi}{b} = \dfrac{2\pi}{\pi} = 2$ Replace b by π.

Phase shift $= c = -\dfrac{2}{\pi}$ To the left, since $-\dfrac{2}{\pi} < 0$ ■ ■ ■

PRACTICE PROBLEM 8 Find the period and the phase shift of each function.

a. $y = 3\sin\left(2x + \dfrac{\pi}{4}\right)$ **b.** $y = \cos(\pi x - 1)$ ■

EXAMPLE 9 **Graphing $y = a\sin(bx - k)$**

Graph $y = 3\sin\left(2x - \dfrac{\pi}{2}\right)$ over a one-period interval.

Solution

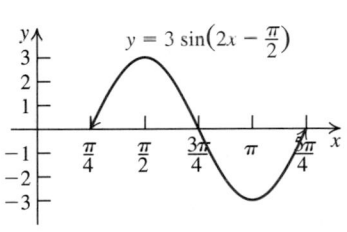

$y = 3\sin\left(2x - \dfrac{\pi}{2}\right)$

FIGURE 5.61

Because $2x - \dfrac{\pi}{2} = 2\left(x - \dfrac{\pi}{4}\right)$, we can write $y = 3\sin\left(2x - \dfrac{\pi}{2}\right) = 3\sin 2\left(x - \dfrac{\pi}{4}\right)$. This is the sinusoidal curve we graphed in the box describing the procedure for graphing the function $y = a\sin b(x - c)$ and $y = a\cos b(x - c)$ on page 553. The graph is shown in Figure 5.61.   ■ ■ ■

PRACTICE PROBLEM 9 Graph $y = 2\cos(3x - \pi)$ over a one-period interval.   ■

Vertical Shifts

Recall that the graph of $y = f(x) + d$ results by shifting the graph of $y = f(x)$ vertically d units up if $d > 0$, and $|d|$ units down if $d < 0$. The next example shows this effect on a sinusoidal graph.

EXAMPLE 10 **Graphing $y = a\sin b(x - c) + d$**

Graph $y = \cos 2\left(x + \dfrac{\pi}{2}\right) + 3$ over a one-period interval.

Solution

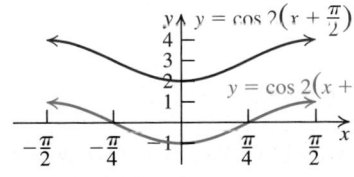

$y = \cos 2\left(x + \dfrac{\pi}{2}\right)$

$y = \cos 2\left(x + \right.$

FIGURE 5.62

In Example 7, we graphed the function $y = \cos 2\left(x + \dfrac{\pi}{2}\right)$ in the process of graphing $y = -\cos 2\left(x + \dfrac{\pi}{2}\right)$. To graph $y = \cos 2\left(x + \dfrac{\pi}{2}\right) + 3$, shift the graph of $y = \cos 2\left(x + \dfrac{\pi}{2}\right)$, up 3 units. See Figure 5.62.   ■ ■ ■

PRACTICE PROBLEM 10 Graph $y = 4\sin\left(3x - \dfrac{\pi}{3}\right) - 2$ over a one-period interval. ■

| EXAMPLE 11 | Modeling the Number of Daylight Hours in Paris |

TABLE 5.5

Daylight hours in Paris	
January	8.8
February	10.2
March	11.9
April	13.7
May	15.3
June	16.1
July	15.7
August	14.3
September	12.6
October	10.8
November	9.2
December	8.3

Source: http://aa.usno.navy.mil/data/docs/Dur_One year.html

Table 5.5 gives the average number of daylight hours in Paris each month. Let y represent the number of daylight hours in Paris in month x, to find a function of the form $y = a\sin b(x - c) + d$ that models the hours of daylight throughout the year.

Solution

Plot the values given in Table 5.5, representing the months by the integers 1 through 12 (Jan. = 1, ..., Dec. = 12). Then sketch a function of the form $y = a\sin b(x - c) + d$ that models the points just graphed. See Figure 5.63.

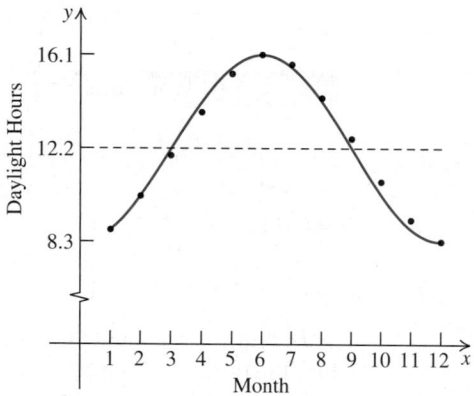

FIGURE 5.63

We want to find the values for the constants a, b, c, and d that will produce the graph shown in Figure 5.63. From Table 5.5, the range of the function is $[8.3, 16.1]$, so

$$\text{Amplitude} = a = \frac{\text{highest value} - \text{lowest value}}{2} = \frac{(16.1 - 8.3)}{2} = 3.9.$$

The sine graph has been shifted vertically by $\dfrac{1}{2}$ (highest value + lowest value), the average of the highest and lowest values. Thus, this average value gives

$$d = \frac{1}{2}(16.1 + 8.3) = 12.2.$$

The weather repeats every 12 months, so the period is 12. Thus, we can find b as follows.

$$\text{period} = \frac{2\pi}{b}$$

$$12 = \frac{2\pi}{b} \qquad \text{Replace period by 12.}$$

$$b = \frac{2\pi}{12} = \frac{\pi}{6} \qquad \begin{array}{l}\text{Multiply both sides by } b \text{, and} \\ \text{divide both sides by 12.}\end{array}$$

$$b \approx 0.52$$

To determine the phase shift, find the value of c for which the input value $\dfrac{2\pi}{12}(x - c)$ for $x = 6$ (when y has the highest value) equals $\dfrac{\pi}{2}$.

$$\frac{2\pi}{12}(x - c) = \frac{\pi}{2} \qquad \text{High value at } \frac{1}{2}(\text{period}) = \frac{1}{2}(12) = 6$$

$$\frac{2\pi}{12}(6 - c) = \frac{\pi}{2} \qquad \text{Replace } x \text{ by } 6.$$

$$c = 3 \qquad \text{Solve for } c.$$

The equation describing the hours of daylight in Paris *in month x* is

$$y = 3.9 \sin\left(\frac{2\pi}{12}\right)(x - 3) + 12.2$$

$$y = 3.9 \sin\frac{\pi}{6}(x - 3) + 12.2. \qquad \blacksquare \; \blacksquare \; \blacksquare$$

PRACTICE PROBLEM 11 Rework Example 11 for the city of Fargo, North Dakota, using the values given in Table 5.6. ■

TABLE 5.6

Daylight hours in Fargo	
January	9
February	10.3
March	11.9
April	13.6
May	15.1
June	15.8
July	15.4
August	14.2
September	12.5
October	10.9
November	9.4
December	8.6

Source: http://aa.usno.navy.mil/data/docs/Dur_One year.html

Simple Harmonic Motion

Frequently, motion caused by vibration, rotation, or oscillation can be described or modeled by trigonometric functions. The motions associated with sound waves, radio waves, alternating electric current, a vibrating guitar string, or the swing of a pendulum are examples of such motion. Another example is the movement of a ball suspended by a spring. If the ball is pulled downward and then released (ignoring the effects of friction and air resistance), the ball will repeatedly move up and down past its rest position. See Figure 5.64.

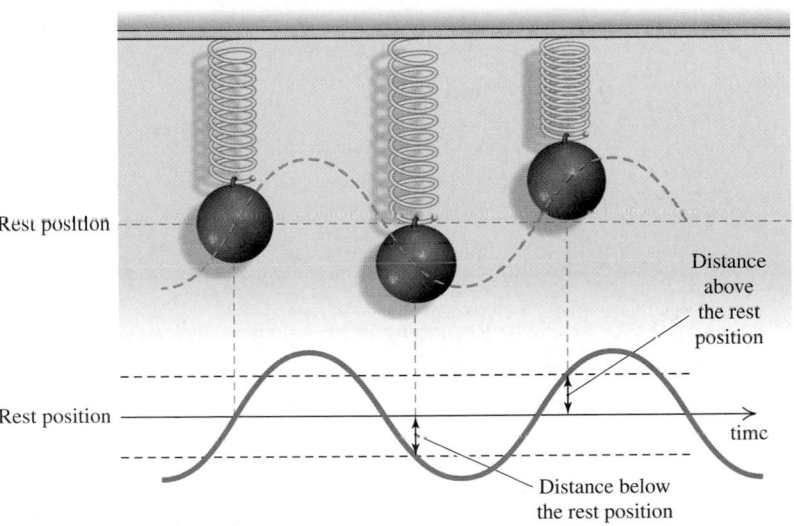

FIGURE 5.64

SIMPLE HARMONIC MOTION

An object whose position relative to an equilibrium position at time t can be described by either

$$y = a \sin \omega t \qquad \text{or} \qquad y = a \cos \omega t \quad (\omega > 0)$$

is said to be in **simple harmonic motion**.

　　The *amplitude,* $|a|$, is the maximum distance the object attains from its equilibrium position. The *period* of the motion, $\dfrac{2\pi}{\omega}$, is the time it takes for the object to complete one full cycle. The **frequency** of the motion is $\dfrac{\omega}{2\pi}$ and gives the number of cycles completed per unit of time.

　　If the distance above and below the rest position of the ball is graphed as a function of time, a sine or a cosine curve results. The amplitude of the curve is the maximum distance above the rest position the ball travels, and one cycle is completed as the ball travels from its highest position to its lowest position and back to its highest position.

EXAMPLE 12　　Simple Harmonic Motion of a Ball Attached to a Spring

Suppose that a ball attached to a spring is pulled down 6 inches and released and the resulting simple harmonic motion has a period of 8 seconds. Write an equation for the ball's simple harmonic motion.

Solution

We must first choose between an equation of the form $y = a \sin \omega t$ or $y = a \cos \omega t$. We start tracking the motion of the ball when $t = 0$. Note that for $t = 0$,

$$y = a \sin (\omega \cdot 0) = a \cdot \sin 0 = a \cdot 0 = 0 \text{ and } y = a \cos (\omega \cdot 0) = a \cdot \cos 0 = a \cdot 1 = a.$$

If we choose to start tracking the ball's motion when we release it after pulling it down 6 inches, we should choose $a = -6$ and $y = -6 \cos \omega t$. Because we pulled the ball *down* in order to start, a is negative. We now have the form of the equation of motion:

$$y = -6 \cos \omega t \qquad \text{When } t = 0, y = -6.$$

$$\text{period} = \frac{2\pi}{\omega} = 8 \qquad \text{The period is given to be 8 seconds.}$$

$$2\pi = 8\omega \qquad \text{Multiply both sides by } \omega.$$

$$\omega = \frac{2\pi}{8} = \frac{\pi}{4} \qquad \text{Divide both sides by 8 and simplify.}$$

Replacing ω by $\dfrac{\pi}{4}$ in $y = -6 \cos \omega t$ yields

$$y = -6 \cos \frac{\pi}{4} t$$

as the equation of the ball's simple harmonic motion.　　　　　　　■ ■ ■

PRACTICE PROBLEM 12　　Rework Example 12 with the motion period of 3 seconds and the ball pulled down 4 inches.　　　　　　　■

A Exercises   Basic Skills and Concepts

In Exercises 1–20, sketch the graph of each given equation over the interval $[-2\pi, 2\pi]$.

1. $y = 2\sin x$ †
2. $y = 4\cos x$ †

3. $y = -\dfrac{1}{2}\sin x$ †
4. $y = -2\sin x$ †

5. $y = \dfrac{3}{2}\cos x$ †
6. $y = \dfrac{5}{4}\sin x$ †

7. $y = \cos 2x$ †
8. $y = \sin 4x$ †

9. $y = \cos\dfrac{2}{3}x$ †
10. $y = \sin\dfrac{4}{3}x$ †

11. $y = \cos\left(x + \dfrac{\pi}{2}\right)$ †
12. $y = \sin\left(x + \dfrac{\pi}{4}\right)$ †

13. $y = \cos\left(x - \dfrac{\pi}{3}\right)$ †
14. $y = \sin(x - \pi)$ †

15. $y = 2\cos\left(x - \dfrac{\pi}{2}\right)$ †
16. $y = 2\sin\left(x + \dfrac{\pi}{3}\right)$ †

17. $y = \sin x + 1$ †
18. $y = \cos x - 2$ †

19. $y = -\cos x + 1$ †
20. $y = \sin x - 3$ †

In Exercises 21–28, find the amplitude, period, and phase shift of each given function.

21. $y = 5\cos(x - \pi)$ †
22. $y = 3\sin\left(x - \dfrac{\pi}{8}\right)$ †

23. $y = 7\cos 9\left(x + \dfrac{\pi}{6}\right)$ †
24. $y = 11\sin 8\left(x + \dfrac{\pi}{3}\right)$ †

25. $y = -6\cos\dfrac{1}{2}(x + 2)$ †
26. $y = 8\sin\dfrac{1}{5}(x + 9)$ †

27. $y = 0.9\sin 0.25\left(x - \dfrac{\pi}{4}\right)$ †
28. $y = \sqrt{5}\cos\pi(x + 1)$ †

In Exercises 29–36, graph each function over a one-period interval.

29. $y = -4\cos\left(x + \dfrac{\pi}{6}\right)$ †
30. $y = -3\sin\left(x - \dfrac{\pi}{6}\right)$ †

31. $y = \dfrac{5}{2}\sin 2\left(x - \dfrac{\pi}{4}\right)$ †
32. $y = \dfrac{3}{2}\cos 2\left(x + \dfrac{\pi}{3}\right)$ †

33. $y = -5\cos 4\left(x - \dfrac{\pi}{6}\right)$ †
34. $y = -3\sin 4\left(x + \dfrac{\pi}{6}\right)$ †

35. $y = \dfrac{1}{2}\sin 4\left(x + \dfrac{\pi}{4}\right) + 2$ †
36. $y = -\dfrac{1}{2}\cos 2\left(x - \dfrac{\pi}{2}\right) - 3$ †

In Exercises 37–46, write each function in the form $y = a\sin b(x - c)$ or $y = a\cos b(x - c)$. Find each period and phase shift.

37. $y = 4\cos\left(2x + \dfrac{\pi}{3}\right)$ †
38. $y = 5\sin\left(3x + \dfrac{\pi}{2}\right)$ †

39. $y = -\dfrac{3}{2}\sin(2x - \pi)$ †
40. $y = -2\cos\left(5x - \dfrac{\pi}{4}\right)$ †

41. $y = 3\cos\pi x$ †
42. $y = \sin\dfrac{\pi x}{3}$ †

43. $y = \dfrac{1}{2}\cos\left(\dfrac{\pi x}{4} + \dfrac{\pi}{4}\right)$ †
44. $y = -\sin\left(\dfrac{\pi x}{6} + \dfrac{\pi}{6}\right)$ †

45. $y = 2\sin(\pi x + 3)$ †
46. $y = -\cos\left(\pi x - \dfrac{1}{4}\right)$ †

B Exercises   Applying the Concepts

47. Pulse and blood pressure. Blood pressure is given by two numbers, written as a fraction: $\dfrac{\text{systolic}}{\text{diastolic}}$. The *systolic* reading is the maximum pressure in an artery, and the *diastolic* reading is the minimum pressure in an artery. As the heart beats, the systolic measurement is taken; when it rests, the diastolic measurement is taken. A reading of $\dfrac{120}{80}$ is considered normal.

Your pulse is the number of heartbeats per minute. Suppose Desmond's blood pressure after t minutes is given by

$$p(t) = 20\sin(140\pi t) + 122,$$

where $p(t)$ is the pressure in millimeters of mercury.

a. Find the period, and explain how it relates to pulse. †
b. Graph the function p over one period. †
c. What is Desmond's blood pressure? †

48. Electrical circuit voltage. The voltage $V(t)$ in an electrical circuit is given by $V(t) = 4.5\cos 160\pi t$, where t is measured in seconds.

a. Find the amplitude and the period for $V(t)$. †
b. Find the frequency of $V(t)$, that is, the number of cycles completed in one second. †
c. Graph $V(t)$ over the interval $\left[0, \dfrac{1}{40}\right]$. †

†Due to space constrictions, answers to these exercises may be found in the Answers beginning on page A–1 in the back of the book.

49. Voltage of an electric outlet. The voltage across the terminals of a typical electric outlet is approximated by $V(t) = 156\sin(120\pi t)$, where t is measured in seconds.

  a. Find the amplitude and the period for $V(t)$. †

  b. Find the frequency of $V(t)$—that is, the number of cycles completed in one second. †

  c. Graph $V(t)$ over the interval $\left[0, \dfrac{1}{30}\right]$. †

50. Oscillating ball. Suppose that a ball attached to a spring is pulled down 5 inches and released and that the resulting simple harmonic motion has a period of 10 seconds. Write an equation of the ball's simple harmonic motion. †

51. Kangaroo population. The kangaroo population in a certain region is given by the function

$$N(t) = 650 + 150\sin 2t,$$

where the time t is measured in years.

  a. What is the largest number of kangaroos present in the region at any time? 800 kangaroos

  b. What is the smallest number of kangaroos present in the region at any time? 500 kangaroos

  c. How much time elapses between occurrences of the largest and the smallest kangaroo population? †

52. Lion and deer populations. The number of deer in a region is given by $D(t) = 450\sin\left(\dfrac{3t}{5}\right) + 1200$, and the number of lions in that same region is given by $L(t) = 225\sin\left(\dfrac{2}{5}(t-2)\right) + 500$, where t is in years.

  a. Graph both functions on the same coordinate plane for $0 \le t \le 10$. †

  b. What can you say about the relationship between these populations, based on the graphs obtained in (a)? †

53. Daylight hours in London. The table gives the average number of daylight hours in London each month, where $x = 1$ represents January. Let y represent the number of daylight hours in London in month x. Find a function of the form $y = a\sin b(x - c) + d$ that models the hours of daylight throughout the year. †

Jan	Feb	Mar	Apr	May	June
8.4	10	11.9	13.9	15.6	16.6

July	Aug	Sept	Oct	Nov	Dec
16.1	14.6	12.6	10.7	8.9	7.9

54. Daylight hours in Washington, DC. The table gives the average number of daylight hours in Washington, DC, each month, where $x = 1$ represents January. Let y represent the number of daylight hours in Washington, DC, in month x. Find a function of the form $y = a\sin b(x - c) + d$ that models the hours of daylight throughout the year. †

Jan	Feb	Mar	Apr	May	June
9.8	10.8	12	13.2	14.3	14.8

July	Aug	Sept	Oct	Nov	Dec
14.6	13.6	12.4	11.2	10.1	9.5

In Exercises 55 and 56, use the table of average monthly temperatures (where Jan = 1, . . ., Dec = 12) to find a function of the form $y = a\sin b(x - c) + d$ that models the temperature in the given city. The four seasons of the year match remarkably well with the quarter periods of the sine function. Since the temperatures repeat each year, the period is 12 months, and so $b = \dfrac{2\pi}{12} = \dfrac{\pi}{6}$. The amplitude $a = \dfrac{1}{2}$ (high temperature − low temperature), and the vertical shift $d = \dfrac{1}{2}$ (high temperature + low temperature). Since the maximum value a of an unshifted sine curve with period 12 occurs at $\dfrac{1}{4}(12) = 3$ units from the start of the cycle, you can find c by solving the equation $c =$ hottest month -3.

55. Average temperature. The monthly average temperatures for Augusta, Maine, are given in the table.

Month	1	2	3	4	5	6	7	8	9	10	11	12
°F	19	22	31	43	54	63	70	67	59	48	37	24

Source: http://www.weatherbase.com/

  a. Find a function of the form $y = a\sin b(x - c) + d$ that models these temperatures. †

  b. Graph the ordered pairs and the function on the same coordinate system. †

  c. Compute the function values for January, April, July, and October, and compare these with the table values for these months. †

56. Average temperatures. The monthly average temperatures for Nashville, Tennessee, are given in the table.

Month	1	2	3	4	5	6	7	8	9	10	11	12
°F	40	45	53	63	71	79	83	81	74	63	52	44

Source: http://www.weatherbase.com/

  a. Find a function of the form $y = a\sin b(x - c) + d$ that models these temperatures. †

  b. Graph the ordered pairs and the function on the same coordinate system. †

  c. Compute the function values for January, April, July, and October and compare these to the table values for these months. †

C Exercises   Beyond the Basics

In Exercises 57–70, graph each equation over the interval $[0, 2\pi]$.

57. $y = 2\sin(3x + \pi)$ †

58. $y = 4\cos\left(2x + \dfrac{\pi}{2}\right)$ †

59. $y = -\dfrac{1}{2}\cos\left(\dfrac{2}{3}x - \dfrac{\pi}{9}\right)$ †

60. $y = -2\sin(\pi x - 2)$ †

61. $y = 3\sin\left(-x + \dfrac{\pi}{4}\right)$ †

62. $y = -2\sin\left(-2x + \dfrac{\pi}{3}\right)$ †

63. $y = 2\cos\left(-3x + \dfrac{\pi}{2}\right) + 2$ †

64. $y = -3\cos\left(-\dfrac{x}{\pi} + \dfrac{1}{2}\right) + 3$ †

65. $y = |\sin x|$ †

66. $y = |\cos x|$ †

67. $y = x \sin x$ †

68. $y = x \cos x$ †

69. $y = \sqrt{x}\, \sin x$ †

70. $y = |x \sin x|$ †

71. Graph the equations $y = x^2$, $y = -x^2$, and $y = x^2 \sin x$ on the same coordinate plane. †

72. We know that $\sin(x + 2\pi) = \sin x$ for all real numbers x. Consequently, if 2π is not the period for the sine function, then $\sin(x + p) = \sin x$ for some real number p, with $0 < p < 2\pi$, and all real numbers x.

a. By evaluating $\sin(x + p) = \sin x$ for $x = 0$, show that if the period is not 2π, then $p = \pi$.

b. Find a value of x for which $\sin(x + \pi) \neq \sin x$ and conclude that the period of the sine function is 2π.

Critical Thinking

73. Suppose that a function of the form $y = a\sin b(x - c) + d$, with $a > 0$, has period $= 20$.

a. In a one-period interval, how many units are there between the value of x at which the maximum value is attained and the value of x at which the minimum value is attained?   10 units

b. In a one-period interval, how many units are there between the value of x at which y has value d and the value of x at which the maximum value is attained?   5 units

74. Suppose the minimum value of a function of the form $y = a\cos b(x - c) + d$, with $a > 0$, occurs at a value of x that is 5 units from the value of x at which the function has the maximum value. What is the period of the function?   10

Graphs of the Other Trigonometric Functions

BEFORE STARTING THIS SECTION, REVIEW

1. Vertical asymptotes (Section 3.5, page 383)

2. Transformations of functions (Section 2.6, page 263)

OBJECTIVES

1 Graph tangent and cotangent functions.

2 Graph cosecant and secant functions.

The U.S.S. Enterprise and Mach Numbers

While Star Trek fans are more interested in warp speed, Mach Numbers are of much more interest to those who fly in the earth's atmosphere.

The Mach number (named after the Austrian physicist Ernst Mach) is the ratio of the speed of the aircraft to the speed of sound. For example, an aircraft traveling at Mach 2 is traveling at twice the speed of sound. An airplane flying at less than the speed of sound is traveling at *subsonic* speed; at the speed of sound (Mach 1), it is traveling at *transonic* speed; at speeds greater than the speed of sound it is traveling at *supersonic* speeds; and at speeds greater than 5 times the speed of sound it is traveling at *hypersonic* speeds. In Example 3, we will see how at supersonic and hypersonic speeds Mach numbers are given as values of the cosecant function, and we will graph a range of Mach numbers that are actually attainable by various military aircrafts.

In this section, you will learn to sketch the graphs of the tangent, cotangent, cosecant, and secant functions. ■

---

1 Graph tangent and cotangent functions.

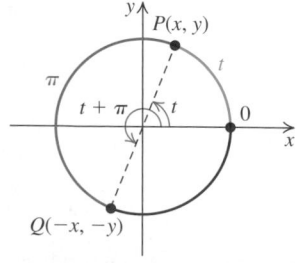

$$\tan(t + \pi) = \frac{-y}{-x} = \frac{y}{x} = \tan t$$

FIGURE 5.65

Graphs of the Tangent and Cotangent Functions

The graph of $y = \tan x$ The tangent function differs from the sine and cosine functions in three significant ways.

1. The tangent function has period π. Figure 5.65 demonstrates the fact that values of the tangent function repeat every π units.

2. Because $\tan x = \dfrac{\sin x}{\cos x}$, we have $\tan x = 0$ when $\sin x = 0$, and $\tan x$ is undefined when $\cos x = 0$. In particular, the tangent is undefined at $\pm\dfrac{\pi}{2}, \pm\dfrac{3\pi}{2}, \pm\dfrac{5\pi}{2}, \ldots$.

3. The tangent function has no amplitude; that is, there are no minimum and maximum y-values. Another way to say this is that the range of $y = \tan x$ is $(-\infty, \infty.)$

Note that $\tan(-x) = \dfrac{\sin(-x)}{\cos(-x)} = \dfrac{-\sin x}{\cos x} = -\tan x$. Thus, the tangent is an odd function, so its graph is symmetric with respect to the origin. To obtain the graph of the tangent function we use the values in Table 5.7 for $y = \tan x$, where x is in the interval $\left[0, \dfrac{\pi}{2}\right)$.

TABLE 5.7

x	0	$\dfrac{\pi}{6}$	$\dfrac{\pi}{4}$	$\dfrac{\pi}{3}$	$\dfrac{7\pi}{18}$	$\dfrac{4\pi}{9}$	$\dfrac{17\pi}{36}$
$y = \tan x$	0	0.6	1	1.7	2.7	5.7	11.4

As x takes on values closer to $\dfrac{\pi}{2}$, we see that the values of $\tan x$ continue to increase; in fact, they increase indefinitely. The decimal value of $\dfrac{\pi}{2}$ is approximately 1.5707963. When $x = \dfrac{89\pi}{180} \approx 1.55$, the value of $\tan x$ is greater than 57; when $x = 1.57$, the value of $\tan x$ is greater than 1255; and when $x = 1.5707$, the value of $\tan x$ is greater than 10,000. The graph of $y = \tan x$ has a vertical asymptote at $x = \dfrac{\pi}{2}$. See Figure 5.66(a).

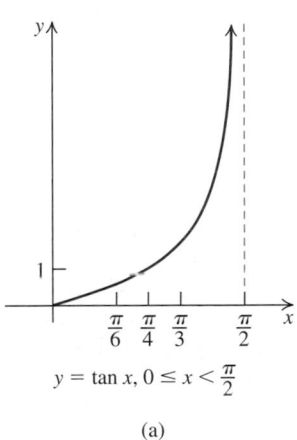

$y = \tan x, \, 0 \le x < \dfrac{\pi}{2}$

(a)

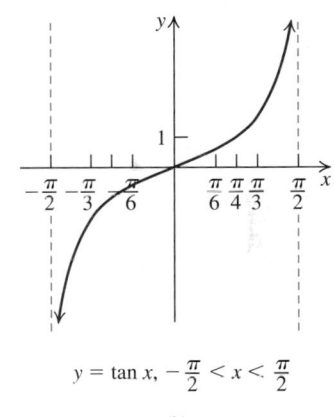

$y = \tan x, \, -\dfrac{\pi}{2} < x < \dfrac{\pi}{2}$

(b)

FIGURE 5.66

The graph of $y = \tan x$ can be extended to the interval $\left(-\dfrac{\pi}{2}, \dfrac{\pi}{2}\right)$ by using the fact that the graph is symmetric with respect to the origin. See Figure 5.66(b).

Because the period of the tangent function is π and we have graphed $y = \tan x$ over an interval of length π, we obtain the complete graph of $y = \tan x$ by repeating the graph in Figure 5.66(b) indefinitely to the left and right, over intervals of length π. We show 3 cycles of the graph in Figure 5.67.

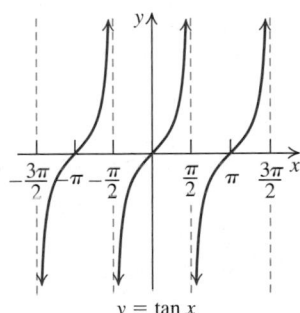

$y = \tan x$

FIGURE 5.67

The graph of $y = \cot x$ The cotangent function also has period π. Since $\cot x = \dfrac{\cos x}{\sin x}$, we have $\cot x = 0$ when $\cos x = 0$, and $\cot x$ is undefined when $\sin x = 0$. In particular, the cotangent function is undefined at $0, \pm\pi, \pm 2\pi, \pm 3\pi, \ldots$.

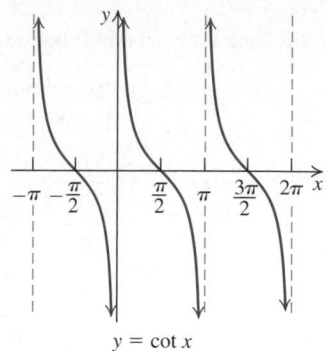

$y = \cot x$

FIGURE 5.68

The cotangent is an odd function because $\cot(-x) = \dfrac{\cos(-x)}{\sin(-x)} = \dfrac{\cos x}{-\sin x} = -\cot x.$

The fact that $\cot x = \dfrac{1}{\tan x}$ tells us that $\tan x$ and $\cot x$ have the same sign everywhere they are both defined and that when $|\tan x|$ is large, $|\cot x|$ is small, and conversely. Three cycles of the graph of the cotangent function are shown in Figure 5.68.

We summarize the essential features of the tangent and cotangent functions and their graphs.

	Main Facts about $y = \tan x$ **and** $y = \cot x$	
	$y = \tan x$	$y = \cot x$
Period	π	π
Domain	All real numbers except odd multiples of $\dfrac{\pi}{2}$.	All real numbers except integer multiples of π.
Range	$(-\infty, \infty)$	$(-\infty, \infty)$
Vertical Asymptotes	$x = a$, where a is an odd multiple of $\dfrac{\pi}{2}$.	$x = a$, where a is an integer multiple of π.
x-intercepts	$a \pm \dfrac{\pi}{2}$, where a is an odd multiple of $\dfrac{\pi}{2}$.	$a \pm \dfrac{\pi}{2}$, where a is an integer multiple of π.
Symmetry	$\tan(-x) = -\tan x$, odd function, symmetric with respect to the origin	$\cot(-x) = -\cot x$, odd function, symmetric with respect to the origin

Graphing $y = a \tan b(x - c)$ The procedure for graphing $y = a \tan b(x - c)$ is based on the essential features of the graph of $y = \tan x$.

FINDING THE SOLUTION: PROCEDURE FOR GRAPHING $y = a \tan b(x - c)$ OR $y = a \cot b(x - c)$

OBJECTIVE

*The **objective** is to graph a function of the form $y = a \tan b(x - c)$ or $y = a \cot b(x - c)$, with $b > 0$, and finding the period and phase shift.*

EXAMPLE

Graph $y = 3 \tan 2\left(x - \dfrac{\pi}{4}\right).$

Step 1 Find the

vertical stretch factor $= |a|$

period $= \dfrac{\pi}{b}$

phase shift $= c$

1. $y = 3 \tan 2\left(x - \dfrac{\pi}{4}\right)$

   $a = 3 \quad b = 2 \quad c = \dfrac{\pi}{4}$

   vertical stretch factor $= |a| = |3| = 3$

   period $= \dfrac{\pi}{b} = \dfrac{\pi}{2}$

   phase shift $= c = \dfrac{\pi}{4}$ To the right, since $\dfrac{\pi}{4} > 0$

Step 2 Locate two adjacent vertical asymptotes. For $y = a \tan b(x - c)$, solve

$$b(x - c) = -\frac{\pi}{2} \text{ and } b(x - c) = \frac{\pi}{2}.$$

For $y = a \cot b(x - c)$, solve $b(x - c) = 0$ and $b(x - c) = \pi$.

2.
$$\begin{aligned} 2\left(x - \frac{\pi}{4}\right) &= -\frac{\pi}{2} \\ x - \frac{\pi}{4} &= -\frac{\pi}{4} \\ x &= -\frac{\pi}{4} + \frac{\pi}{4} \\ x &= 0 \end{aligned} \qquad \begin{aligned} 2\left(x - \frac{\pi}{4}\right) &= \frac{\pi}{2} \\ x - \frac{\pi}{4} &= \frac{\pi}{4} \\ x &= \frac{\pi}{4} + \frac{\pi}{4} \\ x &= \frac{\pi}{2} \end{aligned}$$

Step 3 Divide the interval on the x-axis between the two vertical asymptotes into 4 equal parts, each of length $\dfrac{1}{4}\left(\dfrac{\pi}{b}\right)$.

3. The interval $\left(0, \dfrac{\pi}{2}\right)$ has length $\dfrac{\pi}{2}$.

$$\frac{1}{4}\left(\frac{\pi}{2}\right) = \frac{\pi}{8}$$

The division points of the 4 equal parts of the interval $\left(0, \dfrac{\pi}{2}\right)$ are $0 + \dfrac{\pi}{8}, 0 + 2\left(\dfrac{\pi}{8}\right)$, and $0 + 3\left(\dfrac{\pi}{8}\right)$, or $\dfrac{\pi}{8}, \dfrac{\pi}{4}$, and $\dfrac{3\pi}{8}$.

Step 4 Evaluate the function at the three endpoints of the intervals found in Step 3 that are in the domain of the function.

4.

x	$y = 3\tan 2\left(x - \dfrac{\pi}{4}\right)$
$\dfrac{\pi}{8}$	-3
$\dfrac{\pi}{4}$	0
$\dfrac{3\pi}{8}$	3

Step 5 Sketch the vertical asymptotes, using the values found in Step 2. Connect the points in Step 4 with a smooth curve in the standard shape of a cycle for the given function. Repeat the graph to the left and right over intervals of length $\dfrac{\pi}{b}$ as needed.

5.

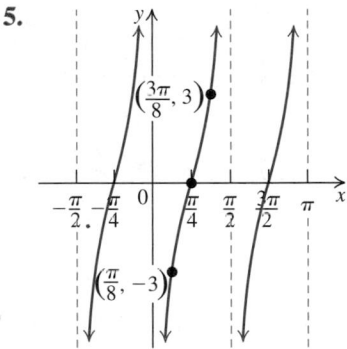

EXAMPLE 1   **Graphing $y = a \cot b(x - c)$**

Graph $y = -4\cot\left(x - \dfrac{\pi}{2}\right)$ over the interval $[-\pi, 2\pi]$.

Solution

Step 1 For $y = -4\cot\left(x - \dfrac{\pi}{2}\right)$, we have $a = -4$, $b = 1$, and $c = \dfrac{\pi}{2}$.

Thus,

$$\text{vertical stretch factor} = |-4|; \qquad \text{period} = \frac{\pi}{1} = \pi; \qquad \text{phase shift} = \frac{\pi}{2}$$

Continued on next page.

Step 2 To locate two adjacent asymptotes, solve the following equations:

$$x - \frac{\pi}{2} = 0 \quad \text{and} \quad x - \frac{\pi}{2} = \pi.$$

$$x = \frac{\pi}{2} \qquad\qquad x = \frac{3\pi}{2}$$

Step 3 The interval $\left(\frac{\pi}{2}, \frac{3\pi}{2} \right)$ has length π.

The division points of $\left(\frac{\pi}{2}, \frac{3\pi}{2} \right)$ are $\frac{\pi}{2} + \frac{1}{4}(\pi) = \frac{3\pi}{4}$,

$\frac{\pi}{2} + \frac{1}{2}(\pi) = \pi$, and $\frac{\pi}{2} + \frac{3}{4}(\pi) = \frac{5\pi}{4}$.

Step 4 Evaluate the function at $\frac{3\pi}{4}$, π, and $\frac{5\pi}{4}$.

x	$y = -4\cot\left(x - \dfrac{\pi}{2} \right)$
$\dfrac{3\pi}{4}$	-4
π	0
$\dfrac{5\pi}{4}$	4

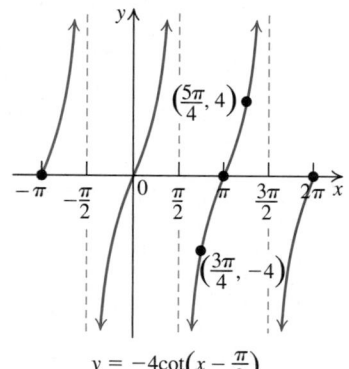

$$y = -4\cot\left(x - \frac{\pi}{2} \right)$$

FIGURE 5.69

Step 5 Sketch the vertical asymptotes at $x = \dfrac{\pi}{2}$ and $x = \dfrac{3\pi}{2}$. Draw the cycle for the cotangent function through the three graph points found in Step **4**.

Repeat the graph to the left or right over intervals of length π. See Figure 5.69. ■ ■ ■

PRACTICE PROBLEM 1 Graph $y = 3\tan\left(x + \dfrac{\pi}{4} \right)$ over the interval $\left(-\dfrac{3\pi}{4}, \dfrac{5\pi}{4} \right)$. ■

2 Graph the cosecant and secant functions.

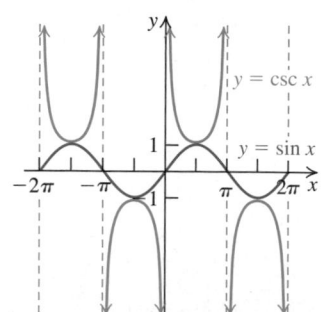

FIGURE 5.70

Graphs of the Secant and Cosecant Functions

We can use the same technique to graph the secant and cosecant functions that we used to graph the cotangent function. Both functions are reciprocal functions; that is,

$$\csc x = \frac{1}{\sin x} \quad \text{and} \quad \sec x = \frac{1}{\cos x}.$$

For every x in the domain of the cosecant function, $\sin x$ and $\csc x$ have the same sign, and when $|\sin x|$ is small, $|\csc x|$ is large, and conversely.

Now $\csc x$ is undefined when $\sin x = 0$. Consequently, $\csc x$ is undefined at $0, \pm\pi, \pm 2\pi, \pm 3\pi, \ldots$ In fact, the graph of the cosecant function has a vertical asymptote at the integer multiples of π, that is, at $0, \pm\pi, \pm 2\pi, \pm 3\pi, \ldots$ Because $\csc x = 1$ whenever $\sin x = 1$ and $\csc x = -1$ when $\sin x = -1$, the graphs of $y = \csc x$ and $y = \sin x$ coincide if $\sin x = \pm 1$. The graphs of $y = \sin x$ and $y = \csc x$ over the interval $[-2\pi, 2\pi]$ are shown in Figure 5.70.

Because $\sec x = \dfrac{1}{\cos x}$, the relationship between the graphs of $y = \sec x$ and $y = \cos x$ is similar to the relationship between the graphs of $y = \sin x$ and $y = \csc x$. The graphs of $y = \cos x$ and $y = \sec x$ over the interval $\left[-\dfrac{3\pi}{2}, \dfrac{5\pi}{2} \right]$ are shown in Figure 5.71.

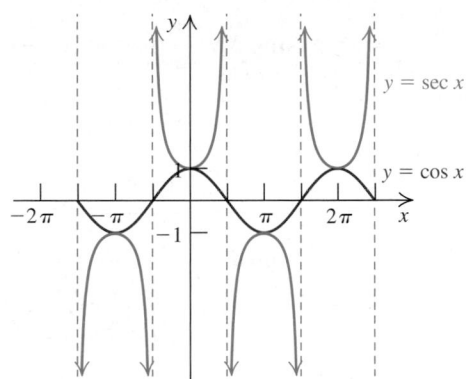

FIGURE 5.71

We summarize the essential facts about the secant and cosecant functions and their graphs.

Main Facts about $y = \csc x$ and $y = \sec x$		
	$y = \csc x$	$y = \sec x$
Period	2π	2π
Domain	All real numbers except integer multiples of π.	All real numbers except odd multiples of $\dfrac{\pi}{2}$.
Range	$(-\infty, -1] \cup [1, \infty)$	$(-\infty, -1] \cup [1, \infty)$
Vertical Asymptotes	$x = a$, where a is an integer multiple of π.	$x = a$, where a is an odd multiple of $\dfrac{\pi}{2}$.
***x*-intercepts**	No x-intercepts	No x-intercepts
Symmetry	$\csc(-x) = -\csc x$, odd function, origin symmetry	$\sec(-x) = \sec x$, even function with y-axis symmetry

The procedures for graphing the functions $y = a \csc b(x - c)$ and $y = a \sec b(x - c)$ rely on those previously described for the related sine and cosine functions.

> **EXAMPLE 2**   **Graphing $y = a \csc b(x - c)$**

Graph $y = 3 \csc 2x$ over a two-period interval.

Solution

Because $\csc 2x = \dfrac{1}{\sin 2x}$, $3 \csc 2x = 3 \sin 2x$ when $\sin 2x = \pm 1$. So, we first graph $y = 3 \sin 2x$.

Continued on next page.

We will follow the steps for graphing a function of this type given in Section 5.4.

Step 1 $y = 3\sin 2x$

amplitude $= 3$,   period $= \dfrac{2\pi}{2} = \pi$,   no phase shift since $c = 0$

Step 2   The starting point for the cycle is $x = 0$. One cycle is graphed over $[0, \pi]$.

Step 3 $\dfrac{1}{4}$ (period) $= \dfrac{1}{4}\pi = \dfrac{\pi}{4}$

starting point $x = 0$,   2nd point $= \dfrac{\pi}{4}$,   3rd point $= 2\left(\dfrac{\pi}{4}\right) = \dfrac{\pi}{2}$,

4th point $= 3\left(\dfrac{\pi}{4}\right) = \dfrac{3\pi}{4}$,   end point $x = 4\left(\dfrac{\pi}{4}\right) = \pi$.

Step 4   Sketch the graph of $y = 3\sin 2x$ through the points $(0, 0), \left(\dfrac{\pi}{4}, 3\right)$, $\left(\dfrac{\pi}{2}, 0\right), \left(\dfrac{3\pi}{4}, -3\right)$, and $(\pi, 0)$. See Figure 5.72.

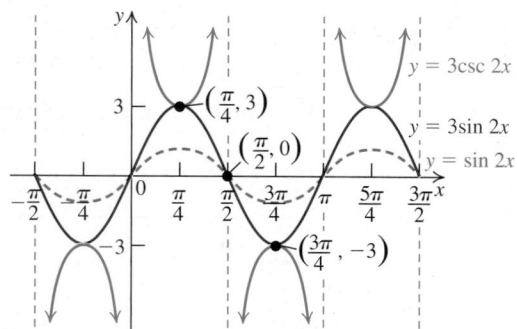

FIGURE 5.72

Step 5   Use the graph from Step **4** to extend the graph to interval $\left(-\dfrac{\pi}{2}, \dfrac{3\pi}{2}\right)$.

Now use the technique that generated the graph of $y = \csc x$ from that of $y = \sin x$ to graph $y = 3\csc 2x$. Start at the common graph points $\left(\dfrac{\pi}{4}, 3\right)$ and $\left(\dfrac{3\pi}{4}, -3\right)$, then use the reciprocal relationship $y = 3\csc 2x = 3\left(\dfrac{1}{\sin 2x}\right)$. See Figure 5.72.   ■ ■ ■

Practice Problem 2   Graph $y = 2\sec 3x$ over a two-period interval.   ■

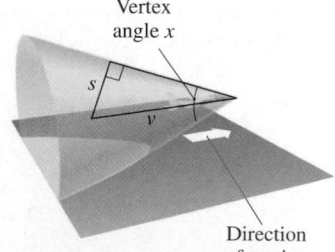

Vertex angle x

Direction of motion

FIGURE 5.73

EXAMPLE 3   **Graphing a Range of Mach Numbers**

When a plane travels at supersonic and hypersonic speeds, small disturbances in the atmosphere are transmitted downstream within a cone. The cone intersects the ground, and the edge of the cone's intersection with the ground can be represented as in Figure 5.73. The sound waves strike the edge of the cone at a right angle. The speed of the sound wave is represented by leg s of the right triangle shown in Figure 5.73. The plane is moving at speed v, which is represented by the hypotenuse of the right triangle in Figure 5.73.

The Mach number, M, is given by

$$M = M(x) = \frac{\text{speed of the aircraft}}{\text{speed of sound}} = \frac{v}{s} = \csc\left(\frac{x}{2}\right),$$

where x is the angle at the vertex of the cone. Graph the Mach number function, $M(x)$, as the angle at the vertex of the cone varies. What is the range of Mach numbers associated with the interval $\left[\frac{\pi}{4}, \pi\right)$?

Solution

Because $\csc\dfrac{x}{2} = \dfrac{1}{\sin\dfrac{x}{2}}$, first graph $y = \sin\dfrac{x}{2}$. For convenience, we have sketched the graph of $y = \sin\dfrac{x}{2}$ over the interval $[0, 2\pi]$. The graph of $y = \csc\dfrac{x}{2}$ is sketched over the interval $(0, 2\pi)$, using the reciprocal connection between the sine graph and the cosecant graph. See Figure 5.74.

$$\text{For } x = \frac{\pi}{4}, y = \csc\frac{x}{2} = \csc\frac{\pi}{8} \approx 2.6.$$

$$\text{For } x = \pi, \ y = \csc\frac{x}{2} = \csc\frac{\pi}{2} = 1.$$

The range of Mach numbers associated with the interval $\left[\dfrac{\pi}{4}, \pi\right)$ is $(1, 2.6]$.   ■ ■ ■

FIGURE 5.74

PRACTICE PROBLEM 3   In Example 3, what is the range of Mach numbers associated with the interval $\left[\dfrac{\pi}{8}, \dfrac{\pi}{4}\right]$?   ■

| **A Exercises** | **Basic Skills and Concepts** |

In Exercises 1–18, graph each function over a one-period interval.

1. $y = \tan\left(x - \dfrac{\pi}{4}\right)$ †

2. $y = \tan\left(x + \dfrac{\pi}{4}\right)$ †

3. $y = \cot\left(x + \dfrac{\pi}{4}\right)$ †

4. $y = \cot\left(x - \dfrac{\pi}{4}\right)$ †

5. $y = \tan 2x$ †

6. $y = \tan\dfrac{x}{2}$ †

7. $y = \cot\dfrac{x}{2}$ †

8. $y = \cot 2x$ †

9. $y = -\tan x$ †

10. $y = -\cot x$ †

11. $y = 3\tan x$ †

12. $y = 3\cot x$ †

13. $y = \sec 2x$ †

14. $y = \sec\dfrac{x}{2}$ †

15. $y = \csc 3x$ †

16. $y = \csc\dfrac{x}{3}$ †

17. $y = \sec(x - \pi)$ †

18. $y = \csc(x \quad \pi)$ †

In Exercises 19–40, graph each function over a two-period interval.

19. $y = \tan 2\left(x + \dfrac{\pi}{2}\right)$ †

20. $y = \tan 2\left(x - \dfrac{\pi}{2}\right)$ †

21. $y = \cot 2\left(x - \dfrac{\pi}{2}\right)$ †

22. $y = \cot 2\left(x + \dfrac{\pi}{2}\right)$ †

†Due to space constrictions, answers to these exercises may be found in the Answers beginning on page A–1 in the back of the book.

23. $y = \tan\dfrac{1}{2}(x + 2\pi)$ †

24. $y = \tan\dfrac{1}{2}(x - 2\pi)$ †

25. $y = \cot\dfrac{1}{2}(x - 2\pi)$ †

26. $y = \cot\dfrac{1}{2}(x + 2\pi)$ †

27. $y = -\dfrac{1}{2}\tan\dfrac{x}{2}$ †

28. $y = -\dfrac{1}{2}\cot\dfrac{x}{2}$ †

29. $y = \sec 4\left(x - \dfrac{\pi}{4}\right)$ †

30. $y = \sec\dfrac{1}{2}\left(x - \dfrac{\pi}{2}\right)$ †

31. $y = -2\sec 3x$ †

32. $y = -3\csc 4x$ †

33. $y = 3\csc\left(x + \dfrac{\pi}{2}\right)$ †

34. $y = 3\sec 2\left(x - \dfrac{\pi}{6}\right)$ †

35. $y = \tan\dfrac{2}{3}\left(x - \dfrac{\pi}{2}\right)$ †

36. $y = 2\cot 2\left(x - \dfrac{\pi}{6}\right)$ †

37. $y = -5\tan 2\left(x + \dfrac{\pi}{3}\right)$ †

38. $y = -3\cot\dfrac{1}{2}\left(x - \dfrac{\pi}{3}\right)$ †

39. $y = \dfrac{1}{3}\cot 2(x - \pi)$ †

40. $y = \dfrac{1}{2}\tan 4\left(x - \dfrac{\pi}{6}\right)$ †

B Exercises   Applying the Concepts

41. Prison searchlight. A dual-beam rotating light on a movie set is positioned as a spotlight shining on a prison wall. The light is 20 feet from the wall and rotates clockwise. The light shines on point P on the wall when first turned on ($t = 0$). After t seconds the distance (in feet) from the beam on the wall to the point P is given by the function

$$d(t) = 20\tan\dfrac{\pi t}{5}.$$

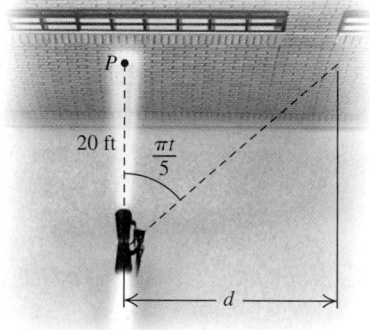

When the light beam is to the right of P, the value of d is positive, and when the beam is to the left of P, the value of d is negative.

a. Graph d over the interval $0 \le t \le 5$. †

b. Since $d(t)$ is undefined for $t = 2.5$, where is the rotating light pointing when $t = 2.5$? †

42. Prison searchlight. In Exercise 41, find the value for b if the light beam is to sweep the entire wall in 10 seconds, and $d(t) = 20\tan bt$. $\dfrac{\pi}{10}$

C Exercises   Beyond the Basics

43. Show that if f is a periodic function with period p, then the reciprocal function $\dfrac{1}{f}$ is also a periodic function with period p.

44. Show that if f is an odd function, then the reciprocal function $\dfrac{1}{f}$ is also an odd function.

45. Show that if f is an even function, then the reciprocal function $\dfrac{1}{f}$ is also an even function.

In Exercises 46–55, graph each function over a two-period interval.

46. $y = 3\tan(-2x)$ †

47. $y = 2\cot(-3x)$ †

48. $y = -2\sec\left(-\dfrac{x}{2}\right)$ †

49. $y = -\dfrac{1}{2}\csc\left(-\dfrac{x}{5}\right)$ †

50. $y = \cot(\pi - x)$ †

51. $y = -\tan\left(\dfrac{\pi}{2} - x\right)$ †

52. $y = -\sec(\pi - 4x)$ †

53. $y = 2\sec(\pi - 2x)$ †

54. $y = 2\tan\left(\dfrac{\pi}{2} - 2x\right) + 1$ †

55. $y = 4\cot(\pi - 4x) + 3$ †

In Exercises 56–59, write an equation for each graph.

56.

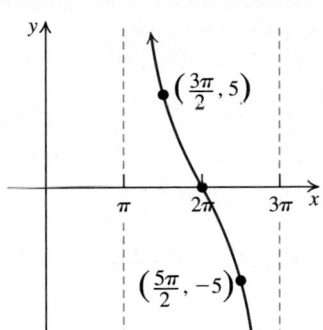

$$y = 5 \cot\left(\frac{x}{2} - \frac{\pi}{2}\right)$$

57.

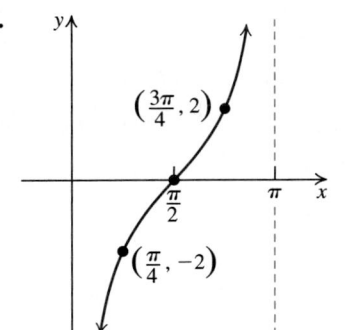

$$y = 2 \tan\left(x + \frac{\pi}{2}\right)$$

58.

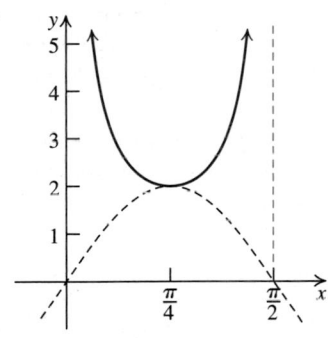

$$y = 2 \csc 2x$$

59.

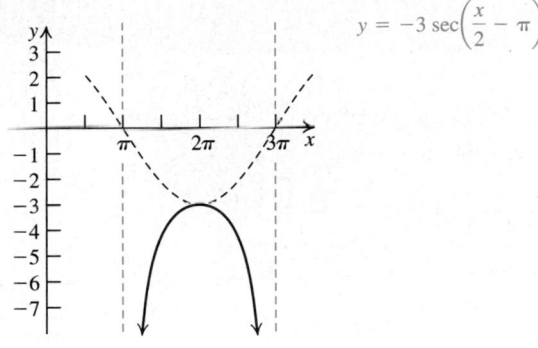

$$y = -3 \sec\left(\frac{x}{2} - \pi\right)$$

Critical Thinking

60. For what number k, with $-2\pi < k < 0$, is $x = k$ a vertical asymptote for $y = \cot\frac{1}{2}\left(x - \frac{\pi}{4}\right)$? $k = -\frac{7\pi}{4}$

61. For what number b does $y = \sec bx$ have period $\frac{\pi}{3}$? 6

SECTION 5.6 | Inverse Trigonometric Functions

BEFORE STARTING THIS SECTION, REVIEW

1. Inverse functions (Section 2.8, page 297)

2. Composition of functions (Section 2.7, page 283)

3. Exact value of the trigonometric functions (Section 5.2, page 521)

OBJECTIVES

1. Use the inverse sine function.

2. Use the inverse cosine function.

3. Use the inverse tangent function.

4. Evaluate inverse trigonometric functions using a calculator.

5. Find exact values of composite functions involving the inverse trigonometric functions.

6. Solve right triangles.

Retail Theft

In 2005, security cameras at Filene's Basement store in Boston filmed a theft coordinated by a thief and an accomplice. The accomplice distracted the salesperson so the thief could steal a $16,000 necklace. Retail theft is a major concern for all retail outlets, from Tiffany & Co. to Wal-Mart.

The National Retail Federation, the industry's largest trade group, and the Retail Industry Leaders Association have instituted password-protected national crime databases online. These databases allow retailers to share information about thefts and determine whether they have been a target of individual shoplifters, who steal for themselves, or organized crime. In addition to participating in the shared databases, many large retailers have their own organized-crime squads. One estimate puts loss to organized theft at over $30 billion annually. In Example 11, we see how methods in this section can be used in an attempt to prevent loss from theft. ■

---

1 Use the inverse sine function.

The Inverse Sine Function

Recall that a function f has an inverse that is also a function if no horizontal line intersects its graph in more than one point. Because every horizontal line $y = b$, where $-1 < b < 1$, intersects the graph of $y = \sin x$ at more than one point, the sine function fails the horizontal line test (so is not one-to-one) and consequently has no inverse.

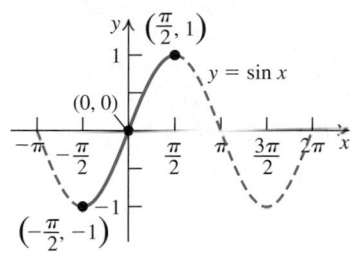

FIGURE 5.75

The solid portion of the sine graph shown in Figure 5.75 is the graph of $y = \sin x$ for $-\dfrac{\pi}{2} \le x \le \dfrac{\pi}{2}$ .When we restrict the domain of $y = \sin x$ to the interval $\left[-\dfrac{\pi}{2}, \dfrac{\pi}{2}\right]$, the resulting function

$$y = \sin x, \quad -\dfrac{\pi}{2} \le x \le \dfrac{\pi}{2}$$

is a one-to-one function (passes the horizontal line text), so its inverse is also a function. Notice that the graph of the restricted function takes on all y-values in the range of $y = \sin x$, which is $[-1, 1]$, and that each of these y-values corresponds to exactly one x-value in the restricted domain $\left[-\dfrac{\pi}{2}, \dfrac{\pi}{2}\right]$. The inverse function for $y = \sin x$, $-\dfrac{\pi}{2} \le x \le \dfrac{\pi}{2}$, is called the **inverse sine**, or **arcsine**, function.

> **INVERSE SINE FUNCTION**
>
> $y = \sin^{-1} x$ means $\sin y = x$, where $-1 \le x \le 1$ and $-\dfrac{\pi}{2} \le y \le \dfrac{\pi}{2}$.
>
> Read $y = \sin^{-1} x$ as "y equals inverse sine at x."

The range of $y = \sin x$ is $[-1, 1]$, so the domain of $y = \sin^{-1} x$ is $[-1, 1]$. The domain of the restricted sine function is $\left[-\dfrac{\pi}{2}, \dfrac{\pi}{2}\right]$, so the range of $y = \sin^{-1} x$ is $\left[-\dfrac{\pi}{2}, \dfrac{\pi}{2}\right]$. The graph of $y = \sin^{-1} x$ is obtained by reflecting the graph of $y = \sin x$, for $-\dfrac{\pi}{2} < x < \dfrac{\pi}{2}$, in the line $y = x$. See Figure 5.76.

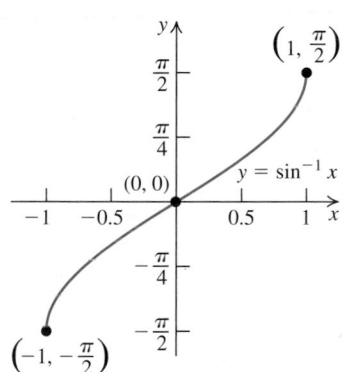

FIGURE 5.76

EXAMPLE 1   **Finding the Exact Values for $y = \sin^{-1} x$**

Find the exact values of y.

a. $y = \sin^{-1} \dfrac{\sqrt{3}}{2}$ **b.** $y = \sin^{-1}\left(-\dfrac{1}{2}\right)$ **c.** $y = \sin^{-1} 3$

Solution

a. $y = \sin^{-1} \dfrac{\sqrt{3}}{2}$ means $\sin y = \dfrac{\sqrt{3}}{2}$ and $-\dfrac{\pi}{2} \le y \le \dfrac{\pi}{2}$.

Since $\sin \dfrac{\pi}{3} = \dfrac{\sqrt{3}}{2}$ and $\dfrac{\pi}{3}$ is in the interval $\left[-\dfrac{\pi}{2}, \dfrac{\pi}{2}\right]$, we have $y = \sin^{-1} \dfrac{\sqrt{3}}{2} - \dfrac{\pi}{3}$.

b. $y = \sin^{-1}\left(-\dfrac{1}{2}\right)$ means $\sin y = -\dfrac{1}{2}$ and $-\dfrac{\pi}{2} \le y \le \dfrac{\pi}{2}$.

Since $\sin\left(-\dfrac{\pi}{6}\right) = -\dfrac{1}{2}$ and $-\dfrac{\pi}{6}$ is in the interval $\left[-\dfrac{\pi}{2}, \dfrac{\pi}{2}\right]$, we have

$$y = \sin^{-1}\left(-\dfrac{1}{2}\right) = -\dfrac{\pi}{6}.$$

c. Since 3 is not in the domain of the inverse sine function, which is $[-1, 1]$, $\sin^{-1} 3$ does not exist.   ■ ■ ■

PRACTICE PROBLEM 1   Find the exact values of y.

a. $y = \sin^{-1}\left(-\dfrac{\sqrt{3}}{2}\right)$ **b.** $y = \sin^{-1}(-1)$ ■

2 Use the inverse cosine function.

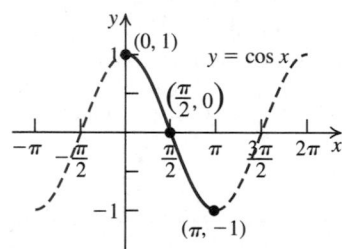

FIGURE 5.77

The Inverse Cosine Function

When we restrict the domain of $y = \cos x$ to the interval $[0, \pi]$, the resulting function, $y = \cos x$ (with $0 \le x \le \pi$), is a one-to-one function. No horizontal line intersects the portion of the graph of $y = \cos x$ corresponding to values of x in $[0, \pi]$ in more than one point. See Figure 5.77. Consequently, the restricted cosine function has an inverse function.

The inverse function for $y = \cos x$, $0 \le x \le \pi$, is called the **inverse cosine**, or **arccosine**, function.

> **INVERSE COSINE FUNCTION**
>
> $y = \cos^{-1}x$ means $\cos y = x$ where $-1 \le x \le 1$ and $0 \le y \le \pi$.
> Read $y = \cos^{-1}x$ as "y equals inverse cosine at x."

STUDY TIP

You can also read $y = \cos^{-1}x$ as "y is the number in the interval $[0, \pi]$ whose cosine is x."

Reflecting the graph of $y = \cos x$, with $0 \le y \le \pi$, in the line $y = x$ produces the graph of $y = \cos^{-1}x$, shown in Figure 5.78.

EXAMPLE 2   **Finding an Exact Value for $\cos^{-1}x$**

Find the exact value of y.

a. $y = \cos^{-1}\dfrac{\sqrt{2}}{2}$ **b.** $y = \cos^{-1}\left(-\dfrac{1}{2}\right)$

Solution

a. $y = \cos^{-1}\dfrac{\sqrt{2}}{2}$ means $\cos y = \dfrac{\sqrt{2}}{2}$ and $0 \le y \le \pi$.

Since $\cos\dfrac{\pi}{4} = \dfrac{\sqrt{2}}{2}$ and $0 \le \dfrac{\pi}{4} \le \pi$, we have

$$y = \cos^{-1}\dfrac{\sqrt{2}}{2} = \dfrac{\pi}{4}.$$

b. $y = \cos^{-1}\left(-\dfrac{1}{2}\right)$ means $\cos y = -\dfrac{1}{2}$ and $0 \le y \le \pi$. Since

$\cos\dfrac{2\pi}{3} = -\dfrac{1}{2}$ and $0 \le \dfrac{2\pi}{3} \le \pi$, we have

$$y = \cos^{-1}\left(-\dfrac{1}{2}\right) = \dfrac{2\pi}{3}.$$ ■ ■ ■

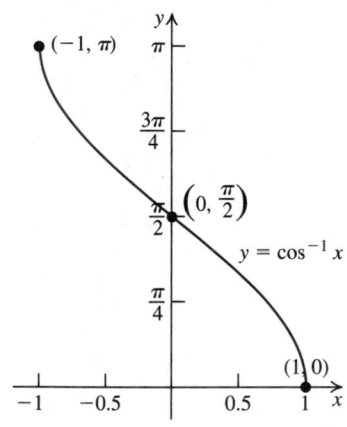

FIGURE 5.78

PRACTICE PROBLEM 2   Find the exact value of y.

a. $y = \cos^{-1}\left(-\dfrac{\sqrt{2}}{2}\right)$ **b.** $y = \cos^{-1}\dfrac{1}{2}$ ■

3 Use the inverse tangent function.

The Inverse Tangent Function

The *inverse tangent function* results from restricting the domain of the tangent function to the interval $\left(-\dfrac{\pi}{2}, \dfrac{\pi}{2}\right)$ to obtain a one-to-one function. The inverse of this restricted tangent function is the **inverse tangent**, or **arctangent**, function.

INVERSE TANGENT FUNCTION

$y = \tan^{-1}x$ means $\tan y = x$, where $-\infty < x < \infty$ and $-\dfrac{\pi}{2} < y < \dfrac{\pi}{2}$.

The graph of $y = \tan^{-1}x$ is obtained by reflecting the graph of $y = \tan x$, with $-\dfrac{\pi}{2} < x < \dfrac{\pi}{2}$, in the line $y = x$. Figure 5.79 shows the graph of the restricted tangent function. The graph of $y = \tan^{-1}x$ is shown in Figure 5.80.

FIGURE 5.79

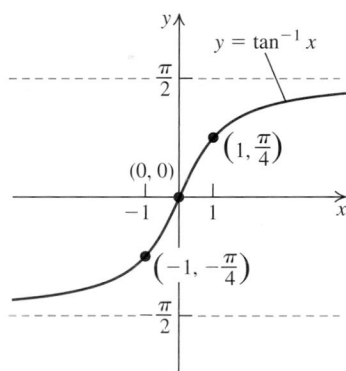

FIGURE 5.80

EXAMPLE 3   **Finding Exact Values for tan⁻¹x**

Find the exact value of y.

a. $y = \tan^{-1}0$ **b.** $y = \tan^{-1}(-\sqrt{3})$

Solution

a. Since $\tan 0 = 0$ and $-\dfrac{\pi}{2} < 0 < \dfrac{\pi}{2}$, we have $y = \tan^{-1}(0) = 0$.

b. Since $\tan\left(-\dfrac{\pi}{3}\right) = -\sqrt{3}$ and $-\dfrac{\pi}{2} < -\dfrac{\pi}{3} < \dfrac{\pi}{2}$, we have

$$y = \tan^{-1}(-\sqrt{3}) = -\dfrac{\pi}{3}.$$

■ ■ ■

PRACTICE PROBLEM 3   Find the exact value of $y = \tan^{-1}\dfrac{\sqrt{3}}{3}$.   ■

Other Inverse Trigonometric Functions

The *inverse secant* and *inverse cosecant* functions are sometimes used with different ranges than we use in this text. Always check the definitions of the domains of these two functions when used outside this course.

Inverse cotangent $y = \cot^{-1} x$ means $\cot y = x$,

                       where $-\infty < x < \infty$ and $0 < y < \pi$.

Inverse cosecant $y = \csc^{-1} x$ means $\csc y = x$,

                       where $|x| \geq 1$ and $-\dfrac{\pi}{2} \leq y \leq \dfrac{\pi}{2}, y \neq 0$.

Inverse secant $y = \sec^{-1} x$ means $\sec y = x$,

                       where $|x| \geq 1$ and $0 \leq y \leq \pi, y \neq \dfrac{\pi}{2}$.

EXAMPLE 4   **Finding the Exact Value for $\csc^{-1} x$**

Find the exact value for $y = \csc^{-1} 2$.

Solution

Since $\csc \dfrac{\pi}{6} = 2$ and $-\dfrac{\pi}{2} \leq \dfrac{\pi}{6} \leq \dfrac{\pi}{2}$, we have $y = \csc^{-1} 2 = \dfrac{\pi}{6}$.   ■ ■ ■

PRACTICE PROBLEM 4   Find the exact value of $y = \sec^{-1} 2$.   ■

Inverse Trigonometric Functions			
Inverse Function	**Equivalent to**	**Domain**	**Range**
$y = \sin^{-1} x$	$\sin y = x$	$[-1, 1]$	$\left[-\dfrac{\pi}{2}, \dfrac{\pi}{2}\right]$
$y = \cos^{-1} x$	$\cos y = x$	$[-1, 1]$	$[0, \pi]$
$y = \tan^{-1} x$	$\tan y = x$	$(-\infty, \infty)$	$\left(-\dfrac{\pi}{2}, \dfrac{\pi}{2}\right)$
$y = \cot^{-1} x$	$\cot y = x$	$(-\infty, \infty)$	$(0, \pi)$
$y = \csc^{-1} x$	$\csc y = x$	$(-\infty, -1] \cup [1, \infty)$	$\left[-\dfrac{\pi}{2}, 0\right) \cup \left(0, \dfrac{\pi}{2}\right]$
$y = \sec^{-1} x$	$\sec y = x$	$(-\infty, -1] \cup [1, \infty)$	$\left[0, \dfrac{\pi}{2}\right) \cup \left(\dfrac{\pi}{2}, \pi\right]$

Using a Calculator with Inverse Functions

In Section 5.3, we defined the six trigonometric functions of *real numbers*, and in this section, we have defined the corresponding six inverse trigonometric functions of real numbers. For example,

$$\sin \frac{\pi}{4} = \frac{\sqrt{2}}{2}$$

and

$$\sin^{-1} \frac{\sqrt{2}}{2} = \frac{\pi}{4}.$$

However, because we also defined the trigonometric functions of *angles* in Section 5.3, it is meaningful, when working with angles in degree measure, to write a statement such as

$$\sin^{-1} \frac{\sqrt{2}}{2} = 45°.$$

When using the inverse trigonometric functions on a calculator to find a real number, or equivalently, an unknown angle measure in radians, be sure to set your calculator to radian mode.

When using a calculator to find $\csc^{-1}x$ or $\sec^{-1}x$, simply find $\sin^{-1}\frac{1}{x}$ and $\cos^{-1}\frac{1}{x}$, respectively. For example, if $\csc^{-1}5 = \theta$, then $\csc\theta = 5$, or $\frac{1}{\sin\theta} = 5$. So $\sin\theta = \frac{1}{5}$ and $\sin^{-1}\left(\frac{1}{5}\right) = \theta$. However, when finding $\cot^{-1}x$, although you begin by finding $\tan^{-1}\frac{1}{x}$, this gives you a value in the interval $\left(-\frac{\pi}{2}, \frac{\pi}{2}\right)$. If $x \geq 0$, this is the correct value, but if $x < 0$, you must add π to $\tan^{-1}\frac{1}{x}$ to get the correct value. That is, for $x < 0$, $\cot^{-1}(x) = \pi + \tan^{-1}\frac{1}{x}$.

When using a calculator to find an unknown angle measure in degrees, be sure to set your calculator to degree measure.

```
sin⁻¹(√(2)/2)
           45.00
cos⁻¹(0)
           90.00
```
```
tan⁻¹(0.45)
       24.22774532
sin⁻¹(0.2)
       11.53695903
■
```

EXAMPLE 5   **Using a Calculator to Find the Values of Inverse Functions**

Use a calculator to find the value of y in radians rounded to four decimal places.

a. $y = \sin^{-1}0.75$ **b.** $y = \cot^{-1}2.8$

Solution

Set your calculator to radian mode.

a. $y = \sin^{-1}0.75 \approx 0.8481$

b. $y = \cot^{-1}2.8 = \tan^{-1}\left(\frac{1}{2.8}\right) \approx 0.3430$

■ ■ ■

PRACTICE PROBLEM 5   Use a calculator to find the value of y in radians rounded to four decimal places.

a. $y = \cos^{-1} 0.22$ **b.** $y = \csc^{-1} 3.5$ ▪

EXAMPLE 6   Using a Calculator to Find the Values of Inverse Functions

Use a calculator to find the value of y in degrees rounded to four decimal places.

a. $y = \tan^{-1} 0.99$ **b.** $y = \sec^{-1} 25$

Solution

Set your calculator to degree mode.

a. $y = \tan^{-1} 0.99 \approx 44.7121°$

b. $y = \sec^{-1} 25 = \cos^{-1}\dfrac{1}{25} \approx 87.7076°$ ▪ ▪ ▪

PRACTICE PROBLEM 6   Repeat Example 6 for each expression.

a. $y = \cot^{-1} 0.75$ **b.** $y = \csc^{-1} 13$ ▪

---

5 Find exact values of composite functions involving the inverse trigonometric functions.

Composition of Trigonometric and Inverse Trigonometric Functions

Recall that if f is a one-to-one function with inverse f^{-1}, then $f^{-1}[f(x)] = x$ for every x in the domain of f and $f[f^{-1}(x)] = x$ for every x in the domain of f^{-1}. This leads to the following formulas for the inverse sine, cosine, and tangent functions:

Inverse Sine	Inverse Cosine	Inverse Tangent
$\sin^{-1}(\sin x) = x,$ $-\dfrac{\pi}{2} \le x \le \dfrac{\pi}{2}$	$\cos^{-1}(\cos x) = x,$ $0 \le x \le \pi$	$\tan^{-1}(\tan x) = x,$ $-\dfrac{\pi}{2} < x < \dfrac{\pi}{2}$
$\sin(\sin^{-1} x) = x,$ $-1 \le x \le 1$	$\cos(\cos^{-1} x) = x,$ $-1 \le x \le 1$	$\tan(\tan^{-1} x) = x,$ $-\infty < x < \infty$

EXAMPLE 7   Finding the Exact Value of $\sin^{-1}(\sin x)$ and $\cos^{-1}(\cos x)$

Find the exact value of

a. $\sin^{-1}\left[\sin\left(-\dfrac{\pi}{8}\right)\right]$ **b.** $\cos^{-1}\left(\cos\dfrac{5\pi}{4}\right)$

Solution

a. Because $-\dfrac{\pi}{2} \le -\dfrac{\pi}{8} \le \dfrac{\pi}{2}$, we have $\sin^{-1}\left[\sin\left(-\dfrac{\pi}{8}\right)\right] = -\dfrac{\pi}{8}$.

b. We cannot use the formula $\cos^{-1}(\cos x) = x$ for $x = \dfrac{5\pi}{4}$, because $\dfrac{5\pi}{4}$ is not in the interval $[0, \pi]$. However, $\cos\dfrac{5\pi}{4} = \cos\left(2\pi - \dfrac{5\pi}{4}\right) = \cos\dfrac{3\pi}{4}$ and $\dfrac{3\pi}{4}$ is in the interval $[0, \pi]$. Thus,

$$\cos^{-1}\left(\cos\frac{5\pi}{4}\right) = \cos^{-1}\left(\cos\frac{3\pi}{4}\right) = \frac{3\pi}{4}.$$ ■ ■ ■

PRACTICE PROBLEM 7   Find the exact value of $\sin^{-1}\left(\sin\dfrac{3\pi}{2}\right)$.   ■

To find the exact values of expressions involving the composition of a trigonometric function and the inverse of a *different* trigonometric function, we use points on the terminal side of an angle in standard position.

EXAMPLE 8   **Finding the Exact Value of a Composite Trigonometric Expression**

Find the exact value of

a. $\cos\left(\tan^{-1}\dfrac{2}{3}\right)$

b. $\sin\left[\cos^{-1}\left(-\dfrac{1}{4}\right)\right]$

Solution

a. Let θ represent the radian measure of the angle in $\left(-\dfrac{\pi}{2}, \dfrac{\pi}{2}\right)$, with $\tan\theta - \dfrac{2}{3}$. Then, since $\tan\theta$ is positive, θ must be positive. We have

$$\theta = \tan^{-1}\frac{2}{3} \quad \text{and} \quad 0 < \theta < \frac{\pi}{2}.$$

Figure 5.81 shows θ in standard position. If (x, y) is a point on the terminal side of θ, then $\tan\theta = \dfrac{y}{x} = \dfrac{2}{3}$.

Consequently, we can choose the point with coordinates $(3, 2)$ to determine the terminal side of θ. Then $x = 3$, $y = 2$ and we have

$$\tan\theta = \frac{2}{3} \quad \text{and} \quad \cos\theta = \frac{3}{r}, \text{ where}$$

$$r = \sqrt{x^2 + y^2} - \sqrt{3^2 + 2^2} = \sqrt{9 + 4} = \sqrt{13}. \text{ Thus,}$$

$$\cos\left(\tan^{-1}\frac{2}{3}\right) = \cos\theta - \frac{3}{r} = \frac{3}{\sqrt{13}} = \frac{3\sqrt{13}}{13}.$$

b. Let θ represent the radian measure of the angle in $[0, \pi]$, with $\cos\theta = -\dfrac{1}{4}$. Then, since $\cos\theta$ is negative, we have

$$\theta = \cos^{-1}\left(-\frac{1}{4}\right) \quad \text{and} \quad \frac{\pi}{2} < \theta < \pi.$$

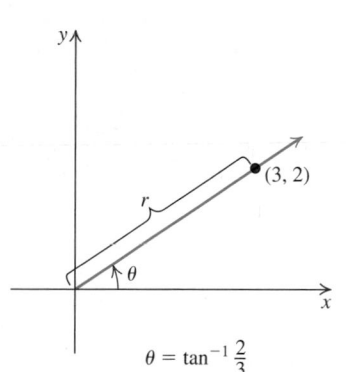

$$\theta = \tan^{-1}\frac{2}{3}$$

FIGURE 5.81

Continued on next page.

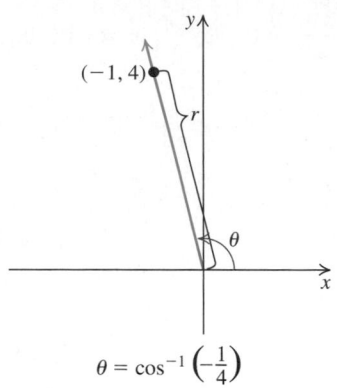

$$\theta = \cos^{-1}\left(-\frac{1}{4}\right)$$

FIGURE 5.82

Figure 5.82 shows θ in standard position. We can choose the point with coordinates $(-1, y)$, a distance of 4 units from the origin, to be on the terminal side of θ.

Then, $\cos\theta = -\dfrac{1}{4}$ and $\sin\theta = \dfrac{y}{4}$, where

$$r = \sqrt{x^2 + y^2} = \sqrt{(1)^2 + y^2} \text{ or } r^2 = 1 + y^2$$

$$4^2 = 1 + y^2 \qquad \text{Replace } r \text{ by 4.}$$

$$15 = y^2 \qquad \text{Simplify.}$$

$$\sqrt{15} = y \qquad y \text{ is positive.}$$

Thus,

$$\sin\left[\cos^{-1}\left(-\frac{1}{4}\right)\right] = \sin\theta = \frac{y}{r} = \frac{\sqrt{15}}{4}. \qquad ■ \ ■ \ ■$$

PRACTICE PROBLEM 8   Find the exact value for $\cos\left[\sin^{-1}\left(-\dfrac{1}{3}\right)\right]$.   ■

6 Solve right triangles.

Learn to Solve Right Triangles

In Section 5.2, you learned to use right triangle trigonometry to find unknown lengths in triangles and to apply this skill to finding unknown distances in applications, such as finding the height of a cloud or the width of a river. Using inverse trigonometric functions provides a way to also find unknown angle measure in right triangles, allowing us to solve applied problems in which angle measures must be found.

To **solve a triangle** means to find all unknown side lengths and angle measures. In this section, we will discuss how to solve right triangles.

In Chapter 7, we will discuss how to solve *oblique triangles*, which do not contain right angles. When solving right triangles, we will solve each triangle $\triangle ABC$, where $\angle C$ is always the right angle, and $\angle A$ and $\angle B$ are the acute angles. (We use A as a shorthand way to write "measure of $\angle A$".) The sides lengths are labeled a, b, and c, where a is the length of the side opposite $\angle A$, and so on. Because $\angle C$ is always the right angle, the length of the hypotenuse will always be c, and the lengths of the legs will be a and b. See Figure 5.83.

In this work, degree measure is traditionally used for the angles. Here are some useful facts about solving right triangles:

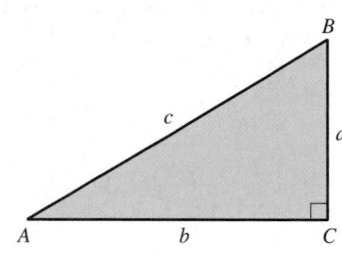

FIGURE 5.83

1. The measure of one angle (the right angle) is automatically given: $C = 90°$.

2. The Pythagorean Theorem allows us to find the length of the third side of any right triangle if two of the side lengths are known.

3. If the measure of one acute angle is given, the measure of the other acute angle can be found from the fact that the two acute angles of any right triangle are complementary.

4. We are able to solve a right triangle if we are given *either* of the following combinations of measurements:

    a. the lengths of any two sides;

    b. the length of any one side and the measure of either of the acute angles.

| EXAMPLE 9 | Solving a Right Triangle, Given One Acute Angle and One Side |

Solve right triangle ABC if $A = 23°$ and $c = 5.8$.

Solution

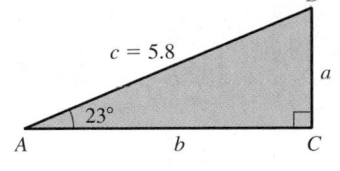

FIGURE 5.84

Sketch the triangle. See Figure 5.84.

   To find a, find a trigonometric function that involves a and the given parts A and c.

$$\sin A = \frac{a}{c} \qquad \text{Definition of sine}$$

$$c \sin A = a \qquad \text{Multiply both sides by } c.$$

$$5.8 \sin 23° = a \qquad \text{Substitute 5.8 for } c \text{ and } 23° \text{ for } A.$$

$$a \approx 2.3 \qquad \text{Use a calculator; round to the nearest tenth.}$$

To find b, find a trigonometric function that involves b and the given parts A and c.

$$\cos A = \frac{b}{c} \qquad \text{Definition of cosine}$$

$$c \cos A = b \qquad \text{Multiply both sides by } c.$$

$$5.8 \cos 23° = b \qquad \text{Substitute 5.8 for } c \text{ and } 23° \text{ for } A.$$

$$b \approx 5.3 \qquad \text{Use a calculator; round to the nearest tenth.}$$

Once a and b have both been found, the Pythagorean Theorem can be used as a check.
   Finally, because $\angle A$ and $\angle B$ are complementary, $B = 90° - 23° = 67°$.   ■ ■ ■

PRACTICE PROBLEM 9   Solve right triangle ABC if $c = 25.8$ and $A = 56°$.   ■

| EXAMPLE 10 | Solving a Right Triangle, Given Two Sides |

Solve right triangle ABC if $a = 9.5$ and $b = 3.4$.

Solution

Sketch the triangle. See Figure 5.85.

   To find A, find a trigonometric function that involves A and the given parts a and b.

$$\tan A = \frac{a}{b} \qquad \text{Definition of tangent}$$

$$\tan A = \frac{9.5}{3.4} \qquad \text{Substitute 9.5 for } a \text{ and 3.4 for } b.$$

$$A = \tan^{-1}\left(\frac{9.5}{3.4}\right) \approx 70.3° \qquad \text{Use a calculator.}$$

FIGURE 5.85

To find c, find a trigonometric function that involves c, A, and a.

$$\sin A = \frac{a}{c} \qquad \text{Definition of sine}$$

$$c \sin A = a \qquad \text{Multiply both sides by } c.$$

$$c = \frac{a}{\sin A} \qquad \text{Divide by } \sin A.$$

$$c = \frac{9.5}{\sin 70.3°} \qquad \text{Substitute 9.5 for } a \text{ and } 70.3° \text{ for } A.$$

$$c \approx 10.1 \qquad \text{Use a calculator; round to the nearest tenth.}$$

Now that all three sides have been found, the Pythagorean Theorem can be used as a check.

Finally, $B = 90° - A$, so $B \approx 90° - 70.3°$, or $B \approx 19.7°$.   ▪ ▪ ▪

PRACTICE PROBLEM 10   Solve right triangle ABC if $b = 24.5$ and $c = 36.9$.   ▪

The process of solving right triangles is useful in many applications. Often, only one unknown side length or angle measure must be found, so it is not necessary to completely solve the triangle.

> **EXAMPLE 11**   **Finding the Rotation Angle for a Security Camera**

A security camera is to be installed 20 feet away from the center of a jewelry counter. The counter is 30 feet long. What angle, to the nearest degree, should the camera rotate through so that it scans the entire counter? See Figure 5.86.

Solution

The counter center B, the camera A, and one end of the counter C form a right triangle. The angle at vertex A is $\dfrac{\theta}{2}$, where θ is the angle through which the camera rotates. (See Figure 5.86.) Note that

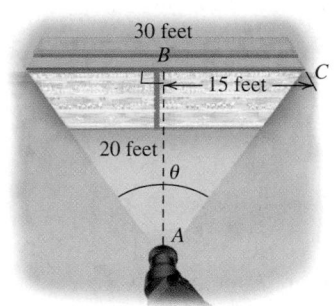

FIGURE 5.86

$$\tan \frac{\theta}{2} = \frac{15}{20} = \frac{3}{4}$$

$$\frac{\theta}{2} = \tan^{-1} \frac{3}{4} \approx 36.87° \qquad \text{Use a calculator in degree mode.}$$

$$\theta \approx 73.74° \qquad\qquad \text{Multiply both sides by 2.}$$

Set the camera to rotate through 74° to scan the entire counter.   ▪ ▪ ▪

PRACTICE PROBLEM 11   Rework Example 11 for a counter that is 20 feet long and a camera set 12 feet from the center of the counter.   ▪

A Exercises   Basic Skills and Concepts

In Exercises 1–20, find each exact value of y, or state that y is undefined.

1. $y = \sin^{-1} 0$ 0

2. $y = \cos^{-1} 0$ †

3. $y = \sin^{-1}\left(-\dfrac{1}{2}\right)$ $-\dfrac{\pi}{6}$

4. $y = \cos^{-1}\left(-\dfrac{\sqrt{3}}{2}\right)$ $\dfrac{5\pi}{6}$

5. $y = \cos^{-1}(-1)$ π

6. $y = \sin^{-1}\dfrac{1}{2}$ $\dfrac{\pi}{6}$

7. $y = \cos^{-1}\dfrac{\pi}{2}$ not defined

8. $y = \sin^{-1}\pi$ not defined

9. $y = \tan^{-1}\sqrt{3}$ †

10. $y = \tan^{-1} 1$ †

11. $y = \tan^{-1}(-1)$ $-\dfrac{\pi}{4}$

12. $y = \tan^{-1}\left(-\dfrac{\sqrt{3}}{3}\right)$ $-\dfrac{\pi}{6}$

13. $y = \cot^{-1}(-1)$ †

14. $y = \cot^{-1} 1$ †

15. $y = \sin^{-1}\left(-\dfrac{\sqrt{2}}{2}\right)$ $-\dfrac{\pi}{4}$

16. $y = \cos^{-1}\left(\dfrac{\sqrt{3}}{2}\right)$ $\dfrac{\pi}{6}$

17. $y = \cot^{-1}\sqrt{3}$ †

18. $y = \cot^{-1}\left(-\sqrt{3}\right)$ †

19. $y = \cos^{-1}(-2)$ not defined

20. $y = \sin^{-1}\sqrt{3}$ not defined

21. $y = \sec^{-1}(-2)$ †

22. $y = \sec^{-1}\sqrt{2}$ †

23. $y = \csc^{-1}\dfrac{2\sqrt{3}}{3}$ $\dfrac{\pi}{3}$

24. $y = \csc^{-1}(2)$ $\dfrac{\pi}{6}$

In Exercises 25–36, find each exact value of y, or state that y is not defined.

25. $y = \sin\left(\sin^{-1}\dfrac{1}{8}\right)$ $\dfrac{1}{8}$

26. $y = \cos\left(\cos^{-1}\dfrac{1}{5}\right)$ $\dfrac{1}{5}$

27. $y = \cos(\cos^{-1} 0.6)$ 0.6

28. $y = \sin(\sin^{-1} 0.8)$ 0.8

---

†Due to space constrictions, answers to these exercises may be found in the Answers beginning on page A–1 in the back of the book.

29. $y = \tan^{-1}\left(\tan\dfrac{\pi}{7}\right)$ $\dfrac{\pi}{7}$

30. $y = \tan^{-1}\left(\tan\dfrac{\pi}{4}\right)$ $\dfrac{\pi}{4}$

31. $y = \tan(\tan^{-1}247)$ 247

32. $y = \tan(\tan^{-1}7)$ 7

33. $y = \sin^{-1}\left(\sin\dfrac{4\pi}{3}\right)$ $-\dfrac{\pi}{3}$

34. $y = \cos^{-1}\left(\cos\dfrac{5\pi}{3}\right)$ $\dfrac{\pi}{3}$

35. $y = \tan^{-1}\left(\tan\dfrac{2\pi}{3}\right)$ $-\dfrac{\pi}{3}$

36. $y = \tan\left(\tan^{-1}\dfrac{2\pi}{3}\right)$ $\dfrac{2\pi}{3}$

In Exercises 37–46, use a calculator to find each value of y in degrees rounded to two decimal places.

37. $y = \cos^{-1}0.6$ 53.13°

38. $y = \sin^{-1}0.23$ 13.29°

39. $y = \sin^{-1}(-0.69)$ −43.63°

40. $y = \cos^{-1}(-0.57)$ 124.75°

41. $y = \sec^{-1}(3.5)$ 73.40°

42. $y = \csc^{-1}(6.8)$ 8.46°

43. $y = \tan^{-1}14$ 85.91°

44. $y = \tan^{-1}50$ 88.85°

45. $y = \tan^{-1}(-42.147)$ −88.64° **46.** $y = \tan^{-1}(-0.3863)$ −21.12°

In Exercises 47–58, use a sketch to find each exact value of y.

47. $y = \cos\left(\sin^{-1}\dfrac{2}{3}\right)$ $\dfrac{\sqrt{5}}{3}$

48. $y = \sin\left(\cos^{-1}\dfrac{3}{4}\right)$ $\dfrac{\sqrt{7}}{4}$

49. $y = \sin\left[\cos^{-1}\left(-\dfrac{4}{5}\right)\right]$ $\dfrac{3}{5}$

50. $y = \cos\left(\sin^{-1}\dfrac{3}{5}\right)$ $\dfrac{4}{5}$

51. $y = \cos\left(\tan^{-1}\dfrac{5}{2}\right)$ $\dfrac{2\sqrt{29}}{29}$

52. $y = \sin\left(\tan^{-1}\dfrac{13}{5}\right)$ $\dfrac{13\sqrt{194}}{194}$

53. $y = \tan\left(\cos^{-1}\dfrac{4}{5}\right)$ $\dfrac{3}{4}$

54. $y = \tan\left[\sin^{-1}\left(-\dfrac{3}{4}\right)\right]$ $-\dfrac{3\sqrt{7}}{7}$

55. $y = \sin(\tan^{-1}4)$ †

56. $y = \cos(\tan^{-1}3)$ †

57. $y = \tan(\sec^{-1}2)$ $\sqrt{3}$

58. $y = \tan[\csc^{-1}(-2)]$ †

In Exercises 59–66, solve each right triangle; angle C is the right angle. Round to the nearest tenth where necessary.

59. $A = 50°, c = 9.2$ $B \approx 40°, a \approx 7.0, b \approx 5.9$

60. $B = 28°, c = 10.5$ $A \approx 62°, a \approx 9.3, b \approx 4.9$

61. $A = 36°, a = 12.0$ $B \approx 54°, c \approx 20.4, b \approx 16.5$

62. $B = 74°, b = 6.3$ $A \approx 16°, a \approx 1.8, c \approx 6.6$

63. $a = 12.5, b = 6.2$ $c \approx 14.0, A \approx 63.6°, B \approx 26.4°$

64. $a = 4.3, b = 8.1$ $c \approx 9.2, A \approx 28°, B \approx 62°$

65. $b = 9.4, c = 14.5$ $a \approx 11, A \approx 49.6°, B \approx 40.4°$

66. $a = 6.2, c = 18.7$ $b \approx 17.6, A \approx 19.4°, B \approx 70.6°$

B Exercises   Applying the Concepts

67. **Sprinkler rotation.** A sprinkler rotates back and forth through an angle θ, as shown in the figure. At a distance of 5 feet from the sprinkler, the rays that form the sides of angle θ are 6 feet apart. Find θ. 62°

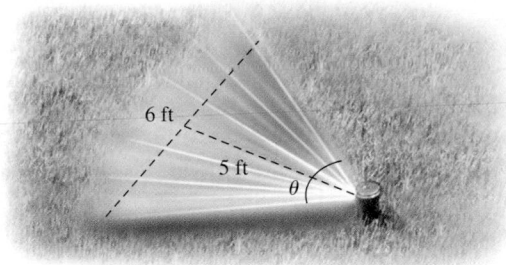

68. **Irradiating flowers.** A tray of flowers is being irradiated by a beam from a rotating lamp, as shown in the figure. If the tray is 8 feet long and the lamp is 2 feet from the center of the tray, through what angle should the lamp rotate to irradiate the full length of the tray? 127°

69. **Motorcycle racing.** A video camera is set up 110 feet at a right angle to a straight quarter-mile racetrack, as shown in the figure. The starting line is to the left, and the finish is to the right. Through what angle must the camera rotate to film the entire race? 159°

70. **Camera's viewing angle.** The viewing angle for the 35-millimeter camera is given (in degrees) by

$$\theta = 2\tan^{-1}\dfrac{18}{x},$$ where x is the focal length of the lens.

The focal length on most adjustable cameras is marked in millimeters on the lens mount.

a. Find the viewing angle, in degrees, if the focal length is 50 millimeters. 39.6°

b. Find the viewing angle, in degrees, if the focal length is 200 millimeters. 10.3°

C Exercises   Beyond the Basics

In Exercises 71–73, determine whether each function is increasing on its domain or decreasing.

71. $y = \sin^{-1}x$ increasing

72. $y = \cos^{-1}x$ decreasing

73. $y = \tan^{-1}x$ increasing

74. Show that

(a) $\sec^{-1}x \neq \dfrac{1}{\cos^{-1}x}$ (b) $\sec^{-1}x = \cos^{-1}\dfrac{1}{x}$

75. Graph the function $y = \cot^{-1}x$. †

76. Graph the function $y = \csc^{-1}x$. †

77. Graph the function $y = \sec^{-1}x$. †

78. For what values of x is $\cot^{-1}(\cot x) = x$ true?

79. For what values of x is $\sec^{-1}(\sec x) = x$ true?

80. For what values of x is $\csc^{-1}(\csc x) = x$ true?

Critical Thinking

In Exercises 81–88, evaluate each expression in terms of x.

81. $\sin(\cos^{-1}x), |x| \leq 1$ $\sqrt{1-x^2}$

82. $\tan(\sin^{-1}x), |x| < 1$

83. $\cos(\tan^{-1}x)$

84. $\sin(\cot^{-1}x)$

85. $\cos(\sin^{-1}x), |x| \leq 1$

86. $\tan(\cos^{-1}x), |x| \leq 1, x \neq 0$

87. $\sin(\tan^{-1}x)$

88. $\cos(\cot^{-1}x)$

Answers:

78. $(0, \pi)$ **79.** $\left[0, \dfrac{\pi}{2}\right) \cup \left(\dfrac{\pi}{2}, \pi\right)$

80. $\left[-\dfrac{\pi}{2}, 0\right) \cup \left(0, \dfrac{\pi}{2}\right]$

Answers:

82. $\dfrac{x}{\sqrt{1-x^2}}$ **83.** $\dfrac{1}{\sqrt{1+x^2}}$ **84.** $\dfrac{1}{\sqrt{1+x^2}}$ **85.** $\sqrt{1-x^2}$

86. $\dfrac{\sqrt{1-x^2}}{x}$ **87.** $\dfrac{x}{\sqrt{x^2+1}}$ **88.** $\dfrac{x}{\sqrt{x^2+1}}$

Summary   Definitions, Concepts, and Formulas

5.1 Angles and Their Measure

i. An **angle** is formed by rotating a ray around its endpoint.

ii. An angle in a rectangular coordinate system is said to be in **standard position** if its vertex is at the origin and its initial side coincides with the positive x-axis. See page 503 for positive and negative angles.

iii. If the terminal side of an angle in standard position lies on the x-axis or the y-axis, the angle is said to be a **quadrantal angle**.

iv. Angles can be measured in **degrees**, where $1° = \dfrac{1}{360}$ of a complete revolution.

v. An **acute angle** is an angle with measure between $0°$ and $90°$, a **right angle** is an angle with measure $90°$, an **obtuse angle** is an angle with measure between $90°$ and $180°$, and a **straight angle** is an angle with measure $180°$.

vi. Angles that have the same initial and terminal sides are called **coterminal** angles.

vii. Angles can also be measured in **radians**. The radian measure of a central angle θ that intercepts an arc of length s on a circle of radius r is $\theta = \dfrac{s}{r}$ radians.

viii. To convert from degrees to radians, multiply degrees by $\dfrac{\pi}{180°}$.

To convert from radians to degrees, multiply radians by $\dfrac{180°}{\pi}$.

ix. Two positive angles are **complements** if their sum is $90°$. Two positive angles are **supplements** if their sum is $180°$.

x. The formula for the length s of the arc intercepted by a central angle θ in a circle of radius r is $s = r\theta$.

xi. If an object travels at a constant speed v on a circle of radius r through an angle of θ radians and an arc of length s, in time t, then the (average) **linear speed** of the object is $v = \dfrac{s}{t}$

and the (average) **angular speed** ω of the object is $\omega = \dfrac{\theta}{t}$.

Further, $v = r\omega$.

xii. Area of a sector $= \dfrac{1}{2}r^2\theta$, r is the radius of the circle, and θ is in radians.

5.2 Right Triangle Trigonometry

i. The right triangle definitions for trigonometric functions of an acute angle θ are given by

$$\sin\theta = \frac{\text{opposite side}}{\text{hypotenuse}} = \frac{a}{c} \qquad \csc\theta = \frac{\text{hypotenuse}}{\text{opposite side}} = \frac{c}{a}$$

$$\cos\theta = \frac{\text{adjacent side}}{\text{hypotenuse}} = \frac{b}{c} \qquad \sec\theta = \frac{\text{hypotenuse}}{\text{adjacent side}} = \frac{c}{b}$$

$$\tan\theta = \frac{\text{opposite side}}{\text{adjacent side}} = \frac{a}{b} \qquad \cot\theta = \frac{\text{adjacent side}}{\text{opposite side}} = \frac{b}{a}$$

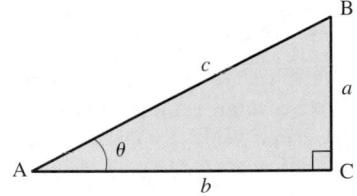

ii. Function values for special angles.

TABLE 5.1

$\theta°$	θ radians	$\sin\theta$	$\cos\theta$	$\tan\theta$	$\csc\theta$	$\sec\theta$	$\cot\theta$
30°	$\dfrac{p}{6}$	$\dfrac{1}{2}$	$\dfrac{\sqrt{3}}{2}$	$\dfrac{\sqrt{3}}{3}$	2	$\dfrac{2\sqrt{3}}{3}$	$\sqrt{3}$
45°	$\dfrac{p}{4}$	$\dfrac{\sqrt{2}}{2}$	$\dfrac{\sqrt{2}}{2}$	1	$\sqrt{2}$	$\sqrt{2}$	1
60°	$\dfrac{p}{3}$	$\dfrac{\sqrt{3}}{2}$	$\dfrac{1}{2}$	$\sqrt{3}$	$\dfrac{2\sqrt{3}}{3}$	2	$\dfrac{\sqrt{3}}{3}$

iii. The value of any trigonometric function of an acute angle θ is equal to the cofunction of the complement of θ.

5.3 Trigonometric Functions of Any Angle

i. Let $P(x,y)$ be any point (other than the origin) on the terminal ray of an angle θ in standard position, and let $r \doteq \sqrt{x^2 + y^2}$, then $r > 0$, and

$$\sin\theta = \frac{y}{r} \qquad \csc\theta = \frac{r}{y} \ (y \neq 0)$$

$$\cos\theta = \frac{x}{r} \qquad \sec\theta = \frac{r}{x} \ (x \neq 0)$$

$$\tan\theta = \frac{y}{x} \ (x \neq 0) \qquad \cot\theta = \frac{x}{y} \ (y \neq 0)$$

ii. Trigonometric function values of coterminal angles

θ in degrees	θ in radians
$\sin\theta = \sin(\theta + n360°)$	$\sin\theta = \sin(\theta + 2\pi n)$
$\cos\theta = \cos(\theta + n360°)$	$\cos\theta = \cos(\theta + 2\pi n)$

These equations hold for any integer n.

iii. **Unit circle** If the terminal side of an angle t intersects the unit circle at the point (x, y), then $\sin t = y$, $\cos t = x$,

$$\tan t = \frac{y}{x}, \ \cot t = \frac{x}{y}, \ \sec t = \frac{1}{x}, \ \text{and } \csc t = \frac{1}{y}.$$

The domain of the sine and cosine functions is $(-\infty, \infty)$, and their range is $[-1, 1]$.

iv. Identities derived from the definition of the trigonometric functions.

1. Reciprocal Identities

$$\csc x = \frac{1}{\sin x} \qquad \sec x = \frac{1}{\cos x} \qquad \cot x = \frac{1}{\tan x}$$

$$\sin x = \frac{1}{\csc x} \qquad \cos x = \frac{1}{\sec x} \qquad \tan x = \frac{1}{\cot x}$$

2. Quotient Identities

$$\tan x = \frac{\sin x}{\cos x} \qquad \cot x = \frac{\cos x}{\sin x}$$

3. Pythagorean Identities

$$\sin^2 x + \cos^2 x = 1 \qquad 1 + \tan^2 x = \sec^2 x$$

$$1 + \cot^2 x = \csc^2 x$$

v. Let θ be an angle in standard position that is not a quadrantal angle. Its **reference angle** is the positive acute angle θ' formed by the terminal side of θ and the positive or negative x-axis. See the Procedure for Using Reference Angles Box on page 537.

vi. Area of a triangle The area of a triangle is one-half the product of the lengths of any two sides and the sine of their included angle.

5.4 Graphs of the Sine and Cosine Functions

i. Definition of the trigonometric function as functions of real numbers

If x is a real number, we define

$$\sin x = \sin(x \text{ radians}) \qquad \cos x = \cos(x \text{ radians})$$
$$\tan x = \tan(x \text{ radians})$$
$$\csc x = \csc(x \text{ radians}) \qquad \sec x = \sec(x \text{ radians})$$
$$\cot x = \cot(x \text{ radians})$$

The left-hand side of each equation is defined for every value of x for which the right-hand side is defined.

ii. Sine and cosine function graphs and properties

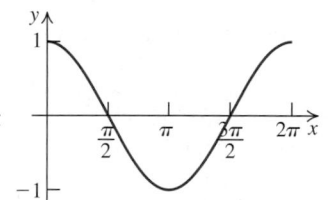

Sine Function

1. Period: 2π
2. Domain: $(-\infty, \infty)$
3. Range: $[-1, 1]$
4. Odd: $\sin(-t) = -\sin t$

Cosine Function

1. Period: 2π
2. Domain: $(-\infty, \infty)$
3. Range: $[-1, 1]$
4. Even: $\cos(t) = \cos t$

iii. The functions $y = a \sin b(x - c) + d$ and $y = a \cos b(x - c) + d$ $(b > 0)$ have amplitude $|a|$, period $\dfrac{2\pi}{b}$, phase shift c, and vertical shift d.

5.5 Graphs of the Other Trigonometric Functions

i. Tangent and cotangent function graphs and properties

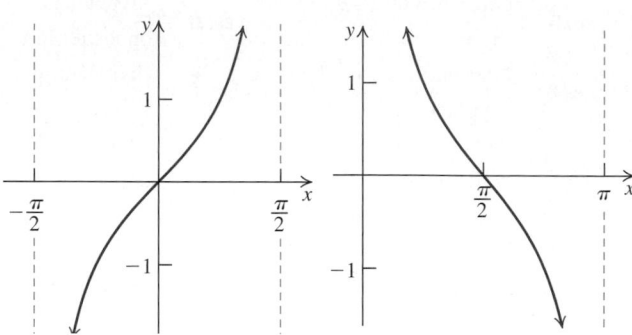

Tangent Function

1. Period: π
2. Domain: All real numbers except for odd multiples of $\dfrac{\pi}{2}$
3. Range: $(-\infty, \infty)$
4. Odd: $\tan(-x) = -\tan x$

Cotangent Function

1. Period: π
2. Domain: All real numbers except for integer multiples of π
3. Range: $(-\infty, \infty)$
4. Odd: $\cot(-x) = -\cot x$

ii. Secant and cosecant function graphs and properties.

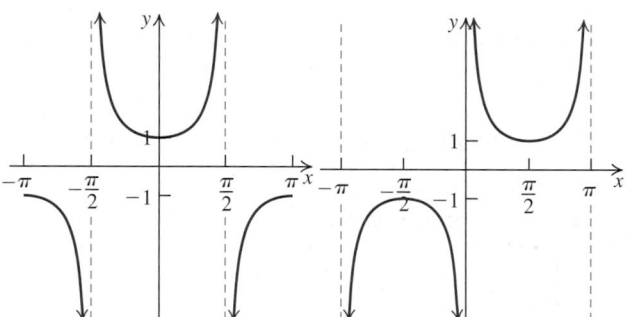

Secant Function

1. Period: 2π
2. Domain: All real numbers except for odd multiples of $\dfrac{\pi}{2}$
3. Range: $(-\infty, -1] \cup [1, \infty)$
4. Even: $\sec(-x) = \sec x$

Cosecant Function

1. Period: 2π
2. Domain: All real numbers except for integer multiples of π
3. Range: $(-\infty, -1] \cup [1, \infty)$
4. Odd: $\csc(-x) = -\csc x$

5.6 Inverse Trigonometric Functions

Inverse Trigonometric Functions			
Inverse Function	**Equivalent to**	**Domain**	**Range**
$y = \sin^{-1}x$	$\sin y = x$	$[-1, 1]$	$\left[-\dfrac{\pi}{2}, \dfrac{\pi}{2}\right]$
$y = \cos^{-1}x$	$\cos y = x$	$[-1, 1]$	$[0, \pi]$
$y = \tan^{-1}x$	$\tan y = x$	$(-\infty, \infty)$	$\left(-\dfrac{\pi}{2}, \dfrac{\pi}{2}\right)$
$y = \cot^{-1}x$	$\cot y = x$	$(-\infty, \infty)$	$(0, \pi)$
$y = \csc^{-1}x$	$\csc y = x$	$(-\infty, -1] \cup [1, \infty)$	$\left[-\dfrac{\pi}{2}, 0\right) \cup \left(0, \dfrac{\pi}{2}\right]$
$y = \sec^{-1}x$	$\sec y = x$	$(-\infty, -1] \cup [1, \infty)$	$\left[0, \dfrac{\pi}{2}\right) \cup \left(\dfrac{\pi}{2}, \pi\right]$

ii. Points on the terminal sides of angles in the standard position are used to find exact values of the composition of a trigonometric function and a different inverse trigonometric function.

iii. Inverse functions are used to solve right-angled triangles.

Review Exercises

In Exercises 1–4, draw each angle in standard position.

1. $240°$ †

2. $-150°$ †

3. $-\dfrac{2\pi}{3}$ †

4. $\dfrac{7\pi}{3}$ †

In Exercises 5–7, convert each angle from degrees to radians. Express each answer as a multiple of π.

5. $20°$ †

6. $36°$ †

7. $-60°$ †

In Exercises 8–10, convert each angle from radians to degrees.

8. $\dfrac{7\pi}{10}$ 126°

9. $\dfrac{5\pi}{18}$ 50°

10. $-\dfrac{4\pi}{9}$ −80°

In Exercises 11 and 12, find the radian measure of a central angle of a circle of radius r that intercepts each arc of length s. Round your answer to three decimal places.

11. 15 inches, $s = 40$ inches 2.667

12. 9 inches, $s = 17$ inches 1.889

In Exercises 13 and 14, find the length of the arc on each circle of radius r intercepted by a central angle θ. Round your answer to three decimal places.

13. $r = 2$ meters, $\theta = 36°$ 1.257 m

14. $r = 0.9$ meter, $\theta = 12°$ 0.188 m

In Exercises 15 and 16, find the exact values for the six trigonometric functions of each angle θ. Rationalize the denominator where necessary.

15.

16.

In Exercises 17–20, use each given trigonometric function value of θ to find the five other trigonometric function values of an acute angle θ. Rationalize the denominators where necessary.

17. $\cos\theta = \dfrac{2}{9}$ †

18. $\sin\theta = \dfrac{1}{5}$ †

19. $\tan\theta - \dfrac{5}{3}$ †

20. $\cot\theta = \dfrac{5}{4}$ †

In Exercises 21–24, a point on the terminal side of an angle θ is given. For each angle, find the exact values of the six trigonometric functions. Rationalize the denominators where necessary.

21. $(2, 8)$ †

22. $(-3, 7)$ †

23. $(-\sqrt{5}, 2)$ †

24. $(-\sqrt{3}, -\sqrt{6})$ †

In Exercises 25–28, use the given information to find the quadrant in which θ lies.

25. $\sin\theta < 0$ and $\cos\theta > 0$ IV **26.** $\sin\theta > 0$ and $\tan\theta > 0$ I

27. $\sin\theta < 0$ and $\cot\theta > 0$ III **28.** $\cos\theta < 0$ and $\csc\theta > 0$ II

In Exercises 29–32, find the exact values of the remaining trigonometric functions of θ from the given information.

29. $\cos\theta = -\dfrac{4}{5}$, θ in quadrant III †

30. $\tan\theta = -\dfrac{5}{12}$, θ in quadrant IV †

31. $\sin\theta = \dfrac{3}{5}$, θ in quadrant II †

32. $\csc\theta = -\dfrac{5}{4}$, θ in quadrant III †

In Exercises 33–36, find the exact value of each trigonometric function by using reference angles. Do not use a calculator.

33. $\cos 150°$ † **34.** $\sin(-300°)$ †

35. $\tan 390°$ † **36.** $\cot -405°$ -1

In Exercises 37–40, sketch the graph of each given equation over the interval $[-2\pi, 2\pi]$.

37. $y = -\dfrac{3}{2}\cos x$ † **38.** $y = \dfrac{5}{2}\sin x$ †

39. $y = 3\sin\left(x - \dfrac{\pi}{3}\right)$ † **40.** $y = 4\cos\left(x + \dfrac{3\pi}{2}\right)$ †

In Exercises 41–44, find the amplitude, period, and phase shift of each given function.

41. $y = 14\sin\left(2x + \dfrac{\pi}{7}\right)$ † **42.** $y = 21\cos\left(8x + \dfrac{\pi}{9}\right)$ †

43. $y = 6\tan\left(2x + \dfrac{\pi}{5}\right)$ † **44.** $y = -11\cot\left(6x + \dfrac{\pi}{12}\right)$ †

In Exercises 45–50, graph each function over a two-period interval.

45. $y = -2\cos\left(x + \dfrac{2\pi}{3}\right)$ † **46.** $y = 3\cos(x - \pi)$ †

47. $y = 5\tan 2\left(x - \dfrac{\pi}{4}\right)$ † **48.** $y = -\cot 2\left(x + \dfrac{\pi}{4}\right)$ †

49. $y = \dfrac{1}{2}\sec\dfrac{x}{2}$ † **50.** $y = -3\csc\dfrac{x}{2}$ †

In Exercises 51–58, find the exact value of y, or state that y is undefined.

51. $y = \cos^{-1}\left(\cos\dfrac{5\pi}{8}\right)$ $\dfrac{5\pi}{8}$ **52.** $y = \sin^{-1}\left(\sin\dfrac{7\pi}{6}\right)$ $-\dfrac{\pi}{6}$

53. $y = \tan^{-1}\left(\tan -\dfrac{2\pi}{3}\right)$ $\dfrac{\pi}{3}$ **54.** $y = \sin\left(\cos^{-1}\dfrac{1}{2}\right)$ $\dfrac{\sqrt{3}}{2}$

55. $y = \cos\left(\sin^{-1}\dfrac{\sqrt{2}}{2}\right)$ $\dfrac{\sqrt{2}}{2}$ **56.** $y = \cos\left(\tan^{-1}\dfrac{3}{4}\right)$ $\dfrac{4}{5}$

57. $y = \tan\left[\cos^{-1}\left(-\dfrac{1}{2}\right)\right]$ $-\sqrt{3}$ **58.** $y = \tan\left[\sin^{-1}\left(-\dfrac{\sqrt{3}}{2}\right)\right]$ $-\sqrt{3}$

In Exercises 59–64, solve triangle ABC. Write angle measures in degrees and round all answers to the nearest tenth.

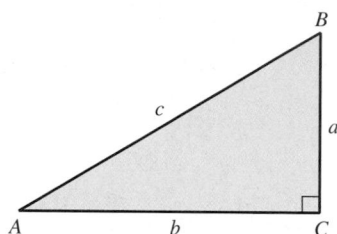

59. $a = 5, c = 13$ $b = 12, A \approx 22.6°, B \approx 67.4°$

60. $a = 2, b = 3$ $c = \sqrt{13}, A \approx 33.7°, B \approx 56.3°$

61. $b = 6, c = 12$ $a = 6\sqrt{3}, A = 60°, B = 30°$

62. $a = 4, m\angle A = 40°$ $B = 50°, c \approx 6.2, b \approx 4.8$

63. $c = 6, m\angle B = 37°$ $A = 53°, a \approx 4.8, b \approx 3.6$

64. $b = 3, m\angle A = 63°$ $B = 27°, a \approx 5.9, c \approx 6.6$

65. A tractor rolls backward so that its wheels turn a quarter of a revolution. If the tires have a radius of 28 inches, how many inches has the tractor moved? ≈ 44 inches

66. What is the radian measure of the smaller central angle made by the hands of a clock at 5:00? Express your answer as a rational multiple of π. †

67. New Orleans, Louisiana, is due south of Dubuque, Iowa. Find the distance between New Orleans (north latitude 29°59′ N) and Dubuque (north latitude 42°31′ N). Use 3960 miles as the value of the radius of Earth. ≈ 866 miles

68. At a time when the sun's rays make a 35° angle with the horizontal, how long is the shadow cast by a man who is 6 foot, 2 inches tall standing on flat ground? 8 ft 10 in.

69. The angle of depression from the top of a tree to a point 85 feet from its base (on flat ground) is found to be 12°. Find the height of the tree to the nearest foot. 18 ft

70. The angle of depression from a helicopter 850 feet directly above a crippled boat to a rescue ship is 40°. How far is the rescue ship from the crippled boat? 1013 ft

71. A gold triangular pendant has two sides of length 1.5 inches, with an included angle of 40°. How many square inches of gold does the pendant contain? ≈ 0.72 square inches

72. The table gives the average number of daylight hours in Santa Fe, New Mexico, each month. Let y represent the number of daylight hours in Santa Fe in month x, and find a function of the form $y = a\sin b(x - c) + d$ that models the hours of daylight throughout the year, where $x = 1$ represents January. †

Jan	Feb	Mar	Apr	May	June
10.1	9.9	12.0	12.7	14.1	14.1

July	Aug	Sept	Oct	Nov	Dec
14.3	13.5	12.0	11.3	10.0	9.8

73. Suppose that a ball attached to a spring is pulled down 11 inches and released and that the resulting simple harmonic motion has a period of 5 seconds. Write an equation of the ball's simple harmonic motion. †

74. At a distance of 200 yards, an observer watches a hot air balloon ascend vertically. (See the figure.) Express the angle of elevation as an inverse trigonometric function of

the height h of the balloon. (Ignore the height of the observer.) †

─ 200 ft ─

Practice Test A

1. Convert $140°$ to radians. 2.4435

2. Convert $\dfrac{7\pi}{5}$ to degrees. 252°

3. If $(2, -5)$ is a point on the terminal side of an angle θ, find $\cos\theta$. †

4. Find the radian measure of a central angle of a circle of radius 10 centimeters that intercepts an arc of length 15 centimeters. 1.5

5. Find the area of a sector of a circle of radius 15 centimeters that intersects an arc of length 10 centimeters. 75 cm²

6. If $\cos\theta = \dfrac{2}{7}$ for an acute angle θ, find $\sin\theta$. $\dfrac{3\sqrt{5}}{7}$

7. If $\tan\theta < 0$ and $\csc\theta > 0$, find the quadrant in which θ lies. †

8. If $\cot\theta = -\dfrac{5}{12}$ and θ is in quadrant IV, find $\sec\theta$. $\dfrac{13}{5}$

9. What is the reference angle for $217°$? 37°

10. If $\cos\dfrac{3\pi}{7} = 0.223$, find $\sin\dfrac{\pi}{14}$. 0.223

11. From a seat 65 meters high on a Ferris wheel, the angle of depression to a hot dog stand is $42°$. How many meters, to

the nearest meter, is the hot dog stand from a point directly below the seat? 72 m

12. Give the amplitude and range for $y = -7\sin x$. †

13. Find the amplitude, period, and phase shift for $y = 19\sin 12(x + 3\pi)$. †

14. Suppose that a ball attached to a spring is pulled down 7 inches and released, and that the resulting simple harmonic motion has a period of 4 seconds. Write an equation for the ball's simple harmonic motion. †

15. Graph $y = -\cos\dfrac{x}{2}$ over a one-period interval. †

16. Graph $y = \sin 2(x - \pi)$ over a one-period interval. †

17. Graph $y = \tan\left(x + \dfrac{\pi}{4}\right)$ over a one-period interval. †

18. Find the exact value of $y = \sin^{-1}\left(-\dfrac{\sqrt{3}}{2}\right)$. $-\dfrac{\pi}{3}$

19. Solve right triangle ABC if $a = 5.6$ and $b = 4.1$. †

20. Find the exact value of $y = \tan\left[\sin^{-1}\left(-\dfrac{1}{3}\right)\right]$. $-\dfrac{\sqrt{2}}{4}$

Practice Test B

Multiple choice—select the correct answer.

1. Convert 160° to radians. b

a. $\dfrac{7\pi}{9}$ **b.** $\dfrac{8\pi}{9}$ **c.** $\dfrac{4\pi}{3}$ **d.** $\dfrac{7\pi}{3}$

2. Convert $\dfrac{13\pi}{5}$ to degrees. d

a. 36°   **b.** 72°   **c.** 108°   **d.** 468°

3. If $(-3, 1)$ is a point on the terminal side of an angle θ, find $\cos\theta$. a

a. $-\dfrac{3\sqrt{10}}{10}$ **b.** $-\dfrac{\sqrt{10}}{10}$

c. $\dfrac{\sqrt{10}}{10}$ **d.** $\dfrac{3\sqrt{10}}{10}$

4. Find the radian measure of a central angle of a circle of radius 8 that intercepts an arc of length 4. a

a. $\dfrac{1}{2}$ **b.** 2   **c.** 32   **d.** 128

5. Find the area of a sector of a circle of radius 6 centimeters that intercepts an arc of length 3 centimeters. d

a. $\dfrac{9}{2}$ cm²   **b.** $\dfrac{27}{2}$ cm²   **c.** 6 cm²   **d.** 9 cm²

6. If $\cos\theta = \dfrac{3}{4}$ for an acute angle θ, find $\sin\theta$. b

a. $\dfrac{3}{\sqrt{7}}$ **b.** $\dfrac{\sqrt{7}}{4}$ **c.** $\dfrac{\sqrt{7}}{3}$ **d.** $\dfrac{4}{3}$

7. If $\sin\theta < 0$ and $\sec\theta > 0$ find the quadrant in which θ lies. d
a. I   **b.** II   **c.** III   **d.** IV

8. If $\tan\theta = \dfrac{12}{5}$ and θ is in quadrant III, find $\csc\theta$. b

a. $-\dfrac{5}{12}$ **b.** $-\dfrac{13}{12}$ **c.** $\dfrac{5}{13}$ **d.** $\dfrac{5}{12}$

9. What is the reference angle for 640°? c
a. 10°   **b.** 60°   **c.** 80°   **d.** 280°

10. In which quadrant is it true that both $\cos\theta > 0$ and $\csc\theta > 0$? a
a. I   **b.** II
c. III   **d.** IV

11. A point on the rim of a wheel with a radius of 50 centimeters has an angular speed of 0.8 radian per second. What is the linear speed of the point? c
a. 4 centimeters per second
b. 6.25 centimeters per second
c. 40 centimeters per second
d. 62.5 centimeters per second

12. If $y = a\cos bx$ has an amplitude of $\dfrac{1}{2}$ and a period of 4π, what are the values of a and b? a

a. $a = \dfrac{1}{2}, b = \dfrac{1}{2}$ **b.** $a = 2, b = \dfrac{1}{2}$

c. $a = \dfrac{1}{2}, b = 2$ **d.** $a = 2, b = 2$

13. Which of the following statements is *false*? b
a. $\sin(-x) = -\sin x$ **b.** $\cos(-x) = -\sin x$
c. $\tan(-x) = -\tan x$ **d.** $\cot(-x) = -\cot x$

14. A 3-foot shrub is 4.5 feet away from a 12-foot streetlight. What length shadow is cast by the shrub? a
a. 1.5 feet   **b.** 2 feet
c. 2.67 feet   **d.** 4 feet

15. Find the amplitude a, period b, and phase shift c for
$$y = -7\cos\frac{1}{6}\left(x - \frac{\pi}{12}\right).\ \text{d}$$

a. $a = 7, b = \dfrac{1}{6}\pi, c = \dfrac{\pi}{12}$

b. $a = 7, b = \dfrac{1}{6}\pi, c = -\dfrac{\pi}{12}$

c. $a = 7, b = 12\pi, c = -\dfrac{\pi}{12}$

d. $a = 7, b = 12\pi, c = \dfrac{\pi}{12}$

16. This is the graph of which function? c

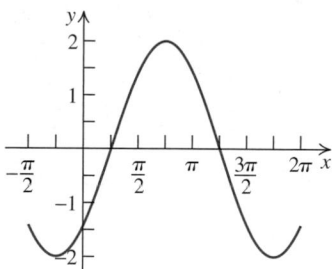

a. $y = -2\sin\left(x + \dfrac{\pi}{2}\right)$ **b.** $y = 2\sin\left(x + \dfrac{\pi}{2}\right)$

c. $y = -2\cos\left(x + \dfrac{\pi}{4}\right)$ **d.** $y = 2\cos\left(x + \dfrac{\pi}{4}\right)$

17. Find the exact value of $y = \cos^{-1}\left(\cos\dfrac{11\pi}{3}\right)$. c

a. $\dfrac{11\pi}{3}$ **b.** $\dfrac{5\pi}{3}$

c. $\dfrac{\pi}{3}$ **d.** $-\dfrac{\pi}{3}$

18. Find the exact value of $y = \cos\left[\sin^{-1}\left(-\dfrac{4}{5}\right)\right]$. a

a. $\dfrac{3}{5}$ **b.** $-\dfrac{3}{5}$ **c.** $\dfrac{3}{4}$ **d.** $-\dfrac{4}{3}$

19. In the right triangle ABC, $a = 12.5$ and $b = 25.4$. Which is closest to $m\angle A$? a
  a. $26.2°$ **b.** $29.5°$ **c.** $60.5°$ **d.** $63.8°$

20. Find the exact value of $y = \cos\left[\tan^{-1}\left(\dfrac{5}{3}\right)\right]$. d

a. $\dfrac{3}{5}$ **b.** $\dfrac{5}{34}$

c. $\dfrac{5\sqrt{34}}{34}$ **d.** $\dfrac{3\sqrt{34}}{34}$

Cumulative Review Exercises Chapters 1–5

1. Solve the equation $3x^2 - 30x + 50 = -24$. †

2. Find all real number solutions of the equation
$(\sqrt{t} + 1)^2 + 2(\sqrt{t} + 1) = 3$. 0

3. Solve the inequality $\dfrac{4 - x}{2x - 4} > 0$ and write the answer in interval notation. $(2, 4)$

4. Write the slope-intercept form of the equation of the line containing the points $(3, -1)$ and $(-6, 5)$. †

5. Find the domain of the function $f(x) = \ln\left(\dfrac{x}{2 - x}\right)$. $(0, 2)$

6. Identify the basic function and then use transformations to sketch the graph of the function $f(x) = 2(x - 3)^2 - 5$. †

7. Use transformations to sketch the graph of the function $f(x) = 4e^x + 1$. †

8. Find and write the domain of $(f \circ g)(x)$ in interval notation if $f(x) = \ln x$, and $g(x) = -\dfrac{1}{x}$. $(-\infty, 0)$

9. Determine whether each function has an inverse function. If so, find an equation for $f^{-1}(x)$.
  a. $f(x) = 3x + 7$ †   **b.** $f(x) = |x|$ †

10. Use synthetic division to find the quotient and remainder:
$\dfrac{2x^4 + 4x^3 + x^2 + x - 2}{x + 2}$ $2x^3 + x - 1$

11. Find the horizontal and the vertical asymptotes of the graph of $f(x) = \dfrac{10 - 3x^2}{x^2 + 4x - 5}$. $y = -3, x = -5, x = 1$

12. Use Rules of Logarithms to rewrite each expression in the expanded form.
  a. $\log\sqrt[3]{\dfrac{x^3 y}{z}}$ †   **b.** $\ln\left(\dfrac{7x^4}{5\sqrt{y}}\right)$ †

13. Sketch the graph of $f(x) = \begin{cases} -\ln x & \text{if } x > 0 \\ \ln|x| & \text{if } x < 0 \end{cases}$. †

14. Solve the equation $\log(x^2 + 9x) = 1$. $(-10, 1)$

15. Find all possible rational zeros of the function $f(x) = 2x^4 + 5x^3 + x^2 + 10x - 6$. †

16. Use the given trigonometric function value of θ to find the 5 other trigonometric function values of an acute angle θ. Rationalize the denominators where necessary.
  a. $\cos\theta = \dfrac{3}{7}$ †   **b.** $\sin\theta = \dfrac{2}{11}$ †

17. Find the exact values of the remaining trigonometric functions of θ from the given information.
  a. $\cos\theta = -\dfrac{4}{5}$, θ in quadrant II †
  b. $\cot\theta = \dfrac{5}{12}$, θ in quadrant III †

18. Sketch the graph of each equation over the interval $[-2\pi, 2\pi]$.
  a. $y = -\dfrac{1}{2}\cos(x + \pi)$ †   **b.** $y = -5\sin\left(x + \dfrac{5\pi}{3}\right)$ †

19. Find the exact value of y, or state that y is undefined.
  a. $y = \cos\left[\sin^{-1}\left(-\dfrac{1}{5}\right)\right]$ $\dfrac{2\sqrt{6}}{5}$
  b. $y = \sin\left(\tan^{-1}\dfrac{7}{2}\right)$ $\dfrac{7\sqrt{53}}{53}$

20. Solve the right triangle ABC if $A = 18°$ and $c = 30.6$.
Answer:
20. $B = 72°$, $a \approx 9.5$, $b \approx 29$.

CHAPTER 6

Analytic Trigonometry

Such varied phenomena as sonic booms from aircraft, musical tones, hours of daylight in a given location, current in an electric circuit, tides, and rainfall, can be described using trigonometric functions. Solutions of trigonometric equations often provide answers to questions about the conditions under which specific characteristics of these phenomena occur. In this chapter we study techniques for solving trigonometric equations.

TOPICS

Trigonometric Identities and Equations

**Hipparchus of Rhodes
(190–120 B.C.)**
Hipparchus was born in Nicaea (now called Iznik) in Bithynia (northwest Turkey), but spent much of his life in Rhodes (Greece). Many historians consider him the founder of trigonometry. He introduced trigonometric functions in the form of a chord table—the ancestor of the sine table found in ancient Indian astronomical works. With his chord table, Hipparchus could solve the height–distance problems of plane trigonometry. In his time, there was no Greek term for trigonometry, because it was not counted as a branch of mathematics. Rather, trigonometry was just an aid to solve problems in astronomy.

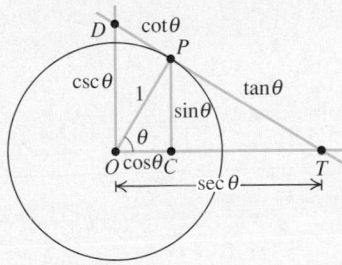

FIGURE 6.1

BEFORE STARTING THIS SECTION, REVIEW

1. Signs of the trigonometric functions (Section 5.3, page 534)

2. LCD and adding rational expressions (Section P.5, page 53)

3. Factoring and special products (Section P.4, page 43)

OBJECTIVES

1 Use fundamental trigonometric identities to evaluate trigonometric functions.

2 Simplify a complicated trigonometric expression.

3 Verify a trigonometric identity.

Visualizing Trigonometric Functions

Trigonometric functions are commonly defined as the ratios of two sides corresponding to an angle in a right triangle. The Greek mathematician Hipparchus was the first to relate trigonometric functions with a circle. We can visualize the trigonometric functions of an acute angle θ as the length of various segments associated with a unit circle. See Figure 6.1.

There are several similar triangles in Figure 6.1. For example, triangles PCT and OCP are similar so that

$$\frac{CT}{PC} = \frac{PC}{OC}. \qquad \text{Sides are proportional.}$$

From Figure 6.1, we have

$$PC = \sin\theta, OC = \cos\theta, \text{ and } CT = OT - OC = \sec\theta - \cos\theta.$$

Substituting these values into the equation $\dfrac{CT}{PC} = \dfrac{PC}{OC}$, we obtain

$$\frac{\sec\theta - \cos\theta}{\sin\theta} = \frac{\sin\theta}{\cos\theta}.$$

In Example 6, we shall verify that this equation is an identity. Recall that an *identity* is an equation that is true for all numbers for which both sides are defined.

In Section 5.3, the six trigonometric functions were defined in terms of the coordinates of a point $P(x, y)$ on a unit circle. Consequently, these functions are related to each other, and any expression containing these functions can be written in several equivalent ways. ■

Fundamental Trigonometric Identities

In Chapter 5, we used the definitions of the trigonometric functions to establish reciprocal, quotient, Pythagorean, and even-odd identities. These are called **fundamental trigonometric identities** and are listed in the next box.

FUNDAMENTAL TRIGONOMETRIC IDENTITIES

1. Reciprocal Identities

$$\csc x = \frac{1}{\sin x} \qquad \sec x = \frac{1}{\cos x} \qquad \cot x = \frac{1}{\tan x}$$

$$\sin x = \frac{1}{\csc x} \qquad \cos x = \frac{1}{\sec x} \qquad \tan x = \frac{1}{\cot x}$$

2. Quotient Identities

$$\tan x = \frac{\sin x}{\cos x} \qquad \cot x = \frac{\cos x}{\sin x}$$

3. Pythagorean Identities

$$\sin^2 x + \cos^2 x = 1 \qquad 1 + \tan^2 x = \sec^2 x \qquad 1 + \cot^2 x = \csc^2 x$$

4. Even-Odd Identities

$$\sin(-x) = -\sin x \qquad \cos(-x) = \cos x \qquad \tan(-x) = -\tan x$$

$$\csc(-x) = -\csc x \qquad \sec(-x) = \sec x \qquad \cot(-x) = -\cot x$$

---

1 Use trigonometric identities to evaluate trigonometric functions.

Evaluating Trigonometric Functions

The next example illustrates the use of a Pythagorean identity to evaluate a related function.

STUDY TIP

It is important to remember that it is the terminal side of an angle that determines the quadrant in which the angle lies. It does *not* matter whether the angle is measured in radians or in degrees.

EXAMPLE 1   **Using a Pythagorean Identity**

If $\cos\theta = -\dfrac{5}{13}$ and $\pi < \theta < \dfrac{3\pi}{2}$, find $\tan\theta$.

Solution

Since $\cos\theta = -\dfrac{5}{13}$, we have

$$\sec\theta = -\frac{13}{5} \qquad \text{Reciprocal identity}$$

$$\tan^2\theta = \sec^2\theta - 1 \qquad \text{Variation of the Pythagorean identity: } 1 + \tan^2\theta = \sec^2\theta$$

$$\tan\theta = \sqrt{\sec^2\theta - 1} \qquad \theta \text{ is in quadrant III, so } \tan\theta \text{ is positive.}$$

$$= \sqrt{\left(-\frac{13}{5}\right)^2 - 1} \qquad \text{Replace } \sec\theta \text{ by } -\frac{13}{5}.$$

$$= \sqrt{\frac{169}{25} - 1} = \sqrt{\frac{144}{25}} = \frac{12}{5}.$$

■ ■ ■

PRACTICE PROBLEM 1   If $\sin\theta = \dfrac{4}{5}$ and $\dfrac{\pi}{2} < \theta < \pi$, find $\cot\theta$.   ■

The next example shows how fundamental trigonometric identities are used to evaluate the remaining trigonometric functions from one specified trigonometric function value.

EXAMPLE 2   **Using the Fundamental Trigonometric Identities**

If $\cot x = \dfrac{3}{4}$ and $\pi < x < \dfrac{3\pi}{2}$, find the values of the remaining trigonometric functions.

Solution

From the given value of $\cot x$, we can find the value of the related function $\csc x$ by using the identity $\csc^2 x = 1 + \cot^2 x$.

$$
\begin{aligned}
\csc^2 x &= 1 + \cot^2 x && \text{Pythagorean identity} \\
&= 1 + \left(\frac{3}{4}\right)^2 && \text{Replace } \cot x \text{ by } \frac{3}{4}. \\
&= 1 + \frac{9}{16} && \left(\frac{3}{4}\right)^2 = \frac{9}{16} \\
\csc^2 x &= \frac{25}{16} && \text{Simplify.} \\
\csc x &= -\frac{5}{4} && \begin{array}{l}\text{Square root property; } x \text{ is in} \\ \text{quadrant III, so } \csc x \text{ is negative.}\end{array} \\
\sin x &= -\frac{4}{5} && \sin x = \frac{1}{\csc x}
\end{aligned}
$$

Multiplying both sides of the quotient identity $\dfrac{\cos x}{\sin x} = \cot x$ by $\sin x$, we have

$$
\begin{aligned}
\cos x &= \cot x \, \sin x \\
&= \left(\frac{3}{4}\right)\left(-\frac{4}{5}\right) && \text{Substitute values of } \cot x \text{ and } \sin x. \\
&= -\frac{3}{5} && \text{Simplify.}
\end{aligned}
$$

We have the following values of the trigonometric functions:

$$
\begin{array}{ll}
\sin x = -\dfrac{4}{5} & \csc x = -\dfrac{5}{4} \\[2ex]
\cos x = -\dfrac{3}{5} & \sec x = \dfrac{1}{\cos x} = -\dfrac{5}{3} \\[2ex]
\cot x = \dfrac{3}{4} & \tan x = \dfrac{1}{\cot x} = \dfrac{4}{3}
\end{array}
$$

■ ■ ■

PRACTICE PROBLEM 2 If $\tan x = -1$ and $\dfrac{\pi}{2} < x < \pi$, find the values of the remaining trigonometric functions. ■

2 Simplify a complicated trigonometric expression.

Simplifying a Trigonometric Expression

The fundamental trigonometric identities are often used for simplifying complicated trigonometric expressions. Recall that when simplifying algebraic expressions, we use properties of real numbers, together with factoring techniques, special product formulas, and rationalizing the denominator. We must also find the least common denominator when adding or subtracting rational expressions. These same techniques together with the fundamental trigonometric identities are used to simplify trigonometric expressions.

> **EXAMPLE 3** **Simplifying by Expressing All Trigonometric Functions in Terms of Sines and Cosines**

Rewrite $\cot x + \tan x + \csc x \sec x$ in terms of sines and cosines and then simplify the resulting expression.

Solution

$$\cot x + \tan x + \csc x \sec x$$

$$= \frac{\cos x}{\sin x} + \frac{\sin x}{\cos x} + \frac{1}{\sin x} \cdot \frac{1}{\cos x} \qquad \text{Quotient and Reciprocal identities}$$

$$= \frac{\cos^2 x}{\sin x \cos x} + \frac{\sin^2 x}{\sin x \cos x} + \frac{1}{\sin x \cos x} \qquad \begin{array}{l}\text{Write each fraction with common denominator} \\ \sin x \cos x.\end{array}$$

$$= \frac{\cos^2 x + \sin^2 x + 1}{\sin x \cos x} \qquad \text{Add numerators.}$$

$$= \frac{1 + 1}{\sin x \cos x} \qquad \sin^2 x + \cos^2 x = 1$$

$$= \frac{2}{\sin x \cos x} \qquad \qquad ■\ ■\ ■$$

PRACTICE PROBLEM 3 Rewrite the expression in terms of sines and cosines and then simplify the resulting expression.

$$\frac{\tan x}{\sec x + 1} + \frac{\tan x}{\sec x - 1} \qquad ■$$

Trigonometric Equations and Identities

To verify that an equation is a trigonometric identity, you must *prove* that both sides of the equation are equal for all values of the variable for which both sides are defined.

Consider the equation:

$$\cos x = \sqrt{1 - \sin^2 x} \qquad (1)$$

Equation (1) is true for infinitely many values of the variable x. In fact, it is true for all values of x in the interval $\left[-\dfrac{\pi}{2}, \dfrac{\pi}{2}\right]$. See Figure 6.2(a).

$$x \text{ in } \left[-\frac{\pi}{2}, \frac{\pi}{2}\right]$$

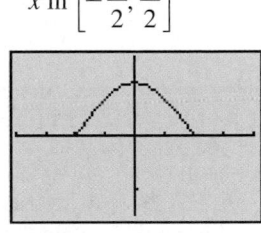

$$Y_1 = \cos x,$$
$$Y_2 = \sqrt{1 - \sin^2 x}$$

$$x \text{ in } \left[-\pi, \pi\right]$$

Graphs of both Y_1 and Y_2.

(a)

The thicker graph is Y_2.

(b)

FIGURE 6.2

Since the domain of both the sine and the cosine functions is the interval $(-\infty, \infty)$, both sides of equation (1) are defined for all real numbers. But for any value of x in the interval $\left(\frac{\pi}{2}, \pi\right]$, the left side of Equation (1) has a negative value (recall that $\cos x$ is negative in quadrant II), while the right side of Equation (1) has a positive value. Thus, Equation (1) is not an identity. See Figure 6.2(b). The graphs in Figure 6.2(b) show that a graphing calculator may be helpful in determining that a given equation is *not* an identity. However, Figure 6.2(a) shows that a graphing calculator cannot be used to verify that a given equation *is* an identity, because you might happen to use a viewing window where the graphs coincide.

EXAMPLE 4   **Proving That an Equation Is Not an Identity**

Prove that the equation

$$(\sin x - \cos x)^2 = \sin^2 x - \cos^2 x$$

is not an identity.

Solution

We prove that the given equation is not an identity by finding at least one value of the variable for which both sides are defined, but for which the two sides of the equation have different values.

Let $x = 0$. We know that $\sin 0 = 0$ and $\cos 0 = 1$.

$$\text{The left side} = (\sin x - \cos x)^2 = (0 - 1)^2 = 1 \qquad \text{Replace } x \text{ by } 0.$$
$$\text{The right side} = \sin^2 x - \cos^2 x = (0)^2 - (1)^2 = -1 \qquad \text{Replace } x \text{ by } 0.$$

Since, for $x = 0$, the two sides of the equation are not equal, the given equation is not an identity.   ■ ■ ■

PRACTICE PROBLEM 4   Prove that the equation $\cos x = 1 - \sin x$ is not an identity.   ■

---

3 Verify a trigonometric identity.

Process of Verifying Trigonometric Identities

The process for verifying a trigonometric identity is different than the process for solving an equation. In verifying an identity, we are given an equation and we wish to show that the equation is true for *all* values of the variable for which both sides of the equation are defined. The following box describes a method of verifying an identity:

VERIFYING TRIGONOMETRIC IDENTITIES

To verify that a given equation is an identity, we transform one side of the equation into the other side by a sequence of steps, each of which produces an identity. The steps involved may be algebraic manipulations or may use known identities.

Note that in verifying an identity, we *do not* just perform the same operation on both sides of the equation.

Methods of Verifying Trigonometric Identities

There is no set procedure for verifying trigonometric identities. Considerable practice and experience are required. In the examples that follow, we suggest five guidelines for verifying trigonometric identities.

1. Start with the more complicated side and transform it to the simpler side.

EXAMPLE 5   Verifying an Identity

Verify the identity:

$$\frac{\csc^2 x - 1}{\cot x} = \cot x$$

Solution

We start with the left side of the equation, because it appears more complicated than the right side.

$$\frac{\csc^2 x - 1}{\cot x} = \frac{\cot^2 x}{\cot x} \qquad \text{Use a variation of the Pythagorean identity } \csc^2 x = 1 + \cot^2 x.$$

$$= \cot x \qquad \text{Remove the common factor } \cot x.$$

The result shows that the left side of the equation is equal to the right side. Hence, the identity has been verified. ■ ■ ■

PRACTICE PROBLEM 5   Verify the identity:

$$\frac{1 - \sin^2 x}{\cos x} = \cos x \qquad\qquad ■$$

2. Stay focused on the answer.

While working on one side of the equation, stay focused on your goal of converting it to the form on the other side. This often helps in deciding what your next step should be.

We next verify the identity proposed in the introduction to this section.

EXAMPLE 6   **Verifying an Identity**

Verify the identity:

$$\frac{\sec\theta - \cos\theta}{\sin\theta} = \frac{\sin\theta}{\cos\theta}$$

Solution

We start with the more complicated left side.

$$\frac{\sec\theta - \cos\theta}{\sin\theta} = \frac{\dfrac{1}{\cos\theta} - \cos\theta}{\sin\theta} \qquad\qquad \sec\theta = \frac{1}{\cos\theta}$$

$$= \frac{\left(\dfrac{1}{\cos\theta} - \cos\theta\right)\cos\theta}{\sin\theta\cos\theta} \qquad \text{Multiply numerator and denominator by } \cos\theta.$$

$$= \frac{\dfrac{1}{\cos\theta}\cdot\cos\theta - \cos^2\theta}{\sin\theta\cos\theta} \qquad \text{Distributive property}$$

$$= \frac{1 - \cos^2\theta}{\sin\theta\cos\theta} \qquad\qquad \text{Simplify.}$$

$$= \frac{\sin^2\theta}{\sin\theta\cos\theta} \qquad\qquad \text{Variation of the Pythagorean identity } \sin^2\theta + \cos^2\theta = 1.$$

$$= \frac{\sin\theta}{\cos\theta} \qquad\qquad \text{Remove the common factor } \sin\theta. \qquad ■ ■ ■$$

PRACTICE PROBLEM 6   In Figure 6.1, triangles OPD and TCP are similar. Thus, $\dfrac{OD}{OP} = \dfrac{PT}{CT}$ leads to the trigonometric equation:

$$\frac{\csc\theta}{1} = \frac{\tan\theta}{\sec\theta - \cos\theta}$$

Verify that the equation is an identity.   ■

3. Convert to sines and cosines.

It may be helpful to rewrite all trigonometric functions in the equation in terms of sines and cosines and then simplify.

EXAMPLE 7   **Verifying by Rewriting with Sines and Cosines**

Verify the identity: $\cot^4 x + \cot^2 x = \cot^2 x \csc^2 x$

Solution

We start with the more complicated left side.

$$\cot^4 x + \cot^2 x = \frac{\cos^4 x}{\sin^4 x} + \frac{\cos^2 x}{\sin^2 x} \qquad\qquad \cot x = \frac{\cos x}{\sin x}$$

$$= \frac{\cos^4 x}{\sin^4 x} + \frac{\cos^2 x}{\sin^2 x}\cdot\frac{\sin^2 x}{\sin^2 x} \qquad \text{The LCD is } \sin^4 x.$$

Continued on next page.

$$= \frac{\cos^4 x + \cos^2 x \sin^2 x}{\sin^4 x} \qquad \text{Add rational expressions.}$$

$$= \frac{\cos^2 x (\cos^2 x + \sin^2 x)}{\sin^4 x} \qquad \text{Factor out } \cos^2 x.$$

$$= \frac{\cos^2 x (1)}{\sin^4 x} \qquad \cos^2 x + \sin^2 x = 1$$

$$= \frac{\cos^2 x}{\sin^2 x} \cdot \frac{1}{\sin^2 x} \qquad \begin{array}{l}\text{Factor to obtain the form} \\ \text{on the right side.}\end{array}$$

$$= \cot^2 x \csc^2 x \qquad \cot x = \frac{\cos x}{\sin x}, \csc x = \frac{1}{\sin x}$$

Because the left side is identical to the right side, the given equation is an identity.

You could also verify the identity in Example 7, as follows:

$$\cot^4 x + \cot^2 x = \cot^2 x (\cot^2 x + 1) \qquad \text{Distributive property}$$

$$= \cot^2 x \csc^2 x \qquad \text{Pythagorean identity}$$

This shows that rewriting the expression using only sines and cosines is not necessarily the quickest way to verify an identity. However, when you are stuck, it may be helpful to try this approach. ■ ■ ■

PRACTICE PROBLEM 7 Verify the identity: $\tan^4 x + \tan^2 x = \tan^2 x \sec^2 x$ ■

4. Work on both sides.

Sometimes it is helpful to work separately on both sides of the equation. Suppose we are to verify the identity $P(x) = Q(x)$. We begin by transforming the left side $P(x)$ into another expression $R(x)$ by using algebraic manipulations and known identities. Then $P(x) = R(x)$ is an identity. Next, we show that the right side, $Q(x)$, can also be transformed into $R(x)$ so that the equation $R(x) = Q(x)$ is an identity. It then follows that $P(x) = Q(x)$ is an identity. The method is illustrated in the next example.

EXAMPLE 8 **Verifying an Identity by Working Both Sides Separately**

Verify the identity:

$$\frac{1}{1 - \sin x} - \frac{1}{1 + \sin x} = \frac{\tan^2 x + \sec^2 x + 1}{\csc x}.$$

Solution

We start with the left side of the equation.

$$\frac{1}{1 - \sin x} - \frac{1}{1 + \sin x} \qquad \text{The LCD is } (1 - \sin x)(1 + \sin x).$$

$$= \frac{1}{1 - \sin x} \cdot \frac{1 + \sin x}{1 + \sin x} - \frac{1}{1 + \sin x} \cdot \frac{1 - \sin x}{1 - \sin x} \qquad \begin{array}{l}\text{Write each expression with a} \\ \text{common denominator.}\end{array}$$

$$= \frac{(1 + \sin x) - (1 - \sin x)}{(1 - \sin x)(1 + \sin x)}$$ Subtract fractions.

$$= \frac{1 + \sin x - 1 + \sin x}{1 - \sin^2 x}$$ Remove parenthesis in the numerator, and multiply factors in the denominator.

$$= \frac{2 \sin x}{\cos^2 x}$$ Simplify numerator, $1 - \sin^2 x = \cos^2 x$.

We now work with the right side.

The goal is to convert it to the form $\frac{2\sin x}{\cos^2 x}$.

$$\frac{\tan^2 x + \sec^2 x + 1}{\csc x}$$

$$= \frac{(\tan^2 x + 1) + \sec^2 x}{\csc x}$$ Regroup terms.

$$= \frac{\sec^2 x + \sec^2 x}{\csc x}$$ $\tan^2 x + 1 = \sec^2 x$

$$= \frac{2 \sec^2 x}{\csc x}$$ Simplify.

$$= 2\left(\frac{1}{\csc x}\right)\sec^2 x$$ Rewrite.

$$= 2\sin x\left(\frac{1}{\cos^2 x}\right)$$ Reciprocal identities

$$= \frac{2 \sin x}{\cos^2 x}$$ Multiply.

Because both sides of the original equation are equal to $\frac{2\sin x}{\cos^2 x}$, the identity is verified. ■ ■ ■

PRACTICE PROBLEM 8   Verify the identity:

$$\tan\theta + \sec\theta = \frac{\csc\theta + 1}{\cot\theta}$$ ■

5. Use conjugates.

It may be helpful to multiply both the numerator and the denominator of a fraction by the same factor. Recall that the sum $a + b$ and the difference $a - b$ are the *conjugates* of each other.

EXAMPLE 9   **Verifying an Identity by Using a Conjugate**

Verify the identity:

$$\frac{\cos x}{1 + \sin x} = \frac{1 - \sin x}{\cos x}$$

Continued on next page.

Solution

We start with the left side of the equation.

$$\frac{\cos x}{1 + \sin x} = \frac{\cos x(1 - \sin x)}{(1 + \sin x)(1 - \sin x)} \qquad \begin{array}{l}\text{Multiply the numerator and the} \\ \text{denominator by } 1 - \sin x, \text{ the conjugate} \\ \text{of } 1 + \sin x.\end{array}$$

$$= \frac{\cos x(1 - \sin x)}{1 - \sin^2 x} \qquad (a + b)(a - b) = a^2 - b^2$$

$$= \frac{\cos x(1 - \sin x)}{\cos^2 x} \qquad 1 - \sin^2 x = \cos^2 x$$

$$= \frac{1 - \sin x}{\cos x} \qquad \begin{array}{l}\text{Remove the common} \\ \text{factor } \cos x.\end{array}$$

■ ■ ■

PRACTICE PROBLEM 9   Verify the identity: $\dfrac{\tan x}{\sec x + 1} = \dfrac{\sec x - 1}{\tan x}$ ■

We summarize guidelines and hints to help you with verifying trigonometric identities.

GUIDELINES FOR VERIFYING TRIGONOMETRIC IDENTITIES

Algebra Operations

Review the use of the algebraic operations for combining fractions by finding the least common denominator.

Fundamental Trigonometric Identities

Review the fundamental trigonometric identities summarized on page 596. Look for an opportunity to apply the fundamental trigonometric identities when working on either side of the identity to be verified. Be thoroughly familiar with alternative forms of fundamental identities. For example, $\sin^2 x = 1 - \cos^2 x$ and $\sec^2 x - \tan^2 x = 1$ are alternative forms of the fundamental identities $\sin^2 x + \cos^2 x = 1$ and $\sec^2 x = 1 + \tan^2 x$, respectively.

1. **Start with the more complicated side.**
    If one side of an identity is more complex than the other side, it is generally helpful to start with the more complicated side and simplify it until it becomes identical to the other side. (See Example 5.)

2. **Stay focused on the answer.**
    While working on one side of the identity, stay focused on your goal of converting it to the form on the other side. (See Example 6.)

3. **Convert to sines and cosines.**
    Rewriting one side of the identity in terms of sines and cosines is often helpful. (See Example 7.)

4. **Work on both sides.**
    Sometimes, it is helpful to work separately on both sides of the equation to transform each side to the same equivalent expression. (See Example 8.)

5. **Use conjugates.**
    In expressions containing $1 + \sin x$, $1 - \sin x$, $1 + \cos x$, $1 - \cos x$, $\sec x + \tan x$, and so on, it is often helpful to multiply both the numerator and the denominator by the appropriate conjugate and then use one of the forms of the Pythagorean identities. (See Example 9.)

A Exercises   Basic Skills and Concepts

1. If $\sin\theta = -\dfrac{12}{13}$ and $\pi < \theta < \dfrac{3\pi}{2}$, find $\cos\theta$. $-\dfrac{5}{13}$

2. If $\sec\theta = \dfrac{5}{4}$ and $\dfrac{3\pi}{2} < \theta < 2\pi$, find $\tan\theta$. $-\dfrac{3}{4}$

3. If $\cot\theta = \dfrac{1}{2}$ and $\pi < \theta < \dfrac{3\pi}{2}$, find $\csc\theta$. $-\dfrac{\sqrt{5}}{2}$

4. If $\cos\theta = -\dfrac{1}{3}$ and $\dfrac{\pi}{2} < \theta < \pi$, find $\tan\theta$. $-2\sqrt{2}$

5. If $\sin x = -\dfrac{2}{3}$, and $\pi < x < \dfrac{3\pi}{2}$, find $\cot x$. $\dfrac{\sqrt{5}}{2}$

6. If $\tan x = \dfrac{1}{2}$, and $\pi < x < \dfrac{3\pi}{2}$, find $\cos x$. $-\dfrac{2\sqrt{5}}{5}$

In Exercises 7–18, use the fundamental identities and the given information to find the exact values of the remaining trigonometric functions of x.

7. $\cos x = -\dfrac{3}{5}$ and $\sin x = \dfrac{4}{5}$ †

8. $\cos x = \dfrac{3}{5}$ and $\sin x = -\dfrac{4}{5}$ †

9. $\sin x = \dfrac{1}{\sqrt{3}}$ and $\cos x = \sqrt{\dfrac{2}{3}}$ †

10. $\sin x = \dfrac{1}{\sqrt{3}}$ and $\cos x = -\sqrt{\dfrac{2}{3}}$ †

11. $\tan x = \dfrac{1}{2}$ and $\sec x = -\dfrac{\sqrt{5}}{2}$ †

12. $\tan x = \dfrac{1}{2}$ and $\sec x = \dfrac{\sqrt{5}}{2}$ †

13. $\csc x = 3$ and $\cot x = 2\sqrt{2}$ †

14. $\csc x = 3$ and $\cot x = -2\sqrt{2}$ †

15. $\cot x = \dfrac{12}{5}$ and $\sin x = -\dfrac{5}{13}$ †

16. $\cot x = -\dfrac{12}{5}$ and $\sin x = -\dfrac{5}{13}$ †

17. $\sec x = 3$ and $\dfrac{3\pi}{2} < x < 2\pi$ †

18. $\tan x = -2$ and $\dfrac{\pi}{2} < x < \pi$ †

In Exercises 19–28, use the fundamental identities and appropriate algebraic operations to simplify each expression.

19. $(1 + \tan x)(1 - \tan x) + \sec^2 x$ 2

20. $(\sec x - 1)(\sec x + 1) - \tan^2 x$ 0

21. $(\sec x + \tan x)(\sec x - \tan x)$ 1

22. $\dfrac{\sec^2 x - 4}{\sec x - 2}$ $\sec x + 2$

23. $\csc^4 x - \cot^4 x$ $\csc^2 x + \cot^2 x$

24. $\sin x \cos x(\tan x + \cot x)$ 1

25. $\dfrac{\sec x \csc x(\sin x + \cos x)}{\sec x + \csc x}$ 1

26. $\dfrac{1}{\csc x + 1} - \dfrac{1}{\csc x - 1}$ $-2\tan^2 x$

27. $\dfrac{\tan^2 x - 2\tan x - 3}{\tan x + 1}$ $\tan x - 3$

28. $\dfrac{\tan^2 x + \sec x - 1}{\sec x - 1}$ $\sec x + 2$

In Exercises 29–72, verify each identity.

29. $\sin x \tan x + \cos x = \sec x$

30. $\cos x \cot x + \sin x = \csc x$

31. $\dfrac{1 - 4\cos^2 x}{1 - 2\cos x} = 1 + 2\cos x$

32. $\dfrac{9 - 16\sin^2 x}{3 + 4\sin x} = 3 - 4\sin x$

33. $(\cos x - \sin x)(\cos x + \sin x) = 1 - 2\sin^2 x$

34. $(\sin x - \cos x)(\sin x + \cos x) = 1 - 2\cos^2 x$

35. $\sin^2 x \cot^2 x + \sin^2 x = 1$

36. $\tan^2 x - \sin^2 x = \sin^4 x \sec^2 x$

37. $\sin^3 x - \cos^3 x = (\sin x - \cos x)(1 + \sin x \cos x)$

38. $\sin^3 x + \cos^3 x = (\sin x + \cos x)(1 - \sin x \cos x)$

39. $\cos^4 x - \sin^4 x = 1 - 2\sin^2 x$

40. $\cos^4 x - \sin^4 x = 2\cos^2 x - 1$

41. $\dfrac{1}{1 - \sin x} + \dfrac{1}{1 + \sin x} = 2\sec^2 x$

42. $\dfrac{1}{1 - \cos x} + \dfrac{1}{1 + \cos x} = 2\csc^2 x$

43. $\dfrac{1}{\csc x - 1} - \dfrac{1}{\csc x + 1} = 2\tan^2 x$

44. $\dfrac{1}{\sec x - 1} + \dfrac{1}{\sec x + 1} = 2\sec x \cot^2 x$

45. $\sec^2 x + \csc^2 x = \sec^2 x \csc^2 x$

46. $\cot^2 x + \tan^2 x = \sec^2 x \csc^2 x - 2$

47. $\dfrac{1}{\sec x - \tan x} + \dfrac{1}{\sec x + \tan x} = \dfrac{2}{\cos x}$

48. $\dfrac{1}{\csc x + \cot x} + \dfrac{1}{\csc x - \cot x} = \dfrac{2}{\sin x}$

†Due to space constrictions, answers to these exercises may be found in the Answers beginning on page A–1 in the back of the book.

49. $\dfrac{\sin x}{1 + \cos x} = \csc x - \cot x$

50. $\dfrac{\sin x}{1 - \cos x} = \csc x + \cot x$

51. $(\sin x + \cos x)^2 = 1 + 2\sin x \cos x$

52. $(\sin x - \cos x)^2 = 1 - 2\sin x \cos x$

53. $(1 + \tan x)^2 = \sec^2 x + 2\tan x$

54. $(1 - \cot x)^2 = \csc^2 x - 2\cot x$

55. $\dfrac{\tan x \sin x}{\tan x + \sin x} = \dfrac{\tan x - \sin x}{\tan x \sin x}$

56. $\dfrac{\cot x \cos x}{\cot x + \cos x} = \dfrac{\cot x - \cos x}{\cot x \cos x}$

57. $(\tan x + \cot x)^2 = \sec^2 x + \csc^2 x$

58. $(1 + \cot^2 x)(1 + \tan^2 x) = \dfrac{1}{\sin^2 x \cos^2 x}$

59. $\dfrac{\sin^2 x - \cos^2 x}{\sec^2 x - \csc^2 x} = \sin^2 x \cos^2 x$

60. $\left(\tan x + \dfrac{1}{\cot x}\right)\left(\cot x + \dfrac{1}{\tan x}\right) = 4$

61. $\dfrac{\tan x}{1 + \sec x} + \dfrac{1 + \sec x}{\tan x} = 2\csc x$

62. $\dfrac{\cot x}{1 + \csc x} + \dfrac{1 + \csc x}{\cot x} = 2\sec x$

63. $\dfrac{\sin x + \tan x}{\cos x + 1} = \tan x$

64. $\dfrac{\sin x}{1 + \tan x} = \dfrac{\cos x}{1 + \cot x}$

65. $\dfrac{\sin x - 2\sin^3 x}{2\cos^3 x - \cos x} = \tan x$

66. $\dfrac{\csc x + \cot x}{\csc x - \cot x} = \dfrac{\sin^2 x}{(1 - \cos x)^2}$

67. $\dfrac{1 - \sin x}{1 - \sec x} - \dfrac{1 + \sin x}{1 + \sec x} = 2\cot x(\cos x - \csc x)$

68. $\dfrac{\sec x + \tan x}{\csc x + \cot x} - \dfrac{\sec x - \tan x}{\csc x - \cot x} = 2(\sec x - \csc x)$

69. $(1 - \tan x)^2 + (1 - \cot x)^2 = (\sec x - \csc x)^2$

70. $\sec^6 x - \tan^6 x = 1 + 3\tan^2 x + 3\tan^4 x$

71. $\dfrac{\cot x + \csc x - 1}{\cot x + \csc x + 1} = \dfrac{1 - \sin x}{\cos x}$

72. $\dfrac{\tan x + \sec x - 1}{\tan x - \sec x + 1} = \dfrac{1 + \sin x}{\cos x}$

B Exercises Applying the Concepts

73. Length of a ladder. A ladder x feet long makes an angle θ with the horizontal and reaches a height of 20 feet.
Then $x = \dfrac{20}{\sin \theta}$. Use a reciprocal identity to rewrite this formula. $20\csc\theta$

74. Distance from a building. From a distance of x feet to a 60-foot-high building, the angle of elevation is θ degrees.
Then $x = \dfrac{60}{\tan \theta}$. Use a reciprocal identity to rewrite this formula. $60\cot\theta$

C Exercises Beyond the Basics

In Exercises 75–84, simplify each expression.

75. $(\sin u \cos v + \cos u \sin v)^2 + (\cos u \cos v - \sin u \sin v)^2$ 1

76. $(\sin u \cos v - \cos u \sin v)^2 + (\cos u \cos v + \sin u \sin v)^2$ 1

77. $3(\sin^4 x + \cos^4 x) - 2(\sin^6 x + \cos^6 x)$ 1

78. $\sin^6 x + \cos^6 x + 3\cos^2 x - 3\cos^4 x$ 1

79. $\dfrac{1 - \cos \theta}{1 + \cos \theta} + \dfrac{1 + \cos \theta}{1 - \cos \theta} - 4\cot^2 \theta$ 2

80. $\dfrac{\cos^3 \theta + \sin^3 \theta}{\cos \theta + \sin \theta} + \dfrac{\cos^3 \theta - \sin^3 \theta}{\cos \theta - \sin \theta}$ 2

81. $\dfrac{\sec^2 \theta + 2\tan^2 \theta}{1 + 3\tan^2 \theta}$ 1

82. $\dfrac{\csc^2 \alpha + \sec^2 \alpha}{\csc^2 \alpha - \sec^2 \alpha} - \dfrac{1 + \tan^2 \alpha}{1 - \tan^2 \alpha}$ 0

83. $\cos^2 x(3 - 4\cos^2 x)^2 + \sin^2 x(3 - 4\sin^2 x)^2$ 1

84. $(\sin \theta + \csc \theta)^2 + (\cos \theta + \sec \theta)^2 - \tan^2 \theta - \cot^2 \theta$ 7

85. If $\sin \theta = \dfrac{a^2 - b^2}{a^2 + b^2}$ and $a > b > 0$, find the values of $\cos \theta$ and $\cot \theta$. Find the quadrant in which θ lies. †

86. Repeat Exercise 85 for $b > a > 0$. †

Critical Thinking

87. If x and y are real numbers, explain why $\sec\theta$ can never be equal to $\dfrac{xy}{x^2 + y^2}$.

88. Find values of t for which $\sin\theta = \dfrac{1 + t^2}{1 - t^2}$ is possible. $t = 0$

89. Find values of a and b for which $\cos^2\theta = \dfrac{a^2 + b^2}{2ab}$ is possible. $a = b$, for $a, b \neq 0$

90. Find values of a and b for which $\csc^2\theta = \dfrac{2\,ab}{a^2 + b^2}$ is possible. $a = b$, for $a, b \neq 0$

91. If $x = r\cos u \cos v$, $y = r\cos u \sin v$, and $z = r\sin u$, verify that $x^2 + y^2 + z^2 = r^2$.

92. If $\tan x + \cot x = 2$, show that
a. $\tan^2 x + \cot^2 x = 2$.
b. $\tan^3 x + \cot^3 x = 2$.

93. If $\sec x + \cos x = 2$, show that
a. $\sec^2 x + \cos^2 x = \sec^4 x + \cos^4 x = 2$;
b. $\sec^3 x + \cos^3 x = 2$.

94. If $\sin x + \sin^2 x = 1$, show that $\cos^2 x + \cos^4 x = 1$.

Group Project

1. Prove that the following inequalities are true for $0 < \theta < \dfrac{\pi}{2}$:

a. $\sin^2\theta + \csc^2\theta \geq 2$
b. $\cos^2\theta + \sec^2\theta \geq 2$
c. $\sec^2\theta + \csc^2\theta \geq 4$

Trigonometric Equations

BEFORE STARTING THIS SECTION, REVIEW

1. Reference angle (Section 5.3, page 535)

2. Periods of trigonometric functions (Section 5.4, page 547)

3. Factoring techniques (Section P.4, page 43)

4. Solving linear and quadratic equations (Section 1.1, page 90)

OBJECTIVES

1 Solve trigonometric equations of the form $a\sin(x - c) = k$, $a\cos(x - c) = k$, and $a\tan(x - c) = k$.

2 Solve trigonometric equations involving multiple angles.

3 Solve trigonometric equations by using the zero-product property.

4 Solve trigonometric equations that contain more than one trigonometric function.

5 Solve trigonometric equations by squaring both sides.

BY THE WAY . . .

The expression *once in a blue moon* means *not often,* but what exactly is a blue moon? The popular definition says that a second full moon in a single calendar month is called a *blue moon.* On average, a blue moon occurs once every two-and-one-half years.

The Phases of the Moon

The Moon orbits Earth and completes one revolution in about 29.5 days (a lunar month). During this period the angle between the Sun, the Earth, and the Moon changes. See Figure 6.3. This causes different amounts of the illuminated Moon to face Earth, and consequently the shape of the Moon appears to change. The shape varies from a **new moon**—the phase of the Moon when the Moon is not visible from Earth (this happens when the Moon is between the Sun and Earth)—to a **half moon**—the phase of the Moon when the Moon looks like half a circular disk to a **full moon**—the phase of the Moon when the Moon looks like a full circular disk in the sky—back to a half moon, and then to a new moon. It is possible to calculate the fraction of the Moon visible from Earth on any given day. Certain fractions, such as the first and last quarters are called **phases of the moon**. In Example 10, we find the visible portion of the Moon by a sinusoidal equation.

FIGURE 6.3

Trigonometric Equations Recall that a *trigonometric equation* is an equation that contains a trigonometric function with a variable. Equations that are true for all values in the domain of the variable are called *identities*. In Section 6.1, we verified trigonometric identities. Equations that are satisfied by some, but not all values of the variable are *conditional* equations. Examples of conditional trigonometric equations include $\sin x = \dfrac{1}{2}$, $\cos 2x = 2 \cos x$, and $\tan^2 x - 4 \sec x + 5 = 0$. For example, $\sin x = \dfrac{1}{2}$ is satisfied by the value $x = \dfrac{\pi}{6}$, but not by the value $x = 0$.

Just as with algebraic equations, solving a trigonometric equation means to find its *solution set*. Some trigonometric equations do not have a solution. For example, the equation $\sin x = 2$ has no solution, since $-1 \le \sin x \le 1$ for all real numbers x.

However, if a trigonometric equation has a solution, then we should expect such an equation to have infinitely many solutions because the trigonometric functions are periodic. We also note that we cannot find an exact solution for every equation. In such cases, we settle for an approximate solution by using a calculator.

In this section, we study those equations that fall into the following three types:

1. Equations that are equivalent to an equation of the form $a \sin(x - c) = k$, $a \cos(x - c) = k$, or $a \tan(x - c) = k$, where a, c, and k are constants;

2. Equations that can be solved by factoring, using the zero-product property;

3. Equations that are equivalent to a polynomial equation in one trigonometric function.

1 Solve trigonometric equations of the form $a\sin(x - c) = k$, $a\cos(x - c) = k$ and $a\tan(x - c) = k$.

Trigonometric Equations of the Form $a\sin(x - c) = k$, $a\cos(x - c) = k$, and $a\tan(x - c) = k$

We begin with some simple equations.

| EXAMPLE 1 | Solving a Trigonometric Equation |

Find all solutions of each equation. Express all solutions in radians.

a. $\sin x = \dfrac{\sqrt{2}}{2}$ **b.** $\cos \theta = -\dfrac{\sqrt{3}}{2}$ **c.** $\tan x = -\sqrt{3}$

Solution

a. We first find the solutions of $\sin x = \dfrac{\sqrt{2}}{2}$ in the interval $[0, 2\pi)$. We know that $\sin \dfrac{\pi}{4} = \dfrac{\sqrt{2}}{2}$; we also know that $\sin x$ is positive only in quadrants I and II. See Figure 6.4. The first and second quadrant angles with reference angle $\dfrac{\pi}{4}$ are:

$$x = \frac{\pi}{4} \quad \text{and} \quad x = \pi - \frac{\pi}{4} = \frac{3\pi}{4}$$

Thus, $x = \dfrac{\pi}{4}$ and $x = \dfrac{3\pi}{4}$ are the only two solutions in the interval $[0, 2\pi)$. Since the sine function is periodic with period 2π, any integer multiple of 2π can be added to

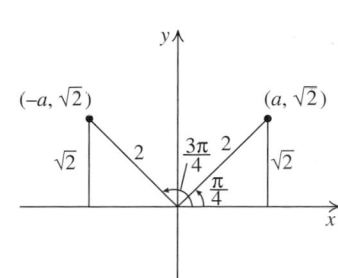

FIGURE 6.4

Continued on next page.

either of these values, and the sine of the resulting value is still $\dfrac{\sqrt{2}}{2}$. Thus, all solutions of the equation $\sin x = \dfrac{\sqrt{2}}{2}$ are given by

$$x = \frac{\pi}{4} + 2n\pi \quad \text{or} \quad x = \frac{3\pi}{4} + 2n\pi,$$

where n is any integer.

b. As in part **a**, we first find all solutions in the interval $[0, 2\pi)$. We know that $\cos\dfrac{\pi}{6} = \dfrac{\sqrt{3}}{2}$; we also know that $\cos\theta$ is negative only in quadrants II and III. See Figure 6.5. The second and third quadrant angles having reference angle $\dfrac{\pi}{6}$ are:

$$\theta = \pi - \frac{\pi}{6} = \frac{5\pi}{6} \quad \text{and} \quad \theta = \pi + \frac{\pi}{6} = \frac{7\pi}{6}$$

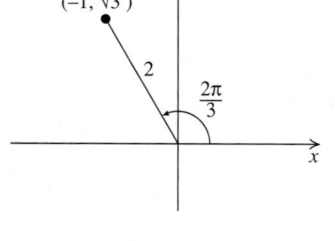

FIGURE 6.5

Thus, $\theta = \dfrac{5\pi}{6}$ and $\theta = \dfrac{7\pi}{6}$ are the only two solutions in the interval $[0, 2\pi)$.

The period of cosine function is 2π, so all solutions of the equation $\cos\theta = -\dfrac{\sqrt{3}}{2}$ are given by

$$\theta = \frac{5\pi}{6} + 2n\pi \quad \text{or} \quad \theta = \frac{7\pi}{6} + 2n\pi,$$

where n is any integer.

c. Because $\tan x$ is a periodic function with period π, we first find all solutions of $\tan x = -\sqrt{3}$ in the interval $[0, \pi)$. We know that $\tan\dfrac{\pi}{3} = \sqrt{3}$; we also know that the tangent is negative in quadrant II. See Figure 6.6. The second quadrant angle with reference angle $\dfrac{\pi}{3}$ is:

$$x = \pi - \frac{\pi}{3} = \frac{2\pi}{3}$$

FIGURE 6.6

Thus, $x = \dfrac{2\pi}{3}$ is the only solution in the interval $[0, \pi)$. Because the period of $\tan x$ is π, all solutions of $\tan x = -\sqrt{3}$ are given by

$$x = \frac{2\pi}{3} + n\pi,$$

where n is any integer. ■ ■ ■

PRACTICE PROBLEM 1 Find all solutions of each equation. Express solutions in radians.

a. $\sin x = 1$ **b.** $\cos x = 1$ **c.** $\tan x = 1$ ■

In Example 1, we were able to find the exact solutions of a trigonometric equation because the angles involved were common angles. In the next example, we find approximate solutions of a trigonometric equation involving other angles.

> **EXAMPLE 2   Finding Approximate Solutions**

a. Find all solutions of $\sin x = 0.3$. Express solutions in degrees rounded to the nearest tenth of a degree.

b. Find all solutions of $\cot x = -3.5$ in the interval $[0, 2\pi)$. Round solutions to four decimal places.

Solution

a. We use the function $\sin^{-1}$ to find the reference angle x' for any angle x with $\sin x = 0.3$.

$$\sin x' = |\sin x| = 0.3 \qquad \text{Given equation}$$
$$x' = \sin^{-1}(0.3) \qquad 0° < x' < 90°$$
$$x' \approx 17.5° \qquad \text{Use a calculator in degree mode.}$$

Since the sine function has positive values in quadrants I and II, we have

$$x \approx 17.5° \quad \text{or} \quad x \approx 180° - 17.5° = 162.5°.$$

The period of sine function is 360°, so all solutions are given by

$$x \approx 17.5° + n \cdot 360° \quad \text{or} \quad x \approx 162.5° + n \cdot 360°,$$

where n is any integer.

b. Since $\cot x = -3.5 = -\dfrac{7}{2}$, we have

$$\tan x = -\frac{2}{7}. \qquad \text{Reciprocal identity}$$

We first find the reference angle x' for any angle x with $\tan x = -\dfrac{2}{7}$. We have

$$\tan x' = |\tan x| = \left|-\frac{2}{7}\right| - \frac{2}{7}.$$

Thus,

$$x' = \tan^{-1}\left(\frac{2}{7}\right) \qquad 0 < x' < \frac{\pi}{2}$$
$$x' \approx 0.2783. \qquad \text{Use a calculator in radian mode.}$$

Because the cotangent function is negative in quadrants II and IV, the required values of x in quadrants II and IV with reference angle 0.2783 are

$$x \approx \pi - 0.2783 \approx 2.8633 \quad \text{and} \quad x \approx 2\pi - 0.2783 \approx 6.0049.$$

These are the only solutions in the interval $[0, 2\pi)$.   ■ ■ ■

PRACTICE PROBLEM 2

a. Find all solutions of $\sec x = 1.5$. Express solutions in degrees rounded to the nearest tenth of a degree.

b. Find all solutions of $\tan x = -2$ in the interval $[0, 2\pi)$. Round solutions to four decimal places.   ■

RECALL

If x' denotes the reference angle for x, then $\sin x = \pm \sin x'$, $\cos x = \pm \cos x'$, $\tan x = \pm \tan x'$. Similar identities hold for $\sec x$, $\csc x$, and $\cot x$.

RECALL

The period of $y = \tan x$ and $y = \cot x$ is π. The period of the other four trigonometric functions is 2π.

In most of our examples, we shall be interested in finding the solutions in the interval $[0, 2\pi)$ for equations involving sine, cosine, secant, and cosecant functions. To find all solutions of such equations, just add $2n\pi$ to each solution obtained in $[0, 2\pi)$. Similarly, to find all solutions of an equation involving tangent or cotangent function, add $n\pi$ to each solution obtained in $[0, \pi)$. When an equation has only a finite number of solutions, we write the solutions using set notation.

EXAMPLE 3   **Solving a Linear Trigonometric Equation**

Find all solutions in the interval $[0, 2\pi)$ of the equation:

$$2\sin\left(x - \frac{\pi}{4}\right) + 1 = 2$$

Solution

Replace $x - \dfrac{\pi}{4}$ by θ in the given equation. We then have

$$2\sin\theta + 1 = 2$$
$$2\sin\theta = 1 \qquad \text{Subtract 1 from both sides.}$$
$$\sin\theta = \frac{1}{2} \qquad \text{Solve for } \sin\theta.$$

$$\text{We know } \sin\frac{\pi}{6} = \frac{1}{2} \qquad \text{See page 522 or from memory.}$$

Since $\sin\theta$ is positive in quadrants I and II only, the solutions of $\sin\theta = \dfrac{1}{2}$ in $[0, 2\pi)$ are:

$$\theta = \frac{\pi}{6} \quad \text{or} \quad \theta = \pi - \frac{\pi}{6} = \frac{5\pi}{6}$$

Now $\theta = x - \dfrac{\pi}{4}$, so $\theta = \dfrac{\pi}{6}$ $\qquad$ or $\qquad$ $\theta = \dfrac{5\pi}{6}$ gives

$x - \dfrac{\pi}{4} = \dfrac{\pi}{6}$	$x - \dfrac{\pi}{4} = \dfrac{5\pi}{6}$ $\qquad$ Replace θ by $x - \dfrac{\pi}{4}$.
$x = \dfrac{\pi}{6} + \dfrac{\pi}{4}$	$x = \dfrac{5\pi}{6} + \dfrac{\pi}{4}$ $\qquad$ Add $\dfrac{\pi}{4}$ to both sides.
$x = \dfrac{2\pi}{12} + \dfrac{3\pi}{12}$	$x = \dfrac{10\pi}{12} + \dfrac{3\pi}{12}$ $\qquad$ LCD is 12.
$x = \dfrac{5\pi}{12}$	$x = \dfrac{13\pi}{12}$ $\qquad$ Simplify.

The solution set in the interval $[0, 2\pi)$ is $\left\{\dfrac{5\pi}{12}, \dfrac{13\pi}{12}\right\}$. $\qquad$ ■ ■ ■

PRACTICE PROBLEM 3   Find all solutions of the equation:

$2\sec(x - 30)° - 1 = \sec(x - 30)° + 3$, in the interval $[0, 360°)$. $\qquad$ ■

2 Solve trigonometric equations involving multiple angles.

Equations Involving Multiple Angles

If x is the measure of an angle, then for any real number k, the number kx is a **multiple angle** of x. Equations such as

$$\sin 3x = \frac{1}{2}, \quad \cos\frac{1}{2}x = 0.7, \quad \text{and} \quad \sin 2x + \sin 4x = 0$$

are examples of trigonometric equations involving multiple angles. You need to be careful when finding all solutions of such equations in the interval $[0, 2\pi)$, as we will see in the next example.

> **EXAMPLE 4   Solving a Trigonometric Equation Containing Multiple Angles**
>
> Find all solutions of the equation $\cos 3x = \dfrac{1}{2}$, in the interval $[0, 2\pi)$.

Solution

Recall that $\cos\theta = \dfrac{1}{2}$ for the acute angle $\theta = \dfrac{\pi}{3}$. Since $\cos\theta$ is positive in quadrants I and IV, we also have $\theta = 2\pi - \dfrac{\pi}{3} = \dfrac{5\pi}{3}$. The period of the cosine function is 2π. Thus, replacing θ by $3x$, all solutions of the equation $\cos 3x = \dfrac{1}{2}$ are given by

$$3x = \frac{\pi}{3} + 2n\pi \quad \text{or} \quad 3x = \frac{5\pi}{3} + 2n\pi \qquad n \text{ any integer}$$

$$x = \frac{\pi}{9} + \frac{2n\pi}{3} \quad \text{or} \quad x = \frac{5\pi}{9} + \frac{2n\pi}{3} \qquad \text{Divide both sides by 3.}$$

To find solutions in the interval $[0, 2\pi)$, try:

$n = -1$	$x = \dfrac{\pi}{9} - \dfrac{2\pi}{3} = -\dfrac{5\pi}{9}$	$x = \dfrac{5\pi}{9} - \dfrac{2\pi}{3} = -\dfrac{\pi}{9}$	
$n = 0$	$x = \dfrac{\pi}{9}$	$x = \dfrac{5\pi}{9}$	
$n = 1$	$x = \dfrac{\pi}{9} + \dfrac{2\pi}{3} = \dfrac{7\pi}{9}$	$x = \dfrac{5\pi}{9} + \dfrac{2\pi}{3} = \dfrac{11\pi}{9}$	
$n - 2$	$x - \dfrac{\pi}{9} + \dfrac{4\pi}{3} - \dfrac{13\pi}{9}$	$x - \dfrac{5\pi}{9} + \dfrac{4\pi}{3} - \dfrac{17\pi}{9}$	
$n = 3$	$x = \dfrac{\pi}{9} + 2\pi = \dfrac{19\pi}{9}$	$x = \dfrac{5\pi}{9} + 2\pi = \dfrac{23\pi}{9}$	

The values resulting from $n = -1$ are too small, and those resulting from $n = 3$ are too large to be in the interval $[0, 2\pi)$. The solutions we want correspond to $n = 0, 1,$ and 2.

In the interval $[0, 2\pi)$, the solution set of the equation $\cos 3x = \dfrac{1}{2}$ is

$$\left\{ \frac{\pi}{9}, \frac{5\pi}{9}, \frac{7\pi}{9}, \frac{11\pi}{9}, \frac{13\pi}{9}, \frac{17\pi}{9} \right\}.$$

■ ■ ■

TECHNOLOGY CONNECTION

〰 If the graphs of $Y_1 = \cos 3x$ and $Y_2 = \dfrac{1}{2}$ are displayed on a graphing calculator, you can see that these graphs intersect in 6 points, corresponding to the six solutions in the interval $[0, 2\pi)$.

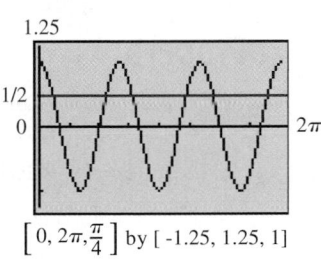

$\left[0, 2\pi, \dfrac{\pi}{4} \right]$ by $[\,-1.25, 1.25, 1\,]$

PRACTICE PROBLEM 4   Find all the solutions of the equation $\sin 2x = \dfrac{1}{2}$ in the interval $[0, 2\pi)$.   ■

EXAMPLE 5   **Solving a Trigonometric Equation Containing a Multiple Angle**

Find all solutions of the equation $\sin\dfrac{x}{2} = -\dfrac{\sqrt{3}}{2}$ in the interval $[0, 2\pi)$.

Solution

We know that $\sin\dfrac{\pi}{3} = \dfrac{\sqrt{3}}{2}$. Since $\sin\theta$ is negative only for θ in quadrants III and IV, the

solutions for $\sin\theta = -\dfrac{\sqrt{3}}{2}$ are the angles in quadrants III and IV with reference angle $\dfrac{\pi}{3}$:

$$\theta = \pi + \frac{\pi}{3} = \frac{4\pi}{3} \quad \text{and} \quad 2\pi - \frac{\pi}{3} = \frac{5\pi}{3}$$

Since the sine function has period 2π, all solutions of $\sin\dfrac{x}{2} = -\dfrac{\sqrt{3}}{2}$ are given by

$$\frac{x}{2} = \frac{4\pi}{3} + 2n\pi \quad \text{or} \quad \frac{x}{2} = \frac{5\pi}{3} + 2n\pi \qquad n \text{ any integer}$$

$$x = \frac{8\pi}{3} + 4n\pi \quad \text{or} \quad x = \frac{10\pi}{3} + 4n\pi \qquad \text{Multiply both sides by 2.}$$

For any integer n, the values of x in both expressions lie outside the interval $[0, 2\pi)$.

For example, for $n = 0$, $x = \dfrac{8\pi}{3} > 2\pi$; and for $n = -1$, $x = \dfrac{8\pi}{3} - 4\pi = -\dfrac{2\pi}{3} < 0$.

Thus, the equation $\sin\dfrac{x}{2} = -\dfrac{\sqrt{3}}{2}$ has no solution in the interval $[0, 2\pi)$, so the solution set is $\varnothing$.   ■ ■ ■

PRACTICE PROBLEM 5   Find all solutions of the equation $\tan\dfrac{x}{2} = \dfrac{1}{\sqrt{3}}$ in the interval $[0, 2\pi)$.   ■

3 Solve trigonometric equations by using the zero-product property.

Trigonometric Equations and the Zero-Product Property

EXAMPLE 6   **Solving an Equation by Using the Zero-Product Property**

Find all solutions of the equation $(2 \sin x - 1)(7 \tan x + 2) = 0$ in the interval $[0, 2\pi)$. Round solutions to four decimal places.

Solution

$$(2 \sin x - 1)(7 \tan x + 2) = 0 \qquad \text{Given equation}$$

$$2 \sin x - 1 = 0 \quad \text{or} \quad 7 \tan x + 2 = 0 \qquad \text{Zero-product property}$$

$$2 \sin x = 1 \qquad\qquad 7 \tan x = -2$$

$$\sin x = \frac{1}{2} \qquad\qquad \tan x = -\frac{2}{7}$$

$$x = \frac{\pi}{6} \text{ or } x = \frac{5\pi}{6} \qquad \Big| \qquad x \approx \pi - 0.2783 \quad \text{or} \quad x \approx 2\pi - 0.2783.$$

$$x \approx 2.8633 \quad \text{or} \quad x \approx 6.0049$$

(See the first part of Example 3.)   (See the first part of Example 2b.)

The given equation has four solutions:

$$x = \frac{\pi}{6}, \ x = \frac{5\pi}{6}, \ x \approx 2.8633, \text{ and } x \approx 6.0049 \qquad ■\ ■\ ■$$

PRACTICE PROBLEM 6   Find all solutions of the equation $(\sin x - 1)(\sqrt{3}\tan x + 1) = 0$ in the interval $[0, 2\pi)$. ■

EXAMPLE 7   **Solving a Quadratic Trigonometric Equation**

Find all solutions of the equation $2\sin^2\theta - 5\sin\theta + 2 = 0$. Express the solutions in radians.

Solution

The given equation is quadratic in $\sin\theta$. We factor the left side and use the zero-product property to solve for $\sin\theta$. We then solve the resulting equation for θ.

$2\sin^2\theta - 5\sin\theta + 2 = 0$	$2x^2 - 5x + 2 = 0$, if $x = \sin\theta$
$(2\sin\theta - 1)(\sin\theta - 2) = 0$	$(2x - 1)(x - 2) = 0$; factor.
$2\sin\theta - 1 = 0 \quad \text{or} \quad \sin\theta - 2 = 0$	Zero-product property
$\sin\theta = \dfrac{1}{2} \qquad \Big| \qquad \sin\theta = 2$	Solve for $\sin\theta$.
$\theta = \dfrac{\pi}{6} \text{ or } \theta = \dfrac{5\pi}{6} \ \Big| \ \sin\theta = 2$ has no solution, since $-1 \le \sin\theta \le 1$.	
See Example 6.	

So, $\theta = \dfrac{\pi}{6}$ and $\theta = \dfrac{5\pi}{6}$ are the only two solutions in the interval $[0, 2\pi)$. Since $\sin\theta$ has period 2π, the solutions of the given equation are

$$\theta = \frac{\pi}{6} + 2n\pi \quad \text{or} \quad \theta = \frac{5\pi}{6} + 2n\pi,$$

where n is any integer. ■ ■ ■

PRACTICE PROBLEM 7   Find all solutions of the equation $2\cos^2\theta - \cos\theta - 1 = 0$. Express the solutions in radians. ■

4 Solve trigonometric equations that contain more than one trigonometric function.

Equations with More than One Trigonometric Function

When a trigonometric equation contains more than one trigonometric function, it is sometimes helpful to use trigonometric identities to convert the equation into an equivalent equation that contains only one trigonometric function.

EXAMPLE 8 Solving a Trigonometric Equation Using Identities

Find all solutions of the equation $2\sin^2\theta + \sqrt{3}\cos\theta + 1 = 0$ in the interval $[0, 2\pi)$.

Solution

The given equation contains both sines and cosines. The Pythagorean identity $\sin^2\theta + \cos^2\theta = 1$ can be used to convert the equation into an equivalent equation that contains cosines only.

$$2\sin^2\theta + \sqrt{3}\cos\theta + 1 = 0 \qquad \text{Given equation}$$
$$2(1 - \cos^2\theta) + \sqrt{3}\cos\theta + 1 = 0 \qquad \text{Replace } \sin^2\theta \text{ by } 1 - \cos^2\theta.$$
$$2 - 2\cos^2\theta + \sqrt{3}\cos\theta + 1 = 0 \qquad \text{Distributive property}$$
$$3 - 2\cos^2\theta + \sqrt{3}\cos\theta = 0 \qquad \text{Combine terms.}$$
$$2\cos^2\theta - \sqrt{3}\cos\theta - 3 = 0 \qquad \text{Multiply both sides by } -1.$$

Use the quadratic formula to solve the last equation for $\cos\theta$.

$$\cos\theta = \frac{-(-\sqrt{3}) \pm \sqrt{(-\sqrt{3})^2 - 4(2)(-3)}}{2(2)} \qquad \text{Use } a = 2, b = -\sqrt{3}, \text{ and } c = -3 \text{ in the quadratic formula.}$$

$$= \frac{\sqrt{3} \pm \sqrt{3 + 24}}{4} \qquad \text{Simplify.}$$

$$= \frac{\sqrt{3} \pm \sqrt{27}}{4} \qquad \text{Simplify.}$$

$$= \frac{\sqrt{3} \pm 3\sqrt{3}}{4} \qquad \sqrt{27} = \sqrt{9 \cdot 3} = \sqrt{9}\sqrt{3} = 3\sqrt{3}$$

Hence,

$$\cos\theta = \frac{\sqrt{3} + 3\sqrt{3}}{4} \qquad \text{or} \qquad \cos\theta = \frac{\sqrt{3} - 3\sqrt{3}}{4}$$

$$= \frac{4\sqrt{3}}{4} \qquad\qquad\qquad = \frac{(-2)\sqrt{3}}{4}$$

$$= \sqrt{3} \qquad\qquad\qquad = -\frac{\sqrt{3}}{2}$$

$$\cos\theta = \sqrt{3} > 1$$

Because $-1 \le \cos\theta \le 1$, the equation $\cos\theta = \sqrt{3}$ has no solution.

The equation $\cos\theta = -\dfrac{\sqrt{3}}{2}$ has two solutions in the interval $[0, 2\pi)$:

$$\theta = \pi - \frac{\pi}{6} = \frac{5\pi}{6} \text{ and}$$

$$\theta = \pi + \frac{\pi}{6} = \frac{7\pi}{6}$$

The solution set for the given equation in the interval $[0, 2\pi)$ is $\left\{\dfrac{5\pi}{6}, \dfrac{7\pi}{6}\right\}$. ■ ■ ■

PRACTICE PROBLEM 8 Find all solutions of the equation $2\cos^2\theta + 3\sin\theta - 3 = 0$ in the interval $[0, 2\pi)$. ■

5 Solve trigonometric equations by squaring both sides.

Extraneous Solutions

In the next example, we solve a trigonometric equation by first squaring both sides of the equation and then using an identity to convert the equation to an equivalent equation containing only one trigonometric function.

Recall that when you square both sides of an equation, you may encounter extraneous solutions. Therefore, you must check the possible solutions by substituting in the original equation.

EXAMPLE 9 **Solving a Trigonometric Equation by Squaring**

Find all solutions of the equation $\sqrt{3}\cos x = \sin x + 1$ in the interval $[0, 2\pi)$.

Solution

$\sqrt{3}\cos x = \sin x + 1$	Original equation
$(\sqrt{3}\cos x)^2 = (\sin x + 1)^2$	Square both sides.
$3\cos^2 x = \sin^2 x + 2\sin x + 1$	Expand the binomial.
$3(1 - \sin^2 x) = \sin^2 x + 2\sin x + 1$	Pythagorean identity
$3 - 3\sin^2 x = \sin^2 x + 2\sin x + 1$	Distributive property
$-4\sin^2 x - 2\sin x + 2 = 0$	Subtract $\sin^2 x + 2\sin x + 1$ from both sides, and simplify.
$2\sin^2 x + \sin x - 1 = 0$	Divide both sides by -2.
$(2\sin x - 1)(\sin x + 1) = 0$	Factor.
$2\sin x - 1 = 0$ or $\sin x + 1 = 0$	Zero-product property
$\sin x = \dfrac{1}{2}$ $\sin x = -1$	Solve for $\sin x$.
$x = \dfrac{\pi}{6}$ or $x = \pi - \dfrac{\pi}{6} = \dfrac{5\pi}{6}$ $x = \dfrac{3\pi}{2}$	Solve for x.

The possible solutions are $\dfrac{\pi}{6}, \dfrac{5\pi}{6}$, and $\dfrac{3\pi}{2}$.

Check:

$$x = \frac{\pi}{6} \qquad\qquad x = \frac{5\pi}{6} \qquad\qquad x = \frac{3\pi}{2}$$

$$\sqrt{3}\cos\frac{\pi}{6} \stackrel{?}{=} \sin\frac{\pi}{6} + 1 \qquad \sqrt{3}\cos\frac{5\pi}{6} \stackrel{?}{=} \sin\frac{5\pi}{6} + 1 \qquad \sqrt{3}\cos\frac{3\pi}{2} \stackrel{?}{=} \sin\frac{3\pi}{2} + 1$$

$$\sqrt{3}\left(\frac{\sqrt{3}}{2}\right) \stackrel{?}{=} \frac{1}{2} + 1 \qquad \sqrt{3}\left(-\frac{\sqrt{3}}{2}\right) \stackrel{?}{=} \frac{1}{2} + 1 \qquad \sqrt{3}(0) \stackrel{?}{=} -1 + 1$$

$$\frac{3}{2} \stackrel{?}{=} \frac{3}{2} \checkmark \qquad\qquad -\frac{3}{2} \stackrel{?}{=} \frac{3}{2} \qquad\qquad 0 \stackrel{?}{=} 0 \checkmark$$

$$\text{Yes} \qquad\qquad\qquad \text{No} \qquad\qquad\qquad \text{Yes}$$

The solution set of the equation in the interval $[0, 2\pi)$ is $\left\{\dfrac{\pi}{6}, \dfrac{3\pi}{2}\right\}$. ■ ■ ■

PRACTICE PROBLEM 9 Find all solutions of the equation $\sqrt{3}\cot\theta + 1 = \sqrt{3}\csc\theta$ in the interval $[0, 2\pi)$. ■

EXAMPLE 10 **The Phases of the Moon**

The Moon orbits Earth in 29.5 days. The portion F of the Moon visible from Earth x days after the new moon is given by the equation

$$F = 0.5\sin\left[\frac{\pi}{14.75}\left(x - \frac{14.75}{2}\right)\right] + 0.5.$$

Find x when 75 percent of the Moon is visible from Earth.

Solution

We are asked to find x when $F = 75$ percent $= 0.75$. We solve the equation

$$0.75 = 0.5\sin\left[\frac{\pi}{14.75}\left(x - \frac{14.75}{2}\right)\right] + 0.5. \qquad \text{Replace } F \text{ by } 0.75.$$

$$0.25 = 0.5\sin\left[\frac{\pi}{14.75}\left(x - \frac{14.75}{2}\right)\right] \qquad \text{Subtract } 0.5 \text{ from both sides.}$$

$$\frac{0.25}{0.5} = \sin\left[\frac{\pi}{14.75}\left(x - \frac{14.75}{2}\right)\right] \qquad \text{Divide both sides by } 0.5.$$

$$\frac{1}{2} = \sin\left[\frac{\pi}{14.75}\left(x - \frac{14.75}{2}\right)\right] \qquad \text{Simplify.}$$

Thus, $\theta = \dfrac{\pi}{14.75}\left(x - \dfrac{14.75}{2}\right)$ is a solution of the equation $\sin\theta = \dfrac{1}{2}$.

We know $\sin\dfrac{\pi}{6} = \dfrac{1}{2}$. Since $\sin\theta$ is positive only in quadrants I and II, we have

$$\frac{\pi}{14.75}\left(x - \frac{14.75}{2}\right) = \frac{\pi}{6} \qquad \text{or} \qquad \frac{\pi}{14.75}\left(x - \frac{14.75}{2}\right) = \frac{5\pi}{6}$$

$$x - \frac{14.75}{2} = \frac{14.75}{6} \qquad\qquad x - \frac{14.75}{2} = \frac{5(14.75)}{6} \qquad \begin{array}{l}\text{Multiply both}\\ \text{sides by } 14.75/\pi.\end{array}$$

$$x = \frac{14.75}{2} + \frac{14.75}{6} \qquad\qquad x = \frac{14.75}{2} + \frac{5(14.75)}{6} \qquad \text{Solve for } x.$$

$$x \approx 9.83 \qquad\qquad\qquad\qquad x \approx 19.67. \qquad \text{Use a calculator.}$$

Thus, 75 percent of the Moon is visible 9.83 (10) days and 19.67 (20) days after the new moon. ■ ■ ■

PRACTICE PROBLEM 10 In Example 10, find x when 30 percent of the Moon is visible from Earth. ■

A Exercises　Basic Skills and Concepts

In Exercises 1–10, find all solutions of each equation. Express the solutions in radians.

1. $\cos x = 0$ †
2. $\sin x = 0$ †

3. $\tan x = -1$ †
4. $\cot x = -1$ †

5. $\cos x = \dfrac{\sqrt{2}}{2}$ †
6. $\sin x = \dfrac{\sqrt{3}}{2}$ †

7. $\cot x = \sqrt{3}$ †
8. $\tan x = -\dfrac{\sqrt{3}}{3}$ $\dfrac{5\pi}{6} + n\pi$

9. $\cos x = -\dfrac{1}{2}$ †
10. $\sin x = -\dfrac{\sqrt{3}}{2}$ †

In Exercises 11–20, find all solutions of each equation. Express the solutions in degrees.

11. $\tan x = \dfrac{\sqrt{3}}{3}$ $30° + 180°n$
12. $\cot x = 1$ $45° + 180°n$

13. $\sin x = -\dfrac{1}{2}$ †
14. $\cos x = \dfrac{1}{2}$ †

15. $\csc x = 1$ $90° + 360°n$
16. $\sec x = -1$ $180° + 360°n$

17. $\sqrt{3}\csc x - 2 = 0$ †
18. $\sqrt{3}\sec x + 2 = 0$ †

19. $2\sec x - 4 = 0$ †
20. $2\csc x + 4 = 0$ †

In Exercises 21–26, find all solutions of each equation in the interval $[0°, 360°)$. Round the answers to the nearest tenth of a degree.

21. $\sin\theta = 0.4$ $23.6°, 156.4°$
22. $\cos\theta = 0.6$ $53.1°, 306.9°$

23. $\sec\theta = 7.2$ †
24. $\csc\theta = -4.5$ †

25. $\tan(\theta - 30°) = -5$ †
26. $\cot(\theta + 30°) = 6$ †

In Exercises 27–32, find all solutions of each equation in the interval $[0, 2\pi)$. Round the solutions to four decimal places.

27. $\csc x = -2$ †
28. $3\sin x - 1 = 0$ †

29. $3\tan x + 4 = 0$ †
30. $2\sec x - 7 = 0$ †

31. $2\csc x + 5 = 0$ †
32. $\cos x = 0.1106$ †

In Exercises 33–40, find all solutions of each equation in the interval $[0, 2\pi)$.

33. $\sin\left(x + \dfrac{\pi}{4}\right) = \dfrac{1}{2}$ $\dfrac{7\pi}{12}, \dfrac{23\pi}{12}$
34. $2\cos\left(x - \dfrac{\pi}{4}\right) + 1 = 0$ †

35. $\sec\left(x - \dfrac{\pi}{8}\right) + 2 = 0$ †
36. $\csc\left(x + \dfrac{\pi}{8}\right) - 2 = 0$ †

37. $\sqrt{3}\tan\left(x - \dfrac{\pi}{6}\right) - 1 = 0$ $\dfrac{\pi}{3}, \dfrac{4\pi}{3}$

38. $\cot\left(x + \dfrac{\pi}{6}\right) + 1 = 0$ $\dfrac{7\pi}{12}, \dfrac{19\pi}{12}$

39. $2\sin\left(x - \dfrac{\pi}{3}\right) + 1 = 0$ $\dfrac{\pi}{6}, \dfrac{3\pi}{2}$

40. $2\cos\left(x + \dfrac{\pi}{3}\right) + \sqrt{2} = 0$ $\dfrac{5\pi}{12}, \dfrac{11\pi}{12}$

In Exercises 41–50, find all solutions of each equation in the interval $[0, 2\pi)$.

41. $\cos 2x = \dfrac{1}{2}$ †
42. $\csc 2x = \dfrac{1}{2}$ ∅

43. $\tan 2x = \dfrac{\sqrt{3}}{3}$ †
44. $\cot 2x = \dfrac{\sqrt{3}}{3}$ †

45. $\sin 3x = \dfrac{1}{2}$ †
46. $\cos 3x = \dfrac{\sqrt{3}}{2}$ †

47. $\cos\dfrac{x}{2} = \dfrac{1}{2}$ $\dfrac{2\pi}{3}$
48. $\csc\dfrac{x}{2} = 2$ $\dfrac{\pi}{3}, \dfrac{5\pi}{3}$

49. $\tan\dfrac{x}{3} = 1$ $\dfrac{3\pi}{4}$
50. $\cot\dfrac{x}{3} = \sqrt{3}$ $\dfrac{\pi}{2}$

In Exercises 51–58, find all solutions of each equation in the interval $[0, 2\pi)$.

51. $(\sin x + 1)(\tan x - 1) = 0$ †
52. $(2\cos x + 1)(\sqrt{3}\tan x - 1) = 0$ †
53. $(\csc x - 2)(\cot x + 1) = 0$ †
54. $(\sqrt{3}\sec x - 2)(\sqrt{3}\cot x + 1) = 0$ †
55. $(\tan x + 1)(2\sin x - 1) = 0$ †
56. $(2\sin x - \sqrt{3})(2\cos x - 1) = 0$ †
57. $(\sqrt{2}\sec x - 2)(2\sin x + 1) = 0$ †
58. $(\cot x - 1)(\sqrt{2}\csc x + 2) = 0$ †

In Exercises 59–66, find all solutions of each equation in the interval $[0, 2\pi)$.

59. $4\sin^2 x = 1$ †
60. $4\cos^2 x = 1$ †

61. $\tan^2 x = 1$ †
62. $\sec^2 x = 2$ †

63. $3\csc^2 x = 4$ †
64. $3\cot^2 x = 1$ †

65. $2\sin^2\theta - \sin\theta - 1 = 0$ †
66. $2\cos^2\theta - 5\cos\theta + 2 = 0$ †

In Exercises 67–76, use trigonometric identities to solve each equation in the interval $[0, 2\pi)$.

67. $\sin x = \cos x$ †
68. $\sqrt{3}\sin x + \cos x = 0$ †

69. $3\sin^2 x = \cos^2 x$ †
70. $3\cos^2 x = \sin^2 x$ †

71. $\cos^2 x - \sin^2 x = 1$ $0, \pi$
72. $2\sin^2 x + \cos x - 1 = 0$ †

†Due to space constrictions, answers to these exercises may be found in the Answers beginning on page A–1 in the back of the book.

73. $2\cos^2 x - 3\sin x - 3 = 0$ †

74. $2\sin^2 x - \cos x - 1 = 0$ †

75. $\sqrt{3}\sec^2 x - 2\tan x - 2\sqrt{3} = 0$ †

76. $\csc^2 x - (\sqrt{3} + 1)\cot x + (\sqrt{3} - 1) = 0$ †

In Exercises 77–80, solve each trigonometric equation in the interval $[0, 2\pi)$ by first squaring both sides.

77. $\sqrt{3}\sin x = 1 + \cos x$ †   **78.** $\tan x + 1 = \sec x$ 0

79. $\sqrt{3}\tan\theta + 1 = \sqrt{3}\sec\theta$ †

80. $\sqrt{3}\cot\theta + 1 = \sqrt{3}\csc\theta$ †

B Exercises   Applying the Concepts

81. Angle of elevation. Find the angle of elevation of the Sun, if the shadow of a tree 24 feet high is $8\sqrt{3}$ feet in length. †

82. Leaning Tower of Pisa. The Leaning Tower of Pisa is 179 feet high and at noon its shadow measures 16.5 feet. At what angle is the tower inclined from the vertical? ≈ 5.3°

83. Returning spacecraft. When a spacecraft re-enters the atmosphere, the angle of re-entry from the horizontal must be between 5.1° and 7.1°. At an angle less than 5.1° the craft would "skip" back into space, and at an angle greater than 7.1° the acceleration forces would be too high and the craft would crash on impact.

A re-entering spacecraft descends a vertical distance of 60 kilometers while traveling a distance of 605 kilometers. Find the angle of re-entry from the horizontal to the nearest tenth of a degree. ≈ 5.7°

84. Electric current. The electric current I (in amperes) produced by an alternator in time t (in seconds) is given by $I = 60\sin(120\pi t)$. Find the smallest possible positive value of t (rounded to four decimal places) such that

a. $I = 30$ amperes,   ≈ 0.0014 sec

b. $I = -20$ amperes.   ≈ 0.0092 sec

85. Simple harmonic motion. A simple harmonic motion is described by the equation $x = 6\sin\left(\dfrac{\pi}{2}t\right)$, where x is the displacement in feet and t is time in seconds. Find positive values of t for which the displacement is 3 feet. †

86. Simple harmonic motion. Repeat Exercise 85 if the simple harmonic motion is described by the equation

$x = 6\cos\left(\dfrac{\pi}{2}t\right)$. $\dfrac{2}{3} + 4n$ sec, $\dfrac{10}{3} + 4n$ sec, n an integer

87. Overcoat sales. The monthly sales of overcoats of the menswear store Suit Yourself in Winterland are approximated by the equation

$$S(x) = 500 + 500\sin\left[\frac{\pi}{4}(x - 2)\right],$$

where x is the month, with $x = 1$ for January. Find the months (after appropriate rounding) in which the number of overcoats sold is

a. 0.   August

b. 1000.   April, December

c. 500.   February, June, October

88. Number of tourists. The weekly number of tourists visiting a tropical island is approximated by the equation

$$y = 20 + 10\sin\left[\frac{\pi}{26}(x - 14)\right],$$

where y is the number of visitors (in thousands) in the xth week of the year, starting with $x = 1$ for the first week in January. Find the week (after appropriate rounding) in which the number of tourists to the island is

a. 30,000.   27

b. 25,000.   19, 36

c. 15,000.   44, 10

89. Average monthly temperature. The average monthly sea surface temperature T (in degrees Fahrenheit) in Paradise Island is approximated by the equation

$$T = 10.5\sin\left[\frac{\pi}{6}(x - 5)\right] + 73.5,$$

where x is the month, with $x = 1$ representing January. Find the months (after appropriate rounding) when the average sea surface temperature is

a. 78.75° F.   June, October

b. 84° F.   August

90. Average monthly snowfall. The average monthly snowfall y (in inches) in Rochester, New York, in the xth month can be approximated by

$$y = 12 + 12\sin\left[\frac{\pi}{4}(x - 2)\right], 1 \le x \le 8,$$

where October = 1, November = 2, December = 3, January = 4, February = 5, March = 6, April = 7, and May = 8.

Find the months (after appropriate rounding) when the average snowfall in Rochester is

a. 24 inches.   January

b. 18 inches.   March, December

C Exercises   Beyond the Basics

In Exercises 91–102, find all solutions of each equation in the interval $[0, 2\pi)$.

91. $\sin^4 2x = 1$ †

92. $\cos^4 2x = 1$ †

93. $2\cos 4x = 1$ †

94. $2\cos 6x = 1$ †

95. $\tan^2 2\theta = 1$ †

96. $\sec^2 2\theta = 1$ †

97. $\sin x \cos x = \sin x$ $\{0, \pi\}$

98. $\cos x(\csc x - 2) = \cos x$ †

99. $\sin x \cos x - \dfrac{\sqrt{3}}{2}\sin x + \dfrac{1}{2}\cos x - \dfrac{\sqrt{3}}{4} = 0$ †

[*Hint:* Factor by grouping.]

100. $2\sin x \tan x + 2\sin x + \tan x + 1 = 0$ †

[*Hint:* Factor by grouping.]

101. $(\tan 2x - 1)(\sin x + 1) = 0$ †

102. $(\sqrt{3}\cot 2x - 1)(2\cos x - 1) = 0$ †

Critical Thinking

103. Solve the following equation: $\sin x \cos x = \dfrac{1}{2}$. †

[*Hint:* Square both sides and replace $\cos^2 x$ by $1 - \sin^2 x$.]

104. Follow the hint given for Exercise 103 to show that the equation $\sin x \cos x = 1$ has no real-number solutions.

Sum and Difference Formulas

BEFORE STARTING THIS SECTION, REVIEW

1. Distance formula (Section 2.1, page 185)

2. Fundamental Trigonometric identities (Section 6.1, page 596)

3. Trigonometric functions of common angles (Section 5.2, page 522)

OBJECTIVES

1 Use the sum and difference formulas for cosine.

2 Use cofunction identities.

3 Use the sum and difference formulas for sine.

4 Use the sum and difference formulas for tangent.

Pure Tones in Music

A vibrating part of an instrument transmits its vibrations to the air, and they travel away as sound waves. The number of complete cycles per second traveled by a wave is called its *frequency* and is denoted by f. The unit of frequency, cycles per second, is also called hertz (abbreviated Hz) after Gustav Hertz, the discoverer of radio waves. The note A on the common musical scale is 440 Hz, which means that when it is played, 440 waves are produced each second; then the time between waves is $\dfrac{1}{440}$ second, and this is the period T of the waves. That is, $T = \dfrac{1}{f}$. You hear the sound produced by note A when the vibration from the source travels to your ear and puts pressure on your eardrum.

A *pure tone* is one in which the vibration is a simple harmonic of just one frequency. The simple harmonic of a pure tone with frequency f can be described by the equation

$$y = a \sin(2\pi ft),$$

where $|a|$ is the amplitude (indicating loudness), t is the time in seconds, and y is the pressure of a pure tone on an eardrum (in pounds per square foot). In Example 10, we consider the pressure due to two pure tones of the same frequency.

In this section, we will develop identities involving the sum and difference of two variables, u and v. The variables represent any two real numbers, or angles, in radian or degree measure. ■

1 Use the sum and difference formulas for cosine.

Sum and Difference Formulas for Cosine

The following identities for $\cos(u - v)$ and $\cos(u + v)$ are called the sum and difference formulas for cosine, respectively.

SUM AND DIFFERENCE FORMULAS FOR COSINE

$$\cos(u + v) = \cos u \cos v - \sin u \sin v$$
$$\cos(u - v) = \cos u \cos v + \sin u \sin v$$

We first derive the difference formula for the cosine:

$$\cos(u - v) = \cos u \cos v + \sin u \sin v$$

Although this identity is true for all real numbers u and v, we prove it for the case when $0 < v < u < 2\pi$. We associate u and v with arcs and angles in a unit circle. Then, by the unit circle definitions of the trigonometric functions (see Section 5.3), the points P and Q on the terminal sides of the angles u and v are labeled as shown in Figure 6.7(a). Now place angle $(u - v)$ in standard position and label the point B on the unit circle corresponding to the terminal side of angle $(u - v)$, as shown in Figure 6.7(b).

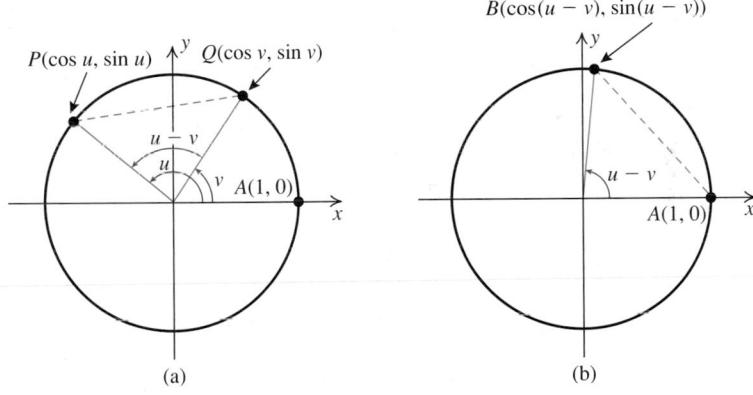

(a)   (b)

FIGURE 6.7

We know that triangle POQ in Figure 6.7(a) is congruent to triangle BOA in Figure 6.7(b) by SAS (side-angle-side congruence). Thus,

$$d(P, Q) = d(A, B)$$

$$[d(P, Q)]^2 = [d(A, B)]^2. \quad (1) \qquad \text{Square both sides.}$$

Now, use the distance formula to simplify the left side of Equation (1).

$$[d(P,Q)]^2 = (\cos u - \cos v)^2 + (\sin u - \sin v)^2 \qquad \text{Distance formula}$$

$$= \cos^2 u - 2\cos u \cos v + \cos^2 v \qquad (a - b)^2 = a^2 - 2ab + b^2$$
$$\quad + \sin^2 u - 2\sin u \sin v + \sin^2 v$$

RECALL

The *distance* $d(P, Q)$ between the points $P(x_1, y_1)$ and $Q(x_2, y_2)$ is given by

$$d(P, Q) = \sqrt{(x_2 - x_1)^2 + (y_2 - y_1)^2}$$

Continued on next page.

$$
\begin{aligned}
&= (\cos^2 u + \sin^2 u) + (\cos^2 v + \sin^2 v) && \text{Combine terms.} \\
&\quad -2(\cos u \cos v + \sin u \sin v) \\
&= 1 + 1 - 2(\cos u \cos v + \sin u \sin v) && \text{Pythagorean identity}
\end{aligned}
$$

Thus,

$$
[d(P, Q)]^2 = 2 - 2(\cos u \cos v + \sin u \sin v) \quad \text{Simplify.}
$$

Now, simplify the right side of Equation (1).

$$
\begin{aligned}
[d(A, B)]^2 &= [\cos(u - v) - 1]^2 + [\sin(u - v) - 0]^2 && \text{Distance formula} \\
&= \cos^2(u - v) - 2\cos(u - v) + 1 + \sin^2(u - v) && \text{Expand binomial.} \\
&= [\cos^2(u - v) + \sin^2(u - v)] + 1 - 2\cos(u - v) && \text{Combine terms.} \\
&= 1 + 1 - 2\cos(u - v) && \text{Pythagorean identity}
\end{aligned}
$$

Thus,

$$
[d(A, B)]^2 = 2 - 2\cos(u - v) \quad \text{Simplify.}
$$

Equate the expressions for $[d(A, B)]^2$ and $[d(P, Q)]^2$.

$$
\begin{aligned}
2 - 2\cos(u - v) &= 2 - 2(\cos u \cos v + \sin u \sin v) && [d(A,B)]^2 = [d(P,Q)]^2 \\
-2\cos(u - v) &= -2(\cos u \cos v + \sin u \sin v) && \text{Subtract 2 from both sides.} \\
\mathbf{\cos(u - v)} &= \mathbf{\cos u \cos v + \sin u \sin v} && \text{Divide both sides by } -2.
\end{aligned}
$$

This proves the formula for the cosine of the difference of two angles.

EXAMPLE 1   **Using the Difference Formula for Cosine**

Find the exact value of $\cos\dfrac{\pi}{12}$ by using $\dfrac{\pi}{12} = \dfrac{\pi}{3} - \dfrac{\pi}{4}$.

Solution

Recall that we know the exact values of the trigonometric functions of $\dfrac{\pi}{3}$ and $\dfrac{\pi}{4}$. We use these values and the difference formula for cosine to evaluate $\cos\dfrac{\pi}{12}$.

$$
\begin{aligned}
\cos\frac{\pi}{12} &= \cos\left(\frac{\pi}{3} - \frac{\pi}{4}\right) && \frac{\pi}{12} = \frac{\pi}{3} - \frac{\pi}{4} \\[2mm]
&= \cos\frac{\pi}{3}\cos\frac{\pi}{4} + \sin\frac{\pi}{3}\sin\frac{\pi}{4} && \text{Formula for } \cos(u - v) \text{ with } u = \frac{\pi}{3} \\
&&& \text{and } v = \frac{\pi}{4} \\[2mm]
&= \frac{1}{2}\cdot\frac{\sqrt{2}}{2} + \frac{\sqrt{3}}{2}\cdot\frac{\sqrt{2}}{2} && \text{Use exact values. (See page 522.)} \\[2mm]
&= \frac{\sqrt{2}}{4} + \frac{\sqrt{6}}{4} && \text{Multiply.} \\[2mm]
&= \frac{\sqrt{2} + \sqrt{6}}{4} && \text{Add.}
\end{aligned}
$$

◼ ◼ ◼

PRACTICE PROBLEM 1   Find the exact value of $\cos 15°$ by using $15° = 45° - 30°$.   ◼

The difference formula for $\cos(u - v)$ is true for all real numbers and angles u and v. We can use this formula and the odd-even identities to prove the formula for $\cos(u + v)$.

$$\cos(u + v) = \cos[u - (-v)] \qquad u + v = u - (-v)$$
$$= \cos u \cos(-v) + \sin u \sin(-v) \qquad \text{Difference formula for cosine}$$
$$= \cos u \cos v + \sin u(-\sin v) \qquad \cos(-v) = \cos v;\ \sin(-v) = -\sin v$$
$$\mathbf{\cos(u + v) = \cos u \cos v - \sin u \sin v} \qquad \text{Simplify.}$$

The last equation is the sum formula for cosine.

EXAMPLE 2   **Using the Sum Formula for Cosine**

Find the exact value of $\cos 75°$ by using $75° = 45° + 30°$.

Solution

$$\cos 75° = \cos(45° + 30°) \qquad 75° = 45° + 30°$$
$$= \cos 45° \cos 30° - \sin 45° \sin 30° \qquad \text{Sum formula for cosine}$$
$$= \frac{\sqrt{2}}{2} \cdot \frac{\sqrt{3}}{2} - \frac{\sqrt{2}}{2} \cdot \frac{1}{2} \qquad \text{Use exact values.}$$
$$= \frac{\sqrt{6}}{4} - \frac{\sqrt{2}}{4} \qquad \text{Multiply.}$$
$$= \frac{\sqrt{6} - \sqrt{2}}{4} \qquad \text{Simplify.} \qquad ■\ ■\ ■$$

PRACTICE PROBLEM 2   Find the exact value of $\cos \dfrac{7\pi}{12}$ by using $\dfrac{7\pi}{12} = \dfrac{\pi}{3} + \dfrac{\pi}{4}$.   ■

2 Use cofunction identities.

Cofunction Identities

Two trigonometric functions f and g are called **cofunctions** if

$$f\left(\frac{\pi}{2} - x\right) = g(x) \quad \text{and} \quad g\left(\frac{\pi}{2} - x\right) = f(x).$$

In order to obtain the sum and difference identities for the sine and tangent functions, we first obtain the cofunction identities from the difference formula for cosine.

$$\cos(u - v) = \cos u \cos v + \sin u \sin v \qquad \text{Difference formula for cosine}$$
$$\cos\left(\frac{\pi}{2} - v\right) = \cos\frac{\pi}{2} \cos v + \sin\frac{\pi}{2} \sin v \qquad \text{Replace } u \text{ by } \frac{\pi}{2}.$$
$$= 0 \cdot \cos v + 1 \cdot \sin v \qquad \cos\frac{\pi}{2} = 0;\ \sin\frac{\pi}{2} = 1$$
$$= \sin v \qquad \text{Simplify.}$$

We obtain a cofunction identity:

$$\mathbf{\cos\left(\frac{\pi}{2} - v\right) = \sin v}$$

This cofunction identity is true for any real number v or angle in radian measure.

If we replace v by $\dfrac{\pi}{2} - v$ in this cofunction identity, we have

$$\cos\left(\frac{\pi}{2} - v\right) = \sin v \qquad \text{Cofunction identity}$$

$$\cos\left[\frac{\pi}{2} - \left(\frac{\pi}{2} - v\right)\right] = \sin\left(\frac{\pi}{2} - v\right) \qquad \text{Replace } v \text{ by } \frac{\pi}{2} - v.$$

$$\cos v = \sin\left(\frac{\pi}{2} - v\right). \qquad \text{Simplify.}$$

Thus,

$$\boldsymbol{\sin\left(\frac{\pi}{2} - v\right) = \cos v}$$

BASIC COFUNCTION IDENTITIES

If v is any real number or angle measured in radians, then

$$\cos\left(\frac{\pi}{2} - v\right) = \sin v$$

$$\sin\left(\frac{\pi}{2} - v\right) = \cos v$$

If angle v is measured in degrees, then replace $\dfrac{\pi}{2}$ by $90°$ in the basic cofunction identities.

EXAMPLE 3   **Using Cofunction Identities**

Prove that for any real number x,

$$\tan\left(\frac{\pi}{2} - x\right) = \cot x.$$

Solution

$$\tan\left(\frac{\pi}{2} - x\right) = \frac{\sin\left(\dfrac{\pi}{2} - x\right)}{\cos\left(\dfrac{\pi}{2} - x\right)} \qquad \text{Quotient identity}$$

$$= \frac{\cos x}{\sin x} \qquad \text{Use cofunction identities.}$$

$$= \cot x \qquad \text{Quotient identity} \qquad ■ ■ ■$$

PRACTICE PROBLEM 3   Prove that for any real number x,

$$\sec\left(\frac{\pi}{2} - x\right) = \csc x. \qquad\qquad ■$$

3 Use sum and difference formulas for sine.

Sum and Difference Formulas for Sine

We use the cofunction identities and the formula for $\cos(u + v)$ to prove the difference formula for the sine function.

$$\sin(u - v) = \cos\left[\frac{\pi}{2} - (u - v)\right] \qquad \text{Cofunction identity}$$

$$= \cos\left[\left(\frac{\pi}{2} - u\right) + v\right] \qquad \frac{\pi}{2} - (u - v) = \left(\frac{\pi}{2} - u\right) + v$$

$$= \cos\left(\frac{\pi}{2} - u\right)\cos v - \sin\left(\frac{\pi}{2} - u\right)\sin v \quad \text{Sum identity for cosine}$$

$$= \sin u \cos v - \cos u \sin v \qquad \text{Cofunction identities}$$

We have established the difference formula for sine:

$$\sin(u - v) = \sin u \cos v - \cos u \sin v$$

This identity is true for all real numbers u and v. If we replace v by $-v$, we obtain the sum formula for sine.

$$\sin(u + v) = \sin[u - (-v)] \qquad u + v = u - (-v)$$

$$= \sin u \cos(-v) - \cos u \sin(-v) \quad \text{Difference formula for sine}$$

$$= \sin u \cos v - \cos u(-\sin v) \qquad \cos(-v) = \cos v; \sin(-v) = -\sin v$$

$$= \sin u \cos v + \cos u \sin v \qquad \text{Simplify.}$$

We have established the sum formula for sine:

$$\sin(u + v) = \sin u \cos v + \cos u \sin v$$

EXAMPLE 4   **Using the Difference Formula for Sine**

Prove the identity: $\sin(\pi - x) = \sin x$.

Solution

$$\sin(u - v) = \sin u \cos v - \cos u \sin v \qquad \text{Difference formula for sine}$$

$$\sin(\pi - x) = \sin \pi \cos x - \cos \pi \sin x \qquad \text{Replace } u \text{ by } \pi \text{ and } v \text{ by } x.$$

$$= (0) \cos x - (-1) \sin x \qquad \sin \pi = 0; \cos \pi = -1$$

$$= \sin x \qquad \text{Simplify.} \qquad ■ ■ ■$$

PRACTICE PROBLEM 4   Use the sum identity for sine to prove that $\sin(\pi + x) = -\sin x$ ■

EXAMPLE 5   **Using the Sum Formula for Sine**

Find the exact value of $\sin 63° \cos 27° + \cos 63° \sin 27°$ without using a calculator.

Solution

The expression $\sin 63° \cos 27° + \cos 63° \sin 27°$ is the right side of the sum formula for

$$\sin(u + v) = \sin u \cos v + \cos u \sin v,$$

with $u = 63°$ and $v = 27°$. Hence,

Continued on next page.

$$\sin 63° \cos 27° + \cos 63° \sin 27° = \sin(63° + 27°)$$
$$= \sin 90°$$
$$= 1.$$

■ ■ ■

PRACTICE PROBLEM 5   Find the exact value of $\sin 43° \cos 13° - \cos 43° \sin 13°$ without using a calculator.   ■

EXAMPLE 6   **Finding the Exact Value of a Sum**

Let $\sin u = -\dfrac{3}{5}$ and $\cos v = \dfrac{12}{13}$, with $\pi < u < \dfrac{3\pi}{2}$ and $\dfrac{3\pi}{2} < v < 2\pi$. Find the exact value of $\sin(u + v)$.

Solution

We are given $\sin u = -\dfrac{3}{5}$, with u in quadrant III.

$$\cos^2 u = 1 - \sin^2 u \qquad \text{Pythagorean identity}$$
$$\cos u = -\sqrt{1 - \sin^2 u} \qquad \cos u \text{ is negative in quadrant III.}$$
$$= -\sqrt{1 - \left(-\frac{3}{5}\right)^2} \qquad \text{Replace } \sin u \text{ by } -\frac{3}{5}.$$
$$= -\sqrt{1 - \frac{9}{25}} \qquad \left(-\frac{3}{5}\right)^2 = \frac{9}{25}$$
$$= -\sqrt{\frac{16}{25}} \qquad 1 - \frac{9}{25} = \frac{25}{25} - \frac{9}{25} = \frac{16}{25}$$
$$= -\frac{4}{5} \qquad \left(\frac{4}{5}\right)^2 = \frac{16}{25}$$

Thus, $\cos u = -\dfrac{4}{5}$.

In the same way, given $\cos v = \dfrac{12}{13}$, with v in quadrant IV, we can find the exact value of $\sin v$.

$$\sin v = -\sqrt{1 - \cos^2 v} \qquad \sin v \text{ is negative in quadrant IV.}$$
$$= -\sqrt{1 - \left(\frac{12}{13}\right)^2} \qquad \text{Replace } \cos v \text{ by } \frac{12}{13}.$$
$$= -\sqrt{\frac{25}{169}} \qquad 1 - \left(\frac{12}{13}\right)^2 = 1 - \frac{144}{169} = \frac{169 - 144}{169}$$
$$= -\frac{5}{13} \qquad \left(\frac{5}{13}\right)^2 = \frac{25}{169}$$

Hence, $\sin v = -\dfrac{5}{13}$.

$$\sin(u + v) = \sin u \cos v + \cos u \sin v \qquad \text{Sum formula for sine}$$

$$= \left(-\frac{3}{5}\right)\left(\frac{12}{13}\right) + \left(-\frac{4}{5}\right)\left(-\frac{5}{13}\right) \qquad \text{Replace values of } \sin u, \ \sin v, \ \cos u, \text{ and } \cos v.$$

$$= -\frac{36}{65} + \frac{20}{65} \qquad \text{Multiply.}$$

$$= -\frac{16}{65} \qquad \text{Simplify.}$$

The exact value of $\sin(u + v)$ is $-\dfrac{16}{65}$.   ■ ■ ■

PRACTICE PROBLEM 6 For the angles u and v in Example 6, find the exact value of $\cos(u + v)$.   ■

EXAMPLE 7   **Verifying an Identity by Using a Sum or Difference Formula**

Verify the identity: $\dfrac{\sin(x - y)}{\cos x \cos y} = \tan x - \tan y.$

Solution

We start with the more complicated left side.

$$\frac{\sin(x - y)}{\cos x \cos y} = \frac{\sin x \cos y - \cos x \sin y}{\cos x \cos y} \qquad \text{Use the formula for } \sin(u - v).$$

$$= \frac{\sin x \cos y}{\cos x \cos y} - \frac{\cos x \sin y}{\cos x \cos y} \qquad \frac{a - b}{c} = \frac{a}{c} - \frac{b}{c}$$

$$= \frac{\sin x}{\cos x} - \frac{\sin y}{\cos y} \qquad \text{Remove common factors.}$$

$$= \tan x - \tan y \qquad \text{Quotient identity}$$

Since the left side is identical to the right side, the given equation is an identity.   ■ ■ ■

PRACTICE PROBLEM 7 Verify the following identity: $\dfrac{\cos(x + y)}{\sin x \sin y} = \cot x \cot y - 1.$ ■

Reduction Formula

Figure 6.8 suggests that a point (a, b) is on the terminal side of the angle θ, if and only if

$$\cos\theta = \frac{a}{\sqrt{a^2 + b^2}} \quad \text{and} \quad \sin\theta = \frac{b}{\sqrt{a^2 + b^2}}.$$

Using these values for $\cos\theta$ and $\sin\theta$ in the sum formula for the sine, we obtain

$$\sin(x + \theta) = \sin x \cos\theta + \cos x \sin\theta \qquad \text{Sum formula for sine}$$

$$\sin(x + \theta) = \sin x \frac{a}{\sqrt{a^2 + b^2}} + \cos x \frac{b}{\sqrt{a^2 + b^2}}$$

Multiplying both sides of this equation by $\sqrt{a^2 + b^2}$, we have

$$\sqrt{a^2 + b^2} \sin(x + \theta) = a \sin x + b \cos x.$$

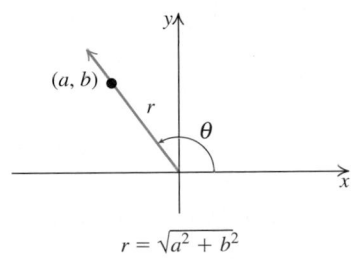

$r = \sqrt{a^2 + b^2}$

FIGURE 6.8

The previous result is called the *reduction formula*.

REDUCTION FORMULA

If (a, b) is any point on the terminal side of an angle θ (radians) in standard position, then
$$a \sin x + b \cos x = \sqrt{a^2 + b^2} \sin(x + \theta)$$
for any real number x.

EXAMPLE 8   Using the Reduction Formula

Find an angle θ, in radians, and a real number A, such that
$$\sin x - \sqrt{3} \cos x = A \sin(x + \theta).$$

Solution

Note that by the reduction formula
$$\sin x - \sqrt{3} \cos x = a \sin x + b \cos x \qquad a = 1 \text{ and } b = -\sqrt{3}$$
$$= A \sin(x + \theta),$$

where $A = \sqrt{a^2 + b^2} = \sqrt{1^2 + (-\sqrt{3})^2} = \sqrt{4} = 2$ and θ is any angle in standard position that has the point $(a, b) = (1, -\sqrt{3})$ on its terminal side. One such angle is $\theta = \tan^{-1}(-\sqrt{3}) = -\dfrac{\pi}{3}$. Then

$$\sin x - \sqrt{3} \cos x = 2 \sin\left[x + \left(-\frac{\pi}{3}\right)\right] = 2 \sin\left(x - \frac{\pi}{3}\right). \qquad \blacksquare\ \blacksquare\ \blacksquare$$

PRACTICE PROBLEM 8   Find an angle θ, in radians, and a real number A, such that
$$\sin x + \sqrt{3} \cos x = A \sin(x + \theta). \qquad \blacksquare$$

EXAMPLE 9   Using the Reduction Formula to Sketch a Graph

Sketch the graph of the equation:
$$y = \sin x - \sqrt{3} \cos x$$

Solution

From Example 8, we have $\sin x - \sqrt{3} \cos x = 2 \sin\left(x - \dfrac{\pi}{3}\right)$. Thus, the graph of $y = \sin x - \sqrt{3} \cos x$, is the same as the graph of $y = 2 \sin\left(x - \dfrac{\pi}{3}\right)$. The graph of $y = 2 \sin\left(x - \dfrac{\pi}{3}\right)$ is a sine wave with amplitude 2, period 2π, and phase shift $\dfrac{\pi}{3}$ units to the right. Two cycles of the graph of $y = 2 \sin\left(x - \dfrac{\pi}{3}\right)$ are shown in Figure 6.9.   ■ ■ ■

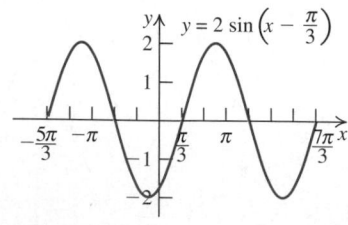

FIGURE 6.9

PRACTICE PROBLEM 9   Sketch two cycles of the graph of $y = \sin x + \sqrt{3} \cos x$.   ■

> **EXAMPLE 10**   **Combining Two Pure Tones**

Suppose that the pressure exerted by two pure tones (in pounds per square foot) after t seconds is given by

$$y_1 = 0.3 \sin(800\pi t) \quad \text{and} \quad y_2 = 0.4 \cos(800\pi t).$$

Find the amplitude, period, frequency, and the phase shift for the total pressure $y = y_1 + y_2$.

Solution

We have $y = 0.3\sin(800\pi t) + 0.4\cos(800\pi t)$. We use the reduction formula with $a = 0.3$ and $b = 0.4$ to rewrite this equation in the form

$$y = A\sin(800\pi t + \theta) = A\sin 800\pi\left(t + \frac{\theta}{800\pi}\right)$$

where

$$A = \sqrt{a^2 + b^2} = \sqrt{(0.3)^2 + (0.4)^2} = 0.5$$

and $(0.3, 0.4)$ is a point on the terminal side of θ. One such angle is $\theta = \tan^{-1}\left(\dfrac{0.4}{0.3}\right)$. For the total pressure,

$$y = A\sin 800\pi\left(t + \frac{\theta}{800\pi}\right)$$

$$= 0.5\sin 800\pi\left(t + \frac{\theta}{800\pi}\right) \qquad A = 0.5, \ \theta = \tan^{-1}\left(\frac{0.4}{0.3}\right)$$

$$\text{amplitude} = 0.5$$

$$\text{period} = \frac{2\pi}{800\pi} = \frac{1}{400}$$

$$\text{frequency} = 400 \qquad\qquad\qquad \text{Frequency} = \frac{1}{\text{period}}$$

$$\text{phase shift} = -\frac{\theta}{800\pi} \approx -0.00037 \qquad\qquad \begin{array}{l}\text{Use a calculator in radian mode.}\\ \theta = \tan^{-1}\left(\dfrac{0.4}{0.3}\right).\end{array} \quad \blacksquare\ \blacksquare\ \blacksquare$$

PRACTICE PROBLEM 10   Find the amplitude, period, frequency, and phase shift of the total pressure due to the pressure from the two pure tones:

$$y_1 = 0.1\sin(400t) \quad \text{and} \quad y_2 = 0.2\cos(400t). \qquad\qquad \blacksquare$$

4 Use the sum and difference formulas for tangent.

Sum and Difference Formulas for Tangent

We use the quotient identity $\tan x = \dfrac{\sin x}{\cos x}$ and the difference formulas for $\sin(u - v)$ and $\cos(u - v)$ to derive a difference formula for $\tan(u - v)$.

$$\tan(u - v) = \frac{\sin(u - v)}{\cos(u - v)} \qquad\qquad \text{Quotient identity}$$

$$= \frac{\sin u \cos v - \cos u \sin v}{\cos u \cos v + \sin u \sin v} \qquad \begin{array}{l}\text{Use formulas for } \sin(u - v)\\ \text{and } \cos(u - v).\end{array}$$

Continued on next page.

$$= \frac{\dfrac{\sin u \, \cancel{\cos v}}{\cos u \, \cancel{\cos v}} - \dfrac{\cancel{\cos u} \, \sin v}{\cancel{\cos u} \, \cos v}}{\dfrac{\cancel{\cos u} \, \cancel{\cos v}}{\cancel{\cos u} \, \cancel{\cos v}} + \dfrac{\sin u \, \sin v}{\cos u \, \cos v}}$$ Divide numerator and denominator by $\cos u \cos v$.

$$= \frac{\dfrac{\sin u}{\cos u} - \dfrac{\sin v}{\cos v}}{1 + \dfrac{\sin u \, \sin v}{\cos u \, \cos v}}$$ Simplify.

$$= \frac{\tan u - \tan v}{1 + \tan u \tan v}$$ Quotient identity

We have derived the difference formula for the tangent:

$$\tan(u - v) = \frac{\tan u - \tan v}{1 + \tan u \tan v}$$

Replacing v by $-v$ in the difference formula, we have

$$\tan(u + v) = \tan[u - (-v)] \qquad u + v = u - (-v)$$

$$= \frac{\tan u - \tan(-v)}{1 + \tan u \tan(-v)} \qquad \text{Use formula for } \tan(u - v).$$

$$= \frac{\tan u - (-\tan v)}{1 + \tan u(-\tan v)} \qquad \tan(-v) = -\tan v$$

$$= \frac{\tan u + \tan v}{1 - \tan u \tan v} \qquad \text{Simplify.}$$

We have obtained the sum formula for tangent:

$$\tan(u + v) = \frac{\tan u + \tan v}{1 - \tan u \tan v}$$

EXAMPLE 11 **Verifying an Identity**

Verify the identity: $\tan(\pi - x) = -\tan x$

Solution

Apply the difference formula for the tangent to $\tan(\pi - x)$.

$$\tan(\pi - x) = \frac{\tan \pi - \tan x}{1 + \tan \pi \tan x} \qquad \text{Replace } u \text{ by } \pi \text{ and } v \text{ by } x \text{ in the formula for } \tan(u - v).$$

$$= \frac{0 - \tan x}{1 + 0 \cdot \tan x} \qquad \tan \pi = 0$$

$$= -\tan x \qquad \text{Simplify.}$$

Thus, the given equation is an identity. ■ ■ ■

PRACTICE PROBLEM 11 Verify the identity: $\tan(\pi + x) = \tan x$ ■

Summary

The important identities involving the sum, difference, and cofunctions of two numbers or angles are summarized next.

SUM AND DIFFERENCE FORMULA

$$\cos(u - v) = \cos u \cos v + \sin u \sin v \qquad \cos(u + v) = \cos u \cos v - \sin u \sin v$$

$$\sin(u - v) = \sin u \cos v - \cos u \sin v \qquad \sin(u + v) = \sin u \cos v + \cos u \sin v$$

$$\tan(u - v) = \frac{\tan u - \tan v}{1 + \tan u \tan v} \qquad \tan(u + v) = \frac{\tan u + \tan v}{1 - \tan u \tan v}$$

COFUNCTION IDENTITIES

$$\sin\left(\frac{\pi}{2} - x\right) = \cos x \qquad \cos\left(\frac{\pi}{2} - x\right) = \sin x \qquad \tan\left(\frac{\pi}{2} - x\right) = \cot x$$

REDUCTION FORMULA

If (a, b) is any point on the terminal side of an angle θ (radians) in standard position, then

$$a \sin x + b \cos x = \sqrt{a^2 + b^2}\, \sin(x + \theta)$$

for any real number x.

A Exercises   Basic Skills and Concepts

In Exercises 1–24, find the exact value of each expression.

1. $\sin(45° + 30°)$ †
2. $\sin(45° - 30°)$ †

3. $\sin(60° - 45°)$ †
4. $\sin(60° + 45°)$ †

5. $\sin(-105°)$ †
6. $\cos 285°$ †

7. $\tan 225°$ 1
8. $\tan(-165°)$ $2 - \sqrt{3}$

9. $\sin\left(\dfrac{\pi}{6} + \dfrac{\pi}{4}\right)$ $\dfrac{\sqrt{6} + \sqrt{2}}{4}$
10. $\cos\left(\dfrac{\pi}{3} - \dfrac{\pi}{4}\right)$ $\dfrac{\sqrt{6} + \sqrt{2}}{4}$

11. $\tan\left(\dfrac{\pi}{4} - \dfrac{\pi}{6}\right)$ $2 - \sqrt{3}$
12. $\cot\left(\dfrac{\pi}{3} - \dfrac{\pi}{4}\right)$ $2 + \sqrt{3}$

13. $\sec\left(\dfrac{\pi}{3} + \dfrac{\pi}{4}\right)$ $-\sqrt{6} - \sqrt{2}$
14. $\csc\left(\dfrac{\pi}{4} - \dfrac{\pi}{3}\right)$ $-\sqrt{6} - \sqrt{2}$

15. $\cos\dfrac{-5\pi}{12}$ $\dfrac{\sqrt{6} - \sqrt{2}}{4}$
16. $\sin\dfrac{7\pi}{12}$ $\dfrac{\sqrt{6} + \sqrt{2}}{4}$

17. $\tan\dfrac{19\pi}{12}$ $-2 - \sqrt{3}$
18. $\sec\dfrac{\pi}{12}$ $\sqrt{6} - \sqrt{2}$

19. $\tan\dfrac{17\pi}{12}$ $2 + \sqrt{3}$
20. $\csc\dfrac{11\pi}{12}$ $\sqrt{6} + \sqrt{2}$

In Exercises 21–34, verify each identity.

21. $\sin\left(x + \dfrac{\pi}{2}\right) = \cos x$
22. $\cos\left(x + \dfrac{\pi}{2}\right) = -\sin x$

23. $\sin\left(x - \dfrac{\pi}{2}\right) = -\cos x$
24. $\cos\left(x - \dfrac{\pi}{2}\right) = \sin x$

25. $\tan\left(x + \dfrac{\pi}{2}\right) = -\cot x$
26. $\tan\left(x - \dfrac{\pi}{2}\right) = -\cot x$

27. $\csc(x + \pi) = -\csc x$
28. $\sec(x + \pi) = -\sec x$

29. $\cos\left(x + \dfrac{3\pi}{2}\right) = \sin x$
30. $\cos\left(x - \dfrac{3\pi}{2}\right) = -\sin x$

31. $\tan\left(x - \dfrac{3\pi}{2}\right) = -\cot x$
32. $\tan\left(x + \dfrac{3\pi}{2}\right) = -\cot x$

33. $\cot(3\pi - x) = -\cot x$
34. $\csc\left(\dfrac{5\pi}{2} - x\right) = \sec x$

In Exercises 35–44, find the exact value of each expression, without using a calculator.

35. $\sin 56° \cos 34° + \cos 56° \sin 34°$ 1

36. $\cos 57° \cos 33° - \sin 57° \sin 33°$ 0

† Due to space constrictions, answers to these exercises may be found in the Answers beginning on page A–1 in the back of the book.

37. $\cos 331° \cos 61° + \sin 331° \sin 61°$ 0

38. $\cos 110° \sin 70° + \sin 110° \cos 70°$ 0

39. $\dfrac{\tan 129° - \tan 84°}{1 + \tan 129° \tan 84°}$ 1

40. $\dfrac{\tan 28° + \tan 17°}{1 - \tan 28° \tan 17°}$ 1

41. $\sin\dfrac{7\pi}{12}\cos\dfrac{3\pi}{12} - \cos\dfrac{7\pi}{12}\sin\dfrac{3\pi}{12}$ $\dfrac{\sqrt{3}}{2}$

42. $\cos\dfrac{5\pi}{12}\cos\dfrac{\pi}{12} - \sin\dfrac{5\pi}{12}\sin\dfrac{\pi}{12}$ 0

43. $\dfrac{\tan\dfrac{5\pi}{12} - \tan\dfrac{2\pi}{12}}{1 + \tan\dfrac{5\pi}{12}\tan\dfrac{2\pi}{12}}$ 1

44. $\dfrac{\tan\dfrac{5\pi}{12} + \tan\dfrac{7\pi}{12}}{1 - \tan\dfrac{5\pi}{12}\tan\dfrac{7\pi}{12}}$ 0

In Exercises 45–50, find the exact value of each expression, given that $\tan u = \dfrac{3}{4}$, with u in quadrant III, and $\sin v = \dfrac{5}{13}$, with v in quadrant II.

45. $\sin(u - v)$ †

46. $\sin(u + v)$ †

47. $\cos(u + v)$ †

48. $\cos(u - v)$ †

49. $\tan(u + v)$ †

50. $\tan(u - v)$ †

In Exercises 51–56, find the exact value of each expression, given that $\cos\alpha = -\dfrac{2}{5}$, with α in quadrant II; and $\sin\beta = -\dfrac{3}{7}$, with β in quadrant IV.

51. $\sin(\alpha - \beta)$ †

52. $\cos(\alpha - \beta)$ †

53. $\csc(\alpha + \beta)$ †

54. $\sec(\alpha + \beta)$ †

55. $\cot(\alpha - \beta)$ †

56. $\cot(\alpha + \beta)$ †

In Exercises 57–64, verify each identity.

57. $\dfrac{\sin(x + y)}{\cos x \cos y} = \tan x + \tan y$

58. $\dfrac{\sin(x + y)}{\sin x \sin y} = \cot x + \cot y$

59. $\dfrac{\cos(x + y)}{\cos x \cos y} = 1 - \tan x \tan y$

60. $\dfrac{\cos(x - y)}{\sin x \sin y} = \cot x \cot y + 1$

61. $\dfrac{\cos(x - y)}{\sin(x + y)} = \dfrac{1 + \cot x \cot y}{\cot x + \cot y}$

62. $\dfrac{\cos(x + y)}{\sin(x - y)} = \dfrac{1 - \cot x \cot y}{\cot x - \cot y}$

63. $\dfrac{\sin(x - y)}{\sin(x + y)} = \dfrac{\cot y - \cot x}{\cot y + \cot x}$

64. $\dfrac{\cos(x + y)}{\cos(x - y)} = \dfrac{\cot x \cot y - 1}{\cot x \cot y + 1}$

In Exercises 65–72, rewrite each equation in the form $y = A\sin(x + \theta)$; graph the resulting equation.

65. $y = \sin x + \cos x$ †

66. $y = \sin x - \cos x$ †

67. $y = 3\sin x + 4\cos x$ †

68. $y = 4\sin x - 3\cos x$ †

69. $y = 5\sin x - 12\cos x$ †

70. $y = 12\sin x + 5\cos x$ †

71. $y = \cos x - 3\sin x$ †

72. $y = 3\cos x - 4\sin x$ †

B Exercises   Applying the Concepts

73. **Analytic geometry.** Let l be a nonvertical line in the coordinate plane. If l makes angle θ with the positive direction of the x-axis, then the slope m of the line l is given by $m = \tan\theta$. Suppose two nonvertical lines l_1 and l_2 intersect in a plane. The slope of l_1 is m_1 and the slope of l_2 is m_2. If $m_1 m_2 \neq -1$, show that the tangent of the acute angle α between the lines l_1 and l_2 is given by $\tan\alpha = \left|\dfrac{m_2 - m_1}{1 + m_1 m_2}\right|$.

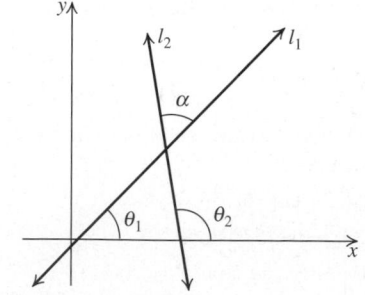

In Exercises 74–76, use Exercise 73 to find the acute angle between the lines l_1 and l_2.

74. **Angle between lines.** $l_1: y = x + 5$, $l_2: y = 4x + 2$. †

75. **Angle between lines.** $l_1: y = 2x + 5$, $l_2: 6x - 3y = 21$.   0

76. **Angle between lines.** $l_1: y = 2x - 4$, $l_2: x + 2y = 7$. †

77. **Combining two pure tones.** The pressure exerted by two pure tones in pounds per square foot is given by the equations $y_1 = 0.4\sin(400t)$ and $y_2 = 0.3\cos(400t)$. Find the amplitude and the phase shift for the total pressure $y = y_1 + y_2$. $A = 0.5, \theta \approx -0.00161$

78. **Combining two pure tones.** Repeat Exercise 77 for $y_1 = 0.05\sin(600t)$ and $y_2 = 0.12\cos(600t)$. $A \approx 0.13, \theta \approx -0.00196$

79. **Simple harmonic motion.** A simple harmonic motion is described by the equation $x = 0.12\sin 2t + 0.5\cos 2t$, where x is the distance from the equilibrium position and t is the time in seconds.

a. Find the amplitude of the motion. $A \approx 0.5142$

b. Find the frequency and the phase shift.   †

80. Simple harmonic motion. Repeat Exercise 79 if the motion is described by the equation $x = \dfrac{1}{2}\sin 3t + \dfrac{1}{3}\cos 3t$.   †

C Exercises   Beyond the Basics

81. Difference quotient. Let $f(x) = \sin x$. Show that

$$\frac{f(x+h) - f(x)}{h} = \sin x\left(\frac{\cos h - 1}{h}\right) + \cos x\left(\frac{\sin h}{h}\right).$$

82. Difference quotient. Let $f(x) = \cos x$. Show that

$$\frac{f(x+h) - f(x)}{h} = \cos x\left(\frac{\cos h - 1}{h}\right) - \sin x\left(\frac{\sin h}{h}\right)$$

In Exercises 83–94, verify each identity.

83. $\cos u \cos(u + v) + \sin u \sin(u + v) = \cos v$

84. $\sin(x + y)\cos y - \cos(x + y)\sin y = \sin x$

85. $\sin 5x \cos 3x - \cos 5x \sin 3x = \sin 2x$

86. $\sin(2x - y)\cos y + \cos(2x - y)\sin y = \sin 2x$

87. $\sin\left(\dfrac{\pi}{2} + x - y\right) = \cos x \cos y + \sin x \sin y$

88. $\cos\left(\dfrac{\pi}{2} + x - y\right) = \cos x \sin y - \sin x \cos y$

89. $\sin(x + y)\sin(x - y) = \sin^2 x - \sin^2 y$

90. $\cos(\alpha + \beta)\cos(\alpha - \beta) = \cos^2\alpha - \sin^2\beta$

91. $\sin^2\left(\dfrac{\pi}{4} + \dfrac{x}{2}\right) - \sin^2\left(\dfrac{\pi}{4} - \dfrac{x}{2}\right) = \sin x$

92. $\cos^2\left(\dfrac{\pi}{4} + \dfrac{x}{2}\right) - \sin^2\left(\dfrac{\pi}{4} - \dfrac{x}{2}\right) = 0$

93. $\dfrac{\sin(\alpha - \beta)}{\sin\alpha \sin\beta} + \dfrac{\sin(\beta - \gamma)}{\sin\beta \sin\gamma} + \dfrac{\sin(\gamma - \alpha)}{\sin\gamma \sin\alpha} = 0$

94. $\dfrac{\sin(\alpha - \beta)}{\cos\alpha \cos\beta} + \dfrac{\sin(\beta - \gamma)}{\cos\beta \cos\gamma} + \dfrac{\sin(\gamma - \alpha)}{\cos\gamma \cos\alpha} = 0$

In Exercises 95–104, find the exact value of each expression.

95. $\cos^2 15° - \cos^2 30° + \cos^2 45° - \cos^2 60° + \cos^2 75°$ †

96. $\sin^2\left(\dfrac{\pi}{8}\right) + \sin^2\left(\dfrac{3\pi}{8}\right) + \sin^2\left(\dfrac{5\pi}{8}\right) + \sin^2\left(\dfrac{7\pi}{8}\right)$ 2

97. $\cos 60° + \cos 80° + \cos 100°$ †

98. $\sin 30° - \sin 70° + \sin 110°$ †

99. $\sin\left[\tan^{-1}\left(-\dfrac{3}{4}\right) + \cos^{-1}\left(\dfrac{4}{5}\right)\right]$ 0

100. $\cos\left[\sin^{-1}\left(-\dfrac{3}{5}\right) + \cos^{-1}\left(\dfrac{3}{5}\right)\right]$ $\dfrac{24}{25}$

101. $\sin\left[\sin^{-1}\left(\dfrac{3}{5}\right) - \cos^{-1}\left(\dfrac{4}{5}\right)\right]$ 0

102. $\cos\left[\sin^{-1}\left(\dfrac{3}{5}\right) + \tan^{-1}\left(-\dfrac{4}{3}\right)\right]$ $\dfrac{24}{25}$

103. $\tan\left[\cos^{-1}\left(\dfrac{4}{5}\right) + \tan^{-1}\left(\dfrac{2}{3}\right)\right]$ $\dfrac{17}{6}$

104. $\tan\left[\sin^{-1}\left(-\dfrac{3}{5}\right) + \cos^{-1}\left(\dfrac{4}{5}\right)\right]$ 0

105. Show that $\tan 70° - \tan 20° = 2\tan 50°$.

106. Show that $\sin(\theta + n\pi) = (-1)^n \sin\theta$.

Critical Thinking

107. Find the exact value of $\tan 1° \tan 2° \tan 3° \ldots \tan 88° \tan 89°$.   †

In Exercises 108–112, assume that x and y are positive numbers in the domain of the inverse function considered. Prove each identity.

108. $\sin^{-1}x \pm \sin^{-1}y = \sin^{-1}(x\sqrt{1 - y^2} \pm y\sqrt{1 - x^2})$

[*Hint:* Let $u = \sin^{-1}x$, and $v = \sin^{-1}y$, and consider $\sin(u \pm v)$.]

109. $\cos^{-1}x + \cos^{-1}y = \cos^{-1}(xy - \sqrt{1 - x^2}\sqrt{1 - y^2})$

110. $\tan^{-1}x + \tan^{-1}y = \begin{cases} \tan^{-1}\left(\dfrac{x + y}{1 - xy}\right), & \text{if } xy < 1 \\ \pi + \tan^{-1}\left(\dfrac{x + y}{1 - xy}\right), & \text{if } xy > 1 \end{cases}$

111. $\sin^{-1}x + \cos^{-1}x = \dfrac{\pi}{2}$

112. Explain why we cannot use the formula for $\tan(u - v)$ to verify that $\tan\left(\dfrac{\pi}{2} - x\right) = \cot x$.

Double-Angle and Half-Angle Formulas

BEFORE STARTING THIS SECTION, REVIEW

1. Sum formulas for sine, cosine, and tangent functions (Section 6.3, page 623)

2. Pythagorean identities (Section 5.3, page 542)

3. Trigonometric functions of common angles (Section 5.2, page 522)

4. Trigonometric equations (Section 6.2, page 609)

OBJECTIVES

1 Use double-angle formulas.

2 Use power-reducing formulas.

3 Use half-angle formulas.

4 Solve trigonometric equations involving multiple angles and half-angles.

Cost of Using an Electric Blanket

Three basic properties of electricity—*voltage*, *current*, and *power*—together with the rate charged by your electric company, are used to find the cost of using an electric device.

Voltage (V) is measured in *volts*. It is the force that pushes electricity through a wire. *Current* (I) measured in *amperes* (amps) measures how much electricity is moving through the device per second. *Power* (P), measured in *watts*, gives the energy consumed per second by an electric device and is defined by the equation

$$P = VI.$$

Your electric company bills you by the kilowatt-hour. When you turn on an electric device that consumes 1000 watts for one hour, it consumes 1 kilowatt-hour. Suppose you live in a community where your electric company charges you at the rate of 8 cents per kilowatt-hour. An electric blanket might use 250 watts (depending on the setting). If you turn it on for 10 hours, it will consume $250 \times 10 = 2500 = 2.5$ kilowatt-hours. This will cost you $(2.5)(8) = 20$ cents.

In Example 5, we use trigonometric identities to compute the *wattage rating* of an electric blanket. ■

1 Use double-angle formulas.

Double-Angle Formulas

Suppose the measure of an angle is x (in radians or degrees); then $2x$ is double the measure of x. The double-angle formulas express the trigonometric function values of $2x$ in terms of function values of x. The sum formulas for the sine, cosine, and tangent functions are

$$\sin(u + v) = \sin u \cos v + \cos u \sin v$$
$$\cos(u + v) = \cos u \cos v - \sin u \sin v$$

and

$$\tan(u + v) = \frac{\tan u + \tan v}{1 - \tan u \tan v}$$

The sum formulas are used to find the double-angle formulas for the sine, cosine, and tangent functions. For example,

$$\sin(u + v) = \sin u \cos v + \cos u \sin v \qquad \text{Sum formula for sines}$$
$$\sin(x + x) = \sin x \cos x + \cos x \sin x \qquad \text{Replace } u \text{ and } v \text{ by } x.$$
$$\sin 2x = 2 \sin x \cos x \qquad \text{Simplify.}$$

The identity

$$\sin 2x = 2 \sin x \cos x$$

is the double-angle formula for the sine function. The double-angle formulas for the cosine and tangent functions are obtained in the same way. We replace both u and v by x (so $u + v = x + x = 2x$) in the sum formulas for $\cos(u + v)$ and $\tan(u + v)$ to obtain:

$$\cos 2x = \cos^2 x - \sin^2 x \qquad \qquad \tan 2x = \frac{2 \tan x}{1 - \tan^2 x}$$

Two other useful forms for $\cos 2x$ are obtained by first replacing $\cos^2 x$ by $1 - \sin^2 x$ and then replacing $\sin^2 x$ by $1 - \cos^2 x$ in the formula for $\cos 2x$.

$$\cos 2x = \cos^2 x - \sin^2 x \qquad \qquad \cos 2x = \cos^2 x - \sin^2 x$$
$$= (1 - \sin^2 x) - \sin^2 x \qquad \qquad = \cos^2 x - (1 - \cos^2 x)$$
$$\cos 2x = 1 - 2 \sin^2 x \qquad \qquad \cos 2x = 2 \cos^2 x - 1$$

We summarize these formulas next.

DOUBLE-ANGLE FORMULAS

$$\sin 2x = 2 \sin x \cos x \qquad \qquad \cos 2x = \cos^2 x - \sin^2 x$$

$$\tan 2x = \frac{2 \tan x}{1 - \tan^2 x} \qquad \qquad \cos 2x = 1 - 2 \sin^2 x$$

$$\cos 2x = 2 \cos^2 x - 1$$

EXAMPLE 1   **Using Double-Angle Formulas**

If $\cos \theta = -\dfrac{3}{5}$ and θ is in quadrant II, find the exact value of each expression.

a. $\sin 2\theta$ **b.** $\cos 2\theta$ **c.** $\tan 2\theta$

Solution

Let (x, y) be the coordinates of a point on the terminal side of θ. Because r represents the distance between (x, y) and the origin, r must be positive. See Figure 6.10. Since

$$\cos \theta = -\frac{3}{5} = \frac{-3}{5} = \frac{x}{r},$$

we choose $x = -3$ and $r = 5$.

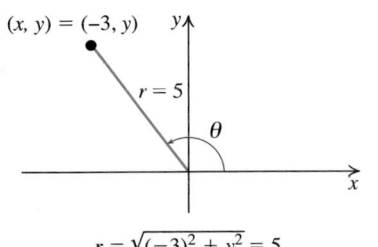

$(x, y) = (-3, y)$

$r = 5$

θ

$r = \sqrt{(-3)^2 + y^2} = 5$

FIGURE 6.10

Continued on next page.

From the relationship $x^2 + y^2 = r^2$, we have

$$y^2 = r^2 - x^2$$

$$\begin{aligned}
y &= \sqrt{r^2 - x^2} & &y \text{ is positive in quadrant II.}\\
&= \sqrt{5^2 - (-3)^2} & &\text{Replace } r \text{ by 5 and } x \text{ by } -3.\\
&= \sqrt{25 - 9} & &\text{Simplify.}\\
&= \sqrt{16} = 4
\end{aligned}$$

Using $x = -3$, $y = 4$, and $r = 5$ we obtain $\sin\theta = \dfrac{y}{r} = \dfrac{4}{5}$, $\tan\theta = \dfrac{y}{x} = \dfrac{4}{-3} = -\dfrac{4}{3}$, and we are given $\cos\theta = -\dfrac{3}{5}$.

a. $\sin 2\theta = 2\sin\theta\cos\theta$ Double-angle formula for sine

$\qquad = 2\left(\dfrac{4}{5}\right)\left(-\dfrac{3}{5}\right)$ Replace $\sin\theta$ by $\dfrac{4}{5}$ and $\cos\theta$ by $-\dfrac{3}{5}$.

$\qquad = -\dfrac{24}{25}$ Simplify.

b. $\cos 2\theta = \cos^2\theta - \sin^2\theta$ Double-angle formula for cosines

$\qquad = \left(-\dfrac{3}{5}\right)^2 - \left(\dfrac{4}{5}\right)^2$ Replace $\cos\theta$ by $-\dfrac{3}{5}$ and $\sin\theta$ by $\dfrac{4}{5}$.

$\qquad = \dfrac{9}{25} - \dfrac{16}{25}$

$\qquad = -\dfrac{7}{25}$ Simplify.

c. $\tan 2\theta = \dfrac{2\tan\theta}{1 - \tan^2\theta}$ Double-angle formula for tangent

$\qquad = \dfrac{2\left(-\dfrac{4}{3}\right)}{1 - \left(-\dfrac{4}{3}\right)^2}$ Replace $\tan\theta$ by $-\dfrac{4}{3}$.

$\qquad = \dfrac{-\dfrac{8}{3}}{1 - \dfrac{16}{9}} = \dfrac{-\dfrac{8}{3}}{-\dfrac{7}{9}}$ Simplify.

$\qquad = \left(-\dfrac{8}{3}\right)\left(-\dfrac{9}{7}\right) = \dfrac{24}{7}$.   Simplify.

You can also find $\tan 2\theta$ by using parts **a** and **b**:

$$\tan 2\theta = \frac{\sin 2\theta}{\cos 2\theta} = \frac{-\dfrac{24}{25}}{-\dfrac{7}{25}} = \frac{24}{7}.$$ ▪ ▪ ▪

PRACTICE PROBLEM 1   If $\sin x = \dfrac{12}{13}$ and $\dfrac{\pi}{2} < x < \pi$, find the exact value of each expression.

a. $\sin 2x$ **b.** $\cos 2x$ **c.** $\tan 2x$ ▪

EXAMPLE 2   Using Double-Angle Formulas

Find the exact value of each expression.

a. $1 - 2\sin^2\left(\dfrac{\pi}{12}\right)$ **b.** $\dfrac{2\tan 22.5°}{1 - \tan^2 22.5°}$

Solution

a. The given expression is the right side of the formula:

$$\cos 2\theta = 1 - 2\sin^2\theta \text{ with } \theta = \frac{\pi}{12}$$

$$1 - 2\sin^2\left(\frac{\pi}{12}\right) = \cos 2\left(\frac{\pi}{12}\right) \qquad \text{Right side equals left side.}$$

$$= \cos\frac{\pi}{6} \qquad 2\left(\frac{\pi}{12}\right) = \frac{\pi}{6}$$

$$= \frac{\sqrt{3}}{2}. \qquad \text{From memory (or see page 522).}$$

b. The given expression is the right side of the formula:

$$\tan 2\theta = \frac{2\tan\theta}{1 - \tan^2\theta}, \text{ with } \theta = 22.5°$$

Thus,

$$\frac{2\tan(22.5°)}{1 - \tan^2 2(22.5°)} = \tan 2(22.5°)$$

$$= \tan 45°$$

$$= 1. \qquad\qquad ■ ■ ■$$

PRACTICE PROBLEM 2   Find the exact value of each expression.

a. $2\cos^2\left(\dfrac{\pi}{12}\right) - 1$ **b.** $\cos^2 22.5° - \sin^2 22.5°$.   ■

EXAMPLE 3   Finding a Triple-Angle Formula for Sines

Verify the identity: $\sin 3x = 3\sin x - 4\sin^3 x$

Solution

We write $3x = 2x + x$ and use the sum formula for sine and the double-angle formulas to verify this identity.

$\sin 3x = \sin(2x + x)$ $3x = 2x + x$

$\qquad = \sin 2x \cos x + \cos 2x \sin x$ Replace u by $2x$ and v by x in the sum formula for $\sin(u + v)$.

$\qquad = (2\sin x \cos x)\cos x + (1 - 2\sin^2 x)\sin x$ Replace $\sin 2x$ by $2\sin x \cos x$ and $\cos 2x$ by $1 - 2\sin^2 x$.

Continued on next page.

$$= 2 \sin x \cos^2 x + \sin x - 2 \sin^3 x \qquad \text{Multiply; distributive property}$$
$$= 2 \sin x (1 - \sin^2 x) + \sin x - 2 \sin^3 x \qquad \cos^2 x = 1 - \sin^2 x$$
$$= 2 \sin x - 2 \sin^3 x + \sin x - 2 \sin^3 x \qquad \text{Distributive property}$$
$$= 3 \sin x - 4 \sin^3 x \qquad \text{Simplify.}$$

We have shown that the left side of the equation is equal to the right side of the equation. The identity is verified. ■ ■ ■

PRACTICE PROBLEM 3   Verify the identity: $\cos 3x = 4 \cos^3 x - 3 \cos x$ ■

The double-angle formulas can be used to express trigonometric functions of $4\theta, 6\theta$, and 8θ in terms of $2\theta, 3\theta$, and 4θ, respectively. For example, the identities

$$\cos 4\theta = 2 \cos^2 2\theta - 1, \quad \sin 6\theta = 2 \sin 3\theta \cos 3\theta, \quad \text{and} \quad \tan 8\theta = \frac{2 \tan 4\theta}{1 - \tan^2 4\theta}$$

can be easily derived from the appropriate double-angle formulas.

2 Use power-reducing formulas.

Power-Reducing Formulas

The purpose of a power-reducing formula is to express the power of a trigonometric function in terms of trigonometric functions with a lower power.

The double-angle formulas for cosines can be used to derive the following *power-reducing formulas:*

POWER-REDUCING FORMULAS

$$\sin^2 x = \frac{1 - \cos 2x}{2} \qquad \cos^2 x = \frac{1 + \cos 2x}{2} \qquad \tan^2 x = \frac{1 - \cos 2x}{1 + \cos 2x}$$

The first two power-reducing formulas can be established by using the appropriate form for the double-angle formulas for $\cos 2x$.

$$\cos 2x = 1 - 2 \sin^2 x \qquad \text{Double-angle formula for } \cos 2x \text{ in terms of sines}$$
$$2 \sin^2 x = 1 - \cos 2x \qquad \text{Add } 2 \sin^2 x - \cos 2x \text{ to both sides and simplify.}$$
$$\sin^2 x = \frac{1 - \cos 2x}{2} \qquad \text{Divide both sides by 2.}$$

This establishes the first formula. Similarly, we can derive the second formula.

$$\cos 2x = 2 \cos^2 x - 1 \qquad \text{Double-angle formula for } \cos 2x \text{ in terms of cosines}$$
$$1 + \cos 2x = 2 \cos^2 x \qquad \text{Add 1 to both sides.}$$
$$\frac{1 + \cos 2x}{2} = \cos^2 x \qquad \text{Divide both sides by 2.}$$

The third formula involving tangents is proved by using the quotient identity and the first two power-reducing formulas.

$$\tan^2 x = \frac{\sin^2 x}{\cos^2 x} \qquad \text{Quotient identity}$$

$$= \dfrac{\dfrac{1 - \cos 2x}{2}}{\dfrac{1 + \cos 2x}{2}}$$
Write power-reducing formulas for $\sin^2 x$ and $\cos^2 x$.

$$= \dfrac{1 - \cos 2x}{1 + \cos x}$$
Multiply numerator and denominator by 2. Simplify.

The power-reducing formulas are very useful in calculus. In these formulas, we express $\sin^2 x$, $\cos^2 x$, and $\tan^2 x$ in terms of trigonometric functions with powers not greater than 1.

EXAMPLE 4   Using Power-Reducing Formulas

Write an equivalent expression for $\cos^4 x$ that contains only first powers of cosines of multiple angles.

Solution

We will make repeated use of power-reducing formulas.

$\cos^4 x = (\cos^2 x)^2$ $\qquad\qquad\qquad a^4 = (a^2)^2$

$\quad = \left(\dfrac{1 + \cos 2x}{2}\right)^2$ $\qquad\quad$ Power-reducing formula:
$\qquad\qquad\qquad\qquad\qquad\qquad \cos^2 x = \dfrac{1 + \cos 2x}{2}$

$\qquad\qquad\qquad\qquad\qquad\qquad \left(\dfrac{1 + b}{2}\right)^2 = \dfrac{(1 + b)^2}{4}$

$\quad = \dfrac{1}{4}(1 + 2\cos 2x + \cos^2 2x)$ $\qquad = \dfrac{1}{4}(1 + 2b + b^2)$ with $b = \cos 2x$

In the power-reducing formula

$\quad = \dfrac{1}{4}\left(1 + 2\cos 2x + \dfrac{1 + \cos 4x}{2}\right)$ $\quad \cos^2 x = \dfrac{1 + \cos 2x}{2}$, replace x by $2x$ to

obtain $\cos^2 2x = \dfrac{1 + \cos 4x}{2}$.

$\quad = \dfrac{1}{4}\left(1 + 2\cos 2x + \dfrac{1}{2} + \dfrac{1}{2}\cos 4x\right)$ $\quad \dfrac{a + b}{c} = \dfrac{a}{c} + \dfrac{b}{c}$

$\quad = \dfrac{1}{4} + \dfrac{2}{4}\cos 2x + \dfrac{1}{8} + \dfrac{1}{8}\cos 4x$ $\qquad$ Distributive property

$\quad = \dfrac{3}{8} + \dfrac{1}{2}\cos 2x + \dfrac{1}{8}\cos 4x$ $\qquad$ Simplify. $\qquad\qquad$ ■ ■ ■

PRACTICE PROBLEM 4   Write an equivalent expression for $\sin^4 x$ that contains only first powers of cosines of multiple angles. ■

Alternating Current

Alternating current (AC) is the electric current that reverses direction, usually many times per second. Most electrical generators produce alternating current. The *wattage rating* of an electric device is $\dfrac{1}{\sqrt{2}} \approx 0.7071$ times the maximum wattage of the device.

EXAMPLE 5 **Finding the Wattage Rating of an Electric Blanket**

The voltage V of household current is given by $V = 170 \sin(120\pi t)$ volts where t is in seconds. Suppose the amount of current passing through an electric blanket is $I = 0.1 \sin(120\pi t)$ amps, where t is in seconds. Find the wattage rating of this electric blanket.

Solution

We have $P = VI$ Power = voltage × current
                      watts = volts × amps

$$P = [170 \sin(120\pi t)][0.1 \sin(120\pi t)]$$ Substitute the given values of V and I.

$$= 17 \sin^2(120\pi t)$$ Multiply.

$$= 17\left[\frac{1 - \cos(240\pi t)}{2}\right]$$ Power-reducing formula

$$P = 8.5 - 8.5 \cos(240\pi t)$$ Simplify.

The maximum value of P is 17 watts; this occurs when $\cos(240\pi t) = -1$.

Hence, the wattage rating for this blanket is $\dfrac{17}{\sqrt{2}} \approx 12$ watts.   ■ ■ ■

PRACTICE PROBLEM 5 In Example 5, find the wattage rating of a lightbulb for which $I = 0.83 \sin(120\pi t)$ amps.   ■

---

3 Use half-angle formulas.

Half-Angle Formulas

If the measure of an angle is θ, then $\dfrac{\theta}{2}$ is half the measure of θ. The half-angle formulas establish trigonometric function values of $\dfrac{\theta}{2}$ in terms of the function values of θ. To derive the half-angle formulas, we replace x by $\dfrac{\theta}{2}$ in the power-reducing formulas and take the square root of both sides. For example,

$$\cos^2 x = \frac{1 + \cos 2x}{2}$$ Power-reducing formula for cosines

$$\cos^2 \frac{\theta}{2} = \frac{1 + \cos 2\left(\frac{\theta}{2}\right)}{2}$$ Replace x by $\dfrac{\theta}{2}$.

$$\cos^2 \frac{\theta}{2} = \frac{1 + \cos \theta}{2}$$ Simplify.

$$\cos \frac{\theta}{2} = \pm\sqrt{\frac{1 + \cos \theta}{2}}.$$ Square-root property

The last equation is called a *half-angle formula* for cosines. The sign, $+$ or $-$, depends on the quadrant in which $\dfrac{\theta}{2}$ lies. Half-angle formulas for sines and tangents can be established in a similar manner.

> **HALF-ANGLE FORMULAS**
>
> $$\sin\frac{\theta}{2} = \pm\sqrt{\frac{1-\cos\theta}{2}}$$
>
> $$\cos\frac{\theta}{2} = \pm\sqrt{\frac{1+\cos\theta}{2}}$$
>
> $$\tan\frac{\theta}{2} = \pm\sqrt{\frac{1-\cos\theta}{1+\cos\theta}}$$
>
> The sign, $+$ or $-$, depends on the quadrant in which $\dfrac{\theta}{2}$ lies.

EXAMPLE 6   Using Half-Angle Formulas

Use a half-angle formula to find the exact value of $\cos 157.5°$.

Solution

Because $157.5° = \dfrac{315°}{2}$, we use the half-angle formula for $\cos\dfrac{\theta}{2}$ with $\theta = 315°$. Note $\dfrac{\theta}{2} = 157.5°$ lies in quadrant II, so that $\cos\dfrac{\theta}{2}$ is negative.

$$\cos 157.5° = \cos\frac{315°}{2}$$

$$= -\sqrt{\frac{1+\cos 315°}{2}} \qquad \text{Half-angle formula for cosines becomes:}$$
$$\cos\frac{\theta}{2} = -\sqrt{\frac{1+\cos\theta}{2}} \text{ with } \frac{\theta}{2} \text{ in quadrant II.}$$

$$= -\sqrt{\frac{1+\cos 45°}{2}} \qquad \cos 315° = \cos(360° - 45°) = \cos 45° = \frac{\sqrt{2}}{2}$$

$$= -\sqrt{\frac{\left(1+\dfrac{\sqrt{2}}{2}\right)\cdot 2}{2\cdot 2}} \qquad \text{Replace } \cos 45° \text{ by } \frac{\sqrt{2}}{2}. \text{ Multiply numerator and denominator by 2.}$$

$$= -\sqrt{\frac{(2+\sqrt{2})}{2\cdot 2}} \qquad \text{Distributive property}$$

$$= -\frac{\sqrt{2+\sqrt{2}}}{2} \qquad \text{Use } \sqrt{\frac{a}{b}} = \frac{\sqrt{a}}{\sqrt{b}} \text{ and simplify.} \qquad ■ \ ■ \ ■$$

PRACTICE PROBLEM 6   Find the exact value of $\sin 112.5°$.   ■

EXAMPLE 7   Finding the Exact Value

Given that $\sin\theta = -\dfrac{5}{13}, \pi < \theta < \dfrac{3\pi}{2}$, find the exact value of each expression.

a. $\sin\dfrac{\theta}{2}$ **b.** $\tan\dfrac{\theta}{2}$

Continued on next page.

Solution

Since θ lies in quadrant III, $\cos\theta$ is negative. Thus,

$$\cos\theta = -\sqrt{1 - \sin^2\theta} \qquad \text{Pythagorean identity}$$

$$\cos\theta = -\sqrt{1 - \left(-\frac{5}{13}\right)^2} \qquad \text{Replace } \sin\theta \text{ by } -\frac{5}{13}.$$

$$= -\sqrt{1 - \frac{25}{169}} \qquad \text{Simplify.}$$

$$= -\sqrt{\frac{169 - 25}{169}} \qquad \text{Simplify.}$$

$$= -\frac{12}{13} \qquad \text{Simplify.}$$

a. Again, since θ lies in quadrant III, $\dfrac{\theta}{2}$ lies in quadrant II. Thus, from the half-angle formula, we have

$$\sin\frac{\theta}{2} = \sqrt{\frac{1 - \cos\theta}{2}} \qquad \sin\frac{\theta}{2} \text{ is positive in quadrant II.}$$

$$= \sqrt{\frac{1 - \left(-\frac{12}{13}\right)}{2}} \qquad \text{Replace } \cos\theta \text{ by } -\frac{12}{13}.$$

$$= \sqrt{\frac{\frac{25}{13}}{2}} \qquad \text{Simplify.}$$

$$= \frac{5}{\sqrt{26}} \qquad \text{Simplify.}$$

$$= \frac{5\sqrt{26}}{26} \qquad \text{Rationalize the denominator.}$$

b. From the half-angle formula, we have

$$\tan\frac{\theta}{2} = -\sqrt{\frac{1 - \cos\theta}{1 + \cos\theta}} \qquad \tan\frac{\theta}{2} \text{ is negative in quadrant II.}$$

$$= -\sqrt{\frac{1 - \left(-\frac{12}{13}\right)}{1 + \left(-\frac{12}{13}\right)}} \qquad \text{Replace } \cos\theta \text{ by } -\frac{12}{13}.$$

$$= -\sqrt{\frac{\frac{25}{13}}{\frac{1}{13}}} \qquad \text{Simplify.}$$

$$= -5 \qquad \text{Simplify.} \qquad\qquad ▪\ ▪\ ▪$$

PRACTICE PROBLEM 7 For θ in Example 7, find $\cos\dfrac{\theta}{2}$. $\qquad\qquad\qquad ▪$

EXAMPLE 8   Verifying a Half-Angle Identity

Verify the identity: $\sin x \cos\dfrac{x}{2} = \sin\dfrac{x}{2}(1 + \cos x)$

Solution

The left side contains $\sin x$, and the right side contains $\sin\dfrac{x}{2}$. Replacing x by $\dfrac{x}{2}$ in the double-angle identity

$$\sin 2x = 2\sin x \cos x$$

yields

$$\sin x = 2\sin\dfrac{x}{2}\cos\dfrac{x}{2} \qquad \sin 2\left(\dfrac{x}{2}\right) = \sin x$$

Begin with the left side of the original equation

$$\sin x \cos\dfrac{x}{2} = 2\sin\dfrac{x}{2}\cos\dfrac{x}{2}\cos\dfrac{x}{2} \qquad \text{Replace } \sin x \text{ by } 2\sin\dfrac{x}{2}\cos\dfrac{x}{2}.$$

$$= 2\sin\dfrac{x}{2}\cos^2\dfrac{x}{2}$$

$$= 2\sin\dfrac{x}{2}\left(\dfrac{1 + \cos 2\left(\dfrac{x}{2}\right)}{2}\right) \qquad \cos^2\dfrac{x}{2} = \dfrac{1 + \cos 2\left(\dfrac{x}{2}\right)}{2}$$

$$= \sin\dfrac{x}{2}(1 + \cos x). \qquad \cos 2\left(\dfrac{x}{2}\right) = \cos x$$

Since the left side is identical to the right side of the equation, the identity is verified. ■ ■ ■

PRACTICE PROBLEM 8   Verify the identity: $\sin\dfrac{x}{2}\sin x = \cos\dfrac{x}{2}(1 - \cos x)$ ■

4 Solve trigonometric equations involving multiple angles and half-angles.

Trigonometric Equations Involving Multiple Angles and Half-Angles

In the next example, we solve a trigonometric equation that involves multiple angles.

EXAMPLE 9   Solving a Trigonometric Equation Involving Multiple Angles

Find all solutions of the equation $2\sin\theta - \sin 3\theta = 0$ in the interval $[0, 2\pi)$.

Solution

$$2\sin\theta - \sin 3\theta = 0 \qquad \text{Given equation.}$$

$$2\sin\theta - (3\sin\theta - 4\sin^3\theta) = 0 \qquad \text{Use } \sin 3\theta = 3\sin\theta - 4\sin^3\theta \text{ from Example 3.}$$

$$2\sin\theta - 3\sin\theta + 4\sin^3\theta = 0 \qquad \text{Distributive property}$$

$$4\sin^3\theta - \sin\theta = 0 \qquad \text{Simplify.}$$

$$\sin\theta(4\sin^2\theta - 1) = 0 \qquad \text{Factor.}$$

$$\sin\theta(2\sin\theta - 1)(2\sin\theta + 1) = 0 \qquad \text{Factor further.}$$

Continued on next page.

$$\sin\theta = 0 \quad \text{or} \quad 2\sin\theta - 1 = 0 \quad \text{or} \quad 2\sin\theta + 1 = 0 \qquad \text{Zero-product property}$$

$\sin\theta = 0$	$2\sin\theta = 1$	$2\sin\theta = -1$
$\sin\theta = 0$	$\sin\theta = \dfrac{1}{2}$	$\sin\theta = -\dfrac{1}{2}$

Solve for $\sin\theta$.

$$\theta = 0 \quad \text{or} \quad \left| \quad \theta = \frac{\pi}{6} \quad \text{or} \quad \right| \quad \theta = \pi + \frac{\pi}{6} = \frac{7\pi}{6}, \quad \text{or} \quad \text{Solve for } \theta \text{ in } [0, 2\pi).$$

$$\theta = \pi \quad \left| \quad \theta = \pi - \frac{\pi}{6} = \frac{5\pi}{6} \quad \right| \quad \theta = 2\pi - \frac{\pi}{6} = \frac{11\pi}{6}$$

The solution set is $\left\{ 0, \dfrac{\pi}{6}, \dfrac{5\pi}{6}, \pi, \dfrac{7\pi}{6}, \dfrac{11\pi}{6} \right\}$. ■ ■ ■

PRACTICE PROBLEM 9   Find all solutions of the equation $\sin\theta - \cos 2\theta = 0$ in the interval $[0, 2\pi)$. ■

EXAMPLE 10   **Solving a Trigonometric Equation Involving Half-Angles**

Find all solutions of the equation $\sin x - \cos\dfrac{x}{2} = 0$ in the interval $[0, 2\pi)$.

Solution

Note that for x to be a solution in the interval $[0, 2\pi)$, the value of $\dfrac{x}{2}$ must be in the interval $[0, \pi)$.

$$\sin x - \cos\frac{x}{2} = 0 \qquad\qquad\qquad \text{Given equation}$$

$$2\sin\frac{x}{2}\cos\frac{x}{2} - \cos\frac{x}{2} = 0 \qquad\qquad 2\sin\frac{x}{2}\cos\frac{x}{2} = \sin 2\left(\frac{x}{2}\right) = \sin x$$

$$\cos\frac{x}{2}\left(2\sin\frac{x}{2} - 1\right) = 0 \qquad\qquad \text{Distributive property}$$

$$\cos\frac{x}{2} = 0 \quad \text{or} \quad 2\sin\frac{x}{2} - 1 = 0 \qquad \text{Zero-product property}$$

$\dfrac{x}{2} = \dfrac{\pi}{2}$	$\sin\dfrac{x}{2} = \dfrac{1}{2}$

Solve for $\dfrac{x}{2}$ in $[0, \pi)$, so that x is in $[0, 2\pi)$.

$$x = \pi \qquad \left| \qquad \frac{x}{2} = \frac{\pi}{6} \quad \text{or} \quad \frac{x}{2} = \frac{5\pi}{6} \right.$$

$$x = \frac{\pi}{3} \quad \text{or} \quad x = \frac{5\pi}{3}$$

The solution set is $\left\{ \dfrac{\pi}{3}, \pi, \dfrac{5\pi}{3} \right\}$. ■ ■ ■

PRACTICE PROBLEM 10   Find all solutions of the equation $\sin x + \cos\dfrac{x}{2} = 0$ in the interval $[0, 2\pi)$. ■

A Exercises   Basic Skills and Concepts

In Exercises 1–6, use the given information about the angle θ to find the exact value of (a) $\sin 2\theta$; (b) $\cos 2\theta$; (c) $\tan 2\theta$.

1. $\sin \theta = \dfrac{3}{5}$, θ in quadrant II †

2. $\cos \theta = -\dfrac{5}{13}$, θ in quadrant III †

3. $\tan \theta = 4$, $\sin \theta < 0$ †

4. $\sec \theta = -\sqrt{3}$, $\sin \theta > 0$ †

5. $\tan \theta = -2$, $\dfrac{\pi}{2} < \theta < \pi$ †

6. $\cot \theta = -7$, $\dfrac{3\pi}{2} < \theta < 2\pi$ †

In Exercises 7–16, use a double-angle formula to find the exact value of each expression.

7. $1 - 2\sin^2 75°$ $-\dfrac{\sqrt{3}}{2}$

8. $\dfrac{2\tan 75°}{1 - \tan^2 75°}$ $-\dfrac{\sqrt{3}}{3}$

9. $2\cos^2 105° - 1$ †

10. $1 - 2\sin^2 165°$ †

11. $\dfrac{2\tan 165°}{1 - \tan^2 165°}$ $-\dfrac{\sqrt{3}}{3}$

12. $2\cos^2 165° - 1$ $\dfrac{\sqrt{3}}{2}$

13. $1 - 2\sin^2\dfrac{\pi}{8}$ $\dfrac{\sqrt{2}}{2}$

14. $2\cos^2\left(-\dfrac{\pi}{8}\right) - 1$ $\dfrac{\sqrt{2}}{2}$

15. $\dfrac{2\tan\left(-\dfrac{5\pi}{12}\right)}{1 - \tan^2\left(-\dfrac{5\pi}{12}\right)}$ $\dfrac{\sqrt{3}}{3}$

16. $1 - 2\sin^2\left(-\dfrac{7\pi}{12}\right)$ $-\dfrac{\sqrt{3}}{2}$

In Exercises 17 and 18, verify each "quadruple-angle" formula.

17. $\sin 4\theta = \cos \theta (4\sin \theta - 8\sin^3 \theta)$

18. $\cos 4\theta = 8\cos^4 \theta - 8\cos^2 \theta + 1$

In Exercises 19–26, verify each identity.

19. $\cos^4 x - \sin^4 x = \cos 2x$

20. $1 + \cos 2x + 2\sin^2 x = 2$

21. $\dfrac{1 + \sin 2x}{\cos 2x} = \dfrac{\cos x + \sin x}{\cos x - \sin x}$

22. $\dfrac{\cos 2x}{\sin 2x} + \dfrac{\sin x}{\cos x} = \csc 2x$

23. $\dfrac{\sin 2x}{\sin x} - \dfrac{\cos 2x}{\cos x} = \sec x$

24. $\dfrac{\cos 3x}{\sin 3x} + \dfrac{\sin x}{\cos x} - \dfrac{\cos 2x}{\sin 3x \cos x}$

25. $\tan 2x + \tan x = \dfrac{\sin 3x}{\cos 2x \cos x}$

26. $\tan 2x - \tan x = \tan x \sec 2x$

In Exercises 27–38, use half-angle formulas to find the exact value of each expression.

27. $\sin\dfrac{\pi}{12}$ †

28. $\sin\dfrac{\pi}{8}$ †

29. $\cos\dfrac{\pi}{8}$ †

30. $\tan\dfrac{\pi}{8}$ †

31. $\sin\left(-\dfrac{3\pi}{8}\right)$ †

32. $\cos\left(-\dfrac{3\pi}{8}\right)$ †

33. $\tan\left(\dfrac{7\pi}{8}\right)$ †

34. $\sec\left(-\dfrac{7\pi}{8}\right)$ †

35. $\tan 112.5°$ †

36. $\cos 112.5°$ †

37. $\sin(-75°)$ †

38. $\tan(-105°)$ †

In Exercises 39–46, use the information about the angle θ to find the exact value of

(a) $\sin\dfrac{\theta}{2}$;   **(b)** $\cos\dfrac{\theta}{2}$;   **(c)** $\tan\dfrac{\theta}{2}$.

39. $\sin \theta = \dfrac{4}{5}$, $\dfrac{\pi}{2} < \theta < \pi$ †

40. $\cos \theta = -\dfrac{12}{13}$, $\pi < \theta < \dfrac{3\pi}{2}$ †

41. $\tan \theta = -\dfrac{2}{3}$, $\dfrac{\pi}{2} < \theta < \pi$ † **42.** $\cot \theta = \dfrac{3}{4}$, $\pi < \theta < \dfrac{3\pi}{2}$ †

43. $\sin \theta = \dfrac{1}{5}$, $\cos \theta < 0$ †   **44.** $\cos \theta = \dfrac{2}{3}$, $\sin \theta < 0$ †

45. $\sec \theta = \sqrt{5}$, $\sin \theta > 0$ †   **46.** $\csc \theta = \sqrt{7}$, $\tan \theta < 0$ †

In Exercises 47–56, verify each identity.

47. $\left(\sin\dfrac{t}{2} + \cos\dfrac{t}{2}\right)^2 = 1 + \sin t$

48. $\left(\sin\dfrac{t}{2} - \cos\dfrac{t}{2}\right)^2 = 1 - \sin t$

49. $2\cos^2\dfrac{x}{2} = \dfrac{\sin^2 x}{1 - \cos x}$

50. $2\sin^2\dfrac{x}{2} = \dfrac{\sin^2 x}{1 + \cos x}$

51. $\tan\dfrac{x}{2} = \dfrac{\sin x}{1 + \cos x}$

52. $\tan\dfrac{x}{2} = \dfrac{1 - \cos x}{\sin x}$

53. $\sin^2\dfrac{x}{2} + \cos x = \cos^2\dfrac{x}{2}$

54. $\cos^2 x + \cos x = 2\cos^2\dfrac{x}{2} - \sin^2 x$

55. $\sin x = \dfrac{2\tan\dfrac{x}{2}}{1 + \tan^2\dfrac{x}{2}}$

56. $\cos x = \dfrac{1 - \tan^2\dfrac{x}{2}}{1 + \tan^2\dfrac{x}{2}}$

† Due to space constrictions, answers to these exercises may be found in the Answers beginning on page A–1 in the back of the book.

In Exercises 57–66, use the power-reducing formulas to rewrite each expression that does not contain trigonometric functions of power greater than 1.

57. $4 \sin^2 x \cos^2 x$ †

58. $\sin^2 x \cos^2 x$ †

59. $4 \sin x \cos x (1 - 2 \sin^2 x)$ † **60.** $4 \sin x \cos x (2 \cos^2 x - 1)$ †

61. $2 \sin 3x \cos 3x (2 \cos^2 3x - 1)$ †

62. $\sin 8x (1 - 2 \sin^2 4x)$ $\sin 8x \cos 8x$

63. $\sin \dfrac{x}{2} \cos \dfrac{x}{2} \left(1 - 2 \sin^2 \dfrac{x}{2} \right)$ $\dfrac{\sin x \cos x}{2}$

64. $\sin x \left(2 \cos^2 \dfrac{x}{2} - 1 \right)$ $\sin x \cos x$

65. $8 \sin^4 \dfrac{x}{2} \cos 2x - 4 \cos x + 3$

66. $8 \cos^4 \dfrac{x}{2} \cos 2x + 4 \cos x + 3$

In Exercises 67–74, find all solutions of each equation in the interval $[0, 2\pi)$.

67. $\sin x - \sin 2x = 0$ †

68. $\sin x - \cos 2x = 0$ †

69. $\cos 2t - 2 \sin^2 t = 0$ †

70. $\cos 2t + 2 \cos^2 t = 0$ †

71. $\sin \dfrac{x}{2} + \sin x = 0$ $\left\{ 0, \dfrac{4\pi}{3} \right\}$

72. $\cos \dfrac{x}{2} + \cos x = 0$ $\left\{ 0, \dfrac{2\pi}{3} \right\}$

73. $\tan \dfrac{x}{2} + \tan x = 0$ $\left\{ 0, \dfrac{2\pi}{3}, \dfrac{4\pi}{3} \right\}$

74. $\cos x - 2 \sin \dfrac{x}{2} \cos \dfrac{x}{2} = 0$ $\left\{ \dfrac{\pi}{4}, \dfrac{5\pi}{4} \right\}$

B Exercises   Applying the Concepts

In Exercises 75–80, assume that the voltage of the current is given by $V = 170 \sin(120\pi t)$, where t is in seconds. Find the wattage rating of each electric device if the current flowing through the device is I amps. Remember, wattage rating of an electric device is $\dfrac{\text{maximum wattage}}{\sqrt{2}}$.

75. Light bulb. $I = 0.832 \sin(120\pi t)$.   100 watts

76. Microwave oven. $I = 7.487 \sin(120\pi t)$.   900 watts

77. Toaster. $I = 9.983 \sin(120\pi t)$.   1200 watts

78. Refrigerator. $I = 6.655 \sin(120\pi t)$.   800 watts

79. Vacuum cleaner. $I = 4.991 \sin(120\pi t)$.   600 watts

80. Television. $I = 2.917 \sin(120\pi t)$.   351 watts

81. Voltage of current. Suppose the voltage of a current is given by $V = 170 \sin(120\pi t)$. Find the first two positive times when the voltage is 85 volts.

82. Voltage of current. Suppose the voltage of a current is given by $V = 160 \sin(120\pi t)$. Find the first two positive times when the voltage is $80\sqrt{3}$ volts.

83. Throwing a football. A quarterback throws a ball with an initial velocity of v_0 feet per second at an angle θ with the horizontal. The horizontal distance x in feet that the ball is thrown is modeled by the equation $x = \dfrac{v_0^2}{16} \sin \theta \cos \theta$. For a fixed v_0, find the angle that produces the maximum distance x. $\left\{ \dfrac{\pi}{4} \right\}$

84. Angle of elevation. A, B, and C are three points on the same horizontal line. The segment CT represents a vertical tower. The angle of elevation of T from the point B is twice that from the point A. The lengths of the segments AB and BC are 80 meters and 50 meters, respectively. Show that the angle of elevation θ from A is given by $\sin^{-1}\left(\dfrac{\sqrt{3}}{4} \right)$.

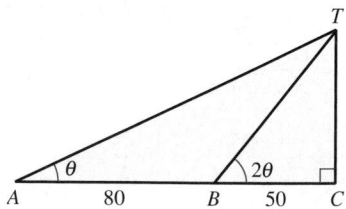

Answers:

81. $\left\{ \dfrac{1}{720}, \dfrac{1}{144} \right\}$

82. $\left\{ \dfrac{1}{360}, \dfrac{1}{180} \right\}$

C Exercises   Beyond the Basics

In Exercises 85–95, verify each identity.

85. $\tan 3x = \dfrac{3\tan x - \tan^3 x}{1 - 3\tan^2 x}$

86. $\dfrac{\sin 3x + \cos 3x}{\cos x - \sin x} = 1 + 2\sin 2x$

87. $\dfrac{\sin x - \cos x}{\sin x + \cos x} - \dfrac{\sin x + \cos x}{\sin x - \cos x} = 2\tan 2x$

88. $\dfrac{2}{\tan x + \cot x} = \sin 2x$

89. $\dfrac{2\sin x}{\cos 3x} = \tan 3x - \tan x$

90. $\cot x - \tan x = 2\cot 2x$

91. $\dfrac{1 - \tan^2\left(\dfrac{\pi}{4} - x\right)}{1 + \tan^2\left(\dfrac{\pi}{4} - x\right)} = \sin 2x$

92. $\dfrac{1 + \sin 2x - \cos 2x}{1 + \sin 2x + \cos 2x} = \tan x$

93. $\sin^2\dfrac{\pi}{8} + \sin^2\dfrac{3\pi}{8} + \sin^2\dfrac{5\pi}{8} + \sin^2\dfrac{7\pi}{8} = 2$

94. $\sin^2\left(\dfrac{\pi}{8} + \dfrac{x}{2}\right) - \sin^2\left(\dfrac{\pi}{8} - \dfrac{x}{2}\right) = \dfrac{1}{\sqrt{2}}\sin x$

95. $\sqrt{2 + \sqrt{2 + 2\cos 4x}} = 2\cos x, \; 0 < x < \dfrac{\pi}{4}$

96. Solve $\sin 2x + \dfrac{1}{\sin 2x} = \dfrac{5}{2}, \; 0 \le x < 2\pi$ $\left\{\dfrac{\pi}{12}, \dfrac{5\pi}{12}, \dfrac{13\pi}{12}, \dfrac{17\pi}{12}\right\}$

Critical Thinking

97. Show that (a) $\sin\dfrac{\pi}{10} = \dfrac{\sqrt{5} - 1}{4}$;

(b) $\cos\dfrac{\pi}{10} = \dfrac{\sqrt{10 + 2\sqrt{5}}}{4}$.

[*Hint:* Let $x = \dfrac{\pi}{10}$. Then $5x = \dfrac{\pi}{2}$ or $3x = \dfrac{\pi}{2} - 2x$.

$\cos 3x = \cos\left(\dfrac{\pi}{2} - 2x\right) = \sin 2x$. Thus,

$4\cos^3 x - 3\cos x = 2\sin x \cos x$,

or $4\cos^2 x - 3 = 2\sin x$ or $4(1 - \sin^2 x) - 3 = 2\sin x$.

Solve this quadratic equation for $\sin x$ to obtain (a).]

98. Use Exercise 97 to find the exact value of each expression.

(a) $\sin\dfrac{\pi}{5}$ (b) $\cos\dfrac{\pi}{5}$ (c) $\sin\dfrac{3\pi}{10}$ (d) $\cos\dfrac{7\pi}{10}$.

Answer:

98. a. $\dfrac{(\sqrt{5} - 1)(\sqrt{10 + 2\sqrt{5}})}{8}$ **b.** $\dfrac{\sqrt{5} + 1}{4}$

c. $\dfrac{\sqrt{5} + 1}{4}$ **d.** $-\dfrac{(\sqrt{5} - 1)(\sqrt{10 + 2\sqrt{5}})}{8}$

Product-to-Sum and Sum-to-Product Formulas

BEFORE STARTING THIS SECTION, REVIEW

1. Sum and difference formulas for sines and cosines (Section 6.3, page 623)

2. Fundamental identities (Section 5.3, page 542)

OBJECTIVES

1 Derive product-to-sum formulas.

2 Derive sum-to-product formulas.

3 Verify trigonometric identities involving multiple angles.

Touch Tone Phones

Dual-tone multi-frequency (DTMF), also known as Touch Tone, tone dialing, or push-button dialing, is a method for instructing a telephone switching network to dial a telephone number. The system was developed by Bell Labs in the late 1950s, and Touch Tone phones were introduced to the public at the 1964 *New York World's Fair.* The dual-tone keypad on a Touch Tone phone is in a format with 4 rows and 3 columns. Each row represents a *low* frequency, and each column represents a *high* frequency, as shown in Figure 6.8. Pressing a button on a Touch Tone phone produces a unique sound. The sound is produced by the sum of two tones (one of low frequency and the other of high frequency) associated with that button, as shown in the figure. In other words, the sound produced is given by $y = y_1 + y_2$, with $y_1 = \sin(2\pi l t)$ and $y_2 = \sin(2\pi h t)$, where l and h are the low and high frequencies (in hertz = Hz) associated with that button.

For example, if you press a single button, such as "1," it will send a sinusoidal tone of two frequencies 697 Hz and 1209 Hz. The sound produced by pressing "1" is represented by the equation

$$y = \sin[2\pi(697)t] + \sin[2\pi(1209)t],$$

or

$$y = \sin(1394\pi t) + \sin(2418\pi t).$$

The two tones are the reason for calling such phones *dual-tone multifrequency phones.* In Example 6, we will analyze the sound produced by the sum of two sine waves. (*Source:* en.wikipedia.org.) ■

FIGURE 6.8

1 Derive product-to-sum formulas.

Product-to-Sum Formulas

The following formulas can be proved by using the sum and difference formulas for the sine and cosine functions:

PRODUCT-TO-SUM FORMULAS

$$\cos x \cos y = \frac{1}{2}[\cos(x - y) + \cos(x + y)]$$

$$\sin x \sin y = \frac{1}{2}[\cos(x - y) - \cos(x + y)]$$

$$\sin x \cos y = \frac{1}{2}[\sin(x + y) + \sin(x - y)]$$

$$\cos x \sin y = \frac{1}{2}[\sin(x + y) - \sin(x - y)]$$

The formulas in the box express the products of the sine values and/or cosine values as the sums or differences of sine or cosine values. The formulas look complicated, but are fairly easy to prove. For example, let's prove the first formula in the box:

$$\cos x \cos y = \frac{1}{2}[\cos(x - y) + \cos(x + y)].$$

We write the difference and sum formulas for cosine, and add.

$\cos(x - y) = \cos x \cos y + \sin x \sin y$	Difference formula for the cosine
$\cos(x + y) = \cos x \cos y - \sin x \sin y$	Sum formula for the cosine
$\cos(x - y) + \cos(x + y) = 2\cos x \cos y + 0$	Add.
$2\cos x \cos y = \cos(x - y) + \cos(x + y)$	Rewrite with the sides reversed.
$\cos x \cos y = \frac{1}{2}[\cos(x - y) + \cos(x + y)]$	Multiply both sides by $\frac{1}{2}$.

Similarly, subtracting $\cos(x + y)$ from $\cos(x - y)$ gives the second formula in the box:

$$\sin x \sin y = \frac{1}{2}[\cos(x - y) - \cos(x + y)]$$

In the same way, starting with the formulas for $\sin(x + y)$ and $\sin(x - y)$, we obtain the third and the fourth formulas in the box.

EXAMPLE 1 **Using a Product-to-Sum Formula**

Write $\sin 5\theta \cos 3\theta$ as the sum or difference of two trigonometric functions.

Solution

Use the identity: $\sin x \cos y = \frac{1}{2}[\sin(x + y) + \sin(x - y)]$

Continued on next page.

$$\sin 5\theta \cos 3\theta = \frac{1}{2}[\sin(5\theta + 3\theta) + \sin(5\theta - 3\theta)] \qquad \text{Replace } x \text{ by } 5\theta \text{ and } y \text{ by } 3\theta.$$

$$= \frac{1}{2}[\sin 8\theta + \sin 2\theta] \qquad \text{Simplify.}$$

$$= \frac{1}{2}\sin 8\theta + \frac{1}{2}\sin 2\theta \qquad \text{Distributive property} \quad ■ \ ■ \ ■$$

PRACTICE PROBLEM 1   Write $\cos 3x \cos x$ as the sum or difference of two functions.   ■

EXAMPLE 2   **Using a Product-to-Sum Formula**

Find the exact value of $\sin 75° \sin 15°$.

Solution

Use the identity: $\sin x \sin y = \frac{1}{2}[\cos(x - y) - \cos(x + y)]$

$$\sin 75° \sin 15° = \frac{1}{2}[\cos(75° - 15°) - \cos(75° + 15°)] \quad \text{Replace } x \text{ by } 75° \text{ and } y \text{ by } 15°.$$

$$= \frac{1}{2}[\cos 60° - \cos 90°] \qquad \text{Simplify.}$$

$$= \frac{1}{2}\left[\frac{1}{2} - 0\right] = \frac{1}{4} \qquad \cos 60° = \frac{1}{2}; \ \cos 90° = 0$$

■ ■ ■

PRACTICE PROBLEM 2   Find the exact value of: $\sin 15° \cos 75°$.   ■

2 Derive sum-to-product formulas.

Sum-to-Product Formula

The following formulas allow us to do just the opposite—rewrite sums or differences of sines and/or cosines as products:

SUM-TO-PRODUCT FORMULAS

$$\cos x + \cos y = 2 \cos\left(\frac{x + y}{2}\right) \cos\left(\frac{x - y}{2}\right)$$

$$\cos x - \cos y = -2 \sin\left(\frac{x + y}{2}\right) \sin\left(\frac{x - y}{2}\right)$$

$$\sin x + \sin y = 2 \sin\left(\frac{x + y}{2}\right) \cos\left(\frac{x - y}{2}\right)$$

$$\sin x - \sin y = 2 \sin\left(\frac{x - y}{2}\right) \cos\left(\frac{x + y}{2}\right)$$

We prove these formulas by using the product-to-sum formulas. For example, we prove the first formula in the box:

$$\cos x + \cos y = 2 \cos\left(\frac{x + y}{2}\right) \cos\left(\frac{x - y}{2}\right)$$

We start with the right side of this formula and use the product-to-sum formulas.

$$2\cos\left(\frac{x+y}{2}\right)\cos\left(\frac{x-y}{2}\right)$$

$$= 2\cdot\frac{1}{2}\left[\cos\left(\frac{x+y}{2}+\frac{x-y}{2}\right)+\cos\left(\frac{x+y}{2}-\frac{x-y}{2}\right)\right]$$ 　　Use the formula for the product of cosines.

$$= \cos\left(\frac{x+y+x-y}{2}\right)+\cos\left(\frac{x+y-x+y}{2}\right)$$ 　　Simplify.

$$= \cos\left(\frac{2x}{2}\right)+\cos\left(\frac{2y}{2}\right)$$ 　　Simplify.

$$= \cos x + \cos y$$ 　　Simplify.

You can verify the other three formulas in the box in a similar way.

EXAMPLE 3　Using Sum-to-Product Formulas

Write each expression as a product of two trigonometric functions and simplify where possible.

a. $\sin 4\theta - \sin 6\theta$　　**b.** $\cos 65° + \cos 55°$

Solution

a. Use the formula: $\sin x - \sin y = 2\sin\left(\frac{x-y}{2}\right)\cos\left(\frac{x+y}{2}\right)$.

$$\sin 4\theta - \sin 6\theta = 2\sin\left(\frac{4\theta-6\theta}{2}\right)\cos\left(\frac{4\theta+6\theta}{2}\right)$$ 　　Replace x by 4θ and y by 6θ.

$$= 2\sin\left(\frac{-2\theta}{2}\right)\cos\left(\frac{10\theta}{2}\right)$$ 　　Simplify.

$$= 2\sin(-\theta)\cos(5\theta)$$ 　　Simplify.

$$= -2\sin\theta\cos 5\theta$$ 　　$\sin(-\theta) = -\sin\theta$

b. Use the formula: $\cos x + \cos y = 2\cos\left(\frac{x+y}{2}\right)\cos\left(\frac{x-y}{2}\right)$.

$$\cos 65° + \cos 55° = 2\cos\left(\frac{65°+55°}{2}\right)\cos\left(\frac{65°-55°}{2}\right)$$ 　　Replace x by $65°$ and y by $55°$.

$$= 2\cos 60°\cos 5°$$ 　　Simplify.

$$= 2\left(\frac{1}{2}\right)\cos 5°$$ 　　$\cos 60° = \frac{1}{2}$

$$= \cos 5°$$ 　　Simplify.　■ ■ ■

PRACTICE PROBLEM 3　Write each expression as a product of two functions and simplify where possible.

a. $\cos 2x - \cos 4x$　　**b.** $\sin 43° + \sin 17°$　　　　　■

In the next example, we will show how to express a sum of a sine and a cosine as a product by first using a cofunction identity.

EXAMPLE 4   **Expressing a Sum of a Sine and a Cosine as a Product**

Write $\sin 5\theta + \cos 3\theta$ as a product of two trigonometric functions.

Solution

Using the cofunction identity $\sin 5\theta = \cos\left(\dfrac{\pi}{2} - 5\theta\right)$, and the formula

$$\cos x + \cos y = 2\cos\left(\frac{x+y}{2}\right)\cos\left(\frac{x-y}{2}\right),\ \text{we have}$$

$$\sin 5\theta + \cos 3\theta = \cos\left(\frac{\pi}{2} - 5\theta\right) + \cos 3\theta \qquad \text{Cofunction identity}$$

$$= 2\cos\left(\frac{\dfrac{\pi}{2} - 5\theta + 3\theta}{2}\right)\cos\left(\frac{\dfrac{\pi}{2} - 5\theta - 3\theta}{2}\right) \qquad \begin{array}{l}\text{Sum-to-product}\\ \text{formula for cosines}\end{array}$$

$$= 2\cos\left(\frac{\pi}{4} - \theta\right)\cos\left(\frac{\pi}{4} - 4\theta\right). \qquad \text{Simplify.} \quad ■\ ■\ ■$$

PRACTICE PROBLEM 4   Write $\sin x - \cos x$ as a product of two trigonometric functions.   ■

Verify Trigonometric Identities

3 Verify trigonometric identities involving multiple angles.

The next example illustrates the use of sum-to-product formulas to verify identities.

EXAMPLE 5   **Verifying an Identity**

Verify each identity.

a. $\dfrac{\sin 5\theta + \sin 9\theta}{\cos 5\theta - \cos 9\theta} = \cot 2\theta$ **b.** $\dfrac{\cos\theta + \cos 2\theta - \cos 3\theta - \cos 4\theta}{\sin\theta + \sin 2\theta + \sin 3\theta + \sin 4\theta} = \tan\theta$

Solution

a. $\dfrac{\sin 5\theta + \sin 9\theta}{\cos 5\theta - \cos 9\theta} = \dfrac{2\sin\dfrac{5\theta + 9\theta}{2}\cos\dfrac{5\theta - 9\theta}{2}}{-2\sin\dfrac{5\theta + 9\theta}{2}\sin\dfrac{5\theta - 9\theta}{2}}$ $\begin{array}{l}\text{Use the formulas for}\\ \sin x + \sin y \text{ and } \cos x + \cos y.\end{array}$

$$= \frac{2\ \cancel{\sin 7\theta}\cos(-2\theta)}{-2\ \cancel{\sin 7\theta}\sin(-2\theta)} \qquad \text{Simplify.}$$

$$= \frac{\cos(-2\theta)}{-\sin(-2\theta)} \qquad \text{Remove the common factors.}$$

$$= \frac{\cos 2\theta}{\sin 2\theta} \qquad \begin{array}{l}\cos(-x) = \cos x, \text{ and}\\ \sin(-x) = -\sin x\end{array}$$

$$= \cot 2\theta \qquad \text{Quotient identity}$$

b. Notice that if we select the numbers (angles) $x = 2\theta$ and $y = \theta$, the resulting angles in the sum-to-product formulas will be $\dfrac{2\theta + \theta}{2} = \dfrac{3\theta}{2}$ and $\dfrac{2\theta - \theta}{2} = \dfrac{\theta}{2}$, neither of which appears on the right side of the identity. However, if we select $x = 3\theta$ and $y = \theta$, then the resulting numbers will be $\dfrac{3\theta + \theta}{2} = 2\theta$ and $\dfrac{3\theta - \theta}{2} = \theta$, and θ is required on the right side.

$$\dfrac{\cos\theta + \cos 2\theta - \cos 3\theta - \cos 4\theta}{\sin\theta + \sin 2\theta + \sin 3\theta + \sin 4\theta}$$ Left side of the identity

$$= \dfrac{(\cos\theta - \cos 3\theta) + (\cos 2\theta - \cos 4\theta)}{(\sin 3\theta + \sin\theta) + (\sin 4\theta + \sin 2\theta)}$$ Regroup terms.

$$= \dfrac{-2\sin\dfrac{\theta + 3\theta}{2}\sin\dfrac{\theta - 3\theta}{2} - 2\sin\dfrac{2\theta + 4\theta}{2}\sin\dfrac{2\theta - 4\theta}{2}}{2\sin\dfrac{3\theta + \theta}{2}\cos\dfrac{3\theta - \theta}{2} + 2\sin\dfrac{4\theta + 2\theta}{2}\cos\dfrac{4\theta - 2\theta}{2}}$$ Use the sum-to-product formulas.

$$= \dfrac{-2\sin 2\theta\sin(-\theta) - 2\sin 3\theta\sin(-\theta)}{2\sin 2\theta\cos\theta + 2\sin 3\theta\cos\theta}$$ Simplify.

$$= \dfrac{2\sin 2\theta\sin\theta + 2\sin 3\theta\sin\theta}{2\sin 2\theta\cos\theta + 2\sin 3\theta\cos\theta}$$ $\sin(-\theta) = -\sin\theta$

$$= \dfrac{\sin\theta(2\sin 2\theta + 2\sin 3\theta)}{\cos\theta(2\sin 2\theta + 2\sin 3\theta)}$$ Distributive property

$$= \dfrac{\sin\theta}{\cos\theta}$$ Remove the common factor.

$$= \tan\theta$$ Quotient identity ■ ■ ■

PRACTICE PROBLEM 5   Verify the identity: $\dfrac{\cos 5x - \cos x}{\sin x - \sin 5x} = \tan 3x$ ■

Analyzing Touch Tone Phones

When a sound of frequency f_1 is combined with a sound of frequency f_2, the resulting sound has frequency $\dfrac{f_1 + f_2}{2}$. In a Touch Tone phone, when you press a button with a low frequency l and high frequency h, the sound produced is modeled by

$$y = \sin(2\pi lt) + \sin(2\pi ht)$$

$$y = 2\sin\left[2\pi\left(\dfrac{l + h}{2}\right)t\right]\cos\left[2\pi\left(\dfrac{l - h}{2}\right)t\right]$$ Sum-to-product formula

$$y = 2\cos\left[2\pi\left(\dfrac{h - l}{2}\right)t\right]\sin\left[2\pi\left(\dfrac{l + h}{2}\right)t\right].$$ $\cos(-\theta) = \cos\theta$

The last equation suggests that the resulting sound may be thought of as a sine wave with frequency of $\dfrac{l + h}{2}$ and variable amplitude of $2\cos\left[2\pi\left(\dfrac{h - l}{2}\right)t\right]$.

FIGURE 6.11

graph of
$$y = 2\cos(484\pi t)\sin[2\pi(1094)t]$$

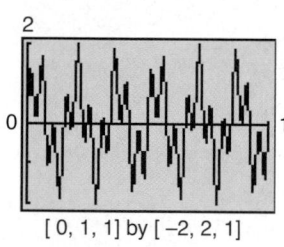

[0, 1, 1] by [−2, 2, 1]

EXAMPLE 6 **Touch Tone Phones**

a. Write an expression that models the tone of the sound produced by pressing the "8" button on your Touch Tone phone. See Figure 6.11.

b. Rewrite the expression from part **a** as a product of two functions.

c. Write the frequency and the variable amplitude of the sound from part **a.**

Solution

a. When the "8" key is pressed, the sound produced (see Figure 6.11) is given by
$$y = \sin[2\pi(852)t] + \sin[2\pi(1336)t] \qquad l = 852, h = 1336$$

b. $y = 2\sin\left[2\pi\left(\dfrac{852+1336}{2}\right)t\right]\cos\left[2\pi\left(\dfrac{852-1336}{2}\right)t\right]$ Sum-to-product formula

$$y = 2\cos[2\pi(242)t]\sin[2\pi(1094)t] \qquad \cos(-\theta) = \cos\theta$$
$$y = 2\cos(484\pi t)\sin[2\pi(1094)t]$$

c. The last equation in part **b** suggests that the sound from pressing the "8" key on a Touch Tone phone has frequency of 1094 Hz and a variable amplitude of $2\cos(484\pi t)$.

■ ■ ■

PRACTICE PROBLEM 6 Repeat Example 5, when you press the "1" button on your Touch Tone phone. ■

A Exercises Basic Skills and Concepts

In Exercises 1–16, use the product-to-sum formulas to rewrite each expression as the sum or difference of two functions. Simplify where possible.

1. $\sin x \cos x$ †
2. $\cos x \cos x$ †
3. $\sin x \sin x$ †
4. $\cos x \sin x$ †
5. $\sin 25° \cos 5°$ †
6. $\sin 40° \sin 20°$ †
7. $\cos 140° \cos 20°$ †
8. $\cos 70° \sin 20°$ †
9. $\sin\dfrac{7\pi}{12}\sin\dfrac{\pi}{12} \quad \dfrac{1}{4}$
10. $\sin\dfrac{3\pi}{8}\cos\dfrac{\pi}{8} \quad \dfrac{1}{2} + \dfrac{\sqrt{2}}{4}$
11. $\cos\dfrac{5\pi}{8}\sin\dfrac{\pi}{8} \quad \dfrac{\sqrt{2}}{4} - \dfrac{1}{2}$
12. $\cos\dfrac{5\pi}{3}\cos\dfrac{\pi}{3} \quad \dfrac{1}{4}$
13. $\sin 5\theta \cos\theta$ †
14. $\cos 3\theta \sin 2\theta$ †
15. $\cos 4x \cos 3x$ †
16. $\sin 5x \sin 2x$ †

In Exercises 17–24, find the exact value of each expression.

17. $\sin 37.5° \sin 7.5°$ †
18. $\cos 52.5° \cos 7.5°$ †
19. $\sin 67.5° \cos 22.5°$ †
20. $\cos 105° \sin 75°$ †
21. $\sin\dfrac{5\pi}{24}\cos\dfrac{\pi}{24} \quad \dfrac{1}{4} + \dfrac{\sqrt{2}}{4}$
22. $\sin\dfrac{7\pi}{12}\sin\dfrac{\pi}{12} \quad \dfrac{1}{4}$
23. $\cos\dfrac{13\pi}{24}\cos\dfrac{5\pi}{24} \quad \dfrac{1}{4} - \dfrac{\sqrt{2}}{4}$
24. $\cos\dfrac{7\pi}{24}\sin\dfrac{\pi}{24} \quad \dfrac{\sqrt{3}}{4} - \dfrac{\sqrt{2}}{4}$

In Exercises 25–44, use sum-to-product formulas to rewrite each expression as a product. Simplify where possible.

25. $\cos 40° - \cos 20°$ †
26. $\sin 22° + \sin 8°$ †
27. $\sin 32° - \sin 16°$ †
28. $\cos 47° + \cos 13°$ †
29. $\sin\dfrac{\pi}{5} + \sin\dfrac{2\pi}{5}$ †
30. $\cos\dfrac{\pi}{12} + \cos\dfrac{\pi}{3}$ †
31. $\cos\dfrac{1}{2} + \cos\dfrac{1}{3}$ †
32. $\sin\dfrac{2}{3} - \sin\dfrac{1}{4} \quad 2\sin\dfrac{5}{24}\cos\dfrac{11}{24}$
33. $\cos 3x + \cos 5x$ †
34. $\sin 5x - \sin 3x$ †
35. $\sin 7x + \sin(-x)$ †
36. $\cos 7x - \cos 3x$ †
37. $\sin x + \cos x$ †
38. $\cos x - \sin x$ †
39. $\sin 2x - \cos 2x$ †
40. $\cos 3x + \sin 3x$ †
41. $\sin 3x + \cos 5x$ †
42. $\sin 5x - \cos x$ †
43. $a(\sin x + \cos x)$ †
44. $a(\sin bx + \cos bx)$ †

In Exercises 45–56, verify each identity.

45. $\dfrac{\sin x + \sin 3x}{\cos x + \cos 3x} = \tan 2x$
46. $\dfrac{\sin 2x + \sin 4x}{\cos 2x + \cos 4x} = \tan 3x$
47. $\dfrac{\cos 3x - \cos 7x}{\sin 7x + \sin 3x} = \tan 2x$
48. $\dfrac{\cos 12x - \cos 4x}{\sin 4x - \sin 12x} = \tan 8x$

†Due to space constrictions, answers to these exercises may be found in the Answers beginning on page A–1 in the back of the book.

49. $\dfrac{\cos 2x + \cos 2y}{\cos 2x - \cos 2y} = \cot(y - x)\cot(y + x)$

50. $\dfrac{\sin 2x + \sin 2y}{\sin 2x - \sin 2y} = \dfrac{\tan(x + y)}{\tan(x - y)}$

51. $\sin x + \sin 2x + \sin 3x = \sin 2x(1 + 2\cos x)$

52. $\cos x + \cos 2x + \cos 3x = \cos 2x(1 + 2\cos x)$

53. $\sin 2x + \sin 4x + \sin 6x = 4\cos x \cos 2x \sin 3x$

54. $\cos x + \cos 3x + \cos 5x + \cos 7x = 4\cos x \cos 2x \cos 4x$

55. $\dfrac{\cos x + \cos 3x + \cos 5x + \cos 7x}{\sin x + \sin 3x + \sin 5x + \sin 7x} = \cot 4x$

56. $\dfrac{\sin 3x + \sin 5x + \sin 7x + \sin 9x}{\cos 3x + \cos 5x + \cos 7x + \cos 9x} = \tan 6x$

B Exercises   Applying the Concepts

57. Touch Tone phone.
  a. Write an expression that models the tone by pressing the "7" button on your Touch Tone phone. See Figure 6.11 (page 656). $y = \sin[2\pi(852)t] + \sin[2\pi(1209)t]$
  b. Rewrite the expression from part (a) as a product of two functions. $y = 2\cos(357\pi t)\sin[2\pi(1030.5)t]$
  c. Write the frequency and the variable amplitude of the sound from part (a). $f = 1030.5$ Hz, $A = 2\cos(357\pi t)$

58. Touch Tone phone. Repeat Exercise 57 if you press the "#" button on your Touch Tone phone. †

59. Beats in music. When two musical tones of slightly different frequencies are played, the sound you hear will fluctuate in volume according to the difference in their frequencies. These are called *beat frequencies*. (The piano tuners use the beat frequency to adjust piano wire until it is at the same frequency as the tuning fork.) Let $y_1 = 0.05\cos(112\pi t)$ and $y_2 = 0.05\cos(120\pi t)$ model two tones.
  a. Write $y = y_1 + y_2$ as the product of two functions. †
  b. How many beats are there? $f = 4$ beats

60. Beats in music. Repeat Exercise 59 for the two tones represented by $y_1 = 0.04\sin(110\pi t)$ and $y_2 = 0.04\sin(114\pi t)$. †

C Exercises   Beyond the Basics

In Exercises 61–70, verify each identity.

61. $\cos 40° + \cos 50° + \cos 70° + \cos 80° = \cos 10° + \cos 20°$

62. $\sin 10° + \sin 20° + \sin 40° + \sin 50° = 2\cos 5° \cos 15°$

63. $\cos 4\theta \cos \theta - \cos 6\theta \cos 9\theta = \sin 5\theta \sin 10\theta$

64. $\cos 38° \cos 46° - \sin 14° \sin 22° = \dfrac{1}{2}\cos 24°$

65. $\cos 20° \cos 100° + \cos 100° \cos 140° -$
  $\cos 140° \cos 200° = -\dfrac{3}{4}$

66. $\sin 25° \sin 35° - \sin 25° \sin 85° - \sin 35° \sin 85° = -\dfrac{3}{4}$

67. $\cos 20° \cos 40° \cos 60° \cos 80° = \dfrac{1}{16}$

68. $\sin 6° \sin 42° \sin 66° \sin 78° = \dfrac{1}{16}$

69. $\dfrac{\sin 3x \cos 5x - \sin x \cos 7x}{\sin x \sin 7x + \cos 3x \cos 5x} = \tan 2x$

70. $\dfrac{\sin 11x \sin x + \sin 7x \sin 3x}{\cos 11x \sin x + \cos 7x \sin 3x} = \tan 8x$

In Exercises 71–76, find all the solutions of each equation in the interval $[0, 2\pi)$.

71. $\cos\theta + \cos 5\theta = 0$ †

72. $\sin\theta + \sin 3\theta = 0$ †

73. $\cos 3\theta - \cos 7\theta = 0$ †

74. $\sin 5\theta - \sin 3\theta = 0$ †

75. $(\sin\theta + \sin 3\theta) - (\cos\theta + \cos 3\theta) = 0$ †

76. $(\sin\theta + \sin 2\theta + \sin 3\theta) - (\cos\theta + \cos 2\theta + \cos 3\theta) = 0$ †

77. Verify the identity:
  $\cos 7x = 2\cos 6x \cos x - 2\cos 4x \cos x + 2\cos 2x \cos x - \cos x$.

78. a. Verify the identity:
  $$4\sin\theta \sin\left(\dfrac{\pi}{3} + \theta\right)\sin\left(\dfrac{\pi}{3} - \theta\right) = \sin 3\theta.$$
  [*Hint:* Recall that $\sin 3\theta = 3\sin\theta - 4\sin^3\theta$.]

  b. Use part (a) to show that
  $$\sin 20° \sin 40° \sin 60° \sin 80° = \dfrac{3}{16}.$$

79. Verify the identity:

$$\frac{\sin(x + 3y) + \sin(3x + y)}{\sin 2x + \sin 2y} = 2\cos(x + y).$$

80. Verify the identity: $\sin^3 x \sin 3x + \cos^3 x \cos 3x = \cos^3 2x$.

81. Verify the following sum-to-product formulas:

a. $\cos x - \cos y = -2\sin\left(\dfrac{x + y}{2}\right)\sin\left(\dfrac{x - y}{2}\right)$

b. $\sin x + \sin y = 2\sin\left(\dfrac{x + y}{2}\right)\cos\left(\dfrac{x - y}{2}\right)$

c. $\sin x - \sin y = 2\sin\left(\dfrac{x - y}{2}\right)\cos\left(\dfrac{x + y}{2}\right)$.

Critical Thinking

82. Supply the reason for each step in verifying the identity:

$$\sin\frac{\pi}{14} \sin\frac{3\pi}{14} \sin\frac{5\pi}{14} = \frac{1}{8}.$$

$$\sin\frac{\pi}{14} \sin\frac{3\pi}{14} \sin\frac{5\pi}{14} = \cos\frac{3\pi}{7} \cos\frac{2\pi}{7} \cos\frac{\pi}{7}$$

$$= \frac{8 \sin\dfrac{\pi}{7} \cos\dfrac{\pi}{7} \cos\dfrac{2\pi}{7} \cos\dfrac{3\pi}{7}}{8 \sin\dfrac{\pi}{7}}$$

$$= \frac{2 \sin\dfrac{4\pi}{7} \cos\dfrac{3\pi}{7}}{8 \sin\dfrac{\pi}{7}}$$

$$= \frac{\sin \pi + \sin\dfrac{\pi}{7}}{8 \sin\dfrac{\pi}{7}}$$

$$= \frac{1}{8}.$$

Group Projects

Assume that $A + B + C = 180°$. Verify each identity.

1. $\sin 2A + \sin 2B + \sin 2C = 4\sin A \sin B \sin C$

2. $\cos 2A + \cos 2B + \cos 2C = -1 - 4\cos A \cos B \cos C$

Summary Definitions, Concepts, and Formulas

6.1 Verifying Trigonometric Identities

Reciprocal Identities

$$\csc x = \frac{1}{\sin x} \qquad \sec x = \frac{1}{\cos x} \qquad \cot x = \frac{1}{\tan x}$$

Quotient Identities

$$\tan x = \frac{\sin x}{\cos x} \qquad \cot x = \frac{\cos x}{\sin x}$$

Pythagorean Identities

$$\sin^2 x + \cos^2 x = 1$$
$$1 + \tan^2 x = \sec^2 x$$
$$1 + \cot^2 x = \csc^2 x$$

Even-Odd Identities

$$\sin(-x) = -\sin x \quad \cos(-x) = \cos x \quad \tan(-x) = -\tan x$$
$$\csc(-x) = -\csc x \quad \sec(-x) = \sec x \quad \cot(-x) = -\cot x$$

See page 600 for *guidelines for verifying trigonometric identities*.

6.2 Trigonometric Equations

A trigonometric equation is an equation that contains a trigonometric function with a variable. Values of the variable that satisfy a trigonometric equations are its *solutions*. Solving a trigonometric equation means to find its *solution set*.

Algebraic techniques are used to solve equations that are in linear, quadratic, or factorable form. Sometimes, trigonometric identities are used to solve trigonometric equations.

6.3 Sum and Difference Formulas

Sum and Difference Formulas

$$\cos(u - v) = \cos u \cos v + \sin u \sin v$$

$$\cos(u + v) = \cos u \cos v - \sin u \sin v$$

$$\sin(u - v) = \sin u \cos v - \cos u \sin v$$

$$\sin(u + v) = \sin u \cos v + \cos u \sin v$$

$$\tan(u - v) = \frac{\tan u - \tan v}{1 + \tan u \tan v}$$

$$\tan(u + v) = \frac{\tan u + \tan v}{1 - \tan u \tan v}$$

Cofunction Identities

$$\sin\left(\frac{\pi}{2} - x\right) = \cos x \quad \cos\left(\frac{\pi}{2} - x\right) = \sin x \quad \tan\left(\frac{\pi}{2} - x\right) = \cot x$$

$$\csc\left(\frac{\pi}{2} - x\right) = \sec x \quad \sec\left(\frac{\pi}{2} - x\right) = \csc x \quad \cot\left(\frac{\pi}{2} - x\right) = \tan x$$

Reduction Formula

If (a, b) is any point on the terminal side of an angle θ in standard position, then $a \sin x + b \cos x = \sqrt{a^2 + b^2}\, \sin(x + \theta)$ for any real number x.

6.4 Double-Angle and Half-Angle Formulas

Double-Angle Formulas

$$\sin 2x = 2 \sin x \cos x$$

$$\cos 2x = \cos^2 x - \sin^2 x$$

$$\cos 2x = 1 - 2 \sin^2 x$$

$$\cos 2x = 2 \cos^2 x - 1$$

$$\tan 2x = \frac{2 \tan x}{1 - \tan^2 x}$$

Power-Reducing Formulas

$$\sin^2 x = \frac{1 - \cos 2x}{2} \quad \cos^2 x = \frac{1 + \cos 2x}{2} \quad \tan^2 x = \frac{1 - \cos 2x}{1 + \cos 2x}$$

Half-Angle Formulas

$$\sin\frac{\theta}{2} = \pm\sqrt{\frac{1 - \cos\theta}{2}}$$

$$\cos\frac{\theta}{2} = \pm\sqrt{\frac{1 + \cos\theta}{2}}$$

$$\tan\frac{\theta}{2} = \pm\sqrt{\frac{1 - \cos\theta}{1 + \cos\theta}}$$

where the sign, $+$ or $-$, depends on the quadrant in which $\frac{\theta}{2}$ lies.

6.5 Product-to-Sum and Sum-to-Product Formulas

Product-to-Sum Formulas

$$\cos x \cos y = \frac{1}{2}[\cos(x - y) + \cos(x + y)]$$

$$\sin x \sin y = \frac{1}{2}[\cos(x - y) - \cos(x + y)]$$

$$\sin x \cos y = \frac{1}{2}[\sin(x + y) + \sin(x - y)]$$

$$\cos x \sin y = \frac{1}{2}[\sin(x + y) - \sin(x - y)]$$

Sum-to-Product Formulas

$$\cos x + \cos y = 2 \cos\left(\frac{x + y}{2}\right) \cos\left(\frac{x - y}{2}\right)$$

$$\cos x - \cos y = -2 \sin\left(\frac{x + y}{2}\right) \sin\left(\frac{x - y}{2}\right)$$

$$\sin x + \sin y = 2 \sin\left(\frac{x + y}{2}\right) \cos\left(\frac{x - y}{2}\right)$$

$$\sin x - \sin y = 2 \sin\left(\frac{x - y}{2}\right) \cos\left(\frac{x + y}{2}\right)$$

Review Exercises

Basic Skills and Concepts

In Exercises 1–4, use the information given to find the exact value of the remaining trigonometric functions of θ.

1. $\sin\theta = -\dfrac{2}{3}$ and $\cos\theta < 0$ †

2. $\tan\theta = -\dfrac{1}{2}$ and $\csc\theta > 0$ †

3. $\sec\theta = 3$ and $\tan\theta < 0$ †

4. $\csc\theta = 5$ and $\cot\theta < 0$ †

In Exercises 5–20, verify each identity.

5. $(\sin x + \cos x)^2 + (\sin x - \cos x)^2 = 2$

6. $(1 - \tan x)^2 + (1 + \tan x)^2 = 2 \sec^2 x$

7. $\dfrac{1 - \tan^2\theta}{1 + \tan^2\theta} = \cos^2\theta - \sin^2\theta$

8. $\dfrac{\sin x + \tan x}{\csc x + \cot x} = \sin^2 x \sec x$

9. $\dfrac{\sin\theta}{1 + \cos\theta} + \dfrac{\sin\theta}{1 - \cos\theta} = 2 \csc\theta$

10. $\tan^2 x \sin^2 x = \tan^2 x - \sin^2 x$

11. $\dfrac{\sin\theta}{1 - \cot\theta} + \dfrac{\cos\theta}{1 - \tan\theta} = \cos\theta + \sin\theta$

12. $\dfrac{\tan\theta - \sin\theta}{\sin^3\theta} = \dfrac{\sec\theta}{1 + \cos\theta}$

13. $\dfrac{\tan x}{\sec x - 1} + \dfrac{\tan x}{\sec x + 1} = 2\csc x$

14. $\dfrac{1}{\csc x - \cot x} - \dfrac{1}{\cot x + \csc x} = 2\cot x$

15. $\dfrac{1 + \sin\theta}{1 - \sin\theta} = (\sec\theta + \tan\theta)^2$

16. $\dfrac{1 - \cos\theta}{1 + \cos\theta} = (\csc\theta - \cot\theta)^2$

17. $\dfrac{\sec x - \tan x}{\sec x + \tan x} = (\sec x - \tan x)^2$

18. $\dfrac{\csc x + \cot x}{\csc x - \cot x} = (\csc x + \cot x)^2$

19. $\dfrac{\sin x - \cos x + 1}{\sin x + \cos x - 1} = \dfrac{\sin x + 1}{\cos x}$

[*Hint:* Multiply the numerator and the denominator of the left side by $\sin x + (1 - \cos x)$.]

20. $\sin^2 x \cot x = \dfrac{2\cos x}{\sin x + \csc x + \cos^2 x \csc x}$

In Exercises 21–26, find all solutions of each equation in the interval $[0, 2\pi)$.

21. $2\cos^2 x - 1 = 0$ †   **22.** $3\tan^2 x - 1 = 0$ †

23. $2\cos^2 x - \cos x - 1 = 0$ †

24. $2\sin^2 x - 5\sin x - 3 = 0$ †

25. $2\sin 3x - 1 = 0$ †

26. $2\cos(2x - 1) - 1 = 0$ †

In Exercises 27–32, solve each equation for θ in the interval $[0°, 360°)$. If necessary, write the answers to the nearest tenth of a degree.

27. $3\sin\theta - 1 = 0$ $\{19.5°, 160.5°\}$

28. $4\cos\theta + 1 = 0$ $\{104.5°, 255.5°\}$

29. $2\sqrt{3}\cos 2\theta - 3 = 0$ $\{15°, 165°, 195°, 345°\}$

30. $(1 - 2\sin 2\theta)(\sqrt{3} + 2\cos 2\theta) = 0$ †

31. $(\sqrt{3}\tan\theta + 1)(2\cos\theta + 1) = 0$ $\{120°, 150°, 240°, 330°\}$

32. $\sqrt{3}\cos\theta = \sin\theta + 1$ $\{30°, 270°\}$

In Exercises 33–40, find the exact value of each expression.

33. $\cos 15°$ †   **34.** $\sin 105°$ †

35. $\csc 75°$ $\sqrt{6} - \sqrt{2}$ **36.** $\tan 75°$ †

37. $\sin 41° \cos 49° + \cos 41° \sin 49°$ 1

38. $\cos 50° \cos 10° - \sin 50° \sin 10°$ †

39. $\dfrac{\tan 69° + \tan 66°}{1 - \tan 69° \tan 66°}$ -1

40. $2\cos 75° \cos 15°$ †

In Exercises 41–44, let $\sin u = \dfrac{4}{5}$, $\cos v = \dfrac{5}{13}$ and $0 < u \le \dfrac{\pi}{2}$, $0 < v \le \dfrac{\pi}{2}$. Find the value of each expression.

41. $\sin(u - v)$ †   **42.** $\cos(u + v)$ †

43. $\cos(u - v)$ †   **44.** $\tan(u - v)$ †

In Exercises 45–62, verify each identity.

45. $\sin(x - y)\cos y + \cos(x - y)\sin y = \sin x$

46. $\cos(x - y)\cos y - \sin(x - y)\sin y = \cos x$

47. $\dfrac{\sin(u + v)}{\sin(u - v)} = \dfrac{\tan u + \tan v}{\tan u - \tan v}$

48. $\dfrac{\tan(x + y)}{\cot(x - y)} = \dfrac{\tan^2 x - \tan^2 y}{1 - \tan^2 x \tan^2 y}$

49. $\dfrac{\sin 4x}{\sin 2x} - \dfrac{\cos 4x}{\cos 2x} = \sec 2x$

50. $\dfrac{\sin 3x}{\sin x} - \dfrac{\cos 3x}{\cos x} = 2$

51. $\sin\left(x - \dfrac{\pi}{6}\right) + \cos\left(x + \dfrac{\pi}{3}\right) = 0$

52. $\cos 2x = \cos^4 x - \sin^4 x$

53. $1 + \tan\theta \tan 2\theta = \sec 2\theta$

54. $\dfrac{\sin\theta + \sin 2\theta}{1 + \cos\theta + \cos 2\theta} = \tan\theta$

55. $\dfrac{\sin\theta + \sin 2\theta}{\cos\theta + \cos 2\theta} = \tan\dfrac{3\theta}{2}$

56. $\dfrac{\sin\theta - \sin 2\theta}{\cos\theta - \cos 2\theta} = -\cot\dfrac{3\theta}{2}$

57. $\dfrac{\sin 5x - \sin 3x}{\sin 5x + \sin 3x} = \dfrac{\tan x}{\tan 4x}$

58. $\dfrac{\cos 5x - \cos 3x}{\cos 5x + \cos 3x} = -\tan x \tan 4x$

59. $\dfrac{\tan 3x + \tan x}{\tan 3x - \tan x} = 2\cos 2x$

60. $\dfrac{\sin 4x}{2(1 + \cos 4x)} = \dfrac{\tan x}{1 - \tan^2 x}$

61. $\dfrac{\sin 3x + \sin 5x + \sin 7x + \sin 9x}{\cos 3x + \cos 5x + \cos 7x + \cos 9x} = \tan 6x$

62. $\dfrac{\cos x + \cos 3x + \cos 5x + \cos 7x}{\sin x + \sin 3x + \sin 5x + \sin 7x} = \cot 4x$

In Exercises 63 and 64, sketch the graph of each equation by first converting it to the form $y = A\sin(x + \theta)$.

63. $y = \sqrt{3}\sin x + \cos x$ †   **64.** $y = \sin x + \sqrt{3}\cos x$ †

In Exercises 65 and 66, assume that $A + B + C = 180°$. Verify each identity.

65. $\sin 2A + \sin 2B - \sin 2C = 4\cos A \cos B \sin C$

66. $\tan A + \tan B + \tan C = \tan A \tan B \tan C$

Applying the Concepts

67. A searchlight beam from a Coast Guard boat shines on a lake at an angle θ to the surface of the water. Viewed by a swimmer under water, the beam appears to make an angle α with the surface of the water, as shown in the figure. Under these circumstances, $\cos\theta = \dfrac{4}{3}\cos\alpha$. Find α if $\cos\theta = \dfrac{2}{3}$. 60°

68. The rabbit population of an area is described by $N(t) = 2400 + 500\sin\pi t$, where $N(t)$ gives the number of rabbits in the area after t years. When will the rabbit population first reach 1900? 1.5 years

69. The voltage from an alternating current generator is given by $V(t) = 160\cos 120\pi t$, where t is measured in seconds. Find the time t when the voltage first equals 80. †

70. A jeweler wants to make a gold pendant in the shape of an isosceles triangle. Express the area of the pendant in terms of $\dfrac{\theta}{2}$, where θ is the angle included by two sides of equal length x. †

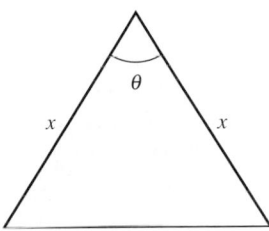

71. If the area of the pendant in Exercise 70 is one square inch, find the angle included between the two sides of equal length when each measures 2 inches. 30°

Practice Test A

1. If $\sin\theta = \dfrac{3}{5}$ and $\cos\theta < 0$, find $\tan\theta$. $-\dfrac{3}{4}$

2. If $\tan x = \dfrac{2}{3}$ and $\csc x < 0$, find $\cos x$. $-\dfrac{3\sqrt{13}}{13}$

In Problems 3–8, verify each identity.

3. $\dfrac{1 - \sin^2 x}{\sin^2 x} = \cot^2 x$

4. $2\sin x\cos x = (\sin x + \cos x + 1)(\sin x + \cos x - 1)$

5. $\sin x\sin\left(\dfrac{\pi}{2} - x\right) = \dfrac{\sin 2x}{2}$

6. $\dfrac{\sin 2x}{2(\cos x + \sin x)} = \dfrac{\sin x}{1 + \tan x}$

7. $\dfrac{\sin 2x + \sin 4x}{\cos 2x + \cos 4x} = \tan 3x$

8. $\cos(x + y)\cos(x - y) = \cos^2 x + \cos^2 y - 1$

In Problems 9 and 10, find all solutions of each equation.

9. $\tan(-x) = 1$ †

10. $\sin 4x = \dfrac{1}{2}$ †

In Problems 11 and 12, find all solutions of each equation in the interval $[0, 2\pi)$.

11. $\cos\dfrac{x}{3} = -\dfrac{\sqrt{2}}{2}$ †

12. $\sin 2x + \cos x = 0$. †

In Problems 13–15, find the exact value of each expression.

13. $\sin 56° + \cos 146°$ 0

14. $\cos 48°\cos 12° - \sin 48°\sin 12°$ †

15. $\sin\dfrac{5\pi}{12}$ $\dfrac{\sqrt{6} + \sqrt{2}}{4}$

16. If $\sin\theta = \dfrac{4}{5}$, find the exact value of $\cos 2\theta$. $-\dfrac{7}{25}$

17. If $\tan\theta = \dfrac{3}{4}$, find the exact value of $\sin 2\theta$. $\dfrac{24}{25}$

18. Determine whether the function $y = \cos\left(\dfrac{\pi}{2} - x\right) + \tan x$ is odd, even, or neither. odd

19. Determine whether $\sin x + \sin y = \sin(x + y)$ is an identity. †

20. The angles of elevation of the top of a tower from two points on the ground at distances 800 and 3200 feet are complementary. Find the height of the tower. 1600 feet

Practice Test B

1. If $\sin\theta = -\dfrac{12}{13}$ and $\pi < \theta < \dfrac{3\pi}{2}$, find $\sec\theta$. a

   a. $-\dfrac{13}{5}$ **b.** $-\dfrac{12}{5}$

   c. $-\dfrac{5}{12}$ **d.** $\dfrac{13}{5}$

2. Which expression is equal to $(\sin x + \cos x)^2 +$ $(\sin x - \cos x)^2$? b

   a. 1   **b.** 2

   c. $\sin x \cos x$ **d.** $4\sin x \cos x$

3. Which expression is equal to $\dfrac{\sin x}{1 + \cos x} + \dfrac{\sin x}{1 - \cos x}$? d

   a. $2\sin x$ **b.** $2\cos x$

   c. $2\sec x$ **d.** $2\csc x$

4. Which expression is equal to $\dfrac{\tan x + \tan y}{\cot x + \cot y}$? b

   a. $\cot x \cot y$ **b.** $\tan x \tan y$

   c. $\sec x \csc y$ **d.** $\sin x \cos y$

5. Which expression is equal to $\dfrac{\sin x + \sin y}{\cos x + \cos y} + \dfrac{\cos x - \cos y}{\sin x - \sin y}$? a

   a. 0   **b.** 1

   c. $\tan x \tan y$ **d.** $\tan x + \tan y$

6. Which expression is equal to $\dfrac{\sin 2x}{1 + \cos 2x}$? b

   a. $\cot x$ **b.** $\tan x$

   c. $\tan 2x$ **d.** $\cot 2x$

7. Which expression is equal to $\dfrac{1 - \cos 2x}{1 + \cos 2x}$? c

   a. $\sin^2 x$ **b.** $\cos^2 x$

   c. $\tan^2 x$ **d.** $\cot^2 x$

8. Which expression is equal to $\dfrac{\sin 3x - \sin x}{\cos x - \cos 3x}$? d

   a. $\tan x$ **b.** $\tan 2x$

   c. $\cot x$ **d.** $\cot 2x$

In Problems 9–11, find all solutions of each equation.

9. $\cot(-x) = -1$ c

   a. $x = \dfrac{\pi}{4} + 2\pi n$, n any integer

   b. $x = \dfrac{3\pi}{4} + 2\pi n$, n any integer

   c. $x = \dfrac{\pi}{4} + \pi n$, n any integer

   d. $x = \dfrac{3\pi}{4} + \pi n$, n any integer

10. $2\cos 4x = -1$ c

   a. $x = \dfrac{2\pi}{3} + 2\pi n$ and $x = \dfrac{4\pi}{3} + 2\pi n$, n any integer

   b. $x = \dfrac{\pi}{3} + \dfrac{n\pi}{2}$ and $x = \dfrac{5\pi}{3} + \dfrac{n\pi}{2}$, n any integer

   c. $x = \dfrac{\pi}{6} + \dfrac{n\pi}{2}$ and $x = \dfrac{\pi}{3} + \dfrac{n\pi}{2}$, n any integer

   d. $x = \dfrac{\pi}{12} + 2\pi n$ and $x = \dfrac{5\pi}{12} + 2\pi n$, n any integer

11. $\sin\dfrac{x}{3} = \dfrac{\sqrt{2}}{2}$ c

   a. $x = \dfrac{\pi}{4} + 2\pi n$ and $x = \dfrac{3\pi}{4} + 2\pi n$, n any integer

   b. $x = \dfrac{\pi}{4} + 6n\pi$ and $x = \dfrac{\pi}{12} + 6n\pi$, n any integer

   c. $x = \dfrac{3\pi}{4} + 6\pi n$ and $x = \dfrac{9\pi}{4} + 6\pi n$, n any integer

   d. $x = \dfrac{3\pi}{4} + 2\pi n$ and $x = \dfrac{5\pi}{4} + 2\pi n$, n any integer

12. Find all the solutions of $\cos x - \sin 2x = 0$ for the interval $[0, 2\pi)$. a

   a. $\left\{\dfrac{\pi}{6}, \dfrac{\pi}{2}, \dfrac{5\pi}{6}, \dfrac{3\pi}{2}\right\}$ **b.** $\left\{\dfrac{\pi}{6}, \dfrac{\pi}{3}, \dfrac{5\pi}{6}, \dfrac{7\pi}{6}\right\}$

   c. $\left\{\dfrac{\pi}{2}, \dfrac{5\pi}{6}, \pi, \dfrac{3\pi}{2}\right\}$ **d.** $\left\{\dfrac{\pi}{6}, \dfrac{\pi}{2}, \dfrac{5\pi}{6}, \dfrac{11\pi}{6}\right\}$

In Problems 13 and 14, find the exact value of each expression.

13. $\sin 71° + \cos 161°$ d

   a. 1.892   **b.** -1.892

   c. 1   **d.** 0

14. $\sin 53° \cos 37° + \cos 53° \sin 37°$ d

   a. $\dfrac{1}{2}$ **b.** $\dfrac{\sqrt{3}}{2}$

   c. 0   **d.** 1

15. If $\sin\theta = \dfrac{2}{3}$, find the exact value of $\cos 2\theta$. b

   a. $\dfrac{1}{3}$ **b.** $\dfrac{1}{9}$

   c. $\dfrac{14}{9}$ **d.** $\dfrac{\sqrt{5}}{3}$

16. If $\tan\theta = \dfrac{4}{3}$, find the exact value of $\sin 2\theta$. a

   a. $\dfrac{24}{25}$ **b.** $\dfrac{4}{5}$

   c. $\dfrac{3}{5}$ **d.** $\dfrac{8}{5}$

17. Which one of the following best describes the symmetry of the graph of $y = \sin\left(\dfrac{\pi}{2} - x\right) + \cot x$? d

 a. Symmetric with respect to the origin.
 b. Symmetric with respect to the x-axis.
 c. Symmetric with respect to the y-axis.
 d. Not symmetric to either axis or the origin.

18. Which pair of values results in a false statement for $\tan(x + y) = \tan x + \tan y$? c

 a. $x = 0, y = \pi$
 b. $x = \dfrac{\pi}{4}, y = -\dfrac{\pi}{4}$

 c. $x = \dfrac{\pi}{4}, y = \dfrac{5\pi}{4}$
 d. $x = \dfrac{\pi}{4}, y = \dfrac{3\pi}{4}$

19. Identify all solutions of $2\cos^2 x = \dfrac{3}{2}$ in the interval $[0, 2\pi)$. d

 a. $\left\{\dfrac{\pi}{6}\right\}$
 b. $\left\{\dfrac{\pi}{6}, \dfrac{5\pi}{6}\right\}$

 c. $\left\{\dfrac{\pi}{6}, \dfrac{11\pi}{6}\right\}$
 d. $\left\{\dfrac{\pi}{6}, \dfrac{5\pi}{6}, \dfrac{7\pi}{6}, \dfrac{11\pi}{6}\right\}$

20. The angle of elevation from a ship moored 3600 feet from the base of a lighthouse to the top of the lighthouse and the angle of depression from the top of the lighthouse to a church 900 feet from its base are complementary. Find the height of the lighthouse. b

 a. 400 feet
 b. 1800 feet

 c. 32,400 feet
 d. 90 feet

Cumulative Review Exercises Chapters 1–6

In Exercises 1–6, solve each equation or inequality.

1. $x^2 + x - 1 = 0$ †

2. $\log_2(x + 1) + \log_2(x - 1) = 1$ $x = \sqrt{3}$

3. $5^{-x} = 9$ †

4. $\sin 2x - \cos x = 0$ $(0 \le x < 2\pi)$ †

5. $x^3 - 4x > 0$ $(-2, 0) \cup (2, \infty)$

6. $\dfrac{2x - 3}{x + 2} - 1 < 0$ $(-2, 5)$

7. If $f(x) = 2x^2 - x + 3$, find $\dfrac{f(x + h) - f(x)}{h}$. $4x - 1 + 2h$

8. If $f(x) = \dfrac{x + 2}{2x - 1}$, find $f^{-1}(x)$. $f^{-1}(x) = \dfrac{x + 2}{2x - 1}$

In Exercises 9–16, sketch the graph of each function $f(x)$ by using transformations on the given basic function.

9. $f(x) = x^2 - 4x - 7$;   use $y = x^2$. †

10. $f(x) = 2\sqrt{x - 3} + 1$;   use $y = \sqrt{x}$. †

11. $f(x) = 2^{x-1} - 2$;   use $y = 2^x$. †

12. $f(x) = 2\ln(x + 1)$;   use $y = \ln x$. †

13. $f(x) = \dfrac{1}{2}\sin 2x$;   use $y = \sin x$. †

14. $f(x) = -2\cos(3x - 1)$;   use $y = \cos x$. †

15. $f(x) = -3\csc x$;   use $y = 3\sin x$. †

16. $f(x) = 2\tan 4x$;   use $y = \tan x$. †

17. Simplify $\dfrac{2\csc^2 x - 5\cot x - 5}{2\cot x + 1}$. $\cot x - 3$

18. Use an identity to find the exact value of $\sec 15°$. $2\sqrt{2} - \sqrt{3}$

19. Verify the identity $\sin\left(x - \dfrac{3\pi}{2}\right) = \cos x$.

20. The height of an observation tower is 125 feet. The base of the tower is 15 feet from the edge of a river. You are on top of the tower, and you measure the angle of depression of a point on the edge directly across the river from you as 51°. How wide is the river? ≈ 86.21 ft

Applications of Trigonometric Functions

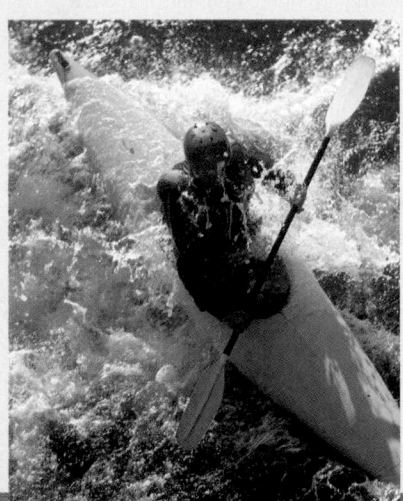

Applications of trigonometry permeate virtually every field, from architecture and bionics to medicine and physics. In this chapter, we introduce vectors and polar coordinates, and investigate the many applications of trigonometry to real-world problems.

TOPICS

The Law of Sines

Mount Everest

In 1852, an unsung hero Radhanath Sickdhar managed to *calculate* the height of Peak XV, an icy peak in the Himalayas. The highest mountain in the world—later named Mount Everest—stood at 29,002 feet. Sickdhar's calculations used triangulations, as well as the phenomenon called refraction—the bending of light rays by the density of Earth's atmosphere. Like George Everest, Sickdhar may have never seen Mount Everest.

BEFORE STARTING THIS SECTION, REVIEW

1. Trigonometric functions (Section 5.2, page 517)

2. Inverse functions (Section 2.8, page 295)

3. Geometric properties of a triangle (Section P.7, page 75)

OBJECTIVES

1 Learn vocabulary and conventions for solving triangles.

2 Derive the Law of Sines.

3 Solve AAS and ASA triangles by using the Law of Sines.

4 Solve for possible triangles in the ambiguous SSA case.

The Great Trigonometric Survey of India

Triangulation is the process of finding the coordinates and the distance to a point by using the *Law of Sines*. Triangulation was used in surveying the Indian subcontinent. The survey, which was called "one of the most stupendous works in the whole history of science," was begun by William Lambton, a British army officer, in 1802. It started in the south of India and extended north to Nepal, a distance of approximately 1600 miles. The survey, which lasted several decades and employed thousands of workers, was named the Great Trigonometric Survey (GTS). In 1818, George Everest (1790–1866), a Welsh surveyor and geographer, was appointed assistant to Lambton. George Everest, who succeeded Lambton in 1823 and was later promoted as surveyor general of India, completed the GTS. Mount Everest was surveyed and named after Everest by his successor Andrew Waugh. In Example 2, we use the Law of Sines to estimate the height of Mount Everest. ■

1 Learn vocabulary and conventions for solving triangles.

RECALL

Two triangles are *congruent* if corresponding sides are congruent (equal in length) and corresponding angles are congruent (equal in measure). An *included side* is the side between two angles, and an *included angle* is the angle between two sides.

Solving Oblique Triangles

The process of finding the unknown side lengths and angle measures in a triangle is called *solving a triangle*. In Section 5.6, you learned techniques of solving right triangles. We now discuss triangles that are not necessarily right triangles. A triangle with no right angle is called an **oblique triangle**. From geometry, we know that two triangles with any of the following sets of given equal parts will always be **congruent:**

    ASA: Two angles and the included side.
    AAS: Two angles and a nonincluded side.
    SAS: Two sides and the included angle.
    SSS: All three sides.

Although **SSA** (two sides and a nonincluded angle) does not guarantee a unique triangle, there can be at most two triangles with the given parts. On the other hand, **AAA** (or **AA**) guarantees only *similar* triangles, not congruent ones, so there are infinitely many triangles with the same three angle measures.

As in our work in Section 5.6 with right triangles, for any triangle *ABC*, we let each letter such as *A* play the dual role of being the vertex *A* and the measure of the angle at *A*. Thus, following the usual convention, the angles of a triangle *ABC* are labeled *A*, *B*, and *C*, and the lengths of their opposite sides are labeled, *a*, *b*, and *c*, respectively. See Figure 7.1.

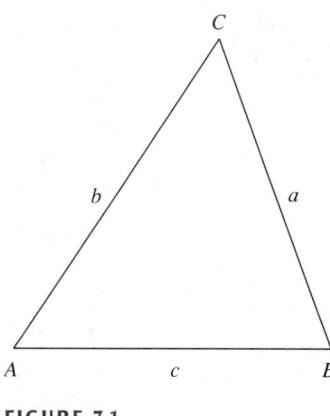

FIGURE 7.1

To solve an oblique triangle, given at least one side and two other measures, we consider four possible cases:

Case 1. Two angles and a side are known (**AAS** and **ASA** triangles).

Case 2. Two sides and an angle opposite one of the given sides are known (**SSA** triangles).

Case 3. Two sides and their included angle are known (**SAS** triangles).

Case 4. All three sides are known (**SSS** triangles).

We now state and derive the *Law of Sines,* which will be used to analyze triangles in Cases 1 and 2. In the next section, we will develop the *Law of Cosines,* which will be needed to solve triangles in Cases 3 and 4.

2 Derive the Law of Sines.

The Law of Sines

THE LAW OF SINES

In a triangle *ABC* with sides of length *a*, *b*, and *c*,

$$\frac{\sin A}{a} = \frac{\sin B}{b} = \frac{\sin C}{c}$$

The Law of Sines is derived by using the right triangles definition of the sine of an acute angle θ:

$$\sin \theta = \frac{\text{opposite}}{\text{hypotenuse}}$$

We begin with an oblique triangle *ABC*. See Figures 7.2 and 7.3. Draw altitude *CD* from the vertex *C* to the side *AB* (or its extension, as in Figure 7.3). Let *h* be the length of segment *CD*.

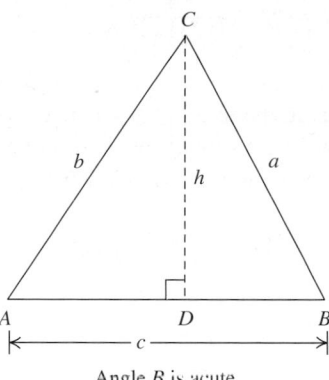

Angle B is acute

FIGURE 7.2

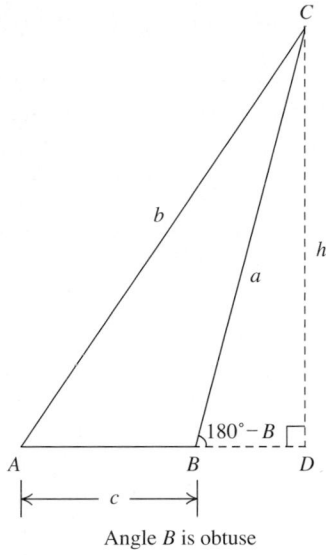

Angle B is obtuse

FIGURE 7.3

In right triangle CDA,

$$\frac{h}{b} = \sin A \text{ or } h = b \sin A.$$

In right triangle CDB,

$$\frac{h}{a} = \sin B \text{ or } h = a \sin B.$$

In right triangle CDA,

$$\frac{h}{b} = \sin A \text{ or } h = b \sin A.$$

In right triangle CDB,

$$\frac{h}{a} = \sin(180° - B) = \sin B$$

or $h = a \sin B.$

Since in each figure $h = b \sin A$ and $h = a \sin B$, we have

$$b \sin A = a \sin B$$

$$\frac{b \sin A}{ab} = \frac{a \sin B}{ab} \qquad \text{Divide both sides by } ab.$$

$$\frac{\sin A}{a} = \frac{\sin B}{b} \qquad \text{Simplify.}$$

Similarly, by drawing altitudes from the other two vertices, we can show that

$$\frac{\sin B}{b} = \frac{\sin C}{c} \quad \text{and} \quad \frac{\sin C}{c} = \frac{\sin A}{a}.$$

The preceding discussion proves the Law of Sines.

THE LAW OF SINES

In any triangle ABC, with sides of length a, b, and c,

$$\frac{\sin A}{a} = \frac{\sin B}{b}, \quad \frac{\sin B}{b} = \frac{\sin C}{c}, \quad \text{and} \quad \frac{\sin C}{c} = \frac{\sin A}{a}$$

We can rewrite these relations in compact notation:

$$\frac{\sin A}{a} = \frac{\sin B}{b} = \frac{\sin C}{c}, \quad \text{or equivalently,} \quad \frac{a}{\sin A} = \frac{b}{\sin B} = \frac{c}{\sin C}$$

3 Solve AAS and ASA triangles by using the Law of Sines.

Solving AAS and ASA Triangles

We next discuss the procedure for solving AAS and ASA triangles of Case 1, where two angles and a side are given. Note that if two angles of a triangle are given, then you also know the third angle (since the sum of the angles of a triangle is 180°). So in this case, we are really dealing with a situation in which all angles and one side of a triangle are known.

FINDING THE SOLUTION: PROCEDURE FOR SOLVING AAS AND ASA TRIANGLES

OBJECTIVE
To solve a triangle if two angles and a side are known.

EXAMPLE
Solve triangle ABC with A = 62°, c = 14 feet, B = 74°. Round side lengths to the nearest tenth.

Step 1 **Find the third angle.** Find the measure of the third angle by subtracting the measures of the known angles from 180°.

1. $C = 180° - A - B$
 $= 180° - 62° - 74°$
 $= 44°$

Step 2 **Make a chart.** Make a chart of the six parts of the triangle, indicating the known parts and the parts to be computed. Make a sketch of the triangle.

2.

$A = 62°$	$a = ?$
$B = 74°$	$b = ?$
$C = 44°$	$c = 14$

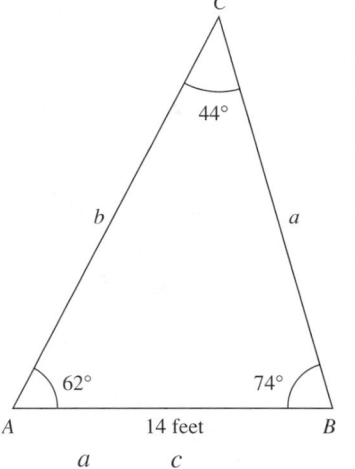

Step 3 **Apply the Law of Sines.** Select two ratios of the Law of Sines in which three of the four quantities are known. Solve for the fourth quantity. Use the form of the Law of Sines in which the unknown quantity is in the numerator.

3. $\dfrac{b}{\sin B} = \dfrac{c}{\sin C}$

$\dfrac{b}{\sin 74°} = \dfrac{14}{\sin 44°}$

$b = \dfrac{14 \sin 74°}{\sin 44°}$

$b \approx 19.4$ feet

$\dfrac{a}{\sin A} = \dfrac{c}{\sin C}$

$\dfrac{a}{\sin 62°} = \dfrac{14}{\sin 44°}$

$a = \dfrac{14 \sin 62°}{\sin 44°}$

$a \approx 17.8$ feet

Step 4 **Show the solution.** Show the solution by completing the chart.

4.

$A = 62°$	$a \approx 17.8$ feet
$B = 74°$	$b \approx 19.4$ feet
$C = 44°$	$c = 14$

EXAMPLE 1 **Using the Law of Sines to Solve an AAS Triangle**

Solve triangle *ABC* with $A = 46°$, $B = 100°$, and $a = 10$ meters. Round side lengths to the nearest tenth.

Solution

Step 1 **Find the third angle.** $C = 180° - A - B$

$= 180 - 46° - 100°$ Replace *A* by 46° and *B* by 100°.

$= 34°$ Simplify.

Step 2   Make a chart.

A = 46°	a = 10
B = 100°	b = ?
C = 34°	c = ?

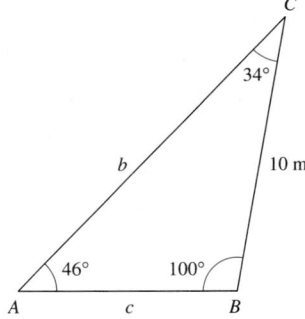

Step 3   Apply the Law of Sines.

$$\frac{b}{\sin B} = \frac{a}{\sin A} \qquad \frac{c}{\sin C} = \frac{a}{\sin A} \qquad \text{The Law of Sines}$$

$$b = \frac{a \sin B}{\sin A} \qquad c = \frac{a \sin C}{\sin A} \qquad \text{Solve for the unknown length.}$$

$$b = \frac{10 \sin 100°}{\sin 46°} \qquad c = \frac{10 \sin 34°}{\sin 46°} \qquad \text{Substitute known values.}$$

$$b \approx 13.7 \text{ meters} \qquad c \approx 7.8 \text{ meters} \qquad \text{Use a calculator.}$$

Step 4   Show the solution.

A = 46°	a = 10 meters
B = 100°	b ≈ 13.7 meters
C = 34°	c ≈ 7.8 meters

■ ■ ■

PRACTICE PROBLEM 1 Solve triangle ABC with $A = 70°$, $B = 65°$, and $a = 16$ inches. Round side lengths to the nearest tenth.   ■

EXAMPLE 2   Height of Mount Everest

From a point on a level plain at the foot of the mountain, a surveyor finds the angle of elevation of the peak of Mount Everest to be 20°. She walks 3465 meters closer (on a direct line between the first point and the base of the mountain) and finds the angle of elevation to be 23°. Estimate the height of the peak of Mount Everest to the nearest meter.

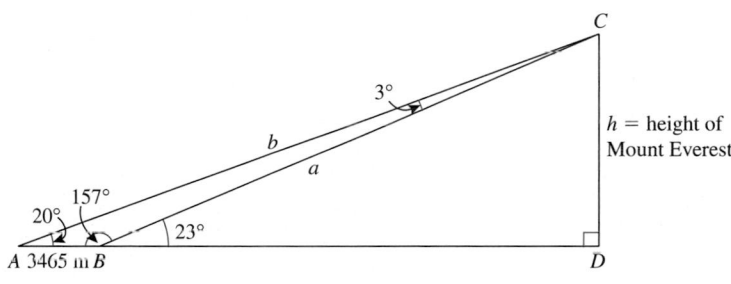

FIGURE 7.4

Solution

In Figure 7.4, consider triangle ABC.

$$m\angle ABC = 180° - 23° = 157°$$

Continued on next page.

Find the third angle in triangle ABC.

$$C = 180° - 20° - 157° = 3°$$

Apply the Law of Sines.

$$\frac{a}{\sin 20°} = \frac{3465}{\sin 3°}$$

$$a = \frac{3465 \sin 20°}{\sin 3°} \approx 22{,}644 \text{ meters}$$

Now in triangle BCD, $\sin 23° = \dfrac{h}{a}$. Thus, $h = a \sin 23° \approx 22{,}644 \sin 23° \approx 8848$ meters.

The height of Mountain Everest is approximately 8848 meters, or about 29,029 feet.   ■ ■ ■

PRACTICE PROBLEM 2   From a point on a level plain at the foot of a mountain, the angle of elevation of the peak is 40°. If you move 2500 feet farther (on a direct line extending from the first point and the base of the mountain), the angle of elevation of the peak is 35°. How high above the plain is the peak? Round your answer to the nearest foot.   ■

4 Solve for possible triangles in the ambiguous SSA case.

Solving SSA Triangles—the Ambiguous Case

In Case 1, where two angles and a side are known, we obtain a unique triangle. However, if the lengths of two sides of a triangle and the measure of the angle opposite one of these sides are given, then depending on these measurements, there may be (1) no such triangle, (2) one such triangle, or (3) two such triangles. For this reason, Case 2 is called the **ambiguous case**.

Suppose we are to draw triangle ABC with given measures of A, a, and b. We draw angle A with the initial side placed horizontally and place the point C on the terminal side of A so that the length of segment AC is b. We are to locate point B on the initial side of A so that the measure of the segment CB is a. See Figure 7.5.

The number of possible triangles depends upon the length h of the altitude from C to the initial side of angle A. Since $\sin A = \dfrac{h}{b}$, we have $h = b \sin A$. Various possibilities for forming triangle ACB are illustrated in Figure 7.6 (where A is an acute angle) and Figure 7.7 (where A is an obtuse angle).

B lies along the initial side of angle A if a triangle exists.

FIGURE 7.5

A is an acute angle

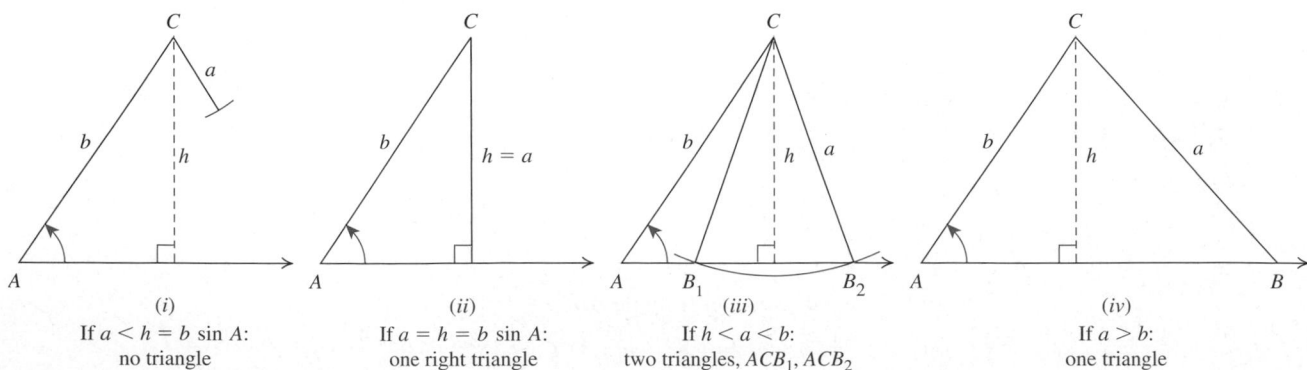

(i)
If $a < h = b \sin A$:
no triangle

(ii)
If $a = h = b \sin A$:
one right triangle

(iii)
If $h < a < b$:
two triangles, ACB_1, ACB_2

(iv)
If $a > b$:
one triangle

FIGURE 7.6

A is an obtuse angle

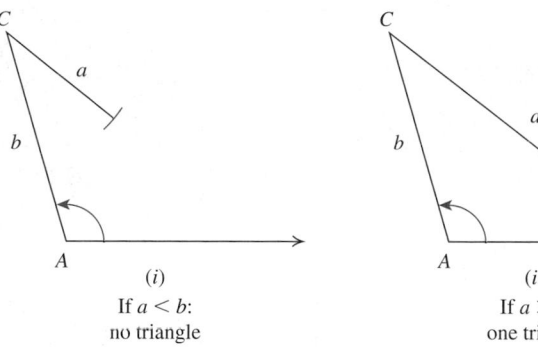

FIGURE 7.7

In practice, you do not need to memorize all the cases involved in solving SSA triangles. We suggest the following procedure to solve SSA triangles:

FINDING THE SOLUTION: PROCEDURE FOR SOLVING SSA TRIANGLES	
OBJECTIVE *To solve a triangle if two sides and an angle opposite one of them is given.*	**EXAMPLE** *Solve triangle ABC with $B = 32°$, $b = 100$ feet, and $c = 150$ feet. Round each answer to the nearest tenth.*

Step 1	**Make a chart** of the six parts, indicating the known parts and the parts to be computed.	**1.**

$A = ?$	$a = ?$
$B = 32°$	$b = 100$
$C = ?$	$c = 150$

Three quantities are known.

Step 2	**Apply the Law of Sines** to the two ratios in which three of the four quantities are known. Solve for the sine of the fourth quantity. Use the form of the Law of Sines in which the unknown quantity is in the numerator.

2. $\dfrac{\sin C}{c} = \dfrac{\sin B}{b}$ The Law of Sines

$\sin C = \dfrac{c \sin B}{b}$ Multiply both sides by c.

$= \dfrac{(150) \sin 32°}{100}$ Substitute values.

$\sin C \approx 0.7949$ Use a calculator.

Step 3	If the sine of the angle, say θ, in Step 2 is greater than 1, there is no triangle with the given measurements. If $\sin \theta$ in Step 2 is between 0 and 1, go to Step 4.

Step 4	Suppose the sine of the angle in Step 2 is x, with $0 < x \le 1$. If $x \ne 1$, there are two possible values for the angle: (*i*) $\theta_1 = \sin^{-1} x$ with $0 < \theta_1 < 90°$ and (*ii*) $\theta_2 = 180° - \theta_1$.

4. $\sin C \approx 0.7949$

Two possible values of C are:

$C_1 \approx \sin^{-1}(0.7949) \approx 52.6°$

$C_2 \approx 180° - 52.6° = 127.4°$

Step 5	If $x \neq 1$, with (known angle) $+ \theta_1 < 180°$ and (known angle) $+ \theta_2 < 180°$, then there are two triangles. Otherwise, there is only one triangle, and if $x = 1$, it is a right triangle.

5. $B + C_1 = 32° + 52.6° = 84.6° < 180°$, and
$B + C_2 = 32° + 127.4° = 159.4° < 180°$.
Thus, there are two triangles with the given measurements.

Step 6	Find the third angle of the triangle(s).

6. $\angle BAC_1 \approx 180° - 32° - 52.6° = 95.4°$

$\angle BAC_2 \approx 180° - 32° - 127.4° = 20.6°$

Step 7	Use the Law of Sines to find the remaining side(s).

7.

$$\frac{a_1}{\sin \angle BAC_1} = \frac{b}{\sin B} \qquad \frac{a_2}{\sin \angle BAC_2} = \frac{b}{\sin B}$$

$$a_1 = \frac{b \sin \angle BAC_1}{\sin B} \qquad a_2 = \frac{b \sin \angle BAC_2}{\sin B}$$

$$a_1 = \frac{100 \sin 95.4°}{\sin 32°} \qquad a_2 = \frac{(100)\sin 20.6°}{\sin 32°}$$

$$a_1 \approx 187.9 \text{ feet} \qquad a_2 \approx 66.4 \text{ feet}$$

Step 8	Show solution(s).

8.

$\triangle BAC_1$

$\angle BAC_1 \approx 95.4°$	$a_1 \approx 187.9$
$B = 32°$	$b = 100$
$C_1 \approx 52.6°$	$c = 150$

$\triangle BAC_2$

$\angle BAC_2 \approx 20.6°$	$a_2 \approx 66.4$
$B = 32°$	$b = 100$
$C_2 \approx 127.4°$	$c = 150$

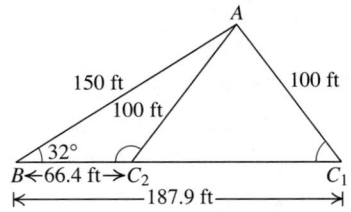

EXAMPLE 3 **Solving an SSA Triangle (No Solution)**

Solve triangle ABC with $A = 50°$, $a = 8$ inches, and $b = 15$ inches.

Solution

Step 1 **Make a chart.**

$A = 50°$	$a = 8$
$B = ?$	$b = 15$
$C = ?$	$c = ?$

Three quantities are known.

Step 2 **Apply the Law of Sines.**

$$\frac{\sin B}{b} = \frac{\sin A}{a} \qquad \text{The Law of Sines}$$

$$\sin B = \frac{b \sin A}{a} \qquad \text{Multiply both sides by } b.$$

$$\sin B = \frac{(15)\sin 50°}{8} \qquad \text{Substitute values.}$$

$$\sin B \approx 1.44 \qquad \text{Use a calculator.}$$

Step 3   Since $\sin B \approx 1.44 > 1$ and the range of the sine function is $[-1, 1]$, we conclude that no triangle exists that is compatible with the given information. ■ ■ ■

PRACTICE PROBLEM 3 Solve triangle ABC with $A = 65°$, $a = 16$ meters, and $b = 30$ meters. ■

> **EXAMPLE 4**   **Solving an SSA Triangle (One Solution)**

Solve triangle ABC with $C = 40°$, $c = 20$ meters, and $a = 15$ meters. Round each answer to the nearest tenth.

Solution

Step 1   **Make a chart.**

$A = ?$	$a = 15$
$B = ?$	$b = ?$
$C = 40°$	$c = 20$

Three quantities are known.

Step 2   **Apply the Law of Sines.**

$$\frac{\sin A}{a} = \frac{\sin C}{c} \qquad \text{The Law of Sines}$$

$$\sin A = \frac{a \sin C}{c} \qquad \text{Multiply both sides by } a.$$

$$= \frac{(15)\sin 40°}{20} \qquad \text{Substitute values.}$$

$$\sin A \approx 0.4821 \qquad \text{Use a calculator.}$$

Step 4 $A = \sin^{-1}(0.4821) \approx 28.8°$. Two possible values of A are $A_1 \approx 28.8°$ and $A_2 \approx 180° - 28.8° = 151.2°$.

Step 5   Since $C + A_2 = 40° + 151.2° = 191.2° > 180°$, there is no triangle with vertex at A_2. Thus, there is only one triangle with measure of angle $A_1 \approx 28.8°$.

Step 6   The third angle at B has measure $\approx 180° - 40° - 28.8° = 111.2°$.

Step 7   Use the Law of Sines to find the remaining side length b.

$$\frac{b}{\sin B} = \frac{c}{\sin C} \qquad \text{The Law of Sines}$$

$$b = \frac{c \sin B}{\sin C} \qquad \text{Multiply both sides by } \sin B.$$

$$= \frac{(20)\sin(111.2°)}{\sin 40°} \qquad \text{Substitute values.}$$

$$b \approx 29.0 \text{ m} \qquad \text{Use a calculator.}$$

Continued on next page.

Step 8 **Show the solution.** See Figure 7.8.

$A_1 \approx 28.8°$	$a = 15$ meters
$B \approx 111.2°$	$b \approx 29.0$ meters
$C = 40°$	$c = 20$ meters

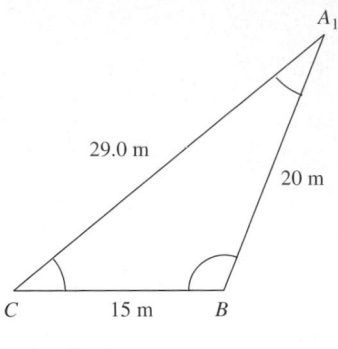

FIGURE 7.8 ■ ■ ■

PRACTICE PROBLEM 4 Solve triangle ABC with $C = 60°$, $c = 50$ feet, and $a = 30$ feet. ■

EXAMPLE 5 **Solving an SSA Triangle (Two Solutions)**

Solve triangle ABC with $A = 47°$, $a = 11$ meters, and $c = 13$ meters. Round each answer to the nearest tenth.

Solution

Step 1 **Make a chart.**

$A = 47°$	$a = 11$	←
$B = ?$	$b = ?$	Three quantities are known.
$C = ?$	$c = 13$	←

Step 2 **Apply the Law of Sines.**

$$\frac{\sin C}{c} = \frac{\sin A}{a} \qquad \text{The Law of Sines}$$

$$\sin C = \frac{c \sin A}{a} \qquad \text{Multiply both sides by } c.$$

$$= \frac{13 \sin 47°}{11} \approx 0.864 \qquad \text{Substitute values and use a calculator.}$$

Step 4 Two possible values of C with $\sin C \approx 0.864$ are

$C_1 \approx \sin^{-1}(0.864) = 59.8°$ and $C_2 \approx 180° - 59.8° = 120.2°$.

Step 5 $A + C_1 = 47° + 59.8° = 106.8° < 180°$, and

$A + C_2 = 47° + 120.2° = 167.2° < 180°$.

There are two triangles with the given measurements.

Step 6 $\angle ABC_1 \approx 180° - 47° - 59.8° = 73.2°$, and

$\angle ABC_2 \approx 180° - 47° - 120.2° = 12.8°$.

Step 7

$$\frac{b_1}{\sin \angle ABC_1} = \frac{a}{\sin a}$$

$$b_1 = \frac{a \sin \angle ABC_1}{\sin A}$$

$$= \frac{11 \sin 73.2°}{\sin 47°}$$

$$\approx 14.4 \text{ meters}$$

$$\frac{b_2}{\sin \angle ABC_2} = \frac{a}{\sin A}$$

$$b_2 = \frac{a \sin \angle ABC_2}{\sin A}$$

$$= \frac{11 \sin 12.8°}{\sin 47°}$$

$$\approx 3.3 \text{ meters}$$

Step 8

$\triangle BAC_1$

$A = 47°$	$a = 11$
$\angle ABC_1 \approx 73.2°$	$b_1 \approx 14.4$
$C_1 \approx 59.8°$	$c = 13$

$\triangle BAC_2$

$A = 47°$	$a = 11$
$\angle ABC_2 \approx 12.8°$	$b_2 \approx 3.3$
$C_2 \approx 120.2°$	$c = 13$

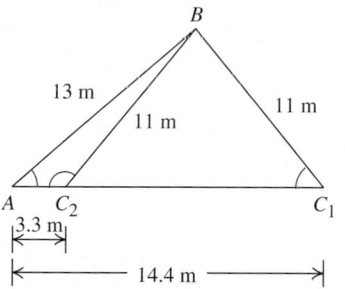

■ ■ ■

PRACTICE PROBLEM 5 Solve triangle ABC with $C = 35°$, $b = 15$ feet, and $c = 12$ feet. Round each answer to the nearest tenth. ■

Bearings

In navigation and surveying, directions are usually given by using *bearings*. A **bearing** is the measure of an acute angle from due north or due south. The bearing $N\,40°\,E$ means $40°$ to the east of due north whereas $S\,30°\,W$ means $30°$ to the west of due south. (See Figure 7.9.)

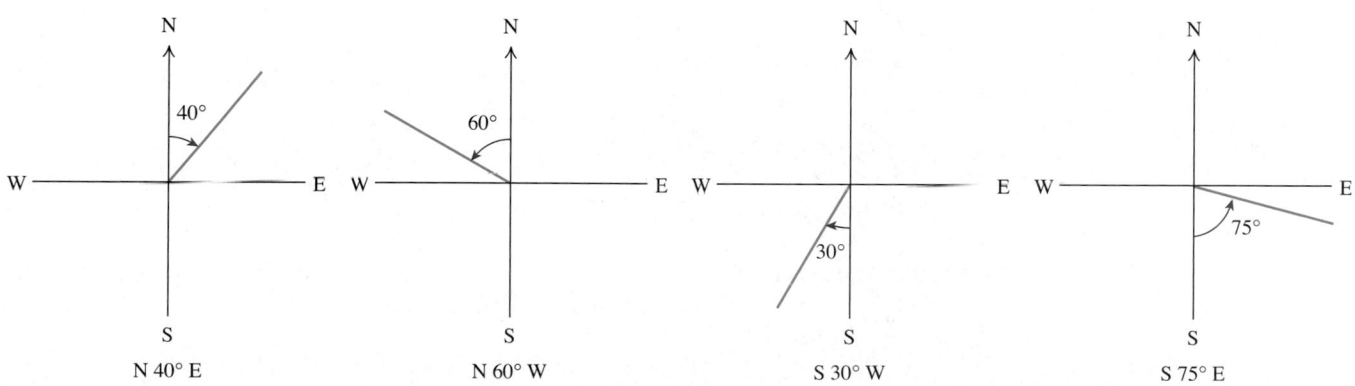

FIGURE 7.9

| EXAMPLE 6 | Navigating Using Bearings |

A ship sailing due west at 20 miles per hour records the bearing of an oil rig at N 55.4° W. An hour and a half later the bearing of the same rig is N 66.8° E.

a. How far is the ship from the oil rig the second time?

b. How close did the ship pass to the oil rig?

Solution

a. In an hour and a half the ship travels $(1.5)(20) = 30$ miles due west. The oil rig (C), the starting point for the ship (A), and the position of the ship after an hour and a half (B) form the vertices of the triangle ABC shown in Figure 7.10.

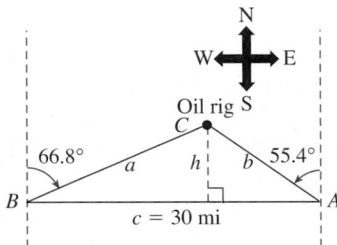

FIGURE 7.10

Then $A = 90° − 55.4° = 34.6°$ and $B = 90° − 66.8° = 23.2°$. Thus, $C = 180° − 34.6° − 23.2° = 122.2°$.

$$\frac{a}{\sin A} = \frac{c}{\sin C} \qquad \text{The Law of Sines}$$

$$a = \frac{c \sin A}{\sin C} \qquad \text{Multiply both sides by } \sin A.$$

$$= \frac{30 \sin 34.6°}{\sin 122.2°} \approx 20 \text{ miles} \qquad \text{Replace } A, C, \text{ and } c \text{ by their values and use a calculator.}$$

The ship is approximately 20 miles from the oil rig when the second bearing is taken.

b. The shortest distance between the ship and the oil rig is the length of the segment h in triangle ABC.

$$\sin B = \frac{h}{a} \qquad \text{Right triangle definition of the sine}$$

$$h = a \sin B \qquad \text{Multiply both sides by } a.$$

$$h \approx 20 \sin 23.2° \qquad \text{Replace } a \text{ and } B \text{ by their values.}$$

$$\approx 7.9 \qquad \text{Use a calculator.}$$

The ship passes within 7.9 miles of the oil rig.   ■ ■ ■

PRACTICE PROBLEM 6   Rework Exercise 6 if the second bearing is taken after two hours and is N 60.4° E, and the ship is traveling at 25 miles per hour.   ■

A Exercises   Basic Skills and Concepts

In Exercises 1–8, solve each triangle. Round each answer to the nearest tenth.

1.

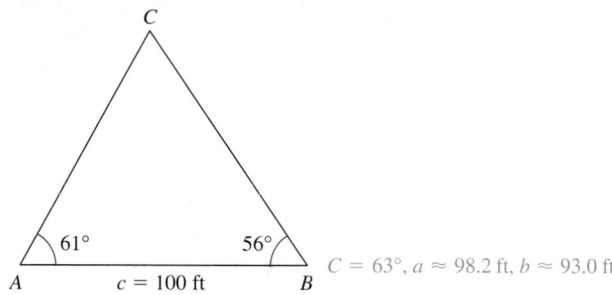

$C = 63°$, $a ≈ 98.2$ ft, $b ≈ 93.0$ ft

2.

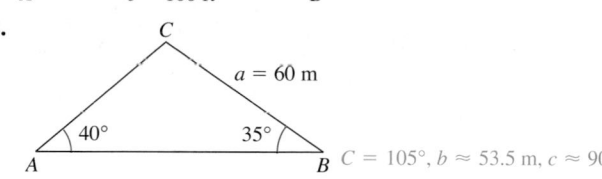

$C = 105°$, $b ≈ 53.5$ m, $c ≈ 90.2$ m

3.

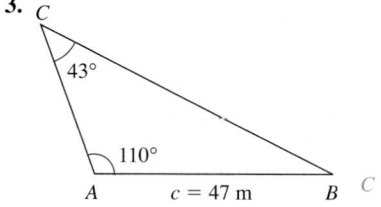

$C = 27°$, $b ≈ 64.8$ m, $c ≈ 31.3$ m

4.

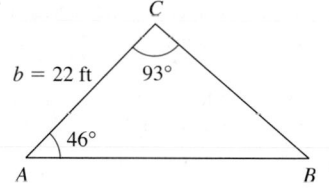

$C = 41°$, $a ≈ 24.1$ ft, $c ≈ 33.5$ ft

5.

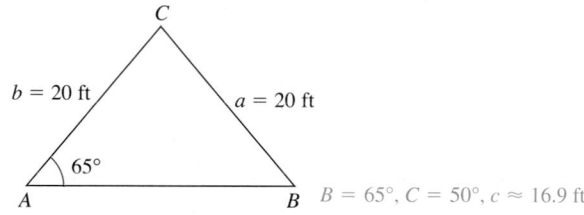

$B = 65°$, $C = 50°$, $c ≈ 16.9$ ft

6.

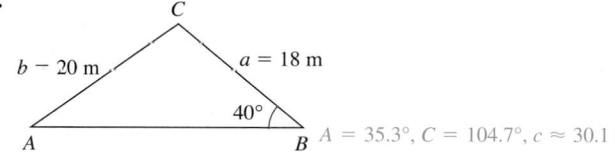

$A = 35.3°$, $C = 104.7°$, $c ≈ 30.1$ m

7.

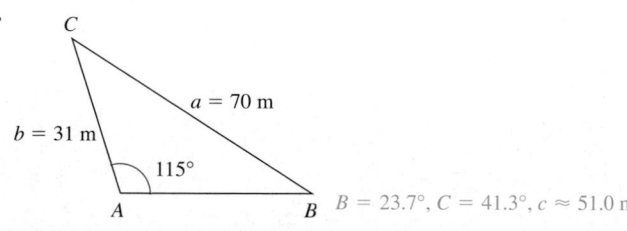

$B = 23.7°$, $C = 41.3°$, $c ≈ 51.0$ m

8.

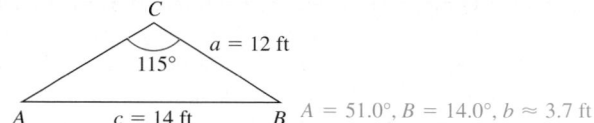

$A = 51.0°$, $B = 14.0°$, $b ≈ 3.7$ ft

In Exercises 9–20, solve triangle ABC. Round each answer to the nearest tenth.

9. $A = 40°$, $B = 35°$, $a = 100$ meters †

10. $A = 80°$, $B = 20°$, $a = 100$ meters †

11. $A = 46°$, $C = 55°$, $a = 75$ centimeters †

12. $A = 35°$, $C = 98°$, $a = 75$ centimeters †

13. $A = 35°$, $C = 47°$, $c = 60$ feet †

14. $A = 44°$, $C = 76°$, $c = 40$ feet †

15. $B = 43°$, $C = 67°$, $b = 40$ inches †

16. $B = 95°$, $C = 35°$, $b = 100$ inches †

17. $B = 110°$, $C = 46°$, $c = 23.5$ feet †

18. $B = 67°$, $C = 63°$, $c = 16.8$ feet †

19. $A = 35.7°$, $B = 45.8°$, $c = 30$ meters †

20. $A = 64.5°$, $B = 54.3°$, $c = 40$ meters †

In Exercises 21–40, solve each SSA triangle. Indicate whether the given measurements result in no triangle, one triangle, or two triangles. Solve each resulting triangle. Round each answer to the nearest tenth.

21. $A = 40°$, $a = 23$, $b = 20$ †

22. $A = 36°$, $a = 30$, $b = 24$ †

23. $A = 30°$, $a = 25$, $b = 50$ †

24. $A = 60°$, $a = 20\sqrt{3}$, $b = 40$ †

25. $A = 40°$, $a = 10$, $b = 20$ No triangle exists.

26. $A = 62°$, $a = 30$, $b = 40$ No triangle exists.

27. $A = 95°$, $a = 18$, $b = 21$ No triangle exists.

28. $A = 110°$, $a = 37$, $b = 41$ No triangle exists.

29. $A = 100°$, $a = 40$, $b = 34$ †

30. $A = 105°$, $a = 70$, $b = 30$ †

31. $B = 50°$, $b = 22$, $c = 40$ No triangle exists.

32. $B = 64°$, $b = 45$, $c = 60$ No triangle exists.

33. $B = 46°$, $b = 35$, $c = 40$ †

34. $B = 32°$, $b = 50$, $c = 60$ †

35. $B = 97°$, $b = 27$, $c = 30$ No triangle exists.

36. $B = 110°$, $b = 19$, $c = 21$ No triangle exists.

37. $A = 42°$, $a = 55$, $c = 62$ †

38. $A = 34°$, $a = 6$, $c = 8$ †

39. $C = 40°$, $a = 3.3$, $c = 2.1$ †

40. $C = 62°$, $a = 50$, $c = 100$ †

†Due to space constrictions, answers to these exercises may be found in the Answers beginning on page A–1 in the back of the book.

B Exercises | Applying the Concepts

41. Finding distance. Angela wishes to find the distance from point A to her friend Carmen's house at point C on the other side of the river. She knows the distance from A to Betty's house at B is 540 feet. (See the figure.) The measurement of angles A and B are 57° and 46°, respectively. Calculate the distance from A to C. Round to the nearest foot. 398 ft

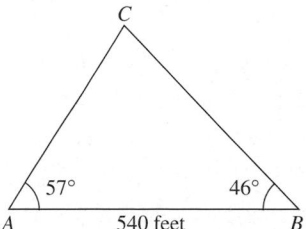

42. Finding distance. In Exercise 41, find the width of the river, assuming that the houses are on the (very straight) banks of the river. 334 ft

43. Projectile. A laser beam with an angle of elevation of 42° is reflected by a target and received 1200 yards from the pointed origin. Assume that the trajectory of the beam forms (approximately) an isosceles triangle.
   a. Find the total distance the beam travels. Round to the nearest yard. 1615 yd
   b. What is the height of the target? Round to the nearest yard. 540 yd

44. Height of a flagpole. Bunty and Bubbly stand 200 feet apart with a flagpole between them. Suppose that the "transit" at each location is 5 feet high. The transit measures the angles of elevation of the top of the flagpole at the two locations to be 30° and 25°, respectively. Find the height of the flagpole. Round to the nearest foot. 57 ft

45. Radio beacon. A ship sailing due east at the rate of 16 miles per hour records the bearing of a radio beacon at N 36.5° E. Two hours later the bearing of the same beacon is N 55.7° W. Round each answer to the nearest tenth of a mile.
   a. How far is the ship from the beacon the second time? †
   b. How close to the beacon did the ship pass? 14.5 mi

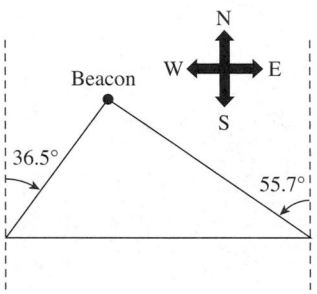

46. Lighthouse. A boat sailing due north at the rate of 14 miles per hour records the bearing of a lighthouse as N 8.4° E. Two hours later, the bearing of the same lighthouse is N 30.9° E. Round the answers to the nearest tenth of a mile.
   a. How far is the ship from the lighthouse the second time? †
   b. If the boat follows the same course and speed, how close to the lighthouse will it approach? 5.5 mi

47. Geostationary satellite. A camel rider was traveling due west at night in the desert. At midnight, his angle of elevation to a satellite was 89°. After traveling west for 20 miles, his angle of elevation to the satellite was 89.05°. The satellite is at a constant height above the ground. How high is the satellite? Round the answer to the nearest mile. 22,912 mi

48. Height of a tower. A flagpole 20 feet tall is placed on top of a tower. At a point on the ground, a surveyor measures the angle of elevation of the bottom of the flag to be 69.6° and that of the top of the flag to be 70.9°. What is the height of the tower, to the nearest foot? 270 ft

Answers:
45. a. 25.7 mi   **46. a.** 10.7 mi

C Exercises Beyond the Basics

49. Suppose that CD bisects angle C of triangle ABC. Show that $\dfrac{AD}{DB} = \dfrac{AC}{CB}$. (See the figure.)

[*Hint:* Apply the Law of Sines to triangles ACD and DCB.]

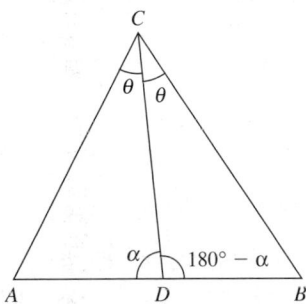

50. A flagpole 15 feet high stands on a building 75 feet high. To an observer at a height of 90 feet, the building and the flag pole subtend equal angles. Find the distance of the observer from the top of the flagpole. [*Hint:* Use Exercise 49.] 18.4 ft

51. A point on an island is located 24 miles southwest of a dock. A ship leaves the dock at 1:00 P.M., traveling west at 12 miles per hour. At what time(s) to the nearest minute is the ship 20 miles from the point? 1:32 PM, 3:18 PM

52. A side of a parallelogram is 60 inches long and makes angles of 28° and 42° with the two diagonals. What are the lengths of the diagonals? Round each answer to the nearest tenth of an inch. 60.0 in., 85.4 in.

53. **Newton's Formula.** In a triangle ABC, prove that
$$\frac{b-c}{a} = \frac{\sin\dfrac{B-C}{2}}{\cos\dfrac{A}{2}}.$$

[*Hint:* Let $\dfrac{a}{\sin A} = \dfrac{b}{\sin B} = \dfrac{c}{\sin C} = k$. Write an expression for $\dfrac{b-c}{a}$ in terms of sines and then use Sum-to-Product and Half-Angle formulas. Note that the formula contains all six parts of a triangle, so it can be used as a check for the solutions of a triangle.]

54. **Mollweide's Formula.** In a triangle ABC, prove that
$$\frac{b+c}{a} = \frac{\cos\dfrac{B-C}{2}}{\sin\dfrac{A}{2}}.$$

55. **Law of Tangents.** In a triangle ABC, prove that
$$\tan\frac{B-C}{2} = \frac{b-c}{b+c}\cot\frac{A}{2}.$$

56. The sides of a triangle are $\sqrt{3}+1$ feet and $\sqrt{3}-1$ feet, and the measure of the angle between these sides is 60°. Use the Law of Tangents (Exercise 55) to find the measure of the difference of the remaining angles. 90°

Critical Thinking

In Exercises 57 and 58, give the most specific description you can for a triangle satisfying the specified conditions. Explain your reasoning.

57. In a triangle ABC, $a\sin A = b\sin B$.

58. In a triangle ABC, $a\cos A = b\cos B$.

Answers:
57. an isosceles triangle with $m\angle A = m\angle B$
58. an isosceles right triangle

The Law of Cosines

BEFORE STARTING THIS SECTION, REVIEW

1. Distance formula (Section 2.1, page 185)

2. Inverse functions (Section 2.8, page 295)

3. Area of a triangle (Section P.7, page 79)

OBJECTIVES

1 Derive the Law of Cosines.

2 Use the Law of Cosines to solve SAS triangles.

3 Use the Law of Cosines to solve SSS triangles.

4 Use Heron's Formula to find the area of a triangle.

Generalizing the Pythagorean Theorem

Suppose that a Boeing 747 jumbo jet is flying over Disney World in Orlando, Florida, at 552 miles per hour and is heading due south to Brazil. Twenty minutes later, an F-16 fighter jet heading due east passes over Disney World at a speed of 1250 miles per hour. By using the Pythagorean Theorem, we can easily calculate the distance d between the two planes t hours after the F-16 passes over Disney World. We have

$$d = \sqrt{(1250t)^2 + \left[\frac{1}{3}(552) + 552t\right]^2} \quad \text{20 minutes} = \frac{1}{3} \text{ hour.}$$

Suppose all the other facts in the problem are unchanged, except that the F-16 has a bearing of N 37° E. Now we can no longer apply the Pythagorean Theorem. In Example 2, we use the Law of Cosines, described in this section, to solve this problem. ▪

1 Derive the Law of Cosines.

The Law of Cosines

The Pythagorean Theorem states that the relationship $c^2 = a^2 + b^2$ holds in a right triangle ABC, where c represents the length of the longest leg. This relationship is not true if the triangle is not a right triangle. The **Law of Cosines** is a generalization of the Pythagorean Theorem that is true in any triangle. This law will be used to solve triangles in which two sides and the included angle are known (SAS triangles), as well as those triangles in which all three sides are known (SSS triangles).

THE LAW OF COSINES

Let A, B, and C denote the measures of the angles of a triangle ABC with opposite sides of lengths a, b, and c, respectively. Then

$$a^2 = b^2 + c^2 - 2bc \cos A,$$
$$b^2 = c^2 + a^2 - 2ca \cos B,$$
$$c^2 = a^2 + b^2 - 2ab \cos C.$$

In words, the square of any side of a triangle is equal to the sum of the squares of the length of the other two sides, less twice the product of the lengths of the other sides and the cosine of their included angle.

Derivation of the Law of Cosines

To derive the Law of Cosines, place triangle ABC in a rectangular coordinate system with the vertex A at the origin and the side c along the positive x-axis. See Figure 7.11.

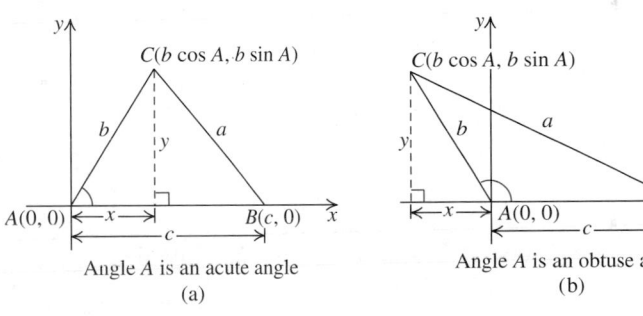

Angle A is an acute angle
(a)

Angle A is an obtuse angle
(b)

FIGURE 7.11

Label the coordinates of the vertices as shown in Figure 7.11. The point $C(x, y)$ on the terminal side of angle A has coordinates $(b \cos A, b \sin A)$ in both Figures 11(a) and 11(b), because

$$\cos A = \frac{x}{b} \qquad \sin A = \frac{y}{b}$$
$$x = b \cos A \qquad y = b \sin A$$

The point B has coordinates $(c, 0)$. Applying the distance formula to the line segment joining $B(c, 0)$ and $C(b \cos A, b \sin A)$, we have

$$a = d(C, B)$$
$$a^2 = [d(C, B)]^2 \qquad \text{Square both sides.}$$
$$a^2 = (b \cos A - c)^2 + (b \sin A - 0)^2 \qquad \text{Distance formula}$$
$$a^2 = b^2 \cos^2 A - 2bc \cos A + c^2 + b^2 \sin^2 A \qquad \text{Expand binomial.}$$
$$a^2 = b^2(\sin^2 A + \cos^2 A) + c^2 - 2bc \cos A \qquad \text{Regroup terms.}$$
$$a^2 = b^2 + c^2 - 2bc \cos A \qquad \sin^2 A + \cos^2 A = 1$$

The last equation is one of the forms of the Law of Cosines. Similarly, by placing the vertex B and then the vertex C at the origin, we obtain the other two forms. Notice that the Law of Cosines becomes the Pythagorean Theorem if the included angle is 90°, because $\cos 90° = 0$.

2 Use the Law of Cosines to solve SAS Triangles.

Solving SAS Triangles

We first describe the general procedure for solving triangles in which two sides and the included angle are known (SAS triangles). This is Case 3 of Section 7.1.

FINDING THE SOLUTION: PROCEDURE FOR SOLVING SAS TRIANGLES

OBJECTIVE	EXAMPLE
To solve triangles in which the measures of two sides and the included angle are known.	*Solve triangle ABC with a = 15 inches, b = 10 inches, and C = 60°. Round each answer to the nearest tenth.*

Step 1 Use the appropriate form of the Law of Cosines to find the side opposite the given angle.

1. Find side c opposite angle C.

$$c^2 = a^2 + b^2 - 2ab\cos C \qquad \text{The Law of Cosines}$$
$$c^2 = (15)^2 + (10)^2 - 2(15)(10)\cos 60° \qquad \text{Substitute values.}$$
$$c^2 = 225 + 100 - 2(15)(10)\left(\frac{1}{2}\right) \qquad \cos 60° = \frac{1}{2}$$
$$c^2 = 175 \qquad \text{Simplify.}$$
$$c = \sqrt{175} \approx 13.2 \qquad \text{Use a calculator.}$$

Step 2 Use the **Law of Sines** to find the angle opposite the shorter of the two given sides. Note that this angle is always an acute angle.

2. Find B:

$$\frac{\sin B}{b} = \frac{\sin C}{c} \qquad \text{The Law of Sines}$$
$$\sin B = \frac{b\sin C}{c} \qquad \text{Multiply both sides by } b.$$
$$\sin B = \frac{10\sin 60°}{\sqrt{175}} \qquad \text{Substitute values.}$$
$$B = \sin^{-1}\left(\frac{10\sin 60°}{\sqrt{175}}\right) \qquad 0° < B \le 90°$$
$$B \approx 40.9° \qquad \text{Use a calculator.}$$

Step 3 Use the angle sum formula to find the third angle.

3. $A = 180° - C - B \qquad A + B + C = 180°$
$A \approx 180° - 60° - 40.9° \qquad$ Substitute values of C and B.
$A \approx 79.1° \qquad$ Simplify.

Step 4 Write the solution.

4.

$A \approx 79.1°$	$a = 15$ inches
$B \approx 40.9°$	$b = 10$ inches
$C = 60°$	$c \approx 13.2$ inches

EXAMPLE 1   **Solving an SAS Triangle**

Solve triangle ABC with $b = 16$ meters, $c = 12$ meters, and $A = 50°$. Round each answer to the nearest tenth.

Solution

Step 1   Find a, the length of the side opposite the given angle A.

$$a^2 = b^2 + c^2 - 2bc\cos A \qquad \text{The Law of Cosines}$$
$$a = \sqrt{b^2 + c^2 - 2bc\cos A} \qquad \text{Square root property; } a > 0$$
$$a = \sqrt{(16)^2 + (12)^2 - 2(16)(12)\cos 50°} \qquad \text{Substitute given values.}$$
$$a \approx 12.376 \text{ meters} \qquad \text{Use a calculator.}$$

Step 2   Find C, the measure of the angle opposite the shorter of the two given sides.

$$\frac{\sin C}{c} = \frac{\sin A}{a} \qquad \text{The Law of Sines}$$

$$\sin C = \frac{c\sin A}{a} \qquad \text{Multiply both sides by } c.$$

$$C = \sin^{-1}\left(\frac{c\sin A}{a}\right) \qquad 0° < C \le 90°$$

$$C = \sin^{-1}\left(\frac{12\sin 50°}{12.376}\right) \qquad \text{Substitute values.}$$

$$C \approx 48.0° \qquad \text{Use a calculator.}$$

Step 3   Find the third angle measure, B.

$$B = 180° - A - C \qquad A + B + C = 180°$$
$$B \approx 180° - 50° - 48° \qquad \text{Substitute values.}$$
$$B \approx 82° \qquad \text{Simplify.}$$

Step 4   The solution of triangle ABC is:

$A = 50°$	$a \approx 12.4$ meters
$B \approx 82°$	$b = 16$ meters
$C \approx 48°$	$c = 12$ meters

■ ■ ■

PRACTICE PROBLEM 1   Solve triangle ABC with $c = 25$, $a = 15$, and $B = 60°$. Round each answer to the nearest tenth.   ■

EXAMPLE 2   **Using the Law of Cosines**

Suppose that a Boeing 747 is flying over Disney World headed due south at 552 miles per hour. Twenty minutes later, an F-16 passes over Disney World with a bearing of N 37° E at a speed of 1250 miles per hour. Find the distance between the two planes 3 hours after the F-16 passes over Disney World. Round the answer to the nearest tenth.

Continued on next page.

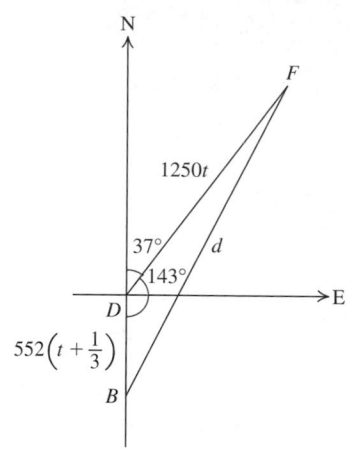

FIGURE 7.12

Solution

Suppose the F-16 has been traveling for t hours after passing over Disney World. Then, because the Boeing 747 had a head start of 20 minutes $= \dfrac{1}{3}$ hour, the Boeing 747 has been traveling $\left(t + \dfrac{1}{3}\right)$ hours due south. The distance d between the two planes is shown in Figure 7.12. Using the Law of Cosines in triangle FDB, we have

$$d^2 = (1250t)^2 + \left[552\left(t + \frac{1}{3}\right)\right]^2 - 2(1250t) \cdot 552\left(t + \frac{1}{3}\right)\cos 143°$$

$$d^2 \approx 28{,}469{,}270.04 \qquad \text{Substitute } t = 3; \text{ use a calculator.}$$

$$d \approx 5335.7 \text{ miles} \qquad \text{Use a calculator.}$$

■ ■ ■

PRACTICE PROBLEM 2   Repeat Example 2 if the F-16 is traveling at a speed of 1375 miles per hour due N 75° E, and the Boeing 747 is traveling with a bearing of S 12° W at 550 miles per hour. ■

---

3 Use the Law of Cosines to solve SSS triangles.

Solving SSS Triangles

We can use the Law of Cosines to solve triangles in which three sides are known (SSS triangles). This is Case 4 of Section 7.1. The procedure for solving SSS triangles is described next.

FINDING THE SOLUTION: PROCEDURE FOR SOLVING SSS TRIANGLES

OBJECTIVE
To solve triangles in which the measures of the three sides are known.

EXAMPLE
Solve triangle ABC with $a = 3.1$ feet, $b = 5.4$ feet, and $c = 7.2$ feet. Round answers to the nearest tenths.

Step 1   Use the Law of Cosines to find the angle opposite the longest side.

1. Find C:

$$c^2 = a^2 + b^2 - 2ab\cos C \qquad \text{The Law of Cosines}$$

$$2ab\cos C = a^2 + b^2 - c^2 \qquad \begin{array}{l}\text{Add } 2ab\cos C - c^2 \\ \text{to both sides.}\end{array}$$

$$\cos C = \frac{a^2 + b^2 - c^2}{2ab} \qquad \text{Solve for } \cos C.$$

$$\cos C = \frac{(3.1)^2 + (5.4)^2 - (7.2)^2}{2(3.1)(5.4)} \qquad \text{Substitute values.}$$

$$\cos C \approx -0.39 \qquad \text{Use a calculator.}$$

$$C \approx \cos^{-1}(-0.39) \qquad 0° < C < 180°$$

$$C \approx 113° \qquad \text{Use a calculator.}$$

Step 2	Use the Law of Sines to find either of the two remaining acute angles.

2. Find B:

$$\frac{\sin B}{b} = \frac{\sin C}{c}$$ The Law of Sines

$$\sin B = \frac{b \sin C}{c}$$ Multiply both sides by b.

$$B = \sin^{-1}\left(\frac{b \sin C}{c}\right)$$ $0° < B < 90°$

$$B = \sin^{-1}\left(\frac{5.4 \sin 113°}{7.2}\right)$$ Substitute values.

$$B \approx 43.7°$$ Use a calculator.

Step 3	Use the angle sum formula to find the third angle.

3. $A = 180° - B - C$ $A + B + C = 180°$

$A \approx 180° - 43.7° - 113°$ Substitute values.

$A \approx 23.3°$ Simplify.

Step 4	Write the solution.

4.

$A \approx 23.3°$	$a = 3.1$ feet
$B \approx 43.7°$	$b = 5.4$ feet
$C \approx 113°$	$c = 7.2$ feet

EXAMPLE 3   **Solving an SSS Triangle**

Solve triangle ABC with $a = 8, b = 5$, and $c = 7$. Round each answer to the nearest tenth.

Solution

Step 1   Find A, the angle opposite the largest side.

$$a^2 = b^2 + c^2 - 2bc \cos A$$ The Law of Cosines

$$\cos A = \frac{b^2 + c^2 - a^2}{2bc}$$ Solve for $\cos A$.

$$= \frac{5^2 + 7^2 - 8^2}{2 \cdot 5 \cdot 7}$$ Substitute given values.

$$\cos A \approx 0.1429$$ Use a calculator.

$$A = \cos^{-1}(0.1429)$$ $0° < A < 180°$

$$A \approx 81.8°$$ Use a calculator.

Step 2   Find B by using the Law of Sines.

$$\frac{\sin B}{b} = \frac{\sin A}{a}$$ The Law of Sines

$$\sin B = \frac{b \sin A}{a}$$ Multiply both sides by b.

Continued on next page.

$$B = \sin^{-1}\left(\frac{b \sin A}{a}\right) \qquad 0° < B < 90°$$

$$B = \sin^{-1}\left(\frac{5 \sin 81.8°}{8}\right) \qquad \text{Substitute values.}$$

$$B \approx 38.2° \qquad \text{Use a calculator.}$$

Step 3 Find C by using the angle sum formula.

$$C = 180° - A - B \qquad A + B + C = 180°$$

$$C \approx 180° - 81.8° - 38.2° \qquad \text{Substitute values.}$$

$$C \approx 60° \qquad \text{Simplify.}$$

Step 4 Write the solution.

$A \approx 81.8°$	$a = 8$
$B \approx 38.2°$	$b = 5$
$C \approx 60°$	$c = 7$

■ ■ ■

PRACTICE PROBLEM 3 Solve triangle ABC with $a = 4.5$, $b = 6.7$, and $c = 5.3$. Round each answer to the nearest tenth. ■

EXAMPLE 4 **Solving an SSS Triangle**

Solve triangle ABC with $a = 2$ meters, $b = 9$ meters, and $c = 5$ meters. Round each answer to the nearest tenth.

Solution

Step 1 We first find B, the angle opposite the longest side.

$$b^2 = c^2 + a^2 - 2ca \cos B \qquad \text{The Law of Cosines}$$

$$\cos B = \frac{c^2 + a^2 - b^2}{2ca} \qquad \text{Solve for } \cos B.$$

$$\cos B = \frac{5^2 + 2^2 - 9^2}{2(5)(2)} \qquad \text{Substitute values.}$$

$$\cos B = -2.6 \qquad \text{Simplify.}$$

■ ■ ■

Since the range of the cosine function is $[-1, 1]$, there is no angle B for which $\cos B = -2.6$. This means that a triangle with the given information cannot exist. Since $2 + 5 < 9$, you can also use the Triangle Inequality from geometry to see that there is no such triangle.

> **RECALL**
>
> The Triangle Inequality states that in any triangle the sum of the lengths of any two sides of a triangle is greater than the length of the third side.

PRACTICE PROBLEM 4 Solve triangle ABC with $a = 2$ inches, $b = 3$ inches, and $c = 6$ inches. ■

4 Use Heron's formula to find the area of a triangle.

Heron's Area Formula

In Section 5.3, you learned that the area K of a triangle ABC, if two sides and their included angle are known, is given by

$$K = \frac{1}{2}ab \sin C = \frac{1}{2}bc \sin A = \frac{1}{2}ca \sin B.$$

The Law of Cosines can be used to derive a formula for the area of a triangle if the length of the three sides (SSS triangles) is known. The formula is called **Heron's formula**.

HERON'S FORMULA FOR SSS TRIANGLES

The area K of a triangle with sides of lengths a, b, and c is given by

$$K = \sqrt{s(s - a)(s - b)(s - c)},$$

where $s = \dfrac{1}{2}(a + b + c)$ is the **semiperimeter**.

In Exercise 54, we ask you to derive Heron's formula.

EXAMPLE 5   Using Heron's Formula

Find the area of triangle ABC with $a = 29$ inches, $b = 25$ inches, and $c = 40$ inches. Round the answer to the nearest tenth.

Solution

We first find the semiperimeter s.

$$s = \frac{a + b + c}{2}$$

$$s = \frac{29 + 25 + 40}{2} = 47$$

$$
\begin{aligned}
\text{Area of the triangle} &= \sqrt{s(s - a)(s - b)(s - c)} && \text{Heron's formula} \\
&= \sqrt{47(47 - 29)(47 - 25)(47 - 40)} && \text{Substitute values.} \\
&\approx 360.9 \text{ square inches.} && \text{Use a calculator.} \quad ■ \quad ■ \quad ■
\end{aligned}
$$

PRACTICE PROBLEM 5   Find the area of triangle ABC with $a = 11$ meters, $b = 17$ meters, and $c = 20$ meters. ■

EXAMPLE 6   Using Heron's Formula

A triangular swimming pool has side lengths 23 feet, 17 feet, and 26 feet. How many gallons of water will fill the pool to a depth of 5 feet? Round answer to the nearest whole number.

Solution

In order to calculate the volume of water in the swimming pool, we first calculate the area of the triangular surface.

We have $a = 23$, $b = 17$, and $c = 26$. So $s = \dfrac{1}{2}(a + b + c) = 33$.

By Heron's formula, the area K of the triangular surface is

$$
\begin{aligned}
K &= \sqrt{s(s - a)(s - b)(s - c)} \\
&= \sqrt{33(33 - 23)(33 - 17)(33 - 26)} && \text{Substitute values for } a, b, c, \text{ and } s. \\
&\approx 192.2498 \text{ square feet.}
\end{aligned}
$$

Continued on next page.

The volume of water in the pool = surface area × depth

$$\approx 192.2498 \times 5$$

$$\approx 961.25 \text{ cubic feet.}$$

One cubic foot contains approximately 7.5 gallons of water. So 961.25 × 7.5 ≈ 7209 gallons of water will fill the pool.   ■ ■ ■

PRACTICE PROBLEM 6   Repeat Example 6 if the swimming pool has side lengths 25 feet, 30 feet, and 33 feet, and the depth of the pool is 5.5 feet.   ■

A Exercises   Basic Skills and Concepts

In Exercises 1–4, solve each triangle. Round each answer to the nearest tenth.

1.

2.

3.

4.

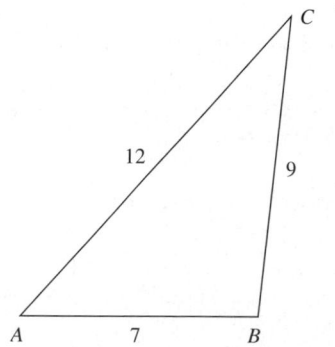

In Exercises 5–20, solve each triangle *ABC*. Round each answer to the nearest tenth. All sides are measured in feet.

5. $a = 15, b = 9, C = 120°$ $c \approx 21, A \approx 38.2°, B \approx 21.8°$

6. $a = 14, b = 10, C = 75°$ $c \approx 15.0, A \approx 64.8°, B \approx 40.2°$

7. $b = 10, c = 12, A = 62°$ $a \approx 11.5, B \approx 50.6°, C \approx 67.4°$

8. $b = 11, c = 16, A = 110°$ $a \approx 22.3, B \approx 27.6°, C \approx 42.4°$

9. $c = 12, a = 15, b = 11$ $A \approx 81.3°, B \approx 46.4°, C \approx 52.3°$

10. $c = 16, a = 11, b = 13$ $A \approx 43.0°, B \approx 53.8°, C \approx 83.2°$

11. $a = 9, b = 13, c = 18$ $A \approx 28.3°, B \approx 43.3°, C \approx 108.4°$

12. $a = 14, b = 6, c = 10$ $A = 120°, B \approx 21.8°, C \approx 38.2°$

13. $a = 2.5, b = 3.7, c = 5.4$ $A \approx 23.7°, B \approx 36.4°, C \approx 119.9°$

14. $a = 4.2, b = 2.9, c = 3.6$ $A \approx 79.7°, B \approx 42.8°, C \approx 57.5°$

15. $b = 3.2, c = 4.3, A = 97.7°$ $a \approx 5.7, B \approx 33.8°, C \approx 48.5°$

16. $b = 5.4, c = 3.6, A = 79.2°$ $a \approx 5.9, B \approx 64.0°, C \approx 36.8°$

17. $c = 4.9, a = 3.9, B = 68.3°$ $b \approx 5.0, A \approx 46.3°, C \approx 65.4°$

18. $c = 7.8, a = 9.8, B = 95.6°$ $b \approx 13.1, A \approx 48.1°, C \approx 36.3°$

19. $a = 2.3, b = 2.8, c = 3.7$ $A \approx 38.4°, B \approx 49.1°, C \approx 92.5°$

20. $a = 5.3, b = 2.9, c = 4.6$ $A \approx 86.8°, B \approx 33.1°, C \approx 60.1°$

In Exercises 21–28, find the area of each triangle by using Heron's formula. Round each answer to the nearest tenth. All sides are measured in inches.

21. $a = 2, b = 3, c = 4$ 2.9 square inches

22. $a = 50, b = 100, c = 130$ 2245.0 square inches

23. $a = 50, b = 50, c = 75$ 1240.2 square inches

24. $a = 100, b = 100, c = 125$ 4878.9 square inches

25. $a = 7.5, b = 4.5, c = 6.0$ 13.5 square inches

26. $a = 8.5, b = 9.0, c = 4.5$ 18.9 square inches

27. $a = 3.7, b = 5.1, c = 4.2$ 7.7 square inches

28. $a = 9.8, b = 5.7, c = 6.5$ 17.7 square inches

†Due to space constrictions, answers to these exercises may be found in the Answers beginning on page A–1 in the back of the book.

B Exercises | Applying the Concepts

In Exercises 29–46, round each answer to the nearest tenth.

29. Chord length. Find the length of the chord intercepted by a central angle of 42° in a circle of radius 8 feet. 5.7 feet

30. Central angle. Find the measure of the central angle of a circle of radius 6 feet that intercepted a chord of length 3.5 feet. 33.9°

31. Tunnel length. Engineers must bore a straight tunnel through the base of a mountain. They select a reference point *C* on the plain surrounding the mountain. The distance from *C* to portal *A* (the starting tunnel point) and portal *B* (the ending tunnel point) are 2352 yards and 1763 yards, respectively. The measure of ∠*ACB* is 41°. How long (to the nearest yard) is the tunnel? 1543.1 yards

32. Pond length. A surveyor needs to find the length of a pond (see figure), but does so indirectly. She selects a point *A* on one side of the pond and measures distances to the points *B* and *C* at opposite ends of the pond to be 537 yards and 823 yards, respectively. The measure of ∠*BAC* is 130°. (See figure.) How long is the pond? 1238.5 yards

33. Roof truss. A roof truss is made in the shape of an inverted V. The lengths of the two edges are 11 feet and 23 feet, respectively. The edges meet at the peak making a 65° angle. Find
a. the width of the truss; 20.9 feet
b. the height of the peak. 11.0 feet

34. Solar panels. A roof of a house addition is being built to accept solar energy panels as shown in the figure. Find
a. the length of the edge *AC* of the truss; 20.8 feet
b. the measure of ∠*BAC*. 79.9°

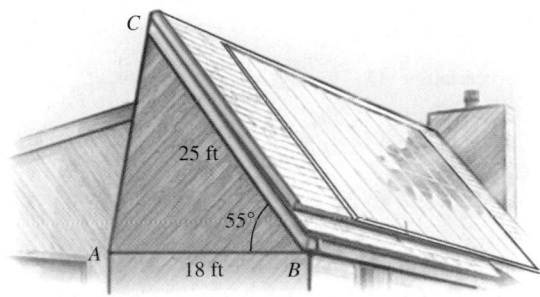

35. Real estate. You have inherited a commercial triangular shaped lot of side lengths 400 feet, 250 feet, and 274 feet. The neighboring property is selling for $1 million dollars per acre. How much is your lot worth? (*Hint:* 1 acre = 43,560 square feet.) $780,000

36. Real estate. Find the area of the quadrangular lot shown in the figure. All measurements are in feet. 1210.5 square feet

37. Swimming pool. Find the number of gallons of water in a triangular swimming pool with sides 11 feet, 16 feet, 19 feet, and a depth of 5 feet. Round your answer to the nearest whole number. [Recall: approximately 7.5 gallons of water are in 1 cubic foot.] 3297 gallons

38. Hikers. Two hikers, Sonia and Tony, leave the same point at the same time. Sonia walks due east at the rate of 3 miles per hour, and Tony walks 45° northeast at the rate of 4.3 miles per hour. How far apart are the hikers after 3 hours? 9.1 miles

39. Distance between ships. Two ships leave the same port, Ship A at 1:00 P.M. and ship B at 3:30 P.M. Ship A sails on a bearing of S 37° E at 18 miles per hour, and B sails on a bearing of N 28° E at 20 miles per hour. How far apart are the ships at 8:00 P.M.? 183.2 miles

40. Navigation. A ship is traveling due north. At two different points *A* and *B*, the navigator of the ship sites a lighthouse at the point *C*, as shown in the accompanying figure.
a. Determine the distance from *B* to *C*. 3689 miles
b. How much farther due north must the ship travel to reach the point closest to the lighthouse? 1634.5 miles

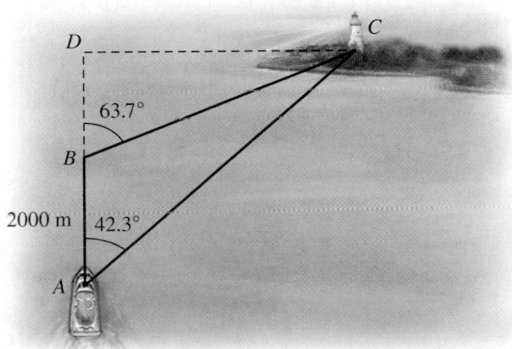

41. Circular gears. Three circles of radii 1.2 inches, 2.2 inches, and 3.1 inches, respectively, are tangent to each other externally. Find the angles of the triangle formed by joining the centers of the circles. $A \approx 86.2°, B \approx 54.0°, C \approx 39.8°$

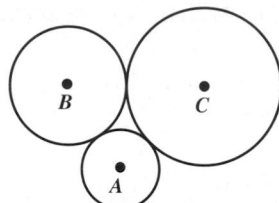

42. Height of a tree. A tree is planted at a point O on horizontal ground. Two points A and B on the ground are 100 feet apart. The angles of elevation of the top of the tree T from the points A and B are 45° and 30°, respectively. The measure of $\angle AOB$ is 60°. Find the height of the tree. 66.4 feet

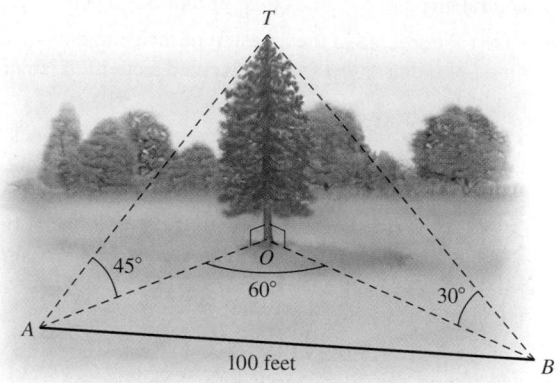

C Exercises   Beyond the Basics

In Exercises 43–46, round each answer to the nearest tenth.

43. A parallelogram has adjacent sides 8 cm and 13 cm. If the shorter diagonal is 11 cm long, find the length of the longer diagonal. 18.6 cm

44. Find the area of the parallelogram of Exercise 43. 87.6 cm²

45. A parallelogram has adjacent sides 10 cm and 15 cm long, and the angle between them is 40°. Find the length of the two diagonals. 9.8 cm, 23.6 cm

46. The length of the two diagonals of a parallelogram are 16 cm and 22 cm. The acute angle between these diagonals is 63°. Find the lengths of the sides of the parallelogram. [*Hint:* The diagonals of a parallelogram bisect each other.] 10.3 cm, 16.3 cm

In Exercises 47–50, triangle ABC has sides a, b, and c, and $s = \dfrac{1}{2}(a + b + c)$. Use the Law of Cosines to prove each identity.

47. $1 - \cos A = \dfrac{(a - b + c)(a + b - c)}{2bc}$

48. $1 - \cos A = \dfrac{2(s - b)(s - c)}{bc}$

49. $1 + \cos A = \dfrac{(b + c + a)(b + c - a)}{2bc}$

50. $1 + \cos A = \dfrac{2s(s - a)}{bc}$

51. Use Half-angle Formula and Exercise 48 to prove the following:
$$\sin\frac{A}{2} = \sqrt{\frac{(s - b)(s - c)}{bc}}.$$

52. Use Half-angle Formula and Exercise 50 to prove the following:
$$\cos\frac{A}{2} = \sqrt{\frac{s(s - a)}{bc}}.$$

53. Use Exercises 51 and 52 to prove that
$$\sin A = \frac{2}{bc}\sqrt{s(s - a)(s - b)(s - c)}.$$

54. Use Exercise 53 to prove Heron's formula.

Critical Thinking

55. Solve triangle ABC with vertices $A(-2, 1)$, $B(5, 3)$, and $C(3, 6)$.

56. Solve triangle ABC with vertices $A(-3, -5)$, $B(6, 10)$, and $C(3, -2)$.

Answers:
55. $a = \sqrt{13}, b = 5\sqrt{2}, c = \sqrt{53}, A \approx 29.1°, B \approx 72.2°, C \approx 78.7°$
56. $a = 3\sqrt{17}, b = 3\sqrt{5}, c = 3\sqrt{34}, A \approx 32.5°, B \approx 16.9°, C \approx 130.6°$

Group Project

You can use the Law of Cosines to solve triangle ABC in the ambiguous case of Section 7.1. For example, to solve triangle ABC with $B = 150°$, $b = 10$, and $c = 6$, use the Law of Cosines to write $b^2 = a^2 + c^2 - 2ac \cos B$.

Substitute values of b, c, and B in this equation to obtain a quadratic equation in a. Find the roots of this equation and interpret your results. Then, again use the Law of Cosines to find A. Then find $C = 180° - A - B$.

Use this technique to solve each triangle ABC.

1. $B = 150°$, $b = 10$, and $c = 6$
2. $A = 30°$, $a = 6$, and $b = 10$
3. $A = 60°$, $a = 12$, and $c = 15$

Answers:
1. $a \approx 4.3$, $A \approx 12.5°$, $C \approx 17.5°$
2. $c \approx 11.98$, $C \approx 93.6°$, $B \approx 56.4°$, $c \approx 5.34$, $C \approx 26.4°$, $B \approx 123.6°$
3. No triangle can be formed.

Vectors

BEFORE STARTING THIS SECTION, REVIEW

1. Pythagorean Theorem (Section P.7, page 77)

2. The Law of Sines (Section 7.1, page 666)

3. The Law of Cosines (Section 7.2, page 681)

OBJECTIVES

1 Represent vectors geometrically.

2 Represent vectors algebraically.

3 Find a unit vector in the direction of V.

4 Write a vector in terms of its magnitude and direction.

5 Find the dot product of two vectors.

6 Find the angle between two vectors.

7 Use the definition of work.

How to Measure Work

If you move an object a distance of d units by applying a force F in the direction of motion, then physicists define the work W done on the object by the force F to be

$$W = Fd$$

Work = (force)(distance).

If the force is measured in pounds and the distance is measured in feet, then the unit of work is *foot-pounds*. Unfortunately, it is not always possible to exert a force in the direction you would like. For example, if you are pulling a child's wagon, then you exert a force in a direction dictated by the position of the handle. In this section, we will give a precise definition of work done by a constant force, and in Example 12 we compute the work done in one such instance. ■

Vectors

Many physical quantities, such as length, area, volume, mass, and temperature, are completely described by their magnitudes in appropriate units. Such quantities are called **scalar quantities**. Other physical quantities, such as velocity, acceleration, and force, are not completely determined until *both* a magnitude (size) and a direction are specified. For example, the movement of wind is usually described by its speed (magnitude) and the direction, say, 15 miles per hour southwest. The wind speed and wind direction together form a **vector quantity** called the *wind velocity*.

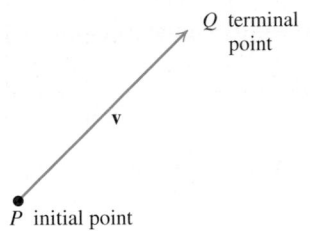

1 Represent vectors geometrically.

FIGURE 7.13

Geometric Vectors

A vector can be represented geometrically by a line segment with an arrowhead. The direction of the arrow specifies the direction of the vector, and the length of the arrow describes its magnitude. The tail of the arrow is called the **initial point** of the vector, and the tip of the arrow the **terminal point**. We shall denote vectors by lowercase boldface type, such as **a**, **b**, **i**, **j**, **u**, **v**, and **w**. When discussing vectors, we refer to real numbers as **scalars**. Scalars will be denoted by lower case italic type, such as a, b, x, y, and z.

As in Figure 7.13, if the initial point of a vector **v** is P and the terminal point is Q, we write

$$\mathbf{v} = \overrightarrow{PQ}.$$

The **magnitude** (or **norm**) of a vector $\mathbf{v} = \overrightarrow{PQ}$, denoted by $\|\mathbf{v}\|$, or $\|\overrightarrow{PQ}\|$, is the length of the vector **v** and is a scalar quantity.

Equivalent Vectors

Two vectors having the same length and same direction are called **equivalent vectors**. Since a vector is determined solely by its length and direction, equivalent vectors are regarded as **equal** even though they may be located in different positions. If **v** and **w** are equivalent, we write **v** = **w**. See Figure 7.14.

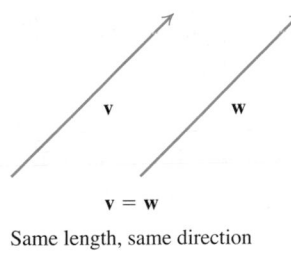

$\mathbf{v} = \mathbf{w}$
Same length, same direction
(a)

$\mathbf{v} \neq \mathbf{u}$
Different length, same direction
(b)

$\mathbf{v} \neq \mathbf{a}$
Same length, different direction
(c)

$\mathbf{v} \neq \mathbf{b}$
Different length, different direction
(d)

FIGURE 7.14

The vector of length zero is called the **zero vector** and is denoted by **0**. The zero vector has zero magnitude and arbitrary direction. If vectors **v** and **a**, as in Figure 7.14(c), have the same length and opposite direction, then **a** is the **opposite vector** of **v** and we write $\mathbf{a} = -\mathbf{v}$.

Adding Vectors

Consider the three vectors shown in Figure 7.15. Imagine the vector $\overrightarrow{PQ}$ as representing the displacement of a particle from the point P to the point Q, followed by displacement of the particle from Q to R (represented by the vector $\overrightarrow{QR}$). The net result is the displacement of the particle from P to R (represented by the vector $\overrightarrow{PR}$). We call $\overrightarrow{PR}$ the sum of the vectors $\overrightarrow{PQ}$ and $\overrightarrow{QR}$ and write

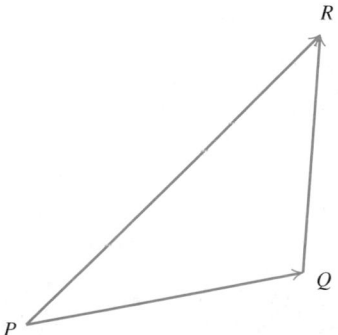

FIGURE 7.15

$$\overrightarrow{PR} = \overrightarrow{PQ} + \overrightarrow{QR}.$$

VECTOR ADDITION (TRIANGLE RULE)

Let **v** and **w** be any two vectors. Place the vector **w** so that its initial point coincides with the terminal point of **v**. The vector **v** + **w**, called the **resultant vector**, is represented by the arrow from the initial point of **v** to the terminal point of **w**.

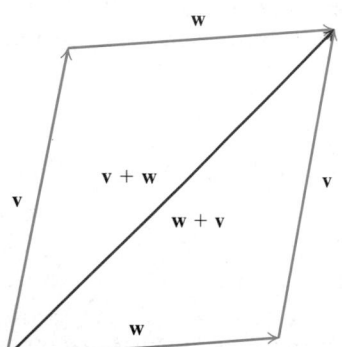

FIGURE 7.16

In Figure 7.16, we have constructed two sums, **v** + **w** and **w** + **v**. It is clear that

$$\mathbf{v} + \mathbf{w} = \mathbf{w} + \mathbf{v}$$

and the sum coincides with the diagonal of the parallelogram determined by **v** and **w** when **v** and **w** have the same initial point.

VECTOR ADDITION (PARALLELOGRAM RULE)

Place vectors **v** and **w** so that their initial points coincide. Form a parallelogram with **v** and **w** as the adjacent sides. The vector with the same initial point as the initial points of **v** and **w** that coincides with the diagonal of the parallelogram represents the resultant vector, **v** + **w**.

Vector subtraction is defined just like the subtraction of real numbers. For any two vectors **v** and **w**, **v** − **w** = **v** + (−**w**), where −**w** is the opposite of **w**. See Figure 7.17.

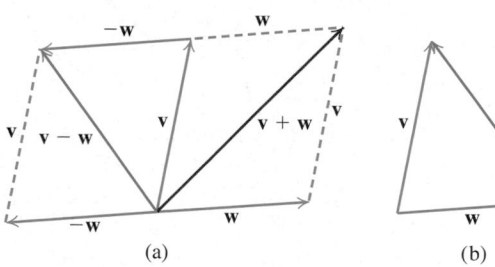

(a)   (b)

FIGURE 7.17

Figure 7.17(b) shows that you can construct the difference vector **v** − **w** without first drawing −**w** as follows: Place the vectors **v** and **w** so that their initial points coincide. Then the vector from the terminal point of **w** to the terminal point of **v** is the vector **v** − **w**.

A second basic arithmetic operation for vectors is **scalar multiplication**.

FIGURE 7.18

SCALAR MULTIPLES OF VECTORS

Let **v** be a vector and c a scalar (a real number). The vector $c\mathbf{v}$ is called the **scalar multiple** of **v**. See Figure 7.18.

If $c > 0$, $c\mathbf{v}$ has the same direction as **v** and magnitude $c\|\mathbf{v}\|$.

If $c < 0$, $c\mathbf{v}$ has the opposite direction as **v** and magnitude $|c|\|\mathbf{v}\|$.

If $c = 0$, $c\mathbf{v} = 0\mathbf{v} = \mathbf{0}$.

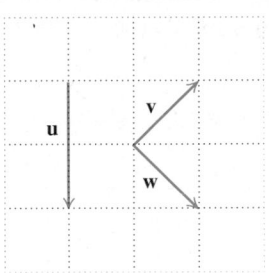

FIGURE 7.19

EXAMPLE 1   Geometric Vectors

Use the vectors **u**, **v**, and **w** in Figure 7.19 to graph each vector.

a. u − 2w   **b. 2v − u + w**

Solution

The graphs are shown in Figure 7.20.

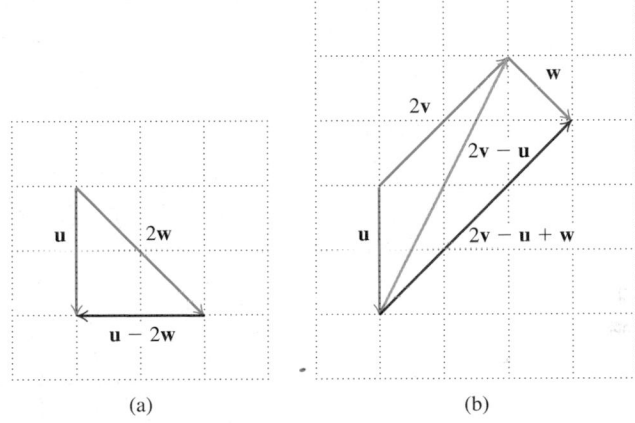

(a)   (b)

FIGURE 7.20   ■ ■ ■

PRACTICE PROBLEM 1   Use the vectors **u**, **v**, and **w** of Figure 7.19 to graph each vector.

a. 2w + v   **b. 2w + v − u**   ■

Algebraic Vectors

2 Represent vectors algebraically.

We now consider vectors in the Cartesian coordinate plane. Since the location of the initial point of a vector is not relevant, we typically draw vectors with their initial point at the origin. Such a vector is called a **position vector**. Note that the terminal point of a position vector will completely determine the vector, so specifying the terminal point will specify the vector. For the position vector **v** with initial point at the origin O and terminal point at $P(v_1, v_2)$, we denote the vector by

$$\mathbf{v} = \overrightarrow{OP} = \langle v_1, v_2 \rangle.$$

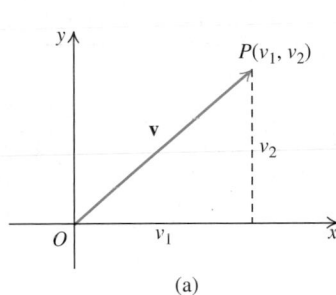

(a)

We call v_1 and v_2 the **components** of the vector **v**; v_1 is the **first component**, and v_2 is the **second component**. Note the difference between the notations for the *point* (v_1, v_2) and the *position vector* $\langle v_1, v_2 \rangle$. The magnitude of the position vector $\mathbf{v} = \langle v_1, v_2 \rangle$ follows directly from the Pythagorean Theorem. See Figure 7.21(a). We have $\|\mathbf{v}\| = \sqrt{v_1^2 + v_2^2}$.

If equivalent vectors, **v** and **w**, are located so that their initial points are at the origin, then their terminal points must coincide (since the equivalent vectors have the same length and same direction). Thus, for the vectors

$$\mathbf{v} = \langle v_1, v_2 \rangle \quad \text{and} \quad \mathbf{w} = \langle w_1, w_2 \rangle,$$
$$\mathbf{v} = \mathbf{w} \quad \text{if and only if} \quad v_1 = w_1 \quad \text{and} \quad v_2 = w_2.$$

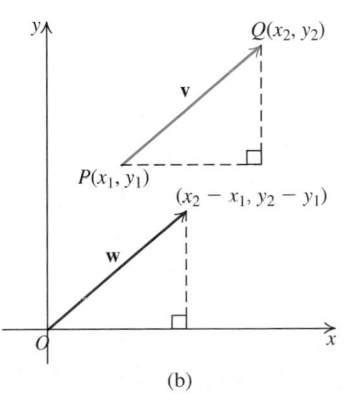

(b)

FIGURE 7.21

We can use congruent triangles to show that any vector **v** with initial point $P(x_1, y_1)$ and terminal point $Q(x_2, y_2)$ is equivalent to the position vector $\mathbf{w} = \langle x_2 - x_1, y_2 - y_1 \rangle$. Thus, any vector in the Cartesian plane can be represented by a position vector. See Figure 7.21(b).

REPRESENTING A VECTOR AS POSITION VECTOR

The vector $\overrightarrow{PQ}$ with initial point $P(x_1, y_1)$ and terminal point $Q(x_2, y_2)$ is equal to the position vector

$$\mathbf{v} = \langle x_2 - x_1, y_2 - y_1 \rangle.$$

EXAMPLE 2   Representing a Vector in the Cartesian Plane

Let $\mathbf{v}$ be the vector with initial point $P(4, -2)$ and terminal point $Q(-1, 3)$. Write $\mathbf{v}$ as a position vector.

Solution

$\mathbf{v}$ has initial point $P(4, -2)$, so $x_1 = 4$ and $y_1 = -2$.

$\mathbf{v}$ has terminal point $Q(-1, 3)$, so $x_2 = -1$ and $y_2 = 3$.

Thus,

$\mathbf{v} = \langle x_2 - x_1, y_2 - y_1 \rangle$	Position vector representation of $\overrightarrow{PQ}$
$\mathbf{v} = \langle -1 - 4, 3 - (-2) \rangle$	Substitute values for $x_1, y_1, x_2,$ and y_2.
$\mathbf{v} = \langle -5, 5 \rangle$	Simplify. ■ ■ ■

PRACTICE PROBLEM 2   Let $\mathbf{w}$ be the vector with initial point $P(-2, 7)$ and terminal point $Q(1, -3)$. Write $\mathbf{w}$ as a position vector.   ■

The zero vector is $\mathbf{0} = \langle 0, 0 \rangle$, and the opposite of the vector $\mathbf{v} = \langle v_1, v_2 \rangle$ is $-\mathbf{v} = \langle -v_1, -v_2 \rangle$.

The following properties describe the arithmetic operations on vectors, using components:

ARITHMETIC OPERATIONS ON VECTORS

If $\mathbf{v} = \langle v_1, v_2 \rangle$ and $\mathbf{w} = \langle w_1, w_2 \rangle$ are vectors and c is any scalar, then

$\mathbf{v} + \mathbf{w} = \langle v_1 + w_1, v_2 + w_2 \rangle$	Vector addition
$\mathbf{v} - \mathbf{w} = \langle v_1 - w_1, v_2 - w_2 \rangle$	Vector subtraction
$c\mathbf{v} = \langle cv_1, cv_2 \rangle$	Scalar multiplication

---

EXAMPLE 3   Operations on Vectors

Let $\mathbf{v} = \langle 2, 3 \rangle$ and $\mathbf{w} = \langle -4, 1 \rangle$. Find each expression.

a. $\mathbf{v} + \mathbf{w}$ **b.** $-2\mathbf{v}$ **c.** $2\mathbf{v} - \mathbf{w}$ **d.** $\|2\mathbf{v} - \mathbf{w}\|$

Solution

a. $\mathbf{v} + \mathbf{w} = \langle 2, 3 \rangle + \langle -4, 1 \rangle = \langle 2 - 4, 3 + 1 \rangle = \langle -2, 4 \rangle$

b. $-2\mathbf{v} = -2\langle 2, 3 \rangle = \langle -2 \cdot 2, -2 \cdot 3 \rangle = \langle -4, -6 \rangle$

c. $2\mathbf{v} - \mathbf{w} = 2\langle 2, 3 \rangle - \langle -4, 1 \rangle$

$= \langle 4, 6 \rangle - \langle -4, 1 \rangle$	Scalar multiplication
$= \langle 4 - (-4), 6 - 1 \rangle$	Vector subtraction
$= \langle 8, 5 \rangle$	Simplify.

d. $\|2\mathbf{v} - \mathbf{w}\| = \|\langle 8, 5 \rangle\|$ From part **c**

   $\|2\mathbf{v} - \mathbf{w}\| = \sqrt{8^2 + 5^2}$ $\mathbf{v} = \langle v_1, v_2 \rangle; \|\mathbf{v}\| = \sqrt{v_1^2 + v_2^2}$

   $\|2\mathbf{v} - \mathbf{w}\| = \sqrt{64 + 25} = \sqrt{89}$ Simplify.   ■ ■ ■

PRACTICE PROBLEM 3   Let $\mathbf{v} = \langle -1, 2 \rangle$ and $\mathbf{w} = \langle 2, -3 \rangle$. Find each expression.

a. $\mathbf{v} + \mathbf{w}$ **b.** $3\mathbf{w}$ **c.** $3\mathbf{w} - 2\mathbf{v}$ **d.** $\|3\mathbf{w} - 2\mathbf{v}\|$ ■

3 Find a unit vector in the direction of *V*.

Unit Vectors

Recall that if $c > 0$ and $\mathbf{v}$ is any vector, then the vector $c\mathbf{v}$ has the same direction as $\mathbf{v}$ and its length is given by

$$\|c\mathbf{v}\| = c\|\mathbf{v}\|.$$

Thus, if $\mathbf{v}$ is a nonzero vector, then letting $c = \dfrac{1}{\|\mathbf{v}\|}$, we have $\left\|\dfrac{1}{\|\mathbf{v}\|}\mathbf{v}\right\| = \dfrac{1}{\|\mathbf{v}\|}\|\mathbf{v}\| = 1$.

Consequently, $\dfrac{1}{\|\mathbf{v}\|}\mathbf{v}$ is a vector of length 1 in the same direction as $\mathbf{v}$. A vector of length 1 is called a **unit vector**.

EXAMPLE 4   **Finding a Unit Vector**

Find a unit vector $\mathbf{u}$ in the direction of $\mathbf{v} = \langle 3, -4 \rangle$.

Solution

First, find magnitude of $\mathbf{v} = \langle 3, -4 \rangle$.

$$\|\mathbf{v}\| = \sqrt{(3)^2 + (-4)^2} \qquad \text{Formula for magnitude}$$
$$\|\mathbf{v}\| = \sqrt{25} = 5 \qquad \text{Simplify.}$$

Now, let

$$\mathbf{u} = \frac{1}{\|\mathbf{v}\|}\mathbf{v} \qquad \text{Multiply } \mathbf{v} \text{ by the scalar } \frac{1}{\|\mathbf{v}\|}.$$

$$\mathbf{u} = \frac{1}{5}\langle 3, -4 \rangle \qquad \text{Substitute values.}$$

$$\mathbf{u} = \left\langle \frac{3}{5}, -\frac{4}{5} \right\rangle \qquad \text{Scalar multiplication}$$

Check that $\|\mathbf{u}\| = 1$:

$$\|\mathbf{u}\| = \sqrt{\left(\frac{3}{5}\right)^2 + \left(-\frac{4}{5}\right)^2} = \sqrt{\frac{9}{25} + \frac{16}{25}} = \sqrt{\frac{25}{25}} = 1.$$

Hence, $\mathbf{u} = \left\langle \dfrac{3}{5}, -\dfrac{4}{5} \right\rangle$ is a unit vector in the same direction as $\mathbf{v}$. (Note that $\mathbf{u}$ is a scalar multiple of $\mathbf{v}$.)   ■ ■ ■

PRACTICE PROBLEM 4   Find a unit vector in the direction of $\mathbf{v} = \langle -12, 5 \rangle$.   ■

In a Cartesian coordinate plane, two unit vectors that lie along the positive coordinate axes are particularly important. These are the vectors

$$\mathbf{i} = \langle 1, 0 \rangle \quad \text{and} \quad \mathbf{j} = \langle 0, 1 \rangle.$$

Every vector $\mathbf{v} = \langle v_1, v_2 \rangle$ can be expressed in terms of $\mathbf{i}$ and $\mathbf{j}$ as follows:

$$
\begin{aligned}
\mathbf{v} = \langle v_1, v_2 \rangle = \langle v_1, 0 \rangle + \langle 0, v_2 \rangle \qquad & \text{Vector addition} \\
= v_1 \langle 1, 0 \rangle + v_2 \langle 0, 1 \rangle \qquad & \text{Scalar multiplication} \\
= v_1 \mathbf{i} + v_2 \mathbf{j} \qquad & \text{Replace } \langle 1, 0 \rangle \text{ by } \mathbf{i} \text{ and } \langle 0, 1 \rangle \text{ by } \mathbf{j}.
\end{aligned}
$$

Thus, a vector $\mathbf{v}$ from $(0, 0)$ to (v_1, v_2) can be represented in the form

$$\mathbf{v} = v_1 \mathbf{i} + v_2 \mathbf{j}$$

with

$$\|\mathbf{v}\| = \sqrt{v_1^2 + v_2^2}.$$

EXAMPLE 5   **Vectors Involving i and j**

Find each expression for $\mathbf{u} = 4\mathbf{i} + 7\mathbf{j}$ and $\mathbf{v} = 2\mathbf{i} + 5\mathbf{j}$.

a. $\mathbf{u} - 3\mathbf{v}$ **b.** $\|\mathbf{u} - 3\mathbf{v}\|$

Solution

a. $\begin{aligned}[t] \mathbf{u} - 3\mathbf{v} &= (4\mathbf{i} + 7\mathbf{j}) - 3(2\mathbf{i} + 5\mathbf{j}) \\ &= 4\mathbf{i} + 7\mathbf{j} - 6\mathbf{i} - 15\mathbf{j} \qquad && \text{Scalar multiplication} \\ &= (4 - 6)\mathbf{i} + (7 - 15)\mathbf{j} \qquad && \text{Group terms} \\ &= -2\mathbf{i} - 8\mathbf{j} \qquad && \text{Simplify.} \end{aligned}$

b. $\begin{aligned}[t] \|\mathbf{u} - 3\mathbf{v}\| &= \|-2\mathbf{i} - 8\mathbf{j}\| \\ &= \sqrt{(-2)^2 + (-8)^2} \qquad && \|v_1\mathbf{i} + v_2\mathbf{j}\| = \sqrt{v_1^2 + v_2^2} \\ &= \sqrt{68} = 2\sqrt{17} \qquad && \text{Simplify.} \end{aligned}$ ■ ■ ■

PRACTICE PROBLEM 5   Find each expression for $\mathbf{u} = -3\mathbf{i} + 2\mathbf{j}$ and $\mathbf{v} = \mathbf{i} + 4\mathbf{j}$.

a. $3\mathbf{u} + 2\mathbf{v}$ **b.** $\|3\mathbf{u} + 2\mathbf{v}\|$ ■

---

4 Write a vector in terms of its magnitude and direction.

Vector in Terms of Magnitude and Direction

Let $\mathbf{v} = \langle v_1, v_2 \rangle$ be a position vector, and suppose that θ is the smallest positive angle that $\mathbf{v}$ makes with the positive x-axis. The angle θ is called the **direction angle** of $\mathbf{v}$. See Figure 7.22.

The length (or magnitude) of the vector $\overrightarrow{OP}$ is $\|\mathbf{v}\|$. Thus,

$$\frac{v_1}{\|\mathbf{v}\|} = \cos\theta \quad \text{and} \quad \frac{v_2}{\|\mathbf{v}\|} = \sin\theta \qquad \text{Definitions of cosine and sine}$$

$$v_1 = \|\mathbf{v}\|\cos\theta \qquad\qquad v_2 = \|\mathbf{v}\|\sin\theta \qquad \text{Multiply both sides by } \|\mathbf{v}\|.$$

Hence,

$$\mathbf{v} = v_1\mathbf{i} + v_2\mathbf{j} \qquad\qquad \text{Write } \mathbf{v} \text{ in terms of } \mathbf{i} \text{ and } \mathbf{j}.$$

$$\mathbf{v} = \|\mathbf{v}\|\cos\theta\,\mathbf{i} + \|\mathbf{v}\|\sin\theta\,\mathbf{j} \qquad \begin{array}{l}\text{Write values of } v_1 \text{ and } v_2 \\ \text{obtained previously.}\end{array}$$

$$\mathbf{v} = \|\mathbf{v}\|(\cos\theta\,\mathbf{i} + \sin\theta\,\mathbf{j}) \qquad \text{Factor out } \|\mathbf{v}\|.$$

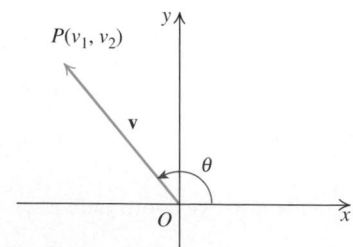

FIGURE 7.22

VECTOR IN TERMS OF MAGNITUDE AND DIRECTION

The formula

$$\mathbf{v} = \|\mathbf{v}\|(\cos\theta\,\mathbf{i} + \sin\theta\,\mathbf{j})$$

expresses a vector $\mathbf{v}$ in terms of its magnitude $\|\mathbf{v}\|$ and its direction angle θ.

Note that any angle coterminal with the direction angle θ of a vector $\mathbf{v}$ may be used in place of θ in the formula $\mathbf{v} = \|\mathbf{v}\|(\cos\theta\,\mathbf{i} + \sin\theta\,\mathbf{j})$.

EXAMPLE 6 **Writing a Vector with Given Length and Direction Angle**

Write the vector of magnitude 3 that makes an angle of $\dfrac{\pi}{3}$ with the positive x-axis.

Solution

Let $\mathbf{v}$ be the required vector. Then,

$$\mathbf{v} = \|\mathbf{v}\|(\cos\theta\,\mathbf{i} + \sin\theta\,\mathbf{j})$$ 　Write $\mathbf{v}$ in terms of its magnitude and direction.

$$\mathbf{v} = 3\left(\cos\frac{\pi}{3}\mathbf{i} + \sin\frac{\pi}{3}\mathbf{j}\right)$$ 　Substitute $\|\mathbf{v}\| = 3$ and $\theta = \dfrac{\pi}{3}$.

$$\mathbf{v} = 3\left(\frac{1}{2}\mathbf{i} + \frac{\sqrt{3}}{2}\mathbf{j}\right)$$ 　$\cos\dfrac{\pi}{3} = \dfrac{1}{2}, \sin\dfrac{\pi}{3} = \dfrac{\sqrt{3}}{2}$

$$\mathbf{v} = \frac{3}{2}\mathbf{i} + \frac{3\sqrt{3}}{2}\mathbf{j}$$ 　Distributive property 　■ ■ ■

PRACTICE PROBLEM 6　Write the vector of magnitude 2 that makes an angle of $\dfrac{11\pi}{6}$ with the positive x-axis. 　■

5 Find the dot product of two vectors.

The Dot Product

The operations involving addition, subtraction, and scalar multiplication produce vectors. We now define a new operation called the *dot product* of two vectors that produces a *scalar*.

THE DOT PRODUCT

For two vectors $\mathbf{v} = \langle v_1, v_2\rangle$ and $\mathbf{w} = \langle w_1, w_2\rangle$, the dot product of $\mathbf{v}$ and $\mathbf{w}$, denoted $\mathbf{v}\cdot\mathbf{w}$, is defined as:

$$\mathbf{v}\cdot\mathbf{w} = \langle v_1, v_2\rangle\cdot\langle w_1, w_2\rangle = v_1 w_1 + v_2 w_2$$

EXAMPLE 7　**Finding the Dot Product**

Find the dot product $\mathbf{v}\cdot\mathbf{w}$.

a.　$\mathbf{v} = \langle 2, -3\rangle$ and $\mathbf{w} = \langle 3, 4\rangle$　**b.**　$\mathbf{v} = -3\mathbf{i} + 5\mathbf{j}$ and $\mathbf{w} = 2\mathbf{i} + 3\mathbf{j}$

Solution

a. $\mathbf{v} \cdot \mathbf{w} = \langle 2, -3 \rangle \cdot \langle 3, 4 \rangle$

$\qquad = (2)(3) + (-3)(4)$ Definition of dot product

$\qquad = 6 - 12 = -6$ Simplify.

b. $\mathbf{v} \cdot \mathbf{w} = (-3\mathbf{i} + 5\mathbf{j}) \cdot (2\mathbf{i} + 3\mathbf{j})$

$\qquad = \langle -3, 5 \rangle \cdot \langle 2, 3 \rangle$ Rewrite as position vectors.

$\qquad = (-3)(2) + (5)(3)$ Definition of dot product

$\qquad = -6 + 15 = 9$ Simplify.   ■ ■ ■

PRACTICE PROBLEM 7   Find the dot product $\mathbf{v} \cdot \mathbf{w}$.

a. $\mathbf{v} = \langle 1, 2 \rangle$ and $\mathbf{w} = \langle -2, 5 \rangle$ b. $\mathbf{v} = 4\mathbf{i} - 3\mathbf{j}$ and $\mathbf{w} = -3\mathbf{i} - 4\mathbf{j}$ ■

We now state the properties of the dot product. These properties can be verified by writing the vectors as position vectors and using the definitions of addition of vectors, scalar multiplication, and the dot product.

PROPERTIES OF THE DOT PRODUCT

If $\mathbf{u}, \mathbf{v},$ and $\mathbf{w}$ are vectors and c is a scalar, then

1. $\mathbf{u} \cdot \mathbf{v} = \mathbf{v} \cdot \mathbf{u}$

2. $\mathbf{u} \cdot (\mathbf{v} + \mathbf{w}) = \mathbf{u} \cdot \mathbf{v} + \mathbf{u} \cdot \mathbf{w}$

3. $\mathbf{0} \cdot \mathbf{v} = 0$

4. $\mathbf{v} \cdot \mathbf{v} = \|\mathbf{v}\|^2$

5. $(c\mathbf{u}) \cdot \mathbf{v} = c(\mathbf{u} \cdot \mathbf{v}) = \mathbf{u} \cdot (c\mathbf{v}).$

---

6 Find the angle between two vectors.

The Angle between Two Vectors

We use the Law of Cosines to find another formula for the dot product. The new formula will be used to find the angle between any two vectors.

Let θ be the angle between the two vectors $\mathbf{v} = \langle v_1, v_2 \rangle$ and $\mathbf{w} = \langle w_1, w_2 \rangle$. See Figure 7.23. Apply the Law of Cosines to the triangle OPQ in Figure 7.23.

FIGURE 7.23

$[d(P, Q)]^2 = \|\mathbf{v}\|^2 + \|\mathbf{w}\|^2 - 2\|\mathbf{v}\|\|\mathbf{w}\|\cos\theta$ The Law of Cosines

$(v_1 - w_1)^2 + (v_2 - w_2)^2$

$\qquad = (v_1^2 + v_2^2) + (w_1^2 + w_2^2) - 2\|\mathbf{v}\|\|\mathbf{w}\|\cos\theta$ Use the distance formula and square of the magnitudes of $\mathbf{v}$ and $\mathbf{w}$.

$v_1^2 - 2v_1w_1 + w_1^2 + v_2^2 - 2v_2w_2 + w_2^2$

$\qquad = v_1^2 + v_2^2 + w_1^2 + w_2^2 - 2\|\mathbf{v}\|\|\mathbf{w}\|\cos\theta$ $(A - B)^2 = A^2 - 2AB + B^2$

$-2v_1w_1 - 2v_2w_2 = -2\|\mathbf{v}\|\|\mathbf{w}\|\cos\theta$ Subtract $v_1^2 + w_1^2 + v_2^2 + w_2^2$ from both sides.

$v_1w_1 + v_2w_2 = \|\mathbf{v}\|\|\mathbf{w}\|\cos\theta$ Divide both sides by -2.

$\mathbf{v} \cdot \mathbf{w} = \|\mathbf{v}\|\|\mathbf{w}\|\cos\theta$ Definition of $\mathbf{v} \cdot \mathbf{w}$

The last equation provides us with another formula for $\mathbf{v} \cdot \mathbf{w}$. Solving the last equation for $\cos\theta$ gives us a formula for finding the angle between two vectors.

THE DOT PRODUCT AND THE ANGLE BETWEEN TWO VECTORS

Let θ $(0 \le \theta \le \pi)$ be the angle between two nonzero vectors $\mathbf{v}$ and $\mathbf{w}$. Then:

$$\mathbf{v} \cdot \mathbf{w} = \|\mathbf{v}\|\|\mathbf{w}\|\cos\theta \quad \text{or} \quad \cos\theta = \frac{\mathbf{v} \cdot \mathbf{w}}{\|\mathbf{v}\|\|\mathbf{w}\|}$$

EXAMPLE 8   **Finding the Dot Product**

Let $\mathbf{v}$ and $\mathbf{w}$ be two vectors of magnitudes 5 and 7, respectively. Let the angle between $\mathbf{v}$ and $\mathbf{w}$ be $75°$. Find $\mathbf{v} \cdot \mathbf{w}$. Round the answer to the nearest tenth.

Solution

$\mathbf{v} \cdot \mathbf{w} = \|\mathbf{v}\|\|\mathbf{w}\|\cos\theta$	Formula for $\mathbf{v} \cdot \mathbf{w}$
$\mathbf{v} \cdot \mathbf{w} = (5)(7)\cos 75°$	Substitute given values.
$\mathbf{v} \cdot \mathbf{w} \approx 9.1$	Use a calculator. ▪ ▪ ▪

PRACTICE PROBLEM 8   Repeat Example 8 if the angle between $\mathbf{v}$ and $\mathbf{w}$ is $60°$. ▪

Since the angle θ between two nonzero vectors $\mathbf{v}$ and $\mathbf{w}$ satisfies $\cos\theta = \dfrac{\mathbf{v} \cdot \mathbf{w}}{\|\mathbf{v}\|\|\mathbf{w}\|}$ and $0 \le \theta \le \pi$, we have $\theta = \cos^{-1}\left(\dfrac{\mathbf{v} \cdot \mathbf{w}}{\|\mathbf{v}\|\|\mathbf{w}\|}\right)$.

EXAMPLE 9   **Finding the Angle between Two Vectors**

Find the angle θ between the vectors $\mathbf{v} = 2\mathbf{i} + 3\mathbf{j}$ and $\mathbf{w} = -3\mathbf{i} + 4\mathbf{j}$. Round the answer to the nearest tenth of a degree.

Solution

$\cos\theta = \dfrac{\mathbf{v} \cdot \mathbf{w}}{\|\mathbf{v}\|\|\mathbf{w}\|}$	Formula for the cosine of the angle between $\mathbf{v}$ and $\mathbf{w}$
$\cos\theta = \dfrac{(2\mathbf{i} + 3\mathbf{j}) \cdot (-3\mathbf{i} + 4\mathbf{j})}{\|2\mathbf{i} + 3\mathbf{j}\|\|-3\mathbf{i} + 4\mathbf{j}\|}$	Substitute expressions for $\mathbf{v}$ and $\mathbf{w}$.
$\cos\theta = \dfrac{(2)(-3) + (3)(4)}{\sqrt{2^2 + 3^2}\sqrt{(-3)^2 + 4^2}}$	Use formulas for the dot product and the magnitude.
$\cos\theta = \dfrac{6}{5\sqrt{13}}$	Simplify.
$\theta = \cos^{-1}\left(\dfrac{6}{5\sqrt{13}}\right)$	$0° \le \theta \le 180°$
$\theta \approx 70.6°$	Use a calculator. ▪ ▪ ▪

PRACTICE PROBLEM 9   Find the angle between the vectors $\mathbf{v} = 2\mathbf{i} - 3\mathbf{j}$ and $\mathbf{w} = 3\mathbf{i} + 5\mathbf{j}$. Round the answer to the nearest tenth of a degree.   ■

EXAMPLE 10   Finding the Magnitude and Direction of the Sum of Two Vectors

Let $\mathbf{v}$ and $\mathbf{w}$ be two vectors in the plane of magnitudes 12 and 7, respectively. The angle between $\mathbf{v}$ and $\mathbf{w}$ is 65°. Find each of the following, rounding answers to the nearest tenths.

a. $\|\mathbf{v} + 2\mathbf{w}\|$

b.   The angle θ between the vectors $\mathbf{v} + 2\mathbf{w}$ and $\mathbf{w}$

RECALL

From geometry we know the following facts about parallelograms:
1. Opposite sides are parallel and equal.
2. The sum of any two adjacent angles is 180°.

Solution

We draw the vectors $\mathbf{v}$, $\mathbf{w}$, $2\mathbf{w}$, and $\mathbf{v} + 2\mathbf{w}$. See Figure 7.24.

FIGURE 7.24

Note that the vector $\mathbf{v} + 2\mathbf{w}$ in Figure 7.24 is the third side of the triangle PRS. In the parallelogram $PQSR$, since the measure of $\angle QPR$ is 65°, the measure of the adjacent $\angle PRS$ is $180° - 65° = 115°$.

a.
$$\|\overrightarrow{PS}\|^2 = \|\overrightarrow{PR}\|^2 + \|\overrightarrow{RS}\|^2 - 2\|\overrightarrow{PR}\|\,\|\overrightarrow{RS}\|\cos 115°$$ Apply the Law of Cosines to triangle PRS.

$$\|\mathbf{v} + 2\mathbf{w}\|^2 = \|2\mathbf{w}\|^2 + \|\mathbf{v}\|^2 - 2\|2\mathbf{w}\|\,\|\mathbf{v}\|\cos 115°$$

$$= (|2|\|\mathbf{w}\|)^2 + \|\mathbf{v}\|^2 - 2|2|\|\mathbf{w}\|\|\mathbf{v}\|\cos 115°$$ $\|2\mathbf{w}\| = |2|\|\mathbf{w}\|$

$$= (2(7))^2 + (12)^2 - 2(2)(7)(12)\cos 115°$$ $|2| = 2, \|\mathbf{w}\| = 7, \|\mathbf{v}\| = 12$

$$\|\mathbf{v} + 2\mathbf{w}\|^2 = 481.9997$$ Use a calculator.

$$\|\mathbf{v} + 2\mathbf{w}\| \approx 21.95 \approx 22.0$$ Take positive square root.

b.   To find angle θ in Figure 7.24, we apply the Law of Sines in triangle PRS.

$$\frac{\sin\theta}{\|\mathbf{v}\|} = \frac{\sin 115°}{\|\mathbf{v} + 2\mathbf{w}\|}$$ The Law of Sines

$$\sin\theta = \frac{\|\mathbf{v}\|\sin 115°}{\|\mathbf{v} + 2\mathbf{w}\|}$$ Multiply both sides by $\|\mathbf{v}\|$.

$$\theta = \sin^{-1}\left(\frac{\|\mathbf{v}\|\sin 115°}{\|\mathbf{v} + 2\mathbf{w}\|}\right)$$ $0° \le \theta \le 90°$

$$\theta = \sin^{-1}\left(\frac{12\sin 115°}{21.95}\right)$$ Substitute values.

$$\theta \approx 29.7°$$ Use a calculator.   ■ ■ ■

PRACTICE PROBLEM 10   Repeat Example 10 if $\|\mathbf{v}\| = 20$ and $\|\mathbf{w}\| = 7$.   ■

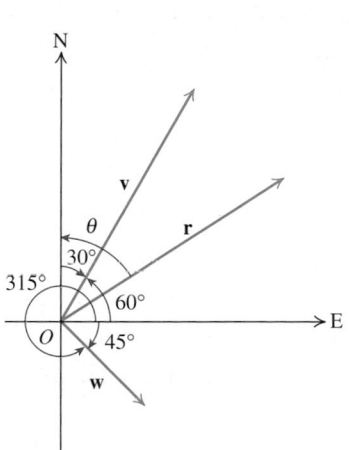

N

v

θ

315°   30°

60°

O   45°

w

r

→E

Vectors are not drawn to scale.

FIGURE 7.25

EXAMPLE 11   Using Vectors in Air Navigation

An F-15 fighter jet is flying over Mount Rushmore at an airspeed (speed in still air) of 800 miles per hour on a bearing of N 30° E. The velocity of wind is 40 miles per hour in the direction of S 45° E. Find the actual speed and direction (relative to the ground) of the plane. Round each answer to the nearest tenth.

Solution

Set up a coordinate system with north along the positive y-axis. See Figure 7.25.
Let **v** be the air velocity of the plane,
w be the wind velocity, and
r be the resultant ground velocity of the plane.
Writing each vector in terms of its magnitude and the reference angle for the direction angle θ that the vector makes with the positive x-axis, we have

$$\mathbf{v} = 800(\cos 60°\mathbf{i} + \sin 60°\mathbf{j}) \qquad 90° - 30° = 60°$$

$$\mathbf{w} = 40[\cos 45°\mathbf{i} - \sin 45°\mathbf{j}] \qquad 45° \text{ is the reference angle for } 315°.$$

The resultant **r** is given by

$$\mathbf{r} = \mathbf{v} + \mathbf{w}$$

$$\mathbf{r} = 800(\cos 60°\mathbf{i} + \sin 60°\mathbf{j}) + 40(\cos 45°\mathbf{i} - \sin 45°\mathbf{j}). \qquad \text{Substitute values of } \mathbf{v} \text{ and } \mathbf{w}.$$

$$\mathbf{r} = (800\cos 60° + 40\cos 45°)\mathbf{i} + (800\sin 60° - 40\sin 45°)\mathbf{j} \qquad \text{Add vectors.}$$

$$\|\mathbf{r}\| = \sqrt{(800\cos 60° + 40\cos 45°)^2 + (800\sin 60° - 40\sin 45°)^2} \qquad \|v_1\mathbf{i} + v_2\mathbf{j}\| = \sqrt{v_1^2 + v_2^2}$$

$$\|\mathbf{r}\| \approx 790.6 \qquad \text{Use a calculator.}$$

The ground speed of the F-15 is approximately 790.6 miles per hour.
To find the actual direction (bearing) of the plane, we find the angle θ between **r** and **j** (unit vector in the direction north).

$$\cos\theta = \frac{\mathbf{j} \cdot \mathbf{r}}{\|\mathbf{j}\|\|\mathbf{r}\|} \qquad \mathbf{j} = 0\mathbf{i} + 1\mathbf{j} \text{ and } \|\mathbf{j}\| = 1$$

$$\approx \frac{800\sin 60° - 40\sin 45°}{790.6} \qquad \text{If } \mathbf{v} = \langle v_1, v_2\rangle, \text{ then } \mathbf{j} \cdot \mathbf{v} = v_2.$$

$$\cos\theta \approx 0.8405 \qquad \text{Use a calculator.}$$

$$\theta \approx \cos^{-1}(0.8405) \approx 32.8° \qquad \text{Use a calculator.}$$

The direction of the F-15 relative to the ground is approximately N 32.8° E.   ■ ■ ■

PRACTICE PROBLEM 11   Repeat Example 11 if the bearing of the plane is N 60° W and the direction of the wind is S 30° W.   ■

7 Use the definition of work.

Work

DEFINITION OF WORK

The work W done by a constant force **F** in moving an object from a point P to a point Q is defined by

$$W = \mathbf{F} \cdot \overrightarrow{PQ}$$

EXAMPLE 12   **Computing Work**

A child pulls a wagon along a level ground, with a force of 40 pounds along the handle on the wagon that makes an angle of 42° with the horizontal. How much work has she done by pulling the wagon 150 feet?

Solution

The work done is

$$W = \mathbf{F} \cdot \overrightarrow{PQ} \qquad\qquad \text{Definition of work}$$
$$= \|\mathbf{F}\|\|\overrightarrow{PQ}\|\cos\theta \qquad \mathbf{u} \cdot \mathbf{v} = \|\mathbf{u}\|\|\mathbf{v}\|\cos\theta$$
$$= (40)(150)\cos 42° \qquad \text{Substitute given values.}$$
$$\approx 4458.87 \text{ foot-pounds.} \qquad \text{Use a calculator.} \quad \blacksquare\ \blacksquare\ \blacksquare$$

PRACTICE PROBLEM 12   In Example 12, compute the work done if the handle on the wagon makes an angle of 60° with the horizontal.   ▪

A Exercises   Basic Skills and Concepts

In Exercises 1–8, use the vectors **u**, **v**, and **w** in the accompanying figure to graph each vector.

1. **u + v** †
2. **3v** †
3. **2u − w** †
4. **w − 2v** †
5. **u + v + w** †
6. **2u − w + v** †
7. **w − 2v + u** †
8. **2v + 3w − u** †

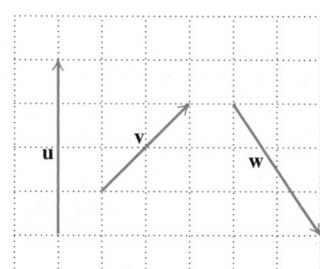

In Exercises 9–16, the vector **v** has initial point P and terminal point Q. Write **v** as a position vector.

9. $P(3, 6), Q(2, 9)$ ⟨−1, 3⟩   10. $P(6, −4), Q(1, 1)$ ⟨−5, 5⟩
11. $P(−5, −2), Q(−3, −4)$ †   12. $P(0, 0), Q(−3, −6)$ †
13. $P(−1, 4), Q(2, −3)$ ⟨3, −7⟩   14. $P(3.5, 2.7), Q(−1.5, 1.3)$ †
15. $P\left(\dfrac{1}{2}, \dfrac{3}{4}\right), Q\left(-\dfrac{1}{2}, -\dfrac{7}{4}\right)$ †   16. $P\left(-\dfrac{2}{3}, \dfrac{4}{9}\right), Q\left(\dfrac{1}{3}, -\dfrac{2}{3}\right)$ †

In Exercises 17–24, let $\mathbf{v} = \langle -1, 2\rangle$ and $\mathbf{w} = \langle 3, -2\rangle$. Find each expression.

17. $\|\mathbf{v}\|$ $\sqrt{5}$ 18. $\|\mathbf{w}\|$ $\sqrt{13}$
19. $\mathbf{v} - \mathbf{w}$ ⟨−4, 4⟩   20. $\mathbf{v} + \mathbf{w}$ ⟨2, 0⟩
21. $2\mathbf{v} - 3\mathbf{w}$ ⟨−11, 10⟩   22. $2\mathbf{w} - 3\mathbf{v}$ ⟨9, −10⟩
23. $\|2\mathbf{v} - 3\mathbf{w}\|$ $\sqrt{221}$ 24. $\|2\mathbf{w} - 3\mathbf{v}\|$ $\sqrt{181}$

In Exercises 25–30, find a unit vector **u** in the direction of the given vector.

25. ⟨1, −1⟩ †   26. ⟨1, 3⟩ †   27. ⟨−4, 3⟩ †
28. ⟨5, −12⟩ †   29. ⟨$\sqrt{2}$, $\sqrt{2}$⟩ †   30. ⟨$\sqrt{5}$, −2⟩ †

In Exercises 31–36, find each expression for $\mathbf{u} = 2\mathbf{i} - 5\mathbf{j}$ and $\mathbf{v} = -3\mathbf{i} - 2\mathbf{j}$.

31. $\mathbf{u} + \mathbf{v}$ $-\mathbf{i} - 7\mathbf{j}$ 32. $\mathbf{u} - \mathbf{v}$ $5\mathbf{i} - 3\mathbf{j}$
33. $2\mathbf{u} - 3\mathbf{v}$ $13\mathbf{i} - 4\mathbf{j}$ 34. $2\mathbf{v} + 3\mathbf{u}$ $-19\mathbf{j}$
35. $\|2\mathbf{u} - 3\mathbf{v}\|$ $\sqrt{185}$ 36. $\|2\mathbf{v} + 3\mathbf{u}\|$ 19

In Exercises 37–44, write the vector **v** in the form $v_1\mathbf{i} + v_2\mathbf{j}$, given $\|\mathbf{v}\|$ and the angle θ that **v** makes with the positive x-axis.

37. $\|\mathbf{v}\| = 2, \theta = 30°$ $\sqrt{3}\mathbf{i} + \mathbf{j}$ 38. $\|\mathbf{v}\| = 5, \theta = 45°$ †
39. $\|\mathbf{v}\| = 4, \theta = 120°$ †   40. $\|\mathbf{v}\| = 3, \theta = 150°$ †
41. $\|\mathbf{v}\| = 3, \theta = \dfrac{5\pi}{3}$ †   42. $\|\mathbf{v}\| = 4, \theta = \dfrac{11\pi}{6}$ †
43. $\|\mathbf{v}\| = 7, \theta = -\dfrac{\pi}{3}$ †   44. $\|\mathbf{v}\| = 8, \theta = \dfrac{3\pi}{4}$ †

In Exercises 45–52, find $\mathbf{u} \cdot \mathbf{v}$.

45. $\mathbf{u} = \langle 1, -2\rangle, \mathbf{v} = \langle 3, 5\rangle$ -7
46. $\mathbf{u} = \langle 1, 3\rangle, \mathbf{v} = \langle -3, 1\rangle$ 0
47. $\mathbf{u} = \langle 2, -6\rangle, \mathbf{v} = \langle 3, 1\rangle$ 0
48. $\mathbf{u} = \langle -1, -2\rangle, \mathbf{v} = \langle -3, -4\rangle$ 11
49. $\mathbf{u} = \mathbf{i} - 3\mathbf{j}, \mathbf{v} = 8\mathbf{i} - 2\mathbf{j}$ 14

---

†Due to space constrictions, answers to these exercises may be found in the Answers beginning on page A–1 in the back of the book.

50. $\mathbf{u} = 6\mathbf{i} - \mathbf{j}, \mathbf{v} = 2\mathbf{i} + 7\mathbf{j}$ 5

51. $\mathbf{u} = 4\mathbf{i} - 2\mathbf{j}, \mathbf{v} = 3\mathbf{j}$ −6

52. $\mathbf{u} = -2\mathbf{i}, \mathbf{v} = 5\mathbf{j}$ 0

In Exercises 53–58, find $\mathbf{u} \cdot \mathbf{v}$, where θ is the angle between the vectors $\mathbf{u}$ and $\mathbf{v}$. Round answers to the nearest tenths.

53. $\|\mathbf{u}\| = 2, \|\mathbf{v}\| = 5, \theta = \dfrac{\pi}{6}$ $5\sqrt{3}$

54. $\|\mathbf{u}\| = 3, \|\mathbf{v}\| = 4, \theta = \dfrac{\pi}{3}$ 6

55. $\|\mathbf{u}\| = 5, \|\mathbf{v}\| = 4, \theta = 65°$ 8.5

56. $\|\mathbf{u}\| = 5, \|\mathbf{v}\| = 3, \theta = 78°$ 3.1

57. $\|\mathbf{u}\| = 3, \|\mathbf{v}\| = 7, \theta = 120°$ −10.5

58. $\|\mathbf{u}\| = 6, \|\mathbf{v}\| = 4, \theta = 150°$ −20.8

In Exercises 59–68, find the angle between the vectors $\mathbf{v}$ and $\mathbf{w}$. Round each answer to the nearest tenth of a degree.

59. $\mathbf{v} = \langle 2, 3 \rangle, \mathbf{w} = \langle 3, 4 \rangle$ 3.2°

60. $\mathbf{v} = \langle -1, 1 \rangle, \mathbf{w} = \langle 5, 12 \rangle$ 67.6°

61. $\mathbf{v} = -2\mathbf{i} - 3\mathbf{j}, \mathbf{w} = \mathbf{i} + \mathbf{j}$ 168.7°

62. $\mathbf{v} = \mathbf{i} - \mathbf{j}, \mathbf{w} = 3\mathbf{i} - 4\mathbf{j}$ 8.1°

63. $\mathbf{v} = 2\mathbf{i} + 5\mathbf{j}, \mathbf{w} = -5\mathbf{i} + 2\mathbf{j}$ 90°

64. $\mathbf{v} = 3\mathbf{i} - 7\mathbf{j}, \mathbf{w} = 7\mathbf{i} + 3\mathbf{j}$ 90°

65. $\mathbf{v} = \mathbf{i} + \mathbf{j}, \mathbf{w} = 3\mathbf{i} + 3\mathbf{j}$ 0°

66. $\mathbf{v} = -2\mathbf{i} + 3\mathbf{j}, \mathbf{w} = -4\mathbf{i} + 6\mathbf{j}$ 0°

67. $\mathbf{v} = -2\mathbf{i} - 3\mathbf{j}, \mathbf{w} = -4\mathbf{i} + 6\mathbf{j}$ 112.6°

68. $\mathbf{v} = -3\mathbf{i} + 4\mathbf{j}, \mathbf{w} = 6\mathbf{i} - 8\mathbf{j}$ 180°

In Exercises 69–76, let $\mathbf{v}$ and $\mathbf{w}$ be two vectors in the plane of magnitudes 12 and 16, respectively. The angle between $\mathbf{v}$ and $\mathbf{w}$ is 50°. Find each expression. Round answers to the nearest tenths.

69. $\|\mathbf{v} + \mathbf{w}\|$ 25.4

70. $\|\mathbf{v} - \mathbf{w}\|$ 12.4

71. $\|2\mathbf{v} + \mathbf{w}\|$ 36.4

72. $\|2\mathbf{v} - \mathbf{w}\|$ 18.4

73. Angle between $\mathbf{v} + \mathbf{w}$ and $\mathbf{w}$ 21.2°

74. Angle between $\mathbf{v} - \mathbf{w}$ and $\mathbf{v}$ 82.0°

75. Angle between $2\mathbf{v} + \mathbf{w}$ and $\mathbf{v}$ 19.7°

76. Angle between $2\mathbf{v} - \mathbf{w}$ and $\mathbf{w}$ 91.8°

B Exercises   Applying the Concepts

77. Wind and vectors. A wind is blowing at 25 miles per hour in the direction N 67° E. Express the wind velocity $\mathbf{v}$ in the form $a\mathbf{i} + b\mathbf{j}$. $23.0\,\mathbf{i} + 9.8\,\mathbf{j}$

78. Wind and vectors. The velocity $\mathbf{v}$ of a wind is given by $\mathbf{v} = 5\mathbf{i} - 12\mathbf{j}$, where the vectors $\mathbf{i}$ and $\mathbf{j}$ represent 1-mile-per-hour winds blowing east and north, respectively. Find the speed (magnitude of $\mathbf{v}$) and the direction of the wind.   13 mi/hr, S 22.6° E

79. Finding resultant force. Two forces of 6 and 8 pounds act at an angle of 30° to each other. Find
a. the resultant force and   13.5 pounds
b. the angle of the resultant force to each of the two forces.   12.8°, 17.2°

80. Repeat Exercise 79, if the two forces act at an angle of 60° to each other.   a. 12.2 pounds   b. 25.3°, 34.7°

81. Air navigation. A plane flies at an airspeed (speed in still air) of 500 miles per hour on a bearing of N 35° E. An east wind (wind from east to west) is blowing at 30 miles per hour. Find the plane's ground speed and direction.   †

82. Air navigation. A plane flies at an airspeed of 550 miles per hour on a straight course from an airfield F. A 30-mile-per-hour wind is blowing from the west. What must be the plane's bearing so that, after one hour of flying time, the plane is due north of F?   N 3.1° W

83. River navigation. A river flowing southward has a current of 4 miles per hour. A motorboat in still water maintains a speed of 15 miles per hour. The motorboat starts at the west shore on a bearing of N 40° E. What is the actual speed and direction of the boat?   12.2 mi/hr, N 52.2° E

84. River crossing. A fisherwoman on the west bank of the river of Exercise 83 sees several people fishing at a spot P directly east of her. If she owns the boat of Exercise 83, what direction should she take to land on the spot P?   N 74.5° E

85. Work. A vector $\mathbf{F}$ represents a force that has a magnitude of 10 pounds, and $\dfrac{2\pi}{3}$ is the angle for its direction. Find the work done by the force in moving an object from the origin to the point $(-6, 3)$. Distance is measured in feet.   56 foot-pounds

86. Work. Two forces $\mathbf{F}_1 = 3\mathbf{i} - 2\mathbf{j}$ and $\mathbf{F}_2 = -4\mathbf{i} + 3\mathbf{j}$ act on an object and move it along a straight line from the point $(8, 4)$ to the point $(3, 5)$. Find the work done by the two forces acting together. The magnitudes of $\mathbf{F}_1$ and $\mathbf{F}_2$ are measured in pounds, and distance is measured in feet.   6 foot-pounds

C Exercises   Beyond the Basics

87. Find the terminal point of $\mathbf{v} = 4\mathbf{i} - 3\mathbf{j}$ if the initial point is $(-2, 1)$. $(2, -2)$

88. Find the initial point of $\mathbf{v} = \langle -3, 5 \rangle$ if the terminal point is $(4, 0)$. $(7, -5)$

89. Let $\mathbf{u} = \langle -1, 2 \rangle$ and $\mathbf{v} = \langle 3, 5 \rangle$. Find a vector $\mathbf{x} = \langle x_1, x_2 \rangle$ that satisfies the equation $2\mathbf{u} - \mathbf{x} = 2\mathbf{x} + 3\mathbf{v}$.

90. Let $P(3, 5)$ and $Q(7, -4)$ be two points in a coordinate plane. Use vectors to find the coordinates of the point on the line segment joining P and Q that is $\dfrac{3}{4}$ of the way from P to Q.

91. Use vectors to find the lengths of the diagonals of the parallelogram determined by $\mathbf{i} + 2\mathbf{j}$ and $\mathbf{i} - \mathbf{j}$. $3, \sqrt{5}$

92. Use vectors to find the fourth vertex of a parallelogram, with three vertices at $(0, 0), (2, 3)$ and $(6, 4)$. [*Hint:* There is more than one answer.] $(4, 1), (-4, -1), (8, 7)$

93. **Parallelogram law:** Show that for any two vectors $\mathbf{u}$ and $\mathbf{v}$,
$$\|\mathbf{u} + \mathbf{v}\|^2 + \|\mathbf{u} - \mathbf{v}\|^2 = 2\|\mathbf{u}\|^2 + 2\|\mathbf{v}\|^2.$$
[*Hint:* $\|\mathbf{a}\|^2 = \mathbf{a} \cdot \mathbf{a}$.]

94. **Polarization identity:** Show that for any two vectors $\mathbf{u}$ and $\mathbf{v}$,
$$\|\mathbf{u} + \mathbf{v}\|^2 - \|\mathbf{u} - \mathbf{v}\|^2 = 4(\mathbf{u} \cdot \mathbf{v}).$$

Critical Thinking

95. Show that the vectors $\mathbf{v} = \langle 2, -5 \rangle$ and $\mathbf{w} = \langle 5, 2 \rangle$ are perpendicular to each other.

96. Let $\mathbf{v} = 3\mathbf{i} + 7\mathbf{j}$. Find a vector perpendicular to $\mathbf{v}$. $7\mathbf{i} - 3\mathbf{j}$

Answers:

89. $\left\langle -\dfrac{11}{3}, -\dfrac{11}{3} \right\rangle$ **90.** $\left(6, -\dfrac{7}{4} \right)$

Polar Coordinates

Bionics

On large construction sites and maintenance projects, it is common to see mechanical systems that lift, dig, and scoop just like biological systems having arms, legs, and hands. The technique of solving mechanical problems with our knowledge of biological systems is called **bionics**. Bionics is used to make robotic devices for the remote-control handling of radioactive materials and the machines that are sent to the Moon or Mars to scoop soil samples, bring them into the space vehicle, perform analysis on them, and then radio the results back to Earth. In Example 4, we use polar coordinates to find the reach of a robotic arm.

Up to now, we have used a rectangular coordinate system to identify points in the plane. In this section, we introduce another coordinate system, called a **polar coordinate system**, that allows us to describe many curves with rather simple equations. The polar coordinate system is believed to have been introduced by Jakob Bernoulli (1654–1705). ■

1 Plot points using polar coordinates.

Polar Coordinates

In a rectangular coordinate system, a point in the plane is described in terms of the horizontal and vertical directed distances from the origin. In a polar coordinate system, we draw a horizontal ray in the plane. The ray is called the **polar axis**, and its endpoint is called the **pole**. A point P in the plane is described by an ordered pair of numbers (r, θ), and we refer to r and θ as **polar coordinates** of P.

Figure 7.26 shows the point $P(r, \theta)$ in the polar coordinate system, where r is the "directed distance" (see Figures 7.26 and 7.29) from the pole O to the point P, and θ is a directed angle from the polar axis to the line segment OP. The angle θ may be measured in degrees or radians. As usual, positive angles are measured counterclockwise from the polar axis, and negative angles are measured clockwise from the polar axis.

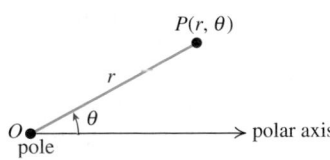

FIGURE 7.26

To locate a point with polar coordinates $(5, 40°)$, we draw an angle θ of measure $40°$ counterclockwise from the polar axis. We then measure 5 units along the terminal side of θ. In Figure 7.27, the points $(5, 40°)$, $(3, 220°)$, $(4, -30°)$, and $(2, 110°)$ are plotted in the polar coordinate system.

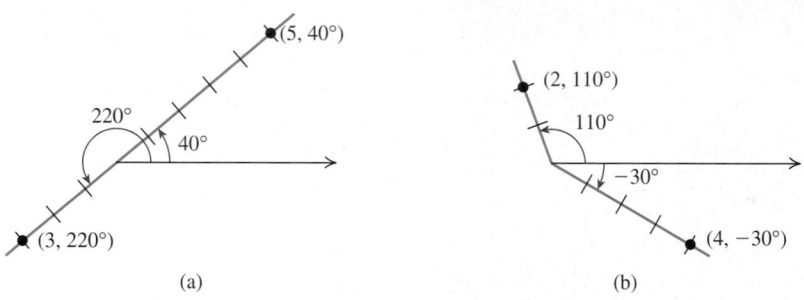

(a)   (b)

FIGURE 7.27

Unlike rectangular coordinates, the polar coordinates of a point are not unique. For example, the polar coordinates $(3, 60°)$, $(3, 420°)$, and $(3, -300°)$ all represent the same point. See Figure 7.28. In general, if a point P has polar coordinates (r, θ), then for any integer n,

$$(r, \theta + n \cdot 360°) \qquad \text{or} \qquad (r, \theta + 2n\pi)$$

↑	↑
if θ is measured in degrees	if θ is measured in radians

are also polar coordinates of P.

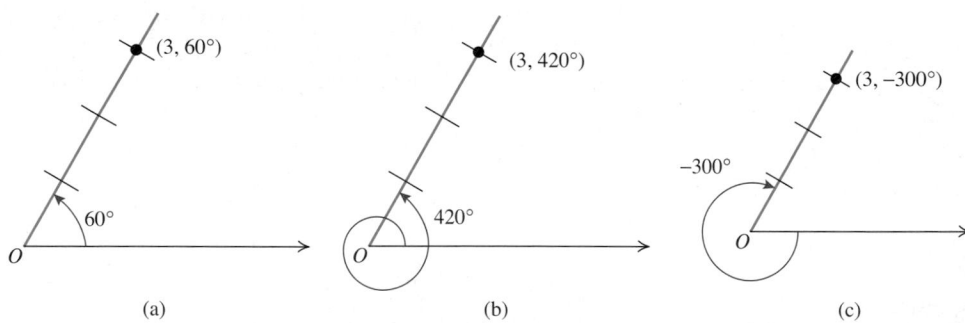

(a)   (b)   (c)

FIGURE 7.28

$P(-4, -30°)$ or $P(4, 150°)$

FIGURE 7.29

When we start graphing curves in polar coordinates, it will be desirable to allow r to be negative. That's why we see the words "directed distance" in the statement defining r. If r is negative, then instead of the point being on the terminal side of the angle, it is $|r|$ units on the extension of the terminal side, which is the ray from the pole that extends in the direction opposite to the terminal side. For example, the point $P(-4, -30°)$ shown in Figure 7.29 is the same point as $(4, 150°)$. Other pairs of polar coordinates for the same point P are $(-4, 330°)$, $(4, -210°)$, and $(4, 510°)$.

EXAMPLE 1   **Finding Different Polar Coordinates**

Plot the point P with polar coordinates $(3, 225°)$. Find another pair of polar coordinates of P for which the following is true.

a. $r < 0$ and $0° < \theta < 360°$

b. $r < 0$ and $-360° < \theta < 0°$

c. $r > 0$ and $-360° < \theta < 0°$

Solution

The point P $(3, 225°)$ is plotted by first drawing the angle of degree measure $225°$ in a counterclockwise direction from the polar axis. Since $r = 3 > 0$, the point P is on the terminal side of the angle, 3 units from the pole. See Figure 7.30.

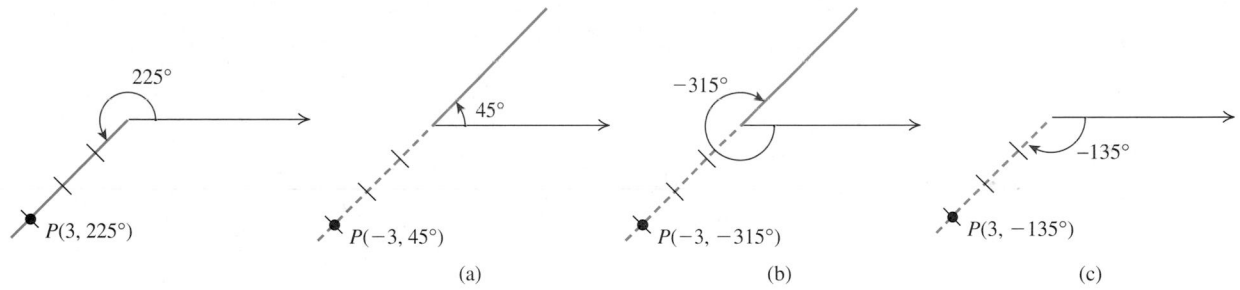

FIGURE 7.30

The answer to parts, **a**, **b**, and **c** are, respectively, $(-3, 45°)$, $(-3, -315°)$, and $(3, -135°)$. See Figure 7.30(a)–(c).   ■ ■ ■

PRACTICE PROBLEM 1   Plot the point P with polar coordinates $(2, -150°)$. Find another pair of polar coordinates of P for which the following is true.

a. $r < 0$ and $0° < \theta < 360°$

b. $r > 0$ and $0° < \theta < 360°$

c. $r < 0$ and $-360° < \theta < 0°$ ■

2 Convert points between polar and rectangular coordinates.

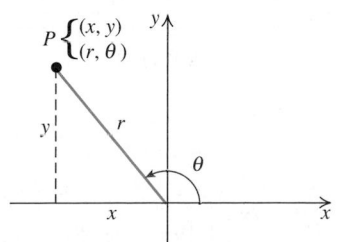

FIGURE 7.31

Relation between Polar and Rectangular Coordinates

Frequently, it is helpful to use both polar and rectangular coordinates in the same problem. To do this, we let the positive x-axis of the rectangular coordinate system serve as the polar axis and the origin as the pole for the polar coordinate system. When this is done, each point P has both polar coordinates (r, θ) and rectangular coordinates (x, y), as shown in Figure 7.31.

From Figure 7.31, we see the following relationships: $x^2 + y^2 = r^2$, $\sin \theta = \dfrac{y}{r}$, $\cos \theta = \dfrac{x}{r}$, and $\tan \theta = \dfrac{y}{x}$. These relationships hold whether $r > 0$ or $r < 0$. These relationships are used to convert the polar coordinates of a point to its rectangular coordinates, and vice versa.

> ## CONVERTING FROM POLAR TO RECTANGULAR COORDINATES
>
> To convert the polar coordinates (r, θ) of a point to rectangular coordinates, use the equations
>
> $$x = r\cos\theta \qquad \text{and} \qquad y = r\sin\theta.$$

TECHNOLOGY CONNECTION

A graphing calculator can be used to check conversions from polar to rectangular coordinates. Choose the appropriate options from the ANGLE menu. The x- and y- coordinates must be calculated separately. The screen shown here is from a calculator set in DEGREE mode.

```
P▸Rx(2,-30)
         1.732050808
√(3)
         1.732050808
P▸Ry(2,-30)
                  -1
■
```

EXAMPLE 2 **Converting from Polar to Rectangular Coordinates**

Convert the polar coordinates of each point to rectangular coordinates.

a. $(2, -30°)$ **b.** $\left(-4, \dfrac{\pi}{3}\right)$

Solution

a.

$x = r\cos\theta$	$y = r\sin\theta$	Conversion equations
$x = 2\cos(-30°)$	$y = 2\sin(-30°)$	Replace r by 2 and θ by $-30°$.
$x = 2\cos 30°$	$y = -2\sin 30°$	$\cos(-\theta) = \cos\theta$, $\sin(-\theta) = -\sin\theta$
$x = 2\left(\dfrac{\sqrt{3}}{2}\right)$	$y = -2\left(\dfrac{1}{2}\right)$	$\cos 30° = \dfrac{\sqrt{3}}{2}$, $\sin 30° = \dfrac{1}{2}$
$x = \sqrt{3}$	$y = -1$	Simplify.

The rectangular coordinates of $(2, -30°)$ are $(\sqrt{3}, -1)$.

b.

$x = r\cos\theta$	$y = r\sin\theta$	Conversion equations
$x = -4\cos\dfrac{\pi}{3}$	$y = -4\sin\dfrac{\pi}{3}$	Replace r by -4 and θ by $\dfrac{\pi}{3}$.
$x = -4\left(\dfrac{1}{2}\right)$	$y = -4\left(\dfrac{\sqrt{3}}{2}\right)$	$\cos\dfrac{\pi}{3} = \dfrac{1}{2}$, $\sin\dfrac{\pi}{3} = \dfrac{\sqrt{3}}{2}$
$x = -2$	$y = -2\sqrt{3}$	Simplify.

The rectangular coordinates of $\left(-4, \dfrac{\pi}{3}\right)$ are $(-2, -2\sqrt{3})$. ■ ■ ■

PRACTICE PROBLEM 2 Convert the polar coordinates of each point to rectangular coordinates.

a. $(-3, 60°)$ **b.** $\left(2, -\dfrac{\pi}{4}\right)$ ■

When converting from rectangular coordinates (x, y) of a point to polar coordinates (r, θ), remember that infinitely many representations are possible. We shall find the polar coordinates (r, θ) of the point (x, y) such that $r > 0$ and $0° \le \theta < 360°$ or $0 \le \theta < 2\pi$.

> ## CONVERTING FROM RECTANGULAR TO POLAR COORDINATES
>
> To convert the rectangular coordinates (x, y) of a point to polar coordinates,
>
> 1. Find the quadrant in which the given point (x, y) lies.
> 2. Use $r = \sqrt{x^2 + y^2}$ to find r.
> 3. Find θ by using $\tan\theta = \dfrac{y}{x}$, and choose θ so that it lies in the same quadrant as the point (x, y).

EXAMPLE 3   Converting from Rectangular to Polar Coordinates

Find polar coordinates (r, θ) of the point P whose rectangular coordinates are $(-2, 2\sqrt{3})$, with $r > 0$ and $0 \le \theta < 2\pi$.

Solution

1. The point $P(-2, 2\sqrt{3})$ lies in quadrant II with $x = -2$ and $y = 2\sqrt{3}$.
2. $r = \sqrt{x^2 + y^2}$ Formula for computing r

    $r = \sqrt{(-2)^2 + (2\sqrt{3})^2}$ Substitute values of x and y.

    $r = \sqrt{4 + 12} = \sqrt{16} = 4$ Simplify.

3. $\tan\theta = \dfrac{y}{x}$ Definition of $\tan\theta$

    $\tan\theta = \dfrac{2\sqrt{3}}{-2}$ Substitute values of y and x.

    $\tan\theta = -\sqrt{3}$ Simplify.

The equation $\tan\theta = -\sqrt{3}$ gives $\theta = \pi - \dfrac{\pi}{3} = \dfrac{2\pi}{3}$ or $\theta = 2\pi - \dfrac{\pi}{3} = \dfrac{5\pi}{3}$. Choose $\theta = \dfrac{2\pi}{3}$, since the terminal side of $\theta = \dfrac{2\pi}{3}$ lies in quadrant II, the quadrant in which the point (x, y) lies.

Thus, the required polar coordinates of $(-2, 2\sqrt{3})$ are $\left(4, \dfrac{2\pi}{3}\right)$.   ■ ■ ■

PRACTICE PROBLEM 3   Find the polar coordinates of the point P whose rectangular coordinates are $(-1, -1)$, with $r > 0$ and $0 \le \theta < 2\pi$.   ■

EXAMPLE 4   Positioning a Robotic Hand

For the robotic arm of Figure 7.32, determine the position of the hand relative to the shoulder. Round all answers to the nearest tenth.

FIGURE 7.32

Solution

The position of the hand, H, relative to the shoulder is determined by finding the polar coordinates (r, θ) of H, with the shoulder O as the pole. Since the length of $\overline{OE}$ is

Continued on next page

16 inches and the segment $\overline{OE}$ makes an angle of $30°$ with the horizontal, we write the vector $\overrightarrow{OE}$ in terms of its components. Thus,

$$\overrightarrow{OE} = \langle 16 \cos 30°, 16 \sin 30° \rangle.$$

Similarly,

$$\overrightarrow{EH} = \langle 12 \cos 45°, 12 \sin 45° \rangle.$$

Then

$$\overrightarrow{OH} = \overrightarrow{OE} + \overrightarrow{EH} \qquad\qquad\qquad \text{Resultant vector}$$
$$= \langle 16 \cos 30°, 16 \sin 30° \rangle + \langle 12 \cos 45°, 12 \sin 45° \rangle$$
$$= \langle 16 \cos 30° + 12 \cos 45°, 16 \sin 30° + 12 \sin 45° \rangle \qquad \text{Vector addition}$$

Thus, the rectangular coordinates (x, y) of H are

$$x = 16 \cos 30° + 12 \cos 45°, \quad y = 16 \sin 30° + 12 \sin 45°.$$

We now convert the coordinates (x, y) to polar coordinates (r, θ) of H.

$$r = \sqrt{x^2 + y^2} \qquad\qquad\qquad\qquad\qquad \text{Formula for } r$$

$$= \sqrt{(16 \cos 30° + 12 \cos 45°)^2 + (16 \sin 30° + 12 \sin 45°)^2} \qquad \begin{array}{l}\text{Substitute values}\\\text{for } x \text{ and } y.\end{array}$$

$$\approx 27.8 \text{ inches}$$

$$\theta = \tan^{-1}\left(\frac{y}{x}\right) \qquad\qquad\qquad\qquad \begin{array}{l}\text{Definition of inverse}\\\text{tangent}\end{array}$$

$$= \tan^{-1}\left(\frac{16 \sin 30° + 12 \sin 45°}{16 \cos 30° + 12 \cos 45°}\right) \qquad \begin{array}{l}\text{Substitute values for}\\x \text{ and } y.\end{array}$$

$$\approx 36.4° \qquad\qquad\qquad\qquad\qquad\qquad \text{Use a calculator.}$$

Thus, the polar coordinates of H relative to the pole O are $(27.8, 36.4°)$.   ■ ■ ■

PRACTICE PROBLEM 4   Repeat Example 4 with $\overline{OE} = 15$ inches and $\overline{EH} = 10$ inches.   ■

3 | Convert equations between rectangular and polar forms.

Converting Equations between Rectangular and Polar Forms

An equation that has the rectangular coordinates x and y as variables is called a **rectangular** (or **Cartesian**) **equation**. Similarly, an equation where the polar coordinates r and θ are the variables is called a **polar equation**. Some examples of polar equations are

$$r = \sin \theta, \quad r = 1 + \cos \theta, \quad \text{and} \quad r = \theta.$$

To convert a rectangular equation to a polar equation, we simply replace x by $r \cos \theta$ and y by $r \sin \theta$, and then simplify where possible.

EXAMPLE 5   **Converting an Equation from Rectangular to Polar Form**

Convert the equation $x^2 + y^2 - 3x + 4 = 0$ to polar form.

Solution

$$x^2 + y^2 - 3x + 4 = 0 \qquad\qquad \text{Given equation}$$
$$(r \cos \theta)^2 + (r \sin \theta)^2 - 3(r \cos \theta) + 4 = 0 \qquad x = r \cos \theta, y = r \sin \theta$$
$$r^2 \cos^2 \theta + r^2 \sin^2 \theta - 3r \cos \theta + 4 = 0 \qquad (ab)^2 = a^2 b^2$$

$$r^2(\cos^2\theta + \sin^2\theta) - 3r\cos\theta + 4 = 0 \qquad \text{Factor out } r^2 \text{ from the first two terms.}$$

$$r^2 - 3r\cos\theta + 4 = 0 \qquad \text{Pythagorean identity:} \\ \sin^2\theta + \cos^2\theta = 1$$

The equation $r^2 - 3r\cos\theta + 4 = 0$ is the polar form of the given rectangular equation.

■ ■ ■

PRACTICE PROBLEM 5   Convert the equation $x^2 + y^2 - 2y + 3 = 0$ to polar form.   ■

Converting an equation from polar to rectangular form will frequently require some ingenuity in order to use the substitutions

$$r^2 = x^2 + y^2, \quad r\cos\theta = x, \quad r\sin\theta = y, \quad \text{and} \quad \tan\theta = \frac{y}{x}.$$

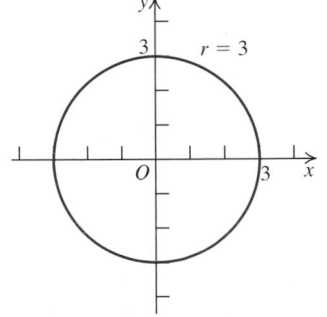

FIGURE 7.33

EXAMPLE 6   **Converting an Equation from Polar to Rectangular Form**

Convert each polar equation to a rectangular equation and identify its graph.

a. $r = 3$ **b.** $\theta = 45°$ **c.** $r = \csc\theta$ **d.** $r = 2\cos\theta$

Solution

a. $r = 3$ Given polar equation

     $r^2 = 9$ Square both sides.

$x^2 + y^2 = 9$ Replace r^2 by $x^2 + y^2$.

The equation $x^2 + y^2 = 9$ is the rectangular form of the polar equation $r = 3$. The graph of the equation $x^2 + y^2 = 9$ or $x^2 + y^2 = 3^2$ is a circle with center at $(0, 0)$ and radius 3. Thus, the graph of the polar equation $r = 3$ is a circle with center at the pole and a radius of 3 units. See Figure 7.33.

b. $\theta = 45°$ Given polar equation

$\tan\theta = \tan 45°$ If $x = y$, then $\tan x = \tan y$.

$\dfrac{y}{x} = 1$ $\tan\theta = \dfrac{y}{x}$ and $\tan 45° = 1$

$y = x$ Multiply both sides by x.

The graph of $y = x$ is a line through the origin, with slope 1. Thus, the graph of the polar equation $\theta = 45°$ is a line through the pole, making an angle of $45°$ with the polar axis. See Figure 7.34.

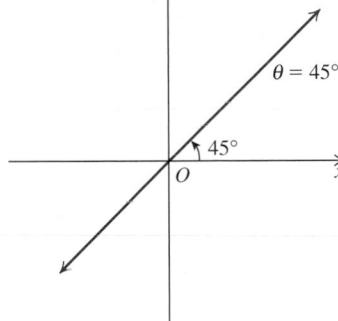

FIGURE 7.34

c. $r = \csc\theta$ Given polar equation

$r = \dfrac{1}{\sin\theta}$ Reciprocal identity

$r\sin\theta = 1$ Multiply both sides by $\sin\theta$.

$y = 1$ Replace $r\sin\theta$ with y.

The graph of $y = 1$ is a horizontal line. Thus, the graph of the polar equation $r = \csc\theta$ is a horizontal line. See Figure 7.35.

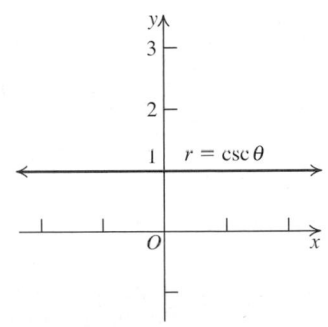

FIGURE 7.35

Continued on next page.

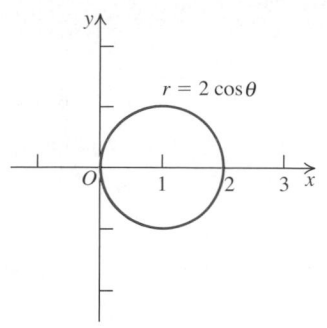

$r = 2\cos\theta$

FIGURE 7.36

d.

$r = 2\cos\theta$	Given polar equation
$r^2 = 2r\cos\theta$	Multiply both sides by r.
$x^2 + y^2 = 2x$	Replace r^2 by $x^2 + y^2$ and $r\cos\theta$ by x.
$x^2 - 2x + y^2 = 0$	Subtract $2x$ from both sides and simplify.
$(x^2 - 2x + 1) + y^2 = 1$	Add 1 to both sides to complete the square.
$(x - 1)^2 + y^2 = 1$	Factor perfect square trinomial.

The graph of equation $(x - 1)^2 + y^2 = 1$ is a circle with center at $(1, 0)$ and radius 1 unit. Then the graph of the polar equation $r = 2\cos\theta$ is the circle shown in Figure 7.36. ■ ■ ■

PRACTICE PROBLEM 6   Convert each polar equation to a rectangular equation and identify its graph.

a. $r = 5$ **b.** $\theta = -\dfrac{\pi}{3}$ **c.** $r = \sec\theta$ **d.** $r = 2\sin\theta$ ■

4 Graph polar equations.

The Graph of a Polar Equation

There are many important polar equations that do not convert "nicely" to rectangular equations. We graph such equations by plotting points in polar coordinates. The graph of a polar equation

$$r = f(\theta)$$

is the set of all points $P(r, \theta)$ that have at least one polar coordinate representation that satisfies the equation. We make a table of several ordered pair solutions (r, θ) of the equation and plot these points. We then join these points with a smooth curve to sketch the graph of the given polar equation.

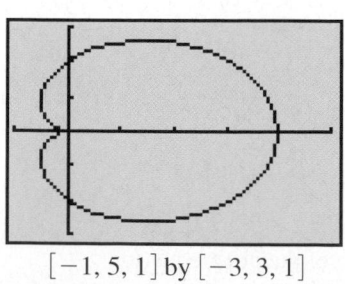
EXAMPLE 7   **Sketching the Graph of a Polar Equation**

Sketch the graph of the polar equation $r = 2(1 + \cos\theta)$.

Solution

Since $\cos\theta$ is an even function (that is, $\cos(-\theta) = \cos\theta$), the graph of $r = 2(1 + \cos\theta)$ is symmetric in the polar axis. Thus, to graph this equation it is sufficient to compute values for $0 \le \theta \le \pi$. We construct Table 7.1 by substituting values for θ at increments of $\pi/6$, and then calculating the corresponding values of r.

TABLE 7.1

θ	0	$\pm\dfrac{\pi}{6}$	$\pm\dfrac{\pi}{3}$	$\pm\dfrac{\pi}{2}$	$\pm\dfrac{2\pi}{3}$	$\pm\dfrac{5\pi}{6}$	$\pm\pi$
$r = 2(1 + \cos\theta)$	4	$2 + \sqrt{3} \approx 3.73$	3	2	1	$2 - \sqrt{3} \approx 0.27$	0

The graph of the equation $r = 2(1 + \cos\theta)$ is shown in Figure 7.37. This type of curve is called a *cardioid* because it resembles a heart. ■ ■ ■

PRACTICE PROBLEM 7   Sketch the graph of the polar equation $r = 2(1 + \sin\theta)$.   ■

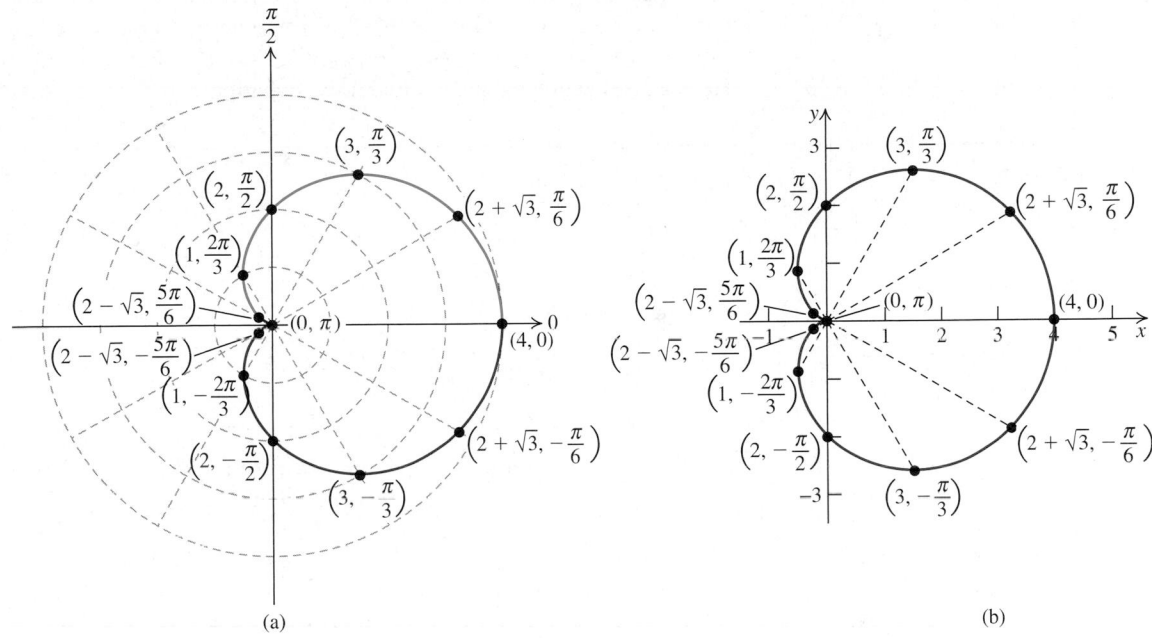

(a)   (b)

FIGURE 7.37

As with Cartesian equations, it is helpful to determine symmetry in the graph of polar equations. If the graph of a polar equation has symmetry, then we can sketch its graph by plotting fewer points.

TESTS FOR SYMMETRY IN POLAR COORDINATES

The graph of a polar equation is symmetric with respect to the following if an equivalent equation results by the given replacements:

Symmetry with respect to the polar axis (x-axis)	**Symmetry with respect to the line $\theta = \dfrac{\pi}{2}$ (y-axis)**	**Symmetry with respect to the pole**

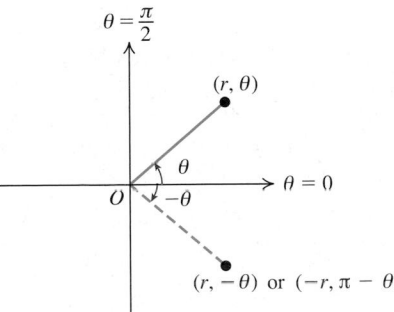

Replace (r, θ) by
$(r, -\theta)$ or $(-r, \pi - \theta)$.

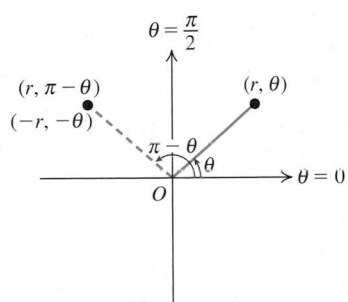

Replace (r, θ) by
$(r, \pi - \theta)$ or $(-r, -\theta)$.

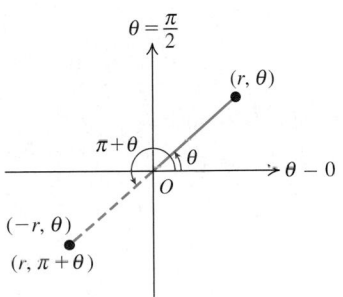

Replace (r, θ) by
$(r, \pi + \theta)$ or $(-r, \theta)$.

Note that if a polar equation fails a test for an indicated symmetry, the graph of the polar equation may or may not exhibit that symmetry. In other words, the tests for polar coordinate symmetry are sufficient for showing symmetry, but are not necessary.

Here are some graphs with simple polar equations:

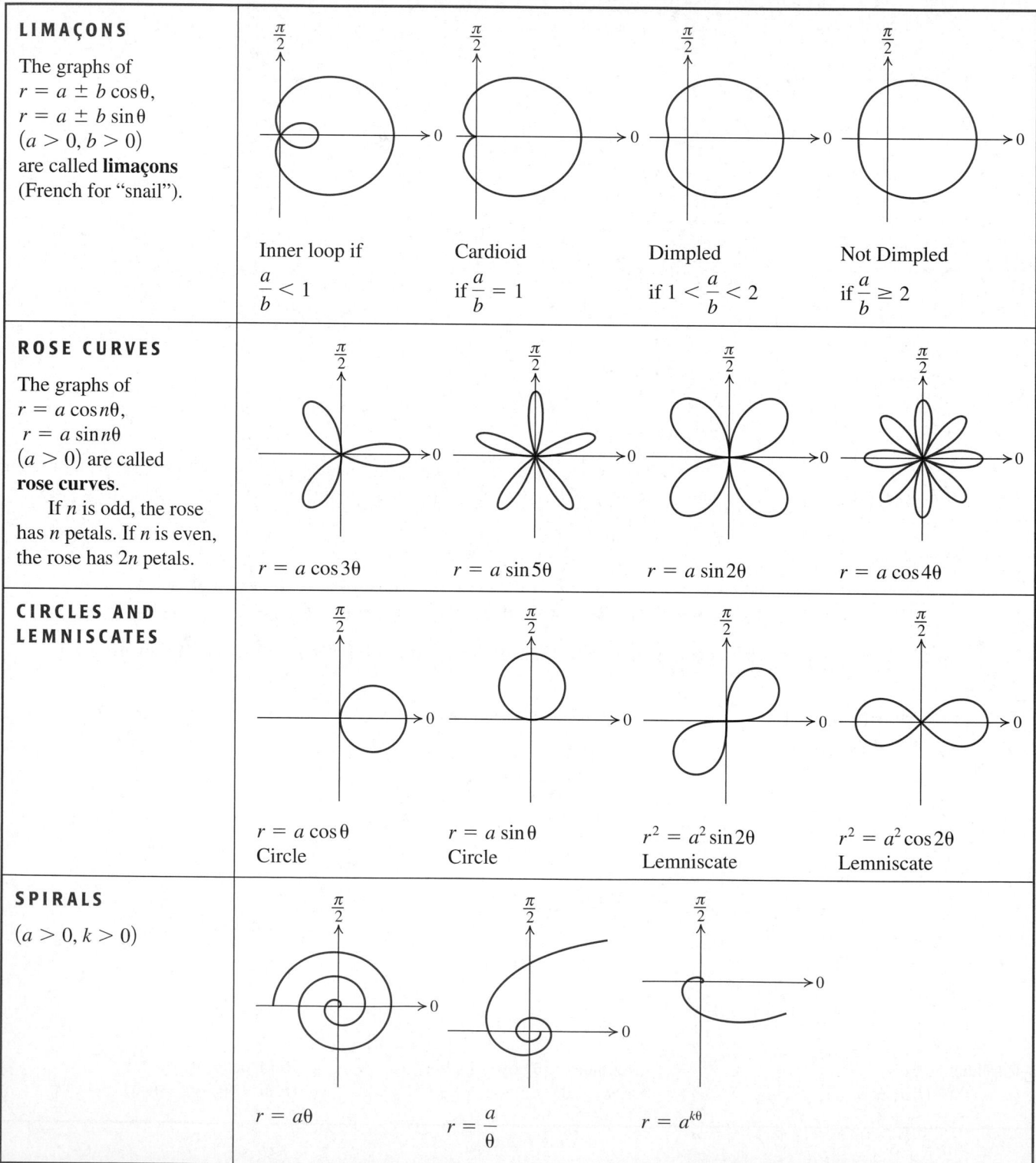

LIMAÇONS

The graphs of
$r = a \pm b \cos\theta$,
$r = a \pm b \sin\theta$
$(a > 0, b > 0)$
are called **limaçons**
(French for "snail").

Inner loop if
$\dfrac{a}{b} < 1$

Cardioid
if $\dfrac{a}{b} = 1$

Dimpled
if $1 < \dfrac{a}{b} < 2$

Not Dimpled
if $\dfrac{a}{b} \geq 2$

ROSE CURVES

The graphs of
$r = a \cos n\theta$,
$r = a \sin n\theta$
$(a > 0)$ are called
rose curves.

If n is odd, the rose has n petals. If n is even, the rose has $2n$ petals.

$r = a \cos 3\theta$ $r = a \sin 5\theta$ $r = a \sin 2\theta$ $r = a \cos 4\theta$

CIRCLES AND LEMNISCATES

$r = a \cos\theta$
Circle

$r = a \sin\theta$
Circle

$r^2 = a^2 \sin 2\theta$
Lemniscate

$r^2 = a^2 \cos 2\theta$
Lemniscate

SPIRALS

$(a > 0, k > 0)$

$r = a\theta$ $r = \dfrac{a}{\theta}$ $r = a^{k\theta}$

A Exercises   Basic Skills and Concepts

In Exercises 1–8, plot the point having the given polar coordinates. Then find different polar coordinates (r, θ) for the same point for which (a) $r < 0$ and $0° \le \theta < 360°$; (b) $r < 0$ and $-360° < \theta < 0°$; (c) $r > 0$ and $-360° < \theta < 0°$.

1. $(4, 45°)$ †
2. $(5, 150°)$ †
3. $(3, 90°)$ †
4. $(2, 240°)$ †
5. $(3, 60°)$ †
6. $(4, 210°)$ †
7. $(6, 300°)$ †
8. $(2, 270°)$ †

In Exercises 9–16, plot the point having the given polar coordinates. Then give two different pairs of polar coordinates of the same point, one with the given value of r, and one with r having the opposite sign of the given value of r.

9. $\left(2, -\dfrac{\pi}{3}\right)$ †
10. $\left(\sqrt{2}, -\dfrac{\pi}{4}\right)$ †
11. $\left(-3, \dfrac{\pi}{6}\right)$ †
12. $\left(-2, \dfrac{3\pi}{4}\right)$ †
13. $\left(-2, -\dfrac{\pi}{6}\right)$ †
14. $(-2, -\pi)$ †
15. $\left(4, \dfrac{7\pi}{6}\right)$ †
16. $(2, 3)$ †

In Exercises 17–24, convert the given polar coordinates of each point to rectangular coordinates.

17. $(3, 60°)$ †
18. $(-2, -30°)$ $(-\sqrt{3}, 1)$
19. $(5, -60°)$ †
20. $(-3, 90°)$ $(0, -3)$
21. $(3, \pi)$ $(-3, 0)$
22. $\left(\sqrt{2}, -\dfrac{\pi}{4}\right)$ $(1, -1)$
23. $\left(-2, -\dfrac{5\pi}{6}\right)$ $(\sqrt{3}, 1)$
24. $\left(-1, \dfrac{7\pi}{6}\right)$ $\left(\dfrac{\sqrt{3}}{2}, \dfrac{1}{2}\right)$

In Exercises 25–32, convert the rectangular coordinates of each point to polar coordinates (r, θ) with $r > 0$ and $0 \le \theta < 2\pi$.

25. $(1, -1)$ †
26. $(-\sqrt{3}, 1)$ †
27. $(3, 3)$ †
28. $(-4, 0)$ $(4, \pi)$
29. $(3, -3)$ †
30. $(2\sqrt{3}, 2)$ †
31. $(-1, \sqrt{3})$ †
32. $(-2, -2\sqrt{3})$ †

In Exercises 33–40, convert each rectangular equation to polar form.

33. $x^2 + y^2 = 16$ $r = 4$
34. $x + y = 1$ †
35. $y^2 = 4x$ $r = 4 \cot \theta \csc \theta$
36. $x^3 = 3y^2$ $r = 3 \tan^2 \theta \sec \theta$
37. $y^2 = 6y - x^2$ $r = 6 \sin \theta$
38. $x^2 - y^2 = 1$ †
39. $xy = 1$ †
40. $x^2 + y^2 - 4x + 6y = 12$ $r^2 - 4r \cos \theta + 6r \sin = 12$

In Exercises 41–48, convert each polar equation to rectangular form. Identify each curve.

41. $r = 2$ $x^2 + y^2 = 4$
42. $r = -3$ $x^2 + y^2 = 9$
43. $\theta = \dfrac{3\pi}{4}$ $y = -x$
44. $\theta = -\dfrac{\pi}{6}$ $y = -\dfrac{\sqrt{3}}{3}x$
45. $r = 4\cos \theta$ $(x - 2)^2 + y^2 = 4$
46. $r = 4\sin \theta$ $x^2 + (y - 2)^2 = 4$
47. $r = -2\sin \theta$ $x^2 + (y + 1)^2 = 1$
48. $r = -3\cos \theta$ †

In Exercises 49–56, sketch the graph of each polar equation by transforming it to rectangular coordinates.

49. $r = -2$ †
50. $r \cos \theta = -1$ †
51. $r \sin \theta = 2$ †
52. $r = \sin \theta$ †
53. $r = 2 \sec \theta$ †
54. $r + 3 \cos \theta = 0$ †
55. $r = \dfrac{1}{\cos \theta + \sin \theta}$ †
56. $r = \dfrac{6}{2\cos \theta + 3\sin \theta}$ †

In Exercises 57–60, sketch the graph of each polar equation by plotting points.

57. $r = 1 - \cos \theta$ †
58. $r = \cos \theta$ †
59. $r = \sin \theta$ †
60. $r = 1 + \sin \theta$ †

†Due to space constrictions, answers to these exercises may be found in the Answers beginning on page A–1 in the back of the book.

B Exercises   Applying the Concepts

In Exercises 61–64, determine the position of the hand relative to the shoulder by considering the robotic arm illustrated in the figure. Round all answers to the nearest tenth.

61. $\alpha = 45°$, $\beta = 30°$ (21.8, 39.6°)

62. $\alpha = -30°$, $\beta = 60°$ (16.1, −0.3°)

63. $\alpha = -70°$, $\beta = 0°$ (18.3, −45.8°)

64. $\alpha = 47°$, $\beta = 17°$ (21.3, 36.2°)

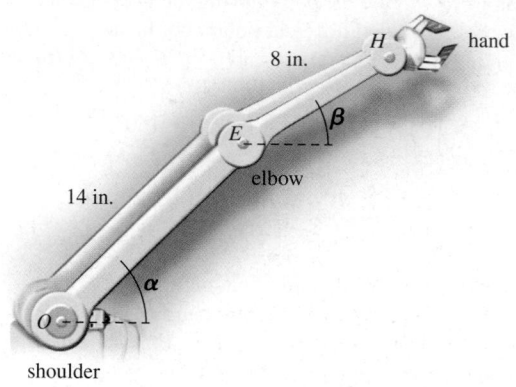

C Exercises   Beyond the Basics

In Exercises 65 and 66, convert each rectangular equation to polar form. Assume that $x \geq 0$, $y \geq 0$, and $\sqrt{x^2 + y^2} < \dfrac{\pi}{2}$.

65. $y = x\tan(\sqrt{x^2 + y^2})$ $r = \theta$

66. $y = x\tan(\ln\sqrt{x^2 + y^2})$ $r = e^{\theta}$

In Exercises 67–72, convert each polar equation to rectangular form.

67. $r(1 - \sin\theta) = 3$ †

68. $r(1 + \cos\theta) = 2$ $y^2 = 4 - 4x$

69. $r\left(1 + \dfrac{1}{2}\cos\theta\right) = 1$ $y^2 = 1 - x - \dfrac{3x^2}{4}$

70. $r\left(1 + \dfrac{3}{4}\sin\theta\right) = 3$ $\dfrac{16x^2}{7} + \left(y + \dfrac{36}{7}\right)^2 = \dfrac{2304}{49}$

71. $r(1 - 3\cos\theta) = 5$ $y^2 - 8x^2 - 30x - 25 = 0$

72. $r(1 - 2\sin\theta) = 4$ $x^2 - 3y^2 - 16y - 16 = 0$

73. Prove that the distance between the points $P(r_1, \theta_1)$ and $Q(r_2, \theta_2)$ is given by

$$d(P, Q) = \sqrt{r_1^2 + r_2^2 - 2r_1 r_2 \cos(\theta_1 - \theta_2)}.$$

74. Prove that the equation $r = a\sin\theta + b\cos\theta$ represents a circle. Find its center and radius. †

75. Prove that the area K of the triangle whose polar coordinates are $(0, 0)$, (r_1, θ_1), and (r_2, θ_2) is given by

$$K = \dfrac{1}{2}r_1 r_2 \sin(\theta_2 - \theta_1).$$ [Assume that $0 \leq \theta_1 < \theta_2 \leq \pi$ and $r_1 > 0$, $r_2 > 0$.]

76. Show that the polar equation of a circle with center (a, θ_0) and radius a is given by $r = 2a\cos(\theta - \theta_0)$. Discuss the cases $\theta_0 = 0$ and $\theta_0 = \dfrac{\pi}{2}$.

Critical Thinking

Determine whether each statement is true or false. Explain your reasoning.

77. The points (r, θ) and $(-r, \theta)$ are symmetric with respect to the y-axis. False

78. The points (r, θ) and $(-r, -\theta)$ are symmetric with respect to the y-axis. True

79. The points (r, θ) and $(r, -\theta)$ are symmetric with respect to the x-axis. True

80. The polar coordinates $(r, -\theta)$ and $(-r, \pi - \theta)$ represent the same point in the plane. True

SECTION 7.5

Polar Form of Complex Numbers; DeMoivre's Theorem

OBJECTIVES

1 Represent complex numbers geometrically.

2 Find the absolute value of complex numbers.

3 Represent the sum of complex numbers geometrically.

4 Write a complex number in polar form.

5 Find the product and quotient of two complex numbers in polar form.

6 Use DeMoivre's Theorem to find powers of a complex number.

7 Use DeMoivre's Theorem to find the nth roots of a complex number.

Alternating Current Circuits

In the early days of the study of alternate current (AC) circuits, scientists concluded that AC circuits were somehow different from the battery-powered direct current (DC) circuits. However, both types of circuits obey exactly the same physical and mathematical laws. The breakthrough in understanding of the AC circuits came in 1893 by Charles Steinmetz. He explained that in AC circuits, the voltage, current, and resistance (called *impedance* in AC circuits) were not scalars, but alternate in direction, and possess frequency and phase shift that must be taken into account. He advocated the use of the polar form of complex numbers to provide a convenient method of symbolically denoting the magnitude, frequency, and phase shift simultaneously for the AC circuit quantities voltage, current, and impedance. Steinmetz eventually became known as "the wizard who generated electricity from the square root of minus one." In Example 7, we use complex numbers to compute the total impedance in an AC circuit. ■

1 Represent complex numbers geometrically.

Geometric Representation of Complex Numbers

Because each complex number $a + bi$ determines a unique ordered pair (a, b) of real numbers, the set of complex numbers can be represented geometrically by points in a rectangular coordinate system. The geometric representation of the complex number $a + bi$

FIGURE 7.38

FIGURE 7.39

2 Find the absolute value of a complex number.

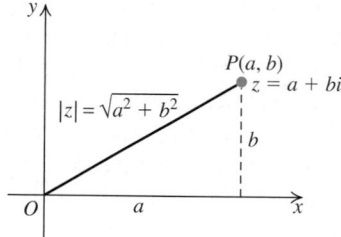

FIGURE 7.40

is the point $P(a, b)$ in a rectangular coordinate system. When a rectangular coordinate system is used to represent complex numbers, the plane is called the **complex plane** or the **Argand plane**. The x-axis is also called the **real axis**, because the real part of a complex number is plotted along the x-axis. Similarly, the y-axis is also called the **imaginary axis**. See Figure 7.38. A complex number $a + bi$ may be viewed as a position vector with initial point $(0, 0)$ and terminal point (a, b).

EXAMPLE 1   **Plotting Complex Numbers**

Plot each complex number in the complex plane.

$$1 + 3i, \quad -2 + 2i, \quad -3, \quad -2i, \quad \text{and} \quad 3 - i$$

Solution

In Figure 7.39, the points A, B, C, D, and E represent the complex numbers $1 + 3i$, $-2 + 2i$, -3, $-2i$, and $3 - i$, respectively.   ■ ■ ■

PRACTICE PROBLEM 1   Plot each complex number in the complex plane.

$$2 + 3i, \quad -3 + 2i, \quad 4, \quad -2 - 3i, \quad \text{and} \quad 3 - 2i$$ ■

The Absolute Value of a Complex Number

Let $P(a, b)$ represent the complex number $z = a + bi$ in a rectangular coordinate system. Then the distance from the origin O to the point $P(a, b)$ is $\sqrt{a^2 + b^2}$. See Figure 7.40. The number $\sqrt{a^2 + b^2}$ is called the *absolute value* (or **magnitude**, or **modulus**) of the complex number $z = a + bi$ and is denoted by $|z|$.

ABSOLUTE VALUE OF A COMPLEX NUMBER

The **absolute value** of a complex number $z = a + bi$ is:
$$|z| = |a + bi| = \sqrt{a^2 + b^2}$$

EXAMPLE 2   **Finding the Absolute Value of a Complex Number**

Find the absolute value of each complex number.

a. $4 + 3i$ **b.** $2 - 3i$ **c.** $-4 + i$ **d.** $-2 - 2i$ **e.** $-3i$

Solution

In each case, we use the formula $|a + bi| = \sqrt{a^2 + b^2}$ and simplify.

a. $|4 + 3i| = \sqrt{4^2 + 3^2} = \sqrt{16 + 9} = \sqrt{25} = 5$

b. $|2 - 3i| = \sqrt{2^2 + (-3)^2} = \sqrt{4 + 9} = \sqrt{13}$

c. $|-4 + i| = |-4 + 1 \cdot i| = \sqrt{(-4)^2 + (1)^2} = \sqrt{16 + 1} = \sqrt{17}$

d. $|-2 - 2i| = \sqrt{(-2)^2 + (-2)^2} = \sqrt{4 + 4} = \sqrt{4 \cdot 2} = 2\sqrt{2}$

e. $|-3i| = |0 - 3i| = \sqrt{0^2 + (-3)^2} = \sqrt{0 + 9} = \sqrt{9} = 3$ ■ ■ ■

PRACTICE PROBLEM 2   Find the absolute value of each complex number.

a. $-5 + 12i$ **b.** -7 **c.** i **d.** $a - bi$ ■

Geometric Representation of the Sum of Complex Numbers

3 Represent the sum of complex numbers geometrically.

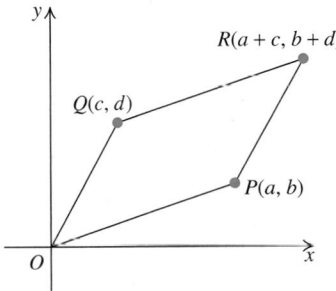

FIGURE 7.41

Suppose we add two complex numbers $a + bi$ and $c + di$. Then, by the definition of addition of complex numbers (see Section 1.3), we have

$$(a + bi) + (c + di) = (a + c) + (b + d)i.$$

If we represent the complex numbers $a + bi$, $c + di$, and $(a + c) + (b + d)i$ by the points P, Q, and R, respectively (see Figure 7.41), then R is the endpoint of the diagonal of the parallelogram with line segments OP and OQ as adjacent sides. This assertion can be easily verified.

$$\text{Slope of } \overline{OP} = \frac{b - 0}{a - 0} = \frac{b}{a}$$

$$\text{Slope of } \overline{QR} = \frac{(b + d) - d}{(a + c) - c} = \frac{b}{a}$$

Therefore, segment OP is parallel to segment QR. Similarly, segment OQ is parallel to segment PR. Hence, quadrilateral $OPRQ$ is a parallelogram.

RECALL

If two distinct lines (or segments on two distinct lines) have the same slope, the lines (or segments) are parallel. A quadrilateral with two pairs of parallel lines is called a *parallelogram*.

EXAMPLE 3   Adding Complex Numbers Geometrically

Add the complex numbers $1 + 3i$ and $-4 + 2i$ geometrically.

Solution

In Figure 7.42, we first locate the points P and Q representing the complex numbers $1 + 3i$ and $-4 + 2i$, respectively. We draw the line segments OP and OQ. We then draw the line segments through P and Q parallel to the line segments OQ and OP, respectively. The point of intersection R represents the complex number $-3 + 5i$, where

$$-3 + 5i = (1 + 3i) + (-4 + 2i).$$ ■ ■ ■

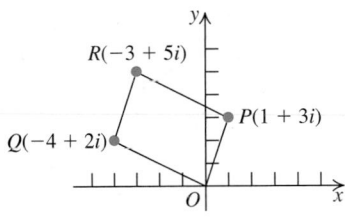

FIGURE 7.42

PRACTICE PROBLEM 3   Add the complex numbers $2 + 3i$ and $1 - 2i$ geometrically.   ■

Polar Form of a Complex Number

4 Write a complex number in polar form.

A complex number z written in the form $z = a + bi$ is said to be in **rectangular form**. The point (a, b) has polar coordinates (r, θ), where $r = \sqrt{a^2 + b^2}$, $a = r \cos\theta$, and $b = r \sin\theta$.

Thus, the complex number $z = a + bi$ can be written in the form

$$z = r \cos\theta + (r \sin\theta)i = r(\cos\theta + i \sin\theta).$$

The representation of a complex number z in the form $r(\cos\theta + i \sin\theta)$ is called the **polar form** or the **trigonometric form** of z.

POLAR FORM OF A COMPLEX NUMBER

The complex number $z = a + bi$ can be written in **polar form**

$$z = r(\cos\theta + i\sin\theta),$$

where $a = r\cos\theta$, $b = r\sin\theta$, $r = \sqrt{a^2 + b^2}$, and $\tan\theta = \dfrac{b}{a}$.

When a nonzero complex number is written in polar form, the positive number r is the **modulus** or **absolute value** of z. The angle θ in the representation is called the **argument** of z (written $\theta = \arg z$).

We note that the angle θ in the polar representation of z is not unique, since for any integer n,

$$r(\cos\theta + i\sin\theta) = r[\cos(\theta + n \cdot 360°) + i\sin(\theta + n \cdot 360°)].$$

Hence, two complex numbers in polar form are equal if and only if their *moduli* (plural of modulus) are equal and their arguments differ by a multiple of 360° (or, in radian measure, their arguments differ by a multiple of 2π).

EXAMPLE 4   **Writing a Complex Number in Polar Form**

Write $z = 1 - \sqrt{3}\,i$ in polar form. Express the argument θ in degrees $0° \le \theta < 360°$.

Solution

To write a nonzero complex number $z = a + bi$ in polar form $z = r(\cos\theta + i\sin\theta)$, we compute $r = \sqrt{a^2 + b^2}$ and determine the appropriate angle θ for which $\tan\theta = \dfrac{b}{a}\,(a \ne 0)$. We choose θ so that it lies in the same quadrant as the point (a, b).

For the complex number $z = 1 - \sqrt{3}\,i$, $a = 1$, and $b = -\sqrt{3}$.

$$
\begin{aligned}
r = \sqrt{a^2 + b^2} &= \sqrt{1^2 + (-\sqrt{3}\,)^2} &&\text{Replace } a \text{ by } 1 \text{ and } b \text{ by } -\sqrt{3}. \\
&= \sqrt{1 + 3} = 2 &&\text{Simplify.}
\end{aligned}
$$

We use $\tan\theta = \dfrac{b}{a}$ with $a = 1$ and $b = -\sqrt{3}$ to find θ.

$$\tan\theta = \frac{b}{a} = \frac{-\sqrt{3}}{1} = -\sqrt{3}$$

We know that $\tan(-60°) = -\tan 60° = -\sqrt{3}$. In Figure 7.43, we note that the argument θ lies in quadrant IV. Thus,

$$\theta = 360° - 60° = 300°.$$

The polar form of $z = 1 - \sqrt{3}\,i$ is

$$
\begin{aligned}
z &= r(\cos\theta + i\sin\theta) \\
&= 2(\cos 300° + i\sin 300°). &&\text{Replace } r \text{ by } 2 \text{ and } \theta \text{ by } 300°. \quad\blacksquare\;\blacksquare\;\blacksquare
\end{aligned}
$$

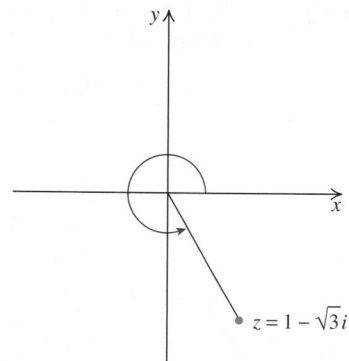

FIGURE 7.43

PRACTICE PROBLEM 4   Write $z = -1 - i$ in polar form. Express the argument θ in radians, $0 \leq \theta < 2\pi$.   ■

EXAMPLE 5   **Writing a Complex Number in Rectangular Form**

Write the complex number $z = 2\left(\cos\dfrac{\pi}{6} + i\sin\dfrac{\pi}{6}\right)$ in rectangular form.

Solution

$$
\begin{aligned}
z &= 2\left(\cos\dfrac{\pi}{6} + i\sin\dfrac{\pi}{6}\right) && \text{Given complex number} \\[2mm]
&= 2\cos\dfrac{\pi}{6} + 2i\sin\dfrac{\pi}{6} && \text{Distributive property} \\[2mm]
&= 2\left(\dfrac{\sqrt{3}}{2}\right) + 2i\left(\dfrac{1}{2}\right) && \cos\dfrac{\pi}{6} = \dfrac{\sqrt{3}}{2}, \sin\dfrac{\pi}{6} = \dfrac{1}{2} \\[2mm]
&= \sqrt{3} + i && \text{Simplify.}
\end{aligned}
$$

The rectangular form of $z = 2\left(\cos\dfrac{\pi}{6} + i\sin\dfrac{\pi}{6}\right)$ is $\sqrt{3} + i$.   ■ ■ ■

PRACTICE PROBLEM 5   Write $z = 4\left(\cos\dfrac{5\pi}{3} + i\sin\dfrac{5\pi}{3}\right)$ in rectangular form.   ■

5 Find the product and quotient of two complex numbers in polar form.

Product and Quotient in Polar Form

The polar representation of complex numbers leads to an interesting interpretation of the product and quotient of two complex numbers.

PRODUCT AND QUOTIENT RULES
FOR TWO COMPLEX NUMBERS IN POLAR FORM

Let $z_1 = r_1(\cos\theta_1 + i\sin\theta_1)$ and $z_2 = r_2(\cos\theta_2 + i\sin\theta_2)$ be two complex numbers in polar form. Then

$$z_1 z_2 = r_1 r_2[\cos(\theta_1 + \theta_2) + i\sin(\theta_1 + \theta_2)] \qquad \text{Product rule}$$

and

$$\dfrac{z_1}{z_2} = \dfrac{r_1}{r_2}[\cos(\theta_1 - \theta_2) + i\sin(\theta_1 - \theta_2)], z_2 \neq 0. \quad \text{Quotient rule}$$

The rules in the box are as follows:

1. To multiply two complex numbers in polar form, multiply their moduli and add arguments.
2. To divide two complex numbers, divide their moduli and subtract arguments.

> **EXAMPLE 6**   **Finding the Product and Quotient of Two Complex Numbers**

Let $z_1 = 3(\cos 65° + i \sin 65°)$ and $z_2 = 4(\cos 15° + i \sin 15°)$.
Find $z_1 z_2$ and $\dfrac{z_1}{z_2}$. Leave the answers in polar form.

Solution

$$z_1 z_2 = 3(\cos 65° + i \sin 65°) \cdot 4(\cos 15° + i \sin 15°)$$ Product of given numbers

$$= 3 \cdot 4[\cos(65° + 15°) + i \sin(65° + 15°)]$$ Multiply moduli and add arguments.

Multiply moduli   Add arguments

$$= 12(\cos 80° + i \sin 80°)$$ Simplify.

$$\frac{z_1}{z_2} = \frac{3(\cos 65° + i \sin 65°)}{4(\cos 15° + i \sin 15°)}$$ Quotient of given numbers

$$= \frac{3}{4}[\cos(65° - 15°) + i \sin(65° - 15°)]$$ Divide moduli and subtract arguments.

Divide moduli   Subtract arguments

$$= \frac{3}{4}(\cos 50° + i \sin 50°)$$ Simplify.   ■ ■ ■

PRACTICE PROBLEM 6   Let $z_1 = 5(\cos 75° + i \sin 75°)$ and $z_2 = 2(\cos 60° + i \sin 60°)$. Find
$z_1 z_2$ and $\dfrac{z_1}{z_2}$. Leave the answers in polar form.   ■

> **EXAMPLE 7**   **Using Complex Numbers in AC Circuits**

In a parallel circuit, the total impedance Z_t is given by

$$Z_t = \frac{Z_1 Z_2}{Z_1 + Z_2}.$$

Find Z_t, if

$$Z_1 = 9(\cos 90° + i \sin 90°) \text{ and } Z_2 = 4[\cos(-60°) + i \sin(-60°)].$$

Solution

We first calculate $Z_1 Z_2$ and $Z_1 + Z_2$.

$$Z_1 Z_2 = 9(\cos 90° + i \sin 90°) \cdot 4[\cos(-60°) + i \sin(-60°)]$$ Substitute values for Z_1 and Z_2.

$$= 9 \cdot 4[\cos(90° - 60°) + i \sin(90° - 60°)]$$ Multiply moduli and add arguments.

$$= 36(\cos 30° + i \sin 30°)$$ Simplify.

To add complex numbers in polar form, convert to rectangular coordinates, perform addition, and then convert back to polar form.

$$Z_1 = 9\cos 90° + 9i\sin 90° = 9i \qquad \cos 90° = 0, \sin 90° = 1$$

$$Z_2 = 4[\cos(-60°) + i\sin(-60°)]$$

$$= 4\cos 60° - 4i\sin 60° \qquad \cos(-\theta) = \cos\theta, \sin(-\theta) = -\sin\theta$$

$$= 4\left(\frac{1}{2}\right) - 4i\left(\frac{\sqrt{3}}{2}\right) \qquad \cos 60° = \frac{1}{2}, \sin 60° = \frac{\sqrt{3}}{2}$$

$$= 2 - 2\sqrt{3}\,i \qquad \text{Simplify.}$$

$$Z_1 + Z_2 = 9i + 2 - 2\sqrt{3}\,i$$

$$Z_1 + Z_2 = 2 + (9 - 2\sqrt{3})i \qquad \text{Regroup.}$$

To write $Z_1 + Z_2$ in polar form, find the values of r and θ.

$$r = \sqrt{a^2 + b^2}$$

$$= \sqrt{2^2 + (9 - 2\sqrt{3})^2} \qquad \text{Replace } a \text{ by 2 and } b \text{ by } 9 - 2\sqrt{3}.$$

$$\approx 5.89 \qquad \text{Use a calculator.}$$

$$\tan\theta = \frac{b}{a} = \frac{9 - 2\sqrt{3}}{2}$$

$$\approx 2.768 \qquad \text{Use a calculator.}$$

$$\theta \approx \tan^{-1}(2.768) \approx 70° \qquad \text{Use a calculator.}$$

The polar form of $Z_1 + Z_2$ is approximately $5.89(\cos 70° + i\sin 70°)$. Thus,

$$Z_t \approx \frac{36(\cos 30° + i\sin 30°)}{5.89(\cos 70° + i\sin 70°)} \qquad \text{Substitute values for } Z_1 Z_2 \text{ and } Z_1 + Z_2.$$

$$= \frac{36}{5.89}[\cos(30° - 70°) + i\sin(30° - 70°)] \qquad \text{Divide moduli and subtract arguments.}$$

$$= \frac{36}{5.89}[\cos(-40°) + i\sin(-40°)] \qquad \text{Simplify.}$$

$$= \frac{36}{5.89}(\cos 40° - i\sin 40°) \qquad \begin{array}{l} \sin(-\theta) = -\sin\theta, \\ \cos(-\theta) = \cos\theta \end{array}$$

$$\approx 6.11(\cos 40° - i\sin 40°). \qquad \blacksquare\ \blacksquare\ \blacksquare$$

PRACTICE PROBLEM 7   Repeat Example 7, with

$$Z_1 = 4(\cos 45° + i\sin 45°) \quad \text{and} \quad Z_2 = 6(\cos 0° + i\sin 0°). \qquad \blacksquare$$

6 Use DeMoivre's Theorem to find powers of a complex number.

Powers of Complex Numbers in Polar Form

Let $z = r(\cos\theta + i\sin\theta)$ be a complex number in polar form. Then

$$z^2 = z \cdot z$$

$$= r(\cos\theta + i\sin\theta) \cdot r(\cos\theta + i\sin\theta) \qquad \text{Form product } z \cdot z.$$

$$= (r \cdot r)[\cos(\theta + \theta) + i\sin(\theta + \theta)] \qquad \text{Multiply moduli and add arguments.}$$

$$= r^2(\cos 2\theta + i\sin 2\theta) \qquad \text{Simplify.}$$

$$z^3 = z^2 \cdot z$$
$$= r^2(\cos 2\theta + i \sin 2\theta) \cdot r(\cos 2\theta + i \sin 2\theta) \quad \text{Polar form of } z^2$$
$$= (r^2 \cdot r)[\cos(2\theta + \theta) + i \sin(2\theta + \theta)] \quad \text{Multiply moduli and add arguments.}$$
$$= r^3(\cos 3\theta + i \sin 3\theta). \quad \text{Simplify.}$$

In a similar way, you can show that

$$z^4 = r^4(\cos 4\theta + i \sin 4\theta).$$

Thus, it is reasonable to make the assertion known as DeMoivre's Theorem. (We omit the proof.)

DeMOIVRE'S THEOREM

Let $z = r(\cos\theta + i\sin\theta)$ be a complex number in polar form. Then, for any integer n,

$$z^n = r^n(\cos n\theta + i \sin n\theta).$$

EXAMPLE 8 **Finding the Power of a Complex Number**

Let $z = 1 + i$. Use DeMoivre's Theorem to find each power of z. Write answers in rectangular form.

a. z^{16} **b.** z^{-10}

Solution

We first convert $z = 1 + i$ to polar form. We find r and θ.

$$r = \sqrt{a^2 + b^2} = \sqrt{1^2 + 1^2} \quad a = 1, b = 1$$
$$= \sqrt{2} \quad \text{Simplify.}$$

and

$$\tan\theta = \frac{b}{a} = \frac{1}{1} = 1, \text{ so}$$

$$\theta = \frac{\pi}{4}$$

a. $z = \sqrt{2}\left(\cos\frac{\pi}{4} + i\sin\frac{\pi}{4}\right)$ Polar form of $z = 1 + i$

$$z^{16} = \left[\sqrt{2}\left(\cos\frac{\pi}{4} + i\sin\frac{\pi}{4}\right)\right]^{16} \quad \text{Raise both sides to the 16th power.}$$

$$= (\sqrt{2})^{16}\left[\cos\left(16 \cdot \frac{\pi}{4}\right) + i\sin\left(16 \cdot \frac{\pi}{4}\right)\right] \quad \text{DeMoivre's Theorem}$$

$$= 2^8[\cos(4\pi) + i\sin(4\pi)] \quad (\sqrt{2})^{16} = (2^{\frac{1}{2}})^{16} = 2^{\frac{1}{2} \cdot 16} = 2^8$$

$$= 256(1 + i \cdot 0) \quad \cos 4\pi = 1, \sin 4\pi = 0$$

$$= 256 \quad \text{Simplify.}$$

TECHNOLOGY CONNECTION

A graphing calculator can be used to find powers of complex numbers or to check your work. The calculator must be set in $a + bi$ mode.

```
(1+i)^(-10)
        -.03125i
Ans►Frac
          -1/32i
■
```

b. $z = \sqrt{2}\left(\cos\dfrac{\pi}{4} + i\sin\dfrac{\pi}{4}\right)$ Polar form of $z = 1 + i$

$z^{-10} = \left[\sqrt{2}\left(\cos\dfrac{\pi}{4} + i\sin\dfrac{\pi}{4}\right)\right]^{-10}$ Raise both sides to the -10th power.

$= (\sqrt{2})^{-10}\left[\cos\left(-10\cdot\dfrac{\pi}{4}\right) + i\sin\left(-10\cdot\dfrac{\pi}{4}\right)\right]$ DeMoivre's Theorem

$= \dfrac{1}{32}\left[\cos\left(-\dfrac{5\pi}{2}\right) + i\sin\left(-\dfrac{5\pi}{2}\right)\right]$ Simplify; $(\sqrt{2})^{-10} = (2^{1/2})^{-10} = 2^{-5} = \dfrac{1}{32}.$

$= \dfrac{1}{32}[0 + i(-1)] = -\dfrac{1}{32}i$ $\cos\left(-\dfrac{5\pi}{2}\right) = 0, \sin\left(-\dfrac{5\pi}{2}\right) = -1$

■ ■ ■

PRACTICE PROBLEM 8   Let $z = -1 + i$. Use DeMoivre's Theorem to find each power of z. Write the answers in rectangular form.

a. z^8 **b.** z^{-12} ■

7 Use DeMoivre's Theorem to find the nth roots of a complex number.

Roots of Complex Numbers

Let z and w be two complex numbers and let n be a positive integer. The complex number z is called the **nth root of** w if

$$z^n = w.$$

We can use DeMoivre's Theorem to find the nth roots of a complex number.

DeMOIVRE'S THEOREM FOR FINDING COMPLEX ROOTS

The nth roots of a complex number $w = r(\cos\theta + i\sin\theta)$, $r > 0$, θ in degrees are given by

$$z_k = r^{1/n}\left[\cos\left(\frac{\theta + 360°k}{n}\right) + i\sin\left(\frac{\theta + 360°k}{n}\right)\right], \quad k = 0, 1, 2, \ldots, n - 1.$$

If θ is in radians, replace $360°$ by 2π in z_k.

The result says that there are exactly n nth roots of a nonzero complex number.

EXAMPLE 9   **Finding the Roots of a Complex Number**

Find the three cube roots of $1 + i$ in polar form, with the argument in degrees.

Solution

In Example 8, we showed that

$$1 + i = \sqrt{2}\left(\cos\frac{\pi}{4} + i\sin\frac{\pi}{4}\right)$$ Polar form of $1 + i$

$$1 + i = \sqrt{2}(\cos 45° + i\sin 45°).$$ Replace $\dfrac{\pi}{4}$ by $45°$.

Continued on next page

RECALL

$\sqrt{2} = 2^{1/2}$, so
$(\sqrt{2})^{1/3} = (2^{1/2})^{1/3} = 2^{1/6}$.

TECHNOLOGY CONNECTION

 A graphing calculator can be used to check complex roots. The calculator must be set in $a + bi$ mode. The screen shown here is from a calculator also set in DEGREE mode.

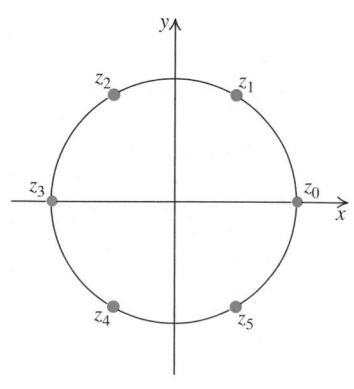

From DeMoivre's Theorem for finding complex roots, with $n = 3$, we have

$$z_k = (\sqrt{2})^{1/3}\left[\cos\left(\frac{45° + 360°k}{3}\right) + i\sin\left(\frac{45° + 360°k}{3}\right)\right], \quad k = 0, 1, 2.$$

We obtain the three cube roots by substituting $k = 0$, 1, and 2 in the expression for z_k and simplifying. We have

$$z_0 = (2)^{\frac{1}{6}}\left[\cos\left(\frac{45° + 360° \cdot 0}{3}\right) + i\sin\left(\frac{45° + 360° \cdot 0}{3}\right)\right] \quad k = 0$$

$$= 2^{\frac{1}{6}}(\cos 15° + i\sin 15°) \qquad\qquad \text{Simplify.}$$

$$z_1 = 2^{\frac{1}{6}}\left[\cos\left(\frac{45° + 360° \cdot 1}{3}\right) + i\sin\left(\frac{45° + 360° \cdot 1}{3}\right)\right] \quad k = 1$$

$$= 2^{\frac{1}{6}}(\cos 135° + i\sin 135°) \qquad\qquad \text{Simplify.}$$

$$z_2 = 2^{\frac{1}{6}}\left[\cos\left(\frac{45° + 360° \cdot 2}{3}\right) + i\sin\left(\frac{45° + 360° \cdot 2}{3}\right)\right] \quad k = 2$$

$$= 2^{\frac{1}{6}}(\cos 255° + i\sin 255°) \qquad\qquad \text{Simplify.}$$

The complex numbers z_0, z_1, and z_2 are the three cube roots of the complex number $1 + i$.   ■ ■ ■

PRACTICE PROBLEM 9   Find the three cube roots of $-1 + i$ in polar form, with the argument in degrees.   ■

The solutions of the equation $z^n = 1$ are called the **nth roots of unity**.

EXAMPLE 10   **Finding nth Roots of Unity**

Find the complex sixth roots of unity. Write the roots in polar form and represent them geometrically.

Solution

The polar form for $1 = 1 + 0i$ is

$$1 = 1(\cos 0° + i\sin 0°).$$

From DeMoivre's Theorem for finding complex roots with $n = 6$, we have

$$z_k = (1)^{1/6}\left[\cos\left(\frac{0° + 360° \cdot k}{6}\right) + i\sin\left(\frac{0° + 360° \cdot k}{6}\right)\right], \quad k = 0, 1, 2, 3, 4, 5.$$

$$z_0 = 1(\cos 0° + i\sin 0°) \qquad \text{Let } k = 0 \text{ in } z_k \text{ and simplify.}$$

$$z_1 = 1(\cos 60° + i\sin 60°) \qquad \text{Let } k = 1 \text{ in } z_k \text{ and simplify.}$$

$$z_2 = 1(\cos 120° + i\sin 120°) \qquad \text{Let } k = 2 \text{ in } z_k \text{ and simplify.}$$

$$z_3 = 1(\cos 180° + i\sin 180°) \qquad \text{Let } k = 3 \text{ in } z_k \text{ and simplify.}$$

$$z_4 = 1(\cos 240° + i\sin 240°) \qquad \text{Let } k = 4 \text{ in } z_k \text{ and simplify.}$$

$$z_5 = 1(\cos 300° + i\sin 300°) \qquad \text{Let } k = 5 \text{ in } z_k \text{ and simplify.}$$

Geometrically, the six roots of unity are equally spaced at 60° intervals on a unit circle. See Figure 7.44.   ■ ■ ■

FIGURE 7.44

PRACTICE PROBLEM 10   Find the complex fourth roots of unity. Write the roots in polar form.   ■

A Exercises   Basic Skills and Concepts

In Exercises 1–8, plot each complex number and find its absolute value.

1. $z = 2$ 2
2. $z = -3$ 3
3. $z = -4i$ 4
4. $z = 2i$ 2
5. $z = 3 + 4i$ 5
6. $z = -1 + 2i$ $\sqrt{5}$
7. $z = -2 - 3i$ $\sqrt{13}$
8. $z = 2 - 5i$ $\sqrt{29}$

In Exercises 9–12, add the given pair of complex numbers geometrically.

9. $z_1 = 2i, z_2 = 3$ †
10. $z_1 = -2, z_2 = -3i$ †
11. $z_1 = 2 + 3i, z_2 = 1 + 2i$ †
12. $z_1 = 3 - 4i, z_2 = -2 + 3i$ †

In Exercises 13–24, write each complex number in polar form. Express the argument θ in degrees, with $0 \le \theta < 360°$.

13. $1 + \sqrt{3}i$ $2(\cos 60° + i\sin 60°)$
14. $-1 + \sqrt{2}i$ $\sqrt{3}(\cos 125.3° + i\sin 125.3°)$
15. $-1 + i$ $\sqrt{2}(\cos 135° + i\sin 135°)$
16. $1 - i$ $\sqrt{2}(\cos 315° + i\sin 315°)$
17. i $\cos 90° + i\sin 90°$
18. $-i$ $\cos 270° + i\sin 270°$
19. 1 $\cos 0° + i\sin 0°$
20. -1 $\cos 180° + i\sin 180°$
21. $3 - 3i$ $3\sqrt{2}(\cos 315° + i\sin 315°)$
22. $4\sqrt{3} + 4i$ $8(\cos 30° + i\sin 30°)$
23. $2 - 2\sqrt{3}i$ $4(\cos 300° + i\sin 300°)$
24. $2 + 3i$ $\sqrt{13}(\cos 56.3° + i\sin 56.3°)$

In Exercises 25–36, write each complex number in rectangular form.

25. $2(\cos 60° + i\sin 60°)$ $1 + \sqrt{3}i$
26. $4(\cos 120° + i\sin 120°)$ $-2 + 2\sqrt{3}i$
27. $3(\cos \pi + i\sin \pi)$ -3
28. $5\left(\cos\dfrac{\pi}{2} + i\sin\dfrac{\pi}{2}\right)$ $5i$
29. $5(\cos 240° + i\sin 240°)$ †
30. $2(\cos 300° + i\sin 300°)$ $1 - \sqrt{3}i$
31. $8(\cos 0° + i\sin 0°)$ 8
32. $2(\cos(-90°)° + i\sin(-90°))$ $-2i$
33. $6\left(\cos\dfrac{5\pi}{6} + i\sin\dfrac{5\pi}{6}\right)$ $-3\sqrt{3} + 3i$
34. $4\left(\cos\dfrac{3\pi}{4} + i\sin\dfrac{3\pi}{4}\right)$ $-2\sqrt{2} + 2\sqrt{2}i$
35. $3\left(\cos\left(-\dfrac{\pi}{3}\right) + i\sin\left(-\dfrac{\pi}{3}\right)\right)$ $\dfrac{3}{2} - \dfrac{3\sqrt{3}}{2}i$
36. $5\left(\cos\left(-\dfrac{7\pi}{6}\right) + i\sin\left(-\dfrac{7\pi}{6}\right)\right)$ $-\dfrac{5\sqrt{3}}{2} + \dfrac{5}{2}i$

In Exercises 37–48, find $z_1 z_2$ and $\dfrac{z_1}{z_2}$. Write each answer in polar form.

37. $z_1 = 4(\cos 75° + i\sin 75°), z_2 = 2(\cos 15° + i\sin 15°)$ †
38. $z_1 = 6(\cos 90° + i\sin 90°), z_2 = 2(\cos 45° + i\sin 45°)$ †
39. $z_1 = 5(\cos 240° + i\sin 240°), z_2 = 2(\cos 60° + i\sin 60°)$ †
40. $z_1 = 10(\cos 135° + i\sin 135°),$
$z_2 = 4(\cos 225° + i\sin 225°)$ †
41. $z_1 = 3(\cos 40° + i\sin 40°), z_2 = 5(\cos 20° + i\sin 20°)$ †
42. $z_1 = 5(\cos 65° + i\sin 65°), z_2 = 2(\cos 25° + i\sin 25°)$ †
43. $z_1 = 1 + i, z_2 = 1 - i$ †
44. $z_1 = 1 + \sqrt{3}i, z_2 = 1 + i$ †
45. $z_1 = -\sqrt{3} + i, z_2 = 2 + 2i$ †
46. $z_1 = 3 + 3i, z_2 = 2 - 2\sqrt{3}i$ †
47. $z_1 = 2\sqrt{2} + 2i, z_2 = \sqrt{3} - i$ †
48. $z_1 = 4\sqrt{3} + 4i, z_2 = 3 - 3i$ †

In Exercises 49–64, use DeMoivre's Theorem to find the indicated power. Write the answers in rectangular form.

49. $\left[2\left(\cos\dfrac{\pi}{3} + i\sin\dfrac{\pi}{3}\right)\right]^{12}$ 2^{12}
50. $\left[\sqrt{2}\left(\cos\dfrac{\pi}{4} + i\sin\dfrac{\pi}{4}\right)\right]^{20}$ -2^{10}
51. $\left[2\left(\cos\left(-\dfrac{3\pi}{4}\right) + i\sin\left(-\dfrac{3\pi}{4}\right)\right)\right]^{6}$ $-64i$
52. $\left(\cos\dfrac{\pi}{27} + i\sin\dfrac{\pi}{27}\right)^{-9}$ $\dfrac{1}{2} - \dfrac{\sqrt{3}}{2}i$
53. $\left[2\left(\cos\left(\dfrac{3\pi}{4}\right) + i\sin\left(\dfrac{3\pi}{4}\right)\right)\right]^{-6}$ $-\dfrac{1}{64}i$
54. $\left[3\left(\cos\left(-\dfrac{5\pi}{6}\right) + i\sin\left(-\dfrac{5\pi}{6}\right)\right)\right]^{16}$ $3^{16}\left(-\dfrac{1}{2} + \dfrac{\sqrt{3}}{2}i\right)$
55. $\left[2\left(\cos\left(-\dfrac{\pi}{4}\right) + i\sin\left(-\dfrac{\pi}{4}\right)\right)\right]^{-10}$ $\dfrac{1}{2^{10}}i$
56. $\left[\dfrac{1}{2}\left(\cos\left(-\dfrac{3\pi}{4}\right) + i\sin\left(-\dfrac{3\pi}{4}\right)\right)\right]^{-6}$ $64i$
57. $(1 - i)^{12}$ -64
58. $(1 - \sqrt{3}i)^{10}$ $-512 + 512\sqrt{3}i$
59. i^{25} i
60. $(-i)^{23}$ i
61. $(3 + 3i)^{8}$ 104,976
62. $(2 - 2i)^{-6}$ †
63. $\left(\dfrac{1}{2} - \dfrac{\sqrt{3}}{2}i\right)^{-8}$ $-\dfrac{1}{2} + \dfrac{\sqrt{3}}{2}i$
64. $\left(\dfrac{\sqrt{3}}{2} + \dfrac{1}{2}i\right)^{10}$ $\dfrac{1}{2} - \dfrac{\sqrt{3}}{2}i$

†Due to space constrictions, answers to these exercises may be found in the Answers beginning on page A–1 in the back of the book.

In Exercises 65–72, find all complex roots. Write your answers in polar form, with the argument θ in degrees with $0 \le \theta < 360°$.

65. Cube roots of 64 †

66. Cube roots of −64 †

67. Square roots of i †

68. Fourth roots of $-i$ †

69. Sixth roots of −1 †

70. Eighth roots of unity †

71. Square roots of $1 - \sqrt{3}i$ †

72. Cube roots of $4 + 4\sqrt{3}i$ †

B Exercises   Applying the Concepts

73. Trigonometry. Use DeMoivre's Theorem to verify each identity.
  a. $\sin 3\theta = 3\sin\theta - 4\sin^3\theta$
  b. $\cos 3\theta = 4\cos^3\theta - 3\cos\theta$

74. Geometry. Show that the area K of a triangle with vertices at the origin O, z_1, and z_2 is given by

$$K = \frac{1}{2}|z_1||z_2|\sin\left(\left|\arg\frac{z_1}{z_2}\right|\right).$$

75. AC circuits. Use Ohm's Law, $I = \dfrac{V}{Z}$, to find the current I, given voltage $V = 120(\cos 60° + i\sin 60°)$ and impedance $Z = 8(\cos 30° + i\sin 30°)$. $15(\cos 30° + i\sin 30°)$

76. AC circuits. Use Ohm's Law from Exercise 75 to find the voltage V, given $I = 6(\cos 40° + i\sin 40°)$ and $Z = 16(\cos 110° + i\sin 110°)$. $96(\cos 150° + i\sin 150°)$

In Exercises 77 and 78, use the formula $Z_t = \dfrac{Z_1 Z_2}{Z_1 + Z_2}$ to find the total impedance in a parallel circuit for the given values of Z_1 and Z_2.

77. $Z_1 = 16(\cos 180° + i\sin 180°)$ and $Z_2 = 2(\cos 150° + i\sin 150°)$ $1.8(\cos 153.2° + i\sin 153.2°)$

78. $Z_1 = 12(\cos 270° + i\sin 270°)$ and $Z_2 = 3(\cos 60° + i\sin 60°)$ $3.8(\cos 50.9° + i\sin 50.9°)$

C Exercises   Beyond the Basics

In Exercises 79–84, use DeMoivre's Theorem to compute each power in polar form, with θ in degrees, with $0 \le \theta < 360°$.

79. $(1 - \sqrt{3}i)^{10}(-2 + 2i)^{-6}$ $2(\cos 30° + i\sin 30°)$

80. $\left(\dfrac{1}{2} + \dfrac{\sqrt{3}}{2}i\right)^8(2 - 2i)^{-6}$ $\dfrac{1}{512}(\cos 30° + i\sin 30°)$

81. $\left(\sin\dfrac{\pi}{6} + i\cos\dfrac{\pi}{6}\right)^{10}$ $\cos 240° + i\sin 240°$

82. $\left(\sin\dfrac{2\pi}{3} + i\cos\dfrac{2\pi}{3}\right)^6$ $\cos 180° + i\sin 180°$

83. $\left(\sin\dfrac{5\pi}{3} + i\cos\dfrac{5\pi}{3}\right)^{-8}$ $\cos 240° + i\sin 240°$

84. $\left(\sin\dfrac{7\pi}{6} + i\cos\dfrac{7\pi}{6}\right)^{-10}$ $\cos 120° + i\sin 120°$

In Exercises 85–88, find all complex solutions of each equation.

85. $z^4 = 1$ †

86. $z^8 = -1$ †

87. $z^3 = 1 + i$ †

88. $z^7 = (1 - i)^2$ †

89. Let $z = \cos\theta + i\sin\theta$, $z \ne 0$. Prove that $\dfrac{1}{z} = \cos\theta - i\sin\theta$.

In Exercises 90–93, let $z = \cos\theta + i\sin\theta$, $z \ne 0$. Use Exercise 89 and DeMoivre's Theorem to prove each identity.

90. $z + \dfrac{1}{z} = 2\cos\theta$

91. $z - \dfrac{1}{z} = 2i\sin\theta$

92. $z^n + \dfrac{1}{z^n} = 2\cos n\theta$

93. $z^n - \dfrac{1}{z^n} = 2i\sin n\theta$

94. Prove that
$$(1 + \cos\theta + i\sin\theta)^n = \left(2\cos\dfrac{\theta}{2}\right)^n\left(\cos\dfrac{n\theta}{2} + i\sin\dfrac{n\theta}{2}\right).$$

Critical Thinking

95. Let n be a positive integer. State whether each of the following is true or false.
  a. $\left(\cos\dfrac{\pi}{6} + i\sin\dfrac{\pi}{6}\right)^n = \cos\dfrac{n\pi}{6} + i\sin\dfrac{n\pi}{6}$ True
  b. $\left(\sin\dfrac{\pi}{3} + i\cos\dfrac{\pi}{3}\right)^n = \sin\dfrac{n\pi}{3} + i\cos\dfrac{n\pi}{3}$ False
  c. $\left[\cos\left(-\dfrac{\pi}{3}\right) + i\sin\left(-\dfrac{\pi}{3}\right)\right]^n = \cos\dfrac{n\pi}{3} - i\sin\dfrac{n\pi}{3}$ True
  d. $\left(\cos\dfrac{\pi}{6} + i\sin\dfrac{\pi}{3}\right)^n = \cos\dfrac{n\pi}{6} + i\sin\dfrac{n\pi}{3}$ False
  e. $(\cos\theta + i\sin\theta)^n = \cos n\theta + i\sin n\theta$ True
  f. $(\cos\theta - i\sin\theta)^n = \cos n\theta - i\sin n\theta$ True
  g. $(\cos\theta + i\sin\theta)^{-n} = \cos n\theta - i\sin n\theta$ True
  h. $(\cos\theta - i\sin\theta)^{-n} = \cos n\theta + i\sin n\theta$ True
  i. $(\sin\theta + i\cos\theta)^n = \sin n\theta + i\cos n\theta$ False
  j. $(\sin\theta + i\cos\theta)^n = \cos n\left(\dfrac{\pi}{2} - \theta\right) + i\sin n\left(\dfrac{\pi}{2} - \theta\right)$ †

Summary Definitions, Concepts, and Formulas

7.1 The Law of Sines

i. In a triangle ABC with sides of length a, b, and c,

$$\frac{\sin A}{a} = \frac{\sin B}{b} = \frac{\sin C}{c}, \text{ or equivalently, } \frac{a}{\sin A} = \frac{b}{\sin B} = \frac{c}{\sin C}.$$

ii. The Law of Sines is used to solve AAS, ASA, and SSA triangles. The SSA case is called the *ambiguous case,* because the information provided may lead to two triangles, one triangle, or no triangle.

7.2 The Law of Cosines

i. In a triangle ABC with sides of lengths a, b, and c,

$$a^2 = b^2 + c^2 - 2bc\cos A;$$
$$b^2 = c^2 + a^2 - 2ca\cos B;$$
$$c^2 = a^2 + b^2 - 2ab\cos C.$$

ii. The Law of Cosines is used to solve SAS and SSS triangles. This law is also used to prove Heron's formula.

iii. **Heron's formula.** The area K of a triangle with sides of lengths a, b, and c is given by

$$K = \sqrt{s(s - a)(s - b)(s - c)},$$

where $s = \dfrac{1}{2}(a + b + c)$ is the *semiperimeter.*

7.3 Vectors

i. A vector $\mathbf{v}$ is a quantity that has both magnitude and direction. A vector is geometrically represented by an arrow.

ii. The magnitude of the scalar product $c\mathbf{v}$ is $|c|$ times the magnitude of $\mathbf{v}$. If $c > 0$, $c\mathbf{v}$ has the direction of $\mathbf{v}$. If $c < 0$, $c\mathbf{v}$ has the opposite direction of $\mathbf{v}$. The zero vector $\mathbf{0}$ has magnitude 0, but arbitrary direction.

iii. We can geometrically add the vectors $\mathbf{v}$ and $\mathbf{w}$ by placing $\mathbf{w}$ so that its initial point coincides with the terminal point of $\mathbf{v}$ and drawing a vector from the initial point of $\mathbf{v}$ to the terminal point of $\mathbf{w}$.

iv. **Algebraic vectors.** A vector $\mathbf{v}$ with initial point at the origin and terminal point (v_1, v_2) is written as $\mathbf{v} = \langle v_1, v_2 \rangle$; v_1 and v_2 are the horizontal and vertical components of $\mathbf{v}$, respectively.

- The magnitude of $\mathbf{v} = \|\mathbf{v}\| = \sqrt{v_1^2 + v_2^2}$. The direction angle of $\mathbf{v}$ is the angle θ that $\mathbf{v}$ makes with the positive x-axis. We have $\cos\theta = \dfrac{v_1}{\|\mathbf{v}\|}$ and $\sin\theta = \dfrac{v_2}{\|\mathbf{v}\|}$, $0° \leq \theta < 360°$.

- The horizontal and vertical components of vector $\mathbf{v}$ with magnitude r and direction angle θ are given by

$$v_1 = r\cos\theta, \; v_2 = r\sin\theta.$$

v. **Vector operations.** For vectors $\mathbf{v} = \langle v_1, v_2 \rangle = v_1\mathbf{i} + v_2\mathbf{j}$ and $\mathbf{w} = \langle w_1, w_2 \rangle = w_1\mathbf{i} + w_2\mathbf{j}$, the following apply:

- **Vector addition:** $\mathbf{v} + \mathbf{w} = \langle v_1 + w_1, v_2 + w_2 \rangle$.

- **Scalar multiplication:** $c\mathbf{v} = \langle cv_1, cv_2 \rangle$.

- **Dot product:** $\mathbf{v} \cdot \mathbf{w} = v_1 w_1 + v_2 w_2$.

$$= \|\mathbf{v}\|\|\mathbf{w}\|\cos\theta, \text{ where } \theta \text{ is the angle between } \mathbf{v} \text{ and } \mathbf{w}.$$

7.4 Polar Coordinates

i. The ordered pair (r, θ) represents a point P in the plane that is a directed distance of r units from the origin (pole) O, where θ is the directed angle between the polar axis (positive x-axis) and the line segment OP. The ordered pair $(r, 0)$ gives the polar coordinates of P.

ii. The polar coordinates of a point $P(r, \theta)$ are not unique. In fact, if n is any integer, then

$$(r, \theta), (r, \theta + 2n\pi), \text{ and } (-r, \theta + \pi + 2n\pi)$$

are all polar coordinates of the same point.

iii. To convert a point from polar coordinates (r, θ) to rectangular coordinates, use the equations $x = r\cos\theta$, $y = \sin\theta$.

iv. To convert a point from rectangular coordinates (x, y) to polar coordinates (r, θ), use the procedure on page 710.

v. A polar equation is an equation whose variables are r and θ.

7.5 Polar Form of Complex Numbers; DeMoivre's Theorem

i. **Geometric representation.** A complex number $z = a + bi$ can be represented as an ordered pair (a, b) in the complex plane.

ii. **Modulus.** $|z| = |a + bi| = \sqrt{a^2 + b^2}$, $|z|$ is called the **modulus** of z.

iii. **Polar form.** The polar form of $z = a + bi$ is

$$z = r(\cos\theta + i\sin\theta), \text{ where } r = \sqrt{a^2 + b^2}, a = r\cos\theta,$$

$b = r\sin\theta$, and $\tan\theta = \dfrac{b}{a}$. The number r is the modulus of z, and θ is called the argument of z (written $\arg z$).

iv. **Multiplication and division.** Let $z_1 = r_1(\cos\theta_1 + i\sin\theta_1)$ and $z_2 = r_2(\cos\theta_2 + i\sin\theta_2)$. Then

$$z_1 z_2 = r_1 r_2[\cos(\theta_1 + \theta_2) + i\sin(\theta_1 + \theta_2)]$$

and

$$\frac{z_1}{z_2} = \frac{r_1}{r_2}[\cos(\theta_1 - \theta_2) + i\sin(\theta_1 - \theta_2)], \quad z_2 \neq 0.$$

v. DeMoivre's Theorem. Let $z = r(\cos\theta + i\sin\theta)$ be a complex number in polar form. Then, for any integer n,

$$[r(\cos\theta + i\sin\theta)]^n = r^n(\cos n\theta + i\sin n\theta).$$

vi. Roots of complex numbers. The n nth roots of a complex number $r(\cos\theta + i\sin\theta)$ are given by

$$z_k = \sqrt[n]{r}\left[\cos\left(\frac{\theta + 2\pi k}{n}\right) + i\sin\left(\frac{\theta + 2\pi k}{n}\right)\right] \text{ or }$$

$$z_k = \sqrt[n]{r}\left[\cos\left(\frac{\theta + 360°k}{n}\right) + i\sin\left(\frac{\theta + 360°k}{n}\right)\right],$$

where $k = 0, 1, 2, \ldots, n - 1$.

Review Exercises

Basic Skills and Concepts

In Exercises 1–8, use the Law of Sines to solve each triangle ABC. Round each answer to the nearest tenth.

1. $A = 40°$, $B = 35°$, $c = 100$ $C = 105°, a \approx 66.5, c \approx 59.4$

2. $B = 30°$, $C = 80°$, $a = 100$ $C = 70°, b \approx 53.2, c \approx 104.8$

3. $A = 45°$, $a = 25$, $b = 75$ No triangle exists.

4. $B = 36°$, $a = 12.5$, $b = 8.7$ †

5. $A = 48.5°$, $C = 57.3°$, $b = 47.3$ †

6. $A = 67°$, $a = 100$, $c = 125$ No triangle exists.

7. $A = 65.2°$, $a = 21.3$, $b = 19$ $B = 54.1°, C = 60.7°, c \approx 20.5$

8. $C = 53°$, $a = 140$, $c = 115$ †

9. In triangle ABC, let $c = 20$ and $B = 60°$. Find a value of b such that C has (i) two possible values, (ii) exactly one value, (iii) no value. †

10. Repeat Exercise 9 for $c = 20$ and $B = 150°$. †

In Exercises 11–18, use the Law of Cosines to solve each triangle ABC. Round each answer to the nearest tenth.

11. $a = 60$, $b = 90$, $c = 125$ $A \approx 26.6°, B \approx 42.1°, C \approx 111.3°$

12. $a = 15$, $b = 9$, $C = 120°$ $A \approx 38.2°, B \approx 21.8°, c = 21$

13. $a = 40$, $c = 38$, $B = 80°$ $A \approx 51.7°, C \approx 48.3°, b \approx 50.2$

14. $a = 10$, $b = 20$, $c = 22$ $A \approx 27.0°, B \approx 65.3°, C \approx 87.7°$

15. $a = 2.6$, $b = 3.7$, $c = 4.8$ $A \approx 32.5°, B \approx 49.8°, C \approx 97.7°$

16. $a = 15$, $c = 26$, $B = 115°$ $A \approx 22.8°, C \approx 42.2°, b \approx 35.1$

17. $a = 12$, $b = 7$, $C = 130°$ $A \approx 32.0°, B \approx 18.0°, c \approx 17.3$

18. $b = 75$, $c = 100$, $A = 80°$ $B \approx 40.3°, C \approx 59.7°, a \approx 114.1$

In Exercises 19–22, find the area of each triangle ABC with the given information. Round each answer to the nearest square unit.

19. $a = 5$ meters, $b = 7$ meters, $c = 10$ meters 16 square meters

20. $a = 2.4$ meters, $b = 3.4$ meters, $c = 4.4$ meters †

21. $A = 65°$, $b = 6$ feet, $c = 4$ feet 11 square feet

22. $A = 115°$, $b = 20$ inches, $a = 30$ inches 140 square inches

In Exercises 23 and 24, let $\mathbf{v}$ be the vector with initial point P and terminal point Q. Write $\mathbf{v}$ as a position vector in terms of $\mathbf{i}$ and $\mathbf{j}$.

23. $P(3, 5)$, $Q(2, 7)$ $-\mathbf{i} + 2\mathbf{j}$ **24.** $P(-1, 3)$, $Q(5, -4)$ $6\mathbf{i} - 7\mathbf{j}$

In Exercises 25–28, let $\mathbf{v} = \langle -2, 3 \rangle$ and $\mathbf{w} = \langle 5, -6 \rangle$. Find each expression.

25. $5\mathbf{v}$ $\langle -10, 15 \rangle$

26. $2\mathbf{v} + \mathbf{w}$ $\langle 1, 0 \rangle$

27. $3\mathbf{v} - 2\mathbf{w}$ $\langle -16, 21 \rangle$

28. $\|\mathbf{v} + \mathbf{w}\|$ $3\sqrt{2}$

In Exercises 29–32, find the unit vector $\mathbf{u}$ in the direction of the vector $\mathbf{v}$.

29. $\mathbf{v} = \mathbf{i} + \mathbf{j}$ †

30. $\mathbf{v} = 2\mathbf{i} - 7\mathbf{j}$ †

31. $\mathbf{v} = \langle 3, -5 \rangle$ †

32. $\mathbf{v} = \langle -5, -2 \rangle$ †

In Exercises 33–36, write $\mathbf{v}$ in terms of $\mathbf{i}$ and $\mathbf{j}$ for the given magnitude $\|\mathbf{v}\|$ and direction angle θ.

33. $\|\mathbf{v}\| = 6$, $\theta = 30°$ †

34. $\|\mathbf{v}\| = 20$, $\theta = 120°$ †

35. $\|\mathbf{v}\| = 12$, $\theta = 225°$ †

36. $\|\mathbf{v}\| = 10$, $\theta = -30°$ †

In Exercises 37–40, find the dot product $\mathbf{v} \cdot \mathbf{w}$.

37. $\mathbf{v} = \langle 2, -3 \rangle$, $\mathbf{w} = \langle 3, 4 \rangle$ -6

38. $\mathbf{v} = \langle -1, -2 \rangle$, $\mathbf{w} = \langle 4, -1 \rangle$ -2

39. $\mathbf{v} = 2\mathbf{i} - 5\mathbf{j}$, $\mathbf{w} = 5\mathbf{i} + 2\mathbf{j}$ 0

40. $\mathbf{v} = 2\mathbf{i} + \mathbf{j}$, $\mathbf{w} = 2\mathbf{i} - \mathbf{j}$ 3

In Exercises 41–44, use the dot product to find the angle θ ($0 \le \theta \le \pi$) between the vectors $\mathbf{v}$ and $\mathbf{w}$. Round your answers to the nearest tenth of a degree.

41. $\mathbf{v} = 2\mathbf{i} + 3\mathbf{j}$, $\mathbf{w} = -\mathbf{i} + 2\mathbf{j}$ $60.3°$

42. $\mathbf{v} = \mathbf{i} + 4\mathbf{j}$, $\mathbf{w} = -4\mathbf{i} - \mathbf{j}$ $118.1°$

43. $\mathbf{v} = \langle 1, 1 \rangle$, $\mathbf{w} = \langle -3, 2 \rangle$ $101.3°$

44. $\mathbf{v} = \langle 1, 5 \rangle$, $\mathbf{w} = \langle 3, -1 \rangle$ $97.1°$

In Exercises 45–48, plot each point in polar coordinates and find its rectangular coordinates.

45. $(24, 30°)$ †

46. $\left(12, -\dfrac{\pi}{3}\right)$ †

47. $\left(-2, -\dfrac{\pi}{4}\right)$ †

48. $\left(-3, -\dfrac{3\pi}{4}\right)$ †

In Exercises 49–52, convert the rectangular coordinates of each point to polar coordinates (r, θ), with $r > 0$ and $0 \le \theta < 2\pi$.

49. $(-2, 2)$ †

50. $(\sqrt{3}, 1)$ †

51. $(2\sqrt{3}, -2)$ †

52. $(-2, -2\sqrt{3})$ †

In Exercises 53–56, convert each rectangular equation to a polar equation.

53. $3x + 2y = 12$ †

54. $x^2 + y^2 = 36$ $\ r = 6$

55. $x^2 + y^2 = 8x$ $\ r = 8\cos\theta$

56. $x^2 + y^2 = 6y$ $\ r = 6\sin\theta$

In Exercises 57–62, convert each polar equation to a rectangular equation.

57. $r = -3$ $\ x^2 + y^2 = 9$

58. $\theta = \dfrac{5\pi}{6}$ $\ y = -\dfrac{\sqrt{3}}{3}x$

59. $r = 3\csc\theta$ $\ y = 3$

60. $r = 2\sec\theta$ $\ x = 2$

61. $r = 1 - 2\sin\theta$ †

62. $r = 3\cos\theta$ $\ x^2 + y^2 = 3x$

In Exercises 63–66, write each complex number in polar form. Express the arguments in radians.

63. $-3i$ †

64. $-1 + i$ †

65. $5\sqrt{3} - 5i$ †

66. $-2 - 2\sqrt{3}i$ †

In Exercises 67–70, write each complex number in rectangular form.

67. $2(\cos 45° + i\sin 45°)$ †

68. $3(\cos 240° + i\sin 240°)$ †

69. $6\left(\cos\dfrac{3\pi}{4} + i\sin\dfrac{3\pi}{4}\right)$ †

70. $4\left(\cos\dfrac{7\pi}{6} + i\sin\dfrac{7\pi}{6}\right)$ †

In Exercises 71–74, find $z_1 z_2$ and $\dfrac{z_1}{z_2}$. Leave your answers in polar form.

71. $z_1 = 3(\cos 25° + \sin 25°)$, $z_2 = 2(\cos 10° + i\sin 10°)$ †

72. $z_1 = 4(\cos 300° + i\sin 300°)$, $z_2 = 2(\cos 20° + i\sin 20°)$ †

73. $z_1 = 2\left(\cos\dfrac{5\pi}{6} + i\sin\dfrac{5\pi}{6}\right)$, $z_2 = 3\left(\cos\dfrac{\pi}{3} + i\sin\dfrac{\pi}{3}\right)$ †

74. $z_1 = 5\left(\cos\dfrac{4\pi}{3} + i\sin\dfrac{4\pi}{3}\right)$, $z_2 = 15\left(\cos\dfrac{\pi}{3} + i\sin\dfrac{\pi}{3}\right)$ †

In Exercises 75–78, use DeMoivre's Theorem to find the indicated power. Write your answers in polar form.

75. $[3(\cos 40° + i\sin 40°)]^3$ †

76. $\left[4\left(\cos\dfrac{\pi}{6} + i\sin\dfrac{\pi}{6}\right)\right]^6$ †

77. $(2 - 2\sqrt{3}i)^6$ †

78. $(2 - 2i)^7$ †

In Exercises 79–82, find all complex roots. Write your answers in polar form, with the arguments in degrees.

79. Cube roots of -125 †

80. Fourth roots of $-16i$ †

81. Fifth roots of $-1 + \sqrt{3}i$ †

82. Sixth roots of $1 - i$ †

Applying the Concepts

83. Width of a river. A surveyor wants to measure the width of a river. She stands at a point A, with point B opposite her on the other side of the river. From A, she walks 320 feet along the bank to a point C. The line CA makes an angle of 40° with the line CB. What is the width of the river? 268.5 feet

84. Angle of elevation of a hill. A tower 120 feet tall is located at the top of a hill. At a point 460 feet down the hill, the angle between the surface of the hill and the line of sight to the top of the tower is 12°. Find the angle of elevation of the hill to a horizontal plane. 25.2°

85. Distance between cars. Two cars start from a point A along two straight roads. The angle between the two roads is 72°. The speeds of the two cars are 55 miles per hour and 65 miles per hour, respectively. How far apart are the two cars after 80 minutes? Round to the nearest tenth of a mile. 94.7 miles

86. Triangular plot. A triangular plot of land has sides of lengths 310 feet, 415 feet, and 175 feet. Find the largest angle between the sides. 114.8°

87. Area. Find the area of the triangular plot in Exercise 86. †

88. Resultant force. Two forces of magnitudes 16 and 20 pounds are acting on an object. The bearings of the forces are N 75° E and S 20° E, respectively. Find the magnitude and the direction of the resultant force, to the nearest tenth. 26.7 pounds, S56.7° E

89. Work. A force of magnitude 30 pounds at an angle of 48° is used to pull a wagon for 60 feet. Find the work done. †

90. AC current. The total impedance in an AC circuit is given by $Z = \dfrac{Z_1 Z_2}{Z_1 + Z_2}$. Find Z if $Z_1 = 20\left(\cos\dfrac{\pi}{6} + i\sin\dfrac{\pi}{6}\right)$ and $Z_2 = 10\left(\cos\dfrac{2\pi}{3} + i\sin\dfrac{2\pi}{3}\right)$. $4\sqrt{5}(\cos 93.5° + i\sin 93.5°)$

Practice Test A

1. In problems 1 – 4, solve triangle ABC. Round each answer to the nearest tenth. $B = 30°, b \approx 13.1, a \approx 23.7$

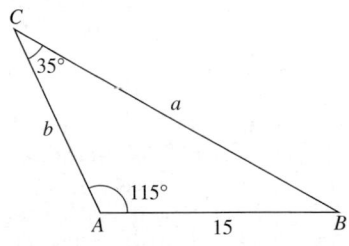

2. $A = 42°, B = 37°, a = 50$ meters. †

3.

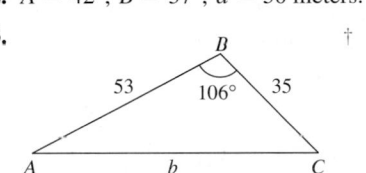

4. $a = 30$ feet, $b = 20$ feet, $c = 25$ feet. †

5. Indicate whether the given measurements result in no triangle, one triangle, or two triangles. Solve each resulting triangle. $A = 43°$, $a = 185$ feet, $b = 248$ feet. †

6. Find the measure of the central angle of a circle of radius 8 feet that intercepts a chord of length 4.5 feet. Round to the nearest tenth of a degree. 32.7°

7. A surveyor, starting from point A, walks 580 feet in the direction N 70.0° E. From that point she walks 725 feet in the direction N 35.0° W. How far, to the nearest foot, is she from her starting point? 803 feet

8. The vector $\mathbf{v}$ has initial point $P(3, 5)$ and terminal point $Q(2, -7)$. Write $\mathbf{v}$ as a position vector. $\langle -1, -12 \rangle$

9. If $\mathbf{v} = \langle -2, 3 \rangle$ and $\mathbf{w} = \langle 1, 5 \rangle$, find $\mathbf{v} - \mathbf{w}$. $\langle -3, -2 \rangle$

10. If $\mathbf{v} = -2\mathbf{i} + 3\mathbf{j}$ and $\mathbf{w} = \mathbf{i} + 5\mathbf{j}$, find $2\mathbf{v} - 3\mathbf{w}$. $-7\mathbf{i} - 9\mathbf{j}$

11. Let $\|\mathbf{v}\| = 3$ and suppose that $\mathbf{v}$ makes an angle of $\theta = -30°$ with the positive x-axis. Write the vector $\mathbf{v}$ in the form $v_1\mathbf{i} + v_2\mathbf{j}$. †

12. Find the dot product $\mathbf{v} \cdot \mathbf{w}$ if $\mathbf{v} = 4\mathbf{i} + 3\mathbf{j}$ and $\mathbf{w} = -\mathbf{i} + 7\mathbf{j}$. 17

13. Find the angle $\theta (0° \le \theta \le 180°)$ between the vectors $\mathbf{v} = 3\mathbf{i} - 4\mathbf{j}$ and $\mathbf{w} = -2\mathbf{i} + 5\mathbf{j}$. Round the answer to the nearest tenth of a degree. 164.9°

14. Convert $(-2, -45°)$ to rectangular coordinates. $(-\sqrt{2}, \sqrt{2})$

15. Convert $(-\sqrt{3}, -1)$ to polar coordinates with $r > 0$ and $0 \le \theta < 2\pi$. †

16. Convert the polar equation $r = -3$ to rectangular form. Identify the curve having this equation. †

17. Write $3\left(\cos\left(\dfrac{2\pi}{3}\right) + i\sin\left(\dfrac{2\pi}{3}\right) \right)$ in rectangular form. †

18. Write $\dfrac{z_1}{z_2}$ in polar form, if $z_1 = 1 - \sqrt{3}i$, $z_2 = -1 + i$, with the argument given in degrees. $\sqrt{2}(\cos 165° + i\sin 165°)$

19. Use DeMoivre's Theorem to find $\left[\sqrt{5}\left(\cos\left(\dfrac{\pi}{4}\right) + i\sin\left(\dfrac{\pi}{4}\right) \right) \right]^{-6}$. Write the answer in rectangular form. †

20. Find all fourth roots of $1 + i$. Express the argument in degrees. †

Practice Test B

1. In triangle ABC, which is closest to the correct value for b? a
   a. $b = 13.4$
   b. $b = 20.8$
   c. $b = 20.2$
   d. $b = 0.05$

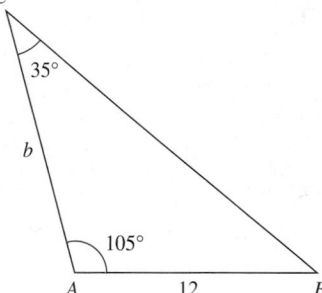

2. In triangle ABC, if $A = 27°$, $B = 50°$, and $a = 25$ meters, which is closest to the correct value for c? c
   a. $c = 0.03$ meter
   b. $c = 42.2$ meters
   c. $c = 53.7$ meters
   d. $c = 0.02$ meter

3. Which statement is true for the measurements $A = 25°$, $a = 25$ feet, $b = 30$ feet? c
   (The angle measurements in choices (c) and (d) are given to the nearest tenth.)
   a. No triangle has these measurements.
   b. One triangle has these measurements.
   c. Two triangles, with $c_1 = 48.7$ and $c_2 = 5.6$, have these measurements (in feet).
   d. Two triangles, with $c_1 = 46$ and $c_2 = 6.4$, have these measurements (in feet).

4. In triangle ABC, which is the closest to the correct value for b? d
   a. $b = 35.8$
   b. $b = 57.2$
   c. $b = 18.7$
   d. $b = 48.4$

5. In triangle ABC, with $b = 8$ feet, $c = 15$ feet, $A = 62°$, which is closest to the correct value for a? c
   a. 8.8 feet   b. 20 feet
   c. 13.3 feet   d. 22.4 feet

6. In triangle ABC, with $a = 12$ feet, $b = 13$ feet, $c = 7$ feet, which is closest to the correct value for A? b
   a. 24°   b. 66°
   c. 81.8°   d. 32.2°

7. Find the measure of the central angle of a circle of radius 9 feet that intercepts a chord of length 3 feet. Round to the nearest tenth of a degree. d
   a. 70.8°   b. 63.6°
   c. 26.4°   d. 19.2°

8. A hunter leaves a straight east–west road at a point A, walking 2 miles at a bearing N 40° W to a point B. From point B, he walks at a bearing of S 20° E and arrives back on the road at a point C. How far, to the nearest tenth of a mile, is point B from point C? c
   a. 4.5 miles   b. 2.9 miles
   c. 1.6 miles   d. 5.3 miles

9. The vector $\mathbf{v}$ has initial point $P(-2, 5)$ and terminal point $Q(3, -1)$. Write $\mathbf{v}$ as a position vector. a
  a. $\langle 5, -6 \rangle$ **b.** $\langle 1, -6 \rangle$
  c. $\langle 1, -4 \rangle$ **d.** $\langle 5, -4 \rangle$

10. If $\mathbf{v} = \langle 1, -4 \rangle$ and $\mathbf{w} = \langle 3, -2 \rangle$, find $\mathbf{v} - \mathbf{w}$. c
  a. $\langle 4, -2 \rangle$ **b.** $\langle 2, 2 \rangle$
  c. $\langle -2, -2 \rangle$ **d.** $\langle 4, -6 \rangle$

11. Let $\mathbf{v} = 7\mathbf{i} + 3\mathbf{j}$ and $\mathbf{w} = -2\mathbf{i} + \mathbf{j}$. Find $2\mathbf{v} - 3\mathbf{w}$. a
  a. $20\mathbf{i} + 3\mathbf{j}$ **b.** $20\mathbf{i} - 3\mathbf{j}$
  c. $8\mathbf{i} - 6\mathbf{j}$ **d.** $8\mathbf{i} + 6\mathbf{j}$

12. Let $\|\mathbf{v}\| = 6$, and suppose that $\mathbf{v}$ makes an angle of $\theta = -60°$ with the positive x-axis. Write the vector $\mathbf{v}$ in the form $v_1\mathbf{i} + v_2\mathbf{j}$. d

  a. $3\sqrt{3}\mathbf{i} - 3\mathbf{j}$ **b.** $3\sqrt{3}\mathbf{i} + 3\mathbf{j}$
  c. $3\mathbf{i} + 3\sqrt{3}\mathbf{j}$ **d.** $3\mathbf{i} - 3\sqrt{3}\mathbf{j}$

13. Find the dot product $\mathbf{v} \cdot \mathbf{w}$ if $\mathbf{v} = -2\mathbf{i} - 5\mathbf{j}$ and $\mathbf{w} = 9\mathbf{i} - 4\mathbf{j}$. d
  a. -38 **b.** 38
  c. $2\mathbf{i} + 20\mathbf{j}$ **d.** 2

14. Find the angle between the vectors $\mathbf{v} = 7\mathbf{i} - \mathbf{j}$ and $\mathbf{w} = \mathbf{i} + \sqrt{2}\mathbf{j}$. Round the answer to the nearest degree. b
  a. $84°$ **b.** $63°$
  c. $32°$ **d.** $17°$

15. Convert $(-4, -30°)$ to rectangular coordinates. c
  a. $\left(-2\sqrt{3}, -2\right)$ **b.** $\left(2, -2\sqrt{3}\right)$
  c. $\left(-2\sqrt{3}, 2\right)$ **d.** $\left(2\sqrt{3}, -2\right)$

16. Convert $\left(3, -\sqrt{3}\right)$ to polar coordinates, with $r > 0$ and $0 \le \theta < 360°$. b
  a. $(12, 330°)$ **b.** $\left(2\sqrt{3}, 330°\right)$
  c. $\left(2\sqrt{3}, 150°\right)$ **d.** $\left(\sqrt{3}, 150°\right)$

17. Which polar equation has a circle for its graph? b
  a. $r = -4\cos\theta + 1$ **b.** $r = -2$
  c. $r\sin\theta = 2$ **d.** $r\cos\theta = 1$

18. Write $5\left(\cos\left(\dfrac{7\pi}{3}\right) + i\sin\left(\dfrac{7\pi}{3}\right)\right)$ in rectangular form. c

  a. $5 + 5\sqrt{3}i$ **b.** $5 - 5\sqrt{3}i$
  c. $\dfrac{5}{2} + \dfrac{5\sqrt{3}}{2}i$ **d.** $\dfrac{5}{2} - \dfrac{5\sqrt{3}}{2}i$

19. Write $\dfrac{z_1}{z_2}$ in polar form, if $z_1 = i$ and $z_2 = 1 - i$. c

  a. $1(\cos 135° + i\sin 135°)$
  b. $\sqrt{2}(\cos 135° + i\sin 135°)$
  c. $\dfrac{\sqrt{2}}{2}(\cos 135° + i\sin 135°)$
  d. $\dfrac{\sqrt{2}}{2}(\cos 315° + i\sin 315°)$

20. Use DeMoivre's Theorem to find $\left[\sqrt{2}\left(\cos\left(\dfrac{\pi}{12}\right) + i\sin\left(\dfrac{\pi}{12}\right)\right)\right]^4$. Write the answer in rectangular form. c

  a. $-2 + 2\sqrt{3}i$ **b.** $\dfrac{1}{2} + \dfrac{\sqrt{3}}{2}i$
  c. $2 + 2\sqrt{3}i$ **d.** $\dfrac{1}{2} - \dfrac{\sqrt{3}}{2}i$

Cumulative Review Exercises   Chapters 1–7

In Exercises 1–4, solve each equation or inequality.

1. $x^2 + 2x + 3 = 0$ $-1 \pm \sqrt{2}i$ **2.** $\dfrac{x^2 - 6x + 8}{x + 3} < 0$ †

3. $x^4 + x^2 - 6 = 0$ †   **4.** $e^x + e^{-x} = 2$ 0

In Exercises 5 and 6, solve each equation for all solutions in the interval $[0, 2\pi)$. Give your answers in radians.

5. $\sin\theta\cos\theta = -\dfrac{\sqrt{3}}{4}$ †

6. $4\sin^2\theta - 1 = 0$ †

In Exercises 7 and 8, find all complex roots. Write your answers in polar form, with the argument in degrees.

7. fourth roots of $\sqrt{3} + i$ †   **8.** sixth roots of -64 †

9. Find the equation of the line in slope-intercept form that passes through the point $(-1, 5)$ and is perpendicular to the line $2x + 3y + 6 = 0$. †

10. Write the following in condensed form:
$2\log x + \dfrac{1}{2}\log(y + 1) - \log(3x + 1)$. $\log\dfrac{x^2\sqrt{y + 1}}{3x + 1}$

In Exercises 11–14, use transformations to sketch the graph of each function.

11. $f(x) = 2\sqrt{x - 1} - 3$ †

12. $f(x) = -|x + 1| + 2$ †

13. $f(x) = -2\cos(3x + \pi)$ †   **14.** $f(x) = 2\sec 3x$ †

15. If $\cos\theta = -\dfrac{5}{13}$ and $\sin\theta > 0$, find $\tan\theta$. $-\dfrac{12}{5}$

16. Use an identity to find the exact value of $\cos 65° \cos 35° + \sin 65° \sin 35°$. †

17. Verify the identity $\dfrac{1}{1 - \cos x} + \dfrac{1}{1 + \cos x} = 2(1 + \cot^2 x)$.

18. Verify the identity $\dfrac{1 + \cos 2x}{\sin 2x} = \cot x$.

19. Solve triangle ABC with $A = 65°$, $B = 46°$, $c = 60$ meters. †

20. A ladder leaning against a vertical wall makes an angle of $47°$ with the ground. The foot of the ladder is 2.3 meters from the wall. Find the length of the ladder. Round to the nearest tenth. 3.4 m

CHAPTER 8

Systems of Equations and Inequalities

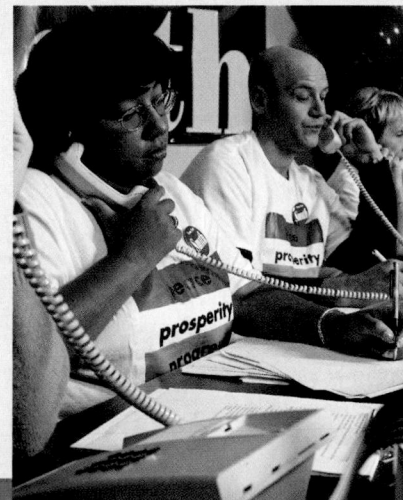

Systems of equations are frequently the tools used to describe relationships among variables representing different, interrelated quantities. These same systems of equations are used to predict results associated with changes in the quantities.

The quantities involved may come from the study of medicine, taxes, elections, business, agriculture, city planning, or any discipline in which multiple quantities interact.

TOPICS

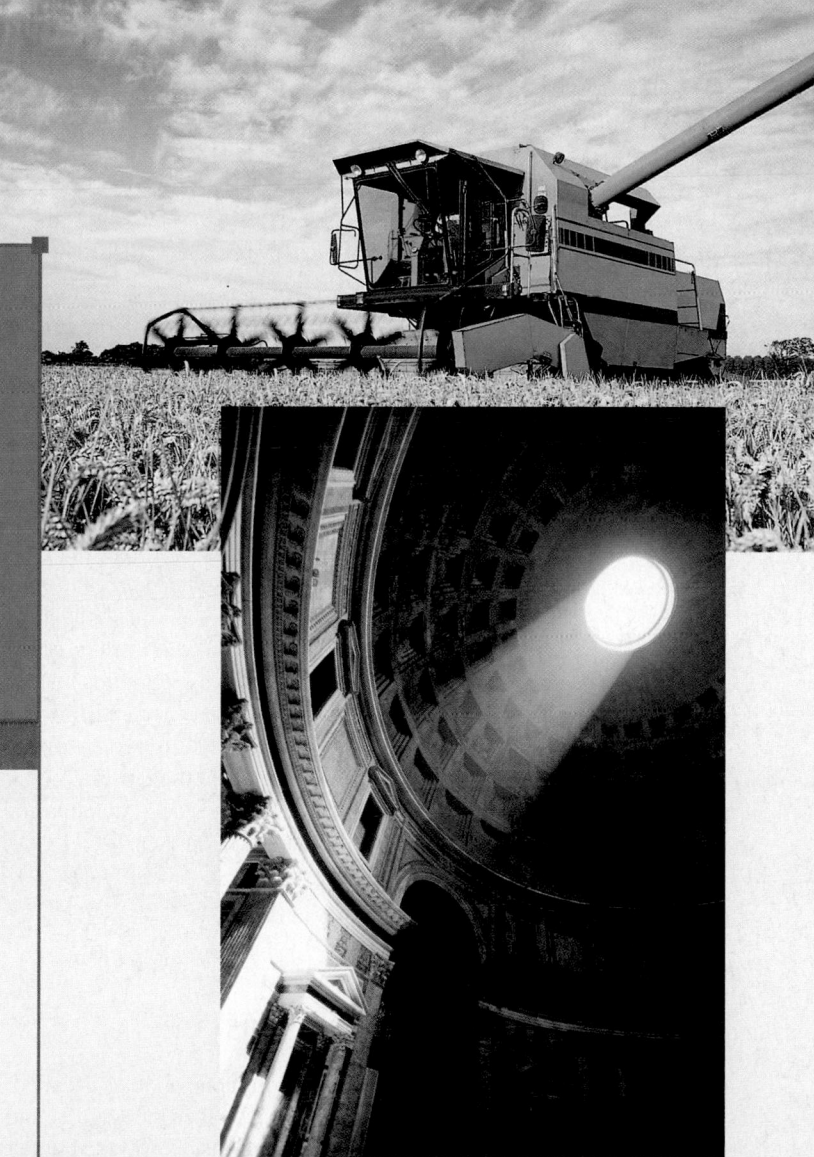

Systems of Linear Equations in Two Variables

**Al-Khwarizmi
(780–850)**

Al-Khwarizmi came to Baghdad from the town of Khwarizm, which is now called *Khivga* and is part of Uzbekistan. The term *algorithm* is a corruption of the name al-khwarizmi. Originally, the word *algorism* was used for the rules for performing arithmetic by using decimal notation. *Algorism* evolved into the word *algorithm* by the 18th century. The word *algorithm* now means a finite set of precise instructions for performing a computation or for solving a problem. (The picture shown is a Soviet postage stamp from 1983 depicting Al-Khwarizmi.)

BEFORE STARTING THIS SECTION, REVIEW

1. Graphs of equations (Section 2.2, page 192)
2. Graphs of linear equations (Section 2.3, page 213)

OBJECTIVES

1. Verify a solution to a system of equations.
2. Solve a system of equations by the graphical method.
3. Solve a system of equations by the substitution method.
4. Solve a system of equations by the elimination method.
5. Solve applied problems by solving systems of equations.

Algebra–Iraq Connection

The most important contributions of the Islamic mathematicians lie in the area of algebra. One of the greatest Islamic scholars was Muhammad ibn Musa al-Khwarizmi (A.D. 780–850). Al-Khwarizmi was one of the first scholars in the House of Wisdom, an academy of scientists, established by caliph al-Mamun in the city of Baghdad in Iraq. Jews, Christians, and Muslims worked together in scholarly pursuits in the academy during this period. The eminent scholar al-Khwarizmi wrote several books on astronomy and mathematics. Western Europeans first learned about algebra from his books. The word *algebra* comes from the Arabic al-jabr, part of the title of his book *Kitab al-jabr wal-muqabala.*

This book was translated into Latin and was a widely used text. The Arabic word *al-jabr* means *restoration,* as in restoring broken parts. (At one time, it was not unusual to see the sign "Algebrista y Sangrador," meaning "bone setter and blood letter," at the entrance of a Spanish barber's shop. The sign informed customers of the barber's side business.) Al-Khwarizmi used the term in the mathematical sense of removing a negative quantity on one side of an equation and restoring it as a positive quantity on the other side. ■

---

1 Verify a solution to a system of equations.

System of Equations

A set of equations with common variables is called a **system of equations.** If each equation in a system of equations is linear, then the set of equations is called a **system of linear equations** or a **linear system of equations.** However, if at least one equation in a system of equations is nonlinear, then the set of equations is called a **nonlinear system of equations.** In this section, we shall study methods of solving a system of two linear equations in two variables. The following two equations form a system of two linear equations in two variables:

$$\begin{cases} 2x - y = 5 \\ x + 2y = 5 \end{cases}$$

We will designate a system of equations by using a left brace with the equations written to the right. A system of equations is sometimes referred to as a set of *simultaneous equations*. A **solution of a system of equations in two variables** x and y is an ordered pair of numbers (a, b) such that when x is replaced by a and y is replaced by b, all the resulting equations in the system are true. The **solution set of a system of equations** is the set of all solutions of the system.

EXAMPLE 1   Verifying a Solution

Verify that the ordered pair $(3, 1)$ is a solution of the system of linear equations

$$\begin{cases} 2x - y = 5 & (1) \\ x + 2y = 5 & (2) \end{cases}$$

Solution

To verify whether the ordered pair $(3, 1)$ is a solution of the system, replace x by 3 and y by 1 in both equations.

Equation (1)	Equation (2)	
$2x - y = 5$	$x + 2y = 5$	
$2(3) - 1 \stackrel{?}{=} 5$	$3 + 2(1) \stackrel{?}{=} 5$	Replace x by 3 and y by 1 in both equations.
$6 - 1 \stackrel{?}{=} 5$	$3 + 2 \stackrel{?}{=} 5$	
$5 = 5 \checkmark$	$5 = 5 \checkmark$	

Since the ordered pair $(3, 1)$ satisfies both equations, it is indeed a solution of the system.

■ ■ ■

PRACTICE PROBLEM 1   Verify that $(1, 3)$ is a solution of the system

$$\begin{cases} x + y = 4 \\ 3x - y = 0 \end{cases}$$

■

In this section, you will learn three methods of solving a system of two equations in two variables: the *graphical method,* the *substitution method,* and the *elimination method.*

2 Learn to solve a system of equations by the graphical method.

Graphical Method

Recall that the graph of a linear equation

$$ax + by = c \qquad (a \text{ and } b \text{ not both zero})$$

is a line. Consider a system of linear equations

$$\begin{cases} a_1x + b_1y = c_1 \\ a_2x + b_2y = c_2 \end{cases}$$

A solution of this system is a point (an ordered pair) that satisfies both equations. Thus, the solution set of this system can be found or estimated by graphing both equations on the same coordinate axes and finding the coordinates of any points of intersection. This procedure is called the **graphical method.**

EXAMPLE 2   **Solving a System by the Graphical Method**

Use the graphical method to solve the system of equations.

$$\begin{cases} 2x - y = 4 & (1) \\ 2x + 3y = 12 & (2) \end{cases}$$

FIGURE 8.1

Solution

Step 1   **Graph both equations on the same coordinate axes.**
  (i)   We first graph Equation (1), $2x - y = 4$, using the intercepts.
     a. Find the y-intercept:
        Set $x = 0$ in $2x - y = 4$ and solve for y.
        We have $2(0) - y = 4$, or $y = -4$, so the y-intercept is -4.
     b. Find the x-intercept:
        Set $y = 0$ in $2x - y = 4$ and solve for x.
        We have $2x - 0 = 4$, or $x = 2$, so the x-intercept is 2.
     The points $(0, -4)$ and $(2, 0)$ are on the graph of Equation (1). The line through these points is sketched in Figure 8.1.

  (ii) We now graph Equation (2), $2x + 3y = 12$, using the intercepts.
        The x-intercept is 6 and the y-intercept is 4.
        The graph of the line $2x + 3y = 12$ is sketched by joining the points $(0, 4)$ and $(6, 0)$. The line through these points is shown in Figure 8.1.

Step 2   **Find the point(s) of intersection of the two graphs.** From Figure 8.1, we observe that the point of intersection of the two graphs is $(3, 2)$.

Step 3   **Check your solution(s).** Replace x by 3 and y by 2 in Equations (1) and (2).

Equation (1)	Equation (2)
$2x - y = 4$	$2x + 3y = 12$
$2(3) - 2 \overset{?}{=} 4$	$2(3) + 3(2) \overset{?}{=} 12$
$6 - 2 \overset{?}{=} 4$	$6 + 6 \overset{?}{=} 12$
$4 = 4 \checkmark$	$12 = 12 \checkmark$
Yes	Yes

Step 4   **Write the solution set for the system.**
The solution set is $\{(3, 2)\}$.   ■ ■ ■

PRACTICE PROBLEM 2   Solve the system of equations graphically.

$$\begin{cases} x + y = 2 \\ 4x + y = -1 \end{cases}$$

■

TECHNOLOGY CONNECTION

In Example 2, solve each equation for y. Graph

$$Y_1 = 2x - 4 \quad \text{and}$$

$$Y_2 = -\frac{2}{3}x + 4$$

on the same screen.

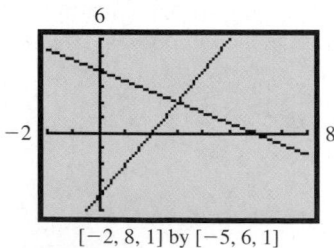

$[-2, 8, 1]$ by $[-5, 6, 1]$

Use the **intersect** feature on your calculator to find the point of intersection.

If a system of equations has at least one solution (as in Example 2), the system is said to be **consistent.** A system of equations with no solution is called **inconsistent.** The solution set of an inconsistent system is the empty set, $\varnothing$.

In general, the solution set of a system of two linear equations in two variables can be classified in one of the following ways (see Figure 8.2):

1. One solution (the lines intersect; see Figure 8.2(a)).
   The system is consistent, and the equations in the system are said to be **independent.**

2. No solution (the lines are parallel; see Figure 8.2(b)).
   The system is inconsistent.

3. Infinitely many solutions (the lines coincide; see Figure 8.2(c)).
   The system is consistent and the equations in the system are said to be **dependent.**

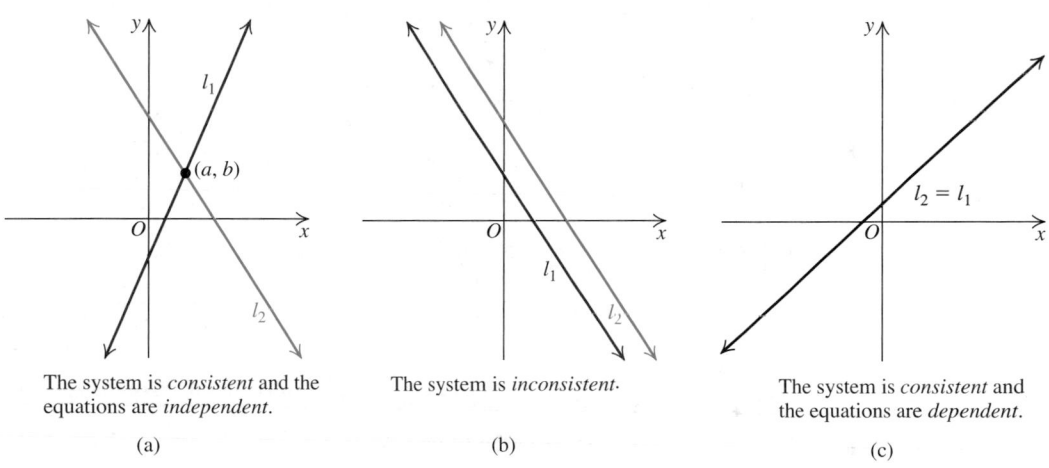

| The system is *consistent* and the equations are *independent.* | The system is *inconsistent.* | The system is *consistent* and the equations are *dependent.* |
| (a) | (b) | (c) |

FIGURE 8.2

---

3 Solve a system of equations by the substitution method.

Substitution Method

A linear system of equations can be solved by the **substitution method.** We next describe and illustrate this method.

FINDING THE SOLUTION: SUBSTITUTION METHOD

OBJECTIVE	EXAMPLE
To reduce the solution of the system to the solution of one equation in one variable by substitution.	Solve. $$\begin{cases} 2x - 5y = 3 & (1) \\ y - 2x = 9 & (2) \end{cases}$$

| **Step 1** | **Solve for one variable.** Choose one of the equations, and express one of the variables in terms of the other variable. | In equation (2), we choose y and express y in terms of x. $$y = 2x + 9 \qquad (3)$$ Solve equation (2) for y. |

Continued on next page.

Step 2	**Substitute.** Substitute the expression obtained in Step 1 into the other equation to obtain an equation in one variable.		

$$2x - 5y = 3 \qquad \text{Equation (1)}$$
$$2x - 5(2x + 9) = 3 \qquad \text{Substitute } 2x + 9 \text{ for } y.$$
$$2x - 10x - 45 = 3 \qquad \text{Distributive property}$$
$$-8x - 45 = 3 \qquad \text{Combine like terms.}$$

Step 3   **Solve** the equation obtained in Step 2.

$$-8x - 45 = 3 \qquad \text{Equation from Step 2}$$
$$-8x = 3 + 45 \qquad \text{Add 45 to both sides.}$$
$$-8x = 48 \qquad \text{Simplify.}$$
$$x = -6 \qquad \text{Solve for } x.$$

Step 4   **Back-substitute.** Substitute the value(s) you obtained in Step 3 back into the expression you found in Step 1. This gives the solution(s).

$$y = 2x + 9 \qquad \text{Equation (3), from Step 1}$$
$$y = 2(-6) + 9 = -3 \qquad \text{Substitute } x = -6.$$

Thus, $x = -6, y = -3$, and the solution set of the system is $\{(-6, -3)\}$.

Step 5   **Check.** Check your answer(s) in the original equations.

Check: $x = -6$ and $y = -3$.

$$2(-6) - 5(-3) \overset{?}{=} 3 \qquad \Big| \qquad -3 - 2(-6) \overset{?}{=} 9$$
$$-12 + 15 \quad = 3 \checkmark \quad \Big| \quad -3 + 12 \quad = 9 \checkmark$$

Since there are many steps involved in the process of solving a system of equations, it is possible that you made arithmetic errors. You should check your solution by substituting it into each equation in the original system.

It is possible that, in the process of solving the equation in Step 3, you obtain an equation of the form $0 = k$ (which can be written as $0x = k$ or $0y = k$), where k is a *nonzero* constant. In such cases, the false statement $0 = k$ indicates that the system is *inconsistent*.

EXAMPLE 3   **Attempting to Solve an Inconsistent System of Equations**

Solve the system of equations.

$$\begin{cases} x + y = 3 & (1) \\ 2x + 2y = 9 & (2) \end{cases}$$

Solution

Step 1   Solve equation (1) for y in terms of x.

$$x + y = 3 \qquad \text{Equation (1)}$$
$$y = 3 - x \qquad \text{Add } -x \text{ to both sides.}$$

Step 2   Substitute into equation (2).

$$2x + 2y = 9 \qquad \text{Equation (2)}$$
$$2x + 2(3 - x) = 9 \qquad \text{Replace } y \text{ by } 3 - x \text{ (from Step 1).}$$

Step 3   Solve for x

$$2x + 6 - 2x = 9 \qquad \text{Distributive property}$$
$$0 = 3 \qquad \text{Subtract 6 from both sides and simplify.}$$

A false statement

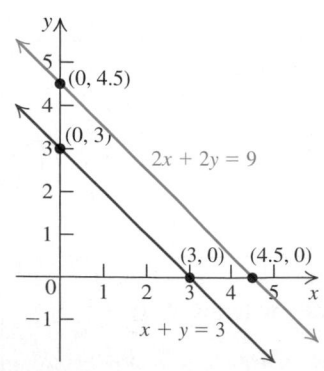

FIGURE 8.3

Since the equation $0 = 3$ is false, the system is inconsistent. Figure 8.3 shows that the graphs of the two equations in this system are parallel lines. Because the lines do not intersect, the system has no solution. The solution set is $\varnothing$.

■ ■ ■

PRACTICE PROBLEM 3   Solve the system of equations.

$$\begin{cases} x - 3y = 1 \\ -2x + 6y = 3 \end{cases}$$ ■

It is also possible that, in the process of solving the equation in Step 3, you obtain an equation of the form $0 = 0$. In such cases the equations in the system are *dependent* and the system has infinitely many solutions.

EXAMPLE 4   **Solving a Dependent System**

Solve the system of equations.

$$\begin{cases} 2x + 4y = 12 & (1) \\ -x - 2y = -6 & (2) \end{cases}$$

Solution

Step 1   Solve equation (2) for x in terms of y.

$-x - 2y = -6$	Equation (2)
$-x = -6 + 2y$	Add $2y$ to both sides.
$x = 6 - 2y$	Multiply both sides by -1.

Step 2   Substitute $(6 - 2y)$ for x in equation (1).

$2x + 4y = 12$	Equation (1)
$2(6 - 2y) + 4y = 12$	Replace x by $6 - 2y$ (from Step 1).

Step 3   Solve for y

$12 - 4y + 4y = 12$	Distributive property
$0 = 0$	Subtract 12 from both sides and simplify.

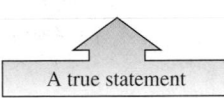

A true statement

The equation $0 = 0$ is true for *every* value of y. Thus, *any* value of y can be used in the equation $x = 6 - 2y$ for back-substitution.

The solutions of the system are of the form $(6 - 2y, y)$ and the solution set is

$$\{(x, y) \mid x = 6 - 2y\}, \text{ or}$$
$$\{(6 - 2y, y) \mid y \text{ a real number}\}$$

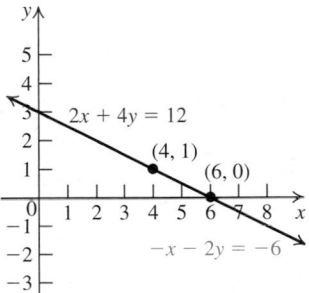

FIGURE 8.4

In other words, the solution set consists of all ordered pairs (x, y) lying on the line with equation $2x + 4y = 12$, as shown in Figure 8.4. The system has infinitely many solutions, one for each value of y. You can find particular solutions by replacing y by any real number. For example, if we let $y = 0$ in $(6 - 2y, y)$, we find that $(6 - 2(0), 0) = (6, 0)$ is a solution of the system. Similarly, letting $y = 1$, we find that $(4, 1)$ is a solution. ■ ■ ■

PRACTICE PROBLEM 4   Solve the system of equations.

$$\begin{cases} -2x + y = -3 \\ 4x - 2y = 6 \end{cases}$$ ■

There are other ways to describe the infinite number of solutions in Example 4. For example, we could solve equation (2) for y:

$$-x - 2y = -6 \qquad (2) \qquad \text{From Example 4}$$
$$-2y = x - 6 \qquad\qquad \text{Add } x \text{ to both sides.}$$
$$y = \frac{6 - x}{2} \qquad\qquad \text{Solve for } y.$$

Hence, every ordered pair of the form $\left(x, \dfrac{6-x}{2}\right)$, where x is any real number, is a solution of the system. Notice that if you let $x = 6$, then $\dfrac{6-x}{2} = \dfrac{0}{2} = 0$, so $(6, 0)$ is one solution of this system. We previously noted this solution in Example 4. In fact, $\left\{\left(x, \dfrac{6-x}{2}\right)\right\}$ and $\{(6 - 2y, y)\}$ describe the same set of ordered pairs. When we write the solution set as $\left\{\left(x, \dfrac{6-x}{2}\right)\right\}$, we say that we have given the solution set with x being *arbitrary,* while when we write $\{(6 - 2y, y)\}$, we have given the solution set with y being *arbitrary.*

4 Solve a system of equations by the elimination method.

Elimination Method

The **elimination method** of solving a system of equations is also called the **addition method.** In this method, you eliminate one of the variables by adding two equations. Here is the procedure.

FINDING THE SOLUTION: ELIMINATION METHOD

OBJECTIVE
To eliminate one variable and reduce the solution of the system to the solution of one equation in one variable.

EXAMPLE
Solve the system.

$$\begin{cases} 2x + 3y = 21 & (1) \\ 3x - 4y = 23 & (2) \end{cases}$$

Step 1 **Adjust the coefficients**. If necessary, multiply both equations by appropriate numbers so as to obtain two new equations in which the coefficients of the variable to be eliminated are the opposites of each other.

We arbitrarily select y as the variable to be eliminated.

$$\begin{cases} 8x + 12y = 84 \\ 9x - 12y = 69 \end{cases}$$

Multiply equation (1) by 4.
Multiply equation (2) by 3.

Coefficients are opposites of each other.

Step 2 **Add the equations.** Add the resulting equations in Step 1 to obtain an equation in one variable.

$$\begin{array}{r} 8x + 12y = 84 \\ 9x - 12y = 69 \\ \hline 17x = 153 \end{array}$$

Adding the two equations from Step 1 eliminates the y-terms.

Step 3 **Solve** the equation obtained in Step 2.

$$17x = 153$$
$$x = \frac{153}{17}$$
$$x = 9$$

Equation from Step 2
Divide both sides by 17.
Simplify.

Step 4	**Back-substitute** the value obtained in Step 3 into one of the original equations to solve for the other variable.	$2x + 3y = 21$	Equation (1)
		$2(9) + 3y = 21$	Replace x by 9.
		$18 + 3y = 21$	$2(9) = 18$
		$3y = 3$	Subtract 18 from both sides.
		$y = 1$	Solve for y.

Step 5 **Write** the solution set from Steps 3 and 4.

The solution set is $\{(9, 1)\}$.

Step 6 **Check** your solution(s) in the original equations (1) and (2).

Check $x = 9$ and $y = 1$.

$$2(9) + 3(1) \stackrel{?}{=} 21 \quad \Big| \quad 3(9) - 4(1) = 23$$
$$18 + 3 = 21 \checkmark \quad \Big| \quad 27 - 4 \quad = 23 \checkmark$$

STUDY TIP

You should use the elimination method when the terms involving one of the variables can easily be eliminated by adding multiples of the equations. Otherwise, use substitution to solve the system. The graphing method is usually used to confirm or visually interpret the result obtained from the other two methods.

Just as in the substitution method, if you add the equations in Step 2 and the resulting equation becomes $0 = k$, where $k \neq 0$, then the system is inconsistent; there are no solutions. As an illustration, if you solve the system of equations in Example 3 by the elimination method, you will obtain the equation $0 = 3$. You now conclude that the system is inconsistent. Similarly, in Step 2, if you obtain $0x + 0y = 0$ (or $0 = 0$), then the equations are dependent.

EXAMPLE 5 **Using the Elimination Method**

Solve the system.

$$\begin{cases} 3x - 4y = 12 & (1) \\ 2x + 5y = 10 & (2) \end{cases}$$

Solution

Step 1 We select the variable y for elimination.

$$\begin{array}{llll} 15x - 20y = & 60 & (3) & \text{Multiply equation (1) by 5.} \\ \underline{8x + 20y = & 40} & (4) & \text{Multiply equation (2) by 4.} \end{array}$$

Step 2 $\qquad\qquad 23x \qquad\quad = 100 \qquad (5) \qquad$ Add (3) and (4).

Step 3 $\qquad\qquad\qquad\qquad x = \dfrac{100}{23} \qquad\qquad$ Solve (5) for x.

Step 4 Back-substitute $x = \dfrac{100}{23}$ in equation (2).

$2x + 5y = 10$	Equation (2)
$2\left(\dfrac{100}{23}\right) + 5y = 10$	Replace x by $\dfrac{100}{23}$.
$5y = 10 - \dfrac{200}{23}$	Subtract $\dfrac{200}{23}$ from both sides.
$5y = \dfrac{30}{23}$	Simplify.
$y = \dfrac{6}{23}$	Solve for y.

STUDY TIP

The graph of a system of equations allows you to use geometric intuition to understand algebra. If the geometric and algebraic representations of a solution do not agree then you must go back and find the error or errors.

Continued on next page.

Step 5   The solution set is $\left\{\left(\dfrac{100}{23}, \dfrac{6}{23}\right)\right\}$.

Step 6   **Check.** You can verify that $x = \dfrac{100}{23}$ and $y = \dfrac{6}{23}$ satisfy both equations (1) and (2).

■ ■ ■

PRACTICE PROBLEM 5   Solve the system.

$$\begin{cases} 3x + 2y = 3 \\ 9x - 4y = 4 \end{cases}$$

■

The next example illustrates how some nonlinear systems can be solved by using substitution of variables to create a linear system and then solving the new system by the elimination method.

EXAMPLE 6	Using the Elimination Method

Solve the system.

$$\begin{cases} \dfrac{2}{x} + \dfrac{5}{y} = -5 & (1) \\ \dfrac{3}{x} - \dfrac{2}{y} = -17 & (2) \end{cases}$$

Solution

Replace $\dfrac{1}{x}$ by u and $\dfrac{1}{y}$ by v. (Recognize that $\dfrac{2}{x} = 2\left(\dfrac{1}{x}\right) = 2u$, etc.) With this substitution, equations (1) and (2) become:

$$\begin{cases} 2u + 5v = -5 & (3) \\ 3u - 2v = -17 & (4) \end{cases}$$

We solve the system made up of equations (3) and (4) for u and v by the elimination method.

Step 1   We select the variable u for elimination.

$6u + 15v = -15$	(5)	Multiply equation (3) by 3.
$-6u + 4v = 34$	(6)	Multiply equation (4) by -2.

Step 2 $\qquad\qquad\qquad 19v = 19$ (7)   Add (5) and (6).

Step 3 $\qquad\qquad\qquad\quad v = 1$ $\qquad\quad$ Divide both sides of (7) by 19.

Step 4   Back-substitute $v = 1$ in equation (3).

$2u + 5v = -5$	Equation (3)
$2u + 5(1) = -5$	Replace v by 1.
$u = -5$	Solve for u.

Step 5 Now solve for x and y, the variables in the original system.

$$u = \frac{1}{x} \qquad \text{and} \qquad v = \frac{1}{y}$$

$-5 = \dfrac{1}{x}$	$1 = \dfrac{1}{y}$ Replace u by -5 and v by 1.
$x = -\dfrac{1}{5}$	$y = 1$ Solve for x and y.

The solution set of the original system is $\left\{\left(-\dfrac{1}{5}, 1\right)\right\}$.

Step 6 You should check to verify that the ordered pair $\left(-\dfrac{1}{5}, 1\right)$ is indeed the solution

of the original system of equations (1) and (2).   ■ ■ ■

PRACTICE PROBLEM 6 Solve the system.

$$\begin{cases} \dfrac{4}{x} + \dfrac{3}{y} = 1 \\[2mm] \dfrac{2}{x} - \dfrac{6}{y} = 3 \end{cases}$$

    ■

5 Solve applied problems by solving systems of equations.

Applications

We can deduce from Section 2.4 that as the price of a product increases, demand for it decreases, and as the price increases, the supply of the product also increases. The **equilibrium point** is the ordered pair (x, p) such that the number of units, x, and the price per unit, p, satisfy *both* the demand and supply equations.

EXAMPLE 7   **Finding the Equilibrium Point**

Find the equilibrium point if the supply and demand functions for a new brand of digital video recorder (DVR) are given by the system

$p = 60 + 0.0012x$	(1)	Supply equation
$p = 80 - 0.0008x$	(2)	Demand equation

where p is the price in dollars and x is the number of units.

Solution

We substitute the value of p from equation (1) into equation (2) and solve the resulting equation.

$p = 80 - 0.0008x$	Demand equation
$60 + 0.0012x = 80 - 0.0008x$	Replace p by $60 + 0.0012x$.
$0.0012x = 20 - 0.0008x$	Subtract 60 from both sides.
$0.002x = 20$	Add $0.0008x$ to both sides.
$x = \dfrac{20}{0.002}$	Divide both sides by 0.002.
$= 10{,}000$	Simplify.

Continued on next page.

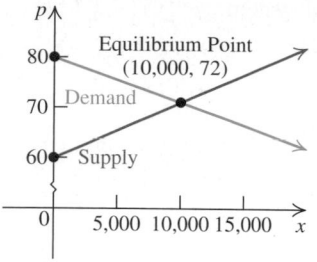

FIGURE 8.5

Thus, the equilibrium point occurs when the supply and demand for DVRs is 10,000 units. To find the price p, we back-substitute $x = 10,000$ into either of the original equations (1) or (2).

$$p = 60 + 0.0012x \qquad \text{Equation (1)}$$
$$= 60 + 0.0012(10,000) \qquad \text{Replace } x \text{ by } 10,000.$$
$$= 72 \qquad \text{Simplify.}$$

The equilibrium point is (10,000, 72). (See Figure 8.5.)

Check. You should verify that the ordered pair (10,000, 72) satisfies both equations (1) and (2).   ■ ■ ■

PRACTICE PROBLEM 7   Find the equilibrium point.

$$\begin{cases} p = 20 + 0.002x & \text{Supply equation} \\ p = 77 - 0.008x & \text{Demand equation} \end{cases} \qquad ■$$

An applied problem involving two unknowns can frequently be solved by setting up equations using variables to represent unknown quantities that are identified in the problem. The general rule is that *the number of equations formed must be equal to the number of unknown quantities involved.*

A Exercises   Basic Skills and Concepts

In Exercises 1–6, determine which ordered pairs are solutions of each system of equations.

1. $\begin{cases} 2x + 3y = 3 \\ 3x - 4y = 13 \end{cases}$ $(1, -3), (3, -1), (6, 3), \left(5, \frac{1}{2}\right)$ (3, −1)

2. $\begin{cases} x + 2y = 6 \\ 3x + 6y = 18 \end{cases}$ $(2, 2), (-2, 4), (0, 3), (1, 2)$ †

3. $\begin{cases} 5x - 2y = 7 \\ -10x + 4y = 11 \end{cases}$ $\left(\frac{5}{4}, 1\right), \left(0, \frac{11}{4}\right), (1, -1), (3, 4)$ ∅

4. $\begin{cases} x - 2y = -5 \\ 3x - y = 5 \end{cases}$ $(1, 3), (-5, 0), (3, 4), (3, -4)$ (3, 4)

5. $\begin{cases} x + y = 1 \\ \frac{1}{2}x + \frac{1}{3}y = 2 \end{cases}$ $(0, 1), (1, 0), \left(\frac{2}{3}, \frac{3}{2}\right), (10, -9)$ (10, −9)

6. $\begin{cases} \dfrac{2}{x} + \dfrac{3}{y} = 2 \\ \dfrac{6}{x} + \dfrac{18}{y} = 9 \end{cases}$ $(3, 2), (2, 3), (4, 3), (3, 4)$ (2, 3)

In Exercises 7–20, determine whether each system is *consistent* or *inconsistent*. If the system is consistent, determine whether the equations are dependent or independent. Do not solve the system.

7. $\begin{cases} y = -2x + 3 \\ y = 3x + 5 \end{cases}$ Independent

8. $\begin{cases} 3x + y = 5 \\ 2x + y = 4 \end{cases}$ Independent

9. $\begin{cases} 2x + 3y = 5 \\ 3x + 2y = 7 \end{cases}$ Independent

10. $\begin{cases} 2x - 4y = 5 \\ 3x + 5y = -6 \end{cases}$ †

11. $\begin{cases} 3x + 5y = 7 \\ 6x + 10y = 14 \end{cases}$ †

12. $\begin{cases} 3x - y = 2 \\ 9x - 3y = 6 \end{cases}$ Dependent

13. $\begin{cases} x + 2y = -5 \\ 2x - y = 4 \end{cases}$ †

14. $\begin{cases} x + 2y = -2 \\ 2x - 3y = 5 \end{cases}$ †

15. $\begin{cases} 2x - 3y = 5 \\ 6x - 9y = 10 \end{cases}$ †

16. $\begin{cases} 3x + y = 2 \\ 15x + 5y = 15 \end{cases}$ †

17. $\begin{cases} -3x + 4y = 5 \\ \dfrac{9}{2}x - 6y = \dfrac{15}{2} \end{cases}$ †

18. $\begin{cases} 6x + 5y = 11 \\ 9x + \dfrac{15}{2}y = 21 \end{cases}$ †

19. $\begin{cases} 7x - 2y = 3 \\ 11x - \dfrac{3}{2}y = 8 \end{cases}$ †

20. $\begin{cases} 4x + 7y = 10 \\ 10x + \dfrac{35}{2}y = 25 \end{cases}$ †

In Exercises 21–30, estimate the solution(s) (if any) of each system by the graphical method. Check your solution(s). For any dependent equations, write your answer with x being arbitrary.

21. $\begin{cases} x + y = 3 \\ x - y = 1 \end{cases}$ †

22. $\begin{cases} x + y = 10 \\ x - y = 2 \end{cases}$ †

23. $\begin{cases} x + 2y = 6 \\ 2x + y = 6 \end{cases}$ †

24. $\begin{cases} 2x - y = 4 \\ x - y = 3 \end{cases}$ †

25. $\begin{cases} 3x - y = -9 \\ y = 3x + 6 \end{cases}$ †

26. $\begin{cases} 5x + 2y = 10 \\ y = -\dfrac{5}{2}x - 5 \end{cases}$ †

†Due to space constrictions, answers to these exercises may be found in the Answers beginning on page A–1 in the back of the book.

27. $\begin{cases} x + y = 7 \\ \quad\quad y = 2x \end{cases}$ †

28. $\begin{cases} y - x = 2 \\ y + x = 9 \end{cases}$ †

29. $\begin{cases} 3x + y = 12 \\ \quad\quad y = -3x + 12 \end{cases}$ †

30. $\begin{cases} 2x + 3y = 6 \\ \quad\quad 6y = -4x + 12 \end{cases}$ †

In Exercises 31–40, solve each system of equations by the substitution method. Check your solutions. For any dependent equations, write your answer with y being arbitrary.

31. $\begin{cases} \quad\quad y = 2x + 1 \\ 5x + 2y = 9 \end{cases}$ †

32. $\begin{cases} \quad\quad x = 3y - 1 \\ 2x - 3y = 7 \end{cases}$ (8, 3)

33. $\begin{cases} 3x - y = 5 \\ x + y = 7 \end{cases}$ (3, 4)

34. $\begin{cases} 2x + y = 2 \\ 3x - y = -7 \end{cases}$ (1, 4)

35. $\begin{cases} 2x - y = 5 \\ -4x + 2y = 7 \end{cases}$ ∅

36. $\begin{cases} 3x + 2y = 5 \\ -9x - 6y = 15 \end{cases}$ ∅

37. $\begin{cases} \dfrac{2}{3}x + \quad y = 3 \\ 3x + 2y = 1 \end{cases}$ (−3, 5)

38. $\begin{cases} x - 2y = 3 \\ 4x + 6y = 3 \end{cases}$ $\left(\dfrac{12}{7}, \dfrac{-9}{14}\right)$

39. $\begin{cases} \quad x - 2y = 5 \\ -3x + 6y = -15 \end{cases}$ †

40. $\begin{cases} x + \quad y = 3 \\ 2x + 2y = 6 \end{cases}$ $\{(3 - y, y)\}$

In Exercises 41–50, solve each system of equations by the elimination method. Check your solutions. For any dependent equations, write your answer with x being arbitrary.

41. $\begin{cases} x - y = 1 \\ x + y = 5 \end{cases}$ (3, 2)

42. $\begin{cases} 2x - 3y = 5 \\ 3x + 2y = 14 \end{cases}$ (4, 1)

43. $\begin{cases} x + \quad y = 0 \\ 2x + 3y = 3 \end{cases}$ (−3, 3)

44. $\begin{cases} x + y = 3 \\ 3x + y = 1 \end{cases}$ (−1, 4)

45. $\begin{cases} 5x - \quad y = 5 \\ 3x + 2y = -10 \end{cases}$ (0, −5)

46. $\begin{cases} 3x - 2y = 1 \\ -7x + 3y = 1 \end{cases}$ (−1, −2)

47. $\begin{cases} \quad x - \quad y = 2 \\ -2x + 2y = 5 \end{cases}$ ∅

48. $\begin{cases} 4x + \quad 7y = -3 \\ -8x - 14y = 6 \end{cases}$ †

49. $\begin{cases} 4x + 6y = 12 \\ 2x + 3y = 6 \end{cases}$ †

50. $\begin{cases} x + \quad y = 5 \\ 2x + 2y = -10 \end{cases}$ ∅

In Exercises 51–70, use any method to solve each system of equations. For any dependent equations, write your answer with y being arbitrary.

51. $\begin{cases} 2x + \quad y = 9 \\ 2x - 3y = 5 \end{cases}$ (4, 1)

52. $\begin{cases} x + 2y = 10 \\ x - 2y = -6 \end{cases}$ (2, 4)

53. $\begin{cases} 2x + 5y = 2 \\ \quad x + 3y = 2 \end{cases}$ (−4, 2)

54. $\begin{cases} 4x - \quad y = 6 \\ 3x - 4y = 11 \end{cases}$ (1, −2)

55. $\begin{cases} 2x + 3y = 7 \\ 3x + \quad y = 7 \end{cases}$ (2, 1)

56. $\begin{cases} x = 3y + 4 \\ x = 5y + 10 \end{cases}$ (−5, −3)

57. $\begin{cases} 2x + 3y = 9 \\ 3x + 2y = 11 \end{cases}$ (3, 1)

58. $\begin{cases} 3x - 4y = 0 \\ \quad\quad y = \dfrac{2x + 1}{3} \end{cases}$ (4, 3)

59. $\begin{cases} \dfrac{x}{4} + \dfrac{y}{6} = 1 \\ x + 2(x - y) = 7 \end{cases}$ †

60. $\begin{cases} \dfrac{x}{3} + \dfrac{y}{5} = 12 \\ x - \quad y = 4 \end{cases}$ (24, 20)

61. $\begin{cases} 3x \quad\quad = 2(x + y) \\ 3x - 5y = 2 \end{cases}$ †

62. $\begin{cases} y + \quad x + 2 = 0 \\ y + 2x + 1 = 0 \end{cases}$ (1, −3)

63. $\begin{cases} 0.2x + 0.7y = 1.5 \\ 0.4x - 0.3y = 1.3 \end{cases}$ (4, 1)

64. $\begin{cases} 0.6x + \quad y = -1 \\ \quad x - 0.5y = 7 \end{cases}$ †

65. $\begin{cases} \dfrac{2}{x} + \dfrac{5}{y} = -5 \\ \dfrac{3}{x} - \dfrac{2}{y} = -17 \end{cases}$ $\left(-\dfrac{1}{5}, 1\right)$

66. $\begin{cases} \dfrac{2}{x} + \dfrac{1}{y} = 3 \\ \dfrac{4}{x} - \dfrac{2}{y} = 0 \end{cases}$ $\left(\dfrac{4}{3}, \dfrac{2}{3}\right)$

67. $\begin{cases} \dfrac{3}{x} + \dfrac{1}{y} = 4 \\ \dfrac{6}{x} - \dfrac{1}{y} = 2 \end{cases}$ $\left(\dfrac{3}{2}, \dfrac{1}{2}\right)$

68. $\begin{cases} \dfrac{6}{x} + \dfrac{3}{y} = 0 \\ \dfrac{4}{x} + \dfrac{9}{y} = -1 \end{cases}$ (14, −7)

69. $\begin{cases} \dfrac{5}{x} + \dfrac{10}{y} = 3 \\ \dfrac{2}{x} - \dfrac{12}{y} = -2 \end{cases}$ (5, 5)

70. $\begin{cases} \dfrac{3}{x} + \dfrac{4}{y} = 1 \\ \dfrac{6}{x} + \dfrac{4}{y} = 3 \end{cases}$ $\left(\dfrac{3}{2}, -4\right)$

B Exercises   Applying the Concepts

In Exercises 71–74, the demand and supply functions of a product are given. In each case, p represents the price in dollars per unit and x represents the number of units in hundreds. Find the equilibrium point.

71. $\begin{cases} 2p + x = 140 \quad \text{Demand equation} \\ 12p - x = 280 \quad \text{Supply equation} \end{cases}$ (80, 30)

72. $\begin{cases} 7p + x = 150 \quad \text{Demand equation} \\ 10p - x = 20 \quad \text{Supply equation} \end{cases}$ (80, 10)

73. $\begin{cases} 2p + x = 25 \quad \text{Demand equation} \\ \quad x - p = 13 \quad \text{Supply equation} \end{cases}$ (17, 4)

74. $\begin{cases} p + 2x = 96 \quad \text{Demand equation} \\ p - \quad x = 39 \quad \text{Supply equation} \end{cases}$ (19, 58)

In Exercises 75–90, use a system of equations to solve each problem.

75. Diameter of a pizza. The sum of the diameters of the largest and the smallest pizza sold at the Monster Pizza Shop is 29 inches. The difference of their diameters is 13 inches. Find the diameters of the largest and the smallest pizza. †

76. Calories in hamburgers. The sum of the number of calories in a hamburger from Boston Burger and a hamburger from Carmen's Broiler is 1130. The difference in the number of calories in the hamburgers is 40. If the Boston Burger has the larger number of calories, how many calories are in each restaurant's hamburger? †

77. Trash composition. Paper and plastic together account for 48% (by weight) of the total trash collected. If the weight of paper trash collected is five times the weight of plastic trash, what percent of the total trash collected is paper and what percent is plastic? †

78. Cost of food and clothing. The average monthly combined cost of food and clothing for the Martínez family is 1000 dollars. If they spend four times as much for food as they do for clothes, what is the average monthly cost of each? †

79. Mardi Gras parade "throws." Levon paid 40 cents for each string of beads and 30 cents for each doubloon (a special coin) he bought to throw from his Mardi Gras float. He paid a total of 265 dollars for the two items. His doubloons and beads combined to a total of 770 "throws." How many doubloons and how many strings of beads did Levon buy? †

80. Halloween candy. Janet bought 135 pieces of candy to give away on Halloween. She bought two kinds of candy, paying 24 cents apiece for one kind and 18 cents apiece for the other. If she spent 26.70 dollars for the candy, how many pieces of each kind did she buy? †

In Exercises 81 and 82, use the information in the following table:

Food Description McDonald's	Fat (gms)	Carb (gms)	Protein (gms)
Breakfast Burrito	20	21	13
Egg McMuffin®	12	27	17

Source: www.shapefit.com/mcdonalds.html
Suppose you are going to eat breakfast at McDonald's during the workweek (Monday–Friday).

81. McDonald's breakfast. Your goal is a total of 123 grams of carbohydrates and 77 grams of protein. How many of each breakfast should you eat during the workweek to reach your goal? 3 Egg McMuffins and 2 Breakfast Burritos

82. McDonald's breakfast. Your goal is a total of 68 grams of fat and 129 grams of carbohydrates. How many of each breakfast should you eat during the workweek to reach your goal? 4 Egg McMuffins and 1 Breakfast Burrito

83. Investment. Last year, Mrs. García invested 50,000 dollars. Part of the money was invested in a real estate venture that paid 7.5% for the year, and the rest was invested in a small-business venture that returned 12% for the year. The combined income from the two investments for the year totaled 5190 dollars. How much did she invest at each rate? †

84. Investment. Mr. Sharma invested a total of 30,000 dollars in two ventures for a year. The annual return from one of them was 8%, and the other paid 10.5% for the year. He received a total income of 2550 dollars from both investments. How much was invested at each rate? †

85. Tutoring other students. A student earns twice as much per hour for tutoring as she does working at McDougal's. If her average wage is 11 dollars and 25 cents per hour, how much does she earn per hour at each job? †

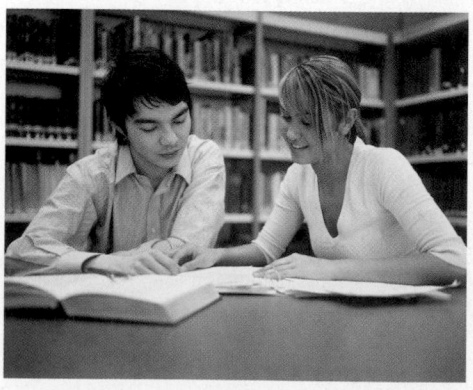

86. Plumber's earnings. A plumber earns 15 dollars per hour more than her apprentice. For a 40-hour week, their combined earnings were 2200 dollars. What is the hourly rate for each?

87. Mixture problem. An herb that sells for 5 dollars and 50 cents per pound is mixed with tea that sells for 3 dollars and 20 cents per pound to produce a 100-pound mix that is worth 3 dollars and 66 cents per pound. How many pounds of each ingredient does the mix contain?

88. Mixture problem. A chemist had a solution of 60% acid. She added some distilled water, reducing the acid concentration to 40%. She then added 1 more liter of water to further reduce the acid concentration to 30%. How much of the 30% solution did she then have? 4 liters

89. Airplane speed. With the help of a tail wind, a plane travels 3000 kilometers in 5 hours. The return trip against the wind requires 6 hours. Assume that the direction and the wind speed are constant. Find both the speed of the plane in still air and the wind speed. [*Hint:* Remember that the wind helps the plane in one direction and hinders it in the other.]

90. Motorboat speed. A motorboat travels up a stream a distance of 12 miles in 2 hours. If the current had been twice as strong, the trip would have taken 3 hours. How long should it take for the return trip down the stream? 1.2 hours

91. Break-even analysis. A local publishing company publishes *City Magazine*. The production and setup costs are 30,000 dollars, and the cost of producing each magazine is 2 dollars. Each magazine sells for 3 dollars and 50 cents. Assume that x magazines are published and sold.
  a. Write the total cost function $y = C(x)$ and the revenue function $y = R(x)$. $C(x) = 30,000 + 2x, R(x) = 3.5x$
  b. Graph both functions from part (a) on the same coordinate plane. †
  c. How many magazines must be sold to break even?
  20,000 magazines

92. Break-even analysis. An electronic manufacturer plans to make digital portable music players (MP4's). Fixed costs will be 750,000 dollars, and it will cost 50 dollars to manufacture each MP4, which will be sold for 125 dollars to the retailers. Assume that x MP4's are manufactured and sold.
  a. Write the total cost function $y = C(x)$ and the revenue function $y = R(x)$. $C(x) = 750,000 + 50x, R(x) = 125x$
  b. Graph both functions from part (a) on the same coordinate plane. †
  c. How many MP4's must be sold to break even?

93. Making a job decision. Shanaysha has two job offers to sell major appliances from two department stores *A* and *B*. Store *A* offers her a fixed salary of 400 dollars per week. Store *B* offers her 150 dollars per week, plus a commission of 4% of her weekly sales. How much should Shanaysha's weekly sales be for the offer from Store *B* to be better than that from Store *A*? Her weekly sales should be more than $6250.

94. Making a job decision. Sheena has two job offers to sell insurance from companies *A* and *B*. Company *A* offers her 25,000 dollars per year, plus 2% of her yearly sales premiums. Company *B* offers her 30,000 dollars per year, plus 1% of her yearly sales premiums. How much must Sheena earn in yearly sales premiums for the offer from Company *B* to be the better offer? If Sheena earns less than $500,000 in sales premiums.

Answers:
86. The plumber earns $35 per hour and her apprentice earns $20 per hour.
87. 20 pounds of herb and 80 pounds of tea
89. The speed of the plane is 550 km/hr and the wind speed is 50 km/hr.
92. c. 10,000 MP4's

C Exercises   Beyond the Basics

95. Solve for x and y.

$$\begin{cases} \dfrac{40}{x+y} + \dfrac{2}{x-y} = 5 \\ \dfrac{25}{x+y} - \dfrac{2}{x-y} = 1 \end{cases} \left(\dfrac{1261}{204}, \dfrac{949}{204} \right)$$

[*Hint:* Let $u = \dfrac{1}{x+y}$ and $v = \dfrac{1}{x-y}$, solve for u and v, and then solve for x and y.]

96. Solve for x and y.

$$\begin{cases} 6x + 3y = 7xy \\ 3x + 9y = 11xy \end{cases} \text{If } xy = 0, \text{ then } (0, 0). \text{ If } xy \neq 0, \text{ then } \left(1, \dfrac{3}{2} \right).$$

[*Hint:* Case (*i*), $xy = 0$; case (*ii*), $xy \neq 0$: Divide by xy.]

97. For what value of the constant c does the following system have only one solution?

$$\begin{cases} x + 2y = 7 \\ 3x + 5y = 11 \quad c = 2 \\ cx + 3y = 4 \end{cases}$$

[*Hint:* Solve the first two equations for x and y, and then substitute the solution into the third equation.]

98. Repeat Exercise 97 for the following system of equations:

$$\begin{cases} 5x + 7y = 11 \\ 13x + 17y = 19 \quad c = 4 \\ 3x + cy = 5 \end{cases}$$

In Exercises 99–101, write your answer in slope–intercept form.

99. Find an equation of the line that passes through the point of intersection of the lines with equations $2x + y = 3$ and $x - 3y = 12$ and that is parallel to the line with equation $3x + 2y = 8$. $y = -\frac{3}{2}x + \frac{3}{2}$

100. Find an equation of the line that passes through the point of intersection of the lines with equations $5x + 2y = 7$ and $6x - 5y = 38$ and that also passes through the point $(1, 3)$.

$$y = -\frac{7}{2}x + \frac{13}{2}$$

101. Find an equation of the line that passes through the point of intersection of the lines with equations $2x + 5y + 7 = 0$ and $13x - 10y + 3 = 0$ and that is perpendicular to the line with equation $7x + 13y = 8$. $y = \frac{13}{7}x + \frac{6}{7}$

Critical Thinking

102. Consider the system of equations

$$\begin{cases} a_1x + b_1y = c_1 \\ a_2x + b_2y = c_2 \end{cases}$$

where $a_1, b_1, c_1, a_2, b_2,$ and c_2 are constants. Find a relationship (an equation) among these constants such that the system of equations has

a. Only one solution. Find the solution in terms of the constants. †

b. No solution. †

c. Infinitely many solutions. †

103. Let $3x + 4y - 12 = 0$ be the equation of a line l_1, and let $P(5, 8)$ be a point.

a. Find an equation of a line l_2 passing through the point P and perpendicular to l_1. $3y - 4x = 4$

b. Find the point Q of the intersection of the two lines l_1 and l_2.

c. Find the distance $d(P, Q)$. This is the distance from the point P to the line l_1. 7

104. Use the procedure outlined in Exercise 103 to show that the (perpendicular) distance from a point $P(x_1, y_1)$ to the line $ax + by + c = 0$ is given by $\dfrac{|ax_1 + by_1 + c|}{\sqrt{a^2 + b^2}}$. †

105. Use the formula from Exercise 104 to find the distance from the given point P to the given line l.

a. $P(2, 3)$, $l: x + y - 7 = 0$ $\sqrt{2}$

b. $P(-2, 5)$, $l: 2x - y + 3 = 0$

c. $P(3, 4)$, $l: 5x - 2y - 7 = 0$ 0

d. $P(0, 0)$, $l: ax + by + c = 0$

Answers

103. b. $\left(\dfrac{4}{5}, \dfrac{12}{5} \right)$

104. a. $b(x - x_1) - a(y - y_1) = 0$

b. $\left(\dfrac{b^2x_1 - aby_1 - ac}{a^2 + b^2}, \dfrac{-abx_1 + a^2y_1 - bc}{a^2 + b^2} \right)$

105. b. $\dfrac{6\sqrt{5}}{5}$

d. $\dfrac{|c|}{\sqrt{a^2 + b^2}}$ if $a \neq 0$ or $b \neq 0$

Systems of Linear Equations in Three Variables

BEFORE STARTING THIS SECTION, REVIEW

1. Solving systems of linear equations (Section 8.1, page 738)

2. Solving a system of equations in two variables (Section 8.1, page 741)

OBJECTIVES

1 Solve a system of linear equations in three variables.

2 Classify systems as consistent and inconsistent.

3 Solve nonsquare systems.

4 Interpret linear systems in three variables geometrically.

5 Use linear systems in applications.

CAT Scans

Computerized axial tomography imaging is more commonly known as a "CAT scan" or "CT scan." Tomography is from the Greek word *tomos*, meaning "slice or section" and *graphia*, meaning "describing." The CAT scan machine was invented in 1972 by British engineer Godfrey Hounsfield and, independently, by physicist Allan Cormack of Tufts University in Massachusetts. Hounsfield never attended a university, but he started experimenting with electrical and mechanical devices as a boy. He shared a Nobel Prize in 1979 with Cormack for inventing the scanner technology and was honored with knighthood in England for his contributions to medicine and science. CAT scanners use X-rays measured outside the patient's body, together with algebraic computations, to construct pictures of the patient's internal body organs, including the brain. Thus, no camera ever *photographs* the brain. The scanner does not "take" any pictures; instead, it *computes* pictures. The principle underlying the working of the CAT scanner is very simple. When an X-ray passes through an object, it loses intensity. The denser the object, the more intensity the X-ray loses. Since tumors are denser than healthy tissues, an unexpected loss of intensity may indicate the presence of a tumor. To obtain sufficient information, a large number of properly arranged X-rays is needed. Imagine a cross section of body tissue with a superimposed mathematical grid. Each region bounded by the grid lines is called a *grid cell*. In an actual CAT scan, each grid cell is 2 square millimeters and contains 10,000 or more biological cells. The grid shown in Figure 8.6 would require many X-rays. Actual CAT scanners work with grids that have 512×512 grid cells and require hundreds of thousands of X-ray beams. In Example 5, we will discuss a simple situation in which X-rays pass through 3 grid cells. ■

Cross section with tumor

FIGURE 8.6 Cross section with tumor

Adapted with permission from *Mathematics Teacher*, May 1996. © 1996 by the National Council of Teachers of Mathematics.

1 Solve a system of linear equations in three variables.

Systems of Linear Equations

A **linear equation in the variables** $x_1, x_2, \ldots, x_n$ is an equation that can be written in the form

$$a_1x_1 + a_2x_2 + \cdots + a_nx_n = b,$$

where b and the *coefficients* $a_1, a_2, \ldots, a_n$ are real numbers. The subscript n may be any positive integer. When n is small—say, between 2 and 5 (as in most textbook examples and exercises)—we normally use x, y, z, u, and v instead of x_1, x_2, x_3, x_4, and x_5. However, in real-life applications, n might be 100 or 1000, or even greater.

A **system of linear equations** (or a **linear system**) in three variables is a collection of two or more linear equations involving the same variables. For example,

$$\begin{cases} x + 3y + z = 0 \\ 2x - y + z = 5 \\ 3x - 3y + 2z = 10 \end{cases}$$

is a system of three linear equations in the three variables x, y, and z. An ordered triple (a, b, c) is a **solution** of a system of three equations in three variables x, y, and z if each equation in the system is a true statement when a, b, and c are substituted for x, y, and z, respectively.

EXAMPLE 1   Verifying a Solution

Determine whether the ordered triple $(2, -1, 3)$ is a solution of the given linear system.

$$\begin{cases} 5x + 3y - 2z = 1 & (1) \\ x - y + z = 6 & (2) \\ 2x + 2y - z = -1 & (3) \end{cases}$$

Solution

To determine whether the ordered triple $(2, -1, 3)$ is a solution of the system, we replace x by 2, y by -1, and z by 3 in all three equations.

Equation (1)	Equation (2)	Equation (3)
$5x + 3y - 2z = 1$	$x - y + z = 6$	$2x + 2y - z = -1$
$5(2) + 3(-1) - 2(3) \stackrel{?}{=} 1$	$2 - (-1) + 3 \stackrel{?}{=} 6$	$2(2) + 2(-1) - (3) \stackrel{?}{=} -1$
$10 - 3 - 6 \stackrel{?}{=} 1$	$2 + 1 + 3 \stackrel{?}{=} 6$	$4 - 2 - 3 \stackrel{?}{=} -1$
$1 = 1 \checkmark$	$6 = 6 \checkmark$	$-1 = -1 \checkmark$

Since the ordered triple $(2, -1, 3)$ satisfies all three equations, it is a solution of the system.

■ ■ ■

PRACTICE PROBLEM 1   Determine whether the ordered triple $(2, -3, 2)$ is a solution of the system.

$$\begin{cases} x + y + z = 1 \\ 3x + 4y + z = -4 \\ 2x + y + 2z = 5 \end{cases}$$

■

We use elimination to convert a system of three equations in the variables x, y, and z into an equivalent system in *triangular form* with leading coefficient 1, as shown below.

$$\begin{cases} x + ay + bz = p & (1) \\ y + cz = q & (2) \\ z = z_0 & (3) \end{cases}$$

We can then solve the system by back substitution.

Toward that end, the following three operations are used to obtain equivalent systems (systems with the same solution set as the original system).

OPERATIONS THAT PRODUCE EQUIVALENT SYSTEMS

1. Interchange the position of any two equations.
2. Multiply any equation by a nonzero constant.
3. Add a nonzero multiple of one equation to another.

A step-by-step procedure called the *Gaussian elimination method* is used to convert a system of linear equations into an equivalent system in triangular form.

FINDING THE SOLUTION: GAUSSIAN ELIMINATION METHOD

OBJECTIVE

To solve a system of three equations in three variables by first converting the system to the form

$$\begin{cases} x + ay + bz = p \\ y + cz = q \\ z = z_0 \end{cases}$$

EXAMPLE

Solve the system of equations.

$$\begin{cases} 3y - z = 5 & (1) \\ 2x + y + z = 9 & (2) \\ x + 2y + 2z = 3 & (3) \end{cases}$$

Step 1 Rearrange the equations, if necessary, to obtain an x-term with a nonzero coefficient in the first equation. Then multiply the first equation by the reciprocal of the coefficient of the x-term to get 1 as a leading coefficient.

Interchange Equations (1) and (3):

$$\begin{cases} x + 2y + 2z = 3 & (3) \\ 2x + y + z = 9 & (2) \\ 3y - z = 5 & (1) \end{cases}$$

The first equation (Equation (3)) already has a leading coefficient of 1.

Step 2 By adding appropriate multiples of the first equation, eliminate any x-terms from the second and third equations. Multiply the resulting second equation by the reciprocal of the coefficient of the y-term to get 1 as a leading coefficient.

To eliminate x from Equation (2), add -2 times Equation (3) to equation (2).

$$\begin{array}{rl} 2x - 4y - 4z = -6 & \quad -2 \text{ times Equation (3)} \\ \underline{2x + y + z = 9} & \quad (2) \\ -3y - 3z = 3 & \quad (4) \qquad \text{Add.} \end{array}$$

$$\begin{cases} x + 2y + 2z = 3 & (3) \\ y + z = -1 & (5) \\ 3y - z = 5 & (1) \end{cases} \quad \text{Multiply Equation (4) by } -\frac{1}{3}.$$

Continued on next page.

| Step 3 | If necessary, by adding an appropriate multiple of the second equation from Step 2, eliminate any y-term from the third equation. Solve the resulting equation for z. |

$$
\begin{aligned}
-3y - 3z &= 3 \\
\underline{3y - z} &= 5 \quad (1) \\
-4z &= 8 \\
z &= -2
\end{aligned}
$$

Multiply Equation (5) by -3.

Add.

Solve for z.

| Step 4 | Back-substitute the value of z from Step 3 into one of the equations in Step 3 that contains only y and z, and solve for y. |

$$
\begin{aligned}
3y - z &= 5 \\
3y - (-2) &= 5 \\
3y + 2 &= 5 \\
y &= 1
\end{aligned}
$$

Equation (1) from Step 3

Substitute $z = -2$.

Solve for y.

| Step 5 | Back-substitute the values of y and z from Steps 3 and 4 in any equation containing x, y, and z, and solve for x. |

$$
\begin{aligned}
x + 2y + 2z &= 3 \\
x + 2(1) + 2(-2) &= 3 \\
x &= 5
\end{aligned}
$$

Equation (3) from Step 1

Substitute $y = 1$, $z = -2$.

Solve for x.

| Step 6 | Write the solution set. |

The solution set is $\{(5, 1, -2)\}$.

| Step 7 | Check your answer in the original equations. |

Check: Verify the solution by substituting $x = 5$, $y = 1$, and $z = -2$ in each of the original equations.

$$
\begin{aligned}
3(1) - (-2) &= 5 \checkmark \quad (1) \\
2(5) + (1) + (-2) &= 9 \checkmark \quad (2) \\
5 + 2(1) + 2(-2) &= 3 \checkmark \quad (3)
\end{aligned}
$$

2 Classify systems as consistent and inconsistent.

Number of Solutions of a Linear System

Just as in the case of two variables, a system of linear equations in three variables may be **consistent** (it has at least one solution) or **inconsistent** (it has no solution). The equations in a consistent system may be **dependent** (the system has infinitely many solutions) or **independent** (the system has one solution).

INCONSISTENT SYSTEM

If, in the process of converting a linear system to triangular form, an equation of the form $0 = a$ occurs, where $a \neq 0$, then the system has no solution and is *inconsistent*.

EXAMPLE 2   Attempting to Solve a Linear System with No Solution

Solve the system of equations.

$$
\begin{cases}
x - y + 2z = 5 & (1) \\
2x + y + z = 7 & (2) \\
3x - 2y + 5z = 20 & (3)
\end{cases}
$$

Solution

Steps 1–2   To eliminate x from Equation (2), add -2 times Equation (1) to Equation (2).

$$
\begin{aligned}
-2x + 2y - 4z &= -10 \\
\underline{2x + y + z} &= 7 \quad (2) \\
3y - 3z &= -3 \quad (4)
\end{aligned}
$$

-2 times Equation (1)

Add.

We next add -3 times Equation (1) to Equation (3) to eliminate x from equation (3).

$$
\begin{array}{ll}
-3x + 3y - 6z = -15 & \quad -3 \text{ times Equation (1)} \\
\underline{3x - 2y + 5z = 20} \quad (3) & \\
y - z = 5 \quad (5) & \quad \text{Add.}
\end{array}
$$

We now have the following system:

$$
\begin{cases}
x - y + 2z = 5 & (1) \\
3y - 3z = -3 & (4) \\
y - z = 5 & (5)
\end{cases}
$$

Step 3   Multiply Equation (4) by $\dfrac{1}{3}$ to obtain

$$
y - z = -1 \qquad (6)
$$

To eliminate y from Equation (5), add -1 times Equation (6) to Equation (5).

$$
\begin{array}{ll}
-y + z = 1 & \quad -1 \text{ times Equation (6)} \\
\underline{y - z = 5} \quad (5) & \\
0 = 6 \quad (7) & \quad \text{Add.}
\end{array}
$$

We now have the system in triangular form:

$$
\begin{cases}
x - y + 2z = 5 & (1) \\
y - z = -1 & (4) \\
0 = 6 & (7)
\end{cases}
$$

False statement

This system is equivalent to the original system. Since equation (7) is false, we conclude that the solution set of the system is $\varnothing$ and the system is inconsistent.

■ ■ ■

PRACTICE PROBLEM 2   Solve the system of equations:

$$
\begin{cases}
2x + 2y + 2z = 12 \\
-3x + y - 11z = -6 \\
2x + y + 4z = -8
\end{cases}
$$

■

DEPENDENT EQUATIONS

If, in the process of converting a linear system to triangular form,

(i)   an equation of the form $0 = a\ (a \neq 0)$ *does not* occur, but

(ii)   an equation of the form $0 = 0$ *does* occur, then the system of equations has infinitely many solutions and the equations are *dependent*.

EXAMPLE 3   **Solving a System with Infinitely Many Solutions**

Solve the system of equations.

$$\begin{cases} x - y + z = 7 & (1) \\ 3x + 2y - 12z = 11 & (2) \\ 4x + y - 11z = 18 & (3) \end{cases}$$

Solution

Steps 1–2   Eliminate x from Equation (2) by adding -3 times Equation (1) to Equation (2).

$$\begin{array}{rll} -3x + 3y - 3z = -21 & & \text{-3 times Equation (1)} \\ \underline{3x + 2y - 12z = 11} & (2) & \\ 5y - 15z = -10 & (4) & \text{Add.} \end{array}$$

Eliminate x from Equation (3) by adding -4 times Equation (1) to Equation (3).

$$\begin{array}{rll} -4x + 4y - 4z = -28 & & \text{-4 times Equation (1)} \\ \underline{4x + y - 11z = 18} & (3) & \\ 5y - 15z = -10 & (5) & \text{Add.} \end{array}$$

We now have the equivalent system:

$$\begin{cases} x - y + z = 7 & (1) \\ 5y - 15z = -10 & (4) \\ 5y - 15z = -10 & (5) \end{cases}$$

Step 3   To eliminate y from Equation (5), add -1 times Equation (4) to Equation (5).

$$\begin{array}{rll} -5y + 15z = 10 & & \text{-1 times Equation (4)} \\ \underline{5y - 15z = -10} & (5) & \\ 0 = 0 & (6) & \text{Add.} \end{array}$$

We finally have the system in triangular form:

$$\begin{cases} x - y + z = 7 & (1) \\ 5y - 15z = -10 & (4) \\ 0 = 0 & (6) \end{cases}$$

A true statement

Notice that the equation $0 = 0$, may be interpreted as $0z = 0$, which is true for every value of z. Solving equation (4) for y, we have $y = 3z - 2$. Substituting $y = 3z - 2$ into equation (1) and solving for x, we obtain

$$\begin{array}{ll} x = y - z + 7 & \text{Solve equation (1) for x.} \\ x = (3z - 2) - z + 7 & \text{Substitute } y = 3z - 2. \\ x = 2z + 5. & \text{Simplify.} \end{array}$$

Thus, every triple $(x, y, z) = (2z + 5, 3z - 2, z)$ is a solution of the system for each value of z. For example, with $z = 0$, the triple $(5, -2, 0)$ is a solution of the system. Similarly, for $z = 1$, the triple $(7, 1, 1)$ is a solution of the system.

Hence, the given system has infinitely many solutions, one for each value of z and the equations are dependent. The solution set for the system is $\{(2z + 5, 3z - 2, z)\}$, with z being arbitrary.   ■ ■ ■

PRACTICE PROBLEM 3   Solve the system of equations.

$$\begin{cases} x + y + z = 5 \\ -4x - y - 8z = -29 \\ 2x + 5y - 2z = 1 \end{cases}$$ ■

3 Solve nonsquare systems.

Nonsquare Systems

Sometimes in a linear system, the number of equations is not the same as the number of variables. Such systems are called **nonsquare linear systems.**

EXAMPLE 4   **Solving a Nonsquare Linear System**

Solve the system of linear equations.

$$\begin{cases} x + 5y + 3z = 7 & (1) \\ 2x + 11y - 4z = 6 & (2) \end{cases}$$

Solution

Steps 1–2   To eliminate x from equation (2), add -2 times equation (1) to equation (2).

$$\begin{array}{rl} -2x - 10y - 6z = -14 & \quad -2 \text{ times equation (1)} \\ \underline{2x + 11y - 4z = 6} & \quad (2) \\ y - 10z = -8 & \quad (3) \qquad \text{Add.} \end{array}$$

We obtain the equivalent system:

$$\begin{cases} x + 5y + 3z = 7 & (1) \\ y - 10z = -8 & (3) \end{cases}$$

Steps 3–4   Since there is no third equation, Steps 3 and 4 are not needed.

Step 5   Solve equation (3) for y in terms of z to obtain

$$y = 10z - 8.$$

Step 6   Back-substitute $y = 10z - 8$ into equation (1), and solve for x.

$$\begin{array}{ll} x + 5y + 3z = 7 & \text{Equation (1)} \\ x + 5(10z - 8) + 3z = 7 & \text{Replace } y \text{ by } 10z - 8. \\ x = -53z + 47 & \text{Solve for } x \end{array}$$

Steps 5 and 6 mean that you can choose any real number for z, and this choice determines both a value for x and a value for y, so that (x, y, z) is a solution of the system. The system has infinitely many solutions, one for each value of z. The solution set is $\{(-53z + 47, 10z - 8, z)\}$ with z being arbitrary.   ■ ■ ■

PRACTICE PROBLEM 4   Solve the system of linear equations.

$$\begin{cases} x + 3y + 2z = 4 \\ 2x + 7y - z = 5 \end{cases}$$ ■

4 Interpret linear systems in three variables geometrically.

Geometric Interpretation

The graph of a linear equation in three variables, such as $ax + by + cz = d$ (where a, b and c are not all zero), is a plane in three-dimensional space. Figure 8.7 shows possible situations for a system of three linear equations in three variables.

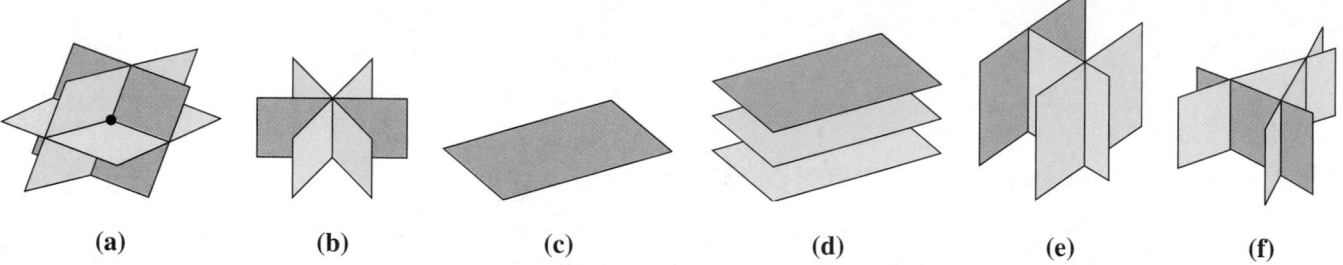

    (a)   **(b)**   **(c)**   **(d)**   **(e)**   **(f)**

FIGURE 8.7

a. Three planes intersect in a single point. The system has only one solution.

b. Three planes intersect in one line. The system has infinitely many solutions.

c. Three planes coincide with each other. The system has infinitely many solutions.

d. There are three parallel planes. The system has no solution.

e. Two parallel planes are intersected by a third plane. The system has no solution.

f. Three planes have no point in common. The system has no solution.

5 Use linear systems in applications.

An Application to CAT Scans

CAT scanners report X-ray data in units called *linear attenuation units* (LAU's), also called *Hounsfield numbers*. The data are reported in such a way that if an X-ray passes through consecutive grid cells, the total weakening of the beam is the sum of the individual decreases. Table 8.1 gives the range of LAU's that determine whether the grid cell contains healthy tissue, tumorous tissue, a bone, or a metal.

TABLE 8.1 CAT Scanner Ranges

Type of Tissue	LAU values
Healthy tissue	0.1625–0.2977
Tumorous tissue	0.2679–0.3930
Bone	0.38757–0.5108
Metal	$1.54-\infty$

Reprinted with permission from *Mathematics Teacher*, May 1996. © 1996 by the National Council of Teachers of Mathematics.

Beam 2   Beam 1

A

B   C

Beam 3

X-ray detector

Three grid cells, three X-rays

FIGURE 8.8 Reprinted with permission from *Mathematics Teacher*, May 1996. © 1996 by the National Council of Teachers of Mathematics.

EXAMPLE 5   **A CAT Scan with Three Grid Cells**

Let A, B, and C be three grid cells as shown in Figure 8.8. A CAT scanner reports the following data for a patient named Monica:

(i)   Beam 1 is weakened by 0.80 unit as it passes through grid cells A and B.

(ii)   Beam 2 is weakened by 0.55 unit as it passes through grid cells A and C.

(iii) Beam 3 is weakened by 0.65 unit as it passes through grid cells B and C.

Use Table 8.1 to determine which grid cells contain each of the types of tissue listed.

Solution

Suppose grid cell A weakens the beam by x units, grid cell B weakens the beam by y units, and grid cell C weakens the beam by z units. Then we have the system:

$$\begin{cases} x + y & = 0.80 \quad (1) \quad \text{(Beam 1)} \\ x \quad\ \ + z = 0.55 \quad (2) \quad \text{(Beam 2)} \\ \quad\ \ y + z = 0.65 \quad (3) \quad \text{(Beam 3)} \end{cases}$$

To solve this system of equations, we use the elimination procedure. Add -1 times Equation (1) to Equation (2).

$$\begin{array}{ll} -x - y \quad\ \ = -0.80 & -1 \text{ times Equation (1)} \\ \underline{\quad x \quad\ \ + z = \quad 0.55 \quad (2)} & \\ \quad -y + z = -0.25 \quad (4) & \text{Add.} \end{array}$$

We obtain the equivalent system:

$$\begin{cases} x + \quad y \quad\ \ = \quad 0.80 \quad (1) \\ \quad -y + z = -0.25 \quad (4) \\ \quad\ \ y + z = \quad 0.65 \quad (3) \end{cases}$$

Add Equation (4) to Equation (3) to get the system:

$$\begin{cases} x + \quad y \quad\ \ = \quad 0.80 \quad (1) \\ \quad -y + \ z = -0.25 \quad (4) \\ \quad\quad\ \ 2z = \quad 0.40 \quad (5) \end{cases}$$

Multiply Equation (5) by $\dfrac{1}{2}$ to obtain $z = 0.20$. Then back-substitute $z = 0.20$ in Equation (4) to get:

$$\begin{array}{ll} -y + 0.20 = -0.25 & \text{Substitute } z = 0.2 \text{ in Equation (4).} \\ -y = -0.45 & \text{Add } -0.20 \text{ to both sides.} \\ y = \quad 0.45 & \text{Multiply both sides by } -1. \end{array}$$

Next, back-substitute $y = 0.45$ in Equation (1) and solve for x:

$$\begin{array}{ll} x + y = 0.80 & \text{Equation (1)} \\ x + 0.45 = 0.80 & \text{Substitute } y = 0.45. \\ x = 0.35 & \text{Solve for } x. \end{array}$$

Now, referring to Table 1, we conclude that cell A contains tumorous tissue (since $x = 0.35$), cell B contains a bone (since $y = 0.45$), and cell C contains healthy tissue (since $z = 0.20$). ■ ■ ■

PRACTICE PROBLEM 5   In Example 5, suppose (*i*) Beam 1 is weakened by 0.65 unit as it passes through grid cells A and B, (*ii*) Beam 2 is weakened by 0.70 unit as it passes through grid cells A and C, and (*iii*) Beam 3 is weakened by 0.55 unit as it passes through grid cells B and C. Use Table 8.1 to determine which grid cells contain each type of tissue listed. ■

A Exercises   Basic Skills and Concepts

In Exercises 1–4, determine whether the given ordered triple (x, y, z) is a solution of the given linear system.

1. $\begin{cases} 2x - 2y - 3z = 1 \\ 3y + 2z = -1 \\ y + z = 0 \end{cases}$ $(1, -1, 1)$ Yes

2. $\begin{cases} 3x - 2y + z = 2 \\ y + z = 5 \\ x + 3z = 8 \end{cases}$ $(2, 3, 2)$ Yes

3. $\begin{cases} x + 3y - 2z = 0 \\ 2x - y + 4z = 5 \\ x - 11y + 14z = 0 \end{cases}$ $(-10, 8, 7)$ No

4. $\begin{cases} x - 4y + 7z = 14 \\ 3x + 8y - 2z = 13 \\ 7x - 8y + 26z = 5 \end{cases}$ $(4, 1, 2)$ No

In Exercises 5–8, solve each triangular linear system.

5. $x + y + z = 4$
$ y - 2z = 4$
$z = -1$ $\{(3, 2, -1)\}$

6. $x + 3y + z = 3$
$ y + 2z = 8$
$z = 5$ †

7. $x - 5y + 3z = -1$
$ y - 2z = -6$
$z = 4$ †

8. $x + 3y + 5z = 0$
$ y + 7z = 2$
$z = \dfrac{1}{2}$ †

9. In the system in Exercise 1, interchange Equations (2) and (3). Write the new equivalent system. In the new system, eliminate y from the last equation. Convert the system to triangular form. †

10. In Exercise 2, interchange Equations (1) and (3). In the new equivalent system, eliminate x from the last equation. Convert the system to triangular form. †

11. Convert the system of Exercise 3 to triangular form. †

12. Convert the system of Exercise 4 to triangular form. †

In Exercises 13–16, convert the system to triangular form and then use back-substitution to solve the system.

13. $\begin{cases} x - y + z = 6 \\ 2y + 3z = 5 \\ 2z = 6 \end{cases}$ $\{(1, -2, 3)\}$

14. $\begin{cases} 4x + 5y + 2z = -3 \\ 3y - z = 14 \\ - 3z = 15 \end{cases}$ $\{(-2, 3, -5)\}$

15. $\begin{cases} 4x + 4y + 4z = 7 \\ 3x - 8y = 14 \\ 4z = -1 \end{cases}$ $\left\{\left(\dfrac{30}{11}, -\dfrac{8}{11}, -\dfrac{1}{4}\right)\right\}$

16. $\begin{cases} 5x + 10y + 10z = 0 \\ 2y + 3z = -0.6 \\ 4z = 1.6 \end{cases}$ $\{(1, -0.9, 0.4)\}$

In Exercises 17–38, find the solution set of each linear system. Identify inconsistent systems and dependent equations.

17. $\begin{cases} x + y + z = 6 \\ x - y + z = 2 \\ 2x + y - z = 1 \end{cases}$ †

18. $\begin{cases} x + y + z = 6 \\ 2x + 3y - z = 5 \\ 3x - 2y + 3z = 8 \end{cases}$ †

19. $\begin{cases} 2x + 3y + z = 9 \\ x + 2y + 3z = 6 \\ 3x + y + 2z = 8 \end{cases}$ †

20. $\begin{cases} 4x + 2y + 3z = 6 \\ x + 2y + 2z = 1 \\ 2x - y + z = -1 \end{cases}$ †

21. $\begin{cases} 3x + y + z = 6 \\ x - y + 4z = -3 \\ 2x + y + 2z = 3 \end{cases}$ †

22. $\begin{cases} 3x + 3y + 2z = 9 \\ 2x - y + 2z = 2 \\ x + 5y - 6z = -9 \end{cases}$ †

23. $\begin{cases} 2x + 3y + 2z = 7 \\ x + 3y - z = -2 \\ x - y + 2z = 8 \end{cases}$ †

24. $\begin{cases} x - y + 2z = 3 \\ 2x + 2y + z = 3 \\ x + y + 3z = 4 \end{cases}$ †

25. $\begin{cases} 4x - 2y + z = 5 \\ 2x + y - 2z = 4 \\ x + 3y - 2z = 6 \end{cases}$ †

26. $\begin{cases} x - 3y + 2z = 9 \\ 2x + 4y - 3z = -9 \\ 3x - 2y + 5z = 12 \end{cases}$ †

27. $\begin{cases} 2x + y + z = 6 \\ x + y - z = 1 \\ x + y + 2z = 4 \end{cases}$ †

28. $\begin{cases} 2x + y - 3z = 7 \\ x - y - 2z = 4 \\ 3x + 3y + 2z = 4 \end{cases}$ †

29. $\begin{cases} 3x + 2y - z = 5 \\ -x + 5y - 2z = 5 \\ 2x - y + 3z = 6 \end{cases}$ †

30. $\begin{cases} 3x - y + z = 1 \\ 2x + y + z = 5 \\ 4x - y + 2z = 4 \end{cases}$ †

31. $\begin{cases} x + y = 0 \\ y + 2z = -4 \\ y + z = 4 - x \end{cases}$ †

32. $\begin{cases} 2x + 4y + 3z = 6 \\ x + 2z = -1 \\ x - 2y + z = -5 \end{cases}$ †

33. $\begin{cases} 2y - z = -4 \\ x + z = 3 \\ 2x + 3y = -1 \end{cases}$ †

34. $\begin{cases} x + y = 9 \\ 2y + 3z = 7 \\ x - 2z = 4 \end{cases}$ †

35. $\begin{cases} 3x -   2z = 11 \\ 2x + y = 8 \\ 2y + 3z = 1 \end{cases}$ †

36. $\begin{cases} 2x + y = 4 \\ x + 2z = 3 \\ 3y - z = 5 \end{cases}$ †

37. $\begin{cases} 2x + 6y + 11 = 0 \\ 6y - 18z + 1 = 0 \end{cases}$ †

38. $\begin{cases} 3x + 5y - 15 = 0 \\ 6x + 20y - 6z = 11 \end{cases}$ †

†Due to space constrictions, answers to these exercises may be found in the Answers beginning on page A–1 in the back of the book.

B Exercises   Applying the Concepts

In Exercises 39–46, use a system of equations to solve each problem.

39. Investment. Miguel invested 20,000 dollars in three different funds that paid 4, 5, and 6 percent, respectively, for the year. The total income for the year from the three funds was 1060 dollars. The income from the 6 percent fund was twice the income from the 5 percent fund. What was the amount invested in each fund? †

40. Number problem. The sum of the digits in a three-digit number is 14. The sum of the hundreds digit and the units digit is equal to the tens digit. If the hundreds digit and the units digit are interchanged, the number is increased by 297. What is the original number? 275

41. Election campaign. Alex, Becky, and Courtney volunteered to assemble (stuff envelopes with newsletters) 741 envelopes for Senator Douglas's reelection campaign. Alex could assemble 124 per hour, Becky 118 per hour, and Courtney 132 per hour. They worked a total of 6 hours. The sum of the number of hours spent by Becky and Courtney was twice that of Alex. How long did each of them work? †

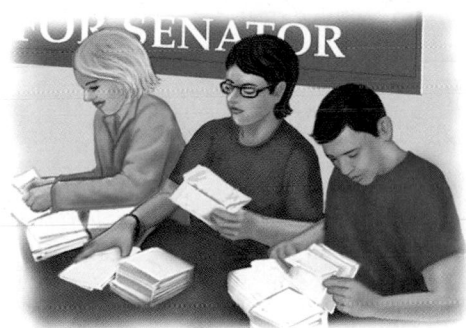

42. Age of students. A college algebra class of 38 students at Central State College was made up of people who were 18, 19, and 20 years of age. The average of their ages was 18.5 years. How many of each age were in the class if the number of 18-year-olds was eight more than the combined number of 19- and 20-year-olds? †

43. Coins in a machine. A vending machine's coin box contains nickels, dimes, and quarters. The total number of coins in the box is 300. The number of dimes is three times the number of nickels and quarters together. If the box

contains 30 dollars and 5 cents, find the number of nickels, dimes, and quarters that it contains. †

44. Sports. The Wildcats scored 46 points in a football game. Twice the number of points resulting from the sum of field goals and extra points equals two more than the number of points from touchdowns. Five times the number of points scored by field goals equals twice the number of points from touchdowns. Find the number of points resulting from touchdowns, field goals, and extra points. [A touchdown = 6 points, a field goal = 3 points, and an extra point = 1 point.] 5 touchdowns, 4 field goals, and 4 extra points

45. Weekly wage. Amy worked 53 hours one week and was paid at three different rates. She earned 7 dollars and 40 cents per hour for her normal daytime work, 9 dollars and 20 cents per hour for night work, and 11 dollars and 75 cents per hour for working on a holiday. If her total gross wages for the week were 452 dollars and 20 cents, and the number of regular daytime hours she worked exceeded the combined hours of night and holiday work by 9 hours, how many hours of each category of work did Amy perform?
31 normal daytime hours, 14 hours at night, and 8 hours on a holiday

46. Components of a product. A manufacturer buys three components—A, B, and C—for use in making a toaster. She used as many units of A as she did of B and C combined. The cost of A, B, and C is 4 dollars, 5 dollars, and 6 dollars per unit, respectively. If she purchased 100 units of these components for a total of 480 dollars, how many units of each did she purchase?

50 units at $4, 20 units at $5, and 30 units at $6

In Exercises 47–50, use Table 8.1 on page 760 and Figure 8.8 to determine which grid cells of the patients contain healthy tissue, tumorous tissue, bone, or metal.

Beam decrease, in LAU's

Patient	Beam 1	Beam 2	Beam 3
47. Vicky	0.54	0.40	0.52 †
48. Yolanda	0.65	0.80	0.75 †
49. Nina	0.51	0.49	0.44 †
50. Srinivasan	0.44	2.21	2.23 †

C Exercises | Beyond the Basics

In Exercises 51–54, write a linear equation of the form $x + by + cz = d$ and that is satisfied by all three of the given ordered triples.

51. $(1, 0, 0)$, $(0, 1, 0)$, $(0, 0, 1)$ $x + y + z = 1$

52. $\left(\frac{1}{3}, 0, 0\right)$, $(0, 4, 3)$, $(1, 2, 2)$ $x + \frac{4}{3}y - \frac{5}{3}z = \frac{1}{3}$

53. $(3, -4, 0)$, $\left(0, \frac{1}{4}, \frac{1}{2}\right)$, $(1, 1, -4)$ $x + \frac{2}{3}y + \frac{1}{3}z = \frac{1}{3}$

54. $(0, 1, -10)$, $\left(\frac{1}{8}, 0, \frac{1}{4}\right)$, $\left(1, \frac{1}{3}, -2\right)$ $x - \frac{111}{14}y - \frac{11}{14}z = -\frac{1}{14}$

In Exercises 55–58, find an equation of the parabola of the form $y = ax^2 + bx + c$ and that passes through the three given points.

55. $(0, 1)$, $(-1, 0)$, $(1, 4)$ $y = x^2 + 2x + 1$

56. $(0, 2)$, $(-1, 30)$, $(2, 6)$ $y = 10x^2 - 18x + 2$

57. $(1, 2)$, $(-1, 4)$, $(2, 4)$ $y = x^2 - x + 2$

58. $(0, 3)$, $(-1, 4)$, $(1, 6)$ $y = 2x^2 + x + 3$

In Exercises 59–62, find an equation of the circle of the form $x^2 + y^2 + ax + by + c = 0$ and that passes through the three given points.

59. $(0, 4)$, $(2\sqrt{2}, 2\sqrt{2})$, $(-4, 0)$ $x^2 + y^2 - 16 = 0$

60. $(0, 3)$, $(0, -1)$, $(\sqrt{3}, 2)$ $x^2 + y^2 - 2y - 3 = 0$

61. $(1, 2)$, $(6, -3)$, $(4, 1)$ $x^2 + y^2 - 2x + 6y - 15 = 0$

62. $(5, 6)$, $(-1, 6)$, $(3, 2)$ $x^2 + y^2 - 4x - 10y + 19 = 0$

In Exercises 63–68, solve the system of equations.

63.
$$\begin{cases} \dfrac{1}{x} + \dfrac{3}{y} - \dfrac{1}{z} = 5 \\[2mm] \dfrac{2}{x} + \dfrac{4}{y} + \dfrac{6}{z} = 4 \\[2mm] \dfrac{2}{x} + \dfrac{3}{y} + \dfrac{1}{z} = 3 \end{cases} \left\{\left(\frac{-9}{14}, \frac{9}{19}, \frac{-9}{2}\right)\right\}$$

64.
$$\begin{cases} \dfrac{1}{x} + \dfrac{2}{y} + \dfrac{3}{z} = 8 \\[2mm] \dfrac{2}{x} + \dfrac{5}{y} + \dfrac{9}{z} = 16 \\[2mm] \dfrac{3}{x} - \dfrac{4}{y} - \dfrac{5}{z} = 32 \end{cases} \left\{\left(\frac{2}{19}, \frac{-2}{3}, 2\right)\right\}$$

$\left[\text{Hint: Let } \dfrac{1}{x} = u, \dfrac{1}{y} = v, \text{ and } \dfrac{1}{z} = w. \text{ Solve for } u, v, \text{ and } w.\right]$

In Exercises 65–66, find the value of c for which the given system has a unique solution.

65.
$$\begin{cases} x + 2y - 5z - 9 = 0 \\ 3x - y + 2z - 14 = 0 \\ 2x + 3y - z - 3 = 0 \\ cx - 5y + z + 3 = 0 \end{cases} \frac{-16}{5}$$

66.
$$\begin{cases} x + 5y + z = 42 \\ 3x + y - 3z = c \\ x - y + 3z = 4 \\ x + y - z = 0 \end{cases} -16$$

67. Find a quadratic function of the form $y = ax^2 + bx + c$ and whose graph passes through the points $(-1, -1)$, $(0, 5)$, and $(2, 5)$. $y = -2x^2 + 4x + 5$

68. Use Table 8.1 on page 760 to investigate four grid cells, arranged in a square, as shown in the given figure. Figures (a) and (b) reprinted with permission from *Mathematics Teacher,* May 1996. © 1996 by National Council of Teachers of Mathematics.

a. For Figure (a), the following data were observed.

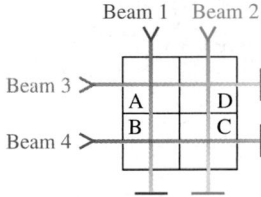

Four grid cells and four X-rays

(a)

1. Beam 1 decreased by 0.60 unit.
2. Beam 2 decreased by 0.75 unit.
3. Beam 3 decreased by 0.65 unit.
4. Beam 4 decreased by 0.70 unit.

Is there sufficient information in Figure (a) to determine which grid cells may contain tumorous tissue?

Answers:
68. a. No. The system has infinitely many solutions.
   b. The system has a unique solution. To see that cell C contains tumorous tissue, use the data for beams 2, 4, and 5 to find that the cell C weakens the beam by 0.3 unit.

b. From two additional X-rays, as shown in Figure (b), the following data were observed.

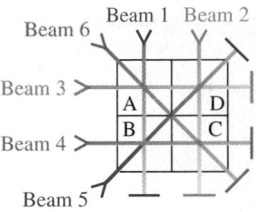

Four grid cells and six X-rays

(b)

5. Beam 5 is decreased by 0.85 unit.
6. Beam 6 is decreased by 0.50 unit.

Show that the six X-rays represented in the two figures are sufficient to locate tumors in this situation, but that, in fact, it is not necessary to use all six rays.

Critical Thinking

69. Write a linear system of three equations in the variables x, y, and z that has $\{(1, -1, 2)\}$ as its solution set.

70. Write a linear system of three equations in the variables x, y and z such that
   a. the system has no solution;
   b. the system has infinitely many solutions.

69. $\begin{cases} x + y - z = -2 \\ 2x - y + 3z = 9 \\ x + y + z = 2 \end{cases}$ Answers may vary.

70. a. $\begin{cases} x + 3y + 3z = 15 \\ x + 2y + z = 1 \\ 2y + 4z = 11 \end{cases}$ Answers may vary.

   b. $\begin{cases} x + 2y - z = 4 \\ x + 3y + 2z = 5 \\ y + 3z = 1 \end{cases}$ Answers may vary.

Partial-Fraction Decomposition

Georg Simon Ohm
(1787–1854)

Georg Ohm was born in Erlangen, Germany. His father, Johann, a mechanic and a self-educated man, was interested in philosophy and mathematics and gave his children an excellent education in physics, chemistry, mathematics, and philosophy through his own teachings. The Ohm's law named in Georg Ohm's honor appeared in his famous pamphlet *Die galvanische Kette, mathematisch bearbeitet* (1827). Ohm's work was not appreciated at all in Germany, where it was first published. Eventually, it was recognized, first by the British Royal Society, which awarded Ohm the Copley Medal in 1841. In 1849, Ohm became a curator of the Bavarian Academy's physical cabinet and began to lecture at the University of Munich. Finally, in 1852 (two years before his death), Ohm achieved his lifelong ambition of becoming chair of physics at the University of Munich.

BEFORE STARTING THIS SECTION, REVIEW

1. Division of polynomials (Section 3.3, page 357)

2. Factoring polynomials (Section P.4, page 41)

3. Irreducible polynomials (Section 3.4, page 377)

4. Rational expressions (Section P.5, page 50)

OBJECTIVES

1 Become familiar with partial fraction decomposition.

2 Decompose $\dfrac{P(x)}{Q(x)}$, where $Q(x)$ has only distinct linear factors.

3 Decompose $\dfrac{P(x)}{Q(x)}$, where $Q(x)$ has repeated linear factors.

4 Decompose $\dfrac{P(x)}{Q(x)}$, where $Q(x)$ has distinct irreducible quadratic factors.

5 Decompose $\dfrac{P(x)}{Q(x)}$, where $Q(x)$ has repeated irreducible quadratic factors.

Ohm's Law

If a voltage is applied across a resistor (such as a wire), a current will flow. Ohm's law states that, in a circuit at constant temperature,

$$I = \frac{V}{R}$$

FIGURE 8.9

where V is the voltage (measured in volts), I is the current (measured in amperes), and R is the resistance (measured in ohms). A **parallel circuit** consists of two or more resistors connected as shown in Figure 8.9. In the figure, the current I from the source divides into two currents, I_1 and I_2, with I_1 going through one resistor and I_2 going through the other, so that $I = I_1 + I_2$. We are interested in finding the total resistance R in the circuit due to the two resistors R_1 and R_2 connected in parallel. Ohm's law can be used to show that in the parallel circuit in Figure 8.9, $\dfrac{1}{R} = \dfrac{1}{R_1} + \dfrac{1}{R_2}$. This is called the *parallel property of resistors*. In Example 6, we will examine the parallel property of resistors by using partial fractions. ■

1 Become familiar with partial-fraction decomposition.

Partial Fractions

In Section P.5, we discussed how to add two rational expressions such as $\dfrac{2}{x+3}$ and $\dfrac{3}{x-1}$. The addition procedure required you to find the least common denominator, rewrite expressions with the same denominator, and then add the corresponding numerators. This procedure gives

$$\frac{2}{x+3} + \frac{3}{x-1} = \frac{5x+7}{(x-1)(x+3)}$$

In some applications of algebra to more advanced mathematics, you need a *reverse* procedure for *splitting* a fraction such as $\dfrac{5x+7}{(x-1)(x+3)}$ into the simpler fractions to obtain

$$\frac{5x+7}{(x-1)(x+3)} = \frac{2}{x+3} + \frac{3}{x-1}$$

Each of the two fractions on the right is called a **partial fraction.** Their sum is called the **partial-fraction decomposition** of the rational expressions on the left.

A rational expression $\dfrac{P(x)}{Q(x)}$ is called **improper** if the degree $P(x) \geq$ degree $Q(x)$, and is called **proper** if degree $P(x) <$ degree $Q(x)$. Examples of improper rational expressions are $\dfrac{x^3}{x^2-1}$, $\dfrac{(x+2)(x-1)}{(x-2)(x+3)}$, and $\dfrac{x^2+x+1}{2x+3}$. Using long division, we can express an improper rational expression $\dfrac{P(x)}{Q(x)}$ as the sum of a polynomial and a proper rational expression.

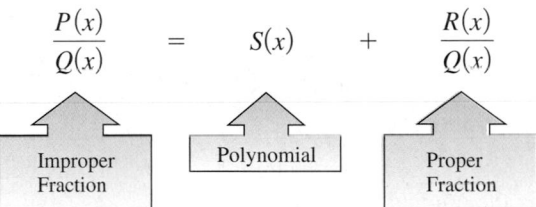

$$\underset{\substack{\text{Improper}\\\text{Fraction}}}{\frac{P(x)}{Q(x)}} = \underset{\text{Polynomial}}{S(x)} + \underset{\substack{\text{Proper}\\\text{Fraction}}}{\frac{R(x)}{Q(x)}}$$

We therefore restrict our discussion of the decomposition of $\dfrac{P(x)}{Q(x)}$ into partial fractions to cases involving proper rational expressions. We also assume that $P(x)$ and $Q(x)$ have no common factor.

The problem of decomposing a proper fraction $\dfrac{P(x)}{Q(x)}$ into partial fractions depends on the type of factors in the denominator $Q(x)$. In this section, we consider four cases for $Q(x)$.

2 Decompose $\dfrac{P(x)}{Q(x)}$, where

$Q(x)$ has only distinct linear factors.

$Q(x)$ Has Only Distinct Linear Factors

CASE 1: THE DENOMINATOR IS THE PRODUCT OF DISTINCT (NONREPEATED) LINEAR FACTORS.

Suppose $Q(x)$ can be factored as

$$Q(x) = (x - a_1)(x - a_2)\cdots(x - a_n),$$

with no factor repeated. The partial-fraction decomposition of $\dfrac{P(x)}{Q(x)}$ is of the form

$$\frac{P(x)}{Q(x)} = \frac{A_1}{x - a_1} + \frac{A_2}{x - a_2} + \cdots + \frac{A_n}{x - a_n},$$

where $A_1, A_2, \ldots, A_n$ are constants to be determined.

The following procedure is used for determining the constants $A_1, A_2, \ldots, A_n$. However, when the number of constants is small, it is more convenient to use the letters $A, B, C, \ldots$, instead of $A_1, A_2, A_3, \ldots$.

FINDING THE SOLUTION: PROCEDURE FOR PARTIAL-FRACTION DECOMPOSITION

OBJECTIVE

To find the partial-fraction decomposition of a rational expression.

EXAMPLE

Find the partial fraction decomposition of $\dfrac{3x + 26}{(x - 3)(x + 4)}$.

Step 1 Write the form of the partial-fraction decomposition with the unknown constants $A, B, C, \ldots$ in the numerators of the decomposition.

$$\frac{3x + 26}{(x - 3)(x + 4)} = \frac{A}{x - 3} + \frac{B}{x + 4}$$

Step 2 Multiply both sides of the equation in Step 1 by the original denominator. Use the distributive property and eliminate common factors. Simplify.

Multiply both sides by $(x - 3)(x + 4)$ and simplify to obtain

$$3x + 26 = (x + 4)A + (x - 3)B$$

$$3x + 26 = (A + B)x + (4A - 3B)$$

Step 3 Write both sides of the equation in Step 2 in descending powers of x, and equate the coefficients of like powers of x.

$$\begin{cases} 3 = A + B & \text{Equate coefficients of } x. \\ 26 = 4A - 3B & \text{Equate constant coefficients.} \end{cases}$$

Step 4 Step 3 will result in a system of linear equations in $A, B, C, \ldots$. Solve this linear system for the constants $A, B, C, \ldots$.

Solving the system of equations in Step 2, we obtain $A = 5$ and $B = -2$.

Step 5 Substitute the values for $A, B, C, \ldots$ obtained in Step 4 into the equation in Step 1, and write the partial-fraction decomposition.

$$\frac{3x + 26}{(x - 3)(x + 4)} = \frac{5}{x - 3} + \frac{-2}{x + 4} \quad \begin{array}{l}\text{Replace } A \text{ by 5 and}\\ B \text{ by } -2 \text{ in Step 1.}\end{array}$$

$$\frac{3x + 26}{(x - 3)(x + 4)} = \frac{5}{x - 3} - \frac{2}{x + 4}$$

EXAMPLE 1	Finding the Partial-Fraction Decomposition When the Denominator Has Only Distinct Linear Factors

Find the partial-fraction decomposition of the expression.

$$\frac{10x - 4}{x^3 - 4x}$$

Solution

First factor the denominator:

$$x^3 - 4x = x(x^2 - 4) \qquad \text{Distributive property}$$
$$= x(x - 2)(x + 2) \qquad x^2 - 4 = (x - 2)(x + 2)$$

Each of the factors x, $x - 2$, and $x + 2$ becomes a denominator for a partial fraction.

Step 1 The partial-fraction decomposition is given by

$$\frac{10x - 4}{x(x - 2)(x + 2)} = \frac{A}{x} + \frac{B}{x - 2} + \frac{C}{x + 2} \qquad \text{Use } A, B, \text{ and } C \text{ instead of } A_1, A_2, \text{ and } A_3.$$

Step 2 Multiply both sides by the common denominator $x(x - 2)(x + 2)$:

Distribute

$$\cancel{x(x - 2)(x + 2)} \left[\frac{10x - 4}{\cancel{x(x - 2)(x + 2)}} \right] - x(x - 2)(x + 2)\left[\frac{A}{x} + \frac{B}{x - 2} + \frac{C}{x + 2} \right]$$

$$10x - 4 = A(x - 2)(x + 2) + Bx(x + 2) + Cx(x - 2) \quad (1) \quad \text{Distributive property; simplify.}$$
$$= A(x^2 - 4) + B(x^2 + 2x) + C(x^2 - 2x) \qquad \text{Multiply.}$$
$$= Ax^2 - 4A + Bx^2 + 2Bx + Cx^2 - 2Cx \qquad \text{Distributive property}$$
$$= (A + B + C)x^2 + (2B - 2C)x - 4A. \qquad \text{Combine like terms.}$$

Step 3 Now use the fact that *two polynomials are equal if and only if the coefficients of the like powers are equal.* Writing $10x - 4 = 0x^2 + 10x - 4$, we have

Coefficients of terms in x

$$0x^2 + 10x - 4 = (A + B + C)x^2 + (2B - 2C)x - 4A.$$

Coefficients
of terms in x^2

Constant terms

Equating corresponding coefficients leads to the system of equations.

$$\begin{cases} A + B + C = 0 & \text{Equate coefficients of } x^2. \\ 2B - 2C = 10 & \text{Equate coefficients of } x. \\ -4A = -4 & \text{Equate constant coefficients.} \end{cases}$$

Continued on next page.

Step 4   Solve the system of equations in Step 3 to obtain $A = 1$, $B = 2$, and $C = -3$. (See Exercise 51.)

Step 5   Since $A = 1$, $B = 2$, and $C = -3$, the partial-fraction decomposition is

$$\frac{10x - 4}{x^3 - 4x} = \frac{1}{x} + \frac{2}{x - 2} + \frac{-3}{x + 2} = \frac{1}{x} + \frac{2}{x - 2} - \frac{3}{x + 2}.$$

In Example 1, the method used to find the constants A, B, and C was to *equate coefficients* of like powers of x and solve the resulting system of linear equations. An alternative (and sometimes quicker) method of finding the constants is to *substitute* well-chosen values for x in the equation (identity) obtained in Step 2.

Alternative Solution of Example 1:

We start with equation (1) from Step 2.

$$10x - 4 = A(x - 2)(x + 2) + Bx(x + 2) + Cx(x - 2) \tag{1}$$

Substitute $x = 2$ in equation (1) to obtain

$$10(2) - 4 = A(2 - 2)(2 + 2) + B(2)(2 + 2) + C(2)(2 - 2)$$
$$16 = 8B \qquad\qquad \text{Simplify.}$$
$$2 = B. \qquad\qquad \text{Solve for } B.$$

Note that we chose $x = 2$ because it causes the terms containing A and C to be 0.
   Now substitute $x = -2$ in equation (1) to obtain

$$10(-2) - 4 = A(-2 - 2)(-2 + 2) + B(-2)(-2 + 2) + C(-2)(-2 - 2)$$
$$-24 = 8C \qquad\qquad \text{Simplify.}$$
$$-3 = C. \qquad\qquad \text{Solve for } C.$$

Finally, substitute $x = 0$ in equation (1) to get

$$10(0) - 4 = A(0 - 2)(0 + 2) + B(0)(0 + 2) + C(0)(0 - 2)$$
$$-4 = -4A \qquad\qquad \text{Simplify.}$$
$$1 = A. \qquad\qquad \text{Solve for } A.$$

Thus, $A = 1$, $B = 2$, $C = -3$, and the partial-fraction decomposition is given (as before) by

$$\frac{10x - 4}{x^3 - 4x} = \frac{1}{x} + \frac{2}{x - 2} + \frac{-3}{x + 2} = \frac{1}{x} + \frac{2}{x - 2} - \frac{3}{x + 2}. \qquad ■ ■ ■$$

PRACTICE PROBLEM 1   Find the partial-fraction decomposition of

$$\frac{3x^2 + 4x + 3}{x^3 - x}. \qquad\qquad ■$$

3 Decompose $\dfrac{P(x)}{Q(x)}$, where $Q(x)$ has repeated linear factors.

$Q(x)$ Has Repeated Linear Factors

CASE 2: THE DENOMINATOR HAS A REPEATED LINEAR FACTOR

Let $(x - a)^m$ be the linear factor $(x - a)$ that is repeated m times in $Q(x)$. Then the portion of the partial-fraction decomposition of $\dfrac{P(x)}{Q(x)}$ that corresponds to the factor $(x - a)^m$ is

$$\frac{A_1}{x - a} + \frac{A_2}{(x - a)^2} + \cdots + \frac{A_m}{(x - a)^m},$$

where $A_1, A_2, \ldots, A_m$ are constants to be determined.

EXAMPLE 2   **Finding the Partial-Fraction Decomposition When the Denominator Has Repeated Linear Factors**

Find the partial-fraction decomposition of $\dfrac{x + 4}{(x + 3)(x - 1)^2}$.

Solution

Step 1   The linear factor $(x - 1)$ is repeated twice and the factor $(x + 3)$ is nonrepeating, so the partial-fraction decomposition has the form

$$\frac{x + 4}{(x + 3)(x - 1)^2} = \frac{A}{x + 3} + \frac{B}{x - 1} + \frac{C}{(x - 1)^2}.$$

Steps 2–4   Multiply both sides of the equation in Step 1 by the original denominator, $(x + 3)(x - 1)^2$, and use the distributive property on the right side to obtain

$$\cancel{(x + 3)(x - 1)^2} \cdot \frac{x + 4}{\cancel{(x + 3)(x - 1)^2}} = (x + 3)(x - 1)^2 \left[\frac{A}{x + 3} + \frac{B}{x - 1} + \frac{C}{(x - 1)^2} \right]$$

$$x + 4 = A(x - 1)^2 + B(x + 3)(x - 1) + C(x + 3)$$

Substitute $x = 1$ in the last equation to obtain

$$1 + 4 = A(1 - 1)^2 + B(1 + 3)(1 - 1) + C(1 + 3)$$

$$5 = 4C \qquad \text{Simplify.}$$

$$C = \frac{5}{4} \qquad \text{Solve for } C.$$

To find the value for A, we substitute $x = -3$ to get

$$-3 + 4 = A(-3 - 1)^2 + B(-3 + 3)(-3 - 1) + C(-3 + 3)$$

$$1 = 16A \qquad \text{Simplify.}$$

$$A = \frac{1}{16} \qquad \text{Solve for } A.$$

Continued on next page.

To obtain the value of B, we replace x by any convenient number, say, 0. We have

$$0 + 4 = A(0 - 1)^2 + B(0 + 3)(0 - 1) + C(0 + 3)$$

$$4 = A - 3B + 3C. \qquad \text{Simplify.}$$

Now replace A by $\dfrac{1}{16}$ and C by $\dfrac{5}{4}$ in the last equation.

$$4 = \frac{1}{16} - 3B + 3\left(\frac{5}{4}\right)$$

$$64 = 1 - 48B + 60 \qquad \text{Multiply both sides by 16.}$$

$$B = -\frac{1}{16} \qquad \text{Solve for } B.$$

We have $A = \dfrac{1}{16}$, $B = -\dfrac{1}{16}$, and $C = \dfrac{5}{4}$.

Step 5 Substitute $A = \dfrac{1}{16}$, $B = -\dfrac{1}{16}$, and $C = \dfrac{5}{4}$ in the decomposition in Step 1 to obtain the partial-fraction decomposition

$$\frac{x + 4}{(x + 3)(x - 1)^2} = \frac{\frac{1}{16}}{x + 3} + \frac{-\frac{1}{16}}{x - 1} + \frac{\frac{5}{4}}{(x - 1)^2},$$

or

$$\frac{x + 4}{(x + 3)(x - 1)^2} = \frac{1}{16(x + 3)} - \frac{1}{16(x - 1)} + \frac{5}{4(x - 1)^2}. \qquad \blacksquare\ \blacksquare\ \blacksquare$$

PRACTICE PROBLEM 2 Find the partial fraction decomposition of

$$\frac{x + 5}{x(x - 1)^2}. \qquad \blacksquare$$

4 Decompose $\dfrac{P(x)}{Q(x)}$, where $Q(x)$ has distinct irreducible quadratic factors.

$Q(x)$ Has Distinct Irreducible Quadratic Factors

CASE 3: THE DENOMINATOR HAS A DISTINCT (NONREPEATED) IRREDUCIBLE QUADRATIC FACTOR.

Suppose $ax^2 + bx + c$ is an irreducible quadratic factor of $Q(x)$. Then the portion of the partial-fraction decomposition of $\dfrac{P(x)}{Q(x)}$ that corresponds to $ax^2 + bx + c$ has the form

$$\frac{Ax + B}{ax^2 + bx + c},$$

where A and B are constants to be determined.

EXAMPLE 3	Finding the Partial-Fraction Decomposition When the Denominator Has a Distinct Irreducible Quadratic Factor

RECALL

The expression $ax^2 + bx + c$ is irreducible if $b^2 - 4ac < 0$. In that case, $ax^2 + bx + c = 0$ has no real solutions.

Find the partial-fraction decomposition of $\dfrac{3x^2 - 8x + 1}{(x - 4)(x^2 + 1)}$.

Solution

Step 1   The factor $x - 4$ is linear and $x^2 + 1$ is irreducible; thus, the partial fraction decomposition has the form

$$\frac{3x^2 - 8x + 1}{(x - 4)(x^2 + 1)} = \frac{A}{x - 4} + \frac{Bx + C}{x^2 + 1}.$$

Step 2   Multiply both sides of the decomposition in Step 1 by the original denominator, $(x - 4)(x^2 + 1)$, and simplify to obtain

$$3x^2 - 8x + 1 = A(x^2 + 1) + (Bx + C)(x - 4).$$

Substitute $x = 4$ to obtain $17 = 17A$, or $A = 1$.

Step 3   Collect like terms, and write both sides of the equation in Step 2 in descending powers of x.

$$3x^2 - 8x + 1 = (A + B)x^2 + (-4B + C)x + (A - 4C)$$

Equate the coefficients of like powers of x to obtain

$$\begin{cases} A + B = 3 & (1) \quad \text{Equate the coefficients of } x^2. \\ -4B + C = -8 & (2) \quad \text{Equate the coefficients of } x. \\ A - 4C = 1 & (3) \quad \text{Equate the constant coefficients.} \end{cases}$$

Step 4   Substitute $A = 1$ in equation (1) to obtain $1 + B = 3$, or $B = 2$.
Substitute $A = 1$ in equation (3) to obtain $1 - 3C = 1$, or $C = 0$.

Step 5   Substitute $A = 1$, $B = 2$, and $C = 0$ into the decomposition in Step 1 to obtain

$$\frac{3x^2 - 8x + 1}{(x - 4)(x^2 + 1)} = \frac{1}{x - 4} + \frac{2x}{x^2 + 1}. \qquad ■ ■ ■$$

PRACTICE PROBLEM 3   Find the partial-fraction decomposition of

$$\frac{3x^2 + 5x - 2}{x(x^2 + 2)}. \qquad ■$$

5 Decompose $\dfrac{P(x)}{Q(x)}$, where

$Q(x)$ has repeated irreducible quadratic factors.

$Q(x)$ Has Repeated Irreducible Quadratic Factors

CASE 4: THE DENOMINATOR HAS A REPEATED IRREDUCIBLE QUADRATIC FACTOR

Suppose the denominator $Q(x)$ has a factor $(ax^2 + bx + c)^m$, where $m \geq 2$ is an integer and $ax^2 + bx + c$ is irreducible. Then the portion of the partial-fraction decomposition of $\dfrac{P(x)}{Q(x)}$ that corresponds to the factor $(ax^2 + bx + c)^m$ has the form

$$\frac{A_1 x + B_1}{ax^2 + bx + c} + \frac{A_2 x + B_2}{(ax^2 + bx + c)^2} + \cdots + \frac{A_m x + B_m}{(ax^2 + bx + c)^m},$$

where $A_1, B_1, A_2, B_2, \dots, A_m, B_m$ are constants to be determined.

EXAMPLE 4 **Finding the Partial-Fraction Decomposition When the Denominator Has a Repeated Irreducible Quadratic Factor**

Find the partial-fraction decomposition of $\dfrac{2x^4 - x^3 + 13x^2 - 2x + 13}{(x - 1)(x^2 + 4)^2}$.

Solution

Step 1 The denominator has a nonrepeating linear factor $(x - 1)$ and an irreducible quadratic factor $(x^2 + 4)$ that appears twice. Thus, the decomposition has the form

$$\frac{2x^4 - x^3 + 13x^2 - 2x + 13}{(x - 1)(x^2 + 4)^2} = \frac{A}{x - 1} + \frac{Bx + C}{x^2 + 4} + \frac{Dx + E}{(x^2 + 4)^2}.$$

Step 2 Multiply both sides of the decomposition in Step 1 by the original denominator $(x - 1)(x^2 + 4)^2$:

Distribute

$$2x^4 - x^3 + 13x^2 - 2x + 13 = (x - 1)(x^2 + 4)^2 \left[\frac{A}{x - 1} + \frac{Bx + C}{x^2 + 4} + \frac{Dx + E}{(x^2 + 4)^2} \right].$$

Now use the distributive property and eliminate common factors to obtain

$$2x^4 - x^3 + 13x^2 - 2x + 13 =$$
$$A(x^2 + 4)^2 + (Bx + C)(x - 1)(x^2 + 4) + (Dx + E)(x - 1).$$

Substitute $x = 1$ and simplify to obtain $25 = 25A$, or $A = 1$.

Steps 3–4 Multiply the factors on the right side of the equation in Step 2 and collect like terms to obtain

$$2x^4 - x^3 + 13x^2 - 2x + 13 =$$
$$(A + B)x^4 + (-B + C)x^3 + (8A + 4B - C + D)x^2 + (-4B + 4C - D + E)x + (16A - 4C - E).$$

Equate the coefficients of like powers of x to get a system of five equations in five variables.

$$\begin{cases} A + B & = 2 \quad (1) \quad \text{Coefficient of } x^4 \\ -B + C & = -1 \quad (2) \quad \text{Coefficient of } x^3 \\ 8A + 4B - C + D & = 13 \quad (3) \quad \text{Coefficient of } x^2 \\ -4B + 4C - D + E = -2 \quad (4) \quad \text{Coefficient of } x \\ 16A - 4C - E = 13 \quad (5) \quad \text{Constant coefficient} \end{cases}$$

Now back-substitute $A = 1$ in Equation (1) to obtain $B = 1$. Again, back-substitute $B = 1$ in Equation (2) to get $C = 0$.

Back-substitute $A = 1$ and $C = 0$ in Equation (5) to obtain $E = 3$. Again, back-substitute $A = 1$, $B = 1$, and $C = 0$ in Equation (3) to get $D = 1$. Hence, $A = 1$, $B = 1$, $C = 0$, $D = 1$, and $E = 3$.

Step 5 Substitute $A = 1$, $B = 1$, $C = 0$, $D = 1$, and $E = 3$ in the equation in Step 1 to obtain the partial-fraction decomposition:

$$\frac{2x^4 - x^3 + 13x^2 - 2x + 13}{(x - 1)(x^2 + 4)^2} = \frac{1}{x - 1} + \frac{x}{x^2 + 4} + \frac{x + 3}{(x^2 + 4)^2}. \qquad ■ ■ ■$$

PRACTICE PROBLEM 4   Find the partial fraction decomposition of

$$\frac{x^2 + 3x + 1}{(x^2 + 1)^2}.$$ ■

EXAMPLE 5   **Learning a Clever Way to Add**

Express the sum

$$\frac{1}{2 \cdot 3} + \frac{1}{3 \cdot 4} + \frac{1}{4 \cdot 5} + \cdots + \frac{1}{2007 \cdot 2008}$$

as a fraction of whole numbers in lowest terms.

Solution

Each term in the sum is of the form $\dfrac{1}{k(k + 1)}$.

The partial-fraction decomposition of $\dfrac{1}{k(k + 1)}$ is given by

$$\frac{1}{k(k + 1)} = \frac{1}{k} - \frac{1}{k + 1}.$$

After decomposing each term into partial fractions

$$\left(\frac{1}{2 \cdot 3} = \frac{1}{2} - \frac{1}{3}, \ \ \frac{1}{3 \cdot 4} = \frac{1}{3} - \frac{1}{4}, \text{ and so on}\right),$$

we find that the sum

$$\frac{1}{2 \cdot 3} + \frac{1}{3 \cdot 4} + \frac{1}{4 \cdot 5} + \cdots + \frac{1}{2007 \cdot 2008}$$

is equal to

$$\left(\frac{1}{2} - \frac{1}{3}\right) + \left(\frac{1}{3} - \frac{1}{4}\right) + \left(\frac{1}{4} - \frac{1}{5}\right) + \cdots + \left(\frac{1}{2007} - \frac{1}{2008}\right).$$

After removing parentheses, we see that most terms cancel in pairs $\left(\text{such as } -\dfrac{1}{3} \text{ and } \dfrac{1}{3}\right),$ leaving just the first and the last term. Hence, the original sum is referred to as a *telescoping sum* that "collapses" to

$$\frac{1}{2} - \frac{1}{2008} = \frac{1004 - 1}{2008} = \frac{1003}{2008}.$$ ■ ■ ■

PRACTICE PROBLEM 5   Express the sum $\dfrac{1}{4 \cdot 5} + \dfrac{1}{5 \cdot 6} + \dfrac{1}{6 \cdot 7} + \cdots + \dfrac{1}{3111 \cdot 3112}$

as a fraction of whole numbers in lowest terms.   ■

EXAMPLE 6   **Calculating the Resistance in a Circuit**

The total resistance R due to two resistances connected in parallel is given by:

$$R = \frac{x(x + 5)}{3x + 10}$$

Continued on next page.

Use partial-fraction decomposition to write $\dfrac{1}{R}$ in terms of partial fractions. What does each term represent?

Solution

From $R = \dfrac{x(x+5)}{3x+10}$, we get:

$$\frac{1}{R} = \frac{3x+10}{x(x+5)} \qquad \text{Take the reciprocal of both sides.}$$

$$\frac{3x+10}{x(x+5)} = \frac{A}{x} + \frac{B}{x+5} \qquad \text{Form of partial-fraction decomposition}$$

$$3x+10 = A(x+5) + Bx \qquad \text{Multiply both sides by } x(x+5) \text{ and simplify.}$$

Substitute $x = 0$ in the last equation to obtain $5A = 10$ or $A = 2$. Now substitute $x = -5$ in the same equation to get $-5 = -5B$, or $B = 1$. Thus, we have

$$\frac{3x+10}{x(x+5)} = \frac{2}{x} + \frac{1}{x+5}, \quad \text{so that}$$

$$\frac{1}{R} = \frac{2}{x} + \frac{1}{x+5} \qquad\qquad \frac{1}{R} = \frac{3x+10}{x(x+5)}$$

$$\frac{1}{R} = \frac{1}{\dfrac{x}{2}} + \frac{1}{x+5} \qquad\qquad \text{Rewrite the right side.}$$

The last equation says that if two resistances $R_1 = \dfrac{x}{2}$ and $R_2 = x+5$ are connected in parallel, they will produce a total resistance R, where $R = \dfrac{x(x+5)}{3x+10}$. ■ ■ ■

PRACTICE PROBLEM 6 Repeat Example 6 if $R = \dfrac{(x+1)(x+2)}{4x+7}$. ■

A Exercises Basic Skills and Concepts

In Exercises 1–10, write the form of the partial-fraction decomposition of each rational expression. You do not need to solve for the constants.

1. $\dfrac{1}{(x-1)(x+2)}$ †

2. $\dfrac{x}{(x+1)(x-3)}$ †

3. $\dfrac{1}{x^2+7x+6} \dfrac{A}{x+6} + \dfrac{B}{x+1}$

4. $\dfrac{3}{x^2-6x+8}$ †

5. $\dfrac{2}{x^3-x^2} \dfrac{A}{x^2} + \dfrac{B}{x-1} + \dfrac{C}{x}$

6. $\dfrac{x-1}{(x+2)^2(x-3)}$ †

7. $\dfrac{x^2-3x+3}{(x+1)(x^2-x+1)}$ †

8. $\dfrac{2x+3}{(x-1)^2(x^2+x+1)}$ †

9. $\dfrac{3x-4}{(x^2+1)^2}$ †

10. $\dfrac{x-2}{(2x+3)^2(x^2+3)^2}$ †

In Exercises 11–42, find the partial-fraction decomposition of each rational expression.

11. $\dfrac{2x+1}{(x+1)(x+2)}$ †

12. $\dfrac{7}{(x-2)(x+5)}$ †

13. $\dfrac{1}{x^2+4x+3}$ †

14. $\dfrac{x}{x^2+5x+6}$ †

15. $\dfrac{2}{x^2+2x} \dfrac{-1}{x+2} + \dfrac{1}{x}$

16. $\dfrac{x+9}{x^2-9} \dfrac{2}{x-3} - \dfrac{1}{x+3}$

17. $\dfrac{x}{(x+1)(x+2)(x+3)}$ †

18. $\dfrac{x^2}{(x-1)(x^2+5x+4)}$ †

19. $\dfrac{x-1}{(x+1)^2} \dfrac{-2}{(x+1)^2} + \dfrac{1}{x+1}$

20. $\dfrac{3x+2}{x^2(x+1)} \dfrac{2}{x^2} + \dfrac{1}{x} - \dfrac{1}{x+1}$

†Due to space constrictions, answers to these exercises may be found in the Answers beginning on page A–1 in the back of the book.

21. $\dfrac{2x^2 + x}{(x + 1)^3}$ †

22. $\dfrac{x}{(x - 1)(x + 1)}$ †

23. $\dfrac{-x^2 + 3x + 1}{x^3 + 2x^2 + x}$ †

24. $\dfrac{5x^2 - 8x + 2}{x^3 - 2x^2 + x}$ †

25. $\dfrac{1}{x^2(x + 1)^2}$ †

26. $\dfrac{2}{(x - 1)^2(x + 3)^2}$ †

27. $\dfrac{1}{(x^2 - 1)^2}$ †

28. $\dfrac{3}{(x^2 - 4)^2}$ †

29. $\dfrac{x - 1}{(2x - 3)^2}$ †

30. $\dfrac{6x + 1}{(3x + 1)^2}$ †

31. $\dfrac{6x + 7}{4x^2 + 12x + 9}$ †

32. $\dfrac{2x + 3}{9x^2 + 30x + 25}$ †

33. $\dfrac{x - 3}{x^3 + x^2} \dfrac{4}{x} - \dfrac{3}{x^2} - \dfrac{4}{x + 1}$ ·

34. $\dfrac{1}{x^3 + x} \dfrac{-x}{x^2 + 1} + \dfrac{1}{x}$

35. $\dfrac{x^2 + 2x + 4}{x^3 + x^2}$ †

36. $\dfrac{x^2 + 2x - 1}{(x - 1)(x^2 + 1)}$ †

37. $\dfrac{x}{x^4 - 1}$ †

38. $\dfrac{3x^3 - 5x^2 + 12x + 4}{x^4 - 16}$ †

39. $\dfrac{1}{x(x^2 + 1)^2}$ †

40. $\dfrac{x^2}{(x^2 + 2)^2}$ †

41. $\dfrac{2x^2 + 3x}{(x^2 + 1)(x^2 + 2)}$ †

42. $\dfrac{x^2 - 2x}{(x^2 + 9)(x^2 + x + 7)}$ †

B Exercises   Applying the Concepts

In Exercises 43–46, express each sum as a fraction of whole numbers in lowest terms.

43. $\dfrac{1}{1 \cdot 2} + \dfrac{1}{2 \cdot 3} + \dfrac{1}{3 \cdot 4} + \cdots + \dfrac{1}{n(n + 1)}$ †

44. $\dfrac{2}{1 \cdot 3} + \dfrac{2}{2 \cdot 4} + \dfrac{2}{3 \cdot 5} + \cdots + \dfrac{2}{100 \cdot 102}$ †

45. $\dfrac{2}{1 \cdot 3} + \dfrac{2}{3 \cdot 5} + \dfrac{2}{5 \cdot 7} + \cdots + \dfrac{2}{(2n - 1)(2n + 1)}$ †

46. $\dfrac{2}{1 \cdot 2 \cdot 3} + \dfrac{2}{2 \cdot 3 \cdot 4} + \dfrac{2}{3 \cdot 4 \cdot 5} + \cdots + \dfrac{2}{100 \cdot 101 \cdot 102}$ †

$$\left[\textit{Hint: Write } \dfrac{2}{k(k + 1)(k + 2)} = \dfrac{1}{k} - \dfrac{2}{k + 1} + \dfrac{1}{k + 2} \right.$$
$$\left. = \dfrac{1}{k} - \dfrac{1}{k + 1} - \dfrac{1}{k + 1} + \dfrac{1}{k + 2}. \right]$$

In Exercises 47–50, the total resistance R in a circuit is given. Use partial-fraction decomposition to write $\dfrac{1}{R}$ in terms of partial fractions. Interpret each term in the partial fraction.

47. **Circuit resistance.** $R = \dfrac{(x + 1)(x + 3)}{2x + 4}$ †

48. **Circuit resistance.** $R = \dfrac{(x + 2)(x + 4)}{7x + 20}$ †

49. **Circuit resistance.** $R = \dfrac{R_1 R_2 R_3}{R_1 R_2 + R_2 R_3 + R_3 R_1}$ †

50. **Circuit resistance.** $R = \dfrac{x(x + 2)(x + 4)}{3x^2 + 12x + 8}$ †

C Exercises   Beyond the Basics

51. Solve the system of equations in Example 1 to verify the values of the constants A, B, and C.

In Exercises 52–60, find the partial-fraction decomposition of each rational expression.

52. $\dfrac{1}{x^3 + 1}$ †

53. $\dfrac{4x}{(x^2 - 1)^2}$ †

54. $\dfrac{2x + 3}{(x^2 + 1)(x + 1)}$ †

55. $\dfrac{x + 1}{(x^2 + 1)(x - 1)^2}$ †

56. $\dfrac{x}{(x^2 + 1)^2(x - 1)}$ †

57. $\dfrac{x^3}{(x + 1)^2(x + 2)^2}$ †

58. $\dfrac{2x^3 + 2x^2 - 1}{(x^2 + x + 1)^2}$ †

59. $\dfrac{15x}{x^3 - 27}$ †

60. $\dfrac{2x^2 - 9x + 10}{x^3 + 8}$ †

61. Find the partial fraction decomposition of $\dfrac{4x}{x^4 + 4}$. †

$[$ *Hint:* $x^4 + 4 = x^4 + 4 + 4x^2 - 4x^2 = (x^2 + 2)^2 - (2x)^2$
$= (x^2 - 2x + 2)(x^2 + 2x + 2)].$

62. Find the partial-fraction decomposition of $\dfrac{x^2 - 8x + 18}{(x - 5)^3}$. †

In Exercises 63–66, find the partial-fraction decomposition by first using long division.

63. $\dfrac{x^2 + 4x + 5}{x^2 + 3x + 2}$ †

64. $\dfrac{(x - 1)(x + 2)}{(x + 3)(x - 4)}$ †

65. $\dfrac{2x^4 + x^3 + 2x^2 - 2x - 1}{(x - 1)(x^2 + 1)}$ †

66. $\dfrac{x^4}{(x - 1)(x - 2)(x - 3)}$ †

Systems of Linear Inequalities; Linear Programming

OBJECTIVES

1 Graph a linear inequality in two variables.

2 Graph linear systems of inequalities in two variables.

3 Apply systems of inequalities to linear programming.

George Dantzig
1914–2005
George Dantzig received numerous honors and awards for his work. Dantzig attributed his success in mathematics to his father who encouraged him to develop his analytic power by making him solve thousands of geometry problems while George was still in high school.

During his first year of graduate studies, Dantzig arrived late in one of Professor Neyman's classes at the University of California at Berkeley. On the blackboard were two problems that Dantzig assumed had been assigned for homework. He submitted his homework a little late. He was surprised to learn that these were the two famous unsolved problems in statistics. The solutions of these problems became part of Dantzig's dissertation for his Ph.D. degree from Berkeley.

The Success of Linear Programming

From 1941 to 1946, George Dantzig was head of the Combat Analysis Branch, U.S. Army Air Corps Headquarters Statistical Control. During this period, he became an expert on planning methods involving troop supply problems that arose during World War II. With a war on several fronts, the size of the problem of coordinating supplies was daunting. This problem was known as *programming*, a military term which at that time referred to plans or schedules for training, logistical supply, or the deployment of forces. Dantzig mechanized the planning process by introducing *linear programming*, where *programming* has the military meaning.

In recent years, linear programming has been applied to problems in almost all areas of human life. A quick check in the library at a university may uncover entire books on linear programming applied to business, agriculture, city planning, and many other areas. Even feedlot operators use linear programming to decide how much and what kinds of food they should give their livestock each day. In Example 5 and in the exercises, we consider several linear programming problems involving two variables. ■

1 Graph a linear inequality in two variables.

Graph of a Linear Inequality in Two Variables

The statements $x + y > 4$, $2x + 3y < 7$, $y \geq x$, and $x + y \leq 9$ are examples of linear inequalities in the variables x and y. As with equations, a **solution of an inequality in two variables** x and y is an ordered pair (a, b) that results in a true statement when x is replaced by a and y is replaced by b in the inequality. For example, the ordered pair $(3, 2)$ is a solution of the inequality $4x + 5y > 11$ because $4(3) + 5(2) = 22 > 11$ is a true statement.

The ordered pair $(1, 1)$ is *not* a solution of the inequality $4x + 5y > 11$, because $4(1) + 5(1) = 9 > 11$ is a false statement. The set of all solutions of an inequality is called the **solution set of the inequality.** The **graph of an inequality in two variables** is the graph of the solution set of the inequality.

EXAMPLE 1   **Graphing a Linear Inequality**

Graph the inequality $2x + y > 6$.

Solution

The explanation that follows will illustrate a relationship between the graph of the inequality $2x + y > 6$ and that of the equation $2x + y = 6$.

Recall that the graph of the equation $2x + y = 6$ (a linear equation in x and y) is a straight line. You can use intercepts to sketch the graph of this line.

The x-intercept is 3 and the y-intercept is 6. The graph of the line joining the points $(3, 0)$ and $(0, 6)$ is shown in Figure 8.10. Solving the equation $2x + y = 6$ for y yields $y = 6 - 2x$. Thus, for each real number a, the point on the line with x-coordinate a has coordinates $(a, 6 - 2a)$. Now, a point $P(a, b)$ in the plane belongs to the graph of the inequality $y > 6 - 2x$ if and only if $b > 6 - 2a$; in other words, if the point $P(a, b)$ lies directly above the point with coordinates $(a, 6 - 2a)$, as shown in Figure 8.10. Thus, the graph of the inequality $2x + y > 6$ consists of all points (x, y) in the plane that lie above the line $2x + y = 6$. The graph of the inequality $2x + y > 6$ is shown shaded in Figure 8.11.

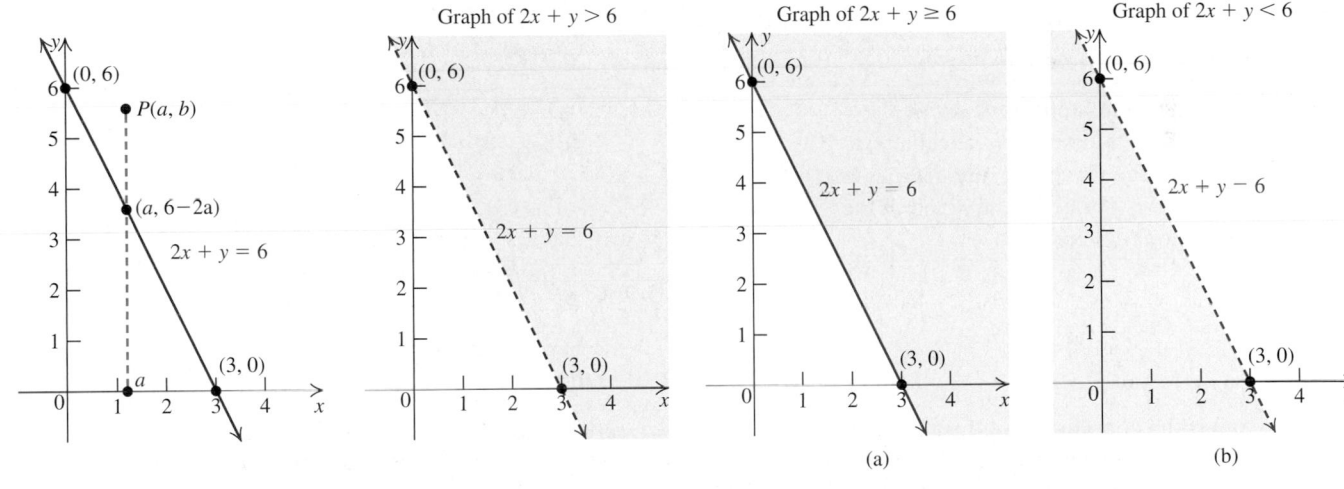

FIGURE 8.10   **FIGURE 8.11**   **FIGURE 8.12**   ■ ■ ■

PRACTICE PROBLEM 1   Graph the inequality $3x + y < 6$.   ■

In Figure 8.11, the graph of the equation $2x + y = 6$ is drawn as a dashed line to indicate that points on the line are *not* included in the solution set of the inequality $2x + y > 6$. The graph of the inequality $2x + y \geq 6$ is shown in Figure 8.12(a), with the graph of the line $2x + y = 6$ shown as a solid line. The solid line indicates that the points on the line *are* included in the solution set. Note that the region below the line $2x + y = 6$ in Figure 8.12(b) is the graph of the inequality $2x + y < 6$.

In general, the graph of the *corresponding equation* of the given inequality (obtained by changing the inequality symbol to an equal sign) will divide the plane into two regions. A line separates a plane into two regions, each called a *half plane*. The line itself is called the **boundary** of each region. *All* the points in one region will satisfy the given inequality, and *none* of the points in the other region will be solutions of the given inequality. You can therefore test a single point called a *test point* to determine which region represents the solution set of the given inequality. This idea leads to the following procedure for sketching the graph of an inequality in two variables.

FINDING THE SOLUTION: PROCEDURE FOR GRAPHING A LINEAR INEQUALITY IN TWO VARIABLES

OBJECTIVE	EXAMPLE
To graph an inequality in two variables.	Graph the linear inequality $y \geq -2x + 4$.

Step 1 Replace the inequality symbol by an equals (=) sign.

$y = -2x + 4$

Step 2 Sketch the graph of the *corresponding equation* in Step 1. Use a dashed line for the boundary if the given inequality sign is $<$ or $>$, and a solid line if the inequality symbol is $\leq$ or $\geq$.

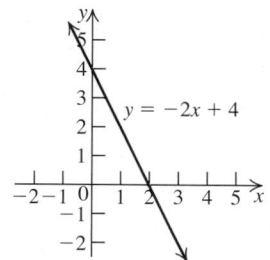

The graph of $y = -2x + 4$.

Step 3 The graph in Step 2 will divide the plane into two regions. Select a *test point* in the plane. Be sure that the test point does not lie on the graph of the equation in Step 1.

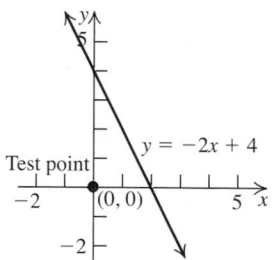

Select $(0, 0)$ as the test point.

Step 4 (*i*) If the coordinates of the test point satisfy the given inequality, then so do all the points of the region that contains the test point. Shade the region that contains the test point.

Since $0 \geq -2(0) + 4$ is false, the coordinates of the test point $(0, 0)$ do *not* satisfy the inequality $y \geq -2x + 4$.
The graph of the solution set of $y \geq -2x + 4$ is shaded in the figure.

(*ii*) If the coordinates of the test point do not satisfy the given inequality, shade the region that does not contain the test point.

The shaded region (including the boundary if it is solid) is the graph of the given inequality.

| EXAMPLE 2 | **Graphing Inequalities** |

Sketch the graph of each of the following inequalities.

a. $x \geq 2$ **b.** $y < 3$ **c.** $x + y < 4$

Solution

Steps	Inequality		
1. Change the inequality to an equality.	**a.** $x \geq 2$ $x = 2$	**b.** $y < 3$ $y = 3$	**c.** $x + y < 4$ $x + y = 4$
2. Graph the equation in Step 1 with a dashed line ($<$ or $>$) or a solid line ($\leq$ or $\geq$).			
3. Select a test point.	Test $(0, 0)$ in $x \geq 2$; $0 \geq 2$ is a false statement. The region not containing $(0, 0)$, together with the vertical line, is the solution set.	Test $(0, 0)$ in $y < 3$; $0 < 3$ is a true statement. The region containing $(0, 0)$ is the solution set.	Test $(0, 0)$ in $x + y < 4$; $0 + 0 < 4$ is a true statement. The region containing $(0, 0)$ is the solution set.
4. Shade the solution set.			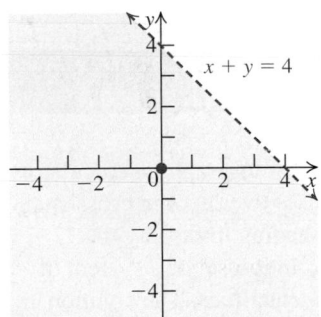

PRACTICE PROBLEM 2   Graph the inequality $x + y > 9$.

TECHNOLOGY CONNECTION

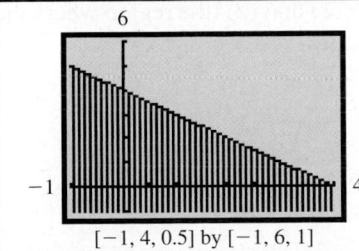

$[-1, 4, 0.5]$ by $[-1, 6, 1]$

Many graphing calculators can graph inequalities in two variables with the SHADE option. Generally, you must solve the associated equation for y if y is not already isolated. Most graphing calculators will not distinguish between a dashed and a solid boundary. The graph of $x + y < 4$ is shown here.

2 Graph linear systems of inequalities in two variables.

Systems of Linear Inequalities in Two Variables

An ordered pair (a, b) is a **solution of a system of inequalities** involving two variables x and y if and only if, when x is replaced by a and y is replaced by b in each inequality of the system, all the resulting statements are true. For example, $(0, 1)$ is a solution of the system

$$\begin{cases} 2x + y \le 1 \\ x - 3y < 0 \end{cases}$$

since $2(0) + 1 \le 1$ and $0 - 3(1) < 0$ are both true statements. The **solution set of a system of inequalities** is the *intersection* of the solution sets of all the inequalities in the system. To find the graph of this solution set, graph the solution set of each inequality in the system (with different-color shadings) on the same coordinate system. Then identify the region common to all the solution sets. (The region where all the shaded parts overlap is the intersection of all the solution sets.)

> **EXAMPLE 3** **Graphing a System of Two Inequalities**
>
> Graph the solution set of the system of inequalities:
>
> $$\begin{cases} 2x + 3y > 6 & (1) \\ y - x \le 0 & (2) \end{cases}$$

Solution

Graph each inequality separately in the same coordinate plane.

Inequality 1	**Inequality 2**
$2x + 3y > 6$	$y - x \le 0$

Step 1 $2x + 3y = 6$ **Step 1** $y - x = 0$

Step 2   Sketch $2x + 3y = 6$ as a dashed line by joining the points $(0, 2)$ and $(3, 0)$.

Step 2   Sketch $y - x = 0$ as a solid line by joining the points $(0, 0)$ and $(1, 1)$.

Step 3   Test $(0, 0)$ in
$$2x + 3y > 6$$
$$2 \cdot 0 + 3 \cdot 0 \overset{?}{>} 6$$
$$0 \overset{?}{>} 6 \quad \text{False}$$

Step 3   Test $(1, 0)$ in
$$y - x \le 0$$
$$0 - 1 \overset{?}{\le} 0$$
$$-1 \overset{?}{\le} 0 \quad \text{True}$$

Step 4   Shade as in Figure 8.13(a).   **Step 4**   Shade as in Figure 8.13(b).

The graph of the solution set of the system of inequalities (1) and (2) (the region where the shadings overlap) is shown shaded in purple in Figure 8.13(c).

TECHNOLOGY CONNECTION

A graphing calculator uses overlapping crosshatch shading to display the solution set of a system of inequalities. The solution set for the system

$$\begin{cases} 2x + 3y > 6 & (1) \\ y - x \le 0 & (2) \end{cases}$$

is shown here.

$[-2, 4, 1]$ by $[-4, 4, 1]$

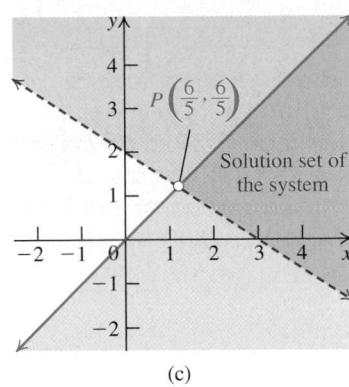

(a)   (b)   (c)

FIGURE 8.13   ■ ■ ■

PRACTICE PROBLEM 3   Graph the solution set of the system of inequalities:

$$\begin{cases} 3x - y > 3 \\ x - y \geq 1 \end{cases}$$ ■

The point $P\left(\dfrac{6}{5}, \dfrac{6}{5}\right)$ in Figure 8.13(c) is the point of intersection of the two lines $2x + 3y = 6$ and $y - x = 0$. Such a point is called a **corner point**, or **vertex** of the solution set. It is found by solving the system of equations $\begin{cases} 2x + 3y = 6 \\ y - x = 0 \end{cases}$.

However, in this case the point $P\left(\dfrac{6}{5}, \dfrac{6}{5}\right)$ is not in the solution set of the given system, because the ordered pair $\left(\dfrac{6}{5}, \dfrac{6}{5}\right)$ satisfies Inequality (2), but does not satisfy Inequality (1) of Example 3. We show P as an open circle.

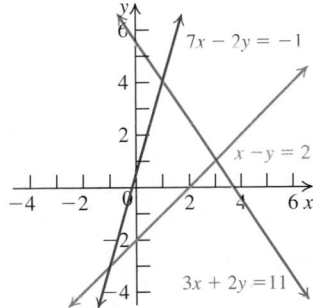

FIGURE 8.14

EXAMPLE 4   **Solving a System of Three Linear Inequalities**

Sketch the graph and label the vertices of the solution set of the following system of linear inequalities:

$$\begin{cases} 3x + 2y \leq 11 & (1) \\ x - y \leq 2 & (2) \\ 7x - 2y \geq -1 & (3) \end{cases}$$

Solution

First, on the same coordinate plane, sketch the graphs of the three linear equations that correspond to the three inequalities. Since either $\leq$ or $\geq$ occurs in all three inequalities, all the corresponding equations are graphed as *solid* lines. (See Figure 8.14.)

Notice that $(0, 0)$ satisfies each of the inequalities, but none of the corresponding equations. You can use $(0, 0)$ as the test point for each inequality.

Continued on next page.

Make the following conclusions:

(i)   Since $(0, 0)$ lies below the line $3x + 2y = 11$, the region on or below the line $3x + 2y = 11$ is in the solution set of Inequality (1).

(ii) Since $(0, 0)$ is above the line $x - y = 2$, the region on or above the line $x - y = 2$ is in the solution set of Inequality (2).

(iii) Finally, since $(0, 0)$ lies below the line $7x - 2y = -1$, the region on or below the line $7x - 2y = -1$ belongs to the solution set of Inequality (3).

The region common to the regions in (*i*), (*ii*), and (*iii*) (including the boundaries) is the solution set of the given system of inequalities. The solution set is the shaded region in Figure 8.15, including the sides of the triangle.

In Figure 8.15, you also see the vertices of the solution set. These vertices are obtained by solving each pair of equations in the system. Since all the vertices are solutions of the given system, they are shown as (filled in) points.

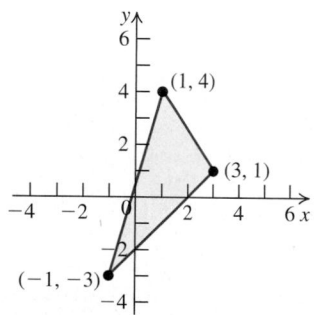

FIGURE 8.15

a. To find the vertex $(3, 1)$, solve the system $\begin{cases} 3x + 2y = 11 & (1) \\ x - y = 2 & (2) \end{cases}$

Solve Equation (2) for x to obtain $x = 2 + y$. Substitute $x = 2 + y$ in Equation (1).

$3x + 2y = 11$	Equation (1)
$3(2 + y) + 2y = 11$	Replace x by $2 + y$ in Equation (1).
$6 + 3y + 2y = 11$	Distributive property
$6 + 5y = 11$	Combine terms.
$y = 1$	Solve for y.

Back-substitute $y = 1$ in Equation (2) to obtain $x = 3$. The vertex is the point $(3, 1)$.

b. You can solve the system of equations $\begin{cases} x - y = 2 \\ 7x - 2y = -1 \end{cases}$ by the substitution method to obtain the vertex $(-1, -3)$.

c. You can solve the system of equations $\begin{cases} 3x + 2y = 11 \\ 7x - 2y = -1 \end{cases}$ by the elimination method to obtain the vertex $(1, 4)$.   ■ ■ ■

PRACTICE PROBLEM 4 Sketch the graph (and label the corner points) of the solution set of the system of inequalities.

$$\begin{cases} 2x + 3y < 16 \\ 4x + 2y \geq 16 \\ 2x - y \leq 8 \end{cases}$$ ■

3 Apply systems of inequalities to linear programming.

Applications: Linear Programming

Recall that if a function f with domain $[a, b]$ has a largest and a smallest value, the largest value is called the *maximum value* and the smallest value is called the *minimum value*. The process of finding the maximum or minimum value of a quanity is called **optimization.** For example, for the function

$$f(x) = x^2, \qquad -2 \leq x \leq 3,$$

the maximum value of f occurs at $x = 3$ and is given by $f(3) = 3^2 = 9$, while the minimum value occurs at $x = 0$ and is given by $f(0) = 0^2 = 0$. (See Figure 8.16.) This is an example of an optimization problem involving one variable.

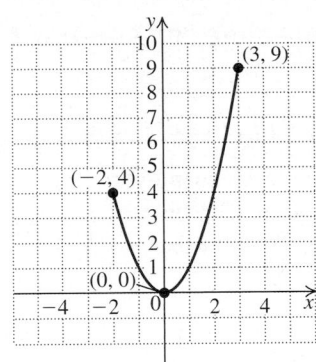

FIGURE 8.16

We now investigate optimization problems involving two variables, say x and y. Consider a two-variable optimization problem in which

1. The quantity f to be maximized or minimized can be written as a linear expression in x and y. That is,

$$f = ax + by, \text{ where } a \neq 0, b \neq 0 \text{ are constants.}$$

2. The domain of the variables x and y is restricted to a region S that is determined by (is a solution set of) a system of linear inequalities.

A problem that satisfies conditions (1) and (2) is called a **linear programming problem.**

The inequalities that determine the region S are called **constraints,** the region S is called the **set of feasible solutions,** and $f = ax + by$ is called the **objective function.** A point in S at which f attains its maximum (or minimum) value, together with the value of f at that point, is called an **optimal solution.**

Now consider the following linear programming problem:

Find values of x and y that will make $f = 2x + 3y$ as large as possible (in other words, that will result in a maximum value for f), where x and y are restricted by the following constraints:

$$\begin{cases} 3x + 5y \leq 15 \\ x \geq 0 \\ y \geq 0 \end{cases}$$

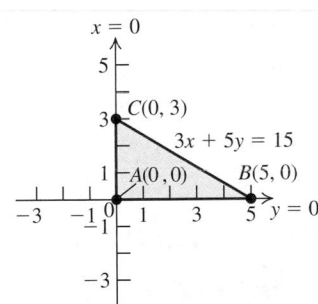

FIGURE 8.17

In order to solve this problem, first sketch the graph of the permissible values of x and y; that is, find the set of feasible solutions determined by the constraints of the problem. Using the method explained in Example 4, you find that the set of feasible solutions is the shaded region shown in Figure 8.17.

Now you have to find the values of $f = 2x + 3y$ at each of the points in the shaded region of Figure 8.17 and then see at which point f takes on the maximum value. However, there are infinitely many points in the shaded region. Since we cannot evaluate f at each point, you need some method other than trial and error to solve the problem.

Fortunately, it can be shown that if there is an optimal solution, it must occur at one of the vertices (corner points) of the feasible solution set. This means that when there is an optimal solution, *we can find the maximum (or minimum) value of f by first computing the value of f at each vertex and then picking the largest (or smallest) value that results.* The following procedure may be used for solving a linear programming problem.

PROCEDURE FOR SOLVING A LINEAR PROGRAMMING PROBLEM

OBJECTIVE	EXAMPLE
To solve a linear programming problem.	

Step 1   Write an expression for the quantity to be maximized or minimized. This expression is the objective function.

Maximize the objective function

$$f = 2x + 3y$$

Step 2   Write all the constraints as linear inequalities.

subject to the constraints:

$$\begin{cases} 3x + 5y \leq 15 \\ \quad x \geq 0 \\ \quad y \geq 0 \end{cases}$$

Step 3   Graph the solution set of the constraint inequalities. This set is the set of feasible solutions.

See Figure 8.17 for the solution set of the constraints.

Step 4   Find all the vertices of the solution set in Step 3 by solving all pairs of corresponding equations for the constraint inequalities.

Find:

$A(0, 0)$ by solving $\begin{cases} x = 0 \\ y = 0 \end{cases}$

$B(5, 0)$ by solving $\begin{cases} y = 0 \\ 3x + 5y = 15 \end{cases}$

and

$C(0, 3)$ by solving $\begin{cases} x \quad\;\; = 0 \\ 3x + 5y = 15 \end{cases}$

Step 5   Find the values of the objective function at each of the vertices of Step 4.

At $A(0, 0)$, $f = 2(0) + 3(0) = 0$.
At $B(5, 0)$, $f = 2(5) + 3(0) = 10$.
At $C(0, 3)$, $f = 2(0) + 3(3) = 9$.

Step 6   The largest of the values (if any) in Step 5 is the maximum value of the objective function, and the smallest of the values (if any) in Step 5 is the minimum value of the objective function.

The objective function f has a maximum value of 10, occurring at $B(5, 0)$. Although you are not asked for the minimum value, it is 0, and it occurs at $A(0, 0)$.

EXAMPLE 5   Nutrition; Minimizing Calories

Fat Albert wishes to go on a crash diet and needs your help in designing a lunch menu. The menu is to include two items: soup and salad. The vitamin units (milligrams) and calorie counts in each ounce of soup and salad are given in Table 8.2.

TABLE 8.2

Item	Vitamin A	Vitamin C	Calories
Soup	1	3	50
Salad	1	2	40

The menu must provide at least:

10 units of Vitamin A
24 units of Vitamin C.

Find the number of ounces of each item in the menu needed to provide the required vitamins with the fewest number of calories.

Solution

a. State the problem mathematically.

Step 1   **Write the objective function.**
Let the lunch menu contain x ounces of soup and y ounces of salad.
You need to minimize the total number of calories in the menu. Since there are 50 calories per ounce of soup (see Table 8.2), the number of calories from x ounces is $50x$. Similarly, there are $40y$ calories from the salad. Hence, the number f of calories provided by the two items is given by the objective function

$$f = 50x + 40y.$$

Step 2   **Write the constraints.** Since each ounce of soup provides 1 unit of vitamin A, and each ounce of salad provides 1 unit of vitamin A, the two items together will provide $1 \cdot x + 1 \cdot y = x + y$ units of vitamin A. The lunch must have at least 10 units of vitamin A; this means that

$$x + y \geq 10.$$

Similarly, the two items will provide $3x + 2y$ units of vitamin C. The menu must provide at least 24 units of vitamin C, so

$$3x + 2y \geq 24.$$

The fact that x and y cannot be negative means that $x \geq 0$ and $y \geq 0$. You now have four constraints.

Summarize your information. Find x and y such that the value of

$$f = 50x + 40y \qquad \text{Objective function from Step 1}$$

is a *minimum,* with the restrictions:

$$\begin{cases} x + \ y \geq 10 \\ 3x + 2y \geq 24 \\ x \geq \ 0 \\ y \geq \ 0 \end{cases} \qquad \text{Constraints from Step 2}$$

b. Solve the linear programming problem.

Step 3   **Graph the set of feasible solutions.**
The set of feasible solutions is shaded in Figure 8.18. This set is bounded by the lines whose equations are

$$x + y = 10, \, 3x + 2y = 24, \, x = 0, \text{ and } y = 0.$$

Step 4   **Find the vertices.** The vertices of the set of feasible solutions are $A(10, 0)$, $B(4, 6)$ and $C(0, 12)$, where:

$$A(10, 0) \text{ is obtained by solving } \begin{cases} y = \ 0 \\ x + y = 10 \end{cases}$$

$$B(4,6) \text{ is obtained by solving } \begin{cases} x + \ y = 10 \\ 3x + 2y = 24 \end{cases}$$

$$C(0, 12) \text{ is obtained by solving } \begin{cases} x = 0 \\ 3x + 2y = 24 \end{cases}$$

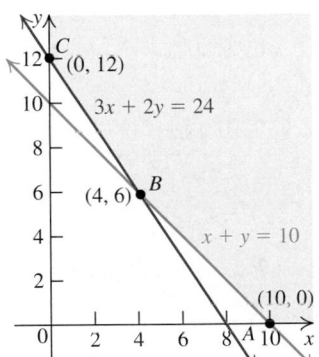

FIGURE 8.18

Continued on next page.

Step 5   **Find the value of f at the vertices.** The value of f at each of the vertices is given in Table 8.3.

TABLE 8.3

Vertex (x, y)	Value of $f = 50x + 40y$
$(10, 0)$	$50(10) + 40(0) = 500$
$(4, 6)$	$50(4) + 40(6) = 440$
$(0, 12)$	$50(0) + 40(12) = 480$

Step 6   **Find the maximum or minimum value of f.** From Table 8.3, the smallest value of f is 440, which occurs when $x = 4$ and $y = 6$.

c. State the conclusion.

The lunch menu for Fat Albert should contain 4 ounces of soup and 6 ounces of salad. His intake of 440 calories will be as small as possible under the given constraints.

■   ■   ■

PRACTICE PROBLEM 5   How does the answer to Example 5 change if 1 ounce of soup contains 30 calories and 1 ounce of salad contains 60 calories?   ■

Notice in Example 5 that the value of the objective function $f = 50x + 40y$ can be made as large as you want by choosing x or y (or both) to be very large. So f has a minimum value of 440, but no maximum value.

A Exercises   Basic Skills and Concepts

In Exercises 1–16, graph each inequality.

1. $x \geq 0$ †

2. $y \geq 0$ †

3. $x > -1$ †

4. $y > 2$ †

5. $x \geq 2$ †

6. $y \leq 3$ †

7. $y - x < 0$ †

8. $y + 2x < 0$ †

9. $x + 2y < 6$ †

10. $3x + 2y < 12$ †

11. $2x + 3y \geq 12$ †

12. $2x + 5y \geq 10$ †

13. $x - 2y \leq 4$ †

14. $3x - 4y \leq 12$ †

15. $3x + 5y < 15$ †

16. $5x + 7y < 35$ †

In Exercises 17–22, determine which ordered pairs are solutions of each system of inequalities.

17. $\begin{cases} x + y < 2 \\ 2x + y \geq 6 \end{cases}$

(a) $(0, 0)$ (b) $(-4, -1)$ (c) $(3, 0)$ (d) $(0, 3)$ None

18. $\begin{cases} x - y < 2 \\ 3x + 4y \geq 12 \end{cases}$

(a) $(0, 0)$ (b) $\left(\dfrac{16}{5}, \dfrac{3}{5}\right)$ (c) $(4, 0)$ (d) $\left(\dfrac{1}{2}, \dfrac{1}{2}\right)$ None

19. $\begin{cases} y < x + 2 \\ x + y \leq 4 \end{cases}$

(a) $(0, 0)$ (b) $(1, 0)$ (c) $(0, 1)$ (d) $(1, 1)$ †

20. $\begin{cases} y \leq 2 - x \\ x + y \leq 1 \end{cases}$

(a) $(0, 0)$ (b) $(0, 1)$ (c) $(1, 2)$ (d) $(-1, -1)$ †

21. $\begin{cases} 3x - 4y \leq 12 \\ x + y \leq 4 \\ 5x - 2y \geq 6 \end{cases}$

(a) $(0, 0)$ (b) $(2, 0)$ (c) $(3, 1)$ (d) $(2, 2)$ $(2, 0), (3, 1), (2, 2)$

22. $\begin{cases} 2 + y \leq 3 \\ x - 2y \leq 3 \\ 5x + 2y \geq 3 \end{cases}$

(a) $(0, 0)$ (b) $(1, 0)$ (c) $(1, 2)$ (d) $(2, 1)$ $(1, 0), (2, 1)$

In Exercises 23–38, graph the solution set of each system of linear inequalities and label the vertices (if any) of the solution set.

23. $\begin{cases} x + y \leq 1 \\ x - y \leq -1 \end{cases}$ †

24. $\begin{cases} x + y \geq 1 \\ y - x \geq 1 \end{cases}$ †

†Due to space constrictions, answers to these exercises may be found in the Answers beginning on page A–1 in the back of the book.

25. $\begin{cases} 3x + 5y \le 15 \\ 2x + 2y \le 8 \end{cases}$ †

26. $\begin{cases} -2x + y \le 2 \\ 3x + 2y \le 4 \end{cases}$ †

27. $\begin{cases} 2x + 3y \le 6 \\ 4x + 6y \ge 24 \end{cases}$ †

28. $\begin{cases} x + 2y \ge 6 \\ 2x + 4y \le 4 \end{cases}$ †

29. $\begin{cases} 3x + y \le 8 \\ 4x + 2y \ge 4 \end{cases}$ †

30. $\begin{cases} x + 2y \le 12 \\ 2x + 4y \ge 8 \end{cases}$ †

31. $\begin{cases} x \ge 0 \\ y \ge 0 \\ x + y \le 1 \end{cases}$ †

32. $\begin{cases} x \ge 0 \\ y \ge 0 \\ x + y > 2 \end{cases}$ †

33. $\begin{cases} x \ge 0 \\ y \ge 0 \\ 2x + 3y \ge 6 \end{cases}$ †

34. $\begin{cases} x \ge 0 \\ y \ge 0 \\ 3x + 4y \le 12 \end{cases}$ †

35. $\begin{cases} x + y \le 1 \\ x - y \ge 1 \\ 2x + y \le 1 \end{cases}$ †

36. $\begin{cases} x + y \le 1 \\ x - y \ge 1 \\ 2x + y \ge 1 \end{cases}$ †

37. $\begin{cases} x + y \le 1 \\ x - y < 2 \\ -x + y \le 3 \\ x + y \ge -4 \end{cases}$ †

38. $\begin{cases} x + y \le -1 \\ 2x - y < -2 \\ -2x + y \le -3 \\ 2x + 2y \le -4 \end{cases}$ †

In Exercises 39–44, use the following figure to indicate the regions (A–G) that correspond to the graph of the given system of inequalities:

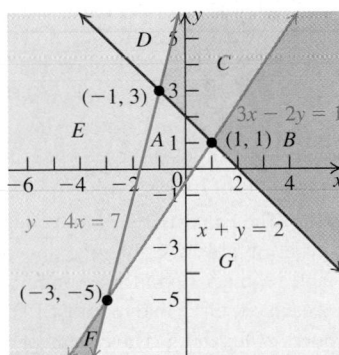

39. $\begin{cases} x + y \le 2 \\ 3x - 2y \le 1 \\ y - 4x \le 7 \end{cases}$ A

40. $\begin{cases} x + y \ge 2 \\ 3x - 2y \le 1 \\ y - 4x \le 7 \end{cases}$ C

41. $\begin{cases} x + y > 2 \\ 3x - 2y \ge 1 \\ y - 4x \le 7 \end{cases}$ B

42. $\begin{cases} x + y > 2 \\ 3x - 2y \le 1 \\ y - 4x \ge 7 \end{cases}$ D

43. $\begin{cases} x + y \le 2 \\ 3x - 2y \le 1 \\ y - 4x \ge 7 \end{cases}$ E

44. $\begin{cases} x + y \le 2 \\ 3x - 2y \ge 1 \\ y - 4x \ge 7 \end{cases}$ F

In Exercises 45–50, find the maximum and the minimum value of each objective function f. The graph of the set of feasible solutions is as follows:

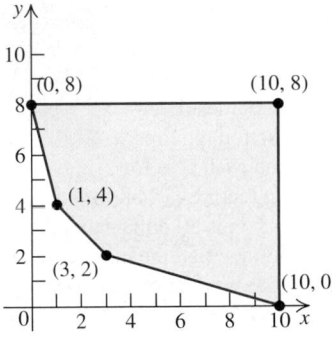

45. $f = x + y$ Max 18, Min 5

46. $f = 2x + y$ Max 28, Min 6

47. $f = x + 2y$ Max 26, Min 7

48. $f = 2x + 5y$ Max 60, Min 16

49. $f = 5x + 2y$ Max 66, Min 13

50. $f = 8x + 5y$ Max 120, Min 28

In Exercises 51–58, you are given an objective function f and a set of constraints. Find the set of feasible solutions determined by the given constraints, and then maximize or minimize the objective function as directed.

51. Maximize $f = 9x + 13y$, subject to the constraints $x \ge 0, y \ge 0, 5x + 8y \le 40, 3x + y \le 12$. †

52. Maximize $f = 7x + 6y$, subject to the constraints $x \ge 0, y \ge 0, 2x + 3y \le 13, x + y \le 5$. †

53. Maximize $f = 5x + 7y$, subject to the constraints $x \ge 0, y \ge 0, x + y \le 70, x + 2y \le 100, 2x + y \le 120$. †

54. Maximize $f = 2x + y$, subject to the constraints $x \ge 0, y \ge 0, x + y \le 5, 2x + 3y \le 21, 4x + 3y \le 24$. †

55. Minimize $f = x + 4y$, subject to the constraints $x \ge 0, y \ge 0, x + 3y \ge 3, 2x + y \ge 2$. †

56. Minimize $f = 5x + 2y$, subject to the constraints $x \ge 0, y \ge 0, 5x + y \ge 10, x + y \ge 6$. †

57. Minimize $f = 13x + 15y$, subject to the constraints $x \ge 0, y \ge 0, 3x + 4y \ge 360, 2x + y \ge 100$. †

58. Minimize $f = 40x + 37y$, subject to the constraints $x \ge 0, y \ge 0, 10x + 3y \ge 180, 2x + 3y \ge 60$. †

B Exercises   Applying the Concepts

59. Agriculture: crop planning. A farmer owns 240 acres of cropland. He can use his land to produce corn and soybeans. A total of 320 labor hours is available to him during the production period of both of these commodities. Each acre for corn production requires 2 hours of labor, and each acre for soybean production requires 1 hour of labor. If the profit per acre in corn production is 50 dollars and that in soybean production is 40 dollars, find the number of acres that he should allocate to the production of corn and soybeans so as to maximize his profit. †

60. Repeat Exercise 59 if the profit per acre in corn production is 30 dollars and that in soybean production is 40 dollars. †

61. Manufacturing: production scheduling. Two machines (I and II) each produce two grades of plywood: Grade A and Grade B. In 1 hour of operation, machine I produces 20 units of Grade A and 10 units of Grade B plywood. Also in 1 hour of operation, machine II produces 30 units of Grade A and 40 units of Grade B plywood. The machines are required to meet a production schedule of at least 1400 units of Grade A and 1200 units of grade B plywood. If the cost of operating machine I is 50 dollars per hour and the cost of operating machine II is 80 dollars per hour, find the number of hours each machine should be operated so as to minimize the cost. †

62. Repeat Exercise 61 if the cost of operating machine I is 70 dollars per hour and the cost of operating machine II is 90 dollars per hour. †

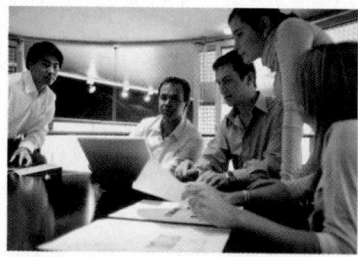

63. Advertising. The Sundial Cheese Company wants to allocate its 6000-dollar advertising budget to two local media—television and newspaper—so that the exposure (number of viewers) to its advertisements is maximized. There are 60,000 viewers exposed to each minute of television time and 20,000 readers exposed to each page of newspaper advertising. Each minute of television time costs 1000 dollars and each page of newspaper advertising costs 500 dollars. How should the company allocate its budget if it has to buy at least 1 minute of television time and at least two pages of newspaper advertising? †

64. Advertising. The Fantastic Bread Company allocates a maximum of 24,000 dollars to advertise its product to two media: television and newspaper. Each hour of television costs 4000 dollars, and each page of newspaper advertising costs 3000 dollars. The exposure from each hour of television time is assumed to be 120,000, and the exposure from each page of newspaper advertising is 80,000. Furthermore, the board of directors has specified that at least 2 hours of television time and one page of newspaper advertising be used. How should the advertising budget be divided so that the exposures to the advertisements are maximized? †

65. Agriculture. A Florida Citrus Company has 480 acres of land for growing oranges and grapefruit. Profits per acre are 40 dollars for oranges and 30 dollars for grapefruit. The total labor hours available during the production are 800. Each acre for oranges uses 2 hours of labor, and each acre for grapefruit uses 1 hour of labor. If the fixed costs are 3000 dollars, what is the maximum profit? †

66. Agriculture. The Florida Juice Company makes two types of fruit punch—Fruity and Tangy—by blending orange juice and apple juice into a mixture. The fruit punch is sold in 5-gallon bottles. A bottle of Fruity earns a profit of 3 dollars, and a bottle of Tangy earns a profit of 2 dollars. A bottle of Fruity requires 3 gallons of orange juice and 2 gallons of apple juice, while a bottle of Tangy requires 4 gallons of orange juice and 1 gallon of apple juice. If 200 gallons of orange juice and 120 gallons of apple juice are available, find the maximum profit for the company. †

67. Manufacturing. The Fantastic Furniture Company manufactures two types of tables: rectangular and circular. Each rectangular table requires 1 hour of assembling and 1 hour of finishing, and each circular table requires 1 hour of assembling and 2 hours of finishing. The company has 20 assemblers and 30 finishers, each of whom works 40 hours per week. Each rectangular table brings a profit of 3 dollars, and each circular table brings a profit of 4 dollars. Suppose that all the tables manufactured will be sold. How many of each type should be made to maximize profits? †

68. Manufacturing. A company produces two products—a portable global positioning system (GPS) and a portable digital video disc (DVD) player, each of which requires three stages of processing. The length of time for processing each unit is given in the following table:

Stage	GPS (hr/unit)	DVD (hr/unit)	Maximum process capacity (hr/day)
I	12	12	840
II	3	6	300
III	8	4	480
Profit per unit	$6	$4	

How many of each product should the company produce per day in order to maximize profit? †

69. Building houses. A contractor has the following materials available: 100 units of concrete, 160 units of wood, and 400 units of glass. He builds houses of two types: terraced houses and cottages. A terraced house requires 1 unit of concrete, 2 units of wood, and 2 units of glass, while a cottage requires 1 unit of concrete, 1 unit of wood and 5 units of glass. A terraced house sells for 40,000 dollars, and a cottage sells for 45,000 dollars. How many houses of each type should the contractor build in order to obtain the maximum amount of money? †

70. Hospitality. Mrs. Adams owns a motel consisting of 300 single rooms and an attached restaurant that serves breakfast. She knows that 30% of the male guests and 50% of the female guests will eat in the restaurant. Suppose that she makes a profit of 18 dollars and 50 cents per day from every guest who eats in her restaurant and 15 dollars per day from every guest who does not eat in her restaurant. If Mrs. Adams never has more than 125 female guests and never more than 220 male guests, find the number of male and female guests that would provide the maximum profit. †

71. Hospitality. In Exercise 70, find Mrs. Adams's maximum profit during a season in which she always has at least 100 guests if she makes a profit of 15 dollars per day from every guest who eats in her restaurant while she suffers a loss of 2 dollars per day from every guest who does not eat in her restaurant. †

72. Transportation. Major Motors, Inc., must produce at least 5000 luxury cars and 12,000 medium-priced cars. The company also must produce at most 30,000 units of compact cars. The company owns two factories: one in Michigan and one in North Carolina. The Michigan factory produces 20, 40, and 60 units of luxury, medium-priced, and compact cars, respectively, per day, while the North Carolina factory produces 10, 30, and 20 luxury, medium-priced, and compact cars, respectively, per day. If the Michigan factory costs 60,000 dollars per day to operate and the North Carolina factory costs 40,000 dollars per day to operate, find the number of days each factory should operate to minimize the cost and meet the requirements. †

73. Nutrition. Elisa Epstein is buying two types of frozen meals: a meal of enchiladas with vegetables and a vegetable loaf meal. She wants to guarantee that she gets a minimum of 60 grams of carbohydrates, 40 grams of proteins, and 35 grams of fats. The enchilada meal contains 5, 3, and 5 grams of carbohydrates, proteins, and fats, respectively, per kilogram, while the vegetable loaf contains 2, 2, and 1 gram of carbohydrates, proteins, and fats, respectively, per kilogram. If the enchilada meal costs 3 dollars and 50 cents per kilogram and the vegetable loaf costs 2 dollars and 25 cents per kilogram, how many kilograms of each should Elisa buy to minimize the cost and still meet the minimum requirement? †

74. Temporary help. The personnel director of the main post office plans to hire extra helpers during the Christmas season to handle the large increase in the volume of mail and delivery. Since office space is limited, the number of temporary workers cannot exceed 10. She hires workers sent by two agencies: Super Temps and Ready Aid. From her past experience, she knows that a typical worker sent by Super Temps can handle 300 letters and 80 packages per day and a typical worker from Ready Aid can handle 600 letters and 40 packages per day. The post office expects that the additional daily volume of letters and packages will be at least 3900 and 560, respectively. The daily wages for a typical worker from Super Temps and Ready Aid are 96 dollars and 86 dollars, respectively. How many workers from each agency should be hired to keep the daily wages to a minimum? †

C Exercises   Beyond the Basics

In Exercises 75–82, write a system of linear inequalities that has the given graph.

75.

76.

77.

78.

79.

80.

81.

82.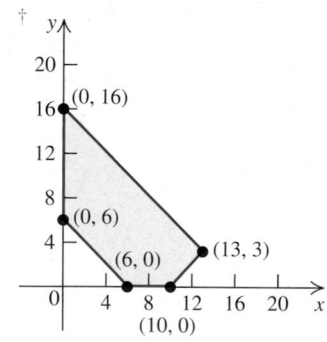

Critical Thinking

In Exercises 83–84, graph the solution set of each inequality.

83. $6 \le 2x + 3y \le 12$ †

84. $|x + 2y| < 4$ †

New York Stock Exchange

Nonlinear Systems of Equations and Inequalities

BEFORE STARTING THIS SECTION, REVIEW

1. Solve systems of linear equations

   (a) The graphical method (Section 8.1, page 739)

   (b) The substitution method (Section 8.1, page 741)

   (c) The elimination method (Section 8.1, page 744)

2. Solve systems of linear inequalities (Section 8.4, page 782)

OBJECTIVES

1 Solve nonlinear systems of equations.

2 Solve a nonlinear system of inequalities.

Investing in the Stock Market

A *stock* is a certificate that shows that you own a small fraction of a corporation. When you own stock in a company, you are referred to as a *shareholder*. When you buy stock, you are paying for a small percentage of everything the company owns and you own a slice of every dollar of profit (or loss) that comes through the door. In essence, a stock is a representation of the amount you own of a company.

Suppose you inherit some money and are interested in investing part of the money in the stock market. You have decided to risk 1000 dollars of your inheritance in the market. Where do you invest your money? (This is a serious question. You may have to do a lot of research on the companies that interest you, or you may have to get help from a broker.)

Suppose you get a tip from a friend who heard it from his brother-in-law (who is a taxi driver and overheard his customer's conversation) that Microsoft is coming out with a new version of Microsoft Windows® that is going to double the company's business. Where do you go to buy Microsoft stock? You go to a broker. A brokerage house (such as Merrill Lynch) is your supermarket of stocks. You call any broker and tell him or her that you have 1000 dollars and want to buy as much Microsoft stock as you can. The broker might tell you, "A share of Microsoft at this time [the price may fluctuate every second] costs 27 dollars [the actual closing price on April 21, 2006, was 27 dollars and 18 cents], and I am going to charge you 55 dollars for my services, so you can buy $\dfrac{1000 - 55}{27} = 35$ shares of Microsoft." You then give the broker the money, and you get the stock. (Usually, the broker doesn't actually give you the paper stock certificate, but rather transfers ownership to you.) So now you are part owner of Microsoft! You have tied your fate to that of Chairman Bill Gates, for better or worse.

You can make a profit on your investment if you sell your stock for more than the total amount you paid for it. You can also make money while you own certain stocks by receiving dividends. A *dividend* on a share of stock is a return on your investment and represents the portion of the company's profits allocated to that share. The dividend can be in the form of cash or additional shares of the company. In Example 3, we discuss such a scenario and solve the problem by using a nonlinear system of equations. ■

1 Solve nonlinear systems of equations.

Nonlinear Systems of Equations

In Sections 8.1, 8.2, and 8.4, we discussed systems of *linear* equations and inequalities. We now consider *nonlinear* systems of equations and inequalities involving two variables. That is, at least one equation or inequality in the system is nonlinear.

To determine whether an ordered pair is a solution of either a linear or a nonlinear system, you check whether it is a solution of each equation or inequality in the system. Thus, $(2, 0)$ is a solution of the system

$$\begin{cases} x^2 + 3y > 3 & (1) \\ 9x^2 - 4y^2 \le 36 & (2) \end{cases}$$

because $2^2 + 3(0) > 3$ and $9(2)^2 - 4(0)^2 \le 36$ are both true statements.

EXAMPLE 1   **Using Substitution to Solve a Nonlinear System**

Solve the system of equations by the substitution method.

$$\begin{cases} 4x + y = -3 & (1) \\ -x^2 + y = 1 & (2) \end{cases}$$

Solution

We follow the same steps that were used in the substitution method for solving a system of linear equations in Section 8.1.

Step 1   **Solve for one variable.** In equation (2), you can express y in terms of x:

$$y = x^2 + 1. \quad (3) \qquad \text{Solve Equation (2) for } y.$$

Step 2   **Substitute.** Substitute $x^2 + 1$ for y in equation (1).

$$\begin{aligned} 4x + y &= -3 && \text{Equation (1)} \\ 4x + (x^2 + 1) &= -3 && \text{Replace } y \text{ by } (x^2 + 1). \\ 4x + x^2 + 1 &= -3 && \text{Remove parentheses.} \\ 4x + x^2 + 4 &= 0 && \text{Add 3 to both sides.} \\ x^2 + 4x + 4 &= 0 && \text{Rewrite in descending powers of } x. \end{aligned}$$

Step 3   **Solve** the equation resulting from Step 2.

$$\begin{aligned} (x + 2)(x + 2) &= 0 && \text{Factor.} \\ x + 2 &= 0 && \text{Zero-product property} \\ x &= -2 && \text{Solve for } x. \end{aligned}$$

Step 4 **Back-substitution.** Substitute $x = -2$ in Equation (3) to obtain the corresponding y-value.

$$y = x^2 + 1 \qquad \text{Equation (3)}$$
$$y = (-2)^2 + 1 \qquad \text{Replace } x \text{ by } -2.$$
$$y = 5 \qquad \text{Simplify.}$$

Since $x = -2$ and $y = 5$, the apparent solution set of the system is $\{(-2, 5)\}$.

Step 5 **Check.** Replace x by -2 and y by 5 in both Equation (1) and Equation (2).

$$4x + y = -3 \qquad\qquad\qquad -x^2 + y = 1$$
$$4(-2) + 5 \overset{?}{=} -3 \qquad\qquad -(-2)^2 + 5 \overset{?}{=} 1$$
$$-8 + 5 \overset{?}{=} -3 \qquad\qquad\quad -4 + 5 \overset{?}{=} 1$$
$$-3 = -3 \checkmark \qquad\qquad\qquad 1 = 1 \checkmark$$

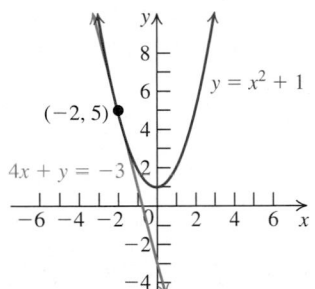

FIGURE 8.19

The graphs of the line $4x + y = -3$ and the parabola $y = x^2 + 1$ confirm that the solution set is $\{(-2, 5)\}$. See Figure 8.19. ▪ ▪ ▪

PRACTICE PROBLEM 1 Solve the system of equations by the substitution method.

$$\begin{cases} x^2 + y = 2 & (1) \\ 2x + y = 3 & (2) \end{cases}$$

▪

EXAMPLE 2 **Using Elimination to Solve a Nonlinear System**

Solve the system of equations by the elimination method.

$$\begin{cases} x^2 + y^2 = 25 & (1) \\ x^2 - y = 5 & (2) \end{cases}$$

Solution

Step 1 **Adjust the coefficients.** Because x has the same power in both equations, we choose the variable x for elimination. We multiply Equation (2) by -1 and obtain the equivalent system:

$$\begin{cases} x^2 + y^2 = 25 & (1) \\ \underline{-x^2 + y = -5} & (3) \qquad \text{Multiply Equation (2) by } -1. \end{cases}$$

Step 2 $\qquad\qquad\qquad\qquad y^2 + y = 20 \quad (4) \qquad$ Add Equations (1) and (3).

Step 3 Solve the equation obtained in Step 2.

$$y^2 + y = 20 \qquad\qquad \text{Equation (4)}$$
$$y^2 + y - 20 = 0 \qquad\qquad \text{Subtract 20 from both sides.}$$
$$(y + 5)(y - 4) = 0 \qquad\qquad \text{Factor.}$$
$$y + 5 = 0 \quad \text{or } y - 4 = 0 \qquad \text{Zero product property}$$
$$y = -5 \text{ or} \qquad y = 4 \qquad \text{Solve for } y.$$

Continued on next page.

To use a graphing calculator to graph the system in Example 2, you must solve $x^2 + y^2 = 25$ for y and enter the two resulting equations.

$$Y_1 = \sqrt{25 - x^2}$$
$$Y_2 = -\sqrt{25 - x^2}$$

Then enter

$$Y_3 = x^2 - 5$$

and use the Zsquare feature.

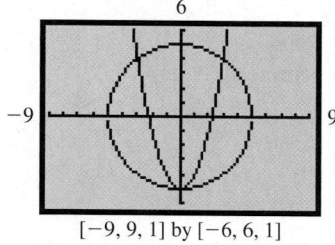

$[-9, 9, 1]$ by $[-6, 6, 1]$

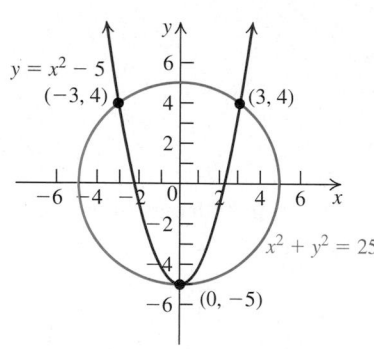

FIGURE 8.20

Step 4   **Back-substitute** the values in one of the original equations to solve for the other variable.

(i)   Substitute $y = -5$ in Equation (2) and solve for x.

$x^2 - y = 5$	Equation (2)
$x^2 - (-5) = 5$	Replace y by -5.
$x^2 + 5 = 5$	Simplify.
$x^2 = 0$	Add -5 to both sides.
$x = 0$	Solve for x.

Thus, $(0, -5)$ is a solution of the system.

(ii)   Substitute $y = 4$ in Equation (2) and solve for x.

$x^2 - y = 5$	Equation (2)
$x^2 - 4 = 5$	Replace y by 4.
$x^2 = 9$	Add 4 to both sides.
$x = \pm 3$	Square root property

Thus, $(3, 4)$ and $(-3, 4)$ are the solutions of the systems.

From (i) and (ii), the apparent solution set for the system is $\{(0, -5), (3, 4), (-3, 4)\}$.

Step 5   **Check.**

	$(0, -5)$	$(3, 4)$	$(-3, 4)$
$x^2 + y^2 = 25$	$0^2 + (-5)^2 \overset{?}{=} 25$	$3^2 + 4^2 \overset{?}{=} 25$	$(-3)^2 + 4^2 \overset{?}{=} 25$
	$25 = 25$ ✓	$9 + 16 = 25$	$9 + 16 \overset{?}{=} 25$
		$25 = 25$ ✓	$25 = 25$ ✓
$x^2 - y = 5$	$0^2 - (-5) \overset{?}{=} 5$	$3^2 - 4 \overset{?}{=} 5$	$(-3)^2 - 4 \overset{?}{=} 5$
	$5 = 5$ ✓	$9 - 4 \overset{?}{=} 5$	$9 - 4 \overset{?}{=} 5$
		$5 = 5$ ✓	$5 = 5$ ✓

The graphs of the circle $x^2 + y^2 = 25$ and the parabola $y = x^2 - 5$ sketched in Figure 8.20 confirm the three solutions.   ■ ■ ■

PRACTICE PROBLEM 2   Solve the system of equations.

$$\begin{cases} x^2 + 2y^2 = 34 \\ x^2 - y^2 = 7 \end{cases}$$ ■

EXAMPLE 3   **Investing in Stocks**

Danielle bought 240 shares of Alpha Airlines stock at 40 dollars per share and paid 100 dollars in broker fees. She kept these shares for three years, during which time she received a number of additional shares of the stock as dividends. At the end of three years, her dividends were worth 2400 dollars, and she sold all her stock and made a profit of 7100 dollars (after paying 100 dollars in broker's commission). How many shares of the stock did she receive as dividends, and what was the selling price of each share of the stock?

Solution

Let $x =$ number of shares she received as dividends

$p =$ selling price per share.

Then

$$xp = 2400 \quad (1) \qquad \text{The total dividend is worth \$2400.}$$

The number of shares she sold at p dollars per share is $240 + x$. Thus,

$$\text{Revenue} = (240 + x)p$$
$$\text{Cost} = (240)(40) + 100 = 9700$$

number of shares bought   commission

price she paid per share

and

$$\text{Revenue} \;-\; \text{Cost} = \text{Profit}$$
$$(240 + x)p - 9700 = 7100$$
$$(240 + x)p = 16{,}800 \qquad \text{Add 9700 to both sides.}$$
$$240p + xp = 16{,}800. \quad (2) \quad \text{Distributive property}$$

We solve the following system of equations

$$\begin{cases} xp = 2400 & (1) \quad \text{Revenue from the dividends} \\ 240p + xp = 16{,}800 & (2) \quad \text{Revenue} - \text{Cost} = \text{Profit} \end{cases}$$

Substitute $xp = 2400$ from Equation (1) into Equation (2):

$$240p + xp = 16{,}800 \qquad (2) \quad \text{Equation (2)}$$
$$240p + 2400 = 16{,}800 \qquad (3) \quad \text{Substitute 2400 for } xp \text{ in (2).}$$
$$240p = 14{,}400 \qquad\qquad \text{Subtract 2400 from both sides.}$$
$$p = 60. \qquad\qquad\quad \text{Solve for } p.$$

Back-substitute $p = 60$ in Equation (1):

$$xp = 2400 \qquad\qquad \text{Equation (1)}$$
$$x(60) = 2400 \qquad\qquad \text{Replace } p \text{ by 60.}$$
$$x = \frac{2400}{60} = 40. \qquad \text{Solve for } x.$$

Danielle received $x = 40$ shares as dividends and sold her stock at $p = 60$ dollars per share.

■ ■ ■

PRACTICE PROBLEM 3   Rework Example 3 if Danielle's dividends were worth \$1950 after 3 years and her profit was \$7850.   ■

2 Solve a nonlinear system of inequalities.

Nonlinear Systems of Inequalities

We first describe a procedure for graphing a nonlinear inequality. Recall from Section 8.4 that the graph of an inequality in two variables is the graph of the solution set of the inequality. This statement applies to both linear and nonlinear inequalities. We use the same *test-point* procedure that was discussed for linear inequalities in Section 8.4.

FINDING THE SOLUTIONS: PROCEDURE FOR GRAPHING A NONLINEAR INEQUALITY IN TWO VARIABLES

OBJECTIVE	EXAMPLE
To graph a nonlinear inequality in two variables.	*Graph $y > x^2 - 2$.*

Step 1   Replace the inequality symbol by an equals $(=)$ sign.

$y = x^2 - 2$

Step 2   Sketch the graph of the *corresponding equation* in Step 1. Use a dashed curve if the given inequality sign is $<$ or $>$ and a solid curve if the inequality symbol is $\leq$ or $\geq$.

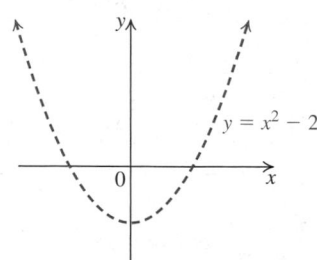

Step 3   The graph in Step 2 will divide the plane into two regions. Select a *test point* in the plane. Be sure that the test point does not lie on the graph of the equation in Step 1.

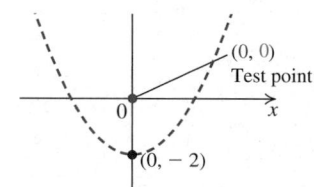

Step 4   (*i*) If the coordinates of the test point satisfy the given inequality, then so do all the points of the region that contains the test point. Shade the region that contains the test point.

(*ii*) If the coordinates of the test point do not satisfy the given inequality, shade the region that does not contain the test point.

The shaded region (along with the boundary if it is a solid curve) is the graph of the given inequality.

Since $0 > 0^2 - 2 = -2$, the coordinates of the test point, $(0, 0)$, satisfy the inequality $y > x^2 - 2$.

The graph of the solution set of $y > x^2 - 2$ is shown shaded.

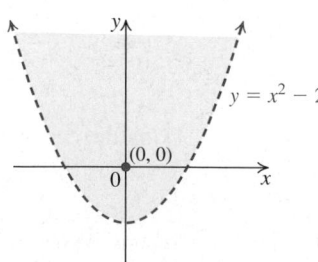

The procedure for solving a nonlinear system of inequalities is identical to the procedure for solving a linear system of inequalities.

EXAMPLE 4 Solving a Nonlinear System of Inequalities

Graph the solution set of the following system of inequalities:

$$\begin{cases} y \le 4 - x^2 & (1) \\ y \ge \dfrac{3}{2}x - 3 & (2) \\ y \ge -6x - 3 & (3) \end{cases}$$

Solution

Graph each inequality separately in the same coordinate plane. Since $(0, 0)$ is not a solution of any of the corresponding equations, use $(0, 0)$ as a test point for each inequality.

Inequality (1)	Inequality (2)	Inequality (3)
$y \le 4 - x^2$	$y \ge \dfrac{3}{2}x - 3$	$y \ge -6x - 3$
Step 1 $y = 4 - x^2$	$y = \dfrac{3}{2}x - 3$	$y = -6x - 3$
Step 2 The graph of $y = 4 - x^2$ is a parabola opening down with vertex $(0, 4)$. Sketch it as a solid curve.	The graph of $y = \dfrac{3}{2}x - 3$ is a line through the points $(0, -3)$ and $(2, 0)$. Sketch a solid line.	The graph of $y = -6x - 3$ is a line through the points $(0, -3)$ and $\left(-\dfrac{1}{2}, 0\right)$. Sketch a solid line.
Step 3 Testing $(0, 0)$ in $y \le 4 - x^2$ gives $0 \le 4$, a true statement. The points that satisfy $y \le 4 - x^2$ are below the parabola.	Testing $(0, 0)$ in $y \ge \dfrac{3}{2}x - 3$ gives $0 \ge -3$, a true statement. The points that satisfy $y \ge \dfrac{3}{2}x - 3$ are above the line $y = \dfrac{3}{2}x - 3$.	Testing $(0, 0)$ in $y \ge -6x - 3$ gives $0 \ge -3$, a true statement. The points that satisfy $y \ge -6x - 3$ are above the line $y = -6x - 3$.
Step 4 Shade the region as in Figure 8.21(a).	Shade the region as in Figure 8.21(b).	Shade the region as in Figure 8.21(c).

The region common to all three graphs is the graph of the solution set of the given system of inequalities. See Figure 8.21(d).

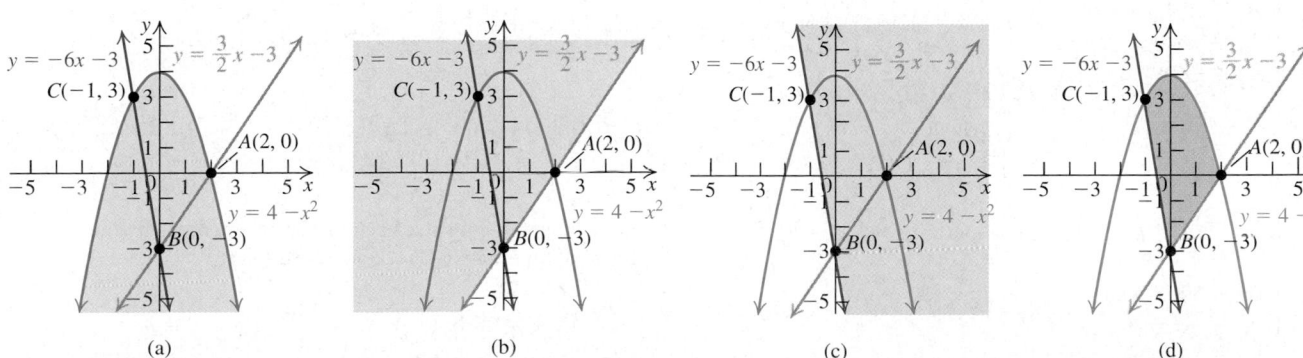

(a)   (b)   (c)   (d)

FIGURE 8.21

The points of intersection of the corresponding equations can be obtained by solving pairs of equations representing the boundaries of the individual regions (in this case, two lines and a parabola.). Using the substitution method, you will find the points A, B, and C shown in Figure 8.21(d).

Point A, $(2, 0)$, is the solution of the system.

$$\begin{cases} y = 4 - x^2 & \text{Boundary of Inequality (1)} \\ y = \dfrac{3}{2}x - 3 & \text{Boundary of Inequality (2)} \end{cases}$$

Point B, $(0, -3)$, is the solution of the system.

$$\begin{cases} y = \dfrac{3}{2}x - 3 & \text{Boundary of Inequality (2)} \\ y = -6x - 3 & \text{Boundary of Inequality (3)} \end{cases}$$

Point C, $(-1, 3)$, is the solution of the system.

$$\begin{cases} y = -6x - 3 & \text{Boundary of Inequality (1)} \\ y = 4 \quad - x^2 & \text{Boundary of Inequality (2)} \end{cases} \quad ■ \ ■ \ ■$$

PRACTICE PROBLEM 4   Graph the solution set of the system of inequalities.

$$\begin{cases} y \ge x^2 + 1 \\ y \le -x + 13 \\ y < 4x + 13 \end{cases} \qquad\qquad ■$$

A Exercises   Basic Skills and Concepts

In Exercises 1–8, determine which of the given ordered pairs are solutions of each system of equations.

1. $\begin{cases} 2x + 3y = 3 \\ x - y^2 = 2 \end{cases}$ $(1, -3), (3, -1), (6, 3), \left(5, \dfrac{1}{2}\right)$ †

2. $\begin{cases} x + 2y = 6 \\ \quad\ y = x^2 \end{cases}$ $(2, 2), (-2, 4), (0, 3), (1, 2)$ †

3. $\begin{cases} 5x - 2y = 7 \\ x^2 + y^2 = 2 \end{cases}$ $\left(\dfrac{5}{4}, 1\right), \left(0, \dfrac{11}{4}\right), (1, -1), (3, 4)$ †

4. $\begin{cases} x - 2y = -5 \\ x^2 + y^2 = 25 \end{cases}$ $(1, 3), (-5, 0), (3, 4), (3, -4)$ †

5. $\begin{cases} 4x^2 + 5y^2 = 180 \\ x^2 - y^2 = 9 \end{cases}$ $(5, 4), (-5, 4), (3, 0), (-5, -4)$ †

6. $\begin{cases} x^2 - y^2 = 3 \\ x^2 - 4x + y^2 = -3 \end{cases}$ $(2, 1), (2, -1), (-2, 1), (-2, -1)$ †

7. $\begin{cases} y = e^{x-1} \\ y = 2x - 1 \end{cases}$ $(1, 1), (0, -1), (2, e), (-1, -3)$ †

8. $\begin{cases} y = \ln(x + 1) \\ y = x \end{cases}$ $(1, 1), (0, 0), (-1, -1), (e - 1, 1)$ †

In Exercises 9–24, solve each system of equations by the substitution method. Check your solutions.

9. $\begin{cases} y = x^2 \\ y = x + 2 \end{cases}$ †

10. $\begin{cases} y = x^2 \\ x + y = 6 \end{cases}$ †

†Due to space constrictions, answers to these exercises may be found in the Answers beginning on page A–1 in the back of the book.

11. $\begin{cases} x^2 - y = 6 \\ x - y = 0 \end{cases}$ †

12. $\begin{cases} x^2 - y = 6 \\ 5x - y = 0 \end{cases}$ †

13. $\begin{cases} x^2 + y^2 = 9 \\ x = 3 \end{cases}$ †

14. $\begin{cases} x^2 + y^2 = 9 \\ y = 3 \end{cases}$ †

15. $\begin{cases} x^2 + y^2 = 5 \\ x - y = -3 \end{cases}$ †

16. $\begin{cases} x^2 + y^2 = 13 \\ 2x - 3y = 0 \end{cases}$ †

17. $\begin{cases} x^2 - 4x + y^2 = -2 \\ x - y = 2 \end{cases}$ †

18. $\begin{cases} x^2 - 8y + y^2 = -6 \\ 2x - y = 1 \end{cases}$ †

19. $\begin{cases} x - y = -2 \\ xy = 3 \end{cases}$ †

20. $\begin{cases} x - 2y = 4 \\ xy = 6 \end{cases}$ †

21. $\begin{cases} 4x^2 + y^2 - 25 \\ x + y = 5 \end{cases}$ †

22. $\begin{cases} x^2 + 4y^2 = 16 \\ x + 2y = 4 \end{cases}$ †

23. $\begin{cases} x^2 - y^2 = 24 \\ 5x - 7y = 0 \end{cases}$ †

24. $\begin{cases} x^2 - 7y^2 = 9 \\ x - y = 3 \end{cases}$ †

In Exercises 25–34, solve each system of equations (only real solutions) by the elimination method. Check your solutions.

25. $\begin{cases} x^2 + y^2 = 20 \\ x^2 - y^2 = 12 \end{cases}$ †

26. $\begin{cases} x^2 + 8y^2 = 9 \\ 3x^2 + y^2 = 4 \end{cases}$ †

27. $\begin{cases} x^2 + 2y^2 = 12 \\ 7y^2 - 5x^2 = 8 \end{cases}$ †

28. $\begin{cases} 3x^2 + 2y^2 = 77 \\ x^2 - 6y^2 = 19 \end{cases}$ †

29. $\begin{cases} x^2 - y = 2 \\ 2x - y = 4 \end{cases}$ †

30. $\begin{cases} x^2 + 3y = 0 \\ x - y = -12 \end{cases}$ †

31. $\begin{cases} x^2 + y^2 = 5 \\ 3x^2 - 2y^2 = -5 \end{cases}$ †

32. $\begin{cases} x^2 + 4y^2 = 5 \\ 9x^2 - y^2 = 8 \end{cases}$ †

33. $\begin{cases} x^2 + y^2 + 2x = 9 \\ x^2 + 4y^2 + 3x = 14 \end{cases}$ †

34. $\begin{cases} x^2 + y^2 = 9 \\ x^2 + y^2 - 18x = 0 \end{cases}$ †

In Exercises 35–48, use any method to solve each system of equations.

35. $\begin{cases} x + y = 8 \\ xy = 15 \end{cases}$ †

36. $\begin{cases} 2x + y = 8 \\ x^2 - y^2 = 5 \end{cases}$ †

37. $\begin{cases} x^2 + y^2 = 2 \\ 3x^2 + 3y^2 = 9 \end{cases}$ †

38. $\begin{cases} x^2 + y^2 = 5 \\ 3x^2 \quad y^2 - 11 \end{cases}$ †

39. $\begin{cases} y^2 = 4x + 4 \\ y = 2x - 2 \end{cases}$ †

40. $\begin{cases} xy = 125 \\ y = x^2 \end{cases}$ †

41. $\begin{cases} x^2 + 4y^2 = 25 \\ x - 2y + 1 = 0 \end{cases}$ †

42. $\begin{cases} y = x^2 - 5x + 4 \\ 3x + y = 3 \end{cases}$ †

43. $\begin{cases} x^2 - 3y^2 = 1 \\ x^2 + 4y^2 = 8 \end{cases}$ †

44. $\begin{cases} 4x^2 - y^2 = 12 \\ 4y^2 - x^2 = 12 \end{cases}$ †

45. $\begin{cases} x^2 - xy + 5x = 4 \\ 2x^2 - 3xy + 10x = -2 \end{cases}$ †

†46. $\begin{cases} x^2 - xy + x = -4 \\ 3x^2 - 2xy - 2x = 4 \end{cases}$ †

47. $\begin{cases} x^2 + y^2 - 8x = -8 \\ x^2 - 4y^2 + 6x = 0 \end{cases}$ †

48. $\begin{cases} 4x^2 + y^2 - 9y = -4 \\ 4x^2 - y^2 - 3y = 0 \end{cases}$ †

In Exercises 49–62, use the procedure for graphing a nonlinear inequality in two variables to graph each inequality.

49. $y \le x^2 + 2$ †

50. $y < x^2 - 3$ †

51. $y > x^2 - 1$ †

52. $y \ge x^2 + 1$ †

53. $y \le (x - 1)^2 + 3$ †

54. $y > -(x + 1)^2 + 4$ †

55. $x^2 + y^2 > 4$ †

56. $x^2 + y^2 \le 9$ †

57. $(x - 1)^2 + (y - 2)^2 \le 9$ †

58. $(x + 2)^2 + (y - 1)^2 > 4$ †

59. $y < 2^x$ †

60. $y \ge e^x$ †

61. $y < \log x$ †

62. $y \ge \ln x$ †

For Exercises 63–68, use the following figure to indicate the region or regions that correspond to the graph of each system of inequalities.

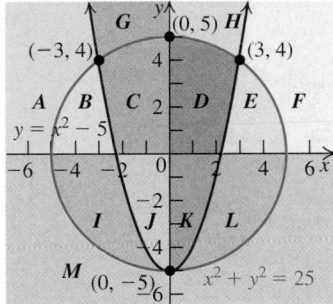

63. $\begin{cases} y \ge x^2 - 5 \\ x^2 + y^2 \le 25 \\ x \ge 0 \end{cases}$ †

64. $\begin{cases} y \ge x^2 - 5 \\ x^2 + y^2 \ge 25 \\ x \ge 0 \end{cases}$ †

65. $\begin{cases} y \le x^2 - 5 \\ x^2 + y^2 \le 25 \\ x \ge 0 \end{cases}$ †

66. $\begin{cases} y \le x^2 - 5 \\ x^2 + y^2 \ge 25 \\ y \ge 0 \end{cases}$ †

67. $\begin{cases} y \le x^2 - 5 \\ x^2 + y^2 \le 25 \\ y \ge 0 \end{cases}$ †

68. $\begin{cases} y \ge x^2 - 5 \\ x^2 + y^2 \le 25 \\ y \ge 0 \end{cases}$ †

In Exercises 69–76, graph the region determined by each system of inequalities and label all points of intersection.

69. $\begin{cases} x + y \le 6 \\ y \ge x^2 \end{cases}$ †

70. $\begin{cases} x + y \ge 6 \\ y \ge x^2 \end{cases}$ †

71. $\begin{cases} y \ge 2x + 1 \\ y \le -x^2 + 2 \end{cases}$ †

72. $\begin{cases} y \le 2x + 1 \\ y \le -x^2 + 2 \end{cases}$ †

73. $\begin{cases} y \ge x \\ x^2 + y^2 \le 1 \end{cases}$ †

74. $\begin{cases} y \le x \\ x^2 + y^2 \le 1 \end{cases}$ †

75. $\begin{cases} x^2 + y^2 \le 25 \\ x^2 + y \le 5 \end{cases}$ †

76. $\begin{cases} x^2 + y^2 \le 25 \\ x^2 + y \ge 5 \end{cases}$ †

B Exercises   Applying the Concepts

In Exercises 77 and 78, the demand and supply functions of a product are given. In each case, p represents the price per unit and x represents the number of units in hundreds. Determine the price that gives market equilibrium and the number of units that are demanded and supplied at that price.

77. $\begin{cases} p + 2x^2 = 96 & \text{Demand equation} \\ p - 13x = 39 & \text{Supply equation} \ \dagger \end{cases}$

78. $\begin{cases} p^2 + 6p + 3x = 75 & \text{Demand equation} \\ -p + x = 13 & \text{Supply equation} \ \dagger \end{cases}$

In Exercises 79–86, use systems of equations to solve the problem.

79. **Numbers.** Find two positive numbers whose sum is 24 and whose product is 143. †

80. **Numbers.** Find two positive numbers whose difference is 13 and whose product is 114. †

81. **Commercial land.** A commercial parcel of land is in the form of a trapezoid with two right angles, as shown in the figure. The oblique side is 100 meters in length, and two sides that meet at the vertex of one of the right angles are equal. The perimeter of the land is 360 meters. Find
   a. The lengths of the remaining sides.
   b. The area of the land. †

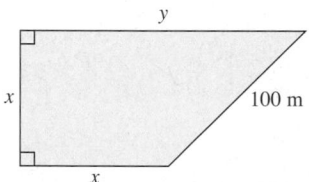

82. **Dividing a pasture.** The area of a rectangular pasture is 8750 square feet. The pasture is divided into three smaller pastures by two fences parallel to the shorter sides.

The widths of two of the larger pastures are the same, and the width of the third is one-half that of the others. Find the dimensions of the original pasture if the perimeter of the smaller of the subdivisions is 190 feet. †

83. **Chartering a fishing boat.** A group of students of a fraternity chartered a fishing boat that would cost 960 dollars. Before the date of the fishing trip, eight more students joined the group and agreed to pay their share of the cost of the charter. The cost per student was reduced by 6 dollars. Find the original number of students in the group and the original cost per student. †

84. **Carpet sale.** A salesperson sold a square carpet and a rectangular carpet whose length was 6 feet more than its width. The combined area of the two carpets was 540 square feet. The price of the square carpet was 12 dollars per square yard, and the price of the rectangular carpet was 10 dollars per square yard. If the sales person received 50 dollars more for the rectangular piece than the square piece, find the dimensions of each carpet. †

85. **Buying and selling stocks.** Flat Fee Brokerage, Inc., charges 100 dollars commission for every transaction (buy or sell) you make. Anju bought a block of stock containing over 400 shares that cost her 10,000 dollars, including the commission. After one year, she received a stock dividend of 30 shares. She then sold all her stock for 3 dollars more per share than it cost and made a profit of 1900 dollars, (after paying the commission). How many shares did she buy and what was the original price of each share? †

86. **Trading stocks.** Repeat Exercise 85 with the following scenario: Anju does not receive dividends and decides to keep 100 shares of the stock. She sells the remaining stock for 10 dollars more per share than it cost and makes a profit of 3900 dollars after paying the commission. †

C Exercises   Beyond the Basics

In Exercises 87–96, graph each inequality.

87. $xy \geq 1$ †

88. $xy < 3$ †

89. $y < 2^x$ †

90. $y \leq 2^{x-1}$ †

91. $y \geq 3^{x-2}$ †

92. $y > -3^x$ †

93. $y \geq \ln x$ †

94. $y < -\ln x$ †

95. $y > \ln(x - 1)$ †

96. $y \leq -\ln(x + 1)$ †

In Exercises 97–98, graph the solution set of each inequality.

97. $1 \leq x^2 + y^2 \leq 9$ †

98. $x^2 \leq y \leq 4x^2$ †

In Exercises 99–104, solve each system of equations and verify the solution graphically.

99. $\begin{cases} y = 3^x + 4 \\ y = 3^{2x} - 2 \end{cases}$ †

100. $\begin{cases} y = \ln x + 1 \\ y = \ln x - 2 \end{cases}$ †

101. $\begin{cases} y = 2^x + 3 \\ y = 2^{2x} + 1 \end{cases}$ †

102. $\begin{cases} y = 2^x + 3 \\ y = 4^x + 1 \end{cases}$ †

103. $\begin{cases} x = 3^y \\ 3^{2y} = 3x - 2 \end{cases}$ †

104. $\begin{cases} x = 3^y \\ x^2 = 3^{y+1} - 2 \end{cases}$ †

In Exercises 105–108, the given circle intersects the given line at the points A and B. Find the coordinates of A and B and compute the distance $d(A,B)$.

105. Circle: $x^2 + y^2 - 7x + 5y + 6 = 0$, line: x-axis. †

106. The circle of Exercise 105 and the y-axis. †

107. Circle: $x^2 + y^2 + 2x - 4y - 5 = 0$, line: $x - y + 1 = 0$. †

108. Circle $x^2 + y^2 - 6x - 8y - 50 = 0$, line $2x + y - 5 = 0$. †

109. Show that the line with equation $x + 2y + 6 = 0$ is a tangent line to the circle with equation $x^2 + y^2 - 2x + 2y - 3 = 0$. (A line that intersects the circle at exactly one point is a **tangent line** to the circle.) †

110. Repeat Exercise 109 for the line with equation $3x - 4y = 0$ and the circle with equation $x^2 + y^2 - 2x - 4y + 4 = 0$. †

Critical Thinking

111. Consider a system of two equations in two variables.

$$\begin{cases} y = mx + b \\ y = Ax^3 + Bx^2 + C + D, A \neq 0 \end{cases}$$ †

Explain whether it is possible for this system to have

a. no real solutions;

b. one real solution;

c. two real solutions;

d. three real solutions;

e. four real solutions;

f. more than four real solutions.

112. Repeat Exercise 111 for the system.

$$\begin{cases} y = mx + b \\ y = Ax^4 + Bx^3 + Cx^2 + Dx + E, A \neq 0 \end{cases}$$ †

Summary   Definitions, Concepts, and Formulas

8.1 Systems of Linear Equations in Two Variables

A **system of equations** is a set of equations with common variables.

A **solution** of a system of equations in two variables x and y is an ordered pair of numbers (a, b) that satisfies all equations in the system. The solution set of a system of two linear equations of the form $ax + by = c$ is the point(s) of intersection of the graphs of the equations.

Systems with no solution are called **inconsistent,** and systems with at least one solution are **consistent.** A system of two linear equations in two variables may have one solution (**independent equations**), no solution (**inconsistent system**), or infinitely many solutions (**dependent equations**).

Three methods of solving a system of equations are (1) the graphical method, (2) the substitution method, and (3) the elimination or addition method.

8.2 Systems of Linear Equations in Three Variables

A **linear equation** in n variables $x_1, x_2, \ldots, x_n$ is an equation that can be written in the form

$$a_1x_1 + a_2x_2 + \cdots + a_nx_n = b,$$

where b and the coefficients $a_1, a_2, \ldots, a_n$ are real numbers.

A system of linear equations can be solved by transforming it into an *equivalent system* that is easier to solve.

The following are operations that produce equivalent systems.

1. Interchange the position of any two equations.

2. Multiply any equation by a nonzero constant.

3. Add a nonzero multiple of one equation to another.

The **Gaussian elimination method** is a procedure for converting a system of linear equations into an equivalent system in *triangular form.*

A linear system may have (*i*) only one solution, (*ii*) infinitely many solutions, or (*iii*) no solution.

8.3 Partial Fractions

In partial-fraction decomposition, we reverse the addition of rational expressions. A rational expression $\dfrac{P(x)}{Q(x)}$ is called a proper fraction if deg $P(x) <$ deg $Q(x)$.

There are four cases to consider in decomposing $\dfrac{P(x)}{Q(x)}$ into partial fractions:

1. $Q(x)$ has only distinct linear factors. (See page 768.)
2. $Q(x)$ has repeated linear factors. (See page 771.)
3. $Q(x)$ has distinct irreducible quadratic factors. (See page 772.)
4. $Q(x)$ has repeated irreducible quadratic factors. (See page 773.)

8.4 Systems of Linear Inequalities

A statement of the form $ax + by < c$ is a linear inequality in the variables x and y. The symbol $<$ may be replaced by $\leq$, $>$, or $\geq$. A procedure for graphing a linear inequality in two variables is described on page 780.

The graph of the solution set of a system of inequalities is obtained by (*i*) first graphing each inequality of the system in the same coordinate plane and then (*ii*) finding the region that is common to every graph in the system.

Linear Programming

In a linear programming model, a quantity f (to be maximized or minimized) that can be expressed in the form $f = ax + by$ is called an **objective function** of the variables x and y. The **constraints** are the restrictions placed on the variables x and y that can be expressed as a system of linear inequalities.

A procedure for solving a linear programming problem is given on page 786.

8.5 Nonlinear Systems

A system of equations (inequalities) in which at least one equation (inequality) is nonlinear is called a **nonlinear system of equations (inequalities).** The methods of substitution, elimination, or graphing is sometimes used to solve a nonlinear system.

Review Exercises

Basic Skills and Concepts

In Exercises 1–16, solve each system of equations by using the method of your choice. Identify systems with no solution and systems with infinitely many solutions.

1. $\begin{cases} 3x - y = -5 \\ x + 2y = 3 \end{cases}$ $\{(-1, 2)\}$

2. $\begin{cases} x + 3y + 6 = 0 \\ y = 4x - 2 \end{cases}$ †

3. $\begin{cases} 2x + 4y = 3 \\ 3x + 6y = 10 \end{cases}$ $\varnothing$

4. $\begin{cases} x - y = 2 \\ 2x - 2y = 9 \end{cases}$ $\varnothing$

5. $\begin{cases} 3x - y = 3 \\ \dfrac{1}{2}x + \dfrac{1}{3}y = 2 \end{cases}$ $\{(2, 3)\}$

6. $\begin{cases} 0.02y - 0.03x = -0.04 \\ 1.5x - y = 3 \end{cases}$ †

7. $\begin{cases} x + 3y + z = 0 \\ 2x - y + z = 5 \\ 3x - 3y + 2z = 10 \end{cases}$ †

8. $\begin{cases} 2x + y = 11 \\ 3y - z = 5 \\ x + 2z = 1 \end{cases}$ †

9. $\begin{cases} x + y = 1 \\ 3y + 2z = 0 \\ 2x - 3z = 7 \end{cases}$ †

10. $\begin{cases} 2x - 3y + z = 2 \\ x - 3y + 2z = -1 \\ 2x + 3y + 2z = 3 \end{cases}$ †

11. $\begin{cases} x + y + z = 1 \\ x + 5y + 5z = -1 \\ 3x - y - z = 4 \end{cases}$ $\varnothing$

12. $\begin{cases} x + 3y - 2z = -4 \\ 2x + 6y - 4z = 3 \\ x + y + z = 1 \end{cases}$ $\varnothing$

13. $\begin{cases} x + 4y + 3z = 1 \\ 2x + 5y + 4z = 4 \end{cases}$ †

14. $\begin{cases} 3x - y + 2z = 9 \\ x - 2y + 3z = 2 \end{cases}$ †

15. $\begin{cases} 3x - y = 2 \\ x + 2y = 9 \\ 3x + y = 10 \end{cases}$ $\varnothing$

16. $\begin{cases} x - 2y = 1 \\ 3x + 4y = 11 \\ 2x + 2y = 7 \end{cases}$ $\varnothing$

In Exercises 17–24, find the partial-fraction decomposition of each rational expression.

17. $\dfrac{1}{(x - 1)(x + 1)}$ †

18. $\dfrac{x}{(x - 2)(x + 2)}$ †

19. $\dfrac{x + 4}{x^2 + 5x + 6}$ †

20. $\dfrac{x + 14}{x^2 + 3x - 4}$ †

21. $\dfrac{3x^2 + x + 1}{x(x - 1)^2}$ †

22. $\dfrac{3x^2 + 2x + 3}{(x^2 - 1)(x + 1)}$ †

23. $\dfrac{x^2 + 2x + 3}{(x^2 + 4)^2}$ †

24. $\dfrac{2x}{x^4 - 1}$ †

In Exercises 25–30, graph each system of inequalities.

25. $\begin{cases} x + y \leq 1 \\ x - y \leq 1 \\ x \geq 0 \end{cases}$ †

26. $\begin{cases} 2x + 3y \leq 6 \\ 4x - 3y \leq 12 \\ x \geq 0 \end{cases}$ †

27. $\begin{cases} 4x + y \leq 7 \\ 2x + 5y \geq -1 \\ x - 2y \geq -5 \end{cases}$ †

28. $\begin{cases} 7x - 2y + 6 \leq 0 \\ x + y + 14 \geq 0 \\ 2x - 3y + 9 \geq 0 \end{cases}$ †

29. $\begin{cases} x + y - 3 \leq 0 \\ 3x - y - 9 \leq 0 \\ y + 3 \geq 0 \\ 7x + 4y + 23 \geq 0 \end{cases}$ †

30. $\begin{cases} x + 5y - 11 \leq 0 \\ 5x + y - 7 \leq 0 \\ x - 5y - 17 \leq 0 \\ 7x + y + 25 \geq 0 \end{cases}$ †

In Exercises 31–34, solve each linear programming problem.

31. Maximize $z = 2x + 3y$, subject to the constraints $x \geq 0, y \geq 0, 3x + 7y \leq 21$. Max of 14 at $x = 7, y = 0$

32. Minimize $z = -5x + 2y$, subject to the constraints $x \geq -2, y \leq 1, x - 2y + 2 \leq 0$. †

33. Minimize $z = x + 3y$, subject to the constraints $2x - 3y + 2 \geq 0, 4x + y - 10 \leq 0, x - 3y - 9 \leq 0, 3x + y + 3 \geq 0$. †

34. Maximize $z = 2x + 5y$, subject to the constraints $x + 3y - 3 \leq 0, 3x - y - 9 \leq 0, x + 4y + 10 \geq 0, 3x - 2y + 2 \geq 0$. †

In Exercises 35–40, solve each nonlinear system of equations.

35. $\begin{cases} x + 3y = 1 \\ x^2 - 3x = 7y + 3 \end{cases}$ †

36. $\begin{cases} 4x - y = 3 \\ y^2 - 2y = x - 2 \end{cases}$ †

37. $\begin{cases} x - y = 4 \\ 5x^2 + y^2 = 24 \end{cases}$ †

38. $\begin{cases} x - 2y = 7 \\ 2x^2 + 3y^2 = 29 \end{cases}$ †

39. $\begin{cases} xy = 2 \\ x^2 + 2y^2 = 9 \end{cases}$ †

40. $\begin{cases} xy = 3 \\ 2x^2 + 3y^2 = 21 \end{cases}$ †

In Exercises 41–46, graph each nonlinear system of inequalities.

41. $\begin{cases} x - y \leq 1 \\ x^2 + y^2 \leq 13 \end{cases}$ †

42. $\begin{cases} x - y \geq 1 \\ x^2 + y^2 \leq 13 \end{cases}$ †

43. $\begin{cases} x - y \leq 1 \\ x^2 + y^2 \leq 13 \\ x \geq 0 \\ y \geq 0 \end{cases}$ †

44. $\begin{cases} x - y \geq 1 \\ x^2 + y^2 \geq 13 \\ x \leq 4 \\ y \geq 0 \end{cases}$ †

45. $\begin{cases} y \leq 3x \\ x^2 + y^2 \leq 25 \\ x \geq 0 \\ y \geq 0 \end{cases}$ †

46. $\begin{cases} y \geq 3x \\ x^2 + y^2 \leq 25 \\ x \geq 0 \\ y \geq 0 \end{cases}$ †

Applying the Concepts

47. **Investment.** A speculator invested part of 15,000 dollars in a high–risk venture and received a return of 12% at the end of the year. The rest of the 15,000 dollars was invested at 4% annual interest. The combined annual income from the two sources was 1300 dollars. How much was invested at each rate? †

48. **Agriculture.** A farmer earns a profit of 525 dollars per acre of tomatoes and 475 dollars per acre of soybeans. His soybean acreage is 5 acres more than twice his tomato acreage. If his total profit from the two crops is 24,500 dollars, how many acres of tomatoes and how many acres of soybeans does he have? †

49. **Geometry.** The area of a rectangle is 63 square feet and its perimeter is 33 feet. What are the dimensions of the rectangle? 10.5 ft by 6ft

50. **Numbers.** Twice the sum of the reciprocals of two numbers is 13, and the product of the numbers is $\dfrac{1}{9}$. Find the numbers. †

51. **Geometry.** The hypotenuse of a right triangle is 17. If one leg of the triangle is increased by 1 and the other leg is increased by 4, the hypotenuse becomes 20. Find the sides of the triangle. 15 and 8

52. **Paper route.** Chris covers her paper route, which is 21 miles long, by 7:30 A.M. each day. If her average rate of travel were 1 mile faster each hour, she would cover the route by 7 A.M. What time does she start in the morning? †

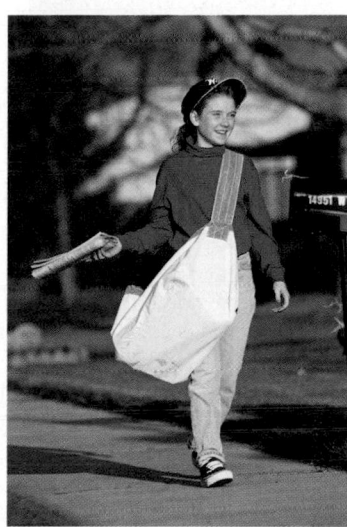

53. **Agriculture.** A rectangular pasture with an area of 6400 square meters is divided into three smaller pastures by two fences parallel to the shorter sides. The width of two of the smaller pastures is the same, and the width of the third is twice that of the others. Find the dimensions of the original pasture if the perimeter of the larger of the subdivisions is 240m. †

54. **Leasing.** Budget Rentals leases its compact cars for 23 dollars per day plus 17 cents per mile. Dollar Rentals leases the same car for 24 dollars per day plus 22 cents per mile.
   a. Find the cost functions describing the daily cost of leasing from each company.†
   b. Graph the two functions in part (a) on the same coordinate axes.†
   c. From which company should you lease the car if you plan to drive (*i*) 50 miles per day; (*ii*) 60 miles per day; (*iii*) 70 miles per day? †

55. **Break-even analysis.** Auto-Sprinkler Corp. manufactures seven-day, 24-hour variable timers for lawn sprinklers. The corporation has a monthly fixed cost of 60,000 dollars and a production cost of 12 dollars for each timer manufactured. Each timer sells for 20 dollars.

a. Write the cost function and the revenue function for selling x timers per month.†

b. Graph the two functions in part (a) on the same coordinate plane, and hence find the break-even point graphically.†

c. Find the break-even point algebraically.†

d. How many timers should be sold in a month to realize a profit (before taxes) of 15% of the cost? †

56. Equilibrium quantity and price. The demand equation for a product is $p = \dfrac{4000}{x}$, where p is the price per unit and x is the number of units of the product. The supply equation for the product is $p = \dfrac{x}{20} + 10$.

a. Find the equilibrium quantity.†

b. Find the equilibrium price.†

c. Graph the supply and demand functions on the same coordinate plane, and label the equilibrium point. †

57. Apartment lease. Alisha and Sunita signed a lease on an apartment for nine months. At the end of six months, Alisha got married and moved out. She paid the landlady an amount equal to the difference between double-occupancy rental and single-occupancy rental for the remaining three months, and Sunita paid the single-occupancy rate for the same three months. If the nine-month rental cost Alisha 2250 dollars and Sunita 3150 dollars what were the single and double monthly rates? $330 for the single and $360 for the double

58. Seating arrangement. The 600 graduating seniors at Central State College are seated in rows, each of which contains the same number of chairs, and every chair is occupied. If five more chairs were in each row, everyone could be seated in four fewer rows. How many chairs are in each row? 25 chairs and 24 rows

59. Passing a final exam. Twenty-six students in a college algebra class took a final exam on which the passing score was 70. The mean score of those who passed was 78, and the mean score of those who failed was 26. The mean of all scores was 72. How many students failed the exam? 3

60. Finding numbers. The average of a and b is 2.5, the average of b and c is 3.8, and the average of a, and c is 3.1. Find the numbers a, b, and c. $a = 1.8, b = 3.2, c = 4.4$

61. May–December match. Steve and his wife Janet have the same birthday. When Steve was as old as Janet is now, he was twice as old as Janet was then. When Janet becomes as old as Steve is now, the sum of their ages will be 119. How old are Steve and Janet now? Janet is 34 and Steve is 51.

62. Percentage increase. Let x and y be positive real numbers. Increasing x by y percent gives 46, while increasing y by x percent gives 21. Find x and y. $x = 40, y = 15$

63. Criminals rob a bank. Three criminals—Butch, Sundance, and Billy—robbed a bank and divided the loot in the following manner: Since Butch planned the job and drove the getaway car, he got 75% as much as Sundance and Billy put together. Since Sundance was an expert safecracker, he got 500 dollars more than 50% of Billy's and Butch's cut put together. Billy got 1000 dollars less than three times the difference of Butch and Sundance's cut. How much did they steal and what was each criminal's take? †

64. Curve fitting. Find all the curves of the form $y = ax^2 + bx + c$ that contain the points $(0, 1)$, $(1, 0)$, and $(-1, 6)$. $y = 2x^2 - 3x + 1$

65. Using exponents. Given that $2^x = 8^y$ and $9^y = 3^{x-2}$, find x and y. $x = 6, y = 2$

66. Area of an octagon. A square of side length 8 has its corners cut off to make it a regular octagon. Find the area of the octagon. (See the figure.) ≈ 53.02 square units

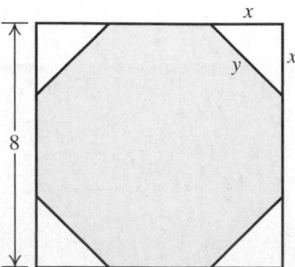

67. Building houses. A builder has 42 units of material and 32 units of labor available during a given period. She builds two-story houses or one-story houses or some of both. Suppose she makes a profit of 10,000 dollars on each two-story house and 4000 dollars on each one-story house. A two-story house requires seven units of material and one unit of labor, whereas a one-story house requires one unit of material and two units of labor. How many houses of each type should she build so as to make a maximum profit? What is the maximum profit? †

Answer:

67. She should build 4 two-story houses and 14 one-story houses to obtain a maximum profit of $96,000.

68. Minimizing cost. An animal food is to be a mixture of two products X and Y. The content and cost of 1 pound of each product is given in the following table:

Product	Protein grams	Fat grams	Carbohydrates grams	Cost
X	180	2	240	$0.75
Y	36	8	200	$0.56

How much of each product should be used to minimize the cost if each bag must contain at least 612 grams of protein, at least 22 grams of fat, and at most 1880 grams of carbohydrates? 3 of product X and 2 of product Y

Practice Test A

In Problems 1–7, solve each system of equations.

1. $\begin{cases} 2x - y = 4 \\ 2x + y = 4 \end{cases}$ (2, 0)

2. $\begin{cases} x + 2y = 8 \\ 3x + 6y = 24 \end{cases}$ †

3. $\begin{cases} -2x + y = 4 \\ 4x - 2y = 4 \end{cases}$ ∅

4. $\begin{cases} 3x + 3y = -15 \\ 2x - 2y = -10 \end{cases}$ †

5. $\begin{cases} \dfrac{5}{3}x + \dfrac{y}{2} = 14 \\ \dfrac{2}{3}x - \dfrac{y}{8} = 3 \end{cases}$ (6, 8)

6. $\begin{cases} y = x^2 \\ 3x - y + 4 = 0 \end{cases}$ †

7. $\begin{cases} x - 3y = -4 \\ 2x^2 + 3x - 3y = 8 \end{cases}$ $\left(-3, \dfrac{1}{3}\right)$, (2, 2)

8. Two gold bars together weigh a total of 485 pounds. One bar weighs 15 pounds more than the other.
   (a) Write a system of equations that describes these relationships. †
   (b) How much does each bar weigh? $x = 250, y = 235$

9. Convert the given system to triangular form.
$$\begin{cases} 2x + y + 2z = 4 \\ 4x + 6y + z = 15 \\ 2x + 2y + 7z = -1 \end{cases} †$$

10. Use back-substitution to solve the given linear system.
$$\begin{cases} x - 6y + 3z = -2 \\ 9y - 5z = 2 \\ 2z = 10 \end{cases} (1, 3, 5)$$

In Exercises 11–13, solve the system of equations.

11. $\begin{cases} x + y + z = 8 \\ 2x - 2y + 2z = 4 \\ x + y - z = 12 \end{cases}$ †

12. $\begin{cases} x + z = -1 \\ 3y + 2z = 5 \\ 3x - 3y + z = -8 \end{cases}$ †

13. $\begin{cases} 2x - y + z = 2 \\ x + y - z = -1 \\ x - 5y + 5z = 7 \end{cases}$ †

14. A vending machine's coin box contains nickels, dimes, and quarters. The total number of coins in the box is 300. The number of dimes is three times the number of nickels and quarters together. If 30 dollars and 65 cents is in the box, find the number of nickels, dimes and quarters that it contains. 53 nickels, 225 dimes, and 22 quarters

For Problems 15 and 16, write the form of the partial-fraction decomposition of the given rational expression. You do not need to solve for the constants.

15. $\dfrac{2x}{(x - 5)(x + 1)}$ †

16. $\dfrac{-5x^2 + x - 8}{(x - 2)(x^2 + 1)^2}$ †

17. Find the partial fraction decomposition of the rational expression
$$\dfrac{x + 3}{(x + 4)^2(x - 7)} †$$

18. Graph the inequality $3x + y < 6$. †

19. Graph the solution set of the system of inequalities:
$$\begin{cases} y - x^2 \leq 3 \\ y - x > 0 \end{cases} †$$

20. Maximize $z = 2x + y$, subject to the constraints $x \geq 0, y \geq 0, x + 3y \leq 3$. Maximum value is 6 at (3, 0)

Practice Test B

In Problems 1–7, solve each system of equations.

1. $\begin{cases} 2x - 3y = 16 \\ x - y = 7 \end{cases}$ a

(a) $\{(5, -2)\}$ (b) $\{(8, 0)\}$

(c) $\{(0, -7)\}$ (d) $\{(4, -3)\}$

2. $\begin{cases} 6x - 9y = -2 \\ 3x - 5y = -6 \end{cases}$ c

(a) $\{(-3, 0)\}$ (b) $\left\{\left(0, \dfrac{5}{6}\right)\right\}$

(c) $\left\{\left(\dfrac{44}{3}, 10\right)\right\}$ (d) $\{(1,1)\}$

3. $\begin{cases} 2x - 5y = 9 \\ 4x - 10y = 18 \end{cases}$ b

(a) $\left\{\left(0, \dfrac{9}{2}\right)\right\}$ (b) $\left\{\left(\dfrac{5}{2}y + \dfrac{9}{2}, y\right)\right\}$

(c) $\left\{\left(x, \dfrac{5}{2}x + \dfrac{9}{2}\right)\right\}$ (d) $\varnothing$

4. $\begin{cases} 3x + 5y = 1 \\ -6x - 10y = 2 \end{cases}$ c

(a) $\left\{\left(0, -\dfrac{1}{5}\right)\right\}$ (b) $\{(2, -1)\}$

(c) $\varnothing$ (d) $\left\{\left(-\dfrac{5}{3}y + \dfrac{1}{3}, y\right)\right\}$

5. $\begin{cases} \dfrac{1}{5}x + \dfrac{2}{5}y = 1 \\ \dfrac{1}{4}x - \dfrac{1}{3}y = \dfrac{-5}{12} \end{cases}$ b

(a) $\{(-15, 10)\}$ (b) $\{(1, 2)\}$

(c) $\{(-10, -15)\}$ (d) $\{(1, 0)\}$

6. $\begin{cases} x - 3y = \dfrac{1}{2} \\ -2x + 6y = -1 \end{cases}$ d

(a) $\left\{\left(\dfrac{1}{2}, 0\right)\right\}$ (b) $\left\{\left(2, \dfrac{1}{2}\right)\right\}$

(c) $\varnothing$ (d) $\left\{\left(3y + \dfrac{1}{2}, y\right)\right\}$

7. $\begin{cases} 3x + 4y = 12 \\ 3x^2 + 16y^2 = 48 \end{cases}$ d

(a) $\{(0, 4), (3, 0)\}$ (b) $\{(0, -4)\}$

(c) $\{(0, -4),(3, 0)\}$ (d) $\left\{(4, 0), \left(2, \dfrac{3}{2}\right)\right\}$

8. Student tickets for a dance cost 2 dollars and nonstudent tickets cost 5 dollars. Three hundred tickets were sold and the total ticket receipts were 975 dollars. How many of each type of ticket were sold? d

(a) 150 student tickets
    150 nonstudent tickets

(b) 200 student tickets
    100 nonstudent tickets

(c) 210 student tickets
    90 nonstudent tickets

(d) 175 student tickets
    125 nonstudent tickets

9. Convert the given system to triangular form. c

$$\begin{cases} x + 3y + 3z = 4 \\ 2x + 5y + 4z = 5 \\ x + 2y + 2z = 6 \end{cases}$$

(a) $x + 3y + 3z = 4$
    $y + 2z = 8$
    $z = 2$

(b) $x + 3y + 3z = 4$
    $2y + z = 1$
    $z = 5$

(c) $x + 3y + 3z = 4$
    $y + 2z = 3$
    $z = 5$

(d) $x + 3y + 3z = 4$
    $2y + z = -2$
    $z = 5$

10. Use back-substitution to solve the given linear system.

$$\begin{cases} 2x + y + z = 0 \\ 10y - 2z = 4 \\ 3z = 9 \end{cases}$$ a

(a) $\{(-2, 1, 3)\}$ (b) $\{(0, -3, 3)\}$

(c) $\{(0, 2, 8)\}$ (d) $\{(-1, 1, 1)\}$

11. Solve the given system of equations or state that the system is inconsistent.

$$\begin{cases} 2x + 13y + 6z = 1 \\ 3x + 10y + 11z = 15 \\ 2x + 10y + 8z = 8 \end{cases}$$ b

(a) $\{(3, -1, -4)\}$ (b) $\{(1, -1, 2)\}$

(c) $\varnothing$ (d) $(1, 6, 8)\}$

12. Solve the given system of equations or state that the system is inconsistent.

$$\begin{cases} 4x - y + 7z = -2 \\ 2x + y + 11z = 13 \\ 3x - y + 4z = -3 \end{cases}$$ d

(a) $\{(-3z + 1, -5z + 11, z)\}$

(b) $\{(-14, -14, 5)\}$

(c) $\left\{\left(-\dfrac{19}{5}, 3, \dfrac{8}{5}\right)\right\}$

(d) $\varnothing$

13. Solve the given system of equations or state that the system is inconsistent.

$$\begin{cases} x - 2y + 3z = 4 \\ 2x - y + z = 1 \\ x + y - 2z = -3 \end{cases}$$ c

(a) $\{(1, 6, 5)\}$ (b) $\{(0, 1, 2)\}$

(c) $\{(x, 5x + 1, 3x + 2)\}$ (d) $\varnothing$

14. Forty-six students will go to one of the countries France, Italy, and Spain for six weeks during the summer. The number of students going to France or Italy is four more than the number going to Spain. The number of students going to France is two less than the number going to Spain. How many students are going to each country? b

(a) France: 23
    Italy: 21
    Spain: 2

(b) France: 19
    Italy: 6
    Spain: 21

(c) France: 21
    Italy: 6
    Spain: 19

(d) France: 2
    Italy: 21
    Spain: 23

For Problems 15 and 16, write the form of the partial-fraction decomposition of the given rational functions. You do not need to solve for the constants.

15. $\dfrac{x}{(x + 2)(x - 7)}$ c

(a) $\dfrac{A}{x + 2} + \dfrac{Bx}{x - 7}$

(b) $\dfrac{Ax}{x + 2} + \dfrac{Bx}{x - 7}$

(c) $\dfrac{A}{x + 2} + \dfrac{B}{x - 7}$

(d) $\dfrac{A}{x + 2} + \dfrac{Bx + C}{x - 7}$

16. $\dfrac{7 - x}{(x - 3)(x + 5)^2}$ a

(a) $\dfrac{A}{x - 3} + \dfrac{B}{x + 5} + \dfrac{C}{(x + 5)^2}$

(b) $\dfrac{A}{x - 3} + \dfrac{B}{x + 5} + \dfrac{Cx + D}{(x + 5)^2}$

(c) $\dfrac{A}{x + 3} + \dfrac{B}{(x + 5)^2}$

(d) $\dfrac{A}{x + 3} + \dfrac{Bx + C}{(x + 5)^2}$

17. Find the partial-fraction decomposition of the rational expression

$$\dfrac{x^2 + 15x + 18}{x^3 - 9x}. \text{ c}$$

(a) $\dfrac{-2}{x} + \dfrac{26}{x - 9}$

(b) $\dfrac{-2}{x} + \dfrac{4}{x + 3} - \dfrac{1}{x - 3}$

(c) $\dfrac{-2}{x} + \dfrac{4}{x - 3} - \dfrac{1}{x + 3}$

(d) $\dfrac{-2}{x} + \dfrac{3x - 15}{x^2 - 9}$

18. Which of the graphs given at the right is the graph of $x + 3y > 3$? b

19. Which of the graphs given at the right is the graph of the solution set of the system of inequalities

$$\begin{cases} y - x^2 + 4 \geq 0 \\ 3x - y \leq 0 \end{cases}? \text{ a}$$

20. Maximize $z = 3x + 21y$, subject to the constraints

$x \geq 0, y \geq 0, 2x + y \leq 8, 2x + 3y \leq 16.$ b

(a) 84

(b) 112

(c) $\dfrac{16}{3}$

(d) 12

(a)

(b)

(c)

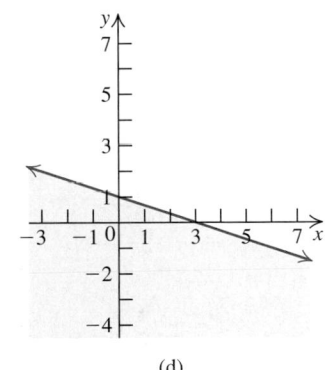

(d)

Figure for Exercise 18

(a)

(b)

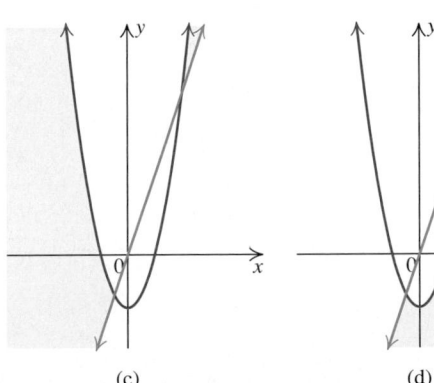

(c)

(d)

Figure for Exercise 19.

Cumulative Review Exercises (Chapters 1–8)

In Exercises 1–10, solve each equation or inequality.

1. $\dfrac{1}{x-1} + \dfrac{4}{x-4} = \dfrac{5}{x-5}$ $\dfrac{5}{2}$

2. $2\left(x + \dfrac{1}{x}\right)^2 - 7\left(x + \dfrac{1}{x}\right) + 5 = 0$ $2, \dfrac{1}{2}, \dfrac{1}{2} + \dfrac{i\sqrt{3}}{2}, \dfrac{1}{2} - \dfrac{i\sqrt{3}}{2}$

3. $\sqrt{3x-5} = x - 3$ 7

4. $\dfrac{x-1}{x+3} \le 0$ $(-3, 1]$

5. $2^{x-1} = 5$ $\dfrac{\ln(2) + \ln(5)}{\ln(2)}$

6. $\log_x 16 = 4$ 2

7. $\log(x-3) + \log(x-1) = \log(2x-5)$ $\{4\}$

8. $\tan x = -1, 0 \le x \le 2\pi$

In Exercises 9–12, use transformations to graph each function.

9. $f(x) = |x+1| - 2$ †

10. $f(x) = -(x-2)^2 + 3$ †

11. $f(x) = 2^{x-1} - 3$ †

12. $f(x) = 2 + 3\sin x$

13. Let $f(x) = 2x - 2$.
  (a) Find $f^{-1}(x)$.
  (b) Graph f and f^{-1} on the same coordinate plane.   †

14. Let $f(x) = x^3 - x^2 + x - 6$

  (a) List all possible rational zeros of f. $\pm 1, \pm 2, \pm 3, \pm 6$
  (b) Use synthetic division to test the possible rational zeros and find a real zero. 2
  (c) Use the zero from part (b) to find all the (real or complex) zeros of $f(x)$.

15. Expand and simplify: $\log_3(9x^4)$. $2 + 4\log_3(x)$

16. A radioactive substance decays so that the amount present in t years is given by $A = A_0 e^{-kt}$, where A_0 is the initial amount. Find the half-life of the substance if
  (a) $k = 0.05$. 13.86
  (b) $k = 0.0002$. 3465.74

17. Verify the identity: $\dfrac{1 + \sec x}{\tan^2 x} = \dfrac{\cos x}{1 - \cos x}$.

18. Solve triangle ABC given that $a = 8$, $b = 5$, and $\angle A = 40°$.

In Exercises 19–20, solve the system of equations.

19. $\begin{cases} 5x - 2y + 25 = 0 \\ 4y - 3x - 29 = 0 \end{cases}$ $\{(-3, 5)\}$

20. $\begin{cases} 2x - y + z = 3 \\ x + 3y - 2z = 11 \\ 3x - 2y + z = 4 \end{cases}$ $\{(3, 2, -1)\}$

Answer:

8. $\left\{\dfrac{3\pi}{4}, \dfrac{7\pi}{4}\right\}$

12. Stretch vertically by a factor of three, shift 2 units up

16. c. $2, \dfrac{-1 \pm i\sqrt{11}}{2}$

18. $B \approx 23.7°, C \approx 116.3°, c \approx 11.2$

CHAPTER 9

Matrices and Determinants

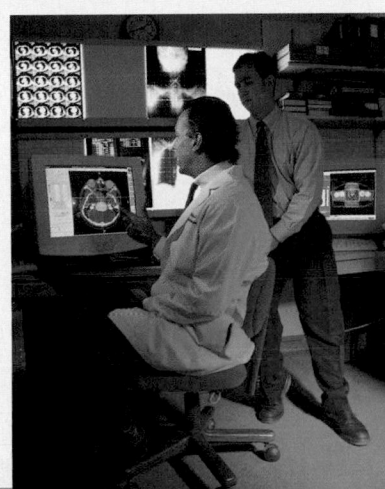

The linear programming problems introduced in the previous chapter involving quantities from the study of such disciplines as medicine, traffic control, structural design, and city planning often involve an extremely large number of variables. To solve such problems successfully requires the use of powerful computers and new techinques. In this chapter, we study matrices and several methods of solving linear systems that are easily implemented on computers.

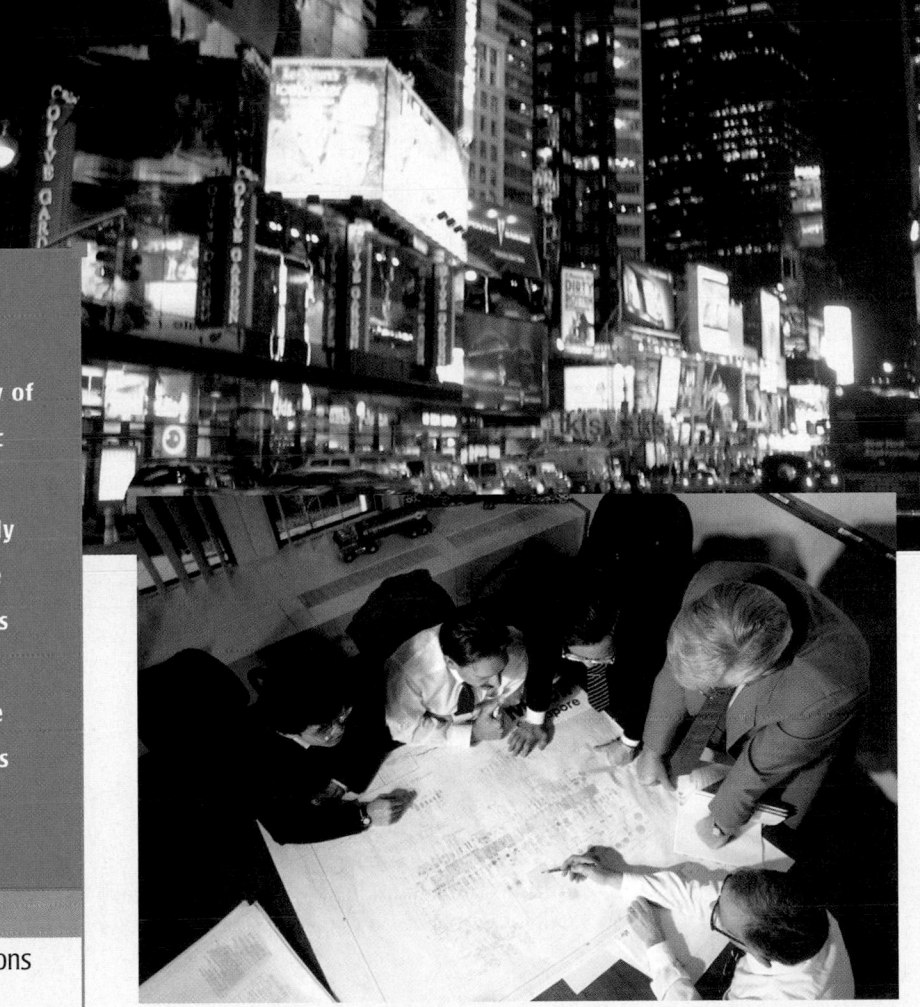

TOPICS

Matrices and Systems of Equations

Wassily Leontief 1906–1999
Leontief studied philosophy, sociology, and economics at the University of Leningrad and earned the degree of Learned Economist in 1925. He continued his studies at the University of Berlin, where he earned his Ph.D. degree. In 1973, the Nobel Prize in Economic Sciences was awarded to Leontief for his work on input–output analysis of the U.S. economy.

BEFORE STARTING THIS SECTION, REVIEW

1. Systems of equations (Section 8.1, page 738)
2. Equivalent systems (Section 8.2, page 755)
3. Gaussian elimination (Section 8.2, page 755)

OBJECTIVES

1 Define a matrix.

2 Use matrices to solve a system.

3 Use Gaussian elimination to solve a system.

4 Use Gauss–Jordan elimination to solve a system.

Leontief Input–Output Model

In 1949, the Russian-born Harvard Professor Wassily Leontief opened the door to a new era in mathematical modeling in economics. He divided the U.S. economy into 500 "sectors," such as the coal, automotive, and communications industries, agriculture, and so on. For each sector, he wrote a linear equation which described how that sector distributed its output to other sectors of the economy. In 1949, the largest computer was the Mark II, and it could not handle the resulting system of 500 equations in 500 variables. Leontief then combined some of the sectors and reduced the system to 42 equations in 42 variables in order to solve the problem. As computers have become more powerful, scientists and engineers can now work on problems far more complex than they even dreamed of a few decades ago. In Example 9, you will explore Leontief's input–output model applied to a simple economy. ■

---

1 Define a matrix.

Definition of a Matrix

The example that follows illustrates how a matrix may arise in a natural way. Great Builders, Incorporated (GBI), builds three types of houses: ranch, colonial, and modern. GBI wants to compare the cost of labor (in millions of dollars) and the cost of material (in millions of dollars) involved in building each type of house during one year. A rectangular array could be used to present the data shown in Table 9.1.

TABLE 9.1

Type of house	Ranch	Colonial	Modern
Cost of labor (in millions)	12	13	14
Cost of material (in millions)	9	11	10

If the pattern in which the type of houses, the cost of labor, and the cost of material as recorded in Table 9.1 is retained, then the array of numbers in the table may be presented simply as

$$\begin{bmatrix} 12 & 13 & 14 \\ 9 & 11 & 10 \end{bmatrix}.$$

This rectangular array of numbers is called a *matrix* (plural, *matrices*). The matrix has two rows (the costs) and three columns (the types of houses).

DEFINITION OF A MATRIX

A **matrix** is a rectangular array of numbers denoted by

$$A = \begin{bmatrix} a_{11} & a_{12} & \cdots & a_{1n} \\ a_{21} & a_{22} & \cdots & a_{2n} \\ \vdots & \vdots & & \vdots \\ a_{m1} & a_{m2} & \cdots & a_{mn} \end{bmatrix} \begin{matrix} \leftarrow \text{Row } 1 \\ \leftarrow \text{Row } 2 \\ \\ \leftarrow \text{Row } m \end{matrix}$$

$$\uparrow \qquad \uparrow \qquad \qquad \uparrow$$
$$\text{Column 1} \quad \text{Column 2} \quad \text{Column } n$$

If a matrix A has m rows and n columns, then A is said to be of **order m by n** (written $m \times n$).

The **entry** or **element** in the ith row and jth column is a real number and is denoted by the *double-subscript* notation a_{ij}. The entry a_{ij} is sometimes referred as the (i, j)**th entry** or the **entry in the (i, j) position,** and we often write

$$A = [a_{ij}].$$

The first subscript, i, in a_{ij} refers to the row number, and the second subscript, j, refers to the column number. For example, the entry a_{24} is the entry in the second row and fourth column of the matrix A.

We also write A_{mn} to indicate that the matrix A has m rows and n columns. If $m = n$, then A is called a **square matrix of order n** and is denoted by A_n. The entries $a_{11}, a_{22}, \ldots, a_{nn}$ form the **main diagonal** of A_n. A $1 \times n$ matrix is called a **row matrix**, and an $n \times 1$ matrix is called a **column matrix**.

EXAMPLE 1   **Determining the Order of Matrices**

Determine the order of each matrix. Identify square, row, and column matrices. Identify entries in the main diagonal of each square matrix.

a. $A = [3]$,   **b.** $B = [3 \quad 5 \quad -7]$,   **c.** $C = \begin{bmatrix} 0 & 1 \\ -3 & 4 \end{bmatrix}$,   **d.** $D = \begin{bmatrix} 1 & 2 & 3 \\ 4 & 5 & 6 \\ 7 & 8 & 9 \end{bmatrix}.$

Solution

a. Matrix A has one row and one column. A is a 1×1 matrix. A is a square matrix of order 1. In A, $a_{11} = 3$.

b. Matrix B has one row and three columns. B is a 1×3 matrix. B is a row matrix.

Continued on next page.

c. Matrix C is a 2×2 matrix. C is a square matrix of order 2. In C, the entries $c_{11} = 0$ and $c_{22} = 4$ form the main diagonal.

d. Matrix D is a 3×3 matrix. D is a square matrix of order 3. In D, the entries $d_{11} = 1$, $d_{22} = 5$, and $d_{33} = 9$ form the main diagonal.   ■ ■ ■

PRACTICE PROBLEM 1   Determine the order of each matrix.

a. $\begin{bmatrix} -1 & 3 \\ 7 & 4 \\ 0 & 0 \end{bmatrix}$ **b.** $\begin{bmatrix} 3 & -8 \end{bmatrix}$ ■

---

2 Use matrices to solve a system.

Using Matrices to Solve Linear Systems

When solving a system of linear equations by the elimination method, the symbols used for the variables have little to do with finding the solution set of the system. It is really the coefficients of the variables and the constants on the right side of the equations that are important. Simply displaying all the numerical information contained in the system gives rise to a matrix. The matrix obtained is called the **augmented matrix** of the system. The matrix containing just the coefficients of the variables is called the **coefficient matrix** of the system. Consider the following system of equations.

$$\begin{cases} x - y - z = 1 \\ 2x - 3y + z = 10 \\ x + y - 2z = 0 \end{cases}$$

Coefficients of x
Coefficients of y
Coefficients of z

Augmented Matrix: $\begin{bmatrix} 1 & -1 & -1 & | & 1 \\ 2 & -3 & 1 & | & 10 \\ 1 & 1 & -2 & | & 0 \end{bmatrix}$

Constants

Coefficient Matrix: $\begin{bmatrix} 1 & -1 & -1 \\ 2 & -3 & 1 \\ 1 & 1 & -2 \end{bmatrix}$

Notice that the numbers in the first column of the augmented matrix are the coefficients of x, those in the second column are the coefficients of y, and those in the third column are the coefficients of z. The constants on the right side of the system are found in the fourth column. The vertical line in the augmented matrix has been inserted just to remind you of the equal signs in the equations. If a particular variable does not appear in one of the equations, you must use a zero in the appropriate position.

EXAMPLE 2   **Writing the Augmented Matrix of a Linear System**

Write the augmented matrix of the linear system.

$$\begin{cases} 2x + 3z = 1 \\ 2z + y = 5 \\ -4x + 5y = 7 \end{cases}$$

TECHNOLOGY CONNECTION

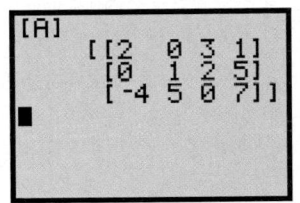 Many graphing calculators have you first name and then insert the entries for a matrix. No vertical line separates the column of constants, but this does not affect any of the matrix operations. The augmented matrix from Example 2 has been named A.

Solution

First write the system with the variables lined up in columns.

$$\begin{cases} 2x & + 3z = 1 \\ y + 2z = 5 \\ -4x + 5y & = 7 \end{cases}$$

Next, insert zeros as coefficients of the missing variables in each equation.

$$\begin{cases} 2x + 0y + 3z = 1 \\ 0x + 1y + 2z = 5 \\ -4x + 5y + 0z = 7 \end{cases}$$

The augmented matrix of the given system is

$$\left[\begin{array}{ccc|c} 2 & 0 & 3 & 1 \\ 0 & 1 & 2 & 5 \\ -4 & 5 & 0 & 7 \end{array}\right].$$

■ ■ ■

PRACTICE PROBLEM 2   Write the augmented matrix of the linear system.

$$\begin{cases} 3y - z = 8 \\ x + 4y = 14 \\ -2y + 9z = 0 \end{cases}$$

■

We can reverse this process and write a linear system from a given augmented matrix. For example, the augmented matrix

$$\left[\begin{array}{ccc|c} 9 & 2 & -1 & 6 \\ 3 & 4 & 7 & -8 \\ 0 & 1 & 5 & 11 \end{array}\right] \text{ corresponds to the system of equations } \begin{cases} 9x + 2y - z = 6 \\ 3x + 4y + 7z = -8. \\ y + 5z = 11 \end{cases}$$

The basic strategy for solving a system of equations is to *replace the given system with an equivalent system* (one with the same solution set) *that is easier to solve.* In the previous chapter we used three basic operations to solve a linear system:

1. Interchange two equations.

2. Multiply all the terms in an equation by a nonzero constant.

3. Add a multiple of one equation to another equation. In other words, replace one equation by the sum of itself and a multiple of another equation.

In matrix terminology, the three operations are called the **elementary row operations**. Two matrices are **row equivalent** if one can be obtained from the other by a sequence of elementary row operations.

Elementary Row Operations		
Row Operation	**In Symbols**	**Description**
1. Interchange two rows.	$R_i \leftrightarrow R_j$	Interchange the ith and jth rows.
2. Multiply a row by a nonzero constant.	cR_j	Multiply the jth row by c.
3. Add a multiple of one row to another row.	$cR_i + R_j \rightarrow R_j$	Replace the jth row by adding c times ith row to it.

TECHNOLOGY CONNECTION

Many graphing calculators provide all three row operations. Consider the matrix A:

Here are some examples of row operations on the matrix A:

Swap rows 1 and 3.

Multiply row 1 by 4.

Add 3 times row 1 to row 2.

EXAMPLE 3   **Applying Elementary Row Operations**

Perform the indicated row operations in the stated order on the matrix

$$A = \begin{bmatrix} 3 & -2 & -3 \\ 2 & 4 & 14 \end{bmatrix}.$$

(a) $R_1 \leftrightarrow R_2$,   **(b)** $\frac{1}{2}R_1$,   **(c)** $-3R_1 + R_2 \to R_2$

Solution

a. $A = \begin{bmatrix} 3 & -2 & -3 \\ 2 & 4 & 14 \end{bmatrix} \xrightarrow{R_1 \leftrightarrow R_2} \begin{bmatrix} 2 & 4 & 14 \\ 3 & -2 & -3 \end{bmatrix} = B$ Interchange 1st and 2nd rows.

b. $B = \begin{bmatrix} 2 & 4 & 14 \\ 3 & -2 & -3 \end{bmatrix} \xrightarrow{\frac{1}{2}R_1} \begin{bmatrix} 1 & 2 & 7 \\ 3 & -2 & -3 \end{bmatrix} = C$ Multiply 1st row by $\frac{1}{2}$.

c. $C = \begin{bmatrix} 1 & 2 & 7 \\ 3 & -2 & -3 \end{bmatrix} \xrightarrow{-3R_1 + R_2 \to R_2} \begin{bmatrix} 1 & 2 & 7 \\ 0 & -8 & -24 \end{bmatrix}$ Add -3 times 1st row to the 2nd row.

■ ■ ■

PRACTICE PROBLEM 3   Perform the row operations of Example 3 in the stated order on the matrix

$$A = \begin{bmatrix} 3 & 4 & 5 \\ 2 & 4 & 6 \end{bmatrix}.$$ ■

   In the next example, we solve a system of equations both with and without matrix notation and place the results side by side for comparison. We solve the system of equations by converting it into triangular form using elimination and then back-substitution.

EXAMPLE 4   **Comparing Linear Systems and Matrices**

Solve the system of linear equations.

$$\begin{cases} x - y - z = 1 & (1) \\ 2x - 3y + z = 10 & (2) \\ x + y - 2z = 0 & (3) \end{cases}$$

Solution

Linear System

$$\begin{cases} x - y - z = 1 & (1) \\ 2x - 3y + z = 10 & (2) \\ x + y - 2z = 0 & (3) \end{cases}$$

Add -2 times equation (1) to equation (2).
Add -1 times equation (1) to equation (3).

$$\begin{cases} x - y - z = 1 & (1) \\ -y + 3z = 8 & (4) \\ 2y - z = -1 & (5) \end{cases}$$

Augmented Matrix

$$A = \begin{bmatrix} 1 & -1 & -1 & | & 1 \\ 2 & -3 & 1 & | & 10 \\ 1 & 1 & -2 & | & 0 \end{bmatrix}$$

Use the first row to produce zeros at the (2, 1) and (3, 1) positions.

$$\xrightarrow[(-1)R_1 + R_3 \to R_3]{-2R_1 + R_2 \to R_2} \begin{bmatrix} 1 & -1 & -1 & | & 1 \\ 0 & -1 & 3 & | & 8 \\ 0 & 2 & -1 & | & -1 \end{bmatrix}$$

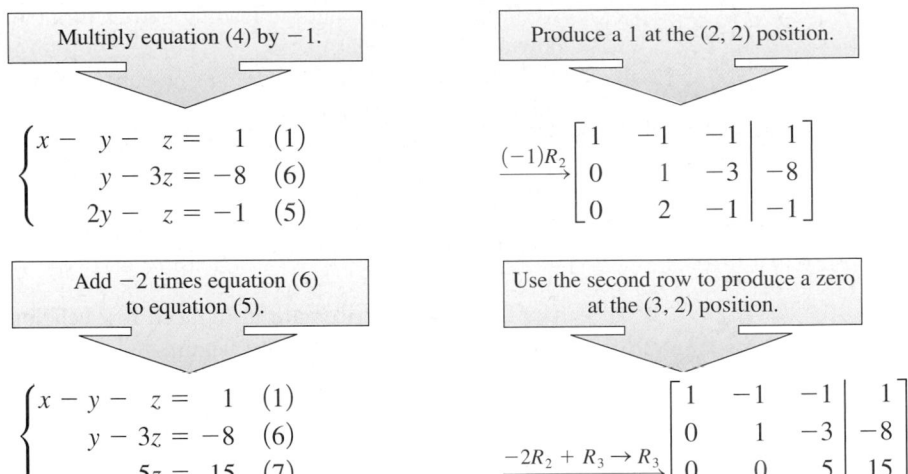

The equation $5z = 15$, which corresponds to row 3 of the final matrix, gives the value $z = 3$. We find y by back-substitution.

$$y - 3z = -8 \qquad \text{Equation (6); final matrix row 2.}$$
$$y - 3(3) = -8 \qquad \text{Replace } z \text{ by 3.}$$
$$y = 1 \qquad \text{Solve for } y.$$

Since $y = 1$ and $z = 3$, we find x by back-substitution.

$$x - y - z = 1 \qquad \text{Equation (1); final matrix row 1.}$$
$$x - 1 - 3 = 1 \qquad \text{Replace } y \text{ by 1 and } z \text{ by 3.}$$
$$x = 5 \qquad \text{Solve for } x.$$

The solution of the system is $x = 5$, $y = 1$, and $z = 3$. You should check this solution by substituting it into the original system of equations. The solution set is $\{(5, 1, 3)\}$.

■ ■ ■

PRACTICE PROBLEM 4   Solve the system of linear equations.

$$\begin{cases} x - 6y + 3z = -2 \\ 3x + 3y - 2z = -2 \\ 2x - 3y + z = -2 \end{cases}$$ ■

The last matrix in the solution of Example 4 is in *row-echelon form*, which is defined next. In the definition, a **nonzero row** means a row that contains at least one nonzero entry; a **leading entry** of a row refers to the leftmost nonzero entry in a nonzero row.

ROW-ECHELON FORM AND REDUCED ROW-ECHELON FORM

An $m \times n$ matrix is in **row-echelon form** if it has the following three properties:

1. All nonzero rows are above the rows consisting entirely of zeros.

2. The leading entry of each nonzero row is a 1.

3. For two successive nonzero rows, the leading 1 in the higher row is farther to the left of the leading 1 in the lower row.

If a matrix in row-echelon form has the following additional property, then it is in **reduced row-echelon form:**

4. Each leading 1 is the only nonzero entry in its column.

Property 3 says that the leading entries form an echelon (steplike) pattern that moves down and to the right.

The following matrices are in row-echelon form, with the starred entries taking on any value, including zero:

$$\begin{bmatrix} 1 & * & * \\ 0 & 1 & * \\ 0 & 0 & 1 \end{bmatrix}, \quad \begin{bmatrix} 1 & * & * & * \\ 0 & 1 & * & * \\ 0 & 0 & 1 & * \end{bmatrix}, \quad \begin{bmatrix} 1 & * & * & * \\ 0 & 0 & 1 & * \\ 0 & 0 & 0 & 1 \\ 0 & 0 & 0 & 0 \end{bmatrix}.$$

The following matrices are in reduced row-echelon form, because the entries above and below the leading 1's are zero (again, the starred entries may take on any value, including zero):

$$\begin{bmatrix} 1 & 0 & 0 \\ 0 & 1 & 0 \\ 0 & 0 & 1 \end{bmatrix}, \quad \begin{bmatrix} 1 & 0 & 0 & * \\ 0 & 1 & 0 & * \\ 0 & 0 & 1 & * \end{bmatrix}, \quad \begin{bmatrix} 1 & * & 0 & 0 \\ 0 & 0 & 1 & 0 \\ 0 & 0 & 0 & 1 \\ 0 & 0 & 0 & 0 \end{bmatrix}.$$

While solving a system of equations, one may transform the augmented matrix by elementary operations into several different matrices, each in row-echelon form, by using different sequences of row operations. However, the *reduced* row-echelon form obtained from a matrix is *unique*. (See Exercise 83.)

3 Use Gaussian elimination to solve a system.

Gaussian Elimination

The method of solving a system of linear equations by transforming the augmented matrix of the system into row-echelon form and then using back-substitution to find the solution set is known as **Gaussian elimination.**

FINDING THE SOLUTION: PROCEDURE FOR SOLVING LINEAR SYSTEMS BY USING GAUSSIAN ELIMINATION

OBJECTIVE	EXAMPLE
To solve a system of linear equations by Gaussian elimination.	Solve the system of equations. $$\begin{cases} x + 2y = -2 \\ 4x + 3y = 7 \end{cases}$$

Step 1 Write the augmented matrix of the system.

$$A = \begin{bmatrix} 1 & 2 & -2 \\ 4 & 3 & 7 \end{bmatrix}$$

Step 2 Use elementary row operations to transform the augmented matrix into row-echelon form.

$$\xrightarrow{-4R_1 + R_2 \rightarrow R_2} \begin{bmatrix} 1 & 2 & -2 \\ 0 & -5 & 15 \end{bmatrix}$$

This operation produces a 0 in the (2, 1) position.

$$\xrightarrow{-\frac{1}{5}R_2} \begin{bmatrix} 1 & 2 & -2 \\ 0 & 1 & -3 \end{bmatrix}$$

This operation produces a 1 in the (2, 2) position.

Step 3   Write the system of linear equations that corresponds to the matrix in row-echelon form that was obtained in Step 2.

$$\begin{cases} x + 2y = -2 & (1) \\ y = -3 & (2) \end{cases}$$

Step 4   Use the system of equations obtained in Step 3, together with back-substitution, to find the solution set of the system.

$$x + 2y = -2$$ Equation (1)

$$x + 2(-3) = -2$$ Replace y by -3.

$$x = 4$$ Solve for x.

The solution set is $\{(4, -3)\}$. You should check the solution by substituting $x = 4$ and $y = -3$ into the original system of equations.

EXAMPLE 5   **Solving a System by Using Gaussian Elimination**

Solve the system of equations by Gaussian elimination.

$$\begin{cases} 2x + y + z = 6 \\ -3x - 4y + 2z = 4 \\ x + y - z = -2 \end{cases}$$

Solution

Step 1   The augmented matrix of the system is

$$A = \begin{bmatrix} 2 & 1 & 1 & 6 \\ -3 & -4 & 2 & 4 \\ 1 & 1 & -1 & -2 \end{bmatrix}$$

Step 2

$$\xrightarrow{R_1 \leftrightarrow R_3} \begin{bmatrix} 1 & 1 & -1 & -2 \\ -3 & -4 & 2 & 4 \\ 2 & 1 & 1 & 6 \end{bmatrix}$$

This operation produces a 1 in the $(1, 1)$ position.

$$\xrightarrow[\substack{-2R_1 + R_3 \to R_3}]{3R_1 + R_2 \to R_2} \begin{bmatrix} 1 & 1 & -1 & -2 \\ 0 & -1 & -1 & -2 \\ 0 & -1 & 3 & 10 \end{bmatrix}$$

This operation produces 0's in the $(2, 1)$ and $(3,1)$ positions.

$$\xrightarrow{(-1)R_2} \begin{bmatrix} 1 & 1 & -1 & -2 \\ 0 & 1 & 1 & 2 \\ 0 & -1 & 3 & 10 \end{bmatrix}$$

This operation produces a 1 in the $(2, 2)$ position.

$$\xrightarrow{R_2 + R_3 \to R_3} \begin{bmatrix} 1 & 1 & -1 & -2 \\ 0 & 1 & 1 & 2 \\ 0 & 0 & 4 & 12 \end{bmatrix}$$

This operation produces a 0 in the $(3, 2)$ position.

Continued on next page.

STUDY TIP

Note that when we perform a row operation such as

$$3R_1 + R_2 \to R_2 \text{ on a matrix,}$$

1. the entries in row 1 are *unchanged;* and
2. we multiply each entry of row 1 by 3 and add this product to the corresponding entries of row 2 to obtain a *new second row*.

$$\xrightarrow{\frac{1}{4}R_3} \begin{bmatrix} 1 & 1 & -1 & -2 \\ 0 & 1 & 1 & 2 \\ 0 & 0 & 1 & 3 \end{bmatrix}$$

This operation produces a 1 in the $(3, 3)$ position.

The last matrix is in row-echelon form.

Step 3 The system of equations corresponding to the last matrix in Step 2 is

$$\begin{cases} x + y - z = -2 & (1) \\ y + z = 2 & (2) \\ z = 3 & (3) \end{cases}$$

Step 4 Equation (3) in Step 3 gives the value $z = 3$. Back-substitute $z = 3$ in Equation (2).

$$\begin{aligned} y + z &= 2 & &\text{Equation (2)} \\ y + 3 &= 2 & &\text{Replace } z \text{ by 3.} \\ y &= -1 & &\text{Solve for } y. \end{aligned}$$

Now back-substitute $z = 3$ and $y = -1$ in Equation (1).

$$\begin{aligned} x + y - z &= -2 & &\text{Equation (1)} \\ x - 1 - 3 &= -2 & &\text{Replace } y \text{ by } -1 \text{ and } z \text{ by 3.} \\ x &= 2 & &\text{Solve for } x. \end{aligned}$$

The solution set for the system is $\{(2, -1, 3)\}$. You should check the solution by substituting these values for x, y, and z into the original system of equations.

■ ■ ■

PRACTICE PROBLEM 5 Solve the system of equations.

$$\begin{cases} 2x + y - z = 7 \\ x - 3y - 3z = 4 \\ 4x + y + z = 3 \end{cases}$$

■

EXAMPLE 6 **Attempting to Solve a System with No Solution**

Solve the system of equations by Gaussian elimination.

$$\begin{cases} y + 5z = -4 \\ x + 4y + 3z = -2 \\ 2x + 7y + z = 8 \end{cases}$$

Solution

Step 1 The augmented matrix of the system is

$$A = \begin{bmatrix} 0 & 1 & 5 & -4 \\ 1 & 4 & 3 & -2 \\ 2 & 7 & 1 & 8 \end{bmatrix}.$$

Step 2
$$\xrightarrow{R_1 \leftrightarrow R_3} \begin{bmatrix} 1 & 4 & 3 & -2 \\ 0 & 1 & 5 & -4 \\ 2 & 7 & 1 & 8 \end{bmatrix}$$

This operation produces a 1 in the $(1, 1)$ position.

$$\xrightarrow{-2R_1 + R_3 \rightarrow R_3} \begin{bmatrix} 1 & 4 & 3 & | & -2 \\ 0 & 1 & 5 & | & -4 \\ 0 & -1 & -5 & | & 12 \end{bmatrix}$$

We already have a 0 in the (2, 1) position. This operation produces a 0 in the (3, 1) position.

$$\xrightarrow{R_2 + R_3 \rightarrow R_3} \begin{bmatrix} 1 & 4 & 3 & | & -2 \\ 0 & 1 & 5 & | & -4 \\ 0 & 0 & 0 & | & 8 \end{bmatrix}$$

This operation produces a 0 in the (3, 2) position.

$$\xrightarrow{\frac{1}{8}R_3} \begin{bmatrix} 1 & 4 & 3 & | & -2 \\ 0 & 1 & 5 & | & -4 \\ 0 & 0 & 0 & | & 1 \end{bmatrix}$$

This operation produces a 1 in the (3, 4) position.

The last matrix is in row-cchelon form.

Step 3 The system of equations corresponding to the last matrix in Step 2 is

$$\begin{cases} x + 4y + 3z = -2 \\ y + 5z = -4 \\ 0 = 1 \end{cases} \quad \text{A false statement}$$

The equation $0 = 1$ can be rewritten as $0x + 0y + 0z = 1$.

Since the equation $0x + 0y + 0z = 1$ is never true, we conclude that this system is inconsistent. Because this system is equivalent to the original system, the original system is also inconsistent.

Step 4 The solution set for the system is $\varnothing$.   ■ ■ ■

PRACTICE PROBLEM 6 Solve the following system of equations by first transforming the augmented matrix into row-echelon form:

$$\begin{cases} 6x + 8y - 14z = 3 \\ 3x + 4y - 7z = 12 \\ 6x + 3y + z = 0 \end{cases}$$ ■

4 Use Gauss–Jordan elimination to solve a system.

Gauss–Jordan Elimination

If we continue the Gaussian elimination procedure until a *reduced* row-echelon form is obtained, the procedure is called **Gauss–Jordan elimination.**

EXAMPLE 7   **Solving a System of Equations by Gauss-Jordan Elimination**

Solve the system given in Example 4 by Gauss–Jordan elimination. Recall that the given system is

$$\begin{cases} x - y - z = 1 \\ 2x - 3y + z = 10 \\ x + y - 2z = 0 \end{cases}$$

Continued on next page.

Solution

We can use an elementary row operation on the final augmented matrix of the system in Example 4 to arrive at an equivalent matrix B in row-echelon form:

$$\left[\begin{array}{ccc|c} 1 & -1 & -1 & 1 \\ 0 & 1 & -3 & -8 \\ 0 & 0 & 5 & 15 \end{array}\right] \xrightarrow{\frac{1}{5}R_3} \left[\begin{array}{ccc|c} 1 & -1 & -1 & 1 \\ 0 & 1 & -3 & -8 \\ 0 & 0 & 1 & 3 \end{array}\right] = B$$

We continue using elementary row operations on the matrix B to obtain an equivalent matrix in reduced row-echelon form.

$$B = \left[\begin{array}{ccc|c} 1 & -1 & -1 & 1 \\ 0 & 1 & -3 & -8 \\ 0 & 0 & 1 & 3 \end{array}\right]$$ The matrix B is in row-echelon form.

$$\xrightarrow{R_2 + R_1 \to R_1} \left[\begin{array}{ccc|c} 1 & 0 & -4 & -7 \\ 0 & 1 & -3 & -8 \\ 0 & 0 & 1 & 3 \end{array}\right]$$ Use the 1 in the $(2, 2)$ position to produce a zero in the $(1, 2)$ position.

$$\xrightarrow[3R_3 + R_2 \to R_2]{4R_3 + R_1 \to R_1} \left[\begin{array}{ccc|c} 1 & 0 & 0 & 5 \\ 0 & 1 & 0 & 1 \\ 0 & 0 & 1 & 3 \end{array}\right]$$ Use the 1 in the $(3, 3)$ position to produce zeros in column 3 above the 1.

We now have an equivalent matrix in reduced row-echelon form. The corresponding system of equations for the last augmented matrix is:

$$\begin{cases} x = 5 \\ y = 1 \\ z = 3 \end{cases}$$

Hence, the solution set is $\{(5, 1, 3)\}$, as in Example 4. ■ ■ ■

PRACTICE PROBLEM 7 Solve the system by using Gauss–Jordan elimination.

$$\begin{cases} 2x - 3y - 2z = 0 \\ x + y - 2z = 7 \\ 3x - 5y - 5z = 3 \end{cases}$$ ■

EXAMPLE 8   **Solving a System with Infinitely Many Solutions**

Solve the system of equations.

$$\begin{cases} x + 2y + 5x = 4 \\ y + 4x = 4 \\ 2x + 4y + 10x = 8 \end{cases}$$

Solution

The augmented matrix of the system is

$$A = \left[\begin{array}{ccc|c} 1 & 2 & 5 & 4 \\ 0 & 1 & 4 & 4 \\ 2 & 4 & 10 & 8 \end{array}\right].$$

You must now change the matrix A to an equivalent matrix in reduced row-echelon form.

Since $a_{11} = 1$ and $a_{21} = 0$, you must produce a zero at the $(3, 1)$ position:

$$A = \begin{bmatrix} 1 & 2 & 5 & | & 4 \\ 0 & 1 & 4 & | & 4 \\ 2 & 4 & 10 & | & 8 \end{bmatrix} \xrightarrow{-2R_1 + R_3 \rightarrow R_3} \begin{bmatrix} 1 & 2 & 5 & | & 4 \\ 0 & 1 & 4 & | & 4 \\ 0 & 0 & 0 & | & 0 \end{bmatrix}$$

Next, produce a zero at the $(1, 2)$ position:

$$\xrightarrow{-2R_2 + R_1 \rightarrow R_1} \begin{bmatrix} 1 & 0 & -3 & | & -4 \\ 0 & 1 & 4 & | & 4 \\ 0 & 0 & 0 & | & 0 \end{bmatrix}$$

The matrix is now in reduced row-echelon form. Converting to a system of equations, we have the equivalent system:

$$x - 3z = -4$$
$$y + 4z = 4$$

Solving for x and y in terms of z, we obtain

$$x = 3z - 4$$
$$y = -4z + 4$$

We thus have infinitely many solutions of the form $(3z - 4, -4z + 4, z)$, where z is any real number. The solution set is $\{(3z - 4, -4z + 4, z)\}$.   ■ ■ ■

PRACTICE PROBLEM 8   Solve the system of equations.

$$\begin{cases} x & + z = -1 \\ & 3y + 2z = 5 \\ 3x - 3y + z = -8 \end{cases}$$ ■

EXAMPLE 9   **Leontief Input–Output Model**

Consider an economy that has steel, coal, and transportation industries. There are two types of demands (measured in dollars) on the production of each industry: interindustry demand and external consumer demand. The demand on the three industries is expressed in Figure 9.1. For example, $1 of transportation output requires $.10 from steel and $.01 from coal.

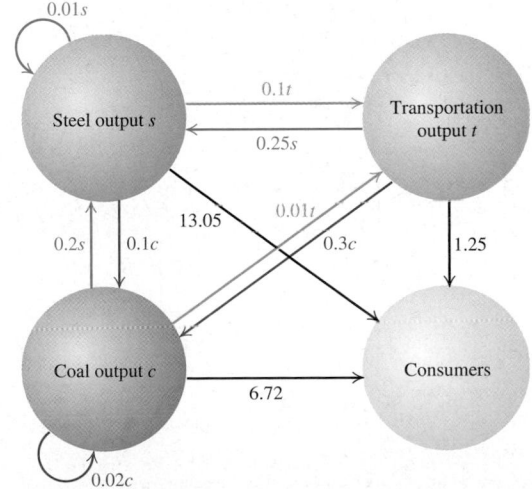

FIGURE 9.1

Continued on next page.

a. Write a system of equations that expresses the demand on the three industries. Assume that all quantities are given in millions of dollars.

b. Verify that $s = 15$, $c = 10$, and $t = 8$ will meet both interindustry and consumer demand.

Solution

a. To satisfy both consumer and interindustry demand, we obtain the following system of linear equations from Figure 9.1 (s denotes total steel output, c total coal output, and t total transportation output):

$$\begin{cases} s = 0.01s + 0.1t + 0.1c + 13.05 & \text{Represents distribution of steel output} \\ c = 0.2s + 0.01t + 0.02c + 6.72. & \text{Represents distribution of coal output} \\ t = 0.25s + 0.3c + 1.25 & \text{Represents distribution of transportation output} \end{cases}$$

You can rewrite this system as

$$\begin{cases} 0.99s - 0.1c - 0.1t = 13.05 & (1) \\ -0.2s + 0.98c - 0.01t = 6.72 & (2) \\ -0.25s - 0.3c + t = 1.25 & (3) \end{cases}$$

b. To verify that the given numbers (obtained by solving the system above using matrices) satisfy these equations, we substitute $s = 15$, $c = 10$, and $t = 8$ into each equation.

$$\begin{aligned} (0.99)(15) - (0.1)(10) - (0.1)(8) &= 13.05 \checkmark \quad (1) \\ (-0.20)(15) + (0.98)(10) - (0.01)(8) &= 6.72 \checkmark \quad (2) \\ (-0.25)(15) - (0.30)(10) + 8 &= 1.25 \checkmark \quad (3) \end{aligned}$$

Thus, output levels of $s = 15$, $c = 10$, and $t = 8$ million dollars will meet interindustry demand, as well as consumer demand, for the three-industry economy. ■ ■ ■

PRACTICE PROBLEM 9   In Example 9, assume that consumer demand (in millions of dollars) is 12.46 for steel, 3 for coal, and 2.7 for transportation.

a. Write a system of equations to express the demand on the three industries.

b. Verify that $s = 14$, $c = 6$, $t = 8$ will meet both interindustry and consumer demand. ■

A Exercises   Basic Skills and Concepts

In Exercises 1–6, determine the order of each matrix.

1. $[7]$ 1×1

2. $[1 \quad 3 \quad 5 \quad 9]$ 1×4

3. $\begin{bmatrix} 3 & 4.3 & 7.5 & 8 \\ 2 & -1 & -3 & 0 \end{bmatrix}$ †

4. $\begin{bmatrix} -1 & 2 & 3 \\ 4 & -5 & 7 \\ 1 & 0 & 0 \end{bmatrix}$ 3×3

5. $\begin{bmatrix} 4 & 5 & 1 \\ 0 & 0 & 0 \end{bmatrix}$ 2×3

6. $\begin{bmatrix} -5 & 2 & 3 & 7 \\ 2.5 & e & -\pi & \frac{1}{2} \\ -e & \pi & 0 & 1 \end{bmatrix}$ †

7. Let $A = \begin{bmatrix} 1 & 2 & 3 & 4 \\ 5 & 6 & 7 & 8 \\ 9 & 10 & 11 & 12 \end{bmatrix}$. Identify the entries a_{13}, a_{31}, a_{33}, and a_{34}. †

8. In matrix A from Exercise 7, identify the (i, j)th location of each entry.

a. 7 a_{23} **b.** 10 a_{32}

c. 4 a_{14} **d.** 12 a_{34}

9. Is the following array a matrix? Why or why not?

$\begin{bmatrix} 2 & 0 & 4 \\ 1 & -3 & 5 \\ 0 & 0 \end{bmatrix}$ No, it is not a rectangular array of numbers.

†Due to space constrictions, answers to these exercises may be found in the Answers beginning on page A–1 in the back of the book.

10. Write the matrix A with the following entries:

$a_{13} = 5$, $a_{22} = 2$, $a_{11} = 6$, $a_{12} = -5$, $a_{23} = 4$, and $a_{21} = 7$. †

In Exercises 11–16, write the augmented matrix for each system of linear equations.

11. $\begin{cases} 2x + 4y = 2 \\ x - 3y = 1 \end{cases}$ †

12. $\begin{cases} x_1 + 2x_2 = 7 \\ 3x_1 + 5x_2 = 11 \end{cases}$ †

13. $\begin{cases} 5x_1 - 11 = 7x_2 \\ 17x_2 - 19 = 13x_1 \end{cases}$ †

14. $\begin{cases} 2v - 10 = 3u \\ 5u + 7 = v \end{cases}$ †

15. $\begin{cases} -x + 2y + 3z = 8 \\ 2x - 3y + 9z = 16 \\ 4x - 5y - 6z = 32 \end{cases}$ †

16. $\begin{cases} x - y = 2 \\ 2x + 3z = -5 \\ y - 2z = 7 \end{cases}$ †

In Exercises 17–20, write the system of linear equations represented by each augmented matrix. Use x, y, and z as the variables.

17. $\left[\begin{array}{ccc|c} 1 & 2 & -3 & 4 \\ -2 & -3 & 1 & 5 \\ 3 & -3 & 2 & 7 \end{array}\right]$ †

18. $\left[\begin{array}{ccc|c} -1 & 2 & 3 & 6 \\ 2 & 3 & 1 & 2 \\ 4 & 3 & 2 & 1 \end{array}\right]$ †

19. $\left[\begin{array}{ccc|c} 1 & -1 & 1 & 2 \\ 2 & 1 & -3 & 6 \end{array}\right]$ †

20. $\left[\begin{array}{ccc|c} 1 & 1 & 1 & 2 \\ 1 & -1 & -1 & 4 \\ 2 & 3 & 1 & 6 \\ -1 & 1 & -1 & 8 \end{array}\right]$ †

In Exercises 21–24, perform the indicated elementary row operations in the stated order.

21. $\begin{bmatrix} 2 & 3 & 5 \\ 1 & 2 & 3 \end{bmatrix}$; (i) $R_1 \leftrightarrow R_2$, (ii) $-2R_1 + R_2 \to R_2$, (iii) $-R_2$ †

22. $\begin{bmatrix} 2 & 4 & 2 \\ 1 & 5 & 7 \end{bmatrix}$; (i) $\frac{1}{2}R_1$, (ii) $(-1)R_1 + R_2 \to R_2$, (iii) $\frac{1}{3}R_2$ †

23. $\begin{bmatrix} 1 & 2 & 3 & 4 \\ 0 & 4 & -3 & 11 \\ 0 & 1 & 5 & -3 \end{bmatrix}$; (i) $R_2 \leftrightarrow R_3$, (ii) $-4R_2 + R_3 \to R_3$, (iii) $-\frac{1}{23}R_3$ †

24. $\begin{bmatrix} 1 & \frac{3}{2} & -2 & \frac{1}{2} \\ 0 & 2 & 3 & 4 \\ -2 & -1 & 7 & 3 \end{bmatrix}$; (i) $2R_1 + R_3 \to R_3$, (ii) $\frac{1}{2}R_2 + R_3 \to R_3$ †

In Exercises 25–28, identify the elementary row operation used and supply the missing entries in each row-equivalent matrix.

25. $\begin{bmatrix} 4 & 5 & -7 \\ 5 & 4 & -2 \end{bmatrix} \to \begin{bmatrix} 1 & ? & -\frac{7}{4} \\ 5 & 4 & -2 \end{bmatrix} \to \begin{bmatrix} 1 & ? & -\frac{7}{4} \\ 0 & -\frac{9}{4} & ? \end{bmatrix} \to$

$\begin{bmatrix} 1 & ? & -\frac{7}{4} \\ 0 & 1 & ? \end{bmatrix}$ †

26. $\begin{bmatrix} 2 & 6 & -8 \\ 3 & -1 & 2 \end{bmatrix} \to \begin{bmatrix} 1 & 3 & -? \\ 3 & -1 & 2 \end{bmatrix} \to \begin{bmatrix} 1 & 3 & ? \\ 0 & -? & 14 \end{bmatrix} \to$

$\begin{bmatrix} 1 & 3 & -? \\ 0 & 1 & ? \end{bmatrix}$ †

27. $\begin{bmatrix} 1 & 4 & 3 & 1 \\ 0 & -3 & -2 & 0 \\ 0 & 7 & 5 & -3 \end{bmatrix} \to \begin{bmatrix} 1 & 4 & 3 & 1 \\ 0 & 1 & ? & 0 \\ 0 & 7 & 5 & -3 \end{bmatrix} \to$

$\begin{bmatrix} 1 & 4 & 3 & 1 \\ 0 & 1 & ? & 0 \\ 0 & 0 & ? & -3 \end{bmatrix} \to \begin{bmatrix} 1 & 4 & 3 & 1 \\ 0 & 1 & ? & 0 \\ 0 & 0 & 1 & ? \end{bmatrix}$ †

28. $\begin{bmatrix} 1 & 1 & 1 & 3 \\ 2 & 3 & 3 & 8 \\ 1 & -3 & -2 & 5 \end{bmatrix} \to \begin{bmatrix} 1 & 1 & 1 & 3 \\ 0 & 1 & ? & 2 \\ 1 & -3 & -2 & 5 \end{bmatrix} \to$

$\begin{bmatrix} 1 & 1 & 1 & 3 \\ 0 & 1 & ? & 2 \\ 0 & -4 & ? & 2 \end{bmatrix} \to \begin{bmatrix} 1 & 1 & 1 & 3 \\ 0 & 1 & ? & 2 \\ 0 & 0 & ? & 10 \end{bmatrix}$ †

In Exercises 29–36, determine whether each matrix is in row-echelon form. If your answer is no, state why not. If your answer is yes, is the matrix in reduced row-echelon form?

29. $\begin{bmatrix} 0 & 1 & 2 \\ 1 & 0 & 3 \end{bmatrix}$ No

30. $\begin{bmatrix} 1 & 2 & 5 \\ 0 & 3 & 6 \end{bmatrix}$ No

31. $\begin{bmatrix} 1 & 0 & 0 & 2 \\ 0 & 1 & 0 & 3 \\ 0 & 0 & 1 & 4 \end{bmatrix}$ The matrix is in reduced row-echelon form because Properties 1–4 are satisfied.

32. $\begin{bmatrix} 0 & 0 & 1 & 2 \\ 0 & 1 & 0 & 1 \\ 1 & 0 & 0 & 3 \end{bmatrix}$ No. Property (3) is not satisfied.

33. $\begin{bmatrix} 1 & 2 & 0 & 2 \\ 0 & 0 & 1 & 5 \end{bmatrix}$ The matrix is in reduced row-echelon form because Properties 1–4 are satisfied.

34. $\begin{bmatrix} 0 & 1 & -1 & -2 & 0 & 2 & 0 \\ 0 & 0 & 0 & 0 & 1 & 2 & 0 \end{bmatrix}$ The matrix is in reduced row-echelon form because Properties 1–4 are satisfied.

35. $\begin{bmatrix} 1 & 0 & 0 & -2 \\ 0 & 1 & 0 & 3 \\ 0 & 0 & 1 & 2 \\ 0 & 0 & 0 & 0 \end{bmatrix}$ The matrix is in reduced row-echelon form because Properties 1–4 are satisfied.

36. $\begin{bmatrix} 1 & 0 & 0 & 3 \\ 0 & 1 & 0 & 4 \\ 0 & 0 & 0 & 5 \\ 0 & 0 & 1 & 3 \end{bmatrix}$ No. Property (3) is not satisfied.

In Exercises 37–46, the augmented matrix of a system of equations has been transformed to an equivalent matrix in row-echelon form or reduced row-echelon form. Using x, y, z, and w as variables, write the system of equations corresponding to the matrix. If the system is consistent, solve it.

37. $\left[\begin{array}{cc|c} 1 & 2 & 1 \\ 0 & 1 & -2 \end{array}\right]$ †

38. $\left[\begin{array}{cc|c} 1 & 0 & 2 \\ 0 & 1 & 3 \end{array}\right]$ †

39. $\left[\begin{array}{ccc|c} 1 & 4 & 2 & 2 \\ 0 & 0 & 1 & 3 \end{array}\right]$ †

40. $\left[\begin{array}{ccc|c} 1 & 2 & 3 & 4 \\ 0 & 0 & 0 & 1 \end{array}\right]$ †

41. $\left[\begin{array}{ccc|c} 1 & 2 & 3 & 2 \\ 0 & 1 & -2 & 4 \\ 0 & 0 & 1 & -1 \end{array}\right]$ †

42. $\left[\begin{array}{ccc|c} 1 & 0 & 2 & 12 \\ 0 & 1 & 3 & 12 \\ 0 & 0 & 1 & 5 \end{array}\right]$ †

43. $\begin{bmatrix} 1 & 0 & 0 & 0 & | & 2 \\ 0 & 1 & 0 & 0 & | & -5 \\ 0 & 0 & 1 & 2 & | & 3 \\ 0 & 0 & 0 & 0 & | & 0 \end{bmatrix}$ † **44.** $\begin{bmatrix} 1 & 0 & 0 & 0 & | & 4 \\ 0 & 1 & 0 & 0 & | & 3 \\ 0 & 0 & 0 & 1 & | & 2 \end{bmatrix}$ †

45. $\begin{bmatrix} 1 & 0 & 0 & 0 & | & -5 \\ 0 & 1 & 0 & 0 & | & 4 \\ 0 & 0 & 1 & 2 & | & 3 \\ 0 & 0 & 0 & 1 & | & 0 \end{bmatrix}$ † **46.** $\begin{bmatrix} 1 & 0 & 0 & 0 & | & 3 \\ 0 & 1 & 0 & 0 & | & 2 \\ 0 & 0 & 1 & 0 & | & 0 \\ 0 & 0 & 0 & 0 & | & 1 \end{bmatrix}$ †

In Exercises 47–60, solve each system of equations by Gaussian elimination.

47. $\begin{cases} x - 2y = 11 \\ 2x - y = 13 \end{cases}$ $\{(5, -3)\}$ **48.** $\begin{cases} 3x - 2y = 4 \\ 4x - 3y = 5 \end{cases}$ $\{(2, 1)\}$

49. $\begin{cases} 2x - 3y = 3 \\ 4x - y = 11 \end{cases}$ $\{(3, 1)\}$ **50.** $\begin{cases} 3x + 2y = 1 \\ 6x + 4y = 3 \end{cases}$ $\varnothing$

51. $\begin{cases} 3x - 5y = 4 \\ 4x - 15y = 13 \end{cases}$ † **52.** $\begin{cases} -2x + 4y = 1 \\ 3x - 5y = -9 \end{cases}$ †

53. $\begin{cases} x - y = 1 \\ 2x + y = 5 \\ 3x - 4y = 2 \end{cases}$ $\{(2, 1)\}$ **54.** $\begin{cases} y = 2x + 1 \\ 3x + 2y + 1.5 = 0 \\ 4x - 2y + 2 = 0 \end{cases}$ †

55. $\begin{cases} x + y + z = 6 \\ x - y + z = 2 \\ 2x + y - z = 1 \end{cases}$ † **56.** $\begin{cases} 2x + 4y + z = 5 \\ x + y + z = 6 \\ 2x + 3y + z = 6 \end{cases}$ †

57. $\begin{cases} 2x + 3y - z = 9 \\ x + y + z = 9 \\ 3x - y - z = -1 \end{cases}$ † **58.** $\begin{cases} x + y + 2z = 4 \\ 2x - y + 3z = 9 \\ 3x - y - z = 2 \end{cases}$ †

59. $\begin{cases} 3x + 2y + 4z = 19 \\ 2x - y + z = 3 \\ 6x + 7y - z = 17 \end{cases}$ † **60.** $\begin{cases} 4x + 3y + z = 8 \\ 2x + y + 4z = -4 \\ 3x + z = 1 \end{cases}$ †

In Exercises 61–66, solve each system of equations by Gauss–Jordan elimination.

61. $\begin{cases} x - y = 1 \\ x - z = -1 \\ 2x + y - z = 3 \end{cases}$ † **62.** $\begin{cases} 4x + 5z = 7 \\ y - 6z = 8 \\ 3x + 4y = 9 \end{cases}$ †

63. $\begin{cases} x + y - z = 4 \\ x + 3y + 5z = 10 \\ 3x + 5y + 3z = 18 \end{cases}$ † **64.** $\begin{cases} x + y + z = -5 \\ 2x - y - z = -4 \\ y + z = -2 \end{cases}$ †

65. $\begin{cases} x + 2y - z = 6 \\ 3x + y + 2z = 3 \\ 2x + 5y + 3z = 9 \end{cases}$ † **66.** $\begin{cases} 2x + 4y - z = 9 \\ x + 3y - 3 = 4 \\ 3x + y + 2z = 7 \end{cases}$ †

67. The reduced row-echelon forms of the augmented matrices of three systems of equations are given. How many solutions does each system have?

a. $\begin{bmatrix} 1 & 0 & | & 2 \\ 0 & 1 & | & 3 \end{bmatrix}$ One solution **b.** $\begin{bmatrix} 1 & 2 & 3 & | & 8 \\ 0 & 0 & 1 & | & 2 \\ 0 & 0 & 0 & | & 0 \end{bmatrix}$ †

c. $\begin{bmatrix} 1 & 0 & | & 2 \\ 0 & 0 & | & 3 \end{bmatrix}$ $\varnothing$

In Exercises 68–70, determine whether the statement is true or false, and justify your answer.

68. If A is a 5×7 matrix, then each column of A has seven entries. False. Each row of A has seven entries.

69. The matrix $E = \begin{bmatrix} 1 & 3 & 0 \\ 0 & 0 & 1 \\ 0 & 0 & 0 \end{bmatrix}$ is in reduced row-echelon form. True

70. If a matrix A is in reduced row-echelon form, then at least one of the entries in each column must be a 1. False

---

B Exercises Applying the Concepts

In Exercises 71–74, Leontief's input–output model of a simplified economy is described. (See Example 9.) For each exercise, do the following.

a. Set up (without solving) a linear system whose solution will represent the required production schedule.
b. Write an augmented matrix for the economy.
c. Solve the system of equations by using part (b) to find the production schedule that will meet interindustry and consumer demand.

71. Two-sector economy. Consider an economy with only two industries: A and B. Suppose industry B needs 10 cents worth of A's product for each 1 dollar of output B produces and that industry A needs 20 cents worth of B's product for each 1 dollar of output A produces. Consumer demand for A's product is 1000 dollars and for B's product is 780 dollars. †

72. A company with two branches. A company has two interacting branches: *A* and *B*. Branch *A* consumes 50 cents of its own output and 20 cents of *B*'s output for every 1 dollar it produces. Branch *B* consumes 60 cents of *A*'s output and 30 cents of its own output for 1 dollar of output. Consumer demand for *A*'s product is 50,000 dollars, and for *B*'s product is 40,000 dollars. †

73. Three-sector economy. An economy has three sectors: labor, transportation, and food industries. Suppose the demand on 1 dollar in labor is 40 cents for transportation and 20 cents for food, the demand on 1 dollar in transportation is 50 cents for labor and 30 cents for transportation, and the demand on 1 dollar in food production is 50 cents for labor, 5 cents for transportation, and 35 cents for food. Outside consumer demand for the current production period is 10,000 dollars for labor, 20,000 dollars for transportation, and 10,000 dollars for food. †

74. Three-sector economy. Consider an economy with three industries *A*, *B*, and *C*, with outputs *a*, *b*, and *c*, respectively. Demand on the three industries is shown in the figure. †

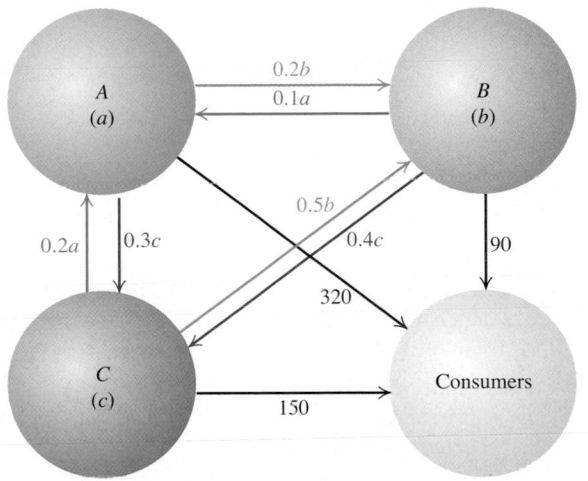

75. Heat transfer. In a study of heat transfer in a grid of wires, the temperature at an exterior node is maintained at a constant value (in °*F*) as shown in the accompanying figure. When the grid is in thermal equilibrium, the temperature at an interior node is the average of the temperatures at the four adjacent nodes. For instance $T_1 = \dfrac{0 + 0 + 300 + T_2}{4}$, or $4T_1 - T_2 = 300$. Find the temperatures T_1, T_2, and T_3 when the grid is in thermal equilibrium. †

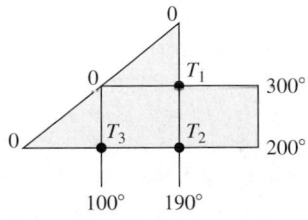

76. Repeat Exercise 75 for the following grid of wires: †

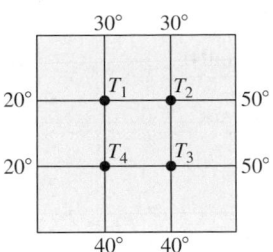

77. Traffic flow. The accompanying figure shows the intersections of one-way streets. The traffic volume during one hour was observed. To keep the traffic moving, traffic controllers use the formula that the number of cars entering an intersection equals the number of cars exiting the intersection.

a. Set up a system of equations that keeps traffic moving. †
b. Solve the system of equations in part (a). †

78. Repeat Exercise 77 for the following pattern of one-way streets. †

79. Modeling. A football was punted. Its height h above the ground at time t was recorded and is given by the following table:

Time t (seconds)	Height h (feet)
$t = 0.5$	31
$t = 1$	51
$t = 2$	67

a. Use the system of equations to find the equation of the parabola of the form $h = at^2 + bt + c$. †
b. What was the hang time (the time it takes for the ball to touch the ground) of the punt? approximately 4 sec
c. What was the maximum height of the ball? 67 ft

C Exercises   Beyond the Basics

80. Partial fractions. Find the partial-fraction decomposition of the rational expression

$$\frac{2x^2 + 22x}{(x-1)^2(x+2)(x+3)}.$$

Use matrix methods to find the partial fractions. †

In Exercises 81 and 82, solve each system of equations by Gauss–Jordan elimination.

81. $\begin{cases} x + y + z + w = 0 \\ x + 3y + 2z + 4w = 0 \\ 2x + z - w = 0 \end{cases}$ $\{(y + 2w, y, -2y - 3w, w)\}$

82. $\begin{cases} x - y + z - w = 4 \\ x + 2y + z + w = 2 \\ 2x + 3y + 4z + 5w = 5 \\ 3x + 4y + 2z - w = 8 \end{cases}$ $\{(1, 0, 2, -1)\}$

83. Let $A = \begin{bmatrix} 1 & 2 & -3 & 1 \\ 1 & 0 & -3 & 2 \\ 0 & 1 & 1 & 0 \\ 2 & 3 & 0 & -2 \end{bmatrix}$.

a. Find two different matrices B and C in row-echelon form that are row equivalent to A. †
b. Show that the reduced row-echelon form of the matrices B and C of part (a) produce the same matrix. †

84. Consider the following system of linear equations:

$$\begin{cases} x + y + z = 6 \\ x - y + z = 2 \\ 2x + y - z = 1 \end{cases}$$

a. Find two different matrices B and C in row-echelon form that yield the same solution set. †

b. Show that the reduced row-echelon form of the matrices B and C of part (a) produces the same matrix. †

85. a. Use the methods of this section to solve a general 2×2 system:

$$\begin{cases} ax + by = m \\ cx + dy = n \end{cases} \dagger$$

b. Under what conditions on the coefficients does the system have (*i*) a unique solution, (*ii*) no solution, and (*iii*) infinitely many solutions? †

86. Construct three different augmented matrices for linear systems whose solution set is $x = 1, y = 0, z = -2$. There are many different correct answers. †

In Exercises 87–88, solve each system of equations by using row operations.

87. $\begin{cases} \log x + \log y + \log z = 6 \\ 3 \log x - \log y + 3 \log z = 10 \\ 5 \log x + 5 \log y - 4 \log z = 3 \end{cases}$ (10, 100, 1000)

[*Hint:* Let $u = \log x, v = \log y,$ and $w = \log z.$]

88. $\begin{cases} 4 \cdot 2^x - 3 \cdot 3^y + 5^z = 1 \\ 2^x + 4 \cdot 3^y - 2 \cdot 5^z = 10 \\ 2 \cdot 2^x - 2 \cdot 3^y + 3 \cdot 5^z = 4 \end{cases}$ $\left\{ \left(1, 1, \frac{\ln 2}{\ln 5} \right) \right\}$

[*Hint:* Let $u = 2^x, v = 3^y,$ and $w = 5^z.$]

89. Find the cubic function $y = ax^3 + bx^2 + cx + d$ whose graph passes through the points $(1, 5), (-1, 1), (2, 7),$ and $(-2, 11)$. †

90. Find the cubic function $y = ax^3 + bx^2 + cx + d$ whose graph passes through the points $(1, 8), (-1, 2), (2, 8),$ and $(-2, 20)$. †

Critical Thinking

91. Find the form of all 2×1 matrices in reduced row-echelon form. †

92. Find the form of all 2×2 matrices in reduced row-echelon form. †

93. Suppose a matrix A is transformed to a matrix B by an elementary row operation. Is there an elementary row operation that transforms B to A? Explain. †

94. Are the following statements true or false? Justify your answers. Suppose a matrix A is in reduced row-echelon form.
   a. If we delete a row of A, then the remaining matrix is in reduced row-echelon form. True
   b. Repeat part (a), replacing "row" by "column." False

In Exercises 95 and 96, state whether the given statement is true or false. Explain.

95. The augmented matrix for the system of equations

$$\begin{cases} 2x + 3y = 5 \\ 3y - 4z = -1 \\ x + 2z = 3 \end{cases} \quad \text{is} \quad \begin{bmatrix} 2 & 3 & 5 \\ 3 & -4 & -1 \\ 1 & 2 & 3 \end{bmatrix}. \; †$$

96. The augmented matrix for the system of equations

$$\begin{cases} 2x - y = 1 \\ 3x + y = 9 \\ 5x - 2y = 4 \end{cases} \quad \text{is} \quad \begin{bmatrix} 2 & -1 & 1 \\ 3x & 1 & 9 \\ 5x & -2y & 4 \end{bmatrix}. \; †$$

SECTION 9.2 | Matrix Algebra

BEFORE STARTING THIS SECTION, REVIEW

1. Properties of real numbers (Section P.1, page 11)
2. Solving systems of equations (Section 8.1, page 755)

OBJECTIVES

1 Define equality of two matrices.

2 Define matrix addition and scalar multiplication.

3 Define matrix multiplication.

4 Apply matrix multiplication to computer graphics.

Computer Graphics

Computer graphics are images displayed on a computer screen. These images can be altered as a result of manipulating the data by computer. Applications of computer graphics are widespread and growing rapidly. Further, computer-aided design (CAD) is an integral part of many engineering processes. Here are some examples in which computer graphics are used:

1. The *automobile industry*. Both CAD and computer-aided manufacturing (CAM) have revolutionized the automotive industry. Many months before a new car is built, engineers design and construct a *mathematical car*—a wire-frame model that exists only in computer memory and on graphics display terminals. The mathematical model organizes and influences each step of the design and manufacture of the car.

2. The *entertainment industry*. Computer graphics are used by the entertainment industry with spectacular success. They were used in *Star Wars* and other movies for special effects, and they are used in the design and creation of arcade games.

3. *Military*. From the very beginning of the widespread use of computers (in the 1960s), computer graphics have been used by the military to prepare for or defend against war. Modern weaponry depends heavily on computer-generated images.

Engineers perform several basic operations on graphic images, such as changing the orientation or scale of a figure, zooming in on small regions, or switching between two- and three-dimensional views. All the manipulations of screen images are accomplished by matrix algebra techniques. In Example 10 and in the exercises, we examine how basic matrix algebra can be used to manipulate graphical images. ■

Equality of Matrices

In the previous section, a matrix was defined as a rectangular array of numbers written within brackets. In this section and the next two, you will be introduced to the operations and uses of matrices. A matrix may be represented in any of the following three ways:

1. A matrix may be denoted by capital letters, such as A, B, C, and so on.
2. A matrix may be denoted by its representative (i, j)th entry: $[a_{ij}]$, $[b_{ij}]$, $[c_{ij}]$, and so on.
3. A matrix may be written as a rectangular array of numbers:

$$A = [a_{ij}] = \begin{bmatrix} a_{11} & a_{12} & \cdots & a_{1n} \\ a_{21} & a_{22} & \cdots & a_{2n} \\ \vdots & \vdots & \cdots & \vdots \\ a_{m1} & a_{m2} & \cdots & a_{mn} \end{bmatrix}.$$

We now examine some *algebraic* properties of matrices. To do so, we shall need the definitions given in this section.

James Joseph Sylvester

(1814–1897)

In 1850, Sylvester coined the term **matrix** to denote a rectangular array of numbers. Sylvester, who was born into a Jewish family in London and studied for several years at Cambridge, was not permitted to take his degree there for religious reasons. Therefore, he received his degree from Trinity College, Dublin. In 1871, he accepted the chair of mathematics at the newly opened Johns Hopkins University in Baltimore. While at Hopkins, Sylvester founded the *American Journal of Mathematics* and helped develop a tradition of graduate education in mathematics in the United States.

EQUALITY OF MATRICES

Two matrices $A = [a_{ij}]$ and $B = [b_{ij}]$ are said to be **equal**, written $A = B$, if

1. A and B have the same order $m \times n$ (that is, A and B have the same number m of rows and same number n of columns) and
2. $a_{ij} = b_{ij}$ for all i and j. (The (i, j)th entry of A is equal to the corresponding (i, j)th entry of B.)

EXAMPLE 1 **Determining Equality of Matrices**

Find x and y such that

$$\begin{bmatrix} x + y & 2 \\ 3 & x - y \end{bmatrix} = \begin{bmatrix} 4 & 2 \\ 3 & 1 \end{bmatrix}.$$

Solution

Because the matrices are equal, they must have identical entries in the corresponding positions. This results in the following system of equations:

$$\begin{cases} x + y = 4 & (1) \\ x - y = 1 & (2) \end{cases}$$

Equate entries in the $(1, 1)$ position.
Equate entries in the $(2, 2)$ position.

Solve this system: Add the two equations to obtain $x = \dfrac{5}{2}$; then substitute $x = \dfrac{5}{2}$ in equation $x - y = 1$ and solve for y to obtain $y = \dfrac{3}{2}$. Thus, $x = \dfrac{5}{2}$ and $y = \dfrac{3}{2}$. ■ ■ ■

PRACTICE PROBLEM 1

Find x and y such that

$$\begin{bmatrix} 1 & 2x - y \\ x + y & 5 \end{bmatrix} = \begin{bmatrix} 1 & 1 \\ 2 & 5 \end{bmatrix}.$$

■

2 Define matrix addition and scalar multiplication.

Matrix Addition and Scalar Multiplication

The addition of two matrices differs somewhat from the ordinary addition of two real numbers. You can add any two real numbers, but this is not necessarily so for any two matrices. The addition of any two matrices is defined only if they have the same order.

MATRIX ADDITION

If $A = [a_{ij}]$ and $B = [b_{ij}]$ are two $m \times n$ matrices, their **sum** $A + B$ is the $m \times n$ matrix defined by

$$A + B = [a_{ij} + b_{ij}],$$

for all i and j.

The definition of matrix addition says that

(i)   two matrices of the same order can be added simply by adding their corresponding entries, but

(ii) the sum of two matrices of different orders is not defined.

EXAMPLE 2   Adding Matrices

Let $A = \begin{bmatrix} -2 & 3 \\ 4 & -1 \\ 0 & 2 \end{bmatrix}$, $B = \begin{bmatrix} 6 & 4 \\ -7 & 9 \\ -8 & -5 \end{bmatrix}$, and $C = \begin{bmatrix} 1 & 2 \\ 3 & 4 \end{bmatrix}$. Find each sum if possible.

a. $A + B$ **b.** $A + C$

Solution

a. Since A and B have the same order, $A + B$ is defined. We have

$$A + B = \begin{bmatrix} -2 & 3 \\ 4 & -1 \\ 0 & 2 \end{bmatrix} + \begin{bmatrix} 6 & 4 \\ -7 & 9 \\ 8 & -5 \end{bmatrix} = \begin{bmatrix} -2+6 & 3+4 \\ 4-7 & -1+9 \\ 0+8 & 2-5 \end{bmatrix} = \begin{bmatrix} 4 & 7 \\ -3 & 8 \\ 8 & -3 \end{bmatrix}.$$

b. $A + C$ is not defined, because A and C do not have the same order.   ■ ■ ■

PRACTICE PROBLEM 2   Let $A = \begin{bmatrix} 2 & -1 & 4 \\ 5 & 0 & 9 \end{bmatrix}$ and $B = \begin{bmatrix} -8 & 2 & 9 \\ 7 & 3 & 6 \end{bmatrix}$. Find $A + B$.   ■

You can also multiply any matrix A by any real number c. The real number c is referred to as a **scalar**, and the multiplication process is called *scalar multiplication*.

SCALAR MULTIPLICATION

Let $A = [a_{ij}]$ be an $m \times n$ matrix, and let c be a real number. Then the **scalar product** of A and c is denoted by cA and is defined by

$$cA = [ca_{ij}].$$

TECHNOLOGY CONNECTION

To produce the sum of two matrices with a graphing calculator, name the matrices and then use the regular addition key with the names of the matrices.

Consider the matrices A and B in Example 2:

```
[A]
     [[-2 3 ]
      [4  -1]
      [0  2 ]]
```

```
[B]
     [[6  4 ]
      [-7 9 ]
      [8  -5]]
```

Their sum is

```
[A]+[B]
     [[4  7 ]
      [-3 8 ]
■     [8  -3]]
```

Thus, to multiply a matrix A by a real number c, you multiply each entry of A by c. When $c = -1$, we frequently write $-A$ instead of $(-1)A$. Further, the *difference* of two matrices, $A - B$, is defined to be the sum $A + (-1)B$.

MATRIX SUBTRACTION

If A and B are two $m \times n$ matrices, then their **difference** is defined by

$$A - B = A + (-1)B.$$

Subtraction $A - B$ is performed by subtracting the corresponding entries of B from A.

TECHNOLOGY CONNECTION

To produce the difference of two matrices with a graphing calculator, name the matrices and then use the regular subtraction key with the names of the matrices. Similarly, to multiply a matrix by a scalar, use the name of the matrix and the regular multiplication key.

Consider the matrices A and B in Example 3:

[A]
```
[[1   2   0]
 [-1  3   1]
 [2  -1   4]]
```

[B]
```
[[2   1   3]
 [1   0  -2]
 [-3  4   5]]
```

We find $3A - 2B$:

```
3*[A]-2*[B]
  [[-1   4   -6]
   [-5   9    7]
   [12 -11    2]]
```

EXAMPLE 3   Performing Scalar Multiplication and Matrix Subtraction

Let $A = \begin{bmatrix} 1 & 2 & 0 \\ -1 & 3 & 1 \\ 2 & -1 & 4 \end{bmatrix}$ and $B = \begin{bmatrix} 2 & 1 & 3 \\ 1 & 0 & -2 \\ -3 & 4 & 5 \end{bmatrix}$. Find the following.

a. $3A$ **b.** $2B$ **c.** $3A - 2B$.

Solution

a. $3A = 3\begin{bmatrix} 1 & 2 & 0 \\ -1 & 3 & 1 \\ 2 & -1 & 4 \end{bmatrix} = \begin{bmatrix} 3(1) & 3(2) & 3(0) \\ 3(-1) & 3(3) & 3(1) \\ 3(2) & 3(-1) & 3(4) \end{bmatrix} = \begin{bmatrix} 3 & 6 & 0 \\ -3 & 9 & 3 \\ 6 & -3 & 12 \end{bmatrix}$

b. $2B = 2\begin{bmatrix} 2 & 1 & 3 \\ 1 & 0 & -2 \\ -3 & 4 & 5 \end{bmatrix} = \begin{bmatrix} 2(2) & 2(1) & 2(3) \\ 2(1) & 2(0) & 2(-2) \\ 2(-3) & 2(4) & 2(5) \end{bmatrix} = \begin{bmatrix} 4 & 2 & 6 \\ 2 & 0 & -4 \\ -6 & 8 & 10 \end{bmatrix}$

c. $3A - 2B = 3A + (-1)2B$

$= \begin{bmatrix} 3 & 6 & 0 \\ -3 & 9 & 3 \\ 6 & -3 & 12 \end{bmatrix} + \begin{bmatrix} -4 & -2 & -6 \\ -2 & 0 & 4 \\ 6 & -8 & -10 \end{bmatrix}$ Substitute from parts **a** and **b**, changing the sign of each entry in B.

$= \begin{bmatrix} 3 + (-4) & 6 + (-2) & 0 + (-6) \\ -3 + (-2) & 9 + 0 & 3 + 4 \\ 6 + 6 & -3 + (-8) & 12 + (-10) \end{bmatrix} = \begin{bmatrix} -1 & 4 & 6 \\ -5 & 9 & 7 \\ 12 & -11 & 2 \end{bmatrix}$ ■ ■ ■

PRACTICE PROBLEM 3   Let $A = \begin{bmatrix} 7 & -4 \\ 3 & 6 \\ 0 & -2 \end{bmatrix}$ and $B = \begin{bmatrix} 1 & -3 \\ 2 & 2 \\ 5 & 8 \end{bmatrix}$. Find $2A - 3B$.   ■

An $m \times n$ matrix whose entries are all equal to 0 is called the $m \times n$ **zero matrix** and is denoted by $\mathbf{0}_{mn}$. When $m = n$, we write $\mathbf{0}_n$. When m and n are understood from the context, we simply write $\mathbf{0}$. The matrix $-A = (-1)A$ is called the **negative** of A. Many of the algebraic properties of matrix addition and scalar multiplication are similar to the familiar properties of real numbers.

> **MATRIX ADDITION AND SCALAR MULTIPLICATION PROPERTIES**
>
> Let A, B, and C be $m \times n$ matrices and c and d be scalars.
>
> **1.** $A + B = B + A$ Commutative property of addition
> **2.** $A + (B + C) = (A + B) + C$ Associative property of addition
> **3.** $A + 0 = 0 + A = A$ Additive identity property
> **4.** $A + (-A) = (-A) + A = 0$ Additive inverse property
> **5.** $(cd)A = c(dA)$ Associative property of scalar multiplication
> **6.** $1A = A$ Scalar identity property
> **7.** $c(A + B) = cA + cB$ Distributive property
> **8.** $(c + d)A = cA + dA$ Distributive property

In the next example, these properties are used to solve an equation involving matrices. Such an equation is called a **matrix equation**.

EXAMPLE 4   Solving a Matrix Equation

Solve the matrix equation $3A + 2X = 4B$ for X, where

$$A = \begin{bmatrix} 2 & 0 \\ 4 & 6 \end{bmatrix} \text{ and } B = \begin{bmatrix} 1 & 3 \\ 5 & 2 \end{bmatrix}.$$

Solution

$3A + 2X = 4B$ The given equation

$2X = 4B - 3A$ Subtract the matrix $3A$ from both sides.

$X = \dfrac{1}{2}(4B - 3A)$ Multiply both sides by $\dfrac{1}{2}$.

$= \dfrac{1}{2}\left(4\begin{bmatrix} 1 & 3 \\ 5 & 2 \end{bmatrix} - 3\begin{bmatrix} 2 & 0 \\ 4 & 6 \end{bmatrix} \right)$ Substitute for A and B.

$= \dfrac{1}{2}\left(\begin{bmatrix} 4 & 12 \\ 20 & 8 \end{bmatrix} - \begin{bmatrix} 6 & 0 \\ 12 & 18 \end{bmatrix} \right)$ Scalar multiplication

$= \dfrac{1}{2}\begin{bmatrix} -2 & 12 \\ 8 & -10 \end{bmatrix}$ Subtract.

$= \begin{bmatrix} -1 & 6 \\ 4 & -5 \end{bmatrix}$ Scalar multiplication

You should check that the matrix $X = \begin{bmatrix} -1 & 6 \\ 4 & -5 \end{bmatrix}$ satisfies the given matrix equation.

■ ■ ■

PRACTICE PROBLEM 4   Solve the matrix equation $5A + 3X = 2B$ for X, where

$$A = \begin{bmatrix} 1 & -1 \\ 3 & 5 \end{bmatrix} \text{ and } B = \begin{bmatrix} 2 & 7 \\ -3 & -5 \end{bmatrix}.$$

■

3 Define matrix multiplication.

Matrix Multiplication

Early in this section, you saw that if A and B are two matrices, then $A + B$ is defined only if both matrices are of the same order. In the case of multiplication, however, there is a different kind of restriction on the orders of the matrices. The general rule is that if A is an $m \times p$ matrix and B is a $p \times n$ matrix, then the *product AB* is defined; otherwise it is not defined.

RULE FOR DEFINING THE PRODUCT *AB*

In order to define the product AB of two matrices A and B, the number of columns of A must be equal to the number of rows of B. If A is an $m \times p$ matrix and B is a $p \times n$ matrix, then the product AB is an $m \times n$ matrix.

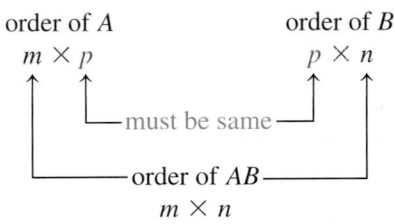

order of A order of B
$m \times p$ $p \times n$

must be same

order of AB
$m \times n$

The diagram in the margin may help in visualizing this restriction.

EXAMPLE 5   Determining the Order of the Product

For each pair of matrices A and B, state whether the product matrix AB is defined. If AB is defined, find the order of the product matrix AB.

a. $A = \begin{bmatrix} 1 & 3 & 5 \end{bmatrix}, B = \begin{bmatrix} 2 \\ 3 \\ 7 \end{bmatrix}$ **b.** $A = \begin{bmatrix} 2 & 3 \\ -1 & 4 \\ 5 & 6 \end{bmatrix}, B = \begin{bmatrix} 2 & 1 & 3 & 5 \\ 4 & -1 & -2 & 6 \end{bmatrix}$

c. $A = \begin{bmatrix} 1 \\ -1 \\ 2 \end{bmatrix}, B = \begin{bmatrix} 2 & 1 & 4 \\ 0 & 2 & 2 \end{bmatrix}$ **d.** $A = \begin{bmatrix} 1 & 0 \\ 0 & 2 \end{bmatrix}, B = \begin{bmatrix} 0 & 1 \\ 3 & 1 \end{bmatrix}$

Solution

a. Yes, the product AB is defined; A is a 1×3 matrix and B is a 3×1 matrix, so the number of columns of A equals the number of rows of B. The product AB is a 1×1 matrix, which has a single entry.

b. Yes, AB is defined; A is a 3×2 matrix and B is a 2×4 matrix, so the number of columns of A equals the number of rows of B. The product AB is a 3×4 matrix.

c. No, AB is not defined; A is a 3×1 matrix and B is a 2×3 matrix, so the number of columns of A does not equal the number of rows of B.

d. Yes, AB is defined; A is a 2×2 matrix and B is a 2×2 matrix, so the product AB is also a 2×2 matrix.   ■ ■ ■

PRACTICE PROBLEM 5   State whether the product matrix AB is defined. If AB is defined, find the order of the product matrix AB.

$$A = \begin{bmatrix} 1 & 4 & 7 \\ 0 & 2 & -2 \end{bmatrix}, B = \begin{bmatrix} 4 \\ 3 \\ -1 \end{bmatrix}$$ ■

Before you actually learn to multiply matrices A and B, consider the next example.

EXAMPLE 6 **Calculating the Total Revenue from Car Sales**

The Zero Down Dealer of Dallas sells new cars. Last month, the dealership sold 10 sports cars (S), 30 compacts (C), and 45 mini-compacts (M). The average price per car of type S, C, and M was 42, 24, and 17 (in thousands of dollars), respectively. Find the total revenue received by the dealership from the sale of these cars last month.

Solution

You can represent the number of cars of each type sold last month by a 1×3 matrix:

$$N = \begin{bmatrix} S & C & M \end{bmatrix} = \begin{bmatrix} 10 & 30 & 45 \end{bmatrix}.$$

Using the price of each type of car, you can construct a 3×1 price matrix:

$$P = \begin{bmatrix} 42 \\ 24 \\ 17 \end{bmatrix}.$$

Then the total revenue R (in thousands of dollars) received by the dealership from the sale of these cars last month is given by $R = 10(42) + 30(24) + 45(17) = 1905$ thousand dollars (or 1,905,000 dollars).

We define the right side of this equation to be the product NP of the two matrices N and P. In matrix notation,

$$NP = \begin{bmatrix} 10 & 30 & 45 \end{bmatrix} \begin{bmatrix} 42 \\ 24 \\ 17 \end{bmatrix} = 10(42) + 30(24) + 45(17) = 1905. \quad ■ ■ ■$$

PRACTICE PROBLEM 6 In Example 6, suppose the average price per car of types S, C, and M were 41, 26, and 19 (in thousands of dollars), respectively. Find the total revenue received by the dealership from the sale of these cars last month. ■

Example 6 leads to the following definition.

PRODUCT OF $1 \times n$ AND $n \times 1$ MATRICES

Suppose

$$A = \begin{bmatrix} a_1 & a_2 & a_3 \cdots a_n \end{bmatrix}$$

is a $1 \times n$ row matrix

and

$$B = \begin{bmatrix} b_1 \\ b_2 \\ \vdots \\ b_n \end{bmatrix}$$

is an $n \times 1$ column matrix. We define the product

$$AB = a_1 b_1 + a_2 b_2 + \cdots + a_n b_n.$$

We make the following observations about this definition.

1. Since A is a $1 \times n$ matrix and B is an $n \times 1$ matrix, the product AB is defined and is a 1×1 matrix.

2. In order to obtain the right side of the product AB, you start by multiplying the left-most entry of A and the top entry of B, then move to the right in A and down in B while multiplying corresponding (first, second, third, etc.) numbers together, and finally add all the resulting products.

EXAMPLE 7   Finding the Product AB

Find AB, where $A = \begin{bmatrix} 2 & 0 & 1 & -2 \end{bmatrix}$ and $B = \begin{bmatrix} 3 \\ 1 \\ -1 \\ 4 \end{bmatrix}$.

Solution

Since A has order 1×4 and B has order 4×1, the product AB is defined. You can apply the product rule to obtain

$$AB = 2(3) + 0(1) + 1(-1) + (-2)(4) = -3.$$

Thus, the product of the 1×4 matrix A and the 4×1 matrix B is the 1×1 matrix $\begin{bmatrix} -3 \end{bmatrix}$, or the number -3.   ■ ■ ■

PRACTICE PROBLEM 7   Find AB, where

$$A = \begin{bmatrix} 3 & -1 & 2 & 7 \end{bmatrix} \quad \text{and} \quad B = \begin{bmatrix} -2 \\ 0 \\ 1 \\ 5 \end{bmatrix}.$$ ■

In Example 7, you may think of the answer -3 as either the 1×1 matrix $\begin{bmatrix} -3 \end{bmatrix}$ or just the number -3. We shall have occasion to make use of both points of view.

The rule for multiplying any two matrices can be reduced to the special case of multiplying a $1 \times p$ matrix by a $p \times 1$ matrix repeatedly.

MATRIX MULTIPLICATION

Let $A = \begin{bmatrix} a_{ij} \end{bmatrix}$ be an $m \times p$ matrix and $B = \begin{bmatrix} b_{ij} \end{bmatrix}$ be a $p \times n$ matrix. Then the **product** AB is the $m \times n$ matrix $C = \begin{bmatrix} c_{ij} \end{bmatrix}$, where the entry c_{ij} of C is obtained by multiplying the ith row (matrix) of A by the jth column (matrix) of B.

The definition of the product AB says that

$$c_{ij} = a_{i1}b_{1j} + a_{i2}b_{2j} + \cdots + a_{ip}b_{pj}.$$

Written in full, the matrix product $AB = C$ in the definition is

$$\begin{bmatrix} a_{11} & a_{12} & \cdots & a_{1p} \\ a_{21} & a_{22} & \cdots & a_{2p} \\ \vdots & \vdots & & \vdots \\ a_{i1} & a_{i2} & \cdots & a_{ip} \\ \vdots & \vdots & & \vdots \\ a_{m1} & a_{m2} & \cdots & a_{mp} \end{bmatrix} \begin{bmatrix} b_{11} & b_{12} & \cdots & b_{1j} & \cdots & b_{1n} \\ b_{21} & b_{22} & \cdots & b_{2j} & \cdots & b_{2n} \\ \cdot & \cdot & & \cdot & & \cdot \\ \cdot & \cdot & \cdots & \cdot & \cdots & \cdot \\ \cdot & \cdot & & \cdot & & \cdot \\ b_{p1} & b_{p2} & \cdots & b_{pj} & \cdots & b_{pn} \end{bmatrix} = \begin{bmatrix} c_{11} & c_{12} & \cdots & c_{1j} & \cdots & c_{1n} \\ \vdots & \vdots & \cdots & \vdots & & \vdots \\ c_{i1} & c_{i2} & \cdots & c_{ij} & \cdots & c_{in} \\ \vdots & \vdots & \vdots & \vdots & & \vdots \\ c_{m1} & c_{m2} & \cdots & c_{mj} & \cdots & c_{mn} \end{bmatrix}$$

To produce the product of two matrices using a graphing calculator, name the matrices and then use the regular multiplication key with the names of the matrices.

Consider the matrices A and B in Example 8.

We find the product AB.

EXAMPLE 8   Finding the Product of Two Matrices

Find the products AB and BA, where

$$A = \begin{bmatrix} 1 & 2 \\ -1 & 3 \end{bmatrix} \quad \text{and} \quad B = \begin{bmatrix} 3 & -2 & 1 \\ 1 & 2 & 3 \end{bmatrix}.$$

Solution

Since A is of order 2×2 and the order of B is 2×3, the product AB is defined and has order 2×3.

Let $AB = C = [c_{ij}]$. By the definition of the product AB, each entry c_{ij} of C is obtained by multiplying the ith row of A by the jth column of B. For example c_{11} is obtained by multiplying the first row of A by the first column of B:

$$\begin{bmatrix} 1 & 2 \\ * & * \end{bmatrix} \begin{bmatrix} 3 & * & * \\ 1 & * & * \end{bmatrix} = \begin{bmatrix} 1(3) + 2(1) & * & * \\ * & * & * \end{bmatrix}.$$

Thus,

$$AB = \begin{bmatrix} 1 & 2 \\ -1 & 3 \end{bmatrix} \begin{bmatrix} 3 & -2 & 1 \\ 1 & 2 & 3 \end{bmatrix}$$

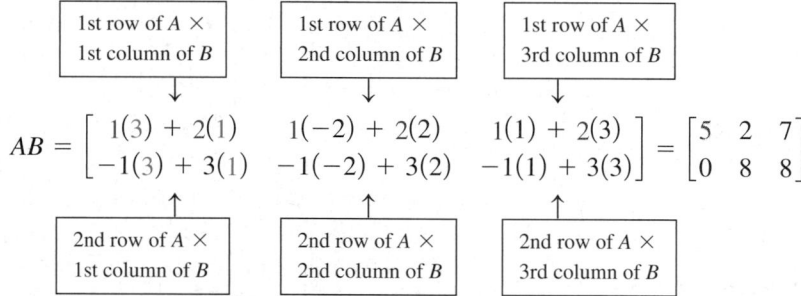

The product BA is not defined, because B is of order 2×3 and A is of order 2×2; that is, the number of columns of B is not the same as the number of rows of A.   ■ ■ ■

PRACTICE PROBLEM 8   Find the products AB and BA, where

$$A = \begin{bmatrix} 5 & 0 \\ 2 & -1 \end{bmatrix} \quad \text{and} \quad B = \begin{bmatrix} 8 & 1 \\ -2 & 6 \\ 0 & 4 \end{bmatrix}.$$

■

In Example 8, it is obvious that $AB \neq BA$, because BA is undefined. Even if both AB and BA are defined, AB may not equal BA, as the next example illustrates.

EXAMPLE 9   Finding the Product of Two Matrices

Find the products AB and BA, where

$$A = \begin{bmatrix} 2 & 3 \\ -1 & 0 \end{bmatrix} \quad \text{and} \quad B = \begin{bmatrix} 3 & 4 \\ 5 & 1 \end{bmatrix}.$$

Solution

$$AB = \begin{bmatrix} 2 & 3 \\ -1 & 0 \end{bmatrix}\begin{bmatrix} 3 & 4 \\ 5 & 1 \end{bmatrix} = \begin{bmatrix} 2(3) + 3(5) & 2(4) + 3(1) \\ -1(3) + 0(5) & -1(4) + 0(1) \end{bmatrix} = \begin{bmatrix} 21 & 11 \\ -3 & -4 \end{bmatrix}$$

$$BA = \begin{bmatrix} 3 & 4 \\ 5 & 1 \end{bmatrix}\begin{bmatrix} 2 & 3 \\ -1 & 0 \end{bmatrix} = \begin{bmatrix} 3(2) + 4(-1) & 3(3) + 4(0) \\ 5(2) + 1(-1) & 5(3) + 1(0) \end{bmatrix} = \begin{bmatrix} 2 & 9 \\ 9 & 15 \end{bmatrix} \quad ■ \ ■ \ ■$$

PRACTICE PROBLEM 9   Find the products AB and BA, where

$$A = \begin{bmatrix} 7 & 1 \\ 0 & 3 \end{bmatrix} \quad \text{and} \quad B = \begin{bmatrix} 2 & -1 \\ 4 & 4 \end{bmatrix}. \qquad ■$$

In Example 9, observe that $AB \neq BA$. Thus, in general, *matrix multiplication is not commutative*. Matrix multiplication, however, does share many of the properties of the multiplication of real numbers. Integral powers of square matrices are defined exactly as for real numbers. That is, $A^n = A \cdot A \cdot A \cdots A$ where n factors of A occur on the right.

PROPERTIES OF MATRIX MULTIPLICATION

Let A, B, and C be matrices and let c be a scalar. Assume that each product and sum is defined. Then

1. $(AB)C = A(BC)$ Associative property of multiplication
2. (i) $A(B + C) = AB + AC$ Distributive property
    (ii) $(A + B)C = AC + BC$ Distributive property
3. $c(AB) = (cA)B = A(cB)$ Associative property of scalar multiplication

---

In the exercises, you will be asked to verify these properties. You will also be asked to note the similarities and differences between the properties of real numbers and the analogous properties of matrices.

4 Apply matrix multiplication to computer graphics.

Computer Graphics

Among the simplest two-dimensional graphics symbols are letters used for labels on a computer screen. The next example illustrates how a letter (or a figure) is transformed when the coordinates of the points on the figure are all multiplied by the same matrix.

EXAMPLE 10   **Transforming a Letter**

The capital letter L in Figure 9.2 is determined by six points (or *vertices*) $P_1 - P_6$. The coordinates of the six points can be stored in a *data matrix D*, together with instructions stating that these vertices are connected by lines.

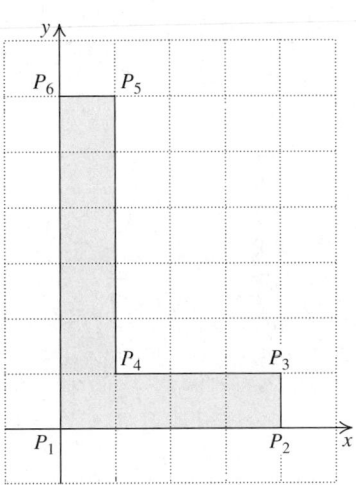

FIGURE 9.2

$$
\begin{array}{c}
\text{Vertex} \\
\downarrow \ \ \downarrow \ \ \downarrow \ \ \downarrow \ \ \downarrow \ \ \downarrow \\
\begin{array}{c} P_1 \ \ P_2 \ \ P_3 \ \ P_4 \ \ P_5 \ \ P_6 \end{array} \\
\begin{array}{l} x\text{-coordinate} \\ y\text{-coordinate} \end{array}
\begin{bmatrix} 0 & 4 & 4 & 1 & 1 & 0 \\ 0 & 0 & 1 & 1 & 6 & 6 \end{bmatrix} = D
\end{array}
$$

Continued on next page.

Given $A = \begin{bmatrix} 1 & 0.25 \\ 0 & 1 \end{bmatrix}$, compute AD. Graph the figure corresponding to the matrix AD by connecting the images of the vertices with the appropriate lines. This produces the complete transformed image of the original figure.

Solution

The columns of the product matrix AD represent the images of the vertices of the letter L.

$$AD = \begin{bmatrix} 1 & 0.25 \\ 0 & 1 \end{bmatrix} \begin{bmatrix} 0 & 4 & 4 & 1 & 1 & 0 \\ 0 & 0 & 1 & 1 & 6 & 6 \end{bmatrix}$$

$$= \begin{bmatrix} 1 \cdot 0 + 0.25 \cdot 0 & 1 \cdot 4 + 0.25 \cdot 0 & 1 \cdot 4 + 0.25 \cdot 1 & 1 \cdot 1 + 0.25 \cdot 1 & 1 \cdot 1 + 0.25 \cdot 6 & 1 \cdot 0 + 0.25 \cdot 6 \\ 0 \cdot 0 + 1 \cdot 0 & 0 \cdot 4 + 1 \cdot 0 & 0 \cdot 4 + 1 \cdot 1 & 0 \cdot 1 + 1 \cdot 1 & 0 \cdot 1 + 1 \cdot 6 & 0 \cdot 0 + 1 \cdot 6 \end{bmatrix}$$

$$\begin{array}{cccccc} P_1' & P_2' & P_3' & P_4' & P_5' & P_6' \end{array}$$

$$= \begin{bmatrix} 0 & 4 & 4.25 & 1.25 & 2.5 & 1.5 \\ 0 & 0 & 1 & 1 & 6 & 6 \end{bmatrix}$$

The transformed vertices are plotted in Figure 9.3, along with connecting line segments that correspond to those in the original figure. Figure 9.3 is the result of the transformation represented by the product matrix AD. ■ ■ ■

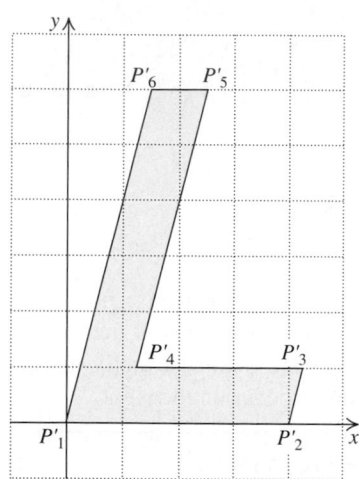

FIGURE 9.3

PRACTICE PROBLEM 10 In Example 10, use the matrix $A = \begin{bmatrix} 0 & 1 \\ 1 & 0.25 \end{bmatrix}$. Graph the figure corresponding to the matrix AD by connecting the images of the vertices with the appropriate lines. ■

A Exercises   Basic Skills and Concepts

In Exercises 1–8, find the values of all variables.

1. $\begin{bmatrix} 2 \\ -3 \end{bmatrix} = \begin{bmatrix} x \\ u \end{bmatrix}$ †

2. $\begin{bmatrix} -\dfrac{y}{2} \\ x \end{bmatrix} = \begin{bmatrix} 4 \\ 3 \end{bmatrix}$ †

3. $\begin{bmatrix} 2 & x \\ y & -3 \end{bmatrix} = \begin{bmatrix} 2 & -1 \\ 3 & -3 \end{bmatrix}$ $x = -1, y = 3$

4. $\begin{bmatrix} 2-x & 1 \\ -2 & 3+y \end{bmatrix} = \begin{bmatrix} 3 & 1 \\ -2 & -3 \end{bmatrix}$ $x = -1, y = -6$

5. $\begin{bmatrix} 2x-3y & -4 \\ 5 & 3x+y \end{bmatrix} = \begin{bmatrix} 1 & -4 \\ 5 & 7 \end{bmatrix}$ $x = 2, y = 1$

6. $\begin{bmatrix} 3x+y & -17 \\ 19 & 2 \end{bmatrix} = \begin{bmatrix} -\dfrac{1}{2} & -17 \\ 19 & 2x+3y \end{bmatrix}$ $x = \dfrac{-1}{2}, y = 1$

7. $\begin{bmatrix} x-y & 1 & 2 \\ 4 & 3x-2y & 3 \\ 5 & 6 & 5x-10y \end{bmatrix} = \begin{bmatrix} -1 & 1 & 2 \\ 4 & -1 & 3 \\ 5 & 6 & 6 \end{bmatrix}$ ∅

8. $\begin{bmatrix} x+y & 2 & 3 \\ 2 & x-y & 4 \\ 3 & 4 & 2x+3y \end{bmatrix} = \begin{bmatrix} -1 & 2 & 3 \\ 2 & 5 & 4 \\ 3 & 4 & -5 \end{bmatrix}$ †

In Exercises 9–16, find each of the following if possible:
a. $A + B$ **b.** $A - B$
c. $-3A$ **d.** $3A - 2B$
e. $(A + B)^2$ **f.** $A^2 - B^2$

9. $A = \begin{bmatrix} 1 & 2 \\ 3 & 4 \end{bmatrix}, B = \begin{bmatrix} -1 & 0 \\ 2 & -3 \end{bmatrix}$ †

10. $A = \begin{bmatrix} \dfrac{1}{3} & 1 \\ -1 & 2 \end{bmatrix}, B = \begin{bmatrix} 1 & 0 \\ 2 & -\dfrac{1}{2} \end{bmatrix}$ †

11. $A = \begin{bmatrix} 2 & 3 \\ -4 & 5 \end{bmatrix}, B = \begin{bmatrix} 1 & 0 & 2 \\ 3 & 1 & 4 \end{bmatrix}$ †

12. $A = \begin{bmatrix} 1 & 2 & 3 \\ -1 & -3 & 4 \end{bmatrix}, B = \begin{bmatrix} 1 & 0 \\ 2 & 3 \\ 1 & 4 \end{bmatrix}$ †

13. $A = \begin{bmatrix} 4 & 0 & -1 \\ -2 & 5 & 2 \\ 0 & 0 & 1 \end{bmatrix}, B = \begin{bmatrix} 3 & 1 & 0 \\ 1 & -4 & 2 \\ 2 & 1 & 3 \end{bmatrix}$ †

14. $A = \begin{bmatrix} 1 & 0 & 2 \\ 2 & 1 & 0 \\ 0 & 1 & 3 \end{bmatrix}, B = \begin{bmatrix} 3 & -1 & 2 \\ 0 & 2 & 1 \\ 1 & 4 & -1 \end{bmatrix}$ †

†Due to space constrictions, answers to these exercises may be found in the Answers beginning on page A–1 in the back of the book.

15. $A = \begin{bmatrix} 1 & 2 & -3 \\ 3 & 4 & 5 \\ 2 & -1 & 0 \end{bmatrix}, B = \begin{bmatrix} 3 & 1 & 0 \\ 1 & -4 & 2 \\ 2 & 1 & 3 \end{bmatrix}$ †

16. $A = \begin{bmatrix} 1 & 0 & 2 \\ 2 & 1 & 0 \\ 0 & 1 & 3 \end{bmatrix}, B = \begin{bmatrix} 3 & -1 & 2 \\ 0 & 2 & 1 \\ 1 & 4 & -1 \end{bmatrix}$ †

In Exercises 17–24, solve each matrix equation for X, where

$$A = \begin{bmatrix} 2 & 3 & -1 \\ 1 & -2 & 4 \end{bmatrix} \quad \text{and} \quad B = \begin{bmatrix} -2 & 1 & 0 \\ 2 & 3 & 4 \end{bmatrix}.$$

17. $A + X = B$ †
18. $B + X = A$ †
19. $2X - A = B$ †
20. $2X - B = A$ †
21. $2X + 3A = B$ †
22. $3X + 2A = B$ †
23. $2A + 3B + 4X = 0$ †
24. $3X - 2A + 5B = 0$ †

In Exercises 25–34, find each product if possible.
a. AB **b.** BA

25. $A = \begin{bmatrix} 1 & 2 \\ 3 & 4 \end{bmatrix}, B = \begin{bmatrix} -2 & 1 \\ 3 & 5 \end{bmatrix}$ †

26. $A = \begin{bmatrix} 3 & 2 \\ 1 & 5 \\ 0 & 1 \end{bmatrix}, B = \begin{bmatrix} 1 & 3 & -2 \\ 2 & 5 & 0 \end{bmatrix}$ †

27. $A = \begin{bmatrix} 2 & -1 & 0 \\ -3 & 1 & 2 \end{bmatrix}, B = \begin{bmatrix} 1 & 5 \\ -2 & 3 \\ 4 & 0 \end{bmatrix}$ †

28. $A = \begin{bmatrix} 1 & 2 & 3 \\ 4 & 5 & 6 \end{bmatrix}, B = \begin{bmatrix} -1 & -3 & -6 \\ 2 & 5 & 7 \end{bmatrix}$ †

29. $A = \begin{bmatrix} 2 & 3 & 5 \end{bmatrix}, B = \begin{bmatrix} 1 \\ -2 \\ 4 \end{bmatrix}$ †

30. $A = \begin{bmatrix} 1 \\ 2 \\ -1 \end{bmatrix}, B = \begin{bmatrix} -3 & 0 & 2 \end{bmatrix}$ †

31. $A = \begin{bmatrix} 1 & 2 & 3 \end{bmatrix}, B = \begin{bmatrix} 1 & 2 & -1 \\ 0 & 3 & 1 \\ 2 & 0 & -3 \end{bmatrix}$ †

32. $A = \begin{bmatrix} 4 & -6 & 2 \\ 2 & 3 & 0 \\ 1 & 2 & -3 \end{bmatrix}, B = \begin{bmatrix} -2 & 0 & 1 \end{bmatrix}$ †

33. $A = \begin{bmatrix} 2 & 0 & 1 \\ 1 & 4 & 2 \\ 3 & -1 & 0 \end{bmatrix}, B = \begin{bmatrix} 3 & 1 & 0 \\ -1 & 2 & 0 \\ 4 & 5 & 2 \end{bmatrix}$ †

34. $A = \begin{bmatrix} 3 & -1 & 2 \\ 0 & 4 & -3 \\ 1 & -2 & 2 \end{bmatrix}, B = \begin{bmatrix} 2 & -5 & 0 \\ -1 & 2 & -1 \\ 3 & 0 & 2 \end{bmatrix}$ †

35. Let $A = \begin{bmatrix} 3 & 1 & 2 \\ 0 & 4 & 3 \\ 1 & -2 & 2 \end{bmatrix}$ and $B = \begin{bmatrix} 2 & 5 & 0 \\ 1 & 2 & -1 \\ 3 & 0 & 2 \end{bmatrix}$.

Verify that $AB \neq BA$. †

36. Let $A = \begin{bmatrix} 5 & 2 & 4 \\ -6 & -3 & 10 \\ -2 & 6 & 5 \end{bmatrix}$ and $B = \begin{bmatrix} 4 & 1 & 2 \\ -3 & 0 & 5 \\ -1 & 3 & 4 \end{bmatrix}$.

Verify that $AB = BA$. †

In Exercises 37–40, let

$$A = \begin{bmatrix} 1 & 2 \\ 3 & 4 \end{bmatrix}, B = \begin{bmatrix} 2 & -3 \\ 3 & 5 \end{bmatrix}, \quad \text{and} \quad C = \begin{bmatrix} 0 & 1 \\ 2 & 4 \end{bmatrix}.$$

37. Verify the associative property for multiplication: $(AB)C = A(BC)$.

38. Verify the distributive property $A(B + C) = AB + AC$.

39. Verify the distributive property $(A + B)C = AC + BC$.

40. For any real number c, verify that $c(AB) = (cA)(B) = A(cB)$.

41. **Cost matrix.** The Build-Rite Co. is building an apartment complex. The cost of purchasing and transporting specific amounts of steel, glass, and wood (in appropriate units) from two different locations is given by the following matrices:

$$\begin{array}{ccc} \text{Steel} & \text{Glass} & \text{Wood} \end{array}$$
$$A = \begin{bmatrix} 7 & 3 & 18 \\ 4 & 1 & 3 \end{bmatrix} \begin{array}{l} \text{Cost of Material} \\ \text{Transportation Cost} \end{array}$$

$$B = \begin{bmatrix} 6 & 2 & 20 \\ 3 & 1 & 4 \end{bmatrix} \begin{array}{l} \text{Cost of Material} \\ \text{Transportation Cost} \end{array}$$

Find the matrix representing the total cost of material and transportation for steel, glass, and wood from both locations. †

42. Repeat Exercise 41 if the order from location A is tripled and the order from location B is doubled. †

43. **Stock purchase.** Ms. Goodbyer plans to buy 100 shares of computer stock, 300 shares of oil stock, and 400 shares of automobile stock. The computer stock is selling for 60 dollars a share, oil stock is selling for 38 dollars a share, and automobile stock is selling for 17 dollars a share. Use matrix multiplication to calculate the total cost of Ms. Goodbyer's purchases. $24,200

44. Product export. The International Export Corporation received an export order for three of its products, say, A, B, and C. The export order is (in thousands) for 50 of product A, 75 of product B, and 150 of product C. The material cost, labor, and profit (each in appropriate units) required to produce each unit of the product are given in the following table:

$$\begin{array}{c} \\ \text{Product A} \\ \text{Product B} \\ \text{Product C} \end{array} \begin{array}{ccc} \text{Material} & \text{Labor} & \text{Profit} \\ \left[\begin{array}{ccc} 20 & 2 & 20 \\ 15 & 3 & 25 \\ 25 & 1 & 15 \end{array}\right] \end{array}$$

Use matrix multiplication to compute the total material cost, total labor, and total profit if the entire export order is filled. †

45. Executive compensation. The Multinational Oil Corporation pays its top executives a salary, a cash bonus, and shares of its stock annually. In 2005, the chairman of the board received 2.5 million dollars in salary, a 1.5 million dollar bonus, and 50,000 shares of stock; the president of the company received one-half of the compensation of the chairman; and each of the four vice presidents was paid 100,000 dollars in salary, a 150,000 dollars bonus, and 5000 shares of stock.

a. Express payments to these executives in salary, bonus, and stock as a 3 × 3 matrix. †

b. Express the number of executives of each rank as a column matrix. †

c. Use matrix multiplication to compute the total amount the company paid to each executive in each category in 2005. †

46. Calories and protein. The Browns (B) and Newgards (N) are neighboring families. The Brown family has two men, three women, and one child, while the Newgard family has one man, one woman, and two children. Both families are weight watchers. They have the same dietician, who recommends the following daily allowance of calories and proteins:

Calories
　male adults: 2400 calories
　female adults: 1900 calories
　children : 1800 calories
Protein (in grams)
　male adults: 55
　female adults: 45
　children: 33

Represent the preceding information in matrix form. Use matrix multiplication to compute the total requirements of calories and proteins for each of the two families. †

In Exercise 47–50, a matrix A is given. Graph the figure represented by the matrix AD, where D is the matrix representation of the letter L of Example 10.

47. $A = \begin{bmatrix} 1 & 0 \\ 0 & -1 \end{bmatrix}$ †

48. $A = \begin{bmatrix} -1 & 0 \\ 0 & 1 \end{bmatrix}$ †

49. $A = \begin{bmatrix} 1 & 0 \\ 0.25 & 1 \end{bmatrix}$ †

50. $A = \begin{bmatrix} 1 & -0.25 \\ 0 & 1 \end{bmatrix}$ †

C Exercises ┃ Beyond the Basics

51. Let $A = \begin{bmatrix} 0 & 3 \\ 0 & 0 \end{bmatrix}$, $B = \begin{bmatrix} 2 & 1 \\ 3 & 0 \end{bmatrix}$ and $C = \begin{bmatrix} 5 & 4 \\ 3 & 0 \end{bmatrix}$.

Verify that $AB = AC$. This example shows that $AB = AC$ does not, in general, imply that $B = C$. †

52. Let $A = \begin{bmatrix} 2 & -3 & -5 \\ -1 & 4 & 5 \\ 1 & -3 & -4 \end{bmatrix}$ and $B = \begin{bmatrix} -1 & 3 & 5 \\ 1 & -3 & -5 \\ -1 & 3 & 5 \end{bmatrix}$.

Verify that $AB = \mathbf{0}$. This example shows that $AB = \mathbf{0}$ does not imply that $A = \mathbf{0}$ or $B = \mathbf{0}$. Answers will vary.

53. Select appropriate 2 × 2 matrices A and B to show that, in general, $(A + B)^2 \neq A^2 + 2AB + B^2$. †

54. Repeat Exercise 53 to show that in general $A^2 - B^2 \neq (A - B)(A + B)$. †

 55. Let $A = \begin{bmatrix} 1 & -2 & 3 \\ 2 & -4 & 1 \\ 3 & -5 & 2 \end{bmatrix}$. Show that

$3A^2 - 2A + I = \begin{bmatrix} 17 & -23 & 15 \\ -13 & 30 & 10 \\ -9 & 22 & 21 \end{bmatrix}$, where $I = \begin{bmatrix} 1 & 0 & 0 \\ 0 & 1 & 0 \\ 0 & 0 & 1 \end{bmatrix}$.

56. Let $A = \begin{bmatrix} 1 & 3 & 2 \\ 2 & 0 & 3 \\ 1 & -1 & 1 \end{bmatrix}$. Show that

$$A^3 - 3A^2 + A - I = \begin{bmatrix} -3 & 14 & -3 \\ 5 & -2 & 8 \\ 5 & -7 & 6 \end{bmatrix},$$

where I is given in Exercise 55.

57. If possible, find a matrix B such that $\begin{bmatrix} 2 & 3 \\ 1 & 2 \end{bmatrix} B = \begin{bmatrix} 1 & 0 \\ 0 & 1 \end{bmatrix}$. †

58. If possible find a matrix B such that

$$\begin{bmatrix} 1 & -2 \\ -2 & 4 \end{bmatrix} B = \begin{bmatrix} 1 & 0 \\ 0 & 1 \end{bmatrix}. \quad \text{Not possible}$$

59. Find x and y if

$$\left(4 \begin{bmatrix} 2 & -1 & 3 \\ 1 & 0 & 2 \end{bmatrix} - \begin{bmatrix} 1 & 2 & -1 \\ 2 & -3 & 4 \end{bmatrix} \right) \begin{bmatrix} 2 \\ -1 \\ 1 \end{bmatrix} = \begin{bmatrix} x \\ y \end{bmatrix}. \quad †$$

60. Find x, y, and z if

$$\begin{bmatrix} 3 & 2 & -1 \\ 4 & 9 & 2 \\ 5 & 0 & -2 \end{bmatrix} \begin{bmatrix} x \\ y \\ z \end{bmatrix} = \begin{bmatrix} 0 \\ 7 \\ 2 \end{bmatrix}. \quad x = 2, y = -1, z = 4$$

Critical Thinking

61. Let A be a $3 \times n$ matrix and B be a $5 \times m$ matrix.
 a. Under what conditions is AB defined? What is the order of AB when this product is defined? †
 b. Repeat part (a) for BA. †

62. Let $A = \begin{bmatrix} 3 & -1 & 0 \\ -2 & 3 & 1 \end{bmatrix}$, $B = \begin{bmatrix} 2 \\ 3 \\ 4 \end{bmatrix}$, and $C = \begin{bmatrix} -1 & 2 \end{bmatrix}$. In which order should all three matrices be multiplied to produce a number? $(CA)B$

Group Project

Market share. The Asma Corporation (A), Bronkial Brothers (B), and Coufmore Company (C) simultaneously decide to introduce a new cigarette at a time when each company has one-third of the market. During the year, the following occurs:

(i) A retains 40% of its customers and loses 30% to B and 30% to C.

(ii) B retains 30% of its customers and loses 60% to A and 10% to C.

(iii) C retains 30% of its customers and loses 60% to A and 10% to B.

The foregoing information can be represented by the *transition matrix*

$$P = \begin{array}{c} \\ A \\ B \\ C \end{array} \begin{array}{ccc} A & B & C \\ \begin{bmatrix} 0.4 & 0.3 & 0.3 \\ 0.6 & 0.3 & 0.1 \\ 0.6 & 0.1 & 0.3 \end{bmatrix} \end{array}.$$

Write the initial market share as $X = \begin{bmatrix} \dfrac{1}{3} & \dfrac{1}{3} & \dfrac{1}{3} \end{bmatrix}$.

a. Compute XP^2 and interpret your result.

b. Compute XP^3, XP^4, XP^5; observe the pattern for the long run. Describe the long-term market share for each company.

The Matrix Inverse

BEFORE STARTING THIS SECTION, REVIEW

1. Matrix multiplication (Section 9.2, page 837)

2. Equality of matrices (Section 9.2, page 831)

3. Gauss–Jordan elimination procedure (Section 9.1, page 821)

4. Leontieff input–output model (Section 9.1, page 823)

OBJECTIVES

1 Verify the multiplicative inverse of a matrix.

2 Find the inverse of a matrix.

3 Find the inverse of a 2×2 matrix.

4 Use matrix inverses to solve systems of linear equations.

5 Use matrix inverses in applied problems.

Coding and Decoding Messages

Imagine that you are a secret agent who is looking for spies in different parts of the world. Periodically, you communicate with your headquarters via your laptop or by satellite. You expect that your communications will be intercepted. So, before you broadcast any message, you must devise a scheme to hide the message. Matrix multiplication can be used to encode and decode your messages.

First, you might replace each letter in the message by some symbol—say, a number—and send the message as a sequence of numbers. The problem with this approach is that it is rather easy to crack such a code. For example, if letters, such as *e*, are always represented by the same symbol, then a code breaker (hacker) can make good guesses about the symbols that represent each letter and eventually translate your entire message. There is a better way to hide your message. A message written with a secret code is called a *cryptogram*. In Example 9, we will show you how to encode and decode a message. ■

1 Verify the multiplicative inverse of a matrix.

The Multiplicative Inverse of a Matrix

In arithmetic, you know that if a is a nonzero real number, then a has a unique reciprocal, denoted by $\dfrac{1}{a}$, or a^{-1}. The number a^{-1} is called the **multiplicative inverse** of a, and

$$aa^{-1} = a^{-1}a = 1.$$

Arthur Cayley

(1821–1895)

English mathematicians of the first third of the 19th century attempted to extend the basic ideas of algebra and to determine exactly how much one can generalize the properties of integers to other types of quantities. Although Sylvester (see page 595) coined the term *matrix*, it was Cayley who developed the algebra of matrices. Cayley studied mathematics at Trinity College, Cambridge, but, because there was no suitable teaching job available, decided to become a lawyer. Although he became skilled in legal work, he regarded the law as just a way to support himself. During his legal career, he was able to write more than 300 mathematical papers. In 1863, Cambridge University established a new post in mathematics and offered it to Cayley. He accepted the job eagerly, even though it paid less money than he made as a lawyer.

Similarly, certain square matrices have *multiplicative inverses,* with an identity matrix acting as "1." We define the multiplicative **inverse of a matrix** as follows:

THE INVERSE OF A MATRIX

Let A be an $n \times n$ matrix and let I_n be the $n \times n$ identity matrix that has 1s on the main diagonal and 0s elsewhere. If there is an $n \times n$ matrix B such that

$$AB = I_n \quad \text{and} \quad BA = I_n,$$

then B is called the **inverse** of A and we write $B = A^{-1}$ (read "A inverse").

Notice that if B is the inverse of A, then A is the inverse of B. We write I instead of I_n when n is known from the context.

EXAMPLE 1   Verify the Inverse of a Matrix

Show that B is the inverse of A, where

$$A = \begin{bmatrix} 1 & 3 \\ 2 & 7 \end{bmatrix} \text{ and } B = \begin{bmatrix} 7 & -3 \\ -2 & 1 \end{bmatrix}.$$

Solution

You need to verify that $AB = I$ and $BA = I$.

$$AB = \begin{bmatrix} 1 & 3 \\ 2 & 7 \end{bmatrix}\begin{bmatrix} 7 & -3 \\ -2 & 1 \end{bmatrix} = \begin{bmatrix} 1(7) + 3(-2) & 1(-3) + 3(1) \\ 2(7) + 7(-2) & 2(-3) + 7(1) \end{bmatrix} = \begin{bmatrix} 1 & 0 \\ 0 & 1 \end{bmatrix} = I$$

$$BA = \begin{bmatrix} 7 & -3 \\ -2 & 1 \end{bmatrix}\begin{bmatrix} 1 & 3 \\ 2 & 7 \end{bmatrix} = \begin{bmatrix} 7(1) + (-3)(2) & 7(3) + (-3)(7) \\ (-2)(1) + 1(2) & (-2)(3) + 1(7) \end{bmatrix} = \begin{bmatrix} 1 & 0 \\ 0 & 1 \end{bmatrix} = I$$

Since $AB = I$ and $BA = I$, it follows that $B = A^{-1}$. ■ ■ ■

PRACTICE PROBLEM 1   Show that B is the inverse of A, where

$$A = \begin{bmatrix} 3 & 2 \\ 2 & 1 \end{bmatrix} \quad \text{and} \quad B = \begin{bmatrix} -1 & 2 \\ 2 & -3 \end{bmatrix}.$$ ■

Recall that, in general (even for square matrices), $AB \neq BA$. However, if A and B are square matrices with $AB = I$, then it can be shown that $BA = I$. Therefore, to determine whether A and B are inverses, you need only check that either $AB = I$ or $BA = I$.

In working with real numbers, you know that if $a = 0$, then a^{-1} does not exist. So it should not come as a surprise that if A is a square *zero* matrix, then A^{-1} does not exist. Surprisingly, there are also nonzero matrices that do not have inverses.

EXAMPLE 2   Proving that a Particular Nonzero Matrix Has No Inverse

Show that the matrix

$$A = \begin{bmatrix} 2 & 0 \\ 0 & 0 \end{bmatrix}$$

does not have an inverse.

Continued on next page.

Solution

Suppose A has an inverse

$$B = \begin{bmatrix} x & y \\ z & w \end{bmatrix}.$$

Then you have

$$\begin{bmatrix} 2 & 0 \\ 0 & 0 \end{bmatrix} \begin{bmatrix} x & y \\ z & w \end{bmatrix} = \begin{bmatrix} 1 & 0 \\ 0 & 1 \end{bmatrix} \qquad AB = I$$

Multiply the two matrices on the left side to obtain

$$\begin{bmatrix} 2x & 2y \\ 0 & 0 \end{bmatrix} = \begin{bmatrix} 1 & 0 \\ 0 & 1 \end{bmatrix}$$

Since these two matrices are equal, you must have

$$0 = 1. \qquad \text{Equate the entries in the } (2, 2) \text{ position.}$$

Because $0 = 1$ is a false statement, the matrix A does not have an inverse. ■ ■ ■

PRACTICE PROBLEM 2 Show that the matrix $A = \begin{bmatrix} 3 & 1 \\ 3 & 1 \end{bmatrix}$ does not have an inverse. ■

2 Find the inverse of a matrix.

Finding the Inverse of a Matrix

It can be shown that if a square matrix A has an inverse, then the inverse is unique. This means that a square matrix cannot have more than one inverse. If a matrix A has an inverse, then A is called **invertible** or **nonsingular.** A square matrix that does not have an inverse is called a **singular** matrix. The next example illustrates a technique for finding the inverse of an invertible matrix.

EXAMPLE 3 Finding the Inverse of a Matrix

Find the inverse of the matrix $A = \begin{bmatrix} 1 & 2 \\ 3 & 5 \end{bmatrix}$.

Solution

Let $B = \begin{bmatrix} x & y \\ z & w \end{bmatrix}$ be the inverse of the matrix A. Then

$$AB = I \qquad \text{Definition of inverse.}$$

$$\begin{bmatrix} 1 & 2 \\ 3 & 5 \end{bmatrix} \begin{bmatrix} x & y \\ z & w \end{bmatrix} = \begin{bmatrix} 1 & 0 \\ 0 & 1 \end{bmatrix} \qquad \text{Substitute for } A, B, \text{ and } I.$$

$$\begin{bmatrix} x + 2z & y + 2w \\ 3x + 5z & 3y + 5w \end{bmatrix} = \begin{bmatrix} 1 & 0 \\ 0 & 1 \end{bmatrix}. \qquad \text{Multiply matrices } A \text{ and } B.$$

Equating corresponding entries in the last matrix equation yields two systems of linear equations.

$$\begin{cases} x + 2z = 1 \\ 3x + 5z = 0 \end{cases} \qquad \text{Equate the entries in the } (1, 1) \\ \text{and } (2, 1) \text{ positions.}$$

$$\begin{cases} y + 2w = 0 \\ 3y + 5w = 1 \end{cases} \qquad \text{Equate the entries in the } (1, 2) \\ \text{and } (2, 2) \text{ positions.}$$

Let's solve the two systems by Gauss–Jordan elimination.

System of equations	Matrix form
$\begin{cases} x + 2z = 1 \\ 3x + 5z = 0 \end{cases}$	$\begin{bmatrix} 1 & 2 & 1 \\ 3 & 5 & 0 \end{bmatrix}$
$\begin{cases} y + 2w = 0 \\ 3y + 5w = 1 \end{cases}$	$\begin{bmatrix} 1 & 2 & 0 \\ 3 & 5 & 1 \end{bmatrix}$

Notice that the coefficient matrix for both systems of equations is the original matrix:

$$A = \begin{bmatrix} 1 & 2 \\ 3 & 5 \end{bmatrix}.$$

Thus, the calculations involved in the Gauss–Jordan elimination on the coefficient matrix A will be the same for both systems. Therefore, you can solve both systems at once by considering the "doubly augmented" matrix

$$C = \begin{bmatrix} 1 & 2 & 1 & 0 \\ 3 & 5 & 0 & 1 \end{bmatrix}.$$

Note that the matrix C is formed by adjoining the identity matrix I to matrix A. Thus,

$$C = [A \mid I].$$

Now apply Gauss–Jordan elimination to the matrix C.

$$C = \begin{bmatrix} 1 & 2 & 1 & 0 \\ 3 & 5 & 0 & 1 \end{bmatrix} \xrightarrow{-3R_1 + R_2 \to R_2} \begin{bmatrix} 1 & 2 & 1 & 0 \\ 0 & -1 & -3 & 1 \end{bmatrix} \xrightarrow{(-1)R_2} \begin{bmatrix} 1 & 2 & 1 & 0 \\ 0 & 1 & 3 & -1 \end{bmatrix}$$

$$\xrightarrow{-2R_2 + R_1 \to R_1} \begin{bmatrix} 1 & 0 & -5 & 2 \\ 0 & 1 & 3 & -1 \end{bmatrix}$$

Converting the last matrix back into two systems of equations, we have

$$\begin{bmatrix} 1 & 0 & -5 \\ 0 & 1 & 3 \end{bmatrix} \text{ represents } \begin{cases} 1 \cdot x + 0 \cdot z = -5 \\ 0 \cdot x + 1 \cdot z = 3 \end{cases} \text{ or } \begin{cases} x = -5 \\ z = 3 \end{cases}$$

Similarly,

$$\begin{bmatrix} 1 & 0 & 2 \\ 0 & 1 & -1 \end{bmatrix} \text{ represents } \begin{cases} 1 \cdot y + 0 \cdot w = 2 \\ 0 \cdot y + 1 \cdot w = -1 \end{cases} \text{ or } \begin{cases} y = 2 \\ w = -1 \end{cases}$$

We conclude that $x = -5$, $y = 2$, $z = 3$, and $w = -1$.

Since $B = \begin{bmatrix} x & y \\ z & w \end{bmatrix}$, it follows that

$$B = \begin{bmatrix} -5 & 2 \\ 3 & -1 \end{bmatrix} = A^{-1}.$$

You should check that $B = A^{-1}$ by multiplication:

$$AA^{-1} = \begin{bmatrix} 1 & 2 \\ 3 & 5 \end{bmatrix} \begin{bmatrix} -5 & 2 \\ 3 & -1 \end{bmatrix} = \begin{bmatrix} 1(-5) + 2(3) & 1(2) + 2(-1) \\ 3(-5) + 5(3) & 3(2) + 5(-1) \end{bmatrix} = \begin{bmatrix} 1 & 0 \\ 0 & 1 \end{bmatrix} = I.$$

■ ■ ■

PRACTICE PROBLEM 3   Find the inverse of the matrix $A = \begin{bmatrix} 1 & -2 \\ 2 & 1 \end{bmatrix}$.   ■

The procedure employed in Example 3 can be used to find the inverse of any square matrix A (if the inverse of A exists).

PROCEDURE FOR FINDING THE INVERSE OF A MATRIX

Let A be an $n \times n$ matrix.

1. Form the $n \times 2n$ augmented matrix $[A \mid I]$, where I is the $n \times n$ identity matrix.
2. If there is a sequence of row operations that transforms A into I, then this same sequence of row operations will transform $[A \mid I]$ into $[I \mid B]$, where $B = A^{-1}$.
3. Check your work by showing that $AA^{-1} = I$.

If it is not possible to transform A into I by row operations, then A does not have an inverse. (This occurs if, at any step in the process, you obtain a matrix $[C \mid D]$ in which C has a row of zeros.)

EXAMPLE 4   Finding the Inverse of a Matrix

Find the inverse (if it exists) of the matrix $A = \begin{bmatrix} 1 & 2 & 3 \\ 2 & 5 & 7 \\ 2 & 4 & 6 \end{bmatrix}$.

Solution

Step 1   Start by adjoining the identity matrix $I = \begin{bmatrix} 1 & 0 & 0 \\ 0 & 1 & 0 \\ 0 & 0 & 1 \end{bmatrix}$ to the matrix A to form

the augmented matrix $[A \mid I]$.

$$[A \mid I] = \begin{bmatrix} 1 & 2 & 3 & | & 1 & 0 & 0 \\ 2 & 5 & 7 & | & 0 & 1 & 0 \\ 2 & 4 & 6 & | & 0 & 0 & 1 \end{bmatrix}.$$

Step 2   Perform row operations on $[A \mid I]$ to transform it to a matrix of the form $[I \mid B]$.

$$\begin{bmatrix} 1 & 2 & 3 & | & 1 & 0 & 0 \\ 2 & 5 & 7 & | & 0 & 1 & 0 \\ 2 & 4 & 6 & | & 0 & 0 & 1 \end{bmatrix} \xrightarrow[\substack{-2R_1 + R_3 \to R_3}]{-2R_1 + R_2 \to R_2} \begin{bmatrix} 1 & 2 & 3 & | & 1 & 0 & 0 \\ 0 & 1 & 1 & | & -2 & 1 & 0 \\ 0 & 0 & 0 & | & -2 & 0 & 1 \end{bmatrix} = [C \mid D].$$

Since the third row of matrix C consists of zeros, it is impossible to transform A into I by row operations. Hence, A is *not* invertible.   ■ ■ ■

PRACTICE PROBLEM 4   Find the inverse (if it exists) of the matrix $A = \begin{bmatrix} 1 & 4 & -2 \\ -1 & 1 & 2 \\ 3 & 7 & -6 \end{bmatrix}$.   ■

EXAMPLE 5   **Finding the Inverse of a Matrix**

Find the inverse (if it exists) of the matrix $A = \begin{bmatrix} 1 & 1 & 0 \\ 0 & 3 & 1 \\ 2 & 3 & 3 \end{bmatrix}$.

Solution

Step 1   Start with the matrix

$$[A \mid I] = \begin{bmatrix} 1 & 1 & 0 & | & 1 & 0 & 0 \\ 0 & 3 & 1 & | & 0 & 1 & 0 \\ 2 & 3 & 3 & | & 0 & 0 & 1 \end{bmatrix}. \quad I = I_3$$

Step 2   Use row operations on $[A \mid I]$. Then $[A \mid I] \rightarrow$

$$\xrightarrow[\substack{\frac{1}{3}R_2 \to R_2 \\ -2R_1 + R_3 \to R_3}]{} \begin{bmatrix} 1 & 1 & 0 & | & 1 & 0 & 0 \\ 0 & 1 & \frac{1}{3} & | & 0 & \frac{1}{3} & 0 \\ 0 & 1 & 3 & | & -2 & 0 & 1 \end{bmatrix} \xrightarrow[(-1)R_2 + R_3 \to R_3]{} \begin{bmatrix} 1 & 1 & 0 & | & 1 & 0 & 0 \\ 0 & 1 & \frac{1}{3} & | & 0 & \frac{1}{3} & 0 \\ 0 & 0 & \frac{8}{3} & | & -2 & -\frac{1}{3} & 1 \end{bmatrix}$$

$$\xrightarrow[\frac{3}{8}R_3]{} \begin{bmatrix} 1 & 1 & 0 & | & 1 & 0 & 0 \\ 0 & 1 & \frac{1}{3} & | & 0 & \frac{1}{3} & 0 \\ 0 & 0 & 1 & | & -\frac{6}{8} & -\frac{1}{8} & \frac{3}{8} \end{bmatrix} \xrightarrow[-\frac{1}{3}R_3 + R_2 \to R_2]{} \begin{bmatrix} 1 & 1 & 0 & | & 1 & 0 & 0 \\ 0 & 1 & 0 & | & \frac{2}{8} & \frac{3}{8} & -\frac{1}{8} \\ 0 & 0 & 1 & | & -\frac{6}{8} & -\frac{1}{8} & \frac{3}{8} \end{bmatrix}$$

$$\xrightarrow[(-1)R_2 + R_1 \to R_1]{} \begin{bmatrix} 1 & 0 & 0 & | & \frac{6}{8} & -\frac{3}{8} & \frac{1}{8} \\ 0 & 1 & 0 & | & \frac{2}{8} & \frac{3}{8} & -\frac{1}{8} \\ 0 & 0 & 1 & | & -\frac{6}{8} & -\frac{1}{8} & \frac{3}{8} \end{bmatrix}.$$

Hence, A is invertible and

$$A^{-1} = \begin{bmatrix} \frac{6}{8} & -\frac{3}{8} & \frac{1}{8} \\ \frac{2}{8} & \frac{3}{8} & -\frac{1}{8} \\ -\frac{6}{8} & -\frac{1}{8} & \frac{3}{8} \end{bmatrix} = \frac{1}{8} \begin{bmatrix} 6 & -3 & 1 \\ 2 & 3 & -1 \\ -6 & -1 & 3 \end{bmatrix}.$$

Step 3   You should verify that $AA^{-1} = I$.   ■ ■ ■

PRACTICE PROBLEM 5   Find the inverse (if it exists) of the matrix $A = \begin{bmatrix} 1 & 2 & 3 \\ -2 & 3 & 1 \\ 4 & 5 & -2 \end{bmatrix}$.   ■

3 Find the inverse of a 2 × 2 matrix.

A Rule for Finding the Inverse of a 2 × 2 Matrix

You can quickly determine whether any 2 × 2 matrix is invertible. If a matrix has an inverse, then you can use the rule given next to find its inverse.

A RULE FOR FINDING THE INVERSE OF A 2 × 2 MATRIX

The matrix

$$A = \begin{bmatrix} a & b \\ c & d \end{bmatrix}$$

is invertible if and only if $ad - bc \neq 0$. Moreover, if $ad - bc \neq 0$, then the inverse is given by

$$A^{-1} = \frac{1}{ad - bc}\begin{bmatrix} d & -b \\ -c & a \end{bmatrix}.$$

If $ad - bc = 0$, the matrix A does not have an inverse.

EXAMPLE 6   **Finding the Inverse of a 2 × 2 Matrix**

Find the inverse (if it exists) of each matrix.

a. $A = \begin{bmatrix} 5 & 2 \\ 4 & 3 \end{bmatrix}$ **b.** $B = \begin{bmatrix} 4 & 6 \\ 2 & 3 \end{bmatrix}$

Solution

a. For the matrix A, $a = 5, b = 2, c = 4$, and $d = 3$.
Here, $ad - bc = (5)(3) - (2)(4) = 15 - 8 = 7 \neq 0$. Thus, A is invertible, and

$$A^{-1} = \frac{1}{7}\begin{bmatrix} 3 & -2 \\ -4 & 5 \end{bmatrix} \qquad \text{Substitute for } a, b, c, \text{ and } d \text{ in } \frac{1}{ad - bc}\begin{bmatrix} d & -b \\ -c & a \end{bmatrix}.$$

$$= \begin{bmatrix} \dfrac{3}{7} & -\dfrac{2}{7} \\ -\dfrac{4}{7} & \dfrac{5}{7} \end{bmatrix} \qquad \text{Scalar multiplication}$$

You should verify that $AA^{-1} = I$.

b. For the matrix B, $a = 4, b = 6, c = 2$, and $d = 3$, so $ad - bc = (4)(3) - (6)(2) = 12 - 12 = 0$. Thus, the matrix B does not have an inverse.   ■ ■ ■

PRACTICE PROBLEM 6   Find the inverse (if it exists) of each matrix.

a. $A = \begin{bmatrix} 8 & 2 \\ 4 & 1 \end{bmatrix}$ **b.** $B = \begin{bmatrix} 8 & -2 \\ 3 & 1 \end{bmatrix}.$ ■

4 Use matrix inverses to solve systems of linear equations.

Solving Systems of Linear Equations by Using Matrix Inverses

Matrix multiplication can be used to write a system of linear equations in matrix form.

System of equations	Matrix form
$\begin{cases} 3x - 2y = 4 \\ 4x - 3y = 5 \end{cases}$	$\begin{bmatrix} 3 & -2 \\ 4 & -3 \end{bmatrix} \begin{bmatrix} x \\ y \end{bmatrix} = \begin{bmatrix} 4 \\ 5 \end{bmatrix}$
$\begin{cases} 2x_1 + 4x_2 - x_3 = 9 \\ 3x_1 + x_2 + 2x_3 = 7 \\ x_1 + 3x_2 - 3x_3 = 4 \end{cases}$	$\begin{bmatrix} 2 & 4 & -1 \\ 3 & 1 & 2 \\ 1 & 3 & -3 \end{bmatrix} \begin{bmatrix} x_1 \\ x_2 \\ x_3 \end{bmatrix} = \begin{bmatrix} 9 \\ 7 \\ 4 \end{bmatrix}$

Thus, solving a system of linear equations amounts to solving a corresponding matrix equation of the form

$$AX = B,$$

where A is the coefficient matrix of the system, X is the column matrix containing the variables, and B is the column matrix of the constants on the right side of the equal sign of the linear system.

If A is a square matrix *and* A is invertible, then the matrix equation $AX = B$ has a unique solution. In this case, you find X by multiplying each side of the equation by the inverse of A.

$AX = B$	Given equation
$A^{-1}(AX) = A^{-1}B$	Be careful to multiply by A^{-1} on the left on both sides of the equation, since multiplication of matrices is not commutative.
$(A^{-1}A)X = A^{-1}B$	Associative property
$IX = A^{-1}B$	$A^{-1}A = I$
$X = A^{-1}B$	I is the identity matrix.

EXAMPLE 7   **Solving a Linear System by Using an Inverse Matrix**

Use a matrix inverse to solve the linear system: $\begin{cases} x + y = 4 \\ 3y + z = 7 \\ 2x + 3y + 3z = 21 \end{cases}$

Solution

First rewrite the system of equations by inserting zeros as coefficients of the missing variables.

$$\begin{cases} x + y + 0z = 4 \\ 0x + 3y + z = 7 \\ 2x + 3y + 3z = 21 \end{cases}$$

Continued on next page.

The linear system in matrix form can be written as

$$\underbrace{\begin{bmatrix} 1 & 1 & 0 \\ 0 & 3 & 1 \\ 2 & 3 & 3 \end{bmatrix}}_{\substack{\uparrow \\ A}} \underbrace{\begin{bmatrix} x \\ y \\ z \end{bmatrix}}_{\substack{\uparrow \\ X}} = \underbrace{\begin{bmatrix} 4 \\ 7 \\ 21 \end{bmatrix}}_{\substack{\uparrow \\ B}}.$$

We need to solve the matrix equation $AX = B$ for X. Since the matrix A is invertible (see Example 5), the system has a unique solution $X = A^{-1}B$. Use

$$A^{-1} = \frac{1}{8}\begin{bmatrix} 6 & -3 & 1 \\ 2 & 3 & -1 \\ -6 & -1 & 3 \end{bmatrix} \qquad \text{Computed in Example 5}$$

$$X = A^{-1}B$$

$$= \frac{1}{8}\begin{bmatrix} 6 & -3 & 1 \\ 2 & 3 & -1 \\ -6 & -1 & 3 \end{bmatrix}\begin{bmatrix} 4 \\ 7 \\ 21 \end{bmatrix} \qquad \text{Substitute for } A^{-1} \text{ and } B.$$

$$= \frac{1}{8}\begin{bmatrix} 6(4) - 3(7) + 1(21) \\ 2(4) + 3(7) - 1(21) \\ -6(4) - 1(7) + 3(21) \end{bmatrix} \qquad \text{Matrix multiplication}$$

$$= \frac{1}{8}\begin{bmatrix} 24 \\ 8 \\ 32 \end{bmatrix} = \begin{bmatrix} 3 \\ 1 \\ 4 \end{bmatrix}.$$

Now,

$$X = \begin{bmatrix} x \\ y \\ z \end{bmatrix} = \begin{bmatrix} 3 \\ 1 \\ 4 \end{bmatrix}$$

gives $x = 3$, $y = 1$, and $z = 4$. You should check this solution in the original system of equations. The solution set is $\{(3, 1, 4)\}$. ▪ ▪ ▪

PRACTICE PROBLEM 7   Solve the linear system.

$$\begin{cases} 3x + 2y + 3z = 9 \\ 3x + y = 12 \\ x + z = 6 \end{cases}$$ ▪

5 Use matrix inverses in applied problems.

Applications of Matrix Inverses

The Leontief Input–Output Model   We can make use of the inverse of a matrix to analyze input–output types of models that we studied in Section 9.1.

Suppose an oversimplified economy depends upon two products: energy (E) and food (F). To produce one unit of E requires $\frac{1}{4}$ unit of E and $\frac{1}{2}$ unit of F. To produce one unit of

F requires $\dfrac{1}{3}$ unit of E and $\dfrac{1}{4}$ unit of F. Then the interindustry consumption is given by the following matrix.

$$A = \begin{array}{cc} & \begin{array}{cc} E & F \end{array} \\ \begin{bmatrix} \dfrac{1}{4} & \dfrac{1}{3} \\ \dfrac{1}{2} & \dfrac{1}{4} \end{bmatrix} & \begin{array}{c} E \\ F \end{array} \end{array}$$

The matrix A is the **interindustry technology input–output matrix,** or simply the **technology matrix,** of the system. If the system is producing x_1 units of energy and x_2 units of food, then the column matrix $X = \begin{bmatrix} x_1 \\ x_2 \end{bmatrix}$ is called the **gross production matrix.**

Consequently,

$$AX = \begin{bmatrix} \dfrac{1}{4} & \dfrac{1}{3} \\ \dfrac{1}{2} & \dfrac{1}{4} \end{bmatrix} \begin{bmatrix} x_1 \\ x_2 \end{bmatrix} = \begin{bmatrix} \dfrac{1}{4}x_1 + \dfrac{1}{3}x_2 \\ \dfrac{1}{2}x_1 + \dfrac{1}{4}x_2 \end{bmatrix} \begin{array}{l} \leftarrow \text{units consumed by } E \\ \leftarrow \text{units consumed by } F \end{array}$$

represents the interindustry consumptions. If the column matrix $D = \begin{bmatrix} d_1 \\ d_2 \end{bmatrix}$ represents consumer demand, then

$$\begin{array}{ll} D = X - AX & \text{Gross production minus interindustry consumption} \\ \quad = IX - AX & I \text{ is the identity matrix.} \\ D = (I - A)X & \text{Distributive property} \\ (I - A)^{-1}D = (I - A)^{-1}(I - A)X & \text{Multiply both sides by } (I - A)^{-1} \text{ if } I - A \text{ is invertible.} \\ (I - A)^{-1}D = IX & (I - A)^{-1}(I - A) = I \\ \quad = X. & I \text{ is the identity matrix.} \end{array}$$

Hence, if $(I - A)$ is invertible, then the gross production matrix is: $X = (I - A)^{-1}D$.

> **EXAMPLE 8**   Using the Leontief Input–Output Model

In the preceding discussion, suppose the consumer demand for energy is 1000 units and that for food is 3000 units. Find the level of production (X) that will meet interindustry and consumer demand.

Solution

For the matrix A, we have

$$I - A = \begin{bmatrix} 1 & 0 \\ 0 & 1 \end{bmatrix} - \begin{bmatrix} \dfrac{1}{4} & \dfrac{1}{3} \\ \dfrac{1}{2} & \dfrac{1}{4} \end{bmatrix} = \begin{bmatrix} \dfrac{3}{4} & -\dfrac{1}{3} \\ -\dfrac{1}{2} & \dfrac{3}{4} \end{bmatrix}.$$

Continued on next page.

Use the formula for the inverse of a 2×2 matrix to obtain

$$(I - A)^{-1} = \dfrac{1}{\dfrac{3}{4} \cdot \dfrac{3}{4} - \left(-\dfrac{1}{3}\right)\left(-\dfrac{1}{2}\right)}\begin{bmatrix} \dfrac{3}{4} & \dfrac{1}{3} \\ \dfrac{1}{2} & \dfrac{3}{4} \end{bmatrix}$$

Use the formula for the inverse of a 2×2 matrix.

$$= \dfrac{48}{19}\begin{bmatrix} \dfrac{3}{4} & \dfrac{1}{3} \\ \dfrac{1}{2} & \dfrac{3}{4} \end{bmatrix} = \dfrac{1}{19}\begin{bmatrix} 36 & 16 \\ 24 & 36 \end{bmatrix}.$$

Simplify.

Hence, the gross production matrix X is given by

$$X = (I - A)^{-1}D = \dfrac{1}{19}\begin{bmatrix} 36 & 16 \\ 24 & 36 \end{bmatrix}\begin{bmatrix} 1000 \\ 3000 \end{bmatrix}$$

Substitute for $(I - A)^{-1}$ and D.

$$= \dfrac{1}{19}\begin{bmatrix} 84{,}000 \\ 132{,}000 \end{bmatrix} = \begin{bmatrix} \dfrac{84{,}000}{19} \\ \dfrac{132{,}000}{19} \end{bmatrix}.$$

Thus, to meet the consumer demand for 1000 units of energy and 3000 units of food, the energy produced must be $\dfrac{84{,}000}{19}$ units and food production must be $\dfrac{132{,}000}{19}$ units. ■ ■ ■

PRACTICE PROBLEM 8   In Example 8, find the level of production (X) that will meet both the interindustry and consumer demand if consumer demand for energy is 800 units and consumer demand for food is 3400 units. ■

Cryptography

To encode or decode a message, first associate each letter in the message with a number, in the obvious manner. The blank corresponds to 0.

blank	A	B	C	D	E	F	G	H	I	J	K	L	M
0	1	2	3	4	5	6	7	8	9	10	11	12	13
	N	O	P	Q	R	S	T	U	V	W	X	Y	Z
	14	15	16	17	18	19	20	21	22	23	24	25	26

For example, the message

JOHNSON IS IN DANGER

becomes:

10 15 8 14 19 15 14 0 9 19 0 9 14 0 4 1 14 7 5 18
J   O   H N   S   O   N   I S   I N   D A N   G E R

This message is easy to decode, so we will make the coding more complicated. First partition these 20 numbers into groups of three, enclosed in brackets, and insert zeros at the end of the last bracket if necessary.

[10 15 8] [14 19 15] [14 0 9] [19 0 9] [14 0 4] [1 14 7] [5 18 0]

J   O   H   N   S   O   N   I   S   I   N   D   A   N   G   E   R

It is more convenient to write these seven groups of three numbers each as the seven columns of a 3×7 matrix

$$M = \begin{bmatrix} 10 & 14 & 14 & 19 & 14 & 1 & 5 \\ 15 & 19 & 0 & 0 & 0 & 14 & 18 \\ 8 & 15 & 9 & 9 & 4 & 7 & 0 \end{bmatrix}.$$

Now choose any invertible 3×3 matrix A, say,

$$A = \begin{bmatrix} 1 & 2 & 3 \\ 1 & 3 & 3 \\ 1 & 2 & 4 \end{bmatrix}.$$

The matrix A can be used to convert the message into code, and then A^{-1} is used to decode the message, as you will see in the next example. The matrix A is called the **coding matrix.**

EXAMPLE 9   **Encoding and Decoding a Message**

Encode and decode the message

JOHNSON IS IN DANGER

by using the matrix A given previously.

Solution

Step 1   Express the message numerically, and partition the numbers into groups of three:

10 15 8, 14 19 15, 14 0 9, 19 0 9, 14 0 4, 1 14 7, 5 18 0

Step 2   Write each group of three numbers in Step 1 as a column of a matrix M:

$$M = \begin{bmatrix} 10 & 14 & 14 & 19 & 14 & 1 & 5 \\ 15 & 19 & 0 & 0 & 0 & 14 & 18 \\ 8 & 15 & 9 & 9 & 4 & 7 & 0 \end{bmatrix}.$$

Step 3   Select an invertible 3×3 matrix A, such as

$$A = \begin{bmatrix} 1 & 2 & 3 \\ 1 & 3 & 3 \\ 1 & 2 & 4 \end{bmatrix}.$$

Step 4   Multiply the matrices in Steps 2 and 3 to form AM.

$$AM = \begin{bmatrix} 1 & 2 & 3 \\ 1 & 3 & 3 \\ 1 & 2 & 4 \end{bmatrix} \begin{bmatrix} 10 & 14 & 14 & 19 & 14 & 1 & 5 \\ 15 & 19 & 0 & 0 & 0 & 14 & 18 \\ 8 & 15 & 9 & 9 & 4 & 7 & 0 \end{bmatrix}$$

$$= \begin{bmatrix} 64 & 97 & 41 & 46 & 26 & 50 & 41 \\ 79 & 116 & 41 & 46 & 26 & 64 & 59 \\ 72 & 112 & 50 & 55 & 30 & 57 & 41 \end{bmatrix} \qquad \text{Matrix multiplication}$$

The coded message sent will be the numbers from column 1 of AM, followed by the numbers from column 2, and so on:

Continued on next page.

64 79 72 97 116 112 41 41 50 46 46 55 26 26 30 50 64 57 41 59 41

Step 5   To decode the message in Step 4, write the numbers received in the message in groups of three and as columns of the matrix AM. Find the **decoding matrix** A^{-1} of the coding matrix A. You can verify that

$$A^{-1} = \begin{bmatrix} 6 & -2 & -3 \\ -1 & 1 & 0 \\ -1 & 0 & 1 \end{bmatrix}.$$

Step 6   Compute the message matrix M.

$$M = A^{-1}(AM) = \begin{bmatrix} 6 & -2 & -3 \\ -1 & 1 & 0 \\ -1 & 0 & 1 \end{bmatrix} \begin{bmatrix} 64 & 97 & 41 & 46 & 26 & 50 & 41 \\ 79 & 116 & 41 & 46 & 26 & 64 & 59 \\ 72 & 112 & 50 & 55 & 30 & 57 & 41 \end{bmatrix}$$

$$= \begin{bmatrix} 10 & 14 & 14 & 19 & 14 & 1 & 5 \\ 15 & 19 & 0 & 0 & 0 & 14 & 18 \\ 8 & 15 & 9 & 9 & 4 & 7 & 0 \end{bmatrix} \quad \text{Matrix multiplication}$$

Step 7   Finally, convert the numerical message from the matrix M in Step 6 back into English.

JOHNSON IS IN DANGER.   ■ ■ ■

PRACTICE PROBLEM 9   Rework Example 9, replacing the message JOHNSON IS IN DANGER with the message JACK IS NOW SAFE.   ■

A Exercises Basic Skills and Concepts

In Exercises 1–10, determine whether B is the inverse of A by computing AB and BA.

1. $A = \begin{bmatrix} 1 & 2 \\ 1 & 3 \end{bmatrix}, B = \begin{bmatrix} 3 & -2 \\ -1 & 1 \end{bmatrix}$ Yes

2. $A = \begin{bmatrix} 3 & 2 \\ 4 & 3 \end{bmatrix}, B = \begin{bmatrix} 3 & -2 \\ -4 & 3 \end{bmatrix}$ Yes

3. $A = \begin{bmatrix} 3 & 2 \\ 1 & 4 \end{bmatrix}, B = \begin{bmatrix} \dfrac{2}{5} & -\dfrac{1}{5} \\ -\dfrac{1}{10} & \dfrac{3}{10} \end{bmatrix}$ Yes

4. $A = \begin{bmatrix} 2 & -3 \\ 4 & -3 \end{bmatrix}, B = \begin{bmatrix} -\dfrac{1}{2} & \dfrac{1}{2} \\ -\dfrac{2}{3} & \dfrac{1}{3} \end{bmatrix}$ Yes

5. $A = \begin{bmatrix} 1 & 0 & -1 \\ -1 & 1 & 1 \end{bmatrix}, B = \begin{bmatrix} 2 & 1 \\ 1 & 1 \\ 1 & 1 \end{bmatrix}$ No

6. $A = \begin{bmatrix} -2 & 1 & 3 \\ 0 & -1 & 1 \\ 1 & 2 & 0 \end{bmatrix}, B = \dfrac{1}{8}\begin{bmatrix} -2 & 6 & 4 \\ 1 & -3 & 2 \\ 1 & 5 & 2 \end{bmatrix}$ Yes

7. $A = \begin{bmatrix} 1 & -2 & 1 \\ -8 & 6 & -2 \\ 5 & -3 & 1 \end{bmatrix}, B = \dfrac{1}{2}\begin{bmatrix} 0 & 1 & 2 \\ 1 & 2 & 3 \\ 3 & 1 & 1 \end{bmatrix}$ No

8. $A = \begin{bmatrix} 2 & 3 & 1 \\ 1 & 2 & 3 \\ 3 & 1 & 2 \end{bmatrix}, B = \dfrac{1}{18}\begin{bmatrix} 1 & -5 & 7 \\ 7 & 1 & -5 \\ -5 & 7 & 1 \end{bmatrix}$ Yes

9. $A = \begin{bmatrix} 1 & 1 & 1 \\ 1 & 2 & 3 \\ -1 & 1 & -1 \end{bmatrix}, B = \dfrac{1}{4}\begin{bmatrix} 5 & -2 & -1 \\ 2 & 0 & 2 \\ -3 & 2 & -1 \end{bmatrix}$ Yes

10. $A = \begin{bmatrix} 1 & -1 & 0 \\ 0 & 1 & -1 \\ 1 & 0 & 1 \end{bmatrix}, B = \dfrac{1}{2}\begin{bmatrix} 1 & 1 & 1 \\ -1 & 1 & 1 \\ -1 & -1 & 1 \end{bmatrix}$ Yes

In Exercises 11–20, find A^{-1} (if it exists) by forming the matrix $[A|I]$ and using the row operation to obtain $[I|B]$, where $B = A^{-1}$.

11. $A = \begin{bmatrix} 2 & 0 \\ 1 & 3 \end{bmatrix}$ †

12. $A = \begin{bmatrix} 4 & 3 \\ 1 & 0 \end{bmatrix}$ †

13. $A = \begin{bmatrix} 2 & 4 \\ 3 & 6 \end{bmatrix}$ †

14. $A = \begin{bmatrix} 9 & 6 \\ 6 & 4 \end{bmatrix}$ †

†Due to space constrictions, answers to these exercises may be found in the Answers beginning on page A–1 in the back of the book.

15. $A = \begin{bmatrix} 1 & 6 & 4 \\ 0 & 2 & 3 \\ 0 & 1 & 2 \end{bmatrix}$ †

16. $A = \begin{bmatrix} -2 & 1 & 3 \\ 0 & -1 & 1 \\ 1 & 2 & 0 \end{bmatrix}$ †

17. $A = \begin{bmatrix} 2 & 4 & 3 \\ 0 & 1 & 1 \\ 2 & 2 & -1 \end{bmatrix}$ †

18. $A = \begin{bmatrix} 1 & 1 & 5 \\ 4 & 3 & -5 \\ 1 & 1 & 0 \end{bmatrix}$ †

19. $A = \begin{bmatrix} 1 & 2 & -1 \\ -1 & 1 & 2 \\ 2 & -1 & 1 \end{bmatrix}$ †

20. $A = \begin{bmatrix} 1 & 2 & 3 \\ 2 & 3 & 0 \\ 0 & 1 & 2 \end{bmatrix}$ †

In Exercises 21–26, find the inverse (if it exists) of $A = \begin{bmatrix} a & b \\ c & d \end{bmatrix}$ by using the formula $A^{-1} = \dfrac{1}{ad - bc}\begin{bmatrix} d & -b \\ -c & a \end{bmatrix}$. Check that $A^{-1}A = I$.

21. $A = \begin{bmatrix} 1 & 0 \\ 3 & 2 \end{bmatrix}$ †

22. $A = \begin{bmatrix} 3 & 4 \\ 5 & 6 \end{bmatrix}$ †

23. $A = \begin{bmatrix} 2 & -3 \\ -3 & 5 \end{bmatrix}$ †

24. $A = \begin{bmatrix} 3 & -4 \\ 2 & -2 \end{bmatrix}$ †

25. $A = \begin{bmatrix} a & -b \\ b & -a \end{bmatrix}, a^2 \neq b^2$ †

26. $A = \begin{bmatrix} 2 & -1 \\ 1 & -1 \end{bmatrix}$ †

In Exercises 27–30, write the given linear system of equations as a matrix equation $AX = B$.

27. $\begin{cases} 2x + 3y = -9 \\ x - 3y = 13 \end{cases}$ †

28. $\begin{cases} 5x - 4y = 7 \\ 4x - 3y = 5 \end{cases}$ †

29. $\begin{cases} 3x + 2y + z = 8 \\ 2x + y + 3z = 7 \\ x + 3y + 2z = 9 \end{cases}$ †

30. $\begin{cases} x + 3y + z = 4 \\ x - 5y + 2z = 7 \\ 3x + y - 4z = -9 \end{cases}$ †

In Exercises 31–34, write each matrix equation as a linear system of equations.

31. $\begin{bmatrix} 1 & -2 \\ 2 & 1 \end{bmatrix}\begin{bmatrix} x \\ y \end{bmatrix} = \begin{bmatrix} 0 \\ 5 \end{bmatrix}$ †

32. $\begin{bmatrix} 2 & 3 \\ 3 & -1 \end{bmatrix}\begin{bmatrix} x_1 \\ x_2 \end{bmatrix} = \begin{bmatrix} 0 \\ 11 \end{bmatrix}$ †

33. $\begin{bmatrix} 2 & 3 & 1 \\ 5 & 7 & -1 \\ 4 & 3 & 0 \end{bmatrix}\begin{bmatrix} x_1 \\ x_2 \\ x_3 \end{bmatrix} = \begin{bmatrix} -1 \\ 5 \\ 5 \end{bmatrix}$ †

34. $\begin{bmatrix} 3 & -2 & 3 \\ 5 & 0 & 4 \\ 2 & 7 & 0 \end{bmatrix}\begin{bmatrix} r \\ s \\ t \end{bmatrix} = \begin{bmatrix} 4 \\ 3 \\ -8 \end{bmatrix}$ †

35. Let $A = \begin{bmatrix} 1 & 2 & 5 \\ 2 & 3 & 8 \\ -1 & 1 & 2 \end{bmatrix}$. Show that $A^{-1} = \begin{bmatrix} 2 & -1 & -1 \\ 12 & -7 & -2 \\ -5 & 3 & 1 \end{bmatrix}$. †

In Exercises 36–38, use the result of Exercise 35 to solve the system of equations.

36. $\begin{cases} x + 2y + 5z = 4 \\ 2x + 3y + 8z = 6 \\ -x + y + 2z = 3 \end{cases}$ †

37. $\begin{cases} x_1 + 2x_2 + 5x_3 = 1 \\ 2x_1 + 3x_2 + 8x_3 = 3 \\ -x_1 + x_2 + 2x_3 = -3 \end{cases}$ †

38. $\begin{cases} x + 2y + 5z = -4 \\ 2x + 3y + 8z = -6 \\ -x + y + 2z = -\dfrac{5}{2} \end{cases}$ †

39. a. Find the inverse of the matrix $A = \begin{bmatrix} 1 & 1 & 1 \\ 1 & 2 & 3 \\ 1 & 4 & 9 \end{bmatrix}$. †

b. Use the result of part (a) to solve the linear system

$$\begin{cases} x + y + z = 6 \\ x + 2y + 3z = 14 \\ x + 4y + 9z = 36 \end{cases}$$ †

40. a. Find the inverse of the matrix $A = \begin{bmatrix} 2 & 4 & -1 \\ 3 & 1 & 2 \\ 1 & 3 & -3 \end{bmatrix}$. †

b. Use the result of part (a) to solve the linear system

$$\begin{cases} 2x + 4y - z = 9 \\ 3x + y + 2z = 7 \\ x + 3y - 3z = 4 \end{cases}$$ †

B Exercises   Applying the Concepts

In Exercises 41–46, solve each linear system by using an inverse matrix.

41. $\begin{cases} -3x + 7y = 17 \\ -5x + 4y = 13 \end{cases}$ †

42. $\begin{cases} x - 7y = 3 \\ 2x + 3y = 23 \end{cases}$ †

43. $\begin{cases} x + y + 2z = 7 \\ x - y - 3z = -6 \\ 2x + 3y + z = 4 \end{cases}$ †

44. $\begin{cases} x + y + z = 6 \\ 2x - 3y + 3z = 5 \\ 3x - 2y - z = -4 \end{cases}$ †

45. $\begin{cases} 2x + 2y + 3z = 7 \\ 5x + 3y + 5z = 3 \\ 3x + 5y + z = -5 \end{cases}$ †

46. $\begin{cases} 9x + 7y + 4z = 12 \\ 6x + 5y + 4z = 5 \\ 4x + 3y + z = 7 \end{cases}$ †

In Exercises 47–50, technology matrix A, representing interindustry demand, and matrix D, representing consumer demand for the sectors in a two- or three-sector economy, are given. Use the matrix equation $X = (I - A)^{-1}D$ to find the production level X that will satisfy both demands.

47. Two-sector economy. In a two-sector economy,

$$A = \begin{bmatrix} 0.1 & 0.4 \\ 0.5 & 0.2 \end{bmatrix}, D = \begin{bmatrix} 50 \\ 30 \end{bmatrix}.$$ †

48. Two-sector economy. In a two-sector economy,

$$A = \begin{bmatrix} 0.2 & 0.5 \\ 0.1 & 0.6 \end{bmatrix}, D = \begin{bmatrix} 11 \\ 18 \end{bmatrix}.$$ †

49. **Three-sector economy.** In a three-sector economy,

$$A = \begin{bmatrix} 0.2 & 0.2 & 0 \\ 0.1 & 0.1 & 0.3 \\ 0.1 & 0 & 0.2 \end{bmatrix}, D = \begin{bmatrix} 400 \\ 600 \\ 800 \end{bmatrix}. \; †$$

50. **Three-sector economy.** In a three-sector economy,

$$A = \begin{bmatrix} 0.5 & 0.4 & 0.2 \\ 0.2 & 0.3 & 0.1 \\ 0.1 & 0.1 & 0.3 \end{bmatrix}, D = \begin{bmatrix} 500 \\ 300 \\ 200 \end{bmatrix}. \; †$$

In Exercises 51 and 52, use a 2 × 2 invertible coding matrix A of

your choice. Remember to partition the numerical message into groups of two. (a) Write a cryptogram for each message. (b) Check by decoding.

51. **Coding and decoding.** CANNOT FIND COLOMBO.

52. **Coding and decoding.** FOUND HEAD OF TERRORIST NETWORK.

In Exercises 53 and 54, use a 3 × 3 invertible coding matrix A of your choice.

53. Code and then decode the message of Exercise 51.

54. Code and then decode the message of Exercise 52.

C Exercises   Beyond the Basics

55. Suppose A is an invertible square matrix.
  a. Is A^{-1} invertible? Why or why not? †
  b. If your answer to part (a) is yes, then what is $(A^{-1})^{-1}$? †

56. Let $A^{-1} = \begin{bmatrix} 2 & 1 \\ 3 & -4 \end{bmatrix}$. Find A. †

57. Let A be a square matrix. Show that if A^2 is invertible, then A must be invertible. [*Hint:* $A^2B = A(AB)$.] †

58. Show that if A is invertible, then A^2 is invertible. †

59. Show that if A and B are $n \times n$ invertible matrices, then AB is invertible and $(AB)^{-1} = B^{-1}A^{-1}$. (Note the order.) †

60. Verify the result of Exercise 59 for

$$A = \begin{bmatrix} 1 & 2 \\ 3 & 4 \end{bmatrix}, B = \begin{bmatrix} -1 & 0 \\ 3 & -2 \end{bmatrix}. \; †$$

61. Let A, B, and C be $n \times n$ matrices such that $AB = AC$. Show that if A is invertible, then $B = C$. †

62. Is the result of Exercise 61 true if A is not invertible? †

63. Let A and B be $n \times n$ matrices such that $AB = A$. Show that if A is invertible, then $B = I$. †

64. Give an example to show that the result of Exercise 63 is not true if A is not invertible. †

65. Let $A = \begin{bmatrix} 3 & 4 \\ 2 & 3 \end{bmatrix}$.

  a. Show that the matrix A satisfies the equation

$$A^2 - 6A + I = 0.$$

  b. Use the equation in part (a) to show that $A^{-1} = 6I - A$.
  c. Use the equation in part (b) to find A^{-1}. †

66. Let $A = \begin{bmatrix} 2 & -1 & 1 \\ -1 & 2 & -1 \\ 1 & -1 & 2 \end{bmatrix}$. Assume that A is invertible.

  a. Show that A satisfies the equation $A^3 - 6A^2 + 9A - 4I = 0.$

  b. Use the equation in part (a) to show that

$$A^{-1} = \frac{1}{4}[A^2 - 6A + 9I].$$

  [*Hint:* Consider the product $\frac{1}{4}[A^2 - 6A + 9I]A$.]

  c. Use part (b) to find A^{-1}. †

Critical Thinking

67. Suppose A and B are 2 × 2 matrices and $B^{-1} = \begin{bmatrix} 1 & 2 \\ 3 & 4 \end{bmatrix}$. Find A

  a. if $AB = \begin{bmatrix} -1 & 3 \\ 0 & 2 \end{bmatrix}$. †

  b. if $BA = \begin{bmatrix} -1 & 3 \\ 0 & 2 \end{bmatrix}$. †

  c. if $B^{-1}AB = \begin{bmatrix} 1 & 1 \\ 1 & 2 \end{bmatrix}$. †

  d. if $BAB^{-1} = \begin{bmatrix} 1 & 1 \\ 1 & 2 \end{bmatrix}$. †

68. a. Is the matrix $\begin{bmatrix} x & -1 \\ 2 & x + 2 \end{bmatrix}$ invertible for all real numbers x? Yes

  b. Is the matrix $\begin{bmatrix} x - 1 & -1 \\ 3 & x - 5 \end{bmatrix}$ invertible for all real numbers x? No

69. True or False? Justify your answers.
  a. If A and B are matrices for which $AB = BA$, then the formula $A^2B = BA^2$ must hold. †
  b. If A and B are invertible matrices, then $A + B$ must be invertible. False. Let $A = I$ and $B = -I$.

70. Give an example of a 2 × 2 matrix A such that $A^2 = 0$. Show that the matrix $I + A$ is invertible and $(I + A)^{-1} = I - A$. †

71. Is it true that every nonsingular matrix is a square matrix? Why or why not? True

SECTION 9.4

Determinants and Cramer's Rule

BEFORE STARTING THIS SECTION, REVIEW

1. Definition of a matrix (Section 9.1, page 813)

2. Systems of equations (Section 8.1, page 738)

3. Inverse of a 2×2 matrix (Section 9.3, page 850)

OBJECTIVES

1. Calculate the determinant of a 2×2 matrix.

2. Find minors and cofactors.

3. Evaluate the determinant of an $n \times n$ matrix.

4. Apply Cramer's Rule.

A Little History of Determinants

It appears that determinants were first investigated in 1683 by the outstanding Japanese mathematician Seki Kōwa in connection with systems of linear equations. Determinants were independently investigated in 1693 by the German mathematician Gottfried Leibniz (1646–1716). The French mathematician Alexandre-Théophile Vandermonde (1735–1796) was the first to give a coherent and systematic exposition of the theory of determinants. Determinants were used extensively in the 19th century by eminent mathematicians such as Cauchy, Jacobi, and Kronecker. Today, determinants are of little numerical value in the large-scale matrix computations that occur so often. Nevertheless, a knowledge of determinants is useful in some applications of matrices. ■

**Seki Kōwa
(1642–1708)**
Seki Kōwa has been called "the Japanese Newton." He was born in the same year as Newton. Like Newton, he acquired much of his knowledge by self-study and was a brilliant problem solver. But the greatest similarity between the two men lies in the claim that Seki Kowa was the creator of *yenri* (calculus). Thus, Seki Kōwa probably invented the calculus in the East just as Newton and Leibniz invented the calculus in the West.

---

1 Calculate the determinant of a 2×2 matrix.

The Determinant of a 2×2 Matrix

Associated with each square matrix A is a number called the *determinant* of A. The determinant of a 2×2 matrix is defined as follows:

STUDY TIP

A determinant can be thought of as a function whose domain is the set of all square matrices and whose range is the set of real numbers.

DETERMINANT OF A 2×2 MATRIX

The **determinant** of the matrix

$$A = \begin{bmatrix} a & b \\ c & d \end{bmatrix}$$

is denoted by $\det(A)$, $|A|$, or $\begin{vmatrix} a & b \\ c & d \end{vmatrix}$ and is defined by

$$\det(A) = |A| = \begin{vmatrix} a & b \\ c & d \end{vmatrix} = ad - bc.$$

To remember this definition, it is helpful to note that you form products along diagonal elements as indicated by the arrows:

$$\begin{bmatrix} a & b \\ c & d \end{bmatrix}.$$
$$-bc \quad +ad$$

You attach a plus sign if you descend from left to right and a minus sign if you descend from right to left. Then you form the sum $ad - bc$.

Recall (page 850) that the matrix $A = \begin{bmatrix} a & b \\ c & d \end{bmatrix}$ is invertible if and only if $ad - bc \neq 0$.

You can rephrase this property by saying that a *matrix of order 2 is invertible if and only if its determinant is nonzero*. If the matrix A is invertible, then its inverse can be expressed in terms of its determinant:

$$A^{-1} = \frac{1}{ad - bc}\begin{bmatrix} d & -b \\ -c & a \end{bmatrix} = \frac{1}{\det(A)}\begin{bmatrix} d & -b \\ -c & a \end{bmatrix}$$

EXAMPLE 1   **Calculating the Determinant of a 2 × 2 Matrix**

Evaluate each determinant.

a. $\begin{vmatrix} 3 & -4 \\ 1 & 5 \end{vmatrix}$ **b.** $\begin{vmatrix} -2 & 3 \\ 4 & -5 \end{vmatrix}$

Solution

a. $\begin{vmatrix} 3 & -4 \\ 1 & 5 \end{vmatrix} = (3)(5) - (-4)(1) = 15 - (-4) = 15 + 4 = 19$

b. $\begin{vmatrix} -2 & 3 \\ 4 & -5 \end{vmatrix} = (-2)(-5) - (3)(4) = 10 - 12 = -2$

■ ■ ■

PRACTICE PROBLEM 1   Evaluate each determinant.

a. $\begin{vmatrix} 5 & 1 \\ 3 & -7 \end{vmatrix}$ **b.** $\begin{vmatrix} 2 & -9 \\ -4 & 18 \end{vmatrix}$ ■

WARNING   Note carefully the notations used for matrices and determinants. Brackets, [ ], are used to denote a matrix, while vertical bars, | |, are used to denote the determinant of a matrix. Remember that *the determinant of a matrix is a number.*

2 Find minors and cofactors.

Minors and Cofactors

In defining the determinants of square matrices of order 3 or higher, it is convenient to have some additional terminology.

MINORS AND COFACTORS IN AN $n \times n$ MATRIX

Let A be an $n \times n$ square matrix. The **minor** M_{ij} of the element a_{ij} is the determinant of the $(n-1) \times (n-1)$ matrix obtained by deleting the ith row and the jth column of A. The **cofactor** A_{ij} of the entry a_{ij} is given by:

$$A_{ij} = (-1)^{i+j} M_{ij}$$

When $i + j$ is an even integer, $(-1)^{i+j} = 1$. When $i + j$ is an odd integer, $(-1)^{i+j} = -1$. Therefore,

$$A_{ij} = \begin{cases} M_{ij} \text{ if } i + j \text{ is an even integer} \\ -M_{ij} \text{ if } i + j \text{ is an odd integer} \end{cases}$$

Notice that, to compute a minor in an $n \times n$ matrix, you must know how to compute the determinant of an $(n-1) \times (n-1)$ matrix. At this point in the text, since you have learned the definition of the determinant of a 2×2 matrix, you can find the minors and cofactors of entries in a 3×3 matrix.

EXAMPLE 2   **Finding Minors and Cofactors**

For the matrix $A = \begin{bmatrix} 2 & 3 & 4 \\ 5 & -3 & -6 \\ 0 & 1 & 7 \end{bmatrix}$, find:

a. the minors M_{11}, M_{23}, and M_{32}

b. the cofactors A_{11}, A_{23}, and A_{32}

Solution

a. (i) To find M_{11}, delete the first row and first column of the matrix A.

$$\begin{bmatrix} 2 & 3 & 4 \\ 5 & -3 & -6 \\ 0 & 1 & 7 \end{bmatrix}$$

Now find the determinant of the resulting matrix.

$$M_{11} = \begin{vmatrix} -3 & -6 \\ 1 & 7 \end{vmatrix} = (-3)(7) - (-6)(1) = -21 + 6 = -15$$

(ii) To find the minor M_{23}, delete the second row and third column of the matrix A.

$$\begin{bmatrix} 2 & 3 & 4 \\ 5 & -3 & -6 \\ 0 & 1 & 7 \end{bmatrix}.$$

Now find the determinant of the resulting matrix.

$$M_{23} = \begin{vmatrix} 2 & 3 \\ 0 & 1 \end{vmatrix} = (2)(1) - (3)(0) = 2$$

Continued on next page.

(iii) To find M_{32}, delete the third row and second column of A.

$$\begin{bmatrix} 2 & 3 & 4 \\ 5 & -3 & -6 \\ 0 & 1 & 7 \end{bmatrix}$$

Find the determinant of the resulting matrix.

$$M_{32} = \begin{vmatrix} 2 & 4 \\ 5 & -6 \end{vmatrix} = (2)(-6) - (4)(5) = -12 - 20 = -32$$

b. To find the cofactors, use the formula $A_{ij} = (-1)^{i+j} M_{ij}$:

$$A_{11} = (-1)^{1+1} M_{11} = (1)(-15) = -15 \qquad (-1)^{1+1} = (-1)^2 = 1; M_{11} = -15$$
$$A_{23} = (-1)^{2+3} M_{23} = (-1)(2) = -2 \qquad (-1)^{2+3} = (-1)^5 = -1; M_{23} = 2$$
$$A_{32} = (-1)^{3+2} M_{32} = (-1)(-32) = 32 \qquad (-1)^{3+2} = (-1)^5 = -1; M_{32} = -32$$

■ ■ ■

PRACTICE PROBLEM 2   For the matrix $A = \begin{bmatrix} 3 & -1 & 2 \\ 4 & 5 & 6 \\ 7 & 1 & 2 \end{bmatrix}$, find:

a. the minors M_{11}, M_{23}, and M_{32}
b. the cofactors A_{11}, A_{23}, and A_{32} ■

3 Evaluate the determinant of an $n \times n$ matrix.

The Determinant of an $n \times n$ Matrix

There are several ways of defining the determinant of a square matrix. Here, we give an *inductive definition*. This means that the definition of the determinant of a matrix of order n uses the determinants of the matrices of order $(n - 1)$.

DETERMINANT OF A SQUARE MATRIX

Let A be a square matrix of order $n \geq 3$. The **determinant** of A is the sum of the entries in any row of A (or column of A), multiplied by their respective cofactors.

Applying the preceding definition to find the determinant of a matrix is called **expanding by cofactors.** Thus, expanding by the cofactors of the ith row gives:

$$\det(A) = a_{i1} A_{i1} + a_{i2} A_{i2} + \cdots + a_{in} A_{in}$$

Similarly, expanding by the cofactors of the jth column yields:

$$\det(A) = a_{1j} A_{1j} + a_{2j} A_{2j} + \cdots + a_{nj} A_{nj}$$

We usually say "expanding by the ith row (column)" instead of "expanding by the cofactors of the ith row (column)."

The "det" option on a graphing calculator is used to find the determinant of a matrix.

EXAMPLE 3   **Calculating the Determinant of a 3 × 3 Matrix**

Find the determinant of $A = \begin{bmatrix} 2 & 3 & 4 \\ 1 & -2 & 2 \\ 3 & 4 & -1 \end{bmatrix}$.

Solution

Expanding by the first row, we have $|A| = a_{11}A_{11} + a_{12}A_{12} + a_{13}A_{13}$ where $a_{11} = 2$, $a_{12} = 3$, $a_{13} = 4$, and

$$A_{11} = (-1)^{1+1}M_{11} = (-1)^{1+1}\begin{vmatrix} -2 & 2 \\ 4 & -1 \end{vmatrix},$$

$$A_{12} = (-1)^{1+2}M_{12} = (-1)^{1+2}\begin{vmatrix} 1 & 2 \\ 3 & -1 \end{vmatrix},$$

$$A_{13} = (-1)^{1+3}M_{13} = (-1)^{1+3}\begin{vmatrix} 1 & -2 \\ 3 & 4 \end{vmatrix}.$$

Thus,

$$\begin{vmatrix} 2 & 3 & 4 \\ 1 & -2 & 2 \\ 3 & 4 & -1 \end{vmatrix} = 2(-1)^{1+1}\begin{vmatrix} -2 & 2 \\ 4 & -1 \end{vmatrix} + 3(-1)^{1+2}\begin{vmatrix} 1 & 2 \\ 3 & -1 \end{vmatrix} + 4(-1)^{1+3}\begin{vmatrix} 1 & -2 \\ 3 & 4 \end{vmatrix}$$

$$= 2(2-8) - 3(-1-6) + 4(4+6) \qquad \text{Evaluate determinants of order 2.}$$

$$= -12 + 21 + 40 = 49. \qquad \text{Simplify.} \qquad ■ \ ■ \ ■$$

PRACTICE PROBLEM 3   Find the determinant of $A = \begin{bmatrix} 2 & -3 & 7 \\ -2 & -1 & 9 \\ 0 & 2 & -9 \end{bmatrix}$.   ■

The definition says that you could expand the determinant by any row or column. For instance, expanding by the third column in A of Example 3, we have

$$\begin{vmatrix} 2 & 3 & 4 \\ 1 & -2 & 2 \\ 3 & 4 & -1 \end{vmatrix} = 4(-1)^{1+3}\begin{vmatrix} 1 & -2 \\ 3 & 4 \end{vmatrix} + 2(-1)^{2+3}\begin{vmatrix} 2 & 3 \\ 3 & 4 \end{vmatrix} + (-1)(-1)^{2+3}\begin{vmatrix} 2 & 3 \\ 1 & -2 \end{vmatrix}$$

$$= 4(4+6) - 2(8-9) - 1(-4-3)$$

$$= 40 + 2 + 7 = 49.$$

4 Apply Cramer's Rule.

Cramer's Rule

You have already learned several methods for solving a system of linear equations. There is another method that uses determinants. This method is called **Cramer's Rule.** To see how the rule works, consider a simple system of two linear equations in two variables.

$$\begin{cases} a_1 x + b_1 y = c_1 & (1) \\ a_2 x + b_2 y = c_2 & (2) \end{cases}$$

We can solve this system by using the elimination method. Let's first eliminate y and solve for x.

$$a_1b_2x + b_1b_2y = c_1b_2 \qquad \text{Multiply Equation (1) by } b_2.$$
$$\underline{-a_2b_1x - b_1b_2y = -c_2b_1} \qquad \text{Multiply Equation (2) by } -b_1.$$
$$(a_1b_2 - a_2b_1)x = c_1b_2 - c_2b_1 \qquad \text{Add to eliminate } y.$$
$$x = \frac{c_1b_2 - c_2b_1}{a_1b_2 - a_2b_1} \qquad \begin{array}{l}\text{Divide both sides by}\\ a_1b_2 - a_2b_1 \text{ if } a_1b_2 - a_2b_1 \neq 0.\end{array}$$

Similarly, by eliminating x and solving for y, we have:

$$y = \frac{a_1c_2 - a_2c_1}{a_1b_2 - a_2b_1} \qquad \text{if } a_1b_2 - a_2b_1 \neq 0.$$

Thus, the solution of the system of equations (1) and (2) is given by:

$$x = \frac{c_1b_2 - c_2b_1}{a_1b_2 - a_2b_1} \quad y = \frac{a_1c_2 - a_2c_1}{a_1b_2 - a_2b_1} \quad \text{provided that } a_1b_2 - a_2b_1 \neq 0.$$

You can write the solution in the form of determinants:

$$x = \frac{\begin{vmatrix} c_1 & b_1 \\ c_2 & b_2 \end{vmatrix}}{\begin{vmatrix} a_1 & b_1 \\ a_2 & b_2 \end{vmatrix}} \quad y = \frac{\begin{vmatrix} a_1 & c_1 \\ a_2 & c_2 \end{vmatrix}}{\begin{vmatrix} a_1 & b_1 \\ a_2 & b_2 \end{vmatrix}} \quad \text{provided that } D = \begin{vmatrix} a_1 & b_1 \\ a_2 & b_2 \end{vmatrix} \neq 0.$$

Note that the denominator of both the x- and the y-values in the solution is the determinant D of the coefficient matrix of the linear system.

Suppose we write $D_x = \begin{vmatrix} c_1 & b_1 \\ c_2 & b_2 \end{vmatrix}$ and $D_y = \begin{vmatrix} a_1 & c_1 \\ a_2 & c_2 \end{vmatrix}$, which are obtained by replacing the column containing the coefficients of x in D and the column containing the coefficients of y in D, by the column of constants, respectively. Then the solution just found can be written as

$$x = \frac{D_x}{D} \quad y = \frac{D_y}{D} \quad \text{provided that } D \neq 0.$$

This representation of the solution is Cramer's Rule for solving a system of linear equations.

CRAMER'S RULE FOR SOLVING TWO EQUATIONS IN TWO VARIABLES

The system

$$\begin{cases} a_1x + b_1y = c_1 \\ a_2x + b_2y = c_2 \end{cases}$$

of two equations in two variables has a unique solution (x, y) given by

$$x = \frac{D_x}{D} \quad \text{and} \quad y = \frac{D_y}{D}$$

provided that $D \neq 0$, where

$$D = \begin{vmatrix} a_1 & b_1 \\ a_2 & b_2 \end{vmatrix}, \quad D_x = \begin{vmatrix} c_1 & b_1 \\ c_2 & b_2 \end{vmatrix}, \quad \text{and} \quad D_y = \begin{vmatrix} a_1 & c_1 \\ a_2 & c_2 \end{vmatrix}.$$

EXAMPLE 4   Using Cramer's Rule

Use Cramer's rule to solve the system: $\begin{cases} 5x + 4y = 1 \\ 2x + 3y = 6 \end{cases}$

Solution

Step 1   Form the determinant D of the coefficient matrix.

$$D = \begin{vmatrix} 5 & 4 \\ 2 & 3 \end{vmatrix} = 15 - 8 = 7$$

Since $D = 7 \neq 0$, the system has a unique solution.

Step 2   Replace the column of coefficients of x in D by the constant terms to obtain

$$D_x = \begin{vmatrix} 1 & 4 \\ 6 & 3 \end{vmatrix} = 3 - 24 = -21.$$

Step 3   Replace the column of coefficients of y in D by the constant terms to obtain

$$D_y = \begin{vmatrix} 5 & 1 \\ 2 & 6 \end{vmatrix} = 30 - 2 = 28.$$

Step 4   By Cramer's Rule,

$$x = \frac{D_x}{D} = \frac{-21}{7} = -3 \quad \text{and} \quad y = \frac{D_y}{D} = \frac{28}{7} = 4.$$

The solution of the system is $x = -3$ and $y = 4$.

The solution set is $\{(-3, 4)\}$.

Check: You should check the solution in the original system.   ▪ ▪ ▪

PRACTICE PROBLEM 4   Use Cramer's Rule to solve the system:

$$\begin{cases} 2x + 3y = 7 \\ 5x + 9y = 4 \end{cases}$$
                                                                                    ▪

   Cramer's rule, as used in Example 4, can be generalized to a system of equations with more than two variables. We state the rule for three equations in three variables.

CRAMER'S RULE FOR SOLVING THREE EQUATIONS IN THREE VARIABLES

The system

$$\begin{cases} a_1 x + b_1 y + c_1 z = k_1 \\ a_2 x + b_2 y + c_2 z = k_2 \\ a_3 x + b_3 y + c_3 z = k_3 \end{cases}$$

of three equations in three variables has a unique solution (x, y, z) given by

$$x = \frac{D_x}{D}, \quad y = \frac{D_y}{D}, \quad \text{and} \quad z = \frac{D_z}{D}$$

provided that $D \neq 0$, where,

(Continued)

**CRAMER'S RULE FOR SOLVING THREE EQUATIONS
IN THREE VARIABLES (CONTINUED)**

$$D = \begin{vmatrix} a_1 & b_1 & c_1 \\ a_2 & b_2 & c_2 \\ a_3 & b_3 & c_3 \end{vmatrix}, \qquad D_x = \begin{vmatrix} k_1 & b_1 & c_1 \\ k_2 & b_2 & c_2 \\ k_3 & b_3 & c_3 \end{vmatrix},$$

$$D_y = \begin{vmatrix} a_1 & k_1 & c_1 \\ a_2 & k_2 & c_2 \\ a_3 & k_3 & c_3 \end{vmatrix}, \text{ and } D_z = \begin{vmatrix} a_1 & b_1 & k_1 \\ a_2 & b_2 & k_2 \\ a_3 & b_3 & k_3 \end{vmatrix}.$$

EXAMPLE 5   **Using Cramer's Rule**

Use Cramer's Rule to solve the system of equations.

$$\begin{cases} 7x + y + z - 1 = 0 \\ 5x + 3z - 2y = 4 \\ 4x - z + 3y = 0 \end{cases}$$

Solution

First rewrite the system of equations so that the terms on the left side of the equals sign are in the proper order and only the constant terms appear on the right side.

$$\begin{cases} 7x + y + z = 1 \\ 5x - 2y + 3z = 4 \\ 4x + 3y - z = 0 \end{cases}$$

STUDY TIP

When you apply Cramer's Rule, make sure that all linear equations are written in the form

$$ax + by + cz = k.$$

Step 1 $D = \begin{vmatrix} 7 & 1 & 1 \\ 5 & -2 & 3 \\ 4 & 3 & -1 \end{vmatrix}$

D is the determinant of the coefficient matrix.

$$= 7\begin{vmatrix} -2 & 3 \\ 3 & -1 \end{vmatrix} - 5\begin{vmatrix} 1 & 1 \\ 3 & -1 \end{vmatrix} + 4\begin{vmatrix} 1 & 1 \\ -2 & 3 \end{vmatrix}$$

Expand by column 1.

$$= 7(2 - 9) - 5(-1 - 3) + 4(3 + 2)$$

Evaluate determinants of order 2.

$$= 7(-7) - 5(-4) + 4(5) = -9$$

Simplify.

Since $D \neq 0$, the system has a unique solution.

Step 2   Replace the first column in D by constant terms, and evaluate the resulting determinant.

$$D_x = \begin{vmatrix} 1 & 1 & 1 \\ 4 & -2 & 3 \\ 0 & 3 & -1 \end{vmatrix}$$

Replace the x-coefficients in the first column in D by the constants.

$$= 1\begin{vmatrix} -2 & 3 \\ 3 & -1 \end{vmatrix} - 4\begin{vmatrix} 1 & 1 \\ 3 & -1 \end{vmatrix} + 0\begin{vmatrix} 1 & 1 \\ -2 & 3 \end{vmatrix}$$

Expand by the 1st column.

$$= 1(2 - 9) - 4(-1 - 3)$$

Evaluate determinants of order 2.

$$= 1(-7) - 4(-4) = 9$$

Simplify.

Step 3   Replace the second column in D by constant terms.

$$D_y = \begin{vmatrix} 7 & 1 & 1 \\ 5 & 4 & 3 \\ 4 & 0 & -1 \end{vmatrix}$$ Replace the 2nd column in D by constants.

$$= -1 \begin{vmatrix} 5 & 3 \\ 4 & -1 \end{vmatrix} + 4 \begin{vmatrix} 7 & 1 \\ 4 & -1 \end{vmatrix} - 0 \begin{vmatrix} 7 & 1 \\ 5 & 3 \end{vmatrix}$$ Expand by the 2nd column, since it contains a zero.

$$= -1(-5 - 12) + 4(-7 - 4)$$ Evaluate determinants of order 2.

$$= 17 - 44 = -27$$ Simplify.

Step 4   Replace the third column in D by constant terms.

$$D_z = \begin{vmatrix} 7 & 1 & 1 \\ 5 & -2 & 4 \\ 4 & 3 & 0 \end{vmatrix}$$ Replace the 3rd column in D by constants.

$$= 1 \begin{vmatrix} 5 & -2 \\ 4 & 3 \end{vmatrix} - 4 \begin{vmatrix} 7 & 1 \\ 4 & 3 \end{vmatrix} + 0 \begin{vmatrix} 7 & 1 \\ 5 & -2 \end{vmatrix}$$ Expand by the 3rd column.

$$= (15 + 8) - 4(21 - 4)$$ Evaluate determinants of order 2.

$$= 23 - 4(17) = -45$$ Simplify.

Step 5   Cramer's Rule gives the following values.

$$x = \frac{D_x}{D} = \frac{9}{-9} = -1$$ From Steps 1 and 2

$$y = \frac{D_y}{D} = \frac{-27}{9} = 3$$ From Steps 1 and 3

$$z = \frac{D_z}{D} = \frac{-45}{-9} = 5$$ From Steps 1 and 4

Hence, the solution set is $\{(-1, 3, 5)\}$.

Check: You should check the solution.   ■ ■ ■

PRACTICE PROBLEM 5   Use Cramer's rule to solve the system.

$$\begin{cases} 3x + 2y + z = 4 \\ 4x + 3y + z = 5 \\ 5x + y + z = 9 \end{cases}$$ ■

WARNING   *It is important to note that Cramer's Rule does not apply if $D = 0$. In this case, the system is either consistent and has dependent equations (has infinitely many solutions) or inconsistent (has no solution). When $D = 0$, use a different method for solving systems of equations to find the solution set.*

A Exercises   Basic Skills and Concepts

In Exercises 1–10, evaluate each determinant.

1. $\begin{vmatrix} 2 & 3 \\ 4 & 5 \end{vmatrix}$ -2

2. $\begin{vmatrix} 3 & -5 \\ 1 & 4 \end{vmatrix}$ 17

3. $\begin{vmatrix} 4 & -2 \\ 3 & -3 \end{vmatrix}$ -6

4. $\begin{vmatrix} -2 & \frac{1}{2} \\ 3 & 1 \end{vmatrix}$ $\frac{-7}{2}$

5. $\begin{vmatrix} -1 & -3 \\ -4 & -5 \end{vmatrix}$ -7

6. $\begin{vmatrix} \frac{1}{2} & \frac{1}{3} \\ \frac{1}{4} & \frac{1}{6} \end{vmatrix}$ 0

7. $\begin{vmatrix} \frac{3}{8} & \frac{1}{2} \\ -\frac{1}{9} & 5 \end{vmatrix}$ $\frac{139}{72}$

8. $\begin{vmatrix} -\frac{1}{2} & \frac{1}{3} \\ \frac{1}{4} & -\frac{1}{3} \end{vmatrix}$ $\frac{1}{12}$

9. $\begin{vmatrix} \sqrt{a} & \sqrt{b} \\ \sqrt{b} & \sqrt{a} \end{vmatrix}$ $a-b$

10. $\begin{vmatrix} \sqrt{3} & 1 \\ -1 & \sqrt{3} \end{vmatrix}$ 4

For Exercises 11–14, consider the matrix

$$A = \begin{bmatrix} 2 & -3 & 4 \\ 1 & -1 & 2 \\ 0 & 1 & 2 \end{bmatrix}.$$

11. Find the minors.
   a. M_{21} **b.** M_{23} **c.** M_{32} †

12. Find the cofactors.
   a. A_{21} **b.** A_{23} **c.** A_{32} †

13. Find the minors.
   a. M_{11} **b.** M_{22} **c.** M_{31} †

14. Find the cofactors.
   a. A_{11} **b.** A_{22} **c.** A_{31} †

In Exercises 15–30, evaluate each determinant.

15. $\begin{vmatrix} 1 & 0 & -1 \\ 0 & 2 & 2 \\ -1 & 0 & 0 \end{vmatrix}$ -2

16. $\begin{vmatrix} 2 & 0 & \frac{1}{2} \\ 1 & 0 & 2 \\ 4 & 0 & -5 \end{vmatrix}$ 0

17. $\begin{vmatrix} 1 & 2 & 3 \\ 0 & 3 & 4 \\ 0 & 0 & 4 \end{vmatrix}$ 12

18. $\begin{vmatrix} 2 & 3 & 4 \\ 0 & -4 & 6 \\ 0 & 0 & -5 \end{vmatrix}$ 40

19. $\begin{vmatrix} 1 & 0 & 0 \\ 2 & 0 & 0 \\ 3 & 4 & 5 \end{vmatrix}$ 0

20. $\begin{vmatrix} -1 & 0 & 0 \\ 3 & 2 & 0 \\ 4 & 5 & -3 \end{vmatrix}$ 6

21. $\begin{vmatrix} 1 & 6 & 0 \\ 2 & 5 & 3 \\ 3 & 4 & 0 \end{vmatrix}$ 42

22. $\begin{vmatrix} 1 & 0 & 2 \\ 0 & 5 & 7 \\ 3 & 1 & 0 \end{vmatrix}$ -37

23. $\begin{vmatrix} 3 & 4 & 1 \\ 1 & 4 & 3 \\ 4 & 3 & 1 \end{vmatrix}$ 16

24. $\begin{vmatrix} 3 & 1 & -2 \\ 4 & 0 & -4 \\ 2 & -1 & -3 \end{vmatrix}$ 0

25. $\begin{vmatrix} 0 & 1 & 6 \\ 1 & 0 & 4 \\ 8 & 3 & 1 \end{vmatrix}$ 49

26. $\begin{vmatrix} 0 & 2 & 3 \\ 1 & 0 & 1 \\ 3 & 2 & 0 \end{vmatrix}$ 12

27. $\begin{vmatrix} a & b & 0 \\ 0 & a & b \\ b & 0 & a \end{vmatrix}$ a^3+b^3

28. $\begin{vmatrix} 0 & z & y \\ z & 0 & x \\ y & x & 0 \end{vmatrix}$ $2xyz$

29. $\begin{vmatrix} a & b & c \\ c & a & b \\ b & c & a \end{vmatrix}$ $a^3+b^3+c^3-3abc$

30. $\begin{vmatrix} u & v & w \\ w & v & u \\ u & v & w \end{vmatrix}$ 0

In Exercises 31–40, use Cramer's Rule (if applicable) to solve each system of equations.

31. $\begin{cases} x + y = 8 \\ x - y = -2 \end{cases}$ $\{(3,5)\}$

32. $\begin{cases} 4x + 3y = -1 \\ 2x - 5y = 9 \end{cases}$ $\left\{\left(\dfrac{11}{13}, \dfrac{-19}{13}\right)\right\}$

33. $\begin{cases} 5x + 3y = 11 \\ 2x + y = 4 \end{cases}$ $\{(1,2)\}$

34. $\begin{cases} 2x - 7y = 13 \\ 5x + 6y = 9 \end{cases}$ $\{(3,-1)\}$

35. $\begin{cases} 2x + 9y = 4 \\ 3x - 2y = 6 \end{cases}$ $\{(2,0)\}$

36. $\begin{cases} 5x + 3y = 1 \\ 2x - 5y = -12 \end{cases}$ $\{(-1,2)\}$

37. $\begin{cases} 2x - 3y = 4 \\ 4x - 6y = 8 \end{cases}$ $\left\{\left(\dfrac{3}{2}y + 2, y\right)\right\}$

38. $\begin{cases} 3x + y = 2 \\ 6x + 2y = 4 \end{cases}$ $\{(x, -3x + 2)\}$

39. $\begin{cases} \dfrac{2}{x} + \dfrac{3}{y} = 2 \\ \dfrac{5}{x} + \dfrac{8}{y} = \dfrac{31}{6} \end{cases}$ $\{(2,3)\}$

40. $\begin{cases} \dfrac{3}{x} - \dfrac{6}{y} = 2 \\ \dfrac{4}{x} + \dfrac{7}{y} = -3 \end{cases}$ $\left\{\left(\dfrac{-45}{4}, \dfrac{-45}{17}\right)\right\}$

[*Hint:* For Exercises 39 and 40, let $u = \dfrac{1}{x}$ and $v = \dfrac{1}{y}$]

In Exercises 41–50, solve each system of equations by means of Cramer's Rule. Use technology to compute the determinants involved.

41. $\begin{cases} x - 2y + z = -1 \\ 3x + y - z = 4 \\ y + z = 1 \end{cases}$ †

42. $\begin{cases} x + 3y = 4 \\ y + 3z = 7 \\ z + 4x = 6 \end{cases}$ †

43. $\begin{cases} x + y - z = -3 \\ 2x + 3y + z = 2 \\ 2y + z = 1 \end{cases}$ †

44. $\begin{cases} 3x + y + z = 10 \\ x + y - z = 0 \\ 5x - 9y = 1 \end{cases}$ †

45. $\begin{cases} x + y + z = 3 \\ 2x - 3y + 5z = 4 \\ x + 2y - 4z = -1 \end{cases}$ †

46. $\begin{cases} x + 2y - z = 3 \\ 3x - y + z = 8 \\ x + y + z = 0 \end{cases}$ †

47. $\begin{cases} 2x - 3y + 5z = 11 \\ 3x + 5y - 2z = 7 \\ x + 2y - 3z = -4 \end{cases}$ †

48. $\begin{cases} x - 3y - 1 = 0 \\ 2x - y - 4z = 2 \\ y + 2z - 4 = 0 \end{cases}$ †

49. $\begin{cases} 5x + 2y + z = 12 \\ 2x + y + 3z = 13 \\ 3x + 2y + 4z = 19 \end{cases}$ †

50. $\begin{cases} 2x + y + z = 7 \\ 3x - y - z = -2 \\ x + 2y - 3z = -4 \end{cases}$ †

†Due to space constrictions, answers to these exercises may be found in the Answers beginning on page A–1 in the back of the book.

B Exercises   Applying the Concepts

Assume that the ***area of a triangle*** with vertices (x_1, y_1), (x_2, y_2), and (x_3, y_3) is equal to the absolute value of D, where

$$D = \frac{1}{2}\begin{vmatrix} x_1 & y_1 & 1 \\ x_2 & y_2 & 1 \\ x_3 & y_3 & 1 \end{vmatrix}.$$

In Exercises 51–54, use determinants to find the area of each triangle.

51. Area of a triangle. The triangle with vertices $(1, 2)$, $(-3, 4)$, and $(4, 6)$.   11

52. Area of a triangle. The triangle with vertices $(3, 1)$, $(4, 2)$, and $(5, 4)$. $\frac{1}{2}$

53. Area of a triangle. The triangle with vertices $(-2, 1)$, $(-3, -5)$, and $(2, 4)$.   10.5

54. Area of a triangle. The triangle with vertices $(-1, 2)$, $(2, 4)$, and the origin.   4

Collinearity. Three points $A(x_1, y_1)$, $B(x_1, y_2)$, and $C(x_3, y_3)$ are *collinear* (lie on the same line) if and only if the area of the triangle ABC is 0. In terms of determinants, three points (x_1, y_1), (x_2, y_2), and (x_3, y_3) are collinear if and only if

$$\begin{vmatrix} x_1 & y_1 & 1 \\ x_2 & y_2 & 1 \\ x_3 & y_3 & 1 \end{vmatrix} = 0.$$

In Exercises 55–58, use determinants to find whether the three given points are collinear.

55. $(0, 3)$, $(-1, 1)$, and $(2, 7)$ Yes

56. $(2, 0)$, $\left(1, \dfrac{1}{2}\right)$, and $(4, -1)$ Yes

57. $(0, -4)$, $(3, -2)$, and $(1, -4)$ No

58. $\left(0, -\dfrac{1}{4}\right)$, $(1, -1)$, and $(2, -2)$ No

Equation of a line. As explained in the discussion of collinearity, three points (x, y), (x_1, y_1), and (x_2, y_2) all lie on the same line if and only if

$$D = \begin{vmatrix} x & y & 1 \\ x_1 & y_1 & 1 \\ x_2 & y_2 & 1 \end{vmatrix} = 0.$$

In other words, a point $P(x, y)$ lies on the line passing through the points (x_1, y_1) and (x_2, y_2) if and only if the determinant $D = 0$. Thus, the equation

$$\begin{vmatrix} x & y & 1 \\ x_1 & y_1 & 1 \\ x_2 & y_2 & 1 \end{vmatrix} = 0.$$

is an equation of the line passing through the points (x_1, y_1) and (x_2, y_2).

In Exercises 59–62, use determinants to write an equation of the line passing through the given points, then evaluate the determinant and write the equation of the line in slope–intercept form.

59. $(-1, -1)$, $(1, 3)$ $y = 2x + 1$

60. $(0, 4)$, $(1, 1)$ $y = -3x + 4$

61. $\left(0, \dfrac{1}{3}\right)$, $(1, 1)$ $y = \dfrac{2}{3}x + \dfrac{1}{3}$

62. $\left(1, -\dfrac{1}{3}\right)$, $(2, 0)$ †

C Exercises   Beyond the Basics

In Exercises 63–67, we list some properties of determinants. These properties are true for $n \times n$ matrices. Verify the properties for $n = 2$ or $n = 3$.

63. If each entry in any row or each entry in any column of a matrix A is zero, then $|A| = 0$. Verify each of the following.

a. $\begin{vmatrix} 0 & 0 \\ 2 & 5 \end{vmatrix} = 0$ **b.** $\begin{vmatrix} 1 & 0 \\ 3 & 0 \end{vmatrix} = 0$

c. $\begin{vmatrix} 1 & -2 & 3 \\ 0 & 0 & 0 \\ 4 & 5 & -7 \end{vmatrix} = 0$ **d.** $\begin{vmatrix} 4 & 5 & 0 \\ 6 & -7 & 0 \\ 8 & 15 & 0 \end{vmatrix} = 0$

64. If a matrix B is obtained from matrix A by interchanging two rows (or columns), then $|B| = -|A|$. Verify each of the following.

a. $\begin{vmatrix} 2 & 3 \\ 4 & 5 \end{vmatrix} = -\begin{vmatrix} 4 & 5 \\ 2 & 3 \end{vmatrix}$

b. $\begin{vmatrix} -5 & 3 \\ 2 & -4 \end{vmatrix} = -\begin{vmatrix} 3 & -5 \\ -4 & 2 \end{vmatrix}$

c. $\begin{vmatrix} 1 & 3 & 5 \\ 0 & 1 & 2 \\ 3 & -1 & 4 \end{vmatrix} = -\begin{vmatrix} 1 & 3 & 5 \\ 3 & -1 & 4 \\ 0 & 1 & 2 \end{vmatrix}$

65. If two rows (or columns) of a matrix A have corresponding entries that are equal, then $|A| = 0$. Verify the following.

a. $\begin{vmatrix} 2 & 3 & 5 \\ -1 & 4 & 8 \\ 2 & 3 & 5 \end{vmatrix} = 0$　**b.** $\begin{vmatrix} 3 & 4 & 3 \\ 1 & 2 & 1 \\ -1 & 6 & -1 \end{vmatrix} = 0$

66. If a matrix B is obtained from a matrix A by multiplying every entry of one row (or one column) by a real number c, then $|B| = c|A|$. Verify each of the following.

a. $\begin{vmatrix} -1 & 2 & 3 \\ 1 \cdot 5 & 4 \cdot 5 & 8 \cdot 5 \\ 2 & 3 & 6 \end{vmatrix} = 5 \begin{vmatrix} -1 & 2 & 3 \\ 1 & 4 & 8 \\ 2 & 3 & 6 \end{vmatrix}$

b. $\begin{vmatrix} 1 & 2 & 3 \\ -1 & 5 & 6 \\ 0 & 2 & 9 \end{vmatrix} = 3 \begin{vmatrix} 1 & 2 & 1 \\ -1 & 5 & 2 \\ 0 & 2 & 3 \end{vmatrix}$

67. If a matrix B is obtained from a matrix A by replacing any row (or column) of A by the sum of that row (or column) and c times another row (or column), then $|B| = |A|$.

Verify that the following two determinants are equal:

$$\begin{vmatrix} 2 & -3 & 4 \\ -4 & 7 & -8 \\ 5 & -1 & 3 \end{vmatrix} \xrightarrow{2R_1 + R_2 \rightarrow R_2} \begin{vmatrix} 2 & -3 & 4 \\ 0 & 1 & 0 \\ 5 & -1 & 3 \end{vmatrix}.$$

68. Evaluate the determinant

$$D = \begin{vmatrix} 1 & 2 & 3 & 3 \\ 4 & 5 & 2 & 1 \\ 1 & 2 & 5 & 3 \\ 2 & 4 & 3 & 7 \end{vmatrix}$$

by following these steps:

(i)　$(-1)R_1 + R_3 \rightarrow R_3$

(ii)　Expand by the cofactors of row 3.

(iii)　In (ii), you will have a determinant of order 3. Evaluate it to obtain the value of D. -6

In Exercises 69–72, use the properties of determinants in Exercises 63–67 to obtain three zeros in one row (or column) and then evaluate the given determinant by evaluating the resulting determinant of order 3.

69. $\begin{vmatrix} 2 & 0 & -3 & 4 \\ 0 & 1 & 0 & 5 \\ 5 & 0 & -9 & 8 \\ 1 & 2 & 0 & 7 \end{vmatrix}$ 21　**70.** $\begin{vmatrix} -3 & 1 & 2 & 3 \\ 0 & -2 & 4 & 7 \\ -9 & 3 & 5 & 2 \\ 2 & -4 & 3 & -12 \end{vmatrix}$ 32

71. $\begin{vmatrix} 5 & 7 & 1 & 2 \\ 6 & 8 & 9 & 3 \\ 24 & 22 & 6 & 10 \\ 21 & 17 & 7 & 10 \end{vmatrix}$ 476　**72.** $\begin{vmatrix} 1 & 2 & 3 & 0 \\ 2 & -3 & 1 & 0 \\ -1 & -3 & 4 & 5 \\ 1 & 3 & 7 & 4 \end{vmatrix}$ -101

In Exercises 73–80, solve each equation for x.

73. $\begin{vmatrix} 3 & 2 \\ 6 & x \end{vmatrix} = 0$　4　**74.** $\begin{vmatrix} 3 & 2 \\ x & 12 \end{vmatrix} = 0$　18

75. $\begin{vmatrix} x & -2 \\ 1 & x-1 \end{vmatrix} = 0$　†　**76.** $\begin{vmatrix} 2x+7 & 4 \\ 1 & x \end{vmatrix} = 0$　$\frac{1}{2}, -4$

77. $\begin{vmatrix} 1 & -3 & 1 \\ 4 & 7 & x \\ 0 & 2 & 2 \end{vmatrix} = 0$　23　**78.** $\begin{vmatrix} x & x+1 & x+2 \\ 2 & 3 & -1 \\ 3 & -2 & 4 \end{vmatrix} = 0$　†

79. $\begin{vmatrix} x & 0 & 1 \\ 0 & x & 0 \\ 1 & 0 & x \end{vmatrix} = 0$　$-1, 0, 1$　**80.** $\begin{vmatrix} x & 2 & 3 \\ x & x & 1 \\ 2 & 0 & 1 \end{vmatrix} = -8$　2, 6

In Exercises 81 and 82, use the formula on page 869 for the area of a triangle.

81. If the area of the triangle formed by the points $(-4, 2)$, $(0, k)$, and $(-2, k)$ is 28 square units, find k. 30

82. If the area of the triangle formed by the points $(2, 3)$, $(1, 2)$, and $(-2, k)$ is 3 square units, find k. -7

Critical Thinking

83. Solve the system by Cramer's Rule.

$$\begin{cases} \dfrac{1}{x-2} + \dfrac{3}{y+1} = 13 \\ \dfrac{4}{x-2} - \dfrac{5}{y+1} = 1 \end{cases} \left\{ \left(\dfrac{9}{4}, \dfrac{-2}{3} \right) \right\}$$

[*Hint:* Do not try to simplify the equations by clearing the denominators, because the resulting equations will not be linear. Instead, let $u = \dfrac{1}{x-2}$ and $v = \dfrac{1}{y+1}$. Solve the system for u and v, and then use this solution to solve for x and y.]

In Exercises 84 and 85, use Cramer's Rule to solve each system of equations.

84. $\begin{cases} \dfrac{6}{x+1} + \dfrac{4}{y-1} = 7 \\ \dfrac{8}{x+1} + \dfrac{5}{y-1} = 9 \end{cases}$ $(1, 2)\}$

85. $\begin{cases} \dfrac{1}{3^x} + \dfrac{4}{4^y} = 25 \\ \dfrac{2}{3^x} - \dfrac{1}{4^y} = 14 \end{cases}$ $\{(-2, -1)\}$

Summary Definitions, Concepts, and Formulas

9.1 Matrices and Systems of Equations

i. **Matrix.** An $m \times n$ matrix is a rectangular array of numbers with m rows and n columns.

ii. **Augmented matrix.** The augmented matrix of a system of linear equations is a matrix whose entries are the coefficients of the variables in the system, together with the constants.

iii. **Elementary row operations.** For an augmented matrix of a system of linear equations, the following row operations will result in the matrix of an equivalent system:

  1. Interchange any two rows.

  2. Multiply any row by a nonzero constant.

  3. Add a multiple of one row to another row.

iv. **Row-echelon form and reduced row-echelon form.** The elementary row operations are used to transform an augmented matrix to row-echelon form or reduced row-echelon form. (See page 817).

v. **Gaussian elimination** is the method of transforming the augmented matrix to row-echelon form and then using back-substitution to find the solution set of a system of linear equations.

vi. **Gauss–Jordan elimination.** If you continue the Gaussian elimination procedure until a reduced row-echelon form is obtained, the procedure is called Gauss–Jordan elimination.

9.2 Matrix Algebra

i. **Equality of matrices.** Two matrices $A = [a_{ij}]$ and $B = [b_{ij}]$ are equal if (i) A and B have the same order $m \times n$ and (ii) all corresponding entries are equal.

ii. **Matrix addition.** The matrices A and B can be added or subtracted if they have the same order. Their sum or difference can be obtained by adding or subtracting the corresponding entries.

iii. **Scalar multiplication.** The product of a matrix by a real number (scalar) is obtained by multiplying every entry of the matrix by the real number.

iv. **Matrix multiplication.** The product AB of two matrices is defined only if the number of columns of A is equal to the number of rows of B. If A is an $m \times p$ matrix and B is a $p \times n$ matrix, then the product AB is an $m \times n$ matrix. The (i, j)th entry of AB is the sum of the products of the corresponding entries in the ith row of A and the jth column of B.

v. **The identity matrix.** The $n \times n$ identity matrix denoted by I_n or I is a matrix that has 1's on the main diagonal and 0's elsewhere. If A is an $n \times n$ matrix, then $AI = IA = A$.

9.3 The Inverse Matrix

i. **Inverse of a matrix.** Let A be an $n \times n$ matrix and I be the $n \times n$ identity matrix. If there is an $n \times n$ matrix B such that $AB = BA = I$, then A is **invertible** and B is called the **inverse** of A. We write $B = A^{-1}$.

ii. **Finding the inverse.** A procedure for finding A^{-1} (if it exists) is given on page 848.

iii. **Inverse of a 2×2 matrix.** The matrix $A = \begin{bmatrix} a & b \\ c & d \end{bmatrix}$ has an inverse if and only if $ad - bc \neq 0$. Moreover, if $ad - bc \neq 0$, then

$$A^{-1} = \frac{1}{ad - bc}\begin{bmatrix} d & -b \\ -c & a \end{bmatrix}.$$

iv. If A is invertible, then the solution of the matrix equation $AX = B$ is $X = A^{-1}B$.

9.4 Determinants and Cramer's Rule

i. **Determinant.** The determinant of a square matrix A is a real number denoted by $\det(A)$ or $|A|$.

ii. The determinant of a 2×2 matrix $A = \begin{bmatrix} a & b \\ c & d \end{bmatrix}$ is defined by $\det(A) = \begin{vmatrix} a & b \\ c & d \end{vmatrix} = ad - bc.$

iii. The determinant of a matrix of order $n \geq 3$ can be found by using the ideas of cofactors. (See page 862.)

iv. **Cramer's Rule** gives formulas for solving a square system of linear equations for which the determinant of the coefficient matrix is nonzero. (See page 864 for solving a system of two equations in two variables and page 865 for solving a system of three equations in three variables).

Review Exercises

Basic Skills and Concepts

In Exercises 1–4, determine the order of each matrix.

1. $\begin{bmatrix} -1 & 2 & 3 & 4 \end{bmatrix}$ 1×4 **2.** $[5]$ 1×1

3. $\begin{bmatrix} 2 & 3 \\ -1 & 2 \\ 0 & 1 \end{bmatrix}$ 3×2 **4.** $\begin{bmatrix} 1 & -1 & 2 & -4 \\ 5 & 4 & 3 & 2 \end{bmatrix}$ 2×4

5. Let A be the matrix of Exercise 4. Identify the entries $a_{12}, a_{14}, a_{23},$ and $a_{21}.$ $a_{12} = -1, a_{14} = -4, a_{23} = 3, a_{21} = 5$

6. Write the 2×3 matrix A with entries $a_{22} = 3, a_{21} = 4,$ $a_{12} = 2, a_{13} = 5, a_{11} = -1,$ and $a_{23} = 1.$ †

In Exercises 7 and 8, write the augmented matrix for each system of linear equations.

7. $\begin{cases} 2x - 3y = 7 \\ 3x + y = 6 \end{cases}$ †   **8.** $\begin{cases} x + y - z = 6 \\ 2x - 3y - 2z = 2 \\ 5x - 3y + z = 8 \end{cases}$ †

In Exercises 9 and 10, convert each matrix to row-echelon form.

9. $\begin{bmatrix} 0 & 1 & 2 & 1 \\ 2 & 0 & 3 & 4 \\ 1 & -2 & 1 & 7 \end{bmatrix}$ †   **10.** $\begin{bmatrix} 3 & -1 & 2 & 12 \\ 1 & 1 & -1 & 2 \\ 1 & 2 & 1 & 7 \end{bmatrix}$ †

In Exercises 11 and 12, convert each matrix to reduced row-echelon form.

11. $\begin{bmatrix} 3 & 1 & 3 & 1 \\ 2 & 1 & 1 & 1 \\ 1 & -1 & -1 & 0 \end{bmatrix}$ †   **12.** $\begin{bmatrix} 3 & 4 & -4 & 2 \\ 2 & 1 & -2 & 1 \\ 1 & 1 & 2 & 1 \end{bmatrix}$ †

In Exercises 13–16, solve each system of equations by Gaussian elimination.

13. $\begin{cases} x + y - z = 0 \\ 2x + y - 2z = 3 \\ 3x - 2y + 3z = 9 \end{cases}$ †   **14.** $\begin{cases} x - y + 2z = 1 \\ x + 3y - z = 6 \\ 2x + y - 3z = 1 \end{cases}$ †

15. $\begin{cases} x - 2y + 3z = -2 \\ 2x - 3y + z = 9 \\ 3x - y + 2z = 5 \end{cases}$ †   **16.** $\begin{cases} 2x + y + z = 7 \\ x + 2y + z = 3 \\ x + 2y + 2z = 6 \end{cases}$ †

In Exercises 17–20, solve each system of equations by Gauss–Jordan elimination.

17. $\begin{cases} x - 2y - 2z = 11 \\ 3x + 4y - z = -2 \\ 4x + 5y + 7z = 7 \end{cases}$ †   **18.** $\begin{cases} x - y - 9z = 1 \\ 3x + 2y - z = 2 \\ 4x + 3y + 3z = 0 \end{cases}$ †

19. $\begin{cases} 2x - y + 3z = 4 \\ x + 3y + 3z = -2 \\ 3x + 2y - 6z = 6 \end{cases}$ †   **20.** $\begin{cases} x - y - 9z = 1 \\ 3x + 2y - z = 2 \\ 4x + 3y + 3z = 0 \end{cases}$ †

21. Find x and y if $\begin{bmatrix} x - y & 0 \\ 1 & x + y \end{bmatrix} = \begin{bmatrix} 1 & 0 \\ 1 & 3 \end{bmatrix}.$ $\{(2, 1)\}$

22. Find x and y if
$$\begin{bmatrix} 2x + 3y & -1 & -2 \\ 0 & 1 & x - y \\ 2 & 3x + 4y & 5 \end{bmatrix} = \begin{bmatrix} 4 & -1 & -2 \\ 0 & 1 & -3 \\ 2 & 5 & 5 \end{bmatrix}.$$ †

23. Let $A = \begin{bmatrix} 1 & 2 \\ -3 & 4 \end{bmatrix}$ and $B = \begin{bmatrix} 2 & -3 \\ -5 & 6 \end{bmatrix}.$ Find each of the following.

a. $A + B$ †   b. $A - B$†

c. $2A$ †   d. $-3B$†

e. $2A - 3B$ †

24. Let $A = \begin{bmatrix} 2 & 0 & -1 \\ 1 & 2 & 2 \\ -2 & 0 & 3 \end{bmatrix}$ and $B = \begin{bmatrix} 0 & 1 & -1 \\ 1 & -1 & 0 \\ -1 & 0 & 1 \end{bmatrix}.$

Find each of the following.

a. $A + B$ †   b. $A - B$†

c. $2A + 3B$ †

25. For the matrices A and B of Exercise 23, solve the matrix equation $3A + 2B - 3X = \mathbf{0}$ for X. †

26. For the matrices A and B of Exercise 24, solve the matrix equation $A - 2X + 2B = \mathbf{0}$ for X. †

In Exercises 27–30, find the following products if possible.
a. AB b. BA

27. $A = \begin{bmatrix} 0 & 1 \\ 2 & 3 \end{bmatrix},$ $B = \begin{bmatrix} -1 & -1 \\ -3 & 4 \end{bmatrix}$ †

28. $A = \begin{bmatrix} 0 & 1 & 2 \\ -1 & 0 & 1 \end{bmatrix},$ $B = \begin{bmatrix} 1 & 2 \\ 3 & -1 \\ 0 & 4 \end{bmatrix}$ †

29. $A = \begin{bmatrix} 1 & 2 & -1 \end{bmatrix},$ $B = \begin{bmatrix} 2 \\ 3 \\ 1 \end{bmatrix}$ †

30. $A = \begin{bmatrix} 1 & 0 \\ 2 & -1 \\ 3 & -2 \end{bmatrix},$ $B = \begin{bmatrix} 1 & 2 & 3 & 4 \\ 2 & -1 & 2 & 3 \end{bmatrix}$ †

31. Find a matrix $A = \begin{bmatrix} x & y \\ z & w \end{bmatrix}$ such that
$$\begin{bmatrix} 1 & 2 \\ 3 & -1 \end{bmatrix} A = \begin{bmatrix} 5 & 6 \\ 1 & -3 \end{bmatrix} . \begin{bmatrix} 1 & 0 \\ 2 & 3 \end{bmatrix}$$

32. Find a matrix $B = \begin{bmatrix} x & y \\ z & w \end{bmatrix}$ such that
$$B \begin{bmatrix} 1 & 2 \\ 3 & -1 \end{bmatrix} = \begin{bmatrix} 5 & 6 \\ 1 & -3 \end{bmatrix} . \begin{bmatrix} \frac{23}{7} & \frac{4}{7} \\ -\frac{8}{7} & \frac{5}{7} \end{bmatrix}$$
Compare your answers for Exercises 31 and 32.

33. Find a matrix $A = \begin{bmatrix} x & y \\ z & w \end{bmatrix}$ such that
$$\begin{bmatrix} 5 & 3 \\ 4 & 2 \end{bmatrix} A = \begin{bmatrix} 1 & 0 \\ 0 & 1 \end{bmatrix} . \begin{bmatrix} -1 & \frac{3}{2} \\ 2 & -\frac{5}{2} \end{bmatrix}$$

34. Find a matrix $A = \begin{bmatrix} x & y \\ z & w \end{bmatrix}$ such that

$$A\begin{bmatrix} 5 & 3 \\ 4 & 2 \end{bmatrix} = \begin{bmatrix} 1 & 0 \\ 0 & 1 \end{bmatrix}. \quad \begin{bmatrix} -1 & \frac{3}{2} \\ 2 & -\frac{5}{2} \end{bmatrix}$$

Compare your answers for Exercises 33 and 34.

35. Let $A = \begin{bmatrix} 0 & 1 \\ -1 & 3 \end{bmatrix}$.

    a. Find A^{-1}. (Use the formula on page 614.) †
    b. Find $(A^2)^{-1}$. †
    c. Find $(A^{-1})^2$. †
    d. Use your answers in parts (b) and (c) to show that $(A^{-1})^2$ is the inverse of A^2.

36. Repeat Exercise 35 for $A = \begin{bmatrix} 3 & 4 \\ 2 & 3 \end{bmatrix}$. †

In Exercises 37–40, show that B is the inverse of A.

37. $A = \begin{bmatrix} 7 & 6 \\ 6 & 5 \end{bmatrix}$, $B = \begin{bmatrix} -5 & 6 \\ 6 & -7 \end{bmatrix}$

38. $A = \begin{bmatrix} -1 & 3 \\ 1 & -4 \end{bmatrix}$, $B = \begin{bmatrix} -4 & -3 \\ -1 & -1 \end{bmatrix}$

39. $A = \begin{bmatrix} 2 & -1 & 0 \\ 1 & 0 & 4 \\ 1 & -1 & 1 \end{bmatrix}$, $B = \frac{1}{5}\begin{bmatrix} 4 & 1 & -4 \\ 3 & 2 & -8 \\ -1 & 1 & 1 \end{bmatrix}$

40. $A = \begin{bmatrix} 2 & 0 & 1 \\ 0 & -1 & 2 \\ 1 & 0 & 1 \end{bmatrix}$, $B = \begin{bmatrix} 1 & 0 & -1 \\ -2 & -1 & 4 \\ -1 & 0 & 2 \end{bmatrix}$

In Exercises 41–44, find the inverse (if it exists) of each matrix.

41. $\begin{bmatrix} 3 & 1 \\ 2 & 4 \end{bmatrix}$ †
    42. $\begin{bmatrix} 3 & -4 \\ 1 & 2 \end{bmatrix}$ †

43. $\begin{bmatrix} 1 & 2 & -2 \\ -1 & 3 & 0 \\ 0 & -2 & 1 \end{bmatrix}$ †
    44. $\begin{bmatrix} 1 & 2 & 1 \\ 2 & 2 & 4 \\ 0 & 0 & 3 \end{bmatrix}$ †

In Exercises 45–50, use an inverse matrix (if possible) to solve each system of linear equations.

45. $\begin{cases} x + 3y = 7 \\ 2x + 5y = 4 \end{cases}$ $\{(-23, 10)\}$
    46. $\begin{cases} 3x + 5y = 4 \\ 2x + 4y = 5 \end{cases}$ $\left\{\left(\dfrac{-9}{2}, \dfrac{7}{2}\right)\right\}$

47. $\begin{cases} x + 3y + 3z = 3 \\ x + 4y + 3z = 5 \\ x + 3y + 4z = 6 \end{cases}$ †
    48. $\begin{cases} x + 2y + 3z = 6 \\ 2x + 4y + 5z = 8 \\ 3x + 5y + 6z = 10 \end{cases}$ †

49. $\begin{cases} x - y + z = 3 \\ 4x + 2y = 5 \\ 7x - y - z = 6 \end{cases}$ †
    50. $\begin{cases} x + 2y + 4z = 7 \\ 4x + 3y - 2z = 6 \\ x - 3z = 4 \end{cases}$ †

In Exercises 51–54, find the determinant of each matrix.

51. $\begin{bmatrix} 2 & -5 \\ 3 & 4 \end{bmatrix}$ 23

52. $\begin{bmatrix} -1 & 4 \\ 11 & -3 \end{bmatrix}$ -41

53. $\begin{bmatrix} 12 & 21 \\ 4 & 7 \end{bmatrix}$ 0
    54. $\begin{bmatrix} -7 & 9 \\ -4 & 5 \end{bmatrix}$ 1

In Exercises 55 and 56, find (a) the minors M_{12}, M_{23}, and M_{22}, and (b) the cofactors A_{12}, A_{23}, and A_{22}, of the given matrix A.

55. $A = \begin{bmatrix} 4 & -1 & 2 \\ -2 & -3 & 5 \\ 0 & 2 & -4 \end{bmatrix}$ †
    56. $A = \begin{bmatrix} 1 & 2 & 3 \\ 4 & 5 & 6 \\ 7 & 8 & 9 \end{bmatrix}$ †

In Exercises 57 and 58, find the determinant of each matrix A by expanding (a) by the second row and (b) by the third column.

57. $A = \begin{bmatrix} 1 & -2 & 3 \\ 4 & -1 & -2 \\ -2 & 1 & 5 \end{bmatrix}$ 35
    58. $A = \begin{bmatrix} 1 & 4 & 3 \\ 6 & 8 & 10 \\ 2 & 5 & 4 \end{bmatrix}$ 8

In Exercises 59 and 60, find the determinant of each matrix A.

59. $A = \begin{bmatrix} 1 & 2 & 0 \\ 0 & 1 & 2 \\ 1 & 0 & 2 \end{bmatrix}$ 6
    60. $A = \begin{bmatrix} 2 & 3 & 4 \\ 2 & 5 & 9 \\ 2 & 7 & 16 \end{bmatrix}$ 8

In Exercises 61–64, use Cramer's Rule to solve each system of equations.

61. $\begin{cases} 5x + 3y = 11 \\ 2x + y = 4 \end{cases}$ $\{(1, 2)\}$
    62. $\begin{cases} 2x - 7y - 13 = 0 \\ 5x + 6y - 9 = 0 \end{cases}$ †

63. $\begin{cases} 3x + y - z = 14 \\ x + 3y - z - 16 \\ x + y - 3z = -10 \end{cases}$ †
    64. $\begin{cases} 2x + 3y - 2z = 0 \\ 5y - 3x + 4z - 9 \\ 3x + 7y - 6z = 4 \end{cases}$ †

In Exercises 65 and 66, solve each equation for x.

65. $\begin{vmatrix} 1 & 2 & 4 \\ -3 & 5 & 7 \\ 1 & x & 4 \end{vmatrix} = 0$ 2
    66. $\begin{vmatrix} 1 & -1 & 2 \\ 0 & x & 1 \\ 3 & 2 & x-1 \end{vmatrix} = 14$ †

67. Show that equation of the line passing through the points $(2, 3)$ and $(1, -4)$ is equivalent to the equation

$$\begin{vmatrix} x & y & 1 \\ 2 & 3 & 1 \\ 1 & -4 & 1 \end{vmatrix} = 0. \text{ (See page 869.)} \; †$$

68. Use a determinant to find the area of the triangle with vertices $A(1, 1)$, $B(4, 3)$, and $C(2, 7)$. (See page 869.) 8

Applying the Concepts

69. **Maximizing profit.** A company is considering which of three methods of production it should use in producing the three products A, B, and C. The number of units of each product produced by each method is shown in this matrix:

$$\begin{array}{c} \\ Method\ 1 \\ Method\ 2 \\ Method\ 3 \end{array} \begin{array}{ccc} A & B & C \\ \begin{bmatrix} 4 & 8 & 2 \\ 5 & 7 & 1 \\ 5 & 4 & 8 \end{bmatrix} \end{array}$$

The profit per unit of the products A, B, and C is 10, 4, and 6 dollars, respectively. Use matrix multiplication to find which method maximizes total profit for the company. †

70. Nutrition. There are two families: Ardestanis (A) and Barkley (B). Family A consists of two adult males, three adult females, and one child. Family B consists of one adult male, one adult female, and two children. Their mutual dietician considers the ages and weights of each member of the two families and recommends daily allowances for calories—adult males 2200, adult females 1700, and children 1500—and for protein—adult males 50 grams, adult females 40 grams, and children 30 grams.

Represent the information in the preceding paragraph by matrices. Use matrix multiplication to calculate the total requirements of calories and proteins for each of the two families. †

In Exercises 71–76, each problem produces a system of linear equations in two or three variables. Use the method of your choice from this chapter to solve the system of equations.

71. Airplane speed. An airplane traveled 1680 miles in 3 hours with the wind. It would have taken 3.5 hours to have made the same trip against the wind. Find the speed of the plane and the velocity of the wind, assuming that both are constant. †

72. Walking speed. In 5 hours, Nertha walks 2 miles farther than Kristina walks in 4 hours; then, in 12 hours, Kristina walks 10 miles farther than Nertha walks in 10 hours. How many miles per hour does each walk? †

73. Friends. Andrew, Bonnie, and Chauncie have 320 dollars among them. Andrew has twice as much as Chauncie, and Bonnie and Chauncie together have 20 dollars less than Andrew. How much money does each have? †

74. Ratio. Steve and Nicole entered a double-decker bus in London on which there were $\frac{5}{8}$ as many men as women. After they boarded the bus, there were $\frac{7}{11}$ as many men as women on the bus. How many people were on the bus before they entered it? 20 males and 32 females

75. Hospital workers. Metropolitan Hospital employs three types of caregivers: registered nurses, licensed practical nurses, and nurse's aides. Each registered nurse is paid 75 dollars per hour, each licensed practical nurse is paid 20 dollars per hour, and each nurse's aide is paid 30 dollars per hour. The hospital has budgeted 4850 dollars per hour for the three categories of caregivers. The hospital requires that each caregiver spend some time in a class learning about advanced medical practices each week: registered nurses, 3 hours; licensed practical nurses, 5 hours; and nurse's aides, 4 hours. The advanced classes can accommodate a maximum of 530 person-hours each week. The hospital needs a total of 130 registered nurses, licensed practical nurses, and nurse's aides to meet the daily needs of the patients. Assume that the allowable payroll is met, the training classes are full, and the patients' needs are met. How many registered nurses, licensed practical nurses, and nurse's aides should the hospital employ? †

76. Sales tax. A drugstore sells three categories of items:
  (i)   medicine, which is not taxed,
  (ii) nonmedical items, which are taxed at the rate of 8%, and
  (iii) beer and cigarettes, which are taxed at the "sin tax" rate of 20%.

Last Friday, the total sales (excluding taxes) of all three items were 18,500 dollars. The total tax collected was 1020 dollars. The sales of medicines exceeded the combined sales of the other items by 3500 dollars. Find the sales in each category. †

Practice Test A

1. Give the order of the matrix and the value of the designated entry of the matrix.

$$\begin{bmatrix} 3 & -1 & -3 & 0 \\ 2 & 4 & 1 & 7 \\ 5 & 0 & 3 & 2 \\ 8 & 10 & 9 & 6 \\ -4 & 0 & 0 & 3 \end{bmatrix}; a_{43} \quad 5 \times 4; 9$$

2. Write an augmented matrix for the system of equations.

$$\begin{cases} 7x - 3y + 9z = 5 \\ -2x + 4y + 3z = -12† \\ 8x - 5y + z = -9 \end{cases}$$

3. Write the system of linear equations represented by the augmented matrix

$$\begin{bmatrix} 4 & 0 & -1 & | & -3 \\ 1 & 3 & 0 & | & 9 \\ 2 & 7 & 5 & | & 8 \end{bmatrix}$$

Use x, y, and z for the variables. †

4. Find values for the variables so that the matrices

$$\begin{bmatrix} x - 5 & y + 3 \\ z & 9 \end{bmatrix} = \begin{bmatrix} 5 & 13 \\ 0 & 9 \end{bmatrix}$$

are equal. $(10, 10, 0)$

In Problems 5 and 6, solve the system of equations by using matrices.

5. $\begin{cases} x + 2y + z = 6 \\ x + y - z = 7 \\ 2x - y + 2z = -3 \end{cases}$ $\{(2, 3, -2)\}$

6. $\begin{cases} 2x + y - 4z = 6 \\ -x + 3y - z = -2 \\ 2x - 6y + 2z = 4 \end{cases}$ $\left\{\left(\frac{20}{7} + \frac{11}{7}z, \frac{2}{7} + \frac{6}{7}z, z\right)\right\}$

7. Let $A = \begin{bmatrix} 5 & -2 \\ 4 & 0 \\ 7 & 6 \end{bmatrix}$ and $B = \begin{bmatrix} -3 & -1 \\ 0 & -8 \\ -4 & 6 \end{bmatrix}$. Find $A - B$. †

In Problems 8 and 9, find the product AB, or state that AB is not defined.

8. $A = \begin{bmatrix} 3 & -7 & 2 \end{bmatrix}$, $B = \begin{bmatrix} 0 \\ 1 \\ 4 \end{bmatrix}$ $AB = [1]$

9. $A = \begin{bmatrix} -4 & 1 & 2 \\ -9 & 0 & 3 \end{bmatrix}$ $B = \begin{bmatrix} 2 & 8 \\ 7 & -5 \end{bmatrix}$ †

For Problems 10–13, let

$$A = \begin{bmatrix} -3 & 1 & 0 \\ 5 & 7 & 2 \end{bmatrix}, \quad B = \begin{bmatrix} -1 & 4 \\ 8 & 2 \end{bmatrix}, \text{ and } C = \begin{bmatrix} 1 & 5 \\ 0 & 4 \end{bmatrix}.$$

10. Find $2A$. †

11. Find $A + BA$. †

12. Find C^2. †

13. Find C^{-1}. †

14. Find the inverse of the matrix

$$A = \begin{bmatrix} 2 & 1 & 3 \\ 1 & 2 & -1 \\ 3 & 1 & 5 \end{bmatrix}. †$$

15. Write the linear system

$$\begin{cases} 5x + 2y = 32 \\ 3x + y = 18 \end{cases}$$

as a matrix equation in the form $AX = B$, where A is the coefficient matrix and B is the constant matrix. †

16. Write the matrix equation

$$\begin{bmatrix} 12 & -3 \\ -2 & 7 \end{bmatrix}\begin{bmatrix} x \\ y \end{bmatrix} = \begin{bmatrix} 5 \\ -9 \end{bmatrix}$$

as a system of linear equations without matrices. †

17. Solve the matrix equation $A - 5X = 2B$ for X,

where $A = \begin{bmatrix} 1 & 5 & -2 \\ 4 & -2 & 7 \end{bmatrix}$ and $B = \begin{bmatrix} 2 & 5 & -11 \\ 18 & 8 & 11 \end{bmatrix}$. †

In Problems 18 and 19, evaluate the determinant.

18. $\begin{vmatrix} \frac{1}{2} & -\frac{1}{4} \\ \frac{1}{2} & \frac{3}{4} \end{vmatrix}$ $\frac{1}{2}$

19. $\begin{vmatrix} 1 & 3 & 5 \\ 2 & 0 & 10 \\ -3 & 1 & -15 \end{vmatrix}$ 0

20. Use Cramer's Rule to write the solution of the system

$$\begin{cases} 2x - y + z = 3 \\ x + y + z = 6 \\ 4x + 3y - 2z = 4 \end{cases}$$

in the determinant form. (You don't need to find the solution.) †

Practice Test B

1. Give the order of the matrix and the value of the designated entries of the matrix.

$$A = \begin{bmatrix} 0 & 3 & 0 & -10 & 6 \\ 14 & -5 & 7 & -7 & 8 \\ -15 & 9 & -6 & 13 & -2 \\ 0.4 & 11 & 4 & -3 & 0 \end{bmatrix}; a_{34} \text{ d}$$

(a) Order: 5×4; $a_{34} = 6$ **(b)** Order: 4×5; $a_{34} = 11$
(c) Order: 20; $a_{34} = -4$ **(d)** Order: 4×5; $a_{34} = 13$

2. Write an augmented matrix for the system of equations

$$\begin{cases} 8x + 4y + 5z = 10 \\ -2x + 3y + 6z = -9. \text{ d} \\ -2x + 8y + 6z = 4 \end{cases}$$

(a) $\begin{bmatrix} 8 & 4 & 5 \\ -2 & 3 & 6 \\ -2 & 8 & 6 \end{bmatrix}$ **(b)** $\begin{bmatrix} 10 & 5 & 4 & 8 \\ -9 & 6 & 3 & -2 \\ 4 & 6 & 8 & -2 \end{bmatrix}$

(c) $\begin{bmatrix} 8 & -2 & -2 & 10 \\ 4 & 3 & 8 & -9 \\ 5 & 6 & 6 & 4 \end{bmatrix}$ **(d)** $\begin{bmatrix} 8 & 4 & 5 & 10 \\ -2 & 3 & 6 & -9 \\ -2 & 8 & 6 & 4 \end{bmatrix}$

3. Write the system of linear equations represented by the augmented matrix

$$\begin{bmatrix} -1 & 7 & 0 & -6 \\ 2 & 0 & 6 & 5 \\ 0 & 8 & -8 & 4 \end{bmatrix}.$$

Use x, y, and z for the variables. d

(a) $\begin{cases} x + 7y + z = -6 \\ 2x + 6z = 5 \\ 8y + 8z = 4 \end{cases}$ **(b)** $\begin{cases} -x + 7y + z = -6 \\ 2x + 6y = 5 \\ 8x - 8y = 4 \end{cases}$

(c) $\begin{cases} -x + 7y + z = -6 \\ 2x + y + 6z = 5 \\ x + 8y - 8z = 4 \end{cases}$ **(d)** $\begin{cases} -x + 7y = -6 \\ 2x + 6z = 5 \\ 8y - 8z = 4 \end{cases}$

4. Find values for the variables so that the matrices

$$\begin{bmatrix} x + 3 & y + 4 \\ 7 & 3 \end{bmatrix} \text{ and } \begin{bmatrix} 9 & 2 \\ 7 & z \end{bmatrix}$$

are equal. c
(a) $x = -6$; $y = 2$; $z = 3$ **(b)** $x = 6$; $y = 9$; $z = 3$
(c) $x = 6$; $y = -2$; $z = 3$ **(d)** $x = 9$; $y = 2$; $z = 3$

5. Find the value of z in the system

$$\begin{cases} 2x + y = 15 \\ 2y + z = 25. \text{ c} \\ 2z + x = 26 \end{cases}$$

(a) 4
(b) 9
(c) 11
(d) 12.

6. Find the value of $4x + 3y + z$ in the system

$$\begin{cases} 2x + y = 17 \\ y + 2z = 15. \text{ d} \\ x + z = 9 \end{cases}$$

(a) 41   **(b)** 43   **(c)** 55   **(d)** 45.

7. Let $A = \begin{bmatrix} -1 & 4 \\ 0 & 4 \\ 8 & -4 \end{bmatrix}$ and $B = \begin{bmatrix} 7 & 2 \\ 17 & 4 \\ 2 & 2 \end{bmatrix}$. Find $A - B$. c

(a) $\begin{bmatrix} 1 & 2 \\ 7 & 0 \\ 6 & -2 \end{bmatrix}$ **(b)** $\begin{bmatrix} 3 & -3 \\ 7 & 0 \\ -6 & 6 \end{bmatrix}$

(c) $\begin{bmatrix} -8 & 2 \\ -17 & 0 \\ 6 & -6 \end{bmatrix}$ **(d)** $\begin{bmatrix} 1 & 5 \\ 7 & 8 \\ 10 & 0 \end{bmatrix}$

In Problems 8 and 9, find the product AB if possible.

8. $A = \begin{bmatrix} -8 & 2 & 9 \end{bmatrix}$, $B = \begin{bmatrix} 3 \\ 0 \\ -3 \end{bmatrix}$ b

(a) $\begin{bmatrix} -24 & 0 & -27 \end{bmatrix}$ **(b)** $\begin{bmatrix} -51 \end{bmatrix}$

(c) $\begin{bmatrix} 210 \end{bmatrix}$ **(d)** $\begin{bmatrix} -24 \\ 0 \\ -27 \end{bmatrix}$

9. $A = \begin{bmatrix} 3 & -2 & 1 \\ 0 & 4 & -2 \end{bmatrix}$, $B = \begin{bmatrix} 5 & 0 \\ -2 & 1 \end{bmatrix}$ a

(a) AB is not defined.   **(b)** $\begin{bmatrix} 15 & -10 & 5 \\ -6 & 8 & -4 \end{bmatrix}$

(c) $\begin{bmatrix} 15 & -6 \\ -10 & 8 \\ 5 & -4 \end{bmatrix}$ **(d)** $\begin{bmatrix} 15 & 0 \\ 0 & 4 \end{bmatrix}$

For Problems 10–13, let

$$A = \begin{bmatrix} 2 & 1 & -3 \\ -5 & 2 & 1 \end{bmatrix}, B = \begin{bmatrix} -3 & 7 \\ 2 & 4 \end{bmatrix}, \text{ and } C = \begin{bmatrix} 5 & 4 \\ 1 & 0 \end{bmatrix}.$$

10. Find $2A$. b

(a) $\begin{bmatrix} 1 & \dfrac{1}{2} & -\dfrac{3}{2} \\ -\dfrac{5}{2} & 1 & \dfrac{1}{2} \end{bmatrix}$ **(b)** $\begin{bmatrix} 4 & 2 & -6 \\ -10 & 4 & 2 \end{bmatrix}$

(c) $\begin{bmatrix} 4 & 3 & -1 \\ -3 & 4 & 3 \end{bmatrix}$ **(d)** $\begin{bmatrix} 0 & -1 & -5 \\ -7 & 0 & -1 \end{bmatrix}$

11. Find $A + BA$. c

(a) $\begin{bmatrix} 2 & -4 & 10 \\ -5 & 4 & 5 \end{bmatrix}$ **(b)** $\begin{bmatrix} 4 & -2 & 6 \\ -10 & 4 & 2 \end{bmatrix}$

(c) $\begin{bmatrix} -39 & 12 & 13 \\ -21 & 12 & -1 \end{bmatrix}$ **(d)** $\begin{bmatrix} -41 & 17 & -2 \\ -16 & 6 & 10 \end{bmatrix}$

12. Find C^2. c

(a) $\begin{bmatrix} 10 & 8 \\ 2 & 0 \end{bmatrix}$ **(b)** $\begin{bmatrix} 41 & 5 \\ 5 & 1 \end{bmatrix}$

(c) $\begin{bmatrix} 29 & 20 \\ 5 & 4 \end{bmatrix}$ **(d)** $\begin{bmatrix} 0 & 4 \\ 1 & 5 \end{bmatrix}$

13. Find C^{-1}. b

(a) $\begin{bmatrix} -\dfrac{5}{4} & 1 \\ \dfrac{1}{4} & 0 \end{bmatrix}$ **(b)** $\begin{bmatrix} 0 & 1 \\ \dfrac{1}{4} & -\dfrac{5}{4} \end{bmatrix}$

(c) $\begin{bmatrix} \dfrac{1}{4} & -\dfrac{5}{4} \\ 0 & 1 \end{bmatrix}$ **(d)** $\begin{bmatrix} 0 & -1 \\ -\dfrac{1}{4} & \dfrac{5}{4} \end{bmatrix}$

14. Find the inverse of the matrix

$$A = \begin{bmatrix} 1 & 0 & 0 \\ 2 & 1 & 0 \\ 3 & -4 & 1 \end{bmatrix}.\ \text{d}$$

(a) $\begin{bmatrix} 1 & 0 & 0 \\ -2 & 1 & 0 \\ 3 & 4 & 1 \end{bmatrix}$ **(b)** $\begin{bmatrix} 1 & 0 & 0 \\ -2 & 1 & 0 \\ -8 & 3 & 1 \end{bmatrix}$

(c) $\begin{bmatrix} 1 & -2 & -11 \\ 0 & 1 & 4 \\ 0 & 0 & 1 \end{bmatrix}$ **(d)** $\begin{bmatrix} 1 & 0 & 0 \\ -2 & 1 & 0 \\ -11 & 4 & 1 \end{bmatrix}$

15. Write the linear system as a matrix equation

$$\begin{cases} 4x + 2y = 15 \\ -2x + 4y = 9 \end{cases}$$

in the form $AX = B$, where A is the coefficient matrix and B is the constant matrix. a

(a) $\begin{bmatrix} 4 & 2 \\ -2 & 4 \end{bmatrix}\begin{bmatrix} x \\ y \end{bmatrix} = \begin{bmatrix} 15 \\ 9 \end{bmatrix}$ **(b)** $\begin{bmatrix} 4 & 2 \\ 4 & -2 \end{bmatrix}\begin{bmatrix} x \\ y \end{bmatrix} = \begin{bmatrix} 15 \\ 9 \end{bmatrix}$

(c) $\begin{bmatrix} 15 & 2 \\ 9 & -2 \end{bmatrix}\begin{bmatrix} x \\ y \end{bmatrix} = \begin{bmatrix} 4 \\ 4 \end{bmatrix}$ **(d)** $\begin{bmatrix} 4 & -2 \\ 2 & 4 \end{bmatrix}\begin{bmatrix} x \\ y \end{bmatrix} = \begin{bmatrix} 15 \\ 9 \end{bmatrix}$

16. Write the matrix equation

$$\begin{bmatrix} -3 & 9 \\ -8 & -4 \end{bmatrix}\begin{bmatrix} x \\ y \end{bmatrix} = \begin{bmatrix} -4 \\ -5 \end{bmatrix}$$

as a system of linear equations. a

(a) $\begin{cases} -3x + 9y = -4 \\ -8x - 4y = -5 \end{cases}$ **(b)** $\begin{cases} -3x + 9y = -4 \\ -4x - 8y = -5 \end{cases}$

(c) $\begin{cases} 9x - 3y = -4 \\ -8x - 4y = -5 \end{cases}$ **(d)** $\begin{cases} -3x + 9y = 4 \\ -8x - 4y = 5 \end{cases}$

17. Let $A = \begin{bmatrix} -2 & -3 & 1 \\ -5 & 3 & -2 \end{bmatrix}$ and $B = \begin{bmatrix} -1 & -2 & -1 \\ 1 & 0 & 1 \end{bmatrix}$.

Solve the matrix equation $A - 3X = -5B$ for X. b

(a) $X = \begin{bmatrix} -\dfrac{5}{2} & -\dfrac{9}{2} & -1 \\ -1 & \dfrac{3}{2} & \dfrac{1}{2} \end{bmatrix}$

(b) $X = \begin{bmatrix} -\dfrac{7}{3} & -\dfrac{13}{3} & -\dfrac{4}{3} \\ 0 & 1 & 1 \end{bmatrix}$

(c) $X = \begin{bmatrix} -1 & \dfrac{3}{2} & -1 \\ -\dfrac{5}{2} & -\dfrac{9}{2} & -1 \end{bmatrix}$

(d) $X = \begin{bmatrix} -\dfrac{1}{3} & \dfrac{1}{3} & \dfrac{8}{3} \\ -\dfrac{20}{3} & 3 & -\dfrac{11}{3} \end{bmatrix}$

In Problems 18 and 19, evaluate the determinant.

18. $\begin{vmatrix} -8 & 5 \\ -4 & -1 \end{vmatrix}$ d

(a) -28 **(b)** -44
(c) -12 **(d)** 28

19. $\begin{vmatrix} 2 & 3 & -2 \\ 3 & 0 & -3 \\ -3 & 0 & -5 \end{vmatrix}$ c

(a) -72 **(b)** 18
(c) 72 **(d)** -18

20. Solve the system of equations

$$\begin{cases} x + y + z = -6 \\ x - y + 3z = -22 \\ 2x + y + z = -10 \end{cases}$$

by using Cramer's Rule. b

(a) $\varnothing$ **(b)** $\{(-4, 3, -5)\}$
(c) $\{(-5, -4, 3)\}$ **(d)** $\{(-5, 3, -4)\}$

Cumulative Review Exercises   (Chapters 1–9)

1. If the distance between the points $(2, -3)$ and $(-1, y)$ is five units, find y. $-7, 1$

In Problems 2–8, solve each equation or inequality.

2. $\dfrac{4}{x-1} - \dfrac{3}{x+2} = \dfrac{18}{(x+2)(x-1)}$ 7

3. $|2x - 5| = 3$ $4, 1$

4. $4x^2 = 8x - 13$ †

5. $\left(\dfrac{3x-1}{x+5}\right)^2 - 3\left(\dfrac{3x-1}{x+5}\right) - 28 = 0$ $-9, \dfrac{-19}{7}$

6. $\log_2|x| + \log_2|x + 6| = 4$ $2, -8$

7. $\dfrac{x+2}{2x-1} > 0$ $x < -2$ or $x > \dfrac{1}{2}$

8. $\cos x = -\dfrac{1}{2}, 0 \le x \le 2\pi$

9. Write all possible rational zeros of
$$f(x) = 4x^3 + 8x^2 - 11x + 3. †$$

10. Show that $\dfrac{1}{2}$ is a zero of multiplicity 2 of the function f in Problem 9.

11. The horsepower required to propel a ship varies as the cube of the ship's speed. If the horsepower required for a speed of 15 miles per hour is 10,125, find the horsepower required for a speed of 20 miles per hour.   24,000

12. A city covers an area of 400 square miles. At present, only 2 percent of its area is reserved for parks. In the unincorporated area outside the city limits, 20 percent of the area could be developed into parks. How many square miles of the incorporated area had to be annexed so that the city could develop 12 percent of its area as parks?   500

In Problems 13 and 14, solve the system of equations.

13. $\begin{cases} 3x + y = 2 \\ 4x + 5y = -1 \end{cases}$ $\{(1, -1)\}$

14. $\begin{cases} 2x + y = 5 \\ y^2 - 2y = -3x + 5 \end{cases}$ $\left\{(2,1), \left(\dfrac{5}{4}, \dfrac{5}{2}\right)\right\}$

15. Use transformations to sketch the graph of
$$f(x) = 1 + \cos\left(x - \dfrac{\pi}{4}\right).$$

16. Find the inverse of the matrix $\begin{bmatrix} 1 & 2 & -2 \\ -1 & 3 & 0 \\ 0 & -2 & 1 \end{bmatrix}$ †

17. Use the result in Problem 16 to solve the system of equations
$$\begin{cases} x + 2y - 2z = 5 \\ -x + 3y = 2 \\ -2y + z = -3 \end{cases} \quad \{(1, 1, -1)\}$$

18. If $f(x) = x^2 + 3x - 1$ and $g(x) = x + 2$, find
(a) $F(x) = (f \circ g)(x)$ and (b) $F(4)$. †

19. Let $f(x) = \dfrac{x}{x+4}$. Find $f^{-1}(x)$. $f^{-1}(x) = \dfrac{-4x}{x-1}$

20. Use the power-reducing identity to verify the identity:
$$\sin^4 x = \dfrac{1}{8}\left(3 - 4\cos 2x + \cos 4x\right)$$

Answer:

8. $\left\{\dfrac{2\pi}{3}, \dfrac{4\pi}{3}\right\}$

Answer:

15. Shift the graph of $y = \cos x$ $\pi/4$ units right and then shift it 1 unit up

CHAPTER 10

The Conic Sections

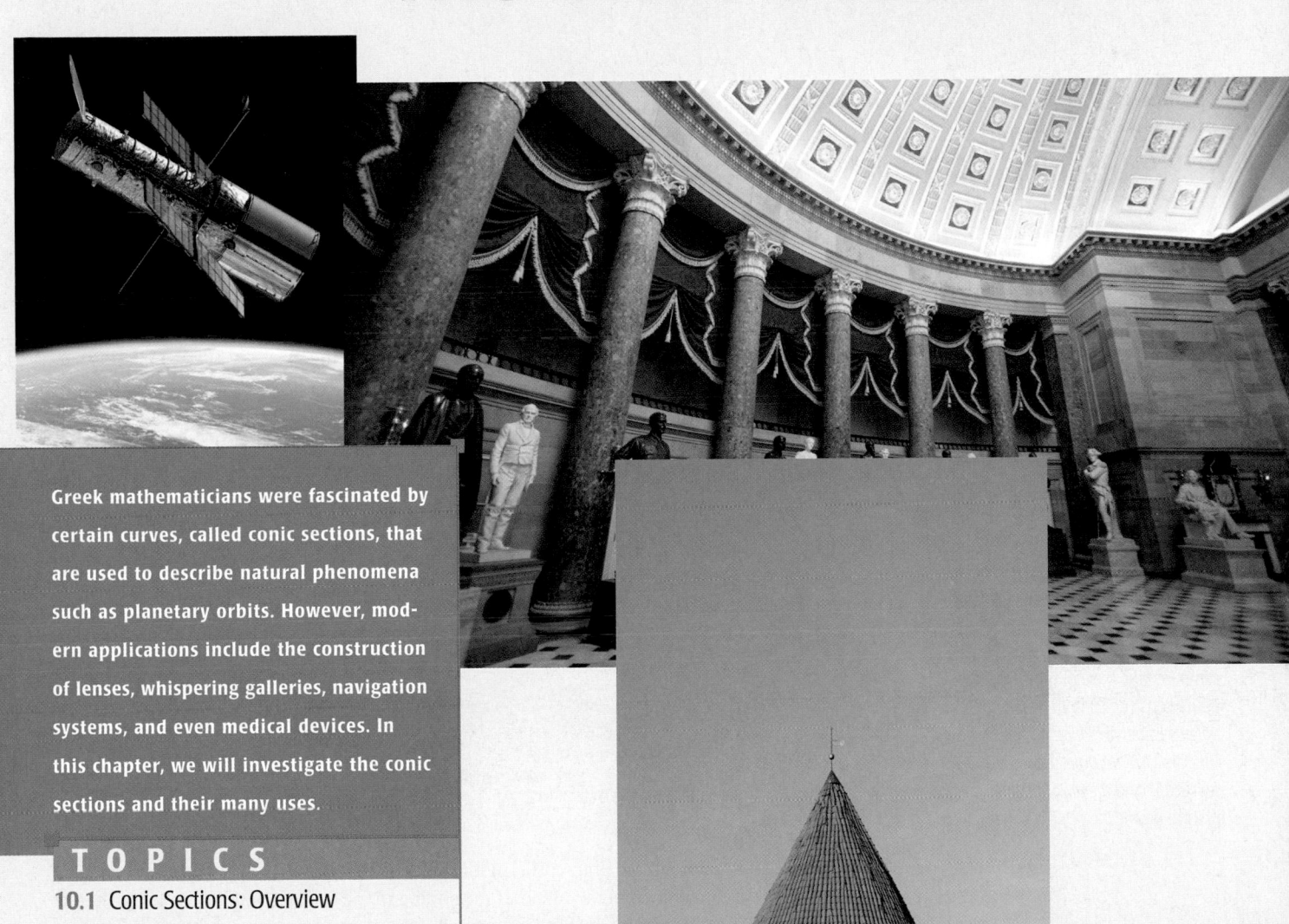

Greek mathematicians were fascinated by certain curves, called conic sections, that are used to describe natural phenomena such as planetary orbits. However, modern applications include the construction of lenses, whispering galleries, navigation systems, and even medical devices. In this chapter, we will investigate the conic sections and their many uses.

TOPICS

Conic Sections: Overview

In this chapter, we study curves called **conic sections.** As the name implies, these curves are the sections of a cone (similar to an ice cream cone) formed when a plane intersects the cone. ■

Apollonius of Perga

(c. 262 B.C. – 190 B.C.)

The mathematician Apollonius was born in Perga, in southern Asia Minor (today known as Murtina in Turkey). He went to Alexandria to study with the successors of Euclid. He became famous in ancient times for his work on astronomy and his eight books on conics. He was able to discover and prove hundreds of beautiful and difficult theorems without modern algebraic symbolism. He is credited with introducing the terms *ellipse, hyperbola,* and *parabola.* The original meaning of these terms compared the base of the geometric figure constructed with the length of a given segment. *Ellipse* meant "deficient," *hyperbola* meant "exceeds," and a *parabola* is "a placing beside."

Euclid defined a cone as a surface generated by rotating a right triangle about one of its legs. However, the following description of a cone given by Apollonius is more appropriate.

RIGHT CIRCULAR CONE

Draw a circle on a flat surface. Draw a line l, called the **axis,** that passes through the center of the circle and is perpendicular to the flat surface. Choose a point V above the flat surface on this line. The surface consisting of all the lines that simultaneously pass through both the point V and the circle is called a **right circular cone** with **vertex** V. The vertex V separates the surface into two parts called **nappes of the cone.** (See Figure 10.1.)

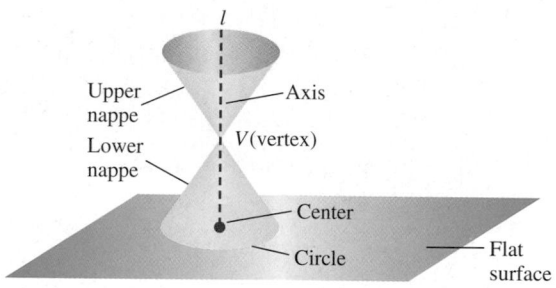

FIGURE 10.1

Suppose we slice the cone in Figure 10.1 with a plane. Then several types of curves called **conic sections** are produced in the plane. If the slicing plane is horizontal (parallel to the flat surface), then a **circle** (Figure 10.2(a)) is formed. However, if the slicing plane is inclined slightly from the horizontal, then an oval-shaped curve called an **ellipse** is formed. In fact, as the angle of the slicing plane increases, more elongated ellipses are formed (Figure 10.2(b)). If the angle of the slicing plane increases still further, so that the slicing plane is parallel to the "side" of the cone, the curve formed is called a **parabola** (Figure 10.2(c)). If the angle of the slicing plane increases yet further so that the slicing plane intersects both nappes of the cone, the resulting curve formed is called a **hyperbola** (Figure 10.2(d)).

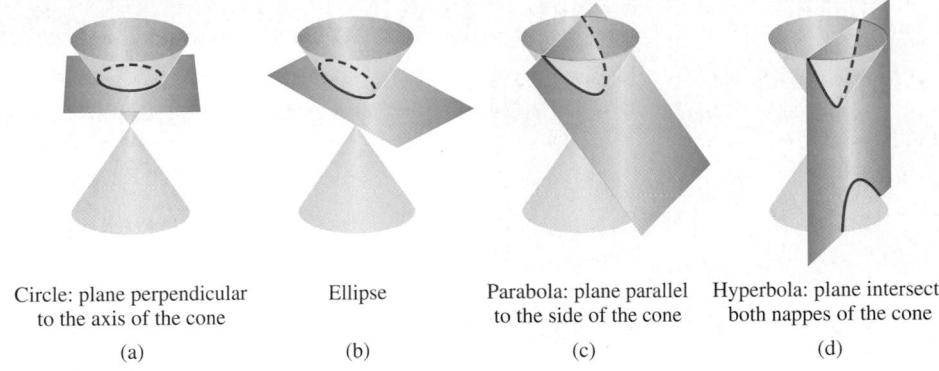

Circle: plane perpendicular
to the axis of the cone

(a)

Ellipse

(b)

Parabola: plane parallel
to the side of the cone

(c)

Hyperbola: plane intersects
both nappes of the cone

(d)

FIGURE 10.2

The point and lines obtained by a slicing plane through the vertex are called **degenerate conic sections.** (See Figure 10.3.)

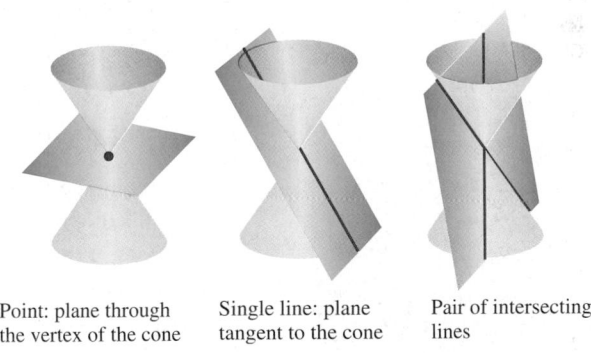

Point: plane through
the vertex of the cone

Single line: plane
tangent to the cone

Pair of intersecting
lines

FIGURE 10.3

Just as a circle (see page 198) is defined as the set of points in the plane at a fixed distance r (the radius) from a fixed point (the center), we can define each of the conic sections just described as a set of points that satisfy certain conditions. These definitions of the conic sections are based on their geometric properties rather than their interpretation as intersections of a plane with a cone. This enables us to keep our work in a two-dimensional setting. Using these definitions, we will derive the equations of the conic sections and show that an equation of the form $Ax^2 + Cy^2 + Dx + Ey + F = 0$ is (except in degenerate cases represented in Figure 10.3) the equation of a parabola, an ellipse, or a hyperbola. (A circle is a special case of an ellipse.)

We study these conic sections because of their practical applications. For example, a satellite dish, a flashlight lens, and a telescope lens have a parabolic shape, the planets travel in elliptical orbits, and comets travel in orbits that are either elliptical or hyperbolic. A comet with an elliptical orbit can be viewed from Earth more than once, while those with a hyperbolic orbit can be viewed only once!

The Parabola

Hubble Telescope

Edwin Hubble
(1889–1953)
Edwin Hubble is renowned for discovering that there are other galaxies in the universe beyond the Milky Way. Hubble then wanted to classify the galaxies according to their content, distance, shape, and brightness patterns. He made the momentous discovery that the galaxies were moving away from each other at a rate proportional to the distance between them (Hubble's Law). This led to the calculation of the point where the expansion began and to confirmation of the Big Bang theory of the origin of the universe. Recent estimates place the age of the universe at about 20 billion years.

BEFORE STARTING THIS SECTION, REVIEW

1. Distance formula (Section 2.1, page 185)

2. Midpoint formula (Section 2.1, page 187)

3. Completing a square (Section 1.4, page 123)

4. Line of symmetry (Section 2.2, page 194)

5. Slopes of perpendicular lines (Section 2.3, page 214)

OBJECTIVES

1 Learn the definition of a parabola.

2 Find an equation of a parabola.

3 Translate a parabola.

4 Use the reflecting property of parabolas.

The Hubble Space Telescope

In 1918, the 2.5-meter (100-inch) Hooker Telescope was installed at Mt. Wilson Observatory in Pasadena, California. With this telescope, astronomer Edwin Hubble measured the distances and velocities of the galaxies. His work led to today's concept of an expanding universe. In 1977, the National Aeronautics and Space Administration (NASA) named its largest, most complex, and most capable orbiting telescope in honor of Edwin Hubble.

On April 25, 1990, the Hubble Space Telescope was deployed into orbit from the space shuttle *Discovery*. However, due to a spherical aberration in the telescope's parabolic mirror, the Hubble had "blurred vision." (See Example 4.) In 1993, astronauts from the space shuttle *Endeavor* installed replacement instruments and supplemental optics to restore the telescope to full optimal performance.

Not since Galileo turned his telescope toward the heavens in 1610 has any event so changed our understanding of the universe as did the deployment of the Hubble Space Telescope. The first instrument of any kind that was specifically designed for routine servicing by spacewalking astronauts, the Hubble telescope brought some stunning pictures from the end of the universe to the general public. ■

---

1 Learn the definition of a parabola.

Definition of a Parabola

In Section 3.1, we stated that the graph of any quadratic function $y = ax^2 + bx + c$, $a \neq 0$, is a parabola. In this section, we give a *geometric* definition of a parabola. Then we derive an equation of a parabola based on the geometric definition.

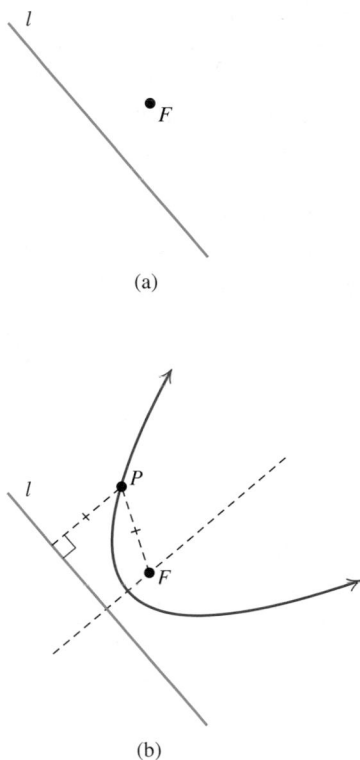

(a)

(b)

FIGURE 10.4

PARABOLA

Let l be a line and F a point in the plane not on the line l. Then the set of all points P in the plane that are the same distance from F as they are from the line l is called a **parabola**. See Figure 10.4. Thus, a parabola is the set of points P for which $d(F, P) = d(P, l)$, where $d(P, l)$ denotes the distance between P and l.

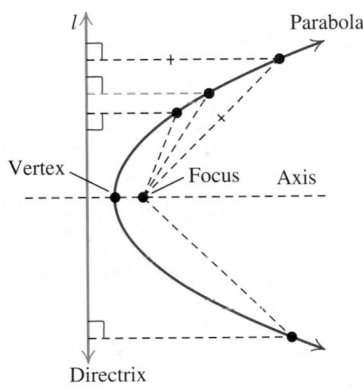

FIGURE 10.5

The line l is called the **directrix** of the parabola, and the point F is called the **focus.** The line through the focus *perpendicular* to the directrix is called the **axis,** or the **axis of symmetry,** of the parabola. The point at which the axis intersects the parabola is called the **vertex.** See Figure 10.5.

Equation of a Parabola

2 Find an equation of a parabola.

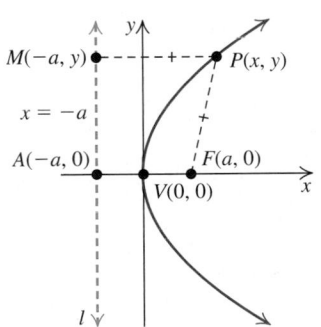

FIGURE 10.6

A coordinate system allows us to translate the geometric description of a parabola into an algebraic equation, called an *equation of the parabola*. An equation of a parabola is particularly simple if you place the vertex V at the origin and the focus on one of the coordinate axes. Suppose for the moment that the focus F is on the positive x-axis . Then F has coordinates of the form $(a, 0)$ with $a > 0$, as shown in Figure 10.6.

The vertex V lies on the parabola with focus F and directrix l, so we have

$$d(V, l) = d(V, F) \qquad \text{Definition of parabola}$$
$$= a.$$

The vertex V at the origin is located midway between the focus and the directrix. Thus, the equation of the directrix is $x = -a$.

Suppose a point $P(x, y)$ lies on the parabola shown in Figure 10.6. Then the distance from the point P to the directrix l is the distance between the points $P(x, y)$ and $M(-a, y)$. Thus, a point $P(x, y)$ lies on this parabola if and only if

$$d(P, F) = d(P, M).$$

Using the distance formula we have

$$d(P, F) = \sqrt{(x-a)^2 + y^2} \quad \text{and} \quad d(P, M) = \sqrt{(x+a)^2}.$$

$$\sqrt{(x-a)^2 + y^2} = \sqrt{(x+a)^2} \qquad d(P, F) = d(P, M)$$

$$(x-a)^2 + y^2 = (x+a)^2 \qquad \text{Square both sides.}$$

$$x^2 - 2ax + a^2 + y^2 = x^2 + 2ax + a^2 \qquad \text{Expand squares.}$$

$$y^2 = 4ax \qquad \text{Simplify.}$$

The equation $y^2 = 4ax$ is called the **standard equation of a parabola with vertex (0, 0) and focus (a, 0).** Similarly, if the focus of a parabola is placed on the negative x-axis, we obtain the equation $y^2 = -4ax$ as the standard equation of a parabola with vertex (0, 0) and focus $(-a, 0)$.

By interchanging the roles of x and y, we find that the equation $x^2 = 4ay$ is the standard equation of a parabola with vertex (0, 0) and focus (0, a). Similarly, the equation $x^2 = -4ay$ is the standard equation of a parabola with vertex (0, 0) and focus (0, $-a$).

Main facts about a parabola with $a > 0$

Standard Equation	$y^2 = 4ax$	$y^2 = -4ax$	$x^2 = 4ay$	$x^2 = -4ay$
Vertex	(0, 0)	(0, 0)	(0, 0)	(0, 0)
Description	Opens right	Opens left	Opens up	Opens down
Axis of Symmetry	$y = 0$ (x-axis)	$y = 0$ (x-axis)	$x = 0$ (y-axis)	$x = 0$ (y-axis)
Focus	$(a, 0)$	$(-a, 0)$	$(0, a)$	$(0, -a)$
Directrix	$x = -a$	$x = a$	$y = -a$	$y = a$
Graph				

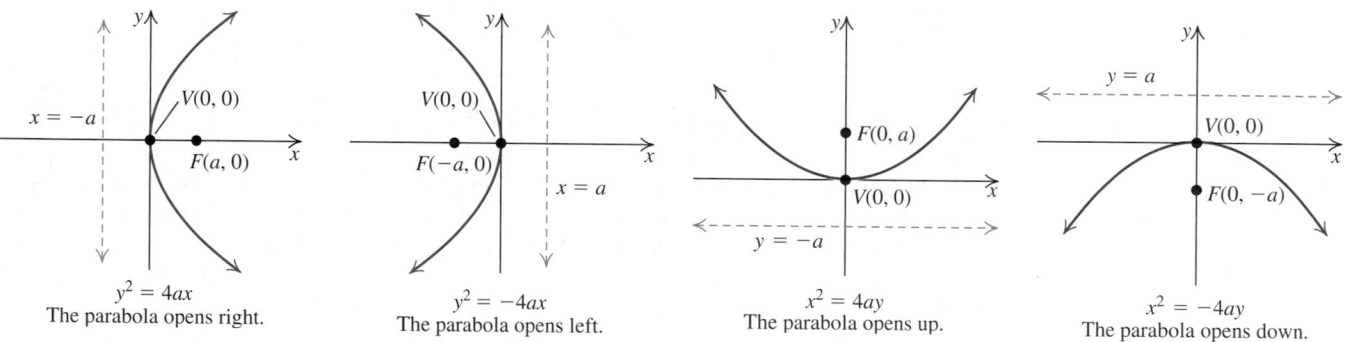

$y^2 = 4ax$	$y^2 = -4ax$	$x^2 = 4ay$	$x^2 = -4ay$
The parabola opens right.	The parabola opens left.	The parabola opens up.	The parabola opens down.

Graph each parabola and specify the vertex, focus, directrix, and axis.

a. $x^2 = -8y$ **b.** $y^2 = 5x$

Solution

a. The equation $x^2 = -8y$ has the standard form $x^2 = -4ay$, so

$$-4a = -8 \qquad \text{Equate coefficients of } y.$$

$$a = 2. \qquad \text{Divide both sides by } -4.$$

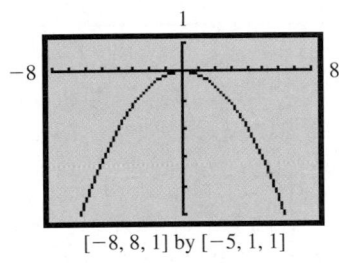
The parabola opens down. The vertex is the origin and the focus is $(0, -2)$. The directrix is the horizontal line $y = 2$; the axis of the parabola is the y-axis. You should plot some additional points to ensure the accuracy of your sketch. Since the focus is $(0, -2)$, substitute $y = -2$ in the equation $x^2 = -8y$ of the parabola to obtain

$$x^2 = (-8)(-2) \qquad \text{Replace } y \text{ by } -2 \text{ in } x^2 = -8y.$$
$$x^2 = 16 \qquad \text{Simplify.}$$
$$x = \pm 4. \qquad \text{Solve for } x.$$

Thus, the points $(4, -2)$ and $(-4, -2)$ are two symmetric points on the parabola to the right and the left of the focus. The graph of this parabola is sketched in Figure 10.7.

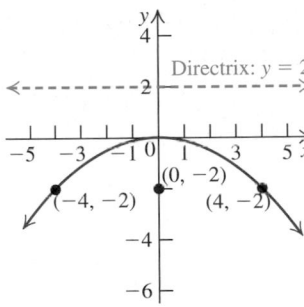

FIGURE 10.7

b. The equation $y^2 = 5x$ has the standard form $y^2 = 4ax$.

$$4a = 5 \qquad \text{Equate coefficients of } x.$$
$$a = \frac{5}{4} \qquad \text{Divide both sides by 4.}$$

The parabola opens to the right. The vertex is the origin and the focus is $\left(\dfrac{5}{4}, 0\right)$. The directrix is the vertical line $x = -a = -\dfrac{5}{4}$; the axis of the parabola is the x-axis.

Two symmetric points on the parabola that are above and below the focus are obtained by substituting $x = \dfrac{5}{4}$ in the equation of the parabola.

$$y^2 = 5x \qquad \text{Equation of the parabola}$$
$$y^2 = 5\left(\frac{5}{4}\right) \qquad \text{Replace } x \text{ by } \frac{5}{4}.$$
$$y^2 = \frac{25}{4} \qquad \text{Simplify.}$$
$$y = \pm\frac{5}{2} \qquad \text{Solve for } y.$$

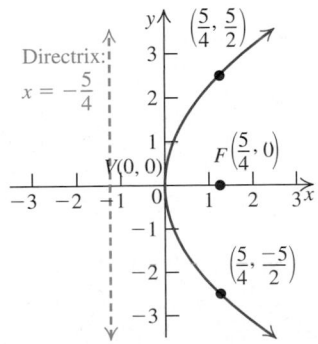

FIGURE 10.8

Thus, the points $\left(\dfrac{5}{4}, \dfrac{5}{2}\right)$ and $\left(\dfrac{5}{4}, -\dfrac{5}{2}\right)$ are two additional points on the parabola. The graph is sketched in Figure 10.8. ■ ■ ■

In order to graph $y^2 = 4ax$, solve the equation for y to obtain

$$y = \pm\sqrt{4ax}.$$

Then graph $Y_1 = \sqrt{4ax}$ and $Y_2 = -\sqrt{4ax}$ in a viewing window. For example, to graph $y^2 = 5x$, you graph

$$Y_1 = \sqrt{5x},\ Y_2 = -\sqrt{5x}.$$

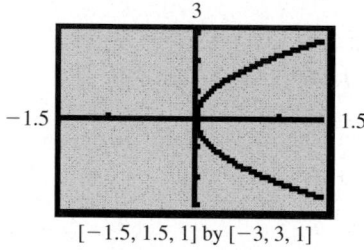

$[-1.5, 1.5, 1]$ by $[-3, 3, 1]$

PRACTICE PROBLEM 1   Graph the parabola and specify the vertex, focus, directrix, and axis.

a. $x^2 = 12y$ **b.** $y^2 = -6x$ ■

The line segment joining the focus and two points symmetric on a parabola is called the *latus rectum* of the parabola.

LATUS RECTUM

The line segment that passes through the focus of a parabola, is perpendicular to the axis of the parabola, and has endpoints on the parabola is called the **latus rectum of the parabola.** Figure 10.9 shows that the length of the latus rectum for the graphs of $y^2 = \pm4ax$ and $x^2 = \pm4ay$ for $a > 0$ is $4a$.

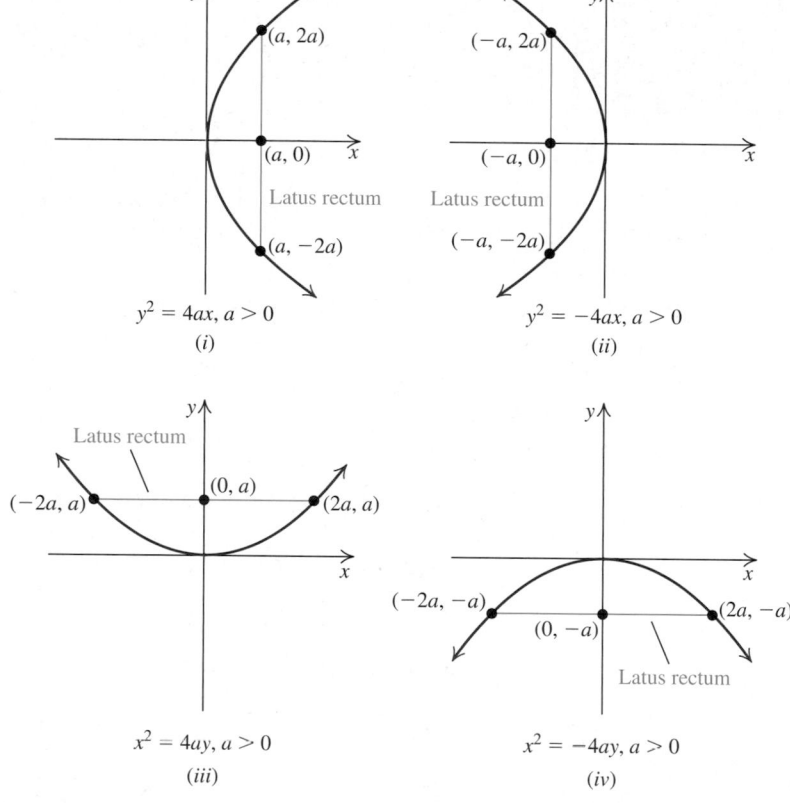

FIGURE 10.9

EXAMPLE 2   **Finding the Equation of a Parabola**

Find the standard equation of a parabola with vertex $(0, 0)$ and satisfying the given description.

a. The focus is $(-3, 0)$.

b. The axis of the parabola is the y-axis, and the graph passes through the point $(-4, 2)$.

Solution

a. The vertex $(0, 0)$ of the parabola and its focus $(-3, 0)$ are on the x-axis, so the parabola opens to the left. Thus, the equation of the parabola is of the form $y^2 = -4ax$ with $a = 3$.

$$y^2 = -4ax \qquad \text{Form of the equation}$$
$$y^2 = -4(3)x \qquad \text{Replace } a \text{ by 3.}$$
$$y^2 = -12x \qquad \text{Simplify.}$$

The equation of the parabola is $\qquad y^2 = -12x.$

b. Since the vertex of the parabola is $(0, 0)$, the axis is the y-axis, and the point $(-4, 2)$ is above the x-axis, the parabola opens up and the equation of the parabola is of the form

$$x^2 = 4ay.$$

Because the parabola passes through the point $(-4, 2)$, the equation $x^2 = 4ay$ is satisfied by $x = -4$ and $y = 2$.

$$x^2 = 4ay \qquad \text{Form of the equation}$$
$$(-4)^2 = 4a(2) \qquad \text{Replace } x \text{ by } -4 \text{ and } y \text{ by 2.}$$
$$16 = 8a \qquad \text{Simplify.}$$
$$2 = a \qquad \text{Divide both sides by 8.}$$

Hence, the equation of the parabola is

$$x^2 = 4ay \qquad \text{Form of the equation}$$
$$x^2 = 4(2)y \qquad \text{Replace } a \text{ by 2.}$$
$$x^2 = 8y. \qquad \text{Simplify.}$$

The equation $x^2 = 8y$ is the required equation of the parabola.   ■ ■ ■

PRACTICE PROBLEM 2 Find the standard equation of a parabola with vertex $(0, 0)$ and satisfying the following conditions.

a. The focus is $(0, 2)$.

b. The axis of the parabola is the x-axis, and the graph passes through $(1, 2)$.   ■

3 Translate a parabola.

Translations of Parabolas

The equation of a parabola with vertex $(0, 0)$ and axis on a coordinate axis is of the form $x^2 = \pm 4ay$ or $y^2 = \pm 4ax$. You can use translations of the graphs of these equations to find the equation of a parabola with vertex (h, k) and axis of symmetry parallel to a coordinate axis. The translations can be obtained by replacing x with $x - h$ (a horizontal shift) and y with $y - k$ (a vertical shift). We now give the standard form of the equations of parabolas with vertex (h, k).

Standard Equation	$(y - k)^2 = 4a(x - h)$	$(y - k)^2 = -4a(x - h)$	$(x - h)^2 = 4a(y - k)$	$(x - h)^2 = -4a(y - k)$
Equation of axis	$y = k$	$y = k$	$x = h$	$x = h$
Description	Opens right	Opens left	Opens up	Opens down
Vertex	(h, k)	(h, k)	(h, k)	(h, k)
Focus	$(h + a, k)$	$(h - a, k)$	$(h, k + a)$	$(h, k - a)$
Directrix	$x = h - a$	$x = h + a$	$y = k - a$	$y = k + a$

Main facts about a parabola with vertex (h, k) and $a > 0$

Graph

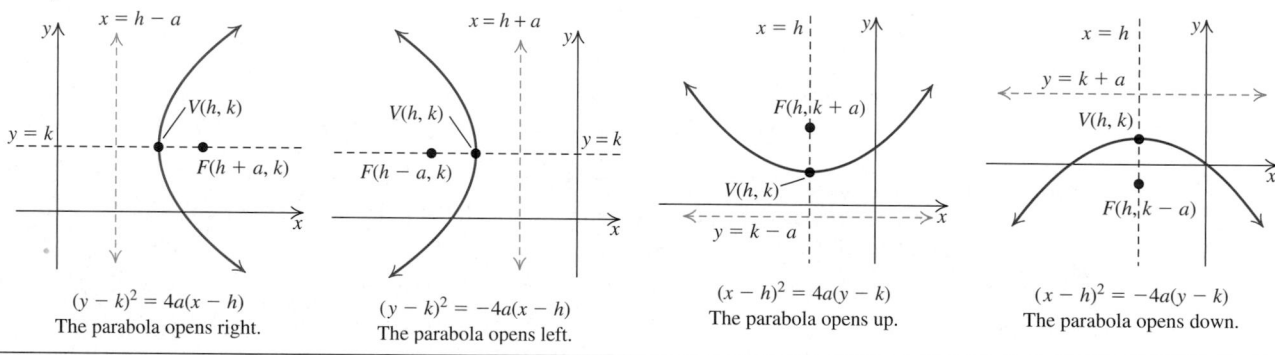

$(y - k)^2 = 4a(x - h)$
The parabola opens right.

$(y - k)^2 = -4a(x - h)$
The parabola opens left.

$(x - h)^2 = 4a(y - k)$
The parabola opens up.

$(x - h)^2 = -4a(y - k)$
The parabola opens down.

Each of the standard equations of a parabola can be expressed in the form

$$Ax^2 + Cy^2 + Dx + Ey + F = 0, \quad AC = 0, A \text{ and } C \text{ not both } 0. \quad (1)$$

For example, the equation $(y + 1)^2 = 4(x - 2)$ can be written as

$$(y + 1)^2 = 4(x - 2) \qquad \text{The given equation}$$
$$y^2 + 2y + 1 = 4x - 8 \qquad (y + 1)^2 = y^2 + 2y + 1$$
$$y^2 - 4x + 2y + 9 = 0. \qquad \text{Add } -4x + 8 \text{ to both sides.}$$

The last equation is in the form of Equation (1) with

$$A = 0, C = 1, D = -4, E = 2, \text{ and } F = 9.$$

A quadratic equation in x and y with either the x^2- or the y^2-term missing (but not both) can be put in standard form by completing the square. Thus, the graph of an equation of the form

$$Ax^2 + Cy^2 + Dx + Ey + F = 0$$

is a parabola if $A = 0$ or $C = 0$, but not both.

Equation (1) is a special case of the more general equation

$$Ax^2 + Bxy + Cy^2 + Dx + Ey + F = 0, \quad (2)$$

called a **second-degree equation,** or **quadratic equation,** in x and y if A, B, and C are not all zero. It can be shown that the graph of Equation (2) is a conic section. If $B = 0$, then Equation (2) reduces to Equation (1), and the conic section has its axis or axes parallel to the coordinate axes. However, if $B \neq 0$, then the graph of the conic section represented by Equation (2) has its axis or axes "tilted" relative to the coordinate axes.

> **EXAMPLE 3** Graphing a Parabola

Find the vertex, focus, and the directrix of the parabola $2y^2 - 8y - x + 7 = 0$. Sketch the graph of the parabola.

Solution

First complete the square on y. Then you can compare the resulting equation with one of the standard forms of the equation of a parabola.

$2y^2 - 8y - x + 7 = 0$	The given equation
$2y^2 - 8y = x - 7$	Isolate terms containing y.
$2(y^2 - 4y) = x - 7$	Factor out the common factor, 2.
$2(y^2 - 4y + 4) = x - 7 + 8$	Add $2 \cdot 4 = 8$ to both sides to complete the square.
$2(y - 2)^2 = x + 1$	$y^2 - 4y + 4 = (y - 2)^2$, simplify.
$(y - 2)^2 = \dfrac{1}{2}(x + 1)$	Divide both sides by 2.

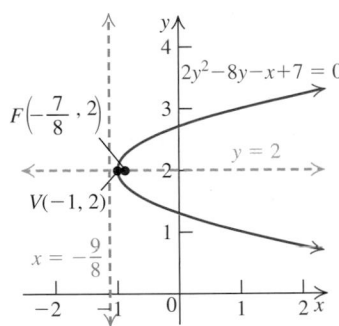

FIGURE 10.10

Now, $(y - 2)^2 = \dfrac{1}{2}(x + 1)$ is one of the standard forms of the parabola. Comparing it with the form $(y - k)^2 = 4a(x - h)$, we have $h = -1$, $k = 2$, and $4a = \dfrac{1}{2}$, or $a = \dfrac{1}{8}$. The parabola opens to the right. The vertex of the parabola is $(h, k) = (-1, 2)$. The focus of the parabola is $(h + a, k) = \left(-1 + \dfrac{1}{8}, 2\right) = \left(-\dfrac{7}{8}, 2\right)$. The directrix is the vertical line $x = h - a = -1 - \dfrac{1}{8} = -\dfrac{9}{8}$. The graph is shown in Figure 10.10.   ■ ■ ■

PRACTICE PROBLEM 3 Find the vertex, focus, and directrix of the parabola

$$2x^2 - 8x - y + 7 = 0.$$

Sketch the graph of the parabola.   ■

---

4 Use the reflecting property of parabolas.

Reflecting Property of Parabolas

A property of parabolas that is useful in applications is their *reflecting property*. The **reflecting property** says that if a reflecting surface has parabolic cross sections with a common focus, then all light rays entering the surface parallel to the axis will be reflected through the focus. (See Figure 10.11(a) on the next page.) This property is used in reflecting telescopes and satellite antennas, since the light rays or radio waves bouncing off a parabolic surface are reflected to the focus, where they are collected and amplified.

Conversely, if a light source is located at the focus of a parabolic reflector, the reflected rays will form a beam parallel to the axis. (See Figure 10.11(b).) This principle is used in flashlights, searchlights, and other such devices.

(a)   (b)

FIGURE 10.11

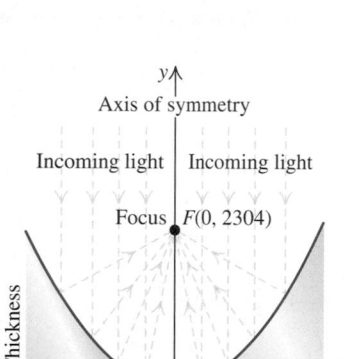

y

Axis of symmetry

Incoming light | Incoming light

Focus | *F*(0, 2304)

Thickness

94.5 in

(Not to scale)

x

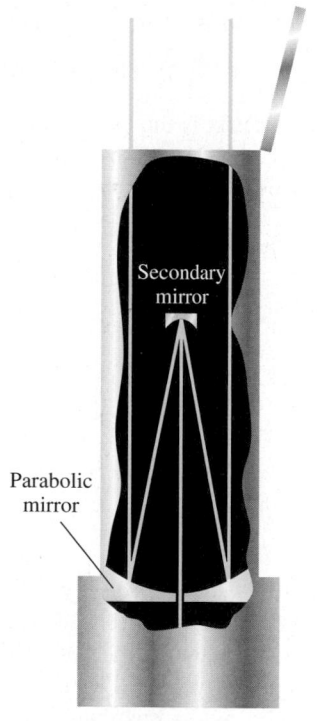

Secondary mirror

Parabolic mirror

(Not to scale)

FIGURE 10.12

EXAMPLE 4   **Calculating Some Properties of the Hubble Space Telescope**

The parabolic mirror used in the Hubble Space Telescope has a diameter of 94.5 inches. (See Figure 10.12.) Find the equation of the parabola if its focus is 2304 inches from the vertex. What is the thickness of the mirror at the edges?

Solution

Position the parabola so that its vertex is the origin and its focus is on the positive *y*-axis. The equation of the parabola is of the form

$$x^2 = 4ay$$
$$x^2 = 4(2304)y \qquad a = 2304$$
$$x^2 = 9216y. \qquad \text{Simplify.}$$

To find the thickness *y* of the mirror at the edge, substitute $x = 47.25$ (half the diameter) in the equation $x^2 = 9216y$ and solve for *y*.

$$(47.25)^2 = 9216y \qquad \text{Replace } x \text{ by } 47.25.$$
$$\frac{(47.25)^2}{9216} = y \qquad \text{Divide both sides by 9216.}$$
$$0.242248 \approx y \qquad \text{Use a calculator.}$$

Thus, the thickness of the mirror at the edges is approximately 0.242248 inch.

The Hubble telescope initially had "blurred vision" because the mirror was ground at the edges to a thickness of 0.24224 inch. In other words, it had been ground 0.000008 inch, or two-millionths of a meter, smaller than it should have been! The problem was fixed in 1993.   ■ ■ ■

PRACTICE PROBLEM 4   A small imitation of the Hubble's parabolic mirror has a diameter of 3 inches. Find the equation of the parabola if its focus is 7.3 inches from the vertex. What is the thickness of the mirror at its edges, correct to four decimal places?   ■

A Exercises   Basic Skills and Concepts

In Exercises 1–8, find the focus and directrix of the parabola with the given equation. Then match each equation to one of the graphs labeled (a) through (h).

1. $x^2 = 2y$ †

2. $9x^2 = 4y$ †

3. $16x^2 = -9y$ †

4. $x^2 = -2y$ †

5. $y^2 = 2x$ †

6. $9y^2 = 16x$ †

7. $9y^2 = -16x$ †

8. $y^2 = -2x$ †

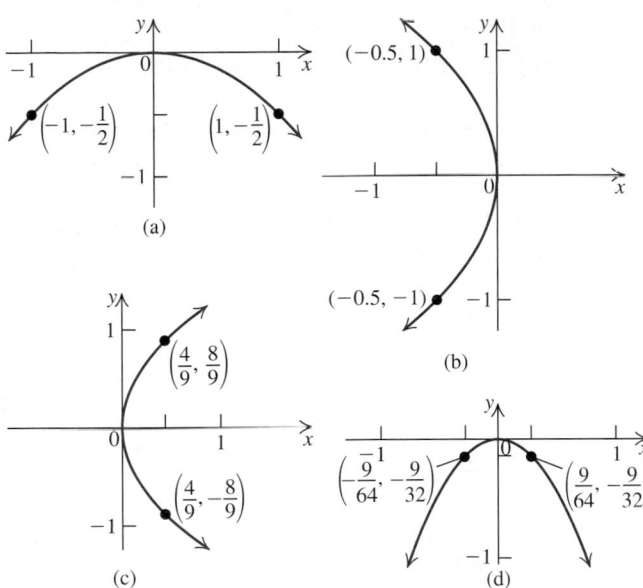

(a)

(b)

(c)

(d)

(e)

(f)

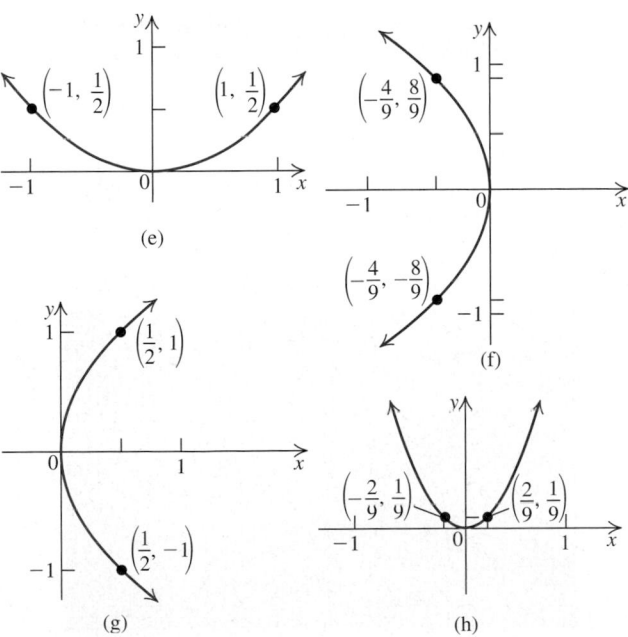

(g)

(h)

In Exercises 9–24, find the standard equation of the parabola that satisfies the given conditions. Also, find the length of the latus rectum of each parabola.

9. Focus: $(0, 2)$; directrix: $y = 4$ †

10. Focus: $(0, 4)$; directrix: $y = -2$ †

11. Focus: $(-2, 0)$; directrix: $x = 3$ †

12. Focus: $(-1, 0)$; directrix: $x = -2$ †

13. Vertex: $(1, 1)$; directrix: $x = 3$ †

14. Vertex: $(1, 1)$ directrix: $y = 2$ †

15. Vertex: $(1, 1)$; directrix: $y = -3$ †

16. Vertex: $(1, 1)$; directrix: $x = -2$ †

17. Vertex: $(1, 0)$; focus: $(3, 0)$ †

18. Vertex: $(0,1)$; focus: $(0, 2)$ †

19. Vertex: $(0, 1)$; focus: $(0, -2)$ †

20. Vertex: $(-1, 0)$; focus: $(-3, 0)$ †

21. Vertex: $(2, 3)$; directrix: $x = 4$ †

22. Vertex: $(2, 3)$; directrix: $y = 4$ †

23. Vertex: $(2, 3)$; directrix: $y = 1$ †

24. Vertex: $(2, 3)$; directrix: $x = 1$ †

In Exercises 25–40, find the vertex, focus, and directrix of each parabola. Graph the equation.

25. $(y - 1)^2 = 2(x + 1)$ †

26. $(y + 2)^2 = 8(x - 3)$ †

27. $(x + 2)^2 = 3(y - 2)$ †

28. $(x - 3)^2 = 4(y + 1)$ †

29. $(y + 1)^2 = -6(x - 2)$ †

30. $(y - 2)^2 = -12(x + 3)$ †

31. $(x - 1)^2 = -10(y - 3)$ †

32. $(x + 2)^2 = -8(y + 3)$ †

33. $y = x^2 + 2x + 2$ †

34. $y = 3x^2 + 6x + 2$ †

35. $2y^2 + 4y - 2x + 1 = 0$ †

36. $3y^2 - 6y + x - 1 = 0$ †

37. $y + x^2 + x + \dfrac{5}{4} = 0$ †

38. $x = 8y^2 + 8y$ †

39. $x = 24y - 3y^2 - 2$ †

40. $y = 16x - 2x^2 + 3$ †

In Exercises 41–48, find two possible equations for the parabola with the given vertex V and passing through the given point P. The axis of symmetry of each parabola is parallel to a coordinate axis.

41. $V(0, 0), P(1, 2)$ †

42. $V(0, 0), P(-3, 2)$ †

43. $V(0, 1), P(2, 3)$ †

44. $V(1, 2), P(2, 1)$ †

45. $V(-2, 1), P(-3, 0)$ †

46. $V(1, -1), P(0, 0)$ †

47. $V(-1, 1), P(0, 2)$ †

48. $V(2, 3), P(3, -1)$ †

B Exercises   Applying the Concepts

49. Satellite dish. A parabolic satellite dish is 40 inches across and 20 inches deep (from the vertex to the plane of the rim). How far from the vertex must the signal-receiving (receptor) unit be located to ensure that it is at the focus of the parabolic cross sections? 5 in.

50. Repeat Exercise 49 if the dish is 8 feet across and 3 feet deep. †

51. Solar heating. A parabolic reflector mirror is to be used for the solar heating of water. The mirror is 18 feet across and 6 feet deep. Where should the heating element be placed in order to heat the water most rapidly? †

52. Flashlights. A parabolic flashlight reflector is to be 4 inches across and 2 inches deep. Where should the light bulb be placed? †

53. Flashlight. The shape of a parabolic flashlight reflector can be described by the equation $x = 4y^2$. Where should the light bulb be placed? †

54. Repeat Exercise 53 if the parabolic flashlight reflector has the shape described by the equation $x = \dfrac{1}{2}y^2$. †

55. Satellite dish. The shape of a parabolic satellite dish can be described by the equation $y = 4x^2$. Where should the microphone be placed? †

56. Repeat Exercise 55 if the shape of the dish can be described by the equation $y = x^2$. †

57. Suspension bridge. The ends of a suspension bridge cable are fastened to the two towers, which are 800 feet apart and 120 feet high. The cable hangs in the shape of a parabola and touches the roadbed midway between the towers. Find the length of the straight wire needed to suspend the roadbed from the cable at a distance of 250 feet from the tower. †

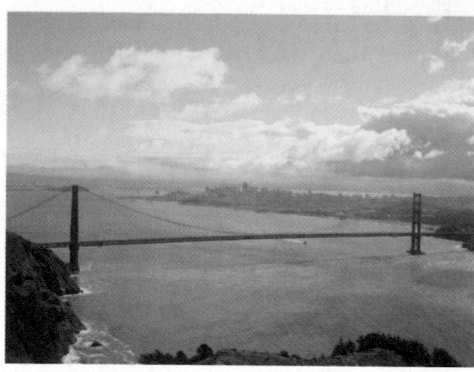

58. Suspension bridge. Repeat Exercise 57 if the suspension bridge cable is at a height of 8 feet above the midway between the towers. †

59. Kicking a football. A football is kicked from the ground 70 yards along a parabolic path. The maximum height of the ball is 30 yards. Find the height of the ball 5 yards before it hits the ground. †

60. Parabolic arch bridge. A parabolic arch of a bridge has a 60-foot base and a height of 24 feet. Find the height of the arch at distances of 5, 10, and 20 feet from the center of the base. †

61. Variable cost. The average variable cost y, in dollars, of a monthly output of x tons of a company producing a metal is given by $y = \dfrac{1}{10}x^2 - 3x + 50$. Find the output and cost at the vertex of the parabola. Output: 15 tons; cost: $27.5

62. Repeat Exercise 61 if the variable cost is given by $y = \dfrac{1}{8}x^2 - 2x + 60$. Output: 8 tons; cost: $52

C Exercises ■ Beyond the Basics

63. Find the coordinates of the points at which the line $2x - 3y + 16 = 0$ intersects the parabola $y^2 = 16x$. †

64. Show that the line $y = 2x + 3$ intersects the parabola $y^2 = 24x$ at only one point. Find the point of intersection. †

65. Find the equation of the directrix of a parabola with vertex $(-2, 2)$ and focus $(-6, 6)$. $y = x - 4$
[*Hint:* Note that the axis of this parabola is *not* parallel to a coordinate axis. Recall that the vertex is midway between the focus and the directrix.]

66. A parabola has focus $(-4, 5)$, and the equation of its directrix is $3x - 4y = 18$.
  a. Find an equation for the axis of the parabola. †
  b. Find the point of intersection of the axis and the directrix. †
  c. Use part (b) to find the vertex of this parabola. $(-1, 1)$

67. Find the equation of two possible parabolas whose latus rectum is the line segment joining the points $(3, 5)$ and $(3, -3)$. †

68. Repeat Exercise 67 if the latus rectum is the line segment joining the points $(-5, 1)$ and $(3, 1)$. †

69. Find an equation of the parabola with axis parallel to the y-axis and passing through the points $(0, 5)$, $(1, 4)$, and $(2, 7)$. †

70. Find an equation of the parabola with axis parallel to the x-axis and passing through the points $(-1, -1)$, $(3, 1)$, and $(4, 0)$. †

71. Find the vertex, focus, directrix, and axis of the parabola
$$x^2 - 8x + 2y + 4 = 0. \; †$$

72. Repeat Exercise 71 for the parabola
$$Ax^2 + Dx + Ey + F = 0, \quad A \neq 0, E \neq 0. \; †$$

73. Find the vertex, focus, directrix, and axis of the parabola
$$y^2 + 3x - 6y + 15 = 0. \; †$$

74. Repeat Exercise 73 for the parabola
$$Cy^2 + Dx + Ey + F = 0, \quad C \neq 0, D \neq 0. \; †$$

Critical Thinking

75. a. Is a parabola always the graph of a function? Why or why not? †
  b. Find all possible values of the slope of the directrix of a parabola such that the parabola is always the graph of a function. 0

76. a. What is the vertex of the parabola $(y - 3)^2 = 12(x - 1)$? (ii)
  (i) $(3, 1)$ (ii) $(1, 3)$
  (iii) $(-3, -1)$ (iv) $(-1, -3)$
  b. What is the equation of the directrix of the parabola $x^2 = 4y$? (iii)
  (i) $x + 1 = 0$ †
  (ii) $x - 1 = 0$ †
  (iii) $y + 1 = 0$ †
  (iv) $y - 1 = 0$ †

Group Projects

1. It can be proved that the distance d from a point (x_1, y_1) to a line $ax + by + c = 0$ is given by
$$d = \frac{|ax_1 + by_1 + c|}{\sqrt{a^2 + b^2}}.$$
Use this fact and the definition of a parabola to find an equation of the parabola whose focus is $(4, 5)$ and whose directrix is the line $3x + 4y = 7$. Find an equation for the axis of this parabola. †

2. Given that the vertex of a parabola is $(6, -3)$ and the directrix is the line $3x - 5y + 1 = 0$, find the coordinates of the focus. $(9, -8)$

The Ellipse

Lithotripter

BEFORE STARTING THIS SECTION, REVIEW

1. Distance formula (Section 2.1, page 185)
2. Completing the square (Section 1.4, page 123)
3. Midpoint formula (Section 2.1, page 187)
4. Transformations of graphs (Section 2.6, page 263)
5. Symmetry (Section 2.2, page 194)

OBJECTIVES

1 Learn the definition of an ellipse.

2 Find an equation of an ellipse.

3 Translate an ellipse.

4 Use ellipses in applications.

What Is Lithotripsy?

Lithotripsy is a combination of two words: *litho* and *tripsy*. In Greek the word *lith* denotes a stone and the word *tripsy* means "crushing." The complete medical term for lithotripsy is *extracorporeal shock-wave lithotripsy* (ESWL). Lithotripsy is a medical procedure in which a kidney stone is crushed into small sandlike pieces with the help of ultrasound high-energy shock waves, without breaking the skin.

The lithotripsy machine is called *lithotripter*. The technology for the lithotripter was developed in Germany. The first successful treatment of a patient by a lithotripter was in February 1980 at Munich University. In the beginning, the patient had to lie in an elliptical tank filled with water, and only small-sized kidney stones were crushed. But as the medical research advanced, newer machines with better technology were manufactured. Now there is no need to keep the patient unconscious with an empty stomach, nor is the tub of water required.

In Example 5, you will see how the *reflecting property* of an ellipse is used in lithotripsy. ■

---

1 Learn the definition of an ellipse.

Definition of Ellipse

ELLIPSE

An **ellipse** is the set of all points in the plane, the sum of whose distances from two fixed points is a constant. The fixed points are called the **foci** (the plural of *focus*) of the ellipse.

FIGURE 10.13

You can draw an ellipse with the use of thumbtacks, string, and a pencil. Cut a piece of string of any length. Stick a thumbtack at each of the two points (the foci), and tie one end of the string to each tack. Place a pencil inside the loop of the string and pull it taut. Move the pencil, keeping the string taut at all times. The pencil traces an ellipse, as shown in Figure 10.13.

The points of intersection of the ellipse with the line through the foci are called the **vertices** (plural of vertex). The line segment connecting the vertices is the **major axis** of the ellipse. The midpoint of the major axis is the **center** of the ellipse. The line segment that is perpendicular to the major axis at the center and with endpoints on the ellipse is called the **minor axis**. (See Figure 10.14.)

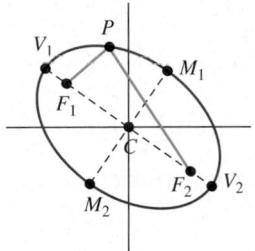

Points F_1 and F_2 are the foci.
Points V_1 and V_2 are the vertices.
Point C is the center.
Segment $\overline{V_1 V_2}$ is the major axis.
Segment $\overline{M_1 M_2}$ is the minor axis.
The sum of the distances $\overline{PF_1} + \overline{PF_2}$ from any point P on the ellipse to the foci is constant.

FIGURE 10.14

2 Find an equation of an ellipse.

Equation of an Ellipse

In order to obtain an equation of an ellipse, it is convenient to place the major axis of the ellipse along one of the coordinate axes, with the center of the ellipse at the origin. The center is the midpoint of the line segment having the foci as endpoints. We will begin with the case in which the major axis lies along the x-axis. Let $F_1(-c, 0)$ and $F_2(c, 0)$ be the coordinates of the foci. (See Figure 10.15.) To simplify the equation, it is customary to let $2a$ be the constant distance referred to in the definition. Let $P(x, y)$ be a point on the ellipse. Then

$$d(P, F_1) + d(P, F_2) = 2a$$ Definition of ellipse

$$\sqrt{(x + c)^2 + y^2} + \sqrt{(x - c)^2 + y^2} = 2a$$ Use the distance formula.

$$\sqrt{(x + c)^2 + y^2} = 2a - \sqrt{(x - c)^2 + y^2}$$ Isolate a radical.

$$(x + c)^2 + y^2 = (2a - \sqrt{(x - c)^2 + y^2})^2$$ Square both sides.

$$x^2 + 2cx + c^2 + y^2 = 4a^2 - 4a\sqrt{(x - c)^2 + y^2}$$
$$+ (x - c)^2 + y^2$$ Expand squares.

$$x^2 + 2cx + c^2 + y^2 = 4a^2 - 4a\sqrt{(x - c)^2 + y^2}$$
$$+ x^2 - 2cx + c^2 + y^2$$ Expand squares.

$$4cx - 4a^2 = -4a\sqrt{(x - c)^2 + y^2}$$ Isolate the radical and simplify.

$$cx - a^2 = -a\sqrt{(x - c)^2 + y^2}$$ Divide both sides by 4.

$$(cx - a^2)^2 = a^2[(x - c)^2 + y^2]$$ Square both sides.

$$c^2x^2 - 2a^2cx + a^4 = a^2(x^2 - 2cx + c^2 + y^2) \qquad \text{Expand squares.}$$

$$(c^2 - a^2)x^2 - a^2y^2 = a^2c^2 - a^4 \qquad \begin{array}{l}\text{Simplify and} \\ \text{rearrange.}\end{array}$$

$$(a^2 - c^2)x^2 + a^2y^2 = a^2(a^2 - c^2). \quad (1) \qquad \begin{array}{l}\text{Multiply both} \\ \text{sides by } -1 \text{ and} \\ \text{factor } a^4 - a^2c^2.\end{array}$$

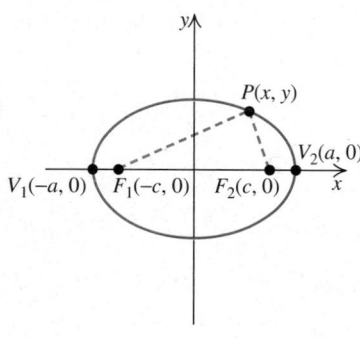

FIGURE 10.15

Now consider triangle F_1PF_2 in Figure 10.15. The *triangle inequality* from geometry states that the sum of the lengths of any two sides of a triangle is greater than the length of the third side, so, for this triangle, we have

$$d(P, F_1) + d(P, F_2) > d(F_1, F_2)$$

$$2a > 2c \qquad 2a = d(P, F_1) + d(P, F_2); d(F_1, F_2) = 2c$$

$$a > c \qquad \text{Divide both sides by 2.}$$

$$a^2 > c^2. \qquad \text{Square both sides.}$$

Therefore, $a^2 - c^2 > 0$. Writing $b^2 = a^2 - c^2$, we obtain

$$(a^2 - c^2)x^2 + a^2y^2 = a^2(a^2 - c^2) \qquad \text{Equation (1)}$$

$$b^2x^2 + a^2y^2 = a^2b^2 \qquad \text{Replace } a^2 - c^2 \text{ by } b^2.$$

$$\frac{x^2}{a^2} + \frac{y^2}{b^2} = 1. \quad (2) \qquad \text{Divide both sides by } a^2b^2.$$

The last equation is the **standard form of the equation of an ellipse** with center $(0, 0)$ and foci $(-c, 0)$ and $(c, 0)$, where $b^2 = a^2 - c^2$.

Let's find the x- and y-intercepts for the graph of the ellipse with equation

$$\frac{x^2}{a^2} + \frac{y^2}{b^2} = 1. \qquad \text{Equation (2)}$$

To find the x-intercepts, set $y = 0$ in Equation (2) to obtain

$$\frac{x^2}{a^2} = 1$$

$$x^2 = a^2 \qquad \text{Multiply both sides by } a^2.$$

$$x = \pm a. \qquad \text{Square root property}$$

The x-intercepts of the graph are $-a$ and a. The points corresponding to these x-intercepts are called the **vertices** of the ellipse. The distance between the vertices $V_1(-a, 0)$ and $V_2(a, 0)$ is $2a$. Thus, the length of the major axis is $2a$. The y-intercepts of the ellipse (found by setting $x = 0$ in Equation (2)) are $-b$ and b, so the endpoints of the minor axis are $(0, -b)$ and $(0, b)$. Hence, the length of the minor axis is $2b$. (See the left-hand figure in the table on page 897.)

Similarly, by reversing the roles of x and y, an equation of the ellipse with center $(0, 0)$ and foci $(0, -c)$ and $(0, c)$ on the y-axis is given by

$$\frac{x^2}{b^2} + \frac{y^2}{a^2} = 1, \text{ where } b^2 = a^2 - c^2. \quad (3)$$

In Equation (3), the major axis, of length $2a$, is along the y-axis and the minor axis, of length $2b$, is along the x-axis. (See the right-hand figure in the table on page 897.)

If the major axis of an ellipse is along or parallel to the *x*-axis, the ellipse is called a **horizontal ellipse,** while an ellipse with major axis along or parallel to the *y*-axis is called a **vertical ellipse.**

We summarize the facts about horizontal and vertical ellipses with center $(0, 0)$. By the equation of a major or minor axis, we mean the equation of the line on which that axis lies.

Main facts about an ellipse with center $(0, 0)$

Standard Equation	$\dfrac{x^2}{a^2} + \dfrac{y^2}{b^2} = 1; \, a > b > 0$ **(Horizontal ellipse)**	$\dfrac{x^2}{b^2} + \dfrac{y^2}{a^2} = 1; \, a > b > 0$ **(Vertical ellipse)**
Relationship between a, b, and c	$b^2 = a^2 - c^2$	$b^2 = a^2 - c^2$
Equation of major axis	$y = 0$ (*x*-axis)	$x = 0$ (*y*-axis)
Length of major axis	$2a$	$2a$
Equation of minor axis	$x = 0$ (*y*-axis)	$y = 0$ (*x*-axis)
Length of minor axis	$2b$	$2b$
Vertices on major axis, a units from the center	$(\pm a, 0)$	$(0, \pm a)$
Foci on major axis, c units from the center	$(\pm c, 0)$	$(0, \pm c)$
Endpoints of minor axis	$(0, \pm b)$	$(\pm b, 0)$
Symmetry	The graph is symmetric with respect to the *x*-axis, *y*-axis, and origin.	The graph is symmetric with respect to the *x*-axis, *y*-axis, and origin.
Graph	 $\dfrac{x^2}{a^2} + \dfrac{y^2}{b^2} = 1$ Horizontal ellipse	 $\dfrac{x^2}{b^2} + \dfrac{y^2}{a^2} = 1$ Vertical ellipse

EXAMPLE 1   Finding an Equation of an Ellipse

Find the standard form of the equation of the ellipse that has vertex $(5, 0)$ and foci $(\pm 4, 0)$.

Solution

Since the foci are $(-4, 0)$ and $(4, 0)$, the major axis is on the *x*-axis. You are given that $c = 4$ and $a = 5$. You can obtain the value of b^2 from the relationship between a, b, and c.

Continued on next page.

$$b^2 = a^2 - c^2 \qquad \text{Relation between } a, b, \text{ and } c.$$

$$b^2 = (5)^2 - (4)^2 \qquad \text{Replace } c \text{ by 4 and } a \text{ by 5.}$$

$$b^2 = 25 - 16 = 9 \qquad \text{Solve for } b^2.$$

$$\frac{x^2}{a^2} + \frac{y^2}{b^2} = 1 \qquad \text{Standard form with major axis along the } x \text{ axis}$$

$$\frac{x^2}{25} + \frac{y^2}{9} = 1 \qquad \text{Replace } a^2 \text{ by 25 and } b^2 \text{ by 9.} \qquad ▪ \ ▪ \ ▪$$

PRACTICE PROBLEM 1 Find the standard form of the equation of the ellipse that has vertex $(0, 10)$ and foci $(0, -8)$ and $(0, 8)$. ▪

EXAMPLE 2 **Graphing an Ellipse**

Sketch a graph of the ellipse whose equation is $9x^2 + 4y^2 = 36$. Find the foci of the ellipse.

Solution

First write the equation in standard form:

$$9x^2 + 4y^2 = 36 \qquad \text{Given equation}$$

$$\frac{9x^2}{36} + \frac{4y^2}{36} = 1 \qquad \text{Divide both sides by 36.}$$

$$\frac{x^2}{4} + \frac{y^2}{9} = 1. \qquad \text{Simplify.}$$

larger denominator

Since the denominator in the y^2-term is larger than the denominator in the x^2-term, the ellipse is a vertical ellipse. Here, $a^2 = 9$ and $b^2 = 4$, so $c^2 = a^2 - b^2 = 9 - 4 = 5$. Thus, $a = 3, b = 2$, and $c = \sqrt{5}$. From the table on page 897, we know the following features of the ellipse:

Vertices: $(0, \pm 3)$
Foci: $(0, \pm \sqrt{5})$
Length of major axis: $2(3) = 6$
Length of minor axis: $2(2) = 4$

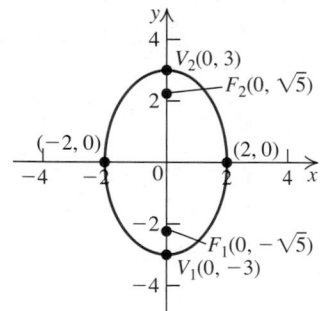

FIGURE 10.16

The graph of the ellipse is shown in Figure 10.16. ▪ ▪ ▪

PRACTICE PROBLEM 2 Sketch a graph of the ellipse whose equation is $4x^2 + y^2 = 16$. ▪

3 Translate an ellipse.

Translations of Ellipses

The graph of the equation

$$\frac{x^2}{a^2} + \frac{y^2}{b^2} = 1$$

is an ellipse with center $(0, 0)$ and major axis along a coordinate axis. Just as in the case of a parabola, horizontal and vertical shifts can be used to obtain the graph of an ellipse whose equation is

$$\frac{(x - h)^2}{a^2} + \frac{(y - k)^2}{b^2} = 1.$$

The center of such an ellipse is (h, k), and its major axis is parallel to a coordinate axis.

Main facts about horizontal and vertical ellipses with center (h, k)		
Standard Equation	$\frac{(x - h)^2}{a^2} + \frac{(y - k)^2}{b^2} = 1;$ $a > b > 0$ **(Horizontal ellipse)**	$\frac{(x - h)^2}{b^2} + \frac{(y - k)^2}{a^2} = 1;$ $a > b > 0$ **(Vertical ellipse)**
Center	(h, k)	(h, k)
Equation of major axis	$y = k$	$x = h$
Length of major axis	$2a$	$2a$
Equation of minor axis	$x = h$	$y = k$
Length of minor axis	$2b$	$2b$
Vertices	$(h + a, k), (h - a, k)$	$(h, k + a), (h, k - a)$
Endpoints of minor axis	$(h, k - b), (h, k + b)$	$(h - b, k), (h + b, k)$
Foci	$(h + c, k), (h - c, k)$	$(h, k + c), (h, k - c)$
Equation involving $a, b,$ and c	$c^2 = a^2 - b^2$	$c^2 = a^2 - b^2$
Symmetry	The graph is symmetric about the lines $x = h$ and $y = k$.	The graph is symmetric about the lines $x = h$ and $y = k$.
Graph		

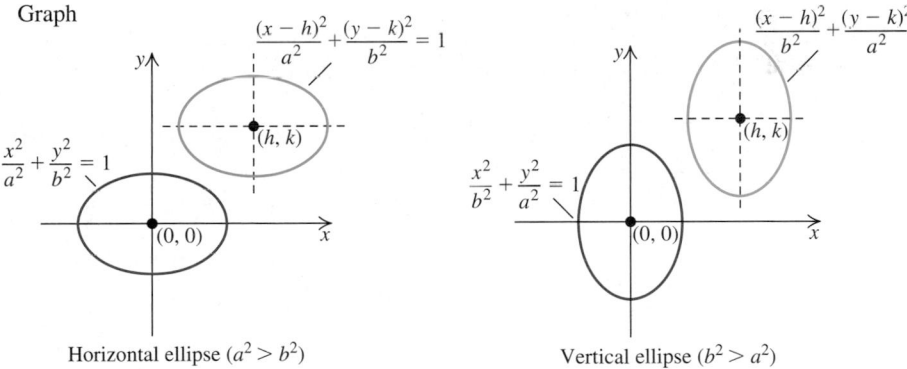

Horizontal ellipse $(a^2 > b^2)$ Vertical ellipse $(b^2 > a^2)$

RECALL

The midpoint of the segment joining (x_1, y_1) and (x_2, y_2) is

$$\left(\frac{x_1 + x_2}{2}, \frac{y_1 + y_2}{2}\right).$$

EXAMPLE 3   Finding the Equation of an Ellipse

Find an equation of the ellipse that has foci $(-3, 2)$ and $(5, 2)$, and has a major axis of length 10.

Solution

Since the foci $(-3, 2)$ and $(5, 2)$ lie on the horizontal line $y = 2$, the given ellipse is a horizontal ellipse. The center of the ellipse is the midpoint of the line segment joining the foci. Using the midpoint formula yields

Continued on next page.

$$h = \frac{-3 + 5}{2} = 1$$

$$k = \frac{2 + 2}{2} = 2.$$

Center (1, 2)

$F_1(-3, 2)$ $F_2(5, 2)$

FIGURE 10.17

The center of the ellipse is (1, 2). (See Figure 10.17.) Since the length of the major axis is 10, the vertices must be at a distance $a = 5$ units from the center.

In Figure 10.17, notice that the foci are four units from the center. Thus, $c = 4$. Then use the equation $b^2 = a^2 - c^2$ to obtain b^2:

$$b^2 = a^2 - c^2 = (5)^2 - (4)^2 = 25 - 16 = 9.$$

Since the major axis is horizontal, the standard form of the equation of the ellipse is

$$\frac{(x - h)^2}{a^2} + \frac{(y - k)^2}{b^2} = 1 \qquad a > b > 0$$

$$\frac{(x - 1)^2}{25} + \frac{(y - 2)^2}{9} = 1. \qquad \text{Replace } h \text{ by 1, } k \text{ by 2,} \\ a^2 \text{ by 25, and } b^2 \text{ by 9.}$$

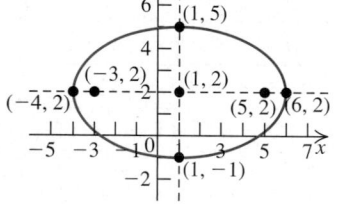

FIGURE 10.18

Now, for this horizontal ellipse with center (1, 2), we have $a = 5$, $b = 3$, and $c = 4$.

Vertices

$$(h \pm a, k) = (1 \pm 5, 2) = (-4, 2) \text{ and } (6, 2).$$

Endpoints of Minor Axis

$$(h, k \pm b) = (1, 2 \pm 3) = (1, -1) \text{ and } (1, 5).$$

Use the center and these four points to sketch the graph, shown in Figure 10.18. ■ ■ ■

PRACTICE PROBLEM 3   Find an equation of the ellipse that has foci at $(2, -3)$ and $(2, 5)$ and has a major axis of length 10.   ■

Both standard forms of the equations of an ellipse with center (h, k) can be put into the form

$$Ax^2 + Cy^2 + Dx + Ey + F = 0, \qquad A \neq 0 \text{ and } AC > 0. \quad (4)$$

For example, consider the ellipse with equation

$$\frac{(x - 1)^2}{4} + \frac{(y + 2)^2}{9} = 1.$$

$$9(x - 1)^2 + 4(y + 2)^2 = 36 \qquad \text{Multiply both sides by 36.}$$

$$9(x^2 - 2x + 1) + 4(y^2 + 4y + 4) = 36 \qquad \text{Expand squares.}$$

$$9x^2 - 18x + 9 + 4y^2 + 16y + 16 = 36 \qquad \text{Distributive property}$$

$$9x^2 + 4y^2 - 18x + 16y - 11 = 0 \qquad \text{Simplify.}$$

Comparing this equation with Equation (4), we have

$$A = 9, C = 4, D = -18, E = 16, \text{ and } F = -11.$$

Conversely, Equation (4) can be put into a standard form for an ellipse by completing the squares in both of the variables x and y.

EXAMPLE 4   **Converting to Standard Form**

Find the center, vertices, and foci of the ellipse with equation

$$3x^2 + 4y^2 + 12x - 8y - 32 = 0.$$

Solution

Complete squares on x and y.

$3x^2 + 4y^2 + 12x - 8y - 32 = 0$	Original equation
$(3x^2 + 12x) + (4y^2 - 8y) = 32$	Group like terms.
$3(x^2 + 4x) + 4(y^2 - 2y) = 32$	Factor out 3 and 4.
$3(x^2 + 4x + 4) + 4(y^2 - 2y + 1) = 32 + 12 + 4$	Complete squares on x and y.

$3(x + 2)^2 + 4(y - 1)^2 = 48$	Simplify.
$\dfrac{(x + 2)^2}{16} + \dfrac{(y - 1)^2}{12} = 1$	Divide both sides by 48.

larger denominator

The last equation is the standard form for a horizontal ellipse with center $(-2, 1)$, $a^2 = 16$, $b^2 = 12$, and $c^2 = a^2 - b^2 = 16 - 12 = 4$. Thus, $a = 4$, $b = \sqrt{12} = 2\sqrt{3}$, and $c = 2$.
From the table on page 899, we have the following information:
The length of the major axis is $2a = 8$.
The length of the minor axis is $2b = 4\sqrt{3}$.

Center:	$(h, k) = (-2, 1)$
Foci:	$(h \pm c, k) = (-2 \pm 2, 1)$
	$= (-4, 1)$ and $(0, 1)$
Vertices:	$(h \pm a, k) = (-2 \pm 4, 1)$
	$= (-6, 1)$ and $(2, 1)$
Endpoints of minor axis:	$(h, k \pm b) = (-2, 1 \pm 2\sqrt{3})$
	$= (-2, 1 + 2\sqrt{3})$ and $(-2, 1 - 2\sqrt{3})$
	$\approx (-2, 4.46)$ and $(-2, -2.46)$

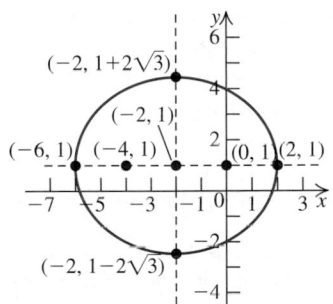

FIGURE 10.19

The graph of the ellipse is shown in Figure 10.19.   ■ ■ ■

PRACTICE PROBLEM 4   Find the center, vertices, and foci of the ellipse with equation

$$x^2 + 4y^2 - 6x + 8y - 29 = 0.$$ ■

A *circle* is an ellipse in which the two foci coincide at the center. Conversely, if the two foci of an ellipse coincide, then $2c = 0$ (remember, $2c$ is the distance between the two foci of an ellipse), so $c = 0$. Again, from the relationship $c^2 = a^2 - b^2 = 0$, we have $a = b$. Thus, the equation for the ellipse becomes the equation for a circle of radius $r = a$ and having the same center as that of the ellipse.

4 | Use ellipses in applications.

Applications

There are many applications of ellipses. We mention just a few:

1. The orbits of the planets are ellipses with the sun at one focus. This fact alone is sufficient to explain the overwhelming importance of ellipses since the 17th century, when Kepler and Newton did their monumental work in astronomy.

2. Newton also reasoned that comets move in elliptical orbits about the sun. His friend, Edmund Halley, used this information to predict that a certain comet (now called Halley's comet) reappears about every 77 years. Halley saw the comet in 1682 and correctly predicted its return in 1759. The last sighting of the comet was in 1986, and it is due to return in 2061. A recent study shows that Halley's comet has made approximately 2000 cycles so far and has about the same number to go before the sun erodes it away completely. (See Exercise 63.)

3. An electron in an atom moves in an elliptical orbit with the nucleus at one focus.

4. **The reflecting property of ellipses.** The *reflecting property* for an ellipse says that a ray of light originating at one focus will be reflected to the other focus. (See Figure 10.20.) Sound waves also follow such paths. This property is used in the construction of "whispering galleries," such as the gallery at St. Paul's Cathedral in London. Such rooms have ceilings whose cross sections are elliptical with common foci. As a result, sounds emanating from one focus are reflected by the ceiling to the other focus. Thus, a whisper at one focus may not be audible at all at a nearby place, but may nevertheless be clearly heard far off at the other focus.

Example 5 illustrates how the *reflecting property* of an ellipse is used in lithotripsy. Recall from the introduction to this section, a *lithotripter* is a machine that is designed to crush kidney stones into small sandlike pieces with the help of high-energy shock waves. To focus these shock waves accurately, a lithotripter uses the reflective property of ellipses. A patient is carefully positioned so that the kidney stone is at one focus of the ellipsoid (a three-dimensional ellipse) and the shock-producing source is placed at the other focus. The high-energy shock waves generated at this focus are concentrated on the kidney stone at the other focus, thus pulverizing it without harming the patient.

Edmund Halley

(1656–1742)

Edmund Halley was a friend of Isaac Newton. Although he is known primarily for calculating the orbit of Halley's comet, he was also a biologist, a geologist, a sea captain, a spy, and the author of the first actuarial mortality tables.

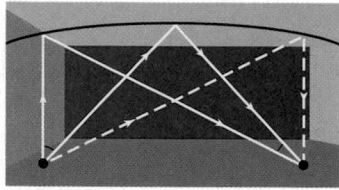

FIGURE 10.20

EXAMPLE 5   **Lithotripsy**

An elliptical water tank has a major axis of length 6 feet and a minor axis of length 4 feet. The source of high-energy shock waves from a lithotripter is placed at one focus of the tank. In order to smash the kidney stone of a patient, how far should the stone be positioned from the source?

Solution

Since the length of the major axis of the ellipse is 6 feet, we have

$$2a = 6$$
$$a = 3. \quad \text{Divide both sides by 2.}$$

Similarly, the minor axis of 4 feet gives

$$2b = 4$$
$$b = 2. \qquad \text{Divide both sides by 2.}$$

Use the equation $c^2 = a^2 - b^2$ to find c. We have

$$c^2 = (3)^2 - (2)^2 = 9 - 4 = 5$$
$$c = \pm\sqrt{5}. \qquad \text{Square root property}$$

If we position the center of ellipse at $(0, 0)$ and the major axis along the x-axis, then the foci of the ellipse are $(-\sqrt{5}, 0)$ and $(\sqrt{5}, 0)$. The distance between these foci is $2\sqrt{5} \approx 4.472$ feet. The kidney stone should be positioned 4.472 feet from the source of the shock waves. ▪ ▪ ▪

PRACTICE PROBLEM 5 In Example 5, if the tank has a major axis of 8 feet and a minor axis of 4 feet, how far should the stone be positioned from the source? ▪

A Exercises Basic Skills and Concepts

In Exercises 1–20, find the vertices and foci for each ellipse. Graph each equation.

1. $\dfrac{x^2}{16} + \dfrac{y^2}{4} = 1$ †

2. $\dfrac{x^2}{4} + \dfrac{y^2}{16} = 1$ †

3. $\dfrac{x^2}{9} + y^2 = 1$ †

4. $x^2 + \dfrac{y^2}{4} = 1$ †

5. $\dfrac{x^2}{25} + \dfrac{y^2}{16} = 1$ †

6. $\dfrac{x^2}{25} + \dfrac{y^2}{9} = 1$ †

7. $\dfrac{x^2}{16} + \dfrac{y^2}{36} = 1$ †

8. $\dfrac{x^2}{9} + \dfrac{y^2}{16} = 1$ †

9. $x^2 + y^2 = 4$ †

10. $x^2 + y^2 = 16$ †

11. $x^2 + 4y^2 = 4$ †

12. $9x^2 + y^2 = 9$ †

13. $9x^2 + 4y^2 = 36$ †

14. $4x^2 + 25y^2 = 100$ †

15. $3x^2 + 4y^2 = 12$ †

16. $4x^2 + 5y^2 = 20$ †

17. $5x^2 - 10 = -2y^2$ †

18. $3y^2 = 21 - 7x^2$ †

19. $2x^2 + 3y^2 = 7$ †

20. $3x^2 + 4y^2 = 11$ †

In Exercises 21–34, find the standard form of the equation for the ellipse satisfying the given conditions. Graph the equation.

21. Foci: $(\pm1, 0)$; vertex $(3, 0)$ †

22. Foci: $(\pm3, 0)$; vertex $(5, 0)$ †

23. Foci: $(0, \pm2)$; vertex $(0, 4)$ †

24. Foci: $(0, \pm3)$; vertex $(0, -6)$ †

25. Foci: $(\pm4, 0)$; y-intercepts: ±3 †

26. Foci: $(\pm3, 0)$; y-intercepts: ±4 †

27. Foci: $(0, \pm2)$; x-intercepts: ±4 †

28. Foci: $(0, \pm3)$; x-intercepts: ±5 †

29. Center $(0, 0)$, vertical major axis of length 10, and minor axis of length 6 †

30. Center $(0, 0)$, vertical major axis of length 8, and minor axis of length 4 †

31. Center $(0, 0)$; vertices $(\pm6, 0)$; $c = 3$ †

32. Center $(0, 0)$; vertices $(0, \pm5)$; $c = 3$ †

33. Center $(0, 0)$; foci $(0, \pm2)$; $b = 3$ †

34. Center $(0, 0)$; foci $(\pm3, 0)$; $b = 2$ †

In Exercises 35–50, find the center, foci, and vertices of each ellipse. Graph each equation.

35. $\dfrac{(x - 1)^2}{4} + \dfrac{(y - 1)^2}{9} = 1$ †

36. $\dfrac{(x - 1)^2}{4} + \dfrac{(y - 1)^2}{16} = 1$ †

37. $\dfrac{x^2}{16} + \dfrac{(y + 3)^2}{4} = 1$ †

38. $\dfrac{(x + 2)^2}{4} + \dfrac{y^2}{9} = 1$ †

39. $3(x - 1)^2 + 4(y + 2)^2 = 12$ †

40. $9(x + 1)^2 + 4(y - 2)^2 = 36$ †

41. $4(x + 3)^2 + 5(y - 1)^2 = 20$ †

42. $25(x - 2)^2 + 4(y + 5)^2 = 100$ †

43. $5x^2 + 9y^2 + 10x - 36y - 4 = 0$ †

44. $9x^2 + 4y^2 + 72x - 24y + 144 = 0$ †

45. $9x^2 + 5y^2 + 36x - 40y + 71 = 0$ †

46. $3x^2 + 4y^2 + 12x - 16y - 32 = 0$ †

47. $x^2 + 2y^2 - 2x + 4y + 1 = 0$ †

48. $2x^2 + 2y^2 - 12x - 8y + 3 = 0$ †

49. $2x^2 + 9y^2 - 4x + 18y + 12 = 0$ †

50. $3x^2 + 2y^2 + 12x - 4y + 15 = 0$ †

†Due to space constrictions, answers to these exercises may be found in the Answers beginning on page A–1 in the back of the book.

B Exercises   Beyond the Basics

51. Semielliptical arch. A portion of an arch in the shape of a *semiellipse* (half of an ellipse) is 50 feet wide at the base and has a maximum height of 20 feet. Find the height of the arch at a distance of 10 feet from the center. (See the figure.) †

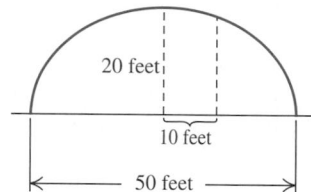

52. In Exercise 51, find the distance between the two points at the base where the height of the arch is 10 feet. 43.3 ft

53. Semielliptical arch bridge. A bridge is built in the shape of a semielliptical arch. The span of the bridge is 150 meters and its maximum height is 45 meters. There are two vertical supports, each at a distance of 25 meters from the central position. Find their heights. 42.4 m

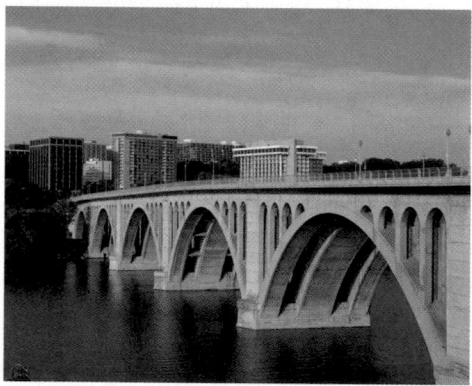

54. Elliptical billiard table. Some billiard tables (similar to pool tables, but without pockets) are manufactured in the shape of an ellipse. The foci of such tables are plainly marked for the convenience of the players. An elliptical billiard table is 6 feet long and 4 feet wide. Find the location of the foci. 2.2 ft from the center, along the major axis.

55. "Ellipti-pool." In Exercise 54, suppose there is a pocket at one of the foci. A pool shark places the ball at the table and bets that he will be able to make the ball fall into the pocket 10 out of 10 times. Explain why you should or should not accept the bet. †

56. Whispering gallery. The vertical cross section of the dome of Statuary Hall in Washington, DC, is semielliptical. The hall is 96 feet long and 23 feet high. It is said that John C. Calhoun used the whispering-gallery phenomenon to eavesdrop on his adversaries. Where should Calhoun and his foes be standing for the maximum whispering effect? †

57. Whispering gallery. The vertical cross section of the dome of the Mormon Tabernacle in Salt Lake City, Utah, is semielliptical in shape. The cross section is 250 feet long with a maximum height of 80 feet. Where should two people stand in order to maximize the whispering effect? †

In Exercises 58–61, use the fact (discovered by Johannes Kepler in 1609) that the planets move in elliptical orbits with the sun at one of the foci. Astronomers have measured the *perihelion* (the smallest distance from the planet to the sun) and *aphelion* (the largest distance from the planet to the sun) for each of the planets. The distances given in Table 10.1 are in millions of miles.

TABLE 10.1

Planet	Perihelion	Aphelion
Mercury	28.56	43.88
Venus	66.74	67.68
Earth	91.38	94.54
Mars	128.49	154.83
Jupiter	460.43	506.87
Saturn	837.05	936.37
Uranus	1699.45	1866.59
Neptune	2771.72	2816.42
Pluto	2749.57	4582.61

58. **Mars.** Find an equation of Mars's orbit about the sun. [*Hint*: Set up a coordinate system with the sun at one focus and the major axis lying on the *x*-axis. (See the figure.) Calculate *a* from the equation $2a = \text{aphelion} + \text{perihelion}$. Calculate *c* from the equation $c = a - \text{perihelion}$. Calculate b^2 from the equation $b^2 = a^2 - c^2$. Write the equation $\frac{x^2}{a^2} + \frac{y^2}{b^2} = 1$.] †

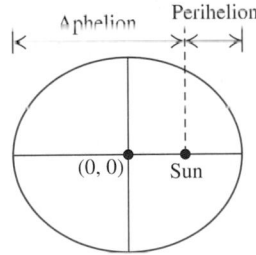

59. **Earth.** Write an equation for the orbit of Earth about the sun. †

60. **Mercury.** Write an equation for the orbit of the planet Mercury about the sun. †

61. **Saturn.** Write an equation for the orbit of the planet Saturn about the sun. †

62. **Moon.** The moon orbits Earth in an elliptical path with Earth at one focus. The major and minor axes of the orbit have lengths of 768,806 kilometers and 767,746 kilometers, respectively. Find the perihelion and aphelion of the orbit. †

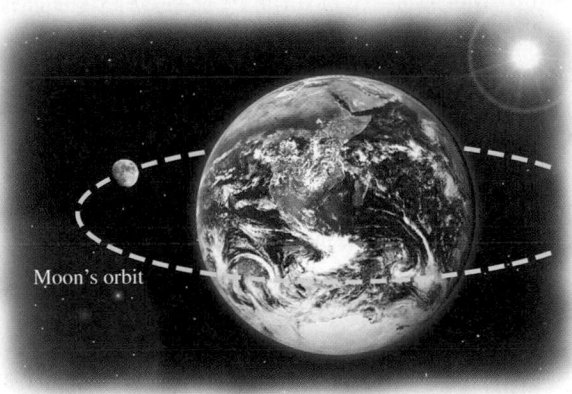

Moon's orbit

63. **Halley's comet.** In 1682, Edmund Halley (1656–1742) identified the orbit of a certain comet (now called Halley's comet) as an elliptical orbit about the sun, with the sun at one focus. He calculated the length of its major axis to be approximately 5.39×10^9 kilometers and minor axis approximately 1.36×10^9 kilometers. Find the perihelion and aphelion of the orbit of Halley's comet. †

64. **Orbit of a satellite.** Assume that Earth is a sphere with a radius of 3960 miles. A satellite has an elliptical orbit around Earth with the center of Earth as one of its foci. The maximum and minimum heights of the satellite from the surface of Earth are 164 miles and 110 miles, respectively. Find an equation for the orbit of the satellite. †

C Exercises Beyond the Basics

65. Find an equation of the ellipse in standard form with center $(0, 0)$, with major axis of length 10, and passing through the point $\left(-3, \dfrac{16}{5}\right)$. †

66. Find an equation of the ellipse in standard form with center $(0, 0)$, with major axis of length 6, and passing through the point $\left(1, \dfrac{3\sqrt{5}}{2}\right)$. †

67. Find the lengths of the major and minor axes of the ellipse
$$\frac{x^2}{b^2} + \frac{y^2}{a^2} = 1,$$
given that the ellipse passes through the points $(2, 1)$ and $(1, -3)$. †

68. Find an equation of the ellipse in standard form with center $(2, 1)$ and passing through the points $(10, 1)$ and $(6, 2)$. †

69. The **eccentricity** of an ellipse, denoted by e, is defined as
$$e = \frac{\text{Distance between the foci}}{\text{Distance between the vertices}} = \frac{2c}{2a} = \frac{c}{a}.$$
What happens when $e = 0$? †

In Exercises 70–74, use the definition of e given in Exercise 69 to determine the eccentricity of each ellipse. (This e has nothing to do with the number e, discussed in Chapter 4, that is base for natural logarithms.)

70. $\dfrac{x^2}{16} + \dfrac{y^2}{9} = 1$ $\dfrac{\sqrt{7}}{4}$

71. $20x^2 + 36y^2 = 720$ $\dfrac{2}{3}$

72. $x^2 + 4y^2 = 1$ $\dfrac{\sqrt{3}}{2}$

73. $\dfrac{(x+1)^2}{25} + \dfrac{(y-2)^2}{9} = 1$ †

74. $x^2 + 2y^2 - 2x + 4y + 1 = 0$ †

75. An ellipse has its major axis along the x-axis and minor axis along the y-axis. Its eccentricity is $\dfrac{1}{2}$ and the distance between the foci is 4. Find an equation of the ellipse. †

76. Find an equation of the ellipse whose major axis has end points $(-3, 0)$ and $(3, 0)$, and that has eccentricity $\dfrac{1}{3}$. †

77. A point $P(x, y)$ moves so that its distance from the point $(4, 0)$ is always one-half its distance from the line $x = 16$. Show that the equation of the path of P is an ellipse of eccentricity $\dfrac{1}{2}$. †

78. A point, $P(x, y)$ moves so that its distance from the point $(0, 2)$ is always one-third of its distance from the line $y = 10$. Show that the equation of the path of P is an ellipse of eccentricity $\dfrac{1}{3}$. †

79. The **latus rectum of an ellipse** is the line segment passing through a focus and that is perpendicular to the major axis and has endpoints on the ellipse. Show that the length of the latus rectum of an ellipse is $\dfrac{2b^2}{a}$, where b is half the length of the minor axis and a is half the length of the major axis. †

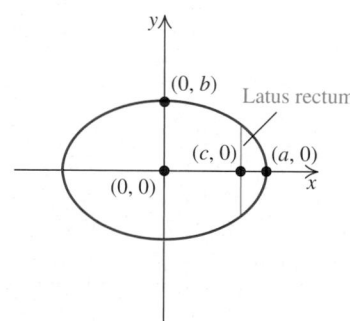

80. Find an equation of the ellipse with center $(0, 0)$, major axis along the x-axis, eccentricity $\dfrac{1}{\sqrt{2}}$, and latus rectum of length 3 units. †

In Exercises 81–84, find all points of intersection of the given curves by solving systems of nonlinear equations. Sketch the graphs of the curves and show the points of intersection.

81. $\begin{cases} x + 3y = -2 \\ 4x^2 + 3y^2 = 7 \end{cases}$ †

82. $\begin{cases} x^2 = 2y \\ 2x^2 + y^2 = 12 \end{cases}$ †

83. $\begin{cases} x^2 + y^2 = 20 \\ 9x^2 + y^2 = 36 \end{cases}$ †

84. $\begin{cases} 9x^2 + 16y^2 = 36 \\ 18x^2 + 5y^2 = 45 \end{cases}$ †

Critical Thinking

85. Find the number of circles with a radius of three units that touch both of the coordinate axes. Write the equation of each circle.

86. Find the number of ellipses with a major axis and a minor axis of lengths six units and four units, respectively, that touch both axes. Write the equation of each ellipse. †

Answer:

85. 4 circles: $(x - 3)^2 + (y - 3)^2 = 9$, $(x + 3)^2 + (y - 3)^2 = 9$, $(x + 3)^2 + (y + 3)^2 = 9$, $(x - 3)^2 + (y + 3)^2 = 9$.

The Hyperbola

BEFORE STARTING THIS SECTION, REVIEW

1. Distance formula (Section 2.1, page 185)

2. Midpoint formula (Section 2.1, page 187)

3. Completing the square (Section 1.4, page 123)

4. Oblique asymptotes (Section 3.5, page 393)

5. Transformations of graphs (Section 2.6, page 263)

6. Symmetry (Section 2.2, page 194)

OBJECTIVES

1 Learn the definition of a hyperbola.

2 Find the asymptotes of the hyperbola.

3 Graph a hyperbola.

4 Translate hyperbolas.

5 Use hyperbolas in applications.

Alfred Lee Loomis (1887–1975)
Alfred Loomis was an American lawyer, investment banker, physicist, and patron of scientific research. Besides inventing LORAN, he made significant contributions to the ground-based technology for landing airplanes by instruments. President Roosevelt recognized the value of Loomis's work and described him as second perhaps only to Churchill as the civilian most responsible for the Allied victory in World War II.

What Is Loran?

LORAN stands for LOng-RAnge Navigation. The federal government runs the LORAN system, which uses land-based radio navigation transmitters to provide users with information on position and timing. During World War II, Alfred Lee Loomis was selected to chair the National Defense Research Committee. Much of his work focused on the problem of creating a light system for plane-carried radar. As a result of this effort, he invented LORAN, the long-range navigation system whose offshoot LORAN-C remains in widespread use. The navigational method provided by LORAN is based on the principle of determining the points of intersection of two hyperbolas to fix the two-dimensional position of the receiver. In Example 7, we illustrate how this is done.

The LORAN-C system is now being supplemented by the global positioning system (GPS), which works on the same principle as LORAN-C. The GPS system consists of 24 satellites that orbit 11,000 miles above Earth. The GPS was created by the U.S. Department of Defense to provide precise navigation information for targeting weapons systems anywhere in the world. The GPS is available to civilian users worldwide in a degraded mode. It is now used in aviation, navigation, and automobiles. The system is able to provide you with your exact position on Earth anywhere, anytime.

The GPS and LORAN-C work together, giving a highly accurate, duplicate navigation system for the Defense Department. ■

1 Learn the definition of a hyperbola.

Definition of Hyperbola

HYPERBOLA

A **hyperbola** is the set of all points in the plane, the difference of whose distances from two fixed points is constant. The fixed points are called the **foci** of the hyperbola.

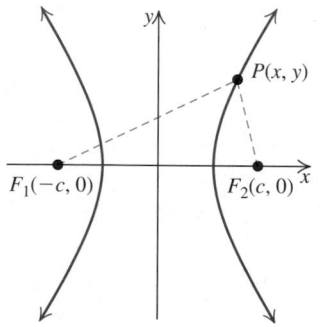

FIGURE 10.21

Figure 10.21 shows a hyperbola in *standard position*, with foci $F_1(-c, 0)$ and $F_2(c, 0)$ on the x-axis at equal distances from the origin. The two parts of the hyperbola are called **branches.**

As in the discussion of ellipses in Section 10.3 (see page 895), we take $2a$ as the positive constant referred to in the definition.

A point $P(x, y)$ lies on a hyperbola if and only if

$$|d(P, F_1) - d(P, F_2)| = 2a \qquad \text{Definition of hyperbola}$$
$$\sqrt{(x + c)^2 + y^2} - \sqrt{(x - c)^2 + y^2} = \pm 2a. \qquad \text{Apply distance formula.}$$

Just as in the case of an ellipse, we eliminate radicals and simplify (see Exercise 79) to obtain the equation:

$$(c^2 - a^2)x^2 - a^2y^2 = a^2(c^2 - a^2) \quad (1)$$

For convenience, we let $b^2 = c^2 - a^2$.

$$(c^2 - a^2)x^2 - a^2y^2 = a^2(c^2 - a^2) \qquad \text{Equation (1)}$$
$$b^2x^2 - a^2y^2 = a^2b^2 \qquad \text{Replace } c^2 - a^2 \text{ by } b^2.$$
$$\frac{x^2}{a^2} - \frac{y^2}{b^2} = 1 \quad (2) \qquad \text{Divide both sides by } a^2b^2.$$

Equation (2) is called the **standard form of the equation of a hyperbola** with center $(0, 0)$. The x-intercepts of the graph of Equation (2) are $-a$ and a. The points corresponding to these x-intercepts are the **vertices** of the hyperbola. The distance between the vertices $V_1(-a, 0)$ and $V_2(a, 0)$ is $2a$. The line segment joining the two vertices is called the **transverse axis.** The midpoint of the transverse axis is the **center** of the hyperbola. The *center* is also the midpoint of the line segment joining the foci. (See Figure 10.22.) The line segment joining the points $(0, -b)$ and $(0, b)$ is called the **conjugate axis.**

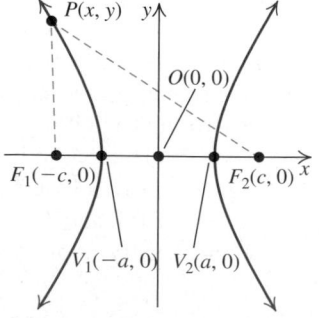

Points F_1 and F_2 are foci.
Points V_1 and V_2 are vertices.
Point O is the center.
Segment $\overline{V_1V_2}$ is the transverse axis.
The difference of the distances $\left|\overline{PF_1} - \overline{PF_2}\right|$ from any point P on the hyperbola is constant.

FIGURE 10.22

Similarly, an equation of a hyperbola with center $(0, 0)$ and foci $(0, -c)$ and $(0, c)$ on the y-axis is given by:

$$\frac{y^2}{a^2} - \frac{x^2}{b^2} = 1, \text{ where } b^2 = c^2 - a^2 \quad (3)$$

Here, the vertices are $(0, -a)$ and $(0, a)$. The transverse axis of length $2a$ of the graph of equation (3) lies on the y-axis, and its conjugate axis is the segment joining the points $(-b, 0)$ and $(b, 0)$ of length $2b$ that lies on the x-axis.

We now summarize important properties and facts about hyperbolas with center $(0, 0)$ and transverse axis on a coordinate axis.

Main facts about hyperbolas centered at $(0, 0)$		
Standard Equation	$\dfrac{x^2}{a^2} - \dfrac{y^2}{b^2} = 1; a > 0, b > 0$	$\dfrac{y^2}{a^2} - \dfrac{x^2}{b^2} = 1; a > 0, b > 0$
Equation of transverse axis	$y = 0$ (x-axis)	$x = 0$ (y-axis)
Length of transverse axis	$2a$	$2a$
Equation of conjugate axis	$x = 0$ (y-axis)	$y = 0$ (x-axis)
Length of conjugate axis	$2b$	$2b$
Vertices	$(\pm a, 0)$	$(0, \pm a)$
Endpoints of conjugate axis	$(0, \pm b)$	$(\pm b, 0)$
Foci	$(\pm c, 0)$, where $c^2 = a^2 + b^2$	$(0, \pm c)$ where $c^2 = a^2 + b^2$
Description	Hyperbola has a *left branch* and a *right branch*. (Hyperbola opens left and right.)	Hyperbola has an *upper branch* and a *lower branch*. (Hyperbola opens up and down.)
Graph		

EXAMPLE 1   **Determining the Orientation of a Hyperbola**

Does the hyperbola

$$\frac{x^2}{4} - \frac{y^2}{10} = 1$$

have its transverse axis on the x-axis or y-axis?

Continued on next page.

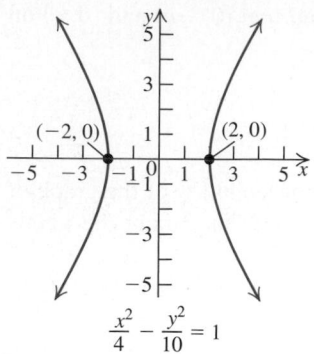

$$\frac{x^2}{4} - \frac{y^2}{10} = 1$$

FIGURE 10.23

Solution

Unlike the horizontal or vertical orientation of an ellipse, the orientation (left–right branches or up–down branches) of a hyperbola is determined, not by examining the relative sizes of the denominators under the x^2- and y^2-terms, but rather *by noting where the minus sign occurs in the standard equation.* From the table on page 909, we see that the transverse axis is on the x-axis when the minus sign precedes the y^2-term and is on the y-axis when the minus sign precedes the x^2-term. In the equation in this example, the minus sign precedes the y^2-term, so the transverse axis is on the x-axis. See Figure 10.23. ▪ ▪ ▪

PRACTICE PROBLEM 1   Does the hyperbola $\dfrac{y^2}{8} - \dfrac{x^2}{5} = 1$ have its transverse axis on the x-axis or the y-axis? ▪

EXAMPLE 2   **Finding the Vertices and Foci from the Equation of a Hyperbola**

Find the vertices and foci for the hyperbola

$$28y^2 - 36x^2 = 63.$$

Solution

First convert the equation $28y^2 - 36x^2 = 63$ to the standard form.

$28y^2 - 36x^2 = 63$	Given equation
$\dfrac{28y^2}{63} - \dfrac{36x^2}{63} = 1$	Divide both sides by 63.
$\dfrac{4y^2}{9} - \dfrac{4x^2}{7} = 1$	Simplify.
$\dfrac{y^2}{\frac{9}{4}} - \dfrac{x^2}{\frac{7}{4}} = 1$	Divide numerators and denominators of each term by 4.

The last equation is the equation of a hyperbola in standard form with center $(0, 0)$. Since the coefficient of x^2 is negative, the transverse axis lies on the y-axis.

Here $a^2 = \dfrac{9}{4}$ and $b^2 = \dfrac{7}{4}$. The equation $c^2 = a^2 + b^2$ gives the value of c^2:

$$c^2 = a^2 + b^2$$
$$= \frac{9}{4} + \frac{7}{4} \qquad \text{Replace } a^2 \text{ by } \frac{9}{4} \text{ and } b^2 \text{ by } \frac{7}{4}.$$
$$= \frac{16}{4} = 4 \qquad \text{Simplify.}$$

Now, $a^2 = \dfrac{9}{4}$ gives $a = \dfrac{3}{2}$, and $c^2 = 4$ gives $c = 2$, since we require $a > 0$ and $c > 0$.

The vertices of the hyperbola are $\left(0, -\dfrac{3}{2}\right)$ and $\left(0, \dfrac{3}{2}\right)$. The foci of the hyperbola are $(0, -2)$ and $(0, 2)$. ▪ ▪ ▪

PRACTICE PROBLEM 2   Find the vertices and foci for the hyperbola

$$x^2 - 4y^2 = 8.$$ ▪

EXAMPLE 3   **Finding the Equation of a Hyperbola**

Find the standard form of the equation of a hyperbola with vertices $(\pm 4, 0)$ and foci $(\pm 5, 0)$.

Solution

Since the foci of the hyperbola, $(-5, 0)$ and $(5, 0)$, are on the x-axis, the transverse axis of the hyperbola lies on the x-axis. The center of the hyperbola is midway between the foci, at $(0, 0)$. The standard form of such a hyperbola is

$$\frac{x^2}{a^2} - \frac{y^2}{b^2} = 1.$$

You need to find a^2 and b^2.

The distance a between the center $(0, 0)$ to either vertex, $(-4, 0)$ or $(4, 0)$, is 4, so that

$$a = 4$$
$$a^2 = 16. \qquad \text{Square both sides.}$$

The distance c between the center $(0, 0)$ to either focus, $(-5, 0)$ or $(5, 0)$, is 5, so

$$c = 5$$
$$c^2 = 25. \qquad \text{Square both sides.}$$

Now use the equation $b^2 = c^2 - a^2$ to obtain:

$$b^2 = c^2 - a^2$$
$$= 25 - 16 \qquad c^2 = 25 \text{ and } a^2 = 16$$
$$= 9 \qquad\qquad \text{Simplify.}$$

Substitute $a^2 = 16$ and $b^2 = 9$ in $\dfrac{x^2}{a^2} - \dfrac{y^2}{b^2} = 1$ to obtain the standard form of the equation of the hyperbola. The equation is

$$\frac{x^2}{16} - \frac{y^2}{9} = 1.$$ ▪ ▪ ▪

PRACTICE PROBLEM 3   Find the standard form of the equation of a hyperbola with vertices at $(0, \pm 4)$ and foci at $(0, \pm 6)$.   ▪

2 Find the asymptotes of the hyperbola.

The Asymptotes of a Hyperbola

Recall from Section 3.5 that a line $y = mx + b$ is a horizontal asymptote (if $m = 0$) or an oblique asymptote (if $m \neq 0$) of the graph of $y = f(x)$ if the distance from the line to the points on the graph of f approaches 0 as $x \to \infty$ or $x \to -\infty$. When horizontal or oblique asymptotes exist, they provide us with information about the end behavior of the graph of f. This is especially helpful in graphing a hyperbola.

In order to find the asymptotes of the hyperbola with equation $\dfrac{x^2}{a^2} - \dfrac{y^2}{b^2} = 1$, we first solve this equation for y.

$$\frac{x^2}{a^2} - \frac{y^2}{b^2} = 1 \qquad\qquad \text{Given equation of hyperbola}$$

$$-\frac{y^2}{b^2} = -\frac{x^2}{a^2} + 1 \qquad\qquad \text{Subtract } \frac{x^2}{a^2} \text{ from both sides.}$$

$$\frac{y^2}{b^2} = \frac{x^2}{a^2} - 1 \qquad\qquad \text{Multiply both sides by } -1.$$

$$y^2 = b^2\left(\frac{x^2}{a^2} - 1\right) \qquad\qquad \text{Multiply both sides by } b^2.$$

$$y^2 = b^2\left(\frac{x^2}{a^2} - \frac{x^2}{a^2} \cdot \frac{a^2}{x^2}\right) \qquad \text{Write } 1 = \frac{x^2}{a^2} \cdot \frac{a^2}{x^2}.$$

$$y^2 = \frac{b^2 x^2}{a^2}\left(1 - \frac{a^2}{x^2}\right) \qquad\qquad \text{Factor out } \frac{x^2}{a^2}.$$

$$y = \pm\frac{bx}{a}\sqrt{1 - \frac{a^2}{x^2}} \qquad\qquad \text{Square root property}$$

STUDY TIP

There is a convenient device that can be used for obtaining equations of the asymptotes of a hyperbola. Substitute 0 for the 1 on the right side of the equation of the hyperbola, and then solve for y in terms of x. For example, for the hyperbola $\dfrac{x^2}{a^2} - \dfrac{y^2}{b^2} = 1$, replace the 1 on the right side by 0 to obtain $\dfrac{x^2}{a^2} - \dfrac{y^2}{b^2} = 0$. Solve this equation for y:

$$\frac{y^2}{b^2} = \frac{x^2}{a^2}$$

$$y^2 = \frac{b^2}{a^2}x^2.$$

The lines $y = \pm\dfrac{b}{a}x$ are the asymptotes of the hyperbola.

As $x \to \infty$ or as $x \to -\infty$, the quantity $\dfrac{a^2}{x^2}$ approaches 0. Thus, $\sqrt{1 - \dfrac{a^2}{x^2}}$ approaches 1 and the value of y approaches $\pm\dfrac{bx}{a}$. Therefore, the lines $y = \dfrac{b}{a}x$ and $y = -\dfrac{b}{a}x$ are the oblique asymptotes for the graph of the hyperbola $\dfrac{x^2}{a^2} - \dfrac{y^2}{b^2} = 1$. Similarly, you can show that the lines $y = \dfrac{a}{b}x$ and $y = -\dfrac{a}{b}x$ are the oblique asymptotes for the graph of the hyperbola $\dfrac{y^2}{a^2} - \dfrac{x^2}{b^2} = 1$.

THE ASYMPTOTES OF A HYPERBOLA WITH CENTER (0, 0)

1. The graph of the hyperbola $\dfrac{x^2}{a^2} - \dfrac{y^2}{b^2} = 1$ has transverse axis along the x-axis and has the two asymptotes (see Figure 10.24 on page 914)

$$y = \frac{b}{a}x \qquad \text{and} \qquad y = -\frac{b}{a}x.$$

2. The graph of the hyperbola $\dfrac{y^2}{a^2} - \dfrac{x^2}{b^2} = 1$ has transverse axis along the y-axis and has the two asymptotes (see Figure 10.25 on page 914)

$$y = \frac{a}{b}x \qquad \text{and} \qquad y = -\frac{a}{b}x.$$

| EXAMPLE 4 | **Finding the Asymptotes of a Hyperbola** |

Determine the asymptotes of each hyperbola.

a. $\dfrac{x^2}{4} - \dfrac{y^2}{9} = 1$ **b.** $\dfrac{y^2}{9} - \dfrac{x^2}{16} = 1$

Solution

a. The hyperbola $\dfrac{x^2}{4} - \dfrac{y^2}{9} = 1$ is of the form $\dfrac{x^2}{a^2} - \dfrac{y^2}{b^2} = 1$. Thus, $a = 2$ and $b = 3$.

Substitute these values into $y = \dfrac{b}{a}x$ and $y = -\dfrac{b}{a}x$. Thus, the asymptotes of the hyper-

bola $\dfrac{x^2}{4} - \dfrac{y^2}{9} = 1$ are

$$y = \frac{3}{2}x \quad \text{and} \quad y = -\frac{3}{2}x.$$

b. The hyperbola $\dfrac{y^2}{9} - \dfrac{x^2}{16} = 1$ has the form $\dfrac{y^2}{a^2} - \dfrac{x^2}{b^2} = 1$. Thus, $a = 3$ and $b = 4$.

Substitute these values into $y = \dfrac{a}{b}x$ and $y = -\dfrac{a}{b}x$. Thus, the asymptotes of the hyper-

bola $\dfrac{y^2}{9} - \dfrac{x^2}{16} = 1$ are

$$y = \frac{3}{4}x \quad \text{and} \quad y = -\frac{3}{4}x. \qquad ■ ■ ■$$

PRACTICE PROBLEM 4   Determine the asymptotes of the hyperbola $\dfrac{y^2}{4} - \dfrac{x^2}{9} = 1$.   ■

---

3 Graph a hyperbola.

Graphing a Hyperbola with Center $(0, 0)$

Consider the hyperbola with equation

$$\frac{x^2}{a^2} - \frac{y^2}{b^2} = 1.$$

The vertices of this hyperbola are $(-a, 0)$ and $(a, 0)$. The endpoints of the conjugate axis are $(0, -b)$ and $(0, b)$. The rectangle with vertices (a, b), $(-a, b)$, $(-a, -b)$, and $(a, -b)$ is called the **fundamental rectangle** of the hyperbola. (See Figure 10.24.) The diagonals of the fundamental rectangle have slopes $\dfrac{b}{a}$ and $-\dfrac{b}{a}$. Thus, the extensions of these diagonals are the asymptotes of the hyperbola.

The following steps will help you graph a hyperbola with center (0, 0).

Graphing a Hyperbola Centered at (0, 0)

Graph $\dfrac{x^2}{a^2} - \dfrac{y^2}{b^2} = 1$.	Graph $\dfrac{y^2}{a^2} - \dfrac{x^2}{b^2} = 1$.
The hyperbola opens left and right.	The hyperbola opens up and down.

Step 1 (i) **Locate the vertices** at $(-a, 0)$ and $(a, 0)$.

    (ii) Locate the endpoints of the conjugate axis at $(0, -b)$ and $(0, b)$.

Step 1 (i) **Locate the vertices** at $(0, -a)$ and $(0, a)$.

    (ii) Locate the endpoints of the conjugate axis at $(-b, 0)$ and $(b, 0)$.

Step 2 Sketch the fundamental rectangle.

    (i) Draw dashed lines $x = a$ and $x = -a$.

    (ii) Draw dashed lines $y = b$ and $y = -b$.

    The four points of intersection of the four lines form the fundamental rectangle.

Step 2 Sketch the fundamental rectangle.

    (i) Draw dashed lines $y = a$ and $y = -a$.

    (ii) Draw dashed lines $x = b$ and $x = -b$.

    The four points of intersection of the four lines form the fundamental rectangle.

Step 3 Find the asymptotes.
Extend the diagonals of the rectangle in Step 2 to obtain the asymptotes $y = \dfrac{b}{a}x$ and $y = -\dfrac{b}{a}x$.

Step 3 Find the asymptotes.
Extend the diagonals of the rectangle in Step 2 to obtain the asymptotes $y = \dfrac{a}{b}x$ and $y = -\dfrac{a}{b}x$.

Step 4 Sketch the graph.
Draw two branches of the hyperbola opening to the left and right, starting from the vertices and approaching the asymptotes. (See Figure 10.24.)

Step 4 Sketch the graph.
Draw two branches of the hyperbola opening up and down, starting from the vertices and approaching the asymptotes. (See Figure 10.25.)

FIGURE 10.24

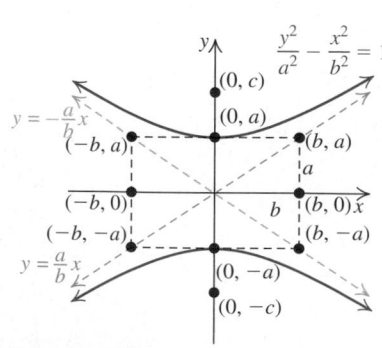

FIGURE 10.25

EXAMPLE 5   **Graphing a Hyperbola**

Graph the hyperbola $16x^2 - 9y^2 = 144$.

Solution

First write the equation in standard form. The right side should be 1, so divide both sides by 144.

$$16x^2 - 9y^2 = 144 \qquad \text{The given equation}$$

$$\frac{16x^2}{144} - \frac{9y^2}{144} = \frac{144}{144} \qquad \text{Divide both sides by 144.}$$

$$\frac{x^2}{9} - \frac{y^2}{16} = 1 \qquad \text{Simplify.}$$

Since the minus sign precedes the y^2-term, the hyperbola opens to the left and right.

Step 1   **Locate the vertices.** The equation of the hyperbola is in the form $\frac{x^2}{a^2} - \frac{y^2}{b^2} = 1$. The transverse axis lies on the x-axis, with $a^2 = 9$ and $b^2 = 16$. Since $a^2 = 9$, $a = 3$. Also, $b^2 = 16$ gives $b = 4$. The vertices of the hyperbola are $(-3, 0)$ and $(3, 0)$. See Figure 10.26(a).
The endpoints of the conjugate axis are $(0, -4)$ and $(0, 4)$.

Step 2   **Draw the fundamental rectangle.** Draw four dashed lines: $x = 3$, $x = -3$, $y = 4$, and $y = -4$. The fundamental rectangle with vertices $(3, 4)$, $(-3, 4)$, $(-3, -4)$, and $(3, -4)$ is formed. See Figure 10.26(b).

Step 3   **Sketch the asymptotes.** Extend the diagonals of the rectangle obtained in Step 2 to sketch the asymptotes: $y = \frac{4}{3}x$ and $y = -\frac{4}{3}x$. See Figure 10.26(c).

Step 4   **Sketch the graph.** Draw two branches of the hyperbola opening to the left and right, starting from the vertices $(-3, 0)$ and $(3, 0)$ and approaching the asymptotes (without crossing them). See Figure 10.26(d). Since $c = \sqrt{a^2 + b^2} = \sqrt{9 + 16} = 5$, the foci of the hyperbola are $(-5, 0)$ and $(5, 0)$.   ■ ■ ■

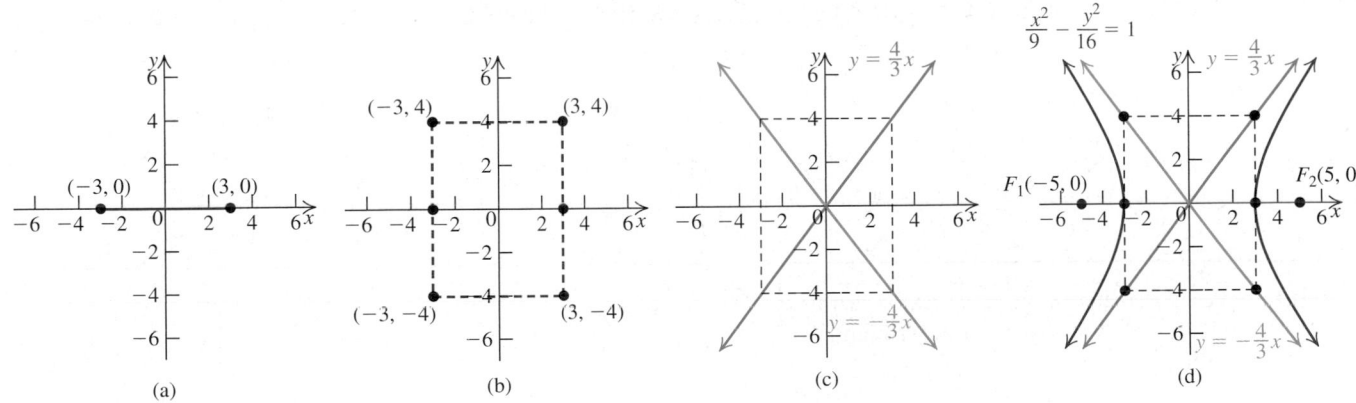

FIGURE 10.26

PRACTICE PROBLEM 5   Graph the hyperbola $25x^2 - 4y^2 = 100$.   ■

4 Translate hyperbolas.

Translations of Hyperbolas

Horizontal and vertical shifts can be used to find the standard form of the equations of hyperbolas centered at (h, k). The properties of such hyperbolas are summarized next.

Main properties of hyperbolas centered at (h, k)		
Standard Equation	$\dfrac{(x - h)^2}{a^2} - \dfrac{(y - k)^2}{b^2} = 1;$ $a > 0, b > 0$	$\dfrac{(y - k)^2}{a^2} - \dfrac{(x - h)^2}{b^2} = 1;$ $a > 0, b > 0$
Equation of transverse axis	$y = k$	$x = h$
Length of transverse axis	$2a$	$2a$
Equation of conjugate axis	$x = h$	$y = k$
Length of conjugate axis	$2b$	$2b$
Center	(h, k)	(h, k)
Vertices	$(h - a, k)$ and $(h + a, k)$	$(h, k - a)$ and $(h, k + a)$
Endpoints of conjugate axis	$(h, k - b)$ and $(h, k + b)$	$(h - b, k)$ and $(h + b, k)$
Foci	$(h - c, k)$ and $(h + c, k);$ $c^2 = a^2 + b^2$	$(h, k - c)$ and $(h, k + c);$ $c^2 = a^2 + b^2$
Asymptotes	$y - k = \pm\dfrac{b}{a}(x - h)$	$y - k = \pm\dfrac{a}{b}(x - h)$

We now describe a procedure for sketching the graph of a hyperbola centered at (h, k).

FINDING THE SOLUTIONS: PROCEDURE FOR SKETCHING THE GRAPH OF A HYPERBOLA CENTERED AT (h, k)

OBJECTIVE

*The **objective** is to sketch the graph of either*
$$\frac{(x - h)^2}{a^2} - \frac{(y - k)^2}{b^2} = 1 \text{ or}$$
$$\frac{(y - k)^2}{a^2} - \frac{(x - h)^2}{b^2} = 1.$$

EXAMPLE.

Sketch the graph of
$$\frac{(x - 1)^2}{4} - \frac{(y + 2)^2}{9} = 1.$$

EXAMPLE.

Sketch the graph of
$$\frac{(y + 2)^2}{9} - \frac{(x - 1)^2}{4} = 1.$$

Step 1   Plot the center (h, k), and draw horizontal and vertical dashed lines through the center.

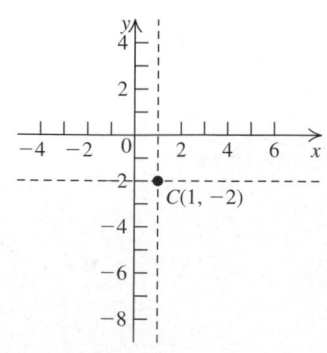

Step 2   Locate the vertices and the endpoints of the conjugate axis. Lightly sketch the fundamental rectangle, with sides parallel to the coordinate axes, through these points.

Step 3   Sketch dashed lines through opposite vertices of the fundamental rectangle. These are the asymptotes.

Step 4   Draw both branches of the hyperbola, through the vertices and approaching the asymptotes.

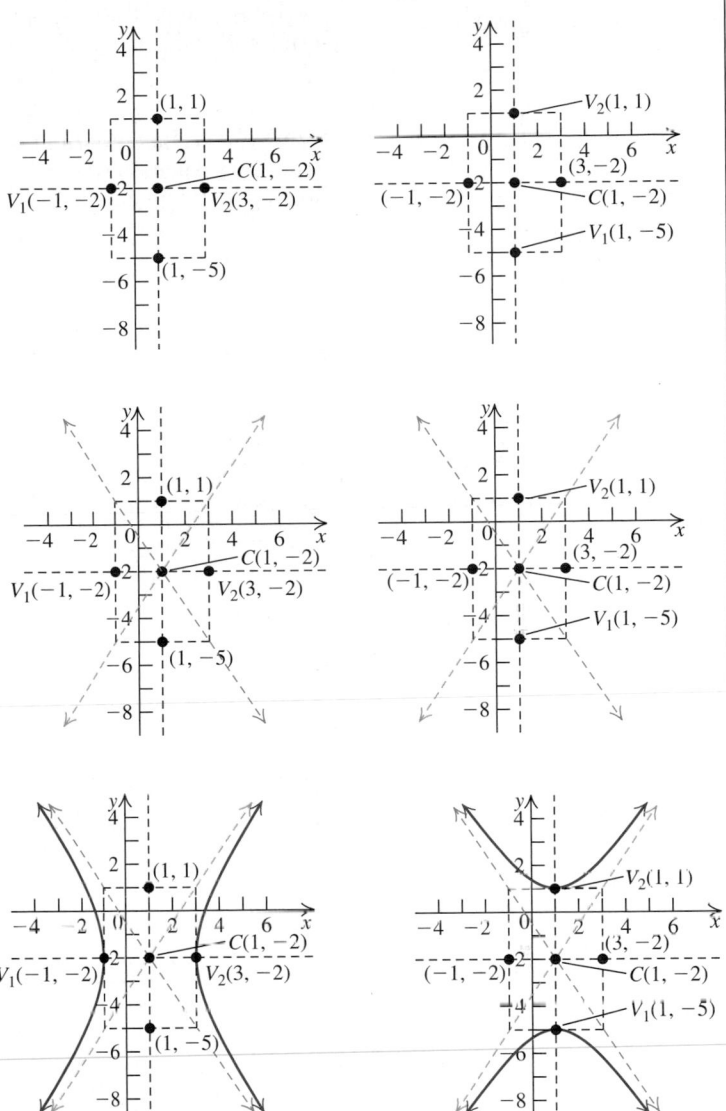

Step 5   The foci are located on the transverse axis, c units from the center, where $c^2 = a^2 + b^2$.

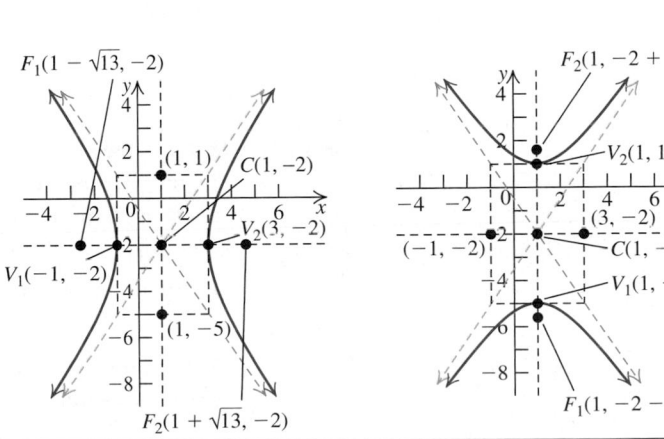

If the binomials in the equation of a hyperbola in standard form are expanded and like terms collected, an equation of the form

$$Ax^2 + Cy^2 + Dx + Ey + F = 0$$

results, with A and C of opposite sign (that is, $AC < 0$.) Conversely, except in degenerate cases, any equation of this form can be put into one of the standard forms of a hyperbola by completing the squares on the x- and y-terms.

EXAMPLE 6   **Graphing a Hyperbola**

Show that $9x^2 - 16y^2 + 18x + 64y - 199 = 0$ is an equation of a hyperbola, and then graph the hyperbola.

Solution

Since we plan on completing squares, first group the x- and y-terms onto the left side and the constants onto the right side.

$9x^2 - 16y^2 + 18x + 64y - 199 = 0$	Given equation
$(9x^2 + 18x) + (-16y^2 + 64y) = 199$	Group terms.
$9(x^2 + 2x) - 16(y^2 - 4y) = 199$	Factor out 9 and -16.
$9(x^2 + 2x + 1) - 16(y^2 - 4y + 4) = 199 + 9 - 64$	Complete the squares by adding the square of half the coefficients to both sides.

$(9)(1) = 9$ was added $(-16)(4) = -64$ was added

$9(x + 1)^2 - 16(y - 2)^2 = 144$	Factor and simplify.
$\dfrac{9(x + 1)^2}{144} - \dfrac{16(y - 2)^2}{144} = 1$	Divide both sides by 144 to obtain 1 on the right side.
$\dfrac{(x + 1)^2}{16} - \dfrac{(y - 2)^2}{9} = 1$	Simplify.

The last equation is the standard form of the equation of a hyperbola with center $(-1, 2)$. Now we sketch the graph of the hyperbola

$$\frac{(x + 1)^2}{16} - \frac{(y - 2)^2}{9} = 1.$$

Steps 1–2   **Locate the vertices.** For this hyperbola with center $(-1, 2)$, $a^2 = 16$ and $b^2 = 9$. Hence, $a = 4$ and $b = 3$. From the table on page 916, with $h = -1$ and $k = 2$, the vertices are

$(h - a, k) = (-1 - 4, 2) = (-5, 2)$ and $(h + a, k) = (-1 + 4, 2) = (3, 2)$.

Draw the fundamental rectangle. The vertices of the fundamental rectangle are $(3, -1), (3, 5), (-5, 5)$, and $(-5, -1)$.

Step 3   **Sketch the asymptotes.** Extend the diagonals of the rectangle obtained in Step 2 to sketch the asymptotes:

$$y - 2 = \frac{3}{4}(x + 1) \quad \text{and} \quad y - 2 = -\frac{3}{4}(x + 1).$$

Step 4   **Sketch the graph.** Draw two branches of the hyperbola opening to the left and right, starting from the vertices $(-5, 2)$ and $(3, 2)$ and approaching the asymptotes (without crossing them). (See Figure 10.27.)

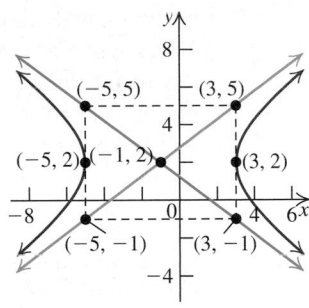

FIGURE 10.27   ■ ■ ■

PRACTICE PROBLEM 6   Show that $x^2 - 4y^2 - 2x + 16y - 20 = 0$ is an equation of a hyperbola, and graph the hyperbola.   ■

5 Use hyperbolas in applications.

Applications

Hyperbolas have many applications. We list a few of them here:

1. Comets that do not move in elliptical orbits around the sun almost always move in hyperbolic orbits. (In theory, they can also move in parabolic orbits.)

2. Boyle's Law states that if a perfect gas is kept at a constant temperature, then its pressure P and volume V are related by the equation $PV = c$, where c is a constant. The graph of this equation is a hyperbola. In Exercise 80(b), you are asked to explore the case where $c = 8$. In this case, the transverse axis is not parallel to a coordinate axis.

3. The hyperbola has the reflecting property that a ray of light from a source at one focus of a hyperbolic mirror (a mirror with hyperbolic cross sections) is reflected along the line through the other focus.
   The reflecting properties of the parabola and hyperbola are combined into one design for a reflecting telescope. (See Figure 10.28.) The parallel rays from a star are finally focused at the eyepiece at F_2.

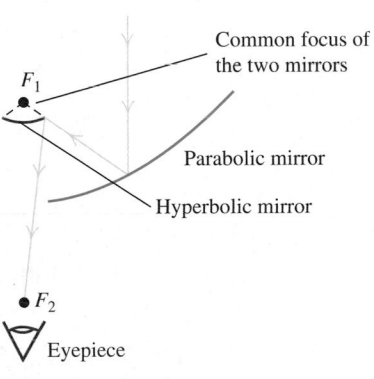

FIGURE 10.28

4. The definition of a hyperbola forms the basis of several important navigational systems.

How Does LORAN Work?

Suppose two stations A and B (several miles apart) transmit synchronized radio signals. The LORAN receiver in your ship measures the difference in reception times of these synchronized signals. The radio signals travel at a speed of 186,000 miles per second. Using this information, you can determine the difference $2a$ in the distance of your ship's receiver from the two transmitters. By the definition of a hyperbola, this information places your ship somewhere on a hyperbola with foci A and B. With two pairs of transmitters, the position of your ship can be determined at a point of intersection of the two hyperbolas (See Exercises 73 and 74).

EXAMPLE 7   Using LORAN

LORAN navigational transmitters A and B are located at $(-130, 0)$ and $(130, 0)$, respectively. A receiver P on a fishing boat somewhere in the first quadrant listens to the pair (A, B) of transmissions and computes the difference of the distances from the boat to A and B as 240 miles. Find the equation of the hyperbola on which P is located.

Solution

With reference to the transmitters A and B, P is located on a hyperbola with $2a = 240$, or $a = 120$, and the hyperbola has foci $(-130, 0)$ and $(130, 0)$.

$$\frac{x^2}{a^2} - \frac{y^2}{b^2} = 1$$ Standard form of the equation of a hyperbola

$$a^2 = (120)^2 = 14{,}400$$ Replace a with 120.

$$b^2 = c^2 - a^2 = (130)^2 - (120)^2 = 2500$$ Replace c with 130 and a with 120.

$$\frac{x^2}{14{,}400} - \frac{y^2}{2500} = 1$$ Replace a^2 with 14,400 and b^2 with 2500.

Thus, the location of the ship lies on a hyperbola (see Figure 10.29) with equation

$$\frac{x^2}{14{,}400} - \frac{y^2}{2500} = 1.$$ ■ ■ ■

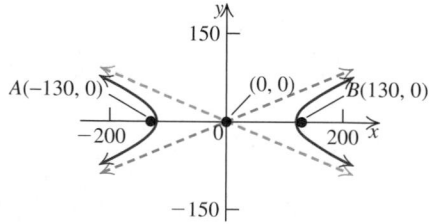

FIGURE 10.29

PRACTICE PROBLEM 7   In Example 7, the transmitters A and B are located at $(-150, 0)$ and $(150, 0)$, respectively, and the difference of the distances from the boat to A and B is 260 miles. Find the equation of the hyperbola on which P is located.   ■

A Exercises   Basic Skills and Concepts

In Exercises 1–8, the equation of a hyperbola is given. Match each equation with its graph shown in (a)–(h).

1. $\dfrac{x^2}{9} - \dfrac{y^2}{4} = 1$ †

2. $\dfrac{x^2}{4} - \dfrac{y^2}{25} = 1$ †

3. $\dfrac{y^2}{25} - \dfrac{x^2}{4} = 1$ †

4. $\dfrac{y^2}{4} - \dfrac{x^2}{9} = 1$ †

5. $4x^2 - 25y^2 = 100$ †

6. $16x^2 - 49y^2 = 196$ †

7. $16y^2 - 9x^2 = 100$ †

8. $9y^2 - 16x^2 = 144$ †

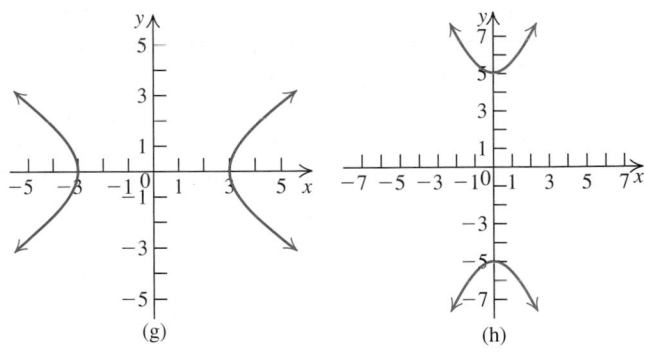

(g)   (h)

In Exercises 9–20, the equation of a hyperbola is given.
  a. Find and plot the vertices, the foci, and the transverse axis of the hyperbola.
  b. State how the hyperbola opens.
  c. Find and plot the vertices of the fundamental rectangle.
  d. Sketch the asymptotes and write their equations.
  e. Graph the hyperbola by using the vertices and the asymptotes.

9. $x^2 - \dfrac{y^2}{4} = 1$ †

10. $y^2 - \dfrac{x^2}{4} = 1$ †

11. $x^2 - y^2 = -1$ †

12. $y^2 - x^2 = -1$ †

13. $9y^2 - x^2 = 36$ †

14. $9x^2 - y^2 = 36$ †

15. $4x^2 - 9y^2 - 36 = 0$ †

16. $4x^2 - 9y^2 + 36 = 0$ †

17. $y = \pm\sqrt{4x^2 + 1}$ †

18. $y = \pm2\sqrt{x^2 + 1}$ †

19. $y = \pm\sqrt{9x^2 - 1}$ †

20. $y = \pm3\sqrt{x^2 - 4}$ †

(a)

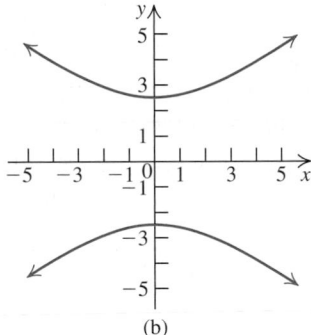

(b)

In Exercises 21–34, find an equation of the hyperbola satisfying the given conditions. Graph the hyperbola.

21. Vertices: $(\pm2, 0)$; foci: $(\pm3, 0)$ †

22. Vertices: $(\pm3, 0)$; foci: $(\pm5, 0)$ †

23. Vertices: $(0, \pm4)$; foci: $(0, \pm6)$ †

24. Vertices: $(0, \pm5)$; foci: $(0, \pm8)$ †

25. Center: $(0, 0)$; vertex: $(0, 2)$; focus: $(0, 5)$ †

26. Center: $(0, 0)$; vertex: $(0, -1)$; focus: $(0, -4)$ †

27. Center: $(0, 0)$; vertex: $(1, 0)$; focus: $(-5, 0)$ †

28. Center: $(0, 0)$; vertex: $(-3, 0)$; focus: $(6, 0)$ †

29. Foci: $(0, \pm5)$; the length of the transverse axis is 6. †

30. Foci: $(\pm2, 0)$; the length of the transverse axis is 2. †

31. Foci: $(\pm\sqrt{5}, 0)$; asymptotes: $y = \pm2x$ †

32. Foci: $(0, \pm10)$; asymptotes: $y = \pm3x$ †

33. Vertices: $(0, \pm4)$; asymptotes: $y = \pm x$ †

34. Vertices: $(\pm3, 0)$; asymptotes: $y = \pm2x$. †

(c)

(d)

(e)

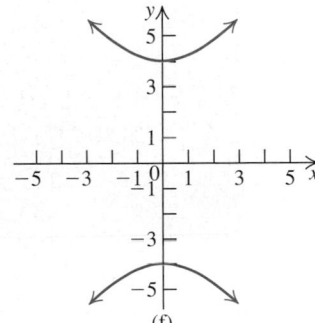

(f)

†Due to space constrictions, answers to these exercises may be found in the Answers beginning on page A–1 in the back of the book.

In Exercises 35–54, the equation of a hyperbola is given.
a. Find and plot the center, vertices, transverse axis, and asymptotes of the hyperbola.
b. Use the vertices and the asymptotes to graph the hyperbola.

35. $\dfrac{(x-1)^2}{9} - \dfrac{(y+1)^2}{16} = 1$ † **36.** $\dfrac{(y-1)^2}{16} - \dfrac{(x+1)^2}{4} = 1$ †

37. $\dfrac{(x+2)^2}{25} - \dfrac{y^2}{49} = 1$ † **38.** $\dfrac{(x+1)^2}{9} - \dfrac{(y+2)^2}{36} = 1$ †

39. $\dfrac{(x+4)^2}{25} - \dfrac{(y+3)^2}{49} = 1$ † **40.** $\dfrac{(x-3)^2}{9} - \dfrac{(y+1)^2}{9} = 1$ †

41. $4x^2 - (y+1)^2 = 25$ † **42.** $9(x-1)^2 - y^2 = 144$ †

43. $(y+1)^2 - 9(x-2)^2 = 25$ †

44. $6(x-4)^2 - 3(y+3)^2 = 4$ †

45. $x^2 - y^2 + 6x = 36$ †

46. $x^2 + 4x - 4y^2 = 12$ †

47. $x^2 - 4y^2 - 4x = 0$ †

48. $x^2 - 2y^2 - 8y = 12$ †

49. $2x^2 - y^2 + 12x - 8y + 3 = 0$ †

50. $y^2 - 9x^2 - 4y - 30x = 33$ †

51. $3x^2 - 18x - 2y^2 - 8y + 1 = 0$ †

52. $4y^2 - 9x^2 - 8y - 36x = 68$ †

53. $y^2 + 2\sqrt{2} - x^2 + 2\sqrt{2}x = 1$ †

54. $x^2 + x = \dfrac{y^2 - 1}{4}$ †

In Exercises 55–64, identify the conic section represented by each equation and sketch the graph.

55. $x^2 - 6x + 12y + 33 = 0$ †

56. $9y^2 = x^2 - 4x$ †

57. $y^2 - 9x^2 = -1$ †

58. $4x^2 + 9y^2 - 8x + 36y + 4 = 0$ †

59. $x^2 + y^2 - 4x + 8y = 16$ †

60. $2y^2 + 3x - 4y - 7 = 0$ †

61. $2x^2 - 4x + 3y + 8 = 0$ †

62. $y^2 - 9x^2 + 18x - 4y = 14$ †

63. $4x^2 + 9y^2 + 8x - 54y + 49 = 0$ †

64. $x^2 - 4y^2 + 6x - 8y + 6 = 0$ †

B Exercises Applying the Concepts

65. **Sound of an explosion.** Points A and B are 1000 meters apart, and it is determined from the sound of an explosion heard at these points at different times that the location of the explosion is 600 meters closer to A than to B. Show that the location of the explosion is restricted to points on a hyperbola, and find the equation of the hyperbola. [*Hint:* Let the coordinates of A be $(-500, 0)$ and those of B be $(500, 0)$.] †

66. **Sound of an explosion.** Points A and B are 2 miles apart. The sound of an explosion at A was heard 3 seconds before it was heard at B. Assume that the sound travels at 1100 feet/second. Show that the location of the explosion is restricted to a hyperbola, and find the equation of the hyperbola. [*Hint:* Recall that 1 mile = 5280 feet.] †

67. **Thunder and lightning.** Thunder is heard by Nicole and Juan, who are 8000 feet apart. Nicole hears the thunder 3 seconds before Juan does. Find the equation of the hyperbola whose points are possible locations where the lightning could have struck. Assume that the sound travels at 1100 feet/second. †

68. **Locating source of thunder.** In Exercise 67, Valerie is at a location midway between Nicole and Juan, and she hears the thunder 2 seconds after Juan does. Determine the location where the lightning strikes in relation to the three people involved. †

69. **LORAN.** Two LORAN stations, A and B, are situated 300 kilometers apart along a straight coastline. Simultaneous radio signals are sent from each station to a ship. The ship receives the signal from A 0.0005 second before the signal from B. Assume that the radio signals travel 300,000 kilometers per second. Find the equation of the hyperbola on which the ship is located. †

70. **LORAN.** In Exercise 69, if the ship were to follow the graph of the hyperbola, determine the location of the ship when it reaches the coastline. $(-75, 0)$

71. **Target practice.** A gun at G and a target at T are 1600 feet apart. The muzzle velocity of the bullet is 2000 feet per second. A person at P hears the crack of the gun and the thud of the bullet at the same time. Show that the possible locations of the person are on a hyperbola. Find the equation of the hyperbola with G at $(-800, 0)$ and T at $(800, 0)$. Assume that the speed of sound is 1100 feet/second. [*Hint:* Show that $|d(P, G) - d(P, T)|$ is a constant.] †

72. **LORAN.** Two LORAN stations, A and B, lie on an east–west line with A 250 miles west of B. A plane is flying west on a line 50 miles north of the line AB. Radio signals are sent (traveling at 980 feet per microsecond) simultaneously from A and B, and

the one sent from B arrives at the plane 500 microseconds before the one from A. Where is the plane? †

73. **Using LORAN.** LORAN navigational transmitters A, B, C, and D are located at $(-100, 0)$, $(100, 0)$, $(0, -150)$, and $(0, 150)$, respectively. A navigator P on a ship somewhere in the second quadrant listens to the pair (A, B) of transmitters and computes the difference of the distances from the ship to A and B as 120 miles. Similarly, by listening to the pair (C, D) of transmitters, navigator P computes the difference of the distances from the ship to C and D as 80 miles. What are the coordinates of the ship? $(-68.5748, 44.2719)$

74. **Using LORAN.** LORAN navigational transmitters A, B, and C are located at $(200, 0)$, $(-200, 0)$, and $(200, 1000)$, respectively. A navigator on a fishing boat listens to the pair (A, B) of transmitters and finds that the difference of the distances from the boat to A and B as 300 miles. She also finds that the difference of the distances from the boat to A and C is 400 miles. Find the possible locations of the boat. †

C Exercises   Beyond the Basics

75. Write the standard form of the equation of the hyperbola for which the difference of the distances from any point on the hyperbola to $(-5, 0)$ and $(5, 0)$ is equal to (a) 2 units; (b) 4 units; (c) 8 units. †

76. Sketch the graphs of all three hyperbolas in Exercise 75 on the same coordinate plane. †

77. Write the standard form of the equation of the hyperbola for which the difference of the distances from any point on the hyperbola to the points F_1 and F_2 is two units, where
   a. F_1 is $(0, 6)$ and F_2 is $(0, -6)$; †
   b. F_1 is $(0, 4)$ and F_2 is $(0, -4)$; †
   c. F_1 is $(0, 3)$ and F_2 is $(0, -3)$. †

78. Sketch the graphs of all three hyperbolas in Exercise 77 on the same coordinate plane. †

79. Rewrite equation
$$\sqrt{(x + c)^2 + y^2} - \sqrt{(x - c)^2 + y^2} = \pm 2a$$
from page 672 as
$$\sqrt{(x + c)^2 + y^2} = \pm 2a + \sqrt{(x - c)^2 + y^2}.$$
Square both sides to obtain
$$(x + c)^2 + y^2 = 4a^2 \pm 4a\sqrt{(x - c)^2 + y^2} + (x - c)^2 + y^2.$$
Simplify, then isolate the radical, and then square both sides again to show that the equation can be simplified to
$$(c^2 - a^2)x^2 - a^2y^2 = a^2(c^2 - a^2). \quad †$$

80. **a.** Let $p > 0$. Show that the graph of the equation $xy = \dfrac{p^2}{2}$ is a hyperbola by showing that this equation is the equa-

tion of the hyperbola with foci (p, p) and $(-p, -p)$ and with difference $2p$ in distance. [*Hint:* Show that the equation
$$\sqrt{(x + p)^2 + (y + p)^2} - \sqrt{(x - p)^2 + (y - p)^2} = 2p$$
simplifies to $xy = \dfrac{p^2}{2}$.] †

   b. Use part (a) to sketch the graph of the hyperbola $xy = 8$. Find the coordinates of the foci. †

81. A hyperbola for which the lengths of the transverse and conjugate axes are equal is called an **equilateral hyperbola.** Show that the asymptotes of an equilateral hyperbola are perpendicular to one another. †

82. The **latus rectum of a hyperbola** is a line segment that passes through a focus, is perpendicular to the transverse axis, and has endpoints on the hyperbola. Show that the length of the latus rectum of the hyperbola
$$\frac{x^2}{a^2} - \frac{y^2}{b^2} = 1 \text{ is } \frac{2b^2}{a}. \quad †$$

83. The *eccentricity* of a hyperbola, denoted by e, is defined by
$$e = \frac{\text{Distance between the } foci}{\text{Distance between the vertices}} = \frac{2c}{2a} = \frac{c}{a}.$$
Show that, for every hyperbola, $e > 1$. What happens when $e = 1$? †

In Exercises 84–88, find the eccentricity and the length of the latus rectum of each hyperbola.

84. $\dfrac{x^2}{16} - \dfrac{y^2}{9} = 1$ †   85. $36x^2 - 25y^2 = 900$ †

86. $x^2 - y^2 = 49$ †

87. $8(x - 1)^2 - (y + 2)^2 = 2$ †

88. $5x^2 - 4y^2 - 10x - 8y - 19 = 0$ †

89. For the hyperbola $\dfrac{x^2}{a^2} - \dfrac{y^2}{b^2} = 1$ with eccentricity e, show that $b^2 = a^2(e^2 - 1)$. †

90. Find an equation of a hyperbola if its foci are $(\pm 6, 0)$ and the length of its latus rectum is 10. †

91. A point $P(x, y)$ moves in the plane so that its distance from the point $(3, 0)$ is always twice its distance from the line $x = -1$. Show that the equation of the path of P is a hyperbola of eccentricity 2. †

92. A point $P(x, y)$ moves in the plane so that its distance from the point $(0, -3)$ is always three times its distance from the line $y = 1$. Show that the equation of the path of P is a hyperbola of eccentricity 3. †

In Exercises 93–98, find all points of intersection of the given curves. Make a sketch of the curves that shows the points of intersection.

93. $y - 2x - 20 = 0$ and $y^2 - 4x^2 = 36$ †

94. $x - 2y^2 = 0$ and $x^2 = 8y^2 + 5$ †

95. $x^2 + y^2 = 15$ and $x^2 - y^2 = 1$ †

96. $x^2 + 9y^2 = 9$ and $4x^2 - 25y^2 = 36$ †

97. $9x^2 + 4y^2 = 72$ and $x^2 - 9y^2 = -77$ †

98. $3y^2 - 7x^2 = 5$ and $9x^2 - 2y^2 = 1$ †

Critical Thinking

99. Explain why each of the following represents a degenerate conic section. Where possible, sketch the graph.

a. $4x^2 - 9y^2 = 0$ †

b. $x^2 + 4y^2 + 6 = 0$

c. $8x^2 + 5y^2 = 0$ †

d. $x^2 + y^2 - 4x + 8y = -20$ †

e. $y^2 - 2x^2 = 0$ †

Answer:

99. b. Since all the terms on the left-hand side are nonnegative and 6 is positive, the left-hand side is always positive. Therefore, there are no x and y values that would satisfy the equation.

Group Project

Discuss the graph of a quadratic equation in x and y of the form

$$Ax^2 + Cy^2 + Dx + Ey + F = 0, \quad AC \neq 0.$$

Rewrite this equation in the form

$$A\left(x^2 + \frac{D}{A}x + \frac{D^2}{4A^2}\right) + C\left(y^2 + \frac{E}{C}y + \frac{E^2}{4C^2}\right) = \frac{D^2}{4A} + \frac{E^2}{4C} - F.$$

Include in your discussion the types of graphs you will obtain in each of the following cases:

i. $A > 0, C > 0$;

ii. $A > 0, C < 0$;

iii. $A < 0, C > 0$,

iv. $A < 0, C < 0$.

In each case, discuss how the classification is affected by the sign of

$$\frac{D^2}{4A} + \frac{E^2}{4C} - F.$$

Summary   Definitions, Concepts, and Formulas

10.1 Conic Sections

Conic sections are the curves formed when a plane intersects the surface of a right circular cone. Except in some degenerate cases, the curves formed are the circle, the ellipse, the parabola, and the hyperbola.

10.2 The Parabola

i.   **Definition.** A **parabola** is the set of all points in the plane that are the same distance from a fixed line and a fixed point not on the line. The fixed line is called the **directrix** and the fixed point is called the **focus.**

ii. **Axis** or **axis of symmetry.** This is the line that passes through the focus and is perpendicular to the directrix.

iii. **Vertex:** This is the point at which the parabola intersects its axis. The vertex is halfway between the focus and the directrix.

iv. **Standard forms of equations of parabolas with vertex at $(0, 0)$ and $a > 0$:**

$$y^2 = \pm 4ax \text{ and } x^2 = \pm 4ay. \text{ (See the table on page 884.)}$$

v.   The **latus rectum** of a parabola is the line segment that passes through the focus, is perpendicular to the axis of the parabola, and has endpoints on the parabola.

vi. **Standard forms of equations of parabolas with vertex (h, k) and $a > 0$** are $(y - k)^2 = \pm 4a(x - h)$ and $(x - h)^2 = \pm 4a(y - k)$. (See the table on page 888.)

10.3 The Ellipse

i.   **Definition.** An **ellipse** is the set of all points in the plane, the sum of whose distances from two fixed points is a constant. The fixed points are called the **foci** of the ellipse.

ii. **Vertices.** These are the two points where the line through the foci intersects the ellipse.

iii. **Major axis.** This is the line segment joining the two vertices of the ellipse.

iv. **Center.** This is the midpoint of the line segment joining the foci. It is also the midpoint of the major axis.

v.   **Minor axis.** This is the line segment that passes through the center of the ellipse, is perpendicular to the major axis, and has endpoints on the ellipse.

vi. **Standard forms of equations of ellipses with center $(0, 0)$, $a > b > 0, c < a$, and $b^2 = a^2 - c^2$ are

$$\frac{x^2}{a^2} + \frac{y^2}{b^2} = 1, \text{ with foci } (\pm c, 0) \text{ and vertices } (\pm a, 0),$$

and

$$\frac{x^2}{b^2} + \frac{y^2}{a^2} = 1, \text{ with foci } (0, \pm c) \text{ and vertices } (0, \pm a).$$

(See the table on page 897.)

vii. **Standard forms of equations of ellipses with center (h, k), $a > b > 0$, and $b^2 = a^2 - c^2$ are

$$\frac{(x-h)^2}{a^2} + \frac{(y-k)^2}{b^2} = 1 \text{ and } \frac{(x-h)^2}{b^2} + \frac{(y-k)^2}{a^2} = 1.$$

(See the table on page 899.)

10.4 The Hyperbola

i.   **Definition.** A **hyperbola** is the set of all points in the plane, the difference of whose distances from two fixed points is a constant. The fixed points are called the **foci** of the hyperbola.

ii. **Vertices.** These are the two points where the line through the foci intersects the hyperbola.

iii. **Transverse axis.** This is the line segment joining the two vertices of the hyperbola.

iv. **Center.** This is the midpoint of the line segment joining the foci. It is also the midpoint of the transverse axis.

v.   **Standard forms of equations of hyperbolas with center $(0, 0), c > a$, and $b^2 = c^2 - a^2$ are

$$\frac{x^2}{a^2} - \frac{y^2}{b^2} = 1, \text{ with foci } (\pm c, 0) \text{ and vertices } (\pm a, 0),$$

and

$$\frac{y^2}{a^2} - \frac{x^2}{b^2} = 1, \text{ with foci } (0, \pm c), \text{ and vertices } (0, \pm a).$$

(See the table on page 909.)

vi. **Conjugate axis.** This is a line segment of length $2b$ that passes through the center of the hyperbola and is perpendicularly bisected by the transverse axis.

vii. **Asymptotes.** The asymptotes of the hyperbola $\dfrac{x^2}{a^2} - \dfrac{y^2}{b^2} = 1$ are the two lines $y = \pm\dfrac{b}{a}x$; the asymptotes of the hyperbola $\dfrac{y^2}{a^2} - \dfrac{x^2}{b^2} = 1$ are the lines $y = \pm\dfrac{a}{b}x$.

viii. **Graphing.** A procedure for graphing a hyperbola centered at $(0, 0)$ is given on page 914.

ix. Standard forms of equations of hyperbolas centered at (h, k) are

$$\frac{(x-h)^2}{a^2} - \frac{(y-k)^2}{b^2} = 1 \text{ and } \frac{(y-k)^2}{a^2} - \frac{(x-h)^2}{b^2} = 1.$$

See the table on page 916. Also see page 916 for a procedure for graphing such hyperbolas.

Review Exercises

In Exercises 1–8, sketch the graph of each parabola. Determine the vertex, focus, axis, and directrix of each parabola.

1. $y^2 = -6x$ †
2. $y^2 = 12x$ †
3. $x^2 = 7y$ †
4. $x^2 = -3y$ †
5. $(x - 2)^2 = -(y + 3)$ †
6. $(y + 1)^2 = 5(x + 2)$ †
7. $y^2 = -4y + 2x + 1$ †
8. $-x^2 + 2x + y = 0$ †

In Exercises 9–12, find an equation of the parabola satisfying the given conditions.

9. Vertex: $(0, 0)$; focus: $(-3, 0)$ $y^2 = -12x$
10. Vertex: $(0, 0)$; focus: $(0, 4)$ $x^2 = 16y$
11. Focus: $(0, 4)$; and directrix: $y = -4$ $x^2 = 16y$
12. Focus: $(-3, 0)$; directrix: $x = 3$ $y^2 = -12x$

In Exercises 13–20, sketch the graph of each ellipse. Determine the foci, vertices, and the endpoints of the minor axis of the ellipse.

13. $\dfrac{x^2}{25} + \dfrac{y^2}{4} = 1$ †
14. $\dfrac{x^2}{9} + \dfrac{y^2}{36} = 1$ †
15. $4x^2 + y^2 = 4$ †
16. $16x^2 + y^2 = 64$ †
17. $16(x + 1)^2 + 9(y + 4)^2 = 144$ †
18. $4(x - 1)^2 + 3(y + 2)^2 = 12$ †
19. $x^2 + 9y^2 + 2x - 18y + 1 = 0$ †
20. $4x^2 + y^2 + 8x - 10y + 13 = 0$ †

In Exercises 21–24, find an equation of the ellipse satisfying the given conditions.

21. Vertices: $(\pm 4, 0)$; endpoints of minor axis: $(0, \pm 2)$ †

22. Vertices: $(0, \pm 6)$; endpoints of minor axis: $(\pm 2, 0)$ †

23. Length of major axis 20; foci: $(\pm 5, 0)$ †

24. Length of minor axis 16; foci: $(0, \pm 6)$ †

In Exercises 25–32, sketch the graph of each hyperbola. Determine the vertices, the foci, and the asymptotes of each hyperbola.

25. $\dfrac{y^2}{16} - \dfrac{x^2}{4} = 1$ †

26. $\dfrac{x^2}{16} - \dfrac{y^2}{9} = 1$ †

27. $8x^2 - y^2 = 8$ †

28. $4y^2 - 4x^2 = 1$ †

29. $\dfrac{(x + 2)^2}{9} - \dfrac{(y - 3)^2}{4} = 1$ †

30. $\dfrac{(y + 1)^2}{6} - \dfrac{(x - 2)^2}{8} = 1$ †

31. $4y^2 - x^2 + 40y - 4x + 60 = 0$ †

32. $4x^2 - 9y^2 + 16x - 54y - 29 = 0$ †

In Exercises 33–36, find an equation of the hyperbola satisfying the given condition.

33. Vertices: $(\pm 1, 0)$; foci: $(\pm 2, 0)$ †

34. Vertices: $(0, \pm 2)$; foci: $(0, \pm 4)$; †

35. Vertices: $(\pm 2, 0)$; asymptotes: $y = \pm 3x$ †

36. Vertices: $(0, \pm 3)$; asymptotes: $y = \pm x$ †

In Exercises 37–48, identify each equation as representing a circle, a parabola, an ellipse, or a hyperbola. Sketch the graph of the conic.

37. $5x^2 - 4y^2 = 20$ †

38. $x^2 - x + y = 1$ †

39. $3x^2 + 4y^2 + 8y - 12x - 6 = 0$ †

40. $2y - x^2 = 0$ †

41. $x^2 + y^2 + 2x - 3 = 0$ †

42. $2x + y^2 = 0$ †

43. $y^2 = x^2 + 3$ †

44. $x^2 = 10 - 3y^2$ †

45. $3x^2 + 3y^2 - 6x + 12y + 5 = 0$ †

46. $y + 2x - x^2 + 2y^2 = 0$ †

47. $9x^2 + 8y^2 = 36$ †

48. $2y^2 + 4y = 3x^2 - 6x + 9$ †

49. Find an equation of the hyperbola whose foci are the vertices of the ellipse $4x^2 + 9y^2 = 36$ and whose vertices are the foci of this ellipse. †

50. Find an equation of the ellipse whose foci are the vertices of the hyperbola $9x^2 - 16y^2 = 144$ and whose vertices are the foci of this hyperbola. †

In Exercises 51–54, find all points of intersection of the given curves, and make a sketch.

51. $x^2 - 4y^2 = 36$ and $x - 2y - 20 = 0$ †

52. $y^2 - 8x^2 = 5$ and $y - 2x^2 = 0$ †

53. $3x^2 - 7y^2 = 5$ and $9y^2 - 2x^2 = 1$ †

54. $x^2 - y^2 = 1$ and $x^2 + y^2 = 7$ †

55. Parabolic curve. Water flowing from the end of a horizontal pipe 20 feet above the ground describes a parabolic curve whose vertex is at the end of the pipe. If, at a point 6 feet below the line of the pipe, the flow of water has curved outward 8 feet beyond a vertical line through the end of the pipe, how far beyond this vertical line will the water strike the ground? 14.6 ft

56. Parabolic arch. A parabolic arch has a height of 20 meters and a width of 36 meters at the base. If the vertex of the parabola is at the top of the arch, find the height of the arch at a distance of 9 meters from the center of the base. 15 m

57. Football. A football is 12 inches long, and a cross section containing a seam is an ellipse with a minor axis of length 7 inches. Suppose every cross section of the ball formed by a plane perpendicular to the major axis of the ellipse is a circle. Find the circumference of such a circular cross section located 2 inches from an end of the ball. 16.4 in

58. Production cost. A company assembles computers at two locations A and B that are 1000 miles apart. The per unit cost of production at location A is $20 less than at location B. Assume that the route of delivery of the computers is along a straight line and that the delivery cost is 25 cents per unit per mile. Find the equation of the curve at any point of which the computers can be supplied from either location at the same cost. †

[*Hint:* Take A at $(-500, 0)$ and B at $(500, 0)$.]

Practice Test A

1. Find the standard form of the parabola with focus $(0, 12)$ and directrix with equation $x = -12$. $(y - 12)^2 = 24(x + 6)$

2. Convert the equation $y^2 - 2y + 8x + 25 = 0$ to the standard form for a parabola by completing the square. †

3. Find the focus and directrix of the parabola with equation $x^2 = -9y$. †

4. Graph the parabola with equation $y^2 = -5x$. †

5. Find the vertex, focus, and directrix of the parabola with equation $(x + 2)^2 = -8(y - 1)$. †

6. The base of a water slide is parabolic in shape and is 6 feet wide and 2 feet deep. Find the height of the slide 1 foot from its center. 2/9 ft

7. Find an equation of the parabola with vertex $(3, -1)$ and directrix $x = -3$. $(y + 1)^2 = 24(x - 3)$

In Problems 8–10, find the standard form of the equation of the ellipse satisfying the given conditions.

8. Foci: $(0, -2)$, $(0, 2)$; vertices: $(0, -4)$, $(0, 4)$ †

9. Foci: $(-2, 0)$, $(2, 0)$; y-intercepts: -5, and 5 †

10. Major axis horizontal and with length 18; minor axis of length 4; center $(0, 0)$ †

11. Graph the ellipse with equation $9x^2 + y^2 = 9$. †

12. Find the vertices and foci for the hyperbola with equation $49y^2 - x^2 = 49$. †

13. Graph the hyperbola with equation $\dfrac{x^2}{49} - \dfrac{y^2}{4} = 1$. †

14. Find the standard form of the equation of the hyperbola with foci $(0, -\sqrt{45})$, $(0, \sqrt{45})$ and vertices $(0, -6)$, $(0, 6)$. †

In Problems 15–16, convert the equation to the standard form for a hyperbola by completing the squares on x and y.

15. $y^2 - x^2 + 2x = 2$ $y^2 - (x - 1)^2 = 1$

16. $x^2 - 2x - 4y^2 - 16y = 19$ †

In Problems 17–20, identify the conic section and sketch its graph.

17. $x^2 - 9y^2 = -16$ †

18. $x^2 - 2y + 4y + 1 = 0$ †

19. $x^2 + y^2 + 2x - 6y = 3$ †

20. $25x^2 + 4y^2 = 100$ †

Practice Test B

1. Find the standard form of the equation of the parabola with focus $(-10, 0)$ and directrix $x = 10$. b
   (a) $y^2 = -10x$ (b) $y^2 = -40x$
   (c) $x^2 = -40y$ (d) $y^2 = 40x$

2. Convert the equation $y^2 - 4y - 5x + 24 = 0$ to the standard form for a parabola by completing the square. b
   (a) $(y + 2)^2 = 5(x - 4)$
   (b) $(y - 2)^2 = 5(x - 4)$
   (c) $(y + 2)^2 = -5(x - 4)$
   (d) $(y - 2)^2 = 5(x + 4)$

3. Find the focus and directrix of the parabola with equation $x = 7y^2$. a

   (a) focus: $\left(\dfrac{1}{28}, 0\right)$, directrix: $x = -\dfrac{1}{28}$

   (b) focus: $\left(0, \dfrac{1}{28}\right)$, directrix: $y = -\dfrac{1}{28}$

   (c) focus: $\left(\dfrac{1}{28}, 0\right)$, directrix: $x = \dfrac{1}{28}$

   (d) focus: $\left(\dfrac{1}{7}, 0\right)$, directrix: $x = -\dfrac{1}{7}$

4. Graph the parabola with equation $y^2 = -7x$. a

   (a)

(b)

(c)

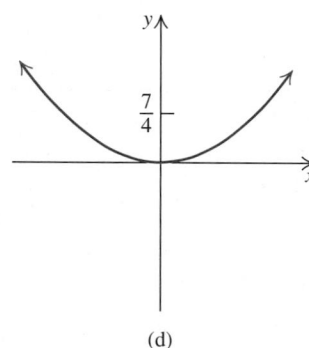

(d)

5. Find the vertex, focus, and directrix of the parabola with equation $(x - 3)^2 = 12(y - 1)$. a

(a) vertex: $(3, 1)$
    focus: $(3, 4)$
    directrix: $y = -2$

(b) vertex: $(-3, -1)$
    focus: $(-3, 2)$
    directrix: $y = -4$

(c) vertex: $(3, 1)$
    focus: $(3, -2)$
    directrix: $x = 4$

(d) vertex: $(1, 3)$
    focus: $(1, 6)$
    directrix: $y = 0$

6. The parabolic arch of a bridge has a 180-foot base and a height of 25 feet. Find the height of the arch 45 feet from the center of the base. d

(a) 12.5 ft
(b) 6.25 ft
(c) 16.7 ft
(d) 18.75 ft

7. Find an equation of the parabola with vertex $(-2, 1)$ and directrix $x = 2$. a

(a) $(y - 1)^2 = -16(x + 2)$
(b) $(y - 1)^2 = 16(x + 2)$
(c) $(y + 2)^2 = -16(x - 1)$
(d) $(y + 2)^2 = 16(x - 1)$

In Problems 8–10, find the standard form of the equation of the ellipse satisfying the given conditions.

8. Foci $(-3, 0)$, $(3, 0)$; vertices $(-5, 0)$, $(5, 0)$ b

(a) $\dfrac{x^2}{9} + \dfrac{y^2}{16} = 1$ (b) $\dfrac{x^2}{25} + \dfrac{y^2}{16} = 1$

(c) $\dfrac{x^2}{9} + \dfrac{y^2}{25} = 1$ (d) $\dfrac{x^2}{16} + \dfrac{y^2}{25} = 1$

9. Foci $(0, -3,)$, $(0, 3)$; y-intercepts $-7, 7$ d

(a) $\dfrac{x^2}{49} + \dfrac{y^2}{40} = 1$ (b) $\dfrac{x^2}{9} + \dfrac{y^2}{49} = 1$

(c) $\dfrac{x^2}{9} + \dfrac{y^2}{40} = 1$ (d) $\dfrac{x^2}{40} + \dfrac{y^2}{49} = 1$

10. Major axis vertical with length 16; length of minor axis = 8; center $(0, 0)$ a

(a) $\dfrac{x^2}{16} + \dfrac{y^2}{64} = 1$ (b) $\dfrac{x^2}{64} + \dfrac{y^2}{256} = 1$

(c) $\dfrac{x^2}{8} + \dfrac{y^2}{64} = 1$ (d) $\dfrac{x^2}{64} + \dfrac{y^2}{16} = 1$

11. Graph the ellipse with equation $9(x - 1)^2 + 4(y - 2)^2 = 36$. a

(a)

(b)

(c)

(b)

(d)

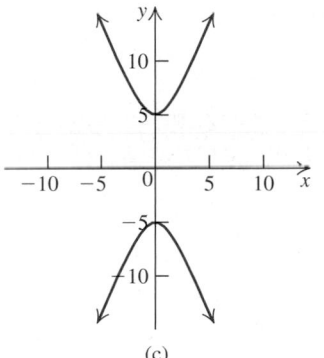

(c)

12. Find the vertices and foci of the hyperbola with equation

$$\frac{x^2}{121} - \frac{y^2}{4} = 1.\ \text{c}$$

(a) vertices: $(-11, 0), (11, 0)$
foci: $(-2, 0), (2, 0)$
(b) vertices: $(0, -1), (0, 11)$
foci: $(-5\sqrt{5}, 0), (5\sqrt{5}, 0)$
(c) vertices: $(-11, 0), (11, 0)$
foci: $(-5\sqrt{5}, 0), (5\sqrt{5}, 0)$
(d) vertices: $(-2, 0), (2, 0)$
foci: $(-5\sqrt{5}, 0), (5\sqrt{5}, 0)$

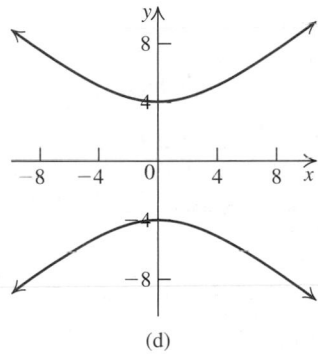

(d)

13. Graph the hyperbola with equation $\dfrac{x^2}{25} - \dfrac{y^2}{4} = 1.$ b

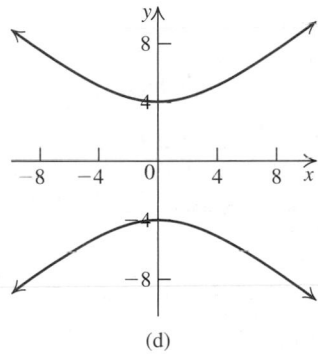

(a)

14. Find the standard form of the equation of the hyperbola with foci $(0, -10), (0, 10)$ and vertices $(0, -5), (0, 5)$. b

(a) $\dfrac{y^2}{25} - \dfrac{x^2}{100} = 1$ **(b)** $\dfrac{y^2}{25} - \dfrac{x^2}{75} = 1$

(c) $\dfrac{x^2}{25} - \dfrac{y^2}{100} = 1$ **(d)** $\dfrac{x^2}{25} - \dfrac{y^2}{75} = 1$

In Problems 15–16, convert the equation to the standard form for a hyperbola by completing the square on x and y.

15. $y^2 - 4x^2 - 2y - 16x - 19 = 0$ c

(a) $\dfrac{(y - 2)^2}{4} - (x + 4)^2 = 1$

(b) $\dfrac{(x - 1)^2}{4} - (y + 2)^2 = 1$

(c) $\dfrac{(y - 1)^2}{4} - (x + 2)^2 = 1$

(d) $(x + 2)^2 - \dfrac{(y - 1)^2}{4} = 1$

16. $4y^2 - 9x^2 - 16y - 36x - 56 = 0$ c

   (a) $\dfrac{(y-2)^2}{4} - \dfrac{(x+2)^2}{9} = 1$

   (b) $\dfrac{(x-2)^2}{4} - \dfrac{(y+2)^2}{9} = 1$

   (c) $\dfrac{(y-2)^2}{9} - \dfrac{(x+2)^2}{4} = 1$

   (d) $\dfrac{(y+2)^2}{9} - \dfrac{(x-2)^2}{4} = 1$

In Problems 17–20, identify the conic section.

17. $3x^2 + 2y^2 - 6x + 4y - 1 = 0$ c

   (a) parabola   **(b)** circle

   (c) ellipse   **(d)** hyperbola

18. $x^2 + 2x + 4y + 5 = 0$ a

   (a) parabola   **(b)** circle

   (c) ellipse   **(d)** hyperbola

19. $4x^2 - y^2 + 16x + 2y + 11 = 0$ d

   (a) parabola   **(b)** circle

   (c) ellipse   **(d)** hyperbola

20. $5y^2 - 3x^2 + 20y - 6x + 2 = 0$ d

   (a) parabola   **(b)** circle

   (c) ellipse   **(d)** hyperbola

Cumulative Review Exercises (Chapters 1–10)

1. Let $f(x) = x^2 - 3x + 2$. Find $\dfrac{f(x+h) - f(x)}{h}$. †

2. Sketch the graph of $f(x) = \sqrt{x+1} - 2$. †

3. Let $f(x) = 2x - 3$. Find the inverse function f^{-1}. Verify that $f(f^{-1}(x)) = x$. †

4. Sketch the graph of $f(x) = \left(\dfrac{1}{2}\right)^{x+2}$. †

5. Solve the equation $\log_5(x-1) + \log_5(x-2) = 3\log_5\sqrt[3]{6}$. †

6. Express

$$\log_a \sqrt[3]{x\sqrt{yz}}$$

in terms of logarithms of x, y, and z. †

7. Solve the inequality

$$\dfrac{x}{x-2} \geq 1.\ \text{Solution: } (2, \infty)$$

Use natural logarithms to solve for t.

In Problems 9–12, solve each system of equations.

8. $\begin{cases} 1.4x - 0.5y = 1.3 \\ 0.4x + 1.1y = 4.1 \end{cases}$ Solution: $x = 2$, $y = 3$

9. $\begin{cases} 2x + y - 4z = 3 \\ x - 2y + 3z = 4 \\ -3x + 4y - z = -2 \end{cases}$ Solution: $x = 4$, $y = 3$, $z = 2$

10. $\begin{cases} y = x^2 - 1 \\ 3x^2 + 8y^2 = 8 \end{cases}$

Answers:

10. $\left\{ \left(\dfrac{\sqrt{26}}{4}, \dfrac{5}{8}\right), \left(-\dfrac{\sqrt{26}}{4}, \dfrac{5}{8}\right) \right\}$

11. If $\cot\theta = \dfrac{5}{2}$ and $\sec\theta < 0$, find $\cos\theta$.

12. If $\cos\theta = -\dfrac{1}{3}$ and θ is in quadrant III, find $\sin 2\theta$.

13. Convert the equation $x^2 + y^2 - 6x + 3 = 0$ to polar form.

14. Find the determinant of the matrix $\begin{bmatrix} 1 & 4 & 7 \\ 2 & 5 & 8 \\ 3 & 6 & 9 \end{bmatrix}$. 0

15. Use Cramer's rule to solve the system of equations:

$$\begin{cases} 2x - 3y = -4 \\ 5x + 7y = 1 \end{cases}$$ Solution: $x = -\dfrac{25}{29}$, $y = \dfrac{22}{29}$

16. Find the inverse of the matrix $A = \begin{bmatrix} 3 & -2 \\ -5 & 4 \end{bmatrix}$.

17. Solve the equation $2x^4 - 5x^2 + 3 = 0$.

In Problems 18–20, an equation of a conic section is given. Identify the conic and sketch its graph.

18. $x^2 - y^2 = -4$ †

19. $9x^2 + 9y^2 = 144$ †

20. Sketch the graph of the rational function $f(x) = \dfrac{x}{x^2 - 16}$.

Answers:

11. $\dfrac{5\sqrt{29}}{29}$ **12.** $-\dfrac{4\sqrt{2}}{9}$ **13.** $r^2 - r\cos\theta + 3 = 0$

17. Solution: $1, -1, \dfrac{1}{2}\sqrt{6}, -\dfrac{1}{2}\sqrt{6}$

CHAPTER 11

Further Topics in Algebra

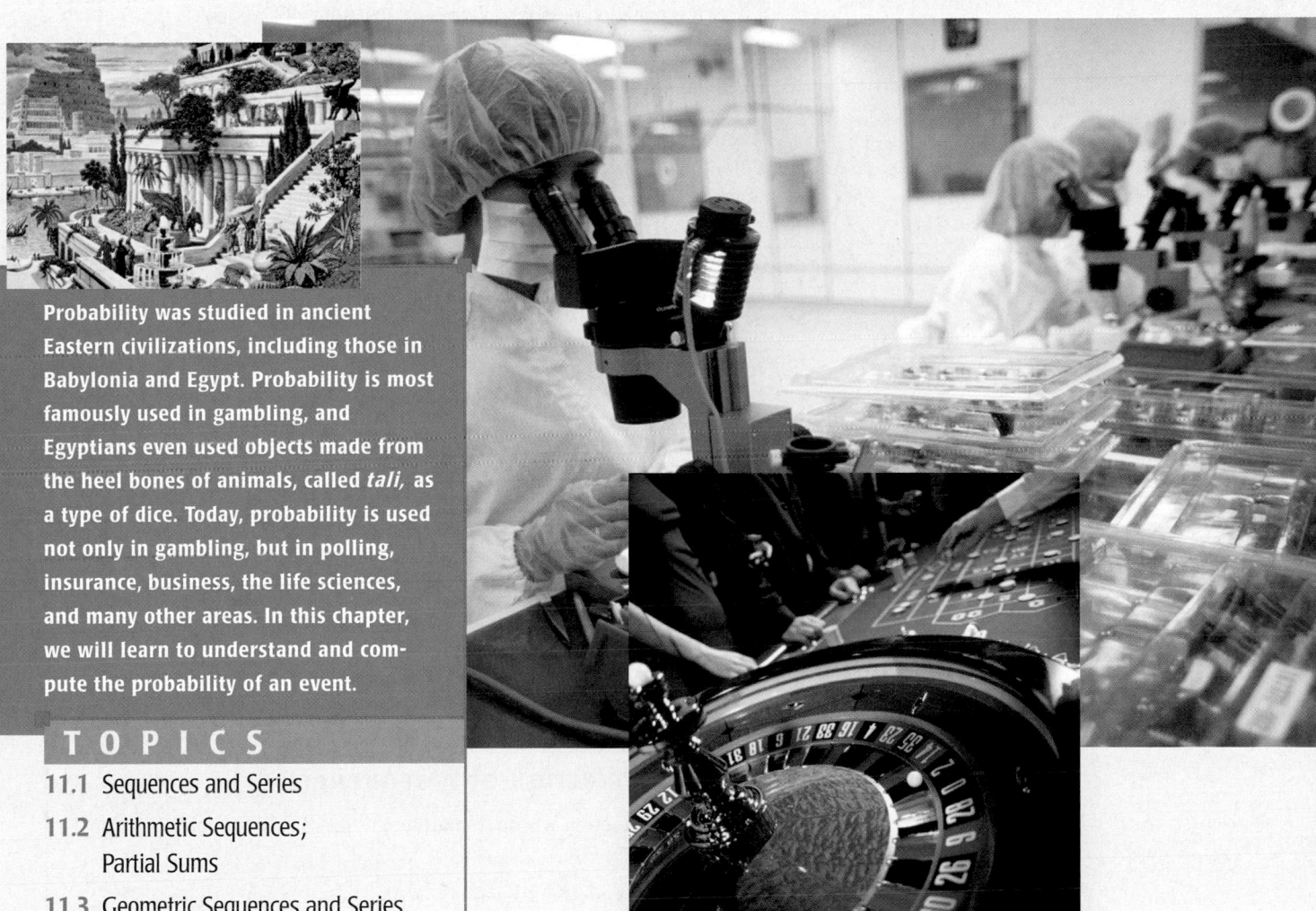

Probability was studied in ancient Eastern civilizations, including those in Babylonia and Egypt. Probability is most famously used in gambling, and Egyptians even used objects made from the heel bones of animals, called *tali,* as a type of dice. Today, probability is used not only in gambling, but in polling, insurance, business, the life sciences, and many other areas. In this chapter, we will learn to understand and compute the probability of an event.

TOPICS

Sequences and Series

BEFORE STARTING THIS SECTION, REVIEW

1. Evaluating algebraic expressions (Section P.1, page 14)

2. Finding functional values (Section 2.4, page 226)

OBJECTIVES

1 Use sequence notation to find specific and general terms in a sequence.

2 Use factorial notation.

3 Use summation notation to write partial sums of a series.

The Family Tree of the Honeybee

The bee that most of us know best is the honeybee, an insect that lives in a colony and has an unusual family tree. Perhaps the most surprising fact about honeybees is that not all of them have two parents. This phenomenon begins with a special female in the colony called the *queen*. There are many other female bees in the colony, called *worker* bees, but unlike the queen bee, they produce no eggs. Male bees do no work and are produced from the queen's unfertilized eggs, so male bees have no father, only a mother. The female bees are produced as a result of the queen bee mating with a male bee. Consequently, all female bees have two parents—a male and a female—whereas male bees have just one parent—a female. In this section, we will study sequences, and in Example 5 we see how a famous sequence accurately counts a honeybee's ancestors. ■

---

1 Use sequence notation to find specific and general terms in a sequence.

Sequences

The word *sequence* is used in mathematics in much the same way it is used in ordinary English. If someone saw a *sequence* of bad movies, you know that the person could list the first bad movie he or she saw, the second bad movie, and so on.

DEFINITION OF A SEQUENCE

An **infinite sequence** is a function whose domain is the set of positive integers. The function values, written as

$$a_1, a_2, a_3, a_4, \ldots, a_n, \ldots$$

are called the **terms** of the sequence. The **nth term, a_n,** is called the **general term** of the sequence.

If the domain of a function consists of only the first n positive integers, the sequence is called a **finite sequence**.

Finite sequences of the form $a_1, a_2, \ldots, a_n$ are often used in computer science. These sequences are called *strings*.

Sometimes it is convenient to use 0 instead of 1 as the first subscript in the subscript notation, and we write the sequence terms as $a_0, a_1, a_2, a_3, \ldots$. The nth term of this sequence is a_{n-1}.

EXAMPLE 1   **Writing the Terms of a Sequence from the General Term**

Write the first four terms of each sequence.

a. $a_n = 5n - 1$ **b.** $a_n = \dfrac{1}{n + 1}$

Solution

The first four terms of each sequence are found by replacing n by the integers 1, 2, 3, and 4 in the equation defining a_n.

a.

$a_n = 5n - 1$	General term of the sequence
$a_1 = 5(1) - 1 = 4$	1st term: Replace n by 1.
$a_2 = 5(2) - 1 = 9$	2nd term: Replace n by 2.
$a_3 = 5(3) - 1 = 14$	3rd term: Replace n by 3.
$a_4 = 5(4) - 1 = 19$	4th term: Replace n by 4.

b.

$a_n = \dfrac{1}{n + 1}$	General term of the sequence
$a_1 = \dfrac{1}{1 + 1} = \dfrac{1}{2}$	1st term: Replace n by 1.
$a_2 = \dfrac{1}{2 + 1} = \dfrac{1}{3}$	2nd term: Replace n by 2.
$a_3 = \dfrac{1}{3 + 1} = \dfrac{1}{4}$	3rd term: Replace n by 3.
$a_4 = \dfrac{1}{4 + 1} = \dfrac{1}{5}$	4th term: Replace n by 4.

■ ■ ■

PRACTICE PROBLEM 1   Write the first four terms of the sequence with general term $a_n = -2^n$. ■

Because it is a function, a sequence has a graph. The graph of the sequence $a_n = 5n - 1$ in Example 1(a) can be obtained from the graph of the function $f(x) = 5x - 1, x > 0$ (see Figure 11.1a) by removing all the graph points except for those whose x-coordinates are positive integers. The remaining points have coordinates (1, 4), (2, 9), (3, 14), (4, 19) and so on. The points $(n, 5n - 1)$ make up the graph of the sequence $f(n) = a_n = 5n - 1$. (See Figure 11.1b for the graph of the first four terms of this sequence.)

We can use subscripts on variables other than a to represent the terms of a sequence. In Example 2, we use the variable b.

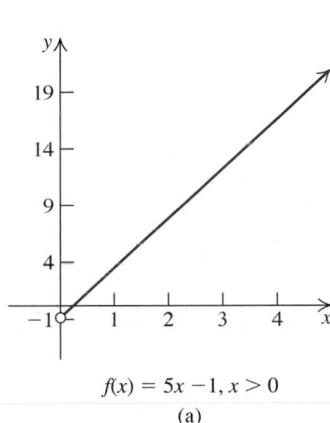

$f(x) = 5x - 1, x > 0$
(a)

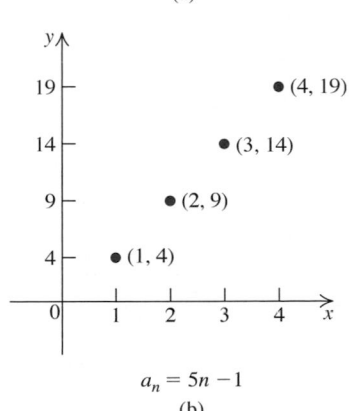

$a_n = 5n - 1$
(b)

FIGURE 11.1

A graphing calculator can write the terms of a sequence and also graph the sequence.

The first four terms of the sequence $a_n = \dfrac{1}{n+1}$ and the graph of this sequence are shown here.

EXAMPLE 2 **Writing the First Several Terms of a Sequence**

Write the first six terms of the sequence defined by:

$$b_n = (-1)^{n+1}\left(\frac{1}{n}\right)$$

Solution

Recall that $(-1)^1 = -1, (-1)^2 = 1, (-1)^3 = -1, (-1)^4 = 1$, and so on; that is, all even powers of -1 equal 1 and all odd powers of -1 equal -1.

$$b_1 = (-1)^{1+1}\left(\frac{1}{1}\right) = (-1)^2(1) = 1$$

$$b_2 = (-1)^{2+1}\left(\frac{1}{2}\right) = (-1)^3\left(\frac{1}{2}\right) = -\frac{1}{2}$$

$$b_3 = (-1)^{3+1}\left(\frac{1}{3}\right) = (-1)^4\left(\frac{1}{3}\right) = \frac{1}{3}$$

$$b_4 = (-1)^{4+1}\left(\frac{1}{4}\right) = (-1)^5\left(\frac{1}{4}\right) = -\frac{1}{4}$$

$$b_5 = (-1)^{5+1}\left(\frac{1}{5}\right) = (-1)^6\left(\frac{1}{5}\right) = \frac{1}{5}$$

$$b_6 = (-1)^{6+1}\left(\frac{1}{6}\right) = (-1)^7\left(\frac{1}{6}\right) = -\frac{1}{6}$$ ▪ ▪ ▪

PRACTICE PROBLEM 2 Write the first six terms of the sequence defined by $a_n = \dfrac{(-1)^n}{n^2}$. ▪

Frequently, the first few terms of a sequence exhibit a pattern that suggests a natural choice for the general term of the sequence.

EXAMPLE 3 **Finding a General Term of a Sequence from a Pattern**

Write the general term a_n for a sequence whose first five terms are given.

a. $1, 4, 9, 16, 25, \ldots$ **b.** $0, \dfrac{1}{2}, -\dfrac{2}{3}, \dfrac{3}{4}, -\dfrac{4}{5}, \ldots$

Solution

Write the position number of the term above each term of the sequence, and look for a pattern that connects the term to the position number of the term.

a. n: 1 2 3 4 5 $\ldots$ n
term: 1, 4, 9, 16, 25, $\cdots$, a_n

Apparent pattern: Here, $1 = 1^2, 4 = 2^2, 9 = 3^2, 16 = 4^2$, and $25 = 5^2$. Each term is the square of the position number of that term. This suggests $a_n = n^2$.

b.

$$n: \quad 1 \quad 2 \quad 3 \quad 4 \quad 5 \quad \dots \quad n$$

$$\text{term:} \quad 0, \quad \frac{1}{2}, \quad -\frac{2}{3}, \quad \frac{3}{4}, \quad -\frac{4}{5}, \quad \dots, \quad a_n$$

Apparent pattern: When the terms alternate in sign, we use factors such as $(-1)^n$ if we want to begin with the factor -1 when $n = 1$, or $(-1)^{n+1}$ if we want to begin with the factor 1 when $n = 1$. Notice that each term can be written as a quotient with denominator equal to the position number and numerator equal to one less than the position number, suggesting the general term $a_n = (-1)^n\left(\dfrac{n-1}{n}\right)$.   ■ ■ ■

PRACTICE PROBLEM 3   Write a general term for a sequence whose first five terms are $0, -\dfrac{1}{2}, \dfrac{2}{3}, -\dfrac{3}{4}, \dfrac{4}{5}, \dots$.   ■

In Example 3, we found the general term of a sequence on the basis of a pattern exhibited in the first few terms of the sequence. However, when only a finite number of successive terms are given without a rule that defines the general term, a *unique* general term cannot be found. To indicate why this is so, consider the two sequences $a_n = n^2$ and $b_n = n^2 + (n-1)(n-2)(n-3)(n-4)$.

The first four terms of these two sequences are identical: 1, 4, 9, 16. However, the fifth term is different: $a_5 = 25$, whereas $b_5 = 49$. Thus, either a_n or b_n could correctly be used as a general term to describe a sequence whose first four terms are 1, 4, 9, and 16. A technique similar to that just used can be employed to show that you can *never* find a unique general term from a finite number of terms in a sequence.

Recursive Formulas

Up to this point, we have expressed the general term as a function of the position of the term in the sequence. A second approach is to define a sequence *recursively*. A **recursive formula** requires that one or more of the first few terms of the sequence be specified and all other terms be defined in relation to previously defined terms. An example will help clarify how this works.

The **Fibonacci sequence** is a famous sequence that is defined recursively and shows up quite frequently in nature. This sequence is defined by first specifying the first two terms: $a_0 = 1$ and $a_1 = 1$. Each subsequent term is found by adding the two terms immediately preceding it. Thus,

$a_0 = 1, a_1 = 1, a_2 = a_0 + a_1 = 1 + 1 = 2$	Add the two given terms.
$a_1 = 1, a_2 = 2, a_3 = a_1 + a_2 = 1 + 2 = 3$	Add the two previous terms.
$a_2 = 2, a_3 = 3, a_4 = a_2 + a_3 = 2 + 3 = 5$	Add the two previous terms.
$a_3 = 3, a_4 = 5, a_5 = a_3 + a_4 = 3 + 5 = 8.$	Add the two previous terms.

The first six terms of the sequence are then

$$1, 1, 2, 3, 5, 8.$$

This sequence can also be defined in subscript notation:

$$a_0 = 1, a_1 = 1, a_k = a_{k-2} + a_{k-1}, \text{ for all } k \geq 2.$$

Leonardo of Pisa (Fibonacci)

(1175–1250)

Leonardo, often known today by the name Fibonacci (son of Bonaccio) was born around 1175. He traveled extensively through North Africa and the Mediterranean, probably on business with his father. At each location, he met with Islamic scholars and absorbed the mathematical knowledge of the Islamic world. After returning to Pisa around 1200, he started writing books on mathematics. He was one of the earliest European writers on algebra. In his most famous book, *Liber abaci,* or *Book of Calculations,* he introduced the Western world to the rules of computing with the new Hindu–Arabic numerals.

Replacing k by 2, 3, 4, and 5, respectively, in the equation $a_k = a_{k-2} + a_{k-1}$ will again produce the values $a_2 = 2$, $a_3 = 3$, $a_4 = 5$, and $a_5 = 8$.

EXAMPLE 4   **Finding Terms of a Recursively Defined Sequence**

Write the first five terms of the recursively defined sequence

$$a_1 = 4, \ a_{n+1} = 2a_n - 9.$$

Solution

We are given the first term of the sequence: $a_1 = 4$.

$a_2 = 2a_1 - 9$	Replace n by 1 in $a_{n+1} = 2a_n - 9$.
$a_2 = 2(4) - 9 = -1$	Replace a_1 by 4.
$a_3 = 2a_2 - 9$	Replace n by 2 in $a_{n+1} = 2a_n - 9$.
$a_3 = 2(-1) - 9 = -11$	Replace a_2 by -1.
$a_4 = 2a_3 - 9$	Replace n by 3 in $a_{n+1} = 2a_n - 9$.
$a_4 = 2(-11) - 9 = -31$	Replace a_3 by -11.
$a_5 = 2a_4 - 9$	Replace n by 4 in $a_{n+1} = 2a_n - 9$.
$a_5 = 2(-31) - 9 = -71$	Replace a_4 by -31.

Thus, the first five terms of the sequence are

$$4, -1, -11, -31, -71. \qquad \blacksquare \ \blacksquare \ \blacksquare$$

PRACTICE PROBLEM 4   Write the first five terms of the recursively defined sequence $a_1 = -3$, $a_{n+1} = 2a_n + 5$. ■

EXAMPLE 5   **Diagramming the Family Tree of a Honeybee**

Find a sequence that accurately counts the ancestors of a male honeybee. The first term of the sequence should give the number of parents of a male honeybee, the second term the number of grandparents, the third term the number of great-grandparents, and so on.

Solution

Recall from the introduction to this section that female honeybees have two parents—a male and a female—but that male honeybees have just one parent—a female.

First, we consider the family tree of a male honeybee. A male bee has 1 parent: a female. Since his mother had 2 parents, he has 2 grandparents. Because his grandmother had 2 parents and his grandfather had only 1 parent, he has 3 great-grandparents.

Now, we count backward using Figure 11.2. You should now recognize terms 1–6 of the Fibonacci sequence: 1, 1, 2, 3, 5, 8. This sequence is defined by $a_0 = 1$, $a_1 = 1$, $a_2 = 2$, and $a_k = a_{k-2} + a_{k-1}$, for all $k \geq 3$. $\qquad \blacksquare \ \blacksquare \ \blacksquare$

PRACTICE PROBLEM 5   Find a sequence that accurately counts the ancestors of a female honeybee. ■

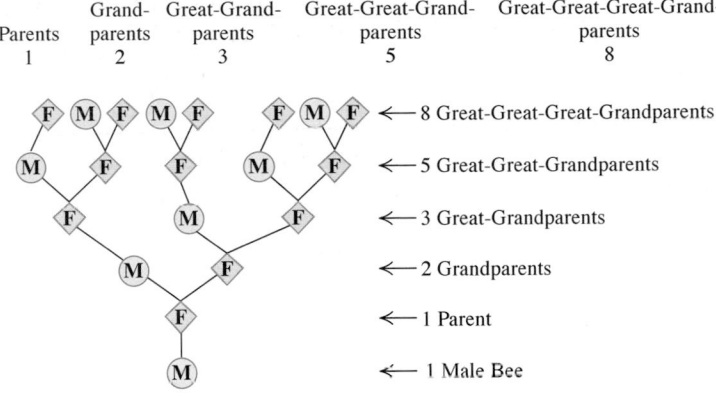

| Parents 1 | Grand-parents 2 | Great-Grand-parents 3 | Great-Great-Grand-parents 5 | Great-Great-Great-Grand-parents 8 |

←— 8 Great-Great-Great-Grandparents

←— 5 Great-Great-Grandparents

←— 3 Great-Grandparents

←— 2 Grandparents

←— 1 Parent

←— 1 Male Bee

FIGURE 11.2

2 Use factorial notation.

Factorial Notation

Special types of products, called factorials, appear in some very important sequences.

DEFINITION OF FACTORIAL

For any positive integer n, n **factorial** (written $n!$) is defined as

$$n! = n \cdot (n - 1) \cdots 4 \cdot 3 \cdot 2 \cdot 1.$$

As a special case, **zero factorial** (written $0!$) is defined as

$$0! = 1.$$

The first eight values of $n!$ are

$0! = 1$ $4! = 4 \cdot 3 \cdot 2 \cdot 1 = 24$

$1! = 1$ $5! = 5 \cdot 4 \cdot 3 \cdot 2 \cdot 1 = 120$

$2! = 2 \cdot 1 = 2$ $6! = 6 \cdot 5 \cdot 4 \cdot 3 \cdot 2 \cdot 1 = 720$

$3! = 3 \cdot 2 \cdot 1 = 6$ $7! = 7 \cdot 6 \cdot 5 \cdot 4 \cdot 3 \cdot 2 \cdot 1 = 5040.$

The values of $n!$ get large very quickly. For example, $10! = 3,628,800$ and $12! = 479,001,600$.

In simplifying some expressions involving factorials, it is helpful to note that

$$\boxed{n! = n \cdot (n - 1)!}$$

TECHNOLOGY CONNECTION

EXAMPLE 6   **Simplifying a Factorial Expression**

Simplify.   **a.** $\dfrac{16!}{14!}$ **b.** $\dfrac{(n + 1)!}{(n - 1)!}$

Solution

a. $\dfrac{16!}{14!} = \dfrac{16 \cdot 15 \cdot 14!}{14!}$ $16! = 16 \cdot 15! = 16 \cdot 15 \cdot 14!$

$= 16 \cdot 15 = 240$ Divide out the factor $14!$

Continued on next page.

b. $\dfrac{(n+1)!}{(n-1)!} = \dfrac{(n+1) \cdot n \cdot (n-1)!}{(n-1)!}$ Use $(n+1)! = (n+1) \cdot n!$

$\qquad\qquad\quad = (n+1)n$ Divide out the common factor $(n-1)!$ ■ ■ ■

PRACTICE PROBLEM 6   Simplify.   **a.** $\dfrac{13!}{12!}$ **b.** $\dfrac{n!}{(n-3)!}$ ■

EXAMPLE 7   **Writing Terms of a Sequence Involving Factorials**

Write the first five terms of the sequence whose general term is: $a_n = \dfrac{(-1)^{n+1}}{n!}$

Solution

Replace n in the formula for the general term by each positive integer from 1 through 5.

$a_1 = \dfrac{(-1)^{1+1}}{1!} = \dfrac{(-1)^2}{1} = 1$ $\qquad$ $a_2 = \dfrac{(-1)^{2+1}}{2!} = \dfrac{(-1)^3}{2} = -\dfrac{1}{2}$

$a_3 = \dfrac{(-1)^{3+1}}{3!} = \dfrac{(-1)^4}{6} = \dfrac{1}{6}$ $\qquad$ $a_4 = \dfrac{(-1)^{4+1}}{4!} = \dfrac{(-1)^5}{24} = -\dfrac{1}{24}$

$a_5 = \dfrac{(-1)^{5+1}}{5!} = \dfrac{(-1)^6}{120} = \dfrac{1}{120}$

Using these five terms, we could write this sequence as

$$1, -\dfrac{1}{2}, \dfrac{1}{6}, -\dfrac{1}{24}, \dfrac{1}{120}, \dots .$$ ■ ■ ■

PRACTICE PROBLEM 7   Write the first five terms of the sequence whose general term is:

$$a_n = \dfrac{(-1)^n 2^n}{n!}$$ ■

3 Use summation notation to write partial sums of a series.

Summation Notation

If we know the general term of a sequence, we can represent a *sum* of terms of the sequence by using *summation* (or *sigma*) *notation*. In this notation, the Greek letter Σ (capital sigma) indicates that we are to *add* the given terms. The letter Σ corresponds to the English letter S, the first letter of the word "sum."

SUMMATION NOTATION

The sum of the first n term of a sequence $a_1, a_2, a_3, \dots , a_n, \dots$ is denoted by

$$\sum_{i=1}^{n} a_i = a_1 + a_2 + a_3 + \cdots + a_n.$$

The letter i in the summation notation is called the **index of summation**, n is called the **upper limit**, and 1 is called the **lower limit**, of the summation.

In summation notation, the index need not start at $i = 1$. Further, any letter may be used in place of the index i.

| EXAMPLE 8 | **Evaluating Sums Given in Summation Notation** |

Find each sum.   **a.** $\displaystyle\sum_{i=1}^{9} i$ **b.** $\displaystyle\sum_{j=4}^{7}(2j^2 - 1)$ **c.** $\displaystyle\sum_{k=0}^{4}\frac{2^k}{k!}$

Solution

a. Replace i with successive integers from 1 to 9 inclusive, and then add.

$$\sum_{i=1}^{9} i = 1 + 2 + 3 + 4 + 5 + 6 + 7 + 8 + 9 = 45.$$

b. The index of summation is j. Evaluate $(2j^2 - 1)$ for all consecutive integers from 4 through 7 inclusive, and then add.

$$\sum_{j=4}^{7}(2j^2 - 1) = [2(4)^2 - 1] + [2(5)^2 - 1] + [2(6)^2 - 1] + [2(7)^2 - 1]$$

$$= 31 + 49 + 71 + 97 = 248$$

c. The index of summation is k. Evaluate $\dfrac{2^k}{k!}$ for consecutive integers 0 through 4, inclusive, and then add.

$$\sum_{k=0}^{4}\frac{2^k}{k!} = \frac{2^0}{0!} + \frac{2^1}{1!} + \frac{2^2}{2!} + \frac{2^3}{3!} + \frac{2^4}{4!}$$

$$= \frac{1}{1} + \frac{2}{1} + \frac{4}{2} + \frac{8}{6} + \frac{16}{24} = 1 + 2 + 2 + \frac{4}{3} + \frac{2}{3} = 7 \qquad ■ ■ ■$$

PRACTICE PROBLEM 8   Find the sum: $\displaystyle\sum_{k=0}^{3}(-1)^k k!$ ■

The familiar properties of real numbers, such as the distributive, commutative, and associative properties, can be used to prove the summation properties listed next.

TECHNOLOGY CONNECTION

✎ A graphing calculator can sum terms of a series. The viewing window shows $\displaystyle\sum_{j=4}^{7}(2j^2 - 1)$. Note that the calculator replaces the variable j with n.

```
sum(seq(2*n^2-1,
n,4,7,1)
              248
■
```

SUMMATION PROPERTIES

Let a_k and b_k represent the general terms of two sequences, and let c represent any real number. Then

1. $\displaystyle\sum_{k-1}^{n} c = c \cdot n$ 　　　　　　　　　　**2.** $\displaystyle\sum_{k=1}^{n} ca_k = c\sum_{k=1}^{n} a_k$

3. $\displaystyle\sum_{k=1}^{n}(a_k + b_k) = \sum_{k=1}^{n} a_k + \sum_{k=1}^{n} b_k$ 　　**4.** $\displaystyle\sum_{k=1}^{n}(a_k - b_k) = \sum_{k=1}^{n} a_k - \sum_{k=1}^{n} b_k$

5. $\displaystyle\sum_{k=1}^{n} a_k = \sum_{k=1}^{j} a_k + \sum_{k=j+1}^{n} a_k$, for $1 \leq j < n$

Series

We all know how to add numbers, but do you think it is possible to add infinitely many numbers? It may come as a surprise that it *is* sometimes possible to add infinitely many numbers, although a complete explanation of this kind of addition must be put off until a calculus course. For now, we need some definitions.

DEFINITION OF SERIES

Let $a_1, a_2, a_3, \ldots, a_k, \ldots$ be an infinite sequence. Then

1. The sum of the first n terms of the sequence is called the **nth partial sum** of the sequence and is denoted by

$$a_1 + a_2 + a_3 + \cdots + a_n = \sum_{i=1}^{n} a_i.$$

2. The sum of all terms of the infinite sequence is called an **infinite series** and is denoted by

$$a_1 + a_2 + a_3 + \cdots + a_n + \cdots = \sum_{i=1}^{\infty} a_i.$$

By contrast with an infinite series, the nth partial sum is a **finite series**.

EXAMPLE 9   **Writing a Partial Sum in Summation Notation**

Write each sum in summation notation.

a. $3 + 5 + 7 + \cdots + 21$ **b.** $\dfrac{1}{4} + \dfrac{1}{9} + \cdots + \dfrac{1}{49}$

Solution

a. The finite series $3 + 5 + 7 + \cdots + 21$ is a sum of consecutive odd numbers from 3 to 21. Each of these numbers can be expressed in the form $2k + 1$, starting with $k = 1$ and ending with $k = 10$. With k as the index of summation with lower limit 1 and upper limit 10, we write

$$3 + 5 + 7 + \cdots + 21 = \sum_{k=1}^{10} (2k + 1)$$

b. The finite series $\dfrac{1}{4} + \dfrac{1}{9} + \cdots + \dfrac{1}{49}$ is a sum of fractions, each of which has numerator 1 and denominator k^2, starting with $k = 2$ and ending with $k = 7$. We write

$$\frac{1}{4} + \frac{1}{9} + \cdots + \frac{1}{49} = \sum_{k=2}^{7} \frac{1}{k^2}$$ ■ ■ ■

PRACTICE PROBLEM 9   Write in summation notation: $2 - 4 + 6 - 8 + 10 - 12 + 14$ ■

A Exercises   Basic Skills and Concepts

In Exercises 1–20, write the first four terms of each sequence.

1. $a_n = 3n - 2$ †

2. $a_n = 2n + 1$ †

5. $a_n = -n^2$ †

6. $a_n = n^3$ †

3. $a_n = 1 - \dfrac{1}{n}$ †

4. $a_n = 1 + \dfrac{1}{n}$ †

7. $a_n = \dfrac{2n}{n + 1}$ †

8. $a_n = \dfrac{3n}{n^2 + 1}$ †

†Due to space constrictions, answers to these exercises may be found in the Answers beginning on page A–1 in the back of the book.

9. $a_n = (-1)^{n+1}$ †

10. $a_n = (-3)^{n-1}$ †

11. $a_n = 3 - \dfrac{1}{2^n}$ †

12. $a_n = \left(\dfrac{3}{2}\right)^n$ †

13. $a_n = 0.6$ †

14. $a_n = -0.4$ †

15. $a_n = \dfrac{(-1)^n}{n!}$ †

16. $a_n = \dfrac{n}{n!}$ †

17. $a_n = (-1)^n 3^{-n}$ †

18. $a_n = (-1)^n 3^{n-1}$ †

19. $a_n = \dfrac{e^n}{2n}$ †

20. $a_n = \dfrac{2^n}{e^n}$ †

In Exercises 21–34, write a general term a_n for each sequence. Assume that n begins with 1.

21. $1, 4, 7, 10, \ldots$ †

22. $7, 9, 11, 13, \ldots$ †

23. $\dfrac{1}{2}, \dfrac{1}{3}, \dfrac{1}{4}, \dfrac{1}{5}, \ldots$ †

24. $\dfrac{2}{3}, \dfrac{3}{4}, \dfrac{4}{5}, \dfrac{5}{6}, \ldots$ †

25. $2, -2, 2, -2, \ldots$ †

26. $-3, 6, -9, 12, \ldots$ †

27. $\dfrac{1}{2}, \dfrac{3}{4}, \dfrac{9}{8}, \dfrac{27}{16}, \ldots$ †

28. $\dfrac{-1}{2}, \dfrac{1}{4}, \dfrac{-1}{8}, \dfrac{1}{16}, \ldots$ †

29. $1 \cdot 2, 2 \cdot 3, 3 \cdot 4, 4 \cdot 5, \ldots$ †

30. $\dfrac{-1}{1 \cdot 2}, \dfrac{1}{2 \cdot 3}, \dfrac{-1}{3 \cdot 4}, \dfrac{1}{4 \cdot 5}, \ldots$ $a_n = \dfrac{(-1)^n}{n(n+1)}$

31. $2 + \dfrac{1}{2}, 2 - \dfrac{1}{3}, 2 + \dfrac{1}{4}, 2 - \dfrac{1}{5}, \ldots$ $a_n = 2 - \dfrac{(-1)^n}{n+1}$

32. $1 + \dfrac{1}{2}, 1 + \dfrac{1}{3}, 1 + \dfrac{1}{4}, 1 + \dfrac{1}{5}, \ldots$ $a_n = 1 + \dfrac{1}{n+1}$

33. $\dfrac{3^2}{2}, \dfrac{3^3}{3}, \dfrac{3^4}{4}, \dfrac{3^5}{5}, \ldots$ †

34. $\dfrac{e}{2}, \dfrac{e^2}{4}, \dfrac{e^3}{8}, \dfrac{e^4}{16}, \ldots$ †

In Exercises 35–44, write the first five terms of the recursively defined sequence.

35. $a_1 = 2, a_{n+1} = a_n + 3$ †

36. $a_1 = 5, a_{n+1} = a_n - 1$ †

37. $a_1 = 3, a_{n+1} = 2a_n$ †

38. $a_1 = 1, a_{n+1} = \dfrac{1}{2}a_n$ †

39. $a_1 = 7, a_{n+1} = -2a_n + 3$ †

40. $a_1 = -4, a_{n+1} = -3a_n - 5$ †

41. $a_1 = 2, a_{n+1} = \dfrac{1}{a_n}$ †

42. $a_1 = -1, a_{n+1} = \dfrac{-1}{a_n}$ †

43. $a_1 = 25, a_{n+1} = \dfrac{(-1)^n}{5a_n}$ †

44. $a_1 = 12, a_{n+1} = \dfrac{(-1)^n}{3a_n}$ †

In Exercises 45–52, simplify the factorial expression.

45. $\dfrac{3!}{5!}$ $\dfrac{1}{20}$

46. $\dfrac{8!}{10!}$ $\dfrac{1}{90}$

47. $\dfrac{12!}{11!}$ 12

48. $\dfrac{20!}{18!}$ 380

49. $\dfrac{n!}{(n+1)!}$ $\dfrac{1}{n+1}$

50. $\dfrac{(n-1)!}{(n-2)!}$ $n-1$

51. $\dfrac{(2n+1)!}{(2n)!}$ $2n+1$

52. $\dfrac{(2n+1)!}{(2n-1)!}$ $4n^2 + 2n$

In Exercises 53–64, find each sum.

53. $\displaystyle\sum_{k=1}^{7} 5$ 35

54. $\displaystyle\sum_{j=1}^{4} 12$ 48

55. $\displaystyle\sum_{j=0}^{5} j^2$ 55

56. $\displaystyle\sum_{k=0}^{4} k^3$ 100

57. $\displaystyle\sum_{i=1}^{5} (2i - 1)$ 25

58. $\displaystyle\sum_{k=0}^{6} (1 - 3k)$ -56

59. $\displaystyle\sum_{j=1}^{7} \dfrac{j+1}{j}$ $\dfrac{1343}{140}$

60. $\displaystyle\sum_{k=0}^{5} \dfrac{1}{k+1}$ $\dfrac{49}{20}$

61. $\displaystyle\sum_{i=1}^{6} (-1)^i 3^{i-1}$ 182

62. $\displaystyle\sum_{k=0}^{4} (-1)^{k+1} k$ -2

63. $\displaystyle\sum_{k=1}^{3} (2 - k^2)$ -8

64. $\displaystyle\sum_{j=0}^{4} (j^3 + 1)$ 105

In Exercises 65–72, write each sum in summation notation.

65. $1 + 3 + 5 + 7 + \cdots + 101$ †

66. $2 + 4 + 6 + 8 + \cdots + 102$ †

67. $\dfrac{1}{5(1)} + \dfrac{1}{5(2)} + \dfrac{1}{5(3)} + \dfrac{1}{5(4)} + \cdots + \dfrac{1}{5(11)}$ $\displaystyle\sum_{k=1}^{11} \dfrac{1}{5k}$

68. $1 + \dfrac{2}{2 \cdot 3} + \dfrac{2}{3 \cdot 4} + \dfrac{2}{4 \cdot 5} + \cdots + \dfrac{2}{9 \cdot 10}$ $\displaystyle\sum_{k=1}^{9} \dfrac{2}{k(k+1)}$

69. $1 - \dfrac{1}{2} + \dfrac{1}{3} - \dfrac{1}{4} + \cdots - \dfrac{1}{50}$ $\displaystyle\sum_{k=1}^{50} \dfrac{(-1)^{k+1}}{k}$

70. $1 - 2 + 3 - 4 + \cdots + (-50)$ †

71. $\dfrac{1}{2} + \dfrac{2}{3} + \dfrac{3}{4} + \dfrac{4}{5} + \cdots + \dfrac{10}{11}$ $\displaystyle\sum_{k=1}^{10} \left(\dfrac{k}{k+1}\right)$

72. $2 + \dfrac{2^2}{2} + \dfrac{2^3}{3} + \dfrac{2^4}{4} + \cdots + \dfrac{2^{10}}{10}$ $\displaystyle\sum_{k=1}^{10} \dfrac{2^k}{k}$

B Exercises   Applying the Concepts

73. Free fall. In the absence of friction, a freely falling body will fall about 16 feet the first second, 48 feet the next second, 80 feet the third second, 112 feet the fourth second, and so on. How far has it fallen during
   a. the seventh second? †   **b.** the nth second? †

74. Bacterial growth. A colony of 1000 bacteria doubles in size every hour. How many bacteria will there be in
   a. 2 hours? †   **b.** 5 hours? †   **c.** n hours? †

75. Workplace fines. A contractor who quits work on a house was told she would be fined 50 dollars if she did not resume work on Monday, 75 dollars if she failed to resume work on Tuesday, 100 dollars on Wednesday, and so on (including weekends). How much will her fine be on the ninth day she fails to show up for work? $250

76. Appreciating value. A painting valued at 30,000 dollars is expected to appreciate 1280 dollars the first year, 1240 dollars the second year, 1200 dollars the third year, and so on. How much will the painting appreciate in
   a. the seventh year? †   **b.** the tenth year? †

77. Cell phone use. At the end of the first six months after a company began providing cell phones to its sales force, it averaged 600 cell minutes per month. For the next four years, its monthly cell phone use doubled every six months. How many cell minutes per month were being used at the end of three years?   19, 200 min

78. Motorcycle acceleration. A motorcycle travels 10 yards the first second and then increases its speed by 20 yards per second in each succeeding second. At this rate, how far will the motorcycle travel during
   a. the eighth second? †   **b.** the nth second? †

79. Compound interest. Suppose 10,000 dollars is deposited into an account that earns 6% interest compounded semiannually. The balance in the account after n compounding periods is given by the sequence

$$A_n = 10,000\left(1 + \frac{0.06}{2}\right)^n, n = 1, 2, 3, \dots.$$

   a. Find the first six terms of this sequence. †
   b. Find the balance in the account after 8 years. $16,047.10

80. Compound interest. Suppose 100 dollars is deposited at the beginning of a year into an account that earns 8% interest compounded quarterly. The balance in the account after n compounding periods is

$$A_n = 100\left(1 + \frac{0.08}{4}\right)^n, n = 1, 2, 3, \dots.$$

   a. Find the first six terms of this sequence. †
   b. Find the balance in the account after ten years. $220.8

81. Real estate value. Analysts estimate that a $100,000 condominium will increase 5% in value each year for the next seven years. Find the value of the condominium in each of those years. Write a formula for a sequence whose first seven terms give these values. †

82. Diminishing savings. Laura withdraws 10% of her 50,000-dollar savings each year. Find the amount remaining in her account for each of the next ten years. Write a formula for a sequence whose first ten terms give these values. †

C Exercises   Beyond the Basics

83. Find a formula for the nth term of the sequence defined recursively by $a_1 = \sqrt{2}, a_{n+1} = \sqrt{2a_n}$. †
   [*Hint:* Write each of the first five terms as a power of 2.]

84. The triangular tiles used in the figures shown have white interiors and gold edges. A sequence of figures is obtained by adding one triangle to the previous figure.

a. Write a recursive sequence whose nth term, a_n, gives the number of gold edges in the nth figure. †
b. Write a recursive sequence whose nth term, b_n, gives the number of gold edges that lie on the perimeter of the nth figure. $b_1 = 3, b_{n+1} = b_n + 1$

One tile   Two tiles   Three tiles

85. The figure shows a sequence of successively smaller squares formed by connecting the midpoints of the sides of the preceding larger square. The area of the largest square is 1.

  a. Write the first five terms of the sequence whose general term, a_n, gives the area of the nth square. †

  b. Write the general term, a_n, of the sequence. †

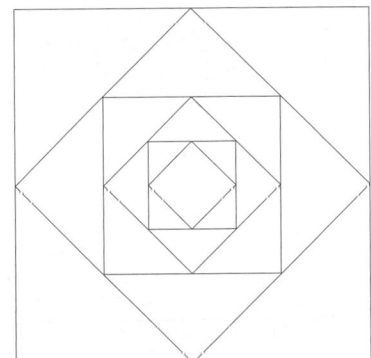

86. A sequence of concentric circles is designed so that the radius of the first circle is 1 and each successive circle has a radius that is twice the length of the radius of the preceding circle. Write a recursive sequence whose nth term, a_n, gives the area of the nth circle. $a_1 = \pi, a_{n+1} = 4a_n$

87. Find the first 10 terms of the sequence defined recursively by $a_1 = a_2 = 1, a_n = a_{a_{n-1}} + a_{n-a_{n-1}}$. In 1989, a prize of 1000 dollars was offered to whoever first discovered (for this sequence) a value of n for which $\left|\dfrac{a_i}{i}\right| - \left|\dfrac{1}{2}\right| < \dfrac{1}{20}$ for all $i > n$.

A mathematician named Colin L. Mallows of AT & T/Bell Laboratories found that $n = 1489$ and claimed the prize. (*Source*: http://el.media.mit.edu/logo-foundation/pubs/papers/easy_as_11223.html)

88. A sequence of numbers $a_0, a_1, a_2, a_3, \ldots$ satisfies the equation

$$a_n{}^2 = (-1)^n a_{n-1} + a_{n+1}.$$

If $a_0 = 1$ and $a_1 = 3$, find a_3. $a_3 = 97$

89. Find a sequence with general term a_m so that

$$\sum_{n=1}^{20} n^2 = \sum_{m=0}^{19} a_m.$$

90. Find a real number c such that

$$\sum_{n=1}^{50} (n-3)^2 = \sum_{n=1}^{50} (n^2 - 6n) + \sum_{n=1}^{50} c. \quad c = 9$$

91. Find a lower limit p and an upper limit q such that

$$\sum_{n=0}^{10} n^3 = \sum_{m=p}^{q} (m+2)^3.$$

92. Give an example of two sequences a_k and b_k such that

$$\sum_{k=1}^{20} a_k b_k \neq \left(\sum_{k=1}^{20} a_k\right)\left(\sum_{k=1}^{20} b_k\right).$$

93. Show that $7! - 2(5!) = 40(5!)$.

94. Show that $\dfrac{10!}{6!4!} + \dfrac{10!}{5!5!} = \dfrac{11!}{6!5!}$.

Critical Thinking

95. Find the largest integer value for the upper limit k if

$$\sum_{n=1}^{k} (n^2 + n)$$

$$= \sum_{n=1}^{k} [(n-1)(n-2)(n-3)(n-4)(n-5) + n^2 + n]. \quad k = 5$$

96. **The Ulam Conjecture.** Define the sequence a_n recursively by

$$a_n = \begin{cases} \dfrac{a_{n-1}}{2} & \text{if } a_{n-1} \text{ is even.} \\[2mm] 3a_{n-1} + 1 & \text{if } a_{n-1} \text{ is odd} \end{cases}$$

The Ulam conjecture says that if your first term a_0 is any positive integer, the sequence a_n will eventually reach the integer 1. Verify the conjecture for $a_0 = 13$.

Answers:

87. $a_1 = 1, a_2 = 1, a_3 = 2, a_4 = 2, a_5 = 3, a_6 = 4, a_7 = 4,$ $a_8 = 4, a_9 = 5, a_{10} = 6$

Answers:

89. $a_m = (m+1)^2$ **91.** $p = -2, q = 8$

92. $a_k = b_k = 1$; Answers may vary.

Arithmetic Sequences; Partial Sums

BEFORE STARTING THIS SECTION, REVIEW

1. The general term of a sequence (Section 11.1, page 932)

2. Partial sums (Section 11.1, page 940)

OBJECTIVES

1 Identify an arithmetic sequence and find its common difference.

2 Find the sum of the first n terms of an arithmetic sequence.

Falling Space Junk

On April 27, 2000, more than 300 kilograms (700 pounds) of "space junk" crashed to the ground in South Africa. The material was eventually identified as part of a Delta 2 rocket used to launch a global positioning satellite in 1996. Once an object begins a free fall toward Earth, it falls (in the absence of friction) 16 feet in the first second, 48 feet in the next second, 80 feet in the third second, and so on. The number of feet traveled in succeeding seconds is the sequence

$$16, 48, 80, 112, \ldots.$$

This is an example of an *arithmetic sequence*. We investigate such a sequence in Example 5. ■

1 Identify an arithmetic sequence and find its common difference.

When the difference between any two consecutive terms of a sequence is always the same number, the sequence is called an *arithmetic sequence*. In other words, the sequence $a_1, a_2, a_3, a_4, \ldots$ is an arithmetic sequence if $a_2 - a_1 = a_3 - a_2 = a_4 - a_3 = \ldots.$

DEFINITION OF ARITHMETIC SEQUENCE

The sequence

$$a_1, a_2, a_3, a_4, \ldots, a_n, \ldots$$

is an **arithmetic sequence,** or an **arithmetic progression,** if there is a number d such that each term in the sequence except the first is obtained from the preceding term by adding d to it. The number d is called the **common difference** of the arithmetic sequence. We have

$$d = a_{n+1} - a_n, \quad n \geq 1.$$

> **EXAMPLE 1**   **Finding the Common Difference**

Find the common difference of each arithmetic sequence.

a. $3, 23, 43, 63, 83, \ldots$ **b.** $29, 19, 9, -1, -11, \ldots$

Solution

a. The common difference is $23 - 3 = 20$ (or $43 - 23$, or $63 - 43$, or $83 - 63$).

b. The common difference is $19 - 29 = -10$ (or $9 - 19$, or $-1 - 9$, or $-11 - (-1)$). ■ ■ ■

PRACTICE PROBLEM 1   Find the common difference of the arithmetic sequence

$$3, -2, -7, -12, -17, \ldots . \qquad ■$$

An arithmetic sequence can be completely specified by giving the first term a_1 and the common difference d. Let's see why. Suppose we are told that the sequence $a_1, a_2, a_3, a_4, \ldots$ is an arithmetic sequence and that $a_1 = 5$ and $d = 4$. Then

$$a_2 - a_1 = 4, \quad \text{so} \quad a_2 = a_1 + 4 = 5 + 4 = 9;$$
$$a_3 - a_2 = 4, \quad \text{so} \quad a_3 = a_2 + 4 = 9 + 4 = 13;$$
$$a_4 - a_3 = 4, \quad \text{so} \quad a_4 = a_3 + 4 = 13 + 4 = 17, \text{ and so on.}$$

Rewriting $d = a_{n+1} - a_n$ as $a_{n+1} = a_n + d$, we have a recursive definition of an arithmetic sequence.

RECURSIVE DEFINITION OF AN ARITHMETIC SEQUENCE

An arithmetic sequence $a_1, a_2, a_3, a_4, \ldots, a_n, \ldots$ can be defined recursively. The recursive formula

$$a_{n+1} = a_n + d \text{ for } n \geq 1$$

defines an arithmetic sequence with first term a_1 and common difference d.

Consider an arithmetic sequence with first term a_1 and common difference d. Using the recursive definition $a_{n+1} = a_n + d$, for $n \geq 1$, we write

$a_1 = a_1$	The first term is a_1.
$a_2 = a_1 + d$	Replace n by 1 in $a_{n+1} = a_n + d$.
$a_3 = a_2 + d = (a_1 + d) + d = a_1 + 2d$	Replace a_2 by $a_1 + d$; simplify.
$a_4 = a_3 + d = (a_1 + 2d) + d = a_1 + 3d$	Replace a_3 by $a_1 + 2d$; simplify.
$a_5 = a_4 + d = (a_1 + 3d) + d = a_1 + 4d$	Replace a_4 by $a_1 + 3d$; simplify.

$$\vdots$$

$$a_n = a_{n-1} + d$$
$$\quad = [a_1 + (n-2)d] + d \qquad \text{Replace } a_{n-1} \text{ by } a_1 + (n-2)d.$$
$$\quad = a_1 + (n-1)d. \qquad \text{Simplify.}$$

Thus, we can find the general term a_n from the values a_1 and d.

---

*n*TH TERM OF AN ARITHMETIC SEQUENCE

If a sequence $a_1, a_2, a_3, \ldots$ is an arithmetic sequence, then its *n*th term, a_n, is given by

$$a_n = a_1 + (n - 1)d,$$

where a_1 is the first term and d is the common difference.

EXAMPLE 2   Finding the *n*th Term of an Arithmetic Sequence

Find an expression for the *n*th term of the arithmetic sequence

$$3, 7, 11, 15, \ldots.$$

Solution

Here, $a_1 = 3$ and $d = 7 - 3 = 4$. Thus, we have

$$
\begin{aligned}
a_n &= a_1 + (n - 1)d && \text{Formula for the *n*th term} \\
&= 3 + (n - 1)4 && \text{Replace } a_1 \text{ by 3 and } d \text{ by 4.} \\
&= 3 + 4n - 4 = 4n - 1 && \text{Simplify.}
\end{aligned}
$$

Note that in the expression $a_n = 4n - 1$, we get the sequence $3, 7, 11, 15, \ldots$ by substituting $n = 1, 2, 3, 4, \ldots.$ ■ ■ ■

PRACTICE PROBLEM 2   Find an expression for the *n*th term of the arithmetic sequence

$$-3, 1, 5, 9, 13, 17, \ldots.$$ ■

EXAMPLE 3   Finding the Common Difference of an Arithmetic Sequence

Find the common difference d and the *n*th term a_n of the arithmetic sequence whose 5th term is 15 and whose 20th term is 45.

Solution

$$
\begin{aligned}
a_n &= a_1 + (n - 1)d && \text{Formula for the *n*th term} \\
45 &= a_1 + (20 - 1)d && \text{Replace } n \text{ by 20; } a_n = a_{20} = 45. \\
(1) \quad 45 &= a_1 + 19d. && \text{Simplify.}
\end{aligned}
$$

Also,

$$
\begin{aligned}
15 &= a_1 + (5 - 1)d && \text{Replace } n \text{ by 5; } a_n = a_5 = 15. \\
(2) \quad 15 &= a_1 + 4d. && \text{Simplify.}
\end{aligned}
$$

Solving the system of equations

$$
\begin{cases}
a_1 + 19d = 45 & (1) \\
a_1 + 4d = 15 & (2)
\end{cases}
$$

gives $d = 2$ and $a_1 = 7$. We substitute $a_1 = 7$ and $d = 2$ in the formula for the *n*th term.

$$
\begin{aligned}
a_n &= a_1 + (n - 1)d && \text{Formula for the *n*th term} \\
a_n &= 7 + (n - 1)2 && \text{Replace } a_1 \text{ by 7 and } d \text{ by 2.} \\
&= 7 + 2n - 2 = 2n + 5 && \text{Simplify.}
\end{aligned}
$$

The nth term of this sequence is given by

$$a_n = 2n + 5, \quad n \geq 1.$$

■ ■ ■

PRACTICE PROBLEM 3   Find the common difference d and the nth term a_n of the arithmetic sequence whose 4th term is 41 and whose 15th term is 8.   ■

---

2 Find the sum of the first n terms of an arithmetic sequence.

Sum of an Arithmetic Sequence

In several applications involving the sum of an arithmetic sequence, the following formula is quite helpful:

$$1 + 2 + 3 \cdots + n = \frac{n(n + 1)}{2}.$$

It is said that Karl Friedrich Gauss (1777–1855) discovered this formula when he realized that any sum of numbers added in reverse order produces the same sum. Thus, if S denotes the sum of the first n natural numbers, then

$$
\begin{array}{ll}
S = \quad 1 \ + \quad 2 \ + \quad 3 \ + \cdots + \quad n & \\
S = \quad n \ + (n - 1) + (n - 2) + \cdots + \quad 1 & \\
\hline
2S = (n + 1) + (n + 1) + (n + 1) + \cdots + (n + 1) & \text{Add } S + S = 2S.
\end{array}
$$

$\underbrace{\qquad\qquad}_{n \text{ terms}}$

$$2S = n(n + 1)$$

$$S = \frac{n(n + 1)}{2}. \qquad\qquad \text{Divide both sides by 2.}$$

For example, we let $n = 100$ to obtain

$$S = 1 + 2 + 3 + \cdots + 100 = \frac{100(100 + 1)}{2}$$

$$= \frac{100(101)}{2} = 5050.$$

We can use the same method Gauss used to discover the sum of the first 100 natural numbers to calculate the sum S_n of the first n terms of any arithmetic sequence.

First we write the sum S_n of the first n terms:

$$S_n = a_1 + (a_1 + d) + (a_1 + 2d) + (a_1 + 3d) + \cdots + a_n.$$

We can also write S_n (with the terms in reverse order) by starting with a_n and *subtracting* the common difference d:

$$S_n = a_n + (a_n - d) + (a_n - 2d) + (a_n - 3d) + \cdots + a_1.$$

Adding the two equations for S_n, we find that the d's in the sums "drop out" (for example, $(a_1 + d) + (a_n - d) = a_1 + a_n$), and we have

$$2S_n = \underbrace{(a_1 + a_n) + (a_1 + a_n) + \cdots + (a_1 + a_n)}_{n \text{ terms.}}.$$

Thus, $$2S_n = n(a_1 + a_n)$$

$$S_n = n\left(\frac{a_1 + a_n}{2}\right) \qquad \text{Divide both sides by 2.}$$

This provides a formula for S_n.

SUM OF n TERMS OF AN ARITHMETIC SEQUENCE

Let $a_1, a_2, a_3, \ldots a_n$ be the first n terms of an arithmetic sequence with common difference d. The sum S_n of these n terms is given by

$$S_n = n\left(\frac{a_1 + a_n}{2}\right)$$

where $a_n = a_1 + (n-1)d$.

EXAMPLE 4   **Finding the Sum of Terms of a Finite Arithmetic Sequence**

Find the sum of the arithmetic sequence of numbers:

$$1 + 4 + 7 + \cdots + 25$$

Solution

We observe that this is an arithmetic sequence with $a_1 = 1$ and $d = 3$. First find the number of terms.

$a_n = a_1 + (n-1)d$	Formula for nth term
$25 = 1 + (n-1)3$	Replace a_n by 25, a_1 by 1, and d by 3.
$24 = (n-1)3$	Subtract 1 from both sides.
$8 = n - 1$	Divide both sides by 3.
$n = 9$	Solve for n.
$S_n = n\left(\dfrac{a_1 + a_n}{2}\right)$	Formula for S_n
$S_9 = 9\left(\dfrac{1 + 25}{2}\right)$	Replace n by 9, a_1 by 1, and $a_n(= a_9)$ by 25.
$= 9(13) = 117$	Simplify.

Thus, $1 + 4 + 7 + \cdots + 25 = 117$.   ■ ■ ■

PRACTICE PROBLEM 4   Find the sum $\dfrac{2}{3} + \dfrac{5}{6} + 1 + \dfrac{7}{6} + \dfrac{4}{3} + \dfrac{3}{2} + \dfrac{5}{3} + \dfrac{11}{6} + 2 + \dfrac{13}{6}.$ ■

EXAMPLE 5   **Calculating the Distance Traveled by a Freely Falling Object**

In the introduction to this section, we described the arithmetic sequence 16, 48, 80, 112, ... whose terms gave the number of feet that freely falling space junk falls in successive seconds. For this sequence, find:

a. the common difference d **b.** the nth term a_n

c. the distance the object travels in 10 seconds

Solution

a. The common difference $d = a_2 - a_1 = 48 - 16 = 32$.

b.
$a_n = a_1 + (n-1)d$	Formula for the nth term
$= 16 + (n-1)32$	Replace a_1 by 16 and d by 32.
$= 32n - 16$	Simplify.

c. The sum of the first ten terms of this sequence gives the distance the object travels in 10 seconds.

$$a_n = 32n - 16 \qquad \text{From part b}$$

$$a_{10} = 32(10) - 16 \qquad \text{Replace } n \text{ by 10.}$$

$$= 304$$

$$S_n = n\left(\frac{a_1 + a_n}{2}\right) \qquad \text{Formula for } S_n$$

$$S_{10} = 10\left(\frac{16 + 304}{2}\right) \qquad \text{Replace } n \text{ by 10, } a_1 \text{ by 16, and } a_n(= a_{10}) \text{ by 304.}$$

$$= 1600 \qquad \text{Simplify.}$$

The object falls 1600 feet in 10 seconds.   ■ ■ ■

PRACTICE PROBLEM 5 In Example 5, find the distance the object travels during the 11th through 15th seconds.   ■

A Exercises   Basic Skills and Concepts

In Exercises 1–14, determine whether each sequence is arithmetic. For those which are, find the first term a_1 and the common difference d.

1. $1, 2, 3, 4, 5, \ldots$ †

2. $1, 3, 5, 7, 9, \ldots$ †

3. $2, 5, 8, 11, 14, \ldots$ †

4. $10, 7, 4, 1, -2, \ldots$ †

5. $1, \frac{1}{2}, 0, -\frac{1}{2}, -\frac{1}{4}, \ldots$ †

6. $2, 4, 8, 16, 32, \ldots$ †

7. $1, -1, 2, -2, 3, \ldots$ †

8. $-\frac{1}{4}, \frac{1}{4}, \frac{3}{4}, \frac{5}{4}, \frac{7}{4}, \ldots$ †

9. $0.6, 0.2, -0.2, -0.6, -1, \ldots$ Arithmetic; $a_1 = 0.6, d = -0.4$

10. $2.3, 2.7, 3.1, 3.5, 3.9, \ldots$ Arithmetic; $a_1 = 2.3, d = 0.4$

11. $a_n = 2n + 6$ †

12. $a_n = 1 - 5n$ †

13. $a_n = 1 - n^2$ †

14. $a_n = 2n^2 - 3$ †

In Exercises 15–24, find an expression for the nth term of the arithmetic sequence.

15. $5, 8, 11, 14, 17, \ldots$ †

16. $4, 7, 10, 13, 16, \ldots$ †

17. $11, 6, 1, -4, -9, \ldots$ †

18. $9, 5, 1, -3, -7, \ldots$ †

19. $\frac{1}{2}, \frac{1}{4}, 0, -\frac{1}{4}, -\frac{1}{2}, \ldots$ †

20. $\frac{2}{3}, \frac{5}{6}, 1, \frac{7}{6}, \frac{4}{3}, \ldots$ †

21. $-\frac{3}{5}, -1, -\frac{7}{5}, -\frac{9}{5}, -\frac{11}{5}, \ldots$ †

22. $\frac{1}{2}, 2, \frac{7}{2}, 5, \frac{13}{2}, \ldots$ $a_n = \frac{3n - 2}{2}$

23. $e, 3 + e, 6 + e, 9 + e, 12 + e, \ldots$ $a_n = 3n + e - 3$

24. $2\pi, 2(\pi + 2), 2(\pi + 4), 2(\pi + 6), 2(\pi + 8) \ldots,$ †

In Exercises 25–30, find the common difference d and the nth term a_n of the arithmetic sequence with the specified terms.

25. 4th term 21; 10th term 60 †

26. 3rd term 15; 21st term 87 †

27. 7th term 8; 15th term -8 $d = -2, a_n = 22 - 2n$

28. 5th term 12; 18th term -1 $d = -1, a_n = 17 - n$

29. 3rd term 7; 23rd term 17 †

30. 11th term -1; 31st term 5 †

In Exercises 31–40, find the sum of each arithmetic sequence.

31. $1 + 2 + 3 + \cdots + 50$ 1275

32. $2 + 4 + 6 + \cdots + 102$ 2652

33. $1 + 3 + 5 + \cdots + 99$ 2500

34. $5 + 10 + 15 + \cdots + 200$ 4100

35. $3 + 6 + 9 + \cdots + 300$ 15,150

36. $4 + 7 + 10 + \cdots + 301$ 15,250

37. $2 - 1 - 4 - \cdots - 34$ -208

38. $-3 - 8 - 13 - \cdots - 48$ -255

39. $\frac{1}{3} + 1 + \frac{5}{3} + \cdots + 7$ $\frac{121}{3}$

40. $\frac{3}{5} + 2 + \frac{17}{5} + \cdots + \frac{101}{5}$ 156

†Due to space constrictions, answers to these exercises may be found in the Answers beginning on page A–1 in the back of the book.

In Exercises 41–46, find the sum of the first n terms of the given arithmetic sequence.

41. $2, 7, 12, \ldots; n = 50$ 6225

42. $8, 10, 12, \ldots; n = 40$ 1880

43. $-15, -11, -7, \ldots; n = 20$ 460

44. $-20, -13, -6, \ldots; n = 25$ 1600

45. $3.5, 3.7, 3.9, \ldots; n = 100$ 1340

46. $-7, -6.5, -6, \ldots; n = 80$ 1020

B Exercises   Applying the Concepts

In Exercises 47–53 assume that the indicated sequence is arithmetic.

47. **Orange picking.** When Eric started work as an orange picker, he picked 10 oranges in the first minute, 12 in the second minute, 14 in the third minute, and so on. How many oranges did Eric pick in the first half hour? 1170

48. **Exercise.** Walking up a steep hill, Jan walks 60 feet in the first minute, 57 feet in the second minute, 54 feet in the third minute and so on.
  a. How far will Jan walk in the nth minute? $63 - 3n$ ft
  b. How far will Jan walk in the first 15 minutes? 585 ft

49. **Contest winner.** A contest winner will receive money each month for three years. The winner receives 50 dollars the first month, 75 dollars the second month, 100 dollars the third month, and so on. How much money will the winner have collected after 30 months? $12,375

50. **Salary.** Darren took a 12-month temporary job with a monthly salary that increased a fixed amount each month. He can't recall the starting salary, but does remember that he was paid 820 dollars at the end of the third month and 910 dollars for his last month's work. How much was Darren's total pay for the entire 12 months? $10,260

51. **Hourly wage.** Antonio's new weekend job started him with an hourly wage of 12 dollars and 75 cents. He is guaranteed a raise of 25 cents an hour every three months for the next four years. What will Antonio's hourly wage be at the end of four years? $16.75

52. **Competing job offers.** Denzel is considering offers from two companies. A marketing company pays 32,500 dollars the first year and guarantees a raise of 1300 dollars each year; an exporting company pays 36,000 dollars the first year, with a guaranteed raise of 400 dollars each year. Over a five-year period, which company will pay more? How much more? The exporting company pays $8500 more.

53. **Theater seating.** A theater has 25 rows of seats. The first row has 20 seats, the second row 22 seats, the third row 24 seats, and so on. How many seats are there in the theater? 1100

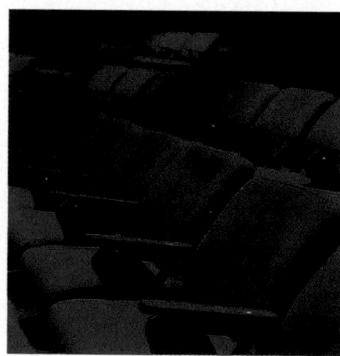

54. **Bricks in a driveway.** A brick driveway has 50 rows of bricks. The first row has 16 bricks and the 50th row has 65 bricks. Assuming that the sequence of numbers giving the number of bricks in rows 1 through 50 is arithmetic, how many bricks does the driveway contain? 2025

55. **Stacked logs.** A stack of logs has 28 rows. The bottom row has 40 logs and the top row has 8 logs. Assuming the sequence of numbers that gives the number of logs in succeeding rows is arithmetic, how many logs does the stack contain? 672

C Exercises   Beyond the Basics

56. Elena wanted to teach her young daughter Sophia about saving. She gave Sophia 10 cents the first day, and an additional 5 cents per day on each subsequent day. After a while, Sophia counted her money and found that she had saved a total of 3 dollars and 25 cents. How many days had she been saving? 10

57. Only 3 customers showed up for the opening day of a flea market. However, 9 came the second day, and an additional 6 customers came on each subsequent day. After several days, there was a total of 192 customers. How many days had the flea market been open? 8

58. Find the sum of all the natural numbers between 45 and 100 that are divisible by 3. 1368

59. Find the sum of all the natural numbers between 26 and 120 that are divisible by 7. 1029

60. A sequence is **harmonic** if the reciprocals of the terms of the sequence form an arithmetic sequence. Is the sequence $\dfrac{1}{2}, \dfrac{3}{5}, \dfrac{3}{4}, 1, \ldots$ harmonic? Explain your reasoning.

61. Consider the harmonic sequence $\dfrac{2}{5}, \dfrac{2}{7}, \dfrac{2}{9}, \ldots$
   a. Find the fourth term.
   b. Find the nth term.

Answers:

60. Yes, it is harmonic, because the reciprocals form an arithmetic sequence.

61. a. $\dfrac{2}{11}$ **b.** $\dfrac{2}{2n + 3}$

62. Show that if the numbers a, m, b are consecutive terms in an arithmetic sequence, then $m = \dfrac{a + b}{2}$. We call m the **arithmetic mean** of a and b.

63. If the numbers $a, m_1, m_2, \ldots, m_k, b$ form an arithmetic sequence, we say that the numbers $m_1, m_2, \ldots, m_k$ are k **arithmetic means** between a and b. Insert k arithmetic means between 1 and 30 so that the sum of the resulting series is 465. $k = 28, d = 1$

Critical Thinking

64. Find the nth term of an arithmetic sequence whose first term is 10 and whose 21st term is 0.

65. If a_1 and d are the first term and common difference, respectively, of an arithmetic sequence, find the first term and difference of an arithmetic sequence whose terms are the negatives of the terms in the given sequence.

66. How many terms are there in the series $\displaystyle\sum_{i=22}^{100} 17i^3$? 79

67. The sum of the first n counting numbers is 12,403. Find the value of n. $n = 157$

Answers:

64. $a_n = \dfrac{21 - n}{2}$ **65.** First term: $-a_1$; difference: $-d$

BEFORE STARTING THIS SECTION, REVIEW

1. The general term of a sequence (Section 11.1, page 932)
2. Partial sums (Section 11.1, page 940)

OBJECTIVES

1 Identify a geometric sequence and find its common ratio.

2 Find the sum of a finite geometric sequence.

3 Solve annuity problems.

4 Find the sum of an infinite geometric sequence.

Spreading the Wealth

Cities across the nation compete to host a Super Bowl. Cities across the world compete to host the Olympic Games. What is the incentive? The *multiplier effect* is virtually always listed among the benefits for hosting one of these events. The effect refers to the phenomonon that occurs when money spent directly on an event has a ripple effect on the economy that is many times the amount spent directly on the event.

Suppose, for example, that 10 million dollars is spent directly by tourists for hotels, meals, tickets, cabs, and so on. Some portion of that amount will be respent by its recipients on groceries, clothes, gas, and so on.

This process is repeated over and over, affecting the economy much more than the initial 10 million dollars spent. Under certain assumptions, the spending just described results in an *infinite geometric series*, whose sum is called the *multiplier*. Example 8 illustrates this effect. ■

1 Identify a geometric sequence and find its common ratio.

When the *ratio* of any two consecutive terms of a sequence is always the same number, the sequence is called a *geometric sequence*. In other words, the sequence $a_1, a_2, a_3, a_4, \ldots$ is a geometric sequence if

$$\frac{a_2}{a_1} = \frac{a_3}{a_2} = \frac{a_4}{a_3} = \cdots.$$

DEFINITION OF GEOMETRIC SEQUENCE

The sequence

$$a_1, a_2, a_3, a_4, \ldots, a_n, \ldots$$

is a **geometric sequence,** or a **geometric progression,** if there is a number r such that each term except the first in the sequence is obtained by multiplying the previous term by r. The number r is called the **common ratio** of the geometric sequence.

We have

$$\frac{a_{n+1}}{a_n} = r, \quad n \geq 1.$$

EXAMPLE 1   Finding the Common Ratio

Find the common ratio for each geometric sequence.

a. $2, 10, 50, 250, 1250, \ldots$ **b.** $-162, -54, -18, -6, -2, \ldots$

Solution

a. The common ratio is $\dfrac{10}{2} = 5 \left(\text{or } \dfrac{50}{10}, \text{ or } \dfrac{250}{50}, \text{ or } \dfrac{1250}{250} \right)$.

b. The common ratio is $\dfrac{-54}{-162} = \dfrac{1}{3} \left(\text{or } \dfrac{-18}{-54}, \text{ or } \dfrac{-6}{-18}, \text{ or } \dfrac{-2}{-6} \right)$.   ■ ■ ■

PRACTICE PROBLEM 1   Find the common ratio for the geometric sequence $6, 18, 54, 162, 486, \ldots$ ■

A geometric sequence can be completely specified by giving the first term a_1 and the common ratio r. Suppose, for example, that we are told that the sequence $a_1, a_2, a_3, a_4, \ldots$ is geometric and that $a_1 = 3$ and $r = 4$. Then we can find a_2:

$$\frac{a_2}{a_1} = 4, \text{ so } a_2 = 4a_1 = 4 \cdot 3 = 12.$$

Now we continue:

$$\frac{a_3}{a_2} = 4, \text{ so } a_3 = 4a_2 = 4 \cdot 12 = 48,$$

$$\frac{a_4}{a_3} = 4, \text{ so } a_4 = 4a_3 = 4 \cdot 48 = 192, \text{ and so on.}$$

By rewriting $\dfrac{a_{n+1}}{a_n} = r$ as $a_{n+1} = ra_n$, we have a recursive definition of a geometric sequence.

RECURSIVE DEFINITION OF A GEOMETRIC SEQUENCE

A geometric sequence $a_1, a_2, a_3, a_4, \ldots, a_n, \ldots$ can be defined recursively. The recursive formula

$$a_{n+1} = ra_n, \quad n \geq 1$$

defines a geometric sequence with the first term a_1 and the common ratio r.

EXAMPLE 2   Determining Whether a Sequence Is Geometric

Determine whether each sequence is geometric. If it is, find the first term and the common ratio.

a. $a_n = 4^n$ **b.** $b_n = \dfrac{3}{2^n}$ **c.** $c_n = 1 - 5^n$

Solution

a. The first four terms and the nth term of the sequence a_n are

$$4, 16, 64, 256, \ldots, 4^n, \ldots.$$

We see that $\dfrac{16}{4} = 4, \dfrac{64}{16} = 4$, and $\dfrac{256}{64} = 4$. The sequence appears to be geometric, with $a_1 = 4$ and $r = 4$. To verify this, we check that $\dfrac{a_{n+1}}{a_n} = 4$ for all $n \geq 1$.

Continued on next page.

Since $a_n = 4^n$,

$$a_{n+1} = 4^{n+1} \qquad \text{Replace } n \text{ by } n+1 \text{ in the general term, } a_n.$$

$$\frac{a_{n+1}}{a_n} = \frac{4^{n+1}}{4^n} = 4. \qquad \frac{4^{n+1}}{4^n} = \frac{4^n 4}{4^n} = 4$$

Consequently, $\dfrac{a_{n+1}}{a_n} = 4$ for all $n \geq 1$, and the sequence is geometric.

b. The first four terms of the sequence b_n are

$$\frac{3}{2}, \frac{3}{4}, \frac{3}{8}, \frac{3}{16},$$

and the nth term is $\dfrac{3}{2^n}$.

We see that $\dfrac{3}{4} \div \dfrac{3}{2} = \dfrac{1}{2}, \dfrac{3}{8} \div \dfrac{3}{4} = \dfrac{1}{2}$, and $\dfrac{3}{16} \div \dfrac{3}{8} = \dfrac{1}{2}$. The sequence appears to be geometric, with $b_1 = \dfrac{3}{2}$ and $r = \dfrac{1}{2}$. To verify this, we check that $\dfrac{b_{n+1}}{b_n} = \dfrac{1}{2}$ for all $n \geq 1$.

Since $b_n = \dfrac{3}{2^n}$,

$$b_{n+1} = \frac{3}{2^{n+1}} \qquad \text{Replace } n \text{ by } n+1 \text{ in the general term } b_n.$$

$$\frac{b_{n+1}}{b_n} = \frac{3}{2^{n+1}} \div \frac{3}{2^n} \qquad \frac{b_{n+1}}{b_n} = b_{n+1} \div b_n$$

$$= \frac{3}{2^{n+1}} \cdot \frac{2^n}{3} = \frac{1}{2}$$

Consequently, $\dfrac{b_{n+1}}{b_n} = \dfrac{1}{2}$ for all $n \geq 1$, and the sequence is geometric.

c. The first four terms of the sequence c_n are

$$-4, -24, -124, -624,$$

and the nth term is $1 - 5^n$. This is *not* a geometric sequence, because not all pairs of consecutive terms have identical quotients. The quotient of the first two terms is $\dfrac{-24}{-4} = 6$, but the quotient of the third and second terms is $\dfrac{-124}{-24} = \dfrac{31}{6}$. ■ ■ ■

PRACTICE PROBLEM 2   Determine whether the sequence $a_n = \left(\dfrac{3}{2}\right)^n$ is geometric. If so, find the first term and the common ratio.   ■

From the equation $a_{n+1} = a_n r$ used in the recursive definition of a geometric sequence, we see that each term after the first is obtained by multiplying the preceding term by the common ratio r.

THE GENERAL TERM OF A GEOMETRIC SEQUENCE

Every geometric sequence can be written in the form

$$a_1, a_1r, a_1r^2, a_1r^3, \ldots, a_1r^{n-1}, \ldots,$$

where r is the common ratio. Since $a_1 = a_1(1) = a_1r^0$, the **nth term of the geometric sequence** is

$$a_n = a_1r^{n-1}, \text{ for } n \geq 1.$$

EXAMPLE 3 **Finding Terms in a Geometric Sequence**

For the geometric sequence $1, 3, 9, 27, \ldots$, find each of the following:

a. a_1 **b.** r **c.** a_n

Solution

a. The first term of the sequence is given: $a_1 = 1$.

b. Since we are told the sequence is geometric, we can take the ratio of any two consecutive terms. Using the ratio of the first two terms, we have

$$r = \frac{3}{1} = 3.$$

c. $a_n = a_1r^{n-1}$ Formula for the nth term
   $= (1)(3^{n-1})$ Replace a_1 by 1 and r by 3.
   $= 3^{n-1}$ ■ ■ ■

PRACTICE PROBLEM 3   For the geometric sequence $2, \dfrac{6}{5}, \dfrac{18}{25}, \dfrac{54}{125}, \ldots$, find:

a. a_1 **b.** r **c.** a_n ■

Notice in Example 3 that converting $a_n = 3^{n-1}$ to standard function notation gives us $f(n) = 3^{n-1}$, an exponential function. A geometric sequence with first term a_1 and common ratio r can be viewed as an exponential function $f(n) = a_1r^{n-1}$ with the set of natural numbers as its domain.

EXAMPLE 4 **Finding a Particular Term in a Geometric Sequence**

Find the 23rd term of a geometric sequence whose first term is 10 and whose common ratio is 1.2.

Solution

$$a_n = a_1r^{n-1} \qquad \text{Formula for the } n\text{th term}$$
$$a_{23} = 10(1.2)^{23-1} \qquad \text{Replace } n \text{ by 23, } a_1 \text{ by 10, and } r \text{ by 1.2.}$$
$$= 10(1.2)^{22}$$
$$\approx 552.06 \qquad \text{Use a calculator.} \qquad\qquad ■ ■ ■$$

PRACTICE PROBLEM 4   Find the 18th term of a geometric sequence whose first term is 7 and whose common ratio is 1.5.   ■

<table>
<tr><td>**2** Find the sum of a finite geometric sequence.</td></tr>
</table>

Finding the Sum of a Finite Geometric Sequence

As with arithmetic sequences, it is useful to find a formula for the sum S_n of the first n terms in a geometric sequence.

$$S_n = a_1 + a_1r + a_1r^2 + a_1r^3 + \cdots + a_1r^{n-1} \qquad \text{Definition of } S_n$$

$$rS_n = a_1r + a_1r^2 + a_1r^3 + a_1r^4 + \cdots + a_1r^n \qquad \text{Multiply both sides by } r.$$

$$S_n - rS_n = a_1 - a_1r^n \qquad \text{Subtract the second equation from the first.}$$

$$(1 - r)S_n = a_1(1 - r^n) \qquad \text{Factor both sides.}$$

$$S_n = \frac{a_1(1 - r^n)}{1 - r}, r \neq 1 \qquad \text{Divide both sides by } 1 - r.$$

SUM OF THE TERMS OF A FINITE GEOMETRIC SEQUENCE

Let $a_1, a_2, a_3, \ldots, a_n$ be the first n terms of a geometric sequence with first term a_1 and common ratio r. The sum S_n of these terms is

$$S_n = \sum_{i=1}^{n} a_1 r^{i-1} = \frac{a_1(1 - r^n)}{1 - r}, r \neq 1.$$

A geometric sequence with $r = 1$ is a sequence in which all terms are identical; that is, $a_n = a_1(1)^{n-1} = a_1$. Consequently, the sum of the first n term, S_n, is

$$\underbrace{a_1 + a_1 + \cdots + a_1}_{n \text{ terms}} = na_1.$$

EXAMPLE 5 **Finding the Sum of Terms of a Finite Geometric Sequence**

Find each sum **a.** $\displaystyle\sum_{i=1}^{15} 5(0.7)^{i-1}$. **b.** $\displaystyle\sum_{i=1}^{15} 5(0.7)^{i}$

Solution

a. We can evaluate $\displaystyle\sum_{i=1}^{15} 5(0.7)^{i-1}$ by using the formula for $S_n = \displaystyle\sum_{i=1}^{n} a_1 r^{i-1}$, where $a_1 = 5$ and $r = 0.7$, and $n = 15$.

$$S_{15} = \sum_{i=1}^{15} a_1 r^{i-1} = 5\left[\frac{1 - (0.7)^{15}}{1 - 0.7}\right] \qquad \text{Replace } a_1 \text{ by } 5, r = 0.7, \text{ and } n = 15.$$

$$\approx 16.588 \qquad \text{Use a calculator.}$$

b. $\displaystyle\sum_{i=1}^{15} 5(0.7)^{i} = (0.7)\sum_{i=1}^{15} 5(0.7)^{i-1} \qquad \text{Factor out } 0.7 \text{ from each term.}$

$$\approx (0.7)(16.588) \qquad \text{From part a}$$

$$= 11.6116$$

■ ■ ■

PRACTICE PROBLEM 5   Find the sum $\sum_{i=1}^{17} 3(0.4)^i$.   ■

---

3 Solve annuity problems.

Annuities

One of the most important applications of finite geometric series is the computation of the value of an *annuity*. An **annuity** is a sequence of equal periodic payments. When a fixed rate of compound interest applies to all payments, the sum of all the payments made, plus all interest, can be found by using the formula for the sum of a finite geometric sequence. The **value of an annuity** (also called the **future value of an annuity**) is the sum of all payments and interest. To develop a formula for the value of an annuity, we suppose P dollars is deposited at the end of each year at an annual interest rate i compounded annually.

The compound interest formula $A = P(1 + i)^t$ gives the total value after t years when P dollars earns an annual interest rate i (in decimal form) compounded once a year. At the end of the first year, the initial payment of P dollars is made, and the annuity's value is P dollars. At the end of the second year, P dollars is again deposited. At this time, the first deposit has earned interest during the second year. The value of the annuity after two years is

$$P \quad + \quad P(1 + i).$$

Payment made at the end of year 2   First payment, plus interest earned for one year

The value of the annuity after three years is

$$P \quad + P(1 + i) \quad + P(1 + i)^2$$

Payment made at the end of year 3   Second payment, plus interest earned for one year   First payment, plus interest earned for two years

The value of the annuity after t years is

$$P + P(1 + i) + P(1 + i)^2 + P(1 + i)^3 + \cdots + P(1 + i)^{t-1}.$$

Payment made at end of year t First payment, plus interest earned for $t - 1$ years

The value of the annuity after t years is the sum of a geometric sequence with first term $a_1 = P$ and common ratio $r = 1 + i$. We compute this sum A as

$$A = S_n = \frac{a_1(1 - r^n)}{1 - r} \qquad \text{Formula for } S_n$$

$$A = \frac{P[1 - (1 + i)^t]}{1 - (1 + i)} \qquad \text{Replace } n \text{ by } t, a_1 \text{ by } P, \text{ and } r \text{ by } 1 + i.$$

$$= \frac{P[1 - (1 + i)^t]}{-i} \qquad \text{Simplify.}$$

$$= P\frac{[(1 + i)^t - 1]}{i}. \qquad \text{Multiply numerator and denominator by } -1.$$

RECALL

The sum S_n of the first n terms of a geometric sequence with first term a_1 and common ratio r is given by the formula

$$S_n = \frac{a_1(1 - r^n)}{1 - r}.$$

If interest is compounded n times per year and equal payments are made at the end of each compounding period, we adjust the formula as we did in Section 4.2 to account for the more frequent compounding.

VALUE OF AN ANNUITY

Let P represent the payment in dollars made at the end of each of n compounding periods per year, and let i be the annual interest rate. Then the value A of the annuity after t years is:

$$A = P\frac{\left(1 + \dfrac{i}{n}\right)^{nt} - 1}{\dfrac{i}{n}}$$

EXAMPLE 6   **Finding the Value of an Annuity**

An individual retirement account (IRA) is a common way to save money to provide funds after retirement. Suppose you make payments of 1200 dollars into an IRA at the end of each year at an annual interest rate of 4.5% per year, compounded annually. What is the value of this annuity after 35 years?

Solution

Each annuity payment is $P = \$1200$. The annual interest rate is 4.5%, so $i = 0.045$, and the number of years is $t = 35$. Since interest is compounded annually, $n = 1$. The value of the annuity is then

$$A = 1200\left[\frac{\left(1 + \dfrac{0.045}{1}\right)^{(1)35} - 1}{\dfrac{0.045}{1}}\right].$$

$$= \$97,795.94. \qquad\qquad \text{Use a calculator.}$$

The value of the IRA after 35 years is 97,795 dollars and 94 cents.   ■ ■ ■

PRACTICE PROBLEM 6   If, in Example 6, the end-of-year payments are $1500, the annual interest rate remains 4.5%, compounded annually, and the payments are made for 30 years, what is the value of the annuity?   ■

4 Find the sum of an infinite geometric sequence.

Infinite Geometric Series

The sum S_n of the first n terms of a geometric series is given by the formula $S_n = \dfrac{a_1(1 - r^n)}{1 - r}$.

If this finite sum S_n approaches a number S as $n \to \infty$ (that is, as n gets larger and larger), we say that S is the **sum of the infinite geometric series,** and we write

$$S = \sum_{i=1}^{\infty} a_1 r^{i-1}.$$

If r is any real number with $-1 < r < 1$ (equivalently, $|r| < 1$), then the value of r^n, like the value of $\left(\dfrac{1}{2}\right)^n$, gets closer and closer to 0 as n gets larger and larger. We indicate that the values of r^n approach 0 by writing

$$\lim_{n \to \infty} r^n = 0 \text{ if } |r| < 1.$$

The expression $\lim\limits_{n \to \infty} r^n$ is read "the limit, as n approaches infinity, of r to the n" or "the limit, as n approaches infinity, of r to the nth power."

When $|r| < 1$,

$$S_n = \frac{a_1(1 - r^n)}{1 - r} \to \frac{a_1(1 - 0)}{1 - r} = \frac{a_1}{1 - r} \quad \text{as } n \to \infty.$$

We state this relationship formally.

SUM OF THE TERMS OF AN INFINITE GEOMETRIC SEQUENCE

If $|r| < 1$, the infinite sum

$$a_1 + a_1 r + a_1 r^2 + a_1 r^3 + \cdots + a_1 r^{n-1} + \cdots$$

is given by

$$S = \sum_{i=1}^{\infty} a_1 r^{i-1} = \frac{a_1}{1 - r}.$$

When $|r| \geq 1$, the infinite geometric series does not have a sum. This is because the value of r^n does not approach 0 as $n \to \infty$. For example, if $r = 2$, we have

$$2^1 = 2, 2^2 = 4, 2^3 = 8, 2^4 = 16, 2^5 = 32, 2^6 = 64, \ldots.$$

EXAMPLE 7   **Finding the Sum of an Infinite Geometric Series**

Find the sum $2 + \dfrac{3}{2} + \dfrac{9}{8} + \dfrac{27}{32} + \cdots$.

Solution

The first term $a_1 = 2$, and the common ratio

$$r = \frac{\dfrac{3}{2}}{2} = \frac{3}{4}.$$

Since $|r| = \dfrac{3}{4} < 1$, we can use the formula for the sum of an infinite geometric series.

$$S = \frac{a_1}{1 - r} \qquad \text{Formula for } S$$

$$= \frac{2}{1 - \dfrac{3}{4}} \qquad \text{Replace } a_1 \text{ by 2 and } r \text{ by } \dfrac{3}{4}.$$

$$= 8 \qquad \text{Simplify.} \qquad\qquad ■ ■ ■$$

PRACTICE PROBLEM 7   Find the sum $3 + \dfrac{6}{3} + \dfrac{12}{9} + \dfrac{24}{27} + \cdots$.   ■

EXAMPLE 8   **Calculating the Multiplier Effect**

The host city for the Super Bowl expects that 10,000,000 dollars will be spent by tourists. Assume that 80% of this money is spent again in the city, and then 80% of this second round of spending is spent again, and so on. In the introduction to this section, we said that such a spending pattern results in a geometric series whose sum is called the *multiplier*. Find this series and its sum.

Solution

We start our series with the 10,000,000 dollars brought into the city and add the subsequent amounts spent.

$$10,000,000 + 10,000,000\,(0.80) + 10,000,000\,(0.80)^2 + 10,000,000\,(0.80)^3 + \cdots$$

| original 10,000,000 | 80% of 10,000,000 | 80% of previous amount | 80% of previous amount |

Using the formula $\displaystyle\sum_{i=1}^{\infty} ar^{i-1} = \dfrac{a}{1-r}$ for the sum of an infinite geometric series, we have

$$\sum_{i=1}^{\infty} (10,000,000)(0.80)^{i-1} = \frac{\$10,000,000}{1 - 0.80} = \$50,000,000.$$

This amount should shed some light on why there is so much competition to serve as the host city for a major sports event.   ■ ■ ■

PRACTICE PROBLEM 8   Find the series and the sum that results in Example 8 if 85%, rather than 80%, occurs in the repeated spending.   ■

A Exercises   Basic Skills and Concepts

In Exercises 1–20, determine whether each sequence is geometric. If it is, find the first term and the common ratio.

1. 3, 6, 12, 24, ... †

2. 2, 4, 8, 16, . . . †

3. 1, 5, 10, 20, . . . †

4. 1, 1, 3, 3, 9, 9, . . . †

5. 1, −3, 9, −27, . . . †

6. −1, 2, −4, 8, . . . †

7. 7, −7, 7, −7, . . . †

8. 1, −2, 4, −8, . . . †

9. $9, 3, 1, \dfrac{1}{3}, \ldots$ †

10. $5, 2, \dfrac{4}{5}, \dfrac{8}{25}, \ldots$ †

11. $a_n = \left(-\dfrac{1}{2}\right)^n$ †

12. $a_n = 5\left(\dfrac{2}{3}\right)^n$ †

13. $a_n = 2^{n-1}$ †

14. $a_n = -(1.06)^{n-1}$ †

15. $a_n = 7n^2 + 1$ †

16. $a_n = 1 - (2n)^2$ †

17. $a_n = 3^{-n}$ †

18. $a_n = 50(0.1)^{-n}$ †

19. $a_n = 5^{\frac{n}{2}}$ †

20. $a_n = 7^{\sqrt{n}}$ †

---

†Due to space constrictions, answers to these exercises may be found in the Answers beginning on page A–1 in the back of the book.

In Exercises 21–28, find the first term a_1, the common ratio r, and the nth term a_n for each geometric sequence.

21. 2, 10, 50, 250, . . . †

22. $-3, -6, -12, -24, \ldots$ †

23. $5, \dfrac{10}{3}, \dfrac{20}{9}, \dfrac{40}{27}, \ldots$ †

24. $1, \sqrt{3}, 3, 3\sqrt{3}, \ldots$ †

25. 0.2, −0.6, 1.8, −5.4, . . . †

26. 1.3, −0.26, 0.052, −0.0104, . . . †

27. $\pi^4, \pi^6, \pi^8, \pi^{10}, \ldots$ †

28. $e^2, 1, e^{-2}, e^{-4}, \ldots$ †

In Exercises 29–38, find the indicated term of each geometric sequence.

29. a_7 when $a_1 = 5$ and $r = 2$ $a_7 = 320$

30. a_7 when $a_1 = 8$ and $r = 3$ $a_7 = 5832$

31. a_{10} when $a_1 = 3$ and $r = -2$ $a_{10} = -1536$

32. a_{10} when $a_1 = 7$ and $r = -2$ $a_{10} = -3584$

33. a_6 when $a_1 = \dfrac{1}{16}$ and $r = 3$ $a_6 = \dfrac{243}{16}$

34. a_6 when $a_1 = \dfrac{1}{81}$ and $r = 3$ $a_6 = 3$

35. a_9 when $a_1 = -1$ and $r = \dfrac{5}{2}$ $a_9 = -\dfrac{390,625}{256}$

36. a_9 when $a_1 = -4$ and $r = \dfrac{3}{4}$ $a_9 = -\dfrac{6561}{16,384}$

37. a_{20} when $a_1 = 500$ and $r = -\dfrac{1}{2}$ $a_{20} = -\dfrac{125}{131,072}$

38. a_{20} when $a_1 = 1000$ and $r = -\dfrac{1}{10}$ $a_{20} = -\dfrac{1}{10^{16}}$

In Exercises 39–44, find the sum S_n of the first n terms of each geometric sequence.

39. $\dfrac{1}{10}, \dfrac{1}{2}, \dfrac{5}{2}, \dfrac{25}{2}, \ldots; n = 10$ †

40. $6, 2, \dfrac{2}{3}, \dfrac{2}{9}, \ldots; n = 10$ †

41. $\dfrac{1}{25}, -\dfrac{1}{5}, 1, -5, \ldots; n = 12$ $S_{12} = -\dfrac{40,690,104}{25}$

42. $-10, \dfrac{1}{10}, \dfrac{-1}{1000}, \dfrac{1}{100,000}, \ldots; n = 12$ $S_{12} = -\dfrac{10^{24} - 1}{(101)(10)^{21}}$

43. $5, \dfrac{5}{4}, \dfrac{5}{4^2}, \dfrac{5}{4^3}, \ldots; n = 8$ $S_8 = \dfrac{109,225}{16,384}$

44. $2, \dfrac{2}{5}, \dfrac{2}{5^2}, \dfrac{2}{5^3}, \ldots; n = 8$ $S_8 = \dfrac{195,312}{78,125}$

In Exercises 45–52, find each sum.

45. $\displaystyle\sum_{i=1}^{5} \left(\dfrac{1}{2}\right)^{i-1}$ $\dfrac{31}{16}$

46. $\displaystyle\sum_{i=1}^{5} \left(\dfrac{1}{5}\right)^{i-1}$ $\dfrac{781}{625}$

47. $\displaystyle\sum_{i=1}^{8} 3\left(\dfrac{2}{3}\right)^{i-1}$ $\dfrac{6305}{729}$

48. $\displaystyle\sum_{i=1}^{8} 2\left(\dfrac{3}{5}\right)^{i-1}$ $\dfrac{384,064}{78,125}$

49. $\displaystyle\sum_{i=3}^{10} \dfrac{2^{i-1}}{4}$ 255

50. $\displaystyle\sum_{i=3}^{10} \dfrac{5^{i-1}}{2}$ $1,220,700$

51. $\displaystyle\sum_{i=1}^{20} \left(-\dfrac{3}{5}\right)\left(-\dfrac{5}{2}\right)^{i-1}$ $\dfrac{3(5^{20} - 2^{20})}{35(2)^{19}}$

52. $\displaystyle\sum_{i=1}^{20} \left(-\dfrac{1}{4}\right)(3^{2-i})$ $-\dfrac{3^{20} - 1}{8(3)^{18}}$

In Exercises 53–62, find each sum.

53. $\dfrac{1}{3} + \dfrac{1}{9} + \dfrac{1}{27} + \dfrac{1}{81} + \cdots$ $\dfrac{1}{2}$

54. $\dfrac{5}{2} + \dfrac{5}{4} + \dfrac{5}{8} + \dfrac{5}{16} + \cdots$ 5

55. $-\dfrac{1}{2} + \dfrac{1}{4} - \dfrac{1}{8} + \dfrac{1}{16} - \cdots$ $-\dfrac{1}{3}$

56. $-\dfrac{3}{2} + \dfrac{3}{4} - \dfrac{3}{8} + \dfrac{3}{16} + \cdots$ -1

57. $8 - 2 + \dfrac{1}{2} - \dfrac{1}{8} + \cdots$ $\dfrac{32}{5}$

58. $1 - \dfrac{3}{5} + \dfrac{9}{25} - \dfrac{27}{125} + \cdots$ $\dfrac{5}{8}$

59. $\displaystyle\sum_{n=0}^{\infty} 5\left(\dfrac{1}{3}\right)^n$ $\dfrac{15}{2}$

60. $\displaystyle\sum_{n=0}^{\infty} 3\left(\dfrac{1}{4}\right)^n$ 4

61. $\displaystyle\sum_{n=0}^{\infty} \left(-\dfrac{1}{4}\right)^n$ $\dfrac{4}{5}$

62. $\displaystyle\sum_{n=0}^{\infty} \left(-\dfrac{1}{3}\right)^n$ $\dfrac{3}{4}$

B Exercises **Applying the Concepts**

63. Population growth. The population in a small town is increasing at the rate of 3% per year. If the present population is 20,000, what will the population be at the end of five years? 23,185

64. Growth of a zoo collection. The butterfly collection at a local zoo started with only 25 butterflies. If the number of butterflies doubled each month, how many butterflies were in the collection after 12 months? 102,375

65. Savings growth. Ramón deposits 100 dollars on the last day of each month into a savings account that pays 6% annually, compounded monthly. What is the balance in the account after 36 compounding periods? $3933.61

66. Savings growth. Kat deposits 300 dollars semiannually into a savings account for her son. If the account pays 8% annually, compounded semiannually, what is the balance in the account after 20 compounding periods? $8,933.42

67. Ancestors. Every person has two parents, four grandparents, eight great-grandparents, and so on. Find the number of ancestors a person has in the tenth generation back. 1024

68. Bacterial growth. A colony of bacteria doubles in number every day. If there are 1000 bacteria now,
a. how many will there be in seven days? $1000(2^7 - 1)$
b. in n days? $1000(2^n - 1)$

69. Investment. An actuarial firm budgets a new position at 36,000 dollars for the first year and a 5% raise each year

thereafter. Find the total compensation a successful applicant for the job would receive over the first 20 years of employment. $1,190,374.35

70. Investment. A realtor offers two choices of payment for a small condominium:
a. Pay 4000 dollars per month for the next 25 months.
b. Pay 1 cent the first month, 2 cents the second month, 4 cents the third month, and so on for 25 months.
Which option, a or b, is the better choice for the buyer? Explain your reasoning. a is better.

71. Pendulum motion. The distance traveled by any point on a certain pendulum is 20% less than in the preceding swing. If the length traveled by the pendulum bob during the first swing is 56.25 centimeters, find the total distance the bob has traveled at the end of the fifth swing. 189.09 cm

72. Depreciating a tractor. Every year a tractor loses 20% of the value it had at the beginning of the year. If the tractor now has a value of 120,000 dollars, what will its value be in five years? $39,321.6

73. Rebounding ball. A particular ball always rebounds $\frac{3}{5}$ the distance it falls. If the ball is dropped from a height of 5 meters, how far will it travel before coming to a stop? 12.5 m

74. Rebounding ball. Repeat Exercise 81 if the ball is dropped from a height of 9 meters. 22.5 m

C Exercises **Beyond the Basics**

75. The accompanying figure shows the first six squares in an infinite sequence of successively smaller squares formed by connecting the midpoints of the sides of the preceding larger square. The area of the largest square is 1. Find the total area of the indicated sections that are shaded in every other square as the number of squares increases to infinity. †

76. The accompanying figure shows the first three equilateral triangles in an infinite sequence of successively smaller equilateral triangles formed by connecting the midpoints of the sides of the preceding larger triangle. The largest triangle has sides of length 4. Find the total perimeter of all the triangles. 24

Figure for Exercise 75.

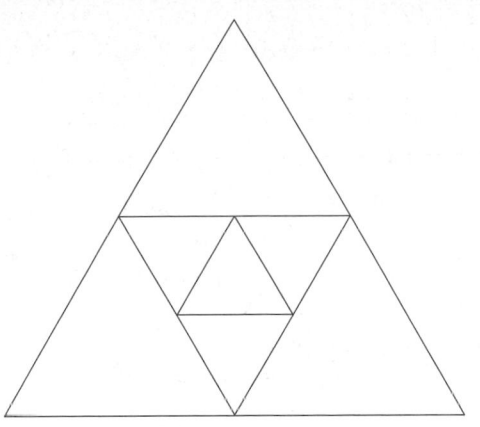

Figure for Exercise 76.

77. Prove that if $a_1, a_2, a_3, \ldots$ is a geometric sequence, then the sequence $\ln a_1, \ln a_2, \ln a_3, \ldots$ is an arithmetic sequence.

78. Prove that if $a_1, a_2, a_3, \ldots$ is a geometric sequence, then $a_1^2, a_2^2, a_3^2, \ldots$ is also a geometric sequence.

79. Show that if $a_1, a_2, a_3, \ldots$ is a geometric sequence with common ratio r, then $\dfrac{1}{a_1}, \dfrac{1}{a_2}, \dfrac{1}{a_3}, \ldots$ is also a geometric sequence, and find its common ratio.

80. Show that if c is any nonzero real number, then

$$c^2, c, 1, \frac{1}{c}, \ldots \text{ is a geometric sequence.}$$

81. Show that if x is any nonzero real number, then

$$x, 2, \frac{4}{x}, \frac{8}{x^2}, \ldots \text{ is a geometric sequence.}$$

82. Show that if a and x are any two nonzero real numbers, then $\dfrac{x}{a}, -1, \dfrac{a}{x}, -\dfrac{a^2}{x^2}, \ldots$ is a geometric sequence.

83. Show that if a, x, and y are any three nonzero real numbers, then $\dfrac{a}{x}, -\dfrac{a}{xy}, \dfrac{a}{xy^2}, \dfrac{-a}{xy^3}, \ldots$ is a geometric sequence.

84. Show that if $a_1, a_2, a_3, \ldots$ is an arithmetic sequence with common difference d, then $2^{a_1}, 2^{a_2}, 2^{a_3}, \ldots$ is a geometric sequence, and find its common ratio.

Critical Thinking

85. If a_n denotes the nth term of an arithmetic sequence with $a_1 = 10$ and $d = 2.7$, and if b_n denotes the nth term of a geometric sequence with $b_1 = 10$ and $r = 2$, which number is larger, a_{1001} or b_{1001}? b_{1001} is larger.

86. If the sum $\dfrac{a(1 - r^n)}{1 - r}$ of the first n terms of a geometric sequence is 1023, find a when $n = 10$ and $r = \dfrac{1}{2}$. $a = 512$

87. Find n and k so that the sum

$$5 + 5 \cdot 2 + 5 \cdot 2^2 + \cdots + 5 \cdot 2^{15} \text{ can be written either as}$$

$$\sum_{i=0}^{n} 5 \cdot 2^i \text{ or as } \sum_{i=1}^{k} 5 \cdot 2^{i-1}. \quad n = 15, k = 16$$

Group Projects

1. The sum of three consecutive terms of a geometric sequence is 35, and their product is 1000. Find the numbers. 5, 10, and 20

[*Hint:* Let $\dfrac{a}{r}$, a, and ar be the three terms of geometric sequence.]

2. The sum of three consecutive terms of an arithmetic sequence is 15. If 1, 4, and 19 are respectively added to the three terms, the resulting numbers form three consecutive terms of a geometric sequence. Find the numbers. †

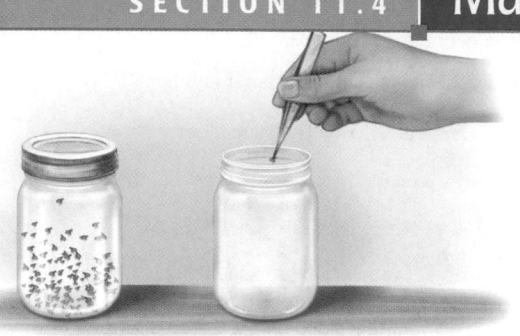

BEFORE STARTING THIS SECTION, REVIEW

1. Natural numbers (Section P.1, page 3)

2. Inequalities (Section P.1, page 5)

3. Exponents (Section P.2, page 19)

4. Series (Section 11.1, page 940)

OBJECTIVE

1 Prove statements by mathematical induction.

Jumping to Conclusions; Good Induction Versus Bad Induction

A scientist had two large jars before him on the laboratory table. The jar on his left contained a hundred fleas; the jar on his right was empty. The scientist carefully lifted a flea from the jar on the left, placed the flea on the table between the two jars, stepped back, and said in a loud voice, "Jump!" The flea jumped and was put into the jar on the right. A second flea was carefully lifted from the jar on the left and placed on the table between the two jars. Again the scientist stepped back and said in a loud voice, "Jump!" The flea jumped and was put into the jar on the right. In the same manner, the scientist treated each of the hundred fleas in the jar on the left, and each flea jumped as ordered. The two jars were then interchanged and the experiment was continued with a slight difference. This time the scientist carefully lifted a flea from the jar on the left, *yanked off its hind legs*, placed the flea on the table between the jars, stepped back and said in a loud voice, "Jump!" The flea did not jump and was put into the jar on the right. A second flea was carefully lifted from the jar on the left, its hind legs yanked off, and then placed on the table between the two jars. Again the scientist stepped back and said in a loud voice, "Jump!" The flea did not jump and was put into the jar on the right. In this manner, the scientist treated each of the hundred fleas in the jar on the left, and in no case did a flea jump when ordered. So the scientist recorded the following inductive statement in his notebook: "A flea, if its hind legs are yanked off, cannot hear." (*Source:* Modified from Howard Eves, *Mathematical Circles.*)

This, of course, is an example of truly bad reasoning. The principle of mathematical induction, demonstrated in Example 2, is the gold standard for reasoning in proving that statements about natural numbers are true. ■

1 Prove statements by mathematical induction.

Suppose your boss wants you to verify that each of a thousand bags contains two specific gold coins. There is only one way to be absolutely sure: You must check every bag. That would take a very long time, but you can eventually finish the job. However, consider the problem of verifying that a statement about the natural numbers, such as

$$1^2 + 2^2 + 3^2 + \cdots + n^2 = \frac{n(n + 1)(2n + 1)}{6}$$

is true for all natural numbers n. Let's first test the statement for several values of n by comparing the value of $1^2 + 2^2 + 3^2 + \cdots + n^2$ in the second column of Table 11.1 with the value of $\dfrac{n(n + 1)(2n + 1)}{6}$ in the third column of Table 11.1.

TABLE 11.1

n	$1^2 + 2^2 + 3^2 + \cdots + n^2$	$\dfrac{n(n + 1)(2n + 1)}{6}$	Equal?
1	$1^2 = 1$	$\dfrac{1(1 + 1)[2(1) + 1]}{6} = 1$	Yes
2	$1^2 + 2^2 = 5$	$\dfrac{2(2 + 1)[2(2) + 1]}{6} = 5$	Yes
3	$1^2 + 2^2 + 3^2 = 14$	$\dfrac{3(3 + 1)[2(3) + 1]}{6} = 14$	Yes
4	$1^2 + 2^2 + 3^2 + 4^2 = 30$	$\dfrac{4(4 + 1)[2(4) + 1]}{6} = 30$	Yes
5	$1^2 + 2^2 + 3^2 + 4^2 + 5^2 = 55$	$\dfrac{5(5 + 1)[2(5) + 1]}{6} = 55$	Yes

We see that the statement is correct for the natural numbers 1, 2, 3, 4, and 5; further, you can continue to verify that the statement is correct for any particular natural number n you try. But is it *always* correct? Clearly, we can't check every natural number!

The principle of *mathematical induction* provides a method for proving that statements about natural numbers are true for *all* natural numbers. The principle is based on the fact that after any natural number n, there is a next-larger natural number $n + 1$ and that any specified natural number can be reached by a finite number of such steps, starting from the natural number 1.

THE PRINCIPLE OF MATHEMATICAL INDUCTION

Let P_n be a statement that involves the natural number n with the following properties:

1. P_1 is true (the statement is true for the natural number 1), and
2. If P_k is a true statement, then P_{k+1} is a true statement.

Then the statement P_n is true for every natural number n.

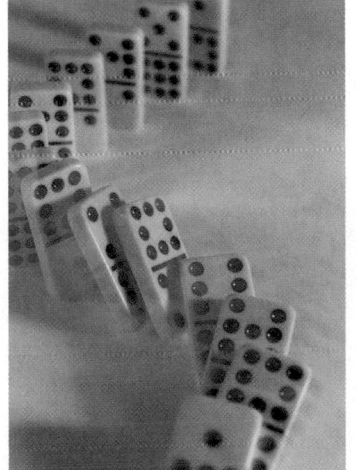

FIGURE 11.3

A common physical interpretation is helpful in understanding why this principle works. Imagine an unending line of dominoes, as shown in Figure 11.3. Suppose the dominoes are arranged so that if *any* domino is knocked down, it will knock down the next domino behind it as well. What will happen if the first domino is knocked down? The answer is that *all* the dominoes will fall. This is because

1. knocking the first domino down causes the second domino to be knocked down, and
2. when the second domino is knocked down, it knocks the third domino down, and so on.

Determining the Statement P_{k+1} from the Statement P_k

In order to successfully use the Principle of Mathematical Induction, you must be able to determine the statement P_{k+1} from a given statement P_k. Suppose the given statement is

$$P_k: k \geq 1;$$

then we have

$$P_{k+1}: k + 1 \geq 1. \qquad \text{Replace } k \text{ by } k + 1 \text{ in } P_k.$$

It is important to recognize that since P_k says "k is greater than or equal to 1," the statement P_{k+1} says "$k + 1$ is greater than or equal to 1." That is, P_{k+1} asserts the same property for $k + 1$ that P_k asserts for k.

EXAMPLE 1 **Determining P_{k+1} from P_k**

Find the statement P_{k+1} from the given statement P_k.

a. $P_k: k < 2^k$ **b.** $P_k: S_k = 3k^2 + 9$ **c.** $P_k: 1 + 2 + 2^2 + 2^3 + \cdots + 2^{k-1} = 2^k - 1$

d. $P_k: 3 + 6 + 9 + 12 + \cdots + 3k = \dfrac{3k(k + 1)}{2}$

Solution

a. $P_k: k < 2^k, \quad P_{k+1}: k + 1 < 2^{k+1}$ \hfill Replace k by $k + 1$.

b. $P_k: S_k = 3k^2 + 9, \quad P_{k+1}: S_{k+1} = 3(k + 1)^2 + 9$ \hfill Replace k by $k + 1$.

c. $P_k: 1 + 2 + 2^2 + 2^3 + \cdots + 2^{k-1} = 2^k - 1$
$P_{k+1}: 1 + 2 + 2^2 + 2^3 + \cdots + 2^{(k+1)-1} = 2^{k+1} - 1$ \hfill Replace k by $k + 1$.

d. $P_k: 3 + 6 + 9 + 12 + \cdots + 3k = \dfrac{3k(k + 1)}{2}$

$P_{k+1}: 3 + 6 + 9 + 12 + \cdots + 3(k + 1) = \dfrac{3(k + 1)[(k + 1) + 1]}{2}$ \hfill Replace k by $k + 1$.

■ ■ ■

PRACTICE PROBLEM 1 Find P_{k+1} for $P_k: (k + 3)^2 > k^2 + 9$. ■

EXAMPLE 2 **Using Mathematical Induction**

Use mathematical induction to prove that, for all natural numbers n,

$$2 + 4 + 6 + \cdots + 2n = n(n + 1).$$

Solution

First we verify that this statement is true for $n = 1$.

Check: $2(1) = 1(1 + 1)$ Replace n by 1 in the original statement.

$2 = 2.$ ✓

The given statement is true for $n = 1$. Thus, the first condition for the principle of mathematical induction holds.

The second condition for the principle of mathematical induction requires two steps.

Step 1   Assume that the formula is true for some unspecified natural number k:

$$P_k: 2 + 4 + 6 + \cdots + 2k = k(k + 1).$$ Assumed true

Step 2   On the basis of the assumption that P_k is true, show that

P_{k+1} is true.

$$P_{k+1}: 2 + 4 + 6 + \cdots + 2(k + 1) = (k + 1)[(k + 1) + 1]$$ Replace k by $k + 1$.

Begin by using P_k, the statement assumed to be true. Add $2(k + 1)$ to both sides of P_k, which again results in a true statement.

$$2 + 4 + 6 + \cdots + 2k = k(k + 1)$$ Assumed true

$$2 + 4 + 6 + \cdots + 2k + 2(k + 1) = k(k + 1) + 2(k + 1)$$ Add $2(k + 1)$ to both sides.

$$2 + 4 + 6 + \cdots + 2k + 2(k + 1) = (k + 1)(k + 2)$$ Factor out the common factor $(k + 1)$ on the right.

> It is not *necessary* to write $2k$ here, because it is understood that $2k$ is the even integer that precedes $2(k + 1)$.

$$2 + 4 + 6 + \cdots + 2(k + 1) = (k + 1)[(k + 1) + 1]$$ Rewrite $(k + 2)$ as $(k + 1) + 1$.

This last equation says that P_{k+1} is true if P_k is assumed to be true. Therefore, by the principle of mathematical induction, the statement

$$2 + 4 + 6 + \cdots + 2n = n(n + 1)$$

is true for every natural number n.   ■ ■ ■

PRACTICE PROBLEM 2   Use mathematical induction to prove that, for all natural numbers n,

$$1 + 2 + 3 + \cdots + n = \frac{n(n + 1)}{2}.$$ ■

EXAMPLE 3   Using Mathematical Induction

Use mathematical induction to prove that

$$2^n > n$$

for all natural numbers n.

Solution

First we show that the given statement is true for $n = 1$.

$$2^1 > 1$$ Replace n by 1 in the original statement.

Continued on next page.

Thus, the inequality is true for $n = 1$.

Next, we assume that, for some unspecified natural number k,

$$P_k: 2^k > k \quad \text{is true.}$$

Then we must use P_k to prove that

$$P_{k+1}: 2^{k+1} > k + 1 \quad \text{is true.}$$

Now, by the product rule of exponents, $2^{k+1} = 2^k \cdot 2^1 = 2^k \cdot 2$, so we can get some information about 2^{k+1} by multiplying both sides of $P_k: 2^k > 2$ by 2.

$2^k > k$	P_k is assumed true.
$2^k \cdot 2 > 2 \cdot k$	Multiply both sides by 2.
$2^{k+1} = 2^k \cdot 2 > 2k = k + k \geq k + 1$	Since $k \geq 1, k + k \geq k + 1$.

Thus, $2^{k+1} > k + 1$ is true.

By the principle of mathematical induction, the statement

$$2^n > n$$

is true for every natural number n.   ▪ ▪ ▪

PRACTICE PROBLEM 3   Use mathematical induction to prove that $3^n > n$ for all natural numbers n.   ▪

A Exercises   Basic Skills and Concepts

In Exercises 1–4, find P_{k+1} from the given statement P_k.

1. $P_k: (k + 1)^2 - 2k = k^2 + 1$ †

2. $P_k: (1 + k)(1 - k) = 1 - k^2$ †

3. $P_k: 2^k > 5k$ $P_{k+1}: 2^{k+1} > 5(k + 1)$

4. $P_k: 1 + 3 + 5 + \cdots + (2k - 1) = k^2$ †

In Exercises 5–28, use mathematical induction to prove that each statement is true for all natural numbers n.

5. $1 + 2 + 3 + \cdots + n = \dfrac{n(n + 1)}{2}$

6. $1 + 3 + 5 + \cdots + (2n - 1) = n^2$

7. $4 + 8 + 12 + \cdots + 4n = 2n(n + 1)$

8. $3 + 6 + 9 + \cdots + 3n = \dfrac{3n(n + 1)}{2}$

9. $1 + 5 + 9 + \cdots + (4n - 3) = n(2n - 1)$

10. $3 + 8 + 13 + \cdots + (5n - 2) = \dfrac{n(5n + 1)}{2}$

11. $3 + 9 + 27 + \cdots + 3^n = \dfrac{3(3^n - 1)}{2}$

12. $5 + 25 + 125 + \cdots + 5^n = \dfrac{5(5^n - 1)}{4}$

13. $\dfrac{1}{1 \cdot 2} + \dfrac{1}{2 \cdot 3} + \dfrac{1}{3 \cdot 4} + \cdots + \dfrac{1}{n(n + 1)} = \dfrac{n}{n + 1}$

14. $\dfrac{1}{2 \cdot 4} + \dfrac{1}{4 \cdot 6} + \dfrac{1}{6 \cdot 8} + \cdots + \dfrac{1}{2n(2n + 2)} = \dfrac{n}{4(n + 1)}$

15. $2 \leq 2^n$ **16.** $2n + 1 \leq 3^n$

17. $n(n + 2) < (n + 1)^2$ **18.** $n \leq n^2$

19. $\dfrac{n!}{n} = (n - 1)!$ **20.** $\dfrac{n!}{(n + 1)!} = \dfrac{1}{n + 1}$

21. $1^2 + 2^2 + 3^2 + \cdots + n^2 = \dfrac{n(n + 1)(2n + 1)}{6}$

22. $1^3 + 2^3 + 3^3 + \cdots + n^3 = \dfrac{n^2(n + 1)^2}{4}$

23. 2 is a factor of $n^2 + n$.   **24.** 2 is a factor of $n^3 + 5n$.

25. 6 is a factor of $n(n + 1)(n + 2)$.

26. 3 is a factor of $n(n + 1)(n - 1)$.

27. $(ab)^n = a^n b^n$ **28.** $\left(\dfrac{a}{b}\right)^n = \dfrac{a^n}{b^n}$

†Due to space constrictions, answers to these exercises may be found in the Answers beginning on page A–1 in the back of the book.

B Exercises   Applying the Concepts

29. Counting hugs. At a family reunion of n people ($n \geq 2$), each person hugs everyone else. Use mathematical induction to show that the number of hugs is $\dfrac{n^2 - n}{2}$.

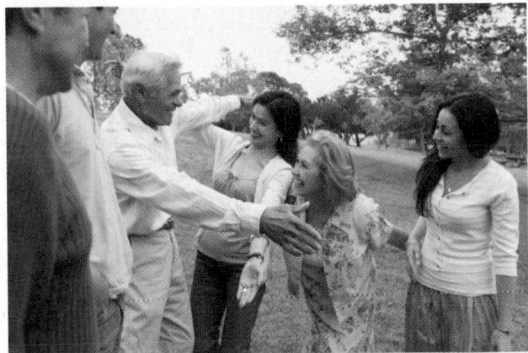

30. Winning prizes. In a contest in which n prizes are possible, a contestant can win any number of the prizes (from 0 to n). Use mathematical induction to show that there are 2^n possible outcomes for the sets of prizes the contestant might win. [*Hint:* If $n = 1$, there are $2(= 2^1)$ outcomes: winning 0 prizes or winning the one prize.]

31. Koch's snowflake. A geometric shape called the Koch snowflake can be formed by starting with an equilateral triangle, as in the figure. Assume each side of the triangle has length 1. On the middle part of each side, construct an equilateral triangle with sides of length $\dfrac{1}{3}$, and erase the side of the smaller triangle that is on the side of the original triangle. Repeat this procedure for each of the smaller triangles. This process produces a figure that resembles a snowflake.

a. Find a formula for the number of sides of the nth figure. Use mathematical induction to prove that this formula is correct. The number of sides of the nth figure is $3(4^{n-1})$.

b. Find a formula for the perimeter of the nth figure. Use mathematical induction to prove that this formula is correct. †

32. Sierpinski's triangle. A geometric figure known as Sierpinski's triangle is constructed by starting with an equilateral triangle as in the figure. Assume that each side of the triangle has length 1. Inside the original triangle, draw a second triangle by connecting the midpoints of the sides of the original triangle. This divides the original triangle into four identical equilateral triangles. Repeat the process by constructing equilateral triangles inside each of the four smaller triangles, again using the midpoints of the sides of the triangle as vertices. Continuing this process with each group of smaller triangles produces Sierpinski's triangle. Coloring each set of smaller triangles helps in following the construction.

a. When a process is repeated over and over, each repetition is called an **iteration.** How many triangles will the fourth iteration have? †

b. How many triangles will the fifth iteration have? †

c. Find a formula for the number of triangles in the nth iteration. Use mathematical induction to prove that this formula is correct. †

33. Towers of Hanoi. Three pegs are attached vertically to a horizontal board, as shown in the figure. One peg has n rings stacked on it, each ring smaller than the one below it. In a game known as the Tower of Hanoi puzzle, all the rings must be moved to a different peg, with only one ring moved at a time, and no ring can be moved on top of a smaller ring. Determine the least number of moves that will accomplish this transfer. Use mathematical induction to prove that your answer is correct. †

34. Exam answer sheets. An exam in which each question is answered with either "True" or "False" has n questions.

   a. If every question is answered, how many answer sheets are possible

      (i)   if $n = 1$? †

      (ii) if $n = 2$? †

b. Find a formula for the number of possible answer sheets for an exam with n questions (for any natural number n), and use mathematical induction to prove that the formula is correct. †

C Exercises   Beyond the Basics

In Exercises 35–43, use mathematical induction to prove each statement for all natural numbers n.

35. 5 is a factor of $8^n - 3^n$.   **36.** 24 is a factor of $5^{2n} - 1$.

37. 64 is a factor of $3^{2n+2} - 8n - 9$.

38. 64 is a factor of $9^n - 8n - 1$.

39. 3 is a factor of $2^{2n+1} + 1$.

40. 5 is a factor of $2^{4n} - 1$.

41. $a - b$ is a factor of $a^n - b^n$.

   [*Hint:* $a^{k+1} - b^{k+1} = a(a^k - b^k) + b^k(a - b)$.]

42. If $a \neq 1$, then $1 + a + a^2 + \cdots + a^{n-1} = \dfrac{a^n - 1}{a - 1}$.

43. $\displaystyle\sum_{k=1}^{n+1} \frac{1}{n + k} \leq \frac{5}{6}$

Critical Thinking

44. Consider the statement "2 is a factor of $4n - 1$ for all natural numbers n." Then P_k: 2 is a factor of $4k - 1$.

    Assume that P_k is true, so that $4k - 1 = 2m$ for some integer m. Then

$$\begin{aligned}
P_{k+1} &= 4(k + 1) - 1 \\
&= 4k + 4 - 1 \\
&= (4k - 1) + 4 \\
&= 2m + 4 \\
&= 2(m + 2).
\end{aligned}$$

Thus, if P_k is true, then P_{k+1} is also true. However, 2 is never a factor of $4n - 1$, since $4n - 1$ is always an odd integer. Explain why this "proof" is not valid.

| # The Binomial Theorem

Blaise Pascal (1623–1662)

BEFORE STARTING THIS SECTION, REVIEW

1. Special products (Section P.3, page 37)

2. Factorials (Section 11.1, page 937)

3. Summation notation (Section 11.1, page 938)

OBJECTIVES

1 Use Pascal's Triangle to compute binomial coefficients.

2 Use Pascal's Triangle to expand a binomial power.

3 Use the Binomial Theorem to expand a binomial power.

4 Find the coefficient of a term in a binomial expansion.

Blaise Pascal

Blaise Pascal was a French mathematician. An evident genius, he was 14 when he began to accompany his father to gatherings of mathematicians that were arranged by Father Marin Mersenne. Pascal presented his own results at one of Mersenne's meetings at the age of 16.

Pascal's desire to help his father with his work collecting taxes led him to invent the first digital calculator, called the Pascalinc. Pascal was also interested in atmospheric pressure, and in 1648 he observed that the pressure of the atmosphere decreased with height and that a vacuum existed above the atmosphere.

Pascal's intense interest in mathematics led him to produce important results related to conic sections and to engage in correspondence with Fermat in which he formulated the foundations for the *theory of probability*. Pascal died a painful death from cancer at the age of 39.

In this section, we study *Pascal's Triangle*. This triangle of numbers contains the important *binomial coefficients*. See Example 1. Pascal's work was influential in Newton's discovery of the general *Binomial Theorem* for fractional and negative powers. ■

Pascaline

Binomial Expansions Recall that a polynomial which has exactly two terms is called a *binomial*. In Section P.3, we introduced the formulas for expanding the binomial powers $(x + y)^2$ and $(x + y)^3$. In the current section, we study a method for expanding $(x + y)^n$ for any positive integer n.

First consider these binomial expansions:

$$(x + y)^1 = x + y$$
$$(x + y)^2 = x^2 + 2xy + y^2$$
$$(x + y)^3 = x^3 + 3x^2y + 3xy^2 + y^3$$
$$(x + y)^4 = x^4 + 4x^3y + 6x^2y^2 + 4xy^3 + y^4$$
$$(x + y)^5 = x^5 + 5x^4y + 10x^3y^2 + 10x^2y^3 + 5xy^4 + y^5$$

The expansions of $(x + y)^2$ and $(x + y)^3$ should be familiar to you; the last three are left for you to verify. Each is a product of the previous binomial and $(x + y)$. For example, $(x + y)^4 = (x + y)^3(x + y)$.

The patterns for expansions of $(x + y)^n$ (with $n = 1, 2, 3, 4, 5$) suggest the following:

1. The expansion of $(x + y)^n$ has $n + 1$ terms.

2. The sum of the exponents on x and y in each term equals n.

3. The exponent on x starts at n $(x^n = x^n \cdot y^0)$ in the first term and decreases by 1 for each term until it is 0 in the last term $(x^0 \cdot y^n = y^n)$.

4. The exponent on y starts at 0 $(x^n = x^n \cdot y^0)$ in the first term and increases by 1 for each term until it is n in the last term $(x^0 \cdot y^n = y^n)$.

5. The variables x and y have symmetrical roles. That is, replacing x by y and y by x in the expansion of $(x + y)^n$ yields the same terms, just in a different order.

You may also have noticed that the coefficients of the first and the last terms are both 1 and the coefficients of the second and the next-to-last terms are equal. In general, the coefficients of

$$x^{n-j}y^j \qquad \text{and} \qquad x^j y^{n-j}$$

are equal for $j = 0, 1, 2, \ldots, n$.

The coefficients in a binomial expansion of $(x + y)^n$ are called the **binomial coefficients**.

1 Use Pascal's Triangle to compute binomial coefficients.

Pascal's Triangle

As early as A.D. 1100, the Chinese scholar Chia Hsien had discovered the secret of the binomial coefficients that was later rediscovered by the French philosopher and mathematician Blaise Pascal (1623–1662). In order to understand Chia Hsien's and Pascal's construction of binomial coefficients, let's first look at the coefficients in these binomial expansions:

$$
\begin{aligned}
(x + y)^0 &= & 1 \\
(x + y)^1 &= & 1x + 1y \\
(x + y)^2 &= & 1x^2 + 2xy + 1y^2 \\
(x + y)^3 &= & 1x^3 + 3x^2y + 3xy^2 + 1y^3 \\
(x + y)^4 &= & 1x^4 + 4x^3y + 6x^2y^2 + 4xy^3 + 1y^4 \\
(x + y)^5 &= & 1x^5 + 5x^4y + 10x^3y^2 + 10x^2y^3 + 5xy^4 + 1y^5.
\end{aligned}
$$

If we remove the variables and the plus signs and list only the coefficients, we get a triangle of numbers composed of the binomial coefficients. This triangle of numbers is known as *Pascal's Triangle*.

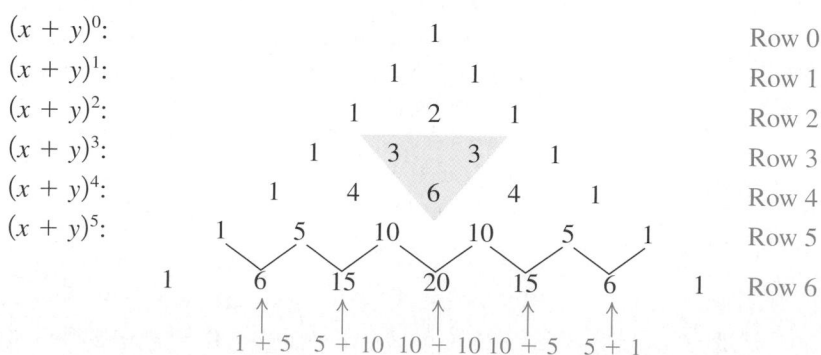

$(x + y)^0$:   Row 0
$(x + y)^1$:   Row 1
$(x + y)^2$:   Row 2
$(x + y)^3$:   Row 3
$(x + y)^4$:   Row 4
$(x + y)^5$:   Row 5
             Row 6

Note the symmetry in Pascal's Triangle. If the triangle were folded vertically down the middle, the numbers on each side of the crease would match. In order to create a new bottom row in the triangle, put the number 1 in the first and the last places of the new row and add two neighboring entries in the previous row.

The top row is called the *zeroth row* because it corresponds to the binomial expansion of $(x + y)^0$. The next row is called the *first row* because it corresponds to the binomial expansion of $(x + y)^1$. All the rows are named so that the *n*th *row* corresponds to the coefficients of $(x + y)^n$.

2 Use Pascal's Triangle to expand a binomial power.

EXAMPLE 1   **Using Pascal's Triangle to Expand a Binomial Power**

Expand $(4y - 2x)^5$.

Solution

From the fifth row of Pascal's Triangle, we see that the binomial coefficients are

$$1, 5, 10, 10, 5, 1.$$

We must make some changes in the expansion

$$(x + y)^5 = x^5 + 5x^4y + 10x^3y^2 + 10x^2y^3 + 5xy^4 + y^5$$

to get the expansion for $(4y - 2x)^5$:

1. x must be replaced by $4y$.

2. y must be replaced by $-2x$.

These changes in $(x + y)^5$ produce

$$(4y - 2x)^5 = [4y + (-2x)]^5 = (4y)^5 + 5(4y)^4(-2x) + 10(4y)^3(-2x)^2$$
$$+ 10(4y)^2(-2x)^3 + 5(4y)(-2x)^4 + (-2x)^5$$
$$= 1024y^5 - 2560y^4x + 2560y^3x^2 - 1280y^2x^3 + 320yx^4 - 32x^5.$$

We note that expanding a *difference* results in alternating signs between terms.

■ ■ ■

PRACTICE PROBLEM 1   Expand $(3y - x)^6$.   ■

3 Use the Binomial Theorem to expand a binomial power.

The coefficients in a binomial expansion can be computed by using ratios of certain factorials. We first introduce the symbol $\dbinom{n}{r}$.

DEFINITION OF $\dbinom{n}{r}$

If r and n are integers with $0 \le r \le n$, then we define

$$\binom{n}{r} = \frac{n!}{r!(n - r)!}$$

TECHNOLOGY CONNECTION

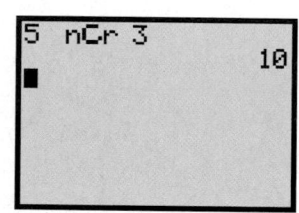 Most graphing calculators can compute the binomial coefficients $\binom{n}{r}$. They frequently use the symbol nCr. Note that $\binom{5}{3}$ is shown as 5 nCr 3 on the viewing screen.

```
5 nCr 3
              10
■
```

EXAMPLE 2   Evaluating $\binom{n}{r}$

Evaluate each binomial coefficient.

a. $\binom{4}{1}$ **b.** $\binom{5}{3}$ **c.** $\binom{9}{0}$ **d.** $\binom{35}{35}$

Solution

a. $\binom{4}{1} = \dfrac{4!}{1!(4-1)!} = \dfrac{4!}{1!3!} = \dfrac{4 \cdot 3 \cdot 2 \cdot 1}{1(3 \cdot 2 \cdot 1)} = \dfrac{4}{1} = 4$

b. $\binom{5}{3} = \dfrac{5!}{3!(5-3!)} = \dfrac{5!}{3!\,2!} = \dfrac{5 \cdot 4 \cdot 3!}{3!\,2!} = \dfrac{5 \cdot 4}{2} = 5 \cdot 2 = 10$

c. $\binom{9}{0} = \dfrac{9!}{0!(9-0)!} = \dfrac{9!}{0!\,9!} = \dfrac{1}{1} = 1$ Recall $0! = 1$.

d. $\binom{35}{35} = \dfrac{35!}{35!(35-35)!} = \dfrac{35!}{35!\,0!} = \dfrac{1}{1} = 1$ ■ ■ ■

PRACTICE PROBLEM 2   Evaluate each binomial coefficient.

a. $\binom{6}{2}$ **b.** $\binom{12}{9}$ ■

Examples 2(c) and 2(d) generalize for $n \geq 0$.

$$\binom{n}{0} = 1 \qquad \text{and} \qquad \binom{n}{n} = 1$$

The symbol $\binom{n}{r}$ is read " n choose r. " It can be shown that $\binom{n}{r}$ is the number of ways of choosing a subset containing exactly r elements from a set with n elements.

The numbers $\binom{n}{r}$ show up as the coefficients in the expansion of a binomial power. For example, $(x + y)^4$ can be written as either

$$(x + y)^4 = x^4 + 4x^3y + 6x^2y^2 + 4xy^3 + y^4$$

or

$$(x + y)^4 = \binom{4}{0}x^4 + \binom{4}{1}x^3y + \binom{4}{2}x^2y^2 + \binom{4}{3}xy^3 + \binom{4}{4}y^4.$$

This result is the **Binomial Theorem** (for $n = 4$), which can be proved by mathematical induction. It provides an efficient method for expanding a binomial power. (See Exercise 58.) The Binomial Theorem can be used to expand a binomial power directly, without reference to Pascal's Triangle. This technique is particularly useful in expanding large powers of a binomial. For example, the expansion of $(x + y)^{20}$ would require that you produce 20 rows of the Pascal Triangle.

THE BINOMIAL THEOREM

If n is a natural number, then the binomial expansion of $(x + y)^n$ is given by

$$(x + y)^n = \binom{n}{0}x^n + \binom{n}{1}x^{n-1}y + \binom{n}{2}x^{n-2}y^2 + \cdots + \binom{n}{r}x^{n-r}y^r + \cdots + \binom{n}{n}y^n$$

$$= \sum_{r=0}^{n} \binom{n}{r}x^{n-r}y^r.$$

The coefficient $\binom{n}{r}$ of $x^{n-r}y^r$ is $\dfrac{n!}{r!(n-r)!}$.

EXAMPLE 3   Expanding a Binomial Power by Using the Binomial Theorem

Find the binomial expansion of $(x - 3y)^4$.

Solution

$$(x - 3y)^4 = [x + (-3y)]^4$$

$$= \binom{4}{0}x^4 + \binom{4}{1}x^3(-3y) + \binom{4}{2}x^2(-3y)^2 + \binom{4}{3}x(-3y)^3 + \binom{4}{4}(-3y)^3$$

$$= \frac{4!}{0!4!}x^4 + \frac{4!}{1!3!}x^3(-3y) + \frac{4!}{2!2!}x^2(-3y)^2 + \frac{4!}{3!1!}x(-3y)^3 + \frac{4!}{4!0!}(-3y)^4$$

$$= x^4 + \frac{4 \cdot 3!}{1! \, 3!}x^3(-3y) + \frac{4 \cdot 3 \cdot 2!}{2! \, 2!}x^2(-3y)^2 + \frac{4 \cdot 3!}{3! \, 1!}x(-3y)^3 + (-3y)^4$$

$$= x^4 + 4x^3(-3y) + \frac{4 \cdot 3}{2!}x^2(-3y)^2 + 4x(-3y)^3 + (-3y)^4$$

$$= x^4 - 12x^3y + 54x^2y^2 - 108xy^3 + 81y^4 \qquad ■ ■ ■$$

PRACTICE PROBLEM 3   Find the binomial expansion of $(3x - y)^4$.   ■

---

4 Find the coefficient of a term in a binomial expansion.

The Binomial Theorem is also useful for finding both a particular term and its coefficient in a binomial expansion.

EXAMPLE 4   Finding a Particular Coefficient in a Binomial Expansion

Find the coefficient of x^9y^3 in the expansion of $(x + y)^{12}$.

Solution

The form of the expansion is

$$(x + y)^{12} = \binom{12}{0}x^{12} + \binom{12}{1}x^{11}y + \binom{12}{2}x^{10}y^2 + \binom{12}{3}x^9y^3 + \cdots + \binom{12}{11}xy^{11} + \binom{12}{12}y^{12}.$$

From the fourth term, $\binom{12}{3}x^9y^3$, the coefficient of x^9y^3 is

$$\binom{12}{3} = \frac{12!}{3!(12 - 3!)} = \frac{12!}{3! \, 9!} = \frac{12 \cdot 11 \cdot 10 \cdot 9!}{3! \, 9!} = 220. \qquad ■ ■ ■$$

PRACTICE PROBLEM 4   Find the coefficient of x^3y^9 in the expansion of $(x + y)^{12}$.   ■

The method illustrated in Example 4 allows us to find any particular term in a binomial expansion without writing out the complete expansion.

PARTICULAR TERM IN A BINOMIAL EXPRESSION

The term containing the factor x^r in the expansion of $(x + y)^n$ is

$$\binom{n}{n-r} x^r y^{n-r}.$$

EXAMPLE 5   **Finding a Particular Term in a Binomial Expansion**

Find the term containing x^{10} in the expansion of $(x + 2a)^{15}$.

Solution

We begin with the formula for the term containing the factor x^r.

$$\binom{n}{n-r} x^r y^{n-r} = \binom{15}{15-10} x^{10}(2a)^{15-10} \qquad \text{Replace } n \text{ by } 15, r \text{ by } 10,$$
$$\text{and } y \text{ by } 2a.$$

$$= \binom{15}{5} x^{10}(2a)^5 \qquad \text{Simplify.}$$

$$= \frac{15!}{5!(15-5)!} x^{10} 2^5 a^5 \qquad \text{Recall } \binom{n}{r} = \frac{n!}{r!(n-r)!}.$$

$$= \frac{15!}{5!\,10!} \cdot 32 x^{10} a^5 \qquad 2^5 = 32$$

$$= \frac{15 \cdot 14 \cdot 13 \cdot 12 \cdot 11 \cdot \cancel{10!}}{5! \cdot \cancel{10!}} \cdot 32 x^{10} a^5$$

$$= 96{,}096 x^{10} a^5 \qquad \text{Use a calculator.} \quad ■ ■ ■$$

PRACTICE PROBLEM 5   Find the term containing x^3 in the expansion of $(x + 2a)^{15}$.   ■

A Exercises   Basic Skills and Concepts

In Exercises 1–10, evaluate each expression.

1. $\dfrac{6!}{3!}$ 120

2. $\dfrac{11!}{9!}$ 110

3. $\dfrac{12!}{11!}$ 12

4. $\dfrac{3!}{0!}$ 6

5. $\dbinom{6}{4}$ 15

6. $\dbinom{6}{3}$ 20

7. $\dbinom{9}{0}$ 1

8. $\dbinom{12}{0}$ 1

9. $\dbinom{7}{1}$ 7

10. $\dbinom{7}{3}$ 35

In Exercises 11–18, use Pascal's Triangle to expand each binomial.

11. $(x + 2)^4$ †

12. $(x + 3)^4$ †

13. $(x - 2)^5$ †

14. $(3 - x)^5$ †

15. $(2 - 3x)^3$ †

16. $(3 - 2x)^3$ †

17. $(2x + 3y)^4$ †

18. $(2x + 5y)^4$ †

In Exercises 19–40, use either the binomial theorem or Pascal's Triangle to expand each binomial.

19. $(x + 1)^4$ †

20. $(x + 2)^4$ †

21. $(x - 1)^5$ †

22. $(1 - x)^5$ †

23. $(y - 3)^3$ †

24. $(2 - y)^5$ †

†Due to space constrictions, answers to these exercises may be found in the Answers beginning on page A–1 in the back of the book.

25. $(x + y)^6$ †

26. $(x - y)^6$ †

27. $(1 + 3y)^5$ †

28. $(2x + 1)^5$ †

29. $(2x + 1)^4$ †

30. $(3x - 1)^4$ †

31. $(x - 2y)^3$ †

32. $(2x - y)^3$ †

33. $(2x + y)^4$ †

34. $(3x - 2y)^4$ †

35. $\left(\dfrac{x}{2} + 2\right)^7$ †

36. $\left(2 - \dfrac{x}{2}\right)^7$ †

37. $\left(a^2 - \dfrac{1}{3}\right)^4$ †

38. $\left(\dfrac{1}{2} - a^2\right)^4$ †

39. $\left(\dfrac{1}{x} + y\right)^3$ †

40. $\left(x + \dfrac{2}{y}\right)^3$ †

In Exercises 41–48, find the specified term.

41. $(x + y)^{10}$; term containing x^7 $120x^7y^3$

42. $(x + y)^{10}$; term containing y^7 $120x^3y^7$

43. $(x - 2)^{12}$; term containing x^3 $-112,640x^3$

44. $(2 - x)^{12}$; term containing x^3 $-112,640x^3$

45. $(2x + 3y)^8$; term containing x^6 $16,128x^6y^2$

46. $(2x + 3y)^8$; term containing y^6 $81,648x^2y^6$

47. $(5x - 2y)^{11}$; term containing y^9 $-704,000x^2y^9$

48. $(7x - y)^{15}$; term containing x^9 $201,969,803,035x^9y^6$

49. Find the value of $(1.2)^5$ by writing it in the form $(1 + 0.2)^5$ and applying the Binomial Theorem.   †

50. Use the method in Exercise 49 to evaluate each expression.
   a. $(2.9)^4$ †   **b.** $(10.4)^3$ †

C Exercises   Beyond the Basics

51. Find the middle term in the expansion of $\left(\sqrt{x} - \dfrac{2}{x^2}\right)^{10}$.   †

52. Find the middle term in the expansion of $\left(\sqrt{x} + \dfrac{1}{x^2}\right)^{10}$.   †

53. Find the middle term in the expansion of $(1 - x^2y^{-3})^{12}$.   †

54. Show that the middle term in the expansion of $(1 + x)^{2n}$ is

$$\dfrac{1 \cdot 3 \cdot 5 \ldots \cdot (2n - 1)}{n!} 2^n x^n.$$

55. Prove that $\dbinom{n}{0} + \dbinom{n}{1} + \dbinom{n}{2} + \cdots + \dbinom{n}{n} = 2^n$.

56. Prove that $\dbinom{n}{0} - \dbinom{n}{1} + \dbinom{n}{2} - \dbinom{n}{3} + \cdots + (-1)^n\dbinom{n}{n} = 0$.

57. Prove that $\dbinom{k}{j} + \dbinom{k}{j-1} = \dbinom{k+1}{j}$.

58. Prove the Binomial Theorem by using the Principle of Mathematical Induction.
   [*Hint:*

$$(x + y)^{k+1} = (x + y)(x + y)^k = (x + y)\sum_{j=0}^{k}\dbinom{k}{j}x^{k-j}y^j$$

$$= \sum_{j=0}^{k}\dbinom{k}{j}x^{k+1-j}y^j + \sum_{j=0}^{k}\dbinom{k}{j}x^{k-j}y^{j+1}.$$

   Use Exercise 57 to show that

$$(x + y)^{k+1} = \sum_{j=0}^{k+1}\dbinom{k+1}{j}x^{k+1-j}y^j.]$$

In Exercises 59–61, find the value of the expression without expanding any term.

59. $(2x - 1)^4 + 4(2x - 1)^3(3 - 2x) + 6(2x - 1)^2(3 - 2x)^2 + 4(2x - 1)(3 - 2x)^3 + (3 - 2x)^4$.   16

60. $(x + 1)^4 - 4(x + 1)^3(x - 1) + 6(x + 1)^2(x - 1)^2 - 4(x + 1)(x - 1)^3 + (x - 1)^4$.   16

61. $(3x - 1)^5 + 5(3x - 1)^4(1 - 2x) + 10(3x - 1)^3(1 - 2x)^2 + 10(3x - 1)^2(1 - 2x)^3 + 5(3x - 1)(1 - 2x)^4 + (1 - 2x)^5$. x^5

62. Find the constant term in each expansion.
   a. $\left(x^2 - \dfrac{1}{x}\right)^9$ 84   **b.** $\left(\sqrt{x} - \dfrac{2}{x^2}\right)^{10}$ 180

63. If the constant term in the expansion of $\left(kx - \dfrac{1}{x^2}\right)^6$ is 240, find k. $k = \pm 2$

64. If the constant term in the expansion of $\left(x^3 + \dfrac{k}{x^8}\right)^{11}$ is 1320, find k. $k = 2$

65. Show that there is no constant term in the expansion of $\left(2x^2 - \dfrac{1}{4x}\right)^{11}$.

Critical Thinking

66. Use the binomial expansion of $(x + y)^6$, with $x = 1$ and $y = 1$, to show that

$$2^6 = \dbinom{6}{0} + \dbinom{6}{1} + \dbinom{6}{2} + \dbinom{6}{3} + \dbinom{6}{4} + \dbinom{6}{5} + \dbinom{6}{6}.$$

67. Use the binomial expansion of $(x + y)^{10}$ to show that

$$\dbinom{10}{0} - \dbinom{10}{1} + \dbinom{10}{2} - \dbinom{10}{3} + \dbinom{10}{4} - \dbinom{10}{5}$$
$$+ \dbinom{10}{6} - \dbinom{10}{7} + \dbinom{10}{8} - \dbinom{10}{9} + \dbinom{10}{10} = 0.$$

68. Use the binomial expansion of $(x + y)^2$ to show that if $x > 0$ and $y > 0$, then $(x + y)^2 > x^2 + y^2$.

69. Use the binomial expansion of $(x + y)^n$ to show that if $x > 0$ and $y > 0$, then $(x + y)^n > x^n + y^n$.

70. Use the binomial expansion of $(1 + x)^n$ to show that if $x > 0$, then $(1 + x)^n > 1 + nx$.

Counting Principles

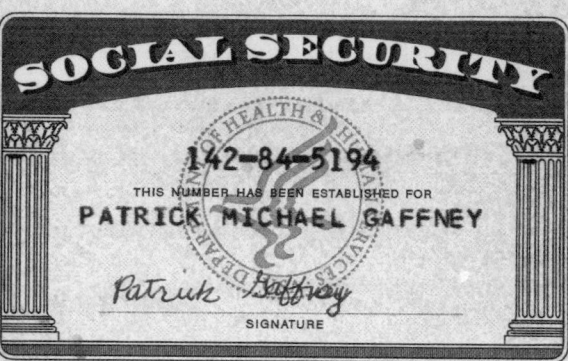

BEFORE STARTING THIS SECTION, REVIEW

1. Exponents (Section P.2, page 19)

2. Factorials (Section 11.1, page 937)

OBJECTIVES

1 Use the Fundamental Counting Principle.

2 Use the formula for permutations.

3 Use the formula for combinations.

4 Use the formula for distinguishable permutations.

The Mystery of Social Security Numbers

Social Security numbers may seem to be assigned almost randomly, but that is not so. Although the details are complicated, here is a brief introduction: First, the format for all Social Security numbers is NNN-NN-NNNN, where N must be one of the numbers 0, 1, 2, 3, 4, 5, 6, 7, 8, 9. U.S. citizens, permanent residents, and certain temporary residents are issued these numbers. For working people, the numbers help track both tax contributions and Social Security benefits.

The first three digits in a Social Security number make up an *area number* assigned to a geographical location. The area number indicates either the state in which the card was issued or the ZIP code in the mailing address provided in the original application.

The middle two digits constitute a *group number* and are designed simply to break the Social Security number into convenient blocks for issuance. The exact procedure is not very enlightening.

The last four digits are *serial numbers* and are assigned within each group from 0001 through 9999.

Various restrictions limit the numbers that can be used. For example, numbers with all zeros in any of the digit blocks (000-xx-xxxx, xxx-00-xxxx, or xxx-xx-0000) are never issued. Even if there were no restrictions, at some point there might be *more people than there are numbers available* in the Social Security format. Thus, the question arises as to how many numbers can be issued in the Social Security format with no restrictions. The answer is 1,000,000,000 (1 billion). (The United States population in October 2006 was about 300,000,000 (300 million).)

In Example 3, you will learn how to calculate the total number of possible Social Security numbers. ■

1 Use the Fundamental Counting Principle.

At first thought, you may feel that you know all there is to know about counting. However, mathematicians have developed a variety of techniques which allow you to determine the number of items that are of interest to you without the effort of listing and counting all of them. We start with an example that easily lists the items to be counted, but that also demonstrates a general counting procedure.

EXAMPLE 1   **Counting Possible Car Selections**

Suppose you are trying to decide between buying a sport-utility vehicle (SUV) and a four-door sedan. The SUV is available in black, red, and silver. The sedan is available in black, blue, and green. In how many ways can you choose a type of car and its color?

Solution

We can represent the possible solutions by using a *tree diagram*, as shown in Figure 11.4. There are two initial choices: an SUV and a sedan. For each of these two choices, there are three additional choices of color, so a total of $2 \cdot 3 = 6$ car selections is possible.

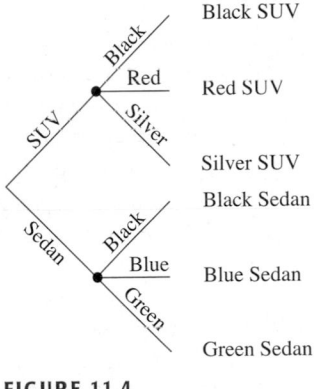

Black SUV

Red SUV

Silver SUV

Black Sedan

Blue Sedan

Green Sedan

FIGURE 11.4   ▪ ▪ ▪

PRACTICE PROBLEM 1   Construct a tree diagram, and determine the number of ways you can choose to take one of three courses—English, French, and math—in either the morning, afternoon, or evening.   ▪

The car selection process in Example 1 involved making two choices. First, choose a type of car; second, choose a color. It is important in this process that the same *number* of choices be available for the second choice, regardless of the result of the first choice. The exact rules for counting by this method are given next.

FUNDAMENTAL COUNTING PRINCIPLE

If a first choice can be made in p different ways, a second choice can be made in q different ways, a third choice can be made in r different ways, and so on, then the sequence of choices can be made in $p \cdot q \cdot r \cdots$ different ways.

EXAMPLE 2   **Counting Music Programs**

A disc jockey wants to pick a song to open a program from among 40 songs by one artist and pick a song to end the program from among 32 songs by a second artist. How many different choices are possible?

Solution

Each choice of an opening and ending song sequence can be obtained as follows:

First, choose an opening song in 40 ways.

Second, choose the song to end the program in 32 ways.

Since no matter which song is chosen to open the program, all 32 songs are available to end the program, the counting principle applies, and there are

$$40 \cdot 32 = 1280$$

possible choices in total for the opening and ending sequences.   ■ ■ ■

PRACTICE PROBLEM 2   Reba gets to choose both dinner and a movie for a Saturday night date. She can choose from any of seven restaurants and five movies. How many different choices are possible?   ■

◆ **WARNING**   You must exercise care in using the Fundamental Counting Principle. Suppose you are trying to decide between buying an SUV and a convertible. The SUV is available only in black, red, or silver, and the convertible is available only in black or red. In how many ways can you choose a type of car and its color? The car and color can be selected by making two choices: type (SUV or convertible), followed by color. But in this situation, the number of ways you can make the second choice depends on the first choice. You can choose from *three* colors for an SUV, but only *two* colors for a convertible. The Fundamental Counting Principle *does not apply*. Fortunately, there are so few different choices here that you can easily list all five: black SUV, red SUV, silver SUV, black convertible, and red convertible.

> **EXAMPLE 3**   **Counting Possible Social Security Numbers**

Social Security numbers have the format NNN-NN-NNNN, where each N must be one of the integers 0, 1, 2, 3, 4, 5, 6, 7, 8, and 9. Assuming that there are no other restrictions, how many such numbers are possible?

Solution

There are nine positions in the format

NNN-NN-NNNN.

Since the number of choices available at each position is not affected by previous choices, the Fundamental Counting Principle can be used. Replace each of the letters N with a blank to be filled in with one of the ten digits 0, 1, 2, 3, 4, 5, 6, 7, 8, and 9.

We have

$$\underline{10} \cdot \underline{10} \cdot \underline{10} \cdot \underline{10} \cdot \underline{10} \cdot \underline{10} \cdot \underline{10} \cdot \underline{10} \cdot \underline{10} = 10^9.$$

Thus, there are $10^9 = 1,000,000,000$ possible Social Security numbers.   ■ ■ ■

PRACTICE PROBLEM 3   In Example 3, suppose we fix the area number for the Social Security number to be 433. How many social security numbers can be assigned to this area—that is, numbers having the form 433-NN-NNNN?   ■

2 Use the formula for permutations.

Permutations

DEFINITION OF PERMUTATION

A **permutation** is an arrangement of n distinct objects in a fixed order in which no object is used more than once. The specific order is important: Each different ordering of the same objects is a different permutation.

EXAMPLE 4　　**Counting Possible Arrangements for a Group Photograph**

How many different ways can five people be arranged in a row for a group photograph?

Solution

To count the number of ways we can arrange five people in a row for a group photograph, we can assign numbers to each of the five photograph positions.

$$\boxed{1}\quad\boxed{2}\quad\boxed{3}\quad\boxed{4}\quad\boxed{5}$$

Then we proceed as follows:
　　First, choosing any of the five people for Position 1 gives 5 ways.
　　Second, choosing one of the four remaining people for Position 2 gives 4 ways.
　　Third, choosing one of the three remaining people for Position 3 gives 3 ways.
　　Fourth, choosing one of the remaining two people for Position 4 gives 2 ways.
　　Fifth, choosing the last person remaining for Position 5 gives 1 way.
　　Using the Fundamental Counting Principle, we see that there are

$$5 \cdot 4 \cdot 3 \cdot 2 \cdot 1 = 5!, \text{ or } 120,$$

possible arrangements.　　　　　　　　　　　　　　　　　　　■ ■ ■

PRACTICE PROBLEM 4　　How many different ways can seven books be arranged on a shelf?　■

　　The technique used in Example 4 can be extended to provide a general formula for counting permutations of n distinct objects.

NUMBER OF PERMUTATIONS OF n OBJECTS

The number of permutations of n distinct objects is

$$n! = n(n - 1) \cdot \cdots \cdot 4 \cdot 3 \cdot 2 \cdot 1.$$

That is, n distinct objects can be arranged in $n!$ different ways.

　　There are occasions upon which some, but not all, of the available objects are to be arranged in a specific order, again with no object being used more than once. You may want to choose r objects from among n available objects. This type of ordering is called a **permutation of n objects taken r at a time.**

EXAMPLE 5   **Counting Prizewinners**

Three prizes (for first, second, and third place) are to be given out in a dog show having 27 contestants. In how many different ways can dogs come in first, second, and third?

Solution

Consider how we might list the prize winners:

Any dog might win first prize; there are 27 possibilities.

Any remaining dog might win second prize; there are 26 possibilities.

Any remaining dog might win third prize; there are 25 possibilities. We can use the Fundamental Counting Principle: There are

$$27 \quad \cdot \quad 26 \quad \cdot \quad 25 = 17{,}550$$

$$\uparrow \qquad \uparrow \qquad \uparrow$$

1st   2nd   3rd

prize   prize   prize

distinct ways that the dogs can come in first, second, and third. This is an example of permutations of 27 objects taken 3 at a time.   ■ ■ ■

PRACTICE PROBLEM 5   There are nine different rides at a state fair. A group has to decide which four rides they will go on and in what order. How many possibilities are there?   ■

PERMUTATIONS OF n OBJECTS TAKEN r AT A TIME

The number of permutations of n distinct objects taken r at a time is denoted by $P(n, r)$, where

$$P(n, r) = \frac{n!}{(n - r)!}$$

$$= n(n - 1)(n - 2)\cdots(n - r + 1).$$

TECHNOLOGY CONNECTION

Most graphing calculators can compute $P(n, r)$. They frequently use the symbol nPr. Note that $P(7, 3)$ is shown as $7\ nPr\ 3$ on the viewing screen.

```
7 nPr 3
              210
```

EXAMPLE 6   **Using the Permutations Formula**

Use the formula for $P(n, r)$ to evaluate each expression.

a. $P(7, 3)$ **b.** $P(6, 0)$

Solution

a.
$$P(7, 3) = \frac{7!}{(7 - 3)!} \qquad \text{\small Replace } n \text{ by 7 and } r \text{ by 3 in } P(n, r).$$

$$= \frac{7!}{4!} = \frac{7 \cdot 6 \cdot 5 \cdot 4!}{4!} = 7 \cdot 6 \cdot 5 = 210$$

b.
$$P(6, 0) = \frac{6!}{(6 - 0)!} \qquad \text{\small Replace } n \text{ by 6 and } r \text{ by 0 in } P(n, r).$$

$$= \frac{6!}{6!} = 1 \qquad\qquad\qquad \blacksquare\ \blacksquare\ \blacksquare$$

PRACTICE PROBLEM 6   Evaluate: **a.** $P(9, 2)$ **b.** $P(n, 0)$ ■

Let's apply the permutations formula to the problem of counting prizewinners in Example 5. The number of permutations of 27 dogs taken 3 at a time is

$$P(27, 3) = \frac{27!}{(27 - 3)!}$$

$$= \frac{27!}{24!} = \frac{27 \cdot 26 \cdot 25 \cdot \cancel{24!}}{\cancel{24!}} = 27 \cdot 26 \cdot 25 = 17,550.$$

This is exactly the answer obtained in Example 5.

3 Use the formula for combinations.

Combinations

Order is not always important in selecting objects. For example, if someone is bringing six movies on a vacation, the order in which the movies were chosen is unimportant.

DEFINITION OF A COMBINATION OF n DISTINCT OBJECTS TAKEN r AT A TIME

When r objects are chosen from n distinct objects without regard to order, we call the set of r objects a **combination of n objects taken r at a time.** The symbol $C(n, r)$ denotes the total number of combinations of n objects taken r at a time.

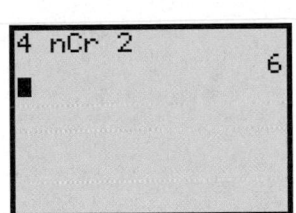
EXAMPLE 7   **Listing Combinations**

List all the combinations of the four mascot names "bears," "bulls," "lions," and "tigers," taken two at a time. In other words, find $C(4, 2)$.

Solution

If "bears" is one of the mascots chosen, the possibilities are {bears, bulls}, {bears, lions} and {bears, tigers}.

If "bulls" is one of the mascots chosen, the remaining possibilities (excluding {bears, bulls}) are {bulls, lions} and {bulls, tigers}.

The final choice of two mascot names is {lions, tigers}.

The combinations of the four mascot names taken two at a time are {bears, bulls}, {bears, lions}, {bears, tigers}, {bulls, lions}, {bulls, tigers} and {lions, tigers}.

Since there are six such combinations, we have $C(4, 2) = 6$.   ■ ■ ■

PRACTICE PROBLEM 7   List all the combinations of the four mascot names "bears," "bulls," "lions," and "tigers," taken three at a time. In other words, find $C(4, 3)$.   ■

In order to find a formula for $C(n, r)$, we begin by comparing $C(n, r)$ with $P(n, r)$, the number of permutations of n objects taken r at a time. Suppose, for example, we have seven distinct objects—A, B, C, D, E, F, and G—and we pick three of them—A, D, and E (a combination of seven objects taken three at a time). This one combination ADE gives $3! = 6$ permutations of seven objects taken three at a time. Here are all the possible arrangements of the letters A, D, and E: ADE, AED, DAE, DEA, EAD, and EDA. Since one combination generates six permutations, there are six ($3!$) times as many permutations of seven objects taken three at a time as there are combinations of seven objects taken three at a time. Thus, $3!(\text{number of combinations}) = (\text{number of permutations})$.

$$3!\,C(7, 3) = P(7, 3)$$

$$C(7, 3) = \frac{P(7, 3)}{3!}$$

$$= \frac{\dfrac{7!}{(7-3)!}}{3!} \qquad \text{Replace } P(7, 3) \text{ by } \frac{7!}{(7-3)!}.$$

$$= \frac{7!}{(7-3)!\,3!} = \frac{7!}{4!\,3!} = \frac{7 \cdot 6 \cdot 5 \cdot \cancel{4!}}{\cancel{4!}\,3!} = \frac{7 \cdot 6 \cdot 5}{3 \cdot 2 \cdot 1} = 35$$

A similar process leads to a more general formula.

THE NUMBER OF COMBINATIONS OF n DISTINCT OBJECTS TAKEN r AT A TIME

The number of combinations of n distinct objects taken r at a time is:

$$C(n, r) = \frac{n!}{(n-r)!\,r!}$$

EXAMPLE 8   Using the Combinations Formula

Use the formula $C(n, r)$ to evaluate each expression.

a. $C(7, 5)$ **b.** $C(8, 0)$ **c.** $C(4, 4)$

a. $C(7, 5) = \dfrac{7!}{(7-5)!\,5!}$ Replace n by 7 and r by 5 in $C(n, r)$.

$$= \frac{7!}{2!\,5!} = \frac{7 \cdot \overset{3}{\cancel{6}} \cdot \cancel{5!}}{2 \cdot 1 \cdot \cancel{5!}} = 21.$$

b. $C(8, 0) = \dfrac{8!}{(8-0)!\,0!}$ Substitute $n = 8$ and $r = 0$ in $C(n, r)$.

$$= \frac{8!}{8!\,0!} = 1.$$

c. $C(4, 4) = \dfrac{4!}{(4-4)!\,4!}$ Substitute $n = 4$ and $r = 4$ in $C(n, r)$.

$$= \frac{4!}{0!\,4!} = 1.$$

■ ■ ■

PRACTICE PROBLEM 8   Evaluate.

a. $C(9, 2)$ **b.** $C(n, 0)$ **c.** $C(n, n)$

■

EXAMPLE 9   **Choosing Pizza Toppings**

How many different ways can five pizza toppings be chosen from the following choices: pepperoni, onions, mushrooms, green peppers, olives, tomatoes, mozzarella, and anchovies?

Solution

Eight toppings are listed, so the question is, how many ways can we pick five things from eight things? That is, we need to find the number of combinations of eight objects taken five at a time, or $C(8, 5)$.

Use the formula $C(n, r) = \dfrac{n!}{(n - r)!\, r!}$.

$$C(8, 5) = \frac{8!}{(8 - 5)!\, 5!} \qquad \text{Replace } n \text{ by 8 and } r \text{ by 5.}$$

$$= \frac{8!}{3!\, 5!} = \frac{8 \cdot 7 \cdot 6}{3 \cdot 2 \cdot 1} = 56.$$

There are 56 ways that five of the eight pizza toppings can be chosen.   ■ ■ ■

PRACTICE PROBLEM 9   A box of assorted chocolates contains 12 different kinds of chocolates. In how many ways can 3 chocolates be chosen?   ■

4 Use the formula for distinguishable permutations.

Distinguishable Permutations

Suppose you were to stand in a line with identical twins. Although the three of you can arrange yourselves in $3! = 6$ different ways, someone who could not tell the twins apart could distinguish only three different arrangements. These three arrangements are called *distinguishable permutations*. To better understand the idea of distinguishable permutations, suppose that we have three tiles with the numbers 1, 2, and 3 printed on the fronts and the letters M O M printed on the backs, respectively.

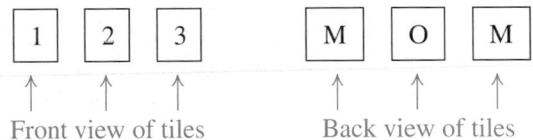

Front view of tiles   Back view of tiles

There are $3! = 6$ permutations of the numbers 1, 2, 3.

Now consider the corresponding arrangements of the letters M, O, and M on the back sides of the tiles as the fronts of the tiles are arranged to show each of the six permutations of 1, 2, 3.

Front View of Tiles	Back View of Tiles
1 2 3	M O M
1 3 2	M M O
2 1 3	O M M
2 3 1	O M M
3 1 2	M M O
3 2 1	M O M

There are only three distinguishable arrangements that appear when the tiles are viewed from the back: MOM, MMO, and OMM.

The front view shows the permutations of three distinct objects, and the back view shows the permutations of three objects, of which two are not distinguishable from each other. We describe this situation in more detail by saying that the three arrangements that arise from the back view are permutations of three objects, of which one is of one kind (in this instance, the letter O) and two are of a second kind (in this instance, the letter M).

The general result is stated next.

DISTINGUISHABLE PERMUTATIONS

The number of distinguishable permutations of n objects of which n_1 are of one kind, n_2 are of a second kind, . . . , and n_k are of a kth kind is

$$\frac{n!}{n_1! \cdot n_2! \cdots \cdots n_k!}$$

where $n_1 + n_2 + \cdots + n_k = n$.

EXAMPLE 10   Distributing Gifts

In how many ways can nine gifts be distributed among three children if each child receives three gifts?

Solution

If we number the gifts 1 through 9 and use A, B, and C to represent the children, we can visualize any distribution of gifts as an arrangement of the letters A, B, and C (each letter being used three times) above the numbers 1 through 9. Here is one possible arrangement:

$$
\begin{array}{ccccccccc}
B & A & A & C & C & B & A & C & B \\
1 & 2 & 3 & 4 & 5 & 6 & 7 & 8 & 9
\end{array}
$$

In this arrangement, child A gets gifts 2, 3, and 7; child B gets gifts 1, 6, and 9; and child C gets gifts 4, 5, and 8.

To count all the possible distributions of gifts, we count the number of permutations of nine objects, of which three are of one kind, three are of a second kind, and three are of a third kind:

$$\frac{9!}{3! \, 3! \, 3!} = 1680$$

There are 1680 ways the nine gifts can be distributed among the three children.   ■ ■ ■

PRACTICE PROBLEM 10   In how many ways can six counselors be sent in pairs to three different locations?   ■

Deciding Whether to Use Permutations, Combinations, or the Fundamental Counting Principle

Suppose 23 students show up late for a private screening of a new movie. Suppose also that there is one seat available in each of the first, second, eighth, and tenth rows and that five students will be allowed to stand in the back of the theater.

Permutations If order is important, use permutations.	In how many ways can 4 of the 23 students be assigned the available seats in Rows 1, 2, 8, and 10? ***Answer:*** $\underset{\text{Row 1}}{23} \cdot \underset{\text{Row 2}}{22} \cdot \underset{\text{Row 8}}{21} \cdot \underset{\text{Row 10}}{20} \cdot = 212{,}520$ ways
Combinations If order is not important, use combinations.	In how many ways can 5 of the 19 students *not given seats* be chosen to stand in the back? ***Answer:*** $C(19, 5) = 11{,}628$ ways
Fundamental Counting Principle Whenever you are making consecutive choices, and the number of choices at each stage is not affected by the way earlier choices were made, you can use the Fundamental Counting Principle.	In how many ways can students be assigned to the available seats and five students be chosen to stand in the back? ***Answer:*** $212{,}520 \times 11{,}628$ ways 　　　　　　　↑　　　　　↑ Assign the four seats.　Pick five students.

Notice that

- Since the Fundamental Counting Principle is used to count permutations, you can always use that principle instead of permutations.
- There are frequently equally good, though different, ways to use counting techniques to solve a problem. For example, we could first choose 5 students to stand in the back of the theater in $C(23, 5)$ ways and then assign the seats in rows 1, 2, 8, and 10 to the 19 remaining students in $19 \cdot 18 \cdot 17 \cdot 16$ ways. The total number of ways students can be assigned to stand in the back and assigned to the available seats is then $C(23, 5) \cdot 19 \cdot 18 \cdot 17 \cdot 16$. You should verify that

$$23 \cdot 22 \cdot 21 \cdot 20 \cdot C(19, 5) = 212{,}520 \times 11{,}628.$$

A Exercises   Basic Skills and Concepts

In Exercises 1–8, use the formula for $P(n, r)$ to evaluate each expression.

1. $P(6, 1)$ 6

2. $P(7, 3)$ 210

3. $P(8, 2)$ 56

4. $P(10, 6)$ 151,200

5. $P(9, 9)$ 362,880

6. $P(5, 5)$ 120

7. $P(7, 0)$ 1

8. $P(4, 0)$ 1

In Exercises 9–16, use the formula for $C(n, r)$ to evaluate each expression.

9. $C(8, 3)$ 56

10. $C(7, 2)$ 21

11. $C(9, 4)$ 126

12. $C(10, 5)$ 252

13. $C(5, 5)$ 1

14. $C(6, 6)$ 1

15. $C(3, 0)$ 1

16. $C(5, 0)$ 1

In Exercises 17–20, use the Fundamental Counting Principle to solve each problem.

17. How many different 2-letter codes can be made up from the 26 capital letters of the alphabet if (a) repeated letters are allowed; (b) repeated letters are not allowed. †

18. How many possible answer sheets are there for a ten-question true–false exam if no answer is left blank? 1024

19. In how many ways can a president and vice-president be chosen from an organization with 50 members? 2450

20. How many four-digit numbers can be formed with the digits 0, 1, 2, 3, 4, 5, 6, 7, 8, and 9 if the first digit cannot be 0? 9000

In Exercises 21–24, use the formula for counting permutations to solve each problem.

21. In how many different ways can the members of a family of four be seated in a row of four chairs? 24

†Due to space constrictions, answers to these exercises may be found in the Answers beginning on page A–1 in the back of the book.

22. Ten teams are entered in a bowling tournament. In how many ways can first, second, and third prizes be awarded? 720

23. Frederico has five shirts, three pairs of pants, and four ties that are appropriate for an interview. If he wears one of each type of apparel, how many different outfits can he wear? 60

24. A choreographer has to arrange eight pieces for a dance program. In how many ways can this be done? 40,320

In Exercises 25–28, use the formula for counting combinations to solve each problem.

25. A pizza menu offers pepperoni, peppers, mushrooms, sausage, and meatballs as extra toppings that can be added to your pizza. How many different pizzas can you order with two additional toppings? 10

26. In how many ways can 2 student representatives be chosen from a class of 15 students? 105

27. Students are allowed to choose 9 out of 11 problems to work for credit on an exam. In how many ways can this be done? 55

28. You have to choose 3 out of 18 potential teammates to help you with a group assignment. In how many ways can this be done? 816

In Exercises 29–34, solve the problem by any appropriate counting method.

29. In how many ways can Ashley choose 4 out of 11 different cans of canned goods to donate to charity? 330

30. In how many ways can a computer store hire a sales clerk and a technician from seven applicants for the clerk position and four applicants for the technician position? 28

31. In how many ways can six people be seated in a row with eight seats, leaving two seats vacant? 20,160

32. Seven students arrive to rent two canoes and three kayaks. In how many ways can two students be selected to rent the canoes and three to rent the kayaks? 210

33. Dakota is trying to decide in which order to visit five prospective colleges. In how many ways can this be done? 120

34. In how many ways can the first 4 numbers be called from the 75 possible bingo numbers? 29,170,800

B Exercises   Applying the Concepts

35. **Area codes.** How many three-digit area codes for telephones are possible if
  a. the first digit cannot be a 0 or 1 and the second digit must be a 0 or 1? 160
  b. there are no restrictions on the second digit? (Previous restrictions were abandoned in 1995.) 800

36. **Radio station call letters.** Radio stations in the United States have call letters that begin with either K or W (for example, WXYZ in Detroit). Some have a total of three letters, and others have four. How many different call-letter selections are possible? 36,504

37. **Fraternity letters.** The Greek alphabet contains 24 letters. How many 3-letter fraternity names can be made with Greek letters
  a. if no repetitions are allowed? 12,144
  b. if repetitions are allowed? 13,824

38. **Codes.** How many three-letter codes can be made from the first ten letters of the alphabet if
  a. no letters are repeated? 720
  b. letters may be repeated? 1000

39. **Supreme Court decisions.** In how many ways can the nine justices of the U.S. Supreme Court reach a majority decision? (The U.S. Supreme Court has nine justices who are appointed for life.) 256

40. **Committee selection.** A club consists of ten members. In how many ways can a committee of four be selected? 210

41. Wardrobe choices. Al's wardrobe consists of eight pairs of slacks, eight shirts, and eight pairs of shoes. He does not want to wear the same outfit on any two days of the year. Will his current wardrobe allow him to do this? Yes.

42. Menu selection. A French restaurant offers two choices of soup, three of salad, eight of an entree, and five of a dessert. How many different complete dinners can you order? 240

43. Housing development. A developer wants to build seven houses, each of a different design. In how many ways can she arrange these homes on a street if
a. there are four lots are on one side of the street and three on the opposite side? 5040
b. there are five lots are on one side of the street and two on the opposite side? 5040

44. Designing exercise sets. The author of a mathematics textbook has seven problems for an exercise set, and she is trying to arrange them in increasing order of difficulty. How many ways can she select the problems if no two of them are equally difficult? In how many ways can the author fail? †

45. Letter selection. From the letters of the word CHARITY, groups of four letters are formed (without regard to order). How many of them will contain
a. both A and R? 10
b. A, but not R? 10
c. neither A nor R? 5

46. Committee selection. In how many ways can a committee of 4 students and 2 professors be formed from 20 students and 8 professors? 135,660

47. Inventory orders. A manufacturer makes shirts in five different colors, seven different neck sizes, and three different sleeve lengths. How many shirts should a department store order in to have one of each type? 105

48. International book codes. All recent books are identified by their International Standard Book Number (ISBN), a ten-digit code assigned by the publisher. A typical ISBN is 0-321-75526-2. The first digit, 0, represents the language of the book (English), the second block of digits, 321, represents the publishing company (Addison-Wesley), the third block of digits, 75526, is the number assigned by the publishing company to that book, and the final digit, 2, is the check digit, which is used to detect the most commonly made errors when ISBNs are copied. How many ISBNs are possible? (Remember that the previous nine digits determine the last digit.) 1,000,000,000

49. Political polling. A senator sends out questionnaires asking his constituents to rank 10 issues of concern to them, such as

crime, education, and taxes, in order of importance. Replies are filed in folders, and two replies are put in the same folder if and only if they give the same ranking to all 10 issues. Find the maximum number of folders that might be needed. 3,628,800

50. Parcel delivery. A UPS driver has to deliver 12 parcels to 12 different addresses. In how many orders can the driver make these deliveries? 479,001,600

51. Circus visit. A father with seven children takes four of them at a time to a circus as often as he can, without taking the same four children more than once. What is the maximum number of times each child will go to the circus, and how many times will the father go? †

52. Arranging books. From six history books, four biology books, and five economics books, in how many ways can a person select three history books, two biology books, and four economics books and arrange them on a shelf? 217,728,000

53. Bingo. Each of four columns on a bingo card contains different numbers chosen in any order from 15. Column "B" chooses from 1 to 15, column "I" from 16 to 30, . . . , and column "O" from 61 to 75. How many different cards are possible? (*Note:* Only four numbers are under column "N," because of the free space.) 111,007,923,832,370,565

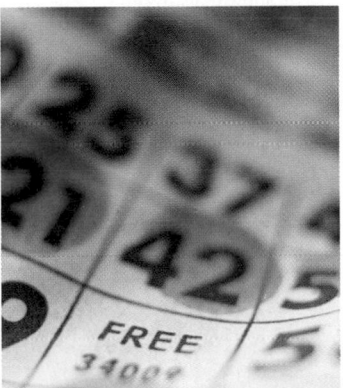

54. Football conferences. The Grid-Iron Football League in Sardonia is divided into two conferences—East and West—each having six members. Each team in the league must play each team in its conference twice and each team in the other conference once during a season. What is the total number of games played in the league? 96

55. Married couples prohibited. In how many ways can a committee of four people be selected from five married couples if no committee is to include husband-and-wife pairs? 80

56. Social club committees. A social club contains seven women and four men. The club wants to select a committee of three to represent it at a state convention. How many of the possible committees contain at least one man? 130

57. Coin gifts. Among Corey's collection of early American coins, he has a half-dollar, a quarter, a nickel, and a penny. He wants to give his younger sister some or all of these four coins. How many different sets of coins can Cory give? 15

58. Meal possibilities. The university cafeteria offers two choices of soups, three of salad, five of main dishes, and six of desserts. How many different four-course meals can you choose? 180

In Exercises 59–62, in how many distinguishable ways can the letters of each word be arranged?

59. TAIWAN 360

60. AMERICA 2520

61. SUCCESS 420

62. ARRANGE 1260

C Exercises   Beyond the Basics

63. A company that supplies temporary help has a contract for 20 weeks to provide three workers per week to an insurance firm. The agreement specifies that in no two weeks can the same three workers be sent to work at the firm. How many different workers are necessary? 6

64. An FM radio station wants to start its evening programming with five songs every day for 21 days without using the same five songs on any two days. What is the smallest number of songs that can be used to accomplish this result? 7

65. In geometry, any two points determine a line. How many lines are determined by 30 given points, no 3 of which lie on the same line? 435

66. In geometry, any 3 noncollinear points determine a triangle. How many triangles can be determined by 21 given points, no 3 of which are collinear? 1330

In Exercises 67–74, solve each equation.

67. $\binom{m+1}{m-1} = 3!$ $m = 3$

68. $6\binom{n-1}{2} = \binom{n+1}{4}$

69. $2\binom{n-1}{2} = \binom{n}{3}$ $n = 6$

70. $\frac{4}{3}\binom{k}{2} = \binom{k+1}{3}$ $k = 3$

71. $\binom{n}{0} + \binom{n}{1} + \binom{n}{2} + \cdots + \binom{n}{n} = 64$ $n = 6$

72. $\binom{k}{1} + \binom{k}{2} + \binom{k}{3} + \cdots + \binom{k}{k-1} = 126$ $k = 7$

73. $\binom{m}{4} = \binom{m}{5}$ $m = 9$

74. $\binom{n}{7} = \binom{n}{3}$ $n = 10$

Critical Thinking

75. How many terms of the form $x^n y^m$ are possible if n and m can be any integer such that $1 \leq n \leq 5$ and $1 \leq m \leq 5$? 25

76. Use the Fundamental Counting Principle to determine the number of terms in the product $(a + b)(x^2 + 2xy + y^2)$. Explain your reasoning. [*Hint:* Each term in the product can be obtained by multiplying one term chosen from each factor.]

Answer:

68. $n = 8$

Answer:

76. There are two terms in the first factor and three in the second, giving $(2)(3) = 6$ possibilities to multiply.

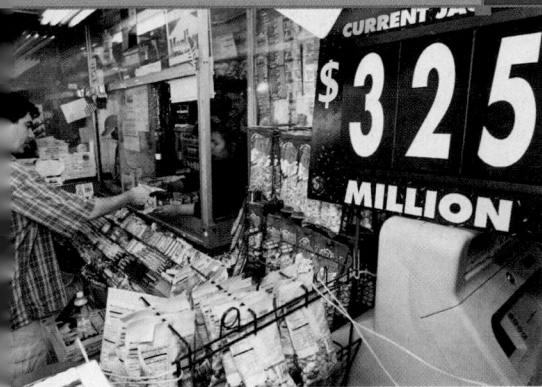

Probability

BEFORE STARTING THIS SECTION, REVIEW

1. Set notation (Section P.1, page 6)

2. Fundamental Counting Principle (Section 11.6, page 979)

3. Permutations (Section 11.6, page 981)

4. Combinations (Section 11.6, page 983)

OBJECTIVES

1 Find the probability of an event.

2 Use the Additive Rule for finding probabilities.

3 Find the probability of mutually exclusive events.

4 Find the probability of the complement of an event.

5 Find experimental probabilities.

Double Lottery Winner

Many people dream of winning a lottery, but only the most optimistic among us dream of winning it twice. When Evelyn Marie Adams won the New Jersey state lottery for the second time, the *New York Times* (February 14, 1986) claimed that the chances of one person winning the lottery twice were about 1 in 17 trillion. Two weeks later, a letter from two statisticians appeared in the *Times* challenging this claim. Although they agreed that any particular person had very little chance of winning a lottery twice, they said that it was almost certain that someone in the United States would win twice. Further, they said that the odds were even for another double lottery win to occur within seven years. In less than two years, Robert Humphries won his second Pennsylvania lottery prize.

Evaluating how likely an event is to occur is the realm of probability, which we study in this section. In Example 4, we determine the probability of winning a lottery in which 6 numbers are randomly selected from the numbers 1 through 53.

The toss of a coin determines which team will kick the ball to the other in order to start a football game. It seems everyone agrees that a coin toss gives both teams the same chance to choose whether to kick or receive the football. The ideas of "chance," "likelihood," and "probability" are all coupled with the desire to quantify expectations about the results of some process. We begin our discussion of probability with some agreements about terminology. ■

1 Find the probability of an event.

The Probability of an Event

Any process that terminates in one or more outcomes (results) is an **experiment**. For example, if we ask people what time of the day they typically eat their first meal, or if we pull balls from a bag of colored balls, we have performed an experiment. The outcomes of the first experiment are the times of day given as responses to our question. The outcomes of the second experiment are the colors of the balls drawn from the bag.

The set of all possible outcomes of a given experiment is called the **sample space** of the experiment. Suppose the experiment is tossing a coin; then the outcome "heads" could be denoted by H and the outcome "tails" by T. The sample space, S, can be written in set notation as

$$S = \{H, T\}.$$

A single die is a cube on which each face contains either one, two, three, four, five, or six dots and no two faces contain the same number of dots. A roll of the die is an experiment, the outcome of which is the number of dots showing on the upper face, and the sample space S can be written in set notation as

$$S = \{1, 2, 3, 4, 5, 6\}.$$

An event is any set of possible outcomes; that is, an **event** is any subset of a sample space. For the die-rolling experiment, one possible event is "The number showing is even." In set notation, we could write $E = \{2, 4, 6\}$ to denote this event. The event "The number showing is a 6" can be written in set notation as $A = \{6\}$.

Outcomes of an experiment are said to be **equally likely** if no outcome should result more often than any other outcome when the experiment is run repeatedly. In both the coin-tossing and the die-rolling experiments, all the outcomes are equally likely.

PROBABILITY OF AN EVENT

If all the outcomes in a sample space S are equally likely, then the **probability** of an event E, denoted $P(E)$, is the ratio of the number of outcomes in E, denoted $n(E)$, to the total number of outcomes in S, denoted $n(S)$. That is,

$$P(E) = \frac{n(E)}{n(S)}.$$

Because E is a subset of S, $0 \leq n(E) \leq n(S)$. Dividing by $n(S)$ yields $0 \leq \dfrac{n(E)}{n(S)} \leq 1$. So the probability $P(E)$ of an event E is a number between 0 and 1 inclusive. If E contains no outcomes, then it is not possible for E to occur and $P(E) = 0$. If $E = S$, then E is certain to occur and $P(E) = 1$.

EXAMPLE 1 **Finding the Probability of an Event**

A single die is rolled. Write each event in set notation and find the probability of the event.

a. E_1: The number 2 is showing.

b. E_2: The number showing is odd.

c. E_3: The number showing is less than 5.

d. E_4: The number showing is greater than or equal to 1.

e. E_5: The number showing is 0.

Solution

The sample space for the experiment of rolling a die is $S = \{1, 2, 3, 4, 5, 6\}$, so $n(S) = 6$.

For any event E, $P(E) = \dfrac{n(E)}{n(S)}$

a. $E_1 = \{2\}$, so $n(E_1) = 1$. $P(E_1) = \dfrac{n(E_1)}{n(S)} = \dfrac{1}{6}$

b. $E_2 = \{1, 3, 5\}$, so $n(E_2) = 3$. $P(E_2) = \dfrac{n(E_2)}{n(S)} = \dfrac{3}{6} = \dfrac{1}{2}$

c. $E_3 = \{1, 2, 3, 4\}$, so $n(E_3) = 4$. $P(E_3) = \dfrac{n(E_3)}{n(S)} = \dfrac{4}{6} = \dfrac{2}{3}$

d. $E_4 = \{1, 2, 3, 4, 5, 6\}$, so $n(E_4) = 6$. $P(E_4) = \dfrac{n(E_4)}{n(S)} - \dfrac{6}{6} = 1$

e. $E_5 = \varnothing$, so $n(E_5) = 0$. $P(E_5) = \dfrac{n(E_5)}{n(S)} = \dfrac{0}{6} = 0$ ■ ■ ■

PRACTICE PROBLEM 1   A single die is rolled. Write each event in set notation and give the probability of each event.

a. E_1: The number showing is even.   **b.** E_2: The number showing is greater than 4.   ■

Notice in Example **1d** that $E_4 = S$, so that the event E_4 is certain to occur on every roll of the die. Every **certain event** has probability 1. On the other hand, in Example **1e** the event $E_5 = \varnothing$, so E_5 never occurs, and $P(E_5) = 0$. An **impossible event** always has probability 0.

EXAMPLE 2   **Tossing a Coin**

What is the probability of getting at least one tail when a coin is tossed twice?

Solution

When a coin is tossed once, there are two equally likely outcomes: heads (H) and tails (T). When the coin is tossed twice, there are two equally likely outcomes for the first toss and, regardless of the first outcome, there are two equally likely outcomes for the second toss. By the Fundamental Counting Principle, there are $2 \cdot 2$, or 4, outcomes when we toss the coin twice. We can represent these outcomes as (first toss, second toss) pairs:

$$S = \{(H, H), (H, T), (T, H), (T, T)\}.$$

Three of these outcomes result in at least one tail—in set notation,

$$E = \{(H, T), (T, H), (T, T)\}.$$

Since $n(S) = 4$, and $n(E) = 3$, we have

$$P(E) = \frac{n(E)}{n(S)} = \frac{3}{4}.$$ ■ ■ ■

PRACTICE PROBLEM 2   What is the probability of getting exactly one head when a coin is tossed twice?   ■

Equally likely outcomes occur in most games of chance that involve tossing coins, rolling dice, or drawing cards. Lotteries and games involving spinning wheels also generate equally likely outcomes.

EXAMPLE 3 Rolling a Pair of Dice

What is the probability of getting a sum of 8 when a pair of dice is rolled?

Solution

There are six equally likely outcomes for each die, so, by the Fundamental Counting Principle, there are $6 \cdot 6$, or 36, equally likely outcomes when a pair of dice is rolled. It is useful to think of having two dice of different colors—say, red and green—in distinguishing the 36 outcomes. In this way, 2 on the red die and 6 on the green die is easily seen to be a different physical outcome from 6 on the red die and 2 on the green die, even though the same sum results.

We can represent the 36 outcomes as (red die, green die) pairs:

$$
\begin{aligned}
S = \{ &(1, 1), (1, 2), (1, 3), (1, 4), (1, 5), (1, 6), \\
&(2, 1), (2, 2), (2, 3), (2, 4), (2, 5), (2, 6), \\
&(3, 1), (3, 2), (3, 3), (3, 4), (3, 5), (3, 6), \\
&(4, 1), (4, 2), (4, 3), (4, 4), (4, 5), (4, 6), \\
&(5, 1), (5, 2), (5, 3), (5, 4), (5, 5), (5, 6), \\
&(6, 1), (6, 2), (6, 3), (6, 4), (6, 5), (6, 6) \}.
\end{aligned}
$$

The ordered pairs in the sample space that are highlighted are the outcomes for which the sum is 8. The event "The sum of the numbers on the dice is 8" is represented in set notation as

$$ E = \{(6, 2), (5, 3), (4, 4), (3, 5), (2, 6)\}. $$

Since $n(E) = 5$ and $n(S) = 36$, we have:

$$ P(E) = \frac{n(E)}{n(S)} = \frac{5}{36} $$

This means that in a random toss of a pair of dice, the probability of getting a sum of 8 is $\dfrac{5}{36}$. ■ ■ ■

PRACTICE PROBLEM 3 What is the probability of getting a sum of 7 when a pair of dice is rolled? ■

EXAMPLE 4 Winning the Florida Lottery

Table tennis balls numbered 1 through 53 are mixed together in a turning drum or basket. Six of the balls are chosen in a random way. To win the lottery, a player must have selected all six of the numbers chosen. The order in which the numbers are chosen does not matter. What is the probability of matching all six numbers?

(*Source:* www.fllottery.com)

Solution

Since the order in which the numbers are selected is not important, the sample space S consists of all sets of 6 numbers that can be selected from 53 numbers. Thus,

$n(S) = C(53, 6) = 22,957,480.$ Because there is only 1 set of 6 numbers that matches the 6 numbers drawn, the probability of the event "guessed all 6 numbers" is

$$P(\text{winning the lottery}) = P(\text{guessed all 6 numbers})$$

$$= \frac{1}{22,957,480} \approx 0.00000004.$$

Whether you say your chances of winning are 1 in 22,957,480 or about 0.00000004, you definitely know they are not very good!   ■ ■ ■

PRACTICE PROBLEM 4   A state lottery requires a winner to correctly select 6 out of 50 numbers. The order of the numbers does not matter. What is the probability of matching all six numbers?   ■

2 Use the Additive Rule for finding probabilities.

The Additive Rule

Consider the experiment of rolling one die. The sample space is $S = \{1, 2, 3, 4, 5, 6\}$, and $n(S) = 6$.

Let E be the event "The number rolled is greater than 4," and let F be the event "The number rolled is even." Then

$$E = \{5, 6\} \qquad \text{and} \qquad F = \{2, 4, 6\}.$$

The event "The number rolled is greater than 4 *and* even" is $E \cap F$.

$$E \cap F = \{6\}$$

Since $n(E) = 2$, $n(F) = 3$, $n(E \cap F) = 1$, and $n(S) = 6$, we have

$$P(E) = \frac{2}{6}, P(F) = \frac{3}{6}, P(E \cap F) = \frac{1}{6}.$$

The event "The number rolled is either greater than 4 *or* even" is $E \cup F$.

$$E \cup F = \{2, 4, 5, 6\}$$

Note that 6 is in *both* E and F, so it is counted once when $n(E)$ is counted and a second time when $n(F)$ is counted. However, 6 is counted only once when $n(E \cup F)$ is counted. We have $n(E \cup F) = n(E) + n(F) - n(E \cap F)$. That is, since 6 was counted twice when adding $n(E) + n(F)$, we must subtract $n(E \cap F)$ to get an accurate count for $E \cup F$.

$$n(E \cup F) = n(E) + n(F) - n(E \cap F)$$

$$\frac{n(E \cup F)}{n(S)} = \frac{n(E)}{n(S)} + \frac{n(F)}{n(S)} - \frac{n(E \cap F)}{n(S)} \qquad \text{Divide both sides by } n(S).$$

$$P(E \cup F) = P(E) + P(F) - P(E \cap F) \qquad \text{Definition of probability}$$

This example illustrates the *Additive Rule*.

THE ADDITIVE RULE

If E and F are events in a sample space, then

$$P(E \cup F) = P(E) + P(F) - P(E \cap F).$$

---

3 Find the probability of mutually exclusive events.

Mutually Exclusive Events

Two events are *mutually exclusive* if it is impossible for both to occur simultaneously. That is, E and F are **mutually exclusive** events if $E \cap F$ contains no outcomes. In this case, $P(E \cap F) = 0$ and the Additive Rule is somewhat simplified.

MUTUALLY EXCLUSIVE EVENTS

If E and F are any events in a sample space and $E \cap F = \varnothing$, then

$$P(E \cup F) = P(E) + P(F).$$

A standard deck of 52 playing cards uses four different designs called suits:

clubs, ♣; diamonds, ♦; hearts, ♥; and spades, ♠.

Each suit has 13 cards: an ace, king, queen, and jack, and cards numbered 2 through 10. The diamond and heart symbols are red, and the club and spade symbols are black. For the purposes of this section, we assume that all decks of cards are standard and well shuffled, so that all cards drawn or dealt from a deck are equally likely.

EXAMPLE 5   **Drawing a Card from a Deck**

A card is drawn from a deck. What is the probability that the card is

a. a king?   **b.** a spade?

c. either a king or a spade?   **d.** a heart or a spade?

Solution

The sample space S is the 52-card deck, so $n(S) = 52$.

a. There are four kings, one in each suit, so

$$P(\text{king}) = \frac{4}{52} = \frac{1}{13}.$$

b. There are 13 spades in the deck, so

$$P(\text{spade}) = \frac{13}{52} = \frac{1}{4}.$$

c. By the Additive Rule, we have

$$P(\text{king or spade}) = P(\text{king}) + P(\text{spade}) - P(\text{king and spade}).$$

Since there is only one card that is both a king and a spade, $P(\text{king and spade}) = \frac{1}{52}$. From parts **a** and **b** in this example,

$$P(\text{king or spade}) = \frac{4}{52} + \frac{13}{52} - \frac{1}{52}$$

$$= \frac{16}{52} = \frac{4}{13}.$$

d. Since no card is both a heart and a spade, the events "Draw a heart" and "Draw a spade" are mutually exclusive. Thus,

$$P(\text{heart or spade}) = P(\text{heart}) + P(\text{spade})$$
$$= \frac{13}{52} + \frac{13}{52} = \frac{1}{2}.$$

■ ■ ■

PRACTICE PROBLEM 5   What is the probability that a card pulled from a deck is a jack or a king?

■

4 Find the probability of the complement of an event.

The Complement of an Event

The **complement of an event** E is the set of all outcomes in the sample space that are *not* in E. The complement of E is denoted by E'. Because every outcome in the sample space is either in E or in E', the event $E \cup E'$ is a certain event and $P(E \cup E') = 1$. Also, E and E' are mutually exclusive events, so $P(E \cup E') = P(E) + P(E')$. Thus, $P(E) + P(E') = 1$ and $P(E') = 1 - P(E)$.

PROBABILITY OF THE COMPLEMENT

If E is any event and E' is its complement, then

$$P(E') = 1 - P(E).$$

EXAMPLE 6   **Finding the Probability of the Complement**

Brandy has applied to receive funding from her company to attend a conference. She knows that her name, along with the names of nine other deserving candidates, was put into a box from which two names will be drawn. What is the probability that Brandy will be one of the two selected?

Solution

It is easier to determine the probability that Brandy will *not* be selected. Since there are nine candidates other than Brandy, there are $C(9, 2)$ ways of selecting two employees not including Brandy. There are $C(10, 2)$ ways of selecting two employees from all ten candidates. Hence, the probability that Brandy is not selected is

$$P(\text{Brandy is not selected}) = \frac{C(9, 2)}{C(10, 2)}$$

$$= \frac{9!}{2! \, 7!} \cdot \frac{2! \, 8!}{10!} = \frac{8}{10} = \frac{4}{5}.$$

The probability that Brandy is selected is

$$P(\text{Brandy is selected}) = 1 - P(\text{Brandy is not selected})$$

$$= 1 - \frac{4}{5} = \frac{1}{5}.$$

■ ■ ■

PRACTICE PROBLEM 6   In Example 6, what is the probability of Brandy being selected if three names are drawn from the box?

■

5 Find experimental probabilities.

Experimental Probabilities

The probabilities we have seen up to this point have been determined by some form of reasoning. For example, although data support the decision to assign the value $\frac{1}{2}$ as the probability of a head resulting from one toss of a coin, the assignment is not *based* on data. This is also true for the probabilities associated with drawing a card, rolling a pair of dice, drawing a ball from an urn, and so on. Probability assigned in this way is called **theoretical probability**.

In contrast, we frequently assign probability values on the basis of observation and the use of data. Typically, an experiment is performed n times (where n is large), and if a particular outcome occurs k times, then the number $\frac{k}{n}$ is often accepted as a reasonable value for the probability of that outcome. When probability is determined in this way, it is called an **experimental probability**. A statement such as "The probability that a 10-year-old child will live to be 95 years old is $\frac{3}{100,000}$" refers to experimental probability.

RELATIVE FREQUENCY PRINCIPLE

If an experiment is performed n times, and an event E occurs k times, then we say that the experimental (or statistical) probability of the event, $P(E)$, is:

$$P(E) = \frac{k}{n}$$

EXAMPLE 7 **Using Data to Estimate Probabilities**

Table 11.2 shows the gender distribution of students at four California City colleges.

TABLE 11.2

College	Male	Female
Los Angeles	6,995	8,179
San Diego	12,251	14,914
San Francisco	16,857	2,000
Sacramento	9,040	11,838

(*Source:* www.areaconnect.com)

Find the probability that a student selected *at random* is:

a. a female   **b.** attending Los Angeles City College

c. a female attending Los Angeles City College

Round your answers to the nearest hundredth.

Solution

The phrase "randomly selected" means that every possible selection is equally likely. In our example, this means that each student is equally likely to be selected. With random selection, the percent of the students in a given category gives the probability that a student in that category will be chosen.

a. The total number of students is 82,074. The total number of female students is 36,931. Thus, $P(\text{female}) = \dfrac{36,931}{82,074} \approx 0.45.$

b. The total number of students is 82,074. The total number of students attending Los Angeles City College is 15,174. Hence,

$$P(\text{attends Los Angeles City College}) = \dfrac{15,174}{82,074} \approx 0.18.$$

c. There are 8179 female students attending Los Angeles City College. Consequently,

$$P(\text{female and attending Los Angeles City College}) = \dfrac{8179}{82,074} \approx 0.10. \qquad ■ ■ ■$$

PRACTICE PROBLEM 7   In Example 7, find the probability that a student selected at random is a male or attends Sacramento College. ■

A Exercises   Basic Skills and Concepts

In Exercises 1–6, write the sample space for each experiment.

1. Students are asked to rank Wendy's, McDonald's, and Burger King in order of preference. †

2. Students are asked to choose either a hamburger or a cheeseburger and then pick Wendy's, McDonalds, or Burger King as the restaurant from which they would prefer to order it. †

3. Two albums are selected from among *Thriller* (Michael Jackson), *The Wall* (Pink Floyd), *Eagles: Their Greatest Hits* (Eagles), and *Led Zeppelin IV* (Led Zeppelin). †

4. Three types of potato chips are selected from among regular salted, regular unsalted, barbecue, cheddar cheese, and sour cream and onion. †

5. Two blanks in a questionnaire are filled in, the first identifying race as white, African-American, Native American, Asian, other, or multiracial, and the second indicating gender as male or female. †

6. A six-sided die is chosen from a box containing a white, a red, and a green die. Then the die is tossed. †

In Exercises 7–10, find the probability of the given event if a year is selected at random.

7. Thanksgiving falls on a Sunday. 0

8. Thanksgiving falls on a Thursday. 1

9. Christmas falls on December 25. 1

10. Christmas falls on January 1. 0

In Exercises 11–20, classify each statement as an example of *theoretical probability* or *experimental probability*.

11. The probability that Ken will go to church next Sunday is 0.85. experimental

12. The probability of exactly two heads when a fair coin is tossed twice is $\dfrac{1}{4}$. theoretical

13. The probability of drawing a heart from a deck of cards is 0.25. theoretical

14. The probability that an American adult will watch a major network's evening newscast is 0.17. experimental

15. The probability that a person driving during the Memorial Day weekend will die in an automobile accident is $\dfrac{1}{58,000}$. †

16. The probability that a student will get a D or an F in a college statistics course is 0.21. experimental

17. The probability of drawing an ace from a deck of cards is $\dfrac{1}{13}$. †

18. The probability that a person will be struck by lightning this year is $\dfrac{1}{727,000}$. experimental

19. The probability that a plane will take off on time from JFK International airport is 0.78. experimental

20. The probability that a college student cheats on an exam is 0.32. experimental

21. Match each given sentence with an appropriate probability. †

An event that	has probability
is very likely to happen	0
will surely happen	0.5
is a rare event	0.001
may or may not happen	1
will never happen	0.999

†Due to space constrictions, answers to these exercises may be found in the Answers beginning on page A–1 in the back of the book.

22. A coin is tossed three times. Rearrange the order of the following events from the most probable event (first) to the least probable event (last):
{exactly two heads}, {the sure event}, {at least one head}, {at least two heads}. †

In Exercises 23–28, a die is rolled. Write each event in set notation and give the probability of each event.

23. The number showing is a 1 or a 6. †

24. The number 5 is showing. †

25. The number showing is greater than 4. †

26. The number showing is a multiple of 3. †

27. The number showing is even. †

28. The number showing is less than 1. $E = \varnothing, P(E) = 0$

In Exercises 29–34, a card is drawn randomly from a standard 52-card deck. Write each event in set notation and find its probability.

29. A queen is drawn. †

30. An ace is drawn. †

31. A heart is drawn. †

32. An ace of hearts or a king of hearts is drawn. †

33. A face card (jack, queen, or king) is drawn. †

34. A heart that is not a face card is drawn. †

In Exercises 35–40, a digit is chosen randomly from the digits 0 through 9, and then 3 is added to the digit and the sum recorded. Write each event in set notation and find the probability of the event.

35. The sum is 11. †

36. The sum is 0. $E = \varnothing, P(E) = 0$

37. The sum is less than 4. †

38. The sum is greater than 8. †

39. The sum is even. †

40. The sum is odd. †

B Exercises   Applying the Concepts

41. **A blind date.** The probability that Tony will like his blind date is 0.3. What is the probability that he will not like his blind date? 0.7

42. **Drawing cards.** The probability of drawing a spade from a standard 52-card deck is 0.25. What is the probability of drawing a card that is not a spade? 0.75

43. **Gender and the Air Force.** In 2006, about 20% of members of the U.S. Air Force were women. What is the probability that an Air Force member chosen at random is a woman? (*Source:* www.af.mil/news) †

44. **Movie attendance.** If 85% of people between the ages of 18 and 24 go to a movie at least once a month, what is the probability that a randomly chosen person in this age group will go to a movie this month? †

45. **Gender and the Marines.** In 2006, about 6% of members of the U.S. Marines were women. What is the probability that a Marine chosen at random is a man? (*Source:* DMDC-June 2005, TFDW-June 2005) †

46. **Movie attendance.** If 20% of people over 65 go to a movie at least once a month, what is the probability that a randomly chosen person over 65 will *not* go to a movie this month? †

47. **Raffles.** One hundred twenty-five tickets were sold at a raffle. If you have 10 tickets, what is the probability of your winning the (only) prize? If there are two prizes, what is the probability of your winning both? †

48. **Committee selection.** To select a committee with two members, two people will be selected at random from a group of four men and four women. What is the probability that a man and a woman will be selected? †

49. **Gender of children.** A couple has two children. Assuming that each child is equally likely to be a boy or a girl, find the probability of having
   a. two boys; †
   b. two girls; †
   c. one boy and one girl. †

50. **Gender of children.** A couple has three children. Assuming that each child is equally likely to be a boy or a girl, find the probability that the couple will have
   a. all girls; †
   b. at least two girls; †
   c. at most two girls; †
   d. exactly two girls. †

51. Car ownership. The following table shows the number of cars owned by each of the 4340 families in a small town:

No. of families	37	1256	2370	526	131	20
No. of cars owned	0	1	2	3	4	5

A family is selected at random. Find the probability that this family owns
a. exactly two cars; †
b. at most two cars; †
c. exactly six cars; 0
d. at most six cars; 1
e. at least one car. †

52. Mammograms. According to the American Cancer Society, 199 of 200 mammograms (for breast cancer screening) turn out to be normal. Find the probability that a mammogram of a woman chosen at random is not normal. †

53. Lactose intolerance. Lactose intolerance (the inability to digest sugars found in dairy products) affects about 20% of non-Hispanic white Americans, and about 75% of African, Asian, and Native Americans. What is the probability that a non-Hispanic white American has no lactose intolerance? Answer the same question for a person in the second group. †

54. Guessing on an exam. A student has just taken a ten-question "true or false" test. If he must guess to answer each of the ten questions, what is the probability that
a. he scores 100% on the test; †
b. he scores 90% on the test; †
c. he scores at least 90% on the test. †

55. Committee selection. A five-person committee is choosing a subcommittee of two of its members. Each member of the committee is of different age. The subcommittee members are chosen at random.
a. What is the probability that the subcommittee will consist of the two oldest members? †
b. What is the probability that the subcommittee consists of the oldest and the youngest members? †

56. How many children do mothers have? The following data are based on statistics published by the U.S. Census Bureau on the eve of Mother's Day in 2000: Among the 35 million mothers in the United States in the age group from 15 to 44 in 1998, 10.7 million had one child, 14.3 million had two children, 6.7 million had three, and 3.3 million had four or more. If a mother from this age group is chosen at random, what is the probability that she has more than one child? 0.6943

57. A test for depression. Suppose that 10% of the U.S. population suffers from depression. A pharmaceutical company is believed to have developed a test with the following results: The test works for 90% of the people who are tested and are actually depressed (as diagnosed through other acceptable methods). In other words, if a patient is actually depressed, then there is a probability of 0.9 that this patient will be diagnosed as a depressed patient by the pharmaceutical company. The test also works for 85% of people who are tested and not depressed. Suppose that the company tests 1000 people for depression. Complete the following table: †

Number of people who are	Depressed according to the test	Normal according to the test
Actually depressed		
Actually normal		

58. Playing marbles. Natasha and Deshawn are playing a game with marbles. Natasha has one marble (call it N) and Deshawn has two (call them M_1 and M_2). They roll their marbles toward a stake in the ground. The person whose marble is closest to the stake wins. Assume that measurements are accurate enough to eliminate ties. List all the sample points. Use the notation M_1NM_2 to denote the sample point when M_1 is closest to the stake and M_2 is farthest from the stake. If they are equally skillful (when the sample points are all equally likely), find the probability that Deshawn wins. †

59. Gender among siblings. If a family with four children is chosen at random, are the children more likely to be three of one gender and one of the other than two boys and two girls? (Assume that each child in a family is equally likely to be a boy or a girl.) †

60. Hospital treatments. Hospital records show that 11% of all patients admitted are admitted for surgical treatment, 15% are admitted for obstetrics, and 3% are admitted for both obstetrics and surgery. What is the probability that a new patient admitted is an obstetrics patient or a surgery patient or both? 0.23

61. Pain relief medicine. A pharmaceutical company testing a new over-the-counter pain relief medicine gave the new medicine, their old medicine, and placebos to different groups of patients. (A placebo is a sugar pill with no medicinal ingredients. However, it sometimes works, supposedly for psychological reason.) The following table shows the results of the tests:

Amount of Pain Relief

Medicine	Some	Complete	None
Placebo	12	4	44
Old	25	25	10
New	18	40	2
Total	55	69	56

Find the probability that a randomly chosen person from the group of 180 people receiving one of the three types of medicines

a. received the placebo or had no pain relief; †

b. received the new medicine or had complete pain relief. †

C Exercises   Beyond the Basics

62. A famous problem called the *birthday problem* asks for the probability that at least two people in a group of people have the same birthday (the same day and the same month, but not necessarily the same year). The best way to approach this problem is to consider the complementary event that no two people have the same birthday. Assume that all birthdays are equally likely.

a. Find the probability that, in a group of two people, both have the same birthday. †

b. Find the probability that, in a group of three people, at least two have the same birthday. †

c. Find the probability that, in a group of 50 people, at least two have the same birthday. †

63. What is the probability that a number between 1 and 1,000,000 contains the digit 3? [*Hint:* Consider the complementary event.] †

64. A business executive types four letters to her clients and then types four envelopes addressed to the clients. What is the probability that if the four letters are randomly placed in envelopes, they are placed in correct envelopes? †

65. Juan gave his telephone number to Maggie. She remembers that the first three digits are 407 and the remaining four digits consist of two 3's, one 6, and one 8. She is not certain about the order of the digits, however. Maggie dials 407-3638. What is the probability that Maggie dialed the correct number? †

Critical Thinking

66. The March 2005 population survey by the U.S. Census Bureau found that among the 187 million people age 25 or older, 59,840,000 reported high school graduation as the highest level of education attained. Find the probability that a person chosen at random from the 187 million in the survey would report his or her highest level of education as high school graduation. †

67. Find the probability of randomly choosing a dark caramel from a box that contains only light and dark caramels and has twice as many light as dark caramels. †

68. If a single die is rolled two times, what is the probability that the second roll will result in a number larger than the first roll? †

Summary   Definitions and Concepts

11.1 Sequences

i. An infinite sequence is a function whose domain is the set of positive integers. The function values $a_1, a_2, a_3, \ldots, a_n, \ldots$ are called the **terms** of the sequence. The term a_n is the **nth term,** or **general term,** of the sequence.

ii. *Recursive formula*

A sequence may be defined recursively, with the nth term of the sequence defined in relation to previous terms.

iii. *Factorial notation*

$$n! = n(n-1)\cdots 3 \cdot 2 \cdot 1 \text{ and } 0! = 1$$

iv. *Summation notation*

$$\sum_{i=1}^{n} a_i = a_1 + a_2 + a_3 + \cdots + a_n$$

v. *Series*

Given an infinite sequence $a_1, a_2, a_3, \ldots, a_n, \ldots$, the sum $\sum_{i=1}^{n} a_i$ is called the **nth partial sum,** and the sum

$$\sum_{i=1}^{\infty} a_i = a_1 + a_2 + a_3 + \cdots \text{ is called an \textbf{infinite series}.}$$

11.2 Arithmetic Sequences

i. A sequence is an **arithmetic sequence** if each term after the first differs from the preceding term by a constant. The constant difference d between the consecutive terms is called the **common difference.** We have $d = a_n - a_{n-1}$ for all $n \geq 1$.

ii. The nth term a_n of the arithmetic sequence $a_1, a_2, a_3 \ldots ,$ $a_n, \ldots$ is given by $a_n = a_1 + (n - 1)d, n \geq 1$, where d is the common difference.

iii. The sum S_n of the first n terms of the arithmetic sequence $a_1, a_2, \ldots , a_n, \ldots$ is given by the formula

$$S_n = n\left(\frac{a_1 + a_n}{2}\right).$$

11.3 Geometric Sequences

i. A sequence is a **geometric sequence** if each term after the first is a constant multiple of the preceding term. The constant ratio r between the consecutive terms is called the **common ratio.** We have $\frac{a_{n+1}}{a_n} = r, n \geq 1$.

ii. The nth term a_n of the geometric sequence $a_1, a_2, a_3, \ldots ,$ $a_n, \ldots$ is given by $a_n = a_1 r^{n-1}, n \geq 1$, where r is the common ratio.

iii. The sum S_n of the first n terms of the geometric sequence $a_1, a_2, \ldots , a_n, \ldots$ with common ratio $r \neq 1$ is given by the formula

$$S_n = \frac{a_1(1 - r^n)}{1 - r}.$$

The **sum S of an infinite geometric sequence** is given by

$$S = \sum_{i=1}^{\infty} a_1 r^{i-1} = \frac{a_1}{1 - r} \text{ if } |r| < 1.$$

iv. An **annuity** is a sequence of equal payments made at equal times. Suppose P is the payment made at the end of each of n compounding periods per year and i is the annual interest rate. Then the value A of the annuity after t years is

$$A = P\frac{\left(1 + \dfrac{i}{n}\right)^{nt} - 1}{\dfrac{i}{n}}.$$

v. If $|r| < 1$, the infinite geometric series $a_1 + a_1 r + a_1 r^2 + \cdots + a_1 r^{n-1} + \cdots$ has the sum $S = \dfrac{a_1}{1 - r}$. When $|r| \geq 1$, the series does not have a sum.

11.4 Mathematical Induction

The statement P_n is true for all positive integers n if the following properties hold:

i. P_1 is true.

ii. If P_k is a true statement, then P_{k+1} is a true statement.

11.5 The Binomial Theorem

i. Binomial coefficient: $\dbinom{n}{j} = \dfrac{n!}{j!(n - j)!}, 0 \leq j \leq n$

$$\binom{n}{0} = 1 = \binom{n}{n}$$

ii. Binomial theorem:

$$(x + y)^n = \binom{n}{0}x^n + \binom{n}{1}x^{n-1}y + \binom{n}{2}x^{n-2}y^2 + \cdots$$

$$+ \binom{n}{j}x^{n-j}y^j + \cdots + \binom{n}{n}y^n$$

$$= \sum_{j=0}^{n}\binom{n}{j}x^{n-j}y^j$$

iii. The term containing the factor x^j in the expansion of $(x + y)^n$ is

$$\binom{n}{n - j}x^j y^{n-j}.$$

11.6 Counting Principles

i. **Fundamental Counting Principle:** If a first choice can be made in p different ways, a second choice in q different ways, a third choice in r different ways, and so on, then the sequence of choices can be made in $p \cdot q \cdot r \cdots$ different ways.

ii. A **permutation** is an arrangement of n distinct objects in a fixed order in which no object is used more than once. The order in an arrangement is important.

iii. **Permutation formula:** The number of permutations of n distinct objects taken r at a time is

$$P(n, r) = \frac{n!}{(n - r)!} = n(n - 1)(n - 2)\ldots(n - r + 1).$$

iv. **Combination formula:** When r objects are chosen from n distinct objects without regard to order, we call the set of r objects a **combination** of n objects taken r at a time. The number of combinations of n distinct objects taken r at a time is denoted by $C(n, r)$, where

$$C(n, r) = \frac{n!}{(n - r)! \, r!}.$$

v. **Distinguishable Permutations:** The number of permutations of n objects of which n_1 are of one kind, n_2 are of a second kind, $\ldots$, and n_k are of a kth kind is

$$\frac{n!}{n_1! \, n_2! \ldots n_k!}$$

where $n_1 + n_2 + \cdots + n_k = n$.

11.7 Probability

i. **Experiment:** Any process that terminates in one or more **outcomes** (results) is an experiment.

ii. **Sample space:** The set of all possible outcomes of an experiment is called the sample space of the experiment.

iii. **Event:** An event is any subset of a sample space.

iv. Equally likely events: Outcomes of an experiment are said to be equally likely if no outcome should result more often than any other outcome when the experiment is performed repeatedly.

v. Probability: If all the outcomes in a sample space S are equally likely, the probability of an event E, denoted $P(E)$, is defined by

$$P(E) = \frac{n(E)}{n(S)},$$

where $n(E)$ is the number of outcomes in E and $n(S)$ is the total number of outcomes in S.

a. The Additive Rule: If E and F are events in a sample space S, then

$$P(E \text{ or } F) = P(E \cup F) = P(E) + P(F) - P(E \cap F).$$

b. If $E \cap F = \varnothing$, E and F are called **mutually exclusive events.** For mutually exclusive events E and F,

$$P(E \cup F) = P(E) + P(F).$$

c. $P(E') = P(\text{not } E) = 1 - P(E)$; the event E' is called the **complement of the event E.**

Review Exercises

In Exercises 1–4, write the first five terms of each sequence.

1. $a_n = 2n - 3$ †

2. $a_n = \dfrac{n(n-2)}{2}$ †

3. $a_n = \dfrac{n}{2n+1}$ †

4. $a_n = (-2)^{n-1}$ †

In Exercises 5 and 6, write a general term a_n for each sequence.

5. $30, 28, 26, 24, \ldots$ †

6. $-1, 2, -4, 8, \ldots$ †

In Exercises 7–10, simplify each expression.

7. $\dfrac{9!}{8!}$ 9

8. $\dfrac{10!}{7!}$ 720

9. $\dfrac{(n+1)!}{n!}$ $n+1$

10. $\dfrac{n!}{(n-2)!}$ $n^2 - n$

In Exercises 11–14, find each sum.

11. $\displaystyle\sum_{k=1}^{4} k^3$ 100

12. $\displaystyle\sum_{j=1}^{5} \dfrac{1}{2j}$ $\dfrac{137}{120}$

13. $\displaystyle\sum_{k=1}^{7} \dfrac{k+1}{k}$ $\dfrac{1343}{140}$

14. $\displaystyle\sum_{k=1}^{5} (-1)^k 3^{k+1}$ -549

In Exercises 15 and 16, write each sum in summation notation.

15. $1 + \dfrac{1}{2} + \dfrac{1}{3} + \dfrac{1}{4} + \cdots + \dfrac{1}{50}$ $\displaystyle\sum_{k=1}^{50} \dfrac{1}{k}$

16. $2 - 4 + 8 - 16 + 32$ †

In Exercises 17–20, determine whether each sequence is arithmetic. If a sequence is arithmetic, find the first term a_1 and the common difference d.

17. $11, 6, 1, -4, \ldots$ †

18. $\dfrac{2}{3}, \dfrac{5}{6}, 1, \dfrac{7}{6}, \ldots$ †

19. $a_n = n^2 + 4$ Not arithmetic

20. $a_n = 3n - 5$ †

In Exercises 21–24, find an expression for the nth term of each arithmetic sequence.

21. $3, 6, 9, 12, 15, \ldots$ $a_n = 3n$

22. $5, 9, 13, 17, 21, \ldots$ †

23. $x, x+1, x+2, x+3, x+4, \ldots$ $a_n = x + n - 1$

24. $3x, 5x, 7x, 9x, 11x, \ldots$ $a_n = (2n+1)x$

In Exercises 25 and 26, find the common difference d and the nth term a_n for each arithmetic sequence.

25. Third term: 7; eighth term: 17 $d = 2, a_n = 2n + 1$

26. 5th term: -16; 20th term: -46 $d = -2, a_n = -2n - 6$

In Exercises 27 and 28, find each sum.

27. $7 + 9 + 11 + 13 + \cdots + 37$ 352

28. $\dfrac{1}{4} + \dfrac{1}{2} + \dfrac{3}{4} + 1 + \cdots + 15$ $\dfrac{915}{2}$

In Exercises 29 and 30, find the sum of the first n terms of each arithmetic sequence.

29. $3, 8, 13, \ldots; n = 40$ 4020

30. $-6, -5.5, -5, \ldots; n = 60$ 525

In Exercises 31–34, determine whether each sequence is geometric. If a sequence is geometric, find the first term a_1 and the common ratio r.

31. $4, -8, 16, -32, \ldots$ †

32. $\dfrac{1}{5}, \dfrac{1}{10}, \dfrac{1}{20}, \dfrac{1}{40}, \ldots$ †

33. $\dfrac{1}{3}, 1, \dfrac{5}{3}, 9, \ldots$ †

34. $a_n = 2^{-n}$ †

In Exercises 35 and 36, for each geometric sequence, find the first term a_1, the common ratio r, and the nth term a_n.

35. $16, -4, 1, -\dfrac{1}{4}, \ldots$ †

36. $-\dfrac{5}{6}, -\dfrac{1}{3}, -\dfrac{2}{15}, -\dfrac{4}{75}, \ldots$ †

In Exercises 37 and 38, find the indicated term of each geometric sequence.

37. a_{10} when $a_1 = 2, r = 3$ $a_{10} = 39{,}366$

38. a_{12} when $a_1 = -2, r = \dfrac{3}{2}$ $a_{12} = -\dfrac{177{,}147}{1024}$

In Exercises 39 and 40, find the sum S_n of the first n terms of each geometric sequence.

39. $\dfrac{1}{10}, \dfrac{1}{5}, \dfrac{2}{5}, \dfrac{4}{5}, \ldots ; n = 12 \quad S_{12} = \dfrac{819}{2}$

40. $2, -1, \dfrac{1}{2}, -\dfrac{1}{4}, \ldots ; n = 10 \quad S_{10} = \dfrac{341}{256}$

In Exercises 41–44, find each sum.

41. $\dfrac{1}{2} + \dfrac{1}{6} + \dfrac{1}{18} + \dfrac{1}{54} + \cdots \quad \dfrac{3}{4}$

42. $-5 - 2 - \dfrac{4}{5} - \dfrac{8}{25} - \cdots \quad -\dfrac{25}{3}$

43. $\displaystyle\sum_{i=1}^{\infty} \left(\dfrac{3}{5}\right)^{i} \quad \dfrac{3}{2}$

44. $\displaystyle\sum_{i=1}^{\infty} 7\left(-\dfrac{1}{4}\right)^{i} \quad -\dfrac{7}{5}$

In Exercises 45 and 46, use mathematical induction to prove that each statement is true for all natural numbers n.

45. $\displaystyle\sum_{k=1}^{n} 2^{k} = 2^{n+1} - 2$ †

46. $\displaystyle\sum_{k=1}^{n} k(k + 1) = \dfrac{n(n + 1)(n + 2)}{3}$ †

In Exercises 47 and 48, evaluate each binomial coefficient.

47. $\dbinom{12}{7} \quad \dbinom{12}{7} = 792$

48. $\dbinom{11}{0} \quad \dbinom{11}{0} = 1$

In Exercises 49 and 50, find each binomial expansion.

49. $(x - 3)^{4}$ †

50. $\left(\dfrac{x}{2} + 2\right)^{6}$ †

In Exercises 51 and 52, find the specified term.

51. $(x + 2)^{12}$; term containing x^{5} $\quad 101{,}376x^{5}$

52. $(x + 2y)^{12}$; term containing x^{7} $\quad 25{,}344x^{7}y^{5}$

In Exercises 53–64, use any method to solve the problem.

53. How many different numbers can be written with the digits 1, 2, 3, and 4 if no digit may be repeated? 24

54. How many ways can horses finish in first, second, and third place in a ten-horse race? 720

55. In how many ways can seven people line up at a ticket window? 5040

56. In a building with seven entrances, in how many ways can you enter the building and leave by a different entrance? 42

57. In how many ways can five movies be listed on a display (vertically, one movie per line)? 120

58. How many different amounts of money can you make with a nickel, a dime, a quarter, and a half-dollar? 15

59. In how many ways can three candies be taken from a box of ten candies? 120

60. In how many ways can 2 face cards be drawn from a standard 52-card deck? 66

61. In how many ways can 2 shirts and three pairs of pants be chosen from 12 shirts and eight pairs of pants? 3696

62. How many doubles teams can be formed from eight tennis players? 28

63. In how many distinguishable ways can the letters of the word R E I T E R A T E be arranged? 15,120

64. A bookshelf has room for four books. How many different arrangements can be made on the shelf from six available books? 360

In Exercises 65–74, find the probability requested.

65. Four silver dollars, all with different dates, are randomly arranged on a horizontal display. What is the probability that the two with the most recent dates will be next to each other? †

66. A jar contains five white, three black, and two green stones. What is the probability of drawing a black stone on a single draw? †

67. The word R A N D O M has been spelled in a game of Scrabble®. If two letters are chosen from this word at random, what is the probability that they are both consonants? †

68. The names of all 30 party guests are placed in a box, and one name is drawn to award a door prize. If you and your date are among the guests, what is the probability that one of you will win the prize? †

69. If two people are chosen at random from a group consisting of five men and three women, what is the probability that one man and one woman are chosen? †

70. A company determines that 32% of the e-mail it receives is junk mail. What is the probability that a randomly chosen e-mail at this company is not junk mail? †

71. If 2 cards are drawn from a standard 52-card deck, what is the probability that both are clubs? †

72. A battery manufacturer inspects 500 batteries and finds that 30 are defective. What is the probability that a randomly selected battery is not defective? †

73. A ball is taken at random from a pool table containing balls numbered 1 through 9. What is the probability of obtaining (a) ball number 7? (b) an even-numbered ball? (c) an odd-numbered ball? †

74. A clothes dryer load contains two shirts, four pairs of socks, and three nightgowns. You pull one item randomly from the dryer.
   a. What is the probability that it is a sock? †
   b. What is the probability that it is a nightgown? †

Practice Test A

In Problems 1 and 2, write the first five terms of each sequence. State whether the sequence is arithmetic or geometric.

1. $a_n = 3(5 - 4n)$ †

2. $a_n = -3(2^n)$ †

3. Write the first five terms of the sequence defined by $a_1 = -2$ and $a_n = 3a_{n-1} + 5$ for $n \geq 2$. †

4. Evaluate $\dfrac{(n-1)!}{n!} \cdot \dfrac{1}{n}$

5. Find a_7 for the arithmetic sequence with $a_1 = -3$ and $d = 4$. $a_7 = 21$

6. Find a_8 for the geometric sequence with $a_1 = 13$ and $r = -\dfrac{1}{2}$. $a_8 = -\dfrac{13}{128}$

In Problems 7–9, find each sum.

7. $\displaystyle\sum_{k=1}^{20}(3k - 2)$ 590

8. $\displaystyle\sum_{k=1}^{5}\left(\dfrac{3}{4}\right)(2^{-k})$ $\dfrac{93}{128}$

9. $\displaystyle\sum_{k=1}^{\infty}18\left(\dfrac{1}{100}\right)^k$; write the answer as a fraction in lowest terms. †

10. Evaluate $\dbinom{13}{0}$. 1

11. Expand $(1 - 2x)^4$. $(1 - 2x)^4 = 16x^4 - 32x^3 + 24x^2 - 8x + 1$

12. Find the term containing x^1 in the expansion of $(2x + 1)^4$. $8x$

13. In how many ways can you answer every question on a true–false test containing ten questions? 1024

In Problems 14 and 15, evaluate each expression.

14. $P(9, 2)$ 72

15. $C(7, 5)$ 21

16. A firm needs to fill two positions—one in accounting and one in human resources. In how many ways can these positions be filled if there are six applicants for the accounting position and ten applicants for the human resources position? 60

17. A state is considering using license plates consisting of two letters followed by a four-digit number. How many distinct license plate numbers can be formed? 6,760,000

18. A box contains five red balls and seven black balls. What is the probability that a ball drawn at random will be red? †

19. What is the probability that a 4 does *not* come upon one roll of a die? †

20. A box contains seven quarters, six dimes, and five nickels. If two coins are drawn at random, what is the probability that both are quarters? †

Practice Test B

In Problems 1 and 2, write the first five terms of each sequence. State whether the sequence is arithmetic or geometric.

1. $a_n = 4(2n - 3)$ c
   a. $-1, 1, 3, 5, 7$; arithmetic
   b. $-1, 1, 3, 5, 7$; geometric
   c. $-4, 4, 12, 20, 28$; arithmetic
   d. $-4, 4, 12, 20, 28$; geometric

2. $a_n = 2(4^n)$ d
   a. $2, 8, 32, 128, 512$; arithmetic
   b. $2, 8, 32, 128, 512$; geometric
   c. $8, 32, 128, 512, 2048$; arithmetic
   d. $8, 32, 128, 512, 2048$; geometric

3. Write the first five terms of the sequence defined by $a_1 = 5$ and $a_n = 2a_{n-1} + 4$ for $n \geq 2$. a
   a. $5, 14, 32, 68, 140$
   b. $5, 14, 19, 24, 29$
   c. $5, 9, 13, 17, 21$
   d. $5, 8, 10, 12, 14$

4. Evaluate $\dfrac{(n + 2)!}{n + 2}$. c
   a. $2!$
   b. 1
   c. $(n + 1)!$
   d. $n + 1$

5. Find a_8 for the arithmetic sequence with $a_1 = -6$ and $d = 3$. a
   a. 15
   b. -271
   c. 30
   d. 18

6. Find a_{10} for the geometric sequence with $a_1 = 247$ and $r = \dfrac{1}{3}$. b
   a. 250
   b. $\dfrac{247}{19,683}$
   c. $\dfrac{247}{59,049}$
   d. $\dfrac{247}{177,147}$

In Problems 7 and 8, find each sum.

7. $\displaystyle\sum_{k=1}^{45}(4k - 7)$ d
   a. 4185
   b. 3735
   c. 4027.5
   d. 3825

8. $\displaystyle\sum_{k=1}^{5}\left(\frac{4}{3}\right)\left(2^{k}\right)$ a

   a. $\dfrac{248}{3}$ **b.** $\dfrac{251}{3}$

   c. $\dfrac{242}{3}$ **d.** $\dfrac{287}{3}$

9. Evaluate $\displaystyle\sum_{k=1}^{\infty}8(-0.3)^{k-1}$. b

   a. 6   **b.** 6.15

   c. -6.15 **d.** -4.15

10. Evaluate $\dbinom{12}{11}$. b

   a. $1.\overline{09}$ **b.** 12

   c. 1   **d.** 11!

11. Expand $(3x-1)^{4}$. a

   a. $81x^{4}-108x^{3}+54x^{2}-12x+1$

   b. $-81x^{4}+108x^{3}-54x^{2}+12x-1$

   c. $-81x^{4}+108x^{3}+54x^{2}+12x+1$

   d. $81x^{4}-108x^{2}+54x-12$

12. Find the coefficient of x in the expansion of $(2x+3)^{3}$. d

   a. 108   **b.** 9

   c. 36   **d.** 54

13. Karen has four necklaces, ten pairs of earrings, and three bracelets. In how many ways can she choose a necklace, a pair of earrings, and a bracelet? c

   a. 40   **b.** 17

   c. 120   **d.** 240

In Problems 14 and 15, evaluate each expression.

14. $P(7,3)$ a

   a. 210   **b.** 840

   c. 1680   **d.** 5040

15. $C(10,7)$ d

   a. 3   **b.** 720

   c. 620,400   **d.** 120

16. How many two-digit numbers can be formed from the digits 0, 1, 2, 3, 4, 5, 6, 7, 8, and 9? No digit can be used more than once. b

   a. 45   **b.** 81

   c. 3,628,880   **d.** 100

17. You have selected eight CDs for your dad, but have only enough money to buy five of them. In how many ways can you select the five if you decide that a particular CD is a "must buy"? d

   a. 56   **b.** 70

   c. 1680   **d.** 35

18. What is the probability of rolling a 5 on one roll of a die? c

   a. $\dfrac{1}{5}$ **b.** 4

   c. $\dfrac{1}{6}$ **d.** 0.05

19. What is the probability of getting a sum greater than 9 when a pair of dice is rolled? a

   a. $\dfrac{1}{6}$ **b.** $\dfrac{1}{4}$

   c. $\dfrac{1}{12}$ **d.** $\dfrac{1}{18}$

20. What is the probability that a card drawn at random from a standard 52-card deck is *not* a spade? d

   a. $\dfrac{2}{5}$ **b.** $\dfrac{1}{4}$

   c. $\dfrac{4}{13}$ **d.** $\dfrac{3}{4}$

Cumulative Review Exercises (Chapters 1–11)

In Problems 1–10, solve each equation or inequality.

1. $|3x-8|=|x|$ †

2. $x^{2}(x^{2}-5)=-4$ †

3. $\log_{2}(3x-5)+\log_{2}x=1$ $x=2$

4. $e^{2x}-e^{x}-2=0$ $x=\ln 2$

5. $\dfrac{6}{x+2}=\dfrac{4}{x}$ $x=4$

6. $2(x-8)^{-1}=(x-2)^{-1}$ $x=-4$

7. $\sqrt{x-3}=\sqrt{x}-1$ $x=4$

8. $x^{2}+4x\ge 0$ †

9. $18\le x^{2}+6x$ †

In Problems 10–11, solve each system.

10. $\begin{cases}5x+4y=6\\4x-3y=11\end{cases}$ $x=2, y=-1$

11. $\begin{cases}x-3y+6z=-8\\5x-6y-2z=7\\3x-2y-10z=11\end{cases}$ †

12. Graph the function $y=\cos\dfrac{2}{3}x$ over one period.

13. Use identities to find the exact value of $\sin\left(-\dfrac{7\pi}{12}\right)$.

14. Write the complex number $2+2\sqrt{3}i$ in polar form.

15. Use transformations to sketch the graph of
$f(x)=\sqrt{x}-3$. †

16. Find the domain of $f(x)=\dfrac{x+3}{x(x+1)}$. †

17. Write $7 \ln x - \ln(x - 5)$ in condensed form. †

18. If $A = \begin{bmatrix} 1 & 0 & -2 \\ 4 & 1 & 0 \\ 1 & 1 & 7 \end{bmatrix}$, find A^{-1}

19. Four students are pairing up to ride two tandem bicycles, each of which accommodates two riders, one in back and one in front. How many ways can this be done if we count arrangements as different if either the front or back rider is different? 12

20. A room has 6 people who are 25 years old or older and 12 people whose age is between 17 and 24. Half of the members of each group have gotten speeding tickets at some time. What is the probability that a person chosen at random from the room will be a person who is 25 years old or older or has gotten a speeding ticket at some time?

Answer:

12.

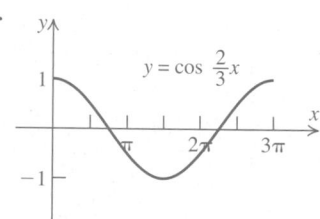

13. $\dfrac{-\sqrt{6} - \sqrt{2}}{4}$

14. $4\left(\cos\dfrac{\pi}{3} + i\sin\dfrac{\pi}{3}\right)$

18. $A^{-1} = \begin{bmatrix} 7 & -2 & 2 \\ -28 & 9 & -8 \\ 3 & -1 & 1 \end{bmatrix}$

Answer:

20. $\dfrac{2}{3}$

Answers

CHAPTER P

Section P.1

Practice Problems

1. **a.** true **b.** true **c.** true
2. $A \cap B = \{0\}$, $A \cup B = \{-4, -3, -2, -1, 0, 1, 2, 3, 4\}$
3. **a.** 10 **b.** 1 **c.** 1
4. 9
5. **a.** 5 **b.** 1 **c.** -33
6. **a.** 2 **b.** $-\dfrac{1}{7}$
7. **a.** $\dfrac{10}{3}$ **b.** $\dfrac{22}{3}$
8. $17°C$
9. $(-\infty, -2) \cup (-2, \infty)$

A Exercises: Basic Skills and Concepts

53. $|3 - 8| = 5$ 54. $|2 - 14| = 12$ 55. $|-6 - 9| = 15$
56. $|-12 - 3| = 15$ 57. $|-20 - (-6)| = 14$
58. $|-14 - (-1)| = 13$
59. $\left|\dfrac{22}{7} - \left(-\dfrac{4}{7}\right)\right| = \dfrac{26}{7}$ 60. $\left|\dfrac{16}{5} - \left(-\dfrac{3}{5}\right)\right| = \dfrac{19}{5}$

61. $1 \le x \le 4$

62. $-2 \le x \le 2$

63. $14 < x < 28$

64. $\dfrac{1}{2} < x < \dfrac{9}{2}$

65. $-3 < x \le 1$

66. $-6 \le x < -2$

67. $x \ge -3$

68. $x \ge 0$

69. $x \le 5$

70. $x \le -1$

71. $-\dfrac{3}{4} < x < \dfrac{9}{4}$

72. $-3 < x < \dfrac{1}{2}$

76. $6x + 10 - 2y$

77. reciprocal: $\dfrac{1}{5}$

80. reciprocal: $\dfrac{10}{17}$

81. additive inverse   82. additive inverse   83. multiplicative identity
84. multiplicative identity   85. multiplicative associative
86. multiplicative associative   87. multiplicative inverse
88. multiplicative inverse   89. additive identity
90. additive identity   92. additive, commutative and associative
107. $(-\infty, -1) \cup (-1, 0) \cup (0, \infty)$ 108. $(-\infty, 0) \cup (0, 5) \cup (5, \infty)$
109. $(-\infty, -2) \cup (-2, 1) \cup (1, \infty)$
110. $(-\infty, -3) \cup (-3, 0) \cup (0, \infty)$ 111. $(-\infty, 0) \cup (0, 2) \cup (2, \infty)$
112. $(-\infty, 3) \cup (3, \infty)$

P.1 B Exercises: Applying the Concepts
115. **a.** people who own either MP3 or DVD player
    b. people who own both MP3 and DVD player
117. $119.5 \le x \le 134.5$ 118. $30 < x \le 107$

Section P.2

Practice Problems

1. **a.** 8 **b.** $9a^2$ **c.** $\dfrac{1}{16}$ 2. **a.** $\dfrac{1}{2}$ **b.** 1 **c.** $\dfrac{4}{9}$
3. **a.** $3x^9$ **b.** 16 4. **a.** 81 **b.** 125 **c.** $\dfrac{2x^7}{3}$
5. **a.** 1 **b.** 1 **c.** $\dfrac{1}{x^8}$ **d.** x^{10} 6. **a.** $\dfrac{2}{x}$ **b.** $\dfrac{25}{x^2}$ **c.** x^3y^6 **d.** $\dfrac{x^6}{y^3}$
7. **a.** $\dfrac{1}{9}$ **b.** $\dfrac{49}{100}$
8. **a.** $\dfrac{1}{4x^8}$ **b.** $-\dfrac{1}{xy^3}$ 9. 7.32×10^5 10. $43 per person

A Exercises: Basic Skills and Concepts
6. Exponent: 2, base: -99 8. Exponent: 7, base: -3
17. $\dfrac{1}{81}$ 18. $\dfrac{1}{49}$ 19. $\dfrac{1}{15625}$ 20. $\dfrac{1}{125}$ 38. $\dfrac{1}{x}$ 39. $\dfrac{y}{x}$ 40. $\dfrac{x^2}{y^2}$
41. $-\dfrac{8}{x}$ 42. $\dfrac{1}{8x}$ 43. $\dfrac{3}{x}$ 44. $\dfrac{3y^2}{x^3}$ 45. $\dfrac{1}{xy^2}$ 46. $\dfrac{1}{x^3y^2}$
47. $\dfrac{1}{x^{12}}$ 48. $\dfrac{1}{x^{10}}$ 53. $\dfrac{4x^2}{y^2}$ 54. $\dfrac{6y^3}{x^3}$ 55. $\dfrac{3x^5}{y^5}$ 56. $-\dfrac{5y^6}{x^6}$

B Exercises: Applying the Concepts
85. **b.** $(3x)(3x) = 9x^2 = 3^2A$
86. **a.** $\pi\left(\dfrac{2d}{2}\right)^2 = 4\pi\left(\dfrac{d}{2}\right)^2 = 2^2A$ **b.** $\pi\left(\dfrac{3d}{2}\right)^2 = 9\pi\left(\dfrac{d}{2}\right)^2 = 3^2A$

Section P.3

Practice Problems
1. 889 ft   2. $5x^3 + 5x^2 + 2x - 4$ 3. $5x^4 - 5x^3 - x^2 - x + 12$
4. $-8x^5 - 4x^4 + 10x^3$ 5. $-10x^4 + x^3 - 33x^2 - 14x$
6. **a.** $4x^2 + 27x - 7$ **b.** $6x^2 - 19x + 10$
7. $9x^2 + 12x + 4$ 8. $1 - 4x^2$ 9. $x^2y + x^3$

A Exercises: Basic Skills and Concepts

1. Yes; $x^2 + 2x + 1$

4. Yes; $x^7 + 3x^5 + 3x^4 - 2x + 1$

6. degree: 2; terms: $-3x^2, 7$ **7.** degree: 4; terms: $-x^4, x^2, 2x, -9$

8. degree: 7; terms: $9x^7, 2x^3, x, -21$

12. $-2x^3 - 3x^2 + 9x - 6$ **13.** $-10x^4 - 6x^3 + 12x^2 - 7x + 17$

17. $2y^3 + y^2 - 2y - 1$ **18.** $6y^2 + 6y + 1$ **21.** $x^3 + 3x^2 + 4x + 2$

22. $2x^3 - 13x^2 + 16x - 5$ **23.** $3x^3 - 5x^2 + 5x - 2$

24. $2x^3 - 5x^2 + 5x + 4$ **25.** $x^2 + 3x + 2$ **26.** $x^2 + 5x + 6$

27. $9x^2 + 9x + 2$ **28.** $2x^2 + 11x + 15$ **29.** $-4x^2 - 7x + 15$

30. $-2x^2 + 11x - 5$ **31.** $6x^2 - 7x + 2$ **32.** $5x^2 - 8x + 3$

33. $4x^2 + 4ax - 15a^2$ **34.** $5x^2 + 23ax - 10a^2$

37. $9x^2 + 27x + 27$ **38.** $-6x^2 + 12x - 8$

41. $27x^3 + 27x^2 + 9x + 1$ **42.** $8x^3 + 36x^2 + 54x + 27$

43. $-4x^2 + 25$ **44.** $-16x^2 + 9$ **47.** $2x^3 - 9x^2 + 19x - 15$

48. $x^3 - 6x^2 + 5x + 6$ **49.** $y^3 + 1$ **50.** $y^3 + 64$ **51.** $x^3 - 216$

52. $x^3 - 1$ **53.** $3x^2 + 11xy + 10y^2$ **54.** $14x^2 + 11xy + 2y^2$

55. $6x^2 + 11xy - 7y^2$ **56.** $2x^2 - xy - 15y^2$ **57.** $x^4 - 2x^2y^2 + y^4$

58. $16x^4 - 8x^2y^2 + y^4$ **59.** $x^3 - 3x^2y + 4y^3$ **60.** $x^3 + 3x^2y - 4y^3$

61. $x^4 - 4x^3y + 16xy^3 - 16y^4$ **62.** $16x^4 + 16x^3y - 4xy^3 - y^4$

B Exercises: Applying the Concepts

63. In 2003, it was $6.02.

Section P.4

Practice Problems

1. a. $2x^3(3x^2 + 7)$ **b.** $7x^2(x^3 + 3x^2 + 5)$

2. a. $(x + 4)(x + 2)$ **b.** $(x - 5)(x + 2)$

3. a. $(x + 2)^2$ **b.** $(3x - 1)^2$

4. a. $(x + 4)(x - 4)$ **b.** $(2x - 5)(2x + 5)$

5. $(x^2 + 9)(x - 3)(x + 3)$

6. a. $(x - 5)(x^2 + 5x + 25)$ **b.** $(3x + 2)(9x^2 - 6x + 4)$

7. 16.224 million dollars

8. a. $(5x + 1)(x + 2)$ **b.** $(3x - 2)(3x - 1)$

9. a. $(x + 3)(x^2 + 1)$ **b.** $(7x - 5)(2x + 1)(2x - 1)$

A Exercises: Basic Skills and Concepts

7. $x^2(x^2 + 2x + 1)$ **8.** $x^2(x^2 - 5x + 7)$ **12.** $ax(x^3 - 2x + 1)$

13. $(x + 3)(x^2 + 1)$ **14.** $(x + 5)(x^2 + 1)$ **15.** $(x - 5)(x^2 + 1)$

16. $(x - 7)(x^2 + 1)$ **17.** $(3x + 2)(2x^2 + 1)$ **18.** $(x + 2)(3x^2 + 1)$

19. $x^2(3x^2 + 1)(4x^3 + 1)$ **20.** $x^2(x^2 + 1)(3x^3 + 1)$

21. $(x + 3)(x + 4)$ **22.** $(x + 3)(x + 5)$ **23.** $(x - 2)(x - 4)$

24. $(x - 2)(x - 7)$ **25.** $(x + 1)(x - 4)$ **26.** $(x + 1)(x - 6)$

29. $(2x + 9)(x - 4)$ **30.** $(2x + 9)(x - 3)$

31. $(2x + 3)(3x + 4)$ **32.** $(2x - 3)(4x + 1)$ **33.** $(3x + 1)(x - 4)$

34. $(x + 1)(5x + 2)$ **36.** $(2x + 1)(2x - 3)$ **50.** $(5x - 7)(5x + 7)$

51. $(x - 1)(x + 1)(x^2 + 1)$ **52.** $(x - 3)(x + 3)(x^2 + 9)$

53. $5(\sqrt{2}x - 1)(\sqrt{2}x + 1)(2x^2 + 1)$

54. $3(\sqrt{2}x - \sqrt{5})(\sqrt{2}x + \sqrt{5})(2x^2 + 5)$

55. $(x + 4)(x^2 - 4x + 16)$ **56.** $(x + 5)(x^2 - 5x + 25)$

57. $(x - 3)(x^2 + 3x + 9)$ **58.** $(x - 6)(x^2 + 6x + 36)$

59. $(2 - x)(4 + 2x + x^2)$ **60.** $(3 - x)(9 + 3x + x^2)$

61. $(2x - 3)(4x^2 + 6x + 9)$ **62.** $(2x - 5)(4x^2 + 10x + 25)$

63. $5(2x + 1)(4x^2 - 2x + 1)$ **64.** $7(x + 2)(x^2 - 2x + 4)$

71. $2(x + 1)(x - 5)$ **72.** $5(x + 2)(x - 4)$ **73.** $(2x - 5)(x + 4)$

74. $(2x + 5)(x - 6)$ **77.** $3x^3(x + 2)^2$

78. $2x^3(x + 4)^2$ **80.** $(4x + 5)(4x - 5)$

85. $x(5x + 2)(9x - 2)$ **86.** $x(5x - 1)(5x + 9)$

87. $a(x + a)(x - 8a)$ **88.** $a(x + 2a)(x - 12a)$

89. $(x + 4 + 4a)(x + 4 - 4a)$ **90.** $(x + 3 + 6a)(x + 3 - 6a)$

91. $3x^3(x + 2y)^2$ **92.** $4x^3(x + 3y)^2$ **93.** $(x + 2 + 5a)(x + 2 - 5a)$

94. $(x + 2 + 4a)(x + 2 - 4a)$ **95.** $2x^4(3x + y)^2$ **96.** $3x^4(2x + y)^2$

B Exercises: Applying the Concepts

97. $x(8 - x)$ **100.** $4(12 - x)(12 + x)$

Section P.5

Practice Problems

1. 0.32   **2. a.** $\dfrac{2x}{3}$ **b.** $\dfrac{x - 2}{x + 2}$ **3.** $\dfrac{x(x - 3)}{14}$

4. a. $\dfrac{7}{x - 6}$ **b.** $\dfrac{1}{x + 4}$ **5. a.** $\dfrac{x(5x - 4)}{(x + 2)(x - 5)}$ **b.** $\dfrac{x(3x + 23)}{(x + 3)(x - 4)}$

6. a. $3x^2(x + 2)^2(x - 2)^2$ **b.** $(x - 5)(x + 5)(x - 1)$

7. a. $\dfrac{x^2 + 2x + 8}{(x + 2)(x - 2)^2}$ **b.** $\dfrac{45 - 7x}{3(x - 5)^2}$ **8.** $\dfrac{1}{x - 5}$ **9.** $\dfrac{25x}{15x - 12}$

A Exercises: Basic Skills and Concepts

3. $\dfrac{3}{x - 1}, x \neq -1, x \neq 1$ **4.** $\dfrac{5}{2 + x}, x \neq -2, x \neq 2$

5. $-\dfrac{2}{x + 3}, x \neq -3, x \neq 3$ **6.** $\dfrac{3}{x - 5}, x \neq -5, x \neq 5$

10. $\dfrac{x - 5}{3}, x \neq 5$ **12.** $\dfrac{4x}{x + 3}, x \neq -3$

13. $\dfrac{x - 10}{x + 7}, x \neq -7, x \neq 1$ **14.** $\dfrac{x + 5}{x - 4}, x \neq 3, x \neq 4$

15. $\dfrac{x + 2}{x - 2}, x \neq -\dfrac{1}{3}, x \neq 0, x \neq 2$

16. $\dfrac{1}{x - 4}, x \neq -\dfrac{1}{3}, x \neq 0, x \neq 4$ **19.** $\dfrac{x + 3}{2(x - 3)}$

20. $\dfrac{(5x + 3)(x + 2)}{4}$ **21.** $\dfrac{x - 1}{x}$ **29.** $\dfrac{5x(x - 3)}{2}$

44. $\dfrac{2x}{(x - 1)^2}$ **45.** $\dfrac{4x}{x - 3}$ **46.** $\dfrac{3x}{(x + 5)^2}$

49. $\dfrac{2(1 - 3x)}{(2x - 1)(2x + 1)}$ **50.** $\dfrac{1 - 8x}{(4x - 1)(4x + 1)}$

51. $-\dfrac{x^3 + 2x^2 + 4x - 8}{x(x - 2)(x + 2)}$ **52.** $\dfrac{2x^3 + 6x^2 - x - 1}{x(x - 1)(x + 1)}$ **54.** $21(1 + 3x)$

55. $(2x - 1)(2x + 1)^2$ **56.** $(3x + 1)(3x - 1)^2$

57. $(x - 1)(x + 1)(x + 2)$ **58.** $(x - 3)(x + 3)(x + 2)$

59. $(x - 1)(x - 4)(x + 2)$ **60.** $(x - 3)(x + 1)(x + 2)$

61. $\dfrac{7x + 15}{(x - 3)(x + 3)}$ **62.** $\dfrac{x(3x + 4)}{(x - 1)(x + 1)}$ **63.** $\dfrac{x(4 - x)}{(x - 2)(x + 2)}$

64. $\dfrac{2x^2 + 6x + 5}{(x - 4)(x + 4)}$ **67.** $\dfrac{2(9x^2 - 5x + 1)}{(3x + 1)(3x - 1)^2}$

68. $\dfrac{2(4x^2 + 3x + 1)}{(2x - 1)(2x + 1)^2}$ **69.** $\dfrac{9(x - 3)}{(x + 4)(x + 5)(x - 5)}$

70. $-\dfrac{7}{(x + 4)(x - 3)}$ **73.** $\dfrac{16a^2}{(x - 5a)(x - 3a)}$

74. $\dfrac{5x^2}{(2x - a)(3x + a)}$ **76.** $-\dfrac{h(2x + h)}{x^2(x + h)^2}$

87. $-\dfrac{1}{x(x + h)}, x \neq -h, x \neq 0$ **88.** $-\dfrac{2x + h}{x^2(x + h)^2}, x \neq -h, x \neq 0$

89. $\dfrac{x}{a}, x \neq -a, x \neq a$

B Exercises: Applying the Concepts

93. a. $\dfrac{3}{100 + x}$ **94. a.** $\dfrac{1500}{200,000 + x}$ **95. a.** $\dfrac{10\pi x^3 + 240}{x}$

96. a. $\dfrac{40x^3 + 360}{x}$ **b.** $3.30

Section P.6

Practice Problems

1. a. 12   **b.** $\dfrac{1}{7}$ **c.** $\dfrac{2}{8}$

2. a. $2\sqrt{5}$ **b.** $4\sqrt{3}$ **c.** $2|x|\sqrt{3}$ **d.** $\dfrac{2|y|\sqrt{5y}}{3\sqrt{3}|x|}$

4. a. $\dfrac{14\sqrt{2}}{8}$ **b.** $-\dfrac{1 + \sqrt{7}}{2}$ **c.** $\dfrac{x\sqrt{x} + 3x}{x - 9}$

5. a. -2 **b.** 2   **c.** 3   **d.** not a real number

6. a. $2\sqrt[3]{9}$ **b.** $2\sqrt[4]{3a^2}$ **7. a.** $13\sqrt{3}$ **b.** 0

8. $\sqrt[10]{972}$ **9. a.** $\dfrac{1}{2}$ **b.** 5   **c.** -2

10. a. $5\sqrt[3]{5}$ **b.** -216 **c.** $\dfrac{1}{1024}$ **d.** not a real number

11. a. $12x^{\frac{7}{10}}$ **b.** $\dfrac{5}{x^{\frac{7}{12}}}$ **c.** $\dfrac{1}{x^{\frac{2}{15}}}$

12. $\dfrac{(2x + 3)(x + 3)^{\frac{1}{2}}}{x + 3}$ **13. a.** $\sqrt[3]{x^2}$ **b.** 5   **c.** x^2

A Exercises: Basic Skills and Concepts

45. $6\sqrt{7}$ **68.** $\dfrac{2x + h - 2\sqrt{x(x + h)}}{h}$ **76.** $-\dfrac{1}{125}$ **77.** $-\dfrac{1}{27}$

86. $\dfrac{1}{9x^4 y^2}$ **87.** $\dfrac{1}{64x^6 y^9}$ **106.** $\sqrt[12]{40m^{11}n^5}$ **107.** $xy(\sqrt[6]{2187xy})$

108. $xy(\sqrt[30]{x^9 y^{13}})$ **109.** $ab(\sqrt[10]{63})$

Section P.7

Practice Problems

1. 10   **2.** 10 feet   **3.** No

B Exercises: Applying the Concepts

32. $4\sqrt{5} \approx 8.94$ ft   **37.** 39 ft^2

Review Exercises

1. d. $\left\{-5, 0, 0.2, 0.\overline{31}, \dfrac{1}{2}, 4\right\}$

f. $\left\{-5, 0, 0.2, 0.\overline{31}, \dfrac{1}{2}, \sqrt{12}, 4, \sqrt[3]{7}\right\}$

6. $-2 \le x < 3$ **7.** $x \le 1$

8. $[1, 4)$ **9.** $(0, \infty)$

24. $\dfrac{1}{729}$ **33.** $\dfrac{1}{4}$ **48.** $\dfrac{x^2}{343y}$ **59.** $\sqrt{6}$ **71.** 2.3051×10^{13}

73. $4x^3 - 12x^2 + 9x - 6$ **74.** $5x^3 + 9x^2 - 11x + 6$

75. $9x^4 + 11x^3 - 12x^2 + 14$ **76.** $15x^4 + 7x^3 + 11x^2 + 2$

83. $(x - 5)(x + 2)$ **84.** $(x + 1)(x + 9)$ **85.** $(6x - 11)(4x + 1)$

86. $3(5x + 6)(x + 1)$ **87.** $(x + 5)(x + 11)$ **88.** $(x - 1)(x^2 + 2)$

89. $(x - 1)(x^3 + 7)$ **91.** $(5x + 4)(2x + 3)$ **92.** $(4x + 3)(2x + 3)$

93. $(4x - 3)(3x + 4)$ **96.** $(4x - 9)(4x + 9)$

100. $(2x - 1)(4x^2 + 2x + 1)$ **101.** $(2x + 3)(4x^2 - 6x + 9)$

102. $7(x - 1)(x^2 + x + 1)$ **103.** $(x - 4)(x + 4)(x + 5)$

104. $(x - 3)(x + 3)(x + 6)$ **115.** $\dfrac{(1 - x)(1 + x + x^2)}{(1 + x)(1 - x + x^2)}$

121. $A = 96, P = 48$ **126.** $\dfrac{20,000}{1,000,000 + x}$

CHAPTER 1

Section 1.1

Practice Problems

1. a. $-\infty, \infty$ **b.** $(-\infty, 2) \cup (2, \infty)$ **c.** $[1, \infty)$

2. $\{-1\}$ **3.** $\{2\}$ **4.** $10°C$

5. $w = \dfrac{P - 2l}{2}$ **6.** 34.3 ft

A Exercises: Basics Skills and Concepts

18. $\left\{-\dfrac{1}{2}\right\}$ **22.** $-\dfrac{1}{2}$ **24.** $\dfrac{3}{5}$ **27.** $\{1\}$ **28.** $\{-8\}$ **31.** $\left\{\dfrac{7}{4}\right\}$

32. $\left\{-\dfrac{1}{16}\right\}$ **34.** $\left\{-\dfrac{35}{4}\right\}$ **37.** $\left\{\dfrac{23}{6}\right\}$ **38.** $\left\{-\dfrac{5}{2}\right\}$

39. $\left\{\dfrac{7}{8}\right\}$ **44.** $\left\{\dfrac{-1}{11}\right\}$ **47.** $r = \dfrac{d}{t}$ **48.** $a = \dfrac{F}{m}$ **49.** $r = \dfrac{C}{2\pi}$

50. $x = \dfrac{A - \pi r^2}{2\pi r}$ **52.** $t = \dfrac{A - P}{rP}$ **53.** $h = \dfrac{2A}{a + b}$

54. $d = \dfrac{T - a}{n - 1}$ **55.** $u = \dfrac{fv}{v - f}$ **56.** $R_2 = \dfrac{RR_1}{R_1 - R}$

57. $m = \dfrac{y - b}{x}$ **58.** $y = \dfrac{c - ax}{b}$

B Exercises: Applying the Concepts

60. 8 ft

C Exercises: Beyond the Basics

77. a. No, because the solution sets are $\{0,1\}$ and $\{1\}$, respectively.
   b. No, because the solution sets are $\{-3, 3\}$ and $\{3\}$ respectively.
   c. No, because the solution sets are $\{0, 1\}$ and $\{0\}$ respectively.
   d. No, because the solution sets are $\{\varnothing\}$ and $\{2\}$ respectively.

78. Division by 0 is used in the proof, since $x = 1$.

84. $\dfrac{a + 3}{a + 2}$

Section 1.2

Practice Problems

1. $3750 in bonds and $11,250 in stocks   **2.** $1500   **3.** 395 m
4. 2.5 hr   **5.** 18 min   **6.** 12.5 gal

A Exercises: Basics Skills and Concepts

2. $\dfrac{5}{6}x$ **3.** $22,000 - x$ **4.** $\dfrac{229.50 - 72}{x}$

5. a. Natasha: $\dfrac{1}{4}t$;   **b.** Natasha's brother: $\dfrac{1}{5}t$.

6. a. Jermaine: $\dfrac{1}{3}t$,   **b.** Ralph: $\dfrac{1}{2}t$.

7. a. $10 - x$ **b.** $4.60x$ **c.** $7.40(10 - x)$

8. a. $15 - x$ **b.** $6.25(15 - x)$ **c.** $5.50x$

9. a. $8 + x$ **b.** $0.8 + x$

10. a. $1 + x$ **b.** $\left(\dfrac{0.25}{1 + x} \times 100\right)\%$

B Exercises: Applying the Concepts
11. $62,000 and $85,000
13. July: 530 tickets; August: 583 tickets.
16. Kevin got $420,000; Kevin's daughter got $210,000; Kevin's dad got $105,000.
17. $1600 invested in high-risk venture and $2600 in savings and loan.
18. $4000 in a tax shelter and $3000 in a bank.
19. Angelina: 30 m/min; Harry: 45 m/min

21. $\dfrac{12}{49}$ qt **23.** $336

27. 75 kg of the 35% chicory and 425 kg of the 15% chicory.
34. nickels and dimes: 46, quarters: 44.
35. 100 mph and 107 mph. **36.** 10 h and 48 min **38.** 305,728
44. 20 tickets for $3.75 and 2 tickets for $4.50 **45.** 6%, 12%
C Exercises: Beyond the Basics
55. 26 min

Section 1.3

Practice Problems

1. a. real $= -1$, imaginary $= 2$ **b.** real $= -\dfrac{1}{3}$, imaginary $= -6$

c. real $= 8$, imaginary $= 0$
2. a. $4 - 2i$ **b.** $-1 + 4i$ **c.** $-2 + 5i$
3. a. $26 + 2i$ **b.** $-15 - 21i$
4. $\dfrac{121}{100} - \dfrac{4}{5}i$ **5. a.** 37 **b.** 4

6. a. $1 + i$ **b.** $-\dfrac{15}{41} - \dfrac{12}{41}i$

A Exercises: Basics Skills and Concepts
1. $x = 3, y = 2$ **2.** $x = 7, y = -2$ **3.** $x = 2, y = -4$
4. $x = 3, y = -5$ **6.** $7 + 3i$ **7.** $-1 - 6i$ **9.** $-5 - 5i$
10. $-3 - 4i$ **24.** $-24 - 29i$ **25.** $-141 - 24\sqrt{3}i$
26. $-164 + 26\sqrt{5}i$ **27.** $26 - 2i$ **28.** $25 + 19i$
29. $\bar{z} = 2 + 3i, z\bar{z} = 13$

30. $\bar{z} = 4 - 5i, z\bar{z} = 41$ **31.** $\bar{z} = \dfrac{1}{2} + 2i, z\bar{z} = \dfrac{17}{4}$

32. $\bar{z} = \dfrac{2}{3} - \dfrac{1}{2}i, z\bar{z} = \dfrac{25}{36}$ **33.** $\bar{z} = \sqrt{2} + 3i, z\bar{z} = 11$

34. $\bar{z} = \sqrt{5} - \sqrt{3}i, z\bar{z} = 8$
B Exercises: Applying the Concepts
50. $\dfrac{241}{82} + \dfrac{37}{82}i$ **51.** $Z = \dfrac{595}{74} + \dfrac{315}{74}i$ **52.** $Z = \dfrac{667}{65} + \dfrac{436}{65}i$

53. $V = 45 + 11i$ **54.** $V = \dfrac{11}{3} - \dfrac{3}{2}i$ **55.** $I = \dfrac{17}{15} + \dfrac{4}{15}i$

56. $I = \dfrac{833}{661} + \dfrac{276}{661}i$

Section 1.4

Practice Problems

1. $\{-21, -4\}$ **2.** $\left\{0, \dfrac{5}{2}\right\}$ **3.** $\{3\}$ **4.** $\{-2 - \sqrt{5}, -2 + \sqrt{5}\}$

5. $\{3 - \sqrt{2}, 3 + \sqrt{2}\}$

6. $\left\{3 - \dfrac{\sqrt{11}}{2}, 3 + \dfrac{\sqrt{11}}{2}\right\}$ **7.** $\left\{-\dfrac{1}{2}, \dfrac{2}{3}\right\}$

8. a. $\left\{-\dfrac{3}{2}i, \dfrac{3}{2}i\right\}$ **b.** $\{2 - 3i, 2 + 3i\}$
9. a. one real **b.** two unequal real **c.** 2 nonreal complex
10. 25.48 ft by 127.41 ft **11.** $18 + 18\sqrt{5} \approx 58.25$ ft
A Exercises: Basics Skills and Concepts

10. $k = \dfrac{3 - \sqrt{7}}{7}$ **17.** $\left\{-3, \dfrac{1}{2}\right\}$ **18.** $\left\{2, \dfrac{5}{2}\right\}$ **19.** $\left\{-1, -\dfrac{2}{3}\right\}$

20. $\left\{-\dfrac{4}{3}, -\dfrac{1}{2}\right\}$ **21.** $\left\{-2, -\dfrac{2}{5}\right\}$ **22.** $\left\{-1, \dfrac{5}{3}\right\}$ **23.** $\left\{-3, \dfrac{5}{2}\right\}$

24. $\left\{-\dfrac{1}{2}, \dfrac{1}{3}\right\}$ **25.** $\left\{-\dfrac{2}{3}, \dfrac{3}{2}\right\}$ **26.** $\{-30, 40\}$ **27.** $\left\{\dfrac{1}{6}, \dfrac{7}{3}\right\}$

28. $\left\{-\dfrac{5}{3}, -\dfrac{3}{2}\right\}$ **29.** $\left\{-\dfrac{25}{2}, 15\right\}$ **30.** $\left\{-\dfrac{9}{4}, -\dfrac{4}{3}\right\}$

36. $\left\{-\dfrac{3}{2}i, \dfrac{3}{2}i\right\}$ **39.** $\dfrac{2}{3} - \dfrac{4}{3}i, \dfrac{2}{3} + \dfrac{4}{3}i$ **40.** $-\dfrac{3}{2} - \dfrac{5}{2}i, -\dfrac{3}{2} + \dfrac{5}{2}i$

45. $\dfrac{49}{4}$ **46.** $\dfrac{9}{4}$ **49.** $\dfrac{a^2}{4}$ **51.** $\{-1 - \sqrt{6}, -1 + \sqrt{6}\}$

52. $\{-3 - \sqrt{2}, -3 + \sqrt{2}\}$ **53.** $\left\{\dfrac{3 - \sqrt{13}}{2}, \dfrac{3 + \sqrt{13}}{2}\right\}$

54. $\left\{\dfrac{1 - \sqrt{13}}{2}, \dfrac{1 + \sqrt{13}}{2}\right\}$ **55.** $\left\{-3, \dfrac{3}{2}\right\}$

56. $\left\{\dfrac{5}{6} - \dfrac{\sqrt{13}}{6}, \dfrac{5}{6} + \dfrac{\sqrt{13}}{6}\right\}$ **57.** $\{1 - i, 1 + i\}$

58. $\{3 - i\sqrt{2}, 3 + i\sqrt{2}\}$ **59.** $\{5 - i\sqrt{3}, 5 + i\sqrt{3}\}$

60. $\left\{-\dfrac{1}{2} - i, -\dfrac{1}{2} + i\right\}$ **61.** $\{6 - \sqrt{33}, 6 + \sqrt{33}\}$

62. $\left\{-\dfrac{3 + \sqrt{19}}{2}, -\dfrac{3 - \sqrt{19}}{2}\right\}$ **63.** $\left\{-\dfrac{7 + \sqrt{13}}{6}, -\dfrac{7 - \sqrt{13}}{6}\right\}$

64. $\left\{\dfrac{3 - \sqrt{41}}{4}, \dfrac{3 + \sqrt{41}}{4}\right\}$ **65.** $\{-1 - \sqrt{5}, -1 + \sqrt{5}\}$

66. $\{-2, -1\}$ **67.** $\left\{-\dfrac{1}{2}, \dfrac{5}{3}\right\}$ **68.** $\{2 - i\sqrt{3}, 2 + i\sqrt{3}\}$

69. $\left\{\dfrac{1 - \sqrt{22}}{3}, \dfrac{1 + \sqrt{22}}{3}\right\}$ **70.** $\left\{-\dfrac{5}{2}, \dfrac{2}{3}\right\}$ **71.** $\left\{-2, -\dfrac{2}{3}\right\}$

72. $\left\{\dfrac{4}{7} - \dfrac{\sqrt{5}}{7}i, \dfrac{4}{7} + \dfrac{\sqrt{5}}{7}i\right\}$ **73.** $\left\{\dfrac{5 - \sqrt{5}}{2}, \dfrac{5 + \sqrt{5}}{2}\right\}$

74. $\{-9 - \sqrt{14}, -9 + \sqrt{14}\}$ **75.** $\left\{\dfrac{1}{4} - \dfrac{\sqrt{7}}{4}i, \dfrac{1}{4} + \dfrac{\sqrt{7}}{4}i\right\}$

76. $\{2 - \sqrt{2}, 2 + \sqrt{2}\}$ **77.** $\left\{-\dfrac{\sqrt{10}}{2}, \dfrac{\sqrt{10}}{2}\right\}$ **79.** $\left\{-\dfrac{5}{3}i, \dfrac{5}{3}i\right\}$

80. $\left\{-\dfrac{2\sqrt{3}}{3}i, \dfrac{2\sqrt{3}}{3}i\right\}$ **81.** $D = 0$, real equal roots
82. $D = -20$, complex roots **83.** $D = 49$, real unequal roots
84. $D = 0$, real equal roots **85.** $D = 1$, real unequal roots
86. $D = -11$, complex roots **87.** $D = 252$, real unequal roots
88. $D = 2$, real unequal roots
B Exercises: Applying the Concepts
102. 442.44 km/h and 542.44 km/h
C Exercises: Beyond the Basics

107. $-2\sqrt{3}$ or $2\sqrt{3}$ **108.** $-\dfrac{4\sqrt{2}}{3}$ or $\dfrac{4\sqrt{2}}{3}$ **110.** $\dfrac{1}{6}$ **111.** $-\dfrac{1}{2}$

112. 1 or 9
113. $ar^2 + br + c = 0 = as^2 + bs + c$

Thus, $ar^2 + br = as^2 + bs \Leftrightarrow a(r^2 - s^2) = -b(r - s) \Leftrightarrow r + s = -\dfrac{b}{a}$

$$(ar^2 + br + c = 0) \cdot \dfrac{1}{a}$$

$$r^2 + \frac{b}{a}r + \frac{c}{a} = 0$$
$$r^2 - (r + s)r + \frac{c}{a} = 0 \Leftrightarrow rs = \frac{c}{a}$$

114. a. $r + s = -\dfrac{5}{3}, rs = -\dfrac{5}{3}$ **b.** $r + s = \dfrac{7}{3}, rs = -\dfrac{1}{3}$

c. $r + s = \sqrt{3}, rs = -\dfrac{4\sqrt{3}}{3}$

d. $r + s = 2 - \sqrt{2}, rs = -5 + 5\sqrt{2}$

117. $ax^2 + bx + c = ax^2 - a(r + s)x + ars = a(x^2 - rx - sx + rs)$
$= a[x(x - r) - s(x - r)] = a(x - r)(x - s)$

Section 1.5

Practice Problems

1. $\{-2, 0, 2\}$ **2.** $\{-2, 2, 5\}$ **3.** $\{-10, 1\}$ **4.** $\{0, 3\}$ **5.** $\{10\}$

6. $\{9\}$ **7.** $\{-6, 7\}$ **8.** $\left\{\dfrac{1}{3}, 1\right\}$ **9.** 60% of the speed of light

A Exercises: Basics Skills and Concepts

8. $\{-8, 2, 6\}$ **13.** $\{1 - \sqrt{2}, 1 + \sqrt{2}\}$

14. $\left\{-\dfrac{1}{2} - \dfrac{\sqrt{5}}{2}, -\dfrac{1}{2} + \dfrac{\sqrt{5}}{2}\right\}$ **15.** $\left\{\dfrac{7}{2} - \dfrac{\sqrt{53}}{2}, \dfrac{7}{2} + \dfrac{\sqrt{53}}{2}\right\}$

16. $\left\{-\dfrac{5}{6} - \dfrac{\sqrt{13}}{6}, -\dfrac{5}{6} + \dfrac{\sqrt{13}}{6}\right\}$ **17.** $\{-3, 5\}$ **18.** $\left\{-\dfrac{3}{2}, 2\right\}$

35. $\{0, 8\}$ **47.** $\{-3, -2, 2, 3\}$ **48.** $\{-2, -\sqrt{3}, \sqrt{3}, 2\}$

49. $\left\{-\dfrac{\sqrt{2}}{2}, \dfrac{\sqrt{2}}{2}, -i, i\right\}$ **50.** $\left\{-\dfrac{1}{3}, \dfrac{1}{3}\right\}$ **53.** $\left\{0, \dfrac{1}{3}\right\}$

54. $\left\{-\dfrac{10}{7}, -\dfrac{2}{7}\right\}$ **64.** $\{-1 - \sqrt{6}, -3, -1 + \sqrt{6}, 1\}$

Section 1.6

Practice Problems

1. a. $(2, \infty)$

b. $(-\infty, 5]$

2. 2.5 hours

3. $\left[-1, \dfrac{3}{2}\right)$

4. $(4, \infty)$

5. $a = -4, b = 11$ **6.** 59°F to 77°F

A Exercises: Basics Skills and Concepts

11. $(-2, 5)$

12. $[-5, 0]$

13. $(0, 4]$

14. $[1, 7)$

15. $[-1, \infty)$

16. $(2, \infty)$

17. $(-\infty, -2]$

18. $(-1, \infty)$

19. $(-\infty, 3)$

20. $(-\infty, 5)$

21. $[-3, \infty)$

22. $(-\infty, 4)$

23. $(-\infty, 2)$

24. $\left[\dfrac{5}{3}, \infty\right)$

25. $(-\infty, -4)$

26. $(-\infty, -1]$

27. $(-\infty, -1)$

28. $[3, \infty)$

29. $(-\infty, 3]$

30. $(-\infty, 4]$

31. $(2, \infty)$

32. $(1, \infty)$

33. $(-\infty, -4]$

34. $(-\infty, -6]$

35. $\left(-\infty, \dfrac{3}{2}\right]$

36. $(-\infty, -20)$

37. $(-\infty, -1]$

38. $[2, \infty)$

39. $[2, \infty)$

40. $(-\infty, 10]$

41. $\left(-\infty, -\dfrac{2}{3}\right]$

42. $(-\infty, -5]$

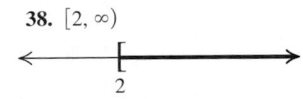

43. $\left(-\infty, -\dfrac{4}{5}\right]$

$-\dfrac{4}{5}$

54. $\left(-1, \dfrac{1}{2}\right]$

Section 1.7

Practice Problems

1. $(-\infty, 1 - \sqrt{3}) \cup (1 + \sqrt{3}, \infty)$

$1-\sqrt{3}$ $1+\sqrt{3}$

2. No   **3.** $(-\infty, -1 - \sqrt{3}) \cup (-1 + \sqrt{3}, \infty)$ **4.** $[-2, 2]$

5. $\left(-\dfrac{1}{3}, \dfrac{1}{3}\right)$

$-\dfrac{1}{3}$ $\dfrac{1}{3}$

A Exercises: Basics Skills and Concepts

1. $(-2, 3)$ **2.** $(-3, 2)$ **3.** $(-5, 2)$
4. $(-\infty, -2) \cup (5, \infty)$ **5.** $[-4, 1]$ **6.** $[-1, 4]$
7. $(-\infty, -1] \cup [6, \infty)$ **8.** $(-\infty, -6] \cup [1, \infty)$
10. $(-\infty, 0) \cup (3, \infty)$ **13.** $(-\infty, -5) \cup (5, \infty)$
16. $(-\infty, 1) \cup (7, \infty)$ **17.** $\left(-\infty, -\dfrac{3}{2}\right] \cup \left[\dfrac{1}{3}, \infty\right)$ **18.** $\left(-\dfrac{1}{2}, 1\right)$
19. $\left[-\dfrac{3}{5}, \dfrac{2}{5}\right]$ **20.** $\left(-\dfrac{7}{12}, 1\right)$ **22.** $(-\infty, -6) \cup (0, \infty)$
23. $\left(-4, \dfrac{3}{2}\right)$ **24.** $\left(-\infty, -\dfrac{7}{3}\right] \cup \left[\dfrac{1}{2}, \infty\right)$ **25.** $(-\infty, -3] \cup [0, 3]$
26. $(-2, 0) \cup (2, \infty)$ **29.** $(1 - \sqrt{3}, 1 + \sqrt{3})$
30. $[2 - \sqrt{5}, 2 + \sqrt{5}]$ **38.** $(-\infty, -\sqrt{3}] \cup \{0\} \cup [\sqrt{3}, \infty)$
42. $(-\infty, -\sqrt{3}) \cup (\sqrt{3}, \infty)$ **44.** $(-\infty -1) \cup (3, \infty)$
48. $(-\infty, 0) \cup (2, \infty)$ **49.** $\left(-\infty, -\dfrac{5}{2}\right] \cup (-2, \infty)$
51. $(-2, 0) \cup (2, \infty)$ **52.** $(-\infty, -3) \cup (1, 2)$
54. $(-3, 0) \cup (4, \infty)$ **55.** $\left(-\infty, \dfrac{4}{3}\right) \cup (2, \infty)$
56. $(-\infty, 2) \cup [3, \infty)$ **61.** $\left(-2, -\dfrac{10}{9}\right) \cup (2, \infty)$
62. $(-\infty, -1) \cup \left(\dfrac{1}{3}, 1\right)$

B Exercises: Applying the Concepts
63. 2 sec to 2.5 sec   **68.** at least 12 m
69. more than 133 cards   **70.** at least 2 cm

Section 1.8

Practice Problems

1. a. $\{2\}$ **b.** $\{-1, 2\}$

2. $\left\{\dfrac{1}{2}\right\}$

3. $[-3, 1]$

-3 1

4. $[270, 420]$

5. $\left(-\infty, -\dfrac{9}{2}\right] \cup \left[\dfrac{3}{2}, \infty\right)$

$-\dfrac{9}{2}$ $\dfrac{3}{2}$

6. a. $(-\infty, \infty)$ **b.** $\varnothing$

A Exercises: Basics Skills and Concepts

9. $\left\{-\dfrac{7}{6}, \dfrac{11}{6}\right\}$ **11.** $\{-2, -1\}$ **17.** $\{-1, 2\}$ **18.** $\left\{0, \dfrac{1}{2}\right\}$
19. $\left\{-1, \dfrac{11}{3}\right\}$ **27.** $(-\infty, -4) \cup (4, \infty)$ **28.** $(-\infty, -5) \cup (5, \infty)$
31. $(-\infty, -3] \cup [3, \infty)$ **32.** $(-\infty, -5) \cup (5, \infty)$
33. $\left(-\dfrac{1}{2}, \dfrac{7}{2}\right)$ **35.** $(-\infty, 1) \cup (4, \infty)$ **36.** $(-\infty, -4] \cup [6, \infty)$
37. $\left[-\dfrac{23}{3}, 5\right]$ **38.** $\left(-2, \dfrac{32}{7}\right)$

41. $(-6, 10)$

-6 ... 10

42. $(-\infty, 2) \cup (6, \infty)$

2 6

43. $[0, 16]$

0 ... 16

44. $\left(-\infty, -\dfrac{47}{2}\right) \cup \left(\dfrac{17}{2}, \infty\right)$

$-\dfrac{47}{2}$ ... $\dfrac{17}{2}$

45. $(-\infty, \infty)$

46. $(-\infty, \infty)$

47. $\left(-\dfrac{8}{9}, \dfrac{22}{9}\right)$

$-\dfrac{8}{9}$ $\dfrac{22}{9}$

48. $[-1, 5]$

-1 5

49. $\left[-\dfrac{10}{3}, 10\right]$

$-\dfrac{10}{3}$ ... 10

50. $\left(-\infty, -\dfrac{2}{3}\right) \cup (2, \infty)$

$-\dfrac{2}{3}$ 2

53. $\left\{-3, -\dfrac{5}{9}\right\}$ **54.** $\left\{-5, -\dfrac{1}{3}\right\}$

C Exercises: Beyond the Basics
65. $\{-2 - 2\sqrt{3}, -2 - \sqrt{2}, -2 + \sqrt{2}, -2 + 2\sqrt{3}\}$
66. $\{-4, -3, 0, 1\}$ **67.** $\left(-\infty, \dfrac{1}{4}\right) \cup \left(\dfrac{3}{4}, \infty\right)$ **70.** $\left(-\dfrac{3}{2}, \dfrac{3}{2}\right)$
79. $|x - 7| > 4$ **80.** $|x - 2| > 3$
81. $|2x - 5| \geq 15$ **82.** $|x + 2| \geq 1$
83. $|2x - a - b| < b - a$ **84.** $|2x - c - d| \leq d - c$
85. $|2x - a - b| > b - a$ **86.** $|2x - c - d| \geq d - c$
89. $\left[-5, \dfrac{5}{3}\right]$ **91.** $\left(-\infty, -\dfrac{7}{2}\right] \cup \left[-\dfrac{1}{6}, \infty\right)$ **92.** $\left(-\infty, -\dfrac{3}{2}\right)$

Critical Thinking
95. $(-\infty, 2] \cup [4, \infty)$

Review Exercises

7. $(-\infty, \infty)$ **8.** $\varnothing$ **10.** $\left\{\dfrac{6}{5}\right\}$ **11.** $\left\{-\dfrac{11}{5}\right\}$ **12.** $\{-3\}$
17. $\left\{-4, -\dfrac{1}{3}\right\}$ **18.** $\left\{-\dfrac{1}{6}, \dfrac{7}{4}\right\}$ **19.** $g = \dfrac{p - k}{t}$
20. $K = \dfrac{4}{R - 3}$ **22.** $r = \dfrac{S - a}{S}$ **26.** $\left\{-\dfrac{3}{2}, 6\right\}$ **27.** $\{-6, 1\}$
28. $\{-1, 2\}$ **31.** $\left\{-1, \dfrac{2}{3}\right\}$ **32.** $\{-5, 3\}$

33. $\left\{\dfrac{3}{2} - \dfrac{\sqrt{13}}{2}, \dfrac{3}{2} + \dfrac{\sqrt{13}}{2}\right\}$ **34.** $\{-3 - \sqrt{7}, -3 + \sqrt{7}\}$

35. $\left\{-1, \dfrac{1}{2}\right\}$ **36.** $\{-2 - \sqrt{3}, -2 + \sqrt{3}\}$

37. $\{2 - 2\sqrt{3}, 2 + 2\sqrt{3}\}$ **38.** $\left\{-1 - \dfrac{\sqrt{10}}{2}, -1 + \dfrac{\sqrt{10}}{2}\right\}$

39. $\left\{\dfrac{1}{4} - \dfrac{\sqrt{17}}{4}, \dfrac{1}{4} + \dfrac{\sqrt{17}}{4}\right\}$ **40.** $\left\{\dfrac{5}{6} - \dfrac{\sqrt{13}}{6}, \dfrac{5}{6} + \dfrac{\sqrt{13}}{6}\right\}$

41. $D = 49$, real, unequal   **42.** $D = 0$, real, equal

43. $D = -16$, no real roots   **44.** $D = 900$, real, unequal

47. $\left\{\dfrac{1}{2}\right\}$ **53.** $\left\{-\dfrac{10}{7}, -\dfrac{2}{7}\right\}$ **55.** $\{-64, 1\}$ **56.** $\{-27, 8\}$

59. $\left\{-3, -\dfrac{1}{2}, \dfrac{1}{2}, 3\right\}$ **62.** $\left\{1 - \dfrac{\sqrt{6}}{3}, 1 + \dfrac{\sqrt{6}}{3}\right\}$

65. $(-\infty, -2)$

66. $(-\infty, 4)$

67. $\left(-\infty, \dfrac{17}{3}\right)$

68. $[-7, \infty)$

69. $\left(-\infty, -\dfrac{6}{7}\right)$

70. $[-9, \infty)$

71. $(-5, 1)$

72. $\left[-\dfrac{2}{3}, 2\right]$

73. $(-\infty, -3] \cup [5, \infty)$

74. $[6, 10]$

75. $[-2, 3]$

76. $(-3, 3)$

77. $\left(\dfrac{3}{2}, \dfrac{16}{3}\right]$

78. $\left(\dfrac{7}{4}, \dfrac{23}{6}\right]$

79. $(-\infty, -3)$

80. $(-\infty, -1] \cup [3, \infty)$

81. $\left(2, \dfrac{5}{2}\right]$

82. $(-\infty, 1)$

83. $\left[-3, \dfrac{5}{3}\right]$

84. $(-\infty, 2] \cup [6, \infty)$

$(-\infty, 1) \cup (3, \infty)$

85.

86. $(-1, 3)$

87. $(-\infty, -1] \cup [9, \infty)$

88. $(-5, 7)$

89. $\dfrac{11}{\pi}$ cm   **93.** 13 cm   **95.** 350 cm

96. \$2600

98. 360 miles of flat terrain with 60 mph, 240 miles of hilly terrain with 40 mph

101. 8 liters of the $4\frac{1}{2}\%$ and 2 liters of the 12%

Practice Test A

8. $\left\{-4, -\dfrac{5}{2}\right\}$ **9.** $\dfrac{1}{9}, \left(x + \dfrac{1}{3}\right)^2$ **10.** $\left\{\dfrac{5}{6} - \dfrac{\sqrt{37}}{6}, \dfrac{5}{6} + \dfrac{\sqrt{37}}{6}\right\}$

17. $\left(-\dfrac{1}{2}, \dfrac{7}{2}\right)$ **19.** $(-\infty, 2]$ **20.** $\left[\dfrac{2}{5}, 2\right]$

CHAPTER 2

Section 2.1

Practice Problems

1.

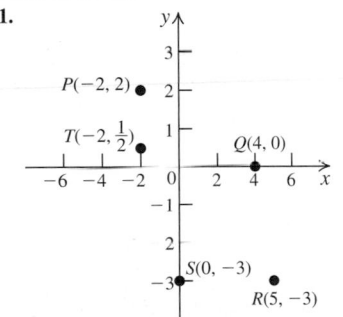

2. (1997, 21.7), (1998, 21.1), (1999, 20.5), (2000, 20.2), (2001, 19.7), (2002, 19.4), (2003, 18.6)

3. $\sqrt{2}$ **4.** Yes   **5.** $60\sqrt{2}$ **6.** $\left(\dfrac{11}{2}, -\dfrac{3}{2}\right)$

A Exercises: Basic Skills and Concepts

1.

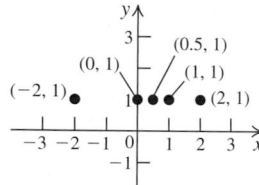

(2, 2), Quadrant I
(3, −1), Quadrant IV
(−1, 0), *x*-axis
(−2, −5), Quadrant III
(0, 0), origin
(−7, 4), Quadrant II
(0, 3), *y*-axis
(−4, 2), Quadrant II

2. a. (1, 0), (2, 0), (3, 0), (4, 0), (5, 0).
The *y*-coordinate is 0.
 b. Horizontal line intersecting the
y-axis at 1.

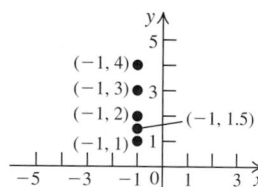

3. a. On the *y*-axis.
 b. Vertical line intersecting the *x*-axis at −1.

4. a. Vertical line intersecting the *x*-axis at −3.
 b. Horizontal line intersecting the *y*-axis at 4.

15. a. $\sqrt{2}|t - k|$ **b.** $\left(\dfrac{t + k}{2}, \dfrac{t + k}{2}\right)$

16. a. $\sqrt{2}|m + n|$ **b.** $\left(\dfrac{m - n}{2}, \dfrac{n - m}{2}\right)$

35. $d(P, R) = d(Q, S) = 17\sqrt{2}$.
36. $d(P, R) = d(Q, S) = 2$.
37. −2 or 6   **38.** $y = 2$ or −8

B Exercises: Applying the Concepts

41.

42.

43.

44.

45.

46. 20,000

47. $92.25 billion in 1998, $108.5 billion in 1999, and $124.75 billion in 2000.

48. $330 billion in 1995, $340 billion in 1996, $350 billion in 1997, $360 billion in 1998, $370 billion in 1999, $380 billion in 2000, and $390 billion in 2001.

50. a.

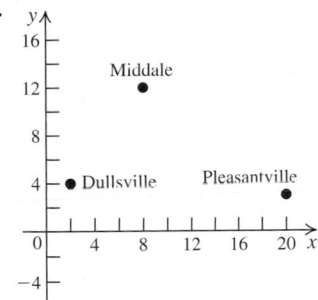

60. c. $\left(\dfrac{2}{3}, \dfrac{5}{3}\right)$ and $\left(\dfrac{7}{3}, \dfrac{4}{3}\right)$

Critical Thinking

62. a. The union of the x-axis and y-axis
   b. The plane without the x-axis and y-axis
63. a. Quadrants I and III
64. b. The plane without the origin
65. Let the point be (x, y).
   $x > 0, y > 0 \rightarrow$ Quadrant I
   $x < 0, y > 0 \rightarrow$ Quadrant II
   $x < 0, y < 0 \rightarrow$ Quadrant III
   $x > 0, y < 0 \rightarrow$ Quadrant IV

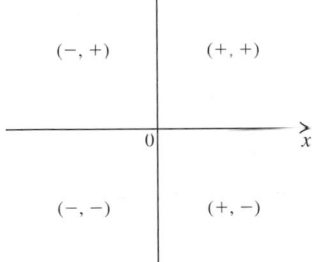

Section 2.2

Practice Problems

1.

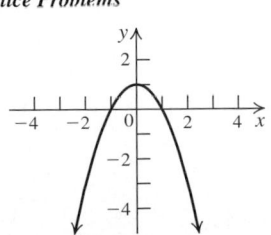

2. x-intercepts: $-2, \dfrac{1}{2}$. y-intercept: -2

3. Symmetric   **4.** Not symmetric
5. Not symmetric with respect to the x-axis, symmetric with respect to the y-axis, not symmetric with respect to the origin
6. a.

b.

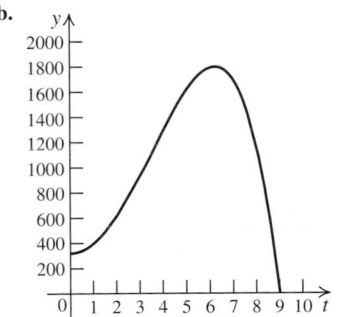

   c. After 9 years
7. $(x - 3)^2 + (y + 6)^2 = 100$
8.

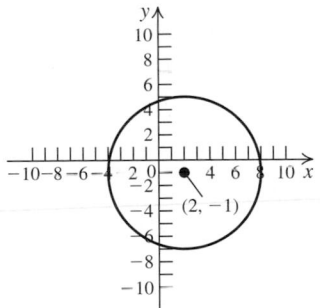

9. $(x + 2)^2 + (y - 3)^2 = 25$

A Exercises: Basic Skills and Concepts

1. On the graph: $(-3, -4), (1, 0), (4, 3)$
   Not on the graph: $(2, 3)$
2. On the graph: $\left(-\dfrac{5}{3}, 0\right), (-1, 1), (1, 4)$
   Not on the graph: $(0, 2)$
3. On the graph: $(3, 2), (0, 1), (8, 3)$
   Not on the graph: $(8, -3)$
4. On the graph: $(1, 1), \left(2, \dfrac{1}{2}\right)$
   Not on the graph: $\left(-3, \dfrac{1}{3}\right), (0, 0)$
5. On the graph: $(1, 0), (2, \sqrt{3}), (2, -\sqrt{3})$
   Not on the graph: $(0, -1)$
6. Each of the points is on the graph.
7. x-intercepts: $-3, 0, 3$. y-intercepts: $-2, 0, 2$
8. x-intercepts: $-2, 4$. y-intercept: -4

9.

10.

11.

12.

13.

14.

15.

16.

17.

18.

19.

20.

21.

22.

23.

24.

25.

26.

27.

28.

29.

30.

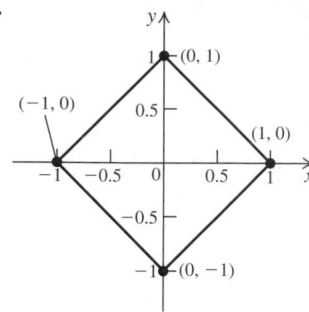

31. x-intercept: 4. y-intercept: 3   **32.** x-intercept: 5. y-intercept: 3

33. x-intercept: $\dfrac{5}{2}$. y-intercept: $\dfrac{5}{3}$ **34.** x-intercept: 2. y-intercept: -3

35. x-intercepts: 2, 4. y-intercept: 8   **36.** x-intercept: 6. y-intercepts: 2, 3

37. x-intercepts: -2, 2. y-intercepts: -2, 2

38. x-intercepts: -3, 3. y-intercept: 3

39. x-intercepts: -1, 1. No y-intercept

41. Not symmetric with respect to the x-axis, symmetric with respect to the y-axis, not symmetric with respect to the origin

42. Symmetric with respect to the x-axis, not symmetric with respect to the y-axis, not symmetric with respect to the origin

43. Not symmetric with respect to the x-axis, not symmetric with respect to the y-axis, symmetric with respect to the origin

44. Not symmetric with respect to the x-axis, not symmetric with respect to the y-axis, symmetric with respect to the origin

45. Not symmetric with respect to the x-axis, symmetric with respect to the y-axis, not symmetric with respect to the origin

46. Not symmetric with respect to the x-axis, symmetric with respect to the y-axis, not symmetric with respect to the origin

47. Not symmetric with respect to the x-axis, not symmetric with respect to the y-axis, symmetric with respect to the origin

48. Not symmetric with respect to the x-axis, symmetric with respect to the y-axis, not symmetric with respect to the origin

49. Not symmetric with respect to the x-axis, not symmetric with respect to the y-axis, symmetric with respect to the origin

50. Symmetric with respect to the x-axis, symmetric with respect to the y-axis, symmetric with respect to the origin

57. $x^2 + (y - 1)^2 = 4$

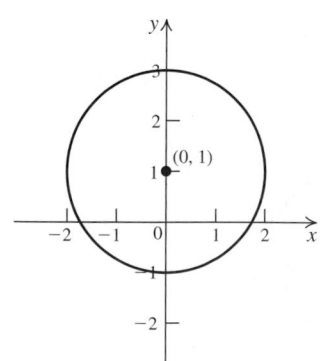

58. $(x - 1)^2 + y^2 = 1$

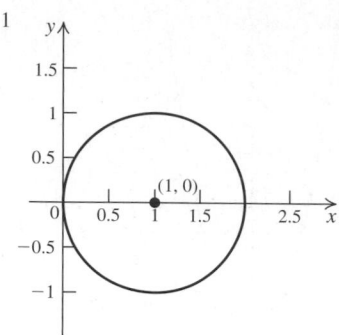

59. $(x + 1)^2 + (y - 2)^2 = 2$

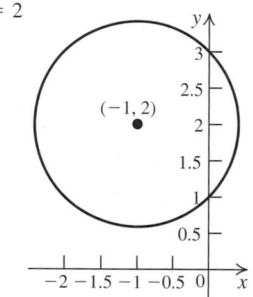

60. $(x + 2)^2 + (y + 3)^2 = 7$

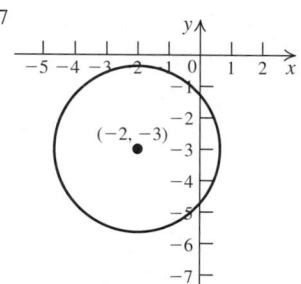

61. $(x - 3)^2 + (y + 4)^2 = 97$

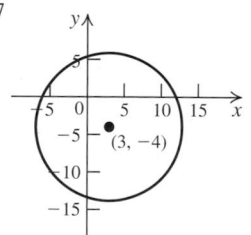

62. $(x - 1)^2 + (y - 2)^2 = 4$

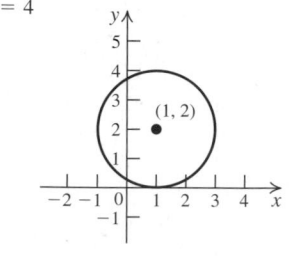

63. $(x - 1)^2 + (y - 2)^2 = 1$

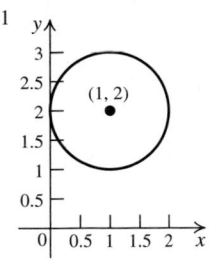

64. $(x - 2)^2 + (y - 5)^2 = 26$

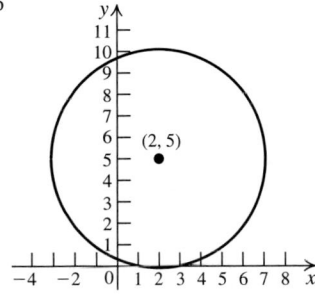

65. Circle. Center: $(1, 1)$. Radius: $\sqrt{6}$

66. Circle. Center: $(2, 1)$. Radius: $2\sqrt{5}$

67. Circle. Center: $(0, -1)$. Radius: 1

68. Circle. Center: $(-1, 0)$. Radius: 1

69. Circle. Center: $\left(\dfrac{1}{2}, 0\right)$. Radius: $\dfrac{1}{2}$

B Exercises: Applying the Concepts

72. $y = \dfrac{1}{3}x - \dfrac{5}{3}$

73. $x = \dfrac{y^2}{4} + 1$

74. $y = \dfrac{x^2}{8} + 2$

75. a. $12 million

    b. $-5.5 million

    c.

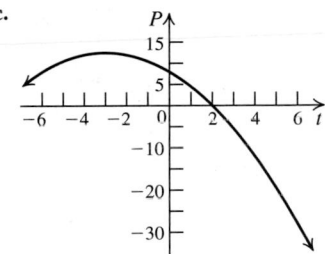

    d. -8 and 2. They represent the months when there is neither profit nor loss.

    e. 8. It represents the profit in July 2004.

76. a.

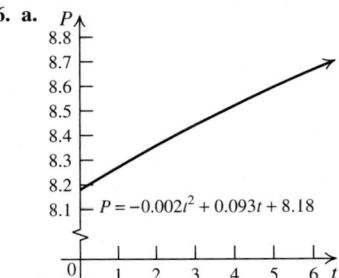

    b. No t-intercept.

    c. 8.18. It represents the number of female students in 1995.

77. a. After 0 second: 320 ft. After 1 second: 432 ft. After 2 seconds: 512 ft. After 3 seconds: 560 ft. After 4 seconds: 576 ft. After 5 seconds: 560 ft. After 6 seconds: 512 ft

    b.

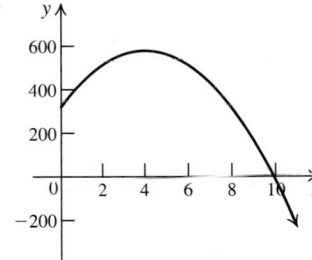

    c. $0 \le t \le 10$

    d. t-intercept: 10. It represents the time when the object hits the ground. y-intercept: 320. It shows the height of the building.

78. a.

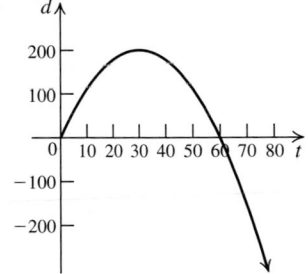

    b. $0 \le t \le 60$

    c. 1 hr

C Exercises: Beyond the Basics

79.

80.

81.

origin symmetry

82.

x-axis symmetry

83.

84.

85.

86.

87.

88.

89. Area: 11π

90. a. ∅

b.

c.

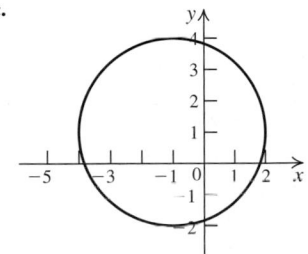

Critical Thinking

91. The graph is the union of the graphs of $y = \sqrt{2x}$ and $y = -\sqrt{2x}$.

95. a.

b.

c.

d.

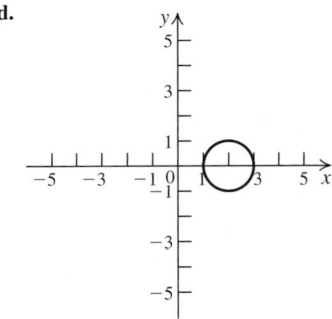

Section 2.3

Practice Problems

1. $-\dfrac{8}{13}$ **2.** $y = -\dfrac{2}{3}x - \dfrac{13}{3}$ **3.** $y = 5x + 11$ **4.** $y = 2x - 3$

5.

6. Undefined; 0

7.

8. Between 176.8 and 179.4 centimeters

9. a. $4x - 3y + 23 = 0$

   b. $5x - 4y - 31 = 0$

A Exercises: Basic Skills and Concepts

1. $\frac{4}{3}$, rising   **4.** Undefined, vertical   **6.** -2.2, falling

8. $\frac{3}{2}$, rising

10. l_1 has slope 1, l_2 has slope 0, l_3 has slope 2, and l_4 has slope $-\frac{4}{3}$.

13. $y = \frac{1}{2}x + 4$

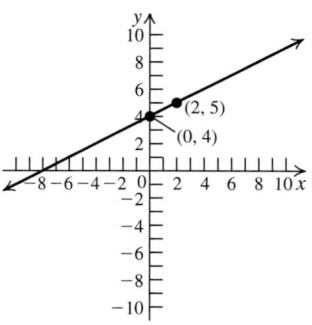

14. $y = -\frac{1}{2}x + 4$

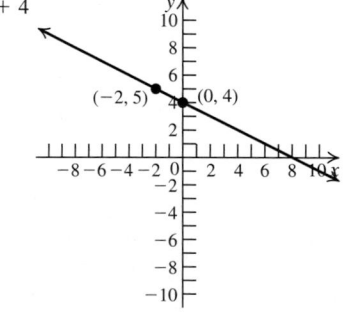

15. $y = -\frac{3}{2}x + 4$

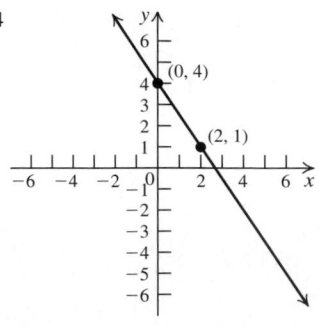

16. $y = \frac{2}{5}x + \frac{2}{5}$

17. $y = -\frac{3}{5}x - 1$

18. $x = 5$

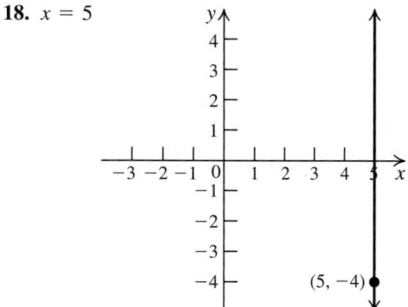

22. $y = \frac{6}{7}x + \frac{37}{7}$ **23.** $y = \frac{2}{3}x + \frac{1}{3}$ **24.** $y = -\frac{6}{7}x - \frac{27}{7}$

35. $y = \frac{4}{3}x + 4$ **36.** $y = -\frac{2}{5}x - 2$ **39.** $y = -5$

40. $x = -3$ **41. c.** perpendicular.   **42. b.** $x = \frac{1}{2}$

43. $m = -\frac{1}{2}$; y-intercept $= 2$

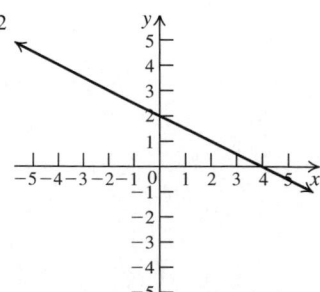

44. $m = \dfrac{1}{3}$; y-intercept $= 3$

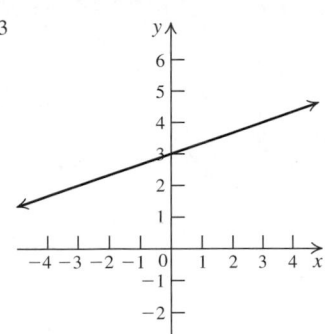

45. $m = \dfrac{3}{2}$; y-intercept $= 3$

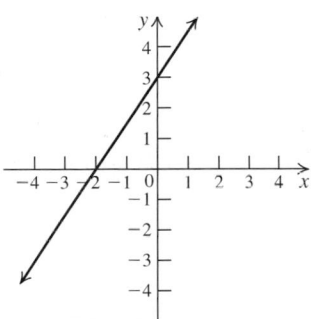

46. $m = -\dfrac{1}{2}$; y-intercept $= \dfrac{15}{4}$

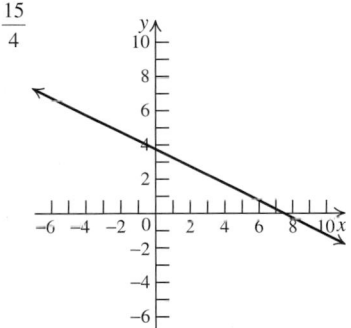

47. m is undefined; no y-intercept

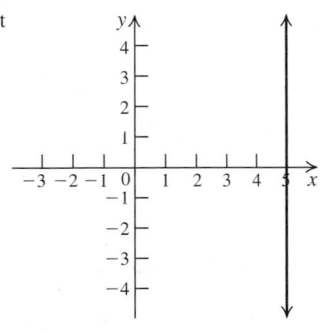

48. $m = 0$; y-intercept $= -\dfrac{5}{2}$

49. m is undefined;
y-intercepts $= y$-axis

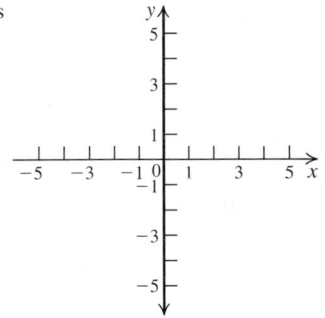

50. $m = 0$; y-intercept $= 0$

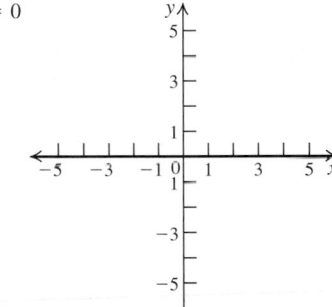

52. $\dfrac{x}{4} + \dfrac{y}{3} = 1$

53. $\dfrac{x}{3} + \dfrac{y}{2} = 1$; x-intercept $= 3$; y-intercept $= 2$

54. $-\dfrac{x}{4} + \dfrac{y}{3} = 1$; x-intercept $= -4$; y-intercept $= 3$

57. $y = x + 2$. Since the coordinates of the point $(-1, 1)$ satisfy this equation, $(-1, 1)$ also lies on this line.

58. They are not collinear.

69. $y = -3x - 2$ **70.** $y = -\dfrac{1}{2}x$ **71.** $y = -\dfrac{1}{6}x + 4$

72. $y = \dfrac{2}{3}x - \dfrac{2}{3}$

B Exercises: Applying the Concepts

73. $\dfrac{1}{10}$ **74.** $|m| = \dfrac{25}{264}$

75. a. x: time in weeks; y: amount of money in the account;
$y = 7x + 130$

b. slope: weekly deposit in the account; y-intercept: initial deposit

76. a. x: number of golf sessions; y: yearly payment to the golf club; $y = 35x + 1000$

b. slope: cost per golf session; y-intercept: annual membership fee

77. a. x: number of hours worked; y: amount of money earned per week;
$$y = \begin{cases} 11x & x \le 40 \\ 16.5x - 220 & x > 40 \end{cases}$$

b. slope: hourly wage; y-intercept: salary for 0 hours of work

78. a. x: number of months one owes on the refrigerator; y: amount owed after x months; $y = -15x + 600$

b. slope: monthly payment; y-intercept: initial change

79. a. x: amount of rupees; y: amount of dollars equal to x rupees; $y = 44x$

b. x: amount of dollars; y: amount of rupees equal to x dollars;
$$y = \frac{1}{44}x$$

80. a. x: number of years after 2004; y: life expectancy of a female born in the United States in the year $x + 2004$; $y = 0.27x + 82.3$

b. slope: rate of increase in the life expectancy of a female born in the United States; y-intercept: current life expectancy of a female born in the United States

81. a. x: number of TV sets produced; y: cost of production for x TV sets; $y = 150x + 10000$

b. slope: marginal cost of a TV set; y-intercept: fixed cost independent of the number of TV sets produced

82. a. x: demand for the product; y: price per unit when the demand is x; $y = -0.1x + 100$

b. slope: rate of increase in the price; y-intercept: price per unit when the demand is zero.

83. a. $v = \$11{,}200$, when $t = 2$

b. $v = \$5{,}600$, when $t = 6$
The tractor's value is $0 at $t = 10$.

84. a. \$750 per yr

b. $V = -750t + 3000$

c.

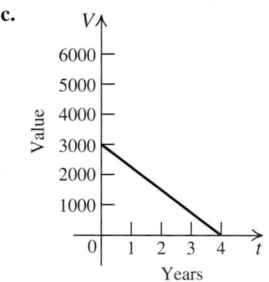

86. a. $C = 0.25x + 30$

b.

c. \$45

d. 71

87. a. $y = 215.8t + 2638$

b.

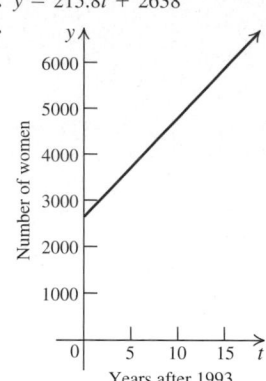

c. $t = 7$; 4149

d. 5875.

88. a. $F = \dfrac{9}{5}C + 32$

b. One degree Celsius change in the temperature is equal to $\dfrac{9}{5}$ degrees change in Fahrenheit.

c. 104°F, 77°F, 23°F, 14°F

d. 37.78°C, 32.22°C, 23.89°C, −23.33°C, −28.89°C

89. a. $q = -160p + 1120$

92. a. $R = 50x$, $C = 25x + 75{,}000$, $P = 25x - 75{,}000$

b.

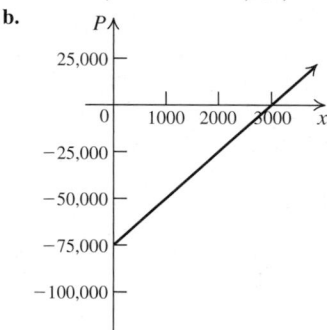

c. slope $= 25$. Rate of increase in the profit per pair of shoes sold

d. y-intercept $= -75{,}000$. Loss if 0 pairs of shoes are sold.

93. a.

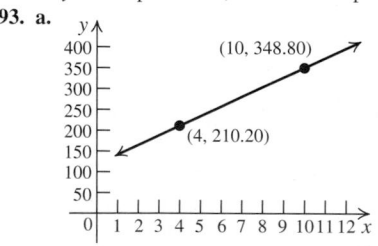

b. Slope: cost of producing one modem. y-intercept: fixed overhead cost

94. b. Slope: monthly increase in the number of viewers. y-intercept: number of viewers at the beginning of the show

C Exercises: Beyond the Basics

98. $c = \dfrac{1}{2}$

106. a. $y = \dfrac{3}{2}x + \dfrac{13}{4}$

Critical Thinking

115. a. This is a family of lines parallel to the line $y = -2x$, and they all have slope equal to -2.

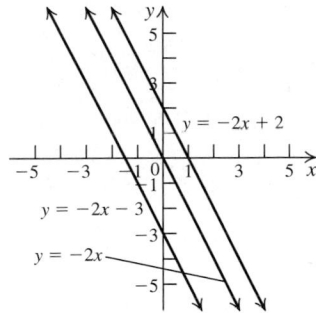

b. This is a family of lines that passes through the point $(0, -4)$, and they all have y-intercept equal to -4.

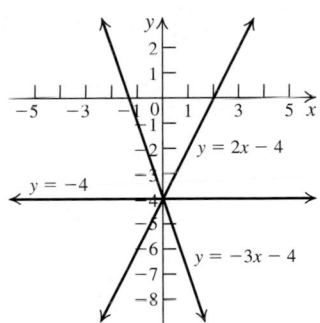

Section 2.4

Practice Problems

1. Domain: $\{-2, -1, 1, 2, 3\}$. Range: $\{-3, -2, 0, 1, 2\}$
2. Answer will vary.   **3. a.** 0   **b.** -7
    c. $-2x^2 - 4hx + 5x - 2h^2 + 5h$ **4. a.** No   **b.** Yes
5. $(-\infty, 1)$ **6.** No   **7. a.** Yes   **b.** $-3, -1$ **c.** -5 **d.** $-5, 1$
8. -4 **9.** $-2x - h + 1$
10. Domain: $[1, \infty)$. Range: $[6, 12)$. The function value at 6 is 11.813.
11. a. $C(x) = 1200x + 100{,}000$ **b.** $R(x) = 2500x$
    c. $P(x) = 1300x - 100{,}000$ **d.** 77

A Exercises: Basic Skills and Concepts

1. Domain: $\{-2, 0, 2\}$. Range: $\{0, 2\}$. Function
2. Domain: $\{3, 4, 5, 6\}$. Range: $\{1\}$. Function
3. Domain: $\{-2, 0, 1, 2\}$. Range: $\{-2, 0, 1, 2\}$. Function
4. Domain: $\{4, 9\}$. Range: $\{-3, -2, 2, 3\}$. Not a function
5. Domain: $\{a, b, c\}$. Range: $\{d, e\}$. Function
6. Domain: $\{a, b, c\}$. Range: $\{d, e, f\}$. Function
7. Domain: $\{a, b, c\}$. Range: $\{1, 2\}$. Function
8. Domain: $\{1, 2, 3\}$. Range: $\{a, b, c, d\}$. Not a function
9. Domain: $\{-2, -1, 1, 2, 3\}$. Range: $\{-2, 1, 2\}$. Function
10. Domain: $\{-2, -1, 1, 3, 4\}$. Range: $\{-4, -2, 1, 2, 4\}$. Not a function
11. Domain: $\{-3, -1, 0, 1, 2, 3\}$. Range: $\{-8, -3, 0, 1\}$. Function
12. Domain: $\{0, 3, 8\}$. Range: $\{-3, -2, -1, 1, 2\}$. Not a function
29. $(-\infty, 9) \cup (9, \infty)$
30. $(-\infty, -9) \cup (-9, \infty)$

31. $(-\infty, -1) \cup (-1, 1) \cup (1, \infty)$
32. $(-\infty, -2) \cup (-2, 2) \cup (2, \infty)$
34. $[-3, 1) \cup (1, \infty)$
37. $(-\infty, -2) \cup (-2, -1) \cup (-1, \infty)$
38. $(-\infty, -3) \cup (-3, -2) \cup (-2, \infty)$
39. $(-\infty, 0) \cup (0, \infty)$
45. $f(3) = 5, f(5) = 7, f(-1) = 1, f(-4) = -2$
46. $g(-2) = 5, g(1) = -4, g(3) = 0, g(4) = 5$
47. $h(-2) = -5, h(-1) = 4, h(0) = 3, h(1) = 4$
49. $f(0) = 1, g(0)$ is not defined,
    $h(0) = \sqrt{2}, f(a) = a^2 - 3a + 1, f(-x) = x^2 + 3x + 1$
50. $f(1) = -1, g(1) = 2, h(1) = 1, g(a) = \dfrac{2}{\sqrt{a}}, g(x^2) = \dfrac{2}{|x|}$
51. $f(-1) = 5, g(-1)$ is not defined,
    $h(-1) = \sqrt{3}, h(c) = \sqrt{2 - c}, h(-x) = \sqrt{2 + x}$
52. $f(4) = 5, g(4) = 1, h(4)$ is not defined,
    $g(2 + k) = \dfrac{2}{\sqrt{2 + k}}, f(a + k) = a^2 + 2ak - 3a + k^2 - 3k + 1$
55. a. $x + h$ **b.** h **c.** 1
56. a. $3x + 3h + 2$ **b.** $3h$ **c.** 3
57. a. $x^2 + 2hx + h^2$ **b.** $2hx + h^2$ **c.** $2x + h$
58. a. $x^2 + 2hx - x + h^2 - h$ **b.** $2hx + h^2 - h$ **c.** $2x + h - 1$
59. a. $2x^2 + 4hx + 3x + 2h^2 + 3h$ **b.** $4hx + 2h^2 + 3h$
    c. $4x + 2h + 3$
60. a. $3x^2 + 6hx - 2x + 3h^2 - 2h + 5$ **b.** $6hx + 3h^2 - 2h$
    c. $6x + 3h - 2$
61. a. 4   **b.** 0   **c.** 0
62. a. -3 **b.** 0   **c.** 0
63. a. $\dfrac{1}{x + h}$ **b.** $-\dfrac{h}{x(x + h)}$ **c.** $-\dfrac{1}{x(x + h)}$
64. a. $-\dfrac{1}{x + h}$ **b.** $\dfrac{h}{x(x + h)}$ **c.** $\dfrac{1}{x(x + h)}$

B Exercises: Applying the Concepts

67. Yes, because there is only one high temperature every day
68. Yes, because the cost of first-class postage on January 1 of any year is a single value
69. No, because Nevada and North Carolina both start with N
70. No, because people with different first names may have the same birthday
73. $A(x) = x^2$. $A(4) = 16$. $A(4)$ represents the area of a square tile with side of length 4.
76. $f(x) = \dfrac{x}{39.37}$. $f(59) \approx 1.5$
79. a. $p(5) = 1150$. If 5000 TVs can be sold, the price per TV is $1150.
    $p(15) = 900$. If 15,000 TVs can be sold, the price per TV is $900.
    $p(30) = 525$. If 30,000 TVs can be sold, the price per TV is $525.
b.

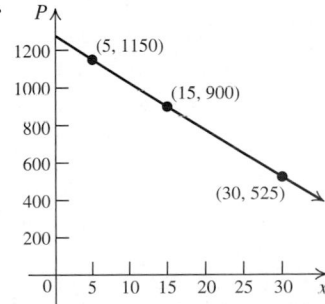

80. a. $R(x) = 1275x - 25x^2$. Domain: $[0, 30]$
b. $R(1) = 1250, R(5) = 5750, R(10) = 10,250, R(15) = 13,500,$
$R(20) = 15,500, R(25) = 16,250, R(30) = 15,750$. They show the amount of revenue for the given number of TVs sold.

c.

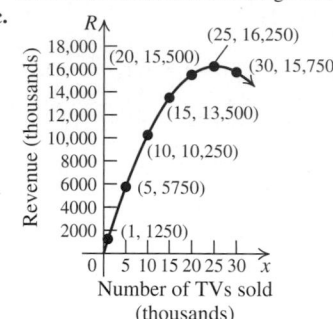

83. a. $[0, 8]$ **b.** $h(2) = 192, h(4) = 256, h(6) = 192$ **c.** 8 sec
d.

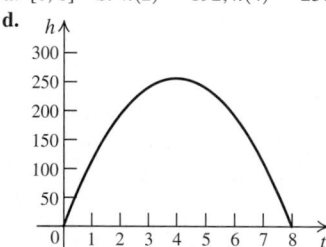

84. c. Based on (a): \$116,450. Based on (b): \$117,640
85. After 4 hours: 12 ml. After 8 hours: 21 ml. After 12 hours: 27.75 ml. After 16 hours: 32.81 ml. After 20 hours: 36.61 ml

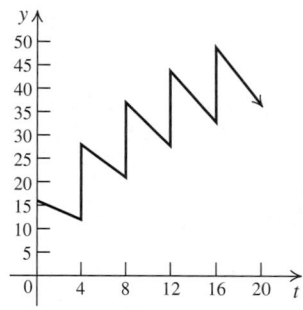

86. 1st day: 400 mg. 2nd day: 500 mg. 3rd day: 525 mg. 4th day: 531.25 mg. 5th day: 532.81 mg. 6th day: 533.2 mg. 7th day: 533.3 mg. 8th day: 533.33 mg. 9th day: 533.33 mg. 10th day: 533.33 mg

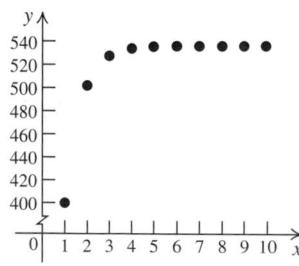

C Exercises: Beyond the Basics
87. a. $f(x) = |x|$ **b.** $f(x) = 0$ **c.** $f(x) = x$

88. a. No, because the domain of f is $[0, \infty)$, while the domain of g is $(-\infty, \infty)$
b. Yes, because $(\sqrt[3]{x})^3 = x$ for every real number x
89. $f(x) = \dfrac{3}{5}x - 3$. Domain: $(-\infty, \infty)$. $f(4) = -\dfrac{3}{5}$
90. $f(x) = \dfrac{x}{x - 1}$. Domain: $(-\infty, 1) \cup (1, \infty)$. $f(4) = \dfrac{4}{3}$
91. $f(x) = \dfrac{4x + 2}{x}$. Domain: $(-\infty, 0) \cup (0, \infty)$. $f(4) = \dfrac{9}{2}$
92. $f(x) = \dfrac{3}{x - 2}$. Domain: $(-\infty, 2) \cup (2, \infty)$. $f(4) = \dfrac{3}{2}$
93. $f(x) = \dfrac{2 - x}{x^2 + 1}$. Domain: $(-\infty, \infty)$. $f(4) = -\dfrac{2}{17}$
94. $f(x) = \dfrac{\sqrt{x}}{x^2 + 2}$. Domain: $[0, \infty)$. $f(4) = \dfrac{1}{9}$
95. No, because they have different domains
96. No, because they have different domains
97. No, because g is not defined at -1
98. No, because f is not defined at -2
99. Yes, because $f(x) = \dfrac{x^2 - 4}{x - 2} = \dfrac{(x + 2)(x - 2)}{x - 2} = x + 2 = g(x),$
since $x = 2$ is outside the given domain
100. Yes, because $f(x) = \dfrac{x - 2}{x^2 - 6x + 8} = \dfrac{x - 2}{(x - 4)(x - 2)} =$
$\dfrac{1}{x - 4} = g(x)$, since $x = 2$ is outside the given domain
102. $b = -4$ or $b = -2$
104. $f(x^2) = 2x^2 - 3, [f(x)]^2 = 4x^2 - 12x + 9$

Section 2.5

Practice Problems
1. $g(x) = 2x + 6$ **2.** 15.524 m
3. $F(-2) = -4, F(3) = 6$

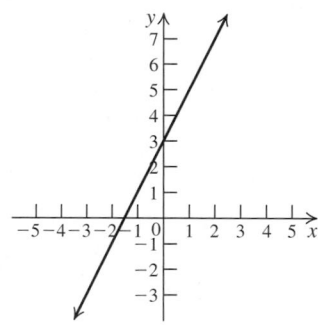

4. $f(-3.4) = -4, f(4.7) = 4$
5. Decreasing on $(-\infty, -3)$, constant on $(-3, 2)$, increasing on $(2, \infty)$
6. $f(-x) = -(-x)^2 = -x^2 = f(x)$; therefore, f is even.

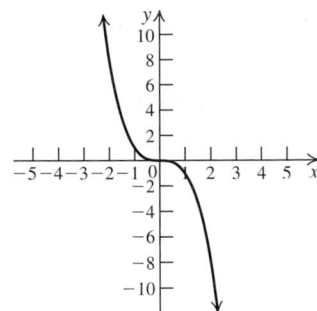

7. $f(-x) = -(-x)^3 = x^3 = -f(x)$; therefore, f is odd.

4. $f(x) = 3x - 2$

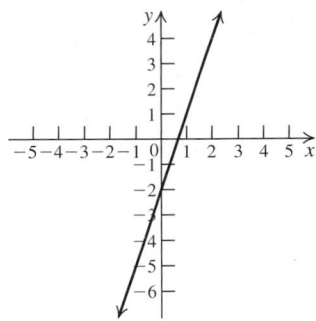

5. $f(x) = -3x + 4$

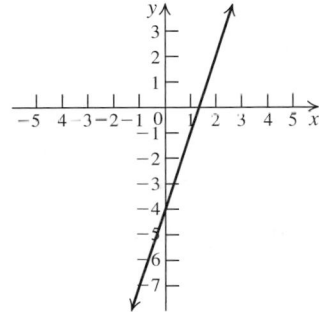

A Exercises: Basic Skills and Concepts

1. $f(x) = x + 1$

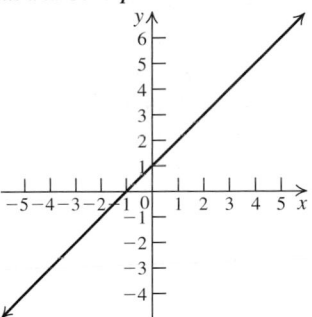

6. $f(x) = 3x - 4$

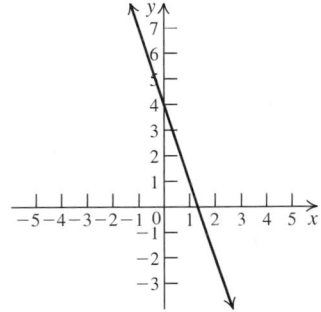

2. $f(x) = x - 1$

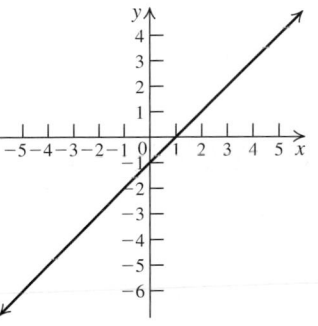

7. $f(x) = \frac{1}{2}x + 3$

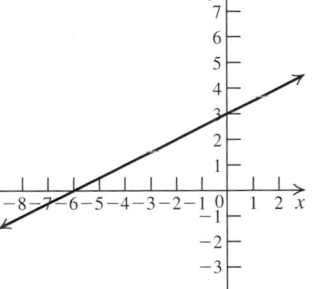

3. $f(x) = 2x + 3$

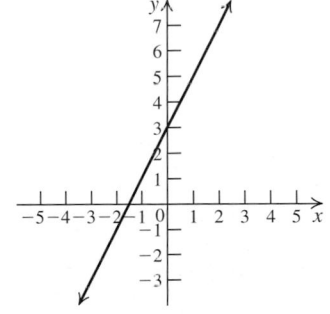

8. $f(x) = \frac{3}{2}x - 1$

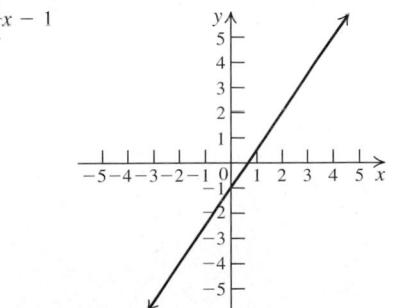

9. $f(x) = -\dfrac{2}{3}x - 1$

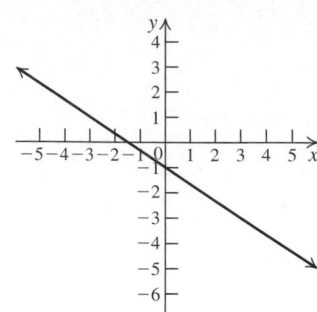

10. $f(x) = -\dfrac{3}{4}x + 1$

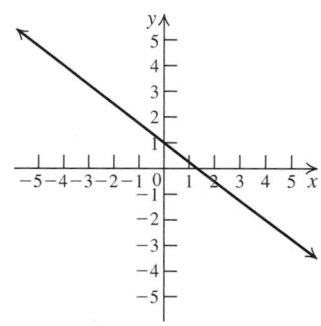

11. a. Domain: $[-2, 6]$. Range: $[-3, 2]$
b. x-intercept: $\dfrac{2}{5}$. y-intercept: $-\dfrac{1}{2}$
c. Increasing on $(-2, 2)$, constant on $(2, 6)$
d. Neither even nor odd

12. a. Domain: $[-3, 0) \cup (0, 3]$. Range: $\{-1, 1\}$
b. No x- or y-intercept
c. Constant on $(-3, 0)$ and $(0, 3)$
d. Odd

13. a. Domain: $[-2, 4]$. Range: $[-1, 2]$
b. x-intercepts: $-2, 0$. y-intercept: 0
c. Decreasing on $(-2, -1)$ and $(2, 4)$, increasing on $(-1, 2)$
d. Neither even nor odd

14. a. Domain: $[-3, 5]$. Range: $[-2, 3]$
b. x-intercept: 0. y-intercept: 0
c. Increasing on $(-3, 5)$
d. Neither even nor odd

15. a. Domain: $(0, \infty)$. Range: $(0, \infty)$
b. No x- or y-intercept
c. Decreasing on $(0, \infty)$
d. Neither even nor odd

16. a. Domain: $(-\infty, 3) \cup (3, \infty)$. Range: $(-\infty, 3) \cup (3, \infty)$
b. x-intercept: 2. y-intercept: 2
c. Decreasing on $(-\infty, 3)$ and $(3, \infty)$
d. Neither even nor odd

17. a. Domain: $(-\infty, \infty)$. Range: $(0, \infty)$
b. No x-intercept. y-intercept: 1
c. Increasing on $(-\infty, \infty)$
d. Neither even nor odd

18. a. Domain: $(0, \infty)$. Range: $(-\infty, \infty)$
b. x-intercept: 1.5. No y-intercept
c. Increasing on $(0, \infty)$
d. Neither even nor odd.

19. a. $f(1) = 2, f(2) = 2, f(3) = 3$
b.

20. a. $g(-1) = -2, g(0) = 0, g(1) = 1$
b.

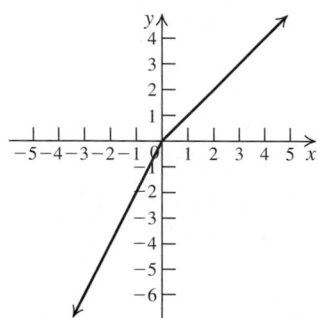

21. a. $f(-15) = -1, f(12) = 1$
b.

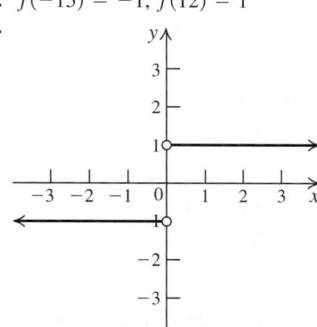

c. Domain: $(-\infty, 0) \cup (0, \infty)$. Range: $\{-1, 1\}$
22. a. $g(-3) = 20, g(1) = 4, g(3) = 10$
b.

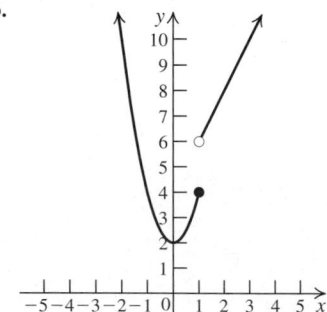

c. Domain: $(-\infty, \infty)$. Range: $[2, \infty)$.
23. constant on $(-\infty, \infty)$ **24.** constant on $(-\infty, \infty)$
25. increasing on $(-\infty, \infty)$ **26.** decreasing on $(-\infty, \infty)$
27. decreasing on $(-\infty, 0)$; increasing on $(0, \infty)$
28. decreasing on $(-\infty, \infty)$ **29.** even   **30.** neither   **31.** neither

32. odd   **41.** neither   **42.** even

43. a. $3 - 4x$ **b.** $6 - 4x$ **c.** $3 + 2x$ **d.** $2x - 3$

   e. $3 - \dfrac{2}{x}$ **f.** $\dfrac{1}{3 - 2x}$

44. a. $10x + 1$ **b.** $10x + 2$ **c.** $-5x + 1$ **d.** $-5x - 1$

   e. $\dfrac{5}{x} + 1$ **f.** $\dfrac{1}{5x + 1}$

45. a. $4x^2 - 4x$ **b.** $2x^2 - 4x$ **c.** $x^2 + 2x$ **d.** $-x^2 + 2x$

   e. $\dfrac{1}{x^2} - \dfrac{2}{x}$ **f.** $\dfrac{1}{x^2 - 2x}$

46. a. $2x - 16x^2$ **b.** $2x - 8x^2$ **c.** $-x - 4x^2$ **d.** $4x^2 - x$

   e. $\dfrac{1}{x} - \dfrac{4}{x^2}$ **f.** $\dfrac{1}{x - 4x^2}$

47. a. $1 - 8x^3$ **b.** $2 - 2x^3$ **c.** $1 + x^3$ **d.** $x^3 - 1$

   e. $1 - \dfrac{1}{x^3}$ **f.** $\dfrac{1}{1 - x^3}$

48. a. $8x^3 + 2x$ **b.** $2x^3 + 2x$ **c.** $-x^3 - x$ **d.** $-x^3 - x$

   e. $\dfrac{1}{x^3} + \dfrac{1}{x}$ **f.** $\dfrac{1}{x^3 + x}$

49. a. $\dfrac{1}{2x}$ **b.** $\dfrac{2}{x}$ **c.** $-\dfrac{1}{x}$ **d.** $-\dfrac{1}{x}$ **e.** x **f.** x

50. a. $\dfrac{1}{2|x|}$ **b.** $\dfrac{2}{|x|}$ **c.** $\dfrac{1}{|x|}$ **d.** $-\dfrac{1}{|x|}$ **e.** $|x|$ **f.** $|x|$

B Exercises: Applying the Concepts

51. a. $f(x) = \dfrac{1}{33.81}x$. Domain: $[0, \infty)$. Range: $[0, \infty)$.

   b. 0.0887. It means that 3 oz = 0.0887 l.

52. a. h-intercept: 117.78. It means that water boils at 0°F at 117,780 feet above sea level. y-intercept: 212. It means that water boils at 212°F at sea level.

   b. Closed interval from 0 to the end of the atmosphere, in feet.

   c. 63,000 feet. It is dangerous because 98.6°F is the temperature of human blood.

53. a. No d-intercept, since $d \geq 0$. y-intercept: 1. It means that the pressure at sea level $(d = 0)$ is 1 atm.

   b. $P(0) = 1, P(10) \approx 1.3, P(33) = 2, P(100) \approx 4.03$

   c. 132 ft

55. b. The y-intercept is the fixed overhead cost.

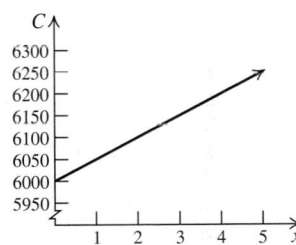

57. c. Ten days after the first of the month

58. a. $f(x) = 15x + 1120$, where x is the number of years since 2002

61. a. $y = \dfrac{2}{27}(x - 150) + 30$ **b.** $\dfrac{1210}{27}$

62. a. $y = \dfrac{1}{3}S + \dfrac{47}{12}$, where S is the size and y is the length

   b. 5.25 in.

63. a.

   b. (i) \$480   **(ii)** \$2000   **(iii)** \$3800

   c. (i) \$15,000   **(ii)** This value is not possible as a liability.

   (iii) \$25,000

64. a. $f(x) = \begin{cases} 0.1x, & \text{if } 0 < x \leq 7300 \\ 0.15x - 365, & \text{if } 7300 < x \leq 29{,}700 \\ 0.25x - 3335, & \text{if } 29{,}700 < x \leq 71{,}950 \\ 0.28x - 5493.5, & \text{if } 71{,}950 < x \leq 150{,}150 \\ 0.33x - 13001, & \text{if } 150{,}150 < x \leq 326{,}450 \\ 0.35x - 19530, & \text{if } x > 326{,}450 \end{cases}$

   x is the taxable income in dollars and $f(x)$ is the tax.

   b. (i) \$5415   **(ii)** \$22,506.5   **(iii)** \$155,470

   c. (i) \$25,766.67   **(ii)** \$64,140   **(iii)** \$144,619.64

C Exercises: Beyond the Basics

65. a. (i) -1 **(ii)** -1 **(iii)** -1

   b. $x = \dfrac{1}{2}$ **c.**

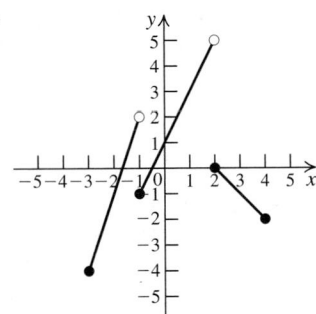

66. a. (i) 3 **(ii)** $-\dfrac{3}{2}$ **(iii)** -3 **(iv)** 3

   b. (i) $x = -\dfrac{1}{2}$ or $x = 1$ **(ii)** $x = -\dfrac{1}{4}$ or $x = \dfrac{1}{2}$

   c.

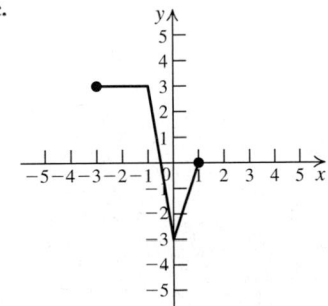

67. a. Domain: $(-\infty, \infty)$. Range: $[0, 1)$.

   b. increasing on $(n, n + 1)$ for every integer n **c.** neither

68. a. Domain: $(-\infty, 0) \cup [1, \infty)$. Range: $\left\{\dfrac{1}{n}: n \neq 0, n \text{ an integer}\right\}$

   b. constant on $(n, n + 1)$ for every nonzero integer n **c.** neither

Critical Thinking

71. b.

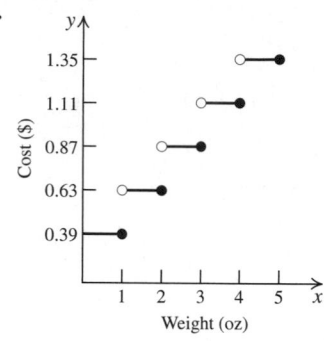

73. a. $C(x) = \begin{cases} 150, & \text{if } x < 100 \\ 0.2[\![x - 99]\!] + 150, & \text{if } x \geq 100 \end{cases}$

b.

Section 2.6

Practice Problems

1.

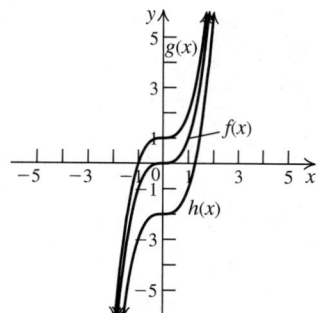

The graph of g is the graph of f shifted 1 unit up; the graph of h is the graph of f shifted 2 units down.

2. $f(x) = (x + 1)^2 - 2$

3.

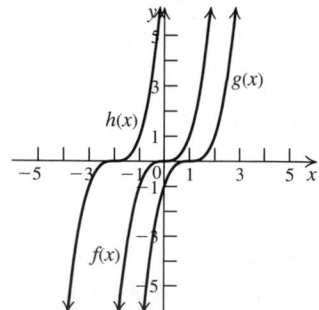

The graph of g is the graph of f shifted 1 unit to the right; the graph of h is the graph of f shifted 2 units to the left.

4.

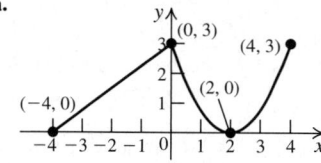

5. Reflect the graph of $y = x^2$ in the x-axis. Then shift it 1 unit to the right and 2 units up.

6.

The graph of g is the graph of f vertically stretched by multiplying each of its y-coordinates by 2.

7. a.

b.

8.

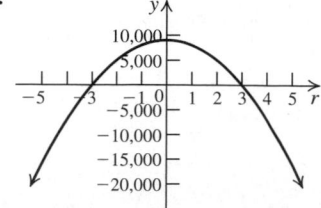

9.

A Exercises: Basic Skills and Concepts

1. a. $g(x)$: Shift two units up. $h(x)$: Shift one unit down.

b.

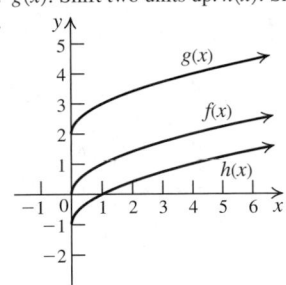

c. $g(x)$: domain: $[0, \infty)$, range: $[2, \infty)$;
$h(x)$: domain: $[0, \infty)$, range: $[-1, \infty)$

2. a. $g(x)$: Shift one unit up. $h(x)$: Shift two units down.

b.

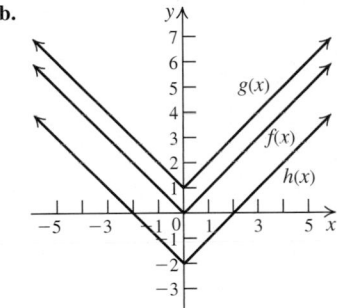

c. $g(x)$: domain: $(-\infty, \infty)$, range: $[1, \infty)$;
$h(x)$: domain: $(-\infty, \infty)$, range: $[-2, \infty)$

3. a. $g(x)$: Shift one unit to the left. $h(x)$: Shift two units to the right.

b.

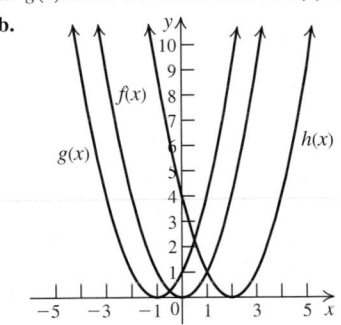

c. $g(x)$: domain: $(-\infty, \infty)$, range: $[0, \infty)$;
$h(x)$: domain: $(-\infty, \infty)$, range: $[0, \infty)$

4. a. $g(x)$: Shift two units to the left. $h(x)$: Shift three units to the right.

b.

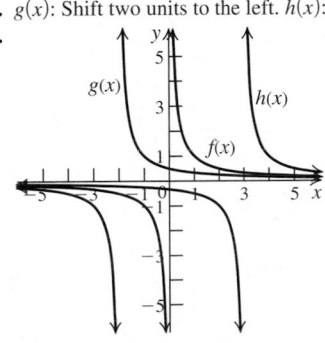

c. $g(x)$: domain: $(-\infty, -2) \cup (-2, \infty)$, range: $(-\infty, 0) \cup (0, \infty)$;
$h(x)$: domain: $(-\infty, 3) \cup (3, \infty)$, range: $(-\infty, 0) \cup (0, \infty)$

5. a. $g(x)$: Reflect in the x-axis. $h(x)$: Reflect in the y-axis.

b.

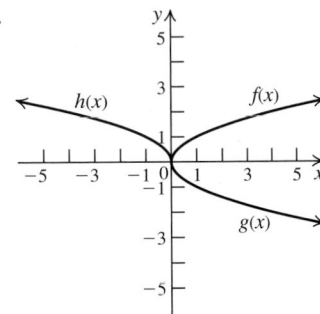

c. $g(x)$: domain: $[0, \infty)$, range: $(-\infty, 0]$;
$h(x)$: domain: $(-\infty, 0]$, range: $[0, \infty)$

6. a. $g(x)$: Reflect in the x-axis; $h(x)$: same as the graph of f

b.

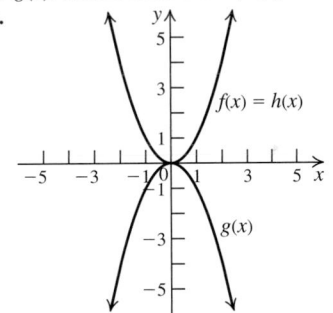

c. $g(x)$: domain: $(-\infty, \infty)$, range: $(-\infty, 0]$;
$h(x)$: domain: $(-\infty, \infty)$, range: $[0, \infty)$

7. a. $g(x)$: Multiply each y-coordinate by 2. $h(x)$: same as the graph of g

b.

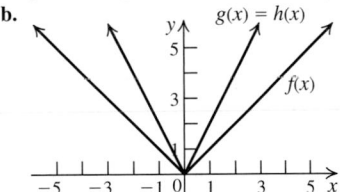

c. $g(x)$: domain: $(-\infty, \infty)$, range: $[0, \infty)$;
$h(x)$: domain: $(-\infty, \infty)$, range: $[0, \infty)$

8. a. $g(x)$: Multiply each y-coordinate by 2. $h(x)$: Multiply each y-coordinate by $\dfrac{1}{2}$.

b.

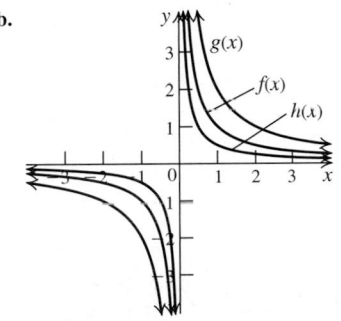

c. $g(x)$: domain: $(-\infty, 0) \cup (0, \infty)$, range: $(-\infty, 0) \cup (0, \infty)$;
$h(x)$: domain: $(-\infty, 0) \cup (0, \infty)$, range: $(-\infty, 0) \cup (0, \infty)$

9. a. $g(x)$: Shift one unit to the left and reflect in the y-axis. $h(x)$: Shift one unit to the left, reflect in the y-axis, reflect in the x-axis, and shift one unit up.

b.

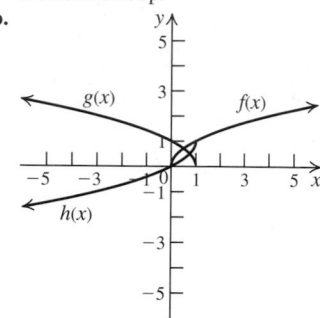

c. $g(x)$: domain: $(-\infty, 1]$, range: $[0, \infty)$;
$h(x)$: domain: $(-\infty, 1]$, range: $(-\infty, 1]$

10. a. $g(x)$: Shift one unit to the right. $h(x)$: Shift one unit to the right and three units up.

b.

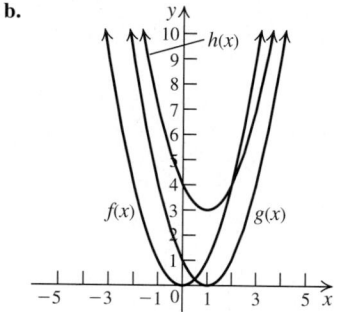

c. $g(x)$: domain: $(-\infty, \infty)$, range: $[0, \infty)$;
$h(x)$: domain: $(-\infty, \infty)$, range: $[3, \infty)$

11. a. $g(x)$: Shift two units to the right and one unit up. $h(x)$: shift one unit to the left, reflect in the x-axis, and shift two units up.

b.

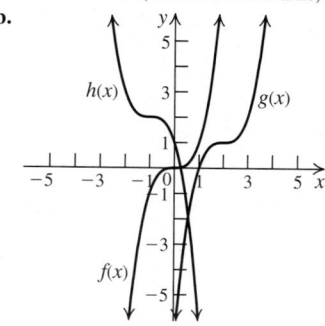

c. $g(x)$: domain: $(-\infty, \infty)$, range: $(-\infty, \infty)$;
$h(x)$: domain: $(-\infty, \infty)$, range: $(-\infty, \infty)$

12. a. $g(x)$: Shift one unit to the right, reflect in the x-axis, and shift two units up. $h(x)$: Multiply each y-coordinate by 3 and shift one unit down.

b.

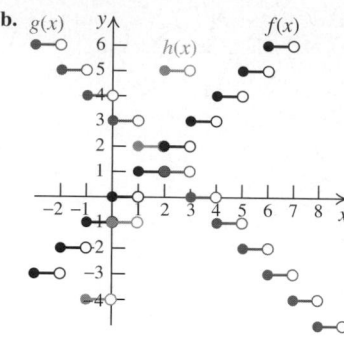

c. $g(x)$: domain :$(-\infty, \infty)$, range: $\{n: \ n$ is an integer$\}$;
$h(x)$: domain: $(-\infty, \infty)$, range: $\{n: \ n = 3k - 1, k$ any integer$\}$

13. a. $g(x)$: Shift one unit up. $h(x)$: Shift one unit to the left.

b.

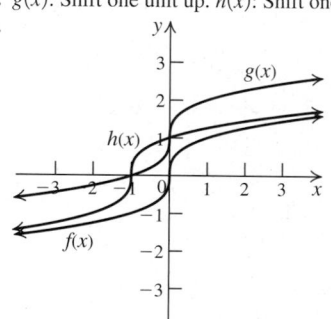

c. $g(x)$: domain: $(-\infty, \infty)$, range:$(-\infty, \infty)$;
$h(x)$: domain :$(-\infty, \infty)$, range :$(-\infty, \infty)$

14. a. $g(x)$: Shift one unit to the left, reflect in the y-axis, multiply each y-coordinate by 2, and shift four units up. $h(x)$: Shift one unit to the right, reflect in the x-axis, and shift three units up.

b.

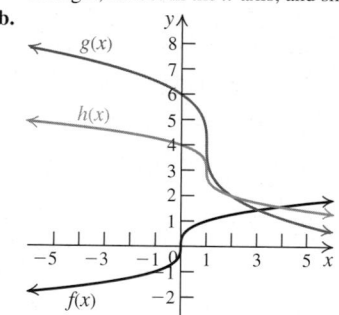

c. $g(x)$: domain: $(-\infty, \infty)$, range: $(-\infty, \infty)$;
$h(x)$: domain: $(-\infty, \infty)$, range: $(-\infty, \infty)$

35.

36.

38.

39.

40.

41.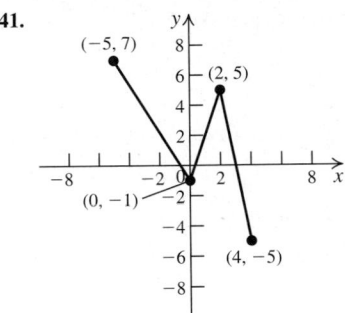

B Exercises: Applying the Concepts

46. $j(x) = \begin{cases} 1.1(x), & \text{if } (x) < 30{,}000 \\ 1.02(x), & \text{if } (x) \geq 30{,}000 \end{cases}$

47. a.

b. $5199.75

49. a.

50. $R(p) = -3(p - 100)^2 + 30{,}000$. Shifting 100 units to the right, stretching by a factor of 3, reflecting in the x-axis, and shifting 30,000 units up

51. The first coordinate gives the month. The second coordinate gives the hours of daylight. From March to September, there is daylight more than half of the day every day. From September to March, more than half of the day is dark every day.

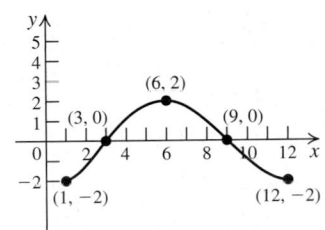

52. The graph shows the number of hours of darkness.

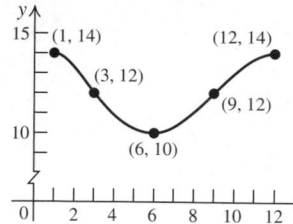

C Exercises: Beyond the Basics

53. Shift one unit to the right, stretch by a factor of 2, reflect in the *x*-axis, and shift three units up.

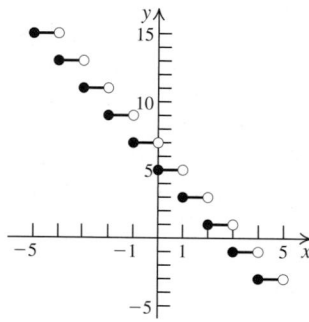

54. Shift two units to the left, stretch by a factor of 3, and shift one unit down.

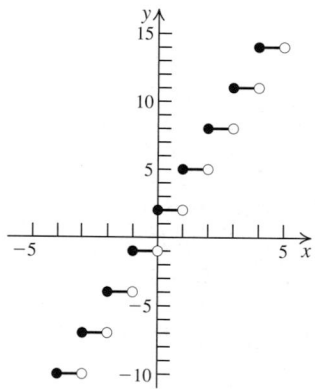

55. Shift two units to the left and four units down.

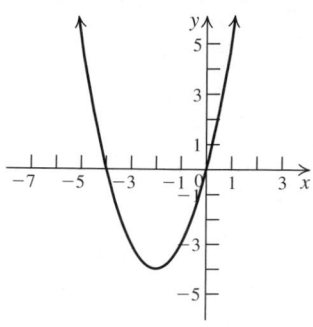

56. $x^2 - 6x = (x^2 - 6x + 9) - 9 = (x - 3)^2 - 9$
Shift three units to the right and nine units down.

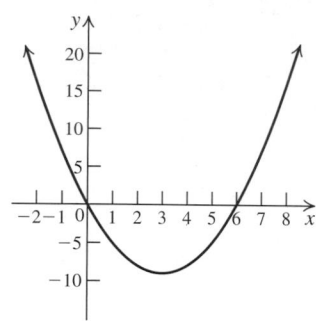

57. $-x^2 + 2x = -(x^2 - 2x + 1) + 1 = -(x - 1)^2 + 1$
Shift one unit to the right, reflect in the *x*-axis, and shift one unit up.

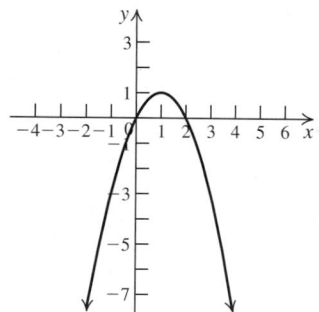

58. $-x^2 - 2x = -(x^2 + 2x + 1) + 1 = -(x + 1)^2 + 1$
Shift one unit to the left, reflect in the *x*-axis, and shift one unit up.

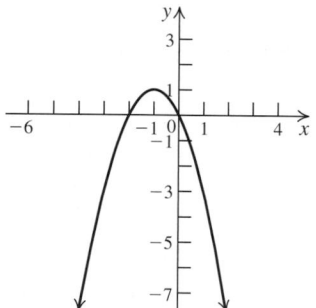

59. $2x^2 - 4x = 2(x^2 - 2x + 1) - 2 = 2(x - 1)^2 - 2$
Shift one unit to the right, stretch by a factor of two, and shift two units down.

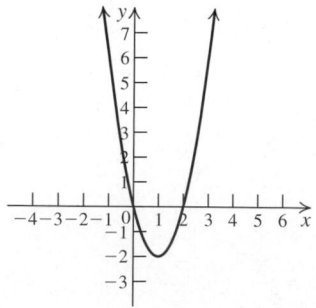

60. $2x^2 + 6x + 3.5 = 2(x^2 + 3x + 2.25) - 1 = 2(x + 1.5)^2 - 1$
Shift 1.5 units to the left, stretch by a factor of two, and shift one down.

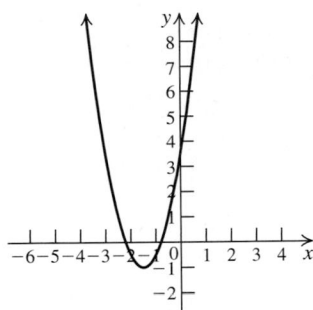

61. $-2x^2 - 8x + 3 = -2(x^2 + 4x + 4) + 11 = -2(x + 2)^2 + 11$
Shift 2 units to the left, stretch by a factor of two, reflect in the x-axis, and shift 11 units up.

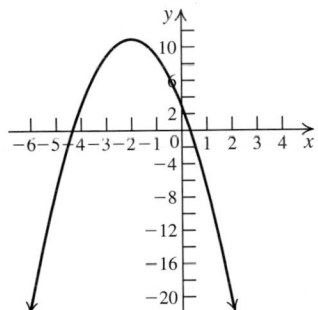

62. $-2x^2 + 2x - 1 = -2(x^2 - x + 0.25) - 0.5 = -2(x - 0.5)^2 - 0.5$
Shift 0.5 unit to the right, stretch by a factor of two, reflect in the x-axis, and shift down by 0.5 unit.

63.

64.

65.

66.

67.

68.

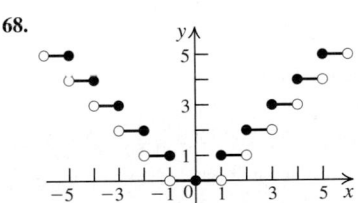

Section 2.7

Practice Problems

1. $(f + g)(x) = x^2 + 3x + 1$
$(f - g)(x) = -x^2 + 3x - 3$
$(fg)(x) = 3x^3 - x^2 + 6x - 2$
$\left(\dfrac{f}{g}\right)(x) = \dfrac{3x - 1}{x^2 + 2}$

2. $(f \circ g)(0) = -5$
$(g \circ f)(0) = 1$

3. $(g \circ f)(x) = 2x^2 - 8x + 9$
$(f \circ g)(x) = 1 - 2x^2$
4. $(g \circ f)(4) = 9$
$(g \circ f)(x) = 2\sqrt{x} + 5$; domain: $[0, \infty)$
5. $(f \circ g)(x) = f(g(x)) = 2(x - 1)^2 + 3 = H(x)$
6. a. $A = 9\pi t^2$
b. $A = 324\pi$ square miles.
7. a. $f(x) = x - 4500$
b. $g(x) = 0.94x$
c. (i) $(f \circ g)(x) = 0.94x - 4500$ **(ii)** $(g \circ f)(x) = 0.94x - 4230$
d. $(g \circ f)(x) - (f \circ g)(x) = 270$

A Exercises: Basic Skills and Concepts

1. a. $(f + g)(-1) = -1$ **b.** $(f - g)(0) = 0$

c. $(f \cdot g)(2) = -8$ **d.** $\left(\dfrac{f}{g}\right)(1) = -2$

2. a. $(f + g)(-1) = 0$ **b.** $(f - g)(0) = 0$

c. $(f \cdot g)(2) = -9$ **d.** $\left(\dfrac{f}{g}\right)(1) = 0$

3. a. $(f + g)(-1) = 0$ **b.** $(f - g)(0) = \dfrac{1}{2}(\sqrt{2} - 2)$

c. $(f \cdot g)(2) = \dfrac{5}{2}$ **d.** $\left(\dfrac{f}{g}\right)(1) = \dfrac{1}{3\sqrt{3}}$

4. a. $(f + g)(-1) = \dfrac{59}{15}$ **b.** $(f - g)(0) = -3$

c. Does not exist **d.** $\left(\dfrac{f}{g}\right)(1) = \dfrac{1}{6}$

5. a. $(f + g)(-1) = 3$ **b.** $(f - g)(0) = -3$

c. $(f \cdot g)(2) = 8$ **d.** $\left(\dfrac{f}{g}\right)(1) = \dfrac{3}{2}$

6. a. $(f + g)(-1) = 25$ **b.** $(f - g)(0) = -21$

c. $(f \cdot g)(2) = 336$ **d.** $\left(\dfrac{f}{g}\right)(1) = \dfrac{4}{27}$

7. a. $(f + g)(x) = x^2 + x - 3$; domain: $(-\infty, \infty)$
b. $(f - g)(x) = -x^2 + x - 3$; domain: $(-\infty, \infty)$
c. $(f \cdot g)(x) = x^3 - 3x^2$; domain: $(-\infty, \infty)$

d. $\left(\dfrac{f}{g}\right)(x) = \dfrac{x - 3}{x^2}$; domain: $(-\infty, 0) \cup (0, \infty)$

e. $\left(\dfrac{g}{f}\right)(x) = \dfrac{x^2}{x - 3}$; domain: $(-\infty, 3) \cup (3, \infty)$

8. a. $(f + g)(x) = x^2 + 2x - 1$; domain: $(-\infty, \infty)$
b. $(f - g)(x) = -x^2 + 2x - 1$; domain: $(-\infty, \infty)$
c. $(f \cdot g)(x) = 2x^3 - x^2$; domain: $(-\infty, \infty)$

d. $\left(\dfrac{f}{g}\right)(x) = \dfrac{2x - 1}{x^2}$; domain: $(-\infty, 0) \cup (0, \infty)$

e. $\left(\dfrac{g}{f}\right)(x) = \dfrac{x^2}{2x - 1}$; domain: $\left(-\infty, \dfrac{1}{2}\right) \cup \left(\dfrac{1}{2}, \infty\right)$

9. a. $(f + g)(x) = x^3 + 2x^2 + 4$; domain: $(-\infty, \infty)$
b. $(f - g)(x) = x^3 - 2x^2 - 6$; domain: $(-\infty, \infty)$
c. $(f \cdot g)(x) = 2x^5 + 5x^3 - 2x^2 - 5$; domain: $(-\infty, \infty)$

d. $\left(\dfrac{f}{g}\right)(x) = \dfrac{x^3 - 1}{2x^2 + 5}$; domain: $(-\infty, \infty)$

e. $\left(\dfrac{g}{f}\right)(x) = \dfrac{2x^2 + 5}{x^3 - 1}$; domain: $(-\infty, 1) \cup (1, \infty)$

10. a. $(f + g)(x) = 2x^2 - 6x + 4$; domain: $(-\infty, \infty)$
b. $(f - g)(x) = 6x - 12$; domain: $(-\infty, \infty)$
c. $(f \cdot g)(x) = x^4 - 6x^3 + 4x^2 + 24x - 32$; domain: $(-\infty, \infty)$

d. $\left(\dfrac{f}{g}\right)(x) = \dfrac{x^2 - 4}{x^2 - 6x + 8}$; domain: $(-\infty, 2) \cup (2, 4) \cup (4, \infty)$

e. $\left(\dfrac{g}{f}\right)(x) = \dfrac{x^2 - 6x + 8}{x^2 - 4}$; domain: $(-\infty, -2) \cup (-2, 2) \cup (2, \infty)$

11. a. $(f + g)(x) = 2x + \sqrt{x} - 1$; domain: $[0, \infty)$
b. $(f - g)(x) = 2x - \sqrt{x} - 1$; domain: $[0, \infty)$
c. $(f \cdot g)(x) = 2x\sqrt{x} - \sqrt{x}$; domain: $[0, \infty)$

d. $\left(\dfrac{f}{g}\right)(x) = \dfrac{2x - 1}{\sqrt{x}}$; domain: $(0, \infty)$

e. $\left(\dfrac{g}{f}\right)(x) = \dfrac{\sqrt{x}}{2x - 1}$; domain: $\left[0, \dfrac{1}{2}\right) \cup \left(\dfrac{1}{2}, \infty\right)$

12. a. $(f + g)(x) = 1$; domain: $(-\infty, 0) \cup (0, \infty)$

b. $(f - g)(x) = 1 - \dfrac{2}{x}$; domain: $(-\infty, 0) \cup (0, \infty)$

c. $(f \cdot g)(x) = \dfrac{x - 1}{x^2}$; domain: $(-\infty, 0) \cup (0, \infty)$

d. $\left(\dfrac{f}{g}\right)(x) = x - 1$; domain: $(-\infty, 0) \cup (0, \infty)$

e. $\left(\dfrac{g}{f}\right)(x) = \dfrac{1}{x - 1}$; domain: $(-\infty, 0) \cup (0, 1) \cup (1, \infty)$

13. $g(f(x)) = 2x^2 + 1$; $g(f(2)) = 9$; $g(f(-3)) = 19$
14. $g(f(x)) = 3|x|^2$; $g(f(2)) = 12$; $g(f(-3)) = 27$
33. a. $(f \circ g)(x) = 2x + 5$; domain: $(-\infty, \infty)$
b. $(g \circ f)(x) = 2x + 1$; domain: $(-\infty, \infty)$
c. $(f \circ f)(x) = 4x - 9$; domain: $(-\infty, \infty)$
d. $(g \circ g)(x) = x + 8$; domain: $(-\infty, \infty)$
34. a. $(f \circ g)(x) = 3x - 8$; domain: $(-\infty, \infty)$
b. $(g \circ f)(x) = 3x - 14$; domain: $(-\infty, \infty)$
c. $(f \circ f)(x) = x - 6$; domain: $(-\infty, \infty)$
d. $(g \circ g)(x) = 9x - 20$; domain: $(-\infty, \infty)$
35. a. $(f \circ g)(x) = -2x^2 - 1$; domain: $(-\infty, \infty)$
b. $(g \circ f)(x) = 4x^2 - 4x + 2$; domain: $(-\infty, \infty)$
c. $(f \circ f)(x) = 4x - 1$; domain: $(-\infty, \infty)$
d. $(g \circ g)(x) = x^4 + 2x^2 + 2$; domain: $(-\infty, \infty)$
36. a. $(f \circ g)(x) = 4x^2 - 3$; domain: $(-\infty, \infty)$
b. $(g \circ f)(x) = 2(2x-3)^2$; domain: $(-\infty, \infty)$
c. $(f \circ f)(x) = 4x - 9$; domain: $(-\infty, \infty)$
d. $(g \circ g)(x) = 8x^4$; domain: $(-\infty, \infty)$
37. a. $(f \circ g)(x) = 8x^2 - 2x - 1$; domain: $(-\infty, \infty)$
b. $(g \circ f)(x) = 4x^2 + 6x - 1$; domain: $(-\infty, \infty)$
c. $(f \circ f)(x) = 8x^4 + 24x^3 + 24x^2 + 9x$; domain: $(-\infty, \infty)$
d. $(g \circ g)(x) = 4x - 3$; domain: $(-\infty, \infty)$
38. a. $(f \circ g)(x) = 4x^2 + 6x$; domain: $(-\infty, \infty)$
b. $(g \circ f)(x) = 2x^2 + 6x$; domain: $(-\infty, \infty)$
c. $(f \circ f)(x) = x^4 + 6x^3 + 12x^2 + 9x$; domain: $(-\infty, \infty)$
d. $(g \circ g)(x) = 4x$; domain: $(-\infty, \infty)$
39. a. $(f \circ g)(x) = x$; domain: $[0, \infty)$
b. $(g \circ f)(x) = |x|$; domain: $(-\infty, \infty)$
c. $(f \circ f)(x) = x^4$; domain: $(-\infty, \infty)$
d. $(g \circ g)(x) = \sqrt[4]{x}$; domain: $[0, \infty)$
40. a. $(f \circ g)(x) = x + 2 + 2\sqrt{x + 2}$; domain: $[-2, \infty)$
b. $(g \circ f)(x) = \sqrt{x^2 + 2x + 2}$; domain: $(-\infty, \infty)$
c. $(f \circ f)(x) = x^4 + 4x^3 + 6x^2 + 4x$; domain: $(-\infty, \infty)$
d. $(g \circ g)(x) = \sqrt{\sqrt{x + 2} + 2}$; domain: $[-2, \infty)$
41. a. $(f \circ g)(x) = -\dfrac{x^2}{x^2 - 2}$;
domain: $(-\infty, -\sqrt{2}) \cup (-\sqrt{2}, 0) \cup (0, \sqrt{2}) \cup (\sqrt{2}, \infty)$

b. $(g \circ f)(x) = (2x-1)^2$; domain: $\left(-\infty, \dfrac{1}{2}\right) \cup \left(\dfrac{1}{2}, \infty\right)$

c. $(f \circ f)(x) = -\dfrac{2x - 1}{2x - 3}$; domain: $\left(-\infty, \dfrac{1}{2}\right) \cup \left(\dfrac{1}{2}, \dfrac{3}{2}\right) \cup \left(\dfrac{3}{2}, \infty\right)$

d. $(g \circ g)(x) = x^4$; domain: $(-\infty, 0) \cup (0, \infty)$

42. a. $(f \circ g)(x) = -\dfrac{1}{x + 1}$; domain: $(-\infty, -1) \cup (-1, \infty)$

b. $(g \circ f)(x) = \dfrac{x - 1}{x}$; domain: $(-\infty, 0) \cup (0, \infty)$

c. $(f \circ f)(x) = x - 2$; domain: $(-\infty, \infty)$

d. $(g \circ g)(x) = \dfrac{x}{2x + 1}$;

domain: $(-\infty, -1) \cup \left(-1, -\dfrac{1}{2}\right) \cup \left(-\dfrac{1}{2}, \infty\right)$

43. a. $(f \circ g)(x) = 2$; domain: $(-\infty, \infty)$

b. $(g \circ f)(x) = -2$; domain: $(-\infty, \infty)$

c. $(f \circ f)(x) = |x|$; domain: $(-\infty, \infty)$

d. $(g \circ g)(x) = -2$; domain: $(-\infty, \infty)$

44. a. $(f \circ g)(x) = 3$; domain: $(-\infty, \infty)$

b. $(g \circ f)(x) = 5$; domain: $(-\infty, \infty)$

c. $(f \circ f)(x) = 3$; domain: $(-\infty, \infty)$

d. $(g \circ g)(x) = 5$; domain: $(-\infty, \infty)$

45. a. $(f \circ g)(x) = \dfrac{2}{1 + x}$; domain: $(-\infty, -1) \cup (-1, 1) \cup (1, \infty)$

b. $(g \circ f)(x) = -2x - 1$; domain: $(-\infty, 0) \cup (0, \infty)$.

c. $(f \circ f)(x) = \dfrac{2x + 1}{x + 1}$; domain: $(-\infty, -1) \cup (-1, 0) \cup (0, \infty)$

d. $(g \circ g)(x) = -\dfrac{1}{x}$; domain: $(-\infty, 0) \cup (0, 1) \cup (1, \infty)$

46. a. $(f \circ g)(x) = \sqrt[3]{x^3 + 2}$; domain: $(-\infty, \infty)$

b. $(g \circ f)(x) = x + 2$; domain: $(-\infty, \infty)$

c. $(f \circ f)(x) = \sqrt[3]{\sqrt[3]{x + 1} + 1}$; domain: $(-\infty, \infty)$

d. $(g \circ g)(x) = (x^3 + 1)^3 + 1$; domain: $(-\infty, \infty)$

B Exercises: Applying the Concepts

57. c. Selling price of x shirts after sales tax

59. b. $P(20) = 50$. Profit made after 20 radios were sold

d. $(R \circ x)(C) = 5C - 1750$. The function represents the revenue in terms of the cost C.

60. a. $g(x) = 0.04x$

b. The after-tax selling price of merchandise worth x dollars

c. $f(x) = 0.02h(x) + 3$. The after-tax shipping-and-handling fee for merchandise for a price of x dollars

d. The total price of merchandise worth x dollars, including the shipping-and-handling fee.

61. a. $f(x) = 0.7x$

b. $g(x) = x - 5$

d. $(f \circ g)(x) = 0.7(x - 5)$

62. c. $(g \circ f)(x) = 0.9(0.8x) = 0.72x$

d. $(f \circ g)(x) = 0.8(0.9x) = 0.72x$

e. They are the same.

63. b. $(f \circ g)(x) = 1.1x + 8.8$. A final test score, that originally was x, after first adding 8 points and then increasing the score by 10%.

c. $(g \circ f)(x) = 1.1x + 8$. A final test score, that originally was x, after first increasing the score by 10% and then adding 8 points.

64. a. A function that models 3% of an amount x.

b. The amount of money that qualified for a 3% bonus.

65. c. The area between the fountain and the fence

68. a. $(f \circ g)(t) = \dfrac{32}{3}\pi t^3$ **b.** $V(t) = \dfrac{32}{3}\pi t^3$

69. a. $f(x) = 1.7559x$ **b.** $g(x) = 0.05328x$

C Exercises: Beyond the Basics

70. f. Odd function

73. a. $h(x) = o(x) + e(x)$, where $e(x) = x^2 + 3$ and $o(x) = -2x$

b. $h(x) = o(x) + e(x)$, where

$e(x) = \dfrac{[x] + [-x]}{2}$ and $o(x) = x + \dfrac{[x] - [-x]}{2}$

Critical Thinking

74. a. Domain: $(-\infty, 0) \cup [1, \infty)$

c. Domain: $[1, 2]$

75. b. Domain: $(-\infty, 0)$

Section 2.8

Practice Problems

1. Inverse $= \{(43, \text{Sophia}), (46, \text{Sal}), (47, \text{Anna}), (47, \text{Dwayne}), (50, \text{Desmonde}), (55, \text{Carl})\}$. Not a function

2. Not one-to-one. The horizontal line $y = 1$ intersects the graph at 2 different points.

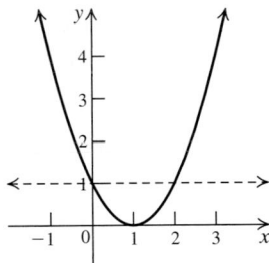

3. a. -3 **b.** 4

4. $(f \circ g)(x) = 3\dfrac{x + 1}{3} - 1 = x + 1 - 1 = x$ and

$(g \circ f)(x) = \dfrac{3x - 1 + 1}{3} = \dfrac{3x}{3} = x$; therefore, f and g are inverses of each other.

5.

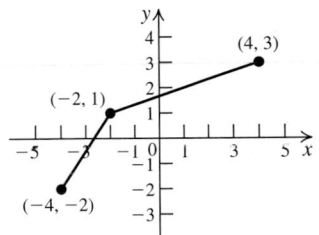

6. $f^{-1}(x) = \dfrac{3x}{1 - x}, x \neq 1$

7. Domain: $(-\infty, -3) \cup (-3, \infty)$; range: $(-\infty, 1) \cup (1, \infty)$

8. $g^{-1}(x) = -\sqrt{x + 1}$

9. 3630 ft

A Exercises: Basic Skills and Concepts

1. Inverse $= \{(01970, \text{Salem MA}), (38736, \text{Doddsville MS}), (68102, \text{Omaha NE}), (94203, \text{Sacramento CA}), (96772, \text{Naalehu HI})\}$. A function

2. Inverse $= \{(23, \text{Equinox}), (26, \text{Malibu}), (27, \text{Colorado}), (27, \text{Impala}), (31, \text{Monte Carlo})\}$. Not a function, because it has two different types of Chevrolet corresponding to 27 miles per gallon

3. Inverse $= \{(-3, 13), (-2, 8), (-1, -1), (1, -1), (2, -8), (3, -13)\}$. A function

4. Inverse $= \{(1, 0), (2, -1), (2, 1), (5, -2), (5, 2), (10, -3), (10, 3)\}$.
Not a function

27.

28.

29.

30.

31.

32.

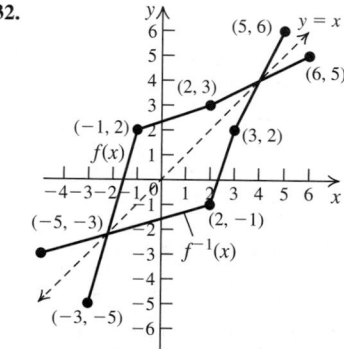

33.

x	3	4	5	6	7
$f^{-1}(x)$	-2	-1	0	1	2

34.

x	-2	0	1	2	3
$f^{-1}(x)$	3	-1	1	-3	5

35. $f(g(x)) = 3\dfrac{x - 1}{3} + 1 = x - 1 + 1 = x,$

$g(f(x)) = \dfrac{3x + 1 - 1}{3} = \dfrac{3x}{3} = x$

36. $f(g(x)) = 3\dfrac{2 - x}{3} = 2 - (2 - x) = x$

$g(f(x)) = \dfrac{2 - (2 - 3x)}{3} = \dfrac{3x}{3} = x$

41. Domain: $(-\infty, -2) \cup (-2, \infty)$. Range: $(-\infty, 1) \cup (1, \infty)$.
42. Domain: $(-\infty, 1) \cup (1, \infty)$. Range: $(-\infty, 3) \cup (3, \infty)$.

43. a. one-to-one   **b.** $f^{-1}(x) = 5 - \dfrac{1}{3}x$

c.

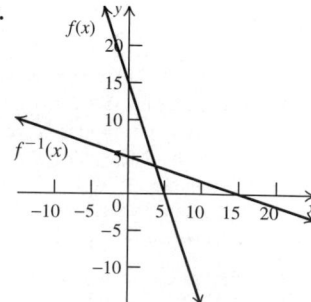

44. a. one-to-one   **b.** $g^{-1}(x) = \dfrac{1}{2}x - \dfrac{5}{2}$

c.

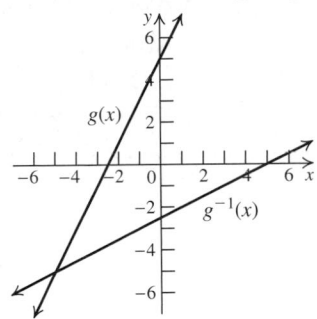

47. a. one-to-one
b. $f^{-1}(x) = (x - 3)^2$
c.

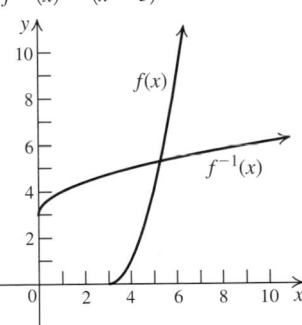

48. a. one-to-one   **b.** $f^{-1}(x) = (x - 4)^2$
c.

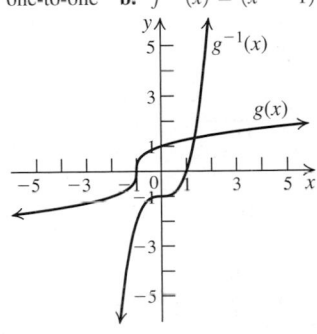

49. a. one-to-one   **b.** $f^{-1}(x) = (x^3 - 1)$
c.

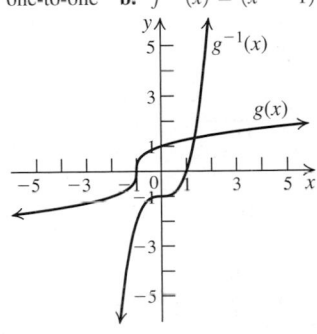

50. a. one-to-one   **b.** $h^{-1}(x) = 1 - x^3$
c.

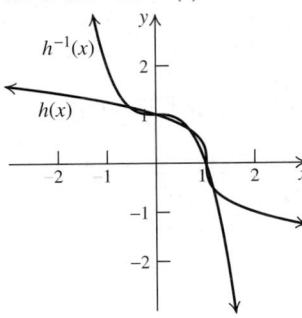

51. a. one-to-one   **b.** $f^{-1}(x) = \dfrac{x + 1}{x}$

c.

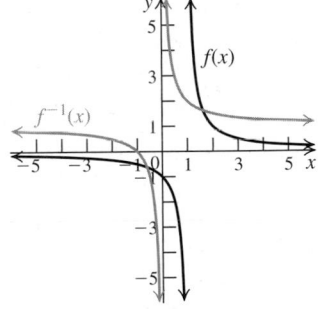

52. a. one-to-one   **b.** $g^{-1}(x) = \dfrac{1}{1 - x}$

c.

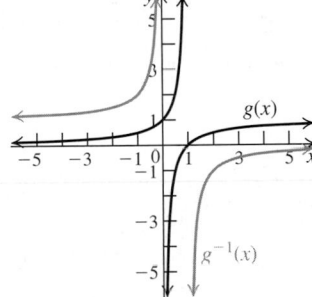

53. a. one-to-one   **b.** $f^{-1}(x) = 2 - x^2$
c.

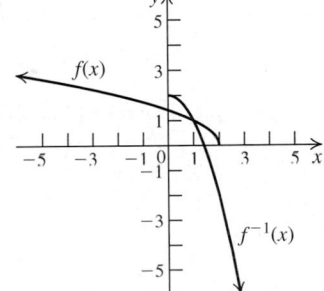

54. a. one-to-one   **b.** $g^{-1}(x) = x^2 - 3$
c.

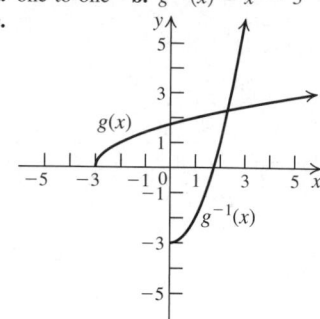

55. $f^{-1}(x) = \dfrac{2x + 1}{x - 1}$. Domain: $(-\infty, 2) \cup (2, \infty)$.
Range: $(-\infty, 1) \cup (1, \infty)$

56. $g^{-1}(x) = \dfrac{x - 2}{1 - x}$ Domain: $(-\infty, -1) \cup (-1, \infty)$.
Range: $(-\infty, 1) \cup (1, \infty)$

57. $f^{-1}(x) = \dfrac{1 - x}{x + 2}$. Domain: $(-\infty, -1) \cup (-1, \infty)$
Range: $(-\infty, -2) \cup (-2, \infty)$

58. $h^{-1}(x) = \dfrac{3x - 1}{x - 1}$. Domain: $(-\infty, 3) \cup (3, \infty)$
Range: $(-\infty, 1) \cup (1, \infty)$

B Exercises Applying the Concepts

59. a. $C(K) = K - 273$. It represents the Celsius temperature corresponding to a given Kelvin temperature.

60. a. $K(F) = \dfrac{5}{9}F + \dfrac{2297}{9}$ **b.** $F(K) = \dfrac{9}{5}K - \dfrac{2297}{5}$. It represents the Fahrenheit temperature corresponding to a given Kelvin temperature.

61. a. $F = \dfrac{9}{5}C + 32$ **b.** $C = \dfrac{5}{9}F - \dfrac{160}{9}$

63. a. Dollars to euros: $f(x) = 0.75x$ (x is the number of dollars, $f(x)$ is the number of euros). Euros to dollars: $g(x) = 1.25x$ (x is the number of euros, $g(x)$ is the number of dollars).
b. $g(f(x)) = 0.9375x \neq x$; therefore, g and f are not inverse functions.

64. a. $x = 20w - 80$. It gives the food sales in terms of his hourly wage.

65. a. $w = \begin{cases} 4 + 0.05x, & \text{if } x > 60 \\ 7, & \text{if } x \leq 60 \end{cases}$
b. It does not have an inverse, because it is constant on $(0, 60)$ and hence is not one-to-one.
c. Restriction of the domain: $[60, \infty)$

66. a. $l = \dfrac{1}{1.11}T$. It shows the length as the function of the period.

67. a. $x = \dfrac{1}{64}V^2$. It gives the height of the water in terms of the velocity.
b. (i) 14.0625 ft   **(ii)** 6.25 ft

68. a. $x = \dfrac{64 - \sqrt{4096 - 8y}}{4}$, $0 \leq y \leq 512$
b. (i) 0.51 ft   **(ii)** 4.69 ft   **(iii)** 16 ft

69. a. The balance due after x months.
b. $f^{-1}(x) = 60 - \dfrac{1}{600}x$. It shows the number of months that have passed from the first payment until the balance due is $\$x$.
c. 24

70. a. $p = 2 - \dfrac{1}{4}\sqrt{2x - 2336}$ $1168 \leq x < 1200$. It shows the price of the computer chips in terms of the demand x.
b. $\$0.75$

C Exercises: Beyond the Basics

73. a.

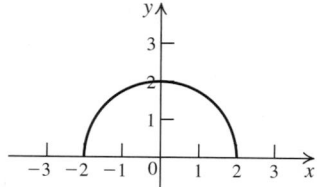

b. No
c. Domain: $[-2, 2]$. Range: $[0, 2]$
75. a.

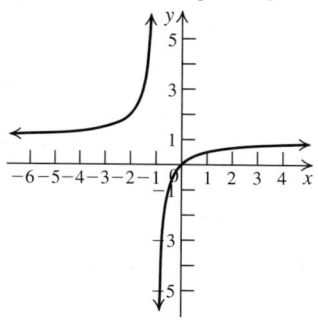

f satisfies the horizontal-line test.
b. $f^{-1}(x) = \dfrac{x}{1 - x}$
c. Domain: $(-\infty, -1) \cup (-1, \infty)$. Range: $(-\infty, 1) \cup (1, \infty)$
76. a.

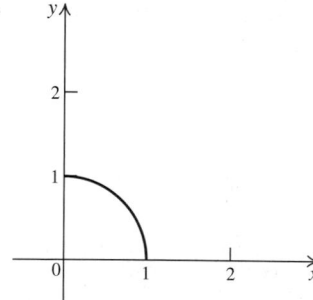

g satisfies the horizontal-line test.
b. $g^{-1}(x) = g(x) = \sqrt{1 - x^2}$
c. Domain = Range = $[0, 1]$
77. a. The midpoint is $M(5, 5)$. Since its coordinates satisfy the equation $y = x$, it lies on the line.
b. The slope of the line segment $\overline{PQ}$ is -1, and the slope of the line $y = x$ is 1. Since $(-1)(1) = -1$, the two lines are perpendicular.

79. a. The graph of g is the graph of f shifted one unit to the right and two units up.

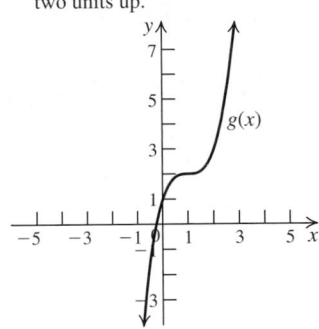

b. $g^{-1}(x) = \sqrt[3]{x - 2} + 1$

c.

80. a. (i) $f^{-1}(x) = \frac{1}{2}x + \frac{1}{2}$ **(ii)** $g^{-1}(x) = \frac{1}{3}x - \frac{4}{3}$

(iii) $(f \circ g)(x) = 6x + 7$ **(iv)** $(g \circ f)(x) = 6x + 1$

(v) $(f \circ g)^{-1}(x) = \frac{1}{6}x - \frac{7}{6}$ **(vi)** $(g \circ f)^{-1}(x) = \frac{1}{6}x - \frac{1}{6}$

(vii) $(f^{-1} \circ g^{-1})(x) = \frac{1}{6}x - \frac{1}{6}$ **(viii)** $(g^{-1} \circ f^{-1})(x) = \frac{1}{6}x - \frac{7}{6}$

b. (i) $(f \circ g)^{-1}(x) - \frac{1}{6}x - \frac{7}{6} - (g^{-1} \circ f^{-1})(x)$

(ii) $(g \circ f)^{-1}(x) = \frac{1}{6}x - \frac{1}{6} = (f^{-1} \circ g^{-1})(x)$

81. a. (i) $f^{-1}(x) = \frac{1}{2}x - \frac{3}{2}$

(ii) $g^{-1}(x) = \sqrt[3]{x} + 1$

(iii) $(f \circ g)(x) = 2x^3 + 1$

(iv) $(g \circ f)(x) = 8x^3 + 36x^2 + 54x + 26$

(v) $(f \circ g)^{-1}(x) = \sqrt[3]{\dfrac{x - 1}{2}}$

(vi) $(g \circ f)^{-1}(x) = \frac{1}{2}\sqrt[3]{x + 1} - \frac{3}{2}$

(vii) $(f^{-1} \circ g^{-1})(x) = \frac{1}{2}\sqrt[3]{x + 1} - \frac{3}{2}$

(viii) $(g^{-1} \circ f^{-1})(x) = \sqrt[3]{\dfrac{x - 1}{2}}$

b. (i) $(f \circ g)^{-1}(x) = \sqrt[3]{\dfrac{x - 1}{2}} = (g^{-1} \circ f^{-1})(x)$

(ii) $(g \circ f)^{-1}(x) = \frac{1}{2}\sqrt[3]{x + 1} - \frac{3}{2} = (f^{-1} \circ g^{-1})(x)$

Critical Thinking

82. No. $f(x) = x^3 - x$ is odd, but it does not have an inverse, because $f(0) = f(1)$, so it is not one-to-one.

83. Yes. The function $f = \{(0, 1)\}$, is even, and it has an inverse: $f^{-1} = \{(1, 0)\}$.

84. Yes, because increasing and decreasing functions are one-to-one

Review Exercises

3. True

9. a. $2\sqrt{5}$ **b.** $(1, 4)$ **c.** $\frac{1}{2}$

10. a. $6\sqrt{2}$ **b.** $(0, 2)$ **c.** -1

11. a. $5\sqrt{2}$ **b.** $\left(\frac{13}{2}, -\frac{11}{2}\right)$ **c.** -1

12. a. $\sqrt{202}$ **b.** $\left(-\frac{5}{2}, -\frac{5}{2}\right)$ **c.** $\frac{11}{9}$

13. a. $\sqrt{34}$ **b.** $\left(\frac{7}{2}, -\frac{9}{2}\right)$ **c.** $\frac{5}{3}$

14. a. $\sqrt{274}$ **b.** $\left(\frac{5}{2}, \frac{1}{2}\right)$ **c.** $-\frac{7}{15}$

16. $d(A, B) = d(B, D) = d(D, C) = d(C, A) = 3\sqrt{5}$, so the four sides have equal length. Therefore, $ABDC$ is a rhombus.

17. $(4, 5)$ **18.** $(5, 10)$ **19.** $\left(\frac{31}{18}, 0\right)$ **20.** $(0, -4)$

21. Not symmetric with respect to the x-axis, symmetric with respect to the y-axis, not symmetric with respect to the origin

22. Not symmetric with respect to the x-axis, not symmetric with respect to the y-axis, symmetric with respect to the origin

23. Symmetric with respect to the x-axis, not symmetric with respect to the y-axis, not symmetric with respect to the origin

24. Symmetric with respect to the x-axis, symmetric with respect to the y-axis, symmetric with respect to the origin

25.

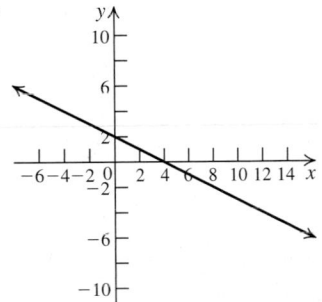

x-intercept: 4. y-intercept: 2. Not symmetric with respect to the x-axis, not symmetric with respect to the y-axis, not symmetric with respect to the origin

26.

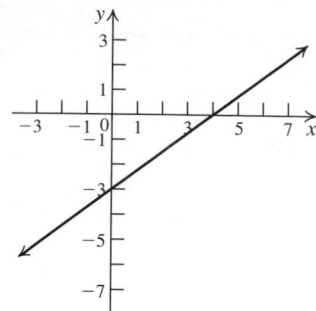

x-intercept: 4. *y*-intercept: −3. Not symmetric with respect to the *x*-axis, not symmetric with respect to the *y*-axis, not symmetric with respect to the origin

27.

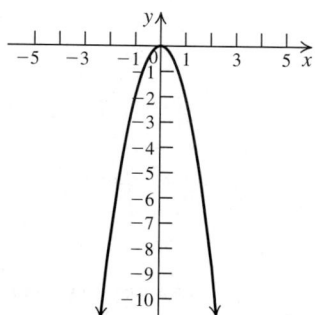

x-intercept: 0. *y*-intercept: 0. Not symmetric with respect to the *x*-axis, symmetric with respect to the *y*-axis, not symmetric with respect to the origin

28.

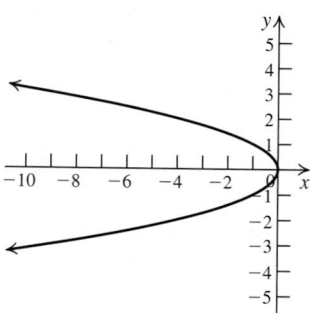

x-intercept: 0. *y*-intercept: 0. Symmetric with respect to the *x*-axis, not symmetric with respect to the *y*-axis, not symmetric with respect to the origin

29.

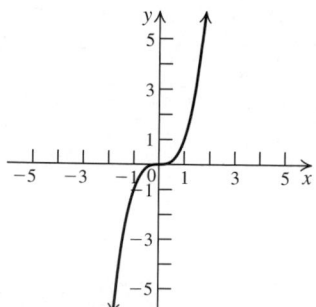

x-intercept: 0. *y*-intercept: 0. Not symmetric with respect to the *x*-axis, not symmetric with respect to the *y*-axis, symmetric with respect to the origin

30.

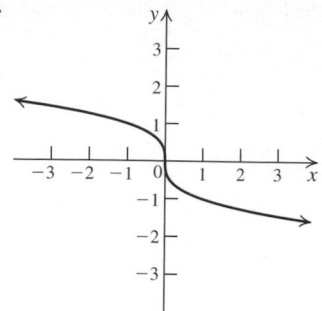

x-intercept: 0. *y*-intercept: 0. Not symmetric with respect to the *x*-axis, not symmetric with respect to the *y*-axis, symmetric with respect to the origin

31.

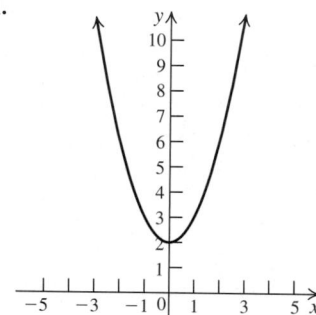

No *x*-intercept. *y*-intercept: 2. Not symmetric with respect to the *x*-axis, symmetric with respect to the *y*-axis, not symmetric with respect to the origin

32.

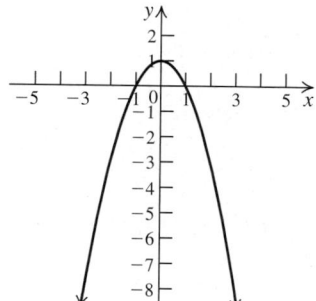

x-intercepts: −1 and 1. *y*-intercept: 1. Not symmetric with respect to the *x*-axis, symmetric with respect to the *y*-axis, not symmetric with respect to the origin

33.

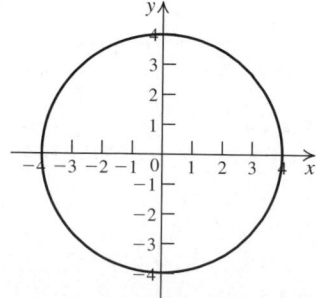

x-intercepts: −4 and 4. *y*-intercepts: −4 and 4. Symmetric with respect to the *x*-axis, symmetric with respect to the *y*-axis, symmetric with respect to the origin

34.

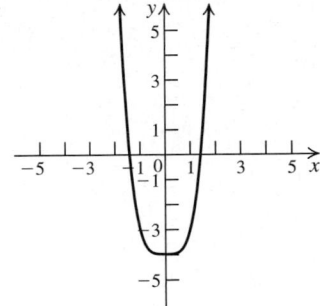

x-intercepts: -2 and 2. y-intercept: -4. Not symmetric with respect to the x-axis, symmetric with respect to the y-axis, not symmetric with respect to the origin

36. $x^2 + (y - 3)^2 = 26$

37. $(x + 2)^2 + (y + 5)^2 = 4$

38. $2x - 5y = 10 \Rightarrow y = \dfrac{2}{5}x - 2$. Line with slope $\dfrac{2}{5}$ and y-intercept -2

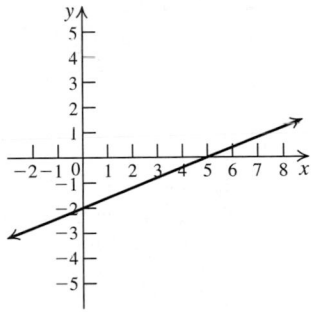

39. $\dfrac{x}{2} - \dfrac{y}{5} = 1 \Rightarrow y = \dfrac{5}{2}x - 5$. Line with slope $\dfrac{5}{2}$ and y-intercept -5

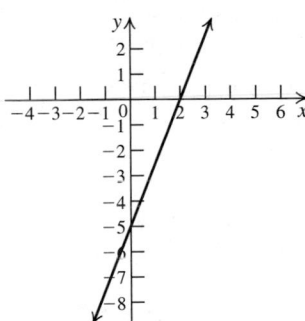

40. Circle centered at $(-1, 3)$ and with radius 4.

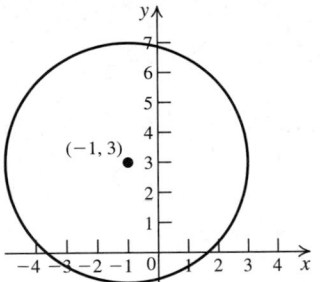

41. $x^2 + y^2 - 2x + 4y - 4 = 0 \Rightarrow (x - 1)^2 + (y + 2)^2 = 9$. Circle centered at $(1, -2)$ and with radius 3

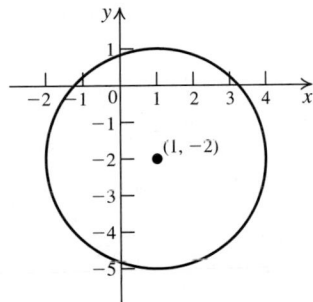

42. $3x^2 + 3y^2 - 6x - 6 = 0 \Rightarrow x^2 + y^2 - 2x - 2 = 0 \Rightarrow$
$(x - 1)^2 + y^2 = 3$. Circle centered at $(1, 0)$ and with radius $\sqrt{3}$.

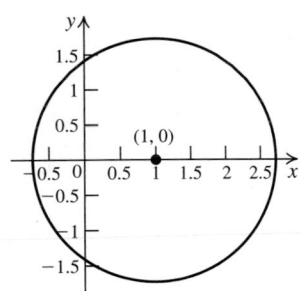

44. $y = -\dfrac{5}{2}x + 5$

49.

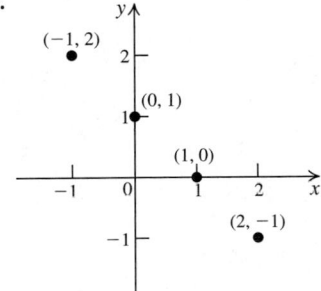

Domain: $\{-1, 0, 1, 2\}$. Range: $\{-1, 0, 1, 2\}$. Function

50.

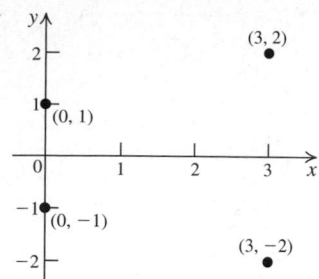

Domain: $\{0, 3\}$. Range: $\{-2, -1, 1, 2\}$. Not a function

51.

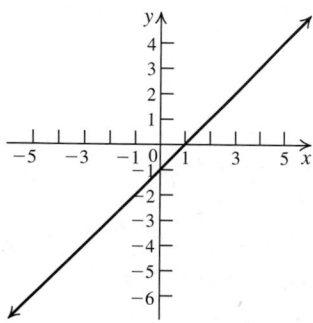

Domain: $(-\infty, \infty)$. Range: $(-\infty, \infty)$. Function

52.

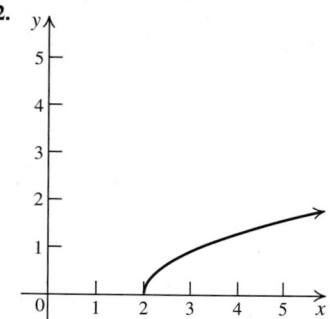

Domain: $[2, \infty)$. Range: $[0, \infty)$. Function

53.

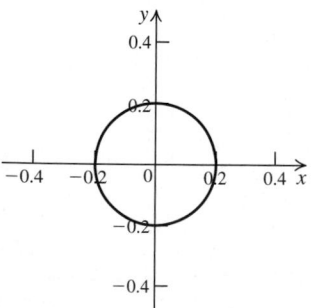

Domain: $[-0.2, 0.2]$. Range: $[-0.2, 0.2]$. Not a function

54.

Domain: $(-\infty, 0]$. Range: $[0, \infty)$. Function

55.

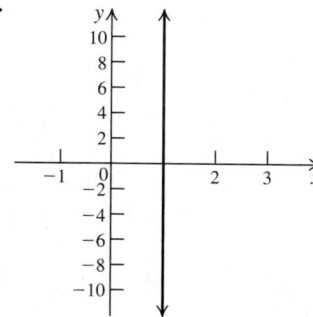

Domain: $\{1\}$. Range: $(-\infty, \infty)$. Not a function

56.

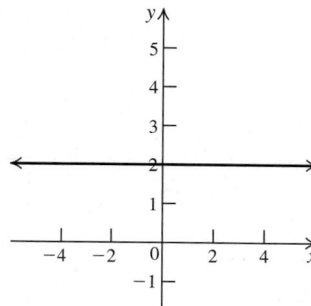

Domain: $(-\infty, \infty)$. Range: $\{2\}$. Function

57.

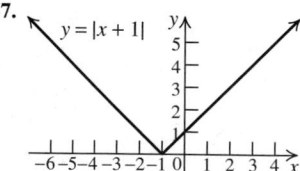

Domain: $(-\infty, \infty)$. Range: $[0, \infty)$. Function

58.

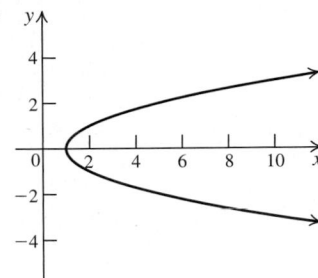

Domain: $[1, \infty)$. Range: $(-\infty, \infty)$. Not a function

77.

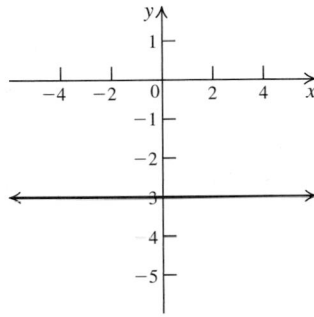

Domain: $(-\infty, \infty)$. Range: $\{-3\}$. Constant on $(-\infty, \infty)$

78.

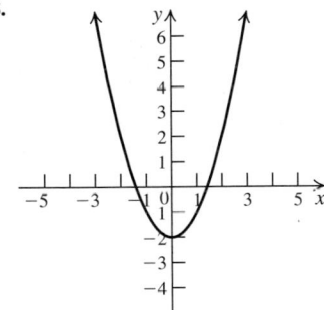

Domain: $(-\infty, \infty)$. Range: $[-2, \infty)$. Decreasing on $(-\infty, 0)$, increasing on $(0, \infty)$

79.

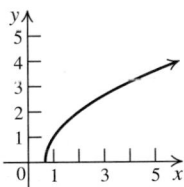

Domain: $\left[\dfrac{2}{3}, \infty\right)$. Range: $[0, \infty)$. Increasing on $\left(\dfrac{2}{3}, \infty\right)$

80.

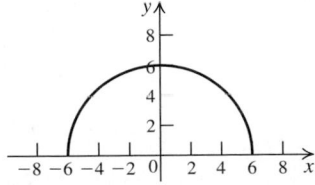

Domain: $[-6, 6]$. Range: $[0, 6]$. Increasing on $(-6, 0)$, decreasing on $(0, 6)$

81.

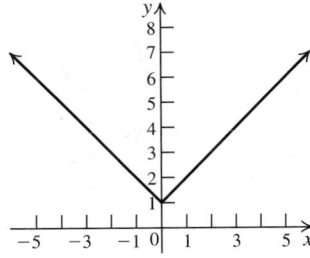

Domain: $(-\infty, \infty)$. Range: $[1, \infty)$. Decreasing on $(-\infty, 0)$, increasing on $(0, \infty)$

82.

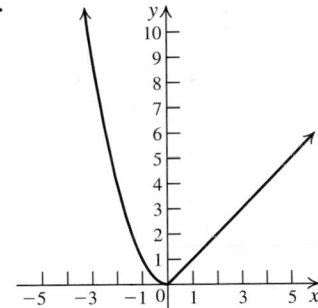

Domain: $(-\infty, \infty)$. Range: $[0, \infty)$. Decreasing on $(-\infty, 0)$, increasing on $(0, \infty)$

83. The graph of g is the graph of f shifted one unit to the left.

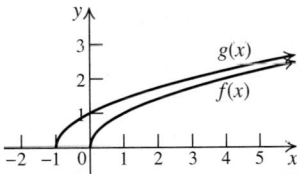

84. The graph of g is the graph of f shifted one unit to the right, stretched by a factor of two, and shifted three units up.

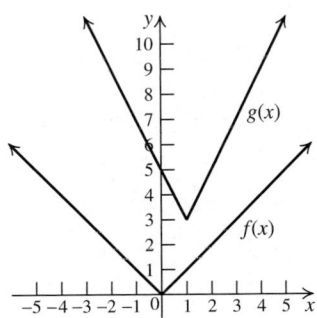

85. The graph of g is the graph of f shifted two units to the right and reflected in the x-axis.

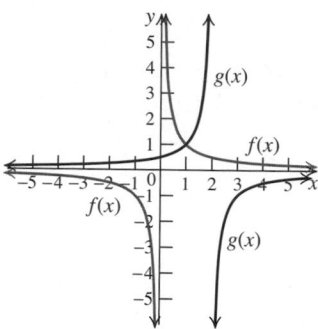

86. The graph of g is the graph of f shifted one unit to the left and two units down.

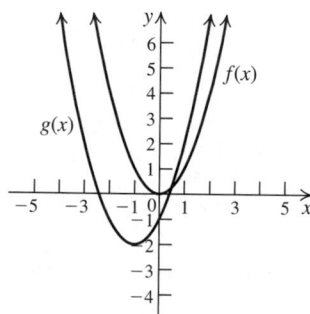

87. Even. Not symmetric with respect to the x-axis, symmetric with respect to the y-axis, not symmetric with respect to the origin

88. Odd. Not symmetric with respect to the x-axis, not symmetric with respect to the y-axis, symmetric with respect to the origin

89. Even. Not symmetric with respect to the x-axis, symmetric with respect to the y-axis, not symmetric with respect to the origin

90. Neither even nor odd. Not symmetric with respect to the x-axis, not symmetric with respect to the y-axis, not symmetric with respect to the origin

91. Neither even nor odd. Not symmetric with respect to the x-axis, not symmetric with respect to the y-axis, not symmetric with respect to the origin

92. Odd. Not symmetric with respect to the x-axis, not symmetric with respect to the y-axis, symmetric with respect to the origin

93. $f(x) = (g \circ h)(x)$, where $g(x) = \sqrt{x}$ and $h(x) = x^2 - 4$

94. $g(x) = (f \circ h)(x)$, where $f(x) = x^{50}$ and $h(x) = x^2 - x + 2$

95. $h(x) = (f \circ g)(x)$, where $f(x) = \sqrt{x}$ and $g(x) = \dfrac{x - 3}{2x + 5}$

96. $H(x) = (f \circ g)(x)$, where $f(x) = x^3 + 5$ and $g(x) = 2x - 1$

97. One-to-one. $f^{-1}(x) = x - 2$

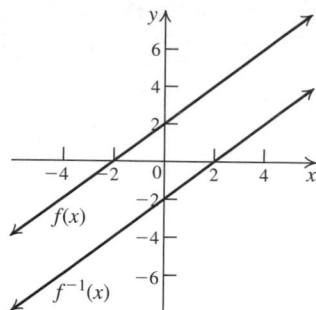

98. One-to-one. $f^{-1}(x) = -\dfrac{1}{2}x + \dfrac{3}{2}$

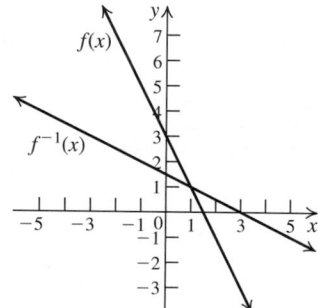

99. One-to-one. $f^{-1}(x) = x^3 + 2$

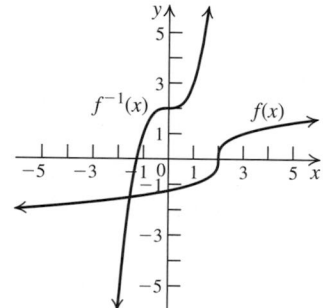

100. One-to-one. $f^{-1}(x) = \dfrac{1}{2}\sqrt[3]{x + 1}$

101. $f^{-1}(x) = \dfrac{2x+1}{1-x}$. Domain: $(-\infty, -2) \cup (-2, \infty)$.

Range: $(-\infty, 1) \cup (1, \infty)$

102. $f^{-1}(x) = \dfrac{x+3}{x-2}$. Domain: $(-\infty, 1) \cup (1, \infty)$.

Range: $(-\infty, 2) \cup (2, \infty)$

103. a. $f(x) = \begin{cases} 3x+6, & \text{if } -3 \le x \le -2 \\ \dfrac{1}{2}x+1, & \text{if } -2 < x < 0 \\ x+1, & \text{if } 0 \le x \le 3 \end{cases}$

b. Domain: $[-3, 3]$. Range: $[-3, 4]$

c. x-intercept: -2. y-intercept: 1

d.

e.

f.

g.

h.

i.

j.

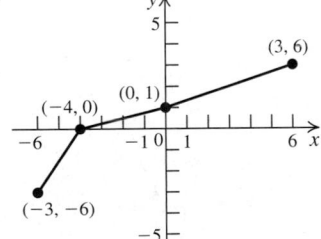

k. It satisfies the horizontal-line test.

l.

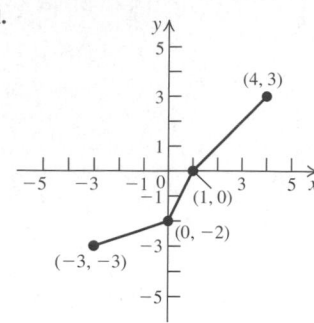

104. b. Slope: the amount of increase in pressure, in pounds per square inch, if the diver descends 1ft deeper. *y*-intercept: the pressure at the surface of the sea

105. a. $C = 0.875w - 22{,}125$

    b. Slope: the cost of disposing 1 pound of waste. *x*-intercept: the amount of waste that can be disposed with no cost. *y*-intercept: the fixed cost

    c. \$510,750

    d. 1,168,142.86 pounds

106. a. 60 mph = 1 mi/min, so if the speedometer is correct, the number of minutes elapsed must be equal to the distance in miles.

    b. Because the odometer reading is based on the speedometer

107. b. She was winning at a rate of \$49/h.

    c. Yes. After 20 hours

108. $f(x) = \begin{cases} 4x, & \text{if } 0 \le x \le 100 \\ 3.2x + 80, & \text{if } 100 < x \le 500 \\ 3x + 180, & \text{if } x > 500 \end{cases}$

109. a. $0.5\sqrt{0.000004t^4 + 0.004t^2 + 5}$

Practice Test A

2. *x*-intercepts: $-1, 0, 3$ *y*-intercept: 0

3.

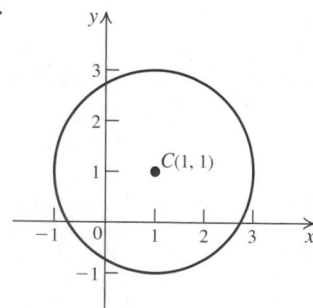

7. -1

9. a. $f(-1) = -3$ **b.** $f(0) = -2$ **c.** $f(1) = -1$

11. $(-\infty, -3] \cup [2, \infty)$

15. Shift the graph of f three units to the right.

19. $A(x) = 100x + 1000$

20. a. \$87.50   **b.** 110 mi

Cumulative Review Exercises (Chapters P–2)

2. a. $(2x - 5)(x + 3)$ **b.** $(x^2 + 4)(x - 2)$

5. b. no solution

6. b. $x = -5; 2$

7. a. $\dfrac{1 \pm \sqrt{23}i}{4}$ **b.** $x = \dfrac{3}{2}$

8. b. $x = \dfrac{3 - \sqrt{13}}{2}; \dfrac{3 + \sqrt{13}}{2}; \dfrac{7 - \sqrt{53}}{2}; \dfrac{7 + \sqrt{53}}{2}$

9. a. $x = \dfrac{7 + \sqrt{17}}{8}$

    b. $x = 0; \dfrac{8}{9}$

10. b. $(-\infty, 3)$

11. a. $(-\infty, 0) \cup (1, \infty)$ **b.** $(-1, 2)$

12. a. $(-\infty, -1) \cup (2, \infty)$

    b. $(-\infty, -1] \cup (2, 5)$

13. b. $[-3, -2]$

14. b. $(-\infty, -1] \cup [4, \infty)$

15. Since the length of the side BC is equal to the length of the side AC (which is 5), the triangle is isosceles.

16.

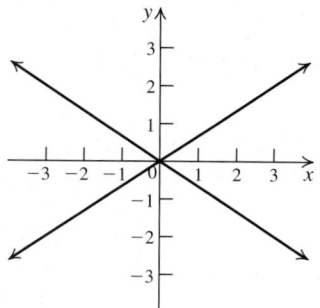

17. All the points satisfy the equation $(x - 2)^2 + (y + 1)^2 = 5^2$, which is a circle with center $(2, -1)$ and radius 5.

24. $x = 5$

27.

28.

29.

30.

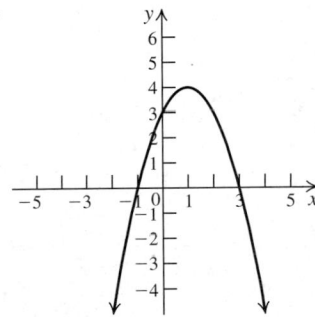

31. She purchased 60 books.

32. The monthly note on a car that was leased for 2 yr is $392.86, and the monthly note on a car that was leased for $1\frac{1}{2}$ years is $642.86.

33. a. $[-1, \infty)$ **b.** x-intercept: 8 y-intercept: -2 **c.** -3 **d.** $(8, \infty)$

34. a. $2, 0, 4$
  b. f decreases on $(-\infty, 0)$ and increases on $(0, \infty)$.

35. a. $(f \circ g)(x) = \dfrac{x}{2 - 2x}$, and its domain is $(-\infty, 0) \cup (0, 1) \cup (1, \infty)$.
  b. $(g \circ f)(x) = 2(x - 2)$, and its domain is $(-\infty, 2) \cup (2, \infty)$.

CHAPTER 3

Section 3.1

Practice Problems

1. $y = 3(x - 1)^2 - 5$

2. The graph is a parabola. $a = -2, h = -1, k = 3$. It opens downward. Vertex: $(-1, 3)$. It is a maximum. x-intercepts:

$$\pm \sqrt{\frac{3}{2}} - 1. \; y\text{-intercept: } 1.$$

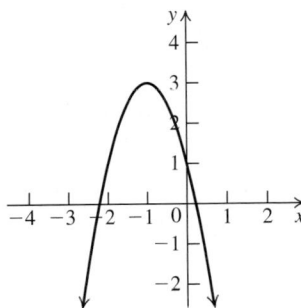

3. The graph is a parabola. $a = 1, b = 4, c = 1$. It opens upward. Vertex: $(-2, -3)$. x-intercepts: $-2 \pm \sqrt{3}$. y-intercept: 1.

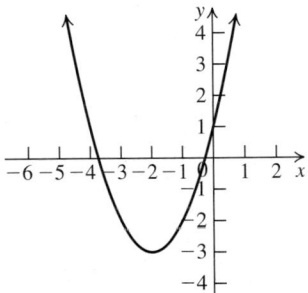

4. $\left[\dfrac{3 - 2\sqrt{3}}{3}, \dfrac{3 + 2\sqrt{3}}{3}\right]$ **5.**

6. 192

A Exercises: Basic Skills and Concepts

18. $y = -\dfrac{4}{9}(x + 3)^2 + 4$

19. $y = \dfrac{11}{49}(x - 2)^2 - 3$ **20.** $y = -\dfrac{2}{3}(x + 3)^2 - 2$

21. $y = -12\left(x - \dfrac{1}{2}\right)^2 + \dfrac{1}{2}$ **22.** $y = \dfrac{3}{2}\left(x + \dfrac{3}{2}\right)^2 - \dfrac{5}{2}$

27. $y = (x + 2)^2 - 4$. The graph is the graph of $y = x^2$ shifted two units to the left and four units down.
Vertex: $(-2, -4)$. Axis: $x = -2$. x-intercepts: -4 and 0.
y-intercept: 0.

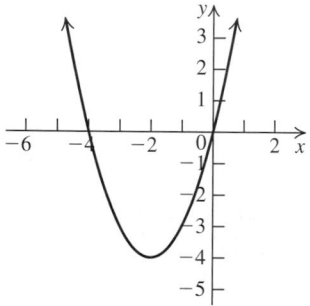

28. $y = (x - 1)^2 + 1$. The graph is the graph of $y = x^2$ shifted one unit to the right and one unit up.
Vertex: $(1, 1)$. Axis: $x = 1$. No x-intercept. y-intercept: 2.

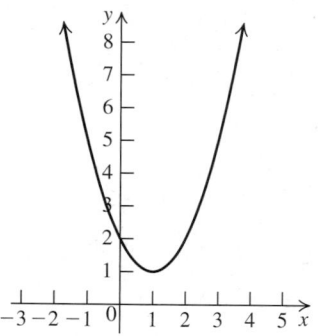

29. $y = -(x - 3)^2 - 1$. The graph is the graph of $y = x^2$ shifted three units to the right, reflected in the x-axis, and shifted one unit down.
Vertex: $(3, -1)$. Axis: $x = 3$. No x-intercept. y-intercept: -10.

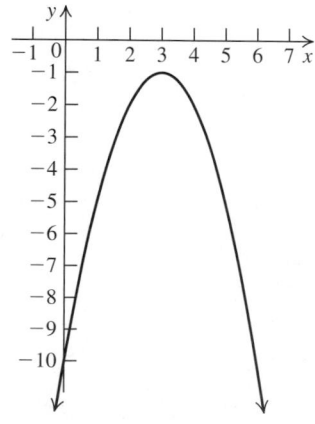

30. $y = -\left(x - \dfrac{3}{2}\right)^2 + \dfrac{41}{4}$. The graph is the graph of $y = x^2$ shifted

$\dfrac{3}{2}$ units to the right, reflected in the x-axis, and shifted $\dfrac{41}{4}$ units up.

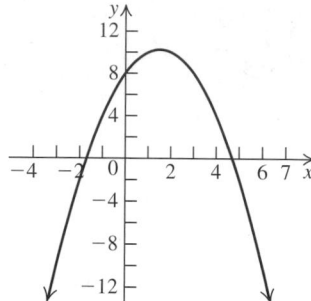

Vertex: $\left(\dfrac{3}{2}, \dfrac{41}{4}\right)$. Axis: $x = \dfrac{3}{2}$. x-intercepts: $\dfrac{3}{2} \pm \dfrac{1}{2}\sqrt{41}$.

y-intercept: 8.

31. $y = 2(x - 2)^2 + 1$. The graph is the graph of $y = x^2$ shifted two units to the right, stretched vertically by a factor of 2, and shifted one unit up.

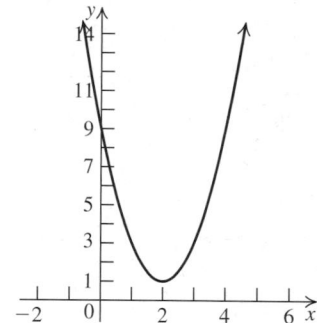

Vertex: $(2, 1)$. Axis: $x = 2$. No x-intercept. y-intercept: 9.

32. $y = 3(x + 2)^2 - 19$. The graph is the graph of $y = x^2$ shifted 2 units to the left, stretched vertically by a factor of 3, and shifted 19 units down.

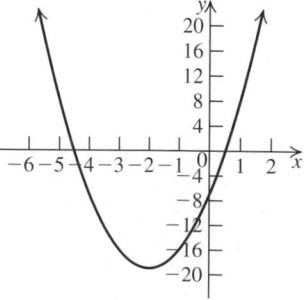

Vertex: $(-2, -19)$. Axis: $x = -2$. x-intercepts: $-2 \pm \dfrac{1}{3}\sqrt{57}$.

y-intercept: -7.

33. $y = -3(x - 3)^2 + 16$. The graph is the graph of $y = x^2$ shifted 3 units to the right, stretched vertically by a factor of 3, reflected in the x-axis, and shifted 16 units up.

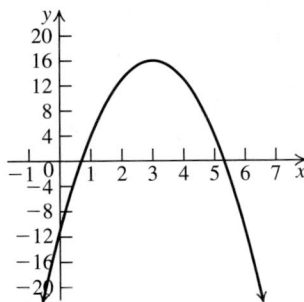

Vertex: $(3, 16)$. Axis: $x = 3$. x-intercepts: $3 \pm \dfrac{4}{3}\sqrt{3}$.
y-intercept: -11.

34. $y = -5(x + 2)^2 + 33$. The graph is the graph of $y = x^2$ shifted 2 units to the left, stretched vertically by a factor of 5, reflected in the x-axis, and shifted 33 units up.

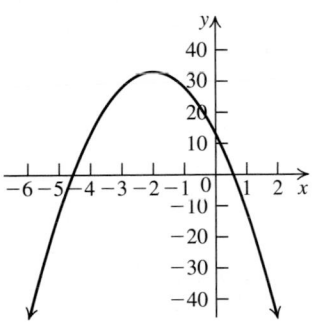

Vertex: $(-2, 33)$. Axis: $x = -2$. x-intercepts: $-2 \pm \dfrac{1}{5}\sqrt{165}$.
y-intercept: 13.

35. $y = \dfrac{1}{2}(x - 2)^2 + 3$. The graph is the graph of $y = x^2$ shifted two

units to the right, compressed vertically by a factor of $\dfrac{1}{2}$, and shifted three units up.

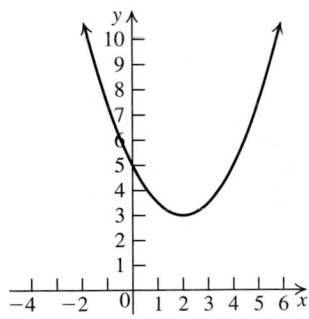

Vertex: $(2, 3)$. Axis: $x = 2$. No x-intercept. y-intercept: 5.

36. $y = \dfrac{3}{4}(x + 4)^2 - 7$. The graph is the graph of $y = x^2$ shifted four

units to the left, compressed vertically by a factor of $\dfrac{3}{4}$, and shifted seven units down.

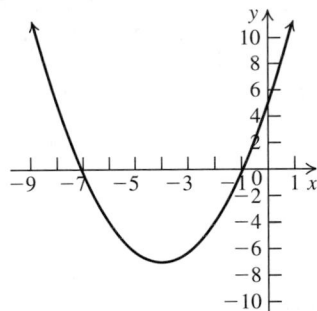

Vertex: $(-4, -7)$. Axis: $x = -4$. x-intercepts: $-4 \pm \dfrac{2}{3}\sqrt{21}$.
y-intercept: 5.

37. $y = -\dfrac{1}{2}(x - 1)^2 - \dfrac{13}{2}$. The graph is the graph of $y = x^2$ shifted

1 unit to the right, compressed vertically by a factor of $\dfrac{1}{2}$, reflected in

the x-axis, and shifted $\dfrac{13}{2}$ units down.

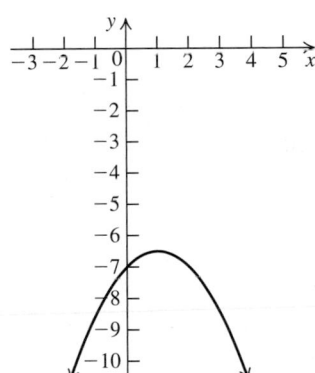

Vertex: $\left(1, -\dfrac{13}{2}\right)$. Axis: $x = 1$. No x-intercept. y-intercept: -7.

38. $y = -\dfrac{1}{4}(x + 1)^2 + \dfrac{13}{4}$. The graph is the graph of $y = x^2$ shifted

1 unit to the left, compressed vertically by a factor of $\dfrac{1}{4}$, reflected in

the x-axis, and shifted $\dfrac{13}{4}$ units up.

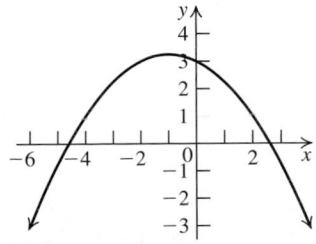

Vertex: $\left(-1, \dfrac{13}{4}\right)$. Axis: $x = -1$. x-intercepts: $-1 \pm \sqrt{13}$.
y-intercept: 3.

39. a. opens up   **b.** $(4,-1)$ **c.** $x = 4$
   d. x-intercepts: 3 and 5; y-intercept: 15.
   e.

40. a. opens up   **b.** $(-4, -3)$ **c.** $x = -4$
   d. x-intercepts: $-4 \pm \sqrt{3}$; y-intercept: 13.
   e.

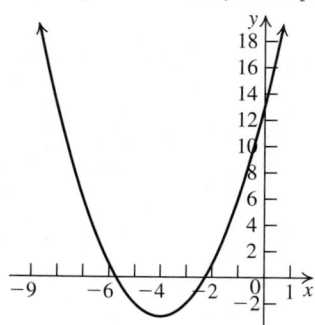

41. a. opens up   **b.** $\left(\frac{1}{2}, \frac{-25}{4}\right)$ **c.** $x = \frac{1}{2}$
   d. x-intercepts: -2 and 3; y-intercept: -6.
   e.

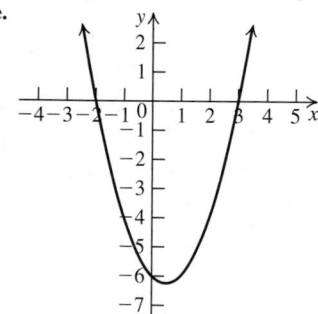

42. a. opens up   **b.** $\left(-\frac{1}{2}, -\frac{9}{4}\right)$ **c.** $x = -\frac{1}{2}$
   d. x-intercepts: -2 and 1;. y-intercept: -2.
   e.

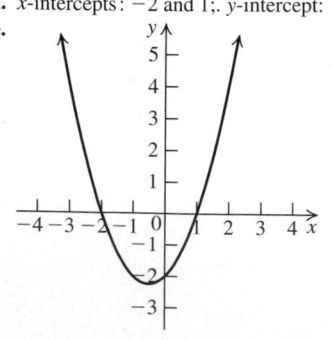

43. a. opens up   **b.** $(1, 3)$ **c.** $x = 1$
   d. x-intercepts: none 2; y-intercept: 4.
   e.

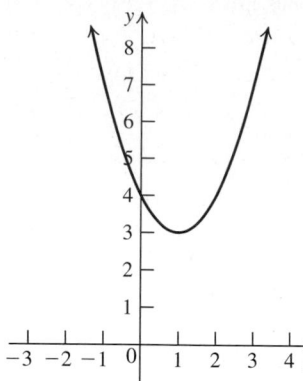

44. a. opens up   **b.** $(2, 1)$ **c.** $x = 2$
   d. x-intercepts: none; y-intercept: 5.
   e.

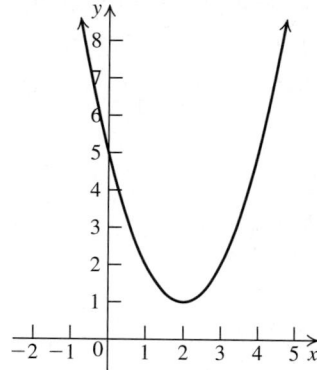

45. a. opens down   **b.** $(-1,7)$ **c.** $x = -1$
   d. x-intercepts: $-1 \pm \sqrt{7}$; y-intercept: 6.
   e.

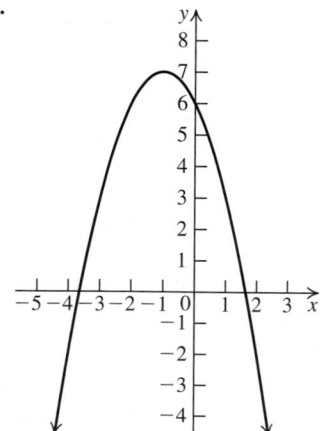

46. a. opens down   **b.** $\left(\dfrac{5}{6}, \dfrac{49}{12}\right)$ **c.** $x = \dfrac{5}{6}$

   d. x-intercepts: $-\dfrac{1}{3}$ and 2; y-intercept: 2.

   e.

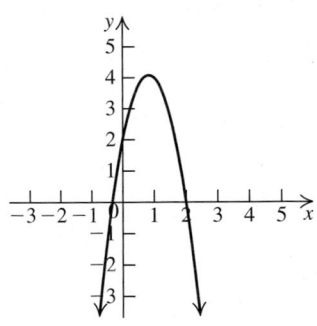

47. a. opens down   **b.** $(6, -2)$ **c.** $x = 6$
   d. x-intercepts: none 5; y-intercept: -110.

   e.

48. a. opens up   **b.** $\left(\dfrac{1}{6}, \dfrac{23}{12}\right)$ **c.** $x = \dfrac{1}{6}$
   d. x-intercepts: none; y-intercept: 2.

   e.

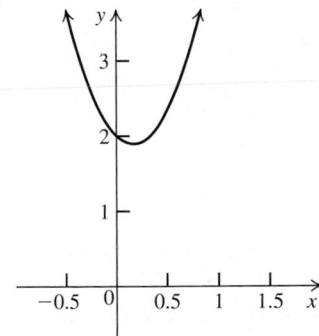

49. a. opens down   **b.** $\left(\dfrac{1}{2}, \dfrac{49}{4}\right)$ **c.** $x = \dfrac{1}{2}$

   d. x-intercepts: -3 and 4; y-intercept: 12.

   e.

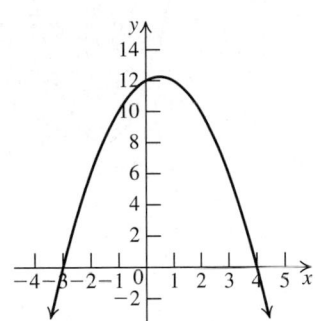

50. a. opens down   **b.** $\left(\dfrac{9}{4}, \dfrac{49}{8}\right)$ **c.** $x = \dfrac{9}{4}$

   d. x-intercepts: $\dfrac{1}{2}$ and 4. y-intercept: -4.

   e.

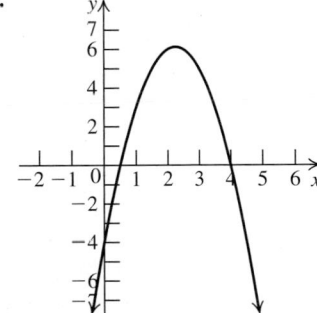

51. a. Minimum: -1 **b.** $[-1, \infty)$
52. a. Maximum: 1   **b.** $(-\infty, 1]$
53. a. Maximum: 0   **b.** $(-\infty, 0]$
54. a. Minimum: 0   **b.** $[0, \infty)$
55. a. Minimum: -5 **b.** $[-5, \infty)$
56. a. Minimum: -17 **b.** $[-17, \infty)$
57. a. Maximum: 16   **b.** $(-\infty, 16]$
58. a. Maximum: 3   **b.** $(-\infty, 3]$

59.

Solution: $[-2, 2]$

60.

Solution: $\varnothing$

61.

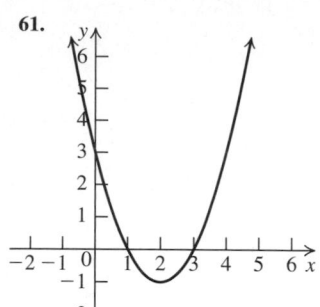

Solution: $(-\infty, 1) \cup (3, \infty)$

62.

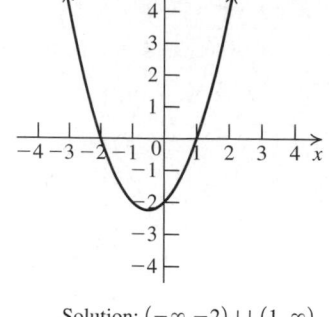

Solution: $(-\infty, -2) \cup (1, \infty)$

82. a.

63.

Solution: $\left(-1, \dfrac{7}{6}\right)$

64.

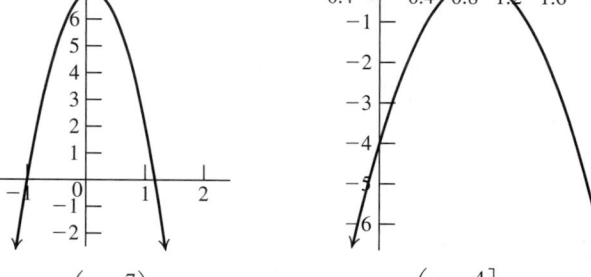

Solution: $\left(-\infty, \dfrac{4}{5}\right] \cup [1, \infty)$

65.

Solution: $(-\infty, \infty)$

66.

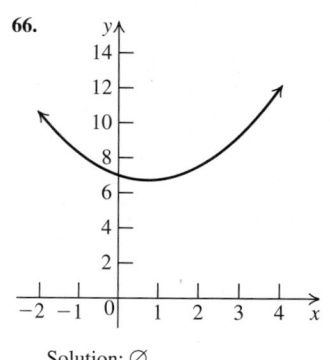

Solution: $\varnothing$

B Exercises: Applying the Concepts

70. $x = 49$. Maximum profit: \$2351.

71. Square with 20-unit sides. Maximum area: 400.

73. Dimensions: 75 m $\times$ 100 m. Area: 7500 m^2.

74. Dimensions: 60 ft $\times$ 37.5 ft. Area: 2250 ft^2.

77. 28 students. Maximum revenue: \$1568.

81. Dimensions of the rectangle: width $= \dfrac{36}{\pi + 4}$ ft, height $= \dfrac{18}{\pi + 4}$ ft.

Section 3.2

Practice Problems

1. $P(x) = 4x^3 + 2x^2 + 5x - 17 = x^3\left(4 + \dfrac{2}{x} + \dfrac{5}{x^2} - \dfrac{17}{x^3}\right)$.

When $|x|$ is large, the terms $\dfrac{2}{x}, \dfrac{5}{x^2}$, and $-\dfrac{17}{x^3}$ are close to 0.

Therefore, $P(x) \approx x^3(4 + 0 + 0 - 0) = 4x^3$.

2. $y \to -\infty$ as $x \to -\infty$ and $y \to -\infty$ as $x \to \infty$ **3.** $\dfrac{3}{2}$

4. $f(1) = -7$, $f(2) = 4$. Since $f(1)$ and $f(2)$ have opposite signs, by the Intermediate Value Theorem f has a real zero between 1 and 2.

5. -5, -1, and 3

6. -5 and -3 with multiplicity 1, and 1 with multiplicity 2

7. 3   **9.** 207.38 1

A Exercises: Basic Skills and Concepts

1. Polynomial function. Degree: 5. Leading term: $2x^5$. Leading coefficient: 2.

4. Polynomial function. Degree: 4. Leading term: $-7x^4$. Leading coefficient: -7.

5. Polynomial function. Degree: 3. Leading term: $\dfrac{2}{3}x^3$. Leading coefficient: $\dfrac{2}{3}$.

8. Not a polynomial.

11. Polynomial function. Degree: 3. Leading term: $\sqrt{2}x^3$. Leading coefficient: $\sqrt{2}$.

12. Polynomial function. Degree: 4. Leading term: πx^4. Leading coefficient: π.

15. Polynomial function. Degree: 0. Leading term: 5. Leading coefficient: 5.

16. Polynomial function. No degree. Leading term: 0. Leading coefficient: 0

31. Zeros: $x = -5$, multiplicity: 1, the graph crosses the x-axis; $x = 1$, multiplicity: 1, the graph crosses the x-axis. Maximum number of turning points: 1.

32. Zeros: $x = -2$, multiplicity: 2, the graph touches but does not cross the x-axis; $x = 3$, multiplicity: 1, the graph crosses the x-axis. Maximum number of turning points: 2.

33. Zeros: $x = -1$, multiplicity: 2, the graph touches but does not cross the x-axis; $x = 1$, multiplicity: 3, the graph crosses the x-axis. Maximum number of turning points: 4.

34. Zeros: $x = -3$, multiplicity: 2, the graph touches but does not cross the x-axis; $x = -1$, multiplicity: 1, the graph crosses the x-axis;

$x = 6$, multiplicity: 1, the graph crosses the x-axis. Maximum number of turning points: 3.

35. Zeros: $x = -\dfrac{2}{3}$, multiplicity: 1, the graph crosses the x-axis; $x = \dfrac{1}{2}$, multiplicity: 2, the graph touches but does not cross the x-axis. Maximum number of turning points: 2.

36. Zeros: $x = 0$, multiplicity: 1, the graph crosses the x-axis; $x = 2$, multiplicity: 1, the graph crosses the x-axis; $x = 4$, multiplicity: 1, the graph crosses the x-axis. Maximum number of turning points: 2.

37. Zeros: $x = 0$, multiplicity: 2, the graph touches but does not cross the x-axis; $x = 3$, multiplicity: 2, the graph touches but does not cross the x-axis. Maximum number of turning points: 3.

38. Zeros: $x = -3$, multiplicity: 1, the graph crosses the x-axis; $x = 3$, multiplicity: 1, the graph crosses the x-axis. Maximum number of turning points: 3.

39. a. $y \to \infty$ as $x \to -\infty$ and $y \to \infty$ as $x \to \infty$ **b.** No zeros
   c. The graph is above the x-axis on $(-\infty, \infty)$.
   d. 3   **e.** f is even.   **f.** 1
   g.

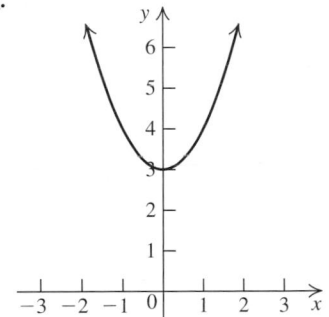

40. a. $y \to \infty$ as $x \to -\infty$ and $y \to \infty$ as $x \to \infty$
   b. Zero: $x = 2$, the graph touches but does not cross the x-axis
   c. The graph is above the x-axis on $(-\infty, 2) \cup (2, \infty)$.
   d. 4   **e.** f is neither even nor odd.   **f.** 1
   g.

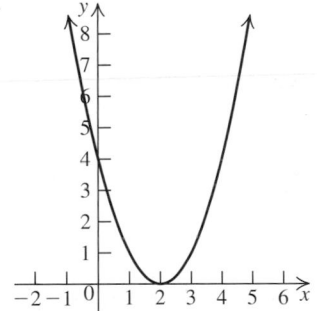

41. a. $y \to \infty$ as $x \to -\infty$ and $y \to \infty$ as $x \to \infty$
   b. Zeros: $x = -7$, the graph crosses the x-axis; $x = 3$, the graph crosses the x-axis.
   c. The graph is above the x-axis on $(-\infty, -7)$ and $(3, \infty)$, and below the x-axis on $(-7, 3)$.
   d. -21 **e.** f is neither even nor odd.   **f.** 1

g.

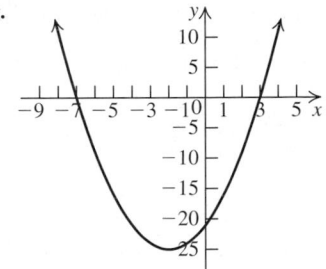

42. a. $y \to -\infty$ as $x \to -\infty$ and $y \to -\infty$ as $x \to \infty$
   b. Zeros: $x = -2$, the graph crosses the x-axis; $x = 6$, the graph crosses the x-axis.
   c. The graph is below the x-axis on $(-\infty, -2)$ and $(6, \infty)$, and above the x-axis on $(-2, 6)$.
   d. 12   **e.** f is neither even, nor odd.   **f.** 1
   g.

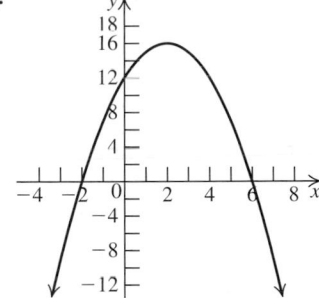

43. a. $y \to \infty$ as $x \to -\infty$ and $y \to -\infty$ as $x \to \infty$
   b. Zeros: $x = -1$, the graph crosses the x-axis; $x = 0$, the graph touches but does not cross the x-axis.
   c. The graph is above the x-axis on $(-\infty, -1)$ and below the x-axis on $(-1, 0) \cup (0, \infty)$.
   d. 0   **e.** f is neither even nor odd.   **f.** 2
   g.

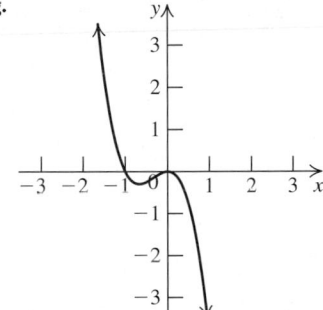

44. a. $y \to \infty$ as $x \to -\infty$ and $y \to -\infty$ as $x \to \infty$
   b. Zeros: $x = -1$, the graph crosses the x-axis; $x = 0$, the graph crosses the x-axis; $x = 1$, the graph crosses the x-axis.

c. The graph is above the x-axis on $(-\infty, -1)$ and $(0, 1)$ and below the x-axis on $(-1, 0)$ and $(1, \infty)$.

d. 0   **e.** f is odd.   **f.** 2

g.

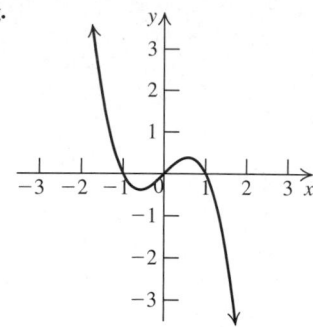

45. a. $y \to \infty$ as $x \to -\infty$ and $y \to \infty$ as $x \to \infty$

b. Zeros: $x = 0$, the graph touches but does not cross the x-axis; $x = 1$, the graph touches but does not cross the x-axis.

c. The graph is above the x-axis on $(-\infty, 0) \cup (0, 1) \cup (1, \infty)$.

d. 0   **e.** f is neither even nor odd.   **f.** 3

g.

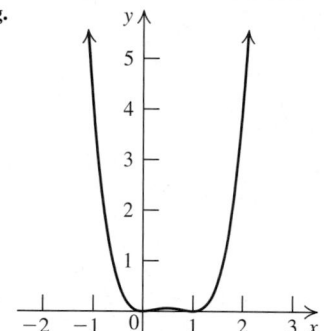

46. a. $y \to \infty$ as $x \to -\infty$ and $y \to \infty$ as $x \to \infty$

b. Zeros: $x = -1$, the graph crosses the x-axis, $x = 0$, the graph touches but does not cross the x-axis; $x = 2$, the graph crosses the x-axis.

c. The graph is above the x-axis on $(-\infty, -1)$ and $(2, \infty)$, and below the x-axis on $(-1, 0) \cup (0, 2)$.

d. 0   **e.** f is neither even nor odd.   **f.** 3

g.

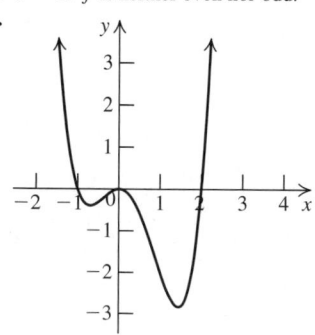

47. a. $y \to \infty$ as $x \to -\infty$ and $y \to \infty$ as $x \to \infty$

b. Zeros: $x = -3$, the graph crosses the x-axis; $x = 1$, the graph touches but does not cross the x-axis; $x = 4$, the graph crosses the x-axis.

c. The graph is above the x-axis on $(-\infty, -3)$ and $(4, \infty)$, and below the x-axis on $(-3, 1) \cup (1, 4)$.

d. -12 **e.** f is neither even nor odd.   **f.** 3

g.

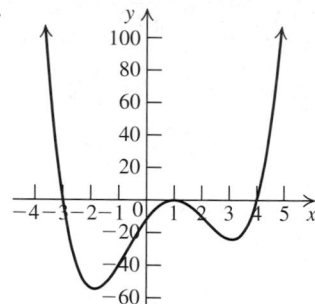

48. a. $y \to \infty$ as $x \to -\infty$ and $y \to \infty$ as $x \to \infty$

b. Zero: $x = -1$, the graph touches but does not cross the x-axis.

c. The graph is above the x-axis on $(-\infty, -1) \cup (-1, \infty)$.

d. 1   **e.** f is neither even nor odd.   **f.** 3

g.

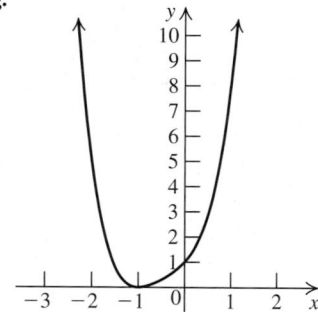

49. a. $y \to \infty$ as $x \to -\infty$ and $y \to -\infty$ as $x \to \infty$

b. Zeros: $x = -1$, the graph touches but does not cross the x-axis; $x = 0$, the graph touches but does not cross the x-axis; $x = 1$, the graph crosses the x-axis.

c. The graph is above the x-axis on $(-\infty, -1) \cup (-1, 0) \cup (0, 1)$ and below the x-axis on $(1, \infty)$.

d. 0   **e.** f is neither even nor odd.   **f.** 4

g.

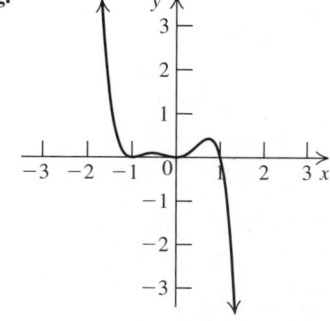

50. a. $y \to \infty$ as $x \to -\infty$ and $y \to -\infty$ as $x \to \infty$

b. Zeros: $x = -2$, the graph touches but does not cross the x-axis; $x = 0$, the graph touches but does not cross the x-axis; $x = 2$, the graph crosses the x-axis.

c. The graph is above the x-axis on $(-\infty, -2) \cup (-2, 0) \cup (0, 2)$ and below the x-axis on $(2, \infty)$.

d. 0   **e.** f is neither even nor odd.   **f.** 4

g.

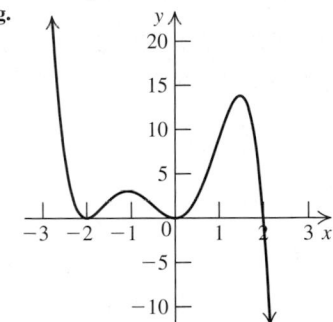

51. a. $y \to \infty$ as $x \to -\infty$ and $y \to \infty$ as $x \to \infty$

b. Zeros: $x = -2$, the graph crosses the x-axis; $x = -1$, the graph crosses the x-axis; $x = 0$, the graph crosses the x-axis; $x = 1$, the graph crosses the x-axis.

c. The graph is above the x-axis on $(-\infty, -2), (-1, 0)$, and $(1, \infty)$, and below the x-axis on $(-2, -1)$ and $(0, 1)$.

d. 0   **e.** f is neither even nor odd.   **f.** 3

g.

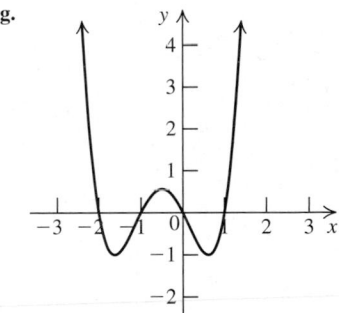

52. a. $y \to -\infty$ as $x \to -\infty$ and $y \to \infty$ as $x \to \infty$

b. Zeros: $x = 0$, the graph touches but does not cross the x-axis; $x = 2$, the graph crosses the x-axis.

c. The graph is below the x-axis on $(-\infty, 0) \cup (0, 2)$ and above the x-axis on $(2, \infty)$.

d. 0   **e.** f is neither even nor odd.   **f.** 4

g.

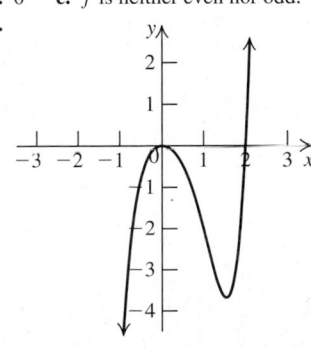

B Exercises: Applying the Concepts

53. a. Zeros: $x = 0$, multiplicity: 2; $x = 4$, multiplicity: 1.

b.

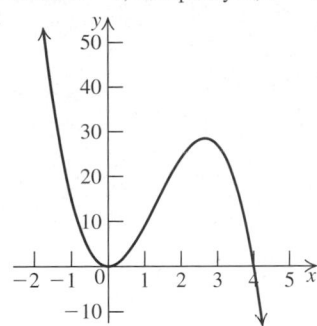

d. Domain: [0, 4]. The portion between the x-intercepts constitutes the graph of $R(x)$.

54. b.

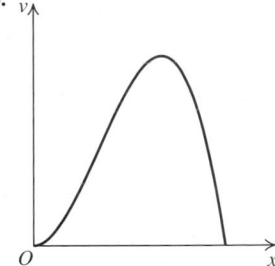

55. a. $R(x) = 27x - \dfrac{1}{90{,}000}x^3$

c.

56. c.

57. a. $V(x) = x(8 - 2x)(15 - 2x)$

b.

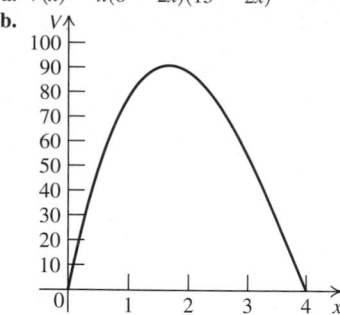

58. a. $V(x) = x^2(108 - 4x)$

b.

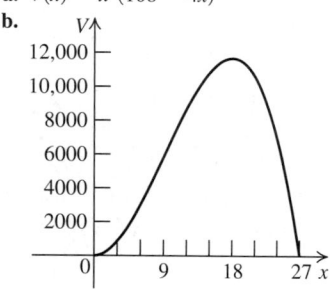

59. a. $V(x) = x^2(62 - 2x)$

b.

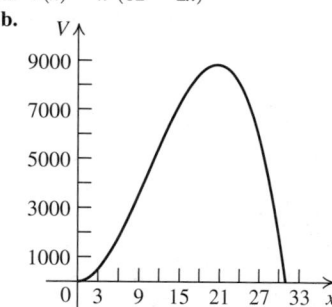

c. 20.67 in. × 20.67 in. × 20.67 in.

60. a. $V(x) = 2x^2(45 - 3x)$

b.

61. a.

62. a.

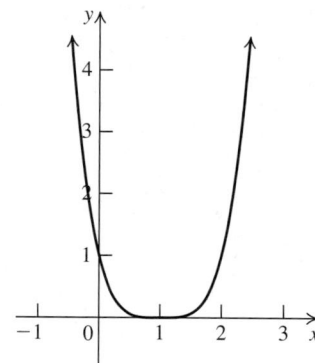

C Exercises: Beyond the Basics

63. The graph of f is the graph of $y = x^4$ shifted one unit to the right.

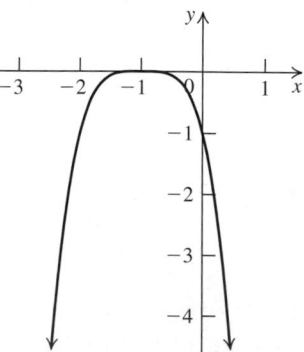

Zero: $x = 1$, multiplicity: 4

64. The graph of f is the graph of $y = x^4$ shifted one unit to the left and reflected in the x-axis.

Zero: $x = -1$, multiplicity: 4

65. The graph of f is the graph of $y = x^4$ shifted two units up.

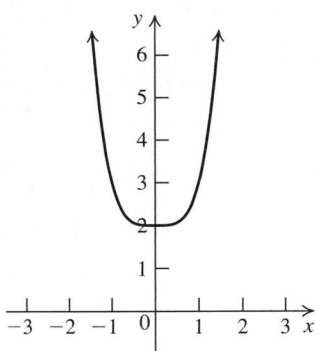

No zeros

66. The graph of f is the graph of $y = x^4$ shifted 81 units up.

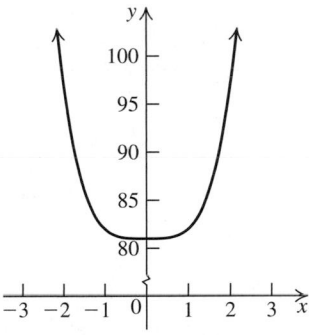

No zeros

67. The graph of f is the graph of $y = x^4$ shifted one unit to the right and reflected in the x-axis.

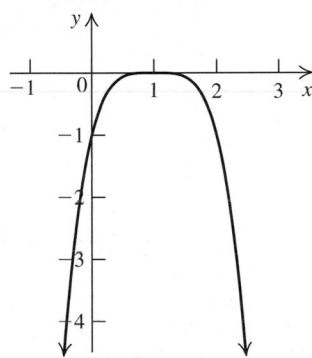

Zero: $x = 1$, multiplicity: 4

68. The graph of f is the graph of $y = x^4$ shifted one unit to the right, compressed by a factor of 2, and shifted by eight units down.

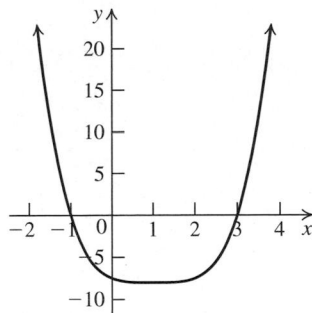

Zero: $x = -1$, multiplicity: 1; $x = 3$, multiplicity: 1

69. The graph of f is the graph of $y = x^5$ shifted one unit up.

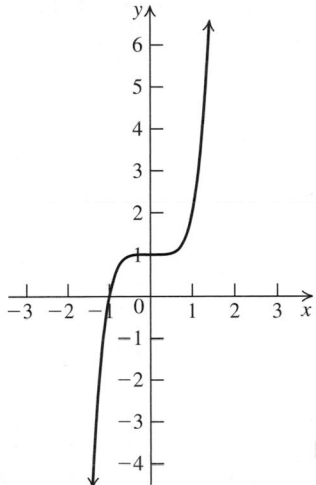

Zero: $x = -1$, multiplicity: 1

70. The graph of f is the graph of $y - x^5$ shifted one unit to the right.

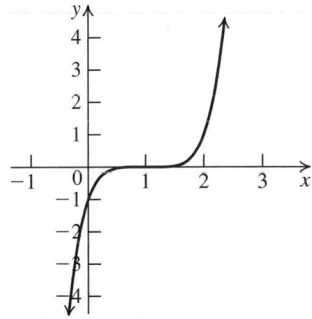

Zero: $x = 1$, multiplicity: 5

71. The graph of f is the graph of $y = x^5$ shifted one unit to the left, compressed by a factor of 4, reflected in the x-axis, and shifted eight units up.

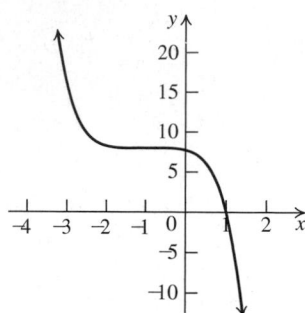

Zero: $x = 1$, multiplicity: 1

72. The graph of f is the graph of $y = x^5$ shifted 1 unit to the left, compressed by a factor of 3, and shifted 81 units up.

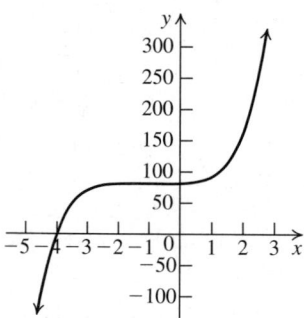

Zero: $x = -4$, multiplicity: 1

75. Maximum vertical distance: 0.25. It occurs at $x \approx 0.71$.

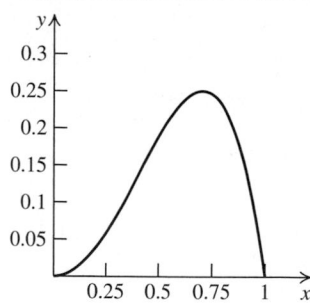

76. Maximum vertical distance: 0.19. It occurs at $x \approx 0.77$.

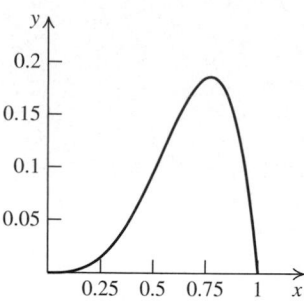

78. $f(x) = -(x + 1)x(x - 1)$

79. $f(x) = 1 - x^4$ **80.** $f(x) = (x + 1)x^2(x - 1)$

Section 3.3

Practice Problems

1. The quotient is $x^2 + x + 3$ and the remainder is $2x - 3$.

2. The quotient is $2x^2 + 7x + 3$ and the remainder is 2.

3. The remainder is 4.   **4.** 32   **5.** $\left\{-2, -\dfrac{2}{3}, 3\right\}$

6. 18   **7.** $\{-2\}$

A Exercises: Basic Skills and Concepts

1. Quotient: $2x - 1$; remainder: 3   **2.** Quotient: $b - 2$; remainder: 0

3. Quotient: $3x - 2$; remainder: 0   **4.** Quotient: $3m + 4$; remainder: 0

5. Quotient: $2x^2 + 2x + \dfrac{7}{2}$; remainder: $\dfrac{15}{2}$

6. Quotient: $2x^2 + \dfrac{10}{3}x + \dfrac{8}{9}$; remainder: $\dfrac{25}{9}$

8. Quotient: $3x^3 - 3x^2 - 3x + 6$; remainder: -13

10. Quotient: $3x^5 - \dfrac{9}{2}x^4 + \dfrac{27}{4}x^3 - \dfrac{81}{8}x^2 + \dfrac{267}{16}x - \dfrac{801}{32}$; remainder: $\dfrac{2723}{32}$

16. Quotient: $\dfrac{1}{2}x^2 - \dfrac{17}{4}x - \dfrac{13}{8}$; remainder: $\dfrac{39}{8}x - \dfrac{63}{8}$

17. Quotient: $x^2 + 5x + 9$; remainder: 6

18. Quotient: $2x^2 + 10x + 31$; remainder: 78

19. Quotient: $9x^2 - 46x + 217$; remainder: -1079

20. Quotient: $x^2 - 8x + 3$; remainder: -2

21. Quotient: $x^3 + x^2 + 3x + 2$; remainder: -5

22. Quotient: $3x^3 + 6x^2 + 6x + 15$; remainder: 23

25. Quotient: $x^4 + 2x^3 - 5x^2 - 3x - 2$; remainder: -3

26. Quotient: $2x^4 - 3x^2 - x + 5$; remainder: -12

27. Quotient: $x^4 - x^3 + x^2 - x + 1$; remainder: 0

28. Quotient: $x^4 + x^3 + x^2 + x + 1$; remainder: 2

29. Quotient: $x^5 - x^4 + 3x^3 - 4x^2 + 4x - 4$; remainder: 9

30. Quotient: $x^6 - x^5 + x^4 - x^3 + x^2 - x + 1$; remainder: -2

31. Quotient: $2x^4 + x^3 + \dfrac{1}{2}x^2 + \dfrac{13}{4}x + \dfrac{13}{8}$; remainder: $\dfrac{125}{16}$

32. Quotient: $6x^3 + 5x^2 + \dfrac{5}{3}x + \dfrac{5}{9}$; remainder: $\dfrac{32}{27}$

33. Quotient: $2x^3 - 3x^2 + \dfrac{3}{2}x + \dfrac{11}{4}$; remainder: $-\dfrac{25}{8}$

34. Quotient: $6x^5 - 4x^4 - \frac{7}{3}x^3 + \frac{14}{9}x^2 + \frac{53}{27}x - \frac{106}{81}$; remainder: $\frac{1184}{243}$

35. Quotient: $-5x^3 + 10x^2 - 20x + 40$; remainder: -80

36. Quotient: $3x^4 + 3x^3 + 3x^2 + 3x + 3$; remainder: 3

57. $\left\{\pm\frac{1}{3}, \pm 1, \pm\frac{5}{3}, \pm 5\right\}$

58. $\left\{\pm\frac{1}{2}, \pm 1\right\}$

59. $\left\{\pm\frac{1}{4}, \pm\frac{1}{2}, \pm\frac{3}{4}, \pm 1, \pm\frac{3}{2}, \pm 2, \pm 3, \pm 6\right\}$

60. $\left\{\begin{array}{llllllll}\pm\frac{1}{6}, & \pm\frac{1}{2}, & \pm 1, & \pm\frac{5}{3}, & \pm\frac{5}{2}, & \pm 5, & \pm 7, & \pm\frac{35}{2}, \\ \pm\frac{1}{3}, & \pm\frac{5}{6}, & \pm\frac{7}{6}, & \pm\frac{7}{3}, & \pm\frac{7}{2}, & \pm\frac{35}{6}, & \pm\frac{35}{3}, & \pm 35\end{array}\right\}$

65. $\left\{-3, \frac{1}{2}, 2\right\}$ **66.** $\frac{2}{3}$

67. $\left\{-2, -\frac{1}{2}, \frac{1}{3}\right\}$ **68.** $-\frac{3}{2}$

69. $-\frac{1}{3}$ **70.** $-\frac{1}{2}$

72. $\left\{-1, \frac{1}{2}\right\}$

73. $\{-3, -1, 1, 4\}$ **74.** $\left\{-2, \frac{1}{3}\right\}$

77. The solution is $x = \pm\sqrt{2}$ and $\sqrt{2}$ is an irrational number.

78. The possible rational zeros are ± 7. Neither satisfies the equation.

79. The possible rational zeros are ± 1. Neither satisfies the equation.

80. The possible rational zeros are ± 1. Neither satisfies the equation.

C Exercises: Beyond the Basics

100. $x^3 - x^2 - 4x + 4 = 0$

Section 3.4

Practice Problems

1. Number of positive zeros: 1; number of negative zeros: 0 or 2

2. Upper bound: 1; lower bound: -4

3. a. $P(x) = 3(x + 2)(x - 1)(x - 1 - i)(x - 1 + i)$

b. $P(x) = 3x^4 - 3x^3 - 6x^2 + 18x - 12$

4. $-3, 2 + 3i, 2 + 3i, 2 - 3i, i, -i$

5. The zeros are $1, 2, 2i$, and $-2i$.

6. The zeros are $2, 4, 1 + i$, and $1 - i$.

A Exercises: Basic Skills and Concepts

1. Number of positive zeros: 0 or 2; number of negative zeros: 1

2. Number of positive zeros: 1; number of negative zeros: 0 or 2

3. Number of positive zeros: 0 or 2; number of negative zeros: 1

4. Number of positive zeros: 1 or 3; number of negative zeros: 1

5. Number of positive zeros: 1 or 3; number of negative zeros: 0 or 2

6. Number of positive zeros: 1 or 3; number of negative zeros: 1

7. Number of positive zeros: 1 or 3; number of negative zeros: 1

8. Number of positive zeros: 1 or 3; number of negative zeros: 0 or 2

13. Upper bound: 31; lower bound: -31

14. Upper bound: 13; lower bound: -1

15. Upper bound: $\frac{7}{2}$; lower bound: $-\frac{7}{2}$

16. Upper bound: $\frac{1}{2}$; lower bound: -5

17. $x = \pm 5i$ **18.** $x = \pm\frac{4}{3}i$ **19.** $x = 2 \pm 3i$ **20.** $x = 1 \pm 3\sqrt{3}i$

21. $x = -2 \pm 3i$ **22.** $x = -1 \pm 4i$

23. $\{2, -1 + \sqrt{3}i, -1 - \sqrt{3}i\}$

24. $\{-1, 1, i, -i\}$ **26.** $(1, 2i, 3i, -3i)$

32. $-1 - i, -2i, 4 - i$

33. $P(x) = 2x^4 - 20x^3 + 70x^2 - 180x + 468$

34. $P(x) = -3x^4 + 18x^3 - 114x^2 + 282x - 663$

38. $-1, 1, 1 + i, 1 - i$

39. $-3, 1, 2 + 2i, 2 - 2i$ **40.** $-\frac{1}{2}, 1, 2i, -2i$

41. $-2, 0, 1, 3 + i, 3 - i$ **42.** $\frac{1}{2}, 2, 3, i, -i$

45. $-\frac{4}{3}, 1 + 3i, 1 - 3i$ **46.** $\frac{1}{3}, 2i, -2i$

47. $\frac{1}{2}, 2 + 3i, 2 - 3i$ **48.** $3, \frac{1}{2} + \frac{1}{2}i, \frac{1}{2} - \frac{1}{2}i$

49. $-1, 0, \frac{3}{2} + \frac{3}{2}i, \frac{3}{2} - \frac{3}{2}i$ **50.** $-2, 0, \frac{1}{3} + \frac{1}{3}i, \frac{1}{3} - \frac{1}{3}i$

51. $-3, 1, 3 + i, 3 - i$ **53.** $\frac{1}{2}, 2, 3, i, -i$

54. $-2, 1$ (with multiplicity 2), $1 + i, 1 - i$

C Exercises: Beyond the Basics

55. There are three cube roots: $1, -\frac{1}{2} + \frac{1}{2}\sqrt{3}i$, and $-\frac{1}{2} - \frac{1}{2}\sqrt{3}i$.

56. The solutions of the equation and the zeros of the polynomial are the same. There are n roots.

Section 3.5

Practice Problems

1. Domain: $(-\infty, -1) \cup (-1, 5) \cup (5, \infty)$

2. $x = -5$ and $x = 2$ **3.** $x = -3$

4. a. $y = \frac{2}{3}$ **b.** No horizontal asymptote

5. x-intercept: 0. y-intercept: 0. Vertical asymptotes: $x = -1$ and $x = 1$. Horizontal asymptote: x-axis. The graph is symmetric with respect to the origin. The graph is above the x-axis on $(-1, 0) \cup (1, \infty)$ and below the x-axis on $(-\infty, -1) \cup (0, 1)$.

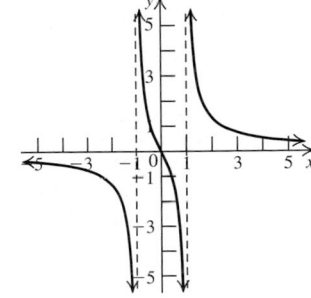

6. x-intercepts: $\pm\dfrac{\sqrt{2}}{2}$. y-intercept: $\dfrac{1}{3}$. Vertical asymptotes: $x = -\dfrac{3}{2}$ and $x = 1$. Horizontal asymptote: $y = 1$. Symmetry: none. The graph is above the x-axis on $\left(-\infty, -\dfrac{3}{2}\right) \cup \left(-\dfrac{\sqrt{2}}{2}, \dfrac{\sqrt{2}}{2}\right) \cup (1, \infty)$ and below the x-axis on $\left(-\dfrac{3}{2}, -\dfrac{\sqrt{2}}{2}\right) \cup \left(\dfrac{\sqrt{2}}{2}, 1\right)$.

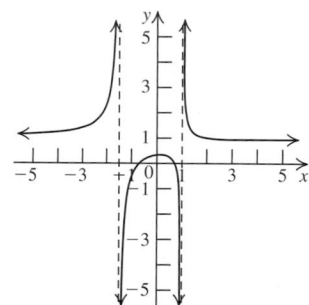

7. No x-intercept. y-intercept: $\dfrac{1}{2}$. No vertical asymptote. Horizontal asymptote: $y = 1$. The graph is symmetric with respect to the y-axis. The graph is above the x-axis on $(-\infty, \infty)$.

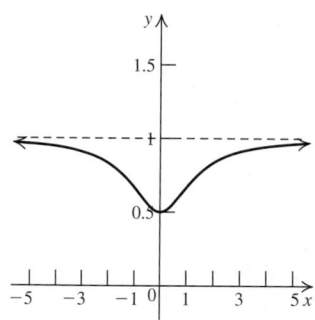

8. No x-intercept. y-intercept: -2. Vertical asymptote: $x = 1$. No horizontal asymptote. $y = x + 1$ is an oblique asymptote. Symmetry: none. The graph is above the x-axis on $(1, \infty)$ and below the x-axis on $(-\infty, 1)$.

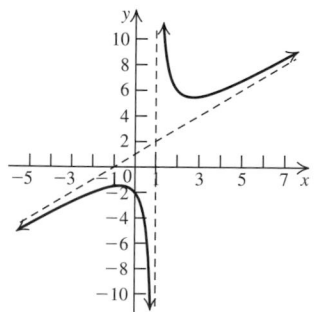

A Exercises: Basic Skills and Concepts
1. $(-\infty, -4) \cup (-4, \infty)$ **2.** $(-\infty, 1) \cup (1, \infty)$
5. $(-\infty, -2) \cup (-2, 3) \cup (3, \infty)$
6. $(-\infty, -1) \cup (-1, 7) \cup (7, \infty)$ **7.** $(-\infty, 2) \cup (2, 4) \cup (4, \infty)$
8. $(-\infty, 1) \cup (1, 2) \cup (2, \infty)$

15. $(-\infty, -2) \cup (-2, 1) \cup (1, \infty)$
16. Two
17. $x = -2$ and $x = 1$
18. $y = 1$

23. $x = -3$ and $x = 2$ **24.** $x = -\dfrac{4}{3}$ and $x = 1$ **25.** $x = -3$
26. $x = -2$, $x = 0$ and $x = 2$ **27.** no vertical asymptote
28. no vertical asymptote   **33.** no horizontal asymptote
43. x-intercept: 0. y-intercept: 0. Vertical asymptote: $x = 3$. Horizontal asymptote: $y = 2$. Symmetry: none. The graph is above the x-axis on $(-\infty, 0) \cup (3, \infty)$ and below the x-axis on $(0, 3)$.

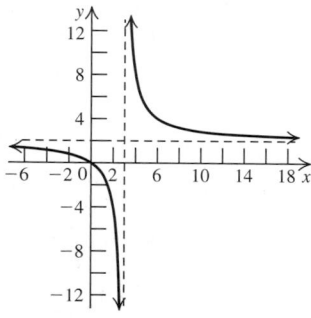

44. x-intercept: 0. y-intercept: 0. Vertical asymptote: $x = 1$. Horizontal asymptote: $y = -1$. Symmetry: none. The graph is above the x-axis on $(0, 1)$ and below the x-axis on $(-\infty, 0) \cup (1, \infty)$.

45. x-intercept: 0. y-intercept: 0. Vertical asymptotes: $x = -2$ and $x = 2$. Horizontal asymptote: x-axis. The graph is symmetric with respect to the origin. The graph is above the x-axis on $(-2, 0) \cup (2, \infty)$, and below the x-axis on $(-\infty, -2) \cup (0, 2)$.

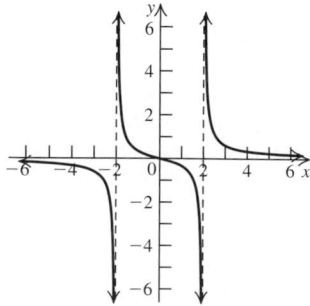

46. *x*-intercept: 0. *y*-intercept: 0. Vertical asymptotes: $x = -1$ and $x = 1$. Horizontal asymptote: *x*-axis. The graph is symmetric with respect to the origin. The graph is above the *x*-axis on $(-\infty, -1) \cup (0, 1)$ and below the *x*-axis on $(-1, 0) \cup (1, \infty)$.

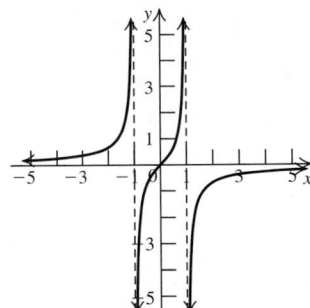

47. *x*-intercept: 0. *y*-intercept: 0. Vertical asymptotes: $x = -2$ and $x = 2$. Horizontal asymptote: $y = 1$. The graph is symmetric with respect to the *y*-axis. The graph is above the *x*-axis on $(-\infty, -2) \cup (2, \infty)$ and below the *x*-axis on $(-2, 2)$.

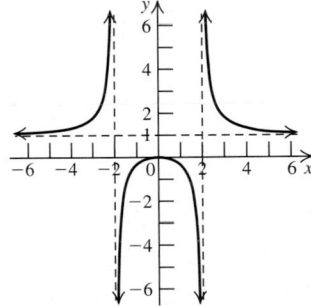

48. *x*-intercept: 0. *y*-intercept: 0. Vertical asymptotes: $x = -2$ and $x = 2$. Horizontal asymptote: $y = -1$. The graph is symmetric with respect to the *y*-axis. The graph is above the *x*-axis on $(-2, 2)$ and below the *x*-axis on $(-\infty, -2) \cup (2, \infty)$.

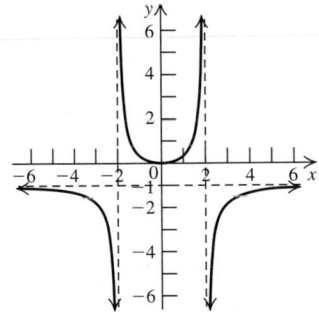

49. *x*-intercept: 0. *y*-intercept: 0. Vertical asymptotes: $x = -3$ and $x = 3$. Horizontal asymptote: $y = -2$. The graph is symmetric in the *y*-axis. The graph is above the *x*-axis on $(-3, 3)$ and below the *x*-axis on $(-\infty, -3) \cup (3, \infty)$.

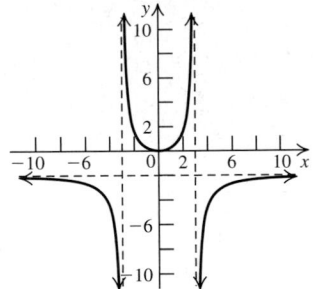

50. *x*-intercepts: $x = \pm2$. No *y*-intercept. Vertical asymptote: $x = 0$. Horizontal asymptote: $y = -1$. The graph is symmetric with respect to the *y*-axis. The graph is above the *x*-axis on $(-2, 0) \cup (0, 2)$ and below the *x*-axis on $(-\infty, -2) \cup (2, \infty)$.

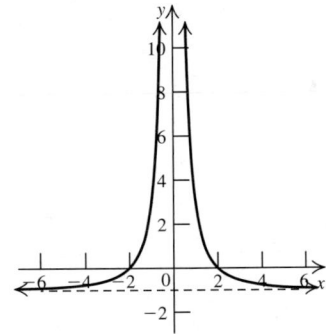

51. No *x*-intercept. *y*-intercept: -1. Vertical asymptotes: $x = -\sqrt{2}$ and $x = \sqrt{2}$. Horizontal asymptote: *x*-axis. The graph is symmetric with respect to the *y*-axis. The graph is above the *x*-axis on $(-\infty, -\sqrt{2}) \cup (\sqrt{2}, \infty)$ and below the *x*-axis on $(-\sqrt{2}, \sqrt{2})$.

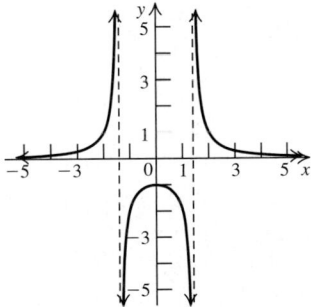

52. No x-intercept. y-intercept: $\dfrac{2}{3}$. Vertical asymptotes: $x = -\sqrt{3}$ and $x = \sqrt{3}$. Horizontal asymptote: x-axis. The graph is symmetric with respect to the y-axis. The graph is above the x-axis on $(-\sqrt{3}, \sqrt{3})$ and below the x-axis on $(-\infty, -\sqrt{3}) \cup (\sqrt{3}, \infty)$.

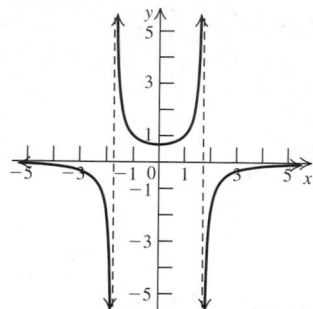

53. x-intercept: -1. y-intercept: $-\dfrac{1}{6}$. Vertical asymptotes: $x = -3$ and $x = 2$. Horizontal asymptote: x-axis. Symmetry: none. The graph is above the x-axis on $(-3, -1) \cup (2, \infty)$, and below the x-axis on $(-\infty, -3) \cup (-1, 2)$.

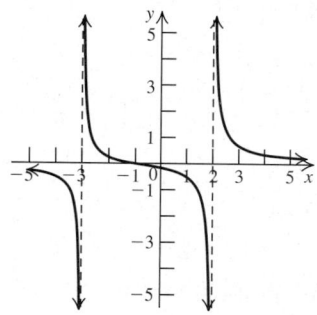

54. x-intercept: 1. y-intercept: $\dfrac{1}{2}$. Vertical asymptotes: $x = -1$ and $x = 2$. Horizontal asymptote: x-axis. Symmetry: none. The graph is above the x-axis on $(-1, 1) \cup (2, \infty)$ and below the x-axis on $(-\infty, -1) \cup (1, 2)$.

55. x-intercept: 0. y-intercept: 0. No vertical asymptote. Horizontal asymptote: $y = 1$. The graph is symmetric with respect to the y-axis. The graph is above the x-axis on $(-\infty, 0) \cup (0, \infty)$.

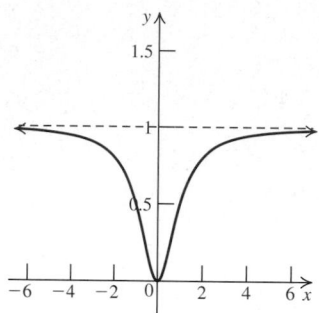

56. x-intercept: 0. y-intercept: 0. No vertical asymptote. Horizontal asymptote: $y = 2$. The graph is symmetric with respect to the y-axis. The graph is above the x-axis on $(-\infty, 0) \cup (0, \infty)$.

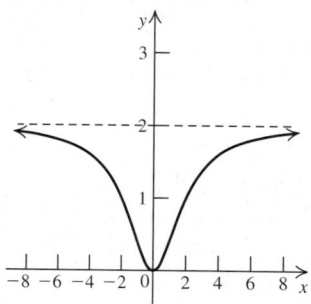

57. x-intercept: ± 2. y-intercept: $\dfrac{4}{9}$. Vertical asymptotes: $x = -3$ and $x = 3$. Horizontal asymptote: $y = 1$. The graph is symmetric with respect to the y-axis. The graph is above the x-axis on $(-\infty, -3) \cup (-2, 2) \cup (3, \infty)$ and below the x-axis on $(-3, -2) \cup (2, 3)$.

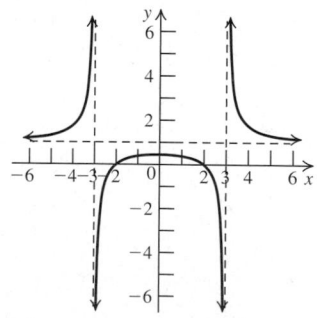

58. No *x*-intercept. *y*-intercept: 4. No vertical asymptote. Horizontal asymptote: *y* = 1. The graph is symmetric with respect to the *y*-axis. The graph is above the *x*-axis on $(-\infty, \infty)$.

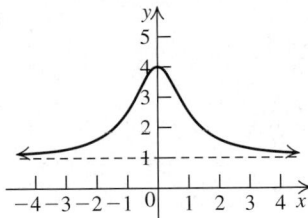

59. No *x*-intercept. *y*-intercept: -2. No vertical asymptote. No horizontal asymptote. Symmetry: none. The graph is above the *x*-axis on $(2, \infty)$ and below the *x*-axis on $(-\infty, 2)$.

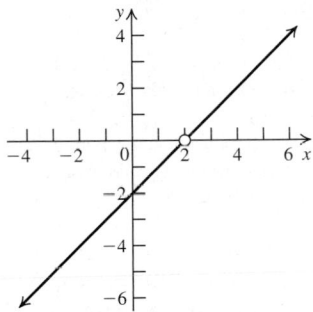

60. No *x*-intercept. *y*-intercept: -1. No vertical asymptote. No horizontal asymptote. Symmetry: none. The graph is above the *x*-axis on $(1, \infty)$ and below the *x*-axis on $(-\infty, 1)$.

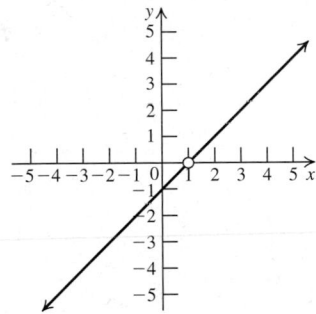

61. No *x*-intercept. *y*-intercept: 1. No vertical asymptote. No horizontal asymptote. Symmetry: none. The graph is above the *x*-axis on $(-\infty, -3) \cup (-3, 4) \cup (4, \infty)$.

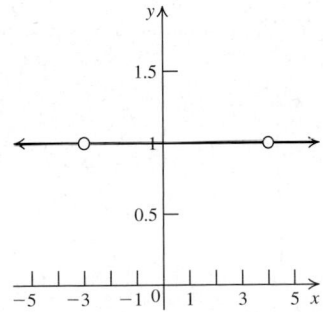

62. No *x*-intercept. *y*-intercept: 1. No vertical asymptote. No horizontal asymptote. Symmetry: none. The graph is above the *x*-axis on $(-\infty, -1) \cup (-1, 1) \cup (1, 2) \cup (2, \infty)$.

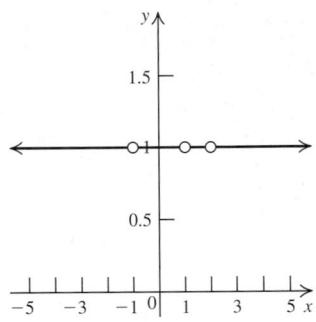

63. Oblique asymptote: *y* = 2*x*

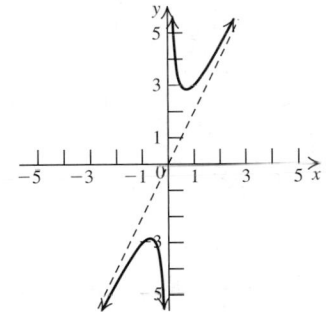

64. Oblique asymptote: *y* = *x*

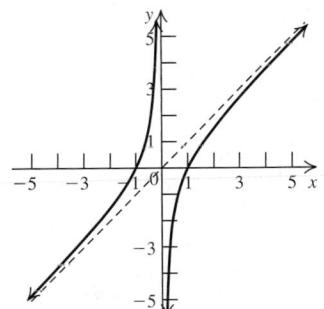

65. Oblique asymptote: *y* = *x*

66. Oblique asymptote: $y = 2x + 1$

67. Oblique asymptote: $y = x - 2$

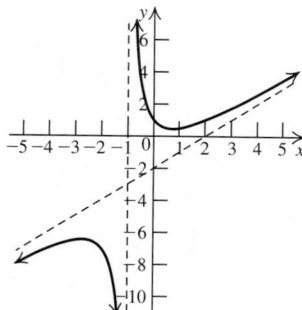

68. Oblique asymptote: $y = 2x - 1$

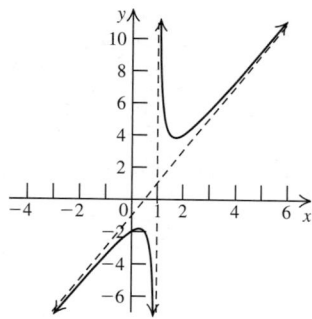

69. Oblique asymptote: $y = x - 2$

70. Oblique asymptote: $y = x$

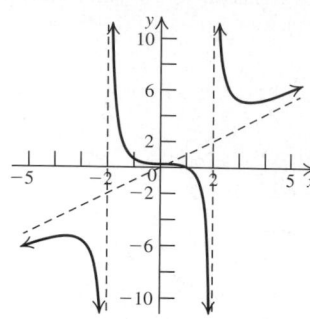

B Exercises: Applying the Concepts

71. a. $C(x) = 0.5x + 2000$ **b.** $\overline{C}(x) = 0.5 + \dfrac{2000}{x}$

    c. $\overline{C}(100) = 20.5, \overline{C}(500) = 4.5, \overline{C}(1000) = 2.5$. These show the average cost of producing 100, 500, and 1000 trinkets, respectively.

    d. Horizontal asymptote: $y = 0.5$. It means that the average cost approaches the fixed daily cost of producing each trinket if the number of trinkets produced approaches ∞.

72. a. $\overline{C}(x) = -0.002x + 6 + \dfrac{7000}{x}$

    b. $\overline{C}(100) = 75.8, \overline{C}(500) = 19, \overline{C}(1000) = 11$. These show the average cost of producing 100, 500, and 1000 CD players, respectively.

    c. Oblique asymptote: $y = -0.002x + 6$. For large values of x, this is a good approximation of the average cost of producing x CD players.

73. a.

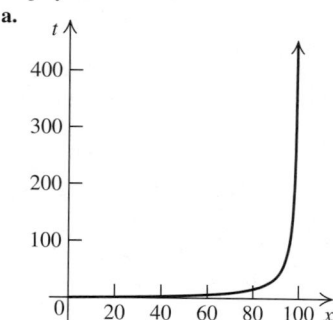

    c. (i) As $x \to 100^-, f(x) \to \infty$.

    (ii) not applicable; the domain is $x < 100$

74. a. $C(50) = 20, C(75) = 40, C(90) = 100, C(99) = 1000$. These show the cost, in millions of dollars, of catching and convicting 50%, 75%, 90%, and 99% of the criminals, respectively.

    b.

75. a. $3.02 billion

b.

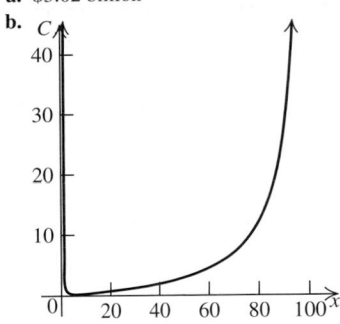

76. a. Horizontal asymptote: $y = a$. Increasing the concentration of the nutrient without bounds pushes the growth rate arbitrarily close to a.

78. a.

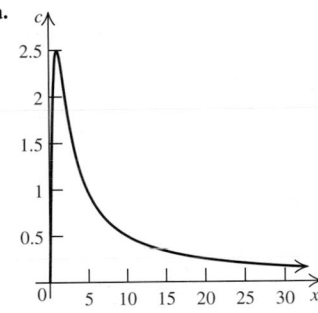

b. Horizontal asymptote: $y = 0$. It means that, as time passes, the concentration of the drug approaches 0.

c. 1 hr after the injection

d. Half an hour and 2 hr after the injection

79. a. $f(x) = \dfrac{10x + 200,000}{x - 2500}$ **c.** More than 25,000.

d. Vertical asymptote: $x = 2500$. Horizontal asymptote: $y = 10$. The vertical asymptote is the number of free samples. The horizontal asymptote is the cost of printing and binding one book.

80. b.

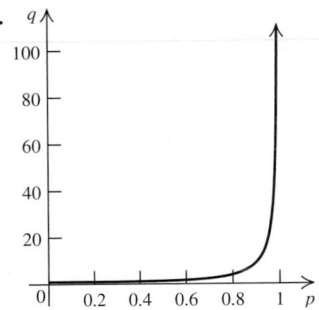

C Exercises: Beyond the Basics

81. Stretch the graph of $y = \dfrac{1}{x}$ vertically by a factor of 2, and reflect the graph in the x-axis.

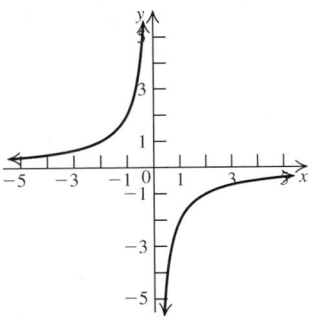

82. Shift the graph of $y = \dfrac{1}{x}$ two units to the right and reflect the graph in the y-axis.

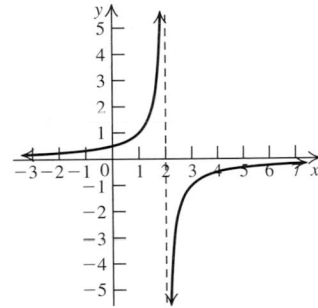

83. Shift the graph of $y = \dfrac{1}{x^2}$ two units to the right.

84. Shift the graph of $y = \dfrac{1}{x^2}$ one unit to the left.

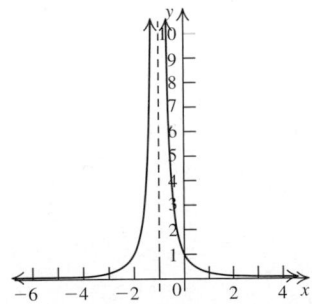

85. Shift the graph of $y = \dfrac{1}{x^2}$ one unit to the right and two units down.

86. Shift the graph of $y = \dfrac{1}{x^2}$ two units to the left and three units up.

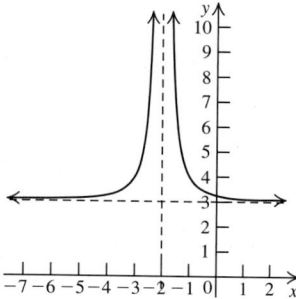

87. Shift the graph of $y = \dfrac{1}{x^2}$ six units to the left.

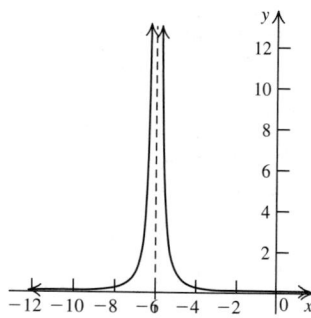

88. Shift the graph of $y = \dfrac{1}{x^2}$ three units to the left and three units up.

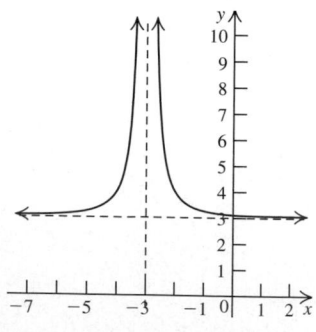

89. Shift the graph of $y = \dfrac{1}{x^2}$ one unit to the right and one unit up.

90. Shift the graph of $y = \dfrac{1}{x^2}$ one unit to the left, stretch the graph vertically by a factor of 5, reflect it in the x-axis, and shift it two units up.

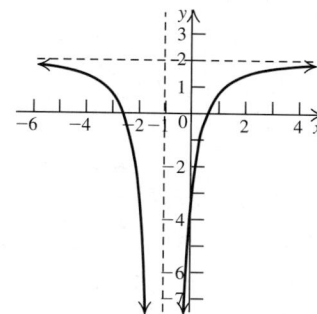

91. a. $f(x) \to 0$ as $x \to -\infty$, $f(x) \to 0$ as $x \to \infty$, $f(x) \to -\infty$ as $x \to 0^-$, and $f(x) \to \infty$ as $x \to 0^+$. No x-intercept. No y-intercept. Vertical asymptote: y-axis. Horizontal asymptote: x-axis. The graph is symmetric with respect to the origin. The graph is above the x-axis on $(0, \infty)$ and below the x-axis on $(-\infty, 0)$.

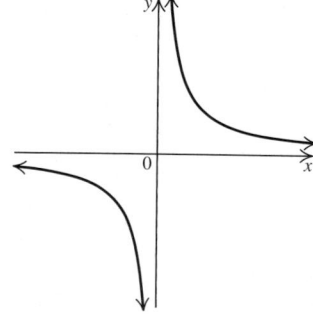

b. $f(x) \to 0$ as $x \to -\infty$, $f(x) \to 0$ as $x \to \infty$,
$f(x) \to \infty$ as $x \to 0^-$, and $f(x) \to -\infty$ as $x \to 0^+$. No x-intercept.
No y-intercept. Vertical asymptote: y-axis. Horizontal asymptote:
x-axis. The graph is symmetric with respect to the origin. The
graph is above the x-axis on $(-\infty, 0)$ and below the x-axis on
$(0, \infty)$.

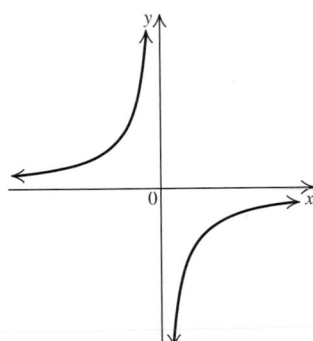

c. $f(x) \to 0$ as $x \to \infty$, $f(x) \to 0$ as $x \to -\infty$,
$f(x) \to \infty$ as $x \to 0^-$, and $f(x) \to \infty$ as $x \to 0^+$. No x-intercept.
No y-intercept. Vertical asymptote: y-axis. Horizontal asymptote:
x-axis. The graph is symmetric with respect to the y-axis. The
graph is above the x-axis on $(-\infty, \infty)$.

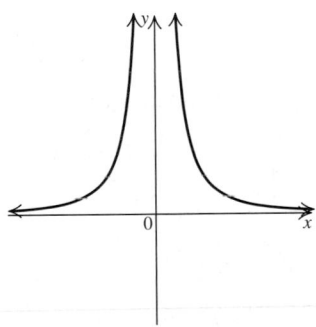

d. $f(x) \to 0$ as $x \to -\infty$, $f(x) \to 0$ as $x \to \infty$,
$f(x) \to -\infty$ as $x \to 0^-$, and $f(x) \to -\infty$ as $x \to 0^+$. No
x-intercept. No y-intercept. Vertical asymptote: y-axis. Horizontal
asymptote: x-axis. The graph is symmetric with respect to the
y-axis. The graph is below the x-axis on $(-\infty, \infty)$.

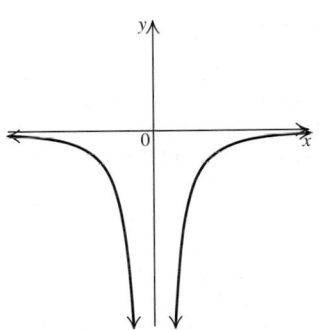

92. a. If c is a zero of $f(x)$, then, since c is not a factor of the numerator,
$x = c$ is a vertical asymptote.
b. Since the numerator is positive, the sign of $f(x)$ and $g(x)$ is the
same.
c. If the graphs intersect for some value x, then $f(x) = g(x)$. It
implies that $f(x) = \dfrac{1}{f(x)}$, from which it follows that $f(x) = \pm 1$.
d. If $f(x)$ increases (decreases, remains constant), the denominator of
$g(x)$ increases (decreases, remains constant). Therefore, $g(x)$
decreases (increases, remains constant).

93.

94.

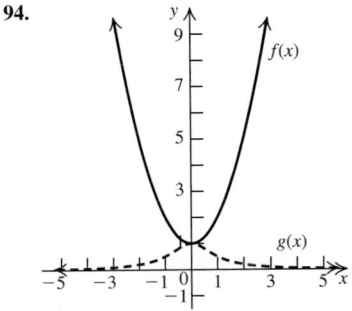

95. $[f(x)]^{-1} = \dfrac{1}{2x + 3}$ and $f^{-1}(x) = \dfrac{1}{2}x - \dfrac{3}{2}$. The two functions are
different.

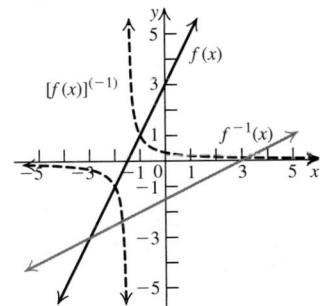

96. $[f(x)]^{-1} = \dfrac{x + 2}{x - 1}$ and $f^{-1}(x) = \dfrac{2x + 1}{1 - x}$.

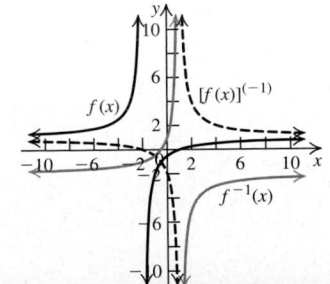

97. $g(x)$ has the oblique asymptote $y = 2x + 3$; $y \to -\infty$ as $x \to -\infty$, and $y \to \infty$ as $x \to \infty$.

98. $f(x) \to \infty$ as $x \to -\infty$, and $f(x) \to \infty$ as $x \to \infty$. $f(x)$ has no oblique asymptote.

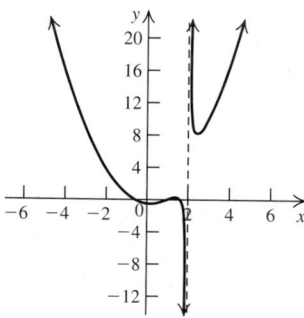

99. Point of intersection: $\left(-\dfrac{1}{3}, 1\right)$; horizontal asymptote $y = 1$

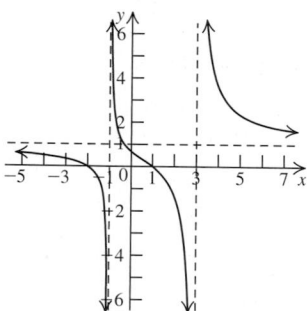

100. Point of intersection: $\left(1, -\dfrac{1}{2}\right)$; horizontal asymptote $y = -\dfrac{1}{2}$

Critical Thinking

101. $f(x) = \dfrac{x + 4}{x - 2}$ **102.** $f(x) = \dfrac{x - 4}{(x - 2)(x + 1)}$

103. $f(x) = \dfrac{4x^2 - 1}{(x - 1)^2}$ **104.** $f(x) = \dfrac{2x^2}{x^2 + 1}$

105. $f(x) = \dfrac{3x^2 - x - 1}{x - 1}$

Section 3.6

Practice Problems

   1. $y = 24$ **2.** 275 **3.** $y = 300$ **4.** $A = 20$

   5. $x = \dfrac{9}{4}$ **6.** $\approx 3.7 \text{ m/sec}^2$

A Exercises: Basic Skills and Concepts

   2. $P = \dfrac{k}{V}$

   5. $V = kx^3y^4$ **6.** $w = \dfrac{k\sqrt{x}}{y}$ **7.** $z = \dfrac{kxu}{v^2}$ **8.** $S = \dfrac{k\sqrt{xy^2z^3}}{u^2}$

   9. $k = \dfrac{1}{2}$, $x = 14$ **10.** $k = \dfrac{3}{2}$, $y = \dfrac{21}{2}$ **15.** $k = 8$, $B = \dfrac{1}{8}$

   16. $k = 10\sqrt[3]{2}$, $x = \dfrac{1}{32}$ **18.** $k = 1$, $m = \dfrac{1}{2}$ **20.** $k = 72$, $u = \dfrac{1}{3}$

   21. $k = \dfrac{1}{17}$, $P = \dfrac{324}{17}$ **22.** $k = \dfrac{1}{13}$, $a = \dfrac{15}{13}$

   24. $k = \dfrac{1}{3}$, $w = \pm 3$ **28.** $y = \dfrac{81}{4}$

B Exercises: Applying the Concepts

   29. $y = Hx$, where y is the speed of the galaxies and x is the distance between them.

   31. a. $y = 30.5x$, where y is the length measured in centimeters and x is the length measured in feet.
     b. (i) 244 cm   **(ii)** 162.67 cm
     c. (i) 1.87 ft   **(ii)** 4.07 ft

   32. a. $y = 2.2x$, where y is the weight measured in pounds and x is the weight measured in kilograms.

   34. \$375. The constant of proportionality is the hourly wage.

   35. $\dfrac{3}{4}$ sec   **38. a.** 13.5 in.^{3} **42.** $2.75 \times 10^{-4}\text{m/s}^2$

   43. a. 1280 candlepower

   44. a. $s = 2\sqrt{6d}$
     b. (i) 37.95 mph   **(ii)** 60 mph   **(iii)** 69.28 mph
     c. 204.17 ft

   45. The length is multiplied by 4.

   47. a. $H = kR^2N$, where k is a constant.

C Exercises: Beyond the Basics

   49. b. $k = 0.0375$ **d.** E is multiplied by 8.   **e.** E is multiplied by 4.

   51. c. The metabolic rate is multiplied by 2.83.

   52. The gravitational attraction between sun and Earth is 168.92 times as strong as the gravitational attraction between Earth and moon.

53. a. $T^2 = \left(\dfrac{4\pi^2}{G}\right)\left(\dfrac{r^3}{M_1 + M_2}\right)$ **b.** 2.01×10^{30} kg

55. a. $R = kN(P - N)$, where k is the constant of variation.

   b. $k = \dfrac{5}{10^6}$ **c.** 125 people per day

Review Exercises

1. (i) opens up   **(ii)** Vertex: $(1, 2)$ **(iii)** Axis: $x = 1$
   (iv) No x-intercept   **(v)** y-intercept: 3
   (vi) decreasing on $(-\infty, 1)$, increasing on $(1, \infty)$

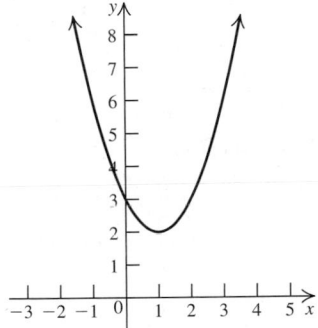

2. (i) opens up   **(ii)** Vertex: $(-2, -3)$ **(iii)** Axis: $x = -2$
   (iv) x-intercepts: $-2 \pm \sqrt{3}$ **(v)** y-intercept: 1
   (vi) decreasing on $(-\infty, -2)$, increasing on $(-2, \infty)$

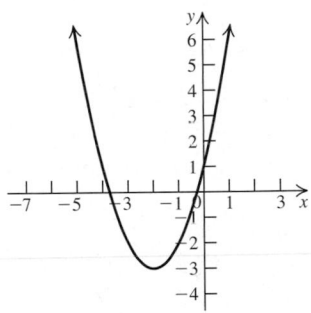

3. (i) opens down   **(ii)** Vertex: $(3, 4)$ **(iii)** Axis: $x = 3$
   (iv) x-intercepts: $3 \pm \sqrt{2}$ **(v)** y-intercept: -14
   (vi) increasing on $(-\infty, 3)$, decreasing on $(3, \infty)$

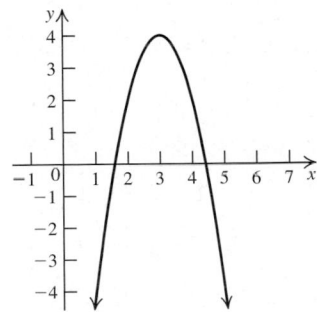

4. (i) opens down   **(ii)** Vertex: $(-1, 2)$ **(iii)** Axis: $x = -1$
   (iv) x-intercepts: $-3, 1$ **(v)** y-intercept: $\dfrac{3}{2}$
   (vi) increasing on $(-\infty, -1)$, decreasing on $(-1, \infty)$

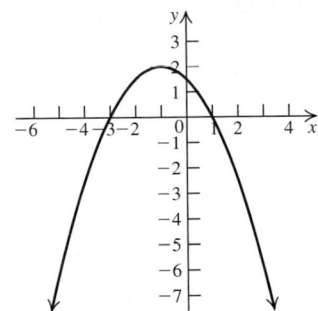

5. (i) opens down   **(ii)** Vertex: $(0, 3)$ **(iii)** Axis: y-axis
   (iv) x-intercepts: $+\dfrac{\sqrt{6}}{2}$ **(v)** y-intercept: 3
   (vi) increasing on $(-\infty, 0)$, decreasing on $(0, \infty)$

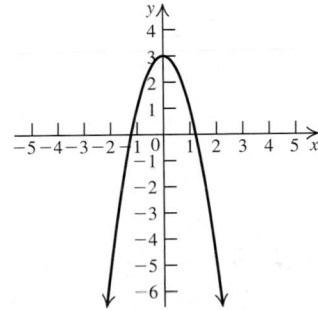

6. (i) opens up   **(ii)** Vertex: $(-1, -3)$ **(iii)** Axis: $x = -1$
   (iv) x-intercepts: $-1 \pm \dfrac{\sqrt{6}}{2}$ **(v)** y-intercept: -1
   (vi) decreasing on $(-\infty, -1)$, increasing on $(-1, \infty)$

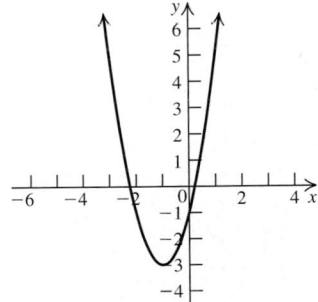

7. (i) opens up   **(ii)** Vertex: $(1, 1)$ **(iii)** Axis: $x = 1$
(iv) No x-intercept   **(v)** y-intercept: 3
(vi) decreasing on $(-\infty, 1)$, increasing on $(1, \infty)$

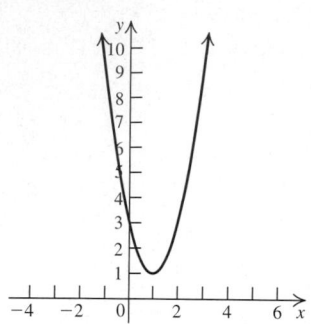

8. (i) opens down   **(ii)** Vertex: $\left(-\dfrac{1}{4}, \dfrac{25}{8}\right)$ **(iii)** Axis: $x = -\dfrac{1}{4}$

(iv) x-intercept: $-\dfrac{3}{2}, 1$ **(v)** y-intercept: 3

(vi) increasing on $\left(-\infty, -\dfrac{1}{4}\right)$, decreasing on $\left(-\dfrac{1}{4}, \infty\right)$

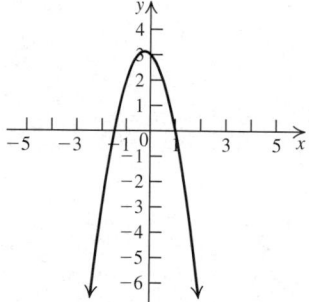

9. (i) opens up   **(ii)** Vertex: $\left(\dfrac{1}{3}, \dfrac{2}{3}\right)$ **(iii)** Axis: $x = \dfrac{1}{3}$

(iv) No x-intercept   **(v)** y-intercept: 1

(vi) decreasing on $\left(-\infty, \dfrac{1}{3}\right)$, increasing on $\left(\dfrac{1}{3}, \infty\right)$

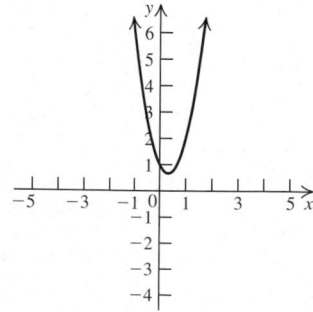

10. (i) opens up   **(ii)** Vertex: $\left(\dfrac{5}{6}, \dfrac{23}{12}\right)$ **(iii)** Axis: $x = \dfrac{5}{6}$
(iv) No x-intercept   **(v)** y-intercept: 4
(vi) decreasing on $\left(-\infty, \dfrac{5}{6}\right)$, increasing on $\left(\dfrac{5}{6}, \infty\right)$

11. Minimum: $(2, -1)$.   **12.** Maximum: $(1, 1)$
13. Maximum: $\left(-\dfrac{3}{4}, \dfrac{25}{8}\right)$ **14.** Minimum: $\left(\dfrac{3}{4}, \dfrac{55}{32}\right)$
15. Shift the graph of $y = x^3$ one unit to the left and two units down.

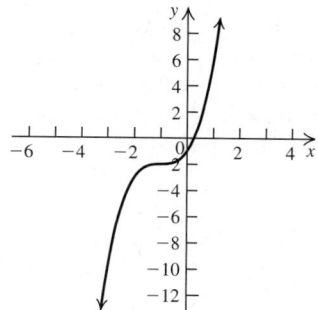

16. Shift the graph of $y = x^4$ one unit to the left and two units up.

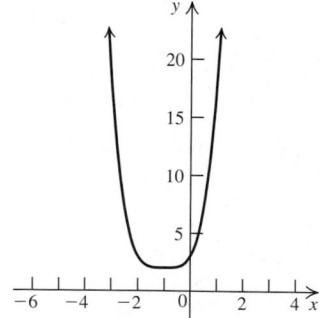

17. Shift the graph of $y = x^3$ one unit right, reflect the resulting graph in the x-axis, and shift it one unit up.

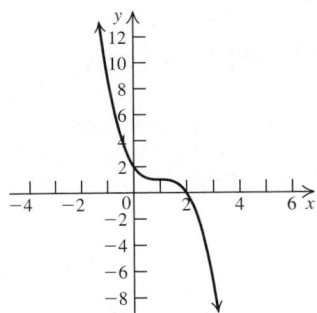

18. Shift the graph of $y = x^4$ three units up.

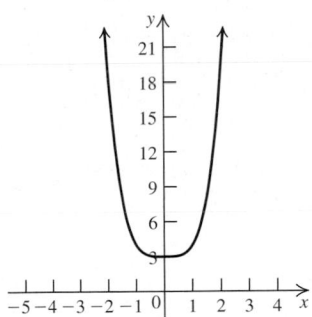

19. (i) $f(x) \to -\infty$ as $x \to -\infty$ and $f(x) \to \infty$ as $x \to \infty$.
  (ii) Zeros: $x = -2$, multiplicity: 1, the graph crosses the x-axis; $x = 0$, multiplicity: 1, the graph crosses the x-axis; $x = 1$, multiplicity: 1, the graph crosses the x-axis.
  (iii) x-intercepts: $-2, 0, 1$; y-intercept: 0
  (iv) The graph is above the x-axis on $(-2, 0) \cup (1, \infty)$ and below the x-axis on $(-\infty, -2) \cup (0, 1)$.
  (v) Symmetry: none
  (vi)

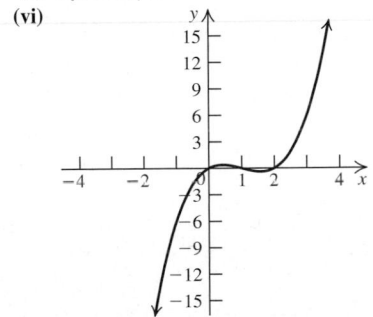

20. (i) $f(x) \to -\infty$ as $x \to -\infty$ and $f(x) \to \infty$ as $x \to \infty$.
  (ii) Zeros: $x = -1$, multiplicity: 1, the graph crosses the x-axis; $x = 0$, multiplicity: 1, the graph crosses the x-axis; $x = 1$, multiplicity: 1, the graph crosses the x-axis.
  (iii) x-intercepts: $-1, 0, 1$. y-intercept: 0
  (iv) The graph is above the x-axis on $(-1, 0) \cup (1, \infty)$ and below the x-axis on $(-\infty, -1) \cup (0, 1)$.
  (v) The graph is symmetric with respect to the origin.

(vi)

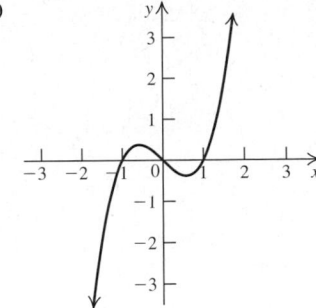

21. (i) $f(x) \to -\infty$ as $x \to -\infty$ and $f(x) \to -\infty$ as $x \to \infty$.
  (ii) Zeros: $x = 0$, multiplicity: 2, the graph touches but does not cross the x-axis; $x = 1$, multiplicity: 2, the graph touches but does not cross the x-axis.
  (iii) x-intercepts: 0, 1; y-intercept: 0
  (iv) The graph is below the x-axis on $(-\infty, 0) \cup (0, 1) \cup (1, \infty)$.
  (v) Symmetry: none
  (vi)

22. (i) $f(x) \to \infty$ as $x \to -\infty$ and $f(x) \to -\infty$ as $x \to \infty$.
  (ii) Zeros: $x = 0$, multiplicity: 3, the graph crosses the x-axis; $x = 2$, multiplicity: 2, the graph touches but does not cross the x-axis.
  (iii) x-intercepts: 0, 2; y-intercept: 0
  (iv) The graph is above the x-axis on $(-\infty, 0)$ and below the x-axis on $(0, 2) \cup (2, \infty)$.
  (v) Symmetry: none
  (vi)

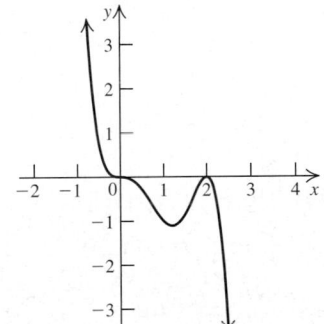

23. (i) $f(x) \to -\infty$ as $x \to -\infty$ and $f(x) \to -\infty$ as $x \to \infty$.
  (ii) Zeros: $x = -1$, multiplicity: 1, the graph crosses the x-axis; $x = 0$, multiplicity: 2, the graph touches but does not cross the x-axis; $x = 1$, multiplicity: 1, the graph crosses the x-axis.
  (iii) x-intercepts: $-1, 0, 1$; y-intercept: 0
  (iv) The graph is above the x-axis on $(-1, 0) \cup (0, 1)$ and below the x-axis on $(-\infty, -1) \cup (1, \infty)$.
  (v) The graph is symmetric with respect to the y-axis.

(vi)

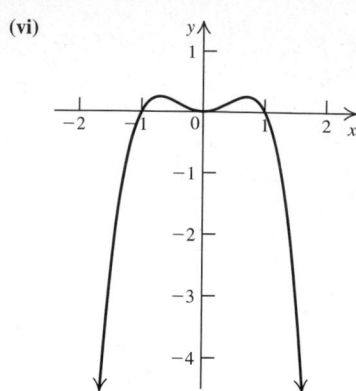

24. (i) $f(x) \to -\infty$ as $x \to -\infty$ and $f(x) \to -\infty$ as $x \to \infty$.

   (ii) Zero: $x = 1$, multiplicity: 2, the graph touches but does not cross the x-axis.

   (iii) x-intercept: 1; y-intercept: -1

   (iv) The graph is below the x-axis on $(-\infty, 1) \cup (1, \infty)$.

   (v) Symmetry: none

   (vi)

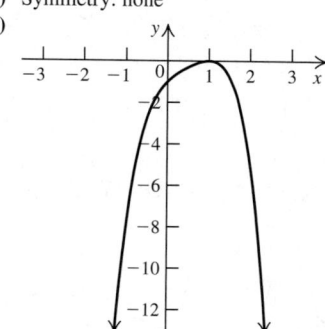

25. Quotient: $2x + 3$; remainder: -7

26. Quotient: $4x - 1$; remainder: 12

27. Quotient: $8x^3 - 12x^2 + 14x - 21$; remainder: 186

29. Quotient: $x^2 + 3x - 3$; remainder: -6

30. Quotient: $-4x^2 - 21x - 131$; remainder: -786

31. Quotient: $2x^3 - 5x^2 + 10x - 17$; remainder: 182

32. Quotient: $3x^4 - 8x^3 + 16x^2 - 31x + 46$; Remainder: -224

38. $-2, \quad \dfrac{7}{4} - \dfrac{\sqrt{33}}{4}, \quad \dfrac{7}{4} + \dfrac{\sqrt{33}}{4}$

40. $\dfrac{1}{4}, \quad -\dfrac{5}{2} + \dfrac{\sqrt{33}}{2}, \quad -\dfrac{5}{2} - \dfrac{\sqrt{33}}{2}$

41. $-6, -3, -2, -1, 1, 2, 3, 6$

42. $\pm\dfrac{1}{9}, \quad \pm\dfrac{2}{9}, \quad \pm\dfrac{1}{3}, \quad \pm\dfrac{4}{9}, \quad \pm\dfrac{2}{3}, \quad \pm\dfrac{8}{9}, \quad \pm 1, \quad \pm\dfrac{4}{3},$

   $\pm\dfrac{16}{9}, \quad \pm 2, \quad \pm\dfrac{8}{3}, \quad \pm 4, \quad \pm\dfrac{16}{3}, \quad \pm 8, \quad \pm 16$

43. $-2, \quad -\dfrac{1}{5}, \quad 0$ **46.** $1, \quad \dfrac{5}{2}$

50. $\dfrac{3}{4}, \quad 2 + i, \quad 2 - i$

51. $2i, \quad -2i, \quad -1 + 2i, \quad -1 - 2i$

54. $\left\{-\dfrac{1}{2}, -\sqrt{6}, \quad \sqrt{6}\right\}$ **55.** $\left\{-1, -\dfrac{1}{2}, \quad \dfrac{3}{2}\right\}$

59. The only possible rational roots are $-2, -1, 1$, and 2. None of them satisfies the equation

60. The only possible rational roots are $-5, -\dfrac{5}{3}, -1, -\dfrac{1}{3}, \dfrac{1}{3}, 1,$

   $\dfrac{5}{3}, 5$. None of them satisfies the equation.

62. 1.60

63. x-intercept: -1. No y-intercept. Vertical asymptote: y-axis. Horizontal asymptote: $y = 1$. Symmetry: none. The graph is above the x-axis on $(-\infty, -1) \cup (0, \infty)$ and below the x-axis on $(-1, 0)$.

64. x-intercept: 2. No y-intercept. Vertical asymptote: y-axis. Horizontal asymptote: $y = -1$. Symmetry: none. The graph is above the x-axis on $(0, 2)$ and below the x-axis on $(-\infty, 0) \cup (2, \infty)$.

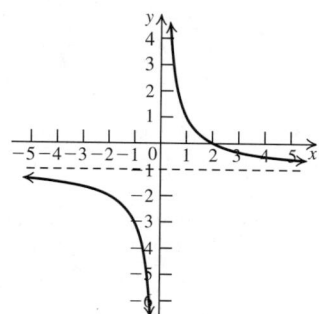

65. x-intercept: 0. y-intercept: 0. Vertical asymptotes: $x = -1$ and $x = 1$. Horizontal asymptote: x-axis. Symmetry: none. The graph is above the x-axis on $(-1, 0) \cup (1, \infty)$ and below the x-axis on $(-\infty, -1) \cup (0, 1)$.

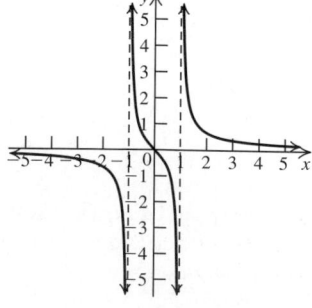

66. x-intercept: ± 3. y-intercept: $\dfrac{9}{4}$. Vertical asymptotes: $x = -2$ and $x = 2$. Horizontal asymptote: $y = 1$. The graph is symmetric with respect to the y-axis. The graph is above the x-axis on $(-\infty, -3) \cup (-2, 2) \cup (3, \infty)$ and below the x-axis on $(-3, -2) \cup (2, 3)$.

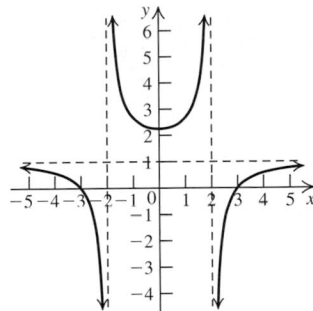

67. x-intercept: 0. y-intercept: 0. Vertical asymptotes: $x = -3$ and $x = 3$. No horizontal asymptote. Symmetry: none. The graph is above the x-axis on $(-3, 0) \cup (3, \infty)$ and below the x-axis on $(-\infty, -3) \cup (0, 3)$.

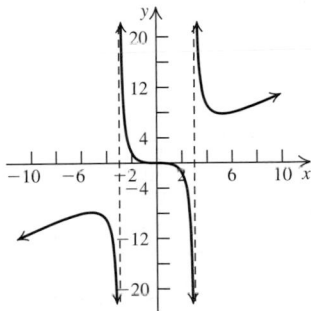

68. x-intercept: -1. y-intercept: $-\dfrac{1}{8}$. Vertical asymptotes: $x = -2$ and $x = 4$. Horizontal asymptote: x-axis. Symmetry: none. The graph is above the x-axis on $(-2, -1) \cup (4, \infty)$ and below the x-axis on $(-\infty, -2) \cup (-1, 4)$.

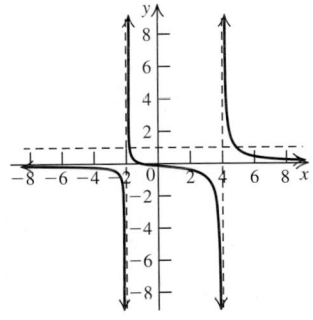

69. x-intercept: 0. y-intercept: 0. Vertical asymptotes: $x = -2$ and $x = 2$. No horizontal asymptote. The graph is symmetric with respect to the y-axis. The graph is above the x-axis on $(-\infty, -2) \cup (2, \infty)$ and below the x-axis on $(-2, 0) \cup (0, 2)$.

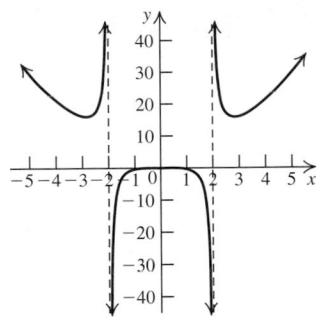

70. x-intercept: 2. y-intercept: $\dfrac{1}{2}$. Vertical asymptote: $x = 4$. Horizontal asymptote: $y = 1$. Symmetry: none. The graph is above the x-axis on $(-\infty, -3) \cup (-3, 2) \cup (4, \infty)$ and below the x-axis on $(2, 4)$.

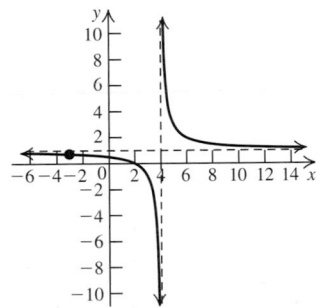

75. Maximum height: 1000. The missile hits the ground at $x = 200$.

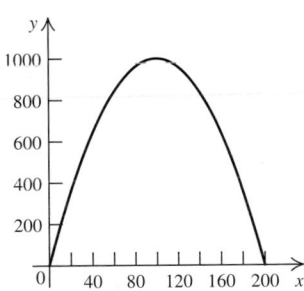

77. $x = 10\sqrt{6}$ ft, $\quad y = \dfrac{20\sqrt{6}}{3}$ ft $\qquad$ **78.** $x = 5\sqrt{30}$ ft, $\quad y = \dfrac{8\sqrt{30}}{3}$ ft

79. a.

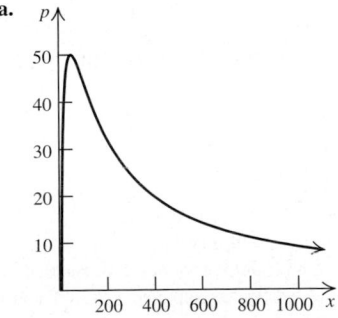

81. a. $P(x) = -\dfrac{3}{1000}x^2 + 20.1x - 150$

   c. $\overline{C}(x) = \dfrac{3}{1000}x + 3.9 + \dfrac{150}{x}$

84. 121 ft   **87. b.** 150 Ω

89. a. $k = \dfrac{1}{200{,}000}$

Practice Test A

1. x-intercepts: $3 \pm \sqrt{7}$.

2.

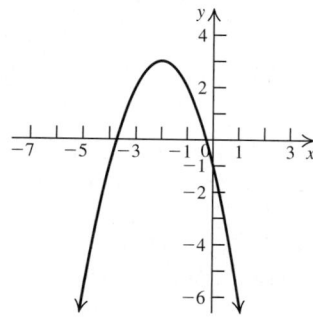

5. Quotient: $x^2 - 4x + 3$; Remainder: 0

6.

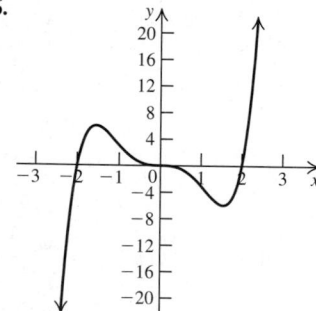

8. Quotient: $-3x^2 + 5x + 1$ **9.** $P(-2) = -53$ **10.** $-2, 2, 5$

11. $0, -\dfrac{1}{2} + \dfrac{\sqrt{61}}{2}, -\dfrac{1}{2} - \dfrac{\sqrt{61}}{2}$

12. $-9, -\dfrac{9}{2}, -3, -\dfrac{3}{2}, -1, -\dfrac{1}{2}, \dfrac{1}{2}, 1, \dfrac{3}{2}, 3, \dfrac{9}{2}, 9$

13. $f(x) \to -\infty$ as $x \to -\infty$ and $f(x) \to \infty$ as $x \to \infty$.

14. $x = -2$, multiplicity: 3; $x = 2$, multiplicity: 1.

15. Number of positive zeros: 0 or 2; number of negative zeros: 1

16. Horizontal asymptote: $y = 2$; vertical asymptotes: $x = -4$ and $x = 5$

---

17. $y = \dfrac{kx}{t^2}$, where k is a constant.

19. 15 thousand units   **20.** $V(x) = x(8 - 2x)(17 - 2x)$

Cumulative Review Exercises (Chapters 1–3)

7. $(2, 3)$.   **8.** $[-4, 2]$

9. $(-\infty, -1] \cup \{2\}$ **10.** $(-2, \infty)$

12. Center: $(-1, 2)$; radius: 3   **14.** $y = -\dfrac{2}{3}x + \dfrac{11}{3}$

15. Domain: $\left(-\infty, -\dfrac{3}{2}\right) \cup \left(-\dfrac{3}{2}, \infty\right)$ **16.** Domain: $(-\infty, 2)$.

17. $f(-2) = 11, f(3) = 6, f(x + h) = x^2 + 2(h - 1)x + h^2 - 2h + 3,$

   $\dfrac{f(x + h) - f(x)}{3} = 2x + h - 2$

18. a. $f(g(x)) = \sqrt{x^2 + 1}$ **b.** $g(f(x)) = x + 1$

   c. $f(f(x)) = \sqrt[4]{x}$ **d.** $g(g(x)) = x^4 + 2x^2 + 2$

19. a. $f(1) = 5, f(3) = 11, f(4) = 6$

   b.

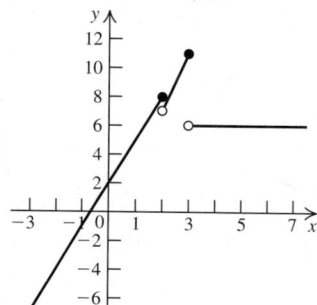

21. a. Shift the graph of $y = \sqrt{x}$ two units to the left.

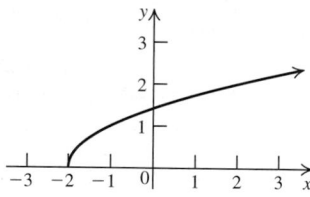

   b. Shift the graph of $y = \sqrt{x}$ one unit to the left stretch the resulting graph horizontally by a factor of 2, reflect it in the x-axis, and shift it three units up.

23.

24.

25.

26.

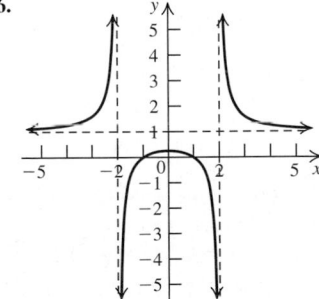

30. $x = 50$

CHAPTER 4

Section 4.1

Practice Problems

1. $f(2) = \dfrac{1}{16} = 0.06$

   $f(0) = 1$

   $f(-1) = 4$

   $f\left(\dfrac{5}{2}\right) = \dfrac{1}{32} = 0.03$

   $f\left(-\dfrac{3}{2}\right) = 8$

2.

3.

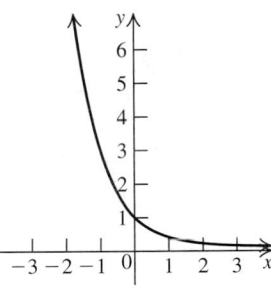

4. $a = \dfrac{1}{5}$ 5. $x = 2$ 6. $x = -1$

7.

8.

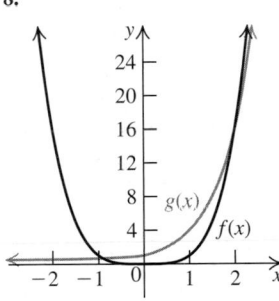

9. $t = 6.$

A Exercises: Basic Skills and Concepts

1. No, the base is not a constant.   2. Yes, the base is 4.   3. Yes, the base is 2.   4. No, the base is 1.   5. No, the base is not a constant.   6. No, the exponent is not a variable.   7. No, the base is not a positive constant.   8. Yes, the base is 1.8.

19.

20.

21.

22.

23.

24.

25.

26.

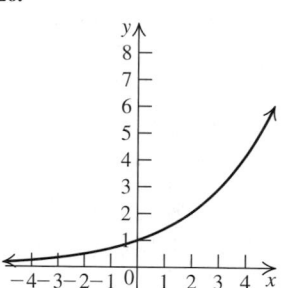

28. Yes, reflection in the y-axis

33. On shifting the graph of $f(x) = 4^x$ (Exercise 19) to the right by 1 unit

34. On reflecting the graph of $g(x) = 10^x$ (Exercise 20) in the x-axis

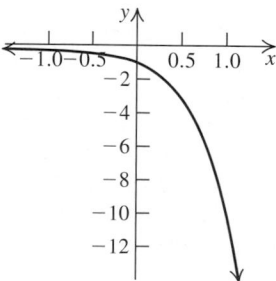

35. Reflect the graph of $h(x) = \left(\dfrac{1}{4}\right)^x$ in the y-axis. (See the graph for Exercise 23).

36. On reflecting the graph of $h(x) = 7^{-x}$ (Exercise 22) in the y-axis, followed by shifting two units up

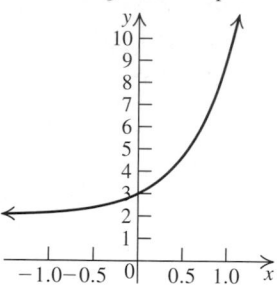

37. On reflecting the graph of $h(x) = \left(\dfrac{1}{4}\right)^x$ (Exercise 23) across the x-axis

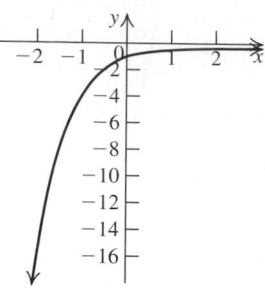

38. On reflecting the graph of $h(x) = 7^{-x}$ (Exercise 22) in the y-axis followed by a reflection across the x-axis and then a shift four units up

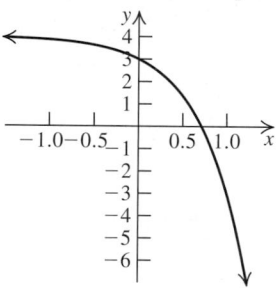

39. On reflecting the graph of $g(x) = \left(\dfrac{3}{2}\right)^{-x}$ (Exercise 21) across the y-axis and then shifting four units up

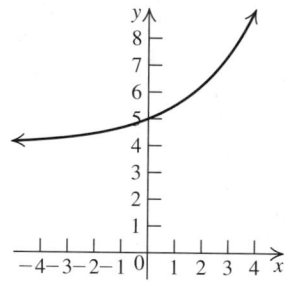

40. On shifting the graph of $f(x) = \left(\dfrac{1}{10}\right)^x$ (Exercise 24) one unit down

41. On reflecting the graph of $f(x) = (1.3)^{-x}$ (Exercise 25) across the x-axis

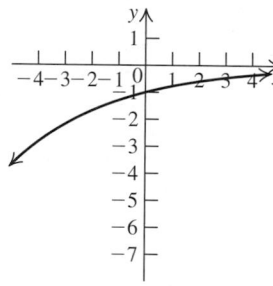

42. On reflecting the graph of $g(x) = (0.7)^{-x}$ (Exercise 26) across x-axis and then shifting two units up

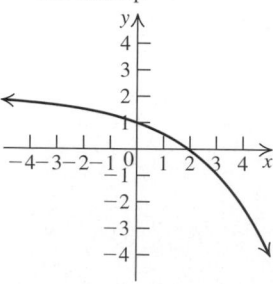

43. Domain $= (-\infty, \infty)$
Range $= (0, \infty)$
Horizontal Asymptote $y = 0$

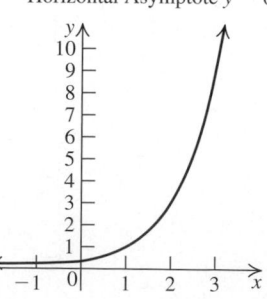

44. Domain $= (-\infty, \infty)$
Range $= (-2, \infty)$
Horizontal Asymptote $y = -2$

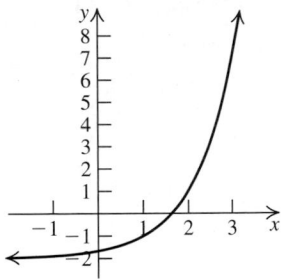

45. Domain $= (-\infty, \infty)$
Range $= (0, \infty)$
Horizontal Asymptote $y = 0$

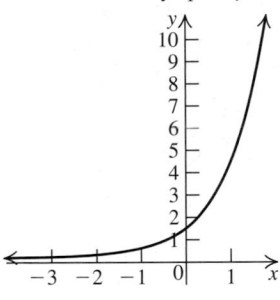

46. Domain $= (-\infty, \infty)$
Range $= (-2, \infty)$
Horizontal Asymptote $y = -2$

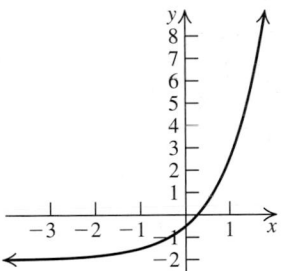

47. Domain $= (-\infty, \infty)$
Range $= (-\infty, 1)$
Horizontal Asymptote $y = 1$

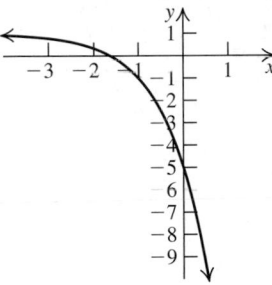

48. Domain $= (-\infty, \infty)$
Range $= (-1, \infty)$
Horizontal Asymptote $y = -1$

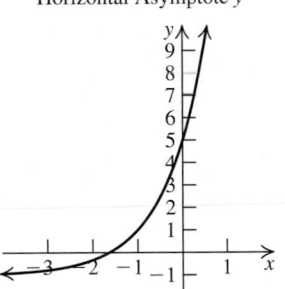

49. Domain $- (-\infty, \infty)$
Range $= (-\infty, 4)$
Horizontal Asymptote $y = 4$

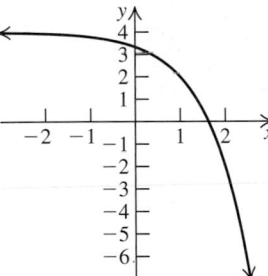

50. Domain $= (-\infty, \infty)$
Range $- (-2, \infty)$
Horizontal Asymptote $y = -2$

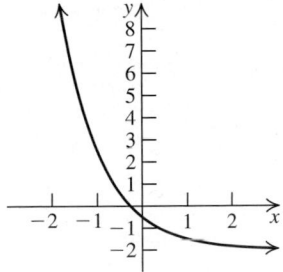

53. $y = 2\left(\dfrac{1}{2}\right)^x - 5$ **75.** $x = \dfrac{1}{8}$

B Exercises: Applying the Concepts
80. $s(0) = 20$
$s(1) = 35$
$s(5) = \dfrac{1570}{32} = 49.0625$
$s(10) = \dfrac{51170}{1024} = 49.9707$

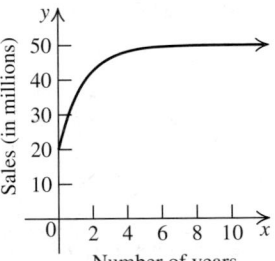

Horizontal asymptote $y = 50$. In the long run, the number of sales approaches, but does not exceed, 50 million.

C Exercises: Beyond the Basics
87. Range $= [1, \infty)$ symmetric in the y-axis.

88.

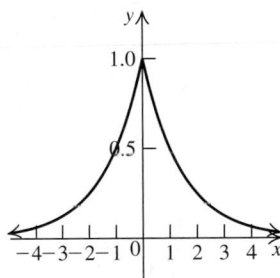

89. Domain $= (-\infty, \infty)$
Range $= [1, \infty)$ symmetric in
the y-axis.

90. a.

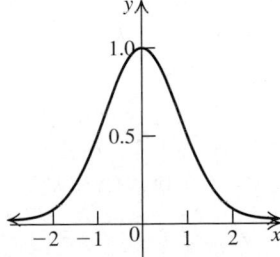

b. Domain $= (-\infty, \infty)$
Range $= (0, 1]$

c. Since $g(-x) = 2^{(-x)^2} = 2^{x^2} \neq h(x)$

92. a. $f(x) + g(x) = 2 \cdot a^x$ **b.** $f(x) - g(x) = 2 \cdot a^{-x}$
c. $[f(x)]^2 - [g(x)]^2 = 4$ **d.** $[f(x)]^2 + [g(x)]^2 = 2(a^{2x} + a^{-2x})$

96. $x = \dfrac{1}{2}, -\dfrac{1}{2}$

98. a. $y = 25 \cdot 2^{\frac{5x}{8}}$

b.

$\approx$ 1233.768 millions
c. After 4.8 yr ($\approx$ in 2000)

99. e. No. The number of AIDS cases from part (c) far exceeds the total population of the United States in 2007.

Critical Thinking

100. The function $y = 2^x$ is an increasing function and is thus one-to-one. The horizontal line $y = k$ for $k > 0$ intersects the graph of $y = 2^x$ in exactly one point.

101. Sketch the graphs of $y = 2^x$ and $y = 2x$. These graphs intersect at $x = 2$ and $x = 1$.

Section 4.2

Practice Problems

1. $ 11,500
2. a. $A = \$11,485.03$ **b.** $I = \$3,485.03$
3. (i) $5325.00 **(ii)** $5330.28 **(iii)** $5333.00 **(iv)** $5334.85
(v) $5335.76
4. $14,764.48
5. a. $4,284,000.00 **b.** $1,911,233,655.42
c. $2,162,832,946.56 **d.** $2,256,324,190.56
6. $y = -e^{x-1} - 2$

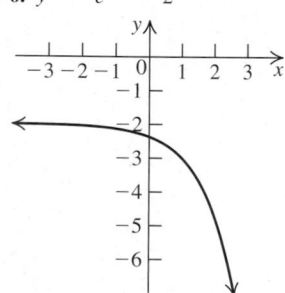

7. a. 11.96229 **b.** 4.76720

A Exercises: Basic Skills and Concepts

1. a. $11,592.208 **b.** $6342.208
2. a. $7936.206 **b.** $4436.206
3. a. $15,304.996 **b.** $9064.996
4. a. $21,207.474 **b.** $13,207.474
5. a. $12,365.409 **b.** $4865.409
6. a. $12,429.419 **b.** $3929.419
7. $4631.934 **8.** $4528.904 **9.** $4493.684 **10.** $4493.289

11. $f(x) = e^{-x}$

12. $f(x) = -e^x$

13. $f(x) = e^{x-2}$

14. $f(x) = e^{2-x}$

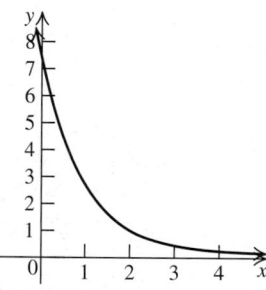

15. $f(x) = 1 + e^x$

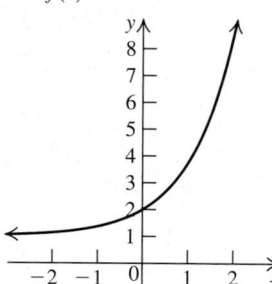

16. $f(x) = 2 - e^{-x}$

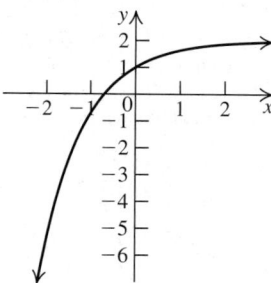

17. $f(x) = -e^{x-2} + 3$

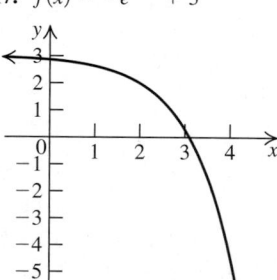

18. $g(x) = 3 + e^{2-x}$

19. $f(x) = e^{|x|}$

20. $g(x) = e^{-|x|}$

43.

44.

C Exercises: Beyond the Basics

Critical Thinking

52. a. $f(0) = 1, f(1) = \dfrac{1}{e} \approx 0.3679, f(2) \approx 0.0183, f(3) \approx 0.0001234$

d.

35.

36.

37.

38.

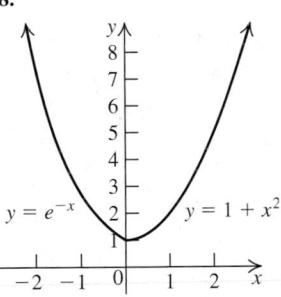

Section 4.3

Practice Problems

1. a. $\log_9\left(\dfrac{1}{3}\right) = -\dfrac{1}{2}$ **b.** $\log_a(p) = q$

2. a. $2^5 = 64$ **b.** $v^w = u$

3. a. 2   **b.** -0.5 **4. a.** 8   **b.** 5

5. $(-\infty, 1)$

6.

7. Shift the graph of $y = \log_2 x$ 3 units right, and reflect the graph in the *x*-axis.

39.

40.

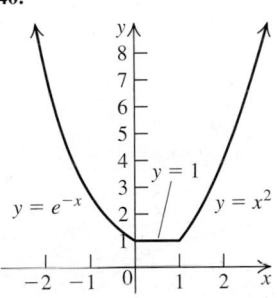

42. $S_5 = 2.716666, S_{10} = 2.7182818,$
    $S_{15} = 2.718281828$

8.

9. a. -1 **b.** 0.693   **10.** 5.423 min
11. a. 30805.03 m^3 **b.** 13.82 yr

A Exercises: Basic Skills and Concepts

1. $\log_5 25 = 2$ **2.** $\log_{81} 9 = \dfrac{1}{2}$ **3.** $\log_{49}\left(\dfrac{1}{7}\right) = -\dfrac{1}{2}$

4. $\log_{\frac{1}{16}}\left(\dfrac{1}{4}\right) = \dfrac{1}{2}$ **5.** $\log_{\frac{1}{16}} 4 = -\dfrac{1}{2}$ **6.** $\log_{a^2} a^4 = 2$

7. $\log_{10} 1 = 0$ **8.** $\log_{10} 10000 = 4$ **9.** $\log_{10} 0.1 = -1$

10. $\log_3 5 = x$ **11.** $\log_a 5 = 2$ **12.** $\log_a \pi = e$ **13.** $2^5 = 32$

14. $7^2 = 49$ **15.** $10^2 = 100$ **16.** $10^1 = 10$ **17.** $10^0 = 1$

18. $a^0 = 1$ **19.** $10^{-2} = 0.01$ **20.** $\left(\dfrac{1}{5}\right)^{-1} = 5$

26. a. $f(x) = \log_2 x$ **b.** $f(x) = \log_3 x$

   c. $f(x) = \log_{\frac{1}{2}} x$ **d.** $f(x) = \log_4 x$

27. Domain $= (-3, \infty)$
   Range $= (-\infty, \infty)$
   Asymptote $x = -3$

28. Domain $= (1, \infty)$
   Range $= (-\infty, \infty)$
   Asymptote $x = 1$

29. Domain $= (0, \infty)$
   Range $= (-\infty, \infty)$
   Asymptote $x = 0$

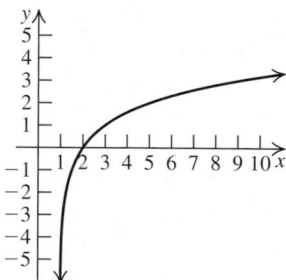

30. Domain $= (0, \infty)$
   Range $= (-\infty, \infty)$
   Asymptote $x = 0$

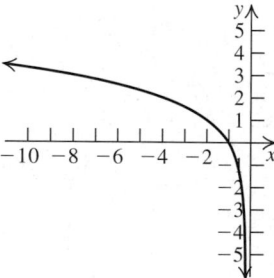

31. Domain $= (-\infty, 0)$
   Range $= (-\infty, \infty)$
   Asymptote $x = 0$

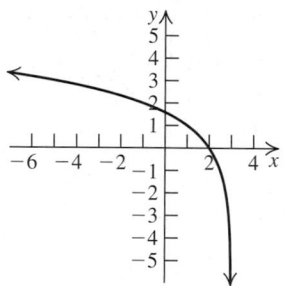

32. Domain $= (-\infty, 0)$
   Range $= (-\infty, \infty)$
   Asymptote $x = 0$

33. Domain $= (0, \infty)$
   Range $= (0, \infty)$
   Asymptote $x = 0$

34. Domain $= (-\infty, 0) \cup (0, \infty)$
   Range $= (-\infty, \infty)$
   Asymptote $x = 0$

35. Domain $= (1, \infty)$
   Range $= (-\infty, \infty)$
   Asymptote $x = 1$

36. Domain $= (-\infty, 0)$
   Range $= (-\infty, \infty)$
   Asymptote $x = 0$

37. Domain $= (-\infty, 3)$
   Range $= (-\infty, \infty)$
   Asymptote $x = 3$

38. Domain $= (0, \infty)$
   Range $= (-\infty, \infty)$
   Asymptote $x = 0$

39. Domain $= (-\infty, 3)$
   Range $= (-\infty, \infty)$
   Asymptote $x = 3$

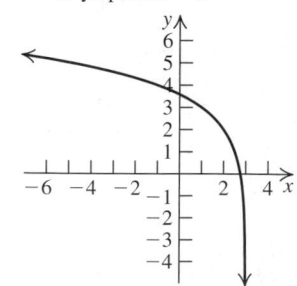

40. Domain $= (-\infty, 3)$
   Range $= (-\infty, \infty)$
   Asymptote $x = 3$

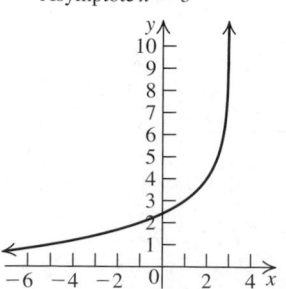

41. Domain $= (-\infty, 0) \cup (0, \infty)$
Range $= (-\infty, \infty)$
Asymptote $x = 0$

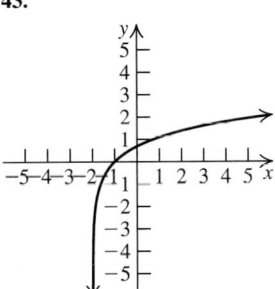

42. Domain $= (-\infty, 0) \cup (0, \infty)$
Range $= (-\infty, \infty)$
Asymptote $x = 0$

43.

44.

45.

46.

47.

48.

49.

50.

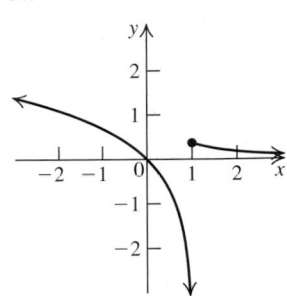

B Exercises: Applying the Concepts

89. a. 48.47   **b.** ≈ 76.83 years   **90.** 43.09 years (≈ 2038)

91. b. 29.96 (≈ 30) years

92. a. $T(n) = 16{,}000e^{-0.25t}$ **b.** ≈ 796.59 m^3 **c.** ≈ 6.4 yr

93. b. 5.5 min

Section 4.4

Practice Problems

1. a. $\log y - \log z$ **b.** $2\log y - 3\log z$

2. a. $\ln(2x - 1) - \ln(x + 4)$ **b.** $\log 2 + \dfrac{1}{2}\log y - \dfrac{1}{2}\log z$

3. $\log\sqrt{x^2 - 1}$ **4.** $\dfrac{\log 1s}{\log 3} \approx 2.46497$ **5. a.** -2 **b.** $\dfrac{1}{7}$

6. $f(x) = 5e\left(\dfrac{1}{5}\ln 20\right)z$ **7.** $t > \approx 13.6$ years   **8.** $\approx 13{,}235$ years

9. $\approx 65.34\%$

A Exercises: Basic Skill and Concepts

13. $\ln(x) + \ln(x - 1)$ **14.** $\log_2 (x - 1) - \log_2 (x + 3)$

15. $\dfrac{1}{2}\log(x^2 + 1) - \log(x + 3)$ **16.** $\ln(x) + \ln(x + 1) - 2\ln(x - 1)$

17. $2\log_3 (x - 1) - 5\log_3 (x + 1)$

18. $\dfrac{2}{3}\log_4 (x - 3) + \dfrac{2}{3}\log_4 (x + 3) - \dfrac{2}{3}\log_4 (x - 2) - \dfrac{2}{3}\log_4 (x - 4)$

19. $\log_b x + \log_b y + \log_b z$ **20.** $\dfrac{1}{2}[\log_b x + \log_b y + \log_b z]$

21. $2\log_b x + 3\log_b y + \log_b z$ **22.** $\log_b x + 2\log_b y - 3\log_b z$

23. $\dfrac{1}{2}\log x + \dfrac{1}{4}(\log y + \log z)$ **24.** $\log_b x + \dfrac{1}{2}(\log_b y + \log_b z)$

B Exercises: Applying the Concepts

61. Rate of growth $\approx 1.375\%$

C Exercises: Beyond the Basics

79.

$[0, 10, 1]$ by $[-4, 4, 1]$

80.

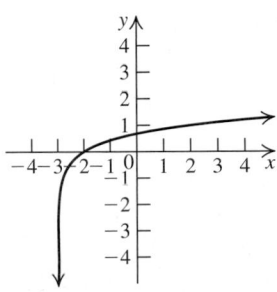

81. The domain of $2 \log(x)$ is $(0, \infty)$, and the domain of $\log(x^2)$ is $(-\infty, 0) \cup (0, \infty)$.

Section 4.5

Practice Problems
1. a. $x = 5$ **b.** $x = \dfrac{2}{3}$ **2.** $x = 1.65$ **3.** $x = 3.82$

4. $x = 1.609$
5. a. United States, 329.10 million; Pakistan, 224.14 million
   b. Sometime in 2020 (after 15.63 yr)
   c. In 27.84 yr (i.e., sometime in 2032)
6. $x = e^{\frac{3}{2}}$ **7.** $\varnothing$ **8.** $x = 9$
9. The average growth rate was approximately 1.74%

B Exercises: Applying the Concepts
63. a.

Item	Canada	Mexico	U.K
Population	32.27 million	136.90 million	61.36 million
Milk price	$3.11	$4.36	$3.39
Bread price	$4.60	$8.52	$5.00

b.

Item	Canada	Mexico	U.K
Population	34.06 million	155.28 million	62.48 million
Milk price	$3.95	$6.96	$4.66
Bread price	$5.84	$3.60	$6.87

67. Canada: In 2032 (after 43.43 yr)
   Mexico: In 2015 (after 26.06 yr)
   UK: In 2026 (after 37.10 yr)
68. In 2002 (after 13.97 yr)

70. a. $\dfrac{\ln 2}{\ln (1 + r)}$ **b.** $t = \dfrac{\ln 2}{r}$ yr

71. a. $k \approx 3.4\%$
   b. ≈ 4.1 million
   c.

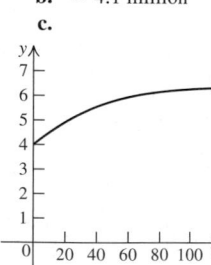

   d. ≈ 4.9 million
   e. 6.4 million

73. a. $a = 4999$ and $k = 0.852$

74. c.

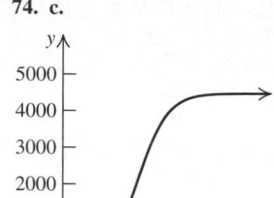

Review Exercises

Basic Skills
19. Domain $= (-\infty, \infty)$
   Range $= (0, \infty)$
   Asymptote $y = 0$

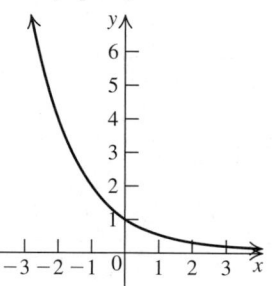

20. Domain $= (-\infty, \infty)$
   Range $= (0, \infty)$
   Asymptote $y = 0$

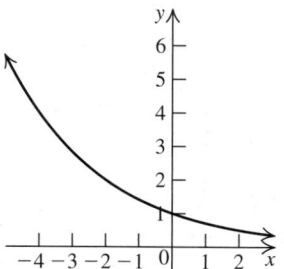

21. Domain $= (-\infty, \infty)$
   Range $= (3, \infty)$
   Asymptote $y = 3$

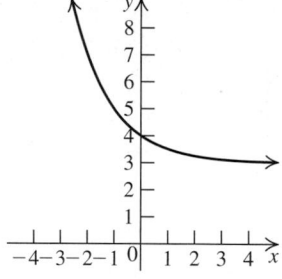

22. Domain $= (-\infty, \infty)$
   Range $= [1, \infty)$

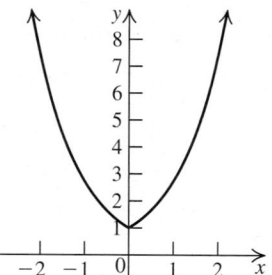

23. Domain $= (-\infty, \infty)$
   Range $= (0, 1]$
   Asymptote $y = 0$

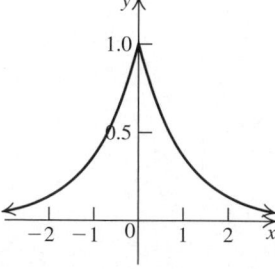

24. Domain $= (-\infty, \infty)$
   Range $= (0, \infty)$
   Asymptote $y = 0$

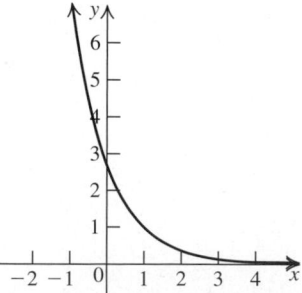

25. Domain $= (-\infty, 0)$
Range $= (-\infty, \infty)$
Asymptote $x = 0$

26. Domain $= (-\infty, \infty)$
Range $= (-\infty, \infty)$
Asymptote $x = 0$

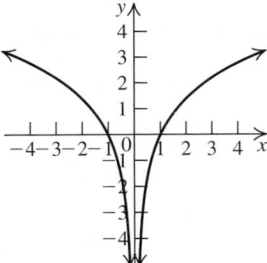

27. Domain $= (1, \infty)$
Range $= (-\infty, \infty)$
Asymptote $x = 1$

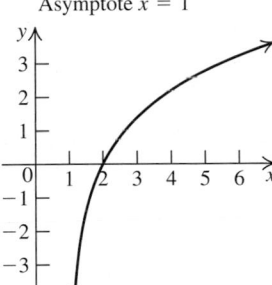

28. Domain $= (-\infty, \infty)$
Range $= (-\infty, 2)$
Asymptote $y = 2$

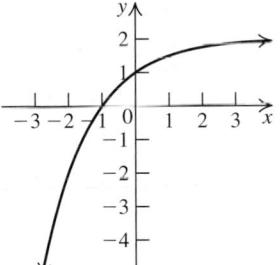

29. Domain $- (-\infty, 0)$
Range $= (0, \infty)$
Asymptote $x = 0$

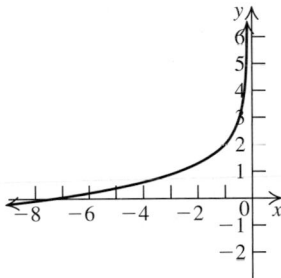

30. Domain $= (-5, \infty)$
Range $= (-\infty, \infty)$
Asymptote $x = -5$

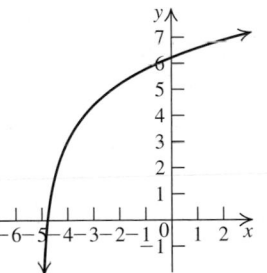

31. a. y-intercept $= 1$,
b. $\lim\limits_{x\to\infty} f(x) - 3$,
$\lim\limits_{x\to-\infty} f(x) = -\infty$

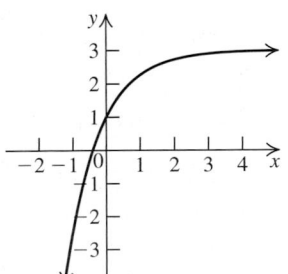

32. a. y-intercept $= 1$,
b. $\lim\limits_{x\to\infty} f(x) = 2.5$,
$\lim\limits_{x\to-\infty} f(x) = 0$

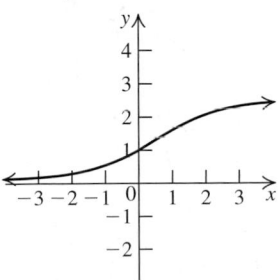

33. a. y-intercept $= 1$,
b. $\lim\limits_{x\to\infty} f(x) = 0$,
$\lim\limits_{x\to-\infty} f(x) = 0$

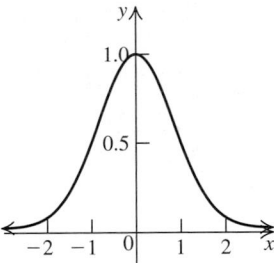

34. a. y-intercept $= 1$,
b. $\lim\limits_{x\to\infty} f(x) = -3$,
$\lim\limits_{x\to-\infty} f(x) = 3$

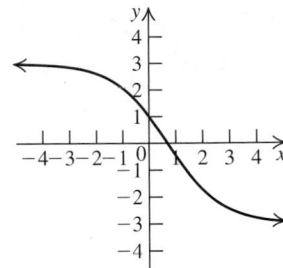

46. $y = \left(\dfrac{1}{x}\right)^{\frac{1}{4}}$ **47.** $y = \dfrac{\sqrt{x^2 - 1}}{x^2 + 1}$ **48.** $y = \dfrac{1}{1 - e^{\frac{1}{x}}}$

53. $\dfrac{\ln(23)}{\ln 3} \approx 2.854$ **54.** $\dfrac{\ln(5.2)}{\ln 2} + 1 \approx 3.379$ **55.** $\dfrac{\ln 19}{\ln 273} \approx 0.525$

58. $\dfrac{1}{2}\left[\dfrac{\ln b}{\ln a} + 1\right]$ **59.** $\left\{e, \dfrac{1}{e}\right\}$ **60.** $\dfrac{\ln 3}{\ln 2} \approx 1.585$

66. $\dfrac{\ln 12}{\ln 3} \approx 2.262$

Applying the Concepts

67. At 5% compounded yearly, A $= \$9849.70$
At 4.75% compounded monthly, A $= \$9754.74$
The 5% investment will provide the greater return.

70. a.

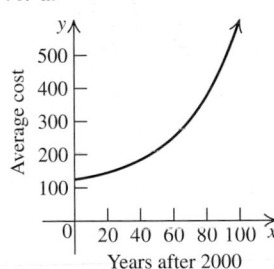

b. $\$133.75$ thousand
c. 59.73 yr

71. a.

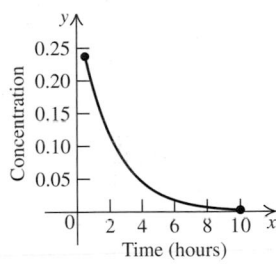

b. ≈ 5 hr

72. a. thickness $= 1/152$ cm **b.** thickness $= 0.01053987$ cm

c. $I = \dfrac{1}{10^{1520}} I_0$

74. a.

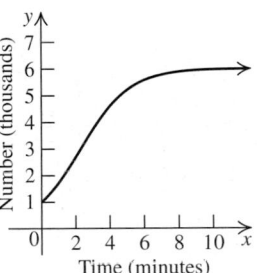

b. 1000 **c.** 4601 **d.** 6000

75. c. ≈ 13.73 mil
78. a. $\approx 3\%$ **b.** $\approx 6\%$
79. c. 200.8
81. b. Remains stationary at 6 gm

Practice Test A

7. $\ln 3x^5$ **12.** $y = \ln(x - 1) + 3$
13.

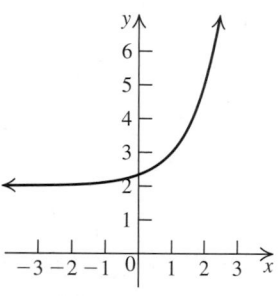

14. $(-\infty, 0)$ **15.** $\ln\dfrac{x^3(x^3 + 2)}{\sqrt{3x^2 + 2}}$ **20.** 22,377

Cumulative Review Exercises (Chapters 1–4)

1. x-intercept 0, y-intercepts 0, 2; Symmetric in y-axis
2. a. $x = -3$ **b.** $x = 5$
4. $y = \dfrac{3}{2}x + 7$
7. Start with $y = \sqrt{x}$, shift one unit left, stretch vertically by a factor of 3, and shift two units down.

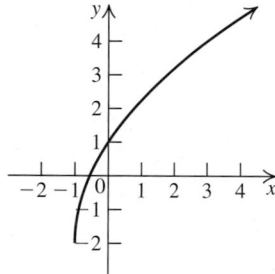

8. $(f \circ g)(z) = 3\sqrt{-\dfrac{1}{x}}$, domain of $f \circ g$ is $(-\infty, 0)$

9. a. Yes, $f^{-1}(x) = \left(\dfrac{x - 1}{2}\right)^{1/3}$

10. a. $Q = 2x, R = x + 1, D = x^2 + 1$

$2x + \dfrac{x + 1}{x^2 + 1}$

b. $Q = 2x^3 + x^2 - 3x + 7, R = -18, D = x + 3$

$2x^3 + x^2 - 3x + 7 - \dfrac{18}{x + 3}$

13. b. $\ln\dfrac{x^3}{y^2}$
16. Rational zeros $\{1, 2\}$; upper bound 4, lower bound -1
17. a. $1, 1, 1, -2, -2, 3$
    b. At $x = 1$ and $x = 3$, the graph crosses the x-axis. At $x = -2$, the graph touches, but does not cross, the x-axis.
    c. $f(x) \to \infty$ as $x \to \infty$; $f(x) \to \infty$ as $x \to -\infty$
    d.

18. d.

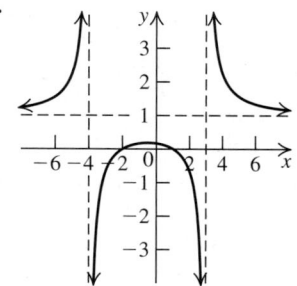

CHAPTER 5

Section 5.1

Practice Problems

1.

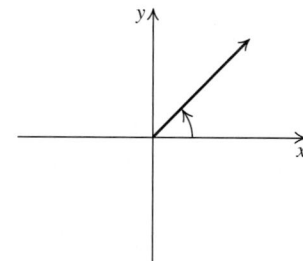

2. a. 13.16°
    b. 41°16′30″
3. $-\dfrac{\pi}{4}$ radians
4. 270°
5. complement = 23°; supplement = 113°
6. 7.85 meters
7. ≈ 790 miles
8. 36π radians per minute ≈ 1131 feet per minute
9. ≈ 52.36 square inches

1.

2.

3.

4.

5.

6.

7.

8.

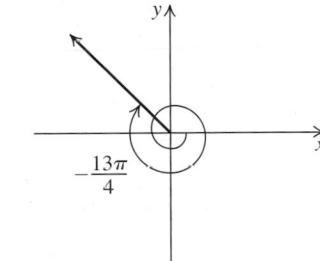

21. $\dfrac{\pi}{4}$ **22.** $\dfrac{\pi}{3}$ **24.** $-\dfrac{7\pi}{6}$ **25.** $\dfrac{7\pi}{4}$

26. $\dfrac{11\pi}{6}$ **27.** $\dfrac{8\pi}{3}$ **28.** $\dfrac{5\pi}{2}$

29. $-\dfrac{17\pi}{6}$ **30.** $-\dfrac{7\pi}{3}$

49. complement: 45°; supplement: 133°

50. complement: 15°; supplement: 105°

51. complement: none because the measure of the angle is greater than 90°; supplement: 60°

52. complement: none because the measure of the angle is greater than 90°; supplement: 20°

53. complement: none because the measure of the angle is greater than 90°; supplement: none because the measure of the angle is greater than 180°

54. complement: none because the measure of the angle is negative; supplement: none because the measure of the angle is negative

B Exercises: Applying the Concepts

65. 70.69 inches   **67.** $\dfrac{2\pi}{3}$ radians   **68.** $\dfrac{7\pi}{6}$ radians

73. a. 120 radians per minute   **b.** 300 radians per minute

74. a. $\omega = 0.07$ radians per second   **b.** $v = 2.13$ meters per second

76. 165 inches/second

77. 84,823.00 inches per minute

C Exercises: Beyond the Basics

93. a. $\omega_A = 176$ radians per second. $v_A = 1056$ inches per second.
    b. $\omega_C = 132$ radians per second. $v_C = 1056$ inches per second.

Critical Thinking

95. The line of latitude through 40°40′13″.

Section 5.2

Practice Problems

1. $\sin\theta = \dfrac{4}{5}$ $\csc\theta = \dfrac{5}{4}$

$\cos\theta = \dfrac{3}{5}$ $\sec\theta = \dfrac{5}{3}$

$\tan\theta = \dfrac{4}{3}$ $\cot\theta = \dfrac{3}{4}$

2. $\sin\theta = \dfrac{2\sqrt{2}}{3}$ $\csc\theta = \dfrac{3\sqrt{2}}{4}$

$\cos\theta = \dfrac{1}{3}$ $\sec\theta = 3$

$\tan\theta = 2\sqrt{2}$ $\cot\theta = \dfrac{\sqrt{2}}{4}$

3. $\csc 45° = \sqrt{2}$; $\sec 45° = \sqrt{2}$; $\cot 45° = 1$

4. $\sin 60° = \dfrac{\sqrt{3}}{2}$ $\csc 60° = \dfrac{2\sqrt{3}}{3}$

$\cos 60° = \dfrac{1}{2}$ $\sec 60° = 2$

$\tan 60° = \sqrt{3}$ $\cot 60° = \dfrac{\sqrt{3}}{3}$

5. a. $\sec 69° \approx 2.7904$
  b. $\cot 15° \approx 3.7321$
6. ≈ 1.096 miles **7.** $\approx 20{,}320$ feet **8.** ≈ 43 feet

A Exercises: Basic Skills and Concepts

1. $\sin\theta = \dfrac{2\sqrt{5}}{25}$ $\csc\theta = \dfrac{5\sqrt{5}}{2}$

$\cos\theta = \dfrac{11\sqrt{5}}{25}$ $\sec\theta = \dfrac{5\sqrt{5}}{11}$

$\tan\theta = \dfrac{2}{11}$ $\cot\theta = \dfrac{11}{2}$

2. $\sin\theta = \dfrac{\sqrt{7}}{2}$ $\csc\theta = \dfrac{2\sqrt{7}}{7}$

$\cos\theta = \dfrac{\sqrt{7}}{2}$ $\sec\theta = \dfrac{2\sqrt{7}}{7}$

$\tan\theta = 1$ $\cot\theta = 1$

3. $\sin\theta = \dfrac{3}{5}$ $\csc\theta = \dfrac{5}{3}$

$\cos\theta = \dfrac{4}{5}$ $\sec\theta = \dfrac{5}{4}$

$\tan\theta = \dfrac{3}{4}$ $\cot\theta = \dfrac{4}{3}$

4. $\sin\theta = \dfrac{8}{17}$ $\csc\theta = \dfrac{17}{8}$

$\cos\theta = \dfrac{15}{17}$ $\sec\theta = \dfrac{17}{15}$

$\tan\theta = \dfrac{8}{15}$ $\cot\theta = \dfrac{15}{8}$

5. $\sin\theta = \dfrac{\sqrt{2}}{10}$ $\csc\theta = 5\sqrt{2}$

$\cos\theta = \dfrac{7\sqrt{2}}{10}$ $\sec\theta = \dfrac{5\sqrt{2}}{7}$

$\tan\theta = \dfrac{1}{7}$ $\cot\theta = 7$

6. $\sin\theta = \dfrac{1}{3}$ $\csc\theta = 3$

$\cos\theta = \dfrac{2\sqrt{2}}{3}$ $\sec\theta = \dfrac{3\sqrt{2}}{4}$

$\tan\theta = \dfrac{\sqrt{2}}{4}$ $\cot\theta = 2\sqrt{2}$

7. $\sin\theta = \dfrac{\sqrt{5}}{3}$ $\csc\theta = \dfrac{3\sqrt{5}}{5}$

$\cos\theta = \dfrac{2}{3}$ $\sec\theta = \dfrac{3}{2}$

$\tan\theta = \dfrac{\sqrt{5}}{2}$ $\cot\theta = \dfrac{2\sqrt{5}}{5}$

8. $\sin\theta = \dfrac{3}{4}$ $\csc\theta = \dfrac{4}{3}$

$\cos\theta = \dfrac{\sqrt{7}}{4}$ $\sec\theta = \dfrac{4\sqrt{7}}{7}$

$\tan\theta = \dfrac{3\sqrt{7}}{7}$ $\cot\theta = \dfrac{\sqrt{7}}{3}$

9. $\sin\theta = \dfrac{5\sqrt{34}}{34}$ $\csc\theta = \dfrac{\sqrt{34}}{5}$

$\cos\theta = \dfrac{3\sqrt{34}}{34}$ $\sec\theta = \dfrac{\sqrt{34}}{3}$

$\tan\theta = \dfrac{5}{3}$ $\cot\theta = \dfrac{3}{5}$

10. $\sin\theta = \dfrac{11\sqrt{157}}{157}$ $\csc\theta = \dfrac{\sqrt{157}}{11}$

$\cos\theta = \dfrac{6\sqrt{157}}{157}$ $\sec\theta = \dfrac{\sqrt{157}}{6}$

$\tan\theta = \dfrac{11}{6}$ $\cot\theta = \dfrac{6}{11}$

11. $\sin\theta = \dfrac{5}{13}$ $\csc\theta = \dfrac{13}{5}$

$\cos\theta = \dfrac{12}{13}$ $\sec\theta = \dfrac{13}{12}$

$\tan\theta = \dfrac{5}{12}$ $\cot\theta = \dfrac{12}{5}$

12. $\sin\theta = \dfrac{1}{4}$ $\csc\theta = 4$

$\cos\theta = \dfrac{\sqrt{15}}{4}$ $\sec\theta = \dfrac{4\sqrt{15}}{15}$

$\tan\theta = \dfrac{\sqrt{15}}{5}$ $\cot\theta = \sqrt{15}$

33. $-\dfrac{1}{2}$ **34.** $-\dfrac{\sqrt{2}}{2}$ **35.** $-\dfrac{\sqrt{3}}{3}$ **37.** $-\dfrac{2\sqrt{3}}{3}$ **38.** $-\dfrac{2\sqrt{3}}{3}$

B Exercises: Applying the Concepts

39. The Empire State Building is approximately 150 meters away and is approximately 381 meters tall.

C Exercises: Beyond the Basics

44. $c \approx 12.806$, $\sin\theta \approx 0.625$, $\tan\theta = 0.8$
45. $c \approx 18.248$, $\sin\theta \approx 0.986$, $\cos\theta \approx 0.164$
46. $\cos\theta \approx 0.291$, $\tan\theta \approx 3.286$
47. $c \approx 33.015$, $\cos\theta \approx 0.818$, $\tan\theta \approx 0.704$
48. $\sin\theta = 0.5$, $b \approx 15.588$, $c = 18$
49. $b \approx 8.660$, $c = 10$
50. $\alpha = 30°$, $b \approx 4.041$, $c \approx 8.083$

Section 5.3

Practice Problems

1. $\sin\theta = -\dfrac{5\sqrt{29}}{29}$ $\csc\theta = -\dfrac{\sqrt{29}}{5}$

   $\cos\theta = \dfrac{2\sqrt{29}}{29}$ $\sec\theta = \dfrac{\sqrt{29}}{2}$

   $\tan\theta = -\dfrac{5}{2}$ $\cot\theta = -\dfrac{2}{5}$

2. **a.** $\sin 180° = 0$ $\csc 180° = $ undefined
   $\cos 180° = -1$ $\sec 180° = -1$
   $\tan 180° = 0$ $\cot 180° = $ undefined
   b. $\sin 270° = -1$ $\csc 270° = -1$
   $\cos 270° = 0$ $\sec 270° = $ undefined
   $\tan 270° = $ undefined $\cot 270° = 0$

3. Quadrant II   **4.** $\sin\theta = -\dfrac{4\sqrt{41}}{41}$, $\sec\theta = \dfrac{\sqrt{41}}{5}$

5. **a.** $5°$ **b.** $\dfrac{\pi}{3}$ **c.** 1.20

6. **a.** $\sin 1035° = -\dfrac{\sqrt{2}}{2}$ **b.** $\cot\dfrac{17\pi}{6} = -\sqrt{3}$

7. 375.2 square feet   **8.** 4.845 square miles

9. $\sin t = \dfrac{\sqrt{5}}{3}$, $\tan t = -\dfrac{\sqrt{5}}{2}$

A Exercises: Basic Skills and Concepts

1. $\sin\theta = \dfrac{3}{5}$ $\csc\theta = \dfrac{5}{3}$

   $\cos\theta = -\dfrac{4}{5}$ $\sec\theta = -\dfrac{5}{4}$

   $\tan\theta = -\dfrac{3}{4}$ $\cot\theta = -\dfrac{4}{3}$

2. $\sin\theta = \dfrac{5\sqrt{34}}{34}$ $\csc\theta = \dfrac{\sqrt{34}}{5}$

   $\cos\theta = -\dfrac{3\sqrt{34}}{34}$ $\sec\theta = -\dfrac{\sqrt{34}}{3}$

   $\tan\theta = -\dfrac{5}{3}$ $\cot\theta = -\dfrac{3}{5}$

3. $\sin\theta = -\dfrac{1}{2}$ $\csc\theta = -2$

   $\cos\theta = -\dfrac{\sqrt{3}}{2}$ $\sec\theta = -\dfrac{2\sqrt{3}}{3}$

   $\tan\theta = \dfrac{\sqrt{3}}{3}$ $\cot\theta = \sqrt{3}$

4. $\sin\theta = -\dfrac{2\sqrt{5}}{5}$ $\csc\theta = -\dfrac{\sqrt{5}}{2}$

   $\cos\theta = -\dfrac{\sqrt{5}}{5}$ $\sec\theta = -\sqrt{5}$

   $\tan\theta = 2$ $\cot\theta = \dfrac{1}{2}$

5. $\sin\theta = \dfrac{\sqrt{2}}{2}$ $\csc\theta = \sqrt{2}$

   $\cos\theta = \dfrac{\sqrt{2}}{2}$ $\sec\theta = \sqrt{2}$

   $\tan\theta = 1$ $\cot\theta = 1$

6. $\sin\theta = -\dfrac{\sqrt{2}}{2}$ $\csc\theta = -\sqrt{2}$

   $\cos\theta = -\dfrac{\sqrt{2}}{2}$ $\sec\theta = -\sqrt{2}$

   $\tan\theta = 1$ $\cot\theta = 1$

7. $\sin\theta = -\dfrac{5}{13}$ $\csc\theta = -\dfrac{13}{5}$

   $\cos\theta = \dfrac{12}{13}$ $\sec\theta = \dfrac{13}{12}$

   $\tan\theta = -\dfrac{5}{12}$ $\cot\theta = -\dfrac{12}{5}$

8. $\sin\theta = -\dfrac{2\sqrt{53}}{53}$ $\csc\theta = -\dfrac{\sqrt{53}}{2}$

   $\cos\theta = \dfrac{7\sqrt{53}}{53}$ $\sec\theta = \dfrac{\sqrt{53}}{7}$

   $\tan\theta = -\dfrac{2}{7}$ $\cot\theta = -\dfrac{7}{2}$

9. Quadrant III   **10.** Quadrant III   **11.** Quadrant II
12. Quadrant III   **13.** Quadrant IV   **14.** Quadrant II
15. Quadrant II   **16.** Quadrant III

17. $\sin\theta = -\dfrac{12}{13}$ $\csc\theta = -\dfrac{13}{12}$

    $\cos\theta = -\dfrac{5}{13}$ $\sec\theta = -\dfrac{13}{5}$

    $\tan\theta = \dfrac{12}{5}$ $\cot\theta = \dfrac{5}{12}$

18. $\sin\theta = -\dfrac{3}{5}$ $\csc\theta = -\dfrac{5}{3}$

    $\cos\theta = \dfrac{4}{5}$ $\sec\theta = \dfrac{5}{4}$

    $\tan\theta = -\dfrac{3}{4}$ $\cot\theta = -\dfrac{4}{3}$

19. $\sin\theta = \dfrac{4}{5}$ $\csc\theta = \dfrac{5}{4}$

    $\cos\theta = -\dfrac{3}{5}$ $\sec\theta = -\dfrac{5}{3}$

    $\tan\theta = -\dfrac{4}{3}$ $\cot\theta = -\dfrac{3}{4}$

20. $\sin\theta = -\dfrac{3}{4}$ $\csc\theta = -\dfrac{4}{3}$

    $\cos\theta = \dfrac{\sqrt{7}}{4}$ $\sec\theta = \dfrac{4\sqrt{7}}{7}$

    $\tan\theta = -\dfrac{3\sqrt{7}}{7}$ $\cot\theta = -\dfrac{\sqrt{7}}{3}$

21. $\sin\theta = \dfrac{3}{5}$ $\csc\theta = \dfrac{5}{3}$

    $\cos\theta = -\dfrac{4}{5}$ $\sec\theta = -\dfrac{5}{4}$

    $\tan\theta = -\dfrac{3}{4}$ $\cot\theta = -\dfrac{4}{3}$

22. $\sin\theta = \dfrac{2\sqrt{13}}{13}$ $\csc\theta = \dfrac{\sqrt{13}}{2}$

    $\cos\theta = \dfrac{3\sqrt{13}}{13}$ $\sec\theta = \dfrac{\sqrt{13}}{3}$

    $\tan\theta = \dfrac{2}{3}$ $\cot\theta = \dfrac{3}{2}$

23. $\sin\theta = -\dfrac{2\sqrt{2}}{3}$ $\csc\theta = -\dfrac{3\sqrt{2}}{4}$

$\cos\theta = \dfrac{1}{3}$ $\sec\theta = 3$

$\tan\theta = -2\sqrt{2}$ $\cot\theta = -\dfrac{\sqrt{2}}{4}$

24. $\sin\theta = \dfrac{2\sqrt{5}}{5}$ $\csc\theta = \dfrac{\sqrt{5}}{2}$

$\cos\theta = -\dfrac{\sqrt{5}}{5}$ $\sec\theta = -\sqrt{5}$

$\tan\theta = -2$ $\cot\theta = -\dfrac{1}{2}$

33. $-\dfrac{1}{2}$ **34.** $-\dfrac{\sqrt{2}}{2}$ **35.** $-\dfrac{\sqrt{3}}{3}$ **37.** $-\dfrac{2\sqrt{3}}{3}$ **38.** $-\dfrac{2\sqrt{3}}{3}$

48. 85.3 sq ft

C Exercises: Beyond the Basics

66. $\sin 0° = \dfrac{\sqrt{0}}{2} = 0$ $\cos 0° = \dfrac{\sqrt{4}}{2} = 1$

$\sin 30° = \dfrac{\sqrt{1}}{2} = \dfrac{1}{2}$ $\cos 30° = \dfrac{\sqrt{3}}{2}$

$\sin 45° = \dfrac{\sqrt{2}}{2}$ $\cos 45° = \dfrac{\sqrt{2}}{2}$

$\sin 60° = \dfrac{\sqrt{3}}{2}$ $\cos 60° = \dfrac{\sqrt{1}}{2} = \dfrac{1}{2}$

$\sin 90° = \dfrac{\sqrt{4}}{2} = 1$ $\cos 90° = \dfrac{\sqrt{0}}{2} = 0$

67. $\cos(\theta + \pi) = \dfrac{-x}{r} = -\dfrac{x}{r} = -\cos\theta$

68. $\sin(\theta + \pi) = \dfrac{-y}{r} = -\dfrac{y}{r} = -\sin\theta$

69. $\tan(\theta + \pi) = \dfrac{-y}{-x} = \dfrac{y}{x} = \tan\theta$

Critical Thinking

81. $\dfrac{1}{2}r^2(\theta - \sin\theta)$

Section 5.4

Practice Problems

1.

2.
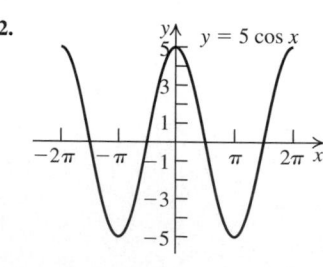

Amplitude = 5; range = $[-5, 5]$

3.

4.

5.
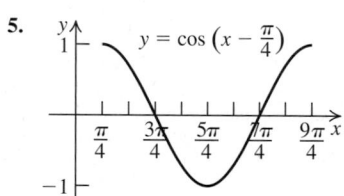

6. Amplitude = $\dfrac{1}{3}$, period = 5π, phase shift = $-\dfrac{\pi}{6}$.

7.
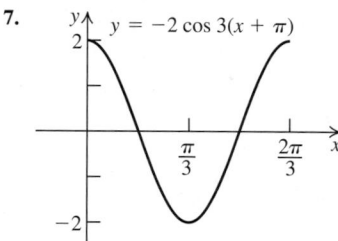

8. a. Period = π, phase shift = $-\dfrac{\pi}{8}$.

   b. Period = 2, phase shift = $\dfrac{1}{\pi}$.

9.

10.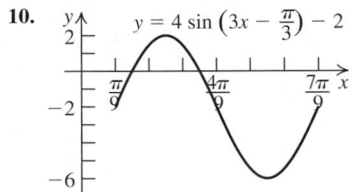
$y = 4 \sin \left(3x - \frac{\pi}{3}\right) - 2$

11.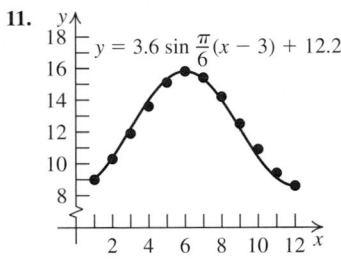
$y = 3.6 \sin \frac{\pi}{6}(x - 3) + 12.2$

12. $y = -4\cos\frac{2\pi}{3}t$

A Exercises: Basic Skills and Concepts

1.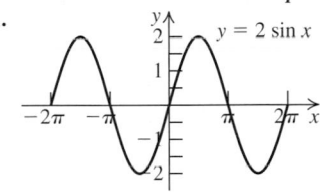
$y = 2 \sin x$

2.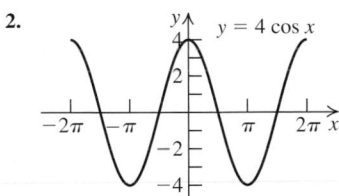
$y = 4 \cos x$

3.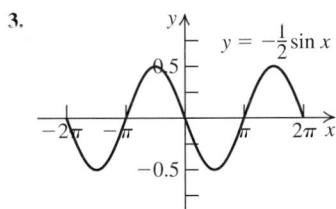
$y = -\frac{1}{2} \sin x$

4.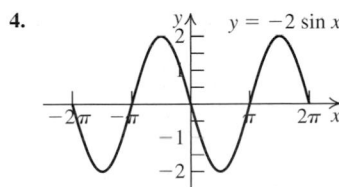
$y = -2 \sin x$

5.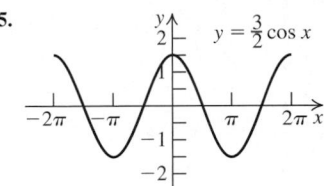
$y = \frac{3}{2} \cos x$

6.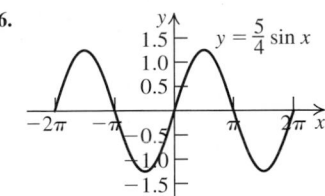
$y = \frac{5}{4} \sin x$

7.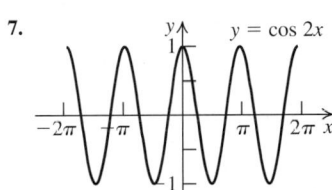
$y = \cos 2x$

8.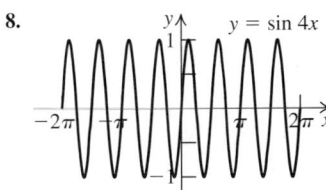
$y = \sin 4x$

9.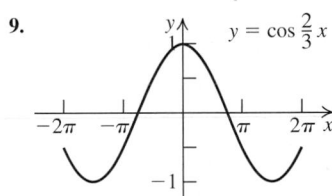
$y = \cos \frac{2}{3}x$

10.
$y = \sin \frac{4}{3}x$

11.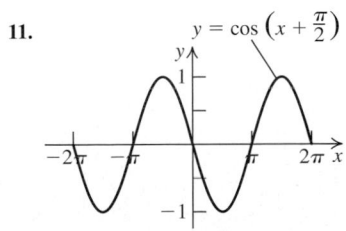
$y = \cos \left(x + \frac{\pi}{2}\right)$

12.

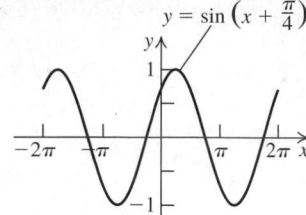

$y = \sin\left(x + \frac{\pi}{4}\right)$

13.

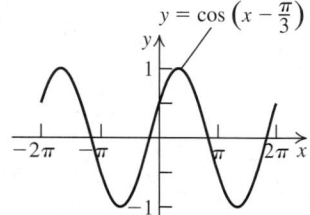

$y = \cos\left(x - \frac{\pi}{3}\right)$

14.

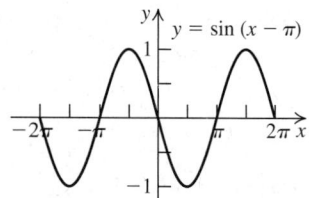

$y = \sin(x - \pi)$

15.

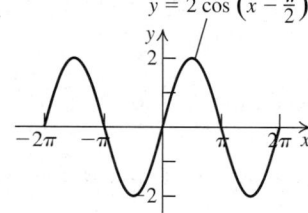

$y = 2\cos\left(x - \frac{\pi}{2}\right)$

16.

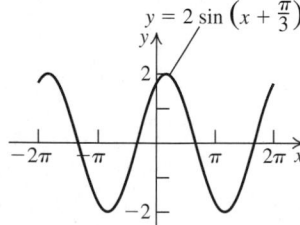

$y = 2\sin\left(x + \frac{\pi}{3}\right)$

17.

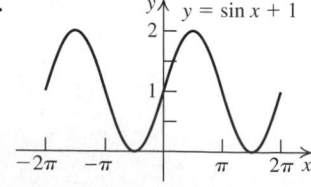

$y = \sin x + 1$

18.

$y = \cos x - 2$

19.

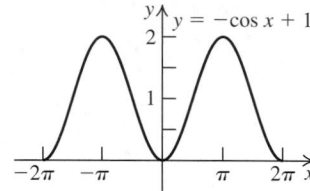

$y = -\cos x + 1$

20.

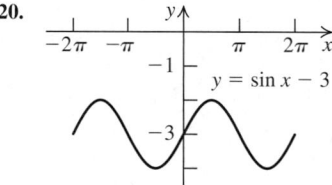

$y = \sin x - 3$

21. Amplitude $= 5$, period $= 2\pi$, phase shift $= \pi$

22. Amplitude $= 3$, period $= 2\pi$, phase shift $= \frac{\pi}{8}$

23. Amplitude $= 7$, period $= \frac{2\pi}{9}$, phase shift $= -\frac{\pi}{6}$

24. Amplitude $= 11$, period $= \frac{\pi}{4}$, phase shift $= -\frac{\pi}{3}$

25. Amplitude $= 6$, period $= 4\pi$, phase shift $= -2$

26. Amplitude $= 8$, period $= 10\pi$, phase shift $= -9$

27. Amplitude $= 0.9$, period $= 8\pi$, phase shift $= \frac{\pi}{4}$

28. Amplitude $= \sqrt{5}$, period $= 2$, phase shift $= -1$

29.

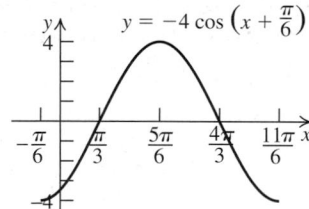

$y = -4\cos\left(x + \frac{\pi}{6}\right)$

30.

$y = -3\sin\left(x - \frac{\pi}{6}\right)$

31.

$$y = \frac{5}{2}\sin 2\left(x - \frac{\pi}{4}\right)$$

32.

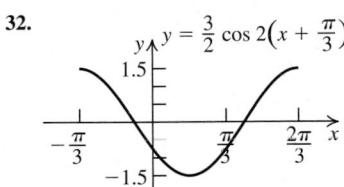
$$y = \frac{3}{2}\cos 2\left(x + \frac{\pi}{3}\right)$$

33.

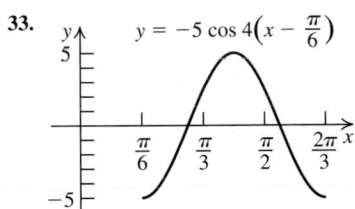
$$y = -5\cos 4\left(x - \frac{\pi}{6}\right)$$

34.

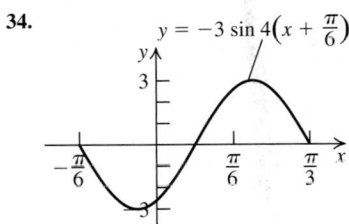
$$y = -3\sin 4\left(x + \frac{\pi}{6}\right)$$

35.

$$y = \frac{1}{2}\sin 4\left(x + \frac{\pi}{4}\right) + 2$$

36.

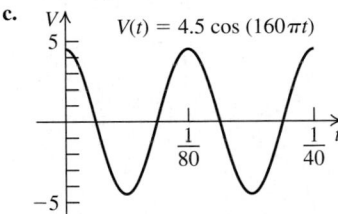
$$y = -\frac{1}{2}\cos 2\left(x - \frac{\pi}{2}\right) - 3$$

37. $y = 4\cos 2\left(x + \frac{\pi}{6}\right)$; period $= \pi$; phase shift $= -\frac{\pi}{6}$

38. $y = 5\sin 3\left(x + \frac{\pi}{6}\right)$; period $= \frac{2\pi}{3}$; phase shift $= -\frac{\pi}{6}$

39. $y = -\frac{3}{2}\sin 2\left(x - \frac{\pi}{2}\right)$; period $= \pi$; phase shift $= \frac{\pi}{2}$

40. $y = -2\cos 5\left(x - \frac{\pi}{20}\right)$; period $= \frac{2\pi}{5}$; phase shift $= \frac{\pi}{20}$

41. $y = 3\cos \pi x$; period $= 2$; phase shift $= 0$

42. $y = \sin \frac{\pi}{3}(x)$; period $= 6$; phase shift $= 0$

43. $y = \frac{1}{2}\cos \frac{\pi}{4}(x + 1)$; period $= 8$; phase shift $= -1$

44. $y = -\sin \frac{\pi}{6}(x + 1)$; period $= 12$; phase shift $= -1$

45. $y = 2\sin \pi\left(x + \frac{3}{\pi}\right)$; period $= 2$; phase shift $= -\frac{3}{\pi}$

46. $y = -\cos \pi\left(x - \frac{1}{4\pi}\right)$; period $= 2$; phase shift $= \frac{1}{4\pi}$

B Exercises: Applying the Concepts

47. a. period $= \frac{1}{70}$. The pulse is the frequency of the function; it says how many times the heart beats in one minute.

b.

$p(t) = 20\sin(140\pi t) + 122$

c. $\frac{142}{102}$

48. a. amplitude $= 4.5$; period $= \frac{1}{80}$

b. frequency $= 80$

c.
$V(t) = 4.5\cos(160\pi t)$

49. a. amplitude $= 156$; period $= \frac{1}{60}$

b. frequency $= 60$

c.
$V(t) = 156\sin(120\pi t)$

50. $y = -5\cos\left(\dfrac{\pi}{5}t\right)$

51. c. $\dfrac{\pi}{2}$ years ≈ 1.57 years

52. a.

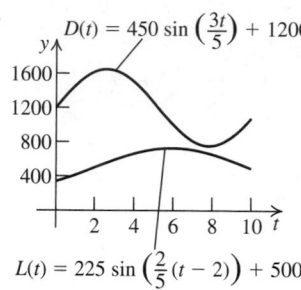

$L(t) = 225 \sin\left(\dfrac{2}{5}(t-2)\right) + 500$

b. As the lion population increases, the deer population decreases. As the lion population decreases, the deer population increases.

53. $y = 4.35\sin\dfrac{\pi}{6}(x-3) + 12.25$

54. $y = 2.65\sin\dfrac{\pi}{6}(x-3) + 12.15$

55. a. $y = 25.5\sin\dfrac{\pi}{6}(x-4) + 44.5$

b.

c. January $= f(1) = 19$; April $= f(4) = 44.5$; July $= f(7) = 70$; October $= f(10) = 44.5$. The computed values are very close to the measured values.

56. a. $y = 21.5\sin\dfrac{\pi}{6}(x-4) + 61.5$

b.

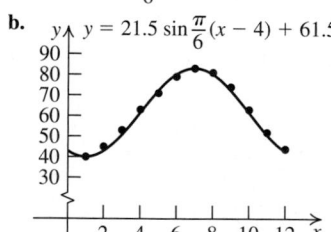

c. January $= f(1) = 40$; April $= f(4) = 61.5$; July $= f(7) = 83$; October $= f(10) = 61.5$.

C Exercises: Beyond the Basics

57.

58.

59.

60.

61.

62.

63.

64.

$y = -3\cos\left(-\dfrac{x}{\pi} + \dfrac{1}{2}\right) + 3$

65.

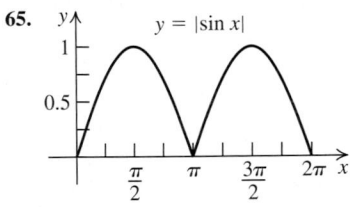

$y = |\sin x|$

66.

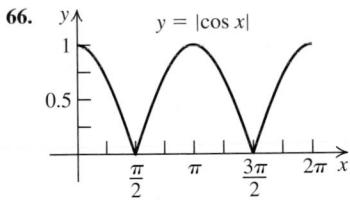

$y = |\cos x|$

67.

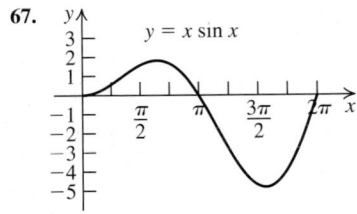

$y = x \sin x$

68.

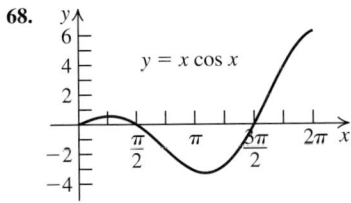

$y = x \cos x$

69.

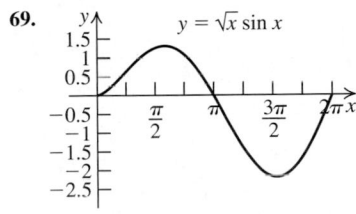

$y = \sqrt{x}\, \sin x$

70.

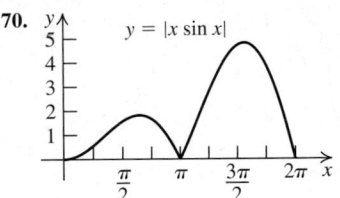

$y = |x \sin x|$

71.

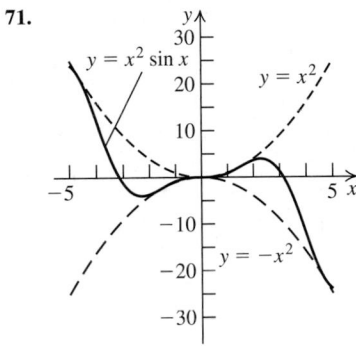

$y = x^2 \sin x$ $y = x^2$ $y = -x^2$

Section 5.5

Practice Problems

1.

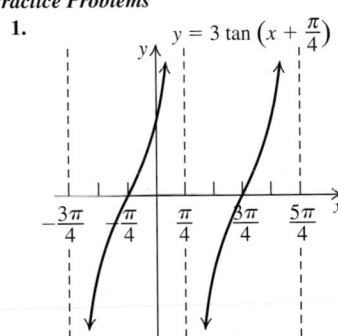

$y = 3\tan\left(x + \dfrac{\pi}{4}\right)$

2.

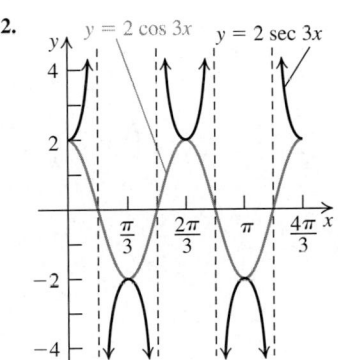

$y = 2\cos 3x$ $y = 2\sec 3x$

3. [5.1, 2.6]

A Exercises: Basic Skills and Concepts

1.

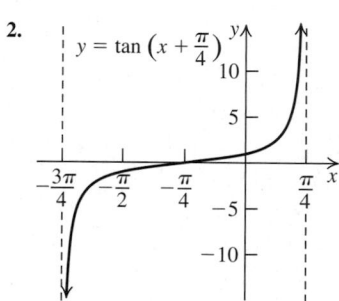

$y = \tan\left(x - \frac{\pi}{4}\right)$

2.

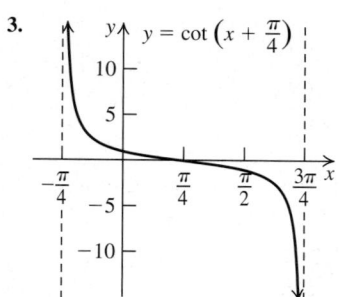

$y = \tan\left(x + \frac{\pi}{4}\right)$

3.

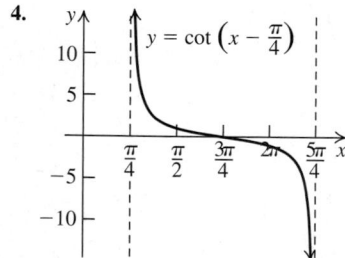

$y = \cot\left(x + \frac{\pi}{4}\right)$

4.

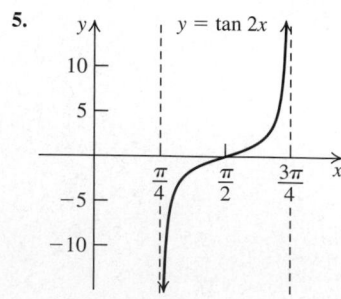

$y = \cot\left(x - \frac{\pi}{4}\right)$

5.

$y = \tan 2x$

6.

$y = \tan\frac{x}{2}$

7.

$y = \cot\frac{x}{2}$

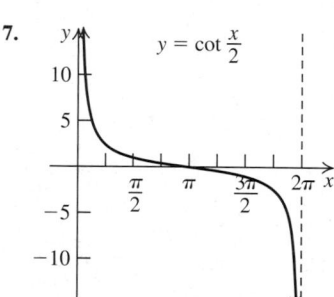

8.

$y = \cot 2x$

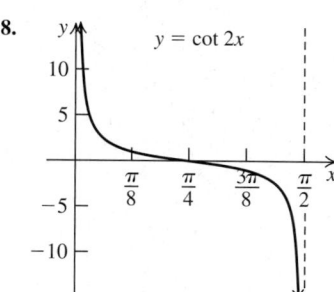

9.

$y = -\tan x$

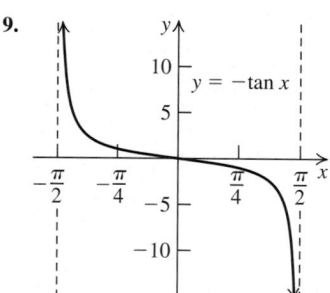

10.

$y = -\cot x$

11.

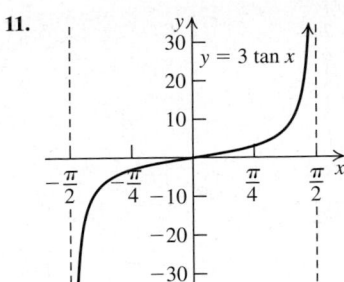

$y = 3 \tan x$

12.

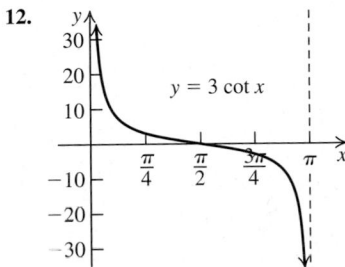

$y = 3 \cot x$

13.

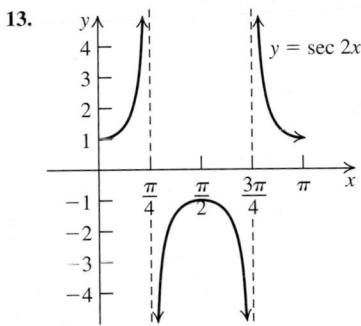

$y = \sec 2x$

14.

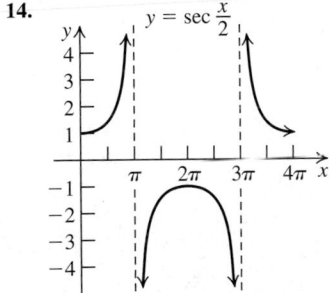

$y = \sec \dfrac{x}{2}$

15.

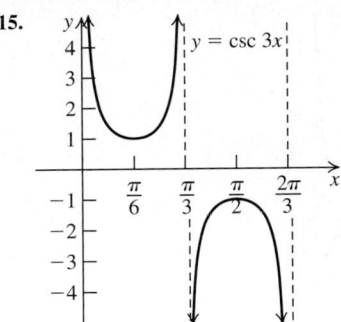

$y = \csc 3x$

16.

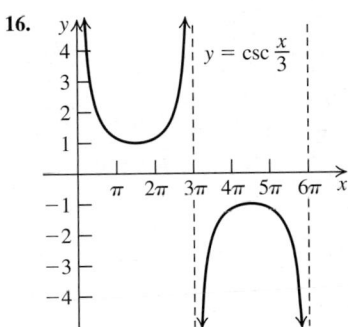

$y = \csc \dfrac{x}{3}$

17.

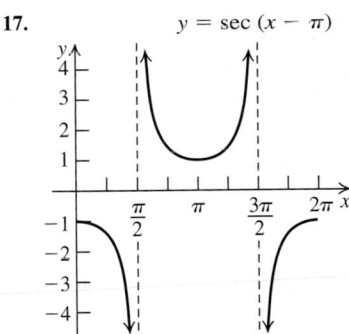

$y = \sec (x - \pi)$

18.

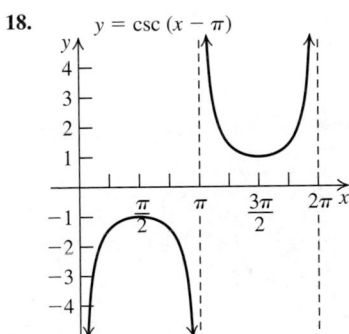

$y = \csc (x - \pi)$

19.

$y = \tan 2\left(x + \frac{\pi}{2}\right)$

20.

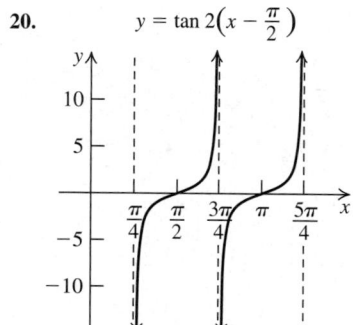

$y = \tan 2\left(x - \frac{\pi}{2}\right)$

21.

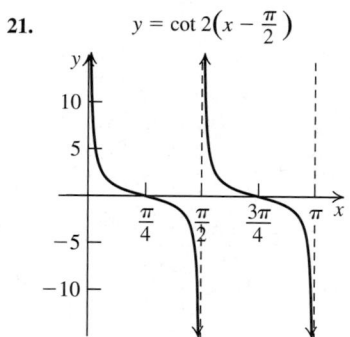

$y = \cot 2\left(x - \frac{\pi}{2}\right)$

22.

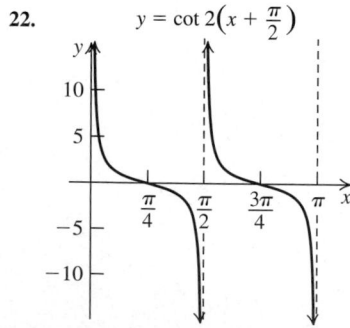

$y = \cot 2\left(x + \frac{\pi}{2}\right)$

23.

$y = \tan \frac{1}{2}(x + 2\pi)$

24.

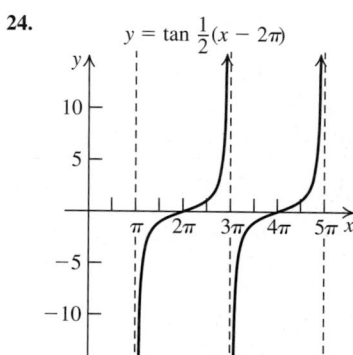

$y = \tan \frac{1}{2}(x - 2\pi)$

25.

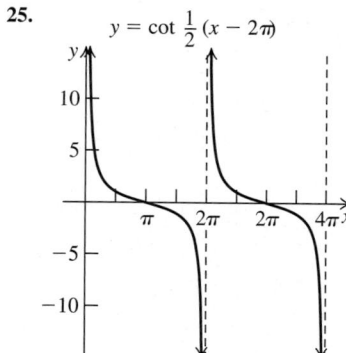

$y = \cot \frac{1}{2}(x - 2\pi)$

26.

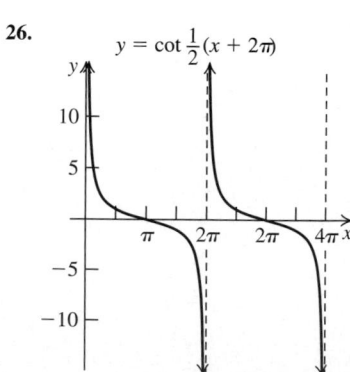

$y = \cot \frac{1}{2}(x + 2\pi)$

27. $y = -\frac{1}{2}\tan\frac{x}{2}$

28. $y = -\frac{1}{2}\cot\frac{x}{2}$

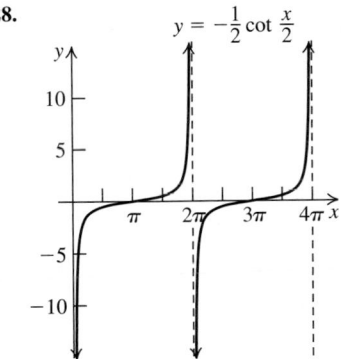

29. $y = \sec 4\left(x - \frac{\pi}{4}\right)$

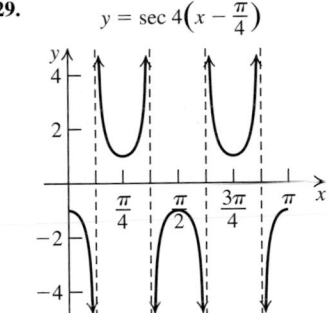

30. $y = \sec\frac{1}{2}\left(x - \frac{\pi}{2}\right)$

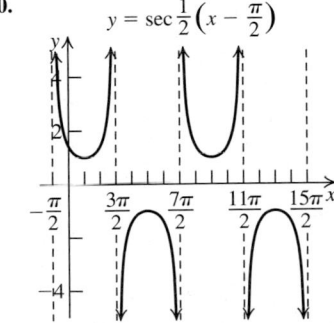

31. $y = -2\sec 3x$

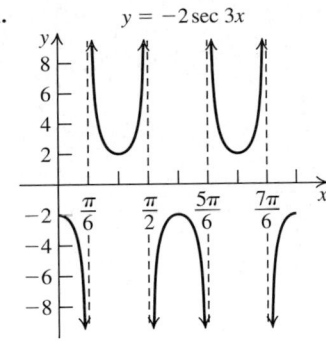

32. $y = -3\csc 4x$

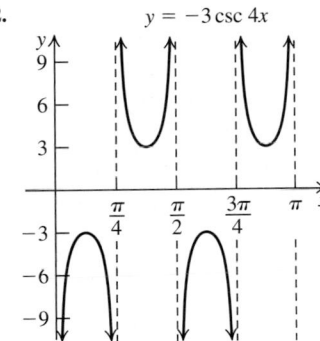

33. $y = 3\csc\left(x + \frac{\pi}{2}\right)$

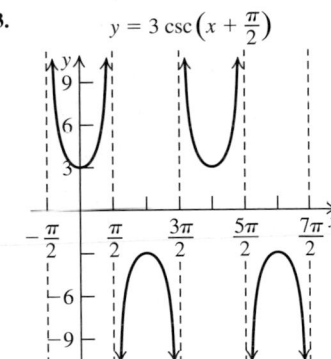

34. $y = 3\sec 2\left(x - \frac{\pi}{6}\right)$

35.

$$y = \tan \frac{2}{3}\left(x - \frac{\pi}{2}\right)$$

36.

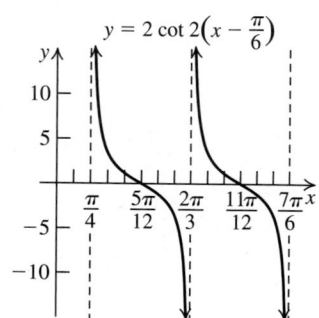

$$y = 2 \cot 2\left(x - \frac{\pi}{6}\right)$$

37.

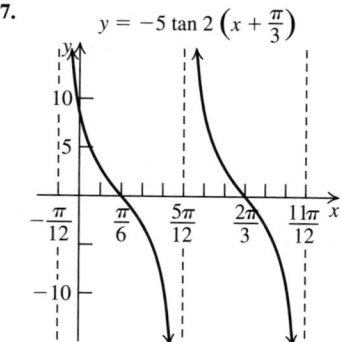

$$y = -5 \tan 2\left(x + \frac{\pi}{3}\right)$$

38.

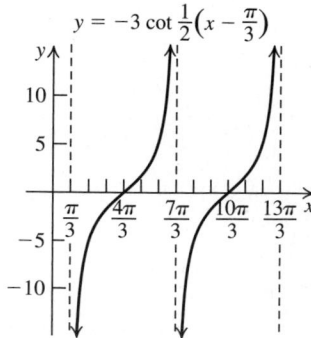

$$y = -3 \cot \frac{1}{2}\left(x - \frac{\pi}{3}\right)$$

39.

$$y = \frac{1}{3} \cot 2\,(x - \pi)$$

40.

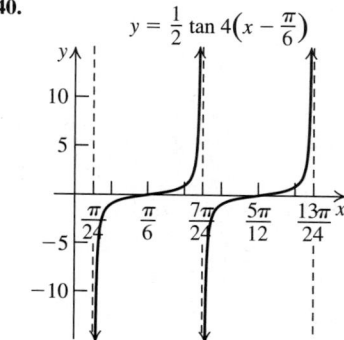

$$y = \frac{1}{2} \tan 4\left(x - \frac{\pi}{6}\right)$$

B Exercises: Applying the Concepts

41. a.

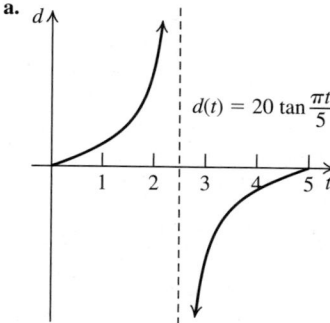

$$d(t) = 20 \tan \frac{\pi t}{5}$$

b. The light is pointing parallel to the wall.

C Exercises: Beyond the Basics

46.

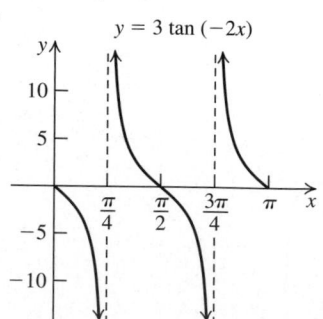

$$y = 3 \tan (-2x)$$

47. $y = 2 \cot(-3x)$

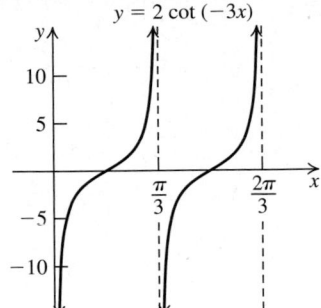

48. $y = -2 \sec\left(-\frac{x}{2}\right)$

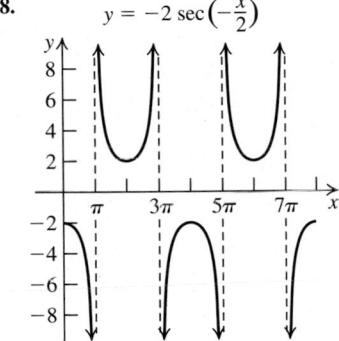

49. $y = -\frac{1}{2} \csc\left(-\frac{x}{5}\right)$

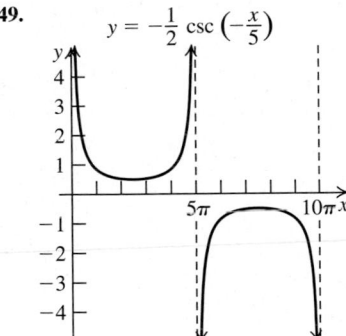

50. $y = \cot(\pi - x)$

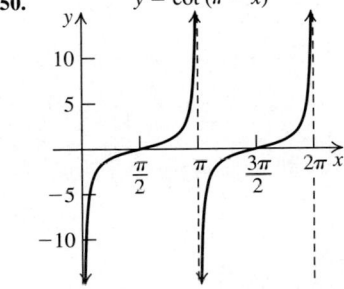

51. $y = -\tan\left(\frac{\pi}{2} - x\right)$

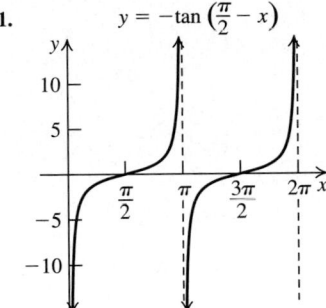

52. $y = -\sec(\pi - 4x)$

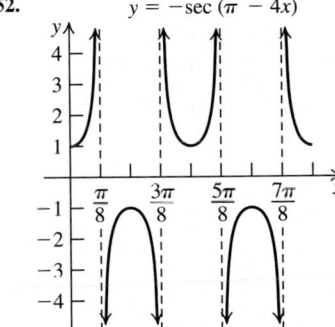

53. $y = 2 \sec(\pi - 2x)$

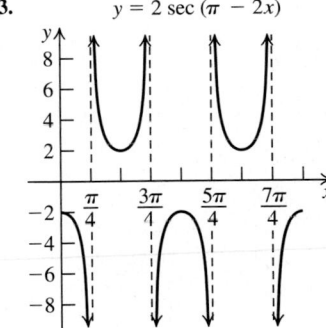

54. $y = 2 \tan\left(\frac{\pi}{2} - 2x\right) + 1$

55.

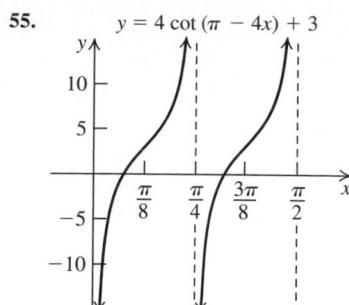

$y = 4 \cot(\pi - 4x) + 3$

Section 5.6

Practice Problems

1. a. $-\dfrac{\pi}{3}$ **b.** $-\dfrac{\pi}{2}$ **2. a.** $\dfrac{3\pi}{4}$ **b.** $\dfrac{\pi}{3}$ **3.** $\dfrac{\pi}{6}$ **4.** $\dfrac{\pi}{3}$

5. a. 1.3490 **b.** 0.2898 **6. a.** 53.13° **b.** 4.41°

7. $-\dfrac{\pi}{2}$ **8.** $\dfrac{2\sqrt{2}}{3}$ **9.** $B = 34°, a \approx 21.4, b \approx 14.4$

10. $A \approx 48.4°, B \approx 41.6°, a \approx 27.6$ **11.** 80°

A Exercises: Basic Skills and Concepts

2. $\dfrac{\pi}{2}$ **9.** $\dfrac{\pi}{3}$ **10.** $\dfrac{\pi}{4}$ **13.** $\dfrac{3\pi}{4}$ **14.** $\dfrac{\pi}{4}$ **17.** $\dfrac{\pi}{6}$ **18.** $\dfrac{5\pi}{6}$

21. $\dfrac{2\pi}{3}$ **22.** $\dfrac{\pi}{4}$ **55.** $\dfrac{4\sqrt{17}}{17}$ **56.** $\dfrac{\sqrt{10}}{10}$ **58.** $-\dfrac{\sqrt{3}}{3}$

C Exercises: Beyond the Basics

75.

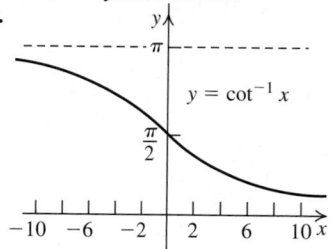

$y = \cot^{-1} x$

76.

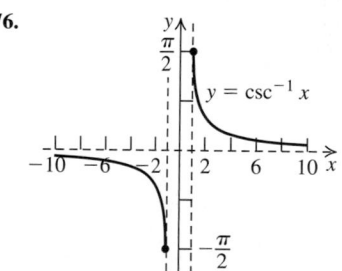

$y = \csc^{-1} x$

77.

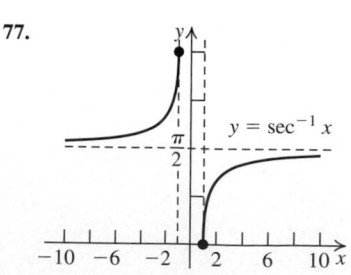

$y = \sec^{-1} x$

Chapter 5 Review Exercises

1.

240°

2.

−150°

3.

$-\dfrac{2\pi}{3}$

4.

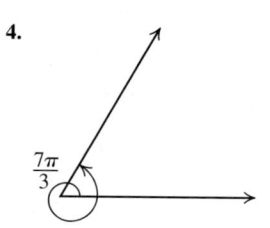

$\dfrac{7\pi}{3}$

5. $\dfrac{\pi}{9}$ **6.** $\dfrac{\pi}{5}$ **7.** $-\dfrac{\pi}{3}$

15. $\sin\theta = \dfrac{\sqrt{5}}{5}, \cos\theta = \dfrac{2\sqrt{5}}{5}, \tan\theta = \dfrac{1}{2}, \cot\theta = 2,$

$\sec\theta = \dfrac{\sqrt{5}}{2}, \csc\theta = \sqrt{5}$

16. $\sin\theta = \dfrac{3\sqrt{58}}{58}, \cos\theta = \dfrac{7\sqrt{58}}{58}, \tan\theta = \dfrac{3}{7}, \cot\theta = \dfrac{7}{3},$

$\sec\theta = \dfrac{\sqrt{58}}{7}, \csc\theta = \dfrac{\sqrt{58}}{3}$

17. $\sin\theta = \dfrac{\sqrt{77}}{9}, \tan\theta = \dfrac{\sqrt{77}}{2}, \cot\theta = \dfrac{2\sqrt{77}}{77}, \sec\theta = \dfrac{9}{2},$

$\csc\theta = \dfrac{9\sqrt{77}}{77}$

18. $\cos\theta = \dfrac{2\sqrt{6}}{5}, \tan\theta = \dfrac{\sqrt{6}}{12}, \cot\theta = 2\sqrt{6}, \sec\theta = \dfrac{5\sqrt{6}}{12}, \csc\theta = 5$

19. $\sin\theta = \dfrac{5\sqrt{34}}{34}, \cos\theta = \dfrac{3\sqrt{34}}{34}, \cot\theta = \dfrac{3}{5}, \sec\theta = \dfrac{\sqrt{34}}{3},$

$\csc\theta = \dfrac{\sqrt{34}}{5}$

20. $\sin\theta = \dfrac{4\sqrt{41}}{41}, \cos\theta = \dfrac{5\sqrt{41}}{41}, \tan\theta = \dfrac{4}{5}, \sec\theta = \dfrac{\sqrt{41}}{5},$

$\csc\theta = \dfrac{\sqrt{41}}{4}$

21. $\sin\theta = \dfrac{4\sqrt{17}}{17}$, $\cos\theta = \dfrac{\sqrt{17}}{17}$, $\tan\theta = 4$, $\cot\theta = \dfrac{1}{4}$, $\sec\theta = \sqrt{17}$, $\csc\theta = \dfrac{\sqrt{17}}{4}$

22. $\sin\theta = \dfrac{7\sqrt{58}}{58}$, $\cos\theta = -\dfrac{3\sqrt{58}}{58}$, $\tan\theta = -\dfrac{7}{3}$, $\cot\theta = -\dfrac{3}{7}$, $\sec\theta = -\dfrac{\sqrt{58}}{3}$, $\csc\theta = \dfrac{\sqrt{58}}{7}$

23. $\sin\theta = \dfrac{2}{3}$, $\cos\theta = -\dfrac{\sqrt{5}}{3}$, $\tan\theta = -\dfrac{2\sqrt{5}}{5}$, $\cot\theta = -\dfrac{\sqrt{5}}{2}$, $\sec\theta = -\dfrac{3\sqrt{5}}{5}$, $\csc\theta = \dfrac{3}{2}$

24. $\sin\theta = -\dfrac{\sqrt{6}}{3}$, $\cos\theta = -\dfrac{\sqrt{3}}{3}$, $\tan\theta = \sqrt{2}$, $\cot\theta = \dfrac{\sqrt{2}}{2}$, $\sec\theta = -\sqrt{3}$, $\csc\theta = -\dfrac{\sqrt{6}}{2}$

29. $\sin\theta = -\dfrac{3}{5}$, $\tan\theta = \dfrac{3}{4}$, $\cot\theta = \dfrac{4}{3}$, $\sec\theta = -\dfrac{5}{4}$, $\csc\theta = -\dfrac{5}{3}$

30. $\sin\theta = -\dfrac{5}{13}$, $\cos\theta = \dfrac{12}{13}$, $\cot\theta = -\dfrac{12}{5}$, $\sec\theta = \dfrac{13}{12}$, $\csc\theta = -\dfrac{13}{5}$

31. $\cos\theta = -\dfrac{4}{5}$, $\tan\theta = -\dfrac{3}{4}$, $\cot\theta = -\dfrac{4}{3}$, $\sec\theta = -\dfrac{5}{4}$, $\csc\theta = \dfrac{5}{3}$

32. $\sin\theta = -\dfrac{4}{5}$, $\cos\theta = -\dfrac{3}{5}$, $\tan\theta = \dfrac{4}{3}$, $\cot\theta = \dfrac{3}{4}$, $\sec\theta = -\dfrac{5}{3}$

33. $-\dfrac{\sqrt{3}}{2}$

34. $\dfrac{\sqrt{3}}{2}$

35. $\dfrac{\sqrt{3}}{3}$

37.

38.

39.

40.

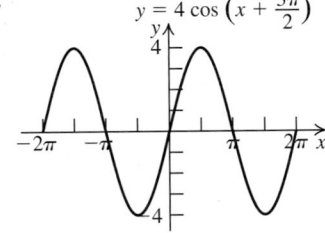

41. Amplitude = 14, period = π, phase shift = $-\dfrac{\pi}{14}$

42. Amplitude = 21, period = $\dfrac{\pi}{4}$, phase shift = $-\dfrac{\pi}{72}$

43. Vertical stretch = 6, period = $\dfrac{\pi}{2}$, phase shift = $-\dfrac{\pi}{10}$

44. Vertical stretch = 11, period = $\dfrac{\pi}{3}$, phase shift = $-\dfrac{\pi}{72}$

45.

46.

47.

48.

$$y = -\cot 2\left(x + \frac{\pi}{4}\right)$$

49.

$$y = \frac{1}{2}\sec\frac{x}{2}$$

50.

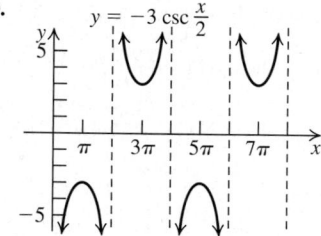

$$y = -3\csc\frac{x}{2}$$

66. $\dfrac{5\pi}{6}$

72. $y = 2.25\sin\dfrac{\pi}{6}(x - 4) + 12.05$ **73.** $y = -11\cos\dfrac{2\pi}{5}t$

74. $\theta = \tan^{-1}\dfrac{h}{200}$

Practice Test A

3. $\dfrac{2\sqrt{29}}{29}$ **7.** Quadrant II   **12.** Amplitude = 7, range = $[-7, 7]$

13. Amplitude = 19, period = $\dfrac{\pi}{6}$, phase shift = -3π

14. $y = -7\cos\left(\dfrac{\pi}{2}t\right)$

15.

$$y = -\cos\frac{x}{2}$$

16.

$$y = \sin 2(x - \pi)$$

17.

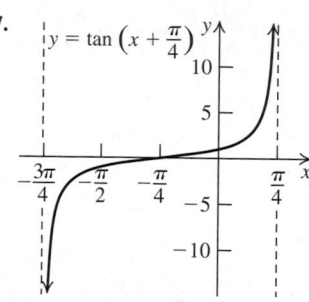

$$y = \tan\left(x + \frac{\pi}{4}\right)$$

19. $c \approx 6.9, A \approx 53.8°, B \approx 36.2°$

Cumulative Review Exercises (Chapters 1–5)

1. $5 \pm \dfrac{\sqrt{3}}{3}$ **4.** $y = -\dfrac{2}{3}x + 1$

6. $f(x) = x^2$

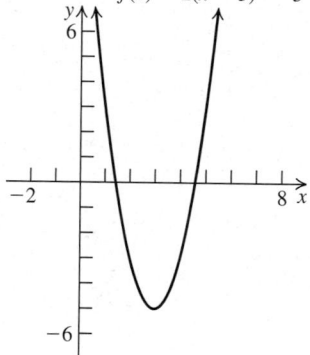

$$f(x) = 2(x - 3)^2 - 5$$

7.

$$f(x) = 4e^x + 1$$

9. a. $f^{-1}(x) = \dfrac{x}{3} - \dfrac{7}{3}$

b. The function does not have an inverse.

12. a. $\log x + \dfrac{1}{3}\log y - \dfrac{1}{3}\log z$

b. $\ln 1.4 + 4\ln x - \dfrac{1}{2}\ln y$

13.

$$f(x) = \begin{cases} -\ln x & \text{if } x > 0 \\ \ln |x| & \text{if } x < 0 \end{cases}$$

15. $\pm 1,\ \pm 2,\ \pm 3,\ \pm 6,\ \pm\dfrac{1}{2},\ \pm\dfrac{3}{2}$

16. a. $\sin\theta = \dfrac{2\sqrt{10}}{7},\ \tan\theta = \dfrac{2\sqrt{10}}{3},\ \cot\theta = \dfrac{3\sqrt{10}}{20},\ \sec\theta = \dfrac{7}{3},$

$\csc\theta - \dfrac{7\sqrt{10}}{20}$

b. $\cos\theta = \dfrac{3\sqrt{13}}{11},\ \tan\theta = \dfrac{2\sqrt{13}}{39},\ \cot\theta = \dfrac{3\sqrt{13}}{2},\ \sec\theta = \dfrac{11\sqrt{13}}{39},$

$\csc\theta = \dfrac{11}{2}$

17. a. $\sin\theta = \dfrac{3}{5},\ \tan\theta = -\dfrac{3}{4},\ \cot\theta = -\dfrac{4}{3},\ \sec\theta = -\dfrac{5}{4},\ \csc\theta = \dfrac{5}{3}$

b. $\sin\theta = \dfrac{12}{13},\ \cos 0 = -\dfrac{5}{13},\ \tan\theta = \dfrac{12}{5},\ \sec\theta = -\dfrac{13}{5},$

$\csc\theta = -\dfrac{13}{12}$

18. a.

$y = -\dfrac{1}{2}\cos(x + \pi)$

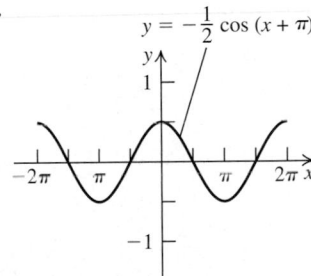

b.

$y = -5\sin\left(x + \dfrac{5\pi}{3}\right)$

CHAPTER 6

Section 6.1

Practice Problems

1. $-\dfrac{3}{4}$

2. $\sin\theta = \dfrac{\sqrt{2}}{2},\ \cos\theta = -\dfrac{\sqrt{2}}{2},\ \cot\theta = -1,\ \sec\theta = -\sqrt{2},\ \csc\theta = \sqrt{2}$

3. $\dfrac{2}{\sin x}$

4. The equation is not an identity. Let $x = 30°$.

A Exercises: Basic Skills and Concepts

7. $\tan x = -\dfrac{4}{3},\ \cot x = -\dfrac{3}{4},\ \sec x = -\dfrac{5}{3},\ \csc x = \dfrac{5}{4}$

8. $\tan x = -\dfrac{4}{3},\ \cot x = -\dfrac{3}{4},\ \sec x = \dfrac{5}{3},\ \csc x = -\dfrac{5}{4}$

9. $\tan x = \dfrac{\sqrt{2}}{2},\ \cot x = \sqrt{2},\ \sec x = \dfrac{\sqrt{6}}{2},\ \csc x = \sqrt{3}$

10. $\tan x = -\dfrac{\sqrt{2}}{2},\ \cot x = -\sqrt{2},\ \sec x = -\dfrac{\sqrt{6}}{2},\ \csc x - \sqrt{3}$

11. $\sin x = -\dfrac{\sqrt{5}}{5},\ \cos x = -\dfrac{2\sqrt{5}}{5},\ \cot x = 2,\ \csc = -\sqrt{5}$

12. $\sin x = \dfrac{\sqrt{5}}{5},\ \cos x = \dfrac{2\sqrt{5}}{5},\ \cot x = 2,\ \csc = \sqrt{5}$

13. $\sin x = \dfrac{1}{3},\ \cos x = \dfrac{2\sqrt{2}}{3},\ \tan x = \dfrac{\sqrt{2}}{4},\ \sec x = \dfrac{3\sqrt{2}}{4}$

14. $\sin x = \dfrac{1}{3},\ \cos x = -\dfrac{2\sqrt{2}}{3},\ \tan x = -\dfrac{\sqrt{2}}{4},\ \sec x = -\dfrac{3\sqrt{2}}{4}$

15. $\cos x = -\dfrac{12}{13},\ \tan x = \dfrac{5}{12},\ \sec x = -\dfrac{13}{12},\ \csc x = -\dfrac{13}{5}$

16. $\cos x = \dfrac{12}{13},\ \tan x = -\dfrac{5}{12},\ \sec x = \dfrac{13}{12},\ \csc x = -\dfrac{13}{5}$

17. $\sin x = -\dfrac{2\sqrt{2}}{3},\ \cos x = \dfrac{1}{3},\ \tan x = -2\sqrt{2},\ \cot x = -\dfrac{\sqrt{2}}{4},$

$\csc x = -\dfrac{3\sqrt{2}}{4}$

18. $\sin x = \dfrac{2\sqrt{5}}{5},\ \cos x = -\dfrac{\sqrt{5}}{5},\ \cot x = -\dfrac{1}{2},\ \sec x = -\sqrt{5},$

$\csc x = \dfrac{\sqrt{5}}{2}$

C Exercises: Beyond the Basics

85. $\cos\theta = \dfrac{2ab}{a^2 + b^2},\ \cot\theta = \dfrac{2ab}{a^2 - b^2};\ \theta$ is in Quadrant 1.

86. $\cos\theta = \dfrac{2ab}{a^2 + b^2},\ \cot\theta = \dfrac{2ab}{a^2 - b^2};\ \theta$ is in Quadrant 4.

Section 6.2

Practice Problems

1. a. $x = \dfrac{\pi}{2} + 2n\pi$ **b.** $x = 0 + 2n\pi$ **c.** $x = \dfrac{\pi}{4} + n\pi$

2. a. $x \approx 48.2°,\ x \approx 311.8°$ **b.** $x \approx \pi - 1.1071,\ x \approx 2\pi - 1.1071$

3. $x \approx 105.5°,\ x \approx 314.5°$ **4.** $\left\{\dfrac{\pi}{12}, \dfrac{5\pi}{12}, \dfrac{13\pi}{12}, \dfrac{17\pi}{12}\right\}$

5. $x = \dfrac{\pi}{3}$ **6.** $x = \dfrac{\pi}{2},\ x = \dfrac{5\pi}{6},\ x = \dfrac{11\pi}{6}$

7. $\theta = 0,\ \theta = \dfrac{2\pi}{3},\ \theta = \dfrac{4\pi}{3}$ **8.** $\theta = \dfrac{\pi}{6},\ \theta = \dfrac{\pi}{2},\ \theta = \dfrac{5\pi}{6}$

9. $\theta = \dfrac{\pi}{3}$

10. 5.44 days and 24.06 days

A Exercises: Basic Skills and Concepts

1. $\dfrac{\pi}{2} + 2n\pi, \dfrac{3\pi}{2} + 2n\pi$ **2.** $0 + 2n\pi, \pi + 2n\pi$ **3.** $\dfrac{3\pi}{4} + n\pi$

4. $\dfrac{3\pi}{4} + n\pi$ **5.** $\dfrac{\pi}{4} + 2n\pi, \dfrac{7\pi}{4} + 2n\pi$ **6.** $\dfrac{\pi}{3} + 2n\pi, \dfrac{2\pi}{3} + 2n\pi$

7. $\dfrac{\pi}{6} + n\pi$ **9.** $\dfrac{2\pi}{3} + 2n\pi, \dfrac{4\pi}{3} + 2n\pi$ **10.** $\dfrac{4\pi}{3} + 2n\pi, \dfrac{5\pi}{3} + 2n\pi$

13. $210° + 360°n, 330° + 360°n$ **14.** $60° + 360°n, 300° + 360°n$

17. $60° + 360°n, 120° + 360°n$ **18.** $150° + 360°n, 210° + 360°n$

19. $60° + 360°n, 300° + 360°n$ **20.** $210° + 360°n, 330° + 360°n$

23. $\{82.0°, 278.0°\}$ **24.** $\{192.8°, 347.2°\}$ **25.** $\{131.3°, 311.3°\}$

26. $\{159.5°, 339.5°\}$ **27.** $\{3.6652, 5.7596\}$ **28.** $\{0.3398, 2.8017\}$

29. $\{2.2143, 5.3559\}$ **30.** $\{1.2810, 5.0021\}$ **31.** $\{3.5531, 5.8717\}$

32. $\{1.4600, 4.8232\}$ **34.** $\left\{\dfrac{11\pi}{12}, \dfrac{19\pi}{12}\right\}$ **35.** $\left\{\dfrac{19\pi}{24}, \dfrac{35\pi}{24}\right\}$

36. $\left\{\dfrac{\pi}{24}, \dfrac{17\pi}{24}\right\}$ **41.** $\left\{\dfrac{\pi}{6}, \dfrac{5\pi}{6}, \dfrac{7\pi}{6}\right\}$

43. $\left\{\dfrac{\pi}{12}, \dfrac{7\pi}{12}, \dfrac{13\pi}{12}, \dfrac{19\pi}{12}\right\}$ **44.** $\left\{\dfrac{\pi}{6}, \dfrac{2\pi}{3}, \dfrac{7\pi}{6}, \dfrac{5\pi}{3}\right\}$

45. $\left\{\dfrac{\pi}{18}, \dfrac{5\pi}{18}, \dfrac{13\pi}{18}, \dfrac{17\pi}{18}, \dfrac{25\pi}{18}, \dfrac{29\pi}{18}\right\}$

46. $\left\{\dfrac{\pi}{18}, \dfrac{11\pi}{18}, \dfrac{13\pi}{18}, \dfrac{23\pi}{18}, \dfrac{25\pi}{18}, \dfrac{35\pi}{18}\right\}$ **51.** $\left\{\dfrac{\pi}{4}, \dfrac{3\pi}{2}, \dfrac{5\pi}{4}\right\}$

52. $\left\{\dfrac{\pi}{6}, \dfrac{2\pi}{3}, \dfrac{7\pi}{6}, \dfrac{4\pi}{3}\right\}$ **53.** $\left\{\dfrac{\pi}{6}, \dfrac{3\pi}{4}, \dfrac{5\pi}{6}, \dfrac{7\pi}{4}\right\}$ **54.** $\left\{\dfrac{\pi}{6}, \dfrac{2\pi}{3}, \dfrac{5\pi}{3}, \dfrac{11\pi}{6}\right\}$

55. $\left\{\dfrac{\pi}{6}, \dfrac{3\pi}{4}, \dfrac{5\pi}{6}, \dfrac{7\pi}{4}\right\}$ **56.** $\left\{\dfrac{\pi}{3}, \dfrac{2\pi}{3}, \dfrac{5\pi}{3}\right\}$ **57.** $\left\{\dfrac{\pi}{4}, \dfrac{7\pi}{6}, \dfrac{7\pi}{4}, \dfrac{11\pi}{6}\right\}$

58. $\left\{\dfrac{\pi}{4}, \dfrac{5\pi}{4}, \dfrac{7\pi}{4}\right\}$ **59.** $\left\{\dfrac{\pi}{6}, \dfrac{5\pi}{6}, \dfrac{7\pi}{6}, \dfrac{11\pi}{6}\right\}$ **60.** $\left\{\dfrac{\pi}{3}, \dfrac{2\pi}{3}, \dfrac{4\pi}{3}, \dfrac{5\pi}{3}\right\}$

61. $\left\{\dfrac{\pi}{4}, \dfrac{3\pi}{4}, \dfrac{5\pi}{4}, \dfrac{7\pi}{4}\right\}$ **62.** $\left\{\dfrac{\pi}{4}, \dfrac{3\pi}{4}, \dfrac{5\pi}{4}, \dfrac{7\pi}{4}\right\}$

63. $\left\{\dfrac{\pi}{3}, \dfrac{2\pi}{3}, \dfrac{4\pi}{3}, \dfrac{5\pi}{3}\right\}$ **64.** $\left\{\dfrac{\pi}{3}, \dfrac{2\pi}{3}, \dfrac{4\pi}{3}, \dfrac{5\pi}{3}\right\}$ **65.** $\left\{\dfrac{\pi}{2}, \dfrac{7\pi}{6}, \dfrac{11\pi}{6}\right\}$

66. $\left\{\dfrac{\pi}{3}, \dfrac{5\pi}{3}\right\}$ **67.** $\left\{\dfrac{\pi}{4}, \dfrac{5\pi}{4}\right\}$ **68.** $\left\{\dfrac{5\pi}{6}, \dfrac{11\pi}{6}\right\}$

69. $\left\{\dfrac{\pi}{6}, \dfrac{5\pi}{6}, \dfrac{7\pi}{6}, \dfrac{11\pi}{6}\right\}$ **70.** $\left\{\dfrac{\pi}{3}, \dfrac{2\pi}{3}, \dfrac{4\pi}{3}, \dfrac{5\pi}{3}\right\}$ **72.** $\left\{0, \dfrac{2\pi}{3}, \dfrac{4\pi}{3}\right\}$

73. $\left\{\dfrac{7\pi}{6}, \dfrac{3\pi}{2}, \dfrac{11\pi}{6}\right\}$ **74.** $\left\{\dfrac{\pi}{3}, \pi, \dfrac{5\pi}{3}\right\}$ **75.** $\left\{\dfrac{\pi}{3}, \dfrac{5\pi}{6}, \dfrac{4\pi}{3}, \dfrac{11\pi}{6}\right\}$

76. $\left\{\dfrac{\pi}{6}, \dfrac{\pi}{4}, \dfrac{7\pi}{6}, \dfrac{5\pi}{4}\right\}$ **77.** $\left\{\dfrac{\pi}{3}, \pi\right\}$ **79.** $\left\{\dfrac{\pi}{6}\right\}$ **80.** $\left\{\dfrac{\pi}{3}\right\}$

B Exercises: Applying the Concepts

81. $\dfrac{\pi}{3}$ **85.** $\dfrac{1}{3} + 4n$ sec, $\dfrac{5}{3} + 4n$ sec, n an integer

C Exercises: Beyond the Basics

91. $\left\{\dfrac{\pi}{4}, \dfrac{3\pi}{4}, \dfrac{5\pi}{4}, \dfrac{7\pi}{4}\right\}$ **92.** $\left\{0, \dfrac{\pi}{2}, \pi, \dfrac{3\pi}{2}\right\}$

93. $\{0.2618, 1.3090, 1.8326, 2.8798, 3.4034, 4.4506, 4.9742, 6.0214\}$

94. $\{0.1745, 0.8727, 1.2217, 1.9199, 2.2689, 2.9671, 3.3161, 4.0143,$
   $4.3633, 5.0615, 5.4105, 6.1087\}$

95. $\left\{\dfrac{\pi}{8}, \dfrac{3\pi}{8}, \dfrac{5\pi}{8}, \dfrac{7\pi}{8}, \dfrac{9\pi}{8}, \dfrac{11\pi}{8}, \dfrac{13\pi}{8}, \dfrac{15\pi}{8}\right\}$ **96.** $\left\{0, \dfrac{\pi}{2}, \pi, \dfrac{3\pi}{2}\right\}$

98. $\left\{\dfrac{\pi}{2}, \dfrac{3\pi}{2}, 0.3398, 2.8018\right\}$ **99.** $\left\{\dfrac{\pi}{6}, \dfrac{7\pi}{6}, \dfrac{11\pi}{6}\right\}$

100. $\left\{\dfrac{3\pi}{4}, \dfrac{7\pi}{6}, \dfrac{7\pi}{4}, \dfrac{11\pi}{6}\right\}$ **101.** $\left\{\dfrac{\pi}{8}, \dfrac{5\pi}{8}, \dfrac{9\pi}{8}, \dfrac{3\pi}{2}, \dfrac{13\pi}{8}\right\}$

102. $\left\{\dfrac{\pi}{6}, \dfrac{\pi}{3}, \dfrac{2\pi}{3}, \dfrac{7\pi}{6}, \dfrac{5\pi}{3}\right\}$

Critical Thinking

103. $\left\{\dfrac{\pi}{4}, \dfrac{5\pi}{4}\right\}$

Section 6.3

Practice Problems

1. $\dfrac{\sqrt{6} + \sqrt{2}}{4}$ **2.** $\dfrac{\sqrt{2} - \sqrt{6}}{4}$ **5.** $\dfrac{1}{2}$

6. $-\dfrac{63}{65}$ **8.** $y = 2\sin\left(x + \dfrac{\pi}{3}\right)$

9.

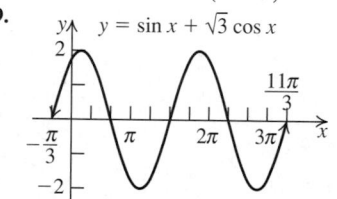
$y = \sin x + \sqrt{3}\cos x$

10. Amplitude $= 0.1\sqrt{5}$, period $= \dfrac{\pi}{200}$, frequency $= \dfrac{200}{\pi}$,
   phase shift ≈ -0.0028

A Exercises: Basic Skills and Concepts

1. $\dfrac{\sqrt{6} + \sqrt{2}}{4}$ **2.** $\dfrac{\sqrt{6} - \sqrt{2}}{4}$ **3.** $\dfrac{\sqrt{6} - \sqrt{2}}{4}$ **4.** $\dfrac{\sqrt{6} + \sqrt{2}}{4}$

5. $-\dfrac{\sqrt{6} + \sqrt{2}}{4}$ **6.** $\dfrac{\sqrt{6} - \sqrt{2}}{4}$ **45.** $\dfrac{56}{65}$ **46.** $\dfrac{16}{65}$ **47.** $\dfrac{63}{65}$

48. $\dfrac{33}{65}$ **49.** $\dfrac{16}{63}$ **50.** $\dfrac{56}{33}$ **51.** $\dfrac{2\sqrt{210} - 6}{35}$

52. $\dfrac{-4\sqrt{10} - 3\sqrt{21}}{35}$ **53.** $\dfrac{35\sqrt{210} - 105}{402}$

54. $\dfrac{35(3\sqrt{21} + 4\sqrt{10})}{29}$ **55.** $\dfrac{-4\sqrt{10} - 3\sqrt{21}}{2\sqrt{210} - 6}$

56. $\dfrac{3\sqrt{21} - 4\sqrt{10}}{2\sqrt{210} + 6}$

65. $y = \sqrt{2}\sin\left(x + \dfrac{\pi}{4}\right)$

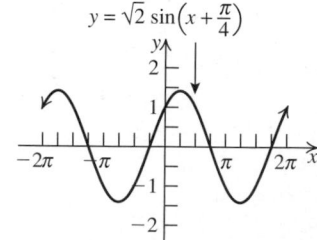
$y = \sqrt{2}\sin\left(x + \dfrac{\pi}{4}\right)$

66. $y = \sqrt{2} \sin\left(x - \dfrac{\pi}{4}\right)$

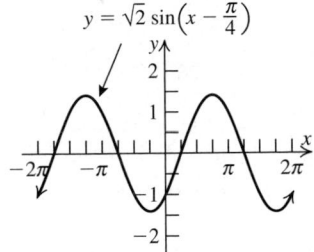

67. $y = 5 \sin(x + 0.927)$

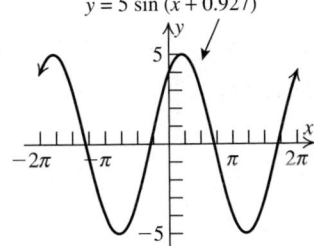

68. $y = 5 \sin(x - 0.644)$

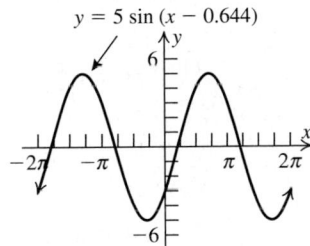

69. $y = 13 \sin(x - 1.176)$

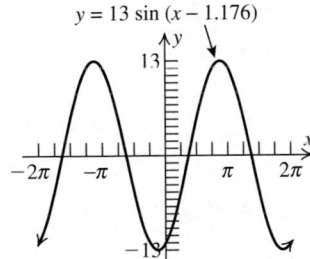

70. $y = 13 \sin(x + 0.395)$

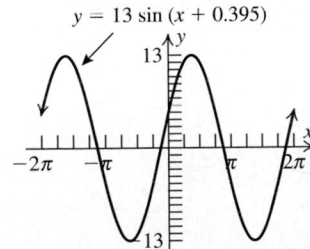

71. $y = \sqrt{10} \sin(x + 2.820)$

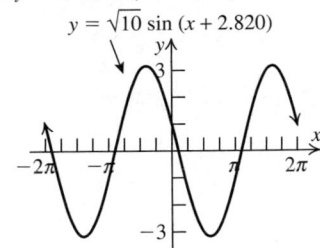

72. $y = 5 \sin(x + 2.498)$

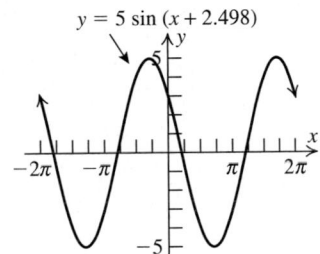

B Exercises: Applying the Concepts

74. $= \tan^{-1}(3/5) \approx 0.5404$ **76.** $\dfrac{\pi}{2}$

79. b. frequency $= \dfrac{1}{\pi}$; phase shift ≈ -0.6676

80. a. $A = \dfrac{\sqrt{13}}{6} \approx 0.6009$

   b. frequency $= \dfrac{3}{2\pi}$; phase shift ≈ -0.196

C Exercises: Beyond the Basics

95. $\dfrac{1}{2}$ **97.** $\dfrac{1}{2}$ **98.** $\dfrac{1}{2}$

Critical Thinking

107. 1

Section 6.4

Practice Problems

1. a. $-\dfrac{120}{169}$ **b.** $-\dfrac{119}{169}$ **c.** $\dfrac{120}{119}$ **2. a.** $\dfrac{\sqrt{3}}{2}$ **b.** $\dfrac{\sqrt{2}}{2}$

4. $\dfrac{3}{8} - \dfrac{1}{2}\cos 2x + \dfrac{1}{8}\cos 4x$ **5.** ≈ 99.8 watts

6. $\dfrac{\sqrt{2 + \sqrt{2}}}{2}$ **7.** $-\dfrac{\sqrt{26}}{26}$ **9.** $\left\{\dfrac{\pi}{6}, \dfrac{3\pi}{2}, \dfrac{5\pi}{6}\right\}$ **10.** $\{\pi\}$

A Exercises: Basic Skills and Concepts

1. a. $-\dfrac{24}{25}$ **b.** $\dfrac{7}{25}$ **c.** $-\dfrac{24}{7}$

2. a. $-\dfrac{120}{169}$ **b.** $-\dfrac{119}{169}$ **c.** $\dfrac{120}{119}$

3. a. $\dfrac{8}{17}$ **b.** $-\dfrac{15}{17}$ **c.** $-\dfrac{8}{15}$

4. a. $-\dfrac{2\sqrt{2}}{3}$ **b.** $-\dfrac{1}{3}$ **c.** $2\sqrt{2}$

5. a. $-\dfrac{4}{5}$ **b.** $-\dfrac{3}{5}$ **c.** $\dfrac{4}{3}$

6. a. $-\dfrac{7}{25}$ **b.** $\dfrac{24}{25}$ **c.** $-\dfrac{7}{24}$ **9.** $-\dfrac{\sqrt{3}}{2}$ **10.** $\dfrac{\sqrt{3}}{2}$

27. $\dfrac{\sqrt{2-\sqrt{3}}}{2}$ **28.** $\dfrac{\sqrt{2-\sqrt{2}}}{2}$ **29.** $\dfrac{\sqrt{2+\sqrt{2}}}{2}$

30. $\dfrac{\sqrt{2-\sqrt{2}}}{\sqrt{2+\sqrt{2}}}$ **31.** $-\dfrac{\sqrt{2+\sqrt{2}}}{2}$ **32.** $\dfrac{\sqrt{2-\sqrt{2}}}{2}$

33. $-\dfrac{\sqrt{2-\sqrt{2}}}{\sqrt{2+\sqrt{2}}}$ **34.** $-\sqrt{2}\sqrt{2-\sqrt{2}}$ **35.** $-\sqrt{2}-1$

36. $-\dfrac{\sqrt{2-\sqrt{2}}}{2}$ **37.** $-\dfrac{\sqrt{2+\sqrt{3}}}{2}$ **38.** $\dfrac{\sqrt{2+\sqrt{3}}}{\sqrt{2-\sqrt{3}}}$

39. a. $\dfrac{2\sqrt{5}}{5}$ **b.** $\dfrac{\sqrt{5}}{5}$ **c.** 2

40. a. $\dfrac{5\sqrt{26}}{26}$ **b.** $-\dfrac{\sqrt{26}}{26}$ **c.** -5

41. a. $\sqrt{\dfrac{13+3\sqrt{13}}{26}}$ **b.** $\sqrt{\dfrac{13-3\sqrt{13}}{26}}$ **c.** $\sqrt{\dfrac{13+3\sqrt{13}}{13-3\sqrt{13}}}$

42. a. $\dfrac{2\sqrt{5}}{5}$ **b.** $-\dfrac{\sqrt{5}}{5}$ **c.** -2

43. a. $\sqrt{\dfrac{5+2\sqrt{6}}{10}}$ **b.** $\sqrt{\dfrac{5-2\sqrt{6}}{10}}$ **c.** $\sqrt{\dfrac{5+2\sqrt{6}}{5-2\sqrt{6}}}$

44. a. $\dfrac{\sqrt{6}}{6}$ **b.** $-\dfrac{\sqrt{30}}{6}$ **c.** $-\dfrac{\sqrt{5}}{5}$

45. a. $\sqrt{\dfrac{5-\sqrt{5}}{10}}$ **b.** $\sqrt{\dfrac{5+\sqrt{5}}{10}}$ **c.** $\sqrt{\dfrac{5-\sqrt{5}}{5+\sqrt{5}}}$

46. a. $\sqrt{\dfrac{7+\sqrt{42}}{14}}$ **b.** $\sqrt{\dfrac{7-\sqrt{42}}{14}}$ **c.** $\sqrt{\dfrac{7+\sqrt{42}}{7-\sqrt{42}}}$

57. $\dfrac{1-\cos 4x}{2}$ **58.** $\dfrac{1-\cos 4x}{8}$ **59.** $\sin 4x$ **60.** $\sin 4x$ **61.** $\dfrac{\sin 12x}{2}$

67. $\left\{0, \dfrac{\pi}{3}, \pi, \dfrac{5\pi}{3}\right\}$ **68.** $\left\{\dfrac{\pi}{6}, \dfrac{3\pi}{2}, \dfrac{5\pi}{6}\right\}$ **69.** $\left\{\dfrac{\pi}{6}, \dfrac{5\pi}{6}, \dfrac{7\pi}{6}, \dfrac{11\pi}{6}\right\}$

70. $\left\{\dfrac{\pi}{3}, \dfrac{2\pi}{3}, \dfrac{4\pi}{3}, \dfrac{5\pi}{3}\right\}$

Section 6.5

Practice Problems

1. $\dfrac{1}{2}\cos 2x + \dfrac{1}{2}\cos 4x$ **2.** $\dfrac{2-\sqrt{3}}{4}$

3. a. $2\sin 3x \sin x$ **b.** $\cos 13°$

4. $\sqrt{2}\sin\left(x - \dfrac{\pi}{4}\right)$

6. a. $y = \sin(2\pi \cdot 697t) + \sin(2\pi \cdot 1209t)$
  b. $y = 2\cos(512\pi t)\sin(2\pi(953t))$
  c. $f = 953\,\text{Hz}$, $A = 2\cos(512\pi t)$

A Exercises: Basic Skills and Concepts

1. $\dfrac{1}{2}\sin 2x$ **2.** $\dfrac{1}{2} + \dfrac{1}{2}\cos 2x$ **3.** $\dfrac{1}{2} - \dfrac{1}{2}\cos 2x$ **4.** $\dfrac{1}{2}\sin 2x$

5. $\dfrac{1}{4} + \dfrac{1}{2}\sin 20°$ **6.** $\dfrac{1}{2}\cos 20° - \dfrac{1}{4}$ **7.** $-\dfrac{1}{4} - \dfrac{1}{2}\cos 20°$

8. $\dfrac{1}{2} - \dfrac{1}{2}\sin 50°$ **13.** $\dfrac{1}{2}\sin 6\theta + \dfrac{1}{2}\sin 4\theta$ **14.** $\dfrac{1}{2}\sin 5\theta - \dfrac{1}{2}\sin\theta$

15. $\dfrac{1}{2}\cos x + \dfrac{1}{2}\cos 7x$ **16.** $\dfrac{1}{2}\cos 3x - \dfrac{1}{2}\cos 7x$ **17.** $\dfrac{\sqrt{3}}{4} - \dfrac{\sqrt{2}}{4}$

18. $\dfrac{\sqrt{2}}{4} + \dfrac{1}{4}$ **19.** $\dfrac{1}{2} + \dfrac{\sqrt{2}}{4}$ **20.** $-\dfrac{1}{4}$ **25.** $-\sin 10°$

26. $2\sin 15° \cos 7°$ **27.** $2\sin 8° \cos 24°$ **28.** $\sqrt{3}\cos 17°$

29. $2\sin\dfrac{3\pi}{10}\cos\dfrac{\pi}{10}$ **30.** $2\cos\dfrac{5\pi}{24}\cos\dfrac{\pi}{8}$ **31.** $2\cos\dfrac{5}{12}\cos\dfrac{1}{12}$

33. $2\cos 4x \cos x$ **34.** $2\sin x \cos 4x$ **35.** $2\sin 3x \cos 4x$

36. $-2\sin 5x \sin 2x$ **37.** $\sqrt{2}\cos\left(x - \dfrac{\pi}{4}\right)$ **38.** $-\sqrt{2}\sin\left(x - \dfrac{\pi}{4}\right)$

39. $\sqrt{2}\sin\left(2x - \dfrac{\pi}{4}\right)$ **40.** $\sqrt{2}\cos\left(3x - \dfrac{\pi}{4}\right)$

41. $2\sin\left(\dfrac{\pi}{4} - x\right)\cos\left(4x - \dfrac{\pi}{4}\right)$ **42.** $2\sin\left(3x - \dfrac{\pi}{4}\right)\cos\left(2x + \dfrac{\pi}{4}\right)$

43. $a\sqrt{2}\cos\left(x - \dfrac{\pi}{4}\right)$ **44.** $a\sqrt{2}\cos\left(bx - \dfrac{\pi}{4}\right)$

B Exercises: Applying the Concepts
58. a. $y = \sin[2\pi(941)t] + \sin[2\pi(1477)t]$
  b. $y = 2\cos(536\pi t)\sin(2\pi(1209)t)$
  c. $f = 1209\,\text{Hz}$, $A = 2\cos(536\pi t)$
59. a. $y = 0.1\cos(116\pi t)\cos(4\pi t)$
60. a. $y = 0.08\cos(2\pi t)\sin(112\pi t)$
  b. $f = 2$ beats per unit time

C Exercises: Beyond the Basics
71. $\left\{\dfrac{\pi}{6}, \dfrac{\pi}{4}, \dfrac{\pi}{2}, \dfrac{3\pi}{4}, \dfrac{5\pi}{6}, \dfrac{7\pi}{6}, \dfrac{5\pi}{4}, \dfrac{3\pi}{2}, \dfrac{7\pi}{4}, \dfrac{11\pi}{6}\right\}$ **72.** $\left\{0, \dfrac{\pi}{2}, \pi, \dfrac{3\pi}{2}\right\}$

73. $\left\{0, \dfrac{\pi}{5}, \dfrac{2\pi}{5}, \dfrac{\pi}{2}, \dfrac{3\pi}{5}, \dfrac{4\pi}{5}, \pi, \dfrac{6\pi}{5}, \dfrac{7\pi}{5}, \dfrac{3\pi}{2}, \dfrac{8\pi}{5}, \dfrac{9\pi}{5}\right\}$

74. $\left\{0, \dfrac{\pi}{8}, \dfrac{3\pi}{8}, \dfrac{5\pi}{8}, \dfrac{7\pi}{8}, \pi, \dfrac{9\pi}{8}, \dfrac{11\pi}{8}, \dfrac{13\pi}{8}, \dfrac{15\pi}{8}\right\}$

75. $\left\{\dfrac{\pi}{8}, \dfrac{\pi}{2}, \dfrac{5\pi}{8}, \dfrac{9\pi}{8}, \dfrac{3\pi}{2}, \dfrac{13\pi}{8}\right\}$ **76.** $\left\{\dfrac{\pi}{8}, \dfrac{5\pi}{8}, \dfrac{2\pi}{3}, \dfrac{9\pi}{8}, \dfrac{4\pi}{3}, \dfrac{13\pi}{8}\right\}$

Review Exercises

1. $\cos\theta = -\dfrac{\sqrt{5}}{3}$, $\tan\theta = \dfrac{2\sqrt{5}}{5}$, $\cot\theta = \dfrac{\sqrt{5}}{2}$,
  $\sec\theta = -\dfrac{3\sqrt{5}}{5}$, $\csc\theta = -\dfrac{3}{2}$

2. $\sin\theta = \dfrac{\sqrt{5}}{5}$, $\cos\theta = -\dfrac{2\sqrt{5}}{5}$, $\cot\theta = -2$,
  $\sec\theta = -\dfrac{\sqrt{5}}{2}$, $\csc\theta = \sqrt{5}$

3. $\sin\theta = -\dfrac{2\sqrt{2}}{3}$, $\cos\theta = \dfrac{1}{3}$, $\tan\theta = -2\sqrt{2}$,
  $\cot\theta = -\dfrac{\sqrt{2}}{4}$, $\csc\theta = -\dfrac{3\sqrt{2}}{4}$

4. $\sin\theta = \dfrac{1}{5}$, $\cos\theta = -\dfrac{2\sqrt{6}}{5}$, $\tan\theta = -\dfrac{\sqrt{6}}{12}$,
  $\cot\theta = -2\sqrt{6}$, $\sec\theta = -\dfrac{5\sqrt{6}}{12}$

21. $\left\{\dfrac{\pi}{4}, \dfrac{3\pi}{4}, \dfrac{5\pi}{4}, \dfrac{7\pi}{4}\right\}$ **22.** $\left\{\dfrac{\pi}{6}, \dfrac{5\pi}{6}, \dfrac{7\pi}{6}, \dfrac{11\pi}{6}\right\}$

23. $\left\{0, \dfrac{2\pi}{3}, \dfrac{4\pi}{3}\right\}$ **24.** $\left\{\dfrac{7\pi}{6}, \dfrac{11\pi}{6}\right\}$

25. $\left\{\dfrac{\pi}{18}, \dfrac{5\pi}{18}, \dfrac{13\pi}{18}, \dfrac{17\pi}{18}, \dfrac{25\pi}{18}, \dfrac{29\pi}{18}\right\}$

26. $\left\{\dfrac{\pi + 3}{6}, \dfrac{5\pi + 3}{6}, \dfrac{7\pi + 3}{6}, \dfrac{11\pi + 3}{6}\right\}$

30. $\{15°, 75°, 105°, 195°, 255°, 285°\}$ **33.** $\dfrac{\sqrt{2 + \sqrt{3}}}{2}$

34. $\dfrac{\sqrt{6} + \sqrt{2}}{4}$ **36.** $\dfrac{3 + \sqrt{3}}{3 - \sqrt{3}}$ **38.** $\dfrac{1}{2}$ **40.** $\dfrac{1}{2}$

41. $-\dfrac{16}{65}$ **42.** $-\dfrac{33}{65}$ **43.** $\dfrac{63}{65}$ **44.** $-\dfrac{16}{63}$

63.

64.

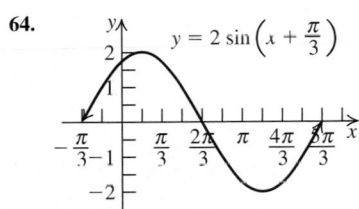

Applying the Concepts

69. $\dfrac{1}{360}\sec$ **70.** $x^2 \sin\dfrac{\theta}{2}\cos\dfrac{\theta}{2}$

Practice Test A

9. $-\dfrac{\pi}{4} + n\pi$ **10.** $\dfrac{\pi}{24} + \dfrac{\pi}{2}n, \dfrac{5\pi}{24} + \dfrac{\pi}{2}n$ **11.** $\dfrac{3\pi}{4}$

12. $\dfrac{\pi}{2}, \dfrac{7\pi}{6}, \dfrac{3\pi}{2}, \dfrac{11\pi}{6}$ **14.** $\dfrac{1}{2}$ **19.** No, let $x = y = \dfrac{\pi}{2}$.

Cumulative Review Exercises (Chapters 1–6)

1. $-\dfrac{1}{2} \pm \dfrac{\sqrt{5}}{2}$ **3.** $x = -\dfrac{\log 9}{\log 5}$ **4.** $\left\{\dfrac{\pi}{6}, \dfrac{\pi}{2}, \dfrac{5\pi}{6}, \dfrac{3\pi}{2}\right\}$

9.

10.

11.

12.

13.

14.

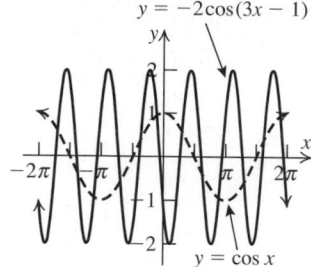

$y = -2\cos(3x - 1)$

$y = \cos x$

15.

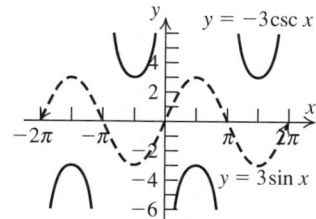

$y = -3\csc x$

$y = 3\sin x$

16.

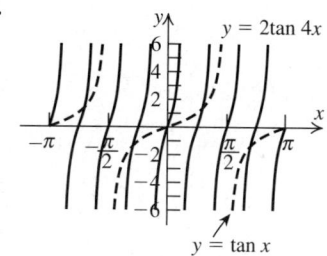

$y = 2\tan 4x$

$y = \tan x$

CHAPTER 7

Section 7.1

Practice Problems

1. $C = 45°, b \approx 15.4$ in., $c \approx 12.0$ in.
2. 10,576 ft   3. No triangle exists.
4. $A \approx 31.3°, B \approx 88.7°, b \approx 57.7$ ft
5. solution 1: $A \approx 99.2°; B \approx 45.8°; a \approx 20.7$
   solution 2: $A \approx 10.8°; B \approx 134.2°; a \approx 3.9$
6. a. ≈ 31.5 mi.   b. ≈ 15.6 mi.

A Exercises: Basic Skills and Concepts

9. $C = 105°, b \approx 89.2$ m, $c \approx 105.3$ m
10. $C = 80°, b \approx 34.7$ m, $c \approx 100$ m
11. $B = 79°, b \approx 102.3$ cm, $c \approx 85.4$ cm
12. $B = 47°, b \approx 95.6$ cm, $c \approx 129.5$ cm
13. $B = 98°, a \approx 47.1$ ft, $b \approx 81.2$ ft
14. $B = 60°, a \approx 28.6$ ft, $b \approx 35.7$ ft
15. $A = 70°, a \approx 55.1$ in., $c \approx 54.0$ in.
16. $A = 50°, a \approx 76.9$ in., $c \approx 57.6$ in.
17. $A = 24°, a \approx 13.3$ ft, $b \approx 30.7$ ft
18. $A = 50°, a \approx 14.4$ ft, $b \approx 17.4$ ft
19. $C = 98.5°, a \approx 17.7$ m, $b \approx 21.7$ m
20. $C = 61.2°, a \approx 41.2$ m, $b \approx 37.1$ m
21. $B \approx 34°, C \approx 106°, c \approx 34.4$
22. $B \approx 28°, C \approx 116°, c \approx 45.9$
23. $C = 90°, B = 60°, c = 25\sqrt{3}$
24. $B = 90°, C = 30°, c = 20$

29. $B \approx 56.8°, C \approx 23.2°, c \approx 16.0$
30. $B \approx 24.5°, C \approx 50.5°, c \approx 56.0$
33. solution 1: $C \approx 55.3°, A \approx 78.7°, a \approx 47.7$;
    solution 2: $C \approx 124.7°, A \approx 9.3°, a \approx 7.9$
34. solution 1: $C \approx 39.5°, A \approx 108.5°, a \approx 89.5$;
    solution 2: $C \approx 140.5°, A \approx 7.5°, a \approx 12.3$
37. solution 1: $C \approx 49.0°, B \approx 89.0°, b \approx 82.2$;
    solution 2: $C \approx 131.0°, B \approx 7.0°, b \approx 10.0$
38. solution 1: $C \approx 48.2°, B \approx 97.8°, b \approx 10.6$;
    solution 2: $C \approx 131.8°, B \approx 14.2°, b \approx 2.6$
39. No triangle exists.
40. $A \approx 26.2°, B \approx 91.8°, b \approx 113.2$

Section 7.2

Practice Problems

1. $b \approx 21.8, A \approx 36.6°, C \approx 83.4°$ 2. 5219.5 miles
3. $A \approx 42.1°, B \approx 85.9°, C \approx 52.0°$ 4. No triangle exists.
5. 93.5 square meters   6. 14,801 gallons

A Exercises: Basic Skills and Concepts

1. $b \approx 20.2, A \approx 44°, C \approx 30°$
2. $a \approx 4.5, B \approx 100.0°, C \approx 45°$
3. $A \approx 130.5°, B \approx 27.1°, C \approx 22.4°$
4. $A \approx 48.2°, B \approx 96.4°, C \approx 35.4°$

Section 7.3

Practice Problems

1. a.

b.

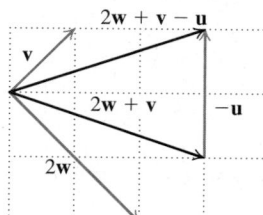

2. $\langle 3, -10 \rangle$ 3. a. $\langle 1, -1 \rangle$ b. $\langle 6, -9 \rangle$ c. $\langle 8, -13 \rangle$ d. $\sqrt{233}$
4. $\left\langle -\dfrac{12}{13}, \dfrac{5}{13} \right\rangle$ 5. a. $-7\mathbf{i} + 14\mathbf{j}$ b. $7\sqrt{5}$ 6. $\sqrt{3}\mathbf{i} - \mathbf{j}$
7. a. 8   b. 0   8. 17.5   9. 115.3°
10. a. 28.9   b. 38.9°   11. a. 801.0 mi/hr   b. N 62.9° W
12. 3000 foot-pounds

A Exercises: Basic Skills and Concepts

1.

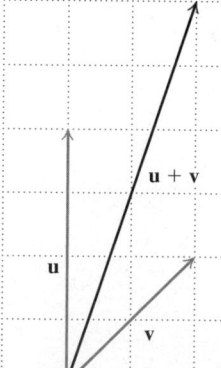

$\mathbf{u} + \mathbf{v}$

$\mathbf{u}$

$\mathbf{v}$

2.

3.

4.

5.

6.

7.

8.

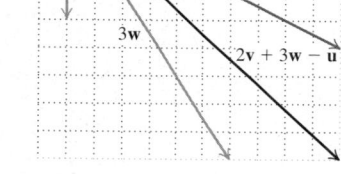

11. $\langle 2, -2 \rangle$ **12.** $\langle -3, -6 \rangle$ **14.** $\langle -5, -1.4 \rangle$

15. $\left\langle -1, -\dfrac{5}{2} \right\rangle$ **16.** $\left\langle 1, -\dfrac{10}{9} \right\rangle$ **25.** $\left\langle \dfrac{\sqrt{2}}{2}, -\dfrac{\sqrt{2}}{2} \right\rangle$

26. $\left\langle \dfrac{\sqrt{10}}{10}, \dfrac{3\sqrt{10}}{10} \right\rangle$ **27.** $\left\langle -\dfrac{4}{5}, \dfrac{3}{5} \right\rangle$ **28.** $\left\langle \dfrac{5}{13}, -\dfrac{12}{13} \right\rangle$

29. $\left\langle \dfrac{\sqrt{2}}{2}, \dfrac{\sqrt{2}}{2} \right\rangle$ **30.** $\left\langle \dfrac{\sqrt{5}}{3}, -\dfrac{2}{3} \right\rangle$ **38.** $\dfrac{5\sqrt{2}}{2}\mathbf{i} + \dfrac{5\sqrt{2}}{2}\mathbf{j}$

39. $-2\mathbf{i} + 2\sqrt{3}\mathbf{j}$ **40.** $-\dfrac{3\sqrt{3}}{2}\mathbf{i} + \dfrac{3}{2}\mathbf{j}$ **41.** $\dfrac{3}{2}\mathbf{i} - \dfrac{3\sqrt{3}}{2}\mathbf{j}$

42. $2\sqrt{3}\mathbf{i} - 2\mathbf{j}$ **43.** $\dfrac{7}{2}\mathbf{i} - \dfrac{7\sqrt{3}}{2}\mathbf{j}$ **44.** $-4\sqrt{2}\mathbf{i} + 4\sqrt{2}\mathbf{j}$

B Exercises: Applying the Concepts
81. 483.4 mi/hr, N 32.1° E

Section 7.4

Practice Problems

1. a.

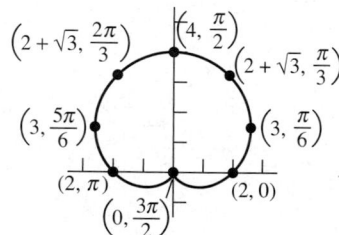

b. $(-2, 30°)$ **c.** $(2, 210°)$ **d.** $(-2, -330°)$

2. a. $\left(-\dfrac{3}{2}, -\dfrac{3\sqrt{3}}{2} \right)$ **b.** $(\sqrt{2}, -\sqrt{2})$ **3.** $\left(\sqrt{2}, \dfrac{5\pi}{4} \right)$

4. $(24.8, 36.0°)$ **5.** $r^2 - 2r\sin\theta + 3 = 0$

6. a. $x^2 + y^2 = 25$; a circle centered at the origin with radius 5
b. $y = -x\sqrt{3}$; a line through the origin with slope $-\sqrt{3}$
c. $x = 1$; a vertical line through $x = 1$
d. $x^2 + (y - 1)^2 = 1$; a circle with center $(0, 1)$ and radius 1

7.

$\left(2 + \sqrt{3}, \dfrac{2\pi}{3} \right)$ $\left(4, \dfrac{\pi}{2} \right)$ $\left(2 + \sqrt{3}, \dfrac{\pi}{3} \right)$ $\left(3, \dfrac{5\pi}{6} \right)$ $\left(3, \dfrac{\pi}{6} \right)$ $(2, \pi)$ $(2, 0)$ $\left(0, \dfrac{3\pi}{2} \right)$

A Exercises: Basic Skills and Concepts

1.

$(4, 45°)$

a. $(-4, 225°)$ **b.** $(-4, -135°)$ **c.** $(4, -315°)$

2.

$(5, 150°)$

a. $(-5, 330°)$ **b.** $(-5, -30°)$ **c.** $(5, -210°)$

3.

$(3, 90°)$

a. $(-3, 270°)$ **b.** $(-3, -90°)$ **c.** $(3, -270°)$

4.

$(2, 240°)$

a. $(-2, 60°)$ **b.** $(-2, -300°)$ **c.** $(2, -120°)$

5.

$(3, 60°)$

a. $(-3, 240°)$ **b.** $(-3, -120°)$ **c.** $(3, -300°)$

6.

(4, 210°)

a. $(-4, 30°)$ **b.** $(-4, -330°)$ **c.** $(4, -150°)$

7.

(6, 300°)

a. $(-6, 120°)$ **b.** $(-6, -240°)$ **c.** $(6, -60°)$

8.

(2, 270°)

a. $(-2, 90°)$ **b.** $(-2, -270°)$ **c.** $(2, -90°)$

9.

$\left(2, -\dfrac{\pi}{3}\right)$

a. $\left(2, \dfrac{5\pi}{3}\right)$ **b.** $\left(-2, \dfrac{2\pi}{3}\right)$

10.

$\left(\sqrt{2}, -\dfrac{\pi}{4}\right)$

a. $\left(\sqrt{2}, \dfrac{7\pi}{4}\right)$ **b.** $\left(-\sqrt{2}, \dfrac{3\pi}{4}\right)$

11.

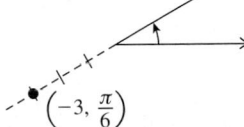

$\left(-3, \dfrac{\pi}{6}\right)$

a. $\left(-3, -\dfrac{11\pi}{6}\right)$ **b.** $\left(3, -\dfrac{5\pi}{6}\right)$

12.

$\left(-2, \dfrac{3\pi}{4}\right)$

a. $\left(-2, -\dfrac{5\pi}{4}\right)$ **b.** $\left(2, -\dfrac{\pi}{4}\right)$

13.

$\left(-2, -\dfrac{\pi}{6}\right)$

a. $\left(-2, \dfrac{11\pi}{6}\right)$ **b.** $\left(2, \dfrac{5\pi}{6}\right)$

14.

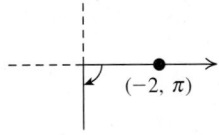

$(-2, \pi)$

a. $(-2, \pi)$ **b.** $(2, 0)$

15.

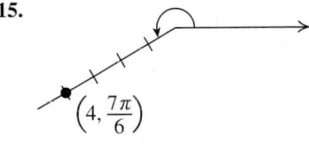

$\left(4, \dfrac{7\pi}{6}\right)$

a. $\left(4, -\dfrac{5\pi}{6}\right)$ **b.** $\left(-4, \dfrac{\pi}{6}\right)$

16.

(2, 3)

a. $(2, -3.28)$ **b.** $(-2, -0.14)$

17. $\left(\dfrac{3}{2}, \dfrac{3\sqrt{3}}{2}\right)$ **19.** $\left(\dfrac{5}{2}, -\dfrac{5\sqrt{3}}{2}\right)$

25. $\left(\sqrt{2}, \dfrac{7\pi}{4}\right)$ **26.** $\left(2, \dfrac{5\pi}{6}\right)$

27. $\left(3\sqrt{2}, \dfrac{\pi}{4}\right)$ **29.** $\left(3\sqrt{2}, \dfrac{7\pi}{4}\right)$

30. $\left(4, \dfrac{\pi}{6}\right)$ **31.** $\left(2, \dfrac{2\pi}{3}\right)$

32. $\left(4, \dfrac{4\pi}{3}\right)$ **34.** $r = \dfrac{1}{\cos\theta + \sin\theta}$

38. $r^2 = \dfrac{1}{\cos^2\theta - \sin^2\theta}$ **39.** $r^2 = \dfrac{1}{\sin\theta \cos\theta}$

48. $\left(x + \dfrac{3}{2}\right)^2 + y^2 = \dfrac{9}{4}$

49.

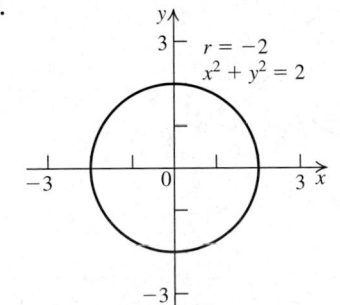

$r = -2$
$x^2 + y^2 = 2$

50.

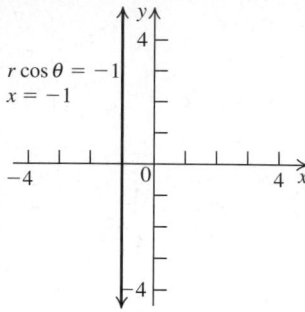

$r\cos\theta = -1$
$x = -1$

51.

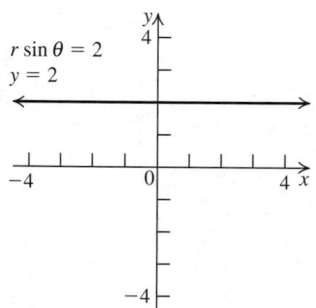

$r\sin\theta = 2$
$y = 2$

52.

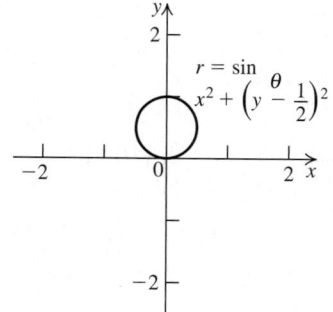

$r = \sin\theta$
$x^2 + \left(y - \frac{1}{2}\right)^2 = \frac{1}{4}$

53.

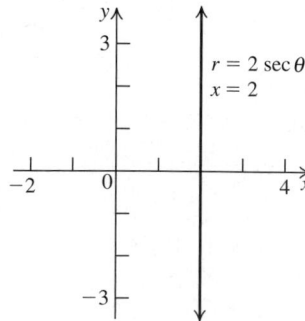

$r = 2\sec\theta$
$x = 2$

54.

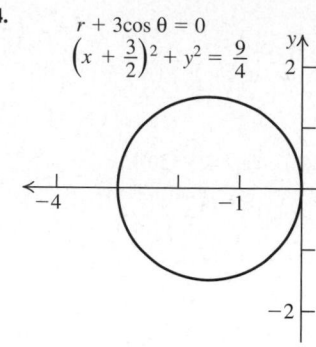

$r + 3\cos\theta = 0$
$\left(x + \frac{3}{2}\right)^2 + y^2 = \frac{9}{4}$

55.

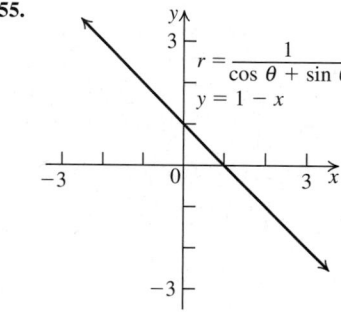

$r = \dfrac{1}{\cos\theta + \sin\theta}$
$y = 1 - x$

56.

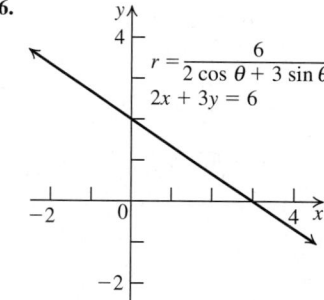

$r = \dfrac{6}{2\cos\theta + 3\sin\theta}$
$2x + 3y = 6$

57.

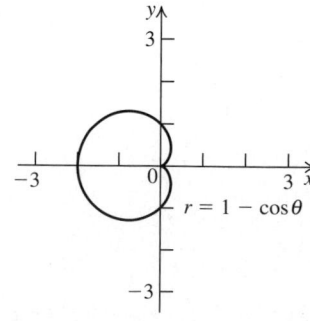

$r = 1 - \cos\theta$

58.

$r = \cos\theta$

59.

$r = \sin\theta$

60.

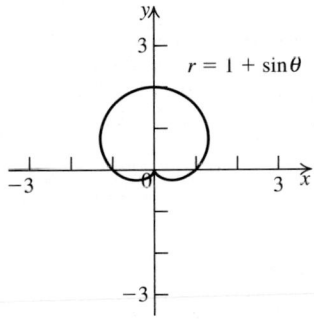

$r = 1 + \sin\theta$

C Exercises: Beyond the Basics

67. $y = \dfrac{x^2}{6} - \dfrac{3}{2}$

74. Center $\left(\dfrac{b}{2}, \dfrac{a}{2}\right)$ and radius $\sqrt{\dfrac{b^2}{4} + \dfrac{a^2}{4}}$.

Section 7.5

Practice Problems

1.

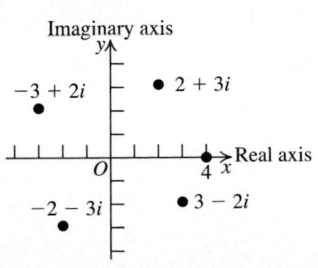

2. a. 13 **b.** 7 **c.** 1 **d.** $\sqrt{a^2 + b^2}$

3.

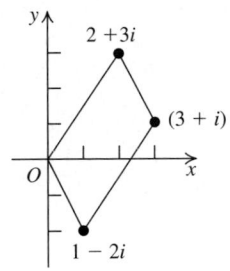

4. $z = \sqrt{2}\left(\cos\dfrac{5\pi}{4} + i\sin\dfrac{5\pi}{4}\right)$

5. $2 - 2\sqrt{3}i$

6. $z_1 z_2 = 10(\cos 135° + i\sin 135°); \dfrac{z_1}{z_2} = \dfrac{5}{2}(\cos 15° + i\sin 15°)$

7. $2.6(\cos 27.2° + i\sin 27.2°)$

8. a. 16 **b.** $-\dfrac{1}{64}$

9. $2^{\frac{1}{6}}(\cos 45° + i\sin 45°)$, $2^{\frac{1}{6}}(\cos 165° + i\sin 165°)$, $2^{\frac{1}{6}}(\cos 285° + i\sin 285°)$

10. $\cos 0° + i\sin 0°$, $\cos 90° + i\sin 90°$, $\cos 180° + i\sin 180°$, $\cos 270° + i\sin 270°$

A Exercises: Basic Skills and Concepts

1–8.

9.

10.

11.

12.

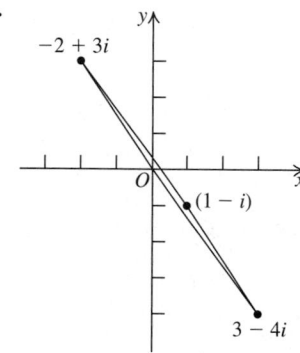

29. $-\dfrac{5}{2} - \dfrac{5\sqrt{3}}{2}i$

37. $z_1 z_2 = 8(\cos 90° + i\sin 90°); \dfrac{z_1}{z_2} = 2(\cos 60° + i\sin 60°)$

38. $z_1 z_2 = 12(\cos 135° + i\sin 135°); \dfrac{z_1}{z_2} = 3(\cos 45° + i\sin 45°)$

39. $z_1 z_2 = 10(\cos 300° + i\sin 300°); \dfrac{z_1}{z_2} = \dfrac{5}{2}(\cos 180° + i\sin 180°)$

40. $z_1 z_2 = 40(\cos 0° + i\sin 0°); \dfrac{z_1}{z_2} = \dfrac{5}{2}(\cos(270°) + i\sin(270°))$

41. $z_1 z_2 = 15(\cos 60° + i\sin 60°); \dfrac{z_1}{z_2} = \dfrac{3}{5}(\cos 20° + i\sin 20°)$

42. $z_1 z_2 = 10(\cos 90° + i\sin 90°); \dfrac{z_1}{z_2} = \dfrac{5}{2}(\cos 40° + i\sin 40°)$

43. $z_1 z_2 = 2(\cos 0° + i\sin 0°); \dfrac{z_1}{z_2} = \cos(90°) + i\sin(90°)$

44. $z_1 z_2 = 2\sqrt{2}(\cos 105° + i\sin 105°); \dfrac{z_1}{z_2} = \sqrt{2}(\cos 15° + i\sin 15°)$

45. $z_1 z_2 = 4\sqrt{2}(\cos 195° + i\sin 195°); \dfrac{z_1}{z_2} = \dfrac{\sqrt{2}}{2}(\cos 105° + i\sin 105°)$

46. $z_1 z_2 = 12\sqrt{2}(\cos 345° + i\sin 345°);$
$\dfrac{z_1}{z_2} = \dfrac{3\sqrt{2}}{4}(\cos(105°) + i\sin(105°))$

47. $z_1 z_2 = 4\sqrt{3}(\cos 5.3° + i\sin 5.3°);$
$\dfrac{z_1}{z_2} = \sqrt{3}(\cos 65.3° + i\sin 65.3°)$

48. $z_1 z_2 = 24\sqrt{2}(\cos 345° + i\sin 345°);$
$\dfrac{z_1}{z_2} = \dfrac{4\sqrt{2}}{3}(\cos(75°) + i\sin(75°))$

62. $-\dfrac{1}{512}i$

65. $4(\cos 0° + i\sin 0°), 4(\cos 120° + i\sin 120°), 4(\cos 240° + i\sin 240°)$

66. $4(\cos 60° + i\sin 60°), 4(\cos 180° + i\sin 180°),$
$4(\cos 300° + i\sin 300°)$

67. $\cos 45° + i\sin 45°, \cos 225° + i\sin 225°$

68. $\cos 67.5° + i\sin 67.5°, \cos 157.5° + i\sin 157.5°,$
$\cos 247.5° + i\sin 247.5°, \cos 337.5° + i\sin 337.5°$

69. $\cos 0° + i\sin 0°, \cos 60° + i\sin 60°, \cos 120° + i\sin 120°,$
$\cos 180° + i\sin 180°, \cos 240° + i\sin 240°, \cos 300° + i\sin 300°$

70. $\cos 0° + i\sin 0°, \cos 45° + i\sin 45°, \cos 90° + i\sin 90°,$
$\cos 135° + i\sin 135°, \cos 180° + i\sin 180°, \cos 225° + i\sin 225°,$
$\cos 270° + i\sin 270°, \cos 315° + i\sin 315°$

71. $\sqrt{2}(\cos 150° + i\sin 150°), \sqrt{2}(\cos 330° + i\sin 330°)$

72. $2(\cos 20° + i\sin 20°), 2(\cos 140° + i\sin 140°),$
$2(\cos 260° + i\sin 260°)$

C Exercises: Beyond the Basics

85. $\cos 0° + i\sin 0°, \cos 90° + i\sin 90°,$
$\cos 180° + i\sin 180°, \cos 270° + i\sin 270°$

86. $\cos 22.5° + i\sin 22.5°, \cos 67.5° + i\sin 67.5°,$
$\cos 112.5° + i\sin 112.5°, \cos 157.5° + i\sin 157.5°,$
$\cos 202.5° + i\sin 202.5°, \cos 247.5° + i\sin 247.5°,$
$\cos 292.5° + i\sin 292.5°, \cos 337.5° + i\sin 337.5°$

87. $2^{\frac{1}{6}}(\cos 15° + i\sin 15°), 2^{\frac{1}{6}}(\cos 135° + i\sin 135°),$
$2^{\frac{1}{6}}(\cos 255° + i\sin 255°)$

88. $2^{\frac{1}{3}}(\cos 38.6° + i\sin 38.6°), 2^{\frac{1}{3}}(\cos 90° + i\sin 90°),$
$2^{\frac{1}{3}}(\cos 141.4° + i\sin 141.4°), 2^{\frac{1}{3}}(\cos 192.9° + i\sin 192.9°),$
$2^{\frac{1}{3}}(\cos 244.3° + i\sin 244.3°), 2^{\frac{1}{3}}(\cos 295.7° + i\sin 295.7°),$
$2^{\frac{1}{3}}(\cos 347.1° + i\sin 347.1°),$

Critical Thinking

95. j. True

Review Exercises

Basic Skills and Concepts

4. $A \approx 57.6°, C \approx 86.4°, c \approx 14.8; A \approx 122.4°, C \approx 21.6°, c \approx 5.4$

5. $B = 74.2°, a \approx 36.8, c \approx 41.4$

8. $A \approx 76.5°, B \approx 50.5°, b \approx 111.2; A \approx 103.5°, B \approx 23.5°, b \approx 57.4$

9. Answers may vary. Sample answers: (i) $10\sqrt{3}$, (ii) 20, (iii) 10

10. Answers may vary. Sample answers: (i) not possible, (ii) 60, (iii) 10

20. 4 square meters

29. $\dfrac{\sqrt{2}}{2}\mathbf{i} + \dfrac{\sqrt{2}}{2}\mathbf{j}$ **30.** $\dfrac{2\sqrt{53}}{53}\mathbf{i} - \dfrac{7\sqrt{53}}{53}\mathbf{j}$

31. $\left\langle \dfrac{3\sqrt{34}}{34}, -\dfrac{5\sqrt{34}}{34} \right\rangle$ **32.** $\left\langle -\dfrac{5\sqrt{29}}{29}, -\dfrac{2\sqrt{29}}{29} \right\rangle$

33. $3\sqrt{3}\mathbf{i} + 3\mathbf{j}$ **34.** $-10\mathbf{i} + 10\sqrt{3}\mathbf{j}$

35. $-6\sqrt{2}\mathbf{i} - 6\sqrt{2}\mathbf{j}$ **36.** $5\sqrt{3}\mathbf{i} - 5\mathbf{j}$

45.

$(12\sqrt{3}, 12)$

46.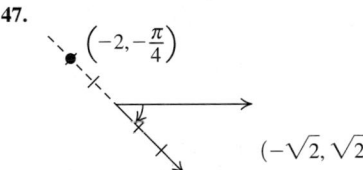

$(6, -6\sqrt{3})$

47.

$\left(-2, -\dfrac{\pi}{4}\right)$

$(-\sqrt{2}, \sqrt{2})$

48.

$\left(-3, \dfrac{-3\pi}{4}\right)$

$\left(\dfrac{3\sqrt{2}}{2}, \dfrac{3\sqrt{2}}{2}\right)$

49. $\left(2\sqrt{2}, \dfrac{3\pi}{4}\right)$ **50.** $\left(2, \dfrac{\pi}{6}\right)$ **51.** $\left(4, \dfrac{11\pi}{6}\right)$ **52.** $\left(4, \dfrac{4\pi}{3}\right)$

53. $r = \dfrac{12}{3\cos\theta + 2\sin\theta}$ **61.** $(x^2 + y^2 + 2y)^2 = x^2 + y^2$

63. $3\left(\cos\dfrac{3\pi}{2} + i\sin\dfrac{3\pi}{2}\right)$ **64.** $\sqrt{2}\left(\cos\dfrac{3\pi}{4} + i\sin\dfrac{3\pi}{4}\right)$

65. $10\left(\cos\dfrac{11\pi}{6} + i\sin\dfrac{11\pi}{6}\right)$ **66.** $4\left(\cos\dfrac{4\pi}{3} + i\sin\dfrac{4\pi}{3}\right)$

67. $\sqrt{2} + \sqrt{2}i$ **68.** $-\dfrac{3}{2} - \dfrac{3\sqrt{3}}{2}i$

69. $-3\sqrt{2} + 3\sqrt{2}i$ **70.** $-2\sqrt{3} - 2i$

71. $z_1 z_2 = 6(\cos 35° + i\sin 35°);\ \dfrac{z_1}{z_2} = \dfrac{3}{2}(\cos 15° + i\sin 15°)$

72. $z_1 z_2 = 8(\cos 320° + i\sin 320°);\ \dfrac{z_1}{z_2} = 2(\cos 280° + i\sin 280°)$

73. $z_1 z_2 = 6\left(\cos\dfrac{7\pi}{6} + i\sin\dfrac{7\pi}{6}\right);\ \dfrac{z_1}{z_2} = \dfrac{2}{3}\left(\cos\dfrac{\pi}{2} + i\sin\dfrac{\pi}{2}\right)$

74. $z_1 z_2 = 75\left(\cos\dfrac{5\pi}{3} + i\sin\dfrac{5\pi}{3}\right);\ \dfrac{z_1}{z_2} = \dfrac{1}{3}(\cos\pi + i\sin\pi)$

75. $27(\cos 120° + i\sin 120°)$ **76.** $4096(\cos\pi + i\sin\pi)$

77. $4096(\cos 0 + i\sin 0)$ **78.** $2^{\frac{21}{2}}\left(\cos\dfrac{\pi}{4} + i\sin\dfrac{\pi}{4}\right)$

79. $5(\cos 60° + i\sin 60°),\ 5(\cos 180° + i\sin 180°),$
$5(\cos 300° + i\sin 300°)$

80. $2(\cos 67.5° + i\sin 67.5°),\ 2(\cos 157.5° + i\sin 157.5°),$
$2(\cos 247.5° + i\sin 247.5°),\ 2(\cos 337.5° + i\sin 337.5°)$

81. $2^{\frac{1}{5}}(\cos 24° + i\sin 24°),\ 2^{\frac{1}{5}}(\cos 96° + i\sin 96°),$
$2^{\frac{1}{5}}(\cos 168° + i\sin 168°),\ 2^{\frac{1}{5}}(\cos 240° + i\sin 240°),$
$2^{\frac{1}{5}}(\cos 312° + i\sin 312°)$

82. $2^{\frac{1}{12}}(\cos(-7.5°) + i\sin(-7.5°)),\ 2^{\frac{1}{12}}(\cos 52.5° + i\sin 52.5°),$
$2^{\frac{1}{12}}(\cos 112.5° + i\sin 112.5°),\ 2^{\frac{1}{12}}(\cos 172.5° + i\sin 172.5°),$
$2^{\frac{1}{12}}(\cos 232.5° + i\sin 232.5°),\ 2^{\frac{1}{12}}(\cos 292.5° + i\sin 292.5°),$
$2^{\frac{1}{12}}(\cos 352.5° + i\sin 352.5°)$

Applying the Concepts
87. 24,625 square feet
89. 1204.4 foot-pounds

Practice Test A

2. $C = 101°,\ b \approx 45.0$ m, $c \approx 73.4$ m
3. $A \approx 28.2°,\ C \approx 45.8°,\ b \approx 71.1$
4. $A \approx 82.8°,\ B \approx 41.4°,\ C \approx 55.8°$
5. Two triangles: $B \approx 66.1°,\ C \approx 70.9°,\ c \approx 256.3$ ft;
$B \approx 113.9°,\ C \approx 23.1°,\ c \approx 106.4$ ft

11. $\dfrac{3\sqrt{3}}{2}\mathbf{i} - \dfrac{3}{2}\mathbf{j}$ **15.** $\left(2, \dfrac{7\pi}{6}\right)$

16. $x^2 + y^2 = 9$; circle with center $(0, 0)$ and radius 3

17. $-\dfrac{3}{2} + \dfrac{3\sqrt{3}}{2}i$ **19.** $\dfrac{1}{125}i$

20. $2^{\frac{1}{8}}(\cos 11.25° + i\sin 11.25°),\ 2^{\frac{1}{8}}(\cos 101.25° + i\sin 101.25°),$
$2^{\frac{1}{8}}(\cos 191.25° + i\sin 191.25°),\ 2^{\frac{1}{8}}(\cos 281.25° + i\sin 281.25°)$

Cumulative Review Exercises (Chapters 1–7)

2. $(-\infty, -3) \cup (2, 4)$ **3.** $\{\pm\sqrt{2}, \pm\sqrt{3}i\}$
5. $\left\{\dfrac{2\pi}{3}, \dfrac{5\pi}{6}, \dfrac{5\pi}{3}, \dfrac{11\pi}{6}\right\}$ **6.** $\left\{\dfrac{\pi}{6}, \dfrac{5\pi}{6}, \dfrac{7\pi}{6}, \dfrac{11\pi}{6}\right\}$
7. $2^{\frac{1}{4}}(\cos 7.5° + i\sin 7.5°),\ 2^{\frac{1}{4}}(\cos 97.5° + i\sin 97.5°),$
$2^{\frac{1}{4}}(\cos 187.5° + i\sin 187.5°),\ 2^{\frac{1}{4}}(\cos 277.5° + i\sin 277.5°),$
8. $2(\cos 30° + i\sin 30°),\ 2(\cos 90° + i\sin 90°),\ 2(\cos 150° + i\sin 150°),$
$2(\cos 210° + i\sin 210°),\ 2(\cos 270° + i\sin 270°),$
$2(\cos 330° + i\sin 330°)$

9. $y = \dfrac{3}{2}x + \dfrac{13}{2}$

11.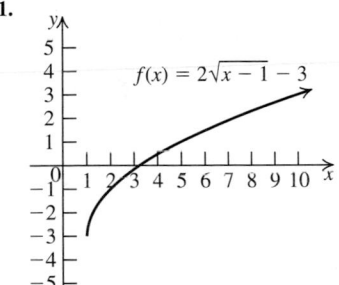

$f(x) = 2\sqrt{x - 1} - 3$

12.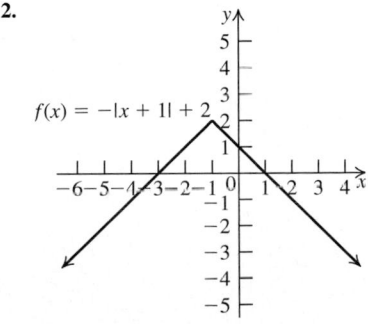

$f(x) = -|x + 1| + 2$

13.

$f(x) = -2\cos(3x + \pi)$

14.

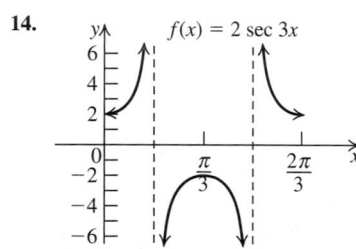

$f(x) = 2\sec 3x$

16. $\dfrac{\sqrt{3}}{2}$

19. $C = 69°$, $a \approx 58.2$ m, $b \approx 46.2$ m

CHAPTER 8

Section 8.1

Practice Problems

1. Equation (1): $(1) + (3) = 4$; Equation (2): $3(1) - 3 = 0$

2. $(-1, 3)$ **3.** $\varnothing$ **4.** $\{(x, 2x - 3)\}$ **5.** $\left\{\left(\dfrac{2}{3}, \dfrac{1}{2}\right)\right\}$

6. $\{(2, -3)\}$ **7.** $\{(5700, 31.4)\}$

A Exercises: Basic Skills and Concepts

2. $(2, 2), (-2, 4), (0, 3)$ **10.** Independent **11.** Dependent

13. Independent **14.** Independent **15.** Inconsistent

16. Inconsistent **17.** Inconsistent **18.** Inconsistent.

19. Independent. **20.** Dependent.

21. $(2, 1)$

22. $(6, 4)$

23. $(2, 2)$

24. $(1, -2)$

25. Inconsistent

26. Inconsistent

27. $\left(\dfrac{7}{3}, \dfrac{14}{3}\right)$

28. $\left(\dfrac{7}{2}, \dfrac{11}{2}\right)$

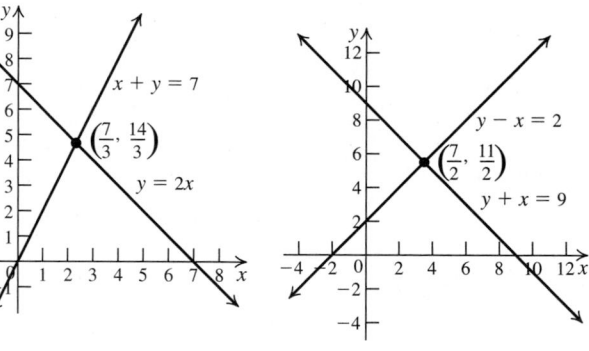

29. $\{(x, 12 - 3x)\}$

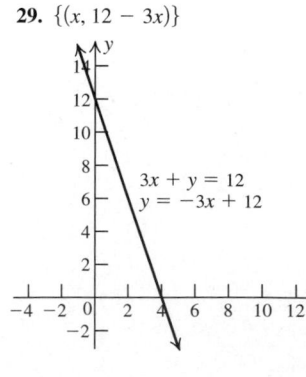

30. $\left\{\left(x, 2 - \dfrac{2}{3}x\right)\right\}$

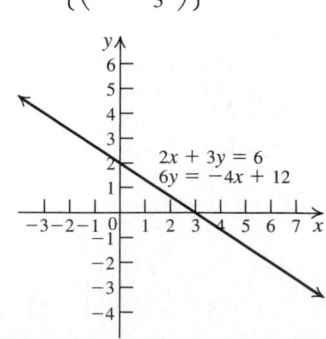

31. $\left(\dfrac{7}{9}, \dfrac{23}{9}\right)$ **39.** $\{(2y + 5, y)\}$ **48.** $\left\{\left(x, \dfrac{-3 - 4x}{7}\right)\right\}$

49. $\left\{\left(x, 2 - \dfrac{2}{3}x\right)\right\}$ **59.** $\left(\dfrac{19}{6}, \dfrac{5}{4}\right)$ **61.** $(4, 2)$ **64.** $(5, -4)$

B Exercises: Applying the Concepts

75. The diameter of the largest pizza is 21 inches, and the diameter of the smallest pizza is 8 inches.

76. The amount of calories in a hamburger from Boston Burger is 585, and the amount of calories in a hamburger from Carmen's Broiler is 545.

77. 8% of the total trash collected is plastic and 40% paper

78. The average monthly cost of food is $800, and the average monthly cost of clothes is $200.

79. 340 beads and 430 doubloons

80. 40 at 24¢ each and 95 at 18¢ each

83. $18,000 at 7.5% and $32,000 at 12%

84. $24,000 at 8% and $6000 at 10.5%

85. $7.50 per hour at McDougals and $15 per hour for tutoring

91. b.

92. b.

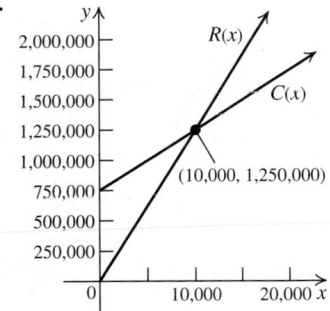

Critical Thinking

102. a. $x = \dfrac{b_2 c_1 - b_1 c_2}{a_1 b_2 - a_2 b_1}$, $y = \dfrac{a_1 c_2 - a_2 c_1}{a_1 b_2 - a_2 b_1}$, where $a_1 b_2 - a_2 b_1 \neq 0$

b. $\dfrac{c_1}{b_1} \neq \dfrac{c_2}{b_2}, \dfrac{a_1}{a_2} = \dfrac{b_1}{b_2}$

c. $\dfrac{a_1}{a_2} = \dfrac{b_1}{b_2} = \dfrac{c_1}{c_2}$

Section 8.2

Practice Problems

1. $(2) + (-3) + (2) = 1$
$3(2) + 4(-3) + (2) = -4$
$2(2) + (-3) + 2(2) = 5$

2. $\varnothing$

3. $\left\{\left(8 - \dfrac{7}{3}z, \dfrac{4}{3}z - 3, z\right)\right\}$

4. $\{(13 - 17z, -3 + 5z, z)\}$

5. Cell A contains bone (since $x = 0.4$), cell B contains healthy tissue (since $y = 0.25$), and cell C contains tumorous tissue (since $z = 0.3$).

A Exercises: Basic Skills and Concepts

6. $\{(4, -2, 5)\}$ **7.** $\{(-3, 2, 4)\}$ **8.** $\left\{\left(2, \dfrac{-3}{2}, \dfrac{1}{2}\right)\right\}$

9. $\begin{cases} x - y - \dfrac{3}{2}z = \dfrac{1}{2} \\ y + z = 0 \\ z = 1 \end{cases}$

10. $\begin{cases} x + 3z = 8 \\ y + z = 5 \\ z = 2 \end{cases}$

11. $\begin{cases} x + 3y - 2z = 0 \\ y - \dfrac{8}{7}z = \dfrac{5}{7} \\ 0 = k, k \neq 0 \end{cases}$

12. $\begin{cases} x - 4y + 7z = 14 \\ y - \dfrac{23}{20}z = \dfrac{-29}{20} \\ 0 = k, k \neq 0 \end{cases}$

17. $\{(1, 2, 3)\}$ **18.** $\{(1, 2, 3)\}$ **19.** $\left\{\left(\dfrac{35}{18}, \dfrac{29}{18}, \dfrac{5}{18}\right)\right\}$

20. $\{(3, 3, -4)\}$ **21.** $\{(2, 1, -1)\}$ **22.** $\{(-1, 2, 3)\}$

23. $\{(3, -1, 2)\}$ **24.** $\{(1, 0, 1)\}$ **25.** $\{(2, 2, 1)\}$

26. $\{(1, -2, 1)\}$ **27.** $\{(3, -1, 1)\}$ **28.** $\{(2, 0, -1)\}$

29. $\{(1, 2, 2)\}$ **30.** $\{(0, 2, 3)\}$ **31.** $\{(12, -12, 4)\}$

32. $\{(-1, 2, 0)\}$ **33.** $\{(1, -1, 2)\}$ **34.** $\{(10, -1, 3)\}$

35. $\{(3, 2, -1)\}$ **36.** $\{(1, 2, 1)\}$

37. Dependent. $\left\{\left(-5 - 9z, \dfrac{-1}{6} + 3z, z\right)\right\}$

38. Dependent. $\left\{\left(\dfrac{49}{6} - z, \dfrac{-19}{10} + \dfrac{3}{5}z, z\right)\right\}$

B Exercises: Applying the Concepts

39. $4000 invested at 4%, $6000 invested at 5%, and $10,000 invested at 6%

41. Alex worked for 2 hours, Becky worked for 2.5 hours, and Courtney worked for 1.5 hours.

42. There are 23 18-year olds, 11 19-year olds, and 4 20-year olds.

43. 56 nickels, 225 dimes, and 19 quarters

47. Cell A contains healthy tissue (since $x = 0.21$), cell B contains tumorous tissue (since $y = 0.33$), and cell C contains healthy tissue (since $z = 0.19$).

48. Cell A contains tumorous tissue (since $x = 0.35$), cell B contains tumorous tissue (since $y = 0.3$), and cell C contains bone (since $z = 0.45$).

49. Cells A, B, and C contain healthy tissue (since $x = 0.28$, $y = 0.23$, and $z = 0.21$).

50. Both cells A and B contain healthy tissue (since $x = 0.21$, $y = 0.23$), and cell C contains metal (since $z = 2$).

Section 8.3

Practice Problems

1. $\dfrac{5}{x - 1} - \dfrac{3}{x} + \dfrac{1}{x + 1}$ **2.** $\dfrac{5}{x} + \dfrac{6}{(x - 1)^2} - \dfrac{5}{x - 1}$

3. $\dfrac{-1}{x} + \dfrac{4x+5}{x^2+2}$ 4. $\dfrac{1}{x^2+1} + \dfrac{3x}{(x^2+1)^2}$

5. $\dfrac{777}{3112}$ 6. $\dfrac{1}{R} = \dfrac{3}{x+1} + \dfrac{1}{x+2} = \dfrac{1}{\frac{x+1}{3}} + \dfrac{1}{x+2}$

A Exercises: Basic Skills and Concepts

1. $\dfrac{A}{x-1} + \dfrac{B}{x+2}$ 2. $\dfrac{A}{x+1} + \dfrac{B}{x-3}$ 4. $\dfrac{A}{x-2} + \dfrac{B}{x-4}$

6. $\dfrac{A}{(x+2)^2} + \dfrac{B}{x-3} + \dfrac{C}{x+2}$ 7. $\dfrac{A}{x+1} + \dfrac{Bx+C}{x^2-x+1}$

8. $\dfrac{A}{(x-1)^2} + \dfrac{Bx+C}{x^2+x+1} + \dfrac{D}{x-1}$ 9. $\dfrac{Ax+B}{x^2+1} + \dfrac{Cx+D}{(x^2+1)^2}$

10. $\dfrac{A}{(2x+3)^2} + \dfrac{Bx+C}{(x^2+3)^2} + \dfrac{D}{2x+3} + \dfrac{Ex+F}{x^2+3}$

11. $\dfrac{3}{x+2} - \dfrac{1}{x+1}$ 12. $\dfrac{1}{x-2} - \dfrac{1}{x+5}$

13. $\dfrac{-1}{2(x+3)} + \dfrac{1}{2(x+1)}$ 14. $\dfrac{3}{x+3} - \dfrac{2}{x+2}$

17. $\dfrac{2}{x+2} - \dfrac{3}{2(x+3)} - \dfrac{1}{2(x+1)}$

18. $\dfrac{16}{15(x+4)} + \dfrac{1}{10(x-1)} - \dfrac{1}{6(x+1)}$

21. $\dfrac{2}{x+1} - \dfrac{3}{(x+1)^2} + \dfrac{1}{(x+1)^3}$

22. $\dfrac{1}{2(x-1)} + \dfrac{1}{2(x+1)}$

23. $\dfrac{1}{x} + \dfrac{3}{(x+1)^2} - \dfrac{2}{x+1}$ 24. $\dfrac{3}{x-1} + \dfrac{2}{x} - \dfrac{1}{(x-1)^2}$

25. $\dfrac{-2}{x} + \dfrac{1}{x^2} + \dfrac{1}{(x+1)^2} + \dfrac{2}{x+1}$

26. $\dfrac{1}{8(x+3)^2} + \dfrac{1}{8(x-1)^2} + \dfrac{1}{16(x+3)} - \dfrac{1}{16(x-1)}$

27. $\dfrac{1}{4(x-1)^2} + \dfrac{1}{4(x+1)^2} + \dfrac{1}{4(x+1)} - \dfrac{1}{4(x-1)}$

28. $\dfrac{-3}{32(x-2)} + \dfrac{3}{16(x+2)^2} + \dfrac{3}{32(x+2)} + \dfrac{3}{16(x-2)^2}$

29. $\dfrac{1}{2(2x-3)} + \dfrac{1}{2(2x-3)^2}$ 30. $\dfrac{2}{3x+1} - \dfrac{1}{(3x+1)^2}$

31. $\dfrac{-2}{(2x+3)^2} + \dfrac{3}{2x+3}$ 32. $\dfrac{-1}{3(3x+5)^2} + \dfrac{2}{3(3x+5)}$

35. $\dfrac{-2}{x} + \dfrac{3}{x+1} + \dfrac{4}{x^2}$ 36. $\dfrac{2}{x^2+1} + \dfrac{1}{x-1}$

37. $\dfrac{-x}{2(x^2+1)} + \dfrac{1}{4(x+1)} + \dfrac{1}{4(x-1)}$

38. $\dfrac{-3}{x^2+4} + \dfrac{1}{x-2} + \dfrac{2}{x+2}$ 39. $\dfrac{-x}{x^2+1} + \dfrac{1}{x} - \dfrac{x}{(x^2+1)^2}$

40. $\dfrac{-2}{(x^2+2)^2} + \dfrac{1}{x^2+2}$ 41. $\dfrac{4-3x}{x^2+2} + \dfrac{-2+3x}{x^2+1}$

42. $\dfrac{-x}{x^2+x+7} + \dfrac{x}{x^2+9}$

B Exercises: Applying the Concepts

43. $\dfrac{n}{n+1}$ 44. $\dfrac{7625}{5151}$ 45. $\dfrac{2n}{2n+1}$ 46. $\dfrac{2575}{5151}$

47. $\dfrac{1}{R} = \dfrac{1}{x+1} + \dfrac{1}{x+3}$

48. $\dfrac{1}{R} = \dfrac{3}{x+2} + \dfrac{4}{x+4} = \dfrac{1}{\left(\frac{x+2}{3}\right)} + \dfrac{1}{\left(\frac{x+4}{4}\right)}$

49. $\dfrac{1}{R} = \dfrac{1}{R_1} + \dfrac{1}{R_2} + \dfrac{1}{R_3}$ 50. $\dfrac{1}{R} = \dfrac{1}{x} + \dfrac{1}{x+2} + \dfrac{1}{x+4}$

C Exercises: Beyond The Basics

52. $\dfrac{-x+2}{3(x^2-x+1)} + \dfrac{1}{3(x+1)}$ 53. $\dfrac{1}{(x-1)^2} - \dfrac{1}{(x+1)^2}$

54. $\dfrac{-x+5}{2(x^2+1)} + \dfrac{1}{2(x+1)}$ 55. $\dfrac{-1}{2(x-1)} + \dfrac{x-1}{2(x^2+1)} + \dfrac{1}{(x-1)^2}$

56. $\dfrac{-x+1}{2(x^2+1)^2} + \dfrac{1}{4(x-1)} + \dfrac{-x-1}{4(x^2+1)}$

57. $\dfrac{-4}{x+2} - \dfrac{8}{(x+2)^2} - \dfrac{1}{(x+1)^2} + \dfrac{5}{x+1}$

58. $\dfrac{2x}{x^2+x+1} + \dfrac{-1-2x}{(x^2+x+1)^2}$ 59. $\dfrac{5}{3(x-3)} + \dfrac{-5x+15}{3(x^2+3x+9)}$

60. $\dfrac{3}{x+2} + \dfrac{-x-1}{x^2-2x+4}$ 61. $\dfrac{1}{x^2-2x+2} - \dfrac{1}{x^2+2x+2}$

62. $\dfrac{3}{(x-5)^3} + \dfrac{1}{x-5} + \dfrac{2}{(x-5)^2}$ 63. $1 + \dfrac{2}{x+1} - \dfrac{1}{x+2}$

64. $1 - \dfrac{4}{7(x+3)} + \dfrac{18}{7(x-4)}$ 65. $2x+3 + \dfrac{2x-1}{x^2+1} + \dfrac{1}{x-1}$

66. $x+6 - \dfrac{16}{x-2} + \dfrac{81}{2(x-3)} + \dfrac{1}{2(x-1)}$

Section 8.4

Practice Problems

1.

2.

3.

4. $(4, 0)$, $(5, 2)$, and $(2, 4)$

5. The minimum number of calories is 300. The lunch then consists of 10 oz of soup and 0 oz of salad.

A Exercises: Basic Skills and Concepts

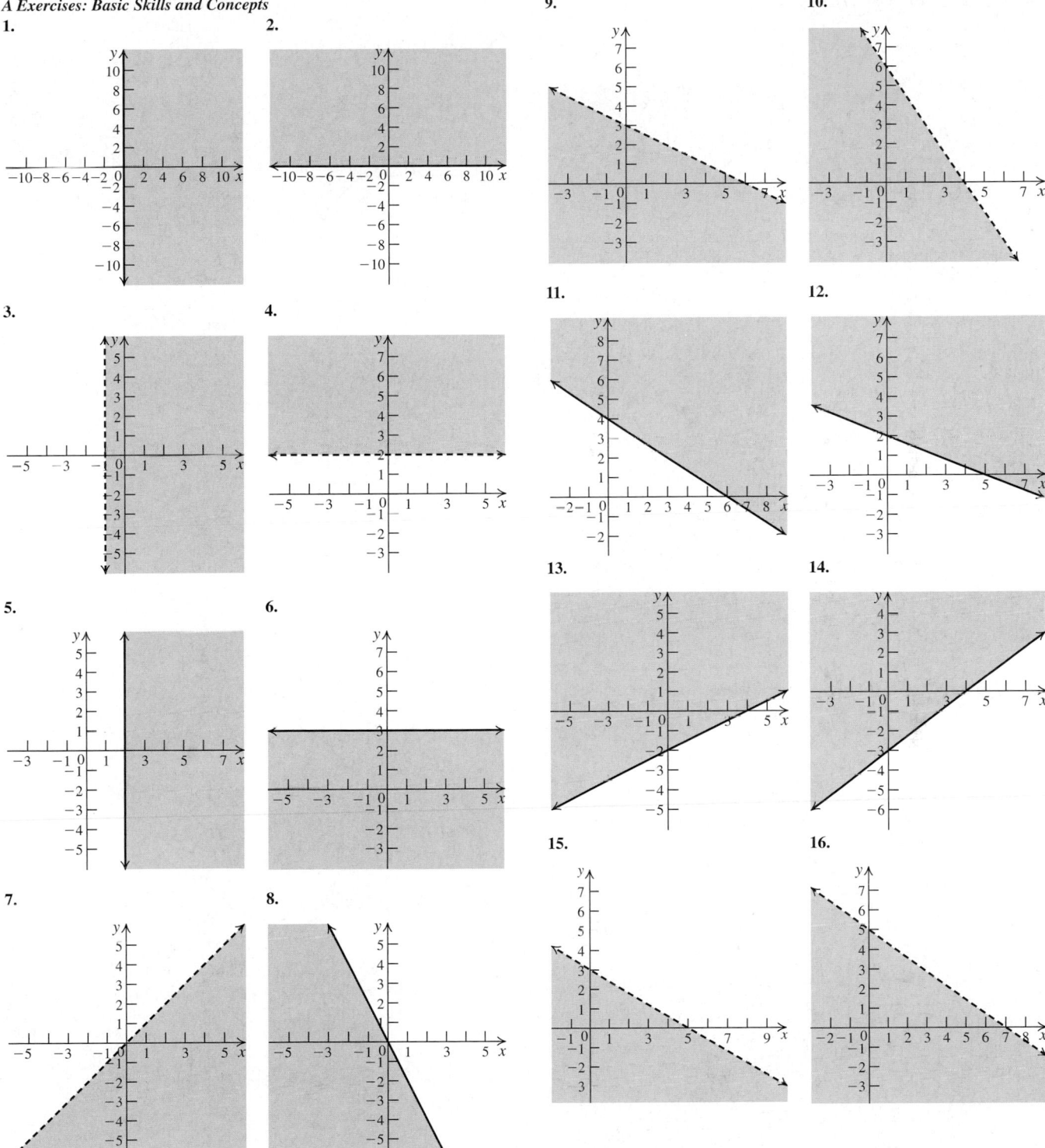

19. (0, 0), (1, 0), (0, 1), (1, 1)

20. (0, 0), (0, 1), (−1, −1)

23.

24.

31.

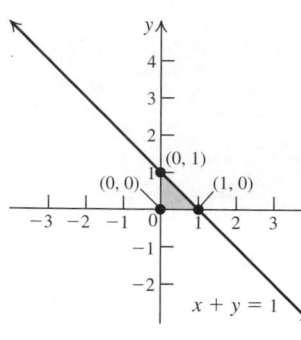

32. There are no vertices of the solution set.

25.

26.

33.

34.

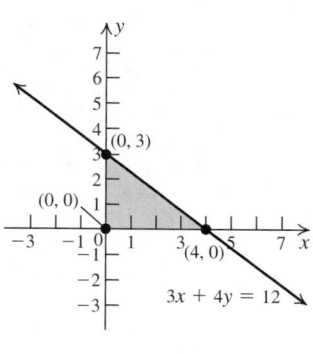

27. There are no vertices of the solution set.

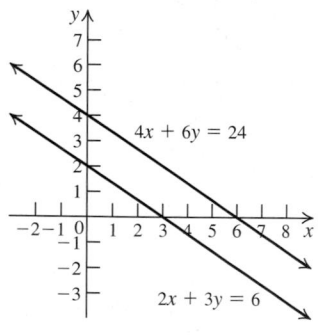

28. There are no vertices of the solution set.

35.

36.

29.

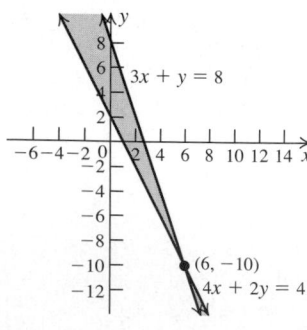

30. There are no vertices of the solution set.

37.

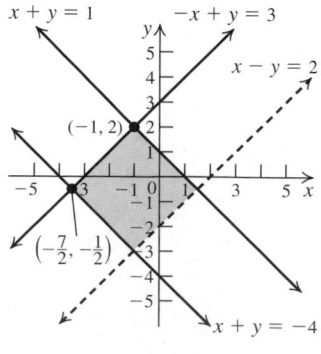

38. There are no vertices of the solution set.

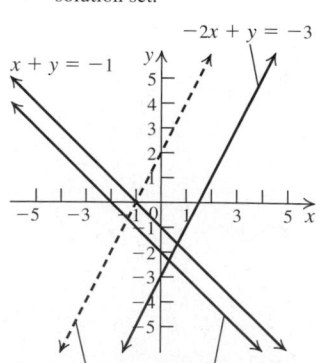

51. Maximum value is $\dfrac{1284}{19}$ at $\left(\dfrac{56}{19}, \dfrac{60}{19}\right)$

52. Maximum value is 35 at (5, 0)

53. Maximum value is 410 at (40, 30)

54. Maximum value is 12 at (6, 0)

55. Minimum value is 3 at (3, 0)

56. Minimum value is 15 at (1, 5)

57. Minimum value is 1364 at (8, 84)

58. Minimum value is 970 at (15, 10)

B Exercises: Applying The Concepts

59. 80 acres of corn and 160 acres of soybeans to obtain a maximum profit of $10,400

60. 0 acres of corn and 240 acres of soybeans to obtain a maximum profit of $9600

61. 40 hours for machine I and 20 hours for machine II to obtain a minimum cost of $3600

62. Machine I should be operated for zero hours and machine II should be operated for 46.7 hours to obtain a minimum cost of $4,200.

63. 5 minutes of television and 2 pages of newspaper advertisement to obtain a maximum of 340,000 viewers

64. 5.25 minutes of television and 1 page of newspaper advertisement to obtain a maximum of 710,000 viewers

65. The maximum profit is $14,600 at (320, 160).

66. The maximum profit is $184 at (56, 8).

67. 400 of both the rectangular and circular table should be made to have a maximum profit of $2,800.

68. 50 GPS's and 20 DVD players should be made to obtain a maximum profit of $380.

69. The contractor should build 33 terraced houses and 66 cottages to obtain a maximum amount of money: $4,290,000.

70. 125 female guests and 175 male guests would provide a maximum profit of $4902.50.

71. Mrs. Adams's maximum profit is $1355 when she has 175 male guests and 125 female guests.

72. The Michigan factory should operate 150 days and the North Carolina factory should operate 200 days for a minimum cost of 17,000,000.

73. Elisa should buy 10 enchilada meals and 5 vegetable loafs to obtain a minimum cost of $46.25.

74. 4 workers from the Ready Aid agency and 5 workers from the Super Temps agency should be hired to keep the daily wages at a minimum of $824.

C Exercises: Beyond the Basics

75. $\begin{cases} x \ge 0 \\ y \ge 0 \\ y \le \dfrac{-2}{3}x + 2 \end{cases}$

76. $\begin{cases} x \ge 0 \\ x \le 2 \\ y \ge 0 \\ y \ge \dfrac{-3}{2}x + 3 \\ y \le 5 \end{cases}$

77. $\begin{cases} x \ge -1 \\ x \le 3 \end{cases}$ 78. $\begin{cases} x \ge 0 \\ x < 2 \end{cases}$

79. $\begin{cases} x \ge 0 \\ y \ge 0 \\ y \le \dfrac{-1}{2}x + 4 \\ y \le \dfrac{-3}{2}x + 6 \end{cases}$

80. $\begin{cases} x \ge 0 \\ y \ge 0 \\ y \le 4 \\ y \le -2x + 8 \end{cases}$ 81. $\begin{cases} x \ge 0 \\ y \ge x - 4 \\ y \ge -x + 6 \\ y \le -x + 16 \end{cases}$

82. $\begin{cases} x \ge 0 \\ y \ge 0 \\ y \le -x + 16 \\ y \ge x - 10 \\ y \ge -x + 6 \end{cases}$

Critical Thinking

83.   84.

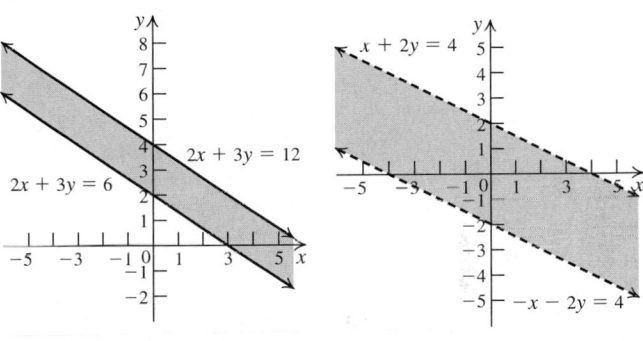

Section 8.5

Practice Problems

1. $\{(1, 1)\}$

2. $\{(4, 3), (-4, 3), (4, -3), (-4, -3)\}$

3. Danielle received $x = 30$ shares as dividends and sold her stock at $p = \$65$ per share.

4.

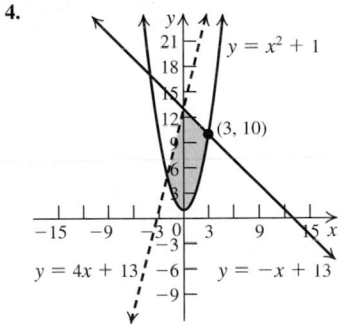

A Exercises: Basic Skills and Concepts

1. $(3, -1)$ 2. $(-2, 4)$ 3. $(1, -1)$ 4. $(-5, 0), (3, 4)$

5. $(5, 4), (-5, 4), (-5, -4)$ 6. $(2, 1), (2, -1)$

7. $(1, 1)$ 8. $(0, 0)$ 9. $\{(-1, 1), (2, 4)\}$

10. $\{(2, 4), (-3, 9)\}$ 11. $\{(3, 3)\}, (-2, -2)\}$

12. $\{(-1, -5), (6, 30)\}$ 13. $\{(3, 0)\}$ 14. $\{(0, 3)\}$

15. $\{(-2, 1), (-1, 2)\}$ 16. $\{(3, 2), (-3, -2)\}$

17. $\{(1, -1), (3, 1)\}$ 18. $\{(1, 1), (3, 5)\}$ 19. $\{(-3, -1), (1, 3)\}$

20. $\{(-2, -3), (6, 1)\}$ 21. $\{(2, 3), (0, 5)\}$ 22. $\{(4, 0), (0, 2)\}$

23. $\{(7, 5), (-7, -5)\}$ 24. $\{(3, 0), (4, 1)\}$

25. $\{(4, 2), (-4, 2), (4, -2), (-4, -2)\}$

26. $\{(1, 1), (-1, 1), (1, -1), (-1, -1)\}$

27. $\{(2, 2), (-2, 2), (2, -2), (-2, -2)\}$

28. $\{(-5, 1), (5, 1), (-5, -1), (5, -1)\}$

29. $\varnothing$ 30. $\varnothing$ 31. $\{(1, 2), (-1, 2), (1, -2), (-1, -2)\}$

32. $\{(1, 1), (-1, 1), (1, -1), (-1, -1)\}$

33. $\left\{(2, 1), (2, -1), \left(\dfrac{-11}{3}, \dfrac{\sqrt{26}}{3}\right), \left(\dfrac{-11}{3}, \dfrac{-\sqrt{26}}{3}\right)\right\}$

34. $\left\{\left(\dfrac{1}{2}, \dfrac{\sqrt{35}}{2}\right), \left(\dfrac{1}{2}, \dfrac{-\sqrt{35}}{2}\right)\right\}$

35. $\{(5, 3), (3, 5)\}$ **36.** $\left\{(3, 2), \left(\dfrac{23}{3}, \dfrac{-22}{3}\right)\right\}$ **37.** $\varnothing$

38. $\{(-2, 1), (2, 1), (-2, -1), (2, -1)\}$

39. $\{(0, -2), (3, 4)\}$ **40.** $\{(5, 25)\}$

41. $\left\{\left(-4, \dfrac{-3}{2}\right), (3, 2)\right\}$ **42.** $\{(1, 0)\}$

43. $\{(-2, 1), (2, 1), (-2, -1), (2, -1)\}$

44. $\{(-2, 2), (2, 2), (-2, -2), (2, -2)\}$

45. $\left\{(2, 5), \left(-7, \dfrac{-10}{7}\right)\right\}$ **46.** $\left\{(-2, -3), \left(6, \dfrac{23}{3}\right)\right\}$

47. $\left\{(2, -2), (2, 2), \left(\dfrac{16}{5}, \dfrac{2\sqrt{46}}{5}\right), \left(\dfrac{16}{5}, \dfrac{-2\sqrt{46}}{5}\right)\right\}$

48. $\left\{(1, 1), (-1, 1), \left(\dfrac{\sqrt{10}}{2}, 2\right), \left(-\dfrac{\sqrt{10}}{2}, 2\right)\right\}$

49.   **50.**

51.   **52.**

53.   **54.**

55.   **56.**

57.   **58.**

59.   **60.**

61.   **62.**

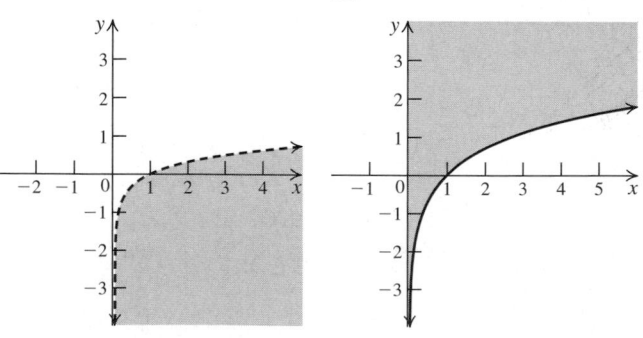

63. D, K   **64.** H   **65.** E, L   **66.** A, F   **67.** E, B   **68.** C, D

69.

70.

71.

72.

73.

74.

75.

76.

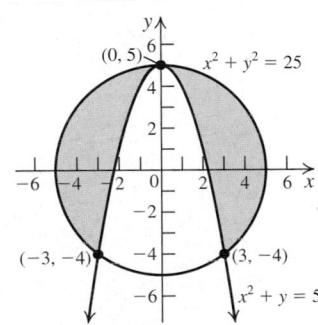

B Exercises: Applying the Concepts

77. $(3, 78)$ **78.** $(16, 3)$ **79.** 11 and 13

80. 6 and 19

81. a. $x = 60$ m, $y = 140$ m   **b.** 6000 m^2

82. 25 ft by 350 ft

83. 32 people and $30

84. 15 ft by 15 ft and 15 ft by 21 ft

85. 450 original shares, purchased at $22 per share

86. 660 original shares, purchased at $15 per share

C Exercises: Beyond the Basics

87.   **88.**

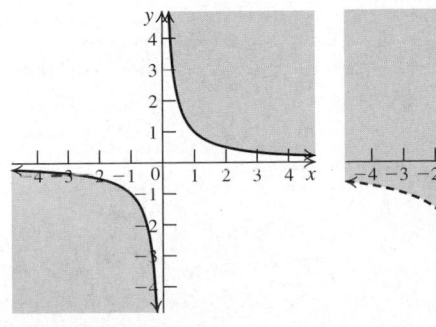

89.

90.

97.

98.

91.

92.

99. $\{(1, 7)\}$

100. $\varnothing$

93.

94.

101. $\{(1, 5)\}$

102. $\{(1, 5)\}$

95.

96.

103. $\left\{(1, 0), \left(2, \dfrac{\ln 2}{\ln 3}\right)\right\}$

104. $\left\{(1, 0), \left(2, \dfrac{\ln 2}{\ln 3}\right)\right\}$

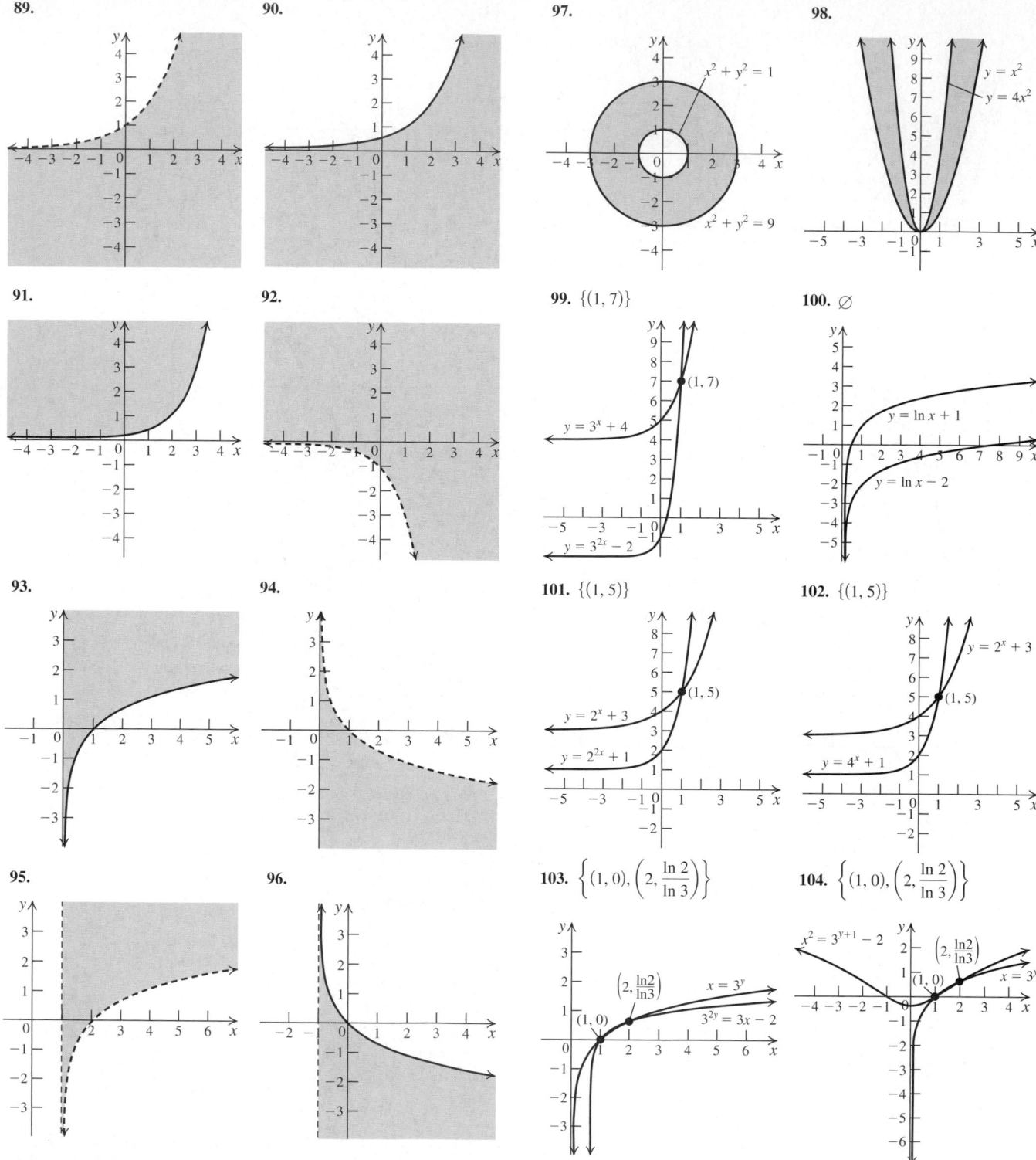

105. $A(1, 0), B(6, 0), d(A, B) = 5$

106. $A(0, -3), B(0, -2), d(A, B) = 1$

107. $A(-2, -1), B(2, 3), d(A, B) = 4\sqrt{2}$

108. $A(1 + \sqrt{14}, 3 - 2\sqrt{14}), B(1 - \sqrt{14}, 3 + 2\sqrt{14}), d(A, B) = 2\sqrt{70}$

109. $(0, -3)$ **110.** $\left(\dfrac{8}{5}, \dfrac{6}{5}\right)$

Critical Thinking

111. a. Not possible   **b.** Possible   **c.** Not possible
   d. Possible   **e.** Not possible   **f.** Not possible

112. a. Possible   **b.** Not possible   **c.** Possible
   d. Not possible   **e.** Possible   **f.** Not possible

Review Exercises

2. $\{(0, -2)\}$ **6.** $\varnothing$ **7.** $\{(1, -1, 2)\}$ **8.** $\{(5, 1, -2)\}$

9. $\{(-1, 2, -3)\}$ **10.** $\left\{\left(2, \dfrac{1}{3}, -1\right)\right\}$

13. $\left\{\left(4 + \dfrac{1}{2}y, y, -1 - \dfrac{3}{2}y\right)\right\}$ **14.** $\{(x, 23 - 7x, 16 - 5x)\}$

17. $\dfrac{1}{2(x - 1)} - \dfrac{1}{2(x + 1)}$ **18.** $\dfrac{1}{2(x + 2)} + \dfrac{1}{2(x - 2)}$

19. $\dfrac{2}{x + 2} - \dfrac{1}{x + 3}$ **20.** $\dfrac{3}{x - 1} - \dfrac{2}{x + 4}$

21. $\dfrac{2}{x - 1} + \dfrac{1}{x} + \dfrac{5}{(x - 1)^2}$ **22.** $\dfrac{2}{x - 1} - \dfrac{2}{(x + 1)^2} + \dfrac{1}{x + 1}$

23. $\dfrac{-1 + 2x}{(x^2 + 4)^2} + \dfrac{1}{x^2 + 4}$ **24.** $\dfrac{1}{2(x - 1)} - \dfrac{x}{x^2 + 1} + \dfrac{1}{2(x + 1)}$

25.

26.

27.

28.

29.

30.

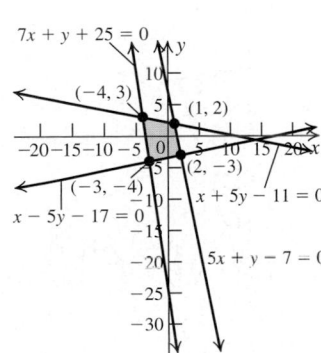

32. Min of 2 at $x = 0, y = 1$.
33. Min of -9 at $x = 0, y = -3$.
34. Max of 6 at $x = 3, y = 0$

35. $\left\{(-2, 1), \left(\dfrac{8}{3}, \dfrac{-5}{9}\right)\right\}$ **36.** $\left\{(1, 1), \left(\dfrac{17}{16}, \dfrac{5}{4}\right)\right\}$

37. $\left\{(2, -2), \left(\dfrac{-2}{3}, \dfrac{-14}{3}\right)\right\}$ **38.** $\left\{(1, -3), \left(\dfrac{31}{11}, \dfrac{-23}{11}\right)\right\}$

39. $\left\{(1, 2), (-1, -2), \left(2\sqrt{2}, \dfrac{\sqrt{2}}{2}\right), \left(-2\sqrt{2}, \dfrac{-\sqrt{2}}{2}\right)\right\}$

40. $\left\{(3, 1), (-3, -1), \left(\dfrac{\sqrt{6}}{2}, \sqrt{6}\right), \left(\dfrac{-\sqrt{6}}{2}, -\sqrt{6}\right)\right\}$

41.

42.

43.

44.

45.

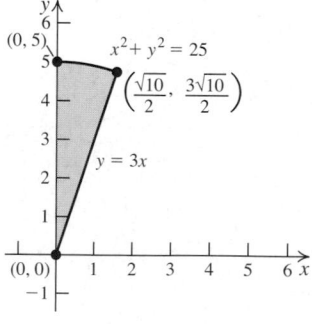

46.

47. \$8750 was invested at 12% and \$6250 was invested at 4%.
48. 35 acres of soybeans and 15 acres of tomatoes
50. $\dfrac{2}{9}$ and $\dfrac{1}{2}$ **52.** 4:00 A.M.
53. The original width is 40 m and the original length is 160 m.
54. **a.** For Budget Rentals, the cost function is $C(x) = 23 + 0.17x$.
For the Dollar Rentals, the cost function is $C(x) = 24 + 0.22x$.
b.

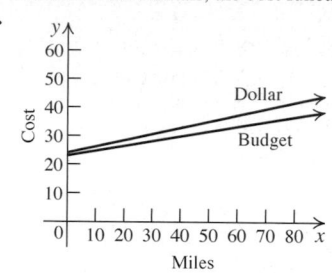

c. For (i), (ii), and (iii), you should lease from Budget Rentals.
55. **a.** $C(x) = 60,000 + 12x, R(x) = 20x$
b.

c. $(7500, 150,000)$
d. 11,129 timers
56. **a.** 200
b. \$20
c.

63. They stole \$35,000, and \$15,000 went to Butch, \$12,000 went to Sundance, and \$8000 went to Billy.

Practice Test A

2. $(8 - 2y, y)$

4. $(-5, 0)$

6. $(-1, 1), (4, 16)$

8. a. $\begin{cases} x + y = 485 \\ x - y = 15 \end{cases}$

9. $x + \dfrac{1}{2}y + z = 2$

$y - \dfrac{3}{4}z = \dfrac{7}{4}$

$z = \dfrac{-27}{23}$

11. $(7, 3, -2)$

12. $\left(x, \dfrac{2x}{3} + \dfrac{7}{3}, -x - 1\right)$

13. $\left(\dfrac{1}{3}, \dfrac{-4}{3} + z, z\right)$

15. $\dfrac{A}{(x - 5)} + \dfrac{B}{(x + 1)}$

16. $\dfrac{A}{x - 2} + \dfrac{Bx + C}{x^2 + 1} + \dfrac{Dx + E}{(x^2 + 1)^2}$

17. $-\dfrac{10}{121(x + 4)} + \dfrac{1}{11(x + 4)^2} + \dfrac{10}{121(x - 7)}$

18.

19.

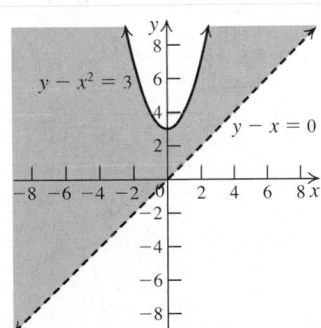

Cumulative Review Exercises (Chapters 1–8)

9.   **10.**

11.

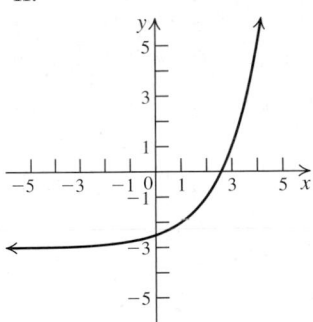

13. a. $f^{-1}(x) - \dfrac{x + 2}{2}$ **b.**

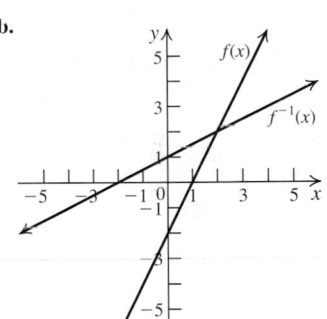

CHAPTER 9

Section 9.1

Practice Problems

1. a. 3×2 **b.** 1×2

2. $\begin{bmatrix} 0 & 3 & -1 & | & 8 \\ 1 & 4 & 0 & | & 14 \\ 0 & -2 & 9 & | & 0 \end{bmatrix}$

3. $\begin{bmatrix} 1 & 2 & 3 \\ 0 & -2 & -4 \end{bmatrix}$ **4.** $\left\{\left(-1, \dfrac{-1}{3}, -1\right)\right\}$

5. $\{(1, 2, -3)\}$ **6.** $\varnothing$ **7.** $\{(1, 2, -2)\}$

8. $\left\{\left(\dfrac{-7}{2} + \dfrac{3}{2}y, y, \dfrac{-3}{2}y + \dfrac{5}{2}\right)\right\}$

9. a. $\begin{cases} s = 0.01s + 0.1\ c + 0.1\ t + 12.46 \\ c = 0.2s + 0.02c + 0.01t + 3 \\ t = 0.25s + 0.3\ c + 2.7 \end{cases}$

b. $(0.99)(14) - (0.1)(6) - (0.1)(8) = 12.46$ ✓
$(-0.20)(14) + (0.98)(6) - (0.01)(8) = 3$ ✓
$(-0.25)(14) - (0.30)(6) + 8 = 2.7$ ✓

A Exercises: Basic Skills and Concepts

3. 2×4 **6.** 3×4

7. $a_{13} = 3, a_{31} = 9, a_{33} = 11, a_{34} = 12$

10. $A = \begin{bmatrix} 6 & -5 & 5 \\ 7 & 2 & 4 \end{bmatrix}$ **11.** $\begin{bmatrix} 2 & 4 & | & 2 \\ 1 & -3 & | & 1 \end{bmatrix}$ **12.** $\begin{bmatrix} 1 & 2 & | & 7 \\ 3 & 5 & | & 11 \end{bmatrix}$

13. $\begin{bmatrix} 5 & -7 & | & 11 \\ -13 & 17 & | & 19 \end{bmatrix}$ **14.** $\begin{bmatrix} -3 & 2 & | & 10 \\ 5 & -1 & | & -7 \end{bmatrix}$

15. $\begin{bmatrix} -1 & 2 & 3 & | & 8 \\ 2 & -3 & 9 & | & 16 \\ 4 & -5 & -6 & | & 32 \end{bmatrix}$ **16.** $\begin{bmatrix} 1 & -1 & 0 & | & 2 \\ 2 & 0 & 3 & | & -5 \\ 0 & 1 & -2 & | & 7 \end{bmatrix}$

17. $\begin{cases} x + 2y - 3z = 4 \\ -2x - 3y + z = 5 \\ 3x - 3y + 2z = 7 \end{cases}$ **18.** $\begin{cases} -x + 2y + 3z = 6 \\ 2x + 3y + z = 2 \\ 4x + 3y + 2z = 1 \end{cases}$

19. $\begin{cases} x - y + z = 2 \\ 2x + y - 3z = 6 \end{cases}$ **20.** $\begin{cases} x + y + z = 2 \\ x - y - z = 4 \\ 2x + 3y + z = 6 \\ -x + y - z = 8 \end{cases}$

21. $\begin{bmatrix} 1 & 2 & 3 \\ 0 & 1 & 1 \end{bmatrix}$ **22.** $\begin{bmatrix} 1 & 2 & 1 \\ 0 & 1 & 2 \end{bmatrix}$

23. $\begin{bmatrix} 1 & 2 & 3 & 4 \\ 0 & 1 & 5 & -3 \\ 0 & 0 & 1 & -1 \end{bmatrix}$ **24.** $\begin{bmatrix} 1 & 1.5 & -2 & .5 \\ 0 & 2 & 3 & 4 \\ 0 & 3 & 4.5 & 6 \end{bmatrix}$

25. $\begin{bmatrix} 4 & 5 & -7 \\ 5 & 4 & -2 \end{bmatrix} \xrightarrow{\frac{1}{4}R_1} \begin{bmatrix} 1 & \frac{5}{4} & -\frac{7}{4} \\ 5 & 4 & -2 \end{bmatrix} \xrightarrow{-5R_1 + R_2 \to R_2}$

$\begin{bmatrix} 1 & \frac{5}{4} & -\frac{7}{4} \\ 0 & -\frac{9}{4} & \frac{27}{4} \end{bmatrix} \xrightarrow{-\frac{4}{9}R_2} \begin{bmatrix} 1 & \frac{5}{4} & -\frac{7}{4} \\ 0 & 1 & -3 \end{bmatrix}$

26. $\begin{bmatrix} 2 & 6 & -8 \\ 3 & -1 & 2 \end{bmatrix} \xrightarrow{\frac{1}{2}R_1} \begin{bmatrix} 1 & 3 & -4 \\ 3 & -1 & 2 \end{bmatrix} \xrightarrow{-3R_1 + R_2 \to R_2}$

$\begin{bmatrix} 1 & 3 & -4 \\ 0 & -10 & 14 \end{bmatrix} \xrightarrow{-\frac{1}{10}R_2} \begin{bmatrix} 1 & 3 & -4 \\ 0 & 1 & -\frac{7}{5} \end{bmatrix}$

27. $\begin{bmatrix} 1 & 4 & 3 & 1 \\ 0 & -3 & -2 & 0 \\ 0 & 7 & 5 & -3 \end{bmatrix} \xrightarrow{-\frac{1}{3}R_2} \begin{bmatrix} 1 & 4 & 3 & 1 \\ 0 & 1 & \frac{2}{3} & 0 \\ 0 & 7 & 5 & -3 \end{bmatrix}$

$\xrightarrow{-7R_2 + R_3 \to R_3} \begin{bmatrix} 1 & 4 & 3 & 1 \\ 0 & 1 & \frac{2}{3} & 0 \\ 0 & 0 & \frac{1}{3} & -3 \end{bmatrix} \xrightarrow{3R_3}$

$\begin{bmatrix} 1 & 4 & 3 & 1 \\ 0 & 1 & \frac{2}{3} & 0 \\ 0 & 0 & 1 & -9 \end{bmatrix}$

28. $\begin{bmatrix} 1 & 1 & 1 & 3 \\ 2 & 3 & 3 & 8 \\ 1 & -3 & -2 & 5 \end{bmatrix} \xrightarrow{-2R_1 + R_2 \to R_2} \begin{bmatrix} 1 & 1 & 1 & 3 \\ 0 & 1 & 1 & 2 \\ 1 & -3 & -2 & 5 \end{bmatrix}$

$\xrightarrow{-R_1 + R_3 \to R_3} \begin{bmatrix} 1 & 1 & 1 & 3 \\ 0 & 1 & 1 & 2 \\ 0 & -4 & -3 & 2 \end{bmatrix}$

$\xrightarrow{4R_2 + R_3 \to R_3} \begin{bmatrix} 1 & 1 & 1 & 3 \\ 0 & 1 & 1 & 2 \\ 0 & 0 & 1 & 10 \end{bmatrix}$

37. $(5, -2)$ $\begin{cases} x + 2y = 1 \\ y = -2 \end{cases}$ **38.** $(2, 3)$ $\begin{cases} x = 2 \\ y = 3 \end{cases}$

39. $(-4 - 4y, y, 3)$ $\begin{cases} x + 4y + 2z = 2 \\ z = 3 \end{cases}$

40. Inconsistent $\begin{cases} x + 2y + 3z = 4 \\ 0z = 1 \end{cases}$

41. $(1, 2, -1)$ $\begin{cases} x + 2y + 3z = 2 \\ y - 2z = 4 \\ z = -1 \end{cases}$

42. $(2, -3, 5)$ $\begin{cases} x + 2z = 12 \\ y + 3z = 12 \\ z = 5 \end{cases}$

43. $(2, -5, -2w + 3, w)$ $\begin{cases} x = 2 \\ y = -5 \\ z + 2w = 3 \end{cases}$

44. $(4, 3, z, 2)$ $\begin{cases} x = 4 \\ y = 3 \\ w = 2 \end{cases}$

45. $(-5, 4, 3, 0)$ $\begin{cases} x = -5 \\ y = 4 \\ z + 2w = 3 \\ w = 0 \end{cases}$ **46.** Inconsistent $\begin{cases} x = 3 \\ y = 2 \\ z = 0 \\ 0w = 1 \end{cases}$

51. $\left\{\left(\dfrac{-1}{5}, \dfrac{-23}{25}\right)\right\}$ **52.** $\left\{\left(\dfrac{-31}{2}, \dfrac{-15}{2}\right)\right\}$

54. $\left\{\left(\dfrac{-1}{2}, 0\right)\right\}$ **55.** $\{(1, 2, 3)\}$ **56.** $\{(2, -1, 5)\}$ **57.** $\{(2, 3, 4)\}$

58. $\{(1, -1, 2)\}$ **59.** $\{(1, 2, 3)\}$ **60.** $\{(1, 2, -2)\}$

61. $\left\{\left(\dfrac{5}{2}, \dfrac{3}{2}, \dfrac{7}{2}\right)\right\}$ **62.** $\left\{\left(\dfrac{283}{81}, -\dfrac{10}{27}, -\dfrac{113}{81}\right)\right\}$

63. $\{(1 + 4z, 3 - 3z, z)\}$ **64.** $\{(-3, -2 - z, z)\}$ **65.** $\{(1, 2, -1)\}$

66. $\{(1, 2, 1)\}$ **67. b.** Infinitely many solutions

B Exercises: Applying the Concepts

71. a. $\begin{cases} a = 0.1b + 1000 \\ b = 0.2a + 780 \end{cases}$

b. $\begin{bmatrix} 1 & -0.1 & | & 1000 \\ -0.2 & 1 & | & 780 \end{bmatrix}$

c. $a = 1100, b = 1000$

72. a. $\begin{cases} a = 0.5a + 0.2b + 50{,}000 \\ b = 0.3b + 0.6a + 40{,}000 \end{cases}$

b. $\begin{bmatrix} 0.5 & -0.2 & | & 50{,}000 \\ -0.6 & 0.7 & | & 40{,}000 \end{bmatrix}$

c. $a = 186{,}957\ b = 217{,}391$

73. a. $l = 0.4t + 0.2f + 10{,}000$
$t = 0.5l + 0.3t + 20{,}000$
$f = 0.5l + 0.05t + 0.35f + 10{,}000$

b. $\begin{bmatrix} 1 & -0.4 & -0.2 & | & 10,000 \\ -0.5 & 0.7 & 0 & | & 20,000 \\ -0.5 & -0.05 & 0.65 & | & 10,000 \end{bmatrix}$

c. food, \$55,000; transportation, \$61,000; labor, \$45,400

74. a. $\begin{cases} a = 0.3c + 0.2b + 320 \\ b = 0.1a + 0.4c + 90 \\ c = 0.5b + 0.2a + 150 \end{cases}$

b. $\begin{bmatrix} 1 & -0.2 & -0.3 & | & 320 \\ -0.1 & 1 & -0.4 & | & 90 \\ -0.2 & -0.5 & 1 & | & 150 \end{bmatrix}$

c. $a = 500, b = 300, c = 400$

75. $T_1 = 110, T_2 = 140, T_3 = 60$

76. $T_1 = 30, T_2 = \dfrac{75}{2}, T_3 = 40, T_4 = \dfrac{65}{2}$

77. a. $\begin{cases} x - y = 70 \\ -x + z = -120 \\ y - z = 50 \end{cases}$

b. $\{(120 + z, 50 + z, z)\}$

78. a. $\begin{cases} x - y = 100 \\ y + w = 200 \\ -x + z = 20 \\ -z - w = -320 \end{cases}$

b. $\{(300 - w, 200 - w, 320 - w, w)\}$

79. a. $h = -16t^2 + 64t + 3$

C Exercises: Beyond the Basics

80. $\dfrac{1}{x-1} + \dfrac{2}{(x-1)^2} - \dfrac{4}{x+2} + \dfrac{3}{x+3}$

83. a. $B = \begin{bmatrix} 1 & \frac{3}{2} & 0 & -1 \\ 0 & 1 & 0 & \frac{1}{2} \\ 0 & 0 & 1 & \frac{1}{2} \\ 0 & 0 & 0 & 1 \end{bmatrix}$, $C = \begin{bmatrix} 1 & 2 & -3 & 1 \\ 0 & 1 & 0 & -\frac{1}{2} \\ 0 & 0 & 1 & \frac{1}{2} \\ 0 & 0 & 0 & 1 \end{bmatrix}$

b. The reduced row-echelon form of the matrices B and C is

$\begin{bmatrix} 1 & 0 & 0 & 0 \\ 0 & 1 & 0 & 0 \\ 0 & 0 & 1 & 0 \\ 0 & 0 & 0 & 1 \end{bmatrix}.$

84. a. Both $B = \begin{bmatrix} 1 & 0.5 & -0.5 & 0.5 \\ 0 & 1 & -1 & -1 \\ 0 & 0 & 1 & 3 \end{bmatrix}$ and $C = \begin{bmatrix} 1 & 1 & 1 & 6 \\ 0 & 1 & 0 & 2 \\ 0 & 0 & 1 & 3 \end{bmatrix}$

yield the solution set $\{(1, 2, 3)\}$.

b. The reduced row-echelon form of the matrices B and C is

$\begin{bmatrix} 1 & 0 & 0 & 1 \\ 0 & 1 & 0 & 2 \\ 0 & 0 & 1 & 3 \end{bmatrix}.$

85. a. $\left\{ \left(\dfrac{dm - nb}{ad - bc}, \dfrac{cm - an}{cb - ad} \right) \right\}$

b. (i) $cb \neq ad$ (ii) $cb = ad$ and $\dfrac{m}{b} \neq \dfrac{n}{d}$ (iii) $cb = ad$ and $\dfrac{m}{b} = \dfrac{n}{d}$

86. $\begin{bmatrix} 1 & 0 & 0 & | & 1 \\ 0 & 1 & 0 & | & 0 \\ 0 & 0 & 1 & | & -2 \end{bmatrix}, \begin{bmatrix} 2 & 1 & 0 & | & 2 \\ 0 & 1 & 0 & | & 0 \\ 0 & 0 & 4 & | & -8 \end{bmatrix}, \begin{bmatrix} 1 & 1 & 1 & | & -1 \\ 0 & 1 & 0 & | & 0 \\ 0 & 1 & 1 & | & -2 \end{bmatrix}$

89. $y = -x^3 + 2x^2 + 3x + 1$

90. $y = -2x^3 + 3x^2 + 5x + 2$

Critical Thinking

91. $\begin{bmatrix} 0 \\ 0 \end{bmatrix}, \begin{bmatrix} 1 \\ 0 \end{bmatrix}$

92. $\begin{bmatrix} 0 & 0 \\ 0 & 0 \end{bmatrix}, \begin{bmatrix} 1 & k \\ 0 & 0 \end{bmatrix}, \begin{bmatrix} 0 & 1 \\ 0 & 0 \end{bmatrix}, \begin{bmatrix} 1 & 0 \\ 0 & 1 \end{bmatrix}$, where k is some constant

93. Yes. The inverse of the operation used to transform A to B

95. False. **96.** False.

Section 9.2

Practice Problems

1. $x = 1, y = 1$ **2.** $\begin{bmatrix} -6 & 1 & 13 \\ 12 & 3 & 15 \end{bmatrix}$

3. $\begin{bmatrix} 11 & 1 \\ 0 & 6 \\ -15 & -28 \end{bmatrix}$ **4.** $X = \begin{bmatrix} -\frac{1}{3} & \frac{19}{3} \\ -7 & -\frac{35}{3} \end{bmatrix}$

5. Yes, the product AB is defined with order 2×1.

6. \$2045 thousand **7.** $[31]$

8. The product AB is not defined. $BA = \begin{bmatrix} 42 & -1 \\ 2 & -6 \\ 8 & -4 \end{bmatrix}$

9. $AB = \begin{bmatrix} 18 & -3 \\ 12 & 12 \end{bmatrix}, BA = \begin{bmatrix} 14 & -1 \\ 28 & 16 \end{bmatrix}$

10. $AD = \begin{bmatrix} 0 & 0 & 1 & 1 & 6 & 6 \\ 0 & 4 & 4.25 & 1.25 & 2.5 & 1.5 \end{bmatrix}$

A Exercises: Basic Skills and Concepts

1. $x = 2, u = -3$ **2.** $x = 3, y = -8$ **8.** $x = 2, y = -3$

9. a. $\begin{bmatrix} 0 & 2 \\ 5 & 1 \end{bmatrix}$ **b.** $\begin{bmatrix} 2 & 2 \\ 1 & 7 \end{bmatrix}$ **c.** $\begin{bmatrix} -3 & -6 \\ -9 & -12 \end{bmatrix}$ **d.** $\begin{bmatrix} 5 & 6 \\ 5 & 18 \end{bmatrix}$

e. $\begin{bmatrix} 10 & 2 \\ 5 & 11 \end{bmatrix}$ **f.** $\begin{bmatrix} 6 & 10 \\ 23 & 13 \end{bmatrix}$

10. a. $\begin{bmatrix} \frac{4}{3} & 1 \\ 1 & \frac{3}{2} \end{bmatrix}$ **b.** $\begin{bmatrix} -\frac{2}{3} & 1 \\ -3 & \frac{5}{2} \end{bmatrix}$ **c.** $\begin{bmatrix} -1 & -3 \\ 3 & -6 \end{bmatrix}$ **d.** $\begin{bmatrix} -1 & 3 \\ -7 & 7 \end{bmatrix}$

e. $\begin{bmatrix} \frac{25}{9} & \frac{17}{6} \\ \frac{17}{6} & \frac{13}{4} \end{bmatrix}$ **f.** $\begin{bmatrix} -\frac{17}{9} & \frac{7}{3} \\ \frac{10}{3} & \frac{11}{4} \end{bmatrix}$

11. a, b, d, e, and f are not defined. **c.** $\begin{bmatrix} -6 & -9 \\ 12 & -15 \end{bmatrix}$

12. a, b, d, e, and f are not defined. **c.** $\begin{bmatrix} -3 & -6 & -9 \\ 3 & 9 & -12 \end{bmatrix}$

13. a. $\begin{bmatrix} 7 & 1 & -1 \\ -1 & 1 & 4 \\ 2 & 1 & 4 \end{bmatrix}$ **b.** $\begin{bmatrix} 1 & -1 & -1 \\ -3 & 9 & 0 \\ -2 & -1 & -2 \end{bmatrix}$

c. $\begin{bmatrix} -12 & 0 & 3 \\ 6 & -15 & -6 \\ 0 & 0 & -3 \end{bmatrix}$ **d.** $\begin{bmatrix} 6 & -2 & -3 \\ -8 & 23 & 2 \\ -4 & -2 & -3 \end{bmatrix}$

e. $\begin{bmatrix} 46 & 7 & -7 \\ 0 & 4 & 21 \\ 21 & 7 & 18 \end{bmatrix}$ **f.** $\begin{bmatrix} 6 & 1 & -7 \\ -21 & 6 & 16 \\ -13 & -1 & -10 \end{bmatrix}$

14. a. $\begin{bmatrix} 4 & -1 & 4 \\ 2 & 3 & 1 \\ 1 & 5 & 2 \end{bmatrix}$ **b.** $\begin{bmatrix} -2 & 1 & 0 \\ 2 & -1 & -1 \\ -1 & -3 & 4 \end{bmatrix}$

c. $\begin{bmatrix} -3 & 0 & -6 \\ -6 & -3 & 0 \\ 0 & -3 & -9 \end{bmatrix}$ **d.** $\begin{bmatrix} -3 & 2 & 2 \\ 6 & -1 & -2 \\ -2 & -5 & 11 \end{bmatrix}$

e. $\begin{bmatrix} 18 & 13 & 23 \\ 15 & 12 & 13 \\ 16 & 24 & 13 \end{bmatrix}$ **f.** $\begin{bmatrix} -10 & -1 & 5 \\ 3 & -7 & 3 \\ 0 & 1 & 2 \end{bmatrix}$

15. a. $\begin{bmatrix} 4 & 3 & -3 \\ 4 & 0 & 7 \\ 4 & 0 & 3 \end{bmatrix}$ **b.** $\begin{bmatrix} -2 & 1 & -3 \\ 2 & 8 & 3 \\ 0 & -2 & -3 \end{bmatrix}$

c. $\begin{bmatrix} -3 & -6 & 9 \\ -9 & -12 & -15 \\ -6 & 3 & 0 \end{bmatrix}$ **d.** $\begin{bmatrix} -3 & 4 & -9 \\ 7 & 20 & 11 \\ 2 & -5 & -6 \end{bmatrix}$

e. $\begin{bmatrix} 16 & 12 & 0 \\ 44 & 12 & 9 \\ 28 & 12 & -3 \end{bmatrix}$ **f.** $\begin{bmatrix} -9 & 14 & 5 \\ 22 & -2 & 13 \\ -14 & -1 & -22 \end{bmatrix}$

16. a. $\begin{bmatrix} 4 & -1 & 4 \\ 2 & 3 & 1 \\ 1 & 5 & 2 \end{bmatrix}$ **b.** $\begin{bmatrix} -2 & 1 & 0 \\ 2 & -1 & -1 \\ -1 & -3 & 4 \end{bmatrix}$ **c.** $\begin{bmatrix} -3 & 0 & -6 \\ -6 & -3 & 0 \\ 0 & -3 & -9 \end{bmatrix}$

d. $\begin{bmatrix} -3 & 2 & 2 \\ 6 & -1 & -2 \\ -2 & -5 & 11 \end{bmatrix}$ **e.** $\begin{bmatrix} 18 & 13 & 23 \\ 15 & 12 & 13 \\ 16 & 24 & 13 \end{bmatrix}$ **f.** $\begin{bmatrix} -10 & -1 & 5 \\ 3 & -7 & 3 \\ 0 & 1 & 2 \end{bmatrix}$

17. $X = \begin{bmatrix} -4 & -2 & 1 \\ 1 & 5 & 0 \end{bmatrix}$ **18.** $X = \begin{bmatrix} 4 & 2 & -1 \\ -1 & -5 & 0 \end{bmatrix}$

19. $X = \begin{bmatrix} 0 & 2 & -\frac{1}{2} \\ \frac{3}{2} & \frac{1}{2} & 4 \end{bmatrix}$ **20.** $X = \begin{bmatrix} 0 & 2 & -\frac{1}{2} \\ \frac{3}{2} & \frac{1}{2} & 4 \end{bmatrix}$

21. $X = \begin{bmatrix} -4 & -4 & \frac{3}{2} \\ -\frac{1}{2} & \frac{9}{2} & -4 \end{bmatrix}$ **22.** $X = \begin{bmatrix} -2 & -\frac{5}{3} & \frac{2}{3} \\ 0 & \frac{7}{3} & \frac{4}{3} \end{bmatrix}$

23. $X = \begin{bmatrix} \frac{1}{2} & -\frac{9}{4} & \frac{1}{2} \\ -2 & -\frac{5}{4} & -5 \end{bmatrix}$ **24.** $X = \begin{bmatrix} \frac{14}{3} & \frac{1}{3} & -\frac{2}{3} \\ -\frac{8}{3} & \frac{19}{3} & -4 \end{bmatrix}$

25. a. $AB = \begin{bmatrix} 4 & 11 \\ 6 & 23 \end{bmatrix}$ **b.** $BA = \begin{bmatrix} 1 & 0 \\ 18 & 26 \end{bmatrix}$

26. a. $AB = \begin{bmatrix} 7 & 19 & -6 \\ 11 & 28 & -2 \\ 2 & 5 & 0 \end{bmatrix}$ **b.** $BA = \begin{bmatrix} 6 & 15 \\ 11 & 29 \end{bmatrix}$

27. a. $AB = \begin{bmatrix} 4 & 7 \\ 3 & -12 \end{bmatrix}$ **b.** $BA = \begin{bmatrix} -13 & 4 & 10 \\ -13 & 5 & 6 \\ 8 & -4 & 0 \end{bmatrix}$

28. The products AB and BA are not defined.

29. a. $AB = [16]$ **b.** $BA = \begin{bmatrix} 2 & 3 & 5 \\ -4 & -6 & -10 \\ 8 & 12 & 20 \end{bmatrix}$

30. a. $AB = \begin{bmatrix} -3 & 0 & 2 \\ -6 & 0 & 4 \\ 3 & 0 & -2 \end{bmatrix}$ **b.** $BA = [-5]$

31. a. $AB = [7 \quad 8 \quad -8]$ **b.** The product BA is not defined.
32. a. The product AB is not defined. **b.** $BA = [-7 \quad 14 \quad -7]$

33. a. $AB = \begin{bmatrix} 10 & 7 & 2 \\ 7 & 19 & 4 \\ 10 & 1 & 0 \end{bmatrix}$ **b.** $BA = \begin{bmatrix} 7 & 4 & 5 \\ 0 & 8 & 3 \\ 19 & 18 & 14 \end{bmatrix}$

34. a. $AB = \begin{bmatrix} 13 & -17 & 5 \\ -13 & 8 & -10 \\ 10 & -9 & 6 \end{bmatrix}$ **b.** $BA = \begin{bmatrix} 6 & -22 & 19 \\ -4 & 11 & -10 \\ 11 & -7 & 10 \end{bmatrix}$

35. $AB = \begin{bmatrix} 13 & 17 & 3 \\ 13 & 8 & 2 \\ 6 & 1 & 6 \end{bmatrix} \neq \begin{bmatrix} 6 & 22 & 19 \\ 2 & 11 & 6 \\ 11 & -1 & 10 \end{bmatrix} = BA$

36. $AB = \begin{bmatrix} 10 & 17 & 36 \\ -25 & 24 & 13 \\ -31 & 13 & 46 \end{bmatrix} = BA$

B Exercises: Applying the Concepts

41. Steel Glass Wood
$C = \begin{bmatrix} 13 & 5 & 38 \\ 7 & 2 & 7 \end{bmatrix}$ Cost of material
Transportation cost

42. Steel Glass Wood
$C = \begin{bmatrix} 33 & 13 & 94 \\ 18 & 5 & 17 \end{bmatrix}$ Cost of material
Transportation cost

44. Materials Labor Profit
$[5875 \quad 475 \quad 5125]$

45. a.   Chairman   President   Vice-president
Salary $\begin{bmatrix} 2,500,000 & 1,250,000 & 100,000 \\ \end{bmatrix}$
Bonus $\begin{bmatrix} 1,500,000 & 750,000 & 150,000 \\ \end{bmatrix}$
Stock $\begin{bmatrix} 50,000 & 25,000 & 5,000 \end{bmatrix}$

b. $\begin{bmatrix} 1 \\ 1 \\ 4 \end{bmatrix}$ Chairman
President
Vice-president

c. $\begin{bmatrix} 4,150,000 \\ 2,850,000 \\ 95,000 \end{bmatrix}$ Total salary
Total bonuses
Total stocks

46.   Male Female Children Calorie Protein
$\begin{matrix} Brown \\ Newgard \end{matrix} \begin{bmatrix} 2 & 3 & 1 \\ 1 & 1 & 2 \end{bmatrix} \begin{bmatrix} 2400 & 55 \\ 1900 & 45 \\ 1800 & 33 \end{bmatrix}$

$= \begin{bmatrix} 12,300 & 278 \\ 7900 & 166 \end{bmatrix}$

For the Brown family, the total calorie requirement is 12,300 and the total protein requirement is 278.
For the Newgard family, the total calorie requirement is 7900 and the total protein requirement is 166.

47. $AD = \begin{bmatrix} 0 & 4 & 4 & 1 & 1 & 0 \\ 0 & 0 & -1 & -1 & -6 & -6 \end{bmatrix}$

48. $AD = \begin{bmatrix} 0 & -4 & -4 & -1 & -1 & 0 \\ 0 & 0 & 1 & 1 & 6 & 6 \end{bmatrix}$

49. $AD = \begin{bmatrix} 0 & 4 & 4 & 1 & 1 & 0 \\ 0 & 1 & 2 & 1.25 & 6.25 & 6 \end{bmatrix}$

50. $AD = \begin{bmatrix} 0 & 4 & 3.75 & 0.75 & -0.5 & -1.5 \\ 0 & 0 & 1 & 1 & 6 & 6 \end{bmatrix}$

C Exercises: Beyond the Basics

51. $AB = \begin{bmatrix} 9 & 0 \\ 0 & 0 \end{bmatrix} = AC$

53. Let $A = \begin{bmatrix} 1 & 2 \\ 3 & 4 \end{bmatrix}$ and $B = \begin{bmatrix} -1 & 0 \\ 2 & -3 \end{bmatrix}$. Then
$(A + B)^2 = \begin{bmatrix} 10 & 2 \\ 5 & 11 \end{bmatrix} \neq \begin{bmatrix} 14 & -2 \\ 17 & 7 \end{bmatrix} = A^2 + 2AB + B^2.$

54. Let $A = \begin{bmatrix} 1 & 2 \\ 3 & 4 \end{bmatrix}$ and $B = \begin{bmatrix} -1 & 0 \\ 2 & -3 \end{bmatrix}$. Then

$$A^2 - B^2 = \begin{bmatrix} 6 & 10 \\ 23 & 13 \end{bmatrix} \neq \begin{bmatrix} 10 & 6 \\ 35 & 9 \end{bmatrix} = (A - B)(A + B).$$

57. $B = \begin{bmatrix} 2 & -3 \\ -1 & 2 \end{bmatrix}$ **59.** $x = 33, y = 5$

Critical Thinking

61. a. AB is defined when $n = 5$ and the order of AB when this product is defined is $3 \times m$.

b. BA is defined when $m = 3$, and the order of BA when this product is defined is $5 \times n$.

Group Project

a. $XP^2 = \begin{bmatrix} \dfrac{37}{75} & \dfrac{19}{75} & \dfrac{19}{75} \end{bmatrix}$

b. $XP^3 = \begin{bmatrix} \dfrac{188}{375} & \dfrac{187}{750} & \dfrac{187}{750} \end{bmatrix}$

$XP^4 = \begin{bmatrix} \dfrac{937}{1875} & \dfrac{469}{1875} & \dfrac{469}{1875} \end{bmatrix}$

$XP^5 = \begin{bmatrix} \dfrac{4688}{9375} & \dfrac{4687}{18,750} & \dfrac{4687}{18,750} \end{bmatrix}$

$XP^n = \begin{bmatrix} 0.5 & 0.25 & 0.25 \end{bmatrix}$

Section 9.3

Practice Problems

1. $\begin{bmatrix} 3 & 2 \\ 2 & 1 \end{bmatrix} \begin{bmatrix} -1 & 2 \\ 2 & -3 \end{bmatrix} = \begin{bmatrix} 1 & 0 \\ 0 & 1 \end{bmatrix}$

2. $\begin{bmatrix} 3x + z & 3y + w \\ 3x + z & 3y + w \end{bmatrix} \neq \begin{bmatrix} 1 & 0 \\ 0 & 1 \end{bmatrix}$, since this implies that $1 = 3x + z = 0$, which is false.

3. $A^{-1} = \begin{bmatrix} \dfrac{1}{5} & \dfrac{2}{5} \\ -\dfrac{2}{5} & \dfrac{1}{5} \end{bmatrix}$

4. The inverse of matrix A does not exist.

5. $A^{-1} = \begin{bmatrix} \dfrac{1}{7} & -\dfrac{19}{77} & \dfrac{1}{11} \\ 0 & \dfrac{2}{11} & \dfrac{1}{11} \\ \dfrac{2}{7} & -\dfrac{3}{77} & -\dfrac{1}{11} \end{bmatrix}$

6. The inverse of matrix A does not exist; $B^{-1} = \begin{bmatrix} \dfrac{1}{14} & \dfrac{1}{7} \\ -\dfrac{3}{14} & \dfrac{4}{7} \end{bmatrix}$.

7. $\left\{ \left(\dfrac{11}{2}, -\dfrac{9}{2}, \dfrac{1}{2} \right) \right\}$ **8.** $X = \begin{bmatrix} \dfrac{83,200}{19} \\ \dfrac{141,600}{19} \end{bmatrix}$

9. $AM = \begin{bmatrix} 1 & 2 & 3 \\ 1 & 3 & 3 \\ 1 & 2 & 4 \end{bmatrix} \begin{bmatrix} 10 & 11 & 19 & 15 & 19 & 5 \\ 1 & 0 & 0 & 23 & 1 & 0 \\ 3 & 9 & 14 & 0 & 6 & 0 \end{bmatrix}$
$= \begin{bmatrix} 21 & 38 & 61 & 61 & 39 & 5 \\ 22 & 38 & 61 & 84 & 40 & 5 \\ 24 & 47 & 75 & 61 & 45 & 5 \end{bmatrix}$

A Exercises: Basic Skills and Concepts

11. $A^{-1} = \begin{bmatrix} \dfrac{1}{2} & 0 \\ -\dfrac{1}{6} & \dfrac{1}{3} \end{bmatrix}$ **12.** $A^{-1} = \begin{bmatrix} 0 & 1 \\ \dfrac{1}{3} & -\dfrac{4}{3} \end{bmatrix}$

13. The inverse of matrix A does not exist.

14. The inverse of matrix A does not exist.

15. $A^{-1} = \begin{bmatrix} 1 & -8 & 10 \\ 0 & 2 & -3 \\ 0 & -1 & 2 \end{bmatrix}$ **16.** $A^{-1} = \begin{bmatrix} -\dfrac{1}{4} & \dfrac{3}{4} & \dfrac{1}{2} \\ \dfrac{1}{8} & -\dfrac{3}{8} & \dfrac{1}{4} \\ \dfrac{1}{8} & \dfrac{5}{8} & \dfrac{1}{4} \end{bmatrix}$

17. $A^{-1} = \begin{bmatrix} \dfrac{3}{4} & -\dfrac{5}{2} & -\dfrac{1}{4} \\ -\dfrac{1}{2} & 2 & \dfrac{1}{2} \\ \dfrac{1}{2} & -1 & -\dfrac{1}{2} \end{bmatrix}$ **18.** $A^{-1} = \begin{bmatrix} 1 & 1 & -4 \\ -1 & -1 & 5 \\ \dfrac{1}{5} & 0 & -\dfrac{1}{5} \end{bmatrix}$

19. $A^{-1} = \begin{bmatrix} \dfrac{3}{14} & -\dfrac{1}{14} & \dfrac{5}{14} \\ \dfrac{5}{14} & \dfrac{3}{14} & -\dfrac{1}{14} \\ -\dfrac{1}{14} & \dfrac{5}{14} & \dfrac{3}{14} \end{bmatrix}$ **20.** $A^{-1} = \begin{bmatrix} \dfrac{3}{2} & -\dfrac{1}{4} & -\dfrac{9}{4} \\ -1 & \dfrac{1}{2} & \dfrac{3}{2} \\ \dfrac{1}{2} & \dfrac{1}{4} & \dfrac{1}{4} \end{bmatrix}$

21. $A^{-1} = \begin{bmatrix} 1 & 0 \\ \dfrac{3}{2} & 1 \\ -\dfrac{3}{2} & \dfrac{1}{2} \end{bmatrix}$ **22.** $A^{-1} = \begin{bmatrix} -3 & 2 \\ \dfrac{5}{2} & -\dfrac{3}{2} \end{bmatrix}$

23. $A^{-1} = \begin{bmatrix} 5 & 3 \\ 3 & 2 \end{bmatrix}$ **24.** $A^{-1} = \begin{bmatrix} -1 & 2 \\ -1 & \dfrac{3}{2} \end{bmatrix}$

25. $A^{-1} = \dfrac{1}{-a^2 + b^2} \begin{bmatrix} -a & b \\ -b & a \end{bmatrix}$, where $a^2 \neq b^2$

26. $A^{-1} = \begin{bmatrix} 1 & -1 \\ 1 & -2 \end{bmatrix}$ **27.** $\begin{bmatrix} 2 & 3 \\ 1 & -3 \end{bmatrix} \begin{bmatrix} x \\ y \end{bmatrix} = \begin{bmatrix} -9 \\ 13 \end{bmatrix}$

28. $\begin{bmatrix} 5 & -4 \\ 4 & -3 \end{bmatrix} \begin{bmatrix} x \\ y \end{bmatrix} = \begin{bmatrix} 7 \\ 5 \end{bmatrix}$ **29.** $\begin{bmatrix} 3 & 2 & 1 \\ 2 & 1 & 3 \\ 1 & 3 & 2 \end{bmatrix} \begin{bmatrix} x \\ y \\ z \end{bmatrix} = \begin{bmatrix} 8 \\ 7 \\ 9 \end{bmatrix}$

30. $\begin{bmatrix} 1 & 3 & 1 \\ 1 & -5 & 2 \\ 3 & 1 & -4 \end{bmatrix} \begin{bmatrix} x \\ y \\ z \end{bmatrix} = \begin{bmatrix} 4 \\ 7 \\ -9 \end{bmatrix}$

31. $\begin{cases} x - 2y = 0 \\ 2x + y = 5 \end{cases}$ **32.** $\begin{cases} 2x_1 + 3x_2 = 0 \\ 3x_1 - x_2 = 11 \end{cases}$

33. $\begin{cases} 2x_1 + 3x_2 + x_3 = -1 \\ 5x_1 + 7x_2 - x_3 = 5 \\ 4x_1 + 3x_2 = 5 \end{cases}$ **34.** $\begin{cases} 3r - 2s + 3t = 4 \\ 5r + 4t = 3 \\ 2r + 7s = -8 \end{cases}$

35. $\begin{bmatrix} 1 & 2 & 5 \\ 2 & 3 & 8 \\ -1 & 1 & 2 \end{bmatrix} \begin{bmatrix} 2 & -1 & -1 \\ 12 & -7 & -2 \\ -5 & 3 & 1 \end{bmatrix} = \begin{bmatrix} 1 & 0 & 0 \\ 0 & 1 & 0 \\ 0 & 0 & 1 \end{bmatrix}$

36. $\{(-1, 0, 1)\}$ **37.** $\{(2, -3, 1)\}$ **38.** $\left\{ \left(\dfrac{1}{2}, -1, -\dfrac{1}{2} \right) \right\}$

39. a. $A^{-1} = \begin{bmatrix} 3 & -\dfrac{5}{2} & \dfrac{1}{2} \\ -3 & 4 & -1 \\ 1 & -\dfrac{3}{2} & \dfrac{1}{2} \end{bmatrix}$ **b.** $\{(1, 2, 3)\}$

40. a. $A^{-1} = \begin{bmatrix} -\dfrac{1}{2} & \dfrac{1}{2} & \dfrac{1}{2} \\ \dfrac{11}{18} & -\dfrac{5}{18} & -\dfrac{7}{18} \\ \dfrac{4}{9} & -\dfrac{1}{9} & -\dfrac{5}{9} \end{bmatrix}$ **b.** $\{(1, 2, 1)\}$

B Exercises: Applying the Concepts

41. $\{(-1, 2)\}$ **42.** $\{(10, 1)\}$ **43.** $\{(2, -1, 3)\}$ **44.** $\{(1, 2, 3)\}$
45. $\{(-5, 1, 5)\}$ **46.** $\{(3, -1, -2)\}$

47. $X = \begin{bmatrix} 100 \\ 100 \end{bmatrix}$ **48.** $X = \begin{bmatrix} \dfrac{1340}{27} \\ \dfrac{1550}{27} \end{bmatrix}$

49. $X = \begin{bmatrix} \dfrac{216{,}000}{277} \\ \dfrac{310{,}000}{277} \\ \dfrac{304{,}000}{277} \end{bmatrix}$ **50.** $X = \begin{bmatrix} \dfrac{61{,}000}{27} \\ \dfrac{32{,}000}{27} \\ \dfrac{7000}{9} \end{bmatrix}$

C Exercises: Beyond the Basics

55. a. Yes, by the definition of *inverse* if $AB = I$, then $BA = I$ and A and B are inverses. **b.** $(A^{-1})^{-1} = A$

56. $A = \begin{bmatrix} \dfrac{4}{11} & \dfrac{1}{11} \\ \dfrac{3}{11} & -\dfrac{2}{11} \end{bmatrix}$

57. $I = A^2B = A(AB)$, so AB is the inverse of A.
58. $I = AB = AIB = A(AB)B = A^2(B^2)$, so B^2 is The inverse of A^2.
59. $ABB^{-1}A^{-1} = AIA^{-1} = AA^{-1} = I$ and $B^{-1}A^{-1}AB = B^{-1}B = I$

60. This is just a direct calculation using $A^{-1} = \begin{bmatrix} -2 & 1 \\ \dfrac{3}{2} & -\dfrac{1}{2} \end{bmatrix}$ and $B^{-1} = \begin{bmatrix} -1 & 0 \\ -\dfrac{3}{2} & -\dfrac{1}{2} \end{bmatrix}$.

61. If A is invertible, there exists some matrix D such that $AD = I$ and $DA = I$. Then $AB = AC \Leftrightarrow DAB = DAC \Leftrightarrow IB = IC \Leftrightarrow B = C$.
62. Not necessarily
63. If A is invertible, there exist some matrix C such that $AC = I$ and $CA = I$. Then $AB = A \Leftrightarrow CAB = CA \Leftrightarrow IB = I \Leftrightarrow B = I$.
64. Let $A = \begin{bmatrix} 2 & 0 \\ 0 & 0 \end{bmatrix}$ and $B = \begin{bmatrix} 1 & 0 \\ 3 & 4 \end{bmatrix}$
65. c. $A^{-1} = \begin{bmatrix} 3 & -4 \\ -2 & 3 \end{bmatrix}$
66. c. $A^{-1} = \begin{bmatrix} \dfrac{3}{4} & \dfrac{1}{4} & -\dfrac{1}{4} \\ \dfrac{1}{4} & \dfrac{3}{4} & \dfrac{1}{4} \\ -\dfrac{1}{4} & \dfrac{1}{4} & \dfrac{3}{4} \end{bmatrix}$

Critical Thinking

67. a. $A = \begin{bmatrix} 8 & 10 \\ 6 & 8 \end{bmatrix}$ **b.** $A = \begin{bmatrix} -1 & 7 \\ -3 & 17 \end{bmatrix}$ **c.** $A = \begin{bmatrix} -1 & -2 \\ \dfrac{5}{2} & 4 \end{bmatrix}$

d. $A = \begin{bmatrix} \dfrac{3}{2} & \dfrac{1}{2} \\ \dfrac{5}{2} & \dfrac{3}{2} \end{bmatrix}$
69. a. True. $A^2B = AAB = ABA = BAA = BA^2$.
70. Let $A = \begin{bmatrix} 0 & -1 \\ 0 & 0 \end{bmatrix}$.

Section 9.4

Practice Problems

1. a. -38 **b.** 0
2. a. $M_{11} = 4, M_{23} = 10, M_{32} = 10$
  b. $A_{11} = 4, A_{23} = -10, A_{32} = -10$
3. 8 **4.** $\{(17, -9)\}$ **5.** $\{(2, -1, 0)\}$

A Exercises: Basic Skills and Concepts

11. a. -10 **b.** 2 **c.** 0 **12. a.** 10 **b.** -2 **c.** 0
13. a. -4 **b.** 4 **c.** -2 **14. a.** -4 **b.** 4 **c.** -2
41. $\{(1, 1, 0)\}$ **42.** $\{(1, 1, 2)\}$
43. $\{(1, -1, 3)\}$ **44.** $\{(2, 1, 3)\}$ **45.** $\{(1, 1, 1)\}$
46. $\{(3, -1, -2)\}$ **47.** $\{(1, 2, 3)\}$ **48.** $\left\{\left(\dfrac{31}{7}, \dfrac{8}{7}, \dfrac{10}{7}\right)\right\}$
49. $\{(1, 2, 3)\}$ **50.** $\{(1, 2, 3)\}$

B Exercises: Applying the Concepts

62. $y = \dfrac{1}{3}x - \dfrac{2}{3}$

C Exercises: Beyond the Basics

75. $\dfrac{1}{2} + \dfrac{1}{2}i\sqrt{7}, \dfrac{1}{2} - \dfrac{1}{2}i\sqrt{7}$, **78.** $\dfrac{-37}{14}$

Review Exercises

6. $\begin{bmatrix} -1 & 2 & 5 \\ 4 & 3 & 1 \end{bmatrix}$ **7.** $\begin{bmatrix} 2 & -3 & | & 7 \\ 3 & 1 & | & 6 \end{bmatrix}$ **8.** $\begin{bmatrix} 1 & 1 & -1 & | & 6 \\ 2 & -3 & -2 & | & 2 \\ 5 & -3 & 1 & | & 8 \end{bmatrix}$

9. $\begin{bmatrix} 1 & -2 & 1 & 7 \\ 0 & 1 & 2 & 1 \\ 0 & 0 & 1 & 2 \end{bmatrix}$ **10.** $\begin{bmatrix} 1 & 2 & 1 & 7 \\ 0 & 1 & 2 & 5 \\ 0 & 0 & 1 & 2 \end{bmatrix}$

11. $\begin{bmatrix} 1 & 0 & 0 & \dfrac{1}{3} \\ 0 & 1 & 0 & \dfrac{1}{2} \\ 0 & 0 & 1 & -\dfrac{1}{6} \end{bmatrix}$ **12.** $\begin{bmatrix} 1 & 0 & 0 & \dfrac{1}{2} \\ 0 & 1 & 0 & \dfrac{1}{4} \\ 0 & 0 & 1 & \dfrac{1}{8} \end{bmatrix}$

13. $\{(2, -3, -1)\}$ **14.** $\{(1, 2, 1)\}$ **15.** $\{(3, -2, -3)\}$
16. $\left\{\left(\dfrac{8}{3}, \dfrac{-4}{3}, 3\right)\right\}$ **17.** $\{(5, -4, 1)\}$ **18.** $\{(-3, 5, -1)\}$
19. $\left\{\left(2, -1, \dfrac{-1}{3}\right)\right\}$ **20.** $\{(-3, 5, -1)\}$ **22.** $\{(-1, 2)\}$

23. a. $\begin{bmatrix} 3 & -1 \\ -8 & 10 \end{bmatrix}$ **b.** $\begin{bmatrix} -1 & 5 \\ 2 & -2 \end{bmatrix}$ **c.** $\begin{bmatrix} 2 & 4 \\ -6 & 8 \end{bmatrix}$
  d. $\begin{bmatrix} -6 & 9 \\ 15 & -18 \end{bmatrix}$ **e.** $\begin{bmatrix} -4 & 13 \\ 9 & -10 \end{bmatrix}$

24. a. $\begin{bmatrix} 2 & 1 & -2 \\ 2 & 1 & 2 \\ -3 & 0 & 4 \end{bmatrix}$ **b.** $\begin{bmatrix} 2 & -1 & 0 \\ 0 & 3 & 2 \\ -1 & 0 & 2 \end{bmatrix}$ **c.** $\begin{bmatrix} 4 & 3 & -5 \\ 5 & 1 & 4 \\ -7 & 0 & 9 \end{bmatrix}$

25. $X = \begin{bmatrix} \dfrac{7}{3} & 0 \\ -\dfrac{19}{3} & 8 \end{bmatrix}$ **26.** $X = \begin{bmatrix} 1 & 1 & -\dfrac{3}{2} \\ \dfrac{3}{2} & 0 & 1 \\ -2 & 0 & \dfrac{5}{2} \end{bmatrix}$

27. $AB = \begin{bmatrix} -3 & 4 \\ -11 & 10 \end{bmatrix},\ BA = \begin{bmatrix} -2 & -4 \\ 8 & 9 \end{bmatrix}$

28. $AB = \begin{bmatrix} 3 & 7 \\ -1 & 2 \end{bmatrix},\ BA = \begin{bmatrix} -2 & 1 & 4 \\ 1 & 3 & 5 \\ -4 & 0 & 4 \end{bmatrix}$

29. $AB = [7],\ BA = \begin{bmatrix} 2 & 4 & -2 \\ 3 & 6 & -3 \\ 1 & 2 & -1 \end{bmatrix}$

30. $AB = \begin{bmatrix} 1 & 2 & 3 & 4 \\ 0 & 5 & 4 & 5 \\ -1 & 8 & 5 & 6 \end{bmatrix}$, BA is not defined

35. a. $\begin{bmatrix} 3 & -1 \\ 1 & 0 \end{bmatrix}$ **b.** $\begin{bmatrix} 8 & -3 \\ 3 & -1 \end{bmatrix}$ **c.** $\begin{bmatrix} 8 & -3 \\ 3 & -1 \end{bmatrix}$

36. a. $\begin{bmatrix} 3 & -4 \\ -2 & 3 \end{bmatrix}$ **b.** $\begin{bmatrix} 17 & -24 \\ -12 & 17 \end{bmatrix}$ **c.** $\begin{bmatrix} 17 & -24 \\ -12 & 17 \end{bmatrix}$

41. $\begin{bmatrix} \dfrac{2}{5} & -\dfrac{1}{10} \\ -\dfrac{1}{5} & \dfrac{3}{10} \end{bmatrix}$ **42.** $\begin{bmatrix} \dfrac{1}{5} & \dfrac{2}{5} \\ -\dfrac{1}{10} & \dfrac{3}{10} \end{bmatrix}$

43. $\begin{bmatrix} 3 & 2 & 6 \\ 1 & 1 & 2 \\ 2 & 2 & 5 \end{bmatrix}$ **44.** $\begin{bmatrix} -1 & 1 & -1 \\ 1 & -\dfrac{1}{2} & \dfrac{1}{3} \\ 0 & 0 & \dfrac{1}{3} \end{bmatrix}$

47. $\{(-12, 2, 3)\}$ **48.** $\{(2, -4, 4)\}$

49. $\left\{\left(\dfrac{7}{6}, \dfrac{1}{6}, 2\right)\right\}$ **50.** $\{(91, -100, 29)\}$

55. a. $M_{12} = 8, M_{23} = 8, M_{22} = -16$
  b. $A_{12} = -8, A_{23} = -8, A_{22} = -16$
56. a. $M_{12} = -6, M_{23} = -6, M_{22} = -12$
  b. $A_{12} = 6, A_{23} = 6, A_{22} = -12$

62. $\{(3, -1)\}$ **63.** $\{(5, 6, 7)\}$

64. $\left\{\left(-2, 1, -\dfrac{1}{2}\right)\right\}$ **66.** $\dfrac{7}{2} + \dfrac{5\sqrt{5}}{2}, \dfrac{7}{2} - \dfrac{5\sqrt{5}}{2}$

67. They both satisfy the equation $y = 7x - 11$.
B Exercises: Applying the Concepts
69. Method 3
70.

	Male	Female	Children	Calories	Protein		Calories	Protein
A	2	3	1	2200	50		11,000	250	A
B	1	1	2	1700	40	$=$	6900	150	B
				1500	30				

71. The speed of the plane is 520 miles per hour and the velocity of the wind is 40 miles per hour.
72. Nertha walks 3.2 miles per hour, and Kristina walks 3.5 miles per hour.
73. Andrew has 170 dollars, Bonnie has 65 dollars, and Chauncie has 85 dollars.
75. 30 registered nurses, 40 licensed practical nurses, and 60 nurse aides
76. The sales of medicine, nonmedical items, and beer and cigarettes were 11,000, 4000, and 3500 dollars, respectively.

Practice Test A

2. $\begin{bmatrix} 7 & -3 & 9 & 5 \\ -2 & 4 & 3 & -12 \\ 8 & -5 & 1 & -9 \end{bmatrix}$

3. $\begin{cases} 4x - \quad\ z = -3 \\ x + 3y \quad\quad = 9 \\ 2x + 7y + 5z = 8 \end{cases}$

7. $A - B = \begin{bmatrix} 8 & -1 \\ 4 & 8 \\ 11 & 0 \end{bmatrix}$

9. The product AB is not defined.
10. $\begin{bmatrix} -6 & 2 & 0 \\ 10 & 14 & 4 \end{bmatrix}$ **11.** $\begin{bmatrix} 20 & 28 & 8 \\ -9 & 29 & 6 \end{bmatrix}$ **12.** $\begin{bmatrix} 1 & 25 \\ 0 & 16 \end{bmatrix}$

13. $\begin{bmatrix} 1 & -\dfrac{5}{4} \\ 0 & \dfrac{1}{4} \end{bmatrix}$ **14.** $\begin{bmatrix} -11 & 2 & 7 \\ 8 & -1 & -5 \\ 5 & -1 & -3 \end{bmatrix}$ **15.** $\begin{bmatrix} 5 & 2 \\ 3 & 1 \end{bmatrix}\begin{bmatrix} x \\ y \end{bmatrix} = \begin{bmatrix} 32 \\ 18 \end{bmatrix}$

16. $\begin{cases} 12x - 3y = 5 \\ -2x + 7y = -9 \end{cases}$ **17.** $X = \begin{bmatrix} -\dfrac{3}{5} & -1 & 4 \\ -\dfrac{32}{5} & -\dfrac{18}{5} & -3 \end{bmatrix}$

20. $x = \dfrac{\begin{vmatrix} 3 & -1 & 1 \\ 6 & 1 & 1 \\ 4 & 3 & -2 \end{vmatrix}}{\begin{vmatrix} 2 & -1 & 1 \\ 1 & 1 & 1 \\ 4 & 3 & -2 \end{vmatrix}}, \quad y = \dfrac{\begin{vmatrix} 2 & 3 & 1 \\ 1 & 6 & 1 \\ 4 & 4 & -2 \end{vmatrix}}{\begin{vmatrix} 2 & -1 & 1 \\ 1 & 1 & 1 \\ 4 & 3 & -2 \end{vmatrix}}, \quad z = \dfrac{\begin{vmatrix} 2 & -1 & 3 \\ 1 & 1 & 6 \\ 4 & 3 & 4 \end{vmatrix}}{\begin{vmatrix} 2 & -1 & 1 \\ 1 & 1 & 1 \\ 4 & 3 & -2 \end{vmatrix}}$

Cumulative Review Exercises (Chapters 1–9)

4. $1 + i\dfrac{3}{2}, 1 - i\dfrac{3}{2}$ **9.** $\pm 1, \pm\dfrac{1}{2}, \pm\dfrac{1}{4}, \pm 3, \pm\dfrac{3}{2}, \pm\dfrac{3}{4}$

16. $A^{-1} = \begin{bmatrix} 3 & 2 & 6 \\ 1 & 1 & 2 \\ 2 & 2 & 5 \end{bmatrix}$

18. a. $F(x) = x^2 + 7x + 9$ **b.** $F(4) = 53$

CHAPTER 10

Section 10.2

Practice Problems

1. a.

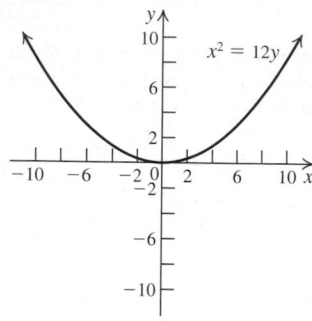

Vertex: $(0, 0)$. Focus: $(0, 3)$. Directrix: $y = -3$. Axis: y-axis.

b.

Vertex: $(0, 0)$. Focus: $\left(-\dfrac{3}{2}, 0\right)$. Directrix: $x = \dfrac{3}{2}$. Axis: x-axis.

2. a. $x^2 = 8y$ b. $y^2 = 4x$

3. Vertex: $(2, -1)$. Focus: $\left(2, -\dfrac{7}{8}\right)$. Directrix: $y = -\dfrac{9}{8}$.

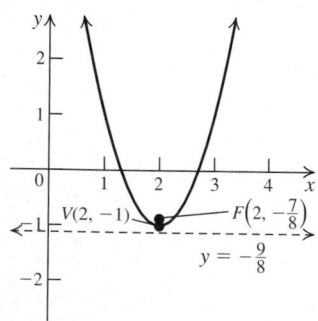

4. Equation: $x^2 = 29.2y$. The thickness of the mirror at the edges is 0.0771 in.

A Exercises: Basic Skills and Concepts

1. Focus: $\left(0, \dfrac{1}{2}\right)$. Directrix: $y = -\dfrac{1}{2}$. Graph: e.

2. Focus: $\left(0, \dfrac{1}{9}\right)$. Directrix: $y = -\dfrac{1}{9}$. Graph: h.

3. Focus: $\left(0, -\dfrac{9}{64}\right)$. Directrix: $y = \dfrac{9}{64}$. Graph: d.

4. Focus: $\left(0, -\dfrac{1}{2}\right)$. Directrix: $y = \dfrac{1}{2}$. Graph: a.

5. Focus: $\left(\dfrac{1}{2}, 0\right)$. Directrix: $x = -\dfrac{1}{2}$. Graph: g.

6. Focus: $\left(\dfrac{4}{9}, 0\right)$. Directrix: $x = -\dfrac{4}{9}$. Graph: c.

7. Focus: $\left(-\dfrac{4}{9}, 0\right)$. Directrix: $x = \dfrac{4}{9}$. Graph: f.

8. Focus: $\left(-\dfrac{1}{2}, 0\right)$. Directrix: $x = \dfrac{1}{2}$. Graph: b.

9. $x^2 = -4(y - 3)$. 4.
10. $x^2 = 12(y - 1)$. 12.

11. $y^2 = -10\left(x - \dfrac{1}{2}\right)$. 10.

12. $y^2 = 2\left(x + \dfrac{3}{2}\right)$. 2.

13. $(y - 1)^2 = -8(x - 1)$. 8.
14. $(x - 1)^2 = -4(y - 1)$. 4.
15. $(x - 1)^2 = 16(y - 1)$. 16.
16. $(y - 1)^2 = 12(x - 1)$. 12.
17. $y^2 = 8(x - 1)$. 8.
18. $x^2 = 4(y - 1)$. 4.
19. $x^2 = -12(y - 1)$. 12.
20. $y^2 = -8(x + 1)$. 8.
21. $(y - 3)^2 = -8(x - 2)$. 8.
22. $(x - 2)^2 = -4(y - 3)$. 4.
23. $(x - 2)^2 = 8(y - 3)$. 8.
24. $(y - 3)^2 = 4(x - 2)$. 4.

25. Vertex: $(-1, 1)$. Focus: $\left(-\dfrac{1}{2}, 1\right)$. Directrix: $x = -\dfrac{3}{2}$.

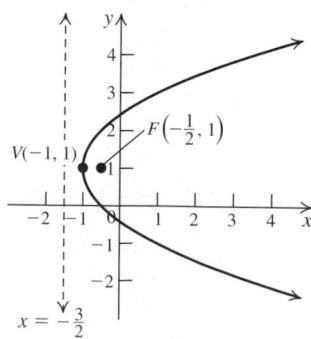

26. Vertex: $(3, -2)$. Focus: $(5, -2)$. Directrix: $x = 1$.

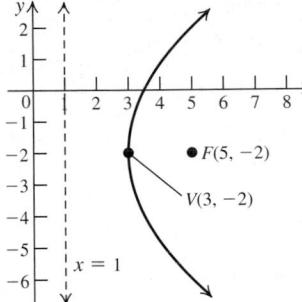

27. Vertex: $(-2, 2)$. Focus: $\left(-2, \frac{11}{4}\right)$. Directrix: $y = \frac{5}{4}$.

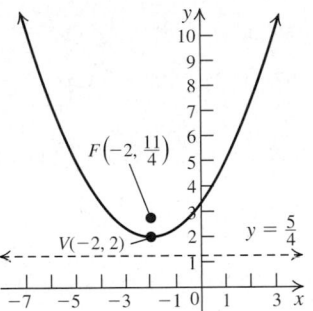

32. Vertex: $(-2, -3)$. Focus: $(-2, -5)$. Directrix: $y = -1$.

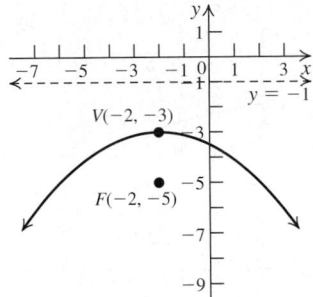

33. Vertex: $(-1, 1)$. Focus: $\left(-1, \frac{5}{4}\right)$. Directrix: $y = \frac{3}{4}$.

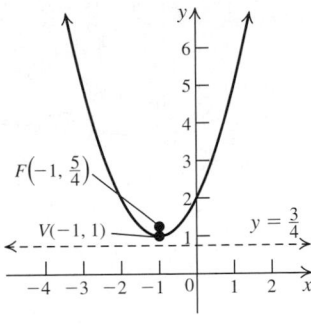

28. Vertex: $(3, -1)$. Focus: $(3, 0)$. Directrix: $y = -2$.

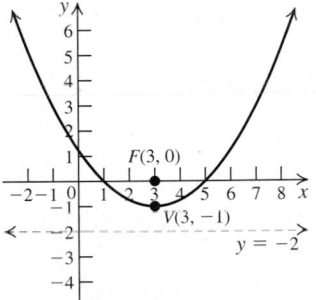

29. Vertex: $(2, -1)$. Focus: $\left(\frac{1}{2}, -1\right)$. Directrix: $x = \frac{7}{2}$.

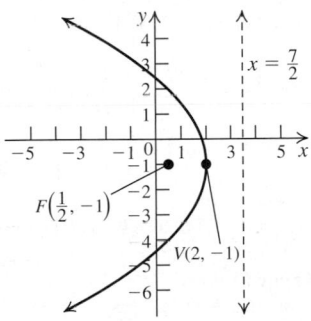

34. Vertex: $(-1, -1)$. Focus: $\left(-1, -\frac{11}{12}\right)$. Directrix: $y = -\frac{13}{12}$.

35. Vertex: $\left(-\frac{1}{2}, -1\right)$. Focus: $\left(-\frac{1}{4}, -1\right)$. Directrix: $x = -\frac{3}{4}$.

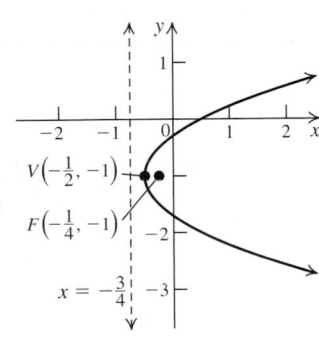

30. Vertex: $(-3, 2)$. Focus: $(-6, 2)$. Directrix: y-axis.

31. Vertex: $(1, 3)$. Focus: $\left(1, \frac{1}{2}\right)$. Directrix: $y - \frac{11}{2}$.

36. Vertex: $(4, 1)$. Focus: $\left(\frac{47}{12}, 1\right)$. Directrix: $x = \frac{49}{12}$.

37. Vertex: $\left(-\frac{1}{2}, -1\right)$. Focus: $\left(-\frac{1}{2}, -\frac{5}{4}\right)$. Directrix: $y = -\frac{3}{4}$.

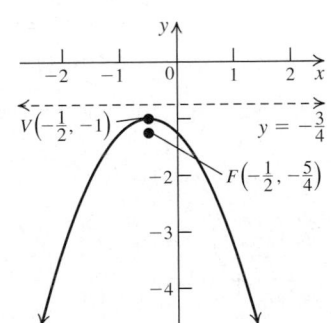

38. Vertex: $\left(-2, -\dfrac{1}{2}\right)$. Focus: $\left(-\dfrac{63}{32}, -\dfrac{1}{2}\right)$. Directrix: $x = -\dfrac{65}{32}$.

39. Vertex: $(46, 4)$. Focus: $\left(\dfrac{551}{12}, 4\right)$. Directrix: $x = \dfrac{553}{12}$.

40. Vertex: $(4, 35)$. Focus: $\left(4, \dfrac{279}{8}\right)$. Directrix: $y = \dfrac{281}{8}$.

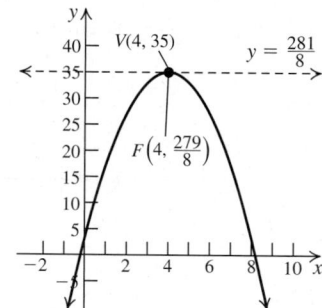

41. $y^2 = 4x$ and $x^2 = \dfrac{1}{2}y$ **42.** $y^2 = -\dfrac{4}{3}x$ and $x^2 = \dfrac{9}{2}y$

43. $(y - 1)^2 = 2x$ and $x^2 = 2(y - 1)$

44. $(y - 2)^2 = x - 1$ and $(x - 1)^2 = -(y - 2)$

45. $(y - 1)^2 = -(x + 2)$ and $(x + 2)^2 = -(y - 1)$

46. $(y + 1)^2 = -(x - 1)$ and $(x - 1)^2 = y + 1$

47. $(y - 1)^2 = x + 1$ and $(x + 1)^2 = y - 1$

48. $(y - 3)^2 = 16(x - 2)$ and $(x - 2)^2 = -\dfrac{1}{4}(y - 3)$

B Exercises: Applying the Concepts

50. $\dfrac{4}{3}$ in.   **51.** $3\dfrac{3}{8}$ ft. from the vertex

52. $\dfrac{1}{2}$ in. from the vertex

53. $\left(\dfrac{1}{16}, 0\right)$ **54.** $\left(\dfrac{1}{2}, 0\right)$

55. $\left(0, \dfrac{1}{16}\right)$ **56.** $\left(0, \dfrac{1}{4}\right)$

57. 16.875 ft   **58.** 23.75 ft

60. 5 ft: 23.3333 ft; 10 ft: 21.3333 ft; 20 ft: 13.3333 ft

C Exercises: Beyond the Basics

63. $(4, 8)$ and $(16, 16)$

64. The only solution of the system
$$y = 2x + 3 \qquad y^2 = 24x$$
is $x = \dfrac{3}{2}, y = 6$. Therefore, the point of intersection is $\left(\dfrac{3}{2}, 6\right)$.

66. a. $y = -\dfrac{4}{3}x - \dfrac{1}{3}$ **b.** $(2, -3)$

67. $(y - 1)^2 = 8(x - 1)$ and $(y - 1)^2 = -8(x - 5)$

68. $(x + 1)^2 = 8(y + 1)$ and $(x + 1)^2 = -8(y - 3)$

69. $\left(x - \dfrac{3}{4}\right)^2 = \dfrac{1}{2}\left(y - \dfrac{31}{8}\right)$

70. $\left(y - \dfrac{1}{3}\right)^2 = -\dfrac{1}{3}\left(x - \dfrac{13}{3}\right)$

71. Vertex: $(4, 6)$. Focus: $\left(4, \dfrac{11}{2}\right)$. Directrix: $y = \dfrac{13}{2}$. Axis: $x = 4$.

72. Vertex: $\left(-\dfrac{D}{2A}, \dfrac{D^2}{4AE} - \dfrac{F}{E}\right)$. Focus: $\left(-\dfrac{D}{2A}, \dfrac{D^2}{4AE} - \dfrac{F}{E} - \dfrac{E}{4A}\right)$.

Directrix: $y = \dfrac{D^2}{4AE} - \dfrac{F}{E} + \dfrac{E}{4A}$. Axis: $x = -\dfrac{D}{2A}$.

73. Vertex: $(-2, 3)$. Focus: $\left(-\dfrac{11}{4}, 3\right)$. Directrix: $x = -\dfrac{5}{4}$. Axis: $y = 3$.

74. Vertex: $\left(\dfrac{E^2}{4CD} - \dfrac{F}{D}, -\dfrac{E}{2C}\right)$. Focus: $\left(\dfrac{E^2}{4CD} - \dfrac{F}{D} - \dfrac{D}{4C}, -\dfrac{E}{2C}\right)$.

Directrix: $x = \dfrac{E^2}{4CD} - \dfrac{F}{D} + \dfrac{D}{4C}$. Axis: $y = -\dfrac{E}{2C}$.

Critical Thinking

75. a. No, because if the axis is horizontal, it does not pass the vertical-line test.

Group Projects

1. $16x^2 + 9y^2 - 24xy - 158x - 194y + 976 = 0$. Axis: $y = \dfrac{4}{3}x - \dfrac{1}{3}$.

Section 10.3

Practice Problems

1. $\dfrac{x^2}{36} + \dfrac{y^2}{100} = 1$

2.

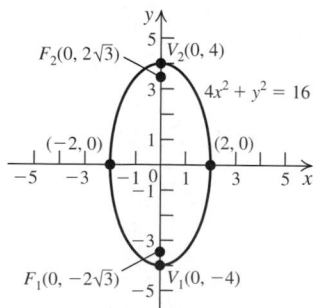

3. $\dfrac{(x - 2)^2}{9} + \dfrac{(y - 1)^2}{25} = 1$

4. Center: $(3, -1)$. Vertices: $(3 + \sqrt{42}, -1)$ and $(3 - \sqrt{42}, -1)$.

Foci: $\left(3 + \dfrac{\sqrt{126}}{2}, -1\right)$ and $\left(3 - \dfrac{\sqrt{126}}{2}, -1\right)$.

5. 6.9282 ft

A Exercises: Basic Skills and Concepts

1. Vertices: $(4, 0)$ and $(-4, 0)$.
Foci: $(2\sqrt{3}, 0)$ and $(-2\sqrt{3}, 0)$.

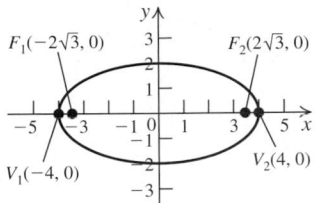

2. Vertices: $(0, 4)$ and $(0, -4)$.
Foci: $(0, 2\sqrt{3})$ and $(0, -2\sqrt{3})$.

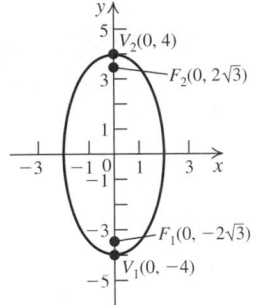

9. Circle centered at the origin with radius 2.

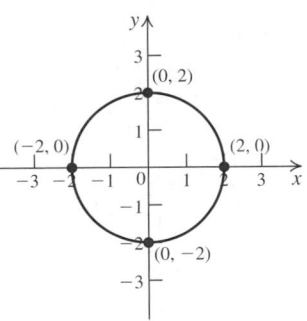

10. Circle centered at the origin with radius 4.

3. Vertices: $(3, 0)$ and $(-3, 0)$.
Foci: $(2\sqrt{2}, 0)$ and $(-2\sqrt{2}, 0)$.

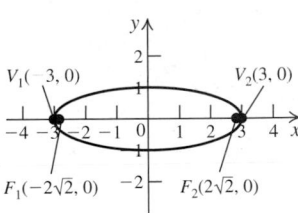

4. Vertices: $(0, 2)$ and $(0, -2)$.
Foci: $(0, \sqrt{3})$ and $(0, -\sqrt{3})$.

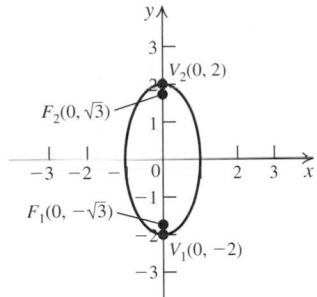

11. Vertices: $(2, 0)$ and $(-2, 0)$.
Foci: $(\sqrt{3}, 0)$ and $(-\sqrt{3}, 0)$.

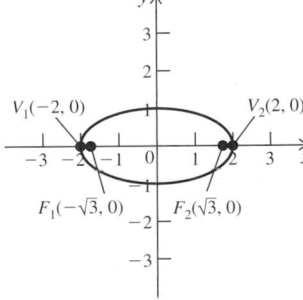

12. Vertices: $(0, 3)$ and $(0, -3)$.
Foci: $(0, 2\sqrt{2})$ and $(0, -2\sqrt{2})$.

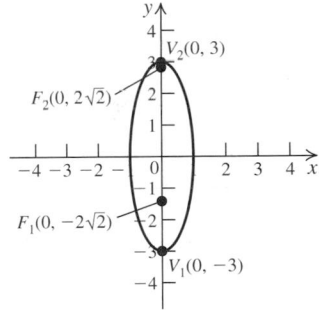

5. Vertices: $(5, 0)$ and $(-5, 0)$.
Foci: $(3, 0)$ and $(-3, 0)$.

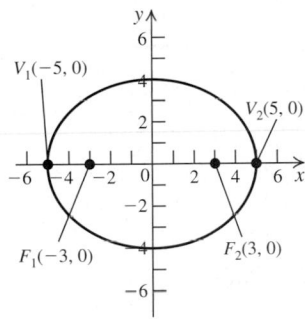

6. Vertices: $(5, 0)$ and $(-5, 0)$.
Foci: $(4, 0)$ and $(-4, 0)$.

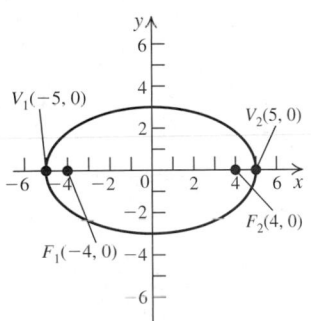

13. Vertices: $(0, 3)$ and $(0, -3)$.
Foci: $(0, \sqrt{5})$ and $(0, -\sqrt{5})$.

14. Vertices: $(5, 0)$ and $(-5, 0)$.
Foci: $(\sqrt{21}, 0)$ and $(-\sqrt{21}, 0)$.

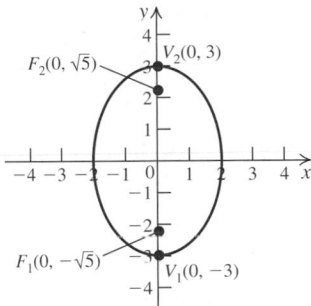

7. Vertices: $(0, 6)$ and $(0, -6)$.
Foci: $(0, 2\sqrt{5})$ and $(0, -2\sqrt{5})$.

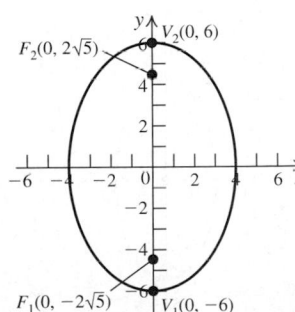

8. Vertices: $(0, 4)$ and $(0, -4)$.
Foci: $(0, \sqrt{7})$ and $(0, -\sqrt{7})$.

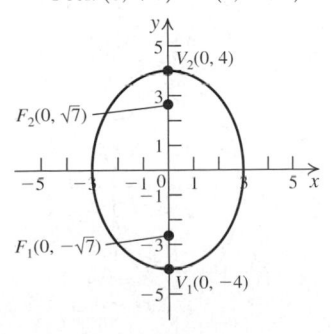

15. Vertices: $(2, 0)$ and $(-2, 0)$.
Foci: $(1, 0)$ and $(-1, 0)$.

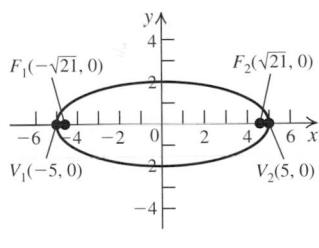

16. Vertices: $(\sqrt{5}, 0)$ and $(-\sqrt{5}, 0)$.
Foci: $(1, 0)$ and $(-1, 0)$.

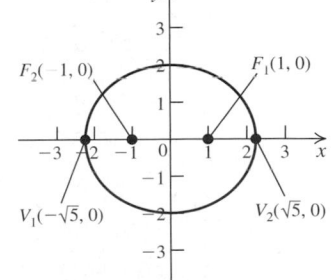

17. Vertices: $(0, \sqrt{5})$ and $(0, -\sqrt{5})$. **18.** Vertices: $(0, \sqrt{7})$ and $(0, -\sqrt{7})$.
Foci: $(0, \sqrt{3})$ and $(0, -\sqrt{3})$.   Foci: $(0, 2)$ and $(0, -2)$.

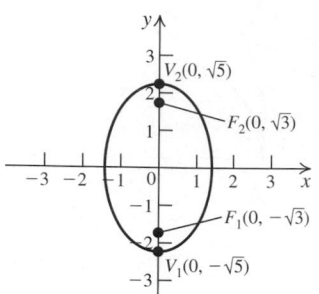

23. $\dfrac{x^2}{12} + \dfrac{y^2}{16} = 1$

24. $\dfrac{x^2}{27} + \dfrac{y^2}{36} = 1$

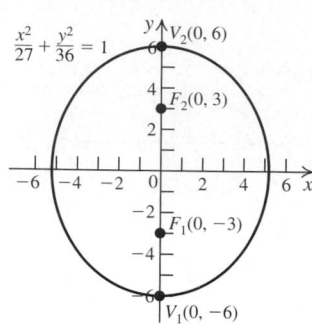

19. Vertices: $\left(\dfrac{\sqrt{14}}{2}, 0\right)$ and $\left(-\dfrac{\sqrt{14}}{2}, 0\right)$. Foci: $\left(\dfrac{\sqrt{42}}{6}, 0\right)$ and $\left(-\dfrac{\sqrt{42}}{6}, 0\right)$.

20. Vertices: $\left(\dfrac{\sqrt{33}}{3}, 0\right)$ and $\left(-\dfrac{\sqrt{33}}{3}, 0\right)$. Foci: $\left(\dfrac{\sqrt{33}}{6}, 0\right)$ and $\left(-\dfrac{\sqrt{33}}{6}, 0\right)$.

25. $\dfrac{x^2}{25} + \dfrac{y^2}{9} = 1$

26. $\dfrac{x^2}{25} + \dfrac{y^2}{16} = 1$

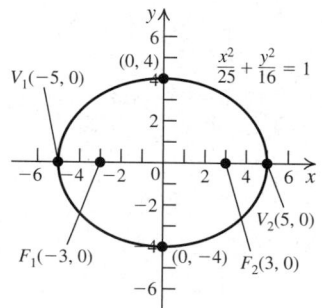

27. $\dfrac{x^2}{16} + \dfrac{y^2}{20} = 1$

28. $\dfrac{x^2}{25} + \dfrac{y^2}{34} = 1$

21. $\dfrac{x^2}{9} + \dfrac{y^2}{8} = 1$

22. $\dfrac{x^2}{25} + \dfrac{y^2}{16} = 1$

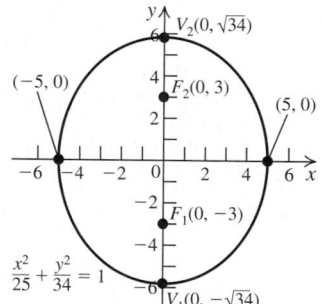

29. $\dfrac{x^2}{9} + \dfrac{y^2}{25} = 1$

30. $\dfrac{x^2}{4} + \dfrac{y^2}{16} = 1$

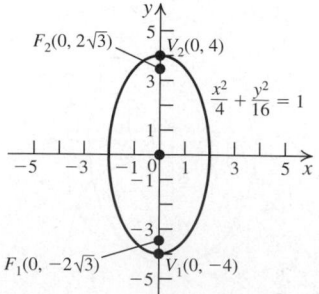

31. $\dfrac{x^2}{36} + \dfrac{y^2}{27} = 1$

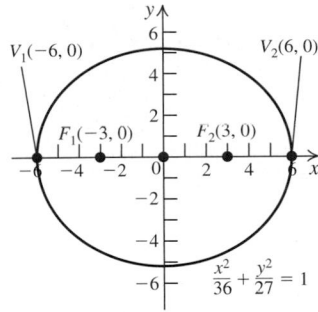

32. $\dfrac{x^2}{16} + \dfrac{y^2}{25} = 1$

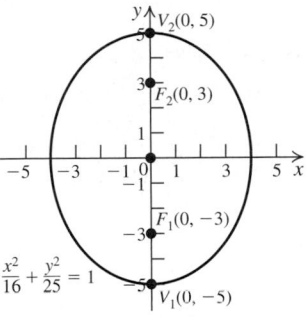

33. $\dfrac{x^2}{9} + \dfrac{y^2}{13} = 1$

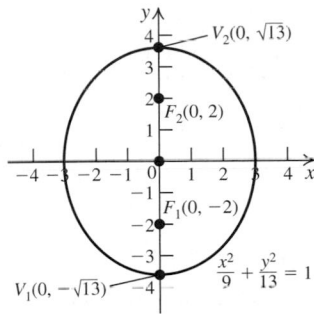

34. $\dfrac{x^2}{13} + \dfrac{y^2}{4} = 1$

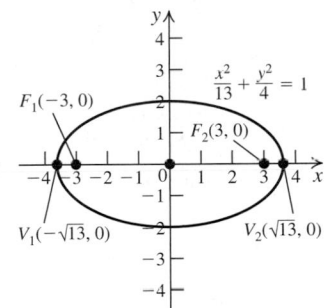

35. Center: $(1, 1)$. Foci:
$(1, 1 + \sqrt{5})$ and $(1, 1 - \sqrt{5})$.
Vertices: $(1, 4)$ and $(1, -2)$.

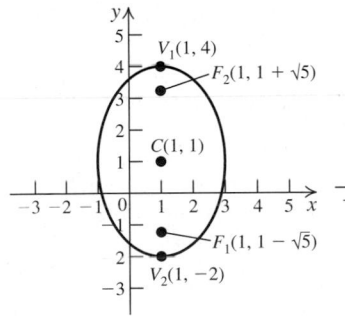

36. Center: $(1, 1)$. Foci: $(1, 1 + 2\sqrt{3})$
and $(1, 1 - 2\sqrt{3})$. Vertices: $(1, 5)$
and $(1, -3)$.

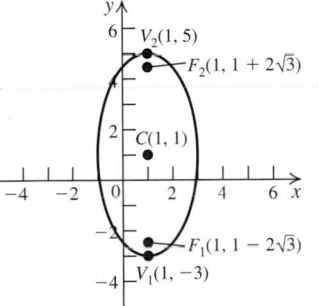

37. Center: $(0, -3)$. Foci:
$(2\sqrt{3}, -3)$ and $(-2\sqrt{3}, -3)$.
Vertices: $(4, -3)$ and $(-4, -3)$.

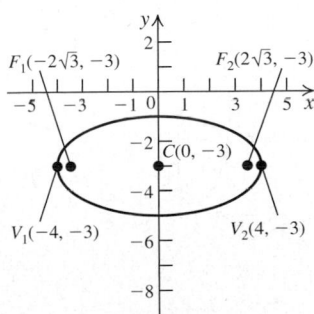

38. Center: $(-2, 0)$. Foci:
$(-2, \sqrt{5})$ and $(-2, -\sqrt{5})$.
Vertices: $(-2, 3)$ and $(-2, -3)$.

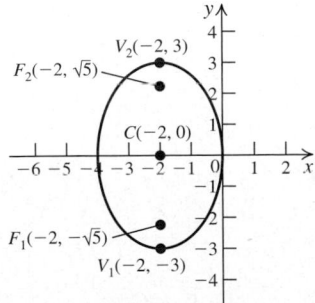

39. Center: $(1, -2)$. Foci: $(2, -2)$
and $(0, -2)$. Vertices: $(3, -2)$
and $(-1, -2)$.

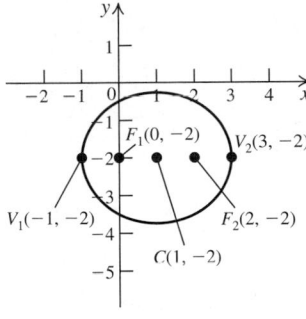

40. Center: $(-1, 2)$. Foci:
$(-1, 2 + \sqrt{5})$ and
$(-1, 2 - \sqrt{5})$.
Vertices: $(-1, 5)$ and $(-1, -1)$.

41. Center: $(-3, 1)$. Foci: $(-2, 1)$
and $(-4, 1)$. Vertices:
$(-3 + \sqrt{5}, 1)$ and
$(-3 - \sqrt{5}, 1)$.

42. Center: $(2, -5)$. Foci:
$(2, -5 + \sqrt{21})$ and
$(2, -5 - \sqrt{21})$. Vertices:
$(2, 0)$ and $(2, -10)$.

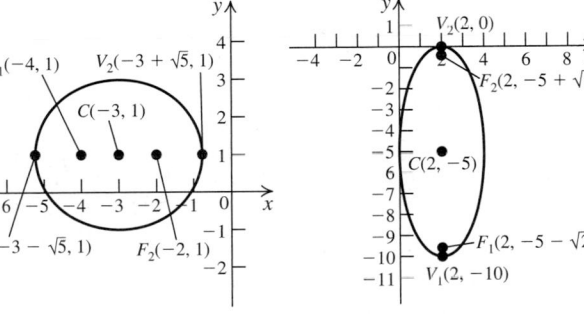

43. Center: $(-1, 2)$. Foci: $(1, 2)$
and $(-3, 2)$. Vertices: $(2, 2)$ and
$(-4, 2)$.

44. Center: $(-4, 3)$. Foci:
$(-4, 3 + \sqrt{5})$ and
$(-4, 3 - \sqrt{5})$.
Vertices: $(-4, 6)$ and $(-4, 0)$.

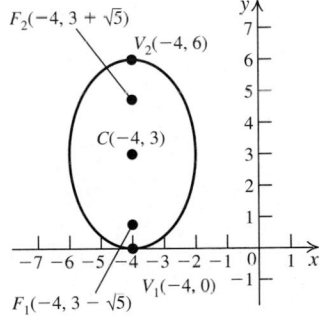

45. Center: $(-2, 4)$. Foci: $(-2, 6)$ and $(-2, 2)$. Vertices: $(-2, 7)$ and $(-2, 1)$.

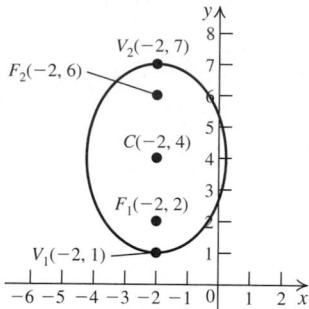

46. Center: $(-2, 2)$. Foci: $(-2 + \sqrt{5}, 2)$ and $(-2 - \sqrt{5}, 2)$. Vertices: $(-2 + 2\sqrt{5}, 2)$ and $(-2 - 2\sqrt{5}, 2)$.

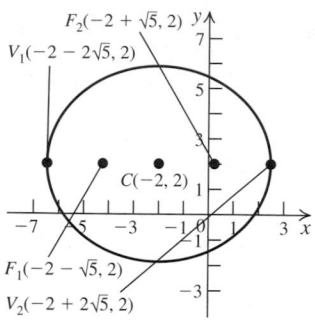

47. Center: $(1, -1)$. Foci: $(2, -1)$ and $(0, -1)$. Vertices: $(1 + \sqrt{2}, -1)$ and $(1 - \sqrt{2}, -1)$.

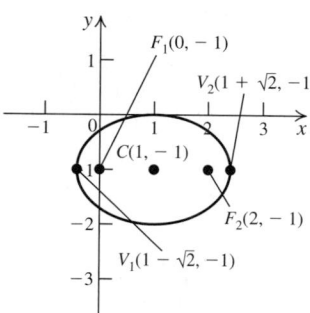

48. Circle centered at $(3, 2)$ with radius $\dfrac{\sqrt{46}}{2}$.

49. No graph.   **50.** No graph.

B Exercises: Applying the Concepts

51. 18.3 ft

55. The bet should not be accepted. The pool shark can hit the ball from any point straight into the pocket, or he can shoot it through the other focus and it will fall into the pocket because of the reflecting property.

56. 5.9 ft from the wall on the opposite sides, along the major axis.

57. 29 ft from the wall on the opposite sides.

58. $\dfrac{x^2}{20{,}067.5556} + \dfrac{y^2}{19{,}894.1067} = 1$

59. $\dfrac{x^2}{8{,}641.5616} + \dfrac{y^2}{8{,}639.0652} = 1$

60. $\dfrac{x^2}{1{,}311.8884} + \dfrac{y^2}{1{,}253.2128} = 1$

61. $\dfrac{x^2}{786{,}254.6241} + \dfrac{y^2}{783{,}788.5085} = 1$

62. Perihelion: 364,224.1427 km. Aphelion: 404,581.8573 km.

63. Perihelion: 8.72×10^7 km. Aphelion: 5.3028×10^9 km.

64. $\dfrac{x^2}{16{,}785{,}409} + \dfrac{y^2}{16{,}784{,}680} = 1$

C Exercises: Beyond the Basics

65. $\dfrac{x^2}{25} + \dfrac{y^2}{16} = 1$ or $\dfrac{x^2}{625} + \dfrac{y^2}{25} = 1$
$\phantom{\dfrac{x^2}{625}}\,_{41}$

66. No solution

67. Major axis: $\dfrac{2\sqrt{105}}{3}$. Minor axis: $\dfrac{\sqrt{70}}{2}$.

68. $(x - 2)^2 + 48(y - 1)^2 = 64$

69. If $e = 0$, the ellipse becomes a circle.

73. $\dfrac{4}{5}$ **74.** $\dfrac{\sqrt{2}}{2}$

75. $\dfrac{x^2}{16} + \dfrac{y^2}{12} = 1$ **76.** $\dfrac{x^2}{9} + \dfrac{y^2}{8} = 1$

77. The distance of P from the point $(4, 0)$ is $\sqrt{(x - 4)^2 + y^2}$, and the distance of P from the line is $|x - 16|$. Hence, the equation of the path of P is $\sqrt{(x - 4)^2 + y^2} = \dfrac{1}{2}|x - 16|$, which, after squaring, gives $(x - 4)^2 + y^2 = \dfrac{1}{4}(x - 16)^2$. This is equivalent to $\dfrac{x^2}{64} + \dfrac{y^2}{48} = 1$, the equation of an ellipse with $a = 8$ and $c = 4$. Therefore, the eccentricity is $\dfrac{1}{2}$.

78. The distance of P from the point $(0, 2)$ is $\sqrt{x^2 + (y - 2)^2}$, and the distance of P from the line is $|y - 10|$. Hence, the equation of the path of P is $\sqrt{x^2 + (y - 2)^2} = \dfrac{1}{3}|y - 10|$, which, after squaring, gives $x^2 + (y - 2)^2 = \dfrac{1}{9}(y - 10)^2$. This is equivalent to $\dfrac{x^2}{8} + \dfrac{(y - 1)^2}{9} = 1$, the equation of an ellipse with $a = 3$ and $c = 1$. Therefore, the eccentricity is $\dfrac{1}{3}$.

79. We can assume without loss of generality that the center of the ellipse is at the origin, the major axis is on the x-axis, and the minor axis is on the y-axis. Thus, the equation of the ellipse is $\dfrac{x^2}{a^2} + \dfrac{y^2}{b^2} = 1$. The length of the latus rectum is the difference in the y-coordinates of the two points on the ellipse with x-coordinate equal to c. Plugging $x = c$ into the equation and using $c^2 = a^2 - b^2$, we obtain $\dfrac{a^2 - b^2}{a^2} + \dfrac{y^2}{b^2} = 1$. The solution of this equation for y is $y = \pm\dfrac{b^2}{a}$. Therefore, the length of the latus rectum is $\dfrac{2b^2}{a}$.

80. $\dfrac{x^2}{9} + \dfrac{y^2}{\frac{9}{2}} = 1$

81. Points of intersection: $\left(-\dfrac{17}{13}, -\dfrac{3}{13}\right)$ and $(1, -1)$.

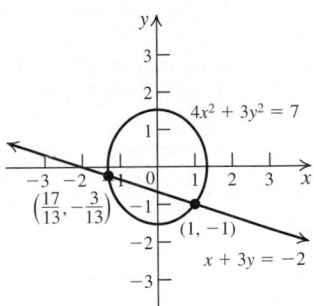

82. Points of intersection: $(-2, 2)$ and $(2, 2)$.

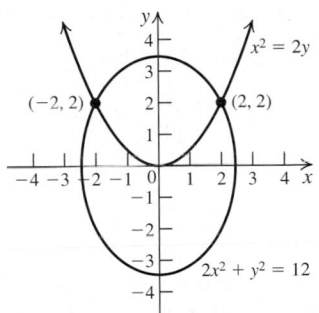

83. Points of intersection: $(\sqrt{2}, 3\sqrt{2}), (\sqrt{2}, -3\sqrt{2}), (-\sqrt{2}, 3\sqrt{2}),$ $(-\sqrt{2}, -3\sqrt{2})$.

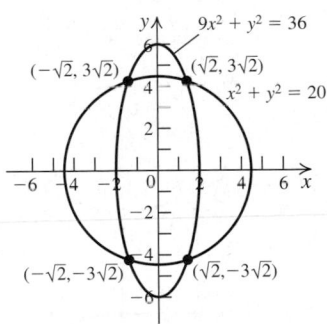

84. Points of intersection: $\left(\dfrac{2\sqrt{5}}{3}, 1\right), \left(\dfrac{2\sqrt{5}}{3}, -1\right), \left(-\dfrac{2\sqrt{5}}{3}, 1\right),$ $\left(-\dfrac{2\sqrt{5}}{3}, -1\right)$.

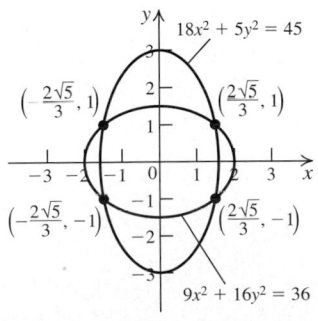

Critical Thinking

86. 8 ellipses: $\dfrac{(x-3)^2}{9} + \dfrac{(y-2)^2}{4} = 1, \dfrac{(x-2)^2}{4} + \dfrac{(y-3)^2}{9} = 1,$

$\dfrac{(x+3)^2}{9} + \dfrac{(y-2)^2}{4} = 1, \dfrac{(x+2)^2}{4} + \dfrac{(y-3)^2}{9} = 1,$

$\dfrac{(x+3)^2}{9} + \dfrac{(y+2)^2}{4} = 1, \dfrac{(x+2)^2}{4} + \dfrac{(y+3)^2}{9} = 1,$

$\dfrac{(x-3)^2}{9} + \dfrac{(y+2)^2}{4} = 1, \dfrac{(x-2)^2}{4} + \dfrac{(y+3)^2}{9} = 1.$

Section 10.4

Practice Problems

1. y-axis

2. Vertices: $(2\sqrt{2}, 0)$ and $(-2\sqrt{2}, 0)$. Foci: $(\sqrt{10}, 0)$ and $(-\sqrt{10}, 0)$.

3. $\dfrac{y^2}{16} - \dfrac{x^2}{20} = 1$ **4.** $y = \dfrac{2}{3}x$ and $y = -\dfrac{2}{3}x$

5. The standard form of the equation is $\dfrac{x^2}{4} - \dfrac{y^2}{25} = 1$. Vertices: $(2, 0)$ and $(-2, 0)$. Endpoints of the conjugate axis: $(0, 5)$ and $(0, -5)$. Asymptotes: $y = \dfrac{5}{2}x$ and $y = -\dfrac{5}{2}x$.

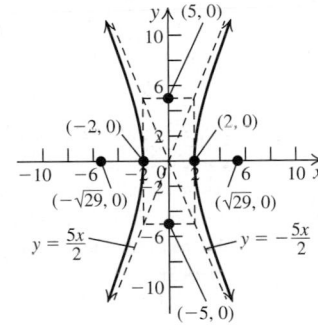

6. $\dfrac{(x-1)^2}{5} - \dfrac{(y-2)^2}{\frac{5}{4}} = 1$. Center: $(1, 2)$. Vertices: $(1 + \sqrt{5}, 2)$ and $(1 - \sqrt{5}, 2)$. Endpoints of the conjugate axis: $\left(1, 2 + \dfrac{\sqrt{5}}{2}\right)$ and $\left(1, 2 - \dfrac{\sqrt{5}}{2}\right)$. Asymptotes: $y - 2 = \pm\dfrac{1}{2}(x - 1)$. Foci: $\left(\dfrac{7}{2}, 2\right)$ and $\left(-\dfrac{3}{2}, 2\right)$.

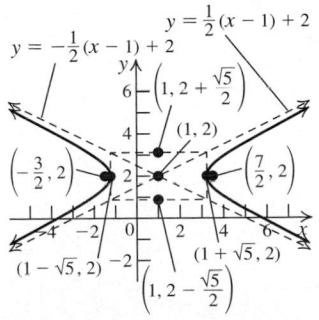

7. $\dfrac{x^2}{16{,}900} - \dfrac{y^2}{5{,}600} = 1$

A Exercises: Basic Skills and Concepts

1. g   **2.** c   **3.** h   **4.** e   **5.** d   **6.** a   **7.** b   **8.** f

9. Vertices: $(1, 0)$ and $(-1, 0)$. Foci: $(\sqrt{5}, 0)$ and $(-\sqrt{5}, 0)$. Transverse axis: x-axis. The hyperbola opens left and right. Vertices of the fundamental rectangle: $(1, 2), (-1, 2), (-1, -2), (1, -2)$. Asymptotes: $y = \pm 2x$.

10. Vertices: $(0, 1)$ and $(0, -1)$. Foci: $(0, \sqrt{5})$ and $(0, -\sqrt{5})$. Transverse axis: y-axis. The hyperbola opens up and down. Vertices of the fundamental rectangle: $(2, 1), (-2, 1), (-2, -1), (2, -1)$.

Asymptotes: $y = \pm \dfrac{1}{2}x$.

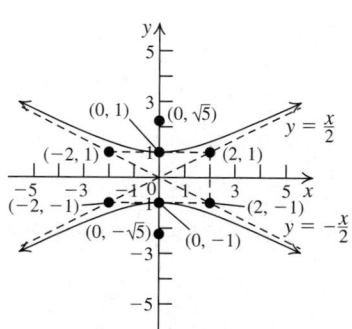

11. Vertices: $(0, 1)$ and $(0, -1)$. Foci: $(0, \sqrt{2})$ and $(0, -\sqrt{2})$. Transverse axis: y-axis. The hyperbola opens up and down. Vertices of the fundamental rectangle: $(1, 1), (-1, 1), (-1, -1), (1, -1)$. Asymptotes: $y = \pm x$.

12. Vertices: $(1, 0)$ and $(-1, 0)$. Foci: $(\sqrt{2}, 0)$ and $(-\sqrt{2}, 0)$. Transverse axis: x-axis. The hyperbola opens left and right. Vertices of the fundamental rectangle: $(1, 1), (-1, 1), (-1, -1), (1, -1)$. Asymptotes: $y = \pm x$.

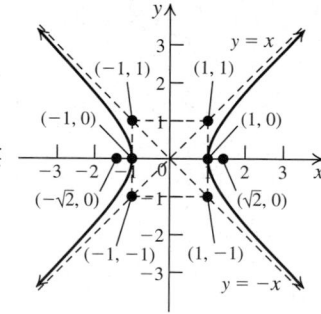

13. Vertices: $(0, 2)$ and $(0, -2)$. Foci: $(0, 2\sqrt{10})$ and $(0, -2\sqrt{10})$. Transverse axis: y-axis. The hyperbola opens up and down. Vertices of the fundamental rectangle: $(6, 2), (-6, 2), (-6, -2), (6, -2)$.

Asymptotes: $y = \pm \dfrac{1}{3}x$.

14. Vertices: $(2, 0)$ and $(-2, 0)$. Foci: $(2\sqrt{10}, 0)$ and $(-2\sqrt{10}, 0)$. Transverse axis: x-axis. The hyperbola opens left and right. Vertices of the fundamental rectangle: $(2, 6), (-2, 6), (-2, -6), (2, -6)$. Asymptotes: $y = \pm 3x$.

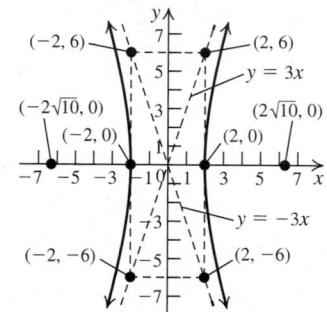

15. Vertices: $(3, 0)$ and $(-3, 0)$. Foci: $(\sqrt{13}, 0)$ and $(-\sqrt{13}, 0)$. Transverse axis: x-axis. The hyperbola opens left and right. Vertices of the fundamental rectangle: $(3, 2), (-3, 2), (-3, -2), (3, -2)$.

Asymptotes: $y = \pm \dfrac{2}{3}x$.

16. Vertices: $(0, 2)$ and $(0, -2)$. Foci: $(0, \sqrt{13})$ and $(0, -\sqrt{13})$. Transverse axis: y-axis. The hyperbola opens up and down. Vertices of the fundamental rectangle: $(3, 2), (-3, 2), (-3, -2), (3, -2)$.

Asymptotes: $y = \pm \dfrac{2}{3}x$.

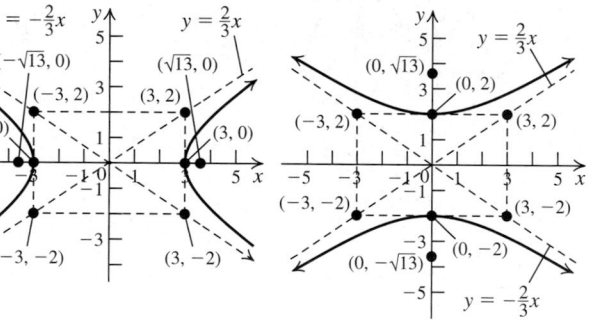

17. Vertices: $(0, 1)$ and $(0, -1)$.

Foci: $\left(0, \dfrac{\sqrt{5}}{2}\right)$ and $\left(0, -\dfrac{\sqrt{5}}{2}\right)$.

Transverse axis: y-axis. The hyperbola opens up and down. Vertices of the fundamental rectangle: $\left(\dfrac{1}{2}, 1\right), \left(-\dfrac{1}{2}, 1\right),$

$\left(-\dfrac{1}{2}, -1\right), \left(\dfrac{1}{2}, -1\right)$.

Asymptotes: $y = \pm 2x$.

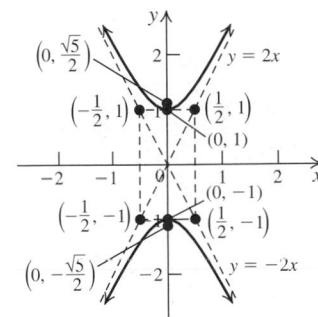

18. Vertices: $(0, 2)$ and $(0, -2)$.
Foci: $(0, \sqrt{5})$ and $(0, -\sqrt{5})$.
Transverse axis: y-axis. The hyperbola opens up and down. Vertices of the fundamental rectangle: $(1, 2), (-1, 2),$ $(-1, -2), (1, -2)$.
Asymptotes: $y = \pm 2x$.

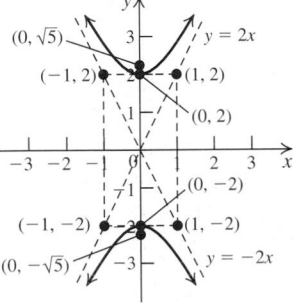

19. Vertices: $\left(\dfrac{1}{3}, 0\right)$ and $\left(-\dfrac{1}{3}, 0\right)$.

Foci: $\left(\dfrac{\sqrt{10}}{3}, 0\right)$ and

$\left(-\dfrac{\sqrt{10}}{3}, 0\right)$. Transverse axis:

x-axis. The hyperbola opens left and right. Vertices of the fundamental rectangle:

$\left(\dfrac{1}{3}, 1\right), \left(-\dfrac{1}{3}, 1\right),$

$\left(-\dfrac{1}{3}, -1\right), \left(\dfrac{1}{3}, -1\right)$.

Asymptotes: $y = \pm 3x$.

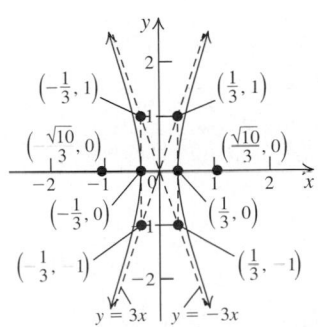

20. Vertices: $(2, 0)$ and $(-2, 0)$.
Foci: $(2\sqrt{10}, 0)$ and $(-2\sqrt{10}, 0)$. Transverse axis: x-axis. The hyperbola opens left and right. Vertices of the fundamental rectangle: $(2, 6),$ $(-2, 6), (-2, -6), (2, -6)$.
Asymptotes: $y = \pm 3x$.

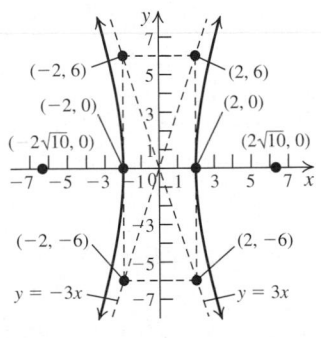

21. $\dfrac{x^2}{4} - \dfrac{y^2}{5} = 1$

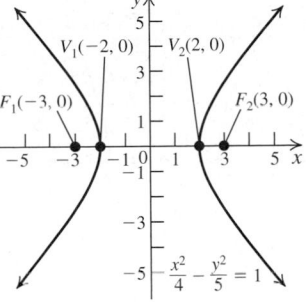

22. $\dfrac{x^2}{9} - \dfrac{y^2}{16} = 1$

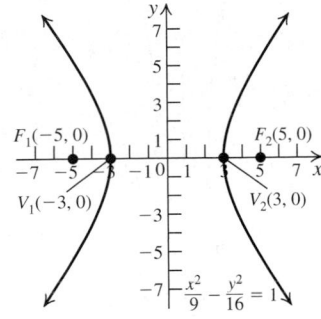

23. $\dfrac{y^2}{16} - \dfrac{x^2}{20} = 1$

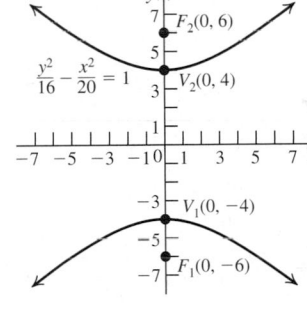

24. $\dfrac{y^2}{25} - \dfrac{x^2}{39} = 1$

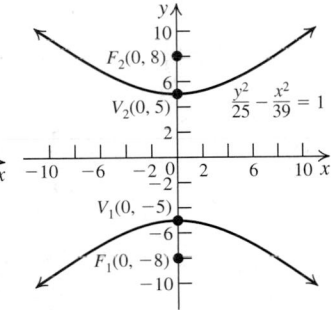

25. $\dfrac{y^2}{4} - \dfrac{x^2}{21} = 1$

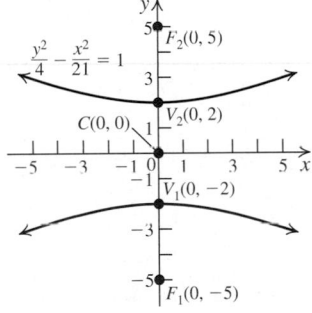

26. $y^2 - \dfrac{x^2}{15} = 1$

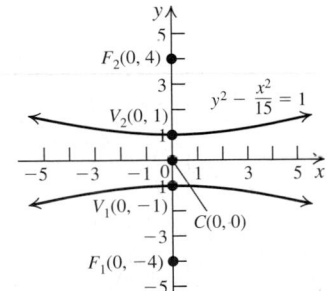

27. $x^2 - \dfrac{y^2}{24} = 1$

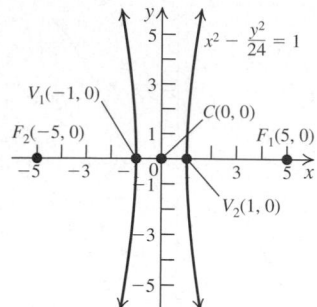

28. $\dfrac{x^2}{9} - \dfrac{y^2}{27} = 1$

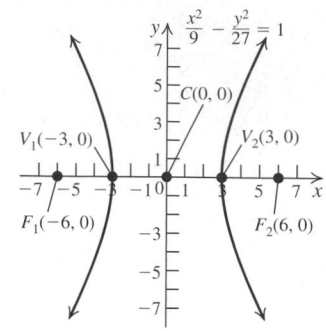

33. $\dfrac{y^2}{16} - \dfrac{x^2}{16} = 1$

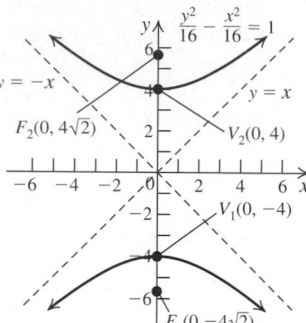

34. $\dfrac{x^2}{9} - \dfrac{y^2}{36} = 1$

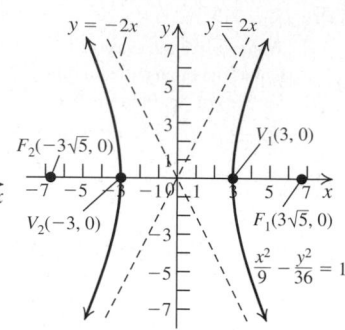

29. $\dfrac{y^2}{9} - \dfrac{x^2}{16} = 1$

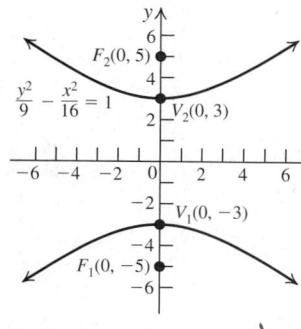

30. $x^2 - \dfrac{y^2}{3} = 1$

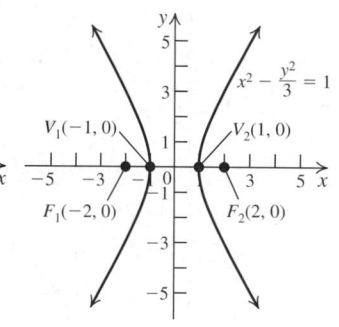

35. Center: $(1, -1)$. Vertices: $(4, -1)$ and $(-2, -1)$. Transverse axis: $y = -1$. Asymptotes:
$$y + 1 = \pm\dfrac{4}{3}(x - 1).$$

36. Center: $(-1, 1)$. Vertices: $(-1, 5)$ and $(-1, -3)$. Transverse axis: $x = -1$. Asymptotes:
$$y - 1 = \pm 2(x + 1).$$

31. $x^2 - \dfrac{y^2}{4} = 1$

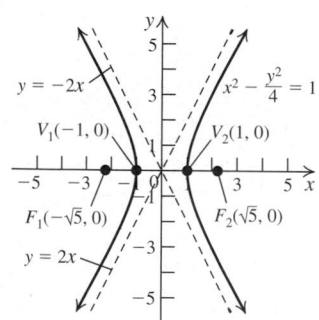

32. $\dfrac{y^2}{90} - \dfrac{x^2}{10} = 1$

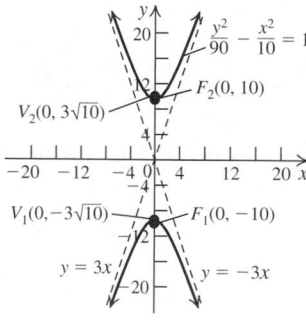

37. Center: $(-2, 0)$. Vertices: $(3, 0)$ and $(-7, 0)$. Transverse axis: x-axis. Asymptotes: $y = \pm\dfrac{7}{5}(x + 2)$.

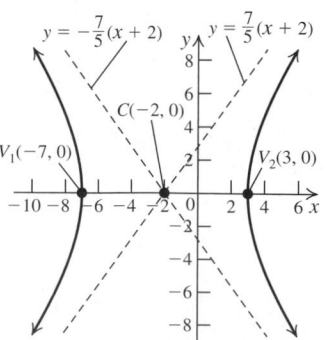

38. Center: $(-1, -2)$. Vertices:
$(2, -2)$ and $(-4, -2)$.
Transverse axis: $y = -2$.
Asymptotes:
$y + 2 = \pm 2(x + 1)$.

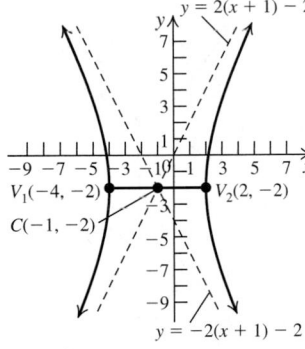

39. Center: $(-4, -3)$. Vertices:
$(1, -3)$ and $(-9, -3)$.
Transverse axis: $y = -3$.
Asymptotes:
$y + 3 = \pm\frac{7}{5}(x + 4)$.

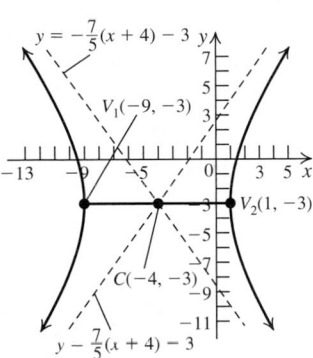

43. Center: $(2, -1)$. Vertices:
$(2, 4)$ and $(2, -6)$. Transverse
axis: $x = 2$. Asymptotes:
$y + 1 = \pm 3(x - 2)$.

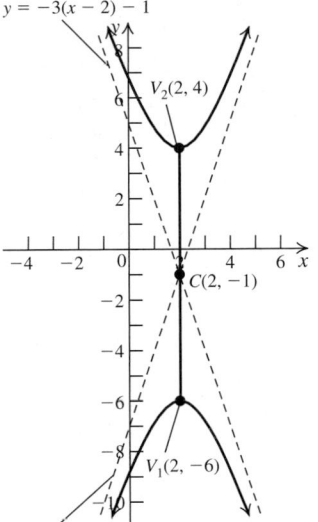

44. Center: $(4, -3)$. Vertices:
$\left(4 + \frac{\sqrt{6}}{3}, -3\right)$ and
$\left(4 - \frac{\sqrt{6}}{3}, -3\right)$. Transverse
axis: $y = -3$. Asymptotes:
$y + 3 = \pm\sqrt{2}(x - 4)$.

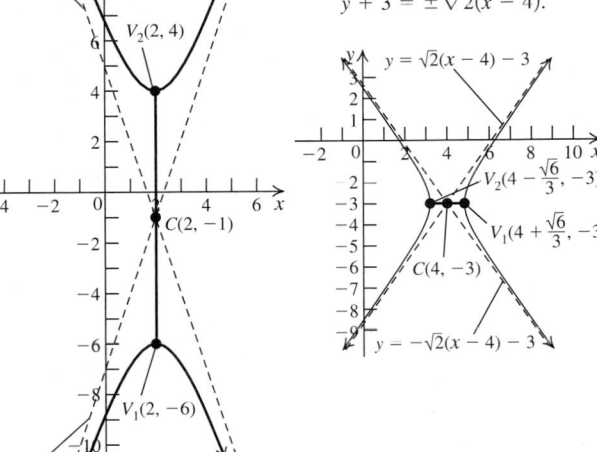

40. Center: $(3, -1)$. Vertices:
$(6, -1)$ and $(0, -1)$. Transverse
axis: $y = -1$. Asymptotes:
$y + 1 = \pm(x - 3)$.

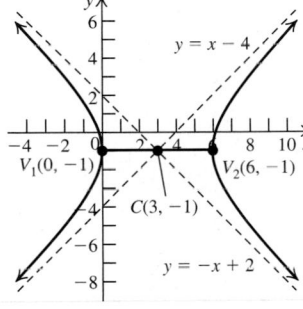

41. Center: $(0, -1)$. Vertices:
$\left(\frac{5}{2}, -1\right)$ and $\left(-\frac{5}{2}, -1\right)$.
Transverse axis: $y = -1$.
Asymptotes: $y + 1 = \pm 2x$.

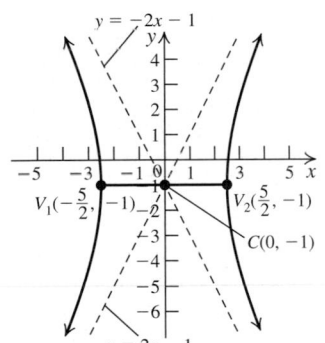

45. Center: $(-3, 0)$. Vertices:
$(-3 + 3\sqrt{5}, 0)$ and
$(-3 - 3\sqrt{5}, 0)$.
Transverse axis: x-axis.
Asymptotes: $y = \pm(x + 3)$.

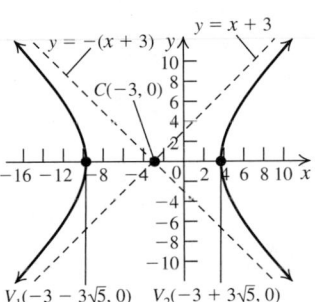

46. Center: $(-2, 0)$. Vertices: $(2, 0)$
and $(-6, 0)$. Transverse axis:
x-axis. Asymptotes:
$y = \pm\frac{1}{2}(x + 2)$.

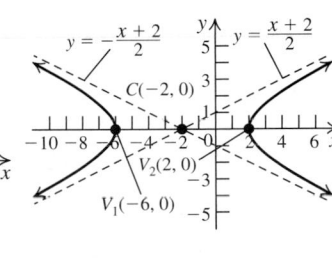

42. Center: $(1, 0)$. Vertices: $(5, 0)$ and $(-3, 0)$. Transverse axis: x-axis.
Asymptotes: $y = \pm 3(x - 1)$.

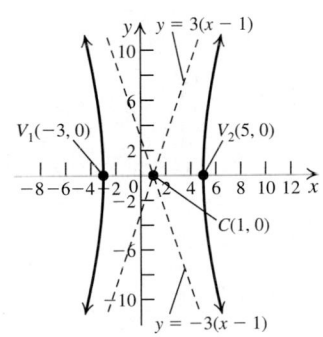

47. Center: (2, 0). Vertices: (4, 0) and (0, 0). Transverse axis: x-axis. Asymptotes:
$$y = \pm\frac{1}{2}(x - 2).$$

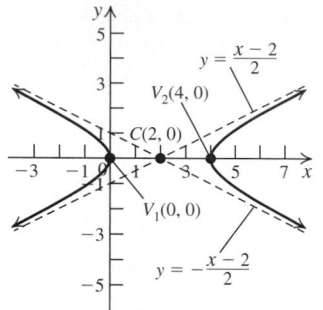

48. Center: (0, −2). Vertices: (2, −2) and (−2, −2). Transverse axis: y = −2.

Asymptotes: $y + 2 = \pm\frac{\sqrt{2}}{2}x.$

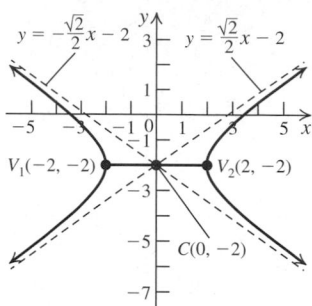

51. Center: (3, −2). Vertices: (3 + √6, −2) and (3 − √6, −2). Transverse axis: y = −2. Asymptotes:
$$y + 2 = \pm\frac{\sqrt{6}}{2}(x - 3).$$

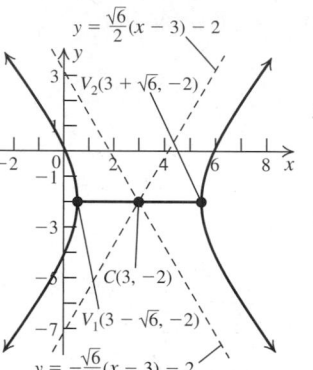

52. Center: (−2, 1). Vertices: (−2, 4) and (−2, −2). Transverse axis: x = −2. Asymptotes:
$$y - 1 = \pm\frac{3}{2}(x + 2).$$

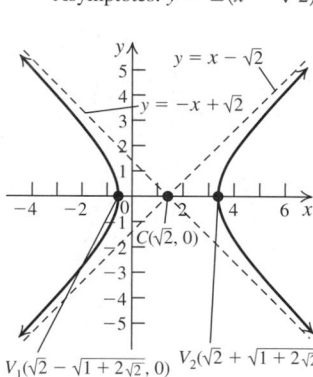

49. Center: (−3, −4). Vertices: (−3, −3) and (−3, −5). Transverse axis: x = −3. Asymptotes:
$$y + 4 = \pm\sqrt{2}(x + 3).$$

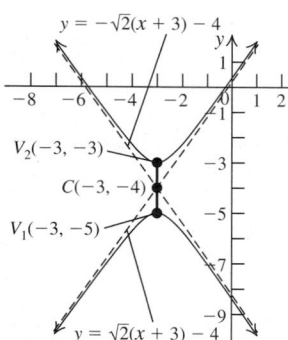

50. Center: $\left(-\frac{5}{3}, 2\right)$. Vertices: $\left(-\frac{5}{3}, 2 + 2\sqrt{3}\right)$ and $\left(-\frac{5}{3}, 2 - 2\sqrt{3}\right)$. Transverse axis: $x = -\frac{5}{3}$. Asymptotes:
$$y - 2 = \pm 3\left(x + \frac{5}{3}\right).$$

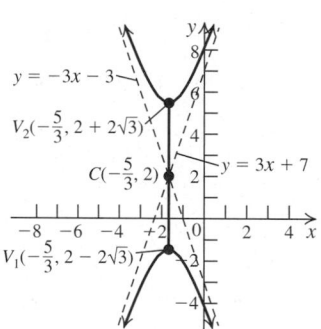

53. Center: (√2, 0). Vertices:
(√2 + √2√2 + 1, 0) and
(√2 − √2√2 + 1, 0).
Transverse axis: x-axis.
Asymptotes: $y = \pm(x - \sqrt{2}).$

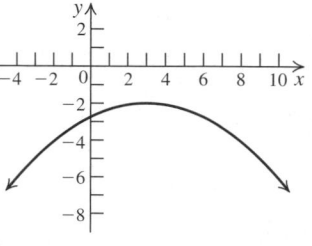

54. This is not a hyperbola, but a pair of lines: $y = \pm 2\left(x + \frac{1}{2}\right).$

55. Parabola

56. Hyperbola

57. Hyperbola

58. Ellipse

63. Ellipse

64. Hyperbola

59. Circle

60. Parabola

61. Parabola

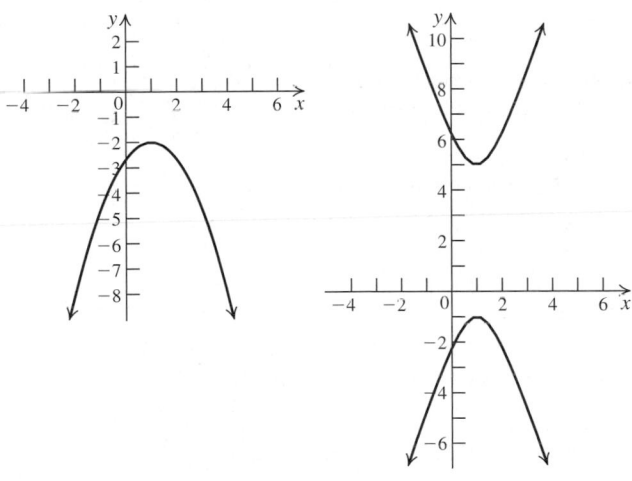

62. Hyperbola

B Exercises: Applying the Concepts

65. The difference in the distances of the location of the explosion from A and B is given: 600 m. Therefore, the location of the explosion is restricted to points on a hyperbola, the length of whose transverse axis is 600 m. Equation: $\dfrac{x^2}{90,000} - \dfrac{y^2}{160,000} = 1$.

66. $(3 \text{ sec}) \times (1100 \text{ ft/sec}) = 3300 \text{ ft}$, so the explosion is 3300 ft closer to A than to B. Therefore, the location of the explosion is restricted to points on a hyperbola, the length of whose transverse axis is 3300 feet. Equation: $\dfrac{x^2}{2,722,500} - \dfrac{y^2}{25,155,900} = 1$.

67. Let the coordinates of Nicole be $(-4000, 0)$ and those of Juan be $(4000, 0)$.

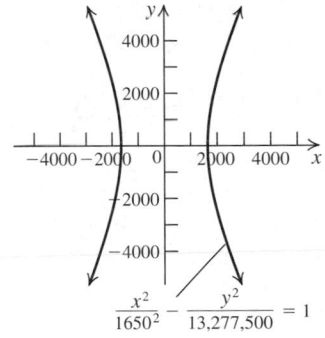

$$\frac{x^2}{1650^2} - \frac{y^2}{13,277,500} = 1$$

68. This is impossible. Since Valerie is at the origin, she must hear the thunder before Juan does.

69. Let the coordinates of A be $(-150, 0)$ and the coordinates of B be $(150, 0)$. Equation: $\dfrac{x^2}{5625} - \dfrac{y^2}{16,875} = 1$.

71. $\dfrac{x^2}{193,600} - \dfrac{y^2}{446,400} = 1$.

72. Let the coordinates of A be $(-125, 0)$ and the coordinates of B be $(125, 0)$. The plane is flying on the line $y = 50$. At the time of receiving the signals, the plane is at $(50.5238, 50)$.

74. Possible locations of the boat: $(-1397.427, 1225.2945)$, $(-281.3655, 209.9383)$, $(359.5894, 288.219)$, $(1059.7444, 925.1969)$.

C Exercises: Beyond the Basics

75. a. $x^2 - \dfrac{y^2}{24} = 1$ **b.** $\dfrac{x^2}{4} - \dfrac{y^2}{21} = 1$ **c.** $\dfrac{x^2}{16} - \dfrac{y^2}{9} = 1$

76.

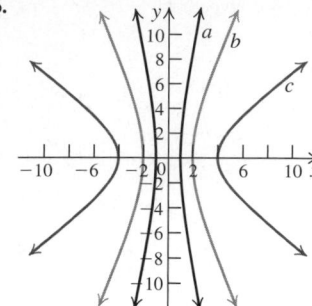

77. a. $y^2 - \dfrac{x^2}{35} = 1$ **b.** $y^2 - \dfrac{x^2}{15} = 1$ **c.** $y^2 - \dfrac{x^2}{8} = 1$

78.

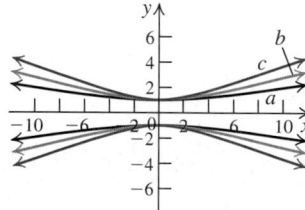

79. After simplification, the equation $(x + c)^2 + y^2 = 4a^2 \pm 4a\sqrt{(x - c)^2 + y^2} + (x - c)^2 + y^2$ becomes $cx = a^2 \pm a\sqrt{(x - c)^2 + y^2}$. Isolating the radical gives $cx - a^2 = \pm a\sqrt{(x - c)^2 + y^2}$. Squaring both sides yields $a^4 - 2a^2cx + c^2x^2 = a^2((x - c)^2 + y^2)$. After simplifying and collecting like terms, we have $(c^2 - a^2)x^2 - a^2y^2 = a^2(c^2 - a^2)$.

80. a. The equation of the hyperbola with foci (p, p) and $(-p, -p)$ and with distance difference $2p$ is $\sqrt{(x + p)^2 + (y + p)^2} - \sqrt{(x - p)^2 + (y - p)^2} = 2p$. Squaring both sides, we obtain $(x + p)^2 + (y + p)^2 + (x - p)^2 + (y - p)^2 - 2\sqrt{(x + p)^2 + (y + p)^2}\sqrt{(x - p)^2 + (y - p)^2} = 4p^2$. Simplifying and isolating the radical yields $x^2 + y^2 - \sqrt{(x + p)^2 + (y + p)^2}\sqrt{(x - p)^2 + (y - p)^2} = 2p^2$. Squaring again and collecting like terms gives $8p^2xy = 4p^4$. Since $p \neq 0$, this is equivalent to $xy = \dfrac{p^2}{2}$.

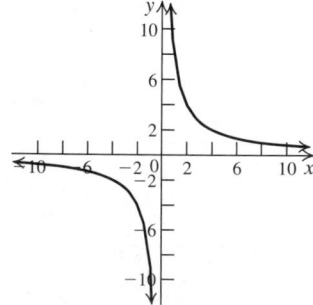

b. Foci: $(4, 4)$ and $(-4, -4)$

81. We may assume without loss of generality that the transverse axis is the x-axis and the conjugate axis is the y-axis. Therefore, the equation of the hyperbola is $\dfrac{x^2}{a^2} - \dfrac{y^2}{b^2} = 1$. Since the hyperbola is equilateral, $a = b$. Thus, the asymptotes are $y = \pm x$. These two lines are perpendicular to one another.

82. One of the foci is $(\sqrt{a^2 + b^2}, 0)$. (Because of symmetry, it does not matter which focus is chosen to calculate the length of the latus rectum.) Therefore, substituting $x = \sqrt{a^2 + b^2}$ in the equation of the hyperbola and solving for y, we get the coordinates of the endpoints of the latus rectum. This gives $y = \pm\dfrac{b^2}{a}$. Hence the length of the latus rectum is $\dfrac{2b^2}{a}$.

83. Since $b > 0$ and $c^2 = a^2 + b^2$, it follows that $c^2 > a^2$, so $c > a$. Therefore, $e > 1$. In the case $e = 1$, the hyperbola becomes the union of two rays.

84. $e = \dfrac{5}{4}$, length of the latus rectum: $\dfrac{9}{2}$.

85. $e = \dfrac{\sqrt{61}}{5}$, length of the latus rectum: $\dfrac{72}{5}$.

86. $e = \sqrt{2}$, length of the latus rectum: 14.

87. $e = 3$, length of the latus rectum: 8.

88. $e = \dfrac{3}{2}$, length of the latus rectum: 5.

89. $e = \dfrac{c}{a} \Rightarrow e^2 = \dfrac{c^2}{a^2} \Rightarrow e^2 = \dfrac{a^2 + b^2}{a^2} \Rightarrow e^2 - 1 = \dfrac{b^2}{a^2} \Rightarrow a^2(e^2 - 1) = b^2$

90. $\dfrac{x^2}{16} - \dfrac{y^2}{20} = 1$

91. The equation of the path of P is $\sqrt{(x - 3)^2 + y^2} = 2|x + 1|$. Squaring both sides, we obtain $(x - 3)^2 + y^2 = 4(x + 1)^2$. After simplifying and rearranging terms, we get $\dfrac{\left(x + \dfrac{7}{3}\right)^2}{\dfrac{64}{9}} - \dfrac{y^2}{\dfrac{64}{3}} = 1$. This is the equation of a hyperbola with $a = \dfrac{8}{3}$ and $c = \dfrac{16}{3}$. Therefore, the eccentricity is 2.

92. The equation of the path of P is $\sqrt{x^2 + (y + 3)^2} = 3|y - 1|$. Squaring both sides, we obtain $x^2 + (y + 3)^2 = 9(y - 1)^2$. After simplifying and rearranging terms, we get $\dfrac{\left(y - \dfrac{3}{2}\right)^2}{\dfrac{9}{4}} - \dfrac{x^2}{18} = 1$. This is the equation of a hyperbola with $a = \dfrac{3}{2}$ and $c = \dfrac{9}{2}$. Therefore, the eccentricity is 3.

93. Points of intersection:

$\left(-\frac{91}{20}, \frac{109}{10}\right)$

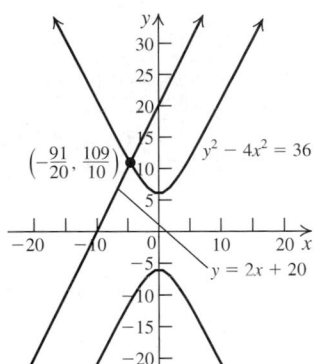

94. Points of intersection:

$\left(5, \frac{1}{2}\sqrt{10}\right), \left(5, -\frac{1}{2}\sqrt{10}\right)$

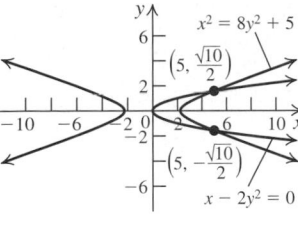

95. Points of intersection:

$(-2\sqrt{2}, -\sqrt{7})$,
$(-2\sqrt{2}, \sqrt{7})$,
$(2\sqrt{2}, -\sqrt{7}), (2\sqrt{2}, \sqrt{7})$

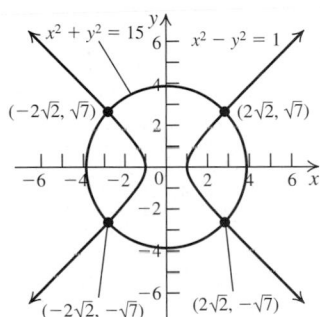

96. Points of intersection: $(-3, 0)$
and $(3, 0)$

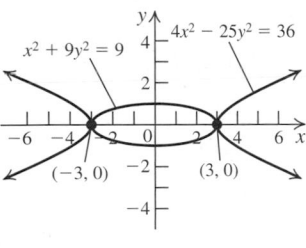

97. Points of intersection:

$(-2, -3), (-2, 3), (2, -3)$,
$(2, 3)$.

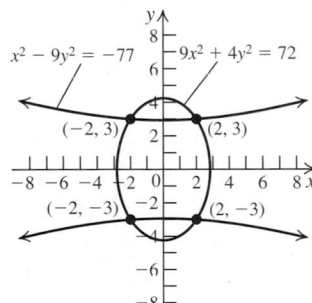

98. Points of intersection:

$(-1, -2), (-1, 2), (1, -2)$,
$(1, 2)$.

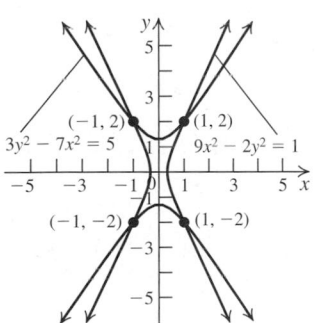

Critical Thinking

99. a. Since $4x^2 - 9y^2 = (2x + 3y)(2x - 3y)$, this is the union of two lines.

c. Since both x^2 and y^2 are nonnegative, the only solution of the equation is $x = y = 0$ (i.e., the origin).

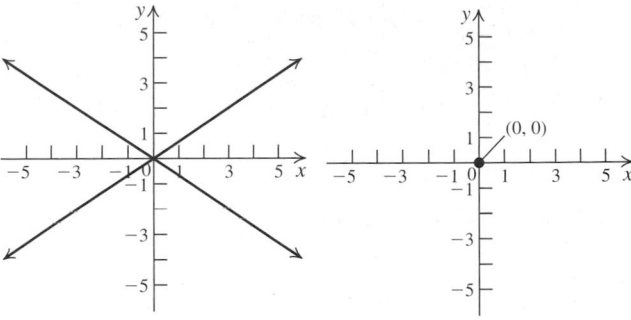

d. After completing the square, we can see that the equation is equivalent to $(x - 2)^2 + (y + 4)^2 = 0$, whose only solution is $x = 2, y = -4$.

e. Since $y^2 - 2x^2 = (y + \sqrt{2}x)(y - \sqrt{2}x)$, this is the union of two lines.

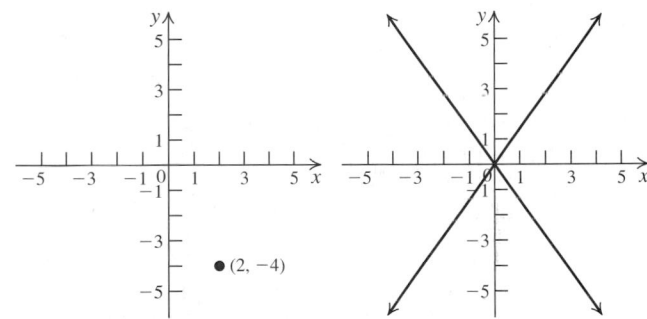

Group Project

The rewritten form of the equation is equivalent to

$$A\left(x + \frac{D}{2A}\right)^2 + C\left(y + \frac{E}{2C}\right)^2 = \frac{D^2}{4A} + \frac{E^2}{4C} - F.$$ If the term on the right-hand side is not zero, then the equation can be written as

$$\frac{\left(x + \frac{D}{2A}\right)^2}{\frac{D^2}{4A^2} + \frac{E^2}{4AC} - AF} + \frac{\left(y + \frac{E}{2C}\right)^2}{\frac{D^2}{4AC} + \frac{E^2}{4C^2} - CF} = 1$$

i. If $\frac{D^2}{4A} + \frac{E^2}{4C} - F = 0$, then the graph consists of one point: $\left(-\frac{D}{2A}, -\frac{E}{2C}\right)$. If $\frac{D^2}{4A} + \frac{E^2}{4C} - F > 0$, then the graph is an ellipse.

If $\frac{D^2}{4A} + \frac{E^2}{4C} - F < 0$, then there is no solution and the graph is empty.

ii. If $\dfrac{D^2}{4A} + \dfrac{E^2}{4C} - F = 0$, then the graph consists of two lines:

$\sqrt{A}\left(x + \dfrac{D}{2A}\right) = \pm\sqrt{-C}\left(y + \dfrac{E}{2C}\right)$. If $\dfrac{D^2}{4A} + \dfrac{E^2}{4C} - F > 0$, then

the graph is a hyperbola with a horizontal transverse axis. If

$\dfrac{D^2}{4A} + \dfrac{E^2}{4C} - F < 0$, then the graph is a hyperbola with a vertical

transverse axis.

iii. If $\dfrac{D^2}{4A} + \dfrac{E^2}{4C} - F = 0$, then the graph consists of two lines:

$\sqrt{-A}\left(x + \dfrac{D}{2A}\right) = \pm\sqrt{C}\left(y + \dfrac{E}{2C}\right)$. If $\dfrac{D^2}{4A} + \dfrac{E^2}{4C} - F > 0$, then

the graph is a hyperbola with a vertical transverse axis. If

$\dfrac{D^2}{4A} + \dfrac{E^2}{4C} - F < 0$, then the graph is a hyperbola with a

horizontal transverse axis.

iv. If $\dfrac{D^2}{4A} + \dfrac{E^2}{4C} - F = 0$, then the graph consists of one point:

$\left(-\dfrac{D}{2A}, -\dfrac{E}{2C}\right)$. If $\dfrac{D^2}{4A} + \dfrac{E^2}{4C} - F > 0$, then there is no solution

and the graph is empty. If $\dfrac{D^2}{4A} + \dfrac{E^2}{4C} - F < 0$, then the graph

is an ellipse.

Review Exercises

1.

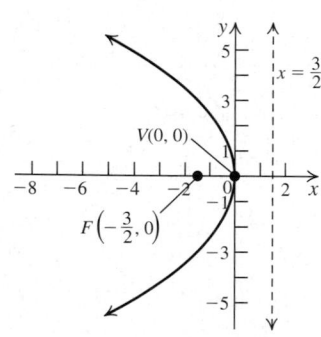

Vertex: $(0, 0)$. Focus: $\left(-\dfrac{3}{2}, 0\right)$.
Axis: x-axis.

Directrix: $x = \dfrac{3}{2}$.

2.

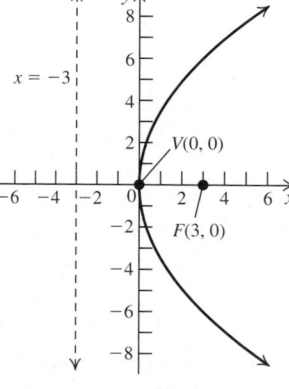

Vertex: $(0, 0)$. Focus: $(3, 0)$.
Axis: x-axis. Directrix:
$x = -3$.

3.

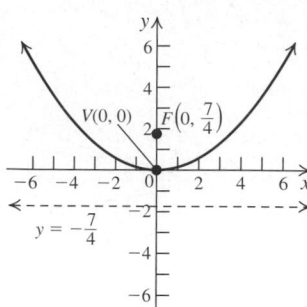

Vertex: $(0, 0)$. Focus: $\left(0, \dfrac{7}{4}\right)$.
Axis: y-axis.

Directrix: $y = -\dfrac{7}{4}$.

4.

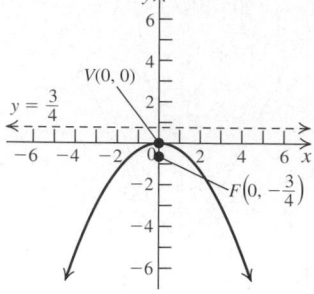

Vertex: $(0, 0)$. Focus: $\left(0, -\dfrac{3}{4}\right)$.
Axis: y-axis.

Directrix: $y = \dfrac{3}{4}$.

5.

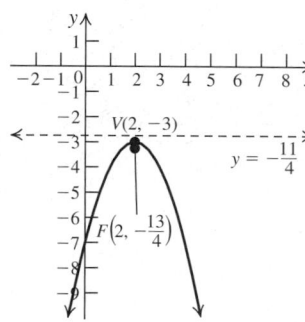

Vertex: $(2, -3)$.

Focus: $\left(2, -\dfrac{13}{4}\right)$.

Axis: $x = 2$.

Directrix: $y = -\dfrac{11}{4}$.

6.

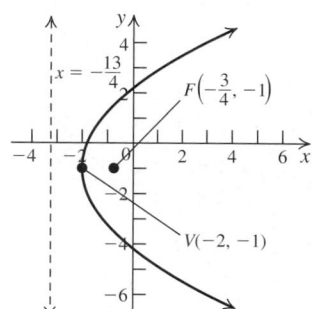

Vertex: $(-2, -1)$.

Focus: $\left(-\dfrac{3}{4}, -1\right)$.

Axis: $y = -1$.

Directrix: $x = -\dfrac{13}{4}$.

7.

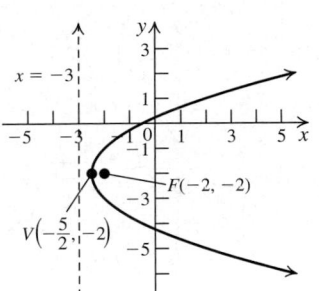

Vertex: $\left(-\dfrac{5}{2}, -2\right)$.

Focus: $(-2, -2)$. Axis: $y = -2$.

Directrix: $x = -3$.

8.

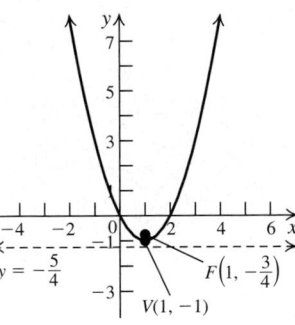

Vertex: $(1, -1)$.

Focus: $\left(1, -\dfrac{3}{4}\right)$. Axis: $x = 1$.

Directrix: $y = -\dfrac{5}{4}$.

15.

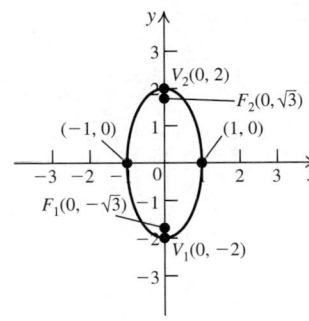

Foci: $(0, \sqrt{3})$ and $(0, -\sqrt{3})$.
Vertices: $(0, 2)$ and $(0, -2)$.
Endpoints of the minor axis:
$(1, 0)$ and $(-1, 0)$.

16.

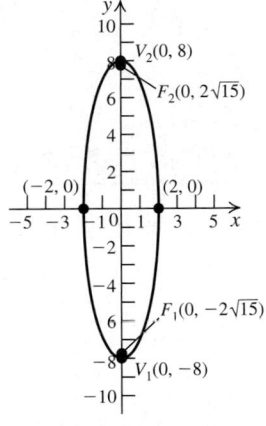

Foci: $(0, 2\sqrt{15})$ and
$(0, -2\sqrt{15})$. Vertices: $(0, 8)$
and $(0, -8)$. Endpoints of the
minor axis: $(2, 0)$ and $(-2, 0)$.

13.

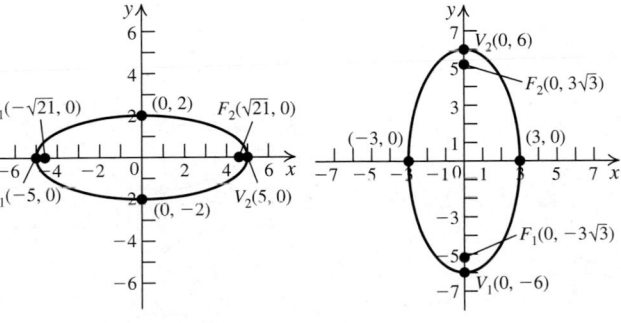

Foci: $(\sqrt{21}, 0)$ and $(-\sqrt{21}, 0)$.
Vertices: $(5, 0)$ and $(-5, 0)$.
Endpoints of the minor axis:
$(0, 2)$ and $(0, -2)$.

14.

Foci: $(0, 3\sqrt{3})$ and $(0, -3\sqrt{3})$.
Vertices: $(0, 6)$ and $(0, -6)$.
Endpoints of the minor axis:
$(3, 0)$ and $(-3, 0)$.

17.

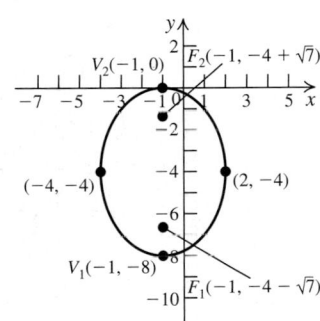

Foci: $(-1, -4 + \sqrt{7})$ and
$(-1, -4 - \sqrt{7})$. Vertices:
$(-1, 0)$ and $(-1, -8)$.
Endpoints of the minor axis:
$(2, -4)$ and $(4, -4)$.

18.

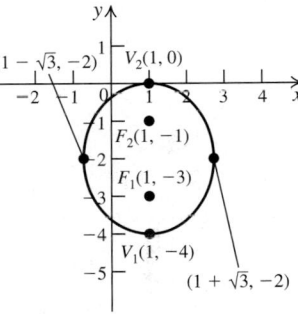

Foci: $(1, -1)$ and $(1, -3)$.
Vertices: $(1, 0)$ and $(1, -4)$.
Endpoints of the minor axis:
$(1 + \sqrt{3},\; 2)$ and
$(1 - \sqrt{3}, -2)$.

19.

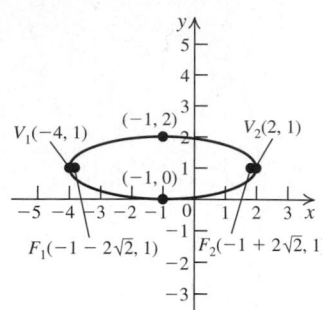

Foci: $(-1 + 2\sqrt{2}, 1)$ and $(-1 - 2\sqrt{2}, 1)$. Vertices: $(2, 1)$ and $(-4, 1)$. Endpoints of the minor axis: $(-1, 2)$ and $(-1, 0)$.

20.

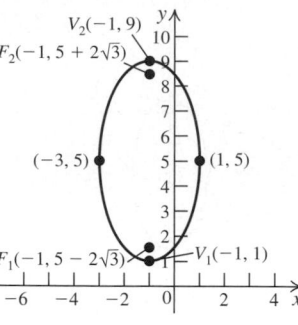

Foci: $(-1, 5 + 2\sqrt{3})$ and $(-1, 5 - 2\sqrt{3})$. Vertices: $(-1, 9)$ and $(-1, 1)$. Endpoints of the minor axis: $(1, 5)$ and $(-3, 5)$.

27.

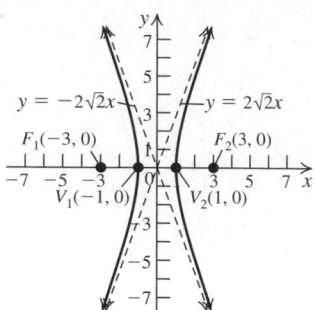

Vertices: $(1, 0)$ and $(-1, 0)$. Foci: $(3, 0)$ and $(-3, 0)$. Asymptotes: $y = \pm 2\sqrt{2}x$.

28.

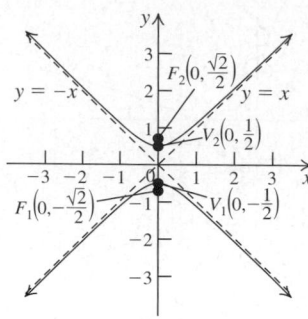

Vertices: $\left(0, \dfrac{1}{2}\right)$ and $\left(0, -\dfrac{1}{2}\right)$. Foci: $\left(0, \dfrac{\sqrt{2}}{2}\right)$ and $\left(0, -\dfrac{\sqrt{2}}{2}\right)$. Asymptotes: $y = \pm x$.

21. $\dfrac{x^2}{16} + \dfrac{y^2}{4} = 1$ **22.** $\dfrac{x^2}{4} + \dfrac{y^2}{36} = 1$

23. $\dfrac{x^2}{100} + \dfrac{y^2}{75} = 1$ **24.** $\dfrac{x^2}{64} + \dfrac{y^2}{100} = 1$

25.

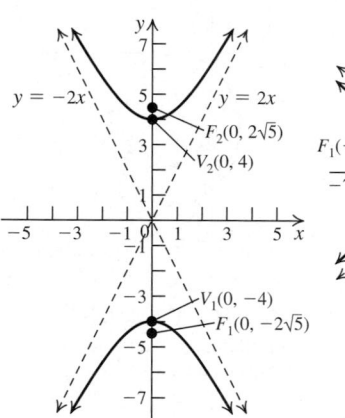

Vertices: $(0, 4)$ and $(0, -4)$. Foci: $(0, 2\sqrt{5})$ and $(0, -2\sqrt{5})$. Asymptotes: $y = \pm 2x$.

26.

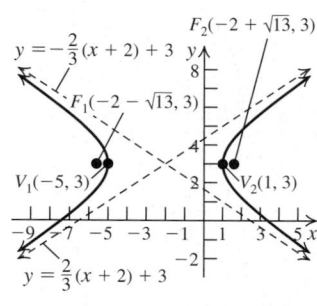

Vertices: $(4, 0)$ and $(-4, 0)$. Foci: $(5, 0)$ and $(-5, 0)$. Asymptotes: $y = \pm\dfrac{3}{4}x$.

29.

Vertices: $(1, 3)$ and $(-5, 3)$. Foci: $(-2 + \sqrt{13}, 3)$ and $(-2 - \sqrt{13}, 3)$. Asymptotes: $y - 3 = \pm\dfrac{2}{3}(x + 2)$.

30.

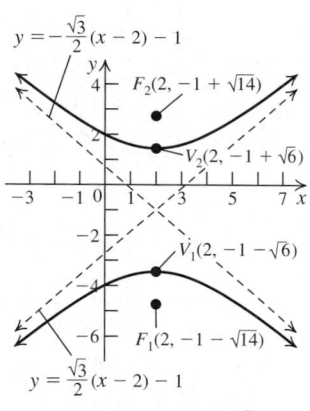

Vertices: $(2, -1 + \sqrt{6})$ and $(2, -1 - \sqrt{6})$. Foci: $(2, -1 + \sqrt{14})$ and $(2, -1 - \sqrt{14})$. Asymptotes: $y + 1 = \pm\dfrac{\sqrt{3}}{2}(x - 2)$.

31.

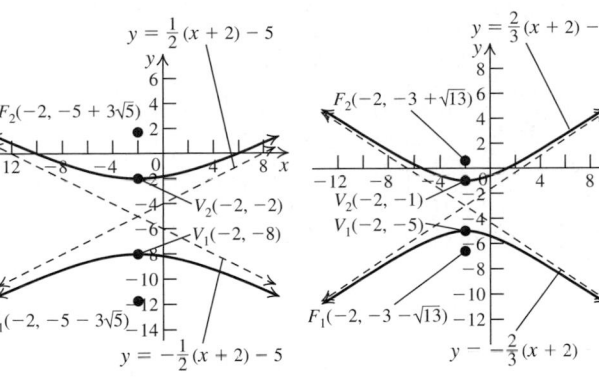

$$y = \frac{1}{2}(x + 2) - 5$$

$F_2(-2, -5 + 3\sqrt{5})$

$V_2(-2, -2)$

$V_1(-2, -8)$

$F_1(-2, -5 - 3\sqrt{5})$

$$y = -\frac{1}{2}(x + 2) - 5$$

Vertices: $(-2, -2)$ and $(-2, -8)$. Foci: $(-2, -5 + 3\sqrt{5})$ and $(-2, -5 - 3\sqrt{5})$. Asymptotes: $y + 5 = \pm\frac{1}{2}(x + 2)$.

32.

$$y = \frac{2}{3}(x + 2) - 3$$

$F_2(-2, -3 + \sqrt{13})$

$V_2(-2, -1)$

$V_1(-2, -5)$

$F_1(-2, -3 - \sqrt{13})$

$$y - -\frac{2}{3}(x + 2) \quad 3$$

Vertices: $(-2, -1)$ and $(-2, -5)$. Foci: $(-2, -3 + \sqrt{13})$ and $(-2, -3 - \sqrt{13})$. Asymptotes: $y + 3 - \pm\frac{2}{3}(x + 2)$.

33. $x^2 - \dfrac{y^2}{3} = 1$ **34.** $\dfrac{y^2}{4} - \dfrac{x^2}{12} = 1$

35. $\dfrac{x^2}{4} - \dfrac{y^2}{36} = 1$ **36.** $\dfrac{y^2}{9} - \dfrac{x^2}{9} = 1$

37. Hyperbola

38. Parabola

39. Ellipse

40. Parabola

41. Circle

42. Parabola

43. Hyperbola

44. Ellipse

45. Circle

46. Hyperbola

47. Ellipse

48. Hyperbola

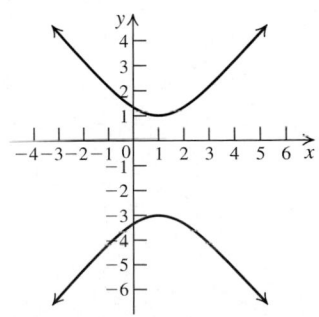

49. $\dfrac{x^2}{5} - \dfrac{y^2}{4} = 1$ **50.** $\dfrac{x^2}{25} + \dfrac{y^2}{9} = 1$

51. Point of intersection:
$\left(\dfrac{109}{10}, -\dfrac{91}{20}\right)$

52. Points of intersection:
$\left(\dfrac{1}{2}\sqrt{10}, 5\right), \left(-\dfrac{1}{2}\sqrt{10}, 5\right)$

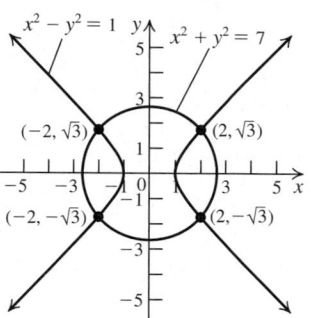

53. Points of intersection: $(2, 1)$,
$(2, -1), (-2, 1), (-2, -1)$.

54. Points of intersection: $(2, \sqrt{3})$,
$(2, -\sqrt{3}), (-2, \sqrt{3})$,
$(-2, -\sqrt{3})$

58. $\dfrac{x}{40} = \sqrt{1 + \dfrac{y^2}{248{,}400}}$

Practice Test A

2. $(y - 1)^2 = -8(x + 3)$

3. Focus: $\left(0, -\dfrac{9}{4}\right)$. Directrix: $y = \dfrac{9}{4}$.

4.

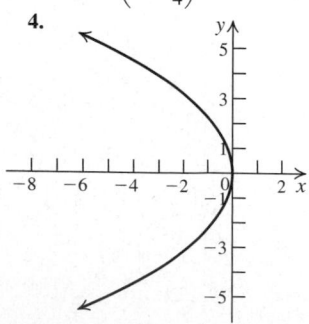

5. Vertex: $(-2, 1)$. Focus: $(-2, -1)$. Directrix: $y = 3$.

8. $\dfrac{x^2}{12} + \dfrac{y^2}{16} = 1$ **9.** $\dfrac{x^2}{29} + \dfrac{y^2}{25} = 1$ **10.** $\dfrac{x^2}{81} + \dfrac{y^2}{4} = 1$

11.

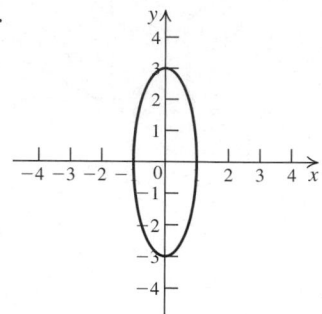

12. Vertices: $(0, 1)$ and $(0, -1)$. Foci: $(0, 5\sqrt{2})$ and $(0, -5\sqrt{2})$.

13.

14. $\dfrac{y^2}{36} - \dfrac{x^2}{9} = 1$ **15.** $y^2 - (x - 1)^2 = 1$

16. $\dfrac{(x - 1)^2}{4} - (y + 2)^2 = 1$

17. Hyperbola

18. Parabola

19. Circle

20. Ellipse

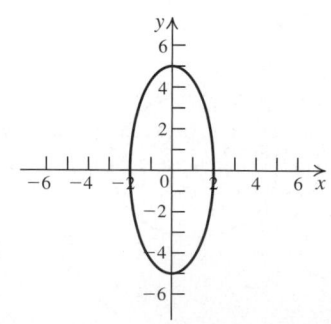

Cumulative Review Exercises (Chapters 1–10)

1. $\dfrac{f(x + h) - f(x)}{h} = 2x + h - 3$

2.

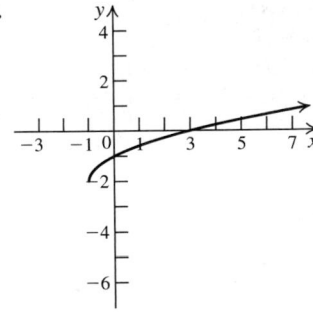

3. $f^{-1}(x) = \dfrac{1}{2}x + \dfrac{3}{2}$.

$f(f^{-1}(x)) = f\left(\dfrac{1}{2}x + \dfrac{3}{2}\right) = 2\left(\dfrac{1}{2}x + \dfrac{3}{2}\right) - 3 = x + 3 - 3 = x$.

4.

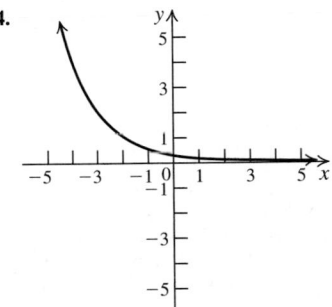

5. Solution: $x = 4$ **6.** $\dfrac{1}{3}\log_a x + \dfrac{1}{6}\log_a y + \dfrac{1}{6}\log_a z$

18. Hyperbola

19. Circle

20.

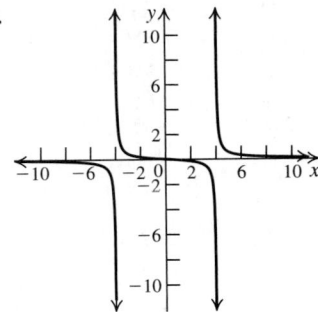

CHAPTER 11

Section 11.1

Practice Problems

1. $a_1 = -2, a_2 = -4, a_3 = -8, a_4 = -16$

2. $a_1 = -1, a_2 = \dfrac{1}{4}, a_3 = -\dfrac{1}{9}, a_4 = \dfrac{1}{16}, a_5 = -\dfrac{1}{25}, a_6 = \dfrac{1}{36}$

3. $a_n = (-1)^{n+1}\left(1 - \dfrac{1}{n}\right)$

4. $a_1 = -3, a_2 = -1, a_3 = 3, a_4 = 11, a_5 = 27$

5. $a_0 = 1, a_1 = 2, a_2 = 3$ and $a_k = a_{k-2} + a_{k-1}$ for all $k \geq 3$.

6. a. 13   **b.** $n(n - 1)(n - 2)$

7. $a_1 = -2, a_2 = 2, a_3 = -\dfrac{4}{3}, a_4 = \dfrac{2}{3}, a_5 = -\dfrac{4}{15}$

8. -4 **9.** $\displaystyle\sum_{k=1}^{7}(-1)^{k+1}(2k)$

A Exercises: Basic Skills and Concepts

1. $a_1 = 1, a_2 = 4, a_3 = 7, a_4 = 10$

2. $a_1 = 3, a_2 = 5, a_3 = 7, a_4 = 9$

3. $a_1 = 0, a_2 = \dfrac{1}{2}, a_3 = \dfrac{2}{3}, a_4 = \dfrac{3}{4}$

4. $a_1 = 2, a_2 = \dfrac{3}{2}, a_3 = \dfrac{4}{3}, a_4 = \dfrac{5}{4}$

5. $a_1 = -1, a_2 = -4, a_3 = -9, a_4 = -16$

6. $a_1 = 1, a_2 = 8, a_3 = 27, a_4 = 64$

7. $a_1 = 1, a_2 = \dfrac{4}{3}, a_3 = \dfrac{3}{2}, a_4 = \dfrac{8}{5}$

8. $a_2 = \dfrac{3}{2}, a_3 = \dfrac{6}{5}, a_4 = \dfrac{9}{10}, a_5 = \dfrac{12}{17}$

9. $a_1 = 1, a_2 = -1, a_3 = 1, a_4 = -1$

10. $a_1 = 1, a_2 = -3, a_3 = 9, a_4 = -27$

11. $a_1 = \dfrac{5}{2}, a_2 = \dfrac{11}{4}, a_3 = \dfrac{23}{8}, a_4 = \dfrac{47}{16}$

12. $a_1 = \dfrac{3}{2}, a_2 = \dfrac{9}{4}, a_3 = \dfrac{27}{8}, a_4 = \dfrac{81}{16}$

13. $a_1 = 0.6, a_2 = 0.6, a_3 = 0.6, a_4 = 0.6$

14. $a_1 = -0.4, a_2 = -0.4, a_3 = -0.4, a_4 = -0.4$

15. $a_1 = -1, a_2 = \dfrac{1}{2}, a_3 = -\dfrac{1}{6}, a_4 = \dfrac{1}{24}$

16. $a_1 = 1, a_2 = 1, a_3 = \dfrac{1}{2}, a_4 = \dfrac{1}{6}$

17. $a_1 = -\dfrac{1}{3}, a_2 = \dfrac{1}{9}, a_3 = -\dfrac{1}{27}, a_4 = \dfrac{1}{81}$

18. $a_1 = -1, a_2 = 3, a_3 = -9, a_4 = 27$

19. $a_1 = \dfrac{e}{2}, a_2 = \dfrac{e^2}{4}, a_3 = \dfrac{e^3}{6}, a_4 = \dfrac{e^4}{8}$

20. $a_1 = \dfrac{2}{e}, a_2 = \dfrac{4}{e^2}, a_3 = \dfrac{8}{e^3}, a_4 = \dfrac{16}{e^4}$

21. $a_n = 3n - 2$ **22.** $a_n = 2n + 5$ **23.** $a_n = \dfrac{1}{n + 1}$

24. $a_n = \dfrac{n + 1}{n + 2}$ **25.** $a_n = (-1)^{n+1}(2)$ **26.** $a_n = (-1)^n(3n)$

27. $a_n = \dfrac{3^{n-1}}{2^n}$ **28.** $a_n = \left(-\dfrac{1}{2}\right)^n$ **29.** $a_n = n(n + 1)$

33. $a_n = \dfrac{3^{n+1}}{n + 1}$ **34.** $a_n = \left(\dfrac{e}{2}\right)^n$

35. $a_1 = 2, a_2 = 5, a_3 = 8, a_4 = 11, a_5 = 14$
36. $a_1 = 5, a_2 = 4, a_3 = 3, a_4 = 2, a_5 = 1$
37. $a_1 = 3, a_2 = 6, a_3 = 12, a_4 = 24, a_5 = 48$
38. $a_1 = 1, a_2 = \dfrac{1}{2}, a_3 = \dfrac{1}{4}, a_4 = \dfrac{1}{8}, a_5 = \dfrac{1}{16}$
39. $a_1 = 7, a_2 = -11, a_3 = 25, a_4 = -47, a_5 = 97$
40. $a_1 = -4, a_2 = 7, a_3 = -26, a_4 = 73, a_5 = -224$
41. $a_1 = 2, a_2 = \dfrac{1}{2}, a_3 = 2, a_4 = \dfrac{1}{2}, a_5 = 2$
42. $a_1 = -1, a_2 = 1, a_3 = -1, a_4 = 1, a_5 = -1$
43. $a_1 = 25, a_2 = -\dfrac{1}{125}, a_3 = -25, a_4 = \dfrac{1}{125}, a_5 = 25$
44. $a_1 = 12, a_2 = -\dfrac{1}{36}, a_3 = -12, a_4 = \dfrac{1}{36}, a_5 = 12$

65. $\displaystyle\sum_{k=1}^{51}(2k - 1)$ **66.** $\displaystyle\sum_{k=1}^{51}2k$ **70.** $\displaystyle\sum_{k=1}^{50}(-1)^{k+1}k$

B Exercises: Applying the Concepts

73. a. 208 ft   **b.** $16 + (N - 1)\, 32$ ft

74. a. 4000   **b.** 32,000   **c.** $(1000)(2^n)$

76. a. \$1040   **b.** \$920   **78. a.** 150 yd   **b.** $20n - 10$ yd

79. a. $A_1 = 10{,}300$ $A_2 = 10{,}609$ $A_3 = 10{,}927.27$ $A_4 = 11{,}255.09$
    $A_5 = 11{,}592.74$ $A_6 = 11{,}940.52$

80. a. $A_1 = 102$ $A_2 = 104.04$ $A_3 = 106.12$ $A_4 = 108.24$ $A_5 = 110.41$
    $A_6 = 112.62$
    b. \$220.80

81. 1st year: \$105,000. 2nd year: \$110,250. 3rd year: \$115,762.5.
    4th year: \$121,550.63. 5th year: \$127,628.16. 6th year: \$134,009.56.
    7th year: \$140,710.04. Formula: $a_n = (100{,}000)(1.05^n)$.

82. 1st year: \$45,000. 2nd year: \$40,500. 3rd year: \$36,450. 4th year:
    \$32,805. 5th year: \$29,524.5. 6th year: \$26,572.05. 7th year:
    \$23,914.85. 8th year: \$21,523.36. 9th year: \$19,371.02. 10th year:
    \$17,433.92. Formula: $a_n = (50{,}000)(0.9^n)$.

C Exercises: Beyond the Basics

83. $a_n = 2^{1 - \frac{1}{2^n}}$

84. a. $a_1 = 3, a_{n+1} = a_n + 2$

85. a. $a_1 = 1, a_2 = \dfrac{1}{2}, a_3 = \dfrac{1}{4}, a_4 = \dfrac{1}{8}, a_5 = \dfrac{1}{16}$ **b.** $a_n = \dfrac{1}{2^{n-1}}$

Section 11.2

Practice Problems

1. -5 **2.** $a_n = 4n - 7$ **3.** $d = -3, a_n = 53 - 3n$
4. $\dfrac{85}{6}$ **5.** 1664 ft

A Exercises: Basic Skills and Concepts

1. Arithmetic; $a_1 = 1, d = 1$ **2.** Arithmetic; $a_1 = 1, d = 2$
3. Arithmetic; $a_1 = 2, d = 3$ **4.** Arithmetic; $a_1 = 10, d = -3$
5. Not Arithmetic   **6.** Not Arithmetic   **7.** Not Arithmetic

8. Arithmetic; $a_1 = -\dfrac{1}{4}, d = \dfrac{1}{2}$ **11.** Arithmetic; $a_1 = 8, d = 2$

12. Arithmetic; $a_1 = -4, d = -5$ **13.** Not arithmetic
14. Not arithmetic   **15.** $a_n = 3n + 2$ **16.** $a_n = 3n + 1$

17. $a_n = 16 - 5n$ **18.** $a_n = 13 - 4n$ **19.** $a_n = \dfrac{3 - n}{4}$

20. $a_n = \dfrac{n + 3}{6}$ **21.** $a_n = -\dfrac{2n + 1}{5}$

24. $a_n = 2(2n + \pi - 2)$ **25.** $d = \dfrac{13}{2}, a_n = \dfrac{13}{2}n - 5$

26. $d = 4, a_n = 4n + 3$ **29.** $d = \dfrac{1}{2}, a_n = \dfrac{n + 11}{2}$

30. $d = \dfrac{3}{10}, a_n = \dfrac{3n - 43}{10}$

Section 11.3

Practice Problems

1. 3   **2.** It is geometric; $a_1 = \dfrac{3}{2}, r = \dfrac{3}{2}$.

3. a. $a_1 = 2$ **b.** $r = \dfrac{3}{5}$ **c.** $a_n = 2\left(\dfrac{3}{5}\right)^{n-1}$

4. 6896.8288   **5.** 2   **6.** \$91,510.60   **7.** 9

8. $\displaystyle\sum_{n=0}^{\infty}(10{,}000{,}000)(0.85)^n = 66{,}666{,}666.67$

A Exercises: Basic Skills and Concepts

1. Geometric; $a_1 = 3, r = 2$ **2.** Geometric; $a_1 = 2, r = 2$
3. Not geometric   **4.** Not geometric
5. Geometric; $a_1 = 1, r = -3$ **6.** Geometric; $a_1 = -1, r = -2$
7. Geometric; $a_1 = 7, r = -1$ **8.** Geometric; $a_1 = 1, r = -2$

9. Geometric; $a_1 = 9, r = \dfrac{1}{3}$ **10.** Geometric; $a_1 = 5, r = \dfrac{2}{5}$

11. Geometric; $a_1 = -\dfrac{1}{2}, r = -\dfrac{1}{2}$ **12.** Geometric; $a_1 = \dfrac{10}{3}, r = \dfrac{2}{3}$

13. Geometric; $a_1 = 1, r = 2$ **14.** Geometric; $a_1 = -1, r = 1.06$
15. Not geometric   **16.** Not geometric

17. Geometric; $a_1 = \dfrac{1}{3}, r = \dfrac{1}{3}$ **18.** Geometric; $a_1 = 500, r = 10$

19. Geometric; $a_1 = \sqrt{5}, r = \sqrt{5}$ **20.** Not geometric

21. $a_1 = 2, r = 5, a_n = (2)(5)^{n-1}$

22. $a_1 = -3, r = 2, a_n = (-3)(2)^{n-1}$

23. $a_1 = 5, r = \dfrac{2}{3}, a_n = (5)\left(\dfrac{2}{3}\right)^{n-1}$

24. $a_1 = 1, r = \sqrt{3}, a_n = (3)^{\frac{n-1}{2}}$

25. $a_1 = 0.2, r = -3, a_n = 0.2(-3)^{n-1}$

26. $a_1 = 1.3, r = -0.2, a_n = \dfrac{1.3}{(-5)^{n-1}}$

27. $a_1 = \pi^4, r = \pi^2, a_n = \pi^{2n+2}$ **28.** $a_1 = e^2, r = \dfrac{1}{e^2}, a_n = \dfrac{1}{e^{2n-4}}$

39. $S_{10} = \dfrac{1{,}220{,}703}{5}$ **40.** $S_{10} = \dfrac{59{,}048}{6561}$

C Exercises: Beyond the Basics

75. $\dfrac{2}{3}$

Group Projects

2. 2, 5, and 8; or 26, 5, and -16

Section 11.4

Practice Problems

1. P_{k+1}: $(k+4)^2 > (k+1)^2 + 9$

A Exercises: Basic Skills and Concepts

1. P_{k+1}: $(k+2)^2 - 2(k+1) = (k+1)^2 + 1$
2. P_{k+1}: $(2+k)(-k) = 1 - (k+1)^2$
4. P_{k+1}: $1 + 3 + 5 + \cdots + (2k-1) + (2k+1) = (k+1)^2$

B Exercises: Applying the Concepts

31. a. The number of sides of the nth figure is $3(4^{n-1})$.

  b. The perimeter of the nth figure is $3\left(\dfrac{4}{3}\right)^{n-1}$.

32. a. 40   **b.** 121
  c. The number of triangles after the nth iteration is $\dfrac{3^n - 1}{2}$.

33. The smallest number of moves to accomplish the transfer is $2^n - 1$.
34. a. (i) 2   **(ii)** 4
  b. The number of answer sheets is 2^n.

Section 11.5

Practice Problems

1. $(3y - x)^6 = 729y^6 - 1458y^5x + 1215y^4x^2 - 540y^3x^3 + 135y^2x^4 - 18yx^5 + x^6$

2. a. $\dbinom{6}{2} = 15$ **b.** $\dbinom{12}{9} - 220$

3. $(3x - y)^4 = 81x^4 - 108x^3y + 54x^2y^2 - 12xy^3 + y^4$
4. 220   **5.** $1{,}863{,}680a^{12}x^3$

A Exercises: Basic Skills and Concepts

11. $(x+2)^4 = x^4 + 8x^3 + 24x^2 + 32x + 16$
12. $(x+3)^4 = x^4 + 12x^3 + 54x^2 + 108x + 81$
13. $(x-2)^5 = x^5 - 10x^4 + 40x^3 - 80x^2 + 80x - 32$
14. $(3-x)^5 = -x^5 + 15x^4 - 90x^3 + 270x^2 - 405x + 243$
15. $(2-3x)^3 = -27x^3 + 54x^2 - 36x + 8$
16. $(3-2x)^3 = -8x^3 + 36x^2 - 54x + 27$
17. $(2x+3y)^4 = 16x^4 + 96x^3y + 216x^2y^2 + 216xy^3 + 81y^4$
18. $(2x+5y)^4 = 16x^4 + 160x^3y + 600x^2y^2 + 1000xy^3 + 625y^4$
19. $(x+1)^4 = x^4 + 4x^3 + 6x^2 + 4x + 1$
20. $(x+2)^4 = x^4 + 8x^3 + 24x^2 + 32x + 16$
21. $(x-1)^5 = x^5 - 5x^4 + 10x^3 - 10x^2 + 5x - 1$
22. $(1-x)^5 = -x^5 + 5x^4 - 10x^3 + 10x^2 - 5x + 1$
23. $(y-3)^3 = y^3 - 9y^2 + 27y - 27$
24. $(2-y)^5 = -y^5 + 10y^4 - 40y^3 + 80y^2 - 80y + 32$
25. $(x+y)^6 = x^6 + 6x^5y + 15x^4y^2 + 20x^3y^3 + 15x^2y^4 + 6xy^5 + y^6$
26. $(x-y)^6 = x^6 - 6x^5y + 15x^4y^2 - 20x^3y^3 + 15x^2y^4 - 6xy^5 + y^6$
27. $(1+3y)^5 = 243y^5 + 405y^4 + 270y^3 + 90y^2 + 15y + 1$
28. $(2x+1)^5 = 32x^5 + 80x^4 + 80x^3 + 40x^2 + 10x + 1$
29. $(2x+1)^4 = 16x^4 + 32x^3 + 24x^2 + 8x + 1$
30. $(3x-1)^4 = 81x^4 - 108x^3 + 54x^2 - 12x + 1$
31. $(x-2y)^3 = x^3 - 6x^2y + 12xy^2 - 8y^3$
32. $(2x-y)^3 = 8x^3 - 12x^2y + 6xy^2 - y^3$
33. $(2x+y)^4 = 16x^4 + 32x^3y + 24x^2y^2 + 8xy^3 + y^4$

34. $(3x-2y)^4 = 81x^4 - 216x^3y + 216x^2y^2 - 96xy^3 + 16y^4$

35. $\left(\dfrac{x}{2} + 2\right)^7 = \dfrac{1}{128}x^7 + \dfrac{7}{32}x^6 + \dfrac{21}{8}x^5 + \dfrac{35}{2}x^4 + 70x^3 + 168x^2 + 224x + 128$

36. $\left(2 - \dfrac{x}{2}\right)^7 = -\dfrac{1}{128}x^7 + \dfrac{7}{32}x^6 - \dfrac{21}{8}x^5 + \dfrac{35}{2}x^4 - 70x^3 + 168x^2 - 224x + 128$

37. $\left(a^2 - \dfrac{1}{3}\right)^4 = a^8 - \dfrac{4}{3}a^6 + \dfrac{2}{3}a^4 - \dfrac{4}{27}a^2 + \dfrac{1}{81}$

38. $\left(\dfrac{1}{2} - a^2\right)^4 = a^8 - 2a^6 + \dfrac{3}{2}a^4 - \dfrac{1}{2}a^2 + \dfrac{1}{16}$

39. $\left(\dfrac{1}{x} + y\right)^3 = y^3 + 3\dfrac{y^2}{x} + 3\dfrac{y}{x^2} + \dfrac{1}{x^3}$

40. $\left(x + \dfrac{2}{y}\right)^3 = x^3 + 6\dfrac{x^2}{y} + 12\dfrac{x}{y^2} + \dfrac{8}{y^3}$

49. 2.48832
50. a. 70.7281
  b. 1124.864

C Exercises: Beyond the Basics

51. $-\dfrac{8064\sqrt{x}}{x^8}$ **52.** $\dfrac{252\sqrt{x}}{x^8}$ **53.** $924\dfrac{x^{12}}{y^{18}}$ **62. b.** 180

Section 11.6

Practice Problems

1.

There are $(3)(3) = 9$ ways to choose a course.
2. 35   **3.** 1,000,000   **4.** 5040   **5.** 3024
6. a. 72   **b.** 1
7. {bears, bulls, lions}, {bears, bulls, tigers}, {bears, lions, tigers}, {bulls, lions, tigers}. $C(4, 3) = 4$
8. a. 36   **b.** 1   **c.** 1   **9.** 220   **10.** 90

A Exercises: Basic Skills and Concepts

17. a. 676   **b.** 650

B Exercises: Applying the Concepts

44. There is only one way to select the problems in increasing order of difficulty. The author can fail in 5,039 ways.
51. The maximum number of times each child will go to the circus is 20. The father goes 35 times.

Section 11.7

Practice Problems

1. a. $E_1 = \{2, 4, 6\}$, $P(E_1) = \frac{1}{2}$ **b.** $E_2 = \{5, 6\}$, $P(E_2) = \frac{1}{3}$

2. $\frac{1}{2}$ **3.** $\frac{1}{6}$ **4.** $\frac{1}{15,890,700}$ **5.** $\frac{2}{13}$ **6.** $\frac{3}{10}$ **7.** 0.69

A Exercises: Basic Skills and Concepts

1. $S = \{$(Wendy's, McDonald's, Burger King), (Wendy's, Burger King, McDonald's), (McDonald's, Wendy's, Burger King), (McDonald's, Burger King, Wendy's), (Burger King, Wendy's, McDonald's), (Burger King, McDonald's, Wendy's)$\}$

2. $S = \{$(hamburger, Wendy's), (hamburger, McDonald's), (hamburger, Burger King), (cheeseburger, Wendy's), (cheeseburger, McDonald's), (cheeseburger, Burger King)$\}$

3. $S = \{\{$Thriller, The Wall$\}$, $\{$Thriller, Eagles: Their Greatest Hits$\}$, $\{$Thriller, Led Zeppelin IV$\}$, $\{$The Wall, Eagles: Their Greatest Hits$\}$, $\{$The Wall, Led Zeppelin IV$\}$, $\{$Eagles: Their Greatest Hits, Led Zeppelin IV$\}\}$

4. $S = \{\{$regular salted, regular unsalted, barbecue$\}$, $\{$regular salted, regular unsalted, cheddar cheese$\}$, $\{$regular salted, regular unsalted, sour cream and onion$\}$, $\{$regular salted, barbecue, cheddar cheese$\}$, $\{$regular salted, barbecue, sour cream and onion$\}$, $\{$regular salted, cheddar cheese, sour cream and onion$\}$, $\{$regular unsalted, barbecue, cheddar cheese$\}$, $\{$regular unsalted, barbecue, sour cream and onion$\}$, $\{$regular unsalted, cheddar cheese, sour cream and onion$\}$, $\{$barbecue, cheddar cheese, sour cream and onion$\}\}$

5. $S = \{$(white, male), (white, female), (African American, male), (African American, female), (Native American, male), (Native American, female), (Asian, male), (Asian, female), (other, male), (other, female), (multiracial, male), (multiracial, female)$\}$

6. $S = \{$(white, 1), (white, 2), (white, 3), (white, 4), (white, 5), (white, 6), (red, 1), (red, 2), (red, 3), (red, 4), (red, 5), (red, 6), (green, 1), (green, 2), (green, 3), (green, 4), (green, 5), (green, 6)$\}$

15. experimental   **17.** theoretical

21. An event that is very likely to happen has probability 0.999. An event that will surely happen has probability 1. An event that is a rare event has probability 0.001. An event that may or may not happen has probability 0.5. An event that will never happen has probability 0.

22. {the sure event}, {at least one head}, {at least two heads}, {exactly two heads}

23. $\frac{1}{3}$ **24.** $\frac{1}{6}$ **25.** $\frac{1}{3}$ **26.** $\frac{1}{3}$ **27.** $\frac{1}{2}$ **29.** $\frac{1}{13}$ **30.** $\frac{1}{13}$

31. $\frac{1}{4}$ **32.** $\frac{1}{26}$ **33.** $\frac{3}{13}$ **34.** $\frac{5}{26}$ **35.** $\frac{1}{10}$ **37.** $\frac{1}{10}$ **38.** $\frac{2}{5}$

39. $\frac{1}{2}$ **40.** $\frac{1}{2}$

B Exercises: Applying the Concepts

43. $\frac{1}{5}$ **44.** $\frac{17}{20}$ **45.** $\frac{47}{50}$ **46.** $\frac{4}{5}$

47. The probability of winning one prize is $\frac{2}{25}$.

The probability of winning both is $\frac{9}{1550}$.

48. $\frac{4}{7}$ **49. a.** $\frac{1}{4}$ **b.** $\frac{1}{4}$ **c.** $\frac{1}{2}$ **50. a.** $\frac{1}{8}$ **b.** $\frac{1}{2}$ **c.** $\frac{7}{8}$

d. $\frac{3}{8}$ **51. a.** $\frac{237}{434}$ **b.** $\frac{3663}{4340}$ **e.** $\frac{4303}{4340}$

52. $\frac{1}{200}$

53. The probability that a non-Hispanic white American has no lactose intolerance is 0.8. The probability for the second group is $\frac{1}{4}$.

54. a. $\frac{1}{1024}$ **b.** $\frac{5}{512}$ **c.** $\frac{11}{1024}$ **55. a.** $\frac{1}{10}$ **b.** $\frac{1}{10}$

57.

Number of people who are	Depressed according to the test	Normal according to the test
Actually depressed	90	10
Actually normal	135	765

58. Sample points: $\{M_1M_2N, M_1NM_2, M_2M_1N, M_2NM_1, NM_1M_2, NM_2M_1\}$.

The probability that Deshawn wins is $\frac{2}{3}$.

59. Three of one gender and one of the other is more likely.

61. a. $\frac{2}{5}$ **b.** $\frac{89}{180}$

C Exercises: Beyond the Basics

62. a. $\frac{1}{365}$ **b.** $\frac{1093}{133,225}$ **c.** $\dfrac{365^{49} - \dfrac{364!}{315!}}{365^{49}}$ **63.** $\frac{468,559}{1,000,000}$

64. $\frac{1}{24}$ **65.** $\frac{1}{12}$

Critical Thinking

66. $\frac{8}{25}$ **67.** $\frac{1}{3}$ **68.** $\frac{5}{12}$

Review Exercises

1. $a_1 = -1, a_2 = 1, a_3 = 3, a_4 = 5, a_5 = 7$

2. $a_1 = -\frac{1}{2}, a_2 = 0, a_3 = \frac{3}{2}, a_4 = 4, a_5 = \frac{15}{2}$

3. $a_1 = \frac{1}{3}, a_2 = \frac{2}{5}, a_3 = \frac{3}{7}, a_4 = \frac{4}{9}, a_5 = \frac{5}{11}$

4. $a_1 = 1, a_2 = -2, a_3 = 4, a_4 = -8, a_5 = 16$

5. $a_n = 32 - 2n$ **6.** $a_n = -(-2)^{n-1}$ **16.** $\sum_{k=1}^{5} - (-2)^k$

17. Arithmetic; $a_1 = 11, d = -5$ **18.** Arithmetic; $a_1 = \frac{2}{3}, d = \frac{1}{6}$

20. Arithmetic; $a_1 = -2, d = 3$

22. $a_n = 4n + 1$ **31.** Geometric; $a_1 = 4, r = -2$

32. Geometric; $a_1 = \frac{1}{5}, r = \frac{1}{2}$ **33.** Not geometric

34. Geometric; $a_1 = \frac{1}{2}, r = \frac{1}{2}$ **35.** $a_1 = 16, r = -\frac{1}{4}, a_n = \frac{(-1)^{n-1}}{4^{n-3}}$

36. $a_1 = -\frac{5}{6}, r = \frac{2}{5}, a_n = -\frac{1}{3}\left(\frac{2}{5}\right)^{n-2}$ **45.** $\frac{7}{9}$ **46.** $\frac{211}{99}$

49. $(x - 3)^4 = x^4 - 12x^3 + 54x^2 - 108x + 81$

50. $\left(\dfrac{x}{2} + 2\right)^6 = \dfrac{1}{64}x^6 + \dfrac{3}{8}x^5 + \dfrac{15}{4}x^4 + 20x^3 + 60x^2 + 96x + 64$

65. $\dfrac{1}{2}$ **66.** $\dfrac{3}{10}$ **67.** $\dfrac{2}{5}$

68. $\dfrac{1}{15}$ **69.** $\dfrac{15}{28}$ **70.** $\dfrac{17}{25}$ **71.** $\dfrac{1}{17}$ **72.** $\dfrac{47}{50}$

73. a. $\dfrac{1}{9}$ **b.** $\dfrac{4}{9}$ **c.** $\dfrac{5}{9}$ **74. a.** $\dfrac{8}{13}$ **b.** $\dfrac{3}{13}$

Practice Test A

1. $a_1 = 3, a_2 = -9, a_3 = -21, a_4 = -33, a_5 = -45$; arithmetic sequence

2. $a_1 = -6, a_2 = -12, a_3 = -24, a_4 = -48, a_5 = -96$; geometric sequence

3. $a_1 = -2, a_2 = -1, a_3 = 2, a_4 = 11, a_5 = 38$

9. $\dfrac{2}{11}$ **18.** $\dfrac{5}{12}$ **19.** $\dfrac{5}{6}$ **20.** $\dfrac{7}{51}$

Cumulative Review Exercises (Chapters 1–11)

1. Solution: $\{2, 4\}$ **2.** Solution: $\{-2, -1, 1, 2\}$

8. $x \in (-\infty, -4] \cup [0, \infty)$

9. $x \in (-\infty, -3 - 3\sqrt{3}] \cup [-3 + 3\sqrt{3}, \infty)$

11. $x = 10, y = 7, z = \dfrac{1}{2}$

15. Shift the graph of $g(x) = \sqrt{x}$ three units to the right.

16. Domain: $(-\infty, -1) \cup (-1, 0) \cup (0, \infty)$

17. $\ln\left(\dfrac{x^7}{x - 5}\right)$

Credits

Chapter P

p. 1, Times Square; Reuters/Corbis.
p. 1, Profit/loss graph; Digital Vision.
p. 1, Mortar and pestle; PhotoDisc.
p. 2, Cricket; BrandX Pictures.
p. 19, Coffee and candy; PhotoDisc.
p. 27, Coffee shop; Corbis RF.
p. 29, Planets; NASA.
p. 30, Leaning tower of Pisa; PhotoDisc.
p. 39, Movie theater box office; PhotoDisc.
p. 39, Cruise ship; Image Source/Getty RF.
p. 40, Drug research and development; PhotoDisc.
p. 50, Pills (drug false positive); PhotoDisc.
p. 60, Water reservoir; Getty RF.
p. 61, Water tower; Getty RF (BrandX Pictures PP).
p. 75, Scarecrow in *Wizard of Oz*; PhotoFest.

Chapter 1

p. 86, Greek architecture; Digital Vision.
p. 86, Fractal; Corbis RF/BrandX Pictures.
p. 86, Spaceship; NASA (PAL).
p. 87, Bungee jumping/bridge; Robert Holmes/Corbis.
p. 93, Bungee jumper and cord; Corbis RF.
p. 95, Rectangular swimming pool; PhotoDisc Red.
p. 96, Digital camera; PhotoDisc (PP).
p. 98, QE2; Pearson Education/PH College (PAL).
p. 107, Pay phone coin box; Beth Anderson.
p. 110, Mandelbrot set; Photo Researchers, Inc. (PAL).
p. 110, Benoit Mandelbrot; Time-Life/Getty Images.
p. 119, Greek architecture; PhotoDisc Red.
p. 119, Parthenon; Corbis RF.
p. 119, Mona Lisa; Art Resource, N.Y./PAL.
p. 120, Pyramid of Giza; Corbis RF.
p. 132, Rectangular concrete patio; PhotoDisc.
p. 135, Albert Einstein; Bettmann/Corbis (PAL).
p. 146, Express train; Digital Vision.
p. 148, Bermuda triangle; Graphic Maps and World Atlas (PAL).
p. 156, Amplifier; PhotoDisc (PP).
p. 156, Car dealer and car lot; PhotoDisc Red.
p. 158, Measuring an accident skid; Arresting Images (PAL).
p. 166, People playing blackjack; PhotoDisc Red.
p. 167, Search plane; MedioImages/Getty RF.
p. 173, Butcher weighing steak; Digital Vision.
p. 173, Woman and fish; PhotoDisc Vol. 43.
p. 177, Shaking hands at party; Digital Vision.

Chapter 2

p. 180, Athletes training; PhotoDisc Blue.
pp. 180, 263, doctor/blood pressure; PhotoDisc.
p. 180, Hurricane map; NASA Headquarters.
p. 181, Descartes and fly; Beth Anderson.
p. 182, Rene Descartes; stamp, public domain.
p. 191, Deer herd; PhotoDisc.
p. 203, Female college students; Getty RF.
p. 203, Diving cage; Getty Images/Science Faction.
p. 206, Wild Bill Longley; RKO/The Kobal Collection.
p. 218, Steep mountain road; PhotoDisc Red.
p. 218, Golfers; Getty RF.
p. 219, New refrigerator; PhotoDisc (PP).
p. 219, Televisions; PhotoDisc.

p. 219, New tractor; PhotoDisc Blue.
p. 219, Band concert; Matt Carmichael/Getty Images (Editorial).
p. 220, Testing lake water; Stephen Frink/Corbis.
p. 223, Drug levels in body; Digital Vision (PP).
p. 224, Movie theater; PhotoDisc Red.
p. 236, Injection in arm; Stockbyte Platinum/Getty RF.
p. 242, Superbowl; Harry How/Getty Image (Sport).
p. 242, Laptop computer; Digital Vision (PP).
p. 243, Bookstore; Corbis RF (PP).
p. 243, Record company; PhotoDisc Red.
p. 244, Aspirin; Beth Anderson.
p. 246, Megatooth shark; Digital Vision.
p. 248, Shark tooth; Corbis RF.
p. 260, Computer printer inventory; PhotoDisc.
p. 260, Apartment for rent; Corbis RF.
p. 261, Child shoe sizes; Beth Anderson.
p. 261, Income taxes; Beth Anderson.
p. 262, Windchill factor; PhotoDisc (PP).
p. 279, Cashmere sweaters; Blend Images/Getty RF.
p. 281, Exxon Valdez oil spill 1989; Natalie Fobes/Corbis.
p. 288, New car; Image Source/Getty RF.
p. 291, Mail order package; Digital Vision.
p. 291, Department store; PhotoDisc Red.
p. 291, Store appliance department; Punchstock/Comstock RF.
p. 294, Diving bell/water pressure; AP/Wideworld Photos.
p. 307, Currency exchange; PhotoDisc Red.
p. 307, Short-order cook; Stockbyte Platinum/Getty RF.

Chapter 3

p. 317, Suspension bridge; PhotoDisc Red.
p. 317, Navigational devices; Beth Anderson.
p. 317, Computer graphics or Mars; PhotoDisc Red.
p. 318, Movie *Yours, Mine and Ours*; Paramount/The Everett Collection.
p. 331, Steer; Glowimages/Getty RF.
p. 331, Arch top window; PhotoDisc.
p. 331, Gateway Arch, St. Louis; PhotoDisc (PP).
p. 351, Khaki slacks; Corbis RF.
p. 352, Orange harvest; PhotoDisc Blue.
p. 352, Airport luggage belt; Digital Vision.
p. 355, Global warming map; Environmental Issues.
p. 364, Petroleum refinery; PhD.
p. 368, Printer; Beth Anderson.
p. 368, Lottery sales; Corbis RF (PP).
p. 370, Gerolamo Cardano; Image Works/Mary Evans Picture Library Ltd (PAL).
p. 381, Federal taxes; PhotoDisc.
p. 397, Portable CD player; PhotoDisc (PP).
p. 397, Las Vegas; PhotoDisc (PP).
p. 398, Polluted or cleaned-up river; BrandX CD Magnificent Landscapes.
p. 398, College bookstore; Digital Vision.
p. 401, Isaac Newton/apple tree; Photo Researchers, Inc. (PAL).
p. 409, Milky Way; NASA Headquarters (PAL).
p. 410, Soybeans; PhotoDisc (PP).
p. 411, Gravity on the moon; NASA/Goddard Space Flight Center (PAL).
p. 411, Gravity on the sun; SOHO/LASCO/ESA & NASA (PAL).
p. 412, Energy from a windmill; PhD.

Chapter 4

p. 421, Crowd of people; Digital Vision.
p. 421, Atomic explosion molecular activity; Digital Vision.

p. 907, Alfred Lee Loomis; SAU.

p. 922, Lightning; PhotoDisc (PP).

Chapter 11

p. 931, Ancient Babylonia; Bettmann/Corbis.

p. 931, Roulette wheel; PhotoDisc.

p. 931, Biologist; PhotoDisc.

p. 932, Honeybee; Photographer's Choice RF.

p. 935, Leonardo of Pisa; The Granger Collection (PAL).

p. 942, Skydivers in free fall; PhotoDisc.

p. 944, Space junk; Photo Researchers, Inc. (PAL).

p. 947, Gauss; Library of Congress.

p. 950, Hiker; Digital Vision.

p. 950, Theatre seating; BrandX Pictures.

p. 952, Effect of Olympics on economy; Ezra Shaw/Getty Images (Sport).

p. 962, Butterfly; Westend61/Getty.

p. 964, Two jars with fleas; Beth Anderson.

p. 965, Falling dominoes; PhotoDisc Blue.

p. 969, People hugging; Blend Images/Getty.

p. 969, Towers of Hanoi; Beth Anderson.

p. 971, Blaise Pascal; PAL/Library of Congress.

p. 971, Pascaline, first digital calculator; Photo Researchers (PAL).

p. 978, Social Security card; Silver Burdett Ginn (PAL).

p. 988, Supreme Court justices; AFP/Getty Images.

p. 989, Bingo card; PhotoDisc.

p. 991, Lottery player; Monika Graff/Getty Images (News).

p. 1000, Female military person; USAF.

p. 1001, Car ownership; PhotoDisc Red.

p. 1001, Hospital treatment; PhotoDisc.

Index of Applications

Physics

Probability

Social Science

Sports/Entertainment

Index

Algebra–Formulas and Definitions

Real-Number Properties

$a + b = b + a$

$(a + b) + c = a + (b + c)$

$a(b + c) = ab + ac$

$a + 0 = 0 + a = a$

$a + (-a) = 0$

$a \cdot 0 = 0 \cdot a = 0$

If $a \cdot b = 0$, then $a = 0$ or $b = 0$.

$ab = ba$

$(ab)c = a(bc)$

$(a + b)c = ac + bc$

$a \cdot 1 = 1 \cdot a = a$

$a\left(\dfrac{1}{a}\right) = 1, a \neq 0$

Absolute Value

$|a| = a$ if $a \geq 0$ and $|a| = -a$ if $a < 0$.

Assume that $a > 0$ and u is an algebraic expression:

$|u| = a$ is equivalent to $u = a$ or $u = -a$.

$|u| < a$ is equivalent to $-a < u < a$.

$|u| > a$ is equivalent to $u < -a$ or $u > a$.

Exponents

$a^n = \underbrace{a \cdot a \cdots a}_{n \text{ factors}}$

$a^0 = 1, a \neq 0$

$a^{-n} = \dfrac{1}{a^n}, a \neq 0$

$a^m a^n = a^{m+n}$

$\dfrac{a^m}{a^n} = a^{m-n}$

$(a^m)^n = a^{mn}$

$(a \cdot b)^n = a^n \cdot b^n$

$\left(\dfrac{a}{b}\right)^n = \dfrac{a^n}{b^n}$

$\left(\dfrac{a}{b}\right)^{-n} = \left(\dfrac{b}{a}\right)^n = \dfrac{b^n}{a^n}$

Logarithms

$y = \log_a x$ means $a^y = x$

$\log_a a^x = x$

$\log_a 1 = 0$

$\log x = \log_{10} x$

$a^{\log_a x} = x$

$\log_a a = 1$

$\ln x = \log_e x$

$\log_a MN = \log_a M + \log_a N$

$\log_a \dfrac{M}{N} = \log_a M - \log_a N$

$\log_a M^r = r \log_a M$

$\log_b x = \dfrac{\log_a x}{\log_a b} = \dfrac{\log x}{\log b} = \dfrac{\ln x}{\ln b}$ (change-of-base formula)

Radicals

$\sqrt{a^2} = |a|$

$\sqrt[n]{a^n} = |a|$ if n is even

$\sqrt[n]{a^n} = a$ if n is odd

$a^{\frac{1}{n}} = \sqrt[n]{a}$

$a^{\frac{m}{n}} = (\sqrt[n]{a})^m = \sqrt[n]{a^m}$

$\sqrt[n]{ab} = \sqrt[n]{a} \cdot \sqrt[n]{b}$

$\sqrt[n]{\dfrac{a}{b}} = \dfrac{\sqrt[n]{a}}{\sqrt[n]{b}}$

Rational Expressions

(Assume all denominators not to be zero.)

$\dfrac{A}{B} \cdot \dfrac{C}{D} = \dfrac{A \cdot C}{B \cdot D}$

$\dfrac{\dfrac{A}{B}}{\dfrac{C}{D}} = \dfrac{A}{B} \div \dfrac{C}{D} = \dfrac{A}{B} \cdot \dfrac{D}{C} = \dfrac{A \cdot D}{B \cdot C}$

$\dfrac{A}{C} \pm \dfrac{B}{C} = \dfrac{A \pm B}{C}$

$\dfrac{A}{B} \pm \dfrac{C}{D} = \dfrac{A \cdot D \pm B \cdot C}{B \cdot D}$

Common Products and Factors

$A^2 - B^2 = (A + B)(A - B)$

$A^2 + 2AB + B^2 = (A + B)^2$

$A^2 - 2AB + B^2 = (A - B)^2$

$A^3 - B^3 = (A - B)(A^2 + AB + B^2)$

$A^3 + B^3 = (A + B)(A^2 - AB + B^2)$

$A^3 + 3A^2 B + 3AB^2 + B^3 = (A + B)^3$

$A^3 - 3A^2 B + 3AB^2 - B^3 = (A - B)^3$

Distance Formula

The distance between $P(x_1, y_1)$ and $Q(x_2, y_2)$ is

$$d(P, Q) = \sqrt{(x_2 - x_1)^2 + (y_2 - y_1)^2}.$$

Midpoint Formula

The midpoint $M(x, y)$ of the line segment with endpoints $P(x_1, y_1)$ and $Q(x_2, y_2)$ is

$$M(x, y) = \left(\dfrac{x_1 + x_2}{2}, \dfrac{y_1 + y_2}{2}\right).$$

Lines

Slope $\quad m = \dfrac{\text{rise}}{\text{run}} = \dfrac{y_2 - y_1}{x_2 - x_1}$

Point-slope form	$y - y_1 = m(x - x_1)$
Slope-intercept form	$y = mx + b$
Horizontal line	$y = k$
Vertical line	$x = k$
General form	$ax + by + c = 0$

Quadratic Formula

The solutions to the equation $ax^2 + bx + c = 0, a \neq 0$, are

$$x = \dfrac{-b \pm \sqrt{b^2 - 4ac}}{2a}.$$

Standard Form of a Circle

$(x - h)^2 + (y - k)^2 = r^2 \quad$ center: (h, k)

radius: r

Standard Form of a Parabola

$(y - k)^2 = \pm 4a(x - h)$ vertex: (h, k) and $(a > 0)$

$(x - h)^2 = \pm 4a(y - k)$

Functions/Graphs

Constant Function
$$f(x) = c$$

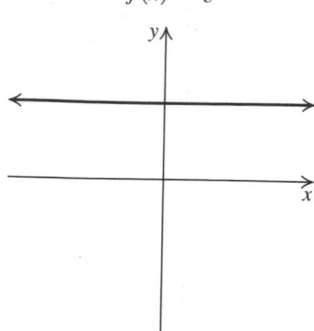

Identity Function
$$f(x) = x$$

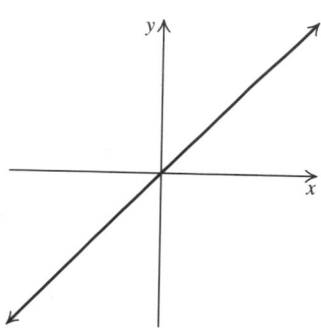

Squaring Function
$$f(x) = x^2$$

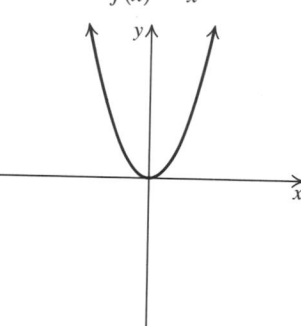

Cubing Function
$$f(x) = x^3$$

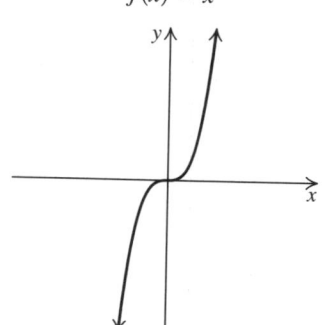

Absolute Value Function
$$f(x) = |x|$$

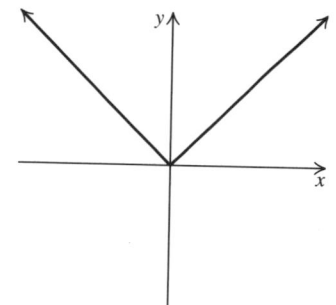

Square Root Function
$$f(x) = \sqrt{x}$$

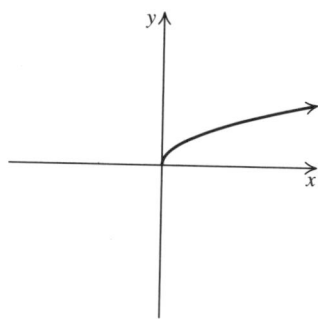

Cube Root Function
$$f(x) = \sqrt[3]{x}$$

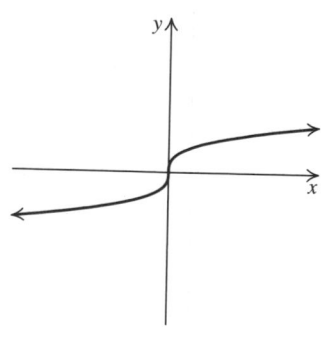

Reciprocal Function
$$f(x) = \frac{1}{x}$$

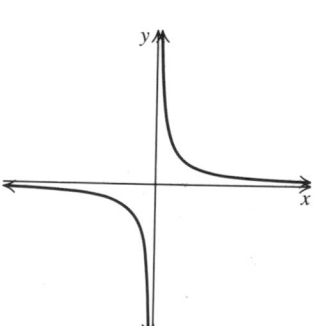

Greatest Integer Function
$$f(x) = [x]$$

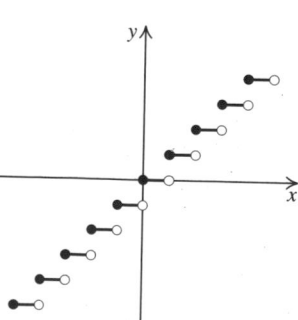